Main-Group Elements

W9-CQI-578

			13 IIIA	14 IVA	15 VA	16 VIA	17 VIIA	18 VIIIA
								2 He 4.002602
			5 B 10.811	6 C 12.0107	7 N 14.0067	8 O 15.9994	9 F 18.9984032	10 Ne 20.1797
10	11 IB	12 IIB	13 Al 26.9815386	14 Si 28.0855	15 P 30.973762	16 S 32.065	17 Cl 35.453	18 Ar 39.948
28 Ni 58.6934	29 Cu 63.546	30 Zn 65.409	31 Ga 69.723	32 Ge 72.64	33 As 74.92160	34 Se 78.96	35 Br 79.904	36 Kr 83.798
46 Pd 106.42	47 Ag 107.8682	48 Cd 112.411	49 In 114.818	50 Sn 118.710	51 Sb 121.760	52 Te 127.60	53 I 126.90447	54 Xe 131.293
78 Pt 195.084	79 Au 196.966569	80 Hg 200.59	81 Tl 204.3833	82 Pb 207.2	83 Bi 208.98040	84 Po (209)	85 At (210)	86 Rn (222)
110 Ds (281)	111 Rg (272)	112 Uub (285)	113 Uut (284)	114 Uuq (289)	115 Uup (288)	116 Uuh (291)		118 Uuo (294)

Inner Transition Metals

62 Sm 150.36	63 Eu 151.964	64 Gd 157.25	65 Tb 158.92535	66 Dy 162.500	67 Ho 164.93032	68 Er 167.259	69 Tm 168.93421	70 Yb 173.04
94 Pu (244)	95 Am (243)	96 Cm (247)	97 Bk (247)	98 Cf (251)	99 Es (252)	100 Fm (257)	101 Md (258)	102 No (259)

A value in parentheses is the mass number of the isotope of the longest half-life.

Permanent names are not yet assigned for elements 112 to 118 (element 117 has not yet been synthesized). These elements are assigned temporary names based on their atomic numbers. See www.webelements.com for more information.

General Chemistry

Chemistry 122 and 123 at Western Washington University

Darrell D. Ebbing | Steven D. Gammon

CENGAGE
Learning™

Australia • Brazil • Japan • Korea • Mexico • Singapore • Spain • United Kingdom • United States

CENGAGE
Learning™

General Chemistry: Chemistry 122 and 123 at Western Washington University

Darrell D. Ebbing | Steven D. Gammon

Executive Editors:
 Maureen Staudt
 Michael Stranz

Senior Project Development Manager:
 Linda DeStefano

Marketing Specialist:
 Sara Mercurio
 Lindsay Shapiro

Senior Production / Manufacturing Manager:
 Donna M. Brown

PreMedia Supervisor:
 Joel Brennecke

Rights & Permissions Specialist:
 Kalina Hintz
 Todd Osborne

Cover Image:
 Getty Images*

* Unless otherwise noted, all cover images used by Custom Solutions, a part of Cengage Learning, have been supplied courtesy of Getty Images with the exception of the Earthview cover image, which has been supplied by the National Aeronautics and Space Administration (NASA).

© 2009 Cengage Learning

ALL RIGHTS RESERVED. No part of this work covered by the copyright herein may be reproduced, transmitted, stored or used in any form or by any means graphic, electronic, or mechanical, including but not limited to photocopying, recording, scanning, digitizing, taping, Web distribution, information networks, or information storage and retrieval systems, except as permitted under Section 107 or 108 of the 1976 United States Copyright Act, without the prior written permission of the publisher.

For product information and technology assistance, contact us at
Cengage Learning Customer & Sales Support, 1-800-354-9706

For permission to use material from this text or product,
submit all requests online at **cengage.com/permissions**
Further permissions questions can be emailed to
permissionrequest@cengage.com

ISBN-13: 978-1-111-03185-5

ISBN-10: 1-111-03185-1

Cengage Learning
5191 Natorp Boulevard
Mason, Ohio 45040
USA

Cengage Learning is a leading provider of customized learning solutions with office locations around the globe, including Singapore, the United Kingdom, Australia, Mexico, Brazil, and Japan. Locate your local office at:
international.cengage.com/region

Cengage Learning products are represented in Canada by Nelson Education, Ltd.

For your lifelong learning solutions, visit **www.cengage.com/custom**

Visit our corporate website at **www.cengage.com**

Printed in the United States of America

Table of Contents

(*Note – this is a "custom" textbook that has been designed specifically for this course in a joint effort between your instructor and the publisher. Please note that some chapters have been removed intentionally and some pages may be black & white as dictated by the changes.)

5

The Gaseous State

Bromine evaporates at room temperature to produce a dense gas, shown being poured from a flask. Compounds that contain bromine are used to disinfect swimming pools and hot tubs.

Contents and Concepts

We will investigate the quantitative relationships that describe the behavior of gases.

This section will develop a model of gases as molecules in constant random motion.

175

Gases have several characteristics that distinguish them from liquids and solids. You can compress gases into smaller and smaller volumes. Anyone who has transported gases such as oxygen compressed in steel cylinders can appreciate this (Figure 5.1). Also, for gases, unlike for liquids and solids, you can relate pressure, volume, temperature, and molar amount of substance with fair accuracy by one simple equation, the ideal gas law. Suppose you wish to determine the amount of oxygen in a cylinder of compressed gas. You measure the pressure (with a gauge), the temperature, and the volume of gas (volume of the tank). Then, using the ideal gas law, you can calculate the amount of gas in the tank.

Kinetic-molecular theory describes a gas as composed of molecules in constant motion. This theory helps explain the simple relationship that exists among the pressure, volume, temperature, and amount of a gas. Kinetic theory has also enhanced our understanding of the flow of fluids, the transmission of sound, and the conduction of heat.

This chapter introduces the empirical gas laws, such as the ideal gas law, and the kinetic-molecular theory that explains these laws. After finishing the chapter, you will be able to answer questions such as, How many grams of oxygen are there in a 50.0-L gas cylinder at 21°C when the oxygen pressure is 15.7 atmospheres? (An atmosphere is a unit of pressure equal to that of the normal atmosphere.) You will also be able to calculate the average speed of an oxygen molecule in this tank (479 m/s, or 1071 mi/hr).

■ **See pages 212–213 for the Media Summary.**

FIGURE 5.1 ▲

Cylinders of gas
Gases such as oxygen and nitrogen can be transported as compressed gases in steel cylinders. Large volumes of gas at normal pressures can be compressed into a small volume. Note the pressure gauges.

Gas Laws

Most substances composed of small molecules are gases under normal conditions or else are easily vaporized liquids. Table 5.1 lists selected gaseous substances and some of their properties.

In the first part of this chapter, we will examine the quantitative relationships, or empirical laws, governing gases. We will first consider the concept of pressure.

TABLE 5.1	Properties of Selected Gases			
Name	Formula	Color	Odor	Toxicity
Ammonia	NH_3	Colorless	Penetrating	Toxic
Carbon dioxide	CO_2	Colorless	Odorless	Nontoxic
Carbon monoxide	CO	Colorless	Odorless	Very toxic
Chlorine	Cl_2	Pale green	Irritating	Very toxic
Hydrogen	H_2	Colorless	Odorless	Nontoxic
Hydrogen sulfide	H_2S	Colorless	Foul	Very toxic
Methane	CH_4	Colorless	Odorless	Nontoxic
Nitrogen dioxide	NO_2	Red-brown	Irritating	Very toxic

| # Gas Pressure and Its Measurement

Pressure is defined as *the force exerted per unit area of surface*. A coin resting on a table exerts a force, and therefore a pressure, downward on the table as a consequence of gravity. The air above the table exerts an additional pressure on the table, because the air is also being pulled downward by gravity.

To obtain the SI unit of pressure and a feeling for its size, let us calculate the pressure on a table from a perfectly flat coin with a radius and mass equal to that of a new penny (9.3 mm in radius and 2.5 g). The force exerted by the coin from gravity equals the mass of the coin times the constant acceleration of gravity. *Acceleration* is the change of speed per unit time, so the SI unit of acceleration is meters per second per second, abbreviated m/s^2. The constant acceleration of gravity is $9.81 \ m/s^2$, and the force on the coin due to gravity is

$$\text{Force} = \text{mass} \times \text{constant acceleration of gravity}$$
$$= (2.5 \times 10^{-3} \ kg) \times (9.81 \ m/s^2) = 2.5 \times 10^{-2} \ kg{\cdot}m/s^2$$

The cross-sectional area of the coin is $\pi \times (\text{radius})^2 = 3.14 \times (9.3 \times 10^{-3} \ m)^2 = 2.7 \times 10^{-4} \ m^2$. Therefore,

$$\text{Pressure} = \frac{\text{force}}{\text{area}} = \frac{2.5 \times 10^{-2} \ kg{\cdot}m/s^2}{2.7 \times 10^{-4} \ m^2} = 93 \ kg/(m{\cdot}s^2)$$

The SI unit of pressure, $kg/(m{\cdot}s^2)$, is given the name **pascal (Pa),** *after the French physicist Blaise Pascal (1623–1662), who studied fluid pressure.* Note that the pressure exerted by a coin the size and mass of a penny is approximately 100 Pa. The pressure exerted by the atmosphere is about 1000 times larger, or about 100,000 Pa. Thus, the pascal is an extremely small unit.

Chemists have traditionally used two other units of pressure, based on the mercury barometer. A **barometer** is *a device for measuring the pressure of the atmosphere*. The mercury barometer consists of a glass tube about one meter long, filled with mercury and inverted in a dish of mercury (Figure 5.2). At sea level the mercury in the tube falls to a height of about 760 mm above the level in the dish. This height is a direct measure of the atmospheric pressure (Figure 5.3). < Air pressure downward on the surface of the mercury in the dish is transmitted through the liquid and exerts a pressure upward at the base of the mercury column, supporting it. A mercury column placed in a sealed flask, as in Figure 5.4, measures the gas pressure in the flask. It acts as a **manometer,** *a device that measures the pressure of a gas or liquid in a vessel.*

The unit **millimeters of mercury (mmHg),** also called the **torr** (after Evangelista Torricelli, who invented the mercury barometer in 1643), is *a unit of pressure equal to that exerted by a column of mercury 1 mm high at 0.00°C.* The **atmosphere (atm)** is a related *unit of pressure equal to exactly 760 mmHg.*

FIGURE 5.2 ▲

A mercury barometer

The height *h* is proportional to the barometric pressure. For that reason, the pressure is often given as the height of the mercury column, in units of millimeters of mercury, mmHg.

Atmospheric, or barometric, pressure depends not only on altitude but also on weather conditions. The "highs" and "lows" of weather reports refer to high- and low-pressure air masses. A high is associated with fair weather; a low brings unsettled weather, or storms.

FIGURE 5.3 ▶ (left)

Atmospheric pressure from air mass

The force of gravity on the mass of a column of air exerts a pressure at the earth's surface. This pressure varies slightly with weather, but is approximately 101 kPa (760 mmHg, or 1 atm).

FIGURE 5.4 ▶ (right)

A flask equipped with a closed-tube manometer

The gas pressure in the flask is proportional to the difference in heights between the liquid levels in the manometer, Δ*h*.

TABLE 5.2	Important Units of Pressure
Unit	Relationship or Definition
Pascal (Pa)	$kg/(m \cdot s^2)$
Atmosphere (atm)	$1\ atm = 1.01325 \times 10^5\ Pa \approx 100\ kPa$
mmHg, or torr	$760\ mmHg = 1\ atm$
Bar	$1.01325\ bar = 1\ atm$

*In 1982, the International Union of Pure and Applied Chemistry (IUPAC) recommended that standard pressure be defined as equal to 1 **bar**, a unit of pressure equal to 1×10^5 Pa, slightly less than 1 atm. Despite this recommendation, 1 atm is still in common use by chemists as the standard pressure. Until the bar is more widely adopted by chemists as the standard unit of pressure, we will continue to use the atmosphere.*

The general relationship between the pressure P and the height h of a liquid column in a barometer or manometer is

$$P = gdh$$

Here g is the constant acceleration of gravity (9.81 m/s^2) and d is the density of the liquid in the manometer. If g, d, and h are in SI units, the pressure is given in pascals. Table 5.2 summarizes the relationships among the various units of pressure. <

Example 5.1 | Converting Units of Pressure

The pressure of a gas in a flask is measured to be 797.7 mmHg using a mercury-filled manometer as in Figure 5.4. What is this pressure in pascals and atmospheres?

Problem Strategy This is a unit conversion problem. To convert to the appropriate units, use the conversion factors presented in Table 5.2 and the techniques presented in Chapter 1. Keep in mind that the conversion 760 mmHg = 1 atm is exact.

Solution Conversion to pascals:

$$797.7\ mmHg \times \frac{1.01325 \times 10^5\ Pa}{760\ mmHg} = \mathbf{1.064 \times 10^5\ Pa}$$

Conversion to atmospheres:

$$797.7\ mmHg \times \frac{1\ atm}{760\ mmHg} = \mathbf{1.050\ atm}$$

Answer Check Pressure conversions between the units of atm and mmHg are very common, so it is helpful to remember the relationship 1 atm = 760 mmHg in order to check your answers quickly.

Exercise 5.1   A gas in a container had a measured pressure of 57 kPa. Calculate the pressure in units of atm and mmHg.

■ See Problems 5.37 and 5.38.

Concept Check 5.1

Suppose that you set up two barometers like the one shown in Figure 5.2. In one of the barometers you use mercury, and in the other you use water. Which of the barometers would have a higher column of liquid, the one with Hg or H$_2$O? Explain your answer.

5.2 | Empirical Gas Laws

All gases under moderate conditions behave quite simply with respect to pressure, temperature, volume, and molar amount. By holding any two of these physical properties constant, it is possible to show a simple relationship between the other two. The discovery of these quantitative relationships, the empirical gas laws, occurred from the mid-seventeenth to the mid-nineteenth century.

TABLE 5.3	Pressure–Volume Data for 1.000 g O_2 at 0°C		
P (atm)	*V* (L)		*PV*
0.2500	2.801		0.7002
0.5000	1.400		0.7000
0.7500	0.9333		0.7000
1.000	0.6998		0.6998
2.000	0.3495		0.6990
3.000	0.2328		0.6984
4.000	0.1744		0.6976
5.000	0.1394		0.6970

(left margin: Increasing pressure; right margin of V column: Increasing volume)

FIGURE 5.5 ▲

Boyle's experiment
The volume of the gas at normal atmospheric pressure (760 mmHg) is 100 mL. When the pressure is doubled by adding 760 mm of mercury, the volume is halved (to 50 mL). Tripling the pressure decreases the volume to one-third of the original (to 33 mL).

FIGURE 5.6 ▲

Model of gas pressure–volume relationship at a constant temperature
(A) When a 1.000-g sample of O_2 gas at 0°C is placed in a container at a pressure of 0.50 atm, it occupies a volume of 1.40 L.
(B) When the pressure on the O_2 sample is doubled to 1.0 atm, the volume is reduced to 0.70 L, which is half the original volume.

Boyle's Law: Relating Volume and Pressure

One characteristic property of a gas is its *compressibility*—its ability to be squeezed into a smaller volume by the application of pressure. By comparison, liquids and solids are relatively incompressible. The compressibility of gases was first studied quantitatively by Robert Boyle in 1661. When he poured mercury into the open end of a J-shaped tube, the volume of the enclosed gas decreased (Figure 5.5). Each addition of mercury increased the pressure on the gas, decreasing its volume. From such experiments, he formulated the law now known by his name. According to **Boyle's law,** *the volume of a sample of gas at a given temperature varies inversely with the applied pressure.* That is, $V \propto 1/P$, where V is the volume, P is the pressure, and $\propto$ means "is proportional to." Thus, if the pressure is doubled, the volume is halved.

Boyle's law can also be expressed in the form of an equation. Putting pressure and volume on the same side of the equation, you can write

> Boyle's law:
> $PV = \text{constant}$ (for a given amount of gas at fixed temperature)

That is, for a given amount of gas at a fixed temperature, the pressure times the volume equals a constant. Table 5.3 gives some pressure and volume data for 1.000 g O_2 at 0°C. Figure 5.6 presents a molecular view of the pressure–volume relationship for two data points in Table 5.3. Note that the product of the pressure and volume for each data pair is nearly constant. By plotting the volume of the oxygen at different pressures (as shown in Figure 5.7), you obtain a graph showing the inverse relationship of P and V.

You can use Boyle's law to calculate the volume occupied by a gas when the pressure changes. Consider the 50.0-L gas cylinder of oxygen mentioned in the chapter opening. The pressure of gas in the cylinder is 15.7 atm at 21°C. What volume of oxygen can you get from the cylinder at 21°C if the atmospheric pressure is 1.00 atm? You can write P_i and V_i for the initial pressure (15.7 atm) and initial volume (50.0 L), and P_f and V_f for the final pressure (1.00 atm) and final volume

FIGURE 5.7 ▶

Gas pressure–volume relationship
(A) Plot of volume vs. pressure for a sample of oxygen. The volume (of 1.000 g O_2 at 0°C) decreases with increasing pressure. When the pressure is doubled (from 0.50 atm to 1.00 atm), the volume is halved (from 1.40 L to 0.70 L). *(B)* Plot of 1/V vs. pressure (at constant temperature) for the same sample. The straight line indicates that volume varies inversely with pressure.

(to be determined). Because the temperature does not change, the product of the pressure and volume remains constant. Thus, you can write

$$P_f V_f = P_i V_i$$

Dividing both sides of the equation by P_f gives

$$V_f = V_i \times \frac{P_i}{P_f}$$

Substituting into this equation yields

$$V_f = 50.0 \text{ L} \times \frac{15.7 \text{ atm}}{1.00 \text{ atm}} = 785 \text{ L}$$

Note that the initial volume is multiplied by a ratio of pressures. You know the oxygen gas is changing to a lower pressure and will therefore expand, so this ratio will be greater than 1. The final volume, 785 L, is that occupied by all of the gas at 1.00 atm pressure. However, because the cylinder holds 50.0 L, only this volume of gas remains in the cylinder. The volume that escapes is (785 − 50.0) L = 735 L.

Example 5.2 | **Using Boyle's Law**

A volume of air occupying 12.0 dm³ at 98.9 kPa is compressed to a pressure of 119.0 kPa. The temperature remains constant. What is the new volume?

Problem Strategy Putting the data for the problem in tabular form, you see what data you have and what you must find. This will suggest the method of solution.

$V_i = 12.0 \text{ dm}^3 \quad P_i = 98.9 \text{ kPa}$ ⎫ Temperature and
$\qquad\qquad\qquad\qquad\qquad\qquad\qquad$ ⎬ moles remain
$V_f = \quad ? \qquad P_f = 119.0 \text{ kPa}$ ⎭ constant.

Because P and V vary but temperature and moles are constant, you use Boyle's law.

Solution Application of Boyle's law gives

$$V_f = V_i \times \frac{P_i}{P_f} = 12.0 \text{ dm}^3 \times \frac{98.9 \text{ kPa}}{119.0 \text{ kPa}} = \textbf{9.97 dm}^3$$

Answer Check In general, when the pressure on a gas increases, the gas is compressed and therefore occupies a smaller volume. When the pressure on a gas decreases, the gas expands—it will occupy a larger volume. Use these concepts to check your answers. In this example, since the pressure increases, the smaller final volume of the answer is what we would expect. (Note that you get the answer to this type of problem by multiplying the volume by a ratio of pressures. This ratio should be less than 1 if the volume decreases, but more than 1 if the volume increases.)

Exercise 5.2 A volume of carbon dioxide gas, CO_2, equal to 20.0 L was collected at 23°C and 1.00 atm pressure. What would be the volume of carbon dioxide collected at 23°C and 0.830 atm?

■ See Problems 5.39, 5.40, 5.41, and 5.42.

FIGURE 5.8 ▶

Effect of temperature on volume of a gas
Left: A balloon immersed in liquid nitrogen shrinks because the air inside contracts in volume. *Right:* When the balloon is removed from the liquid nitrogen, the air inside warms up and the balloon expands to its original size.

Before leaving the subject of Boyle's law, we should note that the pressure–volume product for a gas is not precisely constant. You can see this from the *PV* data given in Table 5.3 for oxygen. In fact, all gases follow Boyle's law at low to moderate pressures but deviate from this law at high pressures. The extent of deviation depends on the gas. We will return to this point at the end of the chapter.

Charles's Law: Relating Volume and Temperature

Temperature also affects gas volume. When you immerse an air-filled balloon in liquid nitrogen ($-196°C$), the balloon shrinks (Figure 5.8). After the balloon is removed from the liquid nitrogen, it returns to its original size. A gas contracts when cooled and expands when heated.

The first ascent of a hot-air balloon carrying people was made on November 21, 1783. A few days later, Jacques Alexandre Charles made an ascent in a hydrogen-filled balloon. On landing, the balloon was attacked and torn to shreds by terrified peasants armed with pitchforks.

One of the first quantitative observations of gases at different temperatures was made by Jacques Alexandre Charles in 1787. Charles was a French physicist and a pioneer in hot-air and hydrogen-filled balloons. < Later, John Dalton (in 1801) and Joseph Louis Gay-Lussac (in 1802) continued these kinds of experiments, which showed that a sample of gas at a fixed pressure increases in volume *linearly* with temperature. By "linearly," we mean that if we plot the volume occupied by a given sample of gas at various temperatures, we get a straight line (Figure 5.9).

When you extend the straight lines in Figure 5.9 from the last experimental point toward lower temperatures—that is, when you *extrapolate* the straight lines backward—you find that they all intersect at a common point. This point occurs at a temperature of $-273.15°C$, where the graph indicates a volume of zero. This seems to say that if the substances remain gaseous, the volumes occupied will be zero at $-273.15°C$. This could not happen, however; all gases liquefy before they reach this temperature, and Charles's law does not apply to liquids. These extrapolations do show that we can express the volume variation of a gas with temperature more simply by choosing a different thermometer scale. Let us see how to do this.

FIGURE 5.9 ▶

Linear relationship of gas volume and temperature at constant pressure
The graph shows gas volume versus temperature for a given mass of gas at 1.00 atm pressure. This linear relationship is independent of amount or type of gas. Note that all lines extrapolate to $-273°C$ at zero volume.

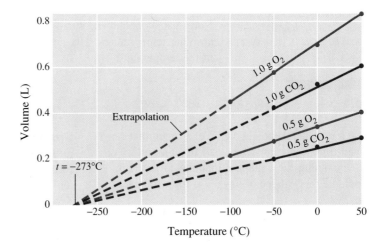

The fact that the volume occupied by a gas varies linearly with degrees Celsius can be expressed mathematically by the following equation:

$$V = bt + a$$

The mathematical equation of a straight line, y = mx + b, is discussed in Appendix A.

where t is the temperature in degrees Celsius and a and b are constants that determine the straight line. < You can eliminate the constant a by observing that $V = 0$ at $t = -273.15$ for any gas. Substituting into the preceding equation, you get

$$0 = b(-273.15) + a \quad \text{or} \quad a = 273.15b$$

The Kelvin temperature scale and a more formal equation for temperature conversion were discussed in Section 1.6.

The equation for the volume can now be rewritten:

$$V = bt + 273.15b = b(t + 273.15)$$

Suppose you use a temperature scale equal to degrees Celsius plus 273.15, which you may recognize as the *Kelvin scale* (an absolute scale). <

$$K = {}^\circ C + 273.15$$

If you write T for the temperature on the Kelvin scale, you obtain

$$V = bT$$

1.0 atm

—0.52 L

—0.26 L

100 K

A

1.0 atm

—0.52 L

—0.26 L

200 K

B

FIGURE 5.10 ▲

Model of the temperature–volume relationship for a gas at a fixed volume *(A)* A 1.0-g sample of O_2 at 100 K and 1.0 atm of pressure occupies a volume of 0.26 L. *(B)* When the absolute temperature of the gas is doubled to 200 K, the volume of O_2 doubles to 0.52 L.

This is **Charles's law,** which we can state as follows: *the volume occupied by any sample of gas at a constant pressure is directly proportional to the absolute temperature.* Thus, doubling the absolute temperature of a gas doubles its volume (Figure 5.10).

Charles's law can be rearranged into a form that is very useful for computation.

> Charles's law:
>
> $$\frac{V}{T} = \text{constant} \quad \text{(for a given amount of gas at a fixed pressure)}$$

This equation says that the volume divided by the absolute temperature, for a sample of gas at a fixed pressure, remains constant.

Consider a sample of gas at a fixed pressure, and suppose the temperature changes from its initial value T_i to a final value T_f. How does the volume change? Because the volume divided by absolute temperature is constant, you can write

$$\frac{V_f}{T_f} = \frac{V_i}{T_i}$$

Or, rearranging slightly,

$$V_f = V_i \times \frac{T_f}{T_i}$$

Note that to obtain the final volume, the initial volume is multiplied by a ratio of absolute temperatures. The next example illustrates a calculation involving a change in the temperature of a gas.

Example 5.3 | Using Charles's Law

Earlier we found that the total volume of oxygen that can be obtained from a particular tank at 1.00 atm and 21°C is 785 L (including the volume remaining in the tank). What would be this volume of oxygen if the temperature had been 28°C?

Problem Strategy You must first convert temperatures to the Kelvin scale. Then, list the data in tabular form so you can easily see what varies and what remains constant. You apply Charles's law when V and T vary and P is constant.

(continued)

(*continued*)

Solution $T_i = (21 + 273)K = 294\ K$

$T_f = (28 + 273)K = 301\ K$

Following is the data table:

$V_i = 785\ L$ $P_i = 1.00\ atm$ $T_i = 294\ K$

$V_f = ?$ $P_f = 1.00\ atm$ $T_f = 301\ K$

Note that T varies and P remains constant, so V must change. These are the conditions needed to apply Charles's law.

$$V_f = V_i \times \frac{T_f}{T_i} = 785\ L \times \frac{301\ K}{294\ K} = \textbf{804 L}$$

Answer Check   In general, when the temperature increases, the volume of gas increases, and when the temperature decreases, the volume of gas decreases. Applying these concepts to check the answer, we verify that when the temperature was increased, the final volume is greater than the starting volume. (Note that you get the answer to this type of problem by multiplying the volume by a ratio of absolute temperatures. This ratio should be more than 1 if the volume increases, but less than 1 if the volume decreases.)

Exercise 5.3   If you expect a chemical reaction to produce 4.38 dm³ of oxygen, O_2, at 19°C and 101 kPa, what will be the volume at 25°C and 101 kPa?

■ See Problems 5.45, 5.46, 5.47, and 5.48.

Although most gases follow Charles's law fairly well, they deviate from it at high pressures and low temperatures.

Combined Gas Law: Relating Volume, Temperature, and Pressure

Boyle's law ($V \propto 1/P$) and Charles's law ($V \propto T$) can be combined and expressed in a single statement: the volume occupied by a given amount of gas is proportional to the absolute temperature divided by the pressure ($V \propto T/P$). You can write this as an equation.

$$V = \text{constant} \times \frac{T}{P} \quad \text{or} \quad \frac{PV}{T} = \text{constant} \qquad \text{(for a given amount of gas)}$$

Consider a problem in which you wish to calculate the final volume of a gas when the pressure and temperature are changed. PV/T is constant for a given amount of gas, so you can write

$$\frac{P_f V_f}{T_f} = \frac{P_i V_i}{T_i}$$

which rearranges to

$$V_f = V_i \times \frac{P_i}{P_f} \times \frac{T_f}{T_i}$$

Thus, the final volume is obtained by multiplying the initial volume by ratios of pressures and absolute temperatures.

Example 5.4 | Using the Combined Gas Law

Modern determination of %N in an organic compound is an automated version of one developed by the French chemist Jean-Baptiste Dumas in 1830. The Dumas method uses hot copper(II) oxide to oxidize C and H in the compound to CO_2 and H_2O (both are trapped chemically) and to convert N in the compound to N_2 gas (Figure 5.11). Using the Dumas

(*continued*)

(continued)

method, 39.8 mg of caffeine gives 10.1 cm^3 of nitrogen gas at 23°C and 746 mmHg. What is the volume of nitrogen at 0°C and 760 mmHg?

FIGURE 5.11 ▲

Oxidation of an organic compound with copper(II) oxide
Left: Molecular model of caffeine, an organic compound. *Center:* A chemist heats caffeine with copper(II) oxide, CuO. CuO oxidizes C and H in the compound to CO_2 and H_2O, and converts N to N_2. *Right:* Copper metal produced by the reaction.

Problem Strategy   As always, you will need to convert temperature to the Kelvin scale and put the data in tabular form to determine the law(s) that apply. In this case, since both pressure and temperature are changing, we should expect to use more than one law to arrive at an answer.

Solution   You first express the temperatures in kelvins:

$$T_i = (23 + 273) \text{ K} = 296 \text{ K}$$

$$T_f = (0 + 273) \text{ K} = 273 \text{ K}$$

Now you put the data for the problem in tabular form:

$$V_i = 10.1 \text{ cm}^3 \quad P_i = 746 \text{ mmHg} \quad T_i = 296 \text{ K}$$

$$V_f = \quad ? \quad\quad P_f = 760 \text{ mmHg} \quad T_f = 273 \text{ K}$$

From the data, you see that you need to use Boyle's and Charles's laws combined to find how V varies as P and T change. Note that the increase in pressure decreases the volume, making the pressure ratio less than 1. The decrease in temperature also decreases the volume, and the ratio of absolute temperatures is less than 1.

$$V_f = V_i \times \frac{P_i}{P_f} \times \frac{T_f}{T_i} = 10.1 \text{ cm}^3 \times \frac{746 \text{ mmHg}}{760 \text{ mmHg}} \times \frac{273 \text{ K}}{296 \text{ K}} = \textbf{9.14 cm}^3$$

Answer Check   This gas sample is undergoing a temperature decrease and a pressure increase. These two changes will have opposite effects on the final gas volume. Considering the magnitude of the changes in temperature and pressure in this problem, we can conclude that the final volume of the gas should not be greatly different from its initial volume.

Exercise 5.4   A balloon contains 5.41 dm^3 of helium, He, at 24°C and 101.5 kPa. Suppose the gas in the balloon is heated to 35°C. If the helium pressure is now 102.8 kPa, what is the volume of the gas?

■ See Problems 5.51 and 5.52.

Concept Check 5.2

To conduct some experiments, a 10.0-L flask equipped with a movable plunger, as illustrated here, is filled with enough H_2 gas to come to a pressure of 20 atm.

a. In the first experiment, we decrease the temperature in the flask by 10°C and then increase the volume. Predict how the pressure in the flask changes during each of these events and, if possible, how the final pressure compares to your starting pressure.

b. Once again we start with the pressure in the flask at 20 atm. The flask is then heated 10°C, followed by a volume decrease. Predict how the pressure in the flask changes during each of these events and, if possible, how the final pressure compares to your starting pressure.

Avogadro's Law: Relating Volume and Amount

In 1808 the French chemist Joseph Louis Gay-Lussac (1778–1850) concluded from experiments on gas reactions that the volumes of reactant gases at the same pressure and temperature are in ratios of small whole numbers *(the law of combining volumes)*. For example, two volumes of hydrogen react with one volume of oxygen gas to produce water.

$$2H_2(g) \ + \ O_2(g) \ \longrightarrow \ 2H_2O(g)$$

2 volumes   1 volume

Three years later, the Italian chemist Amedeo Avogadro (1776–1856) interpreted the law of combining volumes in terms of what we now call **Avogadro's law:** *equal volumes of any two gases at the same temperature and pressure contain the same number of molecules.* Thus, two volumes of hydrogen contain twice the number of molecules as in one volume of oxygen, in agreement with the chemical equation for the reaction.

One mole of any gas contains the same number of molecules (Avogadro's number = 6.02×10^{23}) and by Avogadro's law must occupy the same volume at a given temperature and pressure. This *volume of one mole of gas* is called the **molar gas volume, V_m.** Volumes of gases are often compared at **standard temperature and pressure (STP),** *the reference conditions for gases chosen by convention to be 0°C and 1 atm pressure.* At STP, the molar gas volume is found to be 22.4 L/mol (Figure 5.12).

FIGURE 5.12 ▶

The molar volume of a gas
The box has a volume of 22.4 L, equal to the molar volume of a gas at STP. The basketball is shown for comparison.

A Chemist Looks at . . .

life science

Nitrogen Monoxide Gas and Biological Signaling

In 1998, the Nobel committee awarded its prize in physiology or medicine to three scientists for the astounding discovery that nitrogen monoxide (nitric oxide) gas, NO, functions as the signaling agent between biological cells in a wide variety of chemical processes. Until this discovery, biochemists had thought that the major chemical reactions in a cell always involved very large molecules. Now they discovered that a simple gas, NO, could play a central role in cell chemistry.

Prizewinners Robert Furchgott and Louis Ignarro, independently, unraveled the role of nitrogen monoxide in blood-pressure regulation. Cells in the lining of arteries detect increased blood pressure and respond by producing nitrogen monoxide. NO rapidly diffuses through the artery wall to cells in the surrounding muscle tissue. In response, the muscle tissue relaxes, the blood vessel expands, and the blood pressure drops.

In a related discovery, another prizewinner, Ferid Murad, explained how nitroglycerin works to alleviate the intense chest pain of an angina attack, which results from reduced blood flow to the heart muscle as a result of partial blockage of arteries by plaque. Physicians have prescribed nitroglycerin for angina for more than a century, knowing only that it works. Murad found that nitroglycerin breaks down in the body to form nitrogen monoxide, which relaxes the arteries, allowing greater blood flow to the heart. Alfred Nobel, were he alive today, would no doubt be stunned by this news. Nobel, who established the prizes bearing his name, made his fortune in the nineteenth century from his invention of dynamite, a mixture of nitroglycerin with clay

FIGURE 5.13 ▶

Nitroglycerin patch
Nitroglycerin has been used for more than a hundred years to treat and prevent angina attacks. Here a patient wears a patch that dispenses nitroglycerin steadily over a period of time.

TABLE 5.4	
Molar Volumes of Several Gases at 0.0°C and 1.00 atm	
Gas	Molar Volume (L)
He	22.40
H_2	22.43
O_2	22.39
CO_2	22.29
NH_3	22.09
Ideal gas*	22.41

*An ideal gas follows the empirical gas laws.

We can re-express Avogadro's law as follows: the molar gas volume at a given temperature and pressure is a specific constant independent of the nature of the gas.

> Avogadro's law:
> V_m = specific constant (= 22.4 L/mol at STP)
> (depending on T and P but independent of the gas)

Table 5.4 lists the molar volumes of several gases. The values agree within about 2% of the value expected from the empirical gas laws (the "ideal gas" value). We will discuss the reason for the deviations from this value at the end of this chapter, in the section on real gases.

that tamed the otherwise hazardous explosive. When Nobel had heart trouble, his physician recommended that he eat a small quantity of nitroglycerin; he refused. In a letter, he wrote, "It is ironical that I am now ordered by my physician to eat nitroglycerin." Today, a patient may either take nitroglycerin pills (containing tenths of a milligram of compound in a stabilized mixture) for occasional use or apply a chest patch to dispense nitroglycerin continuously to the skin, where it is absorbed (Figure 5.13).

Research papers on the biological role of nitrogen monoxide now number in the tens of thousands. For example, scientists have found that white blood cells use nitrogen monoxide in a kind of chemical warfare. These cells emit concentrated clouds of NO that surround bacterial or tumor cells, killing them by interfering with certain cell processes. Researchers have also discovered that nitrogen monoxide plays a role in penile erection. Pharmacologists found that the drug Viagra (Figure 5.14) assists in the action of NO in dilating arteries, leading to erection.

FIGURE 5.14 ▲

Viagra

Viagra is marketed as an aid to erectile dysfunction. Sexual stimulation produces nitrogen monoxide, which in turn aids an enzyme in the production of a substance called cGMP that relaxes arterial muscles, allowing blood to flow to the penis. Viagra enhances the action of NO by inhibiting an enzyme that degrades cGMP.

■ See Problems 5.105 and 5.106.

5.3 | The Ideal Gas Law

In the previous section, we discussed the empirical gas laws. Here we will show that these laws can be combined into one equation, called the *ideal gas equation*. Earlier we combined Boyle's law and Charles's law into the equation

$$V = \text{constant} \times \frac{T}{P} \qquad \text{(for a given amount of gas)}$$

This "constant" is independent of the temperature and pressure but does depend on the amount of gas. For one mole, the constant will have a specific value, which we will denote as R. The molar volume, V_m, is

$$V_m = R \times \frac{T}{P}$$

TABLE 5.5

Molar Gas Constant in Various Units

Value of R

0.082058 L·atm/(K·mol)

8.3145 J/(K·mol)*

8.3145 kg·m^2/(s^2·K·mol)

8.3145 kPa·dm^3/(K·mol)

1.9872 cal/(K·mol)*

*The units of pressure times volume are the units of energy—for example, joules (J) or calories (cal).

According to Avogadro's law, the molar volume at a specific value of T and P is a constant independent of the nature of the gas, and this implies that R is a constant independent of the gas. The **molar gas constant, R,** is *the constant of proportionality relating the molar volume of a gas to T/P.* Values of R in various units are given in Table 5.5.

The preceding equation can be written for n moles of gas by multiplying both sides by n.

$$\underbrace{nV_m}_{V} = \frac{nRT}{P} \quad \text{or} \quad PV = nRT$$

Because V_m is the volume per mole, nV_m is the total volume V. *The equation $PV = nRT$, which combines all of the gas laws,* is called the **ideal gas law.**

> Ideal gas law:
> $$PV = nRT$$

The ideal gas law includes all the information contained in Boyle's, Charles's, and Avogadro's laws. In fact, starting with the ideal gas law, you can derive any of the other gas laws.

Example 5.5 | Deriving Empirical Gas Laws from the Ideal Gas Law

Prove the following statement: the pressure of a given amount of gas at a fixed volume is proportional to the absolute temperature. This is sometimes called *Amontons's law*. In 1702 Guillaume Amontons constructed a thermometer based on measurement of the pressure of a fixed volume of air. The principle he employed is now used in special gas thermometers to establish the Kelvin scale.

Problem Strategy   Because we need a relationship between pressure and temperature, the ideal gas law is a logical starting place.

Solution   From the ideal gas law,

$$PV = nRT$$

Solving for P, you get

$$P = \left(\frac{nR}{V}\right)T$$

Note that everything in parentheses in this equation is constant. Therefore, you can write

$$P = \text{constant} \times T$$

Or, expressing this as a proportion,

$$P \propto T$$

Boyle's law and Charles's law follow from the ideal gas law by a similar derivation.

Answer Check   We can apply common experience to qualitatively verify this relationship. Think about what happens to the pressure in a tire when the temperature is increased: the hotter the tire gets, the more the pressure increases.

Exercise 5.5   Show that the moles of gas are proportional to the pressure for constant volume and temperature.

■ See Problems 5.55 and 5.56.

No gas is "ideal." But the ideal gas law is very useful even though it is only an approximation. The behavior of real gases is described at the end of this chapter.

The limitations that apply to Boyle's, Charles's, and Avogadro's laws also apply to the ideal gas law. That is, the ideal gas law is most accurate for low to moderate pressures and for temperatures that are not too low. <

Calculations Using the Ideal Gas Law

The type of problem to which Boyle's and Charles's laws are applied involves a change in conditions (P, V, or T) of a gas. The ideal gas law allows us to solve another type of problem: given any three of the quantities P, V, n, and T, calculate the unknown quantity. Example 5.6 illustrates such a problem.

Example 5.6 | Using the Ideal Gas Law

Answer the question asked in the chapter opening: how many grams of oxygen, O_2, are there in a 50.0-L gas cylinder at 21°C when the oxygen pressure is 15.7 atm?

Problem Strategy In asking for the mass of oxygen, we are in effect asking for moles of gas, n, because mass and moles are directly related. The problem gives P, V, and T, so you can use the ideal gas law to solve for n. The proper value to use for R depends on the units of P and V. Here they are in atmospheres and liters, respectively, so you use $R = 0.0821$ L·atm/(K·mol) from Table 5.5. Once you have solved for n, convert to mass by using the molar mass of oxygen.

Solution The data given in the problem are

Variable	Value
P	15.7 atm
V	50.0 L
T	(21 + 273) K = 294 K
n	?

Solving the ideal gas law for n gives

$$n = \frac{PV}{RT}$$

Substituting the data gives

$$n = \frac{15.7\ \text{atm} \times 50.0\ L}{0.0821\ L\cdot\text{atm}/(K\cdot\text{mol}) \times 294\ K} = 32.5\ \text{mol}$$

and converting moles to mass of oxygen yields

$$32.5\ \text{mol}\ O_2 \times \frac{32.0\ \text{g}\ O_2}{1\ \text{mol}\ O_2} = \mathbf{1.04 \times 10^3\ g\ O_2}$$

Answer Check If you were to forget that oxygen is a diatomic gas with the formula O_2, you would not get this problem right. Keep in mind, too, that the other gaseous diatomic elements are N_2, F_2, and Cl_2.

Exercise 5.6 What is the pressure in a 50.0-L gas cylinder that contains 3.03 kg of oxygen, O_2, at 23°C?

■ See Problems 5.57, 5.58, 5.59, 5.60, 5.61, and 5.62.

Gas Density; Molecular-Mass Determination

The density of a substance is its mass divided by its volume, and because the volume of a gas varies with temperature and pressure, the density of a gas also varies with temperature and pressure (Figure 5.15). In the next example, we use the ideal gas law to calculate the density of a gas at any temperature and pressure. We do this by calculating the moles, and from this the mass, in a liter of gas at the given temperature and pressure; the mass per liter of gas is its density. At the end of this section, we will give an alternative method of solving this problem, using a formula relating density to temperature, pressure, and molecular weight.

Example 5.7 | Calculating Gas Density

What is the density of oxygen, O_2, in grams per liter at 25°C and 0.850 atm?

Problem Strategy The density of a gas is often expressed in g/L. Using the ideal gas law, you can calculate the moles of O_2 in 1 L of O_2. Next, you can convert the moles of O_2 to a mass of O_2, keeping in mind that this mass is the amount of O_2 per liter of O_2 (g/1 L), which is the density.

(continued)

(continued)

Solution   The data given are

Variable	Value
P	0.850 atm
V	1 L (exact value)
T	(25 + 273) K = 298 K
n	?

Therefore,

$$n = \frac{PV}{RT} = \frac{0.850 \text{ atm} \times 1 \text{ L}}{0.0821 \text{ L·atm/(K·mol)} \times 298 \text{ K}} = 0.0347 \text{ mol}$$

Now convert mol O_2 to grams:

$$0.0347 \text{ mol } O_2 \times \frac{32.0 \text{ g } O_2}{1 \text{ mol } O_2} = 1.11 \text{ g } O_2$$

Therefore, the density of O_2 at 25°C and 0.850 atm is **1.11 g/L.**

Suppose you wanted the density of Cl_2, instead of O_2, at this T and P. Only the conversion of moles to mass is affected. The previous calculation becomes

$$0.0347 \text{ mol } Cl_2 \times \frac{70.9 \text{ g } Cl_2}{1 \text{ mol } Cl_2} = 2.46 \text{ g } Cl_2$$

The density of Cl_2 at 25°C and 0.850 atm is 2.46 g/L. Note that the density of a gas is directly proportional to its molecular mass.

Answer Check   Because gases consist of molecules spread very far apart, you should expect any reasonable answer for gas density to be very low when compared to values for liquids and solids. Therefore, gas densities should be on the order of this answer.

Exercise 5.7   Calculate the density of helium, He, in grams per liter at 21°C and 752 mmHg. The density of air under these conditions is 1.188 g/L. What is the difference in mass between 1 liter of air and 1 liter of helium? (This mass difference is equivalent to the buoyant, or lifting, force of helium per liter.)

■ See Problems 5.63, 5.64, 5.65, and 5.66.

FIGURE 5.15 ▲

Hot-air ballooning
A propane gas burner on board a balloon heats the air. The heated air expands, occupying a larger volume; it therefore has a lower density than the surrounding air. The hot air and balloon rise.

FIGURE 5.16 ▲

A gas whose density is greater than that of air
The reddish-brown gas being poured from the flask is bromine. Note how the gas, which is denser than air, hugs the bottom of the beaker.

The previous example demonstrates that the density of a gas is directly proportional to its molecular mass. Bromine, whose molecular mass is five times that of oxygen, is therefore more than five times as dense as air. Figure 5.16 shows bromine gas being poured into a beaker where it displaces the air and fills the beaker.

The relation between density and molecular mass of a gas suggests that you could use a measurement of gas density to determine its molecular mass. In fact, gas-density (vapor-density) measurements provided one of the first methods of determining molecular mass. The method was worked out by the French chemist Jean-Baptiste André Dumas in 1826. It can be applied to any substance that can be vaporized without decomposing.

As an illustration, consider the determination of the molecular mass of halothane, an inhalation anesthetic. The density of halothane vapor at 71°C (344 K) and 768 mmHg (1.01 atm) is 7.05 g/L. To obtain the molecular mass, you calculate the moles of vapor in a given volume. The molar mass equals mass divided by the moles in the same volume. From the density, you see that one liter of vapor has a mass of 7.05 g. The moles in this volume are obtained from the ideal gas law.

$$n = \frac{PV}{RT} = \frac{1.01 \text{ atm} \times 1 \text{ L}}{0.0821 \text{ L·atm}/(\text{K·mol}) \times 344 \text{ K}} = 0.0358 \text{ mol}$$

Therefore, the molar mass, M_m, is

$$M_m = \frac{m}{n} = \frac{7.05 \text{ g}}{0.0358 \text{ mol}} = 197 \text{ g/mol}$$

Thus, the molecular mass is 197 amu.

If you look at what we have done, you will see that all you need to have is the mass of vapor in *any* given volume (for a given T and P). An explicit determination of density is not necessary. You determine the moles of vapor from the volume using the ideal gas law, then determine the molar mass by dividing the mass by moles for this volume. The next example illustrates this. At the end of this section, we will derive an explicit formula for the molecular mass in terms of the density of a gas, which will provide an alternative way to solve this problem.

Example 5.8 | Determining the Molecular Mass of a Vapor

Using the apparatus described in Figure 5.17, a 200.0-mL flask at 99°C and a pressure of 733 mmHg is filled with the vapor of a volatile (easily vaporized) liquid. The mass of the substance in the flask is 0.970 g. What is the molecular mass of the liquid?

Problem Strategy   You can calculate the moles of vapor from the ideal gas law and then calculate the molar mass by dividing mass by moles. Note that the temperature of the vapor is the same as the temperature of the boiling water and that the pressure of the vapor equals the barometric pressure.

Solution   You have the following data for the vapor.

Variable	Value
P	$733 \text{ mmHg} \times \dfrac{1 \text{ atm}}{760 \text{ mmHg}} = 0.964 \text{ atm}$
V	$200.0 \text{ mL} = 0.2000 \text{ L}$
T	$(99 + 273) \text{ K} = 372 \text{ K}$
n	?

From the ideal gas law, $PV = nRT$, you obtain

$$n = \frac{PV}{RT} = \frac{0.964 \text{ atm} \times 0.2000 \text{ L}}{0.0821 \text{ L·atm}/(\text{K·mol}) \times 372 \text{ K}}$$

$$n = 0.00631 \text{ mol}$$

Dividing the mass of the vapor by moles gives you the mass per mole (the molar mass).

$$\text{Molar mass} = \frac{\text{grams vapor}}{\text{moles vapor}} = \frac{0.970 \text{ g}}{0.00631 \text{ mol}} = 154 \text{ g/mol}$$

Thus, the molecular mass is **154 amu**.

Boiling water

Vapor of sample

Sample (should evaporate completely)

FIGURE 5.17 ▲

Finding the vapor density of a substance
After the flask fills with the vapor of the substance at the temperature of the boiling water, you allow the flask to cool so that the vapor condenses. You obtain the mass of the substance (which was vapor) by weighing the flask and substance and then subtracting the mass of the empty flask. The pressure of the vapor equals the barometric pressure, and the temperature equals that of the boiling water.

(continued)

(continued)

Answer Check   No gas has a smaller molar mass than H_2 at 2 g/mol. Therefore, if you obtain an answer that is smaller than this, it must be incorrect. The upper limit on molar masses that you would expect is less definite, but solids and liquids that readily vaporize will have molar masses not much larger than a few hundred. An answer much larger than this should be regarded with suspicion.

Exercise 5.8   A sample of a gaseous substance at 25°C and 0.862 atm has a density of 2.26 g/L. What is the molecular mass of the substance?

■ See Problems 5.67, 5.68, 5.69, and 5.70.

From the ideal gas law, you can obtain an explicit relationship between the molecular mass and density of a gas. Recall that the molar mass ($M_m = m/n$) when expressed in grams per mole is numerically equal to the molecular mass. If you substitute $n = m/M_m$ into the ideal gas law, $PV = nRT$, you obtain

$$PV = \frac{m}{M_m}RT \quad \text{or} \quad PM_m = \frac{m}{V}RT$$

But m/V equals the density, d. Substituting this gives

$$PM_M = dRT$$

We can illustrate the use of this equation by solving Examples 5.7 and 5.8 again. In Example 5.7, we asked, "What is the density of oxygen, O_2, in grams per liter at 25°C (298 K) and 0.850 atm?" You rearrange the previous equation to give an explicit formula for the density and then substitute into this formula.

$$d = \frac{PM_m}{RT} = \frac{0.850 \text{ atm} \times 32.0 \text{ g/mol}}{0.0821 \text{ L·atm/(K·mol)} \times 298 \text{ K}} = 1.11 \text{ g/L}$$

Note that by giving M_m in g/mol and R in L·atm/(K·mol), you obtain the density in g/L.

The question in Example 5.8 is equivalent to the following. What is the molecular mass of a substance weighing 0.970 g whose vapor occupies 200.0 mL (0.2000 L) at 99°C (372 K) and 733 mmHg (0.964 atm)? The density of the vapor is 0.970 g/0.2000 L = 4.85 g/L. To obtain the molecular mass directly, you rearrange the equation $PM_m = dRT$ to give an explicit formula for M_m, then substitute into it.

$$M_m = \frac{dRT}{P} = \frac{4.85 \text{ g/L} \times 0.0821 \text{ L·atm/(K·mol)} \times 372 \text{ K}}{0.964 \text{ atm}} = 154 \text{ g/mol}$$

Concept Check 5.3

Three 3.0-L flasks, each at a pressure of 878 mmHg, are in a room. The flasks contain He, Ar, and Xe, respectively.

a. Which of the flasks contains the most atoms of gas?

b. Which of the flasks has the greatest density of gas?

c. If the He flask were heated and the Ar flask cooled, which of the three flasks would be at the highest pressure?

d. Say the temperature of the He was lowered while that of the Xe was raised. Which of the three flasks would have the greatest number of moles of gas?

5.4 | Stoichiometry Problems Involving Gas Volumes

In Chapter 3 you learned how to find the mass of one substance in a chemical reaction from the mass of another substance in the reaction. Now that you know how to use the ideal gas law, we can extend these types of problems to include gas volumes.

Consider the following reaction, which is often used to generate small quantities of oxygen gas:

$$2KClO_3(s) \xrightarrow[MnO_2]{\Delta} 2KCl(s) + 3O_2(g)$$

Suppose you heat 0.0100 mol of potassium chlorate, $KClO_3$, in a test tube. How many liters of oxygen can you produce at 298 K and 1.02 atm?

You solve such a problem by breaking it into two problems, one involving stoichiometry and the other involving the ideal gas law. You note that 2 mol $KClO_3$ yields 3 mol O_2. Therefore,

$$0.0100 \text{ mol KClO}_3 \times \frac{3 \text{ mol } O_2}{2 \text{ mol KClO}_3} = 0.0150 \text{ mol } O_2$$

Now that you have the moles of oxygen produced, you can use the ideal gas law to calculate the volume of oxygen under the conditions given. You rearrange the ideal gas law, $PV = nRT$, and solve for the volume.

$$V = \frac{nRT}{P}$$

Then you substitute for n, T, and P. Because the pressure is given in units of atmospheres, you choose the value of R in units of L·atm/(K·mol). The answer comes out in liters.

$$V = \frac{0.0150 \text{ mol} \times 0.0821 \text{ L·atm/(K·mol)} \times 298 \text{ K}}{1.02 \text{ atm}} = 0.360 \text{ L}$$

The next example further illustrates this method.

Example 5.9 | Solving Stoichiometry Problems Involving Gas Volumes

Automobiles are being equipped with air bags that inflate on collision to protect the occupants from injury (Figure 5.18). Many such air bags are inflated with nitrogen, N_2, using the rapid reaction of sodium azide, NaN_3, and iron(III) oxide, Fe_2O_3, which is initiated by a spark. The overall reaction is

$$6NaN_3(s) + Fe_2O_3(s) \longrightarrow 3Na_2O(s) + 2Fe(s) + 9N_2(g)$$

How many grams of sodium azide would be required to provide 75.0 L of nitrogen gas at 25°C and 748 mmHg?

Problem Strategy This is a stoichiometry problem and a gas-law problem. The chemical equation relates the moles of NaN_3 to moles of N_2. You can use the ideal gas law to relate the volume of N_2 to moles of N_2 and hence moles of NaN_3. Then you can obtain the grams of NaN_3 from the moles of NaN_3.

Solution Here are the available data:

Variable	Value
P	$748 \text{ mmHg} \times \dfrac{1 \text{ atm}}{760 \text{ mmHg}} = 0.984 \text{ atm}$
V	75.0 L
T	$(25 + 273) \text{ K} = 298 \text{ K}$
n	?

(continued)

(*continued*)

Note that the pressure was converted from mmHg to atmospheres and the temperature from degrees Celsius to kelvins. Rearrange the ideal gas law to obtain *n*.

$$n = \frac{PV}{RT}$$

Substituting from the data gives you the moles of N_2.

$$n = \frac{0.984 \text{ atm} \times 75.0 \text{ L}}{0.0821 \text{ L·atm/(K·mol)} \times 298 \text{ K}} = 3.02 \text{ mol}$$

From the moles of N_2, you use the chemical equation to obtain moles of NaN_3.

$$3.02 \text{ mol } N_2 \times \frac{6 \text{ mol } NaN_3}{9 \text{ mol } N_2} = 2.01 \text{ mol } NaN_3$$

Now you can calculate the grams of NaN_3. The molecular mass of NaN_3 is 65.01 amu.

$$2.01 \text{ mol } NaN_3 \times \frac{65.01 \text{ g } NaN_3}{1 \text{ mol } NaN_3} = \textbf{131 g } NaN_3$$

Answer Check As with any problem, see whether the context can help you evaluate your answer. Here we determined the mass of a substance used to inflate an airbag. Using this problem context, we would expect the amount of NaN_3 not to be many kilograms; otherwise, it wouldn't fit in a steering wheel. Also, it shouldn't be some minuscule amount (1 mol of gas will occupy a volume of about 22 L at STP), because the airbag has a large volume to fill (75.0 L in this case).

FIGURE 5.18 ▲
Automobile air bag
Automobiles are equipped with air bags that inflate during collisions. Most air bags are inflated with nitrogen obtained from the rapid reaction of sodium azide, NaN_3 (the azide ion is N_3^-).

Azide ion

Exercise 5.9 How many liters of chlorine gas, Cl_2, can be obtained at 40°C and 787 mmHg from 9.41 g of hydrogen chloride, HCl, according to the following equation?

$$2KMnO_4(s) + 16HCl(aq) \longrightarrow 8H_2O(l) + 2KCl(aq) + 2MnCl_2(aq) + 5Cl_2(g)$$

■ See Problems 5.73, 5.74, 5.75, 5.76, 5.77, and 5.78.

5.5 | Gas Mixtures; Law of Partial Pressures

While studying the composition of air, John Dalton concluded in 1801 that each gas in a mixture of unreactive gases acts, as far as its pressure is concerned, as though it were the only gas in the mixture. To illustrate, consider two 1-L flasks, one filled with helium to a pressure of 152 mmHg at a given temperature and the other filled with hydrogen to a pressure of 608 mmHg at the same temperature. Suppose all of the helium in the one flask is put in with the hydrogen in the other flask (see Figure 5.19). After the gases are mixed in one flask, each gas occupies a volume of one liter, just as before, and has the same temperature.

According to Dalton, each gas exerts the same pressure it would exert if it were the only gas in the flask. Thus, the pressure exerted by helium in the mixture is 152 mmHg, and the pressure exerted by hydrogen in the mixture is 608 mmHg. The total pressure exerted by the gases in the mixture is 152 mmHg + 608 mmHg = 760 mmHg.

FIGURE 5.19 ▲

An illustration of Dalton's law of partial pressures
The valve connecting the flasks and the valve at the funnel are opened so that flask A fills with mineral oil.
The helium flows into flask B (having the same volume as flask A), where it mixes with hydrogen. Each gas
exerts the pressure it would exert if the other were not there.

Partial Pressures and Mole Fractions

The pressure exerted by a particular gas in a mixture is the **partial pressure** of that
gas. The partial pressure of helium in the preceding mixture is 152 mmHg; the partial pressure of hydrogen in the mixture is 608 mmHg. According to **Dalton's law of
partial pressures,** *the sum of the partial pressures of all the different gases in a mixture is equal to the total pressure of the mixture.*

If you let P be the total pressure and P_A, P_B, P_C, . . . be the partial pressures of
the component gases in a mixture, the law of partial pressures can be written as

Dalton's law of partial pressures:
$$P = P_A + P_B + P_C + \cdots$$

The individual partial pressures follow the ideal gas law. For component A,

$$P_A V = n_A RT$$

where n_A is the number of moles of component A.

The composition of a gas mixture is often described in terms of the mole fractions of component gases. The **mole fraction** of a component gas is *the fraction of
moles of that component in the total moles of gas mixture* (or the fraction of molecules that are component molecules). Because the pressure of a gas is proportional to
moles, for fixed volume and temperature ($P = nRT/V \propto n$), the mole fraction also
equals the partial pressure divided by total pressure.

$$\text{Mole fraction of } A = \frac{n_A}{n} = \frac{P_A}{P}$$

Mole percent equals mole fraction × 100. Mole percent is equivalent to the percentage of the molecules that are component molecules.

Example 5.10 | Calculating Partial Pressures and Mole Fractions of a Gas in a Mixture

A 1.00-L sample of dry air at 25°C and 786 mmHg contains 0.925 g N_2, plus other gases including oxygen, argon, and carbon dioxide. a. What is the partial pressure (in mmHg) of N_2 in the air sample? b. What is the mole fraction and mole percent of N_2 in the mixture?

Problem Strategy The key to understanding how to solve this problem is to assume that each gas in the container is independent of other gases; that is, it occupies the entire volume of the sample. Therefore, each gas in the mixture follows the ideal gas law. Using the ideal gas law, we can solve for the pressure of just the N_2, which is its partial pressure. The mole fraction of N_2 can be calculated from the partial pressure of N_2 and the total pressure of all the gases in the sample.

Solution a. Each gas in a mixture follows the ideal gas law. To calculate the partial pressure of N_2, you convert 0.925 g N_2 to moles N_2.

$$0.925 \text{ g } N_2 \times \frac{1 \text{ mol } N_2}{28.0 \text{ g } N_2} = 0.0330 \text{ mol } N_2$$

You substitute into the ideal gas law (noting that 25°C is 298 K).

$$P_{N_2} = \frac{n_{N_2}RT}{V}$$
$$= \frac{0.0330 \text{ mol} \times 0.0821 \text{ L·atm/(K·mol)} \times 298 \text{ K}}{1.00 \text{ L}}$$
$$= 0.807 \text{ atm } (= \textbf{613 mmHg})$$

b. The mole fraction of N_2 in air is

$$\text{Mole fraction of } N_2 = \frac{P_{N_2}}{P} = \frac{613 \text{ mmHg}}{786 \text{ mmHg}} = \textbf{0.780}$$

Air contains **78.0 mole percent** of N_2.

Answer Check Whenever you are solving for the mole fraction of a substance in a mixture, the number must always be less than 1 (as it was in this problem). Therefore, if you obtain a value greater than 1, it is a sure sign that you have made an error.

Exercise 5.10 A 10.0-L flask contains 1.031 g O_2 and 0.572 g CO_2 at 18°C. What are the partial pressures of oxygen and carbon dioxide? What is the total pressure? What is the mole fraction of oxygen in the mixture?

■ See Problems 5.81, 5.82, 5.83, and 5.84.

Concept Check 5.4

A flask equipped with a valve contains 3.0 mol of H_2 gas. You introduce 3.0 mol of Ar gas into the flask via the valve and then seal the flask.

a. What happens to the pressure of just the H_2 gas in the flask after the introduction of the Ar? If it changes, by what factor does it do so?

b. How do the pressures of the Ar and the H_2 in the flask compare?

c. How does the total pressure in the flask relate to the pressures of the two gases?

Collecting Gases over Water

A useful application of the law of partial pressures arises when you collect gases over water (a method used for gases that do not dissolve appreciably in water). Figure 5.20 shows how a gas, produced by chemical reaction in the flask, is collected by leading it to an inverted tube, where it displaces water. As gas bubbles through the water, the gas picks up molecules of water vapor that mix with it. The partial pressure of water vapor in the gas mixture in the collection tube depends only on the temperature. This partial pressure of water vapor is called the *vapor pressure* of water. < Values of the

Vapor pressure is the maximum partial pressure of the vapor in the presence of the liquid. It is defined more precisely in Chapter 11.

TABLE 5.6	
Vapor Pressure of Water at Various Temperatures*	
Temperature (°C)	Pressure (mmHg)
0	4.6
10	9.2
15	12.8
17	14.5
19	16.5
21	18.7
23	21.1
25	23.8
27	26.7
30	31.8
40	55.3
60	149.4
80	355.1
100	760.0

*Appendix B contains a more complete table.

FIGURE 5.20 ▲

Collection of gas over water

Hydrogen, prepared by the reaction of zinc with hydrochloric acid, is led to an inverted tube initially filled with water. When the gas-collection tube is adjusted so that the water level in the tube is at the same height as the level in the beaker, the gas pressure in the tube equals the barometric pressure (769 mmHg). The total gas pressure equals the sum of the partial pressure of the hydrogen (752 mmHg) and the vapor pressure of water (17 mmHg). For clarity, hydrochloric acid is shown in light brown and hydrogen gas in light blue.

vapor pressure of water at various temperatures are listed in Table 5.6 (see Appendix B for a more complete table). The following example shows how to find the partial pressure and then the mass of the collected gas.

Example 5.11	Calculating the Amount of Gas Collected over Water

Hydrogen gas is produced by the reaction of hydrochloric acid, HCl, on zinc metal.

$$2HCl(aq) + Zn(s) \longrightarrow ZnCl_2(aq) + H_2(g)$$

The gas is collected over water. If 156 mL of gas is collected at 19°C (two significant figures) and 769 mmHg total pressure, what is the mass of hydrogen collected?

Problem Strategy The gas collected is hydrogen mixed with water vapor. To obtain the amount of hydrogen, you must first find its partial pressure in the mixture, using Dalton's law (Step 1). Then you can calculate the moles of hydrogen from the ideal gas law (Step 2). Finally, you can obtain the mass of hydrogen from the moles of hydrogen (Step 3).

Solution

Step 1: The vapor pressure of water at 19°C is 16.5 mmHg. From Dalton's law of partial pressures, you know that the total gas pressure equals the partial pressure of hydrogen, P_{H_2}, plus the partial pressure of water, P_{H_2O}.

$$P = P_{H_2} + P_{H_2O}$$

(continued)

(continued)

Substituting and solving for the partial pressure of hydrogen, you get

$$P_{H_2} = P - P_{H_2O} = (769 - 16.5) \text{ mmHg} = 752 \text{ mmHg}$$

Step 2: Now you can use the ideal gas law to find the moles of hydrogen collected. The data are

Variable	Value
P	$752 \text{ mmHg} \times \dfrac{1 \text{ atm}}{760 \text{ mmHg}} = 0.989 \text{ atm}$
V	$156 \text{ mL} = 0.156 \text{ L}$
T	$(19 + 273) \text{ K} = 292 \text{ K}$
n	?

From the ideal gas law, $PV = nRT$, you have

$$n = \frac{PV}{RT} = \frac{0.989 \text{ atm} \times 0.156 \text{ L}}{0.0821 \text{ L·atm}/(\text{K·mol}) \times 293 \text{ K}} = 0.00644 \text{ mol}$$

Step 3: You convert moles of H_2 to grams of H_2.

$$0.00664 \text{ mol } H_2 \times \frac{2.02 \text{ g } H_2}{1 \text{ mol } H_2} = \mathbf{0.0130 \text{ g } H_2}$$

Answer Check   Note that this problem assumes that the water level in the collection tube is the same as the water level in the beaker (Figure 5.20). This enables us to equate the gas pressure in the collection tube to atmospheric pressure.

Exercise 5.11   Oxygen can be prepared by heating potassium chlorate, $KClO_3$, with manganese dioxide as a catalyst. The reaction is

$$2KClO_3(s) \xrightarrow[\text{MnO}_2]{\Delta} 2KCl(s) + 3O_2(g)$$

How many moles of O_2 would be obtained from 1.300 g $KClO_3$? If this amount of O_2 were collected over water at 23°C and at a total pressure of 745 mmHg, what volume would it occupy?

■ See Problems 5.87 and 5.88.

Kinetic-Molecular Theory

In the following sections, you will see how the interpretation of a gas in terms of the **kinetic-molecular theory** (or simply **kinetic theory**) leads to the ideal gas law. According to this theory, *a gas consists of molecules in constant random motion.* The word *kinetic* describes something in motion. Kinetic energy, E_k, is the energy associated with the motion of an object of mass m. From physics,

$$E_k = \tfrac{1}{2}m \times (\text{speed})^2$$

We will use the concept of kinetic energy in describing the kinetic theory.

FIGURE 5.21 ▲

Kinetic-theory model of gas pressure
According to kinetic theory, gas pressure is the result of the bombardment of the container walls by constantly moving molecules.

Waterston's paper, with the reviewers' comments, was discovered in the Royal Society's files by Lord Rayleigh in 1892. (Rayleigh codiscovered argon and received the 1904 Nobel Prize in physics.)

5.6 | Kinetic Theory of an Ideal Gas

Our present explanation of gas pressure is that it results from the continual bombardment of the container walls by constantly moving molecules (Figure 5.21). This kinetic interpretation of gas pressure was first put forth in 1676 by Robert Hooke, who had been an assistant of Boyle. Hooke did not pursue this idea, however, so the generally accepted interpretation of gas pressure remained the one given by Isaac Newton, a contemporary of Hooke.

According to Newton, the pressure of a gas was due to the mutual repulsions of the gas particles (molecules). These repulsions pushed the molecules against the walls of the gas container, much as coiled springs packed tightly in a box would push against the walls of the box. This interpretation continued to be the dominant view of gas pressure until the mid-nineteenth century.

Despite the dominance of Newton's view, some people followed the kinetic interpretation. In 1738, Daniel Bernoulli, a Swiss mathematician and physicist, gave a quantitative explanation of Boyle's law using the kinetic interpretation. He even suggested that molecules move faster at higher temperatures, in order to explain Amontons's experiments on the temperature dependence of gas volume and pressure. However, Bernoulli's paper attracted little notice. A similar kinetic interpretation of gases was submitted for publication to the Royal Society of London in 1848 by John James Waterston. His paper was rejected as "nothing but nonsense." <

Soon afterward, the scientific climate for the kinetic view improved. The kinetic theory of gases was developed by a number of influential physicists, including James Clerk Maxwell (1859) and Ludwig Boltzmann (in the 1870s). Throughout the last half of the nineteenth century, research continued on the kinetic theory, making it a cornerstone of our present view of molecular substances.

Postulates of Kinetic Theory

Physical theories are often given in terms of *postulates:* the basic statements from which all conclusions or predictions of a theory are deduced. The postulates are accepted as long as the predictions from the theory agree with experiment. If a particular prediction did not agree with experiment, we would limit the area to which the theory applies, modify the postulates, or start over with a new theory.

The kinetic theory of an *ideal gas* (a gas that follows the ideal gas law) is based on five postulates.

Postulate 1: *Gases are composed of molecules whose size is negligible compared with the average distance between them.* Most of the volume occupied by a gas is empty space. This means that you can usually ignore the volume occupied by the molecules.

Postulate 2: *Molecules move randomly in straight lines in all directions and at various speeds.* This means that properties of a gas that depend on the motion of molecules, such as pressure, will be the same in all directions.

Postulate 3: *The forces of attraction or repulsion between two molecules (intermolecular forces) in a gas are very weak or negligible, except when they collide.* < This means that a molecule will continue moving in a straight line with undiminished speed until it collides with another gas molecule or with the walls of the container.

Postulate 4: *When molecules collide with one another, the collisions are elastic.* In an elastic collision, the total kinetic energy remains constant; no kinetic energy is lost. To understand the difference between an elastic and an inelastic collision, compare the collision of two hard steel spheres with

The statements that there are no intermolecular forces and that the volume of molecules is negligible are simplifications that lead to the ideal gas law. But intermolecular forces are needed to explain how we get the liquid state from the gaseous state; it is intermolecular forces that hold molecules together in the liquid state.

FIGURE 5.22 ▶

Elastic collision of steel balls

Left: The steel ball at the left is lifted to give it energy. *Right:* When the steel ball is released, the energy is transmitted through elastic collisions to the ball on the right.

the collision of two masses of putty. The collision of steel spheres is nearly elastic (that is, the spheres bounce off each other and continue moving), but that of putty is not (Figure 5.22). Postulate 4 says that unless the kinetic energy of molecules is removed from a gas—for example, as heat—the molecules will forever move with the same average kinetic energy per molecule.

Postulate 5: *The average kinetic energy of a molecule is proportional to the absolute temperature.* This postulate establishes what we mean by temperature from a molecular point of view: the higher the temperature, the greater the molecular kinetic energy.

Qualitative Interpretation of the Gas Laws

According to the kinetic theory, the pressure of a gas results from the bombardment of container walls by molecules. Both the concentration of molecules (number per unit volume) and the average speed of the molecules are factors in determining this pressure. Molecular concentration and average speed determine the frequency of collisions with the wall. Average molecular speed determines the average force of a collision.

Let's consider how these terms apply to Avogadro's law, which relates the volume of gas to the moles of gas at constant (fixed) temperature and pressure. Constant temperature means that the average kinetic energy of a molecule is constant (Postulate 5). Therefore, the average molecular speed and thus the average molecular force from collision remain constant. Gas pressure depends on the force and frequency of molecular collisions with container walls. Consider the container depicted in Figure 5.23A, where the pressure of the gas molecules in the container equals atmospheric pressure. What happens when you introduce more gas molecules into the container? More moles of gas increase the number of molecules per unit volume (concentration) and therefore increase the frequency of collisions with the container walls. If the volume of the container were fixed, the pressure would increase (Figure 5.23B). However, Avogadro's law requires that the pressure remain constant, so the container volume expands until the concentration and, therefore, the frequency of collisions with container walls decrease (Figure 5.23C). The result is that when you increase the number of moles of gas in a container at a constant pressure and temperature, the volume increases.

The same concepts can be used to discuss Boyle's law. Suppose you increase the volume of a gas while holding both the temperature

A   B   C

FIGURE 5.23 ▲

Molecular description of Avogadro's law

(A) A container where the gas molecules are at atmospheric pressure ($P_{inside} = P_{atm}$). The pressure in the container is due to the force and frequency of molecular collisions with the container walls. *(B)* The container after increasing the number of gas molecules while not allowing the piston to move. Due to the greater concentration of gas (more moles of gas in the same volume), the frequency of collisions of the gas molecules with the walls of the container has increased, causing the pressure to increase ($P_{inside} > P_{atm}$). *(C)* Container after the molecules are allowed to move the piston and increase the volume. The concentration of gas molecules and frequency of collisions with the container walls have decreased, and the pressure of the gas molecules inside the container is again equal to atmospheric pressure ($P_{inside} = P_{atm}$).

A   B

FIGURE 5.24 ▲

Molecular description of Boyle's law
(A) A fixed number of moles of gas in a container at room temperature. The pressure in the container is due to the force and frequency of molecular collisions with the container walls. *(B)* The same number of moles of gas at the same temperature as A, but in a container of greater volume. Because of the larger container volume, the gas concentration is now lower, which leads to a decrease in the frequency of molecular collisions per unit of wall area, resulting in a lower pressure.

| *This derivation is essentially the one given by Daniel Bernoulli.*

| *Consistent with kinetic theory, we assume that the duration of collision of a molecule with a container wall is the same, regardless of the type of molecule.*

| *Recall that kinetic energy is defined as $\frac{1}{2}m$ multiplied by (speed)^2.*

and number of moles of gas constant (Figure 5.24). This decreases the concentration of molecules and the frequency of collisions per unit wall area; the pressure must decrease. Thus, when you increase the volume of a gas while keeping the temperature constant, the pressure decreases.

Now consider Charles's law. If you raise the temperature, you increase the average molecular speed. The average force of a collision increases. If all other factors remained fixed, the pressure would increase. For the pressure to remain constant as it does in Charles's law, it is necessary for the volume to increase so that the number of molecules per unit volume decreases and the frequency of collisions decreases. Thus, when you raise the temperature of a gas while keeping the pressure constant, the volume increases.

The Ideal Gas Law from Kinetic Theory

One of the most important features of kinetic theory is its explanation of the ideal gas law. To show how you can get the ideal gas law from kinetic theory, we will first find an expression for the pressure of a gas. <

According to kinetic theory, the pressure of a gas, P, will be proportional to the frequency of molecular collisions with a surface and to the average force exerted by a molecule in collision.

$$P \propto \text{frequency of collisions} \times \text{average force}$$

The average force exerted by a molecule during a collision depends on its mass m and its average speed u—that is, on its average momentum mu. < In other words, the greater the mass of the molecule and the faster it is moving, the greater the force exerted during collision. The frequency of collisions is also proportional to the average speed u, because the faster a molecule is moving, the more often it strikes the container walls. Frequency of collisions is inversely proportional to the gas volume V, because the larger the volume, the less often a given molecule strikes the container walls. Finally, the frequency of collisions is proportional to the number of molecules N in the gas volume. Putting these factors together gives

$$P \propto \left(u \times \frac{1}{V} \times N \right) \times mu$$

Bringing the volume to the left side, you get

$$PV \propto Nmu^2$$

Because the average kinetic energy of a molecule of mass m and average speed u is $\frac{1}{2}mu^2$, PV is proportional to the average kinetic energy of a molecule. < Moreover, the average kinetic energy is proportional to the absolute temperature (Postulate 5). Noting that the number of molecules, N, is proportional to the moles of molecules, n, you have

$$PV \propto nT$$

You can write this as an equation by inserting a constant of proportionality, R, which you can identify as the molar gas constant.

$$PV = nRT$$

The next two sections give additional deductions from kinetic theory.

5.7 | Molecular Speeds; Diffusion and Effusion

The principal tenet of kinetic theory is that molecules are in constant random motion. Now we will look at the speeds of molecules and at some conclusions of kinetic theory regarding molecular speeds.

FIGURE 5.25 ▲

Maxwell's distribution of molecular speeds
The distributions of speeds of H_2 molecules are shown for 0°C and 500°C. Note that the speed corresponding to the maximum in the curve (the most probable speed) increases with temperature.

According to kinetic theory, the total kinetic energy of a mole of any gas equals $\frac{3}{2}RT$. The average kinetic energy of a molecule, which by definition is $\frac{1}{2}mu^2$, is obtained by dividing $\frac{3}{2}RT$ by Avogadro's number, N_A. Therefore, the kinetic energy is $\frac{1}{2}mu^2 = 3RT/(2N_A)$. Hence $u^2 = 3RT/(N_A m)$. Or, noting that $N_A m$ equals the molar mass M_m, you get $u^2 = 3RT/M_m$, from which you get the text equation.

Molecular Speeds

According to kinetic theory, the speeds of molecules in a gas vary over a range of values. The British physicist James Clerk Maxwell (1831–1879) showed theoretically—and it has since been demonstrated experimentally—that molecular speeds are distributed as shown in Figure 5.25. This distribution of speeds depends on the temperature. At any temperature, the molecular speeds vary widely, but most are close to the average speed, which is close to the speed corresponding to the maximum in the distribution curve. As the temperature increases, the average speed increases.

The **root-mean-square (rms) molecular speed,** u, is *a type of average molecular speed, equal to the speed of a molecule having the average molecular kinetic energy.* It is given by the following formula:

$$u = \sqrt{\frac{3RT}{M_m}} = \left(\frac{3RT}{M_m}\right)^{\frac{1}{2}}$$

where R is the molar gas constant, T is the absolute temperature, and M_m is the molar mass for the gas. This result follows from Postulate 5 of kinetic theory. < Note that of two gases, the one with the higher molar mass will have the lower rms speed.

In applying this equation, *care must be taken to use consistent units.* If SI units are used for R (= 8.31 kg·m²/(s²·K·mol)), T (K), and M_m (kg/mol), as in the following example, the rms speed will be in meters per second. Note that in these units, H_2, whose molecular weight is 2.02 amu, has a molar mass of 2.02 × 10^{-3} kg/mol.

Values of the rms speed calculated from this formula indicate that molecular speeds are astonishingly high. For example, the rms speed of H_2 molecules at 20°C is 1.90 × 10^3 m/s (over 4000 mi/hr).

Example 5.12 | Calculating the rms Speed of Gas Molecules

Calculate the rms speed of O_2 molecules in a cylinder at 21°C and 15.7 atm. See Table 5.5 for the appropriate value of R.

Problem Strategy The rms speed of a gas can be determined by substituting the appropriate values into the preceding equation.

Solution The rms molecular speed is independent of pressure but does depend on the absolute temperature, which is (21 + 273) K = 294 K. To calculate u, it is best to use SI units throughout. In these units, the molar mass of O_2 is 32.0 × 10^{-3} kg/mol, and R = 8.31 kg·m²/(s²·K·mol). Hence,

$$u = \left(\frac{3 \times 8.31 \text{ kg·m}^2/(\text{s}^2 \cdot \text{K} \cdot \text{mol}) \times 294 \text{ K}}{32.0 \times 10^{-3} \text{ kg/mol}}\right)^{\frac{1}{2}} = \textbf{479 m/s}$$

Answer Check When performing calculations that involve this formula, be sure to use the appropriate value of R, (8.31 kg·m²)/(s²·K·mol), and to express the molar mass in units of kg/mol, and the temperature in kelvins.

(continued)

(*continued*)

Exercise 5.12
at 22°C?
What is the rms speed (in m/s) of a carbon tetrachloride molecule

■ See Problems 5.89, 5.90, 5.91, and 5.92.

Exercise 5.13   At what temperature do hydrogen molecules, H_2, have the same rms speed as nitrogen molecules, N_2, at 455°C? At what temperature do hydrogen molecules have the same average kinetic energy?

■ See Problems 5.93 and 5.94.

FIGURE 5.26 ▲

Kinetic-theory model of gas diffusion
A vessel contains two different gases. For clarity, the figure shows the motion of only one molecule. The path of the molecule is chaotic because of the constant collisions with other molecules. After some time, the "green" molecule has by its random motion mixed with the "red" gas. Similar motions of other molecules eventually result in the complete mixing of the two gases.

Diffusion and Effusion

The pleasant odor of apple pie baking in the oven quickly draws people to the kitchen. The spread of an odor is easily explained by kinetic theory. All molecules are in constant, chaotic motion, and eventually a cluster of molecules of a particular substance will spread out to occupy a larger and larger space. Gaseous **diffusion** is *the process whereby a gas spreads out through another gas to occupy the space uniformly.* Figure 5.26 is a kinetic-theory explanation of the diffusion of two gases. An individual molecule moves chaotically as it is buffeted by other molecules. After sufficient time, this constant chaotic motion of molecules results in a complete mixing of the gases. Figure 5.27 demonstrates the diffusion of ammonia gas through air.

When you think about the kinetic-theory calculations of molecular speed, you might ask why diffusion is not even much faster than it is. Why does it take minutes for the gas to diffuse throughout a room when the molecules are moving at perhaps a thousand miles per hour? This was, in fact, one of the first criticisms of kinetic theory. The answer is simply that a molecule never travels very far in one direction (at ordinary pressures) before it collides with another molecule and moves off in another direction. If you could trace out the path of an individual molecule, it would be a zigzagging trail. For a molecule to cross a room, it has to travel many times the straight-line distance.

FIGURE 5.27 ▲

Gaseous diffusion
Left: Concentrated aqueous ammonia in the beaker evolves ammonia gas into the glass tube, which contains a strip of wet indicator paper. In the molecular view there are only nitrogen and oxygen molecules (air) surrounding the indicator paper. *Right:* The indicator changes color as the ammonia gas diffuses upward through the air in the tube. The molecular view depicts the appearance of the NH_3 molecules in the tube due to diffusion.

FIGURE 5.28 ▶

Model of gaseous effusion

According to kinetic theory, gas molecules are in constant random motion. When a molecule in the container happens to hit the small opening, it passes (or effuses) to the outside. The rate of effusion depends on the speed of the molecules—the faster the molecules move, the more likely they are to encounter the opening and pass from the inside of the box to the outside.

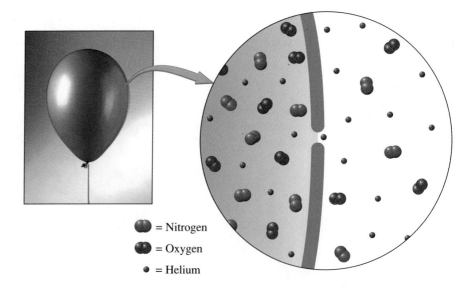

     = Nitrogen

     = Oxygen

     = Helium

Although the rate of diffusion certainly depends in part on the average molecular speed, the effect of molecular collisions makes the theoretical picture a bit complicated. *Effusion*, like diffusion, is a process involving the flow of a gas but is theoretically much simpler.

If you place a container of gas in a vacuum and then make a very small hole in the container, the gas molecules escape through the hole at the same speed they had in the container (Figure 5.28). *The process in which a gas flows through a small hole in a container* is called **effusion.** It was first studied by Thomas Graham, who discovered in 1846 that the rate of effusion of a gas is inversely proportional to the square root of its density. Today we usually state **Graham's law of effusion** in terms of molecular mass: *the rate of effusion of gas molecules from a particular hole is inversely proportional to the square root of the molecular mass of the gas at constant temperature and pressure.*

Let us consider a kinetic-theory analysis of an effusion experiment. Suppose the hole in the container is made small enough so that the gas molecules continue to move randomly (rather than moving together as they would in a wind). When a molecule happens to encounter the hole, it leaves the container. The collection of molecules leaving the container by chance encounters with the hole constitutes the effusing gas. All you have to consider for effusion is the rate at which molecules encounter the hole in the container.

The rate of effusion of molecules from a container depends on three factors: the cross-sectional area of the hole (the larger it is, the more likely molecules are to escape); the number of molecules per unit volume (the more crowded the molecules are, the more likely they are to encounter the hole); and the average molecular speed (the faster the molecules are moving, the sooner they will find the hole and escape).

If you compare the effusion of different gases from the same container, at the same temperature and pressure, the first two factors will be the same. The average molecular speeds will be different, however.

Because the average molecular speed essentially equals $\sqrt{3RT/M_m}$, where M_m is the molar mass, the rate of effusion is proportional to $\sqrt{M_m}$. That is, the rate of effusion is inversely proportional to the square root of the molar mass (or molecular weight), as Graham's law states. The derivation of Graham's law from kinetic theory was considered a triumph of the theory and greatly strengthened confidence in its validity.

Graham's law of effusion:

$$\text{Rate of effusion of molecules} \propto \frac{1}{\sqrt{M_m}} \quad \text{(for the same container at constant } T \text{ and } P)$$

FIGURE 5.29 ▶

The hydrogen fountain
The demonstrator places a beaker containing hydrogen gas over the porous clay container. Hydrogen effuses into the porous container faster than air effuses out. As a result, the pressure inside the porous container and the flask connected to it increases, forcing colored water out the side tube as a stream.

The hydrogen fountain, shown in Figure 5.29, is dependent on the differences in rates of effusion of gases. (Can you explain why a helium-filled balloon loses pressure after a few hours?)

Example 5.13	Calculating the Ratio of Effusion Rates of Gases

Calculate the ratio of effusion rates of molecules of carbon dioxide, CO_2, and sulfur dioxide, SO_2, from the same container and at the same temperature and pressure.

Problem Strategy Here we need to compare the rates of effusion of two gases by taking their rates of effusion. We can use Graham's law of effusion for the two gases to set up a relationship

$$\frac{\text{Rate of effusion of } CO_2}{\text{Rate of effusion of } SO_2} = \frac{\dfrac{1}{\sqrt{M_m(CO_2)}}}{\dfrac{1}{\sqrt{M_m(SO_2)}}}$$

where $M_m(SO_2)$ is the molar mass of SO_2 (64.1 g/mol) and $M_m(CO_2)$ is the molar mass of CO_2 (44.0 g/mol). This equation can be simplified to

$$\frac{\text{Rate of effusion of } CO_2}{\text{Rate of effusion of } SO_2} = \sqrt{\frac{M_m(SO_2)}{M_m(CO_2)}}$$

(Note that the two rates of effusion are inversely proportional to the square roots of the molar masses.)

CO_2; $M_m = 44.0$ g/mol

Solution Substituting these molar masses into the formula gives

$$\frac{\text{Rate of effusion of } CO_2}{\text{Rate of effusion of } SO_2} = \sqrt{\frac{64.1 \text{ g/mol}}{44.0 \text{ g/mol}}} = \textbf{1.21}$$

In other words, carbon dioxide effuses 1.21 times faster than sulfur dioxide (because CO_2 molecules move 1.21 times faster on average than SO_2 molecules).

SO_2; $M_m = 64.1$ g/mol

Answer Check Analyze your answer to make sure that the gas with the lower molar mass has the greater rate of effusion. In this case, the CO_2 would be expected to have the greater effusion rate, so we should expect the effusion rate ratio of CO_2 to SO_2 to be greater than 1.

(continued)

(continued)

Exercise 5.14   If it takes 3.52 s for 10.0 mL of helium to effuse through a hole in a container at a particular temperature and pressure, how long would it take for 10.0 mL of oxygen, O_2, to effuse from the same container at the same temperature and pressure? (Note that the rate of effusion can be given in terms of volume of gas effused per second.)

■ See Problems 5.95, 5.96, 5.97, and 5.98.

Exercise 5.15   If it takes 4.67 times as long for a particular gas to effuse as it takes hydrogen under the same conditions, what is the molecular mass of the gas? (Note that the rate of effusion is inversely proportional to the time it takes for a gas to effuse.)

■ See Problems 5.99 and 5.100.

Graham's law has practical application in the preparation of fuel rods for nuclear fission reactors. Such reactors depend on the fact that the uranium-235 nucleus undergoes fission (splits) when bombarded with neutrons. When the nucleus splits, several neutrons are emitted and a large amount of energy is liberated. These neutrons bombard more uranium-235 nuclei, and the process continues with the evolution of more energy. However, natural uranium consists of 99.27% uranium-238 (which does not undergo fission) and only 0.72% uranium-235 (which does undergo fission). A uranium fuel rod must contain about 3% uranium-235 to sustain the nuclear reaction.

Uranium hexafluoride vapor has a density of 13.0 g/L at 57°C (the temperature at which the solid sublimes). This is more than 12 times as dense as air at the same temperature.

To increase the percentage of uranium-235 in a sample of uranium (a process called *enrichment*), one first prepares uranium hexafluoride, UF_6, a white, crystalline solid that is easily vaporized. < Uranium hexafluoride vapor is allowed to pass through a series of porous membranes. Each membrane has many small holes through which the vapor can effuse. Because the UF_6 molecules with the lighter isotope of uranium travel about 0.4% faster than the UF_6 molecules with the heavier isotope, the gas that passes through first is somewhat richer in uranium-235. When this vapor passes through another membrane, the uranium-235 vapor becomes further concentrated. It takes many effusion stages to reach the necessary enrichment.

Concept Check 5.5

Consider the experimental apparatus shown. In this setup, each round flask contains a gas, and the long tube contains no gas (that is, it is a vacuum).

a. We use 1.0 mol of He for experiment X and 1.0 mol of Ar for experiment Y. If both valves are opened at the same time, which gas would you expect to reach the end of the long tube first?

b. If you wanted the Ar to reach the end of the long tube at the same time as the He, what experimental condition (that is, you cannot change the equipment) could you change to make this happen?

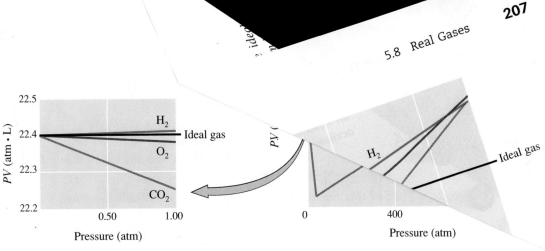

FIGURE 5.30 ▲

Pressure–volume product of gases at different pressures
Right: The pressure–volume product of one mole of various gases at 0°C and at different pressures.
Left: Values at low pressure. For an ideal gas, the pressure–volume product is constant.

5.8 Real Gases

In Section 5.2, we found that, contrary to Boyle's law, the pressure–volume product for O_2 at 0°C was not quite constant, particularly at high pressures (see PV column in Table 5.3). Experiments show that the ideal gas law describes the behavior of real gases quite well at low pressures and moderate temperatures, but not at high pressures and low temperatures.

Figure 5.30 shows the behavior of the pressure–volume product at various pressures for several gases. The gases deviate noticeably from Boyle's law (ideal gas) behavior at high pressures. Also, the deviations differ for each kind of gas. We can explain why this is so by examining the postulates of kinetic theory, from which the ideal gas law can be derived.

Postulate 1 of kinetic theory says that the volume of space occupied by molecules is negligible compared with the total gas volume. To derive the ideal gas law from kinetic theory, we must assume that each molecule is free to move throughout the entire gas volume, V. At low pressures, where the volume of individual molecules is negligible compared with the total volume available (Figure 5.31A), the ideal gas law is a good approximation. At higher pressures, where the volume of individual molecules becomes important (Figure 5.31B), the space through which a molecule can move is significantly different from V.

Postulate 3 says that the forces of attraction between molecules (intermolecular forces) in a gas are very weak or negligible. This is a good approximation at low pressures, where molecules tend to be far apart, because these forces diminish rapidly as the distance between molecules increases. Intermolecular forces become significant at higher pressures, though, because the molecules tend to be close together. Because of these intermolecular forces, the actual pressure of a gas is less than that predicted by ideal gas behavior. As a molecule begins to collide with a wall surface, neighboring molecules pull this colliding molecule slightly away from the wall, giving a reduced pressure (Figure 5.32).

The Dutch physicist J. D. van der Waals (1837–1923) was the first to account for these deviations of a real gas from ideal gas behavior. The **van der Waals equation** is

A   **B**

FIGURE 5.31 ▲

Effect of molecular volume at high pressure

(A) At low pressures, the volume of molecules is a small fraction of the total volume and can be neglected, as in the ideal gas law. *(B)* At high pressures, the volume of molecules is a significant fraction of the total volume and cannot be neglected. The ideal gas law is no longer a good approximation.

FIGURE molecular attractions
Effect pressure
pressure on a wall is due to molecules colliding with it. Here a molecule (shown in red) about to collide with the wall is attracted away from the wall by the weak attractive forces of neighboring molecules (intermolecular forces). As a result, the pressure exerted by the gas is less than that expected in the absence of those forces.

gas law, but includes two constants, a and b, to ideal behavior.

$$\left(P + \frac{n^2a}{V^2}\right)(V - nb) = nRT$$

constants a and b are chosen to fit experiment as closely as possible. Table 5.7 gives values of van der Waals constants for several gases.

You can obtain the van der Waals equation from the ideal gas law, $PV = nRT$, by making the following replacements:

Ideal Gas Equation		**van der Waals Equation**
V	becomes	$V - nb$
P	becomes	$P + n^2a/V^2$

To obtain these substitutions, van der Waals reasoned as follows. The volume available for a molecule to move in equals the gas volume, V, minus the volume occupied by molecules. So he replaced V in the ideal gas law with $V - nb$, where nb represents the volume occupied by n moles of molecules. Then he noted that the total force of attraction on any molecule about to hit a wall is proportional to the concentration of neighboring molecules, n/V. However, the number of molecules about to hit the wall per unit wall area is also proportional to the concentration, n/V. Therefore, the force per unit wall area, or pressure, is reduced from that assumed in the ideal gas law by a factor proportional to n^2/V^2. Letting a be the proportionality constant, we can write

$$P(\text{actual}) = P(\text{ideal}) - n^2a/V^2$$

or

$$P(\text{ideal}) = P(\text{actual}) + n^2a/V^2$$

In other words, you replace P in the ideal gas law by $P + n^2a/V^2$.

The next example illustrates the use of the van der Waals equation to calculate the pressure exerted by a gas under given conditions.

TABLE 5.7	van der Waals Constants for Some Gases		
Gas	a $L^2 \cdot atm/mol^2$	b L/mol	
CO_2	3.658	0.04286	
C_2H_6	5.570	0.06499	
C_2H_5OH	12.56	0.08710	
He	0.0346	0.0238	
H_2	0.2453	0.02651	
O_2	1.382	0.03186	
SO_2	6.865	0.05679	
H_2O	5.537	0.03049	

From Lide, David R., Ed., in *CRC Handbook of Chemistry and Physics,* 74th ed., pp. 6–48. Copyright CRC Press Inc., Boca Raton, Florida, 1993. With the permission of CRC Press, Inc.

| **Example 5.14** | Using the van der Waals Equation |

If sulfur dioxide were an ideal gas, the pressure at 0.0°C exerted by 1.000 mole occupying 22.41 L would be 1.000 atm (22.41 L is the molar volume of an ideal gas at STP). Use the van der Waals equation to estimate the pressure of this volume of 1.000 mol SO_2 at 0.0°C. See Table 5.7 for values of a and b.

Problem Strategy You first rearrange the van der Waals equation to give P in terms of the other variables.

$$P = \frac{nRT}{V - nb} - \frac{n^2a}{V^2}$$

Now you substitute $R = 0.08206$ L·atm/(K·mol), $T = 273.2$ K, $V = 22.41$ L, $a = 6.865$ L^2·atm/mol^2, and $b = 0.05679$ L/mol.

Solution

$$P = \frac{1.000 \text{ mol} \times 0.08206 \text{ L·atm/(K·mol)} \times 273.2 \text{ K}}{22.41 \text{ L} - (1.000 \text{ mol} \times 0.05679 \text{ L/mol})} -$$

$$\frac{(1.000 \text{ mol})^2 \times 6.865 \text{ L}^2\text{·atm/mol}^2}{(22.41 \text{ L})^2}$$

$$= 1.003 \text{ atm} - 0.014 \text{ atm} = \textbf{0.989 atm}$$

Note that the first term, $nRT/(V - nb)$, gives the pressure corrected for molecular volume. This pressure, 1.003 atm, is slightly higher than the ideal value, 1.000 atm, because the volume through which a molecule is free to move, $V - nb$, is smaller than what is assumed for an ideal gas (V). Therefore, the concentration of molecules in this volume is greater, and the number of collisions per unit surface area is expected to be greater. However, the last term, n^2a/V^2, corrects for intermolecular forces, which reduce the force of the collisions, and this reduces the pressure to 0.989 atm.

Answer Check Make sure that you used the appropriate value for the ideal gas constant and that the units of volume and pressure match those given for the constants a and b.

Exercise 5.16 Use the van der Waals equation to calculate the pressure of 1.000 mol ethane, C_2H_6, that has a volume of 22.41 L at 0.0°C. Compare the result with the value predicted by the ideal gas law.

■ See Problems 5.101 and 5.102.

Concept Check 5.6

A 1.00-L container is filled with an ideal gas and the recorded pressure is 350 atm. We then put the same amount of a real gas into the container and measure the pressure.

a. If the real gas molecules occupy a relatively small volume and have large intermolecular attractions, how would you expect the pressures of the two gases to compare?

b. If the real gas molecules occupy a relatively large volume and there are negligible intermolecular attractions, how would you expect the pressures of the two gases to compare?

c. If the real gas molecules occupy a relatively large volume and have large intermolecular attractions, how would you expect the pressures of the two gases to compare?

A Chemist Looks at . . .

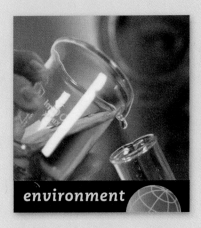

environment

Carbon Dioxide Gas and the Greenhouse Effect

Yes, I know, I shouldn't have left that chocolate bar on the seat of my car, which I parked on a sunny street near the university. You and I know that the interior of such a car can become quite hot. Have you ever wondered why? If the sun's heat energy can get into the car through its window glass, why can't it leave equally well?

Parked cars are similar to greenhouses, which people have used for centuries to protect plants from cold weather. The Swedish chemist Svante Arrhenius, whom you may remember from the previous chapter (for his theory of ionic solutions), realized that carbon dioxide in the atmosphere acts like the glass in a greenhouse. His calculations, published in 1898, were the first to show how sensitive the temperature of the earth might be to the percentage of carbon dioxide in the atmosphere. Arrhenius's reference to the earth's atmospheric envelope, with its carbon dioxide, as a "hothouse" has evolved into our present-day term *greenhouse effect*.

Here is the explanation of the greenhouse effect. The principal gases in the atmosphere are oxygen, O_2, and nitrogen, N_2. These gases are transparent to visible light from the sun, and when this light reaches the surface of the earth, it is absorbed and converted to heat. This heat causes atoms in the earth's surface to vibrate, which then radiate the heat energy as infrared radiation, or heat rays (Figure 5.33). Neither oxygen nor nitrogen absorb infrared radiation, so if the earth's atmosphere contained only these gases, the infrared radiation, or heat rays, would simply escape into outer space; there would be no greenhouse effect. However, other gases in the atmosphere, especially carbon dioxide, do absorb infrared radiation, and it is this absorption that warms the atmosphere and eventually also the earth's surface, giving us a greenhouse effect. The

FIGURE 5.33 ▶

Greenhouse effect of certain gases in the atmosphere
The atmosphere is transparent to sunlight, except for radiation in the far ultraviolet. When sunlight reaches the earth's surface, it is absorbed. The heated surface then radiates the energy back as infrared radiation. The major components of the atmosphere, O_2 and N_2, are transparent to this radiation, but gases such as CO_2, H_2O, CH_4, and chlorofluorocarbons, do absorb infrared rays. These substances in the atmosphere then reradiate the infrared rays, with the result that a significant fraction of the radiation returns to earth. In effect, these gases trap the radiation, acting like the glass on a greenhouse.

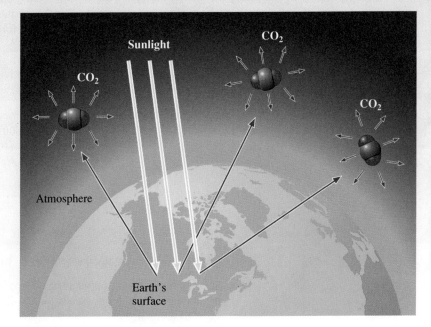

greater the percentage of carbon dioxide in the atmosphere, the warmer the earth should be. (Glass, acting like carbon dioxide, allows visible light to pass into a greenhouse, but absorbs infrared radiation, effectively trapping the heat.)

The greenhouse effect has become associated with the concept of *global warming*. Records kept since the nineteenth century clearly show that the amount of carbon dioxide in the atmosphere has increased dramatically, from about 284 ppm (parts per million) in 1830 to about 370 ppm in 2000 (Figure 5.34). (Parts per million is equivalent to mole percent $\times 10^{-4}$.) Scientists believe that our burning of fossil fuels (coal, oil, and natural gas) is responsible for this change. Moreover, temperature measurements made at the surface of the earth during the past 100 years indicate an average temperature increase of between 0.4°C and 0.8°C. Thus, many climate scientists believe that human activities are at least partially responsible for global warming, and hence, they predict drastic changes in climate.

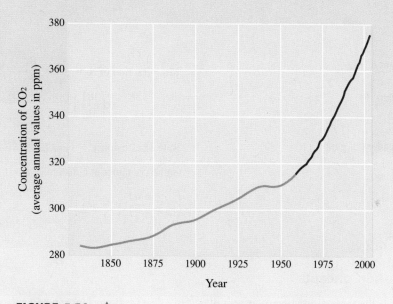

FIGURE 5.34 ▲

Concentrations of carbon dioxide in the atmosphere (average annual values)
Concentrations of carbon dioxide in the atmosphere have been increasing steadily since about 1830. The blue curve is derived from ice core samples (containing air bubbles) obtained from Antarctica. The purple curve is derived from direct measurements of atmospheric carbon dioxide collected since 1958 at Mauna Loa, Hawaii. (*Source of blue curve:* D. M. Etheridge, L. P. Steele, R. L. Langenfelds, R. J. Francey, J. M. Barnola, and V. I. Morgan. 1998. Historical CO_2 records from the Law Dome DE08, DE08-2, and DSS ice cores. In *Trends: A Compendium of Data on Global Change.* Carbon Dioxide Information Analysis Center, Oak Ridge National Laboratory, U.S. Department of Energy, Oak Ridge, Tenn., U.S.A. *Source of purple curve:* C. D. Keeling and T. P. Whorf. 2005. Atmospheric CO_2 records from sites in the SIO air sampling network. In *Trends: A Compendium of Data on Global Change.* Carbon Dioxide Information Analysis Center, Oak Ridge National Laboratory, U.S. Department of Energy, Oak Ridge, Tenn., U.S.A.

■ See Problems 5.107 and 5.108.

A Checklist for Review

Important Terms

pressure (5.1)
pascal (Pa) (5.1)
barometer (5.1)
manometer (5.1)
millimeters of mercury
   (mmHg or torr) (5.1)
atmosphere (atm) (5.1)
bar (5.1)
Boyle's law (5.2)
Charles's law (5.2)

Avogadro's law (5.2)
molar gas volume (V_m) (5.2)
standard temperature and
   pressure (STP) (5.2)
molar gas constant (R) (5.3)
ideal gas law (5.3)
partial pressure (5.5)
Dalton's law of partial
   pressures (5.5)
mole fraction (5.5)

kinetic-molecular theory of gases
   (kinetic theory) (5.6)
root-mean-square (rms)
   molecular speed (5.7)
diffusion (5.7)
effusion (5.7)
Graham's law of
   effusion (5.7)
van der Waals
   equation (5.8)

Key Equations

$PV = \text{constant}$ (constant n, T)

$\dfrac{V}{T} = \text{constant}$ (constant n, P)

$V_m = \text{specific constant}$
(depending on T, P; independent of gas)

$PV = nRT$

$PM_m = dRT$

$P = P_A + P_B + P_C + \cdots$

Mole fraction of $A = \dfrac{n_A}{n} = \dfrac{P_A}{P}$

$u = \sqrt{\dfrac{3RT}{M_m}} = \left(\dfrac{3RT}{M_m}\right)^{\frac{1}{2}}$

Rate of effusion $\}$ $\dfrac{1}{\sqrt{M_m}}$
(same container at constant T, P)

$\left(P + \dfrac{n^2 a}{V^2}\right)(V - nb) = nRT$

Summary of Facts and Concepts

The *pressure* of a gas equals the force exerted per unit area of surface. It is measured by a *manometer* in units of *pascals, millimeters of mercury,* or *atmospheres.*

Gases at low to moderate pressures and moderate temperatures follow the same simple relationships, or gas laws. Thus, for a given amount of gas at constant temperature, the volume varies inversely with pressure *(Boyle's law).* Also, for a given amount of gas at constant pressure, the volume is directly proportional to the absolute temperature *(Charles's law).* These two laws, together with *Avogadro's law* (equal volumes of any two gases at the same temperature and pressure contain the same number of molecules), can be formulated as one equation, $PV = nRT$ *(ideal gas law).* This equation gives the relationship among P, V, n, and T for a gas. It also relates these quantities for each component in a gas mixture. The total gas pressure, P, equals the sum of the partial pressures of each component *(law of partial pressures).*

The ideal gas law can be explained by the *kinetic-molecular theory.* We define an ideal gas as consisting of molecules with negligible volume that are in constant random motion. In the ideal gas model, there are no intermolecular forces between molecules, and the average kinetic energy of molecules is proportional to the absolute temperature. From kinetic theory, one can show that the *rms molecular speed* equals $\sqrt{3RT/M_m}$. Given this result, one can derive *Graham's law of effusion:* the rate of effusion of gas molecules under identical conditions is inversely proportional to the square root of the molecular mass.

Real gases deviate from the ideal gas law at high pressure and low temperature. From kinetic theory, we expect these deviations, because real molecules do have volume and intermolecular forces do exist. These two factors are partially accounted for in the *van der Waals equation.*

Media Summary

Visit the **student website at college.cengage.com/pic/ebbing9e** to help prepare for class, study for quizzes and exams, understand core concepts, and visualize molecular-level interactions. The following media activities are available for this chapter:

Prepare for Class

■ **Video Lessons** *Mini lectures from chemistry experts*
Properties of Gases
Boyle's Law
Charles's Law
The Combined Gas Law
Avogadro's Law
CIA Demonstration: The Potato Cannon
The Ideal Gas Law
Applications of the Ideal Gas Law
Partial Pressure and Dalton's Law
The Kinetic-Molecular Theory of Gases
Molecular Speeds
Effusion and Diffusion
Comparing Real and Ideal Gases

 Improve Your Grade

■ **Visualizations** *Molecular-level animations and lab demonstration videos*
Boyle's Law: A Graphical View
Boyle's Law: A Molecular-Level View
Collapsing Can

Liquid Nitrogen and Balloons
Charles's Law: A Graphical View
Charles's Law: A Molecular-Level View
The Ideal Gas Law: $PV = nRT$
Visualizing Molecular Motion: Single Molecule
Visualizing Molecular Motion: Many Molecules
Kinetic–Molecular Theory/Heat Transfer
Diffusion of Gases
Gaseous Ammonia and Hydrochloric Acid
Effusion of a Gas

■ **Tutorials** *Animated examples and interactive activities*
The Ideal Gas Law

■ **Flashcards** *Key terms and definitions*
Online Flashcards

■ **Self-Assessment Questions** *Additional questions with full worked-out solutions*
6 Self-Assessment Questions

 ACE the Test

Multiple-choice quizzes
3 ACE Practice Tests

Access these resources using the passkey available free with new texts or for purchase separately.

Learning Objectives

5.1 Gas Pressure and Its Measurement

■ Define *pressure* and its units.
■ Convert units of pressure. **Example 5.1**

5.2 Empirical Gas Laws

■ Express *Boyle's law* in words and as an equation.
■ Use Boyle's law. **Example 5.2**
■ Express *Charles's law* in words and as an equation.
■ Use Charles's law. **Example 5.3**
■ Express the *combined gas law* as an equation.
■ Use the combined gas law. **Example 5.4**
■ State *Avogadro's law.*
■ Define *standard temperature and pressure (STP).*

5.3 The Ideal Gas Law

■ State what makes a gas an *ideal gas.*
■ Learn the *ideal gas law* equation.
■ Derive the empirical gas laws from the ideal gas law. **Example 5.5**
■ Use the ideal gas law. **Example 5.6**
■ Calculate gas density. **Example 5.7**
■ Determine the molecular mass of a vapor. **Example 5.8**
■ Use an equation to calculate gas density.

5.4 Stoichiometry Problems Involving Gas Volumes

■ Solving stoichiometry problems involving gas volumes. **Example 5.9**

5.5 Gas Mixture; Law of Partial Pressures

■ Learn the equation for *Dalton's law of partial pressures.*
■ Define the *mole fraction* of a gas.
■ Calculate the partial pressure and mole fractions of a gas in a mixture. **Example 5.10**
■ Describe how gases are collected over water and how to determine the *vapor pressure* of water.
■ Calculate the amount of gas collected over water. **Example 5.11**

5.6 Kinetic Theory of an Ideal Gas

■ List the five postulates of the *kinetic theory.*
■ Provide a qualitative description of the gas laws based on the kinetic theory.

5.7 Molecular Speeds; Diffusion and Effusion

■ Describe how the *root-mean-square (rms) molecular speed* of gas molecules varies with temperature.
■ Describe the molecular-speed distribution of gas molecules at different temperatures.

■ Calculate the rms speed of gas molecules.
  Example 5.12
■ Define *effusion* and *diffusion*.
■ Describe how individual gas molecules move undergoing diffusion.
■ Calculate the ratio of effusion rates of gases.
  Example 5.13

5.8 Real Gases

■ Explain how and why a *real gas* is different from an ideal gas.
■ Use the van der Waals equation. Example 5.14

Self-Assessment and Review Questions

5.1   Define *pressure*. From the definition, obtain the SI unit of pressure in terms of SI base units.

5.2   For what purpose is a manometer used? How does it work?

5.3   What variables determine the height of the liquid in a manometer?

5.4   Starting with Boyle's law (stated as an equation), obtain an equation for the final volume occupied by a gas from the initial volume when the pressure is changed at constant temperature.

5.5   The volume occupied by a gas depends linearly on degrees Celsius at constant pressure, but it is not directly proportional to degrees Celsius. However, it is directly proportional to kelvins. What is the difference between a linear relationship and a direct proportion?

5.6   Explain how you would set up an absolute temperature scale based on the Fahrenheit scale, knowing that absolute zero is −273.15°C.

5.7   Starting with Charles's law (stated as an equation), obtain an equation for the final volume of a gas from its initial volume when the temperature is changed at constant pressure.

5.8   State Avogadro's law in words. How does this law explain the law of combining volumes? Use the gas reaction

$$N_2 + 3H_2 \longrightarrow 2NH_3$$

as an example in your explanation.

5.9   What are the standard conditions for comparing gas volumes?

5.10   What does the term *molar gas volume* mean? What is the molar gas volume (in liters) at STP for an ideal gas?

5.11   Starting from Boyles's, Charles's, and Avogadro's laws, obtain the ideal gas law, $PV = nRT$.

5.12   What variables are needed to describe a gas that obeys the ideal gas law? What are the SI units for each variable?

5.13   What is the value of R in units of L·mmHg/(K·mol)?

5.14   The ideal gas law relates four variables. An empirical gas law relates two variables, assuming the other two are constant. How many empirical gas laws can be obtained? Give statements of each.

5.15   Give the postulates of kinetic theory and state any evidence that supports them.

5.16   Explain Boyle's law in terms of the kinetic theory.

5.17   What is the origin of gas pressure, according to kinetic theory?

5.18   How does the rms molecular speed depend on absolute temperature? on molar volume?

5.19   Explain why a gas appears to diffuse more slowly than average molecular speeds might suggest.

5.20   What is effusion? Why does a gas whose molecules have smaller mass effuse faster than one whose molecules have larger mass?

5.21   Under what conditions does the behavior of a real gas begin to differ significantly from the ideal gas law?

5.22   What is the physical meaning of the a and b constants in the van der Waals equation?

5.23   Which of the following is *not* part of the kinetic molecular theory?

  a. The greater the volume occupied by a given amount of gas, the higher the intermolecular forces.
  b. The average kinetic energy is proportional to the absolute temperature.
  c. Gas particles are in constant motion.
  d. Total kinetic energy is conserved during collision.
  e. Gas molecules have no volume.

5.24   A sample of nitrogen gas is placed into a container at 200 K. If the temperature of the container is reduced by 100°C and the measured pressure decreases by 50%, how does the volume of the container change?

  a. The container volume increases by less than 50%.
  b. The container volume increases by more than 50%.
  c. The container volume doesn't change.
  d. The container volume increases by 50%.
  e. The container volume decreases by 50%.

5.25   At standard temperature and pressure, a 1.00-mol sample of argon gas is vented into a 22.4-L rigid box that already contains 1.00 mol of nitrogen gas. We would expect the argon gas to

  a. decrease the total gas pressure in the box by 50%.
  b. occupy the entire 22.4-L volume of the box.
  c. increase the total gas pressure in the box by less than 50%.
  d. spread out into the box, but the actual volume occupied by the gas cannot be known without pressure information.
  e. occupy only a volume of 11.2 L of the box, since there is already 1.0 mol of nitrogen present in the container.

5.26   A 1-liter container is filled with 2.0 mol Ar, 2.0 mol H_2, and 4.0 mol Kr. Which of the following statements about these gases is *false*?

  a. The Kr is the densest of the three gases.
  b. The mole fraction of Ar in the flask is 0.25.
  c. The total pressure in the flask is four times the pressure of the Ar.
  d. The Ar atoms hit the walls of the flask with the greatest force of the three gases.
  e. H_2 has the highest rms velocity of the three gases.

Concept Explorations

5.27 Gas Laws and Kinetic Theory of Gases I

Shown below are two identical containers labeled A and B. Container A contains a molecule of an ideal gas, and container B contains two molecules of an ideal gas. Both containers are at the same temperature.

a. How do the pressures in the two containers compare? Be sure to explain your answer.

A   B

b. Shown below are four different containers (C, D, E, and F), each with the same volume and at the same temperature. How do the pressures of the gases in the containers compare?

C   D

E   F

c. Container H below has twice the volume of container G. How will the pressure in the containers compare? Explain your reasoning.

G   H

d. How will the pressure of containers G and H compare if you add two more gas molecules to container H?

e. Consider containers J and L below. Container L has twice the volume of container J. Container J is at a temperature of 100 K, and container L is at 200 K. How does the pressure in container J compare with that in container L? Include an explanation as part of your answer.

$T = 100$ K $T = 200$ K

J   L

5.28 Gas Laws and Kinetic Theory of Gases II

Consider the box below that contains a single atom of an ideal gas.

a. Assuming that this gas atom is moving, describe how it creates pressure inside the container.

b. Now consider the two containers below, each at the same temperature. If we were to measure the gas pressure in each container, how would they compare? Explain your answer.

A   B

c. Consider the two containers below, labeled C and D, one with an ideal gas atom and one with ideal gas molecules, each at the same temperature. The gas molecule has more mass than the gas atom. How do the pressures of the two containers compare? Why?

C   D

d. For the containers C and D above, which would have the higher root-mean-square (rms) molecular speed? How does the difference in rms speeds support or contradict the answer you obtained above when you compared the pressures?

e. Consider containers E and F below. How do the pressures in these containers compare? Be sure to explain your answer.

$T = 100$ K $T = 200$ K

E   **F**

f. Consider containers G and H below, one with a gas atom and one with a gas molecule. As before, the gas molecule has more mass than the gas atom. Explain how the pressures in these containers compare.

$T = 100$ K $T = 200$ K

G   **H**

g. Now think about the containers below, I and J. How do the pressures in these containers compare? Be sure to justify your answer.

$T = 200$ K $T = 100$ K

I   **J**

h. Finally, how do the pressures in containers K and L compare?

$T = 200$ K $T = 100$ K

K   **L**

Conceptual Problems

5.29 Using the concepts developed in this chapter, explain the following observations.
 a. Automobile tires are flatter on cold days.
 b. You are not supposed to dispose of aerosol cans in a fire.
 c. The lid of a water bottle pops off when the bottle sits in the sun.
 d. A balloon pops when you squeeze it.

5.30 You have three identical flasks, each containing equal amounts of N_2, O_2, and He. The volume of the N_2 flask is doubled, the O_2 flask volume is halved, and the He flask volume is reduced to one-third of the original volume. Rank the flasks from highest to lowest pressure both before and after the volume is changed and indicate by what factor the pressure has changed.

5.31 Consider the following gas container equipped with a movable piston.

 a. By what factor (increase by 1, decrease by 1.5, etc.) would you change the pressure if you wanted the volume to change from volume C to volume D?
 b. If the piston were moved from volume C to volume A, by what factor would the pressure change?
 c. By what factor would you change the temperature in order to change from volume C to volume B?

 d. If you increased the number of moles of gas in the container by a factor of 2, by what factors would the pressure and the volume change?

5.32 A 3.00-L flask containing 2.0 mol of O_2 and 1.0 mol of N_2 is in a room that is at 22.0°C.
 a. How much (what fraction) of the total pressure in the flask is due to the N_2?
 b. The flask is cooled and the pressure drops. What happens, if anything, to the mole fraction of the O_2 at the lower temperature?
 c. 1.0 L of liquid water is introduced into the flask containing both gases. The pressure is then measured about 45 minutes later. Would you expect the measured pressure to be higher or lower?
 d. Given the information in this problem and the conditions in part c, would it be possible to calculate the pressure in the flask after the introduction of the water? If it is not possible with the given information, what further information would you need to accomplish this task?

5.33 Consider the following setup, which shows identical containers connected by a tube with a valve that is presently closed. The container on the left has 1.0 mol of H_2 gas; the container on the right has 1.0 mol of O_2.

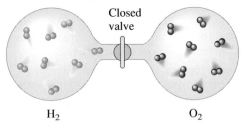

Closed valve

H_2 O_2

Note: Acceptable answers to some of these questions might be "both" or "neither one."

a. Which container has the greatest density of gas?

b. Which container has molecules that are moving at a faster average molecular speed?

c. Which container has more molecules?

d. If the valve is opened, will the pressure in each of the containers change? If it does, how will it change (increase, decrease, or no change)?

e. 2.0 mol of Ar is added to the system with the valve open. What fraction of the total pressure will be due to the H_2?

5.34 Two identical He-filled balloons, each with a volume of 20 L, are allowed to rise into the atmosphere. One rises to an altitude of 3000 m while the other rises to 6000 m.

a. Assuming that the balloons are at the same temperature, which balloon has the greater volume?

b. What information would you need in order to calculate the volume of each of the balloons at their respective heights?

5.35 You have a balloon that contains O_2. What could you do to the balloon in order to double the volume? Be specific in your answers; for example, you could increase the number of moles of O_2 by a factor of 2.

5.36 Three 25.0-L flasks are placed next to each other on a shelf in a chemistry stockroom. The first flask contains He at a pressure of 1.0 atm, the second contains Xe at 1.50 atm, and the third contains F_2 and has a label that says 2.0 mol F_2. Consider the following questions about these flasks.

a. Which flask has the greatest number of moles of gas?

b. If you wanted each of the flasks to be at the same pressure as the He flask, what general things could you do to the other two containers to make this happen?

Practice Problems

Note: In these problems, the final zeros given in temperatures and pressures (for example, 20°C, 760 mmHg) are significant figures.

Units of Pressure

5.37 A gas in a closed-tube manometer (Figure 5.4) has a measured pressure of 0.047 atm. Calculate the pressure in mmHg.

5.38 The barometric pressure measured outside an airplane at 9 km (30,000 ft) was 259 mmHg. Calculate the pressure in kPa.

Empirical Gas Laws

5.39 Suppose you had a 3.15-L sample of neon gas at 21°C and a pressure of 0.951 atm. What would be the volume of this gas if the pressure were increased to 1.292 atm while the temperature remained constant?

5.40 You fill a balloon with helium gas to a volume of 2.68 L at 23°C and 789 mmHg. Now you release the balloon. What would be the volume of helium if its pressure changed to 632 mmHg but the temperature were unchanged?

5.41 You have a cylinder of argon gas at 19.8 atm pressure at 19°C. The volume of argon in the cylinder is 50.0 L. What would be the volume of this gas if you allowed it to expand to the pressure of the surrounding air (0.974 atm)? Assume the temperature remains constant.

5.42 A diving bell is a container open at the bottom. As the bell descends, the water level inside changes so that the pressure inside equals the pressure outside. Initially, the volume of air is 8.58 m^3 at 1.020 atm and 20°C. What is the volume at 1.212 atm and 20°C?

5.43 A McLeod gauge measures low gas pressures by compressing a known volume of the gas at constant temperature. If 315 cm^3 of gas is compressed to a volume of 0.0457 cm^3 under a pressure of 2.51 kPa, what was the original gas pressure?

5.44 If 456 dm^3 of krypton at 101 kPa and 21°C is compressed into a 27.0-dm^3 tank at the same temperature, what is the pressure of krypton in the tank?

5.45 A sample of nitrogen gas at 18°C and 760 mmHg has a volume of 3.92 mL. What is the volume at 0°C and 1 atm of pressure?

5.46 A mole of gas at 0°C and 760 mmHg occupies 22.41 L. What is the volume at 20°C and 760 mmHg?

5.47 Helium gas, He, at 22°C and 1.00 atm occupied a vessel whose volume was 2.54 L. At a pressure of 1.00 atm, what volume would this gas occupy if it were cooled to liquid-nitrogen temperature (−197°C)?

5.48 An experiment called for 4.83 L of sulfur dioxide, SO_2, at 0°C and 1.00 atm. What would be the volume of this gas at 25°C and 1.00 atm?

5.49 A vessel containing 39.5 cm^3 of helium gas at 25°C and 106 kPa was inverted and placed in cold ethanol. As the gas contracted, ethanol was forced into the vessel to maintain the same pressure of helium. If this required 7.7 cm^3 of ethanol, what was the final temperature of the helium?

5.50 A sample of 62.3 cm^3 of argon gas at 18°C was contained at a pressure of 155 kPa in a J-shaped tube with mercury, as in Figure 5.5. Later the temperature changed. When the mercury level was adjusted to give the same pressure of argon, the gas volume changed to 61.2 cm^3. What was the final temperature of the argon?

5.51 A bacterial culture isolated from sewage produced 35.5 mL of methane, CH_4, at 31°C and 753 mmHg. What is the volume of this methane at standard temperature and pressure (0°C, 760 mmHg)?

5.52 Pantothenic acid is a B vitamin. Using the Dumas method, you find that a sample weighing 71.6 mg gives 3.84 mL of nitrogen gas at 23°C and 785 mmHg. What is the volume of nitrogen at STP?

5.53 In the presence of a platinum catalyst, ammonia, NH_3, burns in oxygen, O_2, to give nitric oxide, NO, and water vapor. How many volumes of nitric oxide are obtained from one volume of ammonia, assuming each gas is at the same temperature and pressure?

5.54 Methanol, CH_3OH, can be produced in industrial plants by reacting carbon dioxide with hydrogen in the presence of a catalyst. Water is the other product. How many volumes of hydrogen are required for each volume of carbon dioxide when each gas is at the same temperature and pressure?

Ideal Gas Law

5.55 Starting from the ideal gas law, prove that the volume of a mole of gas is inversely proportional to the pressure at constant temperature (Boyle's law).

5.56 Starting from the ideal gas law, prove that the volume of a mole of gas is directly proportional to the absolute temperature at constant pressure (Charles's law).

5.57 A cylinder of oxygen gas contains 91.3 g O_2. If the volume of the cylinder is 8.58 L, what is the pressure of the O_2 if the gas temperature is 21°C?

5.58 In an experiment, you fill a heavy-walled 5.00-L flask with methane gas, CH_4. If the flask contains 7.13 g of methane at 19°C, what is the gas pressure?

5.59 An experiment calls for 3.50 mol of chlorine, Cl_2. What volume will this be if the gas volume is measured at 34°C and 4.00 atm?

5.60 According to your calculations, a reaction should yield 5.67 g of oxygen, O_2. What do you expect the volume to be at 23°C and 0.985 atm?

5.61 The maximum safe pressure that a certain 4.00-L vessel can hold is 3.50 atm. If the vessel contains 0.410 mol of gas, what is the maximum temperature (in degrees Celsius) to which this vessel can be subjected?

5.62 A 2.50-L flask was used to collect a 5.65-g sample of propane gas, C_3H_8. After the sample was collected, the gas pressure was found to be 741 mmHg. What was the temperature of the propane in the flask?

5.63 What is the density of ammonia gas, NH_3, at 31°C and 751 mmHg? Obtain the density in grams per liter.

5.64 Calculate the density of hydrogen sulfide gas, H_2S, at 56°C and 967 mmHg. Obtain the density in grams per liter.

5.65 Butane, C_4H_{10}, is an easily liquefied gaseous fuel. Calculate the density of butane gas at 0.897 atm and 24°C. Give the answer in grams per liter.

5.66 Chloroform, $CHCl_3$, is a volatile (easily vaporized) liquid solvent. Calculate the density of chloroform vapor at 98°C and 797 mmHg. Give the answer in grams per liter.

5.67 A chemist vaporized a liquid compound and determined its density. If the density of the vapor at 90°C and 753 mmHg is 1.585 g/L, what is the molecular mass of the compound?

5.68 You vaporize a liquid substance at 100°C and 755 mmHg. The volume of 0.548 g of vapor is 237 mL. What is the molecular mass of the substance?

5.69 A 2.56-g sample of a colorless liquid was vaporized in a 250-mL flask at 121°C and 786 mmHg. What is the molecular mass of this substance?

5.70 A 2.30-g sample of white solid was vaporized in a 345-mL vessel. If the vapor has a pressure of 985 mmHg at 148°C, what is the molecular mass of the solid?

5.71 Ammonium chloride, NH_4Cl, is a white solid. When heated to 325°C, it gives a vapor that is a mixture of ammonia and hydrogen chloride.

$$NH_4Cl(s) \longrightarrow NH_3(g) + HCl(g)$$

Suppose someone contends that the vapor consists of NH_4Cl molecules rather than a mixture of NH_3 and HCl. Could you decide between these alternative views on the basis of gas-density measurements? Explain.

5.72 Phosphorus pentachloride, PCl_5, is a white solid that sublimes (vaporizes without melting) at about 100°C. At higher temperatures, the PCl_5 vapor decomposes to give phosphorus trichloride, PCl_3, and chlorine, Cl_2.

$$PCl_5(g) \longrightarrow PCl_3(g) + Cl_2(g)$$

How could gas-density measurements help to establish that PCl_5 vapor is decomposing?

Stoichiometry with Gas Volumes

5.73 Calcium carbide reacts with water to produce acetylene gas, C_2H_2.

$$CaC_2(s) + 2H_2O(l) \longrightarrow Ca(OH)_2(aq) + C_2H_2(g)$$

Calculate the volume (in liters) of acetylene produced at 26°C and 684 mmHg from 0.050 mol CaC_2 and excess H_2O.

5.74 Magnesium metal reacts with hydrochloric acid to produce hydrogen gas, H_2.

$$Mg(s) + 2HCl(aq) \longrightarrow MgCl_2(aq) + H_2(g)$$

Calculate the volume (in liters) of hydrogen produced at 33°C and 665 mmHg from 0.0840 mol Mg and excess HCl.

5.75 Lithium hydroxide, LiOH, is used in spacecraft to recondition the air by absorbing the carbon dioxide exhaled by astronauts. The reaction is

$$2LiOH(s) + CO_2(g) \longrightarrow Li_2CO_3(s) + H_2O(l)$$

What volume of carbon dioxide gas at 21°C and 781 mmHg could be absorbed by 327 g of lithium hydroxide?

5.76 Magnesium burns in air to produce magnesium oxide, MgO, and magnesium nitride, Mg_3N_2. Magnesium nitride reacts with water to give ammonia.

$$Mg_3N_2(s) + 6H_2O(l) \longrightarrow 3Mg(OH)_2(s) + 2NH_3(g)$$

What volume of ammonia gas at 24°C and 753 mmHg will be produced from 4.56 g of magnesium nitride?

5.77 Urea, NH_2CONH_2, is a nitrogen fertilizer that is manufactured from ammonia and carbon dioxide.

$$2NH_3(g) + CO_2(g) \longrightarrow NH_2CONH_2(aq) + H_2O(l)$$

What volume of ammonia at 25°C and 3.00 atm is needed to produce 908 g (2 lb) of urea?

5.78 Nitric acid is produced from nitric oxide, NO, which in turn is prepared from ammonia by the Ostwald process:

$$4NH_3(g) + 5O_2(g) \longrightarrow 4NO(g) + 6H_2O(g)$$

What volume of oxygen at 35°C and 2.15 atm is needed to produce 50.0 g of nitric oxide?

5.79 Ammonium sulfate is used as a nitrogen and sulfur fertilizer. It is produced by reacting ammonia with sulfuric acid. Write the balanced equation for the reaction of gaseous ammonia with sulfuric acid solution. What volume (in liters) of ammonia at 15°C and 1.15 atm is required to produce 150.0 g of ammonium sulfate?

5.80 Sodium hydrogen carbonate is also known as baking soda. When this compound is heated, it decomposes to sodium carbonate, carbon dioxide, and water vapor. Write the balanced equation for this reaction. What volume (in liters) of carbon dioxide gas at 77°C and 756 mmHg will be produced from 26.8 g of sodium hydrogen carbonate?

Gas Mixtures

5.81 Calculate the total pressure (in atm) of a mixture of 0.0200 mol of helium, He, and 0.0100 mol of hydrogen, H_2, in a 2.50-L flask at 10°C. Assume ideal gas behavior.

5.82 Calculate the total pressure (in atm) of a mixture of 0.0300 mol of helium, He, and 0.0200 mol of oxygen, O_2, in a 4.00-L flask at 20°C. Assume ideal gas behavior.

5.83 A 200.0-mL flask contains 1.03 mg O_2 and 0.56 mg He at 15°C. Calculate the partial pressures of oxygen and of helium in the flask. What is the total pressure?

5.84 The atmosphere in a sealed diving bell contained oxygen and helium. If the gas mixture has 0.200 atm of oxygen and a total pressure of 3.00 atm, calculate the mass of helium in 10.0 L of the gas mixture at 20°C.

5.85 The gas from a certain volcano had the following composition in mole percent (that is, mole fraction × 100): 65.0% CO_2, 25.0% H_2, 5.4% HCl, 2.8% HF, 1.7% SO_2, and 0.1% H_2S. What would be the partial pressure of each of these gases if the total pressure of volcanic gas were 760 mmHg?

5.86 In a series of experiments, the U.S. Navy developed an undersea habitat. In one experiment, the mole percent composition of the atmosphere in the undersea habitat was 79.0% He, 17.0% N_2, and 4.0% O_2. What will the partial pressure of each gas be when the habitat is 58.8 m below sea level, where the pressure is 6.91 atm?

5.87 Formic acid, $HCHO_2$, is a convenient source of small quantities of carbon monoxide. When warmed with sulfuric acid, formic acid decomposes to give CO gas.

$$HCHO_2(l) \longrightarrow H_2O(l) + CO(g)$$

If 3.85 L of carbon monoxide was collected over water at 25°C and 689 mmHg, how many grams of formic acid were consumed?

5.88 An aqueous solution of ammonium nitrite, NH_4NO_2, decomposes when heated to give off nitrogen, N_2.

$$NH_4NO_2(s) \longrightarrow 2H_2O(g) + N_2(g)$$

This reaction may be used to prepare pure nitrogen. How many grams of ammonium nitrite must have reacted if 3.75 dm^3 of nitrogen gas was collected over water at 26°C and 97.8 kPa?

Molecular Speeds; Effusion

5.89 Calculate the rms speeds of N_2 molecules at 25°C and at 125°C. Sketch approximate curves of the molecular speed distributions of N_2 at 25°C and at 125°C.

5.90 Calculate the rms speed of Br_2 molecules at 23°C and 1.00 atm. What is the rms speed of Br_2 at 23°C and 1.50 atm?

5.91 Uranium hexafluoride, UF_6, is a white solid that sublimes (vaporizes without melting) at 57°C under normal atmospheric pressure. The compound is used to separate uranium isotopes by effusion. What is the rms speed (in m/s) of a uranium hexafluoride molecule at 57°C?

5.92 For a spacecraft or a molecule to leave the moon, it must reach the escape velocity (speed) of the moon, which is 2.37 km/s. The average daytime temperature of the moon's surface is 365 K. What is the rms speed (in m/s) of a hydrogen molecule at this temperature? How does this compare with the escape velocity?

5.93 At what temperature would CO_2 molecules have an rms speed equal to that of H_2 molecules at 25°C?

5.94 At what temperature does the rms speed of O_2 molecules equal 400. m/s?

5.95 What is the ratio of rates of effusion of N_2 and O_2 under the same conditions?

5.96 Obtain the ratio of rates of effusion of H_2 and H_2Se under the same conditions.

5.97 If 0.10 mol of I_2 vapor can effuse from an opening in a heated vessel in 39 s, how long will it take 0.10 mol H_2 to effuse under the same conditions?

5.98 If it takes 10.6 hours for 1.00 L of nitrogen, N_2, to effuse through the pores in a balloon, how long would it take for 1.00 L of helium, He, to effuse under the same conditions?

5.99 If 4.83 mL of an unknown gas effuses through a hole in a plate in the same time it takes 9.23 mL of argon, Ar, to effuse through the same hole under the same conditions, what is the molecular mass of the unknown gas?

5.100 A given volume of nitrogen, N_2, required 68.3 s to effuse from a hole in a chamber. Under the same conditions, another gas required 85.6 s for the same volume to effuse. What is the molecular mass this gas?

van der Waals Equation

5.101 Calculate the pressure of ethanol vapor, $C_2H_5OH(g)$, at 82.0°C if 1.000 mol $C_2H_5OH(g)$ occupies 30.00 L. Use the van der Waals equation (see Table 5.7 for data). Compare with the result from the ideal gas law.

5.102 Calculate the pressure of water vapor at 120.0°C if 1.000 mol of water vapor occupies 32.50 L. Use the van der Waals equation (see Table 5.7 for data). Compare with the result from the ideal gas law.

5.103 Calculate the molar volume of ethane at 1.00 atm and 0°C and at 10.0 atm and 0°C, using the van der Waals equation. The van der Waals constants are given in Table 5.7. To simplify, note that the term n^2a/V^2 is small compared with P. Hence, it may be approximated with negligible error by substituting nRT/P from the ideal gas law for V in this term. Then the van der Waals equation can be solved for the volume. Compare the results with the values predicted by the ideal gas law.

5.104 Calculate the molar volume of oxygen at 1.00 atm and 0°C and at 10.0 atm and 0°C, using the van der Waals equation. The van der Waals constants are given in Table 5.7. (See the note on solving the equation given in Problem 5.103.) Compare the results with the values predicted by the ideal gas law. Also compare with the values obtained from Table 5.3.

General Problems

5.105 A glass tumbler containing 243 cm^3 of air at 1.00×10^2 kPa (the barometric pressure) and 20°C is turned upside down and immersed in a body of water to a depth of 20.5 m. The air in the glass is compressed by the weight of water above it. Calculate the volume of air in the glass, assuming the temperature and barometric pressure have not changed.

5.106 The density of air at 20°C and 1.00 atm is 1.205 g/L. If this air were compressed at the same temperature to equal the pressure at 40.0 m below sea level, what would be its density? Assume the barometric pressure is constant at 1.00 atm. The density of seawater is 1.025 g/cm^3.

5.107 A flask contains 201 mL of argon at 21°C and 738 mmHg. What is the volume of gas, corrected to STP?

5.108 A steel bottle contains 12.0 L of a gas at 11.0 atm and 20°C. What is the volume of gas at STP?

5.109 A balloon containing 5.0 dm^3 of gas at 14°C and 100.0 kPa rises to an altitude of 2000. m, where the temperature is 20°C. The pressure of gas in the balloon is now 79.0 kPa. What is the volume of gas in the balloon?

5.110 A volume of air is taken from the earth's surface, at 15°C and 1.00 atm, to the stratosphere, where the temperature is −21°C and the pressure is 1.00×10^{-3} atm. By what factor is the volume increased?

5.111 A radioactive metal atom decays (goes to another kind of atom) by emitting an alpha particle (He^{2+} ion). The alpha particles are collected as helium gas. A sample of helium with a volume of 12.05 mL was obtained at 765 mmHg and 23°C. How many atoms decayed during the period of the experiment?

5.112 The combustion method used to analyze for carbon and hydrogen can be adapted to give percentage N by collecting the nitrogen from combustion of the compound as N$_2$. A sample of a compound weighing 8.75 mg gave 1.59 mL N$_2$ at 25°C and 749 mmHg. What is the percentage N in the compound?

5.113 Dry air at STP has a density of 1.2929 g/L. Calculate the average molecular weight of air from the density.

5.114 A hydrocarbon gas has a density of 1.22 g/L at 20°C and 1.00 atm. An analysis gives 80.0% C and 20.0% H. What is the molecular formula?

5.115 A person exhales about 5.8×10^2 L of carbon dioxide per day (at STP). The carbon dioxide exhaled by an astronaut is absorbed from the air of a space capsule by reaction with lithium hydroxide, LiOH.

$$2LiOH(s) + CO_2(g) \longrightarrow Li_2CO_3(s) + H_2O(l)$$

How many grams of lithium hydroxide are required per astronaut per day?

5.116 Pyruvic acid, HC$_3$H$_3$O$_3$, is involved in cell metabolism. It can be assayed for (that is, the amount of it determined) by using a yeast enzyme. The enzyme makes the following reaction go to completion:

$$HC_3H_3O_3(aq) \longrightarrow C_2H_4O(aq) + CO_2(g)$$

If a sample containing pyruvic acid gives 21.2 mL of carbon dioxide gas, CO$_2$, at 349 mmHg and 30°C, how many grams of pyruvic acid are there in the sample?

5.117 Liquid oxygen was first prepared by heating potassium chlorate, KClO$_3$, in a closed vessel to obtain oxygen at high pressure. The oxygen was cooled until it liquefied.

$$2KClO_3(s) \longrightarrow 2KCl(s) + 3O_2(g)$$

If 170. g of potassium chlorate reacts in a 2.50-L vessel, which was initially evacuated, what pressure of oxygen will be attained when the temperature is finally cooled to 25°C? Use the preceding chemical equation and ignore the volume of solid product.

5.118 Raoul Pictet, the Swiss physicist who first liquefied oxygen, attempted to liquefy hydrogen. He heated potassium formate, KCHO$_2$, with KOH in a closed 2.50-L vessel.

$$KCHO_2(s) + KOH(s) \longrightarrow K_2CO_3(s) + H_2(g)$$

If 50.0 g of potassium formate reacts in a 2.50-L vessel, which was initially evacuated, what pressure of hydrogen will be attained when the temperature is finally cooled to 25°C? Use the preceding chemical equation and ignore the volume of solid product.

5.119 A 24.9-mL volume of hydrochloric acid reacts completely with 55.0 mL of aqueous Na$_2$CO$_3$. The reaction is

$$2HCl(aq) + Na_2CO_3(aq) \longrightarrow CO_2(g) + H_2O(l) + 2NaCl(aq)$$

The volume of CO$_2$ formed is 141 mL at 27°C and 727 mmHg. What is the molarity of the HCl solution?

5.120 An 18.6-mL volume of hydrochloric acid reacts completely with a solid sample of MgCO$_3$. The reaction is

$$2HCl(aq) + MgCO_3(s) \longrightarrow CO_2(g) + H_2O(l) + MgCl_2(aq)$$

The volume of CO$_2$ formed is 159 mL at 23°C and 731 mmHg. What is the molarity of the HCl solution?

5.121 A 41.41-mL sample of a 0.1250 M acid reacts with an excess of Na$_2$CO$_3$ to form 150.0 mL CO$_2$ at 646 mmHg and 27°C. If the acid is either HCl or H$_2$SO$_4$, which is it?

5.122 A 48.90-mL sample of a 0.2040 M acid reacts with an excess of Na$_2$CO$_3$ to form 125.0 mL CO$_2$ at 722 mmHg and 17°C. If the acid is either HCl or H$_2$SO$_4$, which is it?

5.123 If the rms speed of NH$_3$ molecules is found to be 0.605 km/s, what is the temperature (in degrees Celsius)?

5.124 If the rms speed of He atoms in the exosphere (highest region of the atmosphere) is 3.53×10^3 m/s, what is the temperature (in kelvins)?

5.125 Calculate the ratio of rates of effusion of ^{235}UF$_6$ and ^{238}UF$_6$, where ^{235}U and ^{238}U are isotopes of uranium. The atomic masses are ^{235}U, 235.04 amu; ^{238}U, 238.05 amu; ^{19}F (the only naturally occurring isotope), 18.998 amu. Carry five significant figures in the calculation.

5.126 Hydrogen has two stable isotopes, ^{1}H and ^{2}H, with atomic masses of 1.0078 amu and 2.0141 amu, respectively. Ordinary hydrogen gas, H$_2$, is a mixture consisting mostly of ^{1}H$_2$ and ^{1}H^{2}H. Calculate the ratio of rates of effusion of ^{1}H$_2$ and ^{1}H^{2}H under the same conditions.

5.127 A 1.000-g sample of an unknown gas at 0°C gives the following data:

P (atm)	V (L)
0.2500	3.1908
0.5000	1.5928
0.7500	1.0601
1.0000	0.7930

Use these data to calculate the value of the molar mass at each of the given pressures from the ideal gas law (we will call this the "apparent molar mass" at this pressure). Plot the apparent molar masses against pressure and extrapolate to find the molar mass at zero pressure. Because the ideal gas law is most accurate at low pressures, this extrapolation will give an accurate value for the molar mass. What is the accurate molar mass?

5.128 Plot the data given in Table 5.3 for oxygen at 0°C to obtain an accurate molar mass for O_2. To do this, calculate a value of the molar mass at each of the given pressures from the ideal gas law (we will call this the "apparent molar mass" at this pressure). On a graph show the apparent molar mass versus the pressure and extrapolate to find the molar mass at zero pressure. Because the ideal gas law is most accurate at low pressures, this extrapolation will give an accurate value for the molar mass. What is the accurate molar mass?

5.129 Carbon monoxide, CO, and oxygen, O_2, react according to

$$2CO(g) + O_2(g) \longrightarrow 2CO_2(g)$$

Assuming that the reaction takes place and goes to completion, determine what substances remain and what their partial pressures are after the valve is opened in the apparatus represented in the accompanying figure. Also assume that the temperature is fixed at 300 K.

5.130 Suppose the apparatus shown in the figure accompanying Problem 5.129 contains H_2 at 0.500 atm in the left vessel separated from O_2 at 1.00 atm in the other vessel. The valve is then opened. If H_2 and O_2 react to give H_2O when the temperature is fixed at 300 K, what substances remain and what are their partial pressures after reaction?

5.131 How does nitrogen monoxide, NO, function in the body to regulate blood pressure?

5.132 How does nitroglycerine alleviate the pain of an angina attack?

5.133 What famous chemist first predicted the greenhouse effect of carbon dioxide gas?

5.134 Explain the greenhouse effect.

Strategy Problems

5.135 A 24.6-mL volume of a hydrochloric acid solution reacts completely with a solid sample of magnesium carbonate, producing 183 mL of CO_2 that is collected over water at 24.0°C and 738 torr total pressure. The reaction is

$$2HCl(aq) + MgCO_3(s) \longrightarrow CO_2(g) + H_2O(l) + MgCl_2(aq)$$

What is the molarity of the HCl solution?

5.136 The graph below represents the distribution of molecular speeds of hydrogen and neon at 200 K.

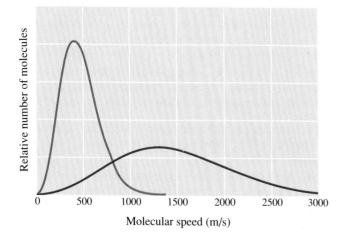

a. Match each curve to the appropriate gas.
b. Calculate the rms speed (in m/s) for each of the gases at 200 K.
c. Which of the gases would you expect to have the greater effusion rate at 200 K? Justify your answer.
d. Calculate the temperature at which the rms speed of the hydrogen gas would equal the rms speed of the neon at 200 K.

5.137 A submersible balloon is sent to the bottom of the ocean. On shore, the balloon had a capacity of 162 L when it was filled at 21.0°C and standard pressure. When it reaches the ocean floor, which is at 5.92°C, the balloon occupies 18.8 L of space. What is the pressure on the ocean floor?

5.138 A given mass of gas occupies a volume of 435 mL at 25°C and 740 mmHg. What will be the new volume at STP?

5.139 A container is filled with 16.0 g of O_2 and 14.0 g of N_2.
a. What is the volume of the container at STP?
b. What is the partial pressure of the O_2 gas?
c. What are the mole fraction and the mole percent of the N_2 in the mixture.

5.140 Sulfur-containing compounds give skunks their potent smell. One of the principal smelly compounds in skunk spray is (*E*)-2-butene-1-thiol, C_4H_7S.
a. What is the root-mean-square (rms) molecular speed of a gas molecule of this compound at 25°C?

b. Using the value from part a, calculate how long it would take a molecule of C_4H_7S to reach your nose if you were 150 m from the skunk.

c. Does the calculation that you performed in part b provide an accurate estimate for the length of time it would take for the molecule to travel 150 m, or is there something that was overlooked in performing the calculation?

5.141 Sulfur hexafluoride, SF_6, is an extremely dense gas. How does its density compare with the density of air? Use a molar mass for air of 29.0 g/mol.

5.142 A rigid 1.0-L container at 75°C is fitted with a gas pressure gauge. A 1.0-mol sample of ideal gas is introduced into the container.

a. What would the pressure gauge in the container be reading in mmHg?

b. Describe the interactions in the container that are causing the pressure.

c. Say the temperature in the container were increased to 150°C. Describe the effect this would have on the pressure, and, in terms of kinetic theory, explain why this change occurred.

5.143 The reaction $8H_2(g) + S_8(l) \longrightarrow 8H_2S(g)$ is run at 125°C and a constant pressure of 12.0 atm. Assuming complete reaction,

what mass of S_8 would be required to produce 6.00×10^2 mL of H_2S gas under these conditions?

5.144 Shown below are three containers of an ideal gas (A, B, and C), each equipped with a movable piston (assume that atmospheric pressure is 1.0 atm).

a. How do the pressures in these containers compare?

b. Are all the gases at the same temperature? If not, compare the temperatures.

c. If you cooled each of the containers in an ice-water bath to 0.0°C, describe how the volumes and pressures of the gases in these containers would compare.

A   **B**   **C**

Cumulative-Skills Problems

5.145 A sample of natural gas is 85.2% methane, CH_4, and 14.8% ethane, C_2H_6, by mass. What is density of this mixture at 18°C and 771 mmHg?

5.146 A sample of a breathing mixture for divers contained 34.3% helium, He; 51.7% nitrogen, N_2; and 14.0% oxygen, O_2 (by mass). What is the density of this mixture at 22°C and 755 mmHg?

5.147 A sample of sodium peroxide, Na_2O_2, was reacted with an excess of water.

$$2Na_2O_2(s) + 2H_2O(l) \longrightarrow 4NaOH(aq) + O_2(g)$$

All of the sodium peroxide reacted, and the oxygen was collected over water at 21°C. The barometric pressure was 771 mmHg. The apparatus was similar to that shown in Figure 5.20. However, the level of water inside the tube was 25.0 cm above the level of water outside the tube. If the volume of gas in the tube is 31.0 mL, how many grams of sodium peroxide were in the sample?

5.148 A sample of zinc metal was reacted with an excess of hydrochloric acid.

$$Zn(s) + 2HCl(aq) \longrightarrow ZnCl_2(aq) + H_2(g)$$

All of the zinc reacted, and the hydrogen gas was collected over water at 17°C; the barometric pressure was 751 mmHg. The apparatus was similar to that shown in Figure 5.20, but the level of water inside the tube was 31.0 cm above the level outside the tube. If the volume of gas in the tube is 22.1 mL, how many grams of zinc were there in the sample?

5.149 A mixture contained calcium carbonate, $CaCO_3$, and magnesium carbonate, $MgCO_3$. A sample of this mixture

weighing 7.85 g was reacted with excess hydrochloric acid. The reactions are

$$CaCO_3(g) + 2HCl(aq) \longrightarrow CaCl_2(aq) + H_2O(l) + CO_2(g)$$
$$MgCO_3(s) + 2HCl(aq) \longrightarrow MgCl_2(aq) + H_2O(l) + CO_2(g)$$

If the sample reacted completely and produced 1.94 L of carbon dioxide, CO_2, at 25°C and 785 mmHg, what were the percentages of $CaCO_3$ and $MgCO_3$ in the mixture?

5.150 A mixture contained zinc sulfide, ZnS, and lead sulfide, PbS. A sample of the mixture weighing 6.12 g was reacted with an excess of hydrochloric acid. The reactions are

$$ZnS(s) + 2HCl(aq) \longrightarrow ZnCl_2(aq) + H_2S(g)$$
$$PbS(s) + 2HCl(aq) \longrightarrow PbCl_2(aq) + H_2S(g)$$

If the sample reacted completely and produced 1.049 L of hydrogen sulfide, H_2S, at 23°C and 745 mmHg, what were the percentages of ZnS and PbS in the mixture?

5.151 A mixture of N_2 and Ne contains equal moles of each gas and has a total mass of 10.0 g. What is the density of this gas mixture at 500 K and 15.00 atm? Assume ideal gas behavior.

5.152 A mixture of Ne and Ar gases at 350 K contains twice as many moles of Ne as of Ar and has a total mass of 50.0 g. If the density of the mixture is 4.00 g/L, what is the partial pressure of Ne?

5.153 An ideal gas with a density of 3.00 g/L has a pressure of 675 mmHg at 25°C. What is the root-mean-square speed of the molecules of this gas?

5.154 The root-mean-square speed of the molecules of an ideal gas at 25°C and a pressure of 2.50 atm is 5.00×10^2 m/s. What is the density of this gas?

6

Thermochemistry

Ammonium dichromate decomposes in a fiery reaction to give a "volcano" of chromium(III) oxide that spews out N_2 gas and H_2O vapor. The color of ruby is due to the chromium(III) ion.

Contents and Concepts

The first part of the chapter lays the groundwork for understanding what we mean by heats of reaction.

Now that we understand the basic properties of heats of reaction and how to measure them, we can explore how to use them.

Nearly all chemical reactions involve either the release or the absorption of heat, a form of energy. The burning of coal and gasoline are dramatic examples of chemical reactions in which a great deal of heat is released. Such reactions are important sources of warmth and energy. Chemical reactions that absorb heat are usually less dramatic. The reaction of barium hydroxide with an ammonium salt is an exception. If crystals of barium hydroxide octahydrate, $Ba(OH)_2 \cdot 8H_2O$, are mixed with crystals of ammonium nitrate, NH_4NO_3, in a flask, the solids form first a slush, then a liquid. Because the reaction mixture absorbs heat from the surroundings, the flask feels cool. It soon becomes so cold that if it is set in a puddle of water on a board, the water freezes; the board can then be inverted with the flask frozen to it (Figure 6.1).

In this chapter, we will be concerned with the quantity of heat released or absorbed in a chemical reaction. We will address several questions: How do you measure the quantity of heat released or absorbed by a chemical reaction? To what extent can you relate the quantity of heat involved in a given reaction to the quantities of heat in other reactions? And how can you use this information?

■ **See pages 252–253 for the Media Summary.**

FIGURE 6.1 ▶

A reaction that absorbs heat
Two crystalline substances, barium hydroxide octahydrate and an ammonium salt, are mixed thoroughly in a flask. Then the flask, which feels quite cold to the touch, is set in a puddle of water on a board. In a couple of minutes, the flask and board are frozen solidly together. The board can then be inverted with the flask frozen to it.

Understanding Heats of Reaction

Thermodynamics is the science of the relationships between heat and other forms of energy. *Thermochemistry* is one area of thermodynamics. It concerns the study of the quantity of heat absorbed or evolved (given off) by chemical reactions. An example of a heat-evolving reaction is the burning of fuel. There may be practical reasons why you want to know the quantity of heat evolved during the burning of a fuel: you could calculate the cost of the fuel per unit of heat energy produced; you could calculate the quantity of heat obtained per unit mass of rocket fuel; and so forth. But there are also theoretical reasons for wanting to know the quantity of heat involved in a reaction. For example, knowing such values, you are able to calculate the amount of energy needed to break a particular kind of chemical bond and so learn something about the strength of that bond. Heat measurements also provide data needed to determine whether a particular chemical reaction occurs and, if so, to what extent. <

These questions concern chemical equilibrium and will be discussed in Chapter 18.

We have just used the terms *energy* and *heat,* assuming you have some idea of what they mean. But to proceed, you will need precise definitions of these and other terms. In the following section, we will define energy and its different forms and introduce units of energy.

6.1 | Energy and Its Units

We can define **energy** briefly as *the potential or capacity to move matter*. According to this definition, energy is not a material thing but rather a property of matter. Energy exists in different forms that can be interconverted. You can see the relationship of a given form of energy to the motion of matter by following its interconversions into different forms.

Consider the interconversions of energy in a steam-driven electrical generator. A fuel is burned to heat water and generate steam. The steam expands against a piston (or turbine), which is connected to a drive shaft that turns an electrical coil in a magnetic field. Electricity is generated in the coil. The fuel contains chemical energy, which is converted to heat. Part of the heat is then converted to motion of the drive shaft, and this motion is converted to electrical energy. The electrical energy could be used to run a motor, transforming the electrical energy back to the energy of motion. Or you could send the electricity into a lightbulb, converting electrical energy to heat energy and light energy. Photovoltaic cells can convert light back to electricity, which could be used to run a motor that can move matter (Figure 6.2). These examples show that energy can exist in different forms, including heat, light, and electrical energy, and these different forms can be interconverted. You also see their relationship to the energy of motion.

In this chapter, we will be especially concerned with the energy of substances, or chemical energy, and its transformation during chemical reaction into heat energy. To prepare for this, we will first explore the quantitative meaning of the energy of motion (*kinetic energy*). Then we will look at the concepts of *potential energy* and of the *internal energy* of substances, which is defined in terms of the kinetic and potential energies of the particles making up the substance.

FIGURE 6.2 ▲

Conversion of light energy to kinetic energy
Solar-powered vehicles use panels of photovoltaic cells.

Kinetic Energy; Units of Energy

Kinetic energy is *the energy associated with an object by virtue of its motion*. An object of mass m and speed or velocity v has kinetic energy E_k equal to

$$E_k = \tfrac{1}{2}mv^2$$

This formula shows that the kinetic energy of an object depends on both its mass and its speed. A heavy object can move more slowly than a light object and still have the same kinetic energy. <

In the previous chapter, we used the symbol u for average molecular speed. Here v is the speed of an individual object or particle.

Consider the kinetic energy of a person whose mass is 59.0 kg and whose speed is 26.8 m/s. (This is equivalent to a person with a mass of 130 lb traveling in an automobile going 60 miles per hour.) You substitute the mass and speed into the formula.

$$E_k = \tfrac{1}{2} \times (59.0 \text{ kg}) \times (26.8 \text{ m/s})^2 = 2.12 \times 10^4 \text{ kg·m}^2/\text{s}^2$$

Note that the unit of energy comes out of the calculation. Because you substituted SI units of mass and speed, you obtain the SI unit of energy. *The SI unit of energy, $kg·m^2/s^2$*, is given the name **joule (J)** (pronounced "jewl") after the English physicist James Prescott Joule (1818–1889), who studied the energy concept. You see that a person weighing 130 lb and traveling 60 miles per hour has a kinetic energy equal to 2.12×10^4 J, or 21.2 kJ (21.2 kilojoules).

The joule is an extremely small unit. To appreciate its size, note that the *watt* is a measure of the quantity of energy used per unit time and equals 1 joule per second. A 100-watt bulb, for example, uses 100 joules of energy every second. A kilowatt-hour, the unit by which electric energy is sold, equals 3600 kilowatt-seconds (there are 3600 seconds in 1 hour), or 3.6 million joules. A household might use something like 1000 kilowatt-hours (3.6 billion joules) of electricity in a month.

The **calorie (cal)** is *a non-SI unit of energy commonly used by chemists, originally defined as the amount of energy required to raise the temperature of one gram of water by one degree Celsius.* This is only an approximate definition, however, because we now know that the energy needed to heat water depends slightly on the temperature of the water. In 1925 the calorie was defined in terms of the joule:

$$1 \text{ cal} = 4.184 \text{ J} \qquad \text{(exact definition)}$$

A person weighing 130 lb and traveling 60 miles per hour has a kinetic energy of

$$2.12 \times 10^4 \text{ J} \times \frac{1 \text{ cal}}{4.184 \text{ J}} = 5.07 \times 10^3 \text{ cal (5.07 kcal)}$$

Example 6.1   Calculating Kinetic Energy

A good pitcher can throw a baseball so that it travels between 60 and 90 miles per hour (although speeds in excess of 100 miles per hour have been recorded). A regulation baseball weighing 143 g (0.143 kg) travels 75 miles per hour (33.5 m/s). What is the kinetic energy of this baseball in joules? in calories?

Problem Strategy Kinetic energy is defined by the formula $E_k = \frac{1}{2}mv^2$. You simply substitute into this formula, making certain that m and v are expressed in the same system of units.

Solution Substitute into the defining equation for the kinetic energy, using SI units.

$$E_k = \frac{1}{2} \times 0.143 \text{ kg} \times (33.5 \text{ m/s})^2 = \textbf{80.2 J}$$

Using the conversion factor 1 cal/4.184 J we obtain

$$80.2 \text{ J} \times \frac{1 \text{ cal}}{4.184 \text{ J}} = \textbf{19.2 cal}$$

Answer Check Make sure that the values for m and v are in the same units; SI units are generally appropriate. The SI unit of mass is kg, and the SI unit of speed is m/s. The answer then comes out in SI units (joules in this case).

Exercise 6.1   An electron, whose mass is 9.11 $\times 10^{-31}$ kg, is accelerated by a positive charge to a speed of 5.0 $\times 10^6$ m/s. What is the kinetic energy of the electron in joules? in calories?

■ See Problems 6.43, 6.44, 6.45, and 6.46.

Potential Energy

Potential energy is *the energy an object has by virtue of its position in a field of force.* For example, water at the top of a dam has potential energy (in addition to whatever kinetic energy it may possess), because the water is at a relatively high position in the gravitational force field of the earth. You can calculate this potential energy of the water from the formula $E_p = mgh$. Here E_p is the potential energy of a quantity of water at the top of the dam, m is the mass of the water, g is the constant acceleration of gravity, and h is the height of the water measured from some standard level. The choice of this standard level is arbitrary, because only *differences* of potential energy are important in any physical situation. It is convenient to choose the standard level to be the surface of the earth. As a quantity of water falls over the dam, its potential energy decreases from mgh at the top of the dam to zero at the earth's surface.

FIGURE 6.3 ▲

Potential energy and kinetic energy
Water at the top of the dam has potential energy. As the water falls over the dam, this potential energy is converted to kinetic energy.

The potential energy of the water at the top of the dam is converted to kinetic energy when the water falls to a lower level. As the water falls, it moves more quickly. The potential energy decreases and the kinetic energy increases. Figure 6.3 shows the potential energy of water being converted to kinetic energy as the water falls over a dam.

Internal Energy

Consider the total energy of a quantity of water as it moves over the dam. This water as a whole has kinetic energy and potential energy. However, we know that water is made up of molecules, which are made up of smaller particles, electrons and nuclei. Each of these particles also has kinetic energy and potential energy. *The sum of the kinetic and potential energies of the particles making up a substance* is referred to as the **internal energy,** U, of the substance. Therefore, the total energy, E_{tot}, of a quantity of water equals the sum of its kinetic and potential energies as a whole ($E_k + E_p$) plus its internal energy.

$$E_{tot} = E_k + E_p + U$$

Normally when you study a substance in the laboratory, the substance is at rest in a vessel. Its kinetic energy as a whole is zero. Moreover, its potential energy as a whole is constant, and you can take it to be zero. In this case, the total energy of the substance equals its internal energy, U.

Law of Conservation of Energy

We have discussed situations in which one form of energy can be converted into another form of energy. For example, when water falls over a dam, potential energy is converted into kinetic energy. Some of the kinetic energy of the water may also be converted into random molecular motion—that is, into internal energy of the water. The total energy, E_{tot}, of the water, however, remains constant, equal to the sum of the kinetic energy, E_k, the potential energy, E_p, and the internal energy, U, of the water.

This result can be stated more generally as the **law of conservation of energy:** *energy may be converted from one form to another, but the total quantity of energy remains constant.*

Concept Check 6.1

A solar-powered water pump has photovoltaic cells that protrude from top panels. These cells collect energy from sunlight, storing it momentarily in a battery, which later runs an electric motor that pumps water up to a storage tank on a hill. What energy conversions are involved in using sunlight to pump water into the storage tank?

6.2 | Heat of Reaction

In the chapter opening, we mentioned chemical reactions (such as the burning of coal) that evolve, or release, heat. We also described a reaction that absorbs heat. Both types of reaction involve a *heat of reaction*. To understand this concept, you need to know what is meant by a thermodynamic *system* and its *surroundings* and to have a precise definition of the term *heat*.

Suppose that you are interested in studying the change of a thermodynamic property (such as internal energy) during a physical or chemical change. *The substance or*

Surroundings

Surroundings

Surroundings

Surroundings

System
(solution of Ba(OH)$_2$
and NH$_4$NO$_3$)

FIGURE 6.4 ▲

Illustration of a thermodynamic system
The *system* consists of the portion of the universe that we choose to study; in this case, it is a solution of Ba(OH)$_2$ and NH$_4$NO$_3$. Everything else, including the reaction vessel, constitutes the *surroundings*.

mixture of substances under study in which a change occurs is called the **thermodynamic system** (or simply **system**). The **surroundings** are *everything in the vicinity of the thermodynamic system* (Figure 6.4).

Definition of Heat

Heat is defined as *the energy that flows into or out of a system because of a difference in temperature between the thermodynamic system and its surroundings.* As long as a system and its surroundings are in thermal contact (that is, they are not thermally insulated from one another), energy (heat) flows between them to establish temperature equality, or *thermal equilibrium.* Heat flows from a region of higher temperature to one of lower temperature; once the temperatures become equal, heat flow stops. Note that once heat flows into a system, it appears in the system as an increase in its internal energy. You would not say that the system has heat, because heat is only an energy flow.

We can explain this flow of energy between two regions of different temperatures in terms of kinetic-molecular theory. Imagine two vessels in contact, each containing oxygen gas and the one on the left being hotter (Figure 6.5). According to kinetic theory, the average speed of molecules in the hotter gas is greater than that of molecules in the colder gas. But as the molecules in their random motions collide with the vessel walls, they lose energy to or gain energy from the walls. The faster molecules tend to slow down, while the slower molecules tend to speed up. Eventually, the average speeds of the molecules in the two vessels (and therefore the temperatures of the two gases) become equal. The net result is that energy is transferred through the vessel walls from the hot gas to the cold gas; that is, heat has flowed from the hotter vessel to the cooler one.

Heat and temperature are sometimes confused. The distinction is clear in the kinetic picture of a gas. According to kinetic theory, the absolute temperature of a gas is directly proportional to the average kinetic energy of the molecules. When you add heat to a gas, you increase its internal energy—and therefore its total kinetic energy. This increase in kinetic energy will be distributed over the molecules in the sample. Therefore, the increase in average kinetic energy per molecule (and thus the increase in temperature) depends on the size of the gas sample. A given quantity of heat will raise the temperature of a sample more if the sample is small.

Heat is denoted by the symbol q. The algebraic sign of q is chosen to be positive if heat is absorbed by the system and negative if heat is evolved. The sign of q can be remembered this way: when heat is absorbed by a system, energy is *added* to it; q is assigned a positive quantity. On the other hand, when heat is evolved by a system, energy is *subtracted* from it; q is assigned a negative number.

Heat of Reaction

Consider a system in which a chemical reaction occurs. Before the reaction, the system and surroundings are at the same temperature, say 25°C. When the reaction starts, however, the temperature changes.

Suppose the temperature of the system falls. In that case, heat flows from the surroundings into the system. When the reaction stops, heat continues to flow until the system returns to the temperature of its surroundings (at 25°C). Heat has flowed into the system; that is, the system has absorbed heat and q is positive.

Suppose, on the other hand, that the temperature of the system rises. In this case, heat flows from the system to the surroundings. When the reaction stops, heat continues to flow until the system returns to the temperature of its surroundings (at 25°C). In this case, heat has flowed out of the system; that is, the system has evolved heat and q is negative.

FIGURE 6.5 ▲

A kinetic-theory explanation of heat
The vessel on the left contains oxygen molecules at a higher temperature than the oxygen molecules on the right. Molecules collide with the vessel walls, thereby losing or gaining energy. The faster molecules tend to slow down, and the slower molecules tend to speed up. The net result is that energy is transferred through the vessel walls from the hot gas to the cold gas. We call this energy transfer *heat.*

FIGURE 6.6

An exothermic process

Left: The test tube contains anhydrous copper(II) sulfate (white crystals) and a thermometer that registers 26.1°C. The graduated cylinder contains water. *Right:* Water from the graduated cylinder has been added to the test tube, where the copper(II) sulfate forms hydrated copper(II) ion (blue color). The thermometer now registers 90.2°C, because the hydration process is exothermic.

$q = +$

Surroundings

Heat ⟶ System ⟵ Heat

Endothermic

$q = -$

Surroundings

Heat ⟵ System ⟶ Heat

Exothermic

The **heat of reaction** (at a given temperature) is *the value of q required to return a system to the given temperature at the completion of the reaction.*

Chemical reactions or physical changes are classified as exothermic or endothermic. An **exothermic process** is *a chemical reaction or a physical change in which heat is evolved* (q is negative); see Figure 6.6. An **endothermic process** is *a chemical reaction or a physical change in which heat is absorbed* (q is positive). Experimentally, you note that in the exothermic reaction, the reaction flask initially warms; in the endothermic reaction, the reaction flask initially cools. We can summarize as follows:

Type of Reaction	Experimental Effect Noted	Result on System	Sign of q
Endothermic	Reaction vessel cools (heat is absorbed)	Energy added	+
Exothermic	Reaction vessel warms (heat is evolved)	Energy subtracted	−

Suppose that in an experiment 1 mol of methane burns in oxygen and evolves 890 kJ of heat: $CH_4(g) + 2O_2(g) \longrightarrow CO_2(g) + 2H_2O(l)$. The reaction is exothermic. Therefore the heat of reaction, q, is −890 kJ.

Or consider the reaction described in the chapter opening, in which crystals of barium hydroxide octahydrate, $Ba(OH)_2 \cdot 8H_2O$, react with crystals of ammonium nitrate, NH_4NO_3.

$$Ba(OH)_2 \cdot 8H_2O(s) + 2NH_4NO_3(s) \longrightarrow 2NH_3(g) + 10H_2O(l) + Ba(NO_3)_2(aq)$$

When 1 mol $Ba(OH)_2 \cdot 8H_2O$ reacts with 2 mol NH_4NO_3, the reaction mixture absorbs 170.8 kJ of heat. The reaction is endothermic. Therefore the heat of reaction, q, is +170.8 kJ.

Exercise 6.2 Ammonia burns in the presence of a platinum catalyst to give nitric oxide, NO.

$$4NH_3(g) + 5O_2(g) \xrightarrow{Pt} 4NO(g) + 6H_2O(l)$$

In an experiment, 4 mol NH_3 is burned and evolves 1170 kJ of heat. Is the reaction endothermic or exothermic? What is the value of q?

■ See Problems 6.47, 6.48, 6.49, and 6.50.

6.3 | Enthalpy and Enthalpy Change

The heat absorbed or evolved by a reaction depends on the conditions under which the reaction occurs. Usually, a reaction takes place in a vessel open to the atmosphere and therefore at the constant pressure of the atmosphere. We will assume that this is the case and write the heat of reaction as q_p, the subscript p indicating that the process occurs at constant pressure.

Enthalpy

There is a property of substances called enthalpy (en'-thal-py) that is related to the heat of reaction q_p. **Enthalpy** (denoted H) is *an extensive property of a substance that can be used to obtain the heat absorbed or evolved in a chemical reaction.* (An extensive property is a property that depends on the amount of substance. Other examples of extensive properties are mass and volume.)

Enthalpy is a state function. A **state function** is *a property of a system that depends only on its present state, which is determined by variables such as temperature and pressure, and is independent of any previous history of the system.* This means that a change in enthalpy does not depend on how the change was made, but only on the initial state and final state of the system. An analogy may clarify the point. Suppose you are hiking in mountainous terrain. You start walking from campsite A, which is at an altitude of 1200 ft above sea level according to your pocket altimeter, and you take the curving, graded path upward to campsite B (Figure 6.7). Alternatively, you could have taken a more direct, but more difficult, route to campsite B. The distances traveled are different; the distance by the graded path is longer than by the more direct route. However, the altitude (height above sea level) of campsite B is independent of how you got there (independent of any history). If you find the altitude of campsite B to be 4800 ft after arriving by the graded path, the altitude will be 4800 ft by any other path (assuming your altimeter is accurate, of course). Moreover, the difference in altitude of the two campsites is independent of the route you take from one to the other. Altitude is analogous to a state function, whereas distance traveled is not.

Enthalpy of Reaction

Consider a chemical reaction system. At first, the enthalpy of the system is that of the reactants. But as the reaction proceeds, the enthalpy changes and finally becomes

FIGURE 6.7 ▶

An analogy to illustrate a state function
The two campsites differ by 3600 ft in altitude. This difference in altitude is independent of the path taken between the campsites. The distance traveled and the things encountered along the way, however, do depend on the path taken. Altitude here is analogous to a thermodynamic state function.

2 mol Na(s) + 2 mol H$_2$O(l)

Enthalpy, H (kJ)

$\Delta H = -368.6$ kJ
(368.6 kJ of heat
is released)

2 mol NaOH(aq) + 1 mol H$_2$(g)

FIGURE 6.8 ▲

An enthalpy diagram
When 2 mol Na(s) and 2 mol H$_2$O(l)
react to give 2 mol NaOH(aq) and 1 mol
H$_2$(g), 368.6 kJ of heat is released, and
the enthalpy of the system decreases by
368.6 kJ.

equal to that of the products. *The change in enthalpy for a reaction at a given temperature and pressure* (called the **enthalpy of reaction**) is obtained by subtracting the enthalpy of the reactants from the enthalpy of the products. We will use the symbol Δ (meaning "change in") and write the change in enthalpy as ΔH. You apply the Δ notation by taking the final value and subtracting the initial value. Thus $\Delta H = H_{final} - H_{initial}$. Since you start from reactants and end with products, the enthalpy of reaction is

$$\Delta H = H(\text{products}) - H(\text{reactants})$$

Because H is a state function, the value of ΔH is independent of the details of the reaction. It depends only on the initial state (the reactants) and the final state (the products).

The key relation in this chapter is that between enthalpy change and heat of reaction:

$$\Delta H = q_p$$

The enthalpy of reaction equals the heat of reaction at constant pressure.

To illustrate the concepts we have introduced, consider the reaction at 25°C of sodium metal and water, carried out in a beaker open to the atmosphere at 1.00 atm pressure.

$$2Na(s) + 2H_2O(l) \longrightarrow 2NaOH(aq) + H_2(g)$$

The metal and water react vigorously and heat evolves. Experiment shows that 2 mol of sodium metal reacts with 2 mol of water to evolve 368.6 kJ of heat. Because heat evolves, the reaction is exothermic, and you write $q_p = -368.6$ kJ. Therefore, the enthalpy of reaction, or change of enthalpy for the reaction, is $\Delta H = -368.6$ kJ. Figure 6.8 shows an *enthalpy diagram* for this reaction.

Enthalpy and Internal Energy

In the preceding discussion, we noted that the enthalpy change equals the heat of reaction at constant pressure. This will be sufficient for the purpose of this chapter, which is to introduce the concepts of heat of reaction and enthalpy change. Later we will look at thermodynamics in more detail. Still, it is useful at this point to note briefly the relationship of enthalpy to internal energy.

The enthalpy, H, is defined precisely as the internal energy, U, plus pressure, P, times volume, V.

$$H = U + PV$$

To obtain some understanding of this equation, consider a reaction system at constant pressure P. We will label the initial quantities (those for reactants) with a subscript i and the final quantities (those for products) with a subscript f. Then

$$\Delta H = H_f - H_i = (U_f + PV_f) - (U_i + PV_i)$$

Collecting the internal-energy terms and the pressure–volume terms, you can rewrite this as

$$\Delta H = (U_f - U_i) + P(V_f - V_i) = \Delta U + P\Delta V$$

We write ΔU for $U_f - U_i$ and ΔV for $V_f - V_i$ and rearrange this as follows:

$$\Delta U = \Delta H - P\Delta V$$

The last term in this equation ($-P\Delta V$) is the energy required by the system to change volume against the constant pressure of the atmosphere. (The minus sign means that energy is required to increase the volume of the system.) This required energy is called the *pressure–volume work*. Thus, the equation says that the internal energy of the

FIGURE 6.9 ▶

Pressure–volume work

In this experiment, we replace the pressure of the atmosphere by a piston-and-weight assembly of equal pressure. As sodium metal reacts with water, the hydrogen gas evolved pushes the piston and weight upward (compare *before* and *after*). It requires work to raise the piston and weight upward in a gravitational field.

Before   After

system changes in two ways. It changes because energy leaves or enters the system as heat (ΔH), and it changes because the system increases or decreases in volume against the constant pressure of the atmosphere (which requires energy $-P\Delta V$).

Consider a specific reaction. When 2 mol of sodium metal and 2 mol of water react in a beaker, 1 mol of hydrogen gas forms and heat evolves. If you measured this heat, you would find it to be -368.6 kJ, indicating that 368.6 kJ of energy has left the system in the form of heat.

Because hydrogen gas forms during the reaction, the volume of the system increases. To expand, the system must push back the atmosphere, and this requires energy equal to the pressure–volume work. It may be easier to see this pressure–volume work if you replace the constant pressure of the atmosphere by an equivalent pressure from a piston-and-weight assembly, as in Figure 6.9. When hydrogen gas is released during the reaction, it pushes upward on the piston and raises the weight. It requires energy to lift a weight upward in a gravitational field. If you calculate this pressure–volume work at 25°C and 1.00 atm pressure, you find that it is $-P\Delta V = -2.5$ kJ.

In the sodium–water reaction, the internal energy changes by -368.6 kJ because heat evolves and changes by -2.5 kJ because pressure–volume work is done. The total change of internal energy is

$$\Delta U = \Delta H - P\Delta V = -368.6 \text{ kJ} - 2.5 \text{ kJ} = -371.1 \text{ kJ}$$

As you can see, ΔU does not differ a great deal from ΔH. This is the case in most reactions, so the heat of reaction at constant pressure is approximately equal to the change of internal energy.

6.4 | Thermochemical Equations

We will often find it convenient to write the enthalpy of reaction, ΔH, with the chemical equation. A **thermochemical equation** is *the chemical equation for a reaction (including phase labels) in which the equation is given a molar interpretation, and the enthalpy of reaction for these molar amounts is written directly after the equation.* For the reaction of sodium and water, you would write

$$2\text{Na}(s) + 2\text{H}_2\text{O}(l) \longrightarrow 2\text{NaOH}(aq) + \text{H}_2(g); \Delta H = -368.6 \text{ kJ}$$

This equation says that 2 mol of sodium reacts with 2 mol of water to produce 2 mol of sodium hydroxide and 1 mol of hydrogen gas, and 368.6 kJ of heat evolves.

Note that the thermochemical equation includes phase labels. This is because the enthalpy change, ΔH, depends on the phase of the substances. Consider the reaction of hydrogen and oxygen to produce water. If the product is water vapor, 2 mol of H_2 burn to release 483.7 kJ of heat.

$$2\text{H}_2(g) + \text{O}_2(g) \longrightarrow 2\text{H}_2\text{O}(g); \Delta H = -483.7 \text{ kJ}$$

On the other hand, if the product is liquid water, the heat released is 571.7 kJ.

$$2H_2(g) + O_2(g) \longrightarrow 2H_2O(l); \Delta H = -571.7 \text{ kJ}$$

In this case, additional heat is released when water vapor condenses to liquid. <

It takes 44.0 kJ of heat to vaporize 1 mol of liquid water at 25°C.

Example 6.2 | Writing Thermochemical Equations

Aqueous sodium hydrogen carbonate solution (baking soda solution) reacts with hydrochloric acid to produce aqueous sodium chloride, water, and carbon dioxide gas. The reaction absorbs 12.7 kJ of heat at constant pressure for each mole of sodium hydrogen carbonate. Write the thermochemical equation for the reaction.

Problem Strategy Remember that the thermochemical equation is the balanced equation for the reaction, given a molar interpretation, with the enthalpy of reaction written directly after it. You need to translate the names of substances given in the problem statement into their formulas and then balance the equation. (This is an acid–base reaction; refer to Section 4.4 for a discussion.) The problem statement gives you the quantity of heat absorbed (heat is added to the system), so the enthalpy change is a positive quantity. Note too that this is the heat absorbed for each mole of sodium hydrogen carbonate.

Solution You first write the balanced chemical equation.

$$NaHCO_3(aq) + HCl(aq) \longrightarrow NaCl(aq) + H_2O(l) + CO_2(g)$$

The equation is for 1 mol $NaHCO_3$, with the absorption of 12.7 kJ of heat. The corresponding ΔH is +12.7 kJ. The thermochemical equation is

$$\textbf{NaHCO}_3(\textbf{aq}) + \textbf{HCl}(\textbf{aq}) \longrightarrow \textbf{NaCl}(\textbf{aq}) + \textbf{H}_2\textbf{O}(l) + \textbf{CO}_2(g); \Delta H = +12.7 \text{ kJ}$$

Answer Check Check that the formulas of the substances in the equation are correct and that the equation is balanced. Also check that the enthalpy of reaction has the correct sign and that its value is for the correct amount of reactant given in the problem statement (1 mol $NaHCO_3$).

Exercise 6.3   A propellant for rockets is obtained by mixing the liquids hydrazine, N_2H_4, and dinitrogen tetroxide, N_2O_4. These compounds react to give gaseous nitrogen, N_2, and water vapor, evolving 1049 kJ of heat at constant pressure when 1 mol N_2O_4 reacts. Write the thermochemical equation for this reaction.

■ See Problems 6.51 and 6.52.

The following are two important rules for manipulating thermochemical equations:

1. When a thermochemical equation is multiplied by any factor, the value of ΔH for the new equation is obtained by multiplying the value of ΔH in the original equation by that same factor.

2. When a chemical equation is reversed, the value of ΔH is reversed in sign.

Consider the thermochemical equation for the synthesis of ammonia.

$$N_2(g) + 3H_2(g) \longrightarrow 2NH_3(g); \Delta H = -91.8 \text{ kJ}$$

Suppose you want the thermochemical equation to show what happens when twice as many moles of nitrogen and hydrogen react to produce ammonia. Because double the amounts of substances are present, the enthalpy of reaction is doubled (enthalpy is an extensive quantity). Doubling the previous equation, you obtain

$$2N_2(g) + 6H_2(g) \longrightarrow 4NH_3(g); \Delta H = -184 \text{ kJ}$$

Suppose you reverse the first equation we wrote for the synthesis of ammonia. Then the reaction is the dissociation of 2 mol of ammonia into its elements. The thermochemical equation is

$$2NH_3(g) \longrightarrow N_2(g) + 3H_2(g); \Delta H = +91.8 \text{ kJ}$$

If you use the molar interpretation of a chemical equation, there is nothing unreasonable about using such coefficients as $\frac{1}{2}$ and $\frac{3}{2}$.

If you want to express this in terms of 1 mol of ammonia, you simply multiply this equation by a factor of $\frac{1}{2}$. ◄

The next example further illustrates the use of these rules of thermochemical equations.

Example 6.3 | Manipulating Thermochemical Equations

When 2 mol $H_2(g)$ and 1 mol $O_2(g)$ react to give liquid water, 572 kJ of heat evolves.

$$2H_2(g) + O_2(g) \longrightarrow 2H_2O(l); \Delta H = -572 \text{ kJ}$$

Write this equation for 1 mol of liquid water. Give the reverse equation, in which 1 mol of liquid water dissociates into hydrogen and oxygen.

Problem Strategy   Recall the rules for manipulating thermochemical equations. When you multiply an equation by a factor, you also multiply ΔH by the same factor. When you reverse an equation, you multiply ΔH by -1.

Solution   You multiply the coefficients and ΔH by $\frac{1}{2}$:

$$H_2(g) + \tfrac{1}{2}O_2(g) \longrightarrow H_2O(l); \Delta H = -286 \text{ kJ}$$

Reversing the equation, you get

$$H_2O(l) \longrightarrow H_2(g) + \tfrac{1}{2}O_2(g); \Delta H = +286 \text{ kJ}$$

Answer Check   If you multiply an equation by a factor, check that every formula and ΔH have been multiplied by that factor.

Exercise 6.4   a. Write the thermochemical equation for the reaction described in Exercise 6.3 for the case involving 1 mol N_2H_4. b. Write the thermochemical equation for the reverse of the reaction described in Exercise 6.3.

■ See Problems 6.53, 6.54, 6.55, and 6.56.

Concept Check 6.2

Natural gas consists primarily of methane, CH_4. It is used in a process called *steam reforming* to prepare a gaseous mixture of carbon monoxide and hydrogen for industrial use.

$$CH_4(g) + H_2O(g) \longrightarrow CO(g) + 3H_2(g); \Delta H = 206 \text{ kJ}$$

The reverse reaction, the reaction of carbon monoxide and hydrogen, has been explored as a way to prepare methane (synthetic natural gas). Which of the following are exothermic? Of these, which one is the most exothermic?

a. $CH_4(g) + H_2O(g) \longrightarrow CO(g) + 3H_2(g)$

b. $2CH_4(g) + 2H_2O(g) \longrightarrow 2CO(g) + 6H_2(g)$

c. $CO(g) + 3H_2(g) \longrightarrow CH_4(g) + H_2O(g)$

d. $2CO(g) + 6H_2(g) \longrightarrow 2CH_4(g) + 2H_2O(g)$

A Chemist Looks at . . .

daily life

Lucifers and Other Matches

Samuel Jones, an Englishman, patented one of the first kinds of matches in 1828. It consisted of a glass bead containing sulfuric acid surrounded by a coating of sugar with an oxidizing agent. You ignited the match by breaking the bead using a pair of pliers or, if you were more daring, your teeth. This action released the acid, which ignited an exothermic reaction in the surrounding combustible materials.

Later Jones began to market a friction match discovered, but not patented, by John Walker. Walker, who had been experimenting with explosives, discovered this match one day when he tried to remove a small glob of a dried mixture of antimony sulfide and potassium chlorate from a stick. He rubbed the stick on the floor and was surprised when it burst into flame. Jones called his matches "Lucifers." They were well named; when lighted, they gave off a shower of sparks and smoky fumes with the acrid odor of sulfur dioxide. Jones had every box inscribed with the warning "Persons whose lungs are delicate should by no means use Lucifers."

A few years later, a Frenchman, Charles Sauria, invented the white phosphorus match, which became an immediate success. When rubbed on a rough surface, the match lighted easily, without hazardous sparks, and smelled better than Lucifers. The match head contained white phosphorus, an oxidizing agent, and glue. White phosphorus is a yellowish-white, waxy substance, often sold in the form of sticks looking something like fat crayons. Unlike crayons, though, white phosphorus ignites spontaneously in air (so it is generally stored under water).

The glue in the match mixture had two purposes: it protected the white phosphorus from air, and it held the match mixture firmly together. The white phosphorus match had one serious drawback. White phosphorus is quite poisonous. Workers in match factories often began to show the agonizing symptoms of "phossy jaw," from white phosphorus poisoning, in which the jawbone disintegrates. The manufacture of white phosphorus matches was outlawed in the early 1900s.

The head of the "strike-anywhere" match, which you can buy today at any grocery store, contains the relatively nontoxic tetraphosphorus trisulfide, P_4S_3, and potassium chlorate, $KClO_3$ (Figure 6.10). By rubbing the match head against a surface, you create enough heat by friction to ignite the match material. Tetraphosphorus trisulfide then burns in air in a very exothermic reaction.

$$P_4S_3(s) + 8O_2(g) \longrightarrow P_4O_{10}(s) + 3SO_2(g);$$
$$\Delta H = -3676 \text{ kJ}$$

Safety matches have a head containing mostly an oxidizing agent and require a striking surface containing nonpoisonous red phosphorus.

FIGURE 6.10 ▲

Strike-anywhere matches
Left: The head of the match contains tetraphosphorus trisulfide and potassium chlorate.
Right: The substances in the match head react when frictional heat ignites the mixture.

■ See Problems 6.121 and 6.122.

6.5 | Applying Stoichiometry to Heats of Reaction

As you might expect, the quantity of heat obtained from a reaction will depend on the amount of reactants. We can extend the method used to solve stoichiometry problems, described in Chapter 3, to problems involving the quantity of heat.

Consider the reaction of methane, CH_4 (the principal constituent of natural gas), burning in oxygen at constant pressure. How much heat could you obtain from 10.0 g of methane, assuming you had an excess of oxygen? You can answer this question if

FIGURE 6.11

Calculating the heat obtained from a reaction

Convert the grams of a reactant or product to moles (using the molar mass). Then convert these moles to kilojoules of heat (using the enthalpy of reaction).

| Grams of A (reactant or product) | × | Conversion factor: g A to mol A (using molar mass) | × | Conversion factor: mol A to kJ (using enthalpy of reaction) | → | Kilojoules of heat |

If you wanted the result in kilocalories, you could convert this answer as follows:

$$556 \text{ kJ} \times \frac{1 \text{ kcal}}{4.184 \text{ kJ}} = 133 \text{ kcal}$$

you know the enthalpy change for the reaction of 1 mol of methane. The thermochemical equation is

$$CH_4(g) + 2O_2(g) \longrightarrow CO_2(g) + 2H_2O(l); \Delta H = -890.3 \text{ kJ}$$

The calculation involves the following conversions:

$$\text{Grams of } CH_4 \longrightarrow \text{moles of } CH_4 \longrightarrow \text{kilojoules of heat}$$

$$10.0 \text{ g } CH_4 \times \frac{1 \text{ mol } CH_4}{16.0 \text{ g } CH_4} \times \frac{-890.3 \text{ kJ}}{1 \text{ mol } CH_4} = -556 \text{ kJ}$$

Figure 6.11 illustrates the general calculation. <

Example 6.4 | **Calculating the Heat of Reaction from the Stoichiometry**

How much heat is evolved when 9.07×10^5 g of ammonia is produced according to the following equation? (Assume that the reaction occurs at constant pressure.)

$$N_2(g) + 3H_2(g) \longrightarrow 2NH_3(g); \Delta H = -91.8 \text{ kJ}$$

Problem Strategy The calculation involves converting grams of NH_3 to moles of NH_3 and then to kilojoules of heat.

$$\text{Grams of } NH_3 \longrightarrow \text{moles of } NH_3 \longrightarrow \text{kilojoules of heat}$$

You obtain the conversion factor for the second step from the thermochemical equation, which says that the production of 2 mol NH_3 is accompanied by $q_p = -91.8$ kJ.

Solution $9.07 \times 10^5 \text{ g } NH_3 \times \dfrac{1 \text{ mol } NH_3}{17.0 \text{ g } NH_3} \times \dfrac{-91.8 \text{ kJ}}{2 \text{ mol } NH_3} = -2.45 \times 10^6 \text{ kJ}$

Thus, **2.45×10^6 kJ of heat evolves.**

Answer Check Make sure that the units in the calculation cancel to give the units of heat. Also note the sign of ΔH to decide whether heat is evolved or absorbed.

Exercise 6.5 How much heat evolves when 10.0 g of hydrazine reacts according to the reaction described in Exercise 6.3?

■ See Problems 6.57, 6.58, 6.59, and 6.60.

6.6 | Measuring Heats of Reaction

So far we have introduced the concept of heat of reaction and have related it to the enthalpy change. We also showed how to display the enthalpy change in a thermochemical equation, and from this equation how to calculate the heat of reaction for any given amount of substance. Now that you have a firm idea of what heats of reaction are, how would you measure them?

First, we need to look at the heat required to raise the temperature of a substance, because a thermochemical measurement is based on the relationship between heat and temperature change. The heat required to raise the temperature of a substance is called its *heat capacity.*

Heat Capacity and Specific Heat

Heat is required to raise the temperature of a given amount of substance, and the quantity of heat depends on the temperature change. The **heat capacity** (C) of a sample of substance is *the quantity of heat needed to raise the temperature of the sample of substance one degree Celsius (or one kelvin).* Changing the temperature of the sample from an initial temperature t_i to a final temperature t_f requires heat equal to

$$q = C\Delta t$$

The heat capacity will depend on whether the process is constant-pressure or constant-volume. We will assume a constant-pressure process unless otherwise stated.

where Δt is the change of temperature and equals $t_f - t_i$. <
Suppose a piece of iron requires 6.70 J of heat to raise the temperature by one degree Celsius. Its heat capacity is therefore 6.70 J/°C. The quantity of heat required to raise the temperature of the piece of iron from 25.0°C to 35.0°C is

$$q = C\Delta t = (6.70 \text{ J/°C}) \times (35.0°\text{C} - 25.0°\text{C}) = 67.0 \text{ J}$$

Heat capacity is directly proportional to the amount of substance. Often heat capacities are listed for molar amounts of substances. The *molar heat capacity* of a substance is its heat capacity for one mole of substance.

Heat capacities are also compared for one-gram amounts of substances. The **specific heat capacity** (or simply **specific heat**) is *the quantity of heat required to raise the temperature of one gram of a substance by one degree Celsius (or one kelvin) at constant pressure.* To find the heat q required to raise the temperature of a sample, you multiply the specific heat of the substance, s, by the mass in grams, m, and the temperature change, Δt.

$$q = s \times m \times \Delta t$$

The specific heats and molar heat capacities of a few substances are listed in Table 6.1. Values depend somewhat on temperature, and those listed are for 25°C. Water has a specific heat of 4.18 J/(g·°C)—that is, 4.18 joules per gram per degree Celsius. In terms of calories, the specific heat of water is 1.00 cal/(g·°C). Example 6.5 illustrates the use of the preceding equation.

TABLE 6.1	Specific Heats and Molar Heat Capacities of Some Substances*	
Substance	Specific Heat J/(g·°C)	Molar Heat Capacity J/(mol·°C)
Aluminum, Al	0.901	24.3
Copper, Cu	0.384	24.4
Ethanol, C_2H_5OH	2.43	112.2
Iron, Fe	0.449	25.1
Water, H_2O	4.18	75.3

*Values are for 25°C.

Example 6.5	Relating Heat and Specific Heat

Calculate the heat absorbed by 15.0 g of water to raise its temperature from 20.0°C to 50.0°C (at constant pressure). The specific heat of water is 4.18 J/(g·°C).

Problem Strategy Note that specific heat is the heat needed to raise the temperature of one gram of substance one degree Celsius. To get the total heat, multiply specific heat by the grams of substance and by the change in degrees Celsius.

(continued)

(continued)

Solution You substitute into the equation

$$q = s \times m \times \Delta t$$

The temperature change is

$$\Delta t = t_f - t_i = 50.0°C - 20.0°C = +30.0°C$$

Therefore,

$$q = 4.18\ \text{J/(g·°C)} \times 15.0\ \text{g} \times (+30.0°C) = \mathbf{1.88 \times 10^3\ J}$$

Answer Check Be sure to put units on quantities in your calculation and to note whether units cancel to give units of heat.

Exercise 6.6 Iron metal has a specific heat of 0.449 J/(g·°C). How much heat is transferred to a 5.00-g piece of iron, initially at 20.0°C, when it is placed in a pot of boiling water? Assume that the temperature of the water is 100.0°C and that the water remains at this temperature, which is the final temperature of the iron.

■ See Problems 6.63 and 6.64.

Measurement of Heat of Reaction

You measure the heat of reaction in a **calorimeter,** *a device used to measure the heat absorbed or evolved during a physical or chemical change.* The device can be as simple as the apparatus sketched in Figure 6.12, which consists of an insulated container (for example, a pair of polystyrene coffee cups) with a thermometer. More elaborate calorimeters are employed when precise measurements are needed for research, although the basic idea remains the same—to measure temperature changes under controlled circumstances and relate these temperature changes to heat.

The coffee-cup calorimeter shown in Figure 6.12 is a constant-pressure calorimeter. The heat of the reaction is calculated from the temperature change caused by the reaction, and since this is a constant-pressure process, the heat can be directly related to the enthalpy change, ΔH. Research versions of a constant-pressure calorimeter are available, and these are used when gases are not involved.

For reactions involving gases, a *bomb calorimeter* is generally used (Figure 6.13). Consider the heat of combustion of graphite, the form of carbon used in the "lead" of a pencil. To measure the heat released when graphite burns in oxygen, a sample of graphite is placed in a small cup in the calorimeter. The graphite is surrounded by oxygen, and the graphite and oxygen are sealed in a steel vessel, or bomb. An electrical circuit is activated to start the burning of the graphite. The bomb is surrounded by water in an insulated container, and the heat of reaction is calculated from the temperature change of the calorimeter caused by the reaction.

Because the reaction in a bomb calorimeter occurs in a closed vessel, the pressure does not generally remain constant. Rather the volume remains constant, and under these conditions the heat of reaction does not in general equal ΔH; a small correction is usually needed. However, this correction is negligible when the reaction does not involve gases or when the number of moles of reactant gas equals the number of moles of product gas, as in the combustion of graphite to carbon dioxide. <

The next example describes the calculations needed to obtain ΔH from calorimetric measurements.

At the end of Section 6.3, we noted that $\Delta H = \Delta U + P\Delta V$. The heat at constant volume equals ΔU. To obtain ΔH, you must add a correction, $P\Delta V$. The change in volume is significant only if there are changes in gas volumes. From the ideal gas law, the molar volume of a gas is RT/P. If the moles of gas that have reacted is n_i and the moles of gas produced is n_f, then $P\Delta V$ equals essentially $RT \times (n_f - n_i)$, or $RT\Delta n$, where Δn refers to the change of moles of gas. To obtain the correction in joules, we use $R = 8.31$ J/(K·mol). Thus, RT at 25°C (298 K) is 8.31 J/(K·mol) $\times 298$ K $= 2.48 \times 10^3$ J/mol. The final result is $\Delta H = \Delta U + (2.48\ kJ) \times \Delta n$.

FIGURE 6.12 ▲

A simple coffee-cup calorimeter
This calorimeter is made of two nested polystyrene coffee cups. The outer cup helps to insulate the reaction mixture from its surroundings. After the reactants are added to the inner cup, the calorimeter is covered to reduce heat loss by evaporation and convection. The heat of reaction is determined by noting the temperature rise or fall.

FIGURE 6.13 ▲

A bomb calorimeter
This type of calorimeter can be used to determine the heat of combustion of a substance. The figure shows a sample of graphite being burned in oxygen within a vessel called the bomb. An electric current passing through the ignition coil starts the graphite burning. The temperature of the water surrounding the bomb rises as heat flows from the exothermic reaction of graphite and oxygen. Example 6.6 illustrates the calculations involved in determining the heat of combustion in such an experiment.

Example 6.6 | Calculating ΔH from Calorimetric Data

Suppose 0.562 g of graphite is placed in a calorimeter with an excess of oxygen at 25.00°C and 1 atm pressure (Figure 6.13). Excess O_2 ensures that all carbon burns to form CO_2. The graphite is ignited, and it burns according to the equation

$$C(graphite) + O_2(g) \longrightarrow CO_2(g)$$

On reaction, the calorimeter temperature rises from 25.00°C to 25.89°C. The heat capacity of the calorimeter and its contents was determined in a separate experiment to be 20.7 kJ/°C. What is the heat of reaction at 25.00°C and 1 atm pressure? Express the answer as a thermochemical equation.

Problem Strategy First, you need to obtain the heat absorbed by the calorimeter when the sample burns, using the calorimeter's temperature rise and its heat capacity. Note that the heat released by reaction of the sample (a negative quantity) equals the heat absorbed by the calorimeter (a positive quantity), except for this sign change. Then, you need to convert this heat to the heat released per mole to obtain ΔH.

Step 1: To obtain heat absorbed by the calorimeter, you reason as follows. The heat released by the reaction is absorbed by the calorimeter and its contents. Let q_{rxn} be the quantity of heat from the reaction mixture, and let C_{cal} be the heat capacity of the calorimeter and contents. The quantity of heat absorbed by the calorimeter is $C_{cal}\Delta t$. This will have the same magnitude as q_{rxn}, but the opposite sign: $q_{rxn} = -C_{cal}\Delta t$.

(continued)

(continued)

Substituting values of C_{cal} and Δt, you obtain the heat q_{rxn} from the sample of C (0.562 g). The factor $(q_{rxn}/0.562$ g C) converts

$$\text{Grams C} \longrightarrow \text{kJ heat}$$

Step 2: What is the heat released from 1 mol C (equal to ΔH)? Convert this amount of C (mathematically) to grams C. Then convert this to kJ heat, using the conversion factor you obtained in Step 1 $(q_{rxn}/0.562$ g C). The conversion steps are

$$\text{Moles C} \longrightarrow \text{grams C} \longrightarrow \text{kJ heat } (\Delta H)$$

Solution

Step 1: The heat from the graphite sample is

$$q_{rxn} = -C_{cal}\Delta t = -20.7 \text{ kJ/°C} \times (25.89°C - 25.00°C)$$
$$= -20.7 \text{ kJ/°C} \times 0.89°C = -18.4 \text{ kJ}$$

An extra figure is retained in q_{rxn} for further computation. The negative sign indicates the reaction is exothermic, as expected for a combustion. The factor to convert grams C to kJ heat is -18.4 kJ/0.562 g C.

Step 2: The conversion of 1 mol C to kJ heat for 1 mol (ΔH) is

$$1 \text{ mol C} \times \frac{12 \text{ g C}}{1 \text{ mol C}} \times \frac{-18.4 \text{ kJ}}{0.562 \text{ g C}} = -3.9 \times 10^2 \text{ kJ}$$

(The final answer has been rounded to two significant figures.) When 1 mol of carbon burns, 3.9×10^2 kJ of heat is released. You can summarize the results by the thermochemical equation:

$$\textbf{C(graphite)} + \textbf{O}_2(g) \longrightarrow \textbf{CO}_2(g); \Delta H = -3.9 \times 10^2 \text{ kJ}$$

Answer Check Go over your calculations carefully. Check that the units within each step cancel properly. Also check that you have the right sign for ΔH; an exothermic reaction will have a negative sign.

Exercise 6.7   Suppose 33 mL of 1.20 M HCl is added to 42 mL of a solution containing excess sodium hydroxide, NaOH, in a coffee-cup calorimeter. The solution temperature, originally 25.0°C, rises to 31.8°C. Give the enthalpy change, ΔH, for the reaction

$$\text{HCl}(aq) + \text{NaOH}(aq) \longrightarrow \text{NaCl}(aq) + \text{H}_2\text{O}(l)$$

Express the answer as a thermochemical equation. For simplicity, assume that the heat capacity and the density of the final solution in the cup are those of water. (In more accurate work, these values must be determined.) Also assume that the total volume of the solution equals the sum of the volumes of HCl(aq) and NaOH(aq).

■ See Problems 6.67, 6.68, 6.69, and 6.70.

Using Heats of Reaction

In the first part of this chapter, we looked at the basic properties of the heat of reaction and how to measure it. Now we want to find how heats of reaction can be used. We will see that the ΔH for one reaction can be obtained from the ΔH's of other reactions. This means that we can tabulate a small number of values and use them to calculate others.

6.7 | Hess's Law

Enthalpy, you may recall, is a state function (Section 6.3). This means that the enthalpy change for a chemical reaction is independent of the path by which the products are obtained. In 1840, the Russian chemist Germain Henri Hess, a professor at the University of St. Petersburg, discovered this result by experiment. **Hess's law of heat summation** states that *for a chemical equation that can be written as the sum of two or more steps, the enthalpy change for the overall equation equals the sum of the enthalpy changes for the individual steps.* In other words, no matter how you go from given reactants to products (whether in one step or several), the enthalpy change for the overall chemical change is the same.

To understand Hess's law fully and to see how you can use it, consider a simple example. Suppose you would like to find the enthalpy change for the combustion of graphite (carbon) to carbon monoxide.

$$2C(graphite) + O_2(g) \longrightarrow 2CO(g)$$

The direct determination of this enthalpy change is very difficult, because once carbon monoxide forms it reacts further with oxygen to yield carbon dioxide. If you do the experiment in an excess of oxygen, you obtain only carbon dioxide, and the enthalpy change is the heat of complete combustion of graphite. On the other hand, if you do the experiment in a limited quantity of oxygen, you obtain a mixture of carbon monoxide and carbon dioxide, and the heat of reaction is a value appropriate for a mixture of these products. How can you obtain the enthalpy change for the preparation of pure carbon monoxide from graphite and oxygen?

The answer is to apply Hess's law. To do this, imagine that the combustion of graphite to carbon monoxide takes place in two separate steps:

$$2C(graphite) + 2O_2(g) \longrightarrow 2CO_2(g) \qquad \text{(first step)}$$

$$2CO_2(g) \longrightarrow 2CO(g) + O_2(g) \qquad \text{(second step)}$$

In the first step, you burn 2 mol of graphite in 2 mol of oxygen to produce 2 mol of carbon dioxide. In the second step, you decompose this carbon dioxide to give 2 mol of carbon monoxide and 1 mol of oxygen. The net result is the combustion of 2 mol of graphite in 1 mol of oxygen to give 2 mol of carbon monoxide. You can obtain this result by adding the two steps, canceling out 2 mol CO_2 and 1 mol O_2 on both sides of the equation.

$$2C(graphite) + \cancel{2}O_2(g) \longrightarrow \cancel{2CO_2(g)}$$
$$\underline{\cancel{2CO_2(g)} \qquad\qquad \longrightarrow 2CO(g) + \cancel{O_2(g)}}$$
$$2C(graphite) + O_2(g) \longrightarrow 2CO(g)$$

According to Hess's law, the enthalpy change for the overall equation (which is the equation you want) equals the sum of the enthalpy changes for the two steps. Now you need to determine the enthalpy changes for the separate steps.

You can determine the enthalpy change for the first step by simply burning graphite in an excess of oxygen, as described in Example 6.6. The result is $\Delta H = -393.5$ kJ per mole of CO_2 formed. For 2 mol CO_2, you multiply by 2.

$$2C(graphite) + 2O_2(g) \longrightarrow 2CO_2(g); \Delta H = (-393.5 \text{ kJ}) \times (2)$$

The second step, the decomposition of carbon dioxide, is not an easy experiment. However, the reverse of this decomposition is simply the combustion of carbon monoxide. You could determine the ΔH for that combustion by burning carbon monoxide in an excess of oxygen. The experiment is similar to the one for the combustion of graphite to carbon dioxide.

$$2CO(g) + O_2(g) \longrightarrow 2CO_2(g); \Delta H = -566.0 \text{ kJ}$$

From the properties of thermochemical equations (Section 6.4), you know that the enthalpy change for the reverse reaction is simply (−1) times the original reaction.

$$2CO_2(g) \longrightarrow 2CO(g) + O_2(g); \Delta H = (-566.0 \text{ kJ}) \times (-1)$$

If you now add these two steps and add their enthalpy changes, you obtain the chemical equation and the enthalpy change for the combustion of carbon monoxide, which is what you wanted.

$2C(\text{graphite}) + 2O_2(g) \longrightarrow 2CO_2(g)$		$\Delta H_1 = (-393.5 \text{ kJ}) \times (2)$
$2CO_2(g) \longrightarrow 2CO(g) + O_2(g)$		$\Delta H_2 = (-566.0 \text{ kJ}) \times (-1)$
$2C(\text{graphite}) + O_2(g) \longrightarrow 2CO(g)$		$\Delta H_3 = -221.0 \text{ kJ}$

You see that the combustion of 2 mol of graphite to give 2 mol of carbon monoxide has an enthalpy change of −221.0 kJ. Figure 6.14 gives an enthalpy diagram showing the relationship among the enthalpy changes for this calculation.

This calculation illustrates how you can use Hess's law to obtain the enthalpy change for a reaction that is difficult to determine by direct experiment. Hess's law is more generally useful, however, in that it allows you to calculate the enthalpy change for one reaction from the values for others, whatever their source. Suppose you are given the following data: <

$$S(s) + O_2(g) \longrightarrow SO_2(g); \Delta H = -297 \text{ kJ} \tag{1}$$

$$2SO_3(g) \longrightarrow 2SO_2(g) + O_2(g); \Delta H = 198 \text{ kJ} \tag{2}$$

How could you use these data to obtain the enthalpy change for the following equation?

$$2S(s) + 3O_2(g) \longrightarrow 2SO_3(g) \tag{3}$$

You need to multiply Equations 1 and 2 by factors (perhaps reversing one or both equations) so that when you add them together you obtain Equation 3. You can usually guess what you need to do to the first two equations to obtain the third one. Note that Equation 3 has a coefficient of 2 for S(s). This suggests that you should multiply Equation 1 by 2 (and multiply the ΔH by 2). Note also that $SO_3(g)$ in Equation 3 is on the right-hand side. This suggests that you should reverse Equation 2 (and multiply the ΔH by −1). Here is the calculation:

$2S(s) + 2O_2(g) \longrightarrow 2SO_2(g)$	$\Delta H = (-297 \text{ kJ}) \times (2)$
$2SO_2(g) + O_2(g) \longrightarrow 2SO_3(g)$	$\Delta H = (198 \text{ kJ}) \times (-1)$
$2S(s) + 3O_2(g) \longrightarrow 2SO_3(g)$	$\Delta H = -792 \text{ kJ}$

The next example gives another illustration of how Hess's law can be used to calculate the enthalpy change for a reaction from the enthalpy values for other reactions. In

We have followed common convention in writing S for the formula of sulfur in Equations 1 and 3, although the molecular formula is S_8. Doing this gives much simpler equations. You might try to do the calculations again, rewriting the equations using S_8 for sulfur. Remember to multiply the value of ΔH in each case by 8.

FIGURE 6.14 ▶

Enthalpy diagram illustrating Hess's law
The diagram shows two different ways to go from graphite and oxygen (reactants) to carbon monoxide (products). Going by way of reactions 1 and 2 is equivalent to the direct reaction 3.

this case, the problem involves three equations from which we obtain a fourth. Although this problem is somewhat more complicated than the one we just did, the basic procedure is the same: Compare the coefficients in the equations. See what factors you need to multiply the equations whose ΔH's you know to obtain the equation you want. Check your results to be sure that the equations (and the ΔH's) add up properly.

| Example 6.7 | Applying Hess's Law |

What is the enthalpy of reaction, ΔH, for the formation of tungsten carbide, WC, from the elements? (Tungsten carbide is very hard and is used to make cutting tools and rock drills.)

$$W(s) + C(graphite) \longrightarrow WC(s)$$

The enthalpy change for this reaction is difficult to measure directly, because the reaction occurs at 1400°C. However, the heats of combustion of the elements and of tungsten carbide can be measured easily:

$$2W(s) + 3O_2(g) \longrightarrow 2WO_3(s); \Delta H = -1685.8 \text{ kJ} \qquad (1)$$

$$C(graphite) + O_2(g) \longrightarrow CO_2(g); \Delta H = -393.5 \text{ kJ} \qquad (2)$$

$$2WC(s) + 5O_2(g) \longrightarrow 2WO_3(s) + 2CO_2(g); \Delta H = -2391.8 \text{ kJ} \qquad (3)$$

Problem Strategy Note that Equations 1, 2, and 3 involve the reactants and products for the desired reaction (as well as their enthalpy changes). You apply Hess's law to these equations, perhaps reversing an equation or multiplying it by a factor, so that when you add all of them together, you obtain the desired equation.

First, look to see whether any equation needs to be reversed to get a reactant or product on the correct side. If you do reverse an equation, remember to change the sign of its ΔH. Second, to obtain the multiplicative factor for each equation, compare that equation with the desired one. For instance, note that Equation 1 has $2W(s)$ on the left side, whereas the desired equation has $W(s)$ on the left. Therefore, you divide Equation 1 (and its ΔH) by 2, or multiply by the factor $\frac{1}{2}$.

Solution Do any equations need to be reversed? Note that you want to end up with $W(s)$ and $C(graphite)$ on the left side and with $WC(s)$ on the right side of the final equation (the formation of WC from its elements). Equation 1 has $W(s)$ on the left, as required after the addition of the equations. Similarly, Equation 2 has $C(graphite)$ on the left, as required. However, Equation 3 has $WC(s)$ on the left, but it should be on the right. Therefore, you reverse Equation 3 (and multiply its ΔH by -1).

$$2WO_3(s) + 2CO_2(g) \longrightarrow 2WC(s) + 5O_2(g); \Delta H = 2391.8 \text{ kJ} \qquad (3')$$

To obtain the multiplicative factor for each equation, you compare Equations 1, 2, and 3', in turn, with the desired equation. We did this earlier (at the end of the Problem Strategy) for Equation 1. Multiplying it by $\frac{1}{2}$, you obtain

$$W(s) + \tfrac{3}{2}O_2(g) \longrightarrow WO_3(s); \Delta H = \tfrac{1}{2} \times (-1685.8 \text{ kJ}) = -842.9 \text{ kJ}$$

Compare Equation 2 with the desired equation. Both have $C(graphite)$ on the left side; therefore, you leave Equation 2 as it is.

$$C(graphite) + O_2(g) \longrightarrow CO_2(g); \Delta H = -393.5 \text{ kJ}$$

Now, compare Equation 3' with the desired equation. Equation 3' has $2WC(s)$ on the right side, whereas the desired equation has $WC(s)$ on the right side. Therefore, you multiply Equation 3' (and its ΔH) by $\frac{1}{2}$.

$$WO_3(s) + CO_2(g) \longrightarrow WC(s) + \tfrac{5}{2}O_2(g); \Delta H = \tfrac{1}{2} \times (2391.8 \text{ kJ}) = 1195.9 \text{ kJ}$$

(continued)

(continued)

Now add these last three equations and their corresponding ΔH's.

$$W(s) + \tfrac{3}{2}O_2(g) \longrightarrow WO_3(s) \qquad \Delta H = -842.9 \text{ kJ}$$
$$C(\text{graphite}) + O_2(g) \longrightarrow CO_2(g) \qquad \Delta H = -393.5 \text{ kJ}$$
$$WO_3(s) + CO_2(g) \longrightarrow WC(s) + \tfrac{5}{2}O_2(g) \qquad \Delta H = 1195.9 \text{ kJ}$$
$$\overline{W(s) + C(\text{graphite}) \longrightarrow WC(s) \qquad \Delta H = -40.5 \text{ kJ}}$$

Answer Check Check that when you add the three equations substances that do not appear in the final one cancel correctly. For example, note that $\tfrac{3}{2}O_2(g)$ and $O_2(g)$ on the left sides of the equations cancel $\tfrac{5}{2}O_2(g)$ on the right side. Then check that the final equation is the one asked for.

Exercise 6.8 Manganese metal can be obtained by reaction of manganese dioxide with aluminum.

$$4Al(s) + 3MnO_2(s) \longrightarrow 2Al_2O_3(s) + 3Mn(s)$$

What is ΔH for this reaction? Use the following data:

$$2Al(s) + \tfrac{3}{2}O_2(g) \longrightarrow Al_2O_3(s); \ \Delta H = -1676 \text{ kJ}$$

$$Mn(s) + O_2(g) \longrightarrow MnO_2(s); \ \Delta H = -520 \text{ kJ}$$

■ See Problems 6.71, 6.72, 6.73, and 6.74.

Concept Check 6.3

The heat of fusion (also called heat of melting), ΔH_{fus}, of ice is the enthalpy change for

$$H_2O(s) \longrightarrow H_2O(l); \ \Delta H_{fus}$$

Similarly, the heat of vaporization, ΔH_{vap}, of liquid water is the enthalpy change for

$$H_2O(l) \longrightarrow H_2O(g); \ \Delta H_{vap}$$

How is the heat of sublimation, ΔH_{sub}, the enthalpy change for the reaction

$$H_2O(s) \longrightarrow H_2O(g); \ \Delta H_{sub}$$

related to ΔH_{fus} and ΔH_{vap}?

6.8 | Standard Enthalpies of Formation

Because Hess's law relates the enthalpy changes of some reactions to the enthalpy changes of others, we only need to tabulate the enthalpy changes of certain types of reactions. We also generally list enthalpy changes only for certain standard thermodynamic conditions (which are not identical to the standard conditions for gases, STP).

The International Union of Pure and Applied Chemistry (IUPAC) recommends that the standard pressure be 1 bar (1×10^5 Pa). Thermodynamic tables are becoming available for 1 bar pressure, and in the future such tables will probably replace those for 1 atm.

The term **standard state** refers to *the standard thermodynamic conditions chosen for substances when listing or comparing thermodynamic data: 1 atm pressure and the specified temperature (usually 25°C).* < These standard conditions are indicated by a superscript degree sign (°). The enthalpy change for a reaction in which reactants in their standard states yield products in their standard states is denoted $\Delta H°$ ("delta H degree," but often read as "delta H zero"). The quantity $\Delta H°$ is called the *standard enthalpy of reaction.*

FIGURE 6.15

FIGURE 6.15

Allotropes of sulfur

Left: An evaporating dish contains rhombic sulfur, the stable form of the element at room temperature. *Right:* When this sulfur is melted, then cooled, it forms long needles of monoclinic sulfur, another allotrope. At room temperature, monoclinic sulfur will slowly change back to rhombic sulfur. Both forms contain the molecule S_8, depicted by the model.

As we will show, it is sufficient to tabulate just the enthalpy changes for formation reactions—that is, for reactions in which compounds are formed from their elements. To specify the formation reaction precisely, however, we must specify the exact form of each element.

Some elements exist in the same physical state (gas, liquid, or solid) in two or more distinct forms. For example, oxygen in any of the physical states occurs both as dioxygen (commonly called simply oxygen), with O_2 molecules, and as ozone, with O_3 molecules. Dioxygen gas is odorless; ozone gas has a characteristic pungent odor. Solid carbon has two principal crystalline forms: graphite and diamond. Graphite is a soft, black, crystalline substance; diamond is a hard, usually colorless crystal. The elements oxygen and carbon are said to exist in different allotropic forms. An **allotrope** is *one of two or more distinct forms of an element in the same physical state* (Figure 6.15).

The **reference form** of an element for the purpose of specifying the formation reaction is usually *the stablest form (physical state and allotrope) of the element under standard thermodynamic conditions.* The reference form of oxygen at 25°C is $O_2(g)$; the reference form of carbon at 25°C is graphite. <

Table 6.2 lists standard enthalpies of formation of substances and ions (a longer table is given in Appendix C). The **standard enthalpy of formation** (also called the **standard heat of formation**) of a substance, denoted ΔH_f°, is *the enthalpy change for the formation of one mole of the substance in its standard state from its elements in their reference form and in their standard states.*

To understand this definition, consider the standard enthalpy of formation of liquid water. Note that the stablest forms of hydrogen and oxygen at 1 atm and 25°C are $H_2(g)$ and $O_2(g)$, respectively. These are therefore the reference forms of the elements. You write the formation reaction for 1 mol of liquid water as follows:

$$H_2(g) + \tfrac{1}{2}O_2(g) \longrightarrow H_2O(l)$$

The standard enthalpy change for this reaction is -285.8 kJ per mole of H_2O. Therefore, the thermochemical equation is

$$H_2(g) + \tfrac{1}{2}O_2(g) \longrightarrow H_2O(l); \ \Delta H_f^\circ = -285.8 \text{ kJ}$$

The values of standard enthalpies of formation listed in Table 6.2 and in other tables are determined by direct measurement in some cases and by applying Hess's law in others. Oxides, such as water, can often be determined by direct calorimetric measurement of the combustion reaction. If you look back at Example 6.7, you will see an illustration of how Hess's law can be used to obtain the enthalpy of formation of tungsten carbide, WC.

Note that the standard enthalpy of formation of an element will depend on the form of the element. For example, the ΔH_f° for diamond equals the enthalpy change

Although the reference form is usually the stablest allotrope of an element, the choice is essentially arbitrary as long as one is consistent.

TABLE 6.2 | Standard Enthalpies of Formation (at 25°C)*

Substance or Ion	ΔH_f° (kJ/mol)	Substance or Ion	ΔH_f° (kJ/mol)	Substance or Ion	ΔH_f° (kJ/mol)
$e^-(g)$	0	$CH_3CHO(g)$	−166.1	$NO_2(g)$	33.10
Bromine		$CH_3CHO(l)$	−191.8	$HNO_3(aq)$	−207.4
$Br(g)$	111.9	**Chlorine**		**Oxygen**	
$Br^-(aq)$	−121.5	$Cl(g)$	121.3	$O(g)$	249.2
$Br^-(g)$	−219.0	$Cl^-(aq)$	−167.2	$O_2(g)$	0
$Br_2(g)$	30.91	$Cl^-(g)$	−234.0	$O_3(g)$	142.7
$Br_2(l)$	0	$Cl_2(g)$	0	$OH^-(aq)$	−230.0
$HBr(g)$	−36.44	$HCl(g)$	−92.31	$H_2O(g)$	−241.8
Calcium		**Fluorine**		$H_2O(l)$	−285.8
$Ca(s)$	0	$F(g)$	79.39	**Silicon**	
$Ca^{2+}(aq)$	−542.8	$F^-(g)$	−255.1	$Si(s)$	0
$CaCO_3(s, \text{calcite})$	−1206.9	$F^-(aq)$	−332.6	$SiCl_4(l)$	−687.0
$CaO(s)$	−635.1	$F_2(g)$	0	$SiF_4(g)$	−1614.9
Carbon		$HF(g)$	−272.5	$SiO_2(s, \text{quartz})$	−910.9
$C(g)$	716.7	**Hydrogen**		**Silver**	
$C(s, \text{diamond})$	1.897	$H(g)$	218.0	$Ag(s)$	0
$C(s, \text{graphite})$	0	$H^+(aq)$	0	$Ag^+(aq)$	105.6
$CCl_4(g)$	−95.98	$H^+(g)$	1536.2	$AgBr(s)$	−100.4
$CCl_4(l)$	−135.4	$H_2(g)$	0	$AgCl(s)$	−127.1
$CO(g)$	−110.5	**Iodine**		$AgF(s)$	−204.6
$CO_2(g)$	−393.5	$I(g)$	106.8	$AgI(s)$	−61.84
$CO_3^{2-}(aq)$	−677.1	$I^-(aq)$	−55.19	**Sodium**	
$CS_2(g)$	116.9	$I^-(g)$	−194.6	$Na(g)$	107.3
$CS_2(l)$	89.70	$I_2(s)$	0	$Na(s)$	0
$HCN(g)$	135.1	$HI(g)$	26.36	$Na^+(aq)$	−240.1
$HCN(l)$	108.9	**Lead**		$Na^+(g)$	609.3
$HCO_3^-(aq)$	−692.0	$Pb(s)$	0	$Na_2CO_3(s)$	−1130.8
Hydrocarbons		$Pb^{2+}(aq)$	−1.7	$NaCl(s)$	−411.1
$CH_4(g)$	−74.87	$PbO(s)$	−219.4	$NaHCO_3(s)$	−950.8
$C_2H_4(g)$	52.47	$PbS(s)$	−98.32	**Sulfur**	
$C_2H_6(g)$	−84.68	**Nitrogen**		$S(g)$	277.0
$C_6H_6(l)$	49.0	$N(g)$	472.7	$S(s, \text{monoclinic})$	0.360
Alcohols		$N_2(g)$	0	$S(s, \text{rhombic})$	0
$CH_3OH(l)$	−238.7	$NH_3(g)$	−45.90	$S_2(g)$	128.6
$C_2H_5OH(l)$	−277.7	$NH_4^+(aq)$	−132.5	$SO_2(g)$	−296.8
Aldehydes		$NO(g)$	90.29	$H_2S(g)$	−20.50
$HCHO(g)$	−117				

*See Appendix C for additional values.

from the stablest form of carbon (graphite) to diamond. The thermochemical equation is

$$C(\text{graphite}) \longrightarrow C(\text{diamond}); \Delta H_f^\circ = 1.9 \text{ kJ}$$

On the other hand, the ΔH_f° for graphite equals zero. Note the values of ΔH_f° for the elements listed in Table 6.2; the reference forms have zero values.

Now let us see how to use standard enthalpies of formation (listed in Table 6.2) to find the standard enthalpy change for a reaction. We will first look at this problem from the point of view of Hess's law. But when we are finished, we will note a pattern in the result, which will allow us to state a simple formula for solving this type of problem.

Consider the equation

$$CH_4(g) + 4Cl_2(g) \longrightarrow CCl_4(l) + 4HCl(g); \Delta H° = ?$$

From Table 6.2 you find the enthalpies of formation for $CH_4(g)$, $CCl_4(l)$, and $HCl(g)$. You can then write the following thermochemical equations:

$$C(graphite) + 2H_2(g) \longrightarrow CH_4(g); \Delta H_f° = -74.9 \text{ kJ} \qquad (1)$$

$$C(graphite) + 2Cl_2(g) \longrightarrow CCl_4(l); \Delta H_f° = -135.4 \text{ kJ} \qquad (2)$$

$$\tfrac{1}{2}H_2(g) + \tfrac{1}{2}Cl_2(g) \longrightarrow HCl(g); \Delta H_f° = -92.3 \text{ kJ} \qquad (3)$$

You now apply Hess's law. Since you want CH_4 to appear on the left, and CCl_4 and 4HCl on the right, you reverse Equation 1 and add Equation 2 and 4 × Equation 3.

$$
\begin{array}{ll}
CH_4(g) \longrightarrow C(graphite) + 2H_2(g) & (-74.9 \text{ kJ}) \times (-1) \\
C(graphite) + 2Cl_2(g) \longrightarrow CCl_4(l) & (-135.4 \text{ kJ}) \times (1) \\
2H_2(g) + 2Cl_2(g) \longrightarrow 4HCl(g) & (-92.3 \text{ kJ}) \times (4) \\
\hline
CH_4(g) + 4Cl_2(g) \longrightarrow CCl_4(l) + 4HCl(g) & \Delta H° = -429.7 \text{ kJ}
\end{array}
$$

The setup of this calculation can be greatly simplified once you closely examine what you are doing. Note that the $\Delta H_f°$ for each compound is multiplied by its coefficient in the chemical equation whose $\Delta H°$ you are calculating. Moreover, the $\Delta H_f°$ for each reactant is multiplied by a negative sign. You can symbolize the enthalpy of formation of a substance by writing the formula in parentheses following $\Delta H_f°$. Then your calculation can be written as follows:

$$\Delta H° = [\Delta H_f°(CCl_4) + 4 \Delta H_f°(HCl)] - [\Delta H_f°(CH_4) + 4 \Delta H_f°(Cl_2)]$$
$$= [(-135.4) + 4(-92.3)] \text{ kJ} - [(-74.9) + 4(0)] \text{ kJ} = -429.7 \text{ kJ}$$

In general, you can calculate the $\Delta H°$ for a reaction by the equation

$$\Delta H° = \Sigma n \Delta H_f°(\text{products}) - \Sigma m \Delta H_f°(\text{reactants})$$

Here Σ is the mathematical symbol meaning "the sum of," and m and n are the coefficients of the substances in the chemical equation.

The next two examples illustrate the calculation of enthalpies of reaction from standard enthalpies of formation.

Example 6.8 | Calculating the Heat of Phase Transition from Standard Enthalpies of Formation

Use values of $\Delta H_f°$ to calculate the heat of vaporization, $\Delta H_{vap}°$, of carbon disulfide at 25°C. The vaporization process is

$$CS_2(l) \longrightarrow CS_2(g)$$

Problem Strategy The vaporization process can be treated like a chemical reaction, with the liquid as the "reactant" and the vapor as the "product." It is convenient to record the values of $\Delta H_f°$ under the formulas in the equation, multiplying them by the coefficients in the equation. You calculate $\Delta H_{vap}°$ by subtracting values for the "reactant" from values for the "product."

(*continued*)

(continued)

Solution Here is the equation for the vaporization, with values of ΔH_f° multiplied by coefficients (here, all 1's).

$$CS_2(l) \longrightarrow CS_2(g)$$
$$\quad 1(89.7) \qquad\qquad 1(116.9) \quad \text{(kJ)}$$

The calculation is

$$\Delta H_{vap}^\circ = \Sigma\, n\, \Delta H_f^\circ(\text{products}) - \Sigma\, m\, \Delta H_f^\circ(\text{reactants})$$
$$= \Delta H_f^\circ[CS_2(g)] - \Delta H_f^\circ[CS_2(l)]$$
$$= (116.9 - 89.7)\ \text{kJ} = \mathbf{27.2\ kJ}$$

CS₂

Answer Check Review your arithmetic carefully. Note that vaporization requires adding heat, so the enthalpy change should be positive.

Exercise 6.9 Calculate the heat of vaporization, ΔH_{vap}°, of water, using standard enthalpies of formation (Table 6.2).

■ See Problems 6.77 and 6.78.

Example 6.9 | Calculating the Enthalpy of Reaction from Standard Enthalpies of Formation

Large quantities of ammonia are used to prepare nitric acid. The first step consists of the catalytic oxidation of ammonia to nitric oxide, NO.

$$4NH_3(g) + 5O_2(g) \xrightarrow{\text{Pt}} 4NO(g) + 6H_2O(g)$$

What is the standard enthalpy change for this reaction? Use Table 6.2 for data.

Problem Strategy You record the values of ΔH_f° under the formulas in the equation, multiplying them by the coefficients in the equation. You calculate ΔH° by subtracting values for the reactants from values for the products.

Solution Here is the equation with the ΔH_f°'s recorded beneath it:

$$4NH_3(g) + 5O_2(g) \longrightarrow 4NO(g) + 6H_2O(g)$$
$$\;\;4(-45.9) \qquad 5(0) \qquad\qquad 4(90.3) \quad 6(-241.8) \quad \text{(kJ)}$$

The calculation is

$$\Delta H^\circ = \Sigma\, n\, \Delta H_f^\circ(\text{products}) - \Sigma\, m\, \Delta H_f^\circ(\text{reactants})$$
$$= [4\, \Delta H_f^\circ(NO) + 6\, \Delta H_f^\circ(H_2O)] - [4\, \Delta H_f^\circ(NH_3) + 5\, \Delta H_f^\circ(O_2)]$$
$$= [4(90.3) + 6(-241.8)]\ \text{kJ} - [4(-45.9) + 5(0)]\ \text{kJ}$$
$$= \mathbf{-906\ kJ}$$

Answer Check Be very careful of arithmetical signs—they are a likely source of mistakes. Also pay particular attention to the state of each substance. Here, for example, you must use the ΔH_f° for $H_2O(g)$, not for $H_2O(l)$.

Exercise 6.10 Calculate the enthalpy change for the following reaction:

$$3NO_2(g) + H_2O(l) \longrightarrow 2HNO_3(aq) + NO(g)$$

Use standard enthalpies of formation.

■ See Problems 6.79, 6.80, 6.81, and 6.82.

Enthalpies of formation can also be defined for ions. It is not possible to make thermal measurements on individual ions, so we must arbitrarily define the standard enthalpy of formation of one ion as zero. Then values for all other ions can be deduced from calorimetric data. The standard enthalpy of formation of $H^+(aq)$ is taken as zero. Values of ΔH_f° for some ions are given in Table 6.2.

Exercise 6.11   Calculate the standard enthalpy change for the reaction of an aqueous solution of barium hydroxide, $Ba(OH)_2$, with an aqueous solution of ammonium nitrate, NH_4NO_3, at 25°C. (Figure 6.1 illustrated this reaction using solids instead of solutions.) The complete ionic equation is

$$Ba^{2+}(aq) + 2OH^-(aq) + 2NH_4^+(aq) + 2NO_3^-(aq) \longrightarrow 2NH_3(g) + 2H_2O(l) + Ba^{2+}(aq) + 2NO_3^-(aq)$$

■ See Problems 6.83 and 6.84.

6.9 | Fuels—Foods, Commercial Fuels, and Rocket Fuels

A *fuel* is any substance that is burned or similarly reacted to provide heat and other forms of energy. The earliest use of fuels for heat came with the control of fire, which was achieved about 750,000 years ago. This major advance allowed the human species to migrate from tropical savannas and eventually to inhabit most of the earth. Through cooking, fire also increased the variety of edible food supplies and provided some protection of the food from bacterial decay. During the mid-eighteenth century, the discovery of the steam engine, which converts the chemical energy latent in fuels to mechanical energy, ushered in the Industrial Revolution. Today fuels not only heat our homes and move our cars but are absolutely necessary for every facet of modern technology. For example, fuels generate the electricity required for our modern computing and communications technologies, and they propel the rocket engines that make possible our explorations of outer space. In this section we will look at foods as fuels; at fossil fuels (which include gas, oil, and coal); at coal gasification and liquefaction; and at rocket fuels.

Foods as Fuels

Foods fill three needs of the body: they supply substances for the growth and repair of tissue, they supply substances for the synthesis of compounds used in the regulation of body processes, and they supply energy. About 80% of the energy we need is for heat. The rest is used for muscular action, chemical processes, and other body processes. <

The human body requires about as much energy in a day as does a 100-watt lightbulb.

The body generates energy from food by the same overall process as combustion, so the overall enthalpy change is the same as the heat of combustion, which can be determined in a calorimeter. You can get some idea of the energy available from carbohydrate foods by looking at a typical one, glucose ($C_6H_{12}O_6$). The thermochemical equation for the combustion of glucose is

$$C_6H_{12}O_6(s) + 6O_2(g) \longrightarrow 6CO_2(g) + 6H_2O(l); \quad \Delta H^\circ = -2803 \text{ kJ}$$

One gram of glucose yields 15.6 kJ (3.73 kcal) of heat when burned.

A representative fat is glyceryl trimyristate, $C_{45}H_{86}O_6$. The equation for its combustion is

$$C_{45}H_{86}O_6(s) + \tfrac{127}{2}O_2(g) \longrightarrow 45CO_2(g) + 43H_2O(l); \quad \Delta H^\circ = -27{,}820 \text{ kJ}$$

In the popular literature of nutrition, the kilocalorie is referred to as the Calorie (capital C). Thus, these values are given as 4.0 Calories and 9.0 Calories.

One gram of this fat yields 38.5 kJ (9.20 kcal) of heat when burned. The average values quoted for carbohydrates and fats are 4.0 kcal/g and 9.0 kcal/g, respectively. < Note

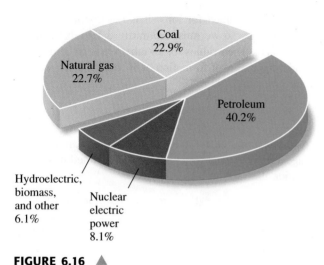

FIGURE 6.16

Sources of energy consumed in the United States (2005)
Data are from *Monthly Energy Review On-line,* http//www.eia.doe.gov.

that fats contain more than twice the fuel value per gram as do carbohydrates. Thus, by storing its fuel as fat, the body can store more fuel for a given mass of body tissue.

Fossil Fuels

All of the fossil fuels in existence today were created millions of years ago when aquatic plants and animals were buried and compressed by layers of sediment at the bottoms of swamps and seas. Over time this organic matter was converted by bacterial decay and pressure to petroleum (oil), gas, and coal. Figure 6.16 gives the percentages of the total energy consumed in the United States from various sources. Fossil fuels account for over 80% of the total.

Anthracite, or hard coal, the oldest variety of coal, was laid down as long as 250 million years ago and may contain over 80% carbon. Bituminous coal, a younger variety of coal, has between 45% and 65% carbon. Fuel values of coals are rated in Btu's (British thermal units) per pound, which are essentially heats of combustion per pound of coal. A typical value is 13,200 Btu/lb. A Btu equals 1054 J, so 1 Btu/lb equals 2.32 J/g. Therefore, the combustion of coal in oxygen yields about 30.6 kJ/g. You can compare this value with the heat of combustion of pure carbon (graphite).

$$C(graphite) + O_2(g) \longrightarrow CO_2(g); \Delta H° = -393.5 \text{ kJ}$$

The value given in the equation is for 1 mol (12.0 g) of carbon. Per gram, you get 32.8 kJ/g, which is comparable with the values obtained for coal.

Natural gas and petroleum together account for nearly three-quarters of the fossil fuels consumed per year. They are very convenient fluid fuels, being easily transportable and having no ash. Purified natural gas is primarily methane, CH_4, but it also contains small amounts of ethane, C_2H_6; propane, C_3H_8; and butane, C_4H_{10}. We would expect the fuel values of natural gas to be close to that for the heat of combustion of methane:

$$CH_4(g) + 2O_2(g) \longrightarrow CO_2(g) + 2H_2O(g); \Delta H° = -802 \text{ kJ}$$

This value of $\Delta H°$ is equivalent to 50.1 kJ per gram of fuel.

Petroleum is a very complicated mixture of compounds. Gasoline, which is obtained from petroleum by chemical and physical processes, contains many different hydrocarbons (compounds of carbon and hydrogen). One such hydrocarbon is octane, C_8H_{18}. The combustion of octane evolves 5074 kJ of heat per mole.

$$C_8H_{18}(l) + \tfrac{25}{2}O_2(g) \longrightarrow 8CO_2(g) + 9H_2O(g); \Delta H° = -5074 \text{ kJ}$$

This value of $\Delta H°$ is equivalent to 44.4 kJ/g. These combustion values indicate another reason why the fluid fossil fuels are popular: they release more heat per gram than coal does.

Coal Gasification and Liquefaction

The major problem with petroleum and natural gas as fuels is their relative short supply. It has been estimated that petroleum supplies will be 80% depleted by about the year 2030. Natural-gas supplies may be depleted even sooner.

Coal supplies, on the other hand, are sufficient to last several more centuries. This abundance has spurred much research into developing commercial methods for converting coal to the more easily handled liquid and gaseous fuels. Most of these methods begin by converting coal to carbon monoxide, CO. One way involves the water–gas reaction.

$$C(s) + H_2O(g) \longrightarrow CO(g) + H_2(g)$$

In this reaction, steam is passed over hot coal. Once a mixture of carbon monoxide and hydrogen is obtained, it can be transformed by various reactions into useful products. For example, in the methanation reaction (discussed at length in Chapter 14), this mixture is reacted over a catalyst to give methane.

$$CO(g) + 3H_2(g) \longrightarrow CH_4(g) + H_2O(g)$$

Different catalysts and different reaction conditions result in liquid fuels. An added advantage of coal gasification and coal liquefaction is that sulfur, normally present in fossil fuels, can be removed during the process. The burning of sulfur-containing coal is a major source of air pollution and acid rain.

Rocket Fuels

Rockets are self-contained missiles propelled by the ejection of gases from an orifice. Usually these are hot gases propelled from the rocket by the reaction of a fuel with an oxidizer. Rockets are believed to have originated with the Chinese—perhaps before the thirteenth century, which is when they began to appear in Europe. However, it was not until the twentieth century that rocket propulsion began to be studied seriously, and since World War II rockets have become major weapons. Space exploration with satellites propelled by rocket engines began in 1957 with the Russian satellite *Sputnik I*. Today weather and communications satellites are regularly put into orbit about the earth using rocket engines.

One of the factors determining which fuel and oxidizer to use is the mass of the fuel and oxidizer required. We have already seen that natural gas and gasoline have higher fuel values per gram than does coal. The difference is caused by the higher hydrogen content of natural gas and gasoline. Hydrogen is the element of lowest density, and at the same time it reacts exothermically with oxygen to give water. You might expect hydrogen and oxygen to be an ideal fuel–oxidizer combination. The thermochemical equation for the combustion of hydrogen is

$$H_2(g) + \tfrac{1}{2}O_2(g) \longrightarrow H_2O(g); \ \Delta H° = -242 \text{ kJ}$$

This value of $\Delta H°$ is equivalent to 120 kJ/g of fuel (H_2) compared with 50 kJ/g of methane. The second and third stages of the *Saturn V* launch vehicle that sent a three-man Apollo crew to the moon used a hydrogen/oxygen system. The launch vehicle contained liquid hydrogen (boiling at $-253°C$) and liquid oxygen, or LOX (boiling at $-183°C$).

The first stage of liftoff used kerosene and oxygen, and an unbelievable 550 metric tons (550×10^3 kg) of kerosene were burned in 2.5 minutes! It is interesting to calculate the average rate of energy production in this 2.5-minute interval. Kerosene is approximately $C_{12}H_{26}$. The thermochemical equation is

$$C_{12}H_{26}(l) + \tfrac{37}{2}O_2(g) \longrightarrow 12CO_2(g) + 13H_2O(g); \ \Delta H° = -7513 \text{ kJ}$$

This value of $\Delta H°$ is equivalent to 44.1 kJ/g. Thus, 550×10^6 g of fuel generated 2.43×10^{10} kJ in 150 s (2.5 min). Each second, the average energy produced was 1.62×10^{11} J. This is equivalent to 1.62×10^{11} watts, or 217 million horsepower (1 horsepower equals 745.7 watts, or J/s).

The landing module for the Apollo mission used a fuel made of hydrazine, N_2H_4, and a derivative of hydrazine. The oxidizer was dinitrogen tetroxide, N_2O_4. These substances are normally liquids and are therefore easier to store than liquid hydrogen and oxygen. The reaction of the oxidizer with hydrazine is

$$2N_2H_4(l) + N_2O_4(l) \longrightarrow 3N_2(g) + 4H_2O(g); \ \Delta H° = -1049 \text{ kJ}$$

Solid propellants are also used as rocket fuels. The mixture used in the booster rockets of the space shuttles (Figure 6.17) is a fuel containing aluminum metal powder. An oxidizer of ammonium perchlorate, NH_4ClO_4, is mixed with the fuel.

FIGURE 6.17 ▲

The launching of a space shuttle
The solid fuel for the booster rockets is a mixture of aluminum metal powder and other materials with ammonium perchlorate as the oxidizer. A cloud of aluminum oxide forms as the rockets burn.

A Checklist for Review

Important Terms

energy (6.1)
kinetic energy (6.1)
joule (J) (6.1)
calorie (cal) (6.1)
potential energy (6.1)
internal energy (6.1)
law of conservation of
  energy (6.1)
thermodynamic system
  (or system) (6.2)

surroundings (6.2)
heat (6.2)
heat of reaction (6.2)
exothermic process (6.2)
endothermic process (6.2)
enthalpy (6.3)
state function (6.3)
enthalpy of reaction (6.3)
thermochemical equation (6.4)
heat capacity (6.6)

specific heat capacity
  (specific heat) (6.6)
calorimeter (6.6)
Hess's law of heat summation (6.7)
standard state (6.8)
allotrope (6.8)
reference form (6.8)
standard enthalpy of formation
  (standard heat of formation) (6.8)

Key Equations

$E_k = \frac{1}{2}mv^2$

$q = C \, \Delta t$

$1 \text{ cal} = 4.184 \text{ J}$

$q = s \times m \times \Delta t$

$\Delta H = q_p$

$\Delta H° = \Sigma \, n \, \Delta H_f°(\text{products}) - \Sigma \, m \, \Delta H_f°(\text{reactants})$

Summary of Facts and Concepts

Energy exists in various forms, including *kinetic energy* and *potential energy*. The SI unit of energy is the *joule* (1 calorie = 4.184 joules). The *internal energy* of a substance is the sum of the kinetic energies and potential energies of the particles making up the substance. According to the *law of conservation of energy,* the total quantity of energy remains constant.

Reactions absorb or evolve definite quantities of heat under given conditions. At constant pressure, this *heat of reaction* is the *enthalpy of reaction, ΔH.* The chemical equation plus ΔH for molar amounts of reactants is referred to as the *thermochemical equation.* With it, you can calculate the heat for any amount of substance by *applying stoichiometry to heats of reaction.* One measures the heat of reaction in a *calorimeter.* Direct calorimetric determination of the heat of reaction requires a reaction that goes to completion without other reactions occurring at the same time. Otherwise, the heat or enthalpy of reaction is determined indirectly from other enthalpies of reaction by using *Hess's law of heat summation.* Thermochemical data are conveniently tabulated as *enthalpies of formation.* If you know the values for each substance in an equation, you can easily compute the enthalpy of reaction. As an application of thermochemistry, the last section of the chapter discusses fuels.

Media Summary

Visit the **student website at college.cengage.com/pic/ebbing9e** to help prepare for class, study for quizzes and exams, understand core concepts, and visualize molecular-level interactions. The following media activities are available for this chapter:

Prepare for Class

■ **Video Lessons** *Mini lectures from chemistry experts*
The Nature of Energy
Energy, Calories, and Nutrition

CIA Demonstration: Cool Fire
Constant-Pressure Calorimetry
Bomb Calorimetry (Constant Volume)
Hess's Law
Enthalpies of Formation

Improve Your Grade

■ **Visualizations** *Molecular-level animations and lab demonstration videos*
Hess's Law

■ **Tutorials** *Animated examples and interactive activities*
Hess's Law
Work, Heat, and Energy Flow

■ **Flashcards** *Key terms and definitions*
Online Flashcards

■ **Self-Assessment Questions** *Additional questions with full worked-out solutions*
6 Self-Assessment Questions

A+ **ACE the Test**

Multiple-choice quizzes
3 ACE Practice Tests

Access these resources using the passkey available free with new texts or for purchase separately.

Learning Objectives

6.1 Energy and Its Units

■ Define *energy, kinetic energy, potential energy,* and *internal energy.*
■ Define the SI unit of energy *joule,* as well as the common unit of energy *calorie.*
■ Calculate the kinetic energy of a moving object. **Example 6.1**
■ State the law of conservation of energy.

6.2 Heat of Reaction

■ Define a *thermodynamic system* and its *surroundings.*
■ Define *heat* and *heat of reaction.*
■ Distinguish between an *exothermic process* and an *endothermic process.*

6.3 Enthalpy and Enthalpy Change

■ Define *enthalpy* and *enthalpy of reaction.*
■ Explain how the terms *enthalpy of reaction* and *heat of reaction* are related.
■ Explain how enthalpy and internal energy are related.

6.4 Thermochemical Equations

■ Define a *thermochemical equation.*
■ Write a thermochemical equation given pertinent information. **Example 6.2**
■ Learn the two rules for manipulating (reversing and multiplying) thermochemical equations.
■ Manipulate a thermochemical equation using these rules. **Example 6.3**

6.5 Applying Stoichiometry to Heats of Reaction

■ Calculate the heat absorbed or evolved from a reaction given its enthalpy of reaction and the mass of a reactant or product. **Example 6.4**

6.6 Measuring Heats of Reaction

■ Define *heat capacity* and *specific heat.*
■ Relate the heat absorbed or evolved to the specific heat, mass, and temperature change.

■ Calculate using this relation between heat and specific heat. **Example 6.5**
■ Define *calorimeter.*
■ Calculate the enthalpy of reaction from calorimetric data (its temperature change and heat capacity). **Example 6.6**

6.7 Hess's Law

■ State Hess's law of heat summation.
■ Apply Hess's law to obtain the enthalpy change for one reaction from the enthalpy changes of a number of other reactions. **Example 6.7**

6.8 Standard Enthalpies of Formation

■ Define *standard state* and *reference form.*
■ Define *standard enthalpy of formation.*
■ Calculate the heat of a phase transition using standard enthalpies of formation for the different phases. **Example 6.8**
■ Calculate the heat (enthalpy) of reaction from the standard enthalpies of formation of the substances in the reaction. **Example 6.9**

6.9 Fuels—Foods, Commercial Fuels, and Rocket Fuels

■ Define *fuel.*
■ Describe the three needs of the body that are fulfilled by foods.
■ Give the approximate average values quoted (per gram) for the heat values (heats of combustion) for fats and for carbohydrates.
■ List the three major fossil fuels.
■ Describe the processes of coal gasification and coal liquefaction.
■ Describe some fuel–oxidizer systems used in rockets.

Self-Assessment and Review Questions

6.1 Define *energy, kinetic energy, potential energy,* and *internal energy.*

6.2 Define the joule in terms of SI base units.

6.3 What is the original definition of the calorie? What is the present definition?

6.4 Describe the interconversions of potential and kinetic energy in a moving pendulum. A moving pendulum eventually comes to rest. Has the energy been lost? If not, what has happened to it?

6.5 Suppose heat flows into a vessel containing a gas. As the heat flows into the gas, what happens to the gas molecules? What happens to the internal energy of the gas?

6.6 Define an *exothermic* reaction and an *endothermic* reaction. Give an example of each.

6.7 The internal energy of a substance is a state function. What does this mean?

6.8 Under what condition is the enthalpy change equal to the heat of reaction?

6.9 How does the enthalpy change for an endothermic reaction occurring at constant pressure?

6.10 Why is it important to give the states of the reactants and products when giving an equation for ΔH?

6.11 If an equation for a reaction is doubled and then reversed, how is the value of ΔH changed?

6.12 Consider the reaction of methane, CH_4, with oxygen, O_2, discussed in Section 6.5. How would you set up the calculation if the problem had been to compute the heat if 10.0 g H_2O were produced (instead of 10.0 g CH_4 reacted)?

6.13 Define the heat capacity of a substance. Define the specific heat of a substance.

6.14 Describe a simple calorimeter. What measurements are needed to determine the heat of reaction?

6.15 What property of enthalpy provides the basis of Hess's law? Explain.

6.16 You discover that you cannot carry out a particular reaction for which you would like the enthalpy change. Does this mean that you will be unable to obtain this enthalpy change? Explain.

6.17 What is meant by the thermodynamic standard state?

6.18 What is meant by the reference form of an element? What is the standard enthalpy of formation of an element in its reference form?

6.19 What is meant by the standard enthalpy of formation of a substance?

6.20 Write the chemical equation for the formation reaction of $H_2S(g)$.

6.21 Is the following reaction the appropriate one to use in determining the enthalpy of formation of methane, $CH_4(g)$? Why or why not?

$$C(g) + 4H(g) \longrightarrow CH_4(g)$$

6.22 What is a fuel? What are the fossil fuels?

6.23 Give chemical equations for the conversion of carbon in coal to methane, CH_4.

6.24 List some rocket fuels and corresponding oxidizers. Give thermochemical equations for the exothermic reactions of these fuels with the oxidizers.

6.25 The equation for the combustion of 2 mol of butane can be written

$$2C_4H_{10}(g) + O_2(g) \longrightarrow 8CO_2(g) + 10H_2O(g); \Delta H < O$$

Which of the following produces the *least* heat?
  a. Burning 1 mol of butane.
  b. Reacting 1 mol of oxygen with excess butane.
  c. Burning enough butane to produce 1 mol of carbon dioxide.
  d. Burning enough butane to produce 1 mol of water.
  e. All of the above reactions (a, b, c, and d) produce the same amount of heat.

6.26 A 5.0-g sample of water starting at 60.0°C loses 418 J of energy in the form of heat. What is the *final* temperature of the water after this heat loss?
  a. 20.°C
  b. 40.°C
  c. 50.°C
  d. 60.°C
  e. 80.°C

6.27 Hypothetical elements A_2 and B_2 react according to the following equation, forming the compound AB.

$$A_2(aq) + B_2(aq) \longrightarrow 2AB(aq); \Delta H° = +271 \text{ kJ/mol}$$

If solutions $A_2(aq)$ and $B_2(aq)$, starting at the same temperature, are mixed in a coffee-cup calorimeter, the reaction that occurs is
  a. exothermic, and the temperature of the resulting solution rises.
  b. endothermic, and the temperature of the resulting solution rises.
  c. endothermic, and the temperature of the resulting solution falls.
  d. exothermic, and the temperature of the resulting solution falls.
  e. exothermic or endothermic, depending on the original and final temperatures.

6.28 Consider the following specific heats of metals.

Metal	Specific Heat
copper	0.385 J/(g·°C)
magnesium	1.02 J/(g·°C)
mercury	0.138 J/(g·°C)
silver	0.237 J/(g·°C)

Four 25-g samples, one of each metal, and four insulated containers with identical water volumes, all start out at room temperature. Now suppose you add exactly the same quantity of heat to each metal sample. Then you place the hot metal samples in different containers of water (that all have the same volume of water). Which of the answers below is true?
  a. The water with the copper will be the hottest.
  b. The water with the magnesium will be the hottest.
  c. The water with the mercury will be the hottest.
  d. The water with the silver will be the hottest.
  e. The temperature of the water will be the same in all the cups.

Concept Explorations

6.29   Thermal Interactions

Part 1: In an insulated container, you mix 200. g of water at 80°C with 100. g of water at 20°C. After mixing, the temperature of the water is 60°C.

   a. How much did the temperature of the hot water change? How much did the temperature of the cold water change? Compare the magnitudes (positive values) of these changes.

   b. During the mixing, how did the heat transfer occur: from hot water to cold, or from cold water to hot?

   c. What quantity of heat was transferred from one sample to the other?

   d. How does the quantity of heat transferred to or from the hot-water sample compare with the quantity of heat transferred to or from the cold-water sample?

   e. Knowing these relative quantities of heat, why is the temperature change of the cold water greater than the magnitude of the temperature change of the hot water.

   f. A sample of hot water is mixed with a sample of cold water that has twice its mass. Predict the temperature change of each of the samples.

   g. You mix two samples of water, and one increases by 20°C, while the other drops by 60°C. Which of the samples has less mass? How do the masses of the two water samples compare?

   h. A 7-g sample of hot water is mixed with a 3-g sample of cold water. How do the temperature changes of the two water samples compare?

Part 2: A sample of water is heated from 10°C to 50°C. Can you calculate the amount of heat added to the water sample that caused this temperature change? If not, what information do you need to perform this calculation?

Part 3: Two samples of water are heated from 20°C to 60°C. One of the samples requires twice as much heat to bring about this temperature change as the other. How do the masses of the two water samples compare? Explain your reasoning.

6.30   Enthalpy

   a. A 100.-g sample of water is placed in an insulated container and allowed to come to room temperature at 21°C. To heat the water sample to 41°C, how much heat must you add to it?

   b. Consider the hypothetical reaction,

$$2X(aq) + Y(l) \longrightarrow X_2Y(aq)$$

   being run in an insulated container that contains 100. g of solution. If the temperature of the solution changes from 21°C to 31°C, how much heat does the chemical reaction produce? How does this answer compare with that in part a? (You can assume that this solution is so dilute that it has the same heat capacity as pure water.)

   c. If you wanted the temperature of 100. g of this solution to increase from 21°C to 51°C, how much heat would you have to add to it? (Try to answer this question without using a formula.)

   d. If you had added 0.02 mol of X and 0.01 mol of Y to form the solution in part b, how many moles of X and Y would you need to bring about the temperature change described in part c.

   e. Judging on the basis of your answers so far, what is the enthalpy of the reaction $2X(aq) + Y(l) \longrightarrow X_2Y(aq)$?

Conceptual Problems

6.31   A small car is traveling at twice the speed of a larger car, which has twice the mass of the smaller car. Which car has the greater kinetic energy? (Or do they both have the same kinetic energy?)

6.32   The equation for the combustion of butane, C_4H_{10}, is

$$C_4H_{10}(g) + \tfrac{13}{2}O_2(g) \longrightarrow 4CO_2(g) + 5H_2O(g)$$

Which one of the following generates the least heat? Why?
   a. burning one mole of butane
   b. reacting one mole of oxygen with excess butane
   c. producing one mole of carbon dioxide by burning butane
   d. producing one mole of water by burning butane

6.33   A 250-g sample of water at 20.0°C is placed in a freezer that is held at a constant temperature of −20.0°C. Considering the water as the "system," answer the following questions:

   a. what is the sign of q_{sys} for the water after it is placed in the freezer?

   b. After a few hours, what will be the state of the water?

   c. How will the initial enthalpy for the water compare with the final enthalpy of the water after it has spent several hours in the freezer?

   d. What will the temperature of the water be after several hours in the freezer?

6.34   A 20.0-g block of iron at 50.0°C and a 20.0 g block of aluminum at 45°C are placed in contact with each other. Assume that heat is only transferred between the two blocks.

   a. Draw an arrow indicating the heat flow between the blocks.

   b. What is the sign of q_{sys} for the aluminum when the blocks first come into contact?

   c. What will you observe when q_{sys} for the iron is zero?

   d. Estimate the temperature of the Al and Fe blocks when q_{sys} of the iron equals q_{sys} of the aluminum.

6.35   What is the enthalpy change for the preparation of one mole of liquid water from the elements, given the following equations?

$$H_2(g) + \tfrac{1}{2}O_2(g) \longrightarrow H_2O(g); \Delta H_f$$

$$H_2O(l) \longrightarrow H_2O(g); \Delta H_{vap}$$

6.36 A block of aluminum and a block of iron, both having the same mass, are removed from a freezer and placed outside on a warm day. When the same quantity of heat has flowed into each block, which block will be warmer? Assume that neither block has yet reached the outside temperature. (See Table 6.1 for the specific heats of the metals.)

6.37 You have two samples of different metals, metal A and metal B, each having the same mass. You heat both metals to 95°C and then place each one into separate beakers containing the same quantity of water at 25°C.

  a. You measure the temperatures of the water in the two beakers when each metal has cooled by 10°C and find that the temperature of the water with metal A is higher than the temperature of the water with metal B. Which metal has the greater specific heat? Explain.

  b. After waiting a period of time, the temperature of the water in each beaker rises to a maximum value. In which beaker does the water rise to the higher value, the one with metal A or the one with metal B? Explain.

6.38 Consider the reactions of silver metal, Ag(s), with each of the halogens: fluorine, $F_2(g)$, chlorine, $Cl_2(g)$, and bromine, $Br_2(l)$. What chapter data could you use to decide which reaction is most exothermic? Which reaction is that?

6.39 Tetraphosphorus trisulfide, P_4S_3, burns in excess oxygen to give tetraphosphorus decoxide, P_4O_{10}, and sulfur dioxide, SO_2. Suppose you have measured the enthalpy change for this reaction. How could you use it to obtain the enthalpy of formation of P_4S_3? What other data do you need?

6.40 A soluble salt, MX_2, is added to water in a beaker. The equation for the dissolving of the salt is:

$$MX_2(s) \longrightarrow M^{2+}(aq) + 2X^-(aq); \quad \Delta H > 0$$

  a. Immediately after the salt dissolves, is the solution warmer or colder?

  b. Indicate the direction of heat flow, in or out of the beaker, while the salt dissolves.

  c. After the salt dissolves and the water returns to room temperature, what is the value of q for the system?

Practice Problems

Energy and Its Units

6.41 Methane, CH_4, is a major component of marsh gas. When 0.5000 mol methane burns to produce carbon dioxide and liquid water, −445.1 kJ of heat is released. What is this heat in kilocalories?

6.42 Hydrogen sulfide, H_2S, is produced during decomposition of organic matter. When 0.5500 mol H_2S burns to produce $SO_2(g)$ and $H_2O(l)$, −309.1 kJ of heat is released. What is this heat in kilocalories?

6.43 A car whose mass is 4.85×10^3 lb is traveling at a speed of 57 miles per hour. What is the kinetic energy of the car in joules? in calories? See Table 1.4 for conversion factors.

6.44 A bullet weighing 245 grains is moving at a speed of 2.52×10^3 ft/s. Calculate the kinetic energy of the bullet in joules and in calories. One grain equals 0.0648 g.

6.45 Chlorine dioxide, ClO_2, is a reddish yellow gas used in bleaching paper pulp. The average speed of a ClO_2 molecule at 25°C is 306 m/s. What is the kinetic energy (in joules) of a ClO_2 molecule moving at this speed?

6.46 Nitrous oxide, N_2O, has been used as a dental anesthetic. The average speed of an N_2O molecule at 25°C is 379 m/s. Calculate the kinetic energy (in joules) of an N_2O molecule traveling at this speed.

Heat of Reaction

6.47 The process of dissolving ammonium nitrate, NH_4NO_3, in water is an endothermic process. What is the sign of q? If you were to add some ammonium nitrate to water in a flask, would you expect the flask to feel warm or cool?

6.48 The decomposition of ozone, O_3, to oxygen, O_2, is an exothermic reaction. What is the sign of q? If you were to touch a flask in which ozone is decomposing to oxygen, would you expect the flask to feel warm or cool?

6.49 Nitric acid, a source of many nitrogen compounds, is produced from nitrogen dioxide. An old process for making nitrogen dioxide employed nitrogen and oxygen.

$$N_2(g) + 2O_2(g) \longrightarrow 2NO_2(g)$$

The reaction absorbs 66.2 kJ of heat per 2 mol NO_2 produced. Is the reaction endothermic or exothermic? What is the value of q?

6.50 Hydrogen cyanide is used in the manufacture of clear plastics such as Lucite and Plexiglas. It is prepared from ammonia and natural gas (CH_4).

$$2NH_3(g) + 3O_2(g) + 2CH_4(g) \longrightarrow 2HCN(g) + 6H_2O(g)$$

The reaction evolves 939 kJ of heat per 2 mol HCN formed. Is the reaction endothermic or exothermic? What is the value of q?

Thermochemical Equations

6.51 When 1 mol of iron metal reacts with hydrochloric acid at constant temperature and pressure to produce hydrogen gas and aqueous iron(II) chloride, 89.1 kJ of heat evolves. Write a thermochemical equation for this reaction.

6.52 When 2 mol of potassium chlorate crystals decompose to potassium chloride crystals and oxygen gas at constant temperature and pressure, 78.0 kJ of heat is given off. Write a thermochemical equation for this reaction.

6.53 When white phosphorus burns in air, it produces tetraphosphorus decoxide.

$$P_4(s) + 5O_2(g) \longrightarrow P_4O_{10}(s); \Delta H = -3010 \text{ kJ}$$

What is ΔH for the following equation?

$$P_4O_{10}(s) \longrightarrow P_4(s) + 5O_2(g)$$

P_4

6.54 Carbon disulfide burns in air, producing carbon dioxide and sulfur dioxide.

$$CS_2(l) + 3O_2(g) \longrightarrow CO_2(g) + 2SO_2(g); \Delta H = -1077 \text{ kJ}$$

What is ΔH for the following equation?

$$\tfrac{1}{2}CS_2(l) + \tfrac{3}{2}O_2(g) \longrightarrow \tfrac{1}{2}CO_2(g) + SO_2(g)$$

CS_2

6.55 Phosphoric acid, H_3PO_4, can be prepared by the reaction of phosphorus(V) oxide, P_4O_{10}, with water.

$$\tfrac{1}{4}P_4O_{10}(s) + \tfrac{3}{2}H_2O(l) \longrightarrow H_3PO_4(aq); \Delta H = -96.2 \text{ kJ}$$

What is ΔH for the reaction involving 1 mol of P_4O_{10}?

$$P_4O_{10}(s) + 6H_2O(l) \longrightarrow 4H_3PO_4(aq)$$

6.56 With a platinum catalyst, ammonia will burn in oxygen to give nitric oxide, NO.

$$4NH_3(g) + 5O_2(g) \longrightarrow 4NO(g) + 6H_2O(g);$$
$$\Delta H = -906 \text{ kJ}$$

What is the enthalpy change for the following reaction?

$$NO(g) + \tfrac{3}{2}H_2O(g) \longrightarrow NH_3(g) + \tfrac{5}{4}O_2(g)$$

Stoichiometry of Reaction Heats

6.57 Colorless nitric oxide, NO, combines with oxygen to form nitrogen dioxide, NO_2, a brown gas.

$$2NO(g) + O_2(g) \longrightarrow 2NO_2(g); \Delta H = -114 \text{ kJ}$$

What is the enthalpy change per gram of nitric oxide?

6.58 Hydrogen, H_2, is used as a rocket fuel. The hydrogen is burned in oxygen to produce water vapor.

$$2H_2(g) + O_2(g) \longrightarrow 2H_2O(g); \Delta H = -484 \text{ kJ}$$

What is the enthalpy change per gram of hydrogen?

6.59 Ammonia burns in the presence of a copper catalyst to form nitrogen gas.

$$4NH_3(g) + 3O_2(g) \longrightarrow 2N_2(g) + 6H_2O(g);$$
$$\Delta H = -1267 \text{ kJ}$$

What is the enthalpy change to burn 35.8 g of ammonia?

6.60 Hydrogen sulfide, H_2S, is a foul-smelling gas. It burns to form sulfur dioxide.

$$2H_2S(g) + 3O_2(g) \longrightarrow 2SO_2(g) + 2H_2O(g);$$
$$\Delta H = -1036 \text{ kJ}$$

Calculate the enthalpy change to burn 28.5 g of hydrogen sulfide.

6.61 Propane, C_3H_8, is a common fuel gas. Use the following to calculate the grams of propane you would need to provide 369 kJ of heat.

$$C_3H_8(g) + 5O_2(g) \longrightarrow 3CO_2(g) + 4H_2O(g);$$
$$\Delta H = -2043 \text{ kJ}$$

6.62 Ethanol, C_2H_5OH, is mixed with gasoline and sold as gasohol. Use the following to calculate the grams of ethanol needed to provide 358 kJ of heat.

$$C_2H_5OH(l) + 3O_2(g) \longrightarrow 2CO_2(g) + 3H_2O(g);$$
$$\Delta H = -1235 \text{ kJ}$$

Heat Capacity and Calorimetry

6.63 You wish to heat water to make coffee. How much heat (in joules) must be used to raise the temperature of 0.180 kg of tap water (enough for one cup of coffee) from 19°C to 96°C (near the ideal brewing temperature)? Assume the specific heat is that of pure water, 4.18 J/(g·°C).

6.64 An iron skillet weighing 1.28 kg is heated on a stove to 178°C. Suppose the skillet is cooled to room temperature, 21°C. How much heat energy (in joules) must be removed to effect this cooling? The specific heat of iron is 0.449 J/(g·°C).

6.65 When steam condenses to liquid water, 2.26 kJ of heat is released per gram. The heat from 168 g of steam is used to heat a room containing 6.44×10^4 g of air (20 ft × 12 ft × 8 ft). The specific heat of air at normal pressure is 1.015 J/(g·°C). What is the change in air temperature, assuming the heat from the steam is all absorbed by air?

6.66 When ice at 0°C melts to liquid water at 0°C, it absorbs 0.334 kJ of heat per gram. Suppose the heat needed to melt 31.5 g of ice is absorbed from the water contained in a glass. If this water has a mass of 0.210 kg and a temperature of 21.0°C, what is the final temperature of the water? (Note that you will also have 31.5 g of water at 0°C from the ice.)

6.67 When 15.3 g of sodium nitrate, $NaNO_3$, was dissolved in water in a calorimeter, the temperature fell from 25.00°C to 21.56°C. If the heat capacity of the solution and the calorimeter is 1071 J/°C, what is the enthalpy change when 1 mol of sodium nitrate dissolves in water? The solution process is

$$NaNO_3(s) \longrightarrow Na^+(aq) + NO_3^-(aq); \Delta H = ?$$

6.68 When 23.6 g of calcium chloride, $CaCl_2$, was dissolved in water in a calorimeter, the temperature rose from 25.0°C to 38.7°C. If the heat capacity of the solution and the calorimeter is 1258 J/°C, what is the enthalpy change when 1.20 mol of calcium chloride dissolves in water? The solution process is

$$CaCl_2(s) \longrightarrow Ca^{2+}(aq) + 2Cl^-(aq)$$

6.69 A sample of ethanol, C_2H_5OH, weighing 2.84 g was burned in an excess of oxygen in a bomb calorimeter. The temperature of the calorimeter rose from 25.00°C to 33.73°C. If the heat capacity of the calorimeter and contents was 9.63 kJ/°C, what is the value of q for burning 1 mol of ethanol at constant volume and 25.00°C? The reaction is

$$C_2H_5OH(l) + 3O_2(g) \longrightarrow 2CO_2(g) + 3H_2O(l)$$

6.70 A sample of benzene, C_6H_6, weighing 3.51 g was burned in an excess of oxygen in a bomb calorimeter. The temperature of the calorimeter rose from 25.00°C to 37.18°C. If the heat capacity of the calorimeter and contents was 12.05 kJ/°C, what is the value of q for burning 1.25 mol of benzene at constant volume and 25.00°C? The reaction is

$$C_6H_6(l) + \tfrac{15}{2}O_2(g) \longrightarrow 6CO_2(g) + 3H_2O(l)$$

Hess's Law

6.71 Hydrazine, N_2H_4, is a colorless liquid used as a rocket fuel. What is the enthalpy change for the process in which hydrazine is formed from its elements?

$$N_2(g) + 2H_2(g) \longrightarrow N_2H_4(l)$$

Use the following reactions and enthalpy changes:

$$N_2H_4(l) + O_2(g) \longrightarrow N_2(g) + 2H_2O(l); \Delta H = -622.2 \text{ kJ}$$
$$H_2(g) + \tfrac{1}{2}O_2(g) \longrightarrow H_2O(l); \Delta H = -285.8 \text{ kJ}$$

6.72 Hydrogen peroxide, H_2O_2, is a colorless liquid whose solutions are used as a bleach and an antiseptic. H_2O_2 can be prepared in a process whose overall change is

$$H_2(g) + O_2(g) \longrightarrow H_2O_2(l)$$

Calculate the enthalpy change using the following data:

$$2H_2O_2(l) \longrightarrow 2H_2O(l) + O_2(g); \Delta H = -196.0 \text{ kJ}$$
$$H_2(g) + \tfrac{1}{2}O_2(g) \longrightarrow H_2O(l); \Delta H = -285.8 \text{ kJ}$$

6.73 Ammonia will burn in the presence of a platinum catalyst to produce nitric oxide, NO.

$$4NH_3(g) + 5O_2(g) \longrightarrow 4NO(g) + 6H_2O(g)$$

What is the heat of reaction at constant pressure? Use the following thermochemical equations:

$$N_2(g) + O_2(g) \longrightarrow 2NO(g); \Delta H = 180.6 \text{ kJ}$$
$$N_2(g) + 3H_2(g) \longrightarrow 2NH_3(g); \Delta H = -91.8 \text{ kJ}$$
$$2H_2(g) + O_2(g) \longrightarrow 2H_2O(g); \Delta H = -483.7 \text{ kJ}$$

6.74 Hydrogen cyanide is a highly poisonous, volatile liquid. It can be prepared by the reaction

$$CH_4(g) + NH_3(g) \longrightarrow HCN(g) + 3H_2(g)$$

What is the heat of reaction at constant pressure? Use the following thermochemical equations:

$$N_2(g) + 3H_2(g) \longrightarrow 2NH_3(g); \Delta H = -91.8 \text{ kJ}$$
$$C(graphite) + 2H_2(g) \longrightarrow CH_4(g); \Delta H = -74.9 \text{ kJ}$$
$$H_2(g) + 2C(graphite) + N_2(g) \longrightarrow 2HCN(g); \Delta H = 270.3 \text{ kJ}$$

6.75 Compounds with carbon–carbon double bonds, such as ethylene, C_2H_4, add hydrogen in a reaction called hydrogenation.

$$C_2H_4(g) + H_2(g) \longrightarrow C_2H_6(g)$$

Calculate the enthalpy change for this reaction, using the following combustion data:

$$C_2H_4(g) + 3O_2(g) \longrightarrow 2CO_2(g) + 2H_2O(l); \Delta H = -1411 \text{ kJ}$$

$$C_2H_6(g) + \tfrac{7}{2}O_2(g) \longrightarrow 2CO_2(g) + 3H_2O(l); \Delta H = -1560 \text{ kJ}$$
$$H_2(g) + \tfrac{1}{2}O_2(g) \longrightarrow H_2O(l); \Delta H = -286 \text{ kJ}$$

6.76 Acetic acid, CH_3COOH, is contained in vinegar. Suppose acetic acid was formed from its elements, according to the following equation:

$$2C(graphite) + 2H_2(g) + O_2(g) \longrightarrow CH_3COOH(l)$$

Find the enthalpy change, ΔH, for this reaction, using the following data:

$$CH_3COOH(l) + 2O_2(g) \longrightarrow 2CO_2(g) + 2H_2O(l); \Delta H = -874 \text{ kJ}$$

$$C(graphite) + O_2(g) \longrightarrow CO_2(g); \Delta H = -394 \text{ kJ}$$

$$H_2(g) + \tfrac{1}{2}O_2(g) \longrightarrow H_2O(l); \Delta H = -286 \text{ kJ}$$

Standard Enthalpies of Formation

6.77 The cooling effect of alcohol on the skin is due to its evaporation. Calculate the heat of vaporization of ethanol (ethyl alcohol), C_2H_5OH.

$$C_2H_5OH(l) \longrightarrow C_2H_5OH(g); \Delta H° = ?$$

The standard enthalpy of formation of $C_2H_5OH(l)$ is -277.7 kJ/mol and that of $C_2H_5OH(g)$ is -235.4 kJ/mol.

6.78 Carbon tetrachloride, CCl_4, is a liquid used as an industrial solvent and in the preparation of fluorocarbons. What is the heat of vaporization of carbon tetrachloride?

$$CCl_4(l) \longrightarrow CCl_4(g); \Delta H° = ?$$

Use standard enthalpies of formation (Table 6.2).

6.79 Hydrogen sulfide gas is a poisonous gas with the odor of rotten eggs. It occurs in natural gas and is produced during the decay of organic matter, which contains sulfur. The gas burns in oxygen as follows:

$$2H_2S(g) + 3O_2(g) \longrightarrow 2H_2O(l) + 2SO_2(g)$$

Calculate the standard enthalpy change for this reaction using standard enthalpies of formation.

6.80 Carbon disulfide is a colorless liquid. When pure, it is nearly odorless, but the commercial product smells vile. Carbon disulfide is used in the manufacture of rayon and cellophane. The liquid burns as follows:

$$CS_2(l) + 3O_2(g) \longrightarrow CO_2(g) + 2SO_2(g)$$

Calculate the standard enthalpy change for this reaction using standard enthalpies of formation.

6.81 Iron is obtained from iron ore by reduction with carbon monoxide. The overall reaction is

$$Fe_2O_3(s) + 3CO(g) \longrightarrow 2Fe(s) + 3CO_2(g)$$

Calculate the standard enthalpy change for this equation. See Appendix C for data.

6.82 The first step in the preparation of lead from its ore (galena, PbS) consists of roasting the ore.

$$2PbS(s) + 3O_2(g) \longrightarrow 2SO_2(g) + 2PbO(s)$$

Calculate the standard enthalpy change for this reaction, using enthalpies of formation (see Appendix C).

6.83 Hydrogen chloride gas dissolves in water to form hydrochloric acid (an ionic solution).

$$HCl(g) \xrightarrow{H_2O} H^+(aq) + Cl^-(aq)$$

Find $\Delta H°$ for the above reaction. The data are given in Table 6.2.

6.84 Carbon dioxide from the atmosphere "weathers," or dissolves, limestone ($CaCO_3$) by the reaction

$$CaCO_3(s) + CO_2(g) + H_2O(l) \longrightarrow$$
$$Ca^{2+}(aq) + 2HCO_3^-(aq)$$

Obtain $\Delta H°$ for this reaction. See Table 6.2 for the data.

6.85 The Group IIA carbonates decompose when heated. For example,

$$MgCO_3(s) \longrightarrow MgO(s) + CO_2(g)$$

Use enthalpies of formation (see Appendix C) and calculate the heat required to decompose 10.0 g of magnesium carbonate.

6.86 The Group IIA carbonates decompose when heated. For example,

$$BaCO_3(s) \longrightarrow BaO(s) + CO_2(g)$$

Use enthalpies of formation (see Appendix C) and calculate the heat required to decompose 10.0 g of barium carbonate.

General Problems

6.87 The energy, E, needed to move an object a distance d by applying a force F is $E = F \times d$. What must be the SI unit of force if this equation is to be consistent with the SI unit of energy for E?

6.88 The potential energy of an object in the gravitational field of the earth is $E_p = mgh$. What must be the SI unit of g if this equation is to be consistent with the SI unit of energy for E_p?

6.89 Liquid hydrogen peroxide has been used as a propellant for rockets. Hydrogen peroxide decomposes into oxygen and water, giving off heat energy equal to 686 Btu per pound of propellant. What is this energy in joules per gram of hydrogen peroxide? (1 Btu = 252 cal; see also Table 1.4.)

6.90 Hydrogen is an ideal fuel in many respects; for example, the product of its combustion, water, is nonpolluting. The heat given off in burning hydrogen to gaseous water is 5.16×10^4 Btu per pound. What is this heat energy in joules per gram? (1 Btu = 252 cal; see also Table 1.4.)

6.91 Niagara Falls has a height of 167 ft (American Falls). What is the potential energy in joules of 1.00 lb of water at the top of the falls if we take water at the bottom to have a potential energy of zero? What would be the speed of this water at the bottom of the falls if we neglect friction during the descent of the water?

6.92 Any object, be it a space satellite or a molecule, must attain an initial upward velocity of at least 11.2 km/s in order to escape the gravitational attraction of the earth. What would be the kinetic energy in joules of a satellite weighing 2354 lb that has the speed equal to this escape velocity of 11.2 km/s?

6.93 When calcium carbonate, $CaCO_3$ (the major constituent of limestone and seashells), is heated, it decomposes to calcium oxide (quicklime).

$$CaCO_3(s) \longrightarrow CaO(s) + CO_2(g); \Delta H = 177.9 \text{ kJ}$$

How much heat is required to decompose 21.3 g of calcium carbonate?

6.94 Calcium oxide (quicklime) reacts with water to produce calcium hydroxide (slaked lime).

$$CaO(s) + H_2O(l) \longrightarrow Ca(OH)_2(s); \Delta H = -65.2 \text{ kJ}$$

The heat released by this reaction is sufficient to ignite paper. How much heat is released when 24.5 g of calcium oxide reacts?

6.95 Formic acid, $HCHO_2$, was first discovered in ants (*formica* is Latin for "ant"). In an experiment, 5.48 g of formic acid was burned at constant pressure.

$$2HCHO_2(l) + O_2(g) \longrightarrow 2CO_2(g) + 2H_2O(l)$$

If 30.3 kJ of heat evolved, what is ΔH per mole of formic acid?

6.96 Acetic acid, $HC_2H_3O_2$, is the sour constituent of vinegar (*acetum* is Latin for "vinegar"). In an experiment, 3.58 g of acetic acid was burned.

$$HC_2H_3O_2(l) + 2O_2(g) \longrightarrow 2CO_2(g) + 2H_2O(l)$$

If 52.0 kJ of heat evolved, what is ΔH per mole of acetic acid?

6.97 Suppose you mix 21.0 g of water at 52.7°C with 54.9 g of water at 31.5°C in an insulated cup. What is the maximum temperature of the solution after mixing?

6.98 Suppose you mix 20.5 g of water at 66.2°C with 45.4 g of water at 35.7°C in an insulated cup. What is the maximum temperature of the solution after mixing?

6.99 A piece of lead of mass 121.6 g was heated by an electrical coil. From the resistance of the coil, the current, and the time the current flowed, it was calculated that 235 J of heat was added to the lead. The temperature of the lead rose from 20.4°C to 35.5°C. What is the specific heat of the lead?

6.100 The specific heat of copper metal was determined by putting a piece of the metal weighing 35.4 g in hot water. The quantity of heat absorbed by the metal was calculated to be 47.0 J from the temperature drop of the water. What was the specific heat of the metal if the temperature of the metal rose 3.45°C?

6.101 A 50.0-g sample of water at 100.00°C was placed in an insulated cup. Then 25.3 g of zinc metal at 25.00°C was added to the water. The temperature of the water dropped to 96.68°C. What is the specific heat of zinc?

6.102 A 19.6-g sample of a metal was heated to 61.67°C. When the metal was placed into 26.7 g of water in a calorimeter, the temperature of the water increased from 25.00°C to 30.00°C. What is the specific heat of the metal?

6.103 A 14.1-mL sample of 0.996 M NaOH is mixed with 32.3 mL of 0.905 M HCl in a coffee-cup calorimeter (see Section 6.6 of your text for a description of a coffee-cup calorimeter). The enthalpy of the reaction, written with the lowest whole-number coefficients, is −55.8 kJ. Both solutions are at 21.6°C prior to mixing and reacting. What is the final temperature of the reaction mixture? When solving this problem, assume that no heat is lost from the calorimeter to the surroundings, the density of all solutions is 1.00 g/mL, the specific heat of all solutions is the same as that of water, and volumes are additive.

6.104 A 29.1-mL sample of 1.05 M KOH is mixed with 20.9 mL of 1.07 M HBr in a coffee-cup calorimeter (see Section 6.6 of your text for a description of a coffee-cup calorimeter). The enthalpy of the reaction, written with the lowest whole-number coefficients, is −55.8 kJ. Both solutions are at 21.8°C prior to mixing and reacting. What is the final temperature of the reaction mixture? When solving this problem, assume that no heat is lost from the calorimeter to the surroundings, the density of all solutions is 1.00 g/mL, and volumes are additive.

6.105 In a calorimetric experiment, 6.48 g of lithium hydroxide, LiOH, was dissolved in water. The temperature of the calorimeter rose from 25.00°C to 36.66°C. What is ΔH for the solution process?

$$LiOH(s) \longrightarrow Li^+(aq) + OH^-(aq)$$

The heat capacity of the calorimeter and its contents is 547 J/°C.

6.106 When 21.45 g of potassium nitrate, KNO_3, was dissolved in water in a calorimeter, the temperature fell from 25.00°C to 14.14°C. What is the ΔH for the solution process?

$$KNO_3(s) \longrightarrow K^+(aq) + NO_3^-(aq)$$

The heat capacity of the calorimeter and its contents is 682 J/°C.

6.107 A 10.00-g sample of acetic acid, $HC_2H_3O_2$, was burned in a bomb calorimeter in an excess of oxygen.

$$HC_2H_3O_2(l) + 2O_2(g) \longrightarrow 2CO_2(g) + 2H_2O(l)$$

The temperature of the calorimeter rose from 25.00°C to 35.84°C. If the heat capacity of the calorimeter and its contents is 13.43 kJ/°C, what is the enthalpy change for the reaction?

6.108 The sugar arabinose, $C_5H_{10}O_5$, is burned completely in oxygen in a calorimeter.

$$C_5H_{10}O_5(s) + 5O_2(g) \longrightarrow 5CO_2(g) + 5H_2O(l)$$

Burning a 0.548-g sample caused the temperature to rise from 20.00°C to 20.54°C. The heat capacity of the calorimeter and its contents is 15.8 kJ/°C. Calculate ΔH for the combustion reaction per mole of arabinose.

6.109 Hydrogen sulfide, H_2S, is a poisonous gas with the odor of rotten eggs. The reaction for the formation of H_2S from the elements is

$$H_2(g) + \tfrac{1}{8}S_8(\text{rhombic}) \longrightarrow H_2S(g)$$

Use Hess's law to obtain the enthalpy change for this reaction from the following enthalpy changes:

$$H_2S(g) + \tfrac{3}{2}O_2(g) \longrightarrow H_2O(g) + SO_2(g); \Delta H = -518 \text{ kJ}$$
$$H_2(g) + \tfrac{1}{2}O_2(g) \longrightarrow H_2O(g); \Delta H = -242 \text{ kJ}$$
$$\tfrac{1}{8}S_8(\text{rhombic}) + O_2(g) \longrightarrow SO_2(g); \Delta H = -297 \text{ kJ}$$

6.110 Ethylene glycol, $HOCH_2CH_2OH$, is used as antifreeze. It is produced from ethylene oxide, C_2H_4O, by the reaction

$$C_2H_4O(g) + H_2O(l) \longrightarrow HOCH_2CH_2OH(l)$$

Use Hess's law to obtain the enthalpy change for this reaction from the following enthalpy changes:

$$2C_2H_4O(g) + 5O_2(g) \longrightarrow 4CO_2(g) + 4H_2O(l);$$
$$\Delta H = -2612.2 \text{ kJ}$$
$$HOCH_2CH_2OH(l) + \tfrac{5}{2}O_2(g) \longrightarrow 2CO_2(g) + 3H_2O(l);$$
$$\Delta H = -1189.8 \text{ kJ}$$

6.111 Hydrogen, H_2, is prepared by *steam reforming,* in which hydrocarbons are reacted with steam. For CH_4,

$$CH_4(g) + H_2O(g) \longrightarrow CO(g) + 3H_2(g)$$

Calculate the enthalpy change $\Delta H°$ for this reaction, using standard enthalpies of formation.

6.112 Hydrogen is prepared from natural gas (mainly methane, CH_4) by partial oxidation.

$$2CH_4(g) + O_2(g) \longrightarrow 2CO(g) + 4H_2(g)$$

Calculate the enthalpy change $\Delta H°$ for this reaction, using standard enthalpies of formation.

6.113 Calcium oxide, CaO, is prepared by heating calcium carbonate (from limestone and seashells).

$$CaCO_3(s) \longrightarrow CaO(s) + CO_2(g)$$

Calculate the standard enthalpy of reaction, using enthalpies of formation. The $\Delta H_f°$ of CaO(s) is −635 kJ/mol. Other values are given in Table 6.2.

6.114 Sodium carbonate, Na_2CO_3, is used to manufacture glass. It is obtained from sodium hydrogen carbonate, $NaHCO_3$, by heating.

$$2NaHCO_3(s) \longrightarrow Na_2CO_3(s) + H_2O(g) + CO_2(g)$$

Calculate the standard enthalpy of reaction, using enthalpies of formation (Table 6.2).

6.115 Calculate the heat released when 2.000 L O_2 with a density of 1.11 g/L at 25°C reacts with an excess of hydrogen to form liquid water at 25°C.

6.116 Calculate the heat released when 4.000 L Cl_2 with a density of 2.46 g/L at 25°C reacts with an excess of sodium metal to form solid sodium chloride at 25°C.

6.117 Sucrose, $C_{12}H_{22}O_{11}$, is common table sugar. The enthalpy change at 25°C and 1 atm for the complete burning of 1 mol of sucrose in oxygen to give $CO_2(g)$ and $H_2O(l)$ is -5641 kJ. From this and from data given in Table 6.2, calculate the standard enthalpy of formation of sucrose.

6.118 Acetone, CH_3COCH_3, is a liquid solvent. The enthalpy change at 25°C and 1 atm for the complete burning of 1 mol of acetone in oxygen to give $CO_2(g)$ and $H_2O(l)$ is -1791 kJ. From this and from data given in Table 6.2, calculate the standard enthalpy of formation of acetone.

6.119 Ammonium nitrate is an oxidizing agent and can give rise to explosive mixtures. A mixture of 2.00 mol of powdered aluminum and 3.00 mol of ammonium nitrate crystals reacts exothermically, yielding nitrogen gas, water vapor, and aluminum oxide. How many grams of the mixture are required to provide 245 kJ of heat? See Appendix C for data.

6.120 The thermite reaction is a very exothermic reaction; it has been used to produce liquid iron for welding. A mixture of 2 mol of powdered aluminum metal and 1 mol of iron(III) oxide yields liquid iron and solid aluminum oxide. How many grams of the mixture are needed to produce 348 kJ of heat? See Appendix C for data.

6.121 Describe the physical characteristics of white phosphorus. Is it found in any modern matches? Why or why not?

6.122 What is the phosphorus compound used in "strike anywhere" matches. What is the chemical equation for the burning of this compound in air?

Strategy Problems

6.123 How fast (in meters per second) must an iron ball with a mass of 56.6 g be traveling in order to have a kinetic energy of 15.75 J? The density of iron is 7.87 g/cm^3.

6.124 Sulfur dioxide gas reacts with oxygen, $O_2(g)$, to produce $SO_3(g)$. This reaction releases 99.0 kJ of heat (at constant pressure) for each mole of sulfur dioxide that reacts. Write the thermochemical equation for the reaction of 2 mol of sulfur dioxide, and then also for the decomposition of 3 mol of sulfur trioxide gas into oxygen gas and sulfur dioxide gas. Do you need any other information to answer either question?

6.125 When solid iron burns in oxygen gas (at constant pressure) to produce $Fe_2O_3(s)$, 1651 kJ of heat is released for every 4 mol of iron burned. How much heat is released when 10.3 g $Fe_2O_3(s)$ is produced (at constant pressure)? What additional information would you need to calculate the heat released to produce this much $Fe_2O_3(s)$ if you burned iron in ozone gas, $O_3(g)$, instead of $O_2(g)$?

6.126 How many grams of oxygen gas are required to produce 7.60 kJ of heat when hydrogen gas burns at constant pressure to produce gaseous water?

$$2H_2(g) + O_2(g) \longrightarrow 2H_2O(g); \Delta H = -484 \text{ kJ}$$

Liquid water has a heat of vaporization of 44.0 kJ per mole at 25°C.

6.127 Hydrogen is burned in oxygen to release heat. How many grams of hydrogen gas must be burned to release enough heat to warm a 50.0-g block of iron, giving 2 mol of water?

$$2H_2(g) + O_2(g) \longrightarrow 2H_2O(g); \Delta H = -484 \text{ kJ}$$

Iron has a specific heat of 0.449 J/(g·°C).

6.128 A piece of iron was heated to 95.4°C and dropped into a constant-pressure calorimeter containing 284 g of water at 32.2°C. The final temperature of the water and iron was 51.9°C. Assuming that the calorimeter itself absorbs a negligible amount of heat, what was the mass (in grams) of the piece of iron? The specific heat of iron is 0.449 J/(g·°C), and the specific heat of water is 4.18 J/(g·°C).

6.129 The enthalpy of combustion, ΔH, for benzoic acid, C_6H_5COOH, is -3226 kJ/mol. When a sample of benzoic acid was burned in a calorimeter (at constant pressure), the temperature of the calorimeter and contents rose from 23.44°C to 27.65°C. The heat capacity of the calorimeter and contents was 12.41 kJ/°C. What mass of benzoic acid was burned?

6.130 Given the following (hypothetical) thermochemical equations:

$$A + B \longrightarrow 2C; \Delta H = -447 \text{ kJ}$$
$$A + 3D \longrightarrow 2E; \Delta H = -484 \text{ kJ}$$
$$2D + B \longrightarrow 2F; \Delta H = -429 \text{ kJ}$$

Calculate ΔH, in kJ, for the equation

$$4E + 5B \longrightarrow 4C + 6F$$

6.131 The head of a "strike anywhere" match contains tetraphosphorus trisulfide, P_4S_3. In an experiment, a student burned this compound in an excess of oxygen and found that it evolved 3651 kJ of heat per mole of P_4S_3 at a constant pressure of 1 atm. She wrote the following thermochemical equation:

$$P_4S_3(s) + 8O_2(g) \longrightarrow P_4O_{10}(s) + 3SO_2(g); \Delta H° = -3651 \text{ kJ}$$

Calculate the standard enthalpy of formation of P_4S_3, using this student's result and the following standard enthalpies of formation: $P_4O_{10}(s)$, -3009.9 kJ/mol; $SO_2(g)$, -296.8 kJ/mol. How does this value compare with the value given in Appendix C?

6.132 Toluene, $C_6H_5CH_3$, has an enthalpy of combustion of -3908 kJ/mol. Using data from Appendix C, calculate the enthalpy of formation of toluene.

Cumulative-Skills Problems

6.133 What will be the final temperature of a mixture made from 25.0 g of water at 15.0°C, from 45.0 g of water at 50.0°C, and from 15.0 g of water at 37.0°C?

6.134 What will be the final temperature of a mixture made from equal masses of the following: water at 25.0°C, ethanol at 35.5°C, and iron at 95°C?

6.135 Graphite is burned in oxygen to give carbon monoxide and carbon dioxide. If the product mixture is 33% CO and 67% CO_2 by mass, what is the heat from the combustion of 1.00 g of graphite?

6.136 A sample of natural gas is 80.0% CH_4 and 20.0% C_2H_6 by mass. What is the heat from the combustion of 1.00 g of this mixture? Assume the products are $CO_2(g)$ and $H_2O(l)$.

6.137 A sample containing 2.00 mol of graphite reacts completely with a limited quantity of oxygen at 25°C and 1.0 atm pressure, producing 481 kJ of heat and a mixture of CO and CO_2. Calculate the masses of CO and CO_2 produced.

6.138 A 10.0-g sample of a mixture of CH_4 and C_2H_4 reacts with oxygen at 25°C and 1 atm to produce $CO_2(g)$ and $H_2O(l)$. If the reaction produces 520 kJ of heat, what is the mass percentage of CH_4 in the mixture?

6.139 How much heat is released when a mixture containing 10.0 g NH_3 and 20.0 g O_2 reacts by the following equation?

$$4NH_3(g) + 5O_2(g) \longrightarrow 4NO(g) + 6H_2O(g);$$
$$\Delta H° = -906 \text{ kJ}$$

6.140 How much heat is released when a mixture containing 10.0 g CS_2 and 10.0 g Cl_2 reacts by the following equation?

$$CS_2(g) + 3Cl_2(g) \longrightarrow S_2Cl_2(g) + CCl_4(g);$$
$$\Delta H° = -230 \text{ kJ}$$

6.141 Consider the Haber process:

$$N_2(g) + 3H_2(g) \longrightarrow 2NH_3(g); \Delta H° = -91.8 \text{ kJ}$$

The density of ammonia at 25°C and 1.00 atm is 0.696 g/L. The density of nitrogen, N_2, is 1.145 g/L, and the molar heat capacity is 29.12 J/(mol·°C). (a) How much heat is evolved in the production of 1.00 L of ammonia at 25°C and 1.00 atm? (b) What percentage of this heat is required to heat the nitrogen required

for this reaction (0.500 L) from 25°C to 400°C, the temperature at which the Haber process is run?

6.142 An industrial process for manufacturing sulfuric acid, H_2SO_4, uses hydrogen sulfide, H_2S, from the purification of natural gas. In the first step of this process, the hydrogen sulfide is burned to obtain sulfur dioxide, SO_2.

$$2H_2S(g) + 3O_2(g) \longrightarrow 2H_2O(l) + 2SO_2(g);$$
$$\Delta H° = -1124 \text{ kJ}$$

The density of sulfur dioxide at 25°C and 1.00 atm is 2.62 g/L, and the molar heat capacity is 30.2 J/(mol·°C). (a) How much heat would be evolved in producing 1.00 L of SO_2 at 25°C and 1.00 atm? (b) Suppose heat from this reaction is used to heat 1.00 L of SO_2 from 25°C and 1.00 atm to 500°C for its use in the next step of the process. What percentage of the heat evolved is required for this?

6.143 The carbon dioxide exhaled in the breath of astronauts is often removed from the spacecraft by reaction with lithium hydroxide.

$$2LiOH(s) + CO_2(g) \longrightarrow Li_2CO_3(s) + H_2O(l)$$

Estimate the grams of lithium hydroxide required per astronaut per day. Assume that each astronaut requires 2.50×10^3 kcal of energy per day. Further assume that this energy can be equated to the heat of combustion of a quantity of glucose, $C_6H_{12}O_6$, to $CO_2(g)$ and $H_2O(l)$. From the amount of glucose required to give 2.50×10^3 kcal of heat, calculate the amount of CO_2 produced and hence the amount of LiOH required. The $\Delta H°_f$ for glucose(s) is -1273 kJ/mol.

6.144 A rebreathing gas mask contains potassium superoxide, KO_2, which reacts with moisture in the breath to give oxygen.

$$4KO_2(s) + 2H_2O(l) \longrightarrow 4KOH(s) + 3O_2(g)$$

Estimate the grams of potassium superoxide required to supply a person's oxygen needs for one hour. Assume a person requires 1.00×10^2 kcal of energy for this time period. Further assume that this energy can be equated to the heat of combustion of a quantity of glucose, $C_6H_{12}O_6$, to $CO_2(g)$ and $H_2O(l)$. From the amount of glucose required to give 1.00×10^2 kcal of heat, calculate the amount of oxygen consumed and hence the amount of KO_2 required. The $\Delta H°_f$ for glucose(s) is -1273 kJ/mol.

11

States of Matter; Liquids and Solids

Liquid butane, C_4H_{10}, in the lighter changes to the gaseous state, which burns when ignited. Butane stoves also employ this change of state.

Contents and Concepts

We look at the changes of state (or phase transitions) a substance can undergo, including vapor pressure, melting point, and freezing point.

We now look at several physical properties of liquids and then explain those properties in terms of intermolecular forces (weak forces between molecules).

We look at the kinds of forces that hold the units of a solid together. Then, we look at crystalline solids and their structure.

olid carbon dioxide is shown in Figure 11.1. It has an interesting property: at normal pressures it passes directly to the gaseous state without first melting to the liquid. This property, together with the fact that this change occurs at $-78°C$, makes solid carbon dioxide useful for keeping materials very cold. Because solid CO_2 cools other objects and does not leave a liquid residue, it is called *dry ice*.

Liquid carbon dioxide is obtained by putting carbon dioxide gas under pressure; it can exist only at pressures greater than 5 atm. In most cases, carbon dioxide is transported as a liquid in high-pressure steel tanks or at low temperature (about $-18°C$) and moderate pressure. When liquid carbon dioxide evaporates (changes to vapor), it absorbs large quantities of heat, cooling as low as $-57°C$. Because of this property, it is used as a refrigerant. Liquid carbon dioxide is often used to freeze foods for grocery stores and fast-food restaurants. If the compressed gas from the evaporating liquid is allowed to expand through a valve, the rapidly cooled vapor forms solid carbon dioxide "snow." (Most gases cool when they expand in this manner; for example, air cools when it escapes from the valve of an inflated tire.) This carbon dioxide snow is compacted into blocks and is the source of dry ice.

Carbon dioxide, like water and most other pure substances, exists in solid, liquid, and gaseous states and can undergo changes from one state to another. Substances change state under various temperature and pressure conditions. Can we obtain some understanding of these conditions for a change of state? Why, for example, is carbon dioxide normally a gas, whereas water is normally a liquid? What are the conditions under which carbon dioxide gas changes to a liquid or to a solid?

FIGURE 11.1 ▲

Dry ice

Dry ice is solid carbon dioxide, CO_2, whose temperature is about $-78°C$. It passes directly from the solid to the gaseous state. The white plumes are composed of ice crystals (H_2O, not CO_2) formed by condensation from the cold air.

These are some of the questions we will examine in this chapter. They concern certain physical properties that, as you will see, can often be related to the bonding and structure of the liquid and solid states.

■ See pages 465–466 for the Media Summary.

11.1 | Comparison of Gases, Liquids, and Solids

The different states of matter were defined in Section 1.4, and the gas laws and the kinetic theory of gases were defined in Chapter 5. Here we want to recall the salient features of those discussions and then compare gases, liquids, and solids. We especially want to compare how these states are viewed in terms of kinetic-molecular theory.

Gases are compressible fluids. According to kinetic-molecular theory, gases are composed of molecules or single atoms that are in constant random motion throughout mostly empty space (unless the gas is highly compressed). A gas is easily compressed because the molecules can be pushed into a smaller space. A gas is fluid because individual molecules can move easily relative to one another.

Liquids are relatively incompressible fluids. According to kinetic-molecular theory, the molecules of a liquid are in constant random motion (as in a gas) but are more tightly packed, so there is much less free space. Because the molecules can move relative to one another as in a gas, a liquid can flow (it is fluid). But the lack of empty space explains why a liquid, unlike a gas, is nearly incompressible.

Solids are nearly incompressible and are rigid, not fluid. Kinetic-molecular theory explains this by saying that the particles making up a solid (which may be

FIGURE 11.2 ▶

Representation of the states of matter
In a solid, the basic units (atoms, ions, or molecules) are closely packed and vibrate about fixed sites. In a liquid, molecules are rather closely packed, similar to those in a molecular solid, but can slip by one another and are in constant random motion. In a gas, molecules are widely spaced and, similar to those in a liquid, are in constant random motion.

Solid

Liquid

Gas

atoms, molecules, or ions) exist in close contact and (unlike those in a gas or liquid) do not move about but oscillate or vibrate about fixed sites. This explains the rigidity of a solid. And, of course, the compact structure explains its incompressibility. Figure 11.2 compares the gaseous, liquid, and solid states in kinetic-molecular terms.

Recall that gases normally follow closely the ideal gas law, $PV = nRT$. The simplicity of this equation is a result of the nearly negligible forces of interaction between molecules and the nearly negligible molecular size compared with the total volume of gas. Still, to be accurate we should account for both of these quantities, and the van der Waals equation, which we discussed in Section 5.8, is one attempt to do this.

$$(P + n^2a/V^2)(V - nb) = nRT$$

In this equation, the constants a and b depend on the nature of the gas. The constant a depends on the magnitude of the intermolecular forces; the constant b depends on the relative size of the molecules.

No such simple equations exist for the liquid and solid states. The size of the particles making up the liquid and solid states cannot be neglected relative to the total volume or accounted for in a simple way. Similarly, the forces of interaction between particles in the liquid and the solid states cannot be neglected; indeed, these forces of interaction are crucial when you describe the properties of the liquid and solid states.

Some of the most important properties of liquids and solids are concerned with changes of physical state. Therefore, we begin with this topic. In later sections, we will look specifically at the liquid and solid states and see how their properties depend on the forces of attraction between particles.

Changes of State

In the chapter opener, we discussed the change of solid carbon dioxide (dry ice) directly to a gas. Such *a change of a substance from one state to another* is called a **change of state** or **phase transition.** In the next sections, we will look at the different kinds of phase transitions and the conditions under which they occur. (A *phase* is a homogeneous portion of a system—that is, a given state of either a substance or a solution.)

11.2 | Phase Transitions

In general, each of the three states of a substance can change into either of the other states by undergoing phase transition.

Melting is *the change of a solid to the liquid state* (melting is also referred to as *fusion*). For example,

$$H_2O(s) \longrightarrow H_2O(l) \qquad \text{(melting, fusion)}$$
ice, snow   liquid water

Freezing is *the change of a liquid to the solid state*. The freezing of liquid water to ice is a common example.

$$H_2O(l) \longrightarrow H_2O(s) \qquad \text{(freezing)}$$
liquid water   ice

The casting of a metal object involves the melting of the metal, then its freezing in a mold.

Vaporization is *the change of a solid or a liquid to the vapor.* For example,

$$H_2O(l) \longrightarrow H_2O(g) \qquad \text{(vaporization)}$$
liquid water   water vapor

The change of a solid directly to the vapor is specifically referred to as **sublimation.** Although the vapor pressure of many solids is quite low, some (usually molecular solids) have appreciable vapor pressure. Ice, for instance, has a vapor pressure of 4.7 mmHg at 0°C. For this reason, a pile of snow slowly disappears in winter even though the temperature is too low for it to melt. The snow is being changed directly to water vapor.

$$H_2O(s) \longrightarrow H_2O(g) \qquad \text{(sublimation)}$$
ice, snow   water vapor

Sublimation can be used to purify solids that readily vaporize. Figure 11.3 shows a simple way to purify iodine by sublimation. Impure iodine is heated in a beaker so that it vaporizes, leaving nonvolatile impurities behind. The vapor crystallizes on the bottom surface of a dish containing ice that rests on top of the beaker. Freeze-drying of foods is a commercial application of sublimation. Brewed coffee, for example, is frozen and placed in a vacuum to remove water vapor. The ice continues to sublime until it is all gone, leaving freeze-dried coffee. Most freeze-dried foods are easily reconstituted by adding water.

Condensation is *the change of a gas to either the liquid or the solid state* (the change of vapor to solid is sometimes called *deposition*). Dew is liquid water formed by condensation of water vapor from the atmosphere. Frost is solid water formed by direct condensation of water vapor from the atmosphere without first forming liquid water. Snow is formed by a similar process in the upper atmosphere.

$$H_2O(g) \longrightarrow H_2O(l) \qquad \text{(condensation)}$$
water vapor   dew

$$H_2O(g) \longrightarrow H_2O(s) \qquad \text{(condensation, deposition)}$$
water vapor   frost, snow

FIGURE 11.3 ▼

Sublimation of iodine

Left: The beaker contains iodine crystals, I_2; a dish of ice rests on top of the beaker. *Right:* Iodine has an appreciable vapor pressure even below its melting point (114°C); thus, when heated carefully, the solid sublimes without melting. The vapor deposits as crystals on the cool underside of the dish.

Solid I_2

Gaseous I_2

When a substance that is normally a gas, such as carbon dioxide, changes to the liquid state, the phase transition is often referred to as *liquefaction*. The following diagram summarizes these phase transitions.

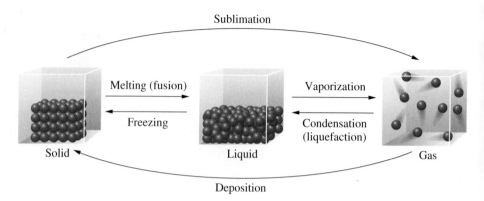

Vapor Pressure

Liquids, and even some solids, are continuously vaporizing. If a liquid is in a closed vessel with space above it, a partial pressure of the vapor state builds up in this space. The **vapor pressure** of a liquid is *the partial pressure of the vapor over the liquid, measured at equilibrium at a given temperature*. To understand what we mean by equilibrium, let us look at a simple method for measuring vapor pressure.

You introduce a few drops of water from a medicine dropper into the mercury column of a barometer (Figure 11.4A). Being less dense than mercury, the water rises in the tube to the top of the mercury, where it evaporates, or vaporizes.

To understand the process of vaporization, it is necessary to realize that the molecules in a liquid have a distribution of kinetic energies (Figure 11.5). Those molecules moving away from the surface and toward the vapor phase will escape only if their kinetic energies are greater than a certain minimum value equal to the potential energy from the attraction of molecules in the body of the liquid.

FIGURE 11.4 ▶

Measurement of the vapor pressure of water

(A) The mercury column drops a distance *h* because of the vapor pressure of water. *(B)* A detail of the upper portion of the tube, showing water molecules evaporating from and condensing on the water surface.

FIGURE 11.5

Distribution of kinetic energies of molecules in a liquid

Distributions of kinetic energies are shown for two different temperatures. The fraction of molecules having kinetic energies greater than the minimum necessary for escape is given by the colored areas (orange for the lower temperature, red area plus orange area at the higher temperature). Note that the fraction of molecules having kinetic energies greater than the minimum value for vaporization increases with temperature.

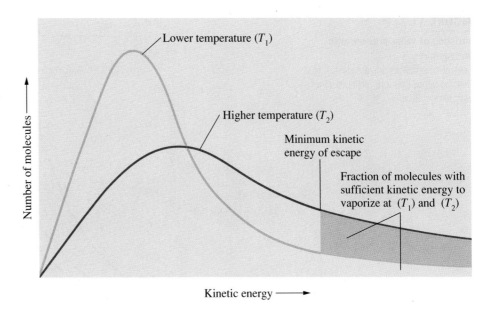

FIGURE 11.6

Rates of vaporization and condensation of a liquid over time

As vaporization continues at a constant rate, the rate of condensation increases. Eventually, the two rates become equal. The partial pressure of vapor reaches a steady value at a given temperature, which is the vapor pressure of the liquid. The process is said to reach equilibrium. The flasks, A, B, and C, present the molecular view of the process at positions A, B, and C on the curve.

As molecules at the surface gain sufficient kinetic energy (through collisions with neighboring molecules), they escape the liquid and go into the space at the top of the barometer column (see Figure 11.4B). More and more water molecules begin to fill this space. As the number of molecules in the vapor state increases, more and more gaseous molecules collide with the liquid water surface, exerting pressure on it. So, as vaporization of water proceeds, the mercury column moves downward.

Some of the molecules in the vapor collide with the liquid surface and stick; that is, the vapor condenses to liquid. The rate of condensation steadily increases as the number of molecules in the volume of vapor increases, until the rate at which molecules are condensing on the liquid equals the rate at which molecules are vaporizing (Figure 11.6).

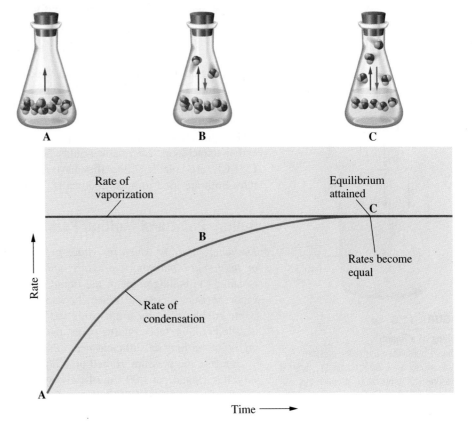

FIGURE 11.7 ▶

Variation of vapor pressure with temperature
Several common liquids are shown. Note that the vapor pressure increases rapidly with temperature.

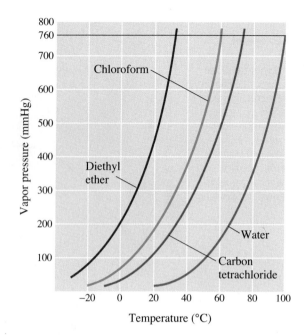

When the rates of vaporization and condensation have become equal, the number of molecules in the vapor at the top of the column in Figure 11.4 stops increasing and remains unchanged. The partial pressure of the vapor (as measured by the change in height of the mercury column) reaches a steady value, which is its vapor pressure. The liquid and vapor are in *equilibrium*. Although the partial pressure of the vapor is unchanging, molecules are still leaving the liquid and coming back to the liquid. For this reason, you speak of this as a *dynamic equilibrium*—one in which the molecular processes (in this case, vaporization and condensation) are continuously occurring. You represent this dynamic equilibrium for the vaporization and condensation of water by the equation with a double arrow.

$$H_2O(l) \rightleftharpoons H_2O(g)$$

As Figure 11.7 demonstrates, the vapor pressure of a substance depends on the temperature. (Appendix B gives a table of the vapor pressures of water at various temperatures.) As the temperature increases, the kinetic energy of molecular motion becomes greater, and the vapor pressure increases. Liquids and solids with relatively high vapor pressure at normal temperatures are said to be *volatile*. Chloroform and carbon tetrachloride are volatile liquids. Naphthalene, $C_{10}H_8$, and *para*-dichlorobenzene, $C_6H_4Cl_2$, are volatile solids: they have appreciable vapor pressures at room temperature. Both are used to make mothballs.

Boiling Point and Melting Point

The temperature at which the vapor pressure of a liquid equals the pressure exerted on the liquid (atmospheric pressure, unless the vessel containing the liquid is closed) is called the **boiling point** of the liquid. As the temperature of a liquid is raised, the vapor pressure increases. When the vapor pressure equals the atmospheric pressure, stable bubbles of vapor form within the body of the liquid (Figure 11.8). This process is called boiling. Once boiling starts, the temperature of the liquid remains at the boiling point (as long as sufficient heat is supplied).

Because the pressure exerted on a liquid can vary, the boiling point of a liquid can vary. For instance, at 1.00 atm (the average atmospheric pressure at sea level), the boiling point of water is 100°C. But at 0.83 atm (the average atmospheric pressure in

Atmospheric pressure

Vapor bubble

FIGURE 11.8 ▲

Boiling of a liquid
A liquid boils when the vapor pressure inside a bubble of vapor equals the external pressure. The temperature at which this occurs is called the boiling point.

TABLE 11.1	Melting Points and Boiling Points (at 1 atm) of Several Substances		
Name	Type of Solid*	Melting Point, °C	Boiling Point, °C
Neon, Ne	Molecular	−249	−246
Hydrogen sulfide, H_2S	Molecular	−86	−61
Chloroform, $CHCl_3$	Molecular	−64	62
Water, H_2O	Molecular	0	100
Acetic acid, $HC_2H_3O_2$	Molecular	17	118
Mercury, Hg	Metallic	−39	357
Sodium, Na	Metallic	98	883
Tungsten, W	Metallic	3410	5660
Cesium chloride, CsCl	Ionic	645	1290
Sodium chloride, NaCl	Ionic	801	1413
Magnesium oxide, MgO	Ionic	2800	3600
Quartz, SiO_2	Covalent network	1610	2230
Diamond, C	Covalent network	3550	4827

*Types of solids are discussed in Section 11.6.

If you want to cook a stew in less time than is possible at atmospheric pressure, you can use a pressure cooker. This is especially valuable at high altitudes, where water boils at a lower temperature. The steam pressure inside the cooker is allowed to build up to a given value before being released by a valve. The stew then boils at a higher temperature and is cooked more quickly.

Denver, Colorado, at 1609 m above sea level), the boiling point of water is 95°C. The *normal boiling point* of a liquid is the boiling point at 1 atm. <

The temperature at which a pure liquid changes to a crystalline solid, or freezes, is called the **freezing point.** The temperature at which a crystalline solid changes to a liquid, or melts, is called the **melting point;** it is identical to the freezing point. The melting or freezing occurs at the temperature where the liquid and solid are in dynamic equilibrium.

$$Solid \rightleftharpoons liquid$$

Unlike boiling points, melting points are affected significantly only by large pressure changes.

Both the melting point and the boiling point are characteristic physical properties of a substance and can be used to help identify it. Table 11.1 gives melting points and boiling points of several substances.

Heat of Phase Transition

Any change of state involves the addition or removal of energy as heat to or from the substance. A simple experiment shows that this is the case. Suppose you add heat at a constant rate to a beaker containing ice at −20°C. In Figure 11.9, we have plotted the temperature of the different phases of water as heat is added. The temperature of the ice begins to rise from −20°C, as you would expect; the addition of heat normally raises the temperature of a substance. At 0°C, the ice begins to melt, so that you get a beaker of ice in water. Note the flat region in the curve, labeled ice and water. Why is this region flat? It means that heat is being added to the system without a change in temperature; the temperature remains at 0°C. This temperature, of course, is the melting point of ice. The heat being added is energy required to melt ice to water at the same temperature. The intermolecular forces binding water molecules to specific sites in the solid phase must be partially broken to allow water molecules the ability to slide over one another easily, as happens in the liquid state. Note the flat regions for each of the phase transitions. Because heat is being added at a constant rate, the length of each flat region is proportional to the *heat of phase transition.*

FIGURE 11.9 ▶

Heating curve for water
Heat is being added at a constant rate to a system containing water. Note the flat regions of the curve. When heat is added during a phase transition, the temperature does not change.

The heat needed for the melting of a solid is called the **heat of fusion** (or *enthalpy of fusion*) and is denoted ΔH_{fus}. For ice, the heat of fusion is 6.01 kJ per mole.

$$H_2O(s) \longrightarrow H_2O(l); \ \Delta H_{fus} = 6.01 \ \text{kJ/mol}$$

The heat needed for the vaporization of a liquid is called the **heat of vaporization** (or *enthalpy of vaporization*) and is denoted ΔH_{vap}. At 100°C, the heat of vaporization of water is 40.7 kJ per mole. ◀

$$H_2O(l) \longrightarrow H_2O(g); \ \Delta H_{vap} = 40.7 \ \text{kJ/mol}$$

The fact that heat is required for vaporization can be demonstrated by evaporating a dish of water inside a vessel attached to a vacuum pump. With the pressure kept low, water evaporates quickly enough to freeze the water remaining in the dish.

Note that much more heat is required for vaporization than for melting. Melting needs only enough energy for the molecules to escape from their sites in the solid. For vaporization, enough energy must be supplied to break most of the intermolecular attractions.

A refrigerator relies on the cooling effect accompanying vaporization. The mechanism contains an enclosed gas that can be liquefied under pressure, such as ammonia or 1,1,1,2-tetrafluoroethane (NFC-134a), CH_2FCF_3. As the liquid is allowed to evaporate, it absorbs heat and thus cools its surroundings (the interior space of the refrigerator). Gas from the evaporation is recycled to a compressor and then to a condenser, where it is liquefied again. Heat leaves the condenser, going into the surrounding air.

Example 11.1 | Calculating the Heat Required for a Phase Change of a Given Mass of Substance

---

A particular refrigerator cools by evaporating liquefied dichlorodifluoromethane, CCl_2F_2. How many kilograms of this liquid must be evaporated to freeze a tray of water at 0°C to ice at 0°C? The mass of the water is 525 g, the heat of fusion of ice is 6.01 kJ/mol, and the heat of vaporization of dichlorodifluoromethane is 17.4 kJ/mol.

Problem Strategy The cooling effect as CCl_2F_2 liquid evaporates is used to freeze water at 0°C to ice. You first need to obtain the quantity of heat removed from the water to freeze it (using the heat of fusion of ice as a conversion factor, converting moles of H_2O to the heat required). Then you use this quantity of heat to determine the amount of CCl_2F_2 to evaporate (now using the heat of vaporization of CCl_2F_2 to convert this quantity of heat to the amount of CCl_2F_2 that must be vaporized).

Solution The heat that must be removed to freeze 525 g of water at 0°C is

$$525 \ \text{g} \ H_2O \times \frac{1 \ \text{mol} \ H_2O}{18.0 \ \text{g} \ H_2O} \times \frac{-6.01 \ \text{kJ}}{1 \ \text{mol} \ H_2O} = -175 \ \text{kJ}$$

(continued)

(continued)

The minus sign indicates that heat energy is taken away from the water. Consequently, the vaporization of dichlorodifluoromethane absorbs 175 kJ of heat. The mass of CCl_2F_2 that must be vaporized to absorb this quantity of heat is

$$175 \text{ kJ} \times \frac{1 \text{ mol } CCl_2F_2}{17.4 \text{ kJ}} \times \frac{121 \text{ g } CCl_2F_2}{1 \text{ mol } CCl_2F_2} = 1.22 \times 10^3 \text{ g } CCl_2F_2$$

1.22 kg of dichlorodifluoromethane must be evaporated.

CCl_2F_2

Answer Check The calculations are similar to the stoichiometry calculations we did in Chapter 3. As in those calculations, make sure that the units properly cancel to convert those of the known quantity to the units of the desired quantity.

Exercise 11.1 The heat of vaporization of ammonia is 23.4 kJ/mol. How much heat is required to vaporize 1.00 kg of ammonia? How many grams of water at 0°C could be frozen to ice at 0°C by the evaporation of this amount of ammonia?

■ See Problems 11.43, 11.44, 11.45, and 11.46.

Concept Check 11.1

$t = 0$

Shown here is a representation of a closed container in which you have just placed 10 L of H_2O. In our experiment, we are going to call this starting point in time $t = 0$ and assume that all of the H_2O is in the liquid phase. We have represented a few of the H_2O molecules in the water as dots.

a. Consider a time $t = 1$, at which some time has passed but the system has not reached equilibrium.
   i. How will the level of the liquid H_2O compare to that at $t = 0$?
   ii. How will the vapor pressure in the flask compare to that at $t = 0$?
   iii. How will the number of H_2O molecules in the vapor state compare to that at $t = 0$?
   iv. How does the rate of evaporation in this system compare to the rate of condensation?
   v. Draw a picture of the system at $t = 1$.

b. Consider a time $t = 2$, at which enough time has passed for the system to reach equilibrium.
   i. How will the level of the liquid H_2O compare to that at $t = 1$?
   ii. How will the vapor pressure in the flask compare to that at $t = 1$?
   iii. How will the number of H_2O molecules in the vapor state compare to that at $t = 1$?
   iv. How does the rate of evaporation in this system compare to the rate of condensation?
   v. Draw a picture of the system at $t = 2$.

Clausius–Clapeyron Equation: Relating Vapor Pressure and Liquid Temperature

We noted earlier that the vapor pressure of a substance depends on temperature. The variation of vapor pressure with temperature of some liquids was given in Figure 11.7.

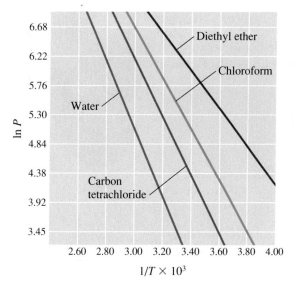

FIGURE 11.10 ▲

Plot of the logarithm of vapor pressure versus 1/T
The liquids shown in Figure 11.7 are replotted in this graph. Note the straight-line relationship.

| See Appendix A for the graphing of
| a straight line.

It can be shown that the logarithm of the vapor pressure of a liquid or solid varies with the absolute temperature according to the following approximate relation:

$$\ln P = -\frac{A}{T} + B$$

Here $\ln P$ is the natural logarithm of the vapor pressure, and A and B are positive constants. You can confirm this relation for the liquids shown in Figure 11.7 by replotting the data. If you put $y = \ln P$ and $x = 1/T$, the previous relation becomes

$$y = -Ax + B$$

This means that if you plot $\ln P$ versus $1/T$, you should get a straight line with slope $-A$. The data of Figure 11.7 are replotted this way in Figure 11.10. <

The previous equation has been derived from thermodynamics, by assuming the vapor behaves like an ideal gas. The result, known as the *Clausius–Clapeyron equation,* shows that the constant A is proportional to the heat of vaporization of the liquid, ΔH_{vap}.

$$\ln P = \frac{-\Delta H_{vap}}{RT} + B$$

A two-point form of the Clausius–Clapeyron equation is very useful for calculations. Let us write the previous equation for two different temperatures:

$$\ln P_2 = \frac{-\Delta H_{vap}}{RT_2} + B$$

$$\ln P_1 = \frac{-\Delta H_{vap}}{RT_1} + B$$

Here P_1 is the vapor pressure at absolute temperature T_1, and P_2 is the vapor pressure at absolute temperature T_2. If you subtract the second equation from the first, you get

$$\ln P_2 - \ln P_1 = \frac{-\Delta H_{vap}}{RT_2} - \frac{-\Delta H_{vap}}{RT_1} + B - B$$

which you can write as

$$\ln \frac{P_2}{P_1} = \frac{\Delta H_{vap}}{R}\left(\frac{1}{T_1} - \frac{1}{T_2}\right)$$

The next two examples illustrate the use of this two-point form of the Clausius–Clapeyron equation.

Example 11.2 | Calculating the Vapor Pressure at a Given Temperature

Estimate the vapor pressure of water at 85°C. Note that the normal boiling point of water is 100°C and that its heat of vaporization is 40.7 kJ/mol.

Problem Strategy   The two-point form of the Clausius–Clapeyron equation relates five quantities: P_1, T_1, P_2, T_2, and ΔH_{vap}. The normal boiling point is the temperature at which

(continued)

(*continued*)

the vapor pressure equals 760 mmHg. Thus, you can let P_1 equal 760 mmHg and T_1 equal 373 K (100°C). Then P_2 would be the vapor pressure at T_2, or 358 K (85°C). The heat of vaporization, ΔH_{vap}, is 40.7×10^3 J/mol. Note that we have expressed this quantity in joules per mole to agree with the units of the molar gas constant, R, which equals 8.31 J/(K·mol).

Solution You can now substitute into the two-point equation (the equation shaded in color just before this example).

$$\ln \frac{P_2}{760 \text{ mmHg}} = \frac{40.7 \times 10^3 \text{ J/mol}}{8.31 \text{ J/(K} \cdot \text{mol)}} \left(\frac{1}{373 \text{ K}} - \frac{1}{358 \text{ K}} \right)$$
$$= (4898 \text{ K}) \times (-1.123 \times 10^{-4}/\text{K}) = -0.550$$

You now want to solve this equation for P_2, which is the vapor pressure of water at 85°C. To do so, you take the antilogarithm (antiln) of both sides of the equation. This gives

$$\frac{P_2}{760 \text{ mmHg}} = \text{antiln}(-0.550)$$

The antiln (-0.550) is $e^{-0.550} = 0.577$. (Appendix A describes how to obtain the antilogarithm.) Thus

$$\frac{P_2}{760 \text{ mmHg}} = 0.577$$

Therefore,

$$P_2 = 0.577 \times 760 \text{ mmHg} = \textbf{439 mmHg}$$

This value may be compared with the experimental value of 434 mmHg, given in Appendix B. Differences from the experimental value stem from the fact that the Clausius–Clapeyron equation is an approximate relation.

Answer Check The result should be less than 760 mmHg, because the vapor pressure is lower at a lower temperature. If you inadvertently dropped the minus sign before taking the antiln, you would have gotten a result larger than 760 mmHg. Also, if you had entered ΔH_{vap} in kilojoules, rather than joules, the result would be close to zero, which is not reasonable given that the water is at 85°C.

Exercise 11.2 Carbon disulfide, CS_2, has a normal boiling point of 46°C and a heat of vaporization of 26.8 kJ/mol. What is the vapor pressure of carbon disulfide at 35°C?

■ See Problems 11.49 and 11.50.

Example 11.3 | Calculating the Heat of Vaporization from Vapor Pressures

Calculate the heat of vaporization of diethyl ether (often called simply "ether"), $C_4H_{10}O$, from the following vapor pressures: 400 mmHg at 18°C and 760 mmHg at 35°C. (Each pressure value has three significant figures.)

Problem Strategy If you let P_1 be 400 mmHg, then T_1 is 291 K (18°C), P_2 is 760 mmHg, and T_2 is 308 K (35°C). You substitute these values into the Clausius–Clapeyron equation.

(*continued*)

(*continued*)

Solution $\ln \dfrac{760 \text{ mmHg}}{400 \text{ mmHg}} = \dfrac{\Delta H_{vap}}{8.31 \text{ J/(K·mol)}} \times \left(\dfrac{1}{291 \text{ K}} - \dfrac{1}{308 \text{ K}} \right)$

$$0.642 = (2.28 \times 10^{-5}) \times \Delta H_{vap}/(\text{J/mol})$$

Therefore,

$$\Delta H_{vap} = 2.82 \times 10^{4} \text{ J/mol} \quad \textbf{(28.2 kJ/mol)}$$

Answer Check Whenever you are dealing with calculated quantities of heat, always make sure that the sign of your answer makes sense. In this case, because vaporization is a process that requires energy, the answer should always be a positive quantity as it is here. Also, enthalpies of vaporization generally fall in the range of tens of kilojoules, so anything much outside that range should be suspect.

Exercise 11.3 Selenium tetrafluoride, SeF_4, is a colorless liquid. It has a vapor pressure of 757 mmHg at 105°C and 522 mmHg at 95°C. What is the heat of vaporization of selenium tetrafluoride?

■ See Problems 11.51 and 11.52.

11.3 | **Phase Diagrams**

As we mentioned in the chapter opening, the solid, liquid, and gaseous states of carbon dioxide exist under different temperature and pressure conditions. A **phase diagram** is *a graphical way to summarize the conditions under which the different states of a substance are stable.*

Melting-Point Curve

Figure 11.11 is a phase diagram for water. It consists of three curves that divide the diagram into regions labeled "solid," "liquid," and "gas." In each region, the indicated state is stable. Every point on each of the curves indicates experimentally determined temperatures and pressures at which two states are in equilibrium. Thus, the curve

FIGURE 11.11 ▶

Phase diagram for water (not to scale)
The curves *AB, AC,* and *AD* divide the diagram into regions that give combinations of temperature and pressure for which only one state is stable. Along any curve, the two states from the adjoining regions are in equilibrium.

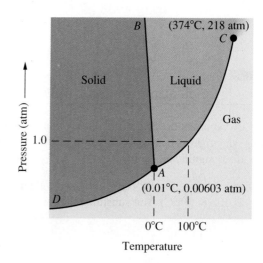

The following is a dramatic demonstration of the effect of pressure on the melting of ice: Suspend a block of ice between two chairs. Then loop a length of wire over the block and place weights on the ends of the wire. The pressure of the wire will melt the ice under it. Liquid water will flow over the top of the wire and freeze again, because it is no longer under the pressure of the wire. As a result, the wire will cut through the ice and fall to the floor, but the block of ice will remain as one piece.

AB, dividing the solid region from the liquid region, represents the conditions under which the solid and liquid are in equilibrium.

$$\text{Solid} \rightleftharpoons \text{liquid}$$

This curve gives the melting points of the solid at various pressures.

Usually, the melting point is only slightly affected by pressure. For this reason, the melting-point curve *AB* is nearly vertical. If a liquid is more dense than the solid, as is the case for water, the melting point decreases with pressure. < The melting-point curve in such cases leans slightly to the left. In the case of ice, the decrease is indeed slight—only 1°C for a pressure increase of 133 atm. For most substances, the liquid state is less dense than the solid. In that case, the melting-point curve leans slightly to the right.

Vapor-Pressure Curves for the Liquid and the Solid

The curve *AC* that divides the liquid region from the gaseous region gives the vapor pressures of the liquid at various temperatures. It also gives the boiling points of the liquid for various pressures. The boiling point of water at 1 atm is shown on the phase diagram (Figure 11.11).

Because the triple point for water occurs at a definite temperature, it is used to define the Kelvin temperature scale. The temperature of water at its triple point is defined to be 273.16 K (0.01°C).

The curve *AD* that divides the solid region from the gaseous region gives the vapor pressures of the solid at various temperatures. This curve intersects the other curves at point *A*, the **triple point,** which is *the point on a phase diagram representing the temperature and pressure at which three phases of a substance coexist in equilibrium.* For water, the triple point occurs at 0.01°C, 0.00603 atm (4.58 mmHg), and the solid, liquid, and vapor phases coexist. <

Suppose a solid is warmed at a pressure below the pressure at the triple point. In a phase diagram, this corresponds to moving along a horizontal line below the triple point. You can see from Figure 11.11 that such a line will intersect curve *AD*, the vapor-pressure curve for the solid. Thus, the solid will pass directly into the gas; that is, the solid will sublime. Freeze-drying of a food (or brewed coffee) is accomplished by placing the frozen food in a vacuum (below 0.00603 atm) so that the ice in it sublimes. Because the food can be dried at a lower temperature than if heat-dried, it retains more flavor and can often be reconstituted by simply adding water.

The triple point of carbon dioxide is at −57°C and 5.1 atm (Figure 11.12 *top*). Therefore, the solid sublimes if warmed at any pressure below 5.1 atm. This is why solid carbon dioxide sublimes at normal atmospheric pressure (1 atm). Above 5.1 atm, however, the solid melts if warmed. Sulfur has a more complicated phase diagram (Figure 11.12 *bottom*). It displays three triple points, one of them involving two different solid forms of sulfur (called rhombic sulfur and monoclinic sulfur), as well as the vapor.

Critical Temperature and Pressure

Imagine an experiment in which liquid and gaseous carbon dioxide are sealed in a thick-walled glass vessel at 20°C. At this temperature, the liquid is in equilibrium with its vapor at a pressure of 57 atm. You observe that the liquid and vapor are separated by a well-defined boundary, or meniscus. Now suppose the temperature is raised. The vapor pressure increases, and at 30°C it is 71 atm. Then, as the temperature approaches 31°C, a curious thing happens. The meniscus becomes fuzzy and less well defined. At 31°C, the meniscus disappears altogether. Above this temperature and above the critical pressure, there is only one fluid state, called a *supercritical fluid* (see Figure 11.13).

The temperature above which the liquid state of a substance no longer exists regardless of the pressure is called the **critical temperature.** For carbon dioxide it is

FIGURE 11.12 ▲

Phase diagrams for carbon dioxide and sulfur (not to scale)

Top: Carbon dioxide. At normal atmospheric pressure (1 atm), the solid sublimes when warmed. *Bottom:* Sulfur. This substance has a complicated phase diagram with three triple points.

FIGURE 11.13 ▶

Observing the critical phenomenon
(A) Carbon dioxide liquid in equilibrium with its vapor at 20°C. *(B)* The same two states in equilibrium at 30°C (just below the critical point); the densities of the liquid and vapor are becoming equal. *(C)* Carbon dioxide at 31°C (the critical temperature); the liquid and vapor now have the same densities—in fact, the distinction between liquid and vapor has disappeared, resulting in what is called a supercritical fluid.

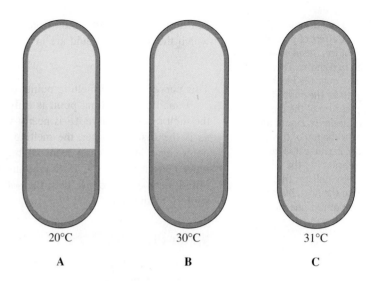

20°C	30°C	31°C
A	B	C

31°C. *The vapor pressure at the critical temperature* is called the **critical pressure** (73 atm for carbon dioxide). It is the minimum pressure that must be applied to a gas at the critical temperature to liquefy it.

On a phase diagram, the preceding experiment corresponds to following the vapor-pressure curve where the liquid and vapor are in equilibrium. Note that this curve in Figure 11.12 *top* ends at a point at which the temperature and pressure have their critical values. This is the *critical point*. If you look at the phase diagram for water, you will see that the vapor-pressure curve for the liquid similarly ends, at point *C*, which is the critical point for water. In this case, the critical temperature is 374°C and the critical pressure is 218 atm.

Many important gases cannot be liquefied at room temperature. Nitrogen, for example, has a critical temperature of −147°C. This means the gas cannot be liquefied until the temperature is below −147°C.

Example 11.4 | Relating the Conditions for the Liquefaction of a Gas to Its Critical Temperature

The critical temperatures of ammonia and nitrogen are 132°C and −147°C, respectively. Explain why ammonia can be liquefied at room temperature by merely compressing the gas to a high enough pressure, whereas the compression of nitrogen requires a low temperature as well.

Problem Strategy Note that above the critical temperature, a gas cannot be liquefied (that is, transformed so that the gas coexists in equilibrium with the liquid). This can occur only below the critical temperature.

Solution **The critical temperature of ammonia is well above room temperature.** If ammonia gas at

room temperature is compressed, it will liquefy. **Nitrogen, however, has a critical temperature well below room temperature.** It cannot be liquefied by compression unless the temperature is below the critical temperature.

Answer Check Make sure that you understand the critical temperature correctly; liquefaction can occur only *below* the critical temperature if sufficient pressure has been applied to the gas.

Exercise 11.4   Describe how you could liquefy the following gases: a. methyl chloride, CH_3Cl (critical point, 144°C, 66 atm); b. oxygen, O_2 (critical point, −119°C, 50 atm).

■ See Problems 11.57 and 11.58.

A Chemist Looks at . . .

Removing Caffeine from Coffee

daily life

Legend has it that a goat herder named Kaldi, in the ancient country of Abyssinia (now Ethiopia, in northeast Africa), discovered the pleasant effect of coffee beans when he noted that his goats danced wildly about after eating the shiny leaves and red berries of a small tree. Later he tried eating the whole berries himself, and he soon found that he was dancing with his goats. Whether the legend is true or not, it does effectively describe the stimulant effect of this berry from the coffee tree. As we now know, coffee, which today is obtained by roasting the berries' green pits, or beans as they are called, contains the stimulant caffeine, a bitter-tasting white substance with the formula $C_8H_{10}N_4O_2$. (Figure 11.14 shows the structural formula of caffeine.)

For those who like the taste of roasted coffee but don't want the caffeine, decaffeinated coffee is available. A German chemist, Ludwig Roselius, first made "decaf" coffee about 1900 by extracting the caffeine from green coffee beans with the solvent chloroform, $CHCl_3$. Later, commercial processes replaced chloroform with the safer organic solvent methylene chloride, CH_2Cl_2. Today, though, most of the commercial decaffeinated coffee produced (Figure 11.15) uses *supercritical* carbon dioxide as the extracting fluid.

In a tank of carbon dioxide under pressure (for example, in a CO_2 fire extinguisher), the substance normally exists as the liquid in equilibrium with its gas phase. But we know from the previous text discussion that above 31°C (88°F), the two phases, gas and liquid, are replaced by a single fluid phase. So, on a hot summer day (above 31°C, or 88°F), the carbon dioxide in such a tank is above its critical temperature and pressure and exists as the supercritical fluid.

Supercritical carbon dioxide is a near-ideal solvent. Under normal conditions, carbon dioxide is not a very good solvent for organic substances, but supercritical carbon dioxide readily dissolves many of these substances, including caffeine. It is nontoxic and nonflammable. It also has no effect on the stratospheric ozone layer, whereas methylene chloride does. (See the essay on stratospheric ozone at the end of Chapter 10.) Carbon dioxide does contribute to the greenhouse effect (discussed in the essay at the end of Chapter 5), but the gas once used can be recirculated for solvent use and not vented to the atmosphere.

Supercritical fluids have gained much attention recently because of the possibility of replacing toxic and environmentally less desirable solvents. For example, at the moment, the usual solvent used to dry-clean clothes is perchloroethylene, CCl_2CCl_2. Although nonflammable and less toxic than carbon tetrachloride, which was the solvent previously used, perchloroethylene is regulated as an air pollutant under the Clean Air Act. Some scientists have shown that you can dry-clean with supercritical carbon dioxide if you use a special detergent.

Substances other than carbon dioxide have also shown intriguing solvent properties. For example, whereas water under normal conditions dissolves ionic and polar substances, above its critical point (374°C, 217 atm) it becomes an excellent solvent for nonpolar substances. Supercritical water and carbon dioxide promise to replace many toxic or environmentally unfriendly organic solvents.

FIGURE 11.15 ▲

Decaf coffee
Coffee that was "naturally decaffeinated" using supercritical carbon dioxide.

FIGURE 11.14 ▶

The caffeine molecule
Space-filling model of caffeine, $C_8H_{10}N_4O_2$.

■ See Problems 11.123 and 11.124.

Concept Check 11.2

When camping at high altitude, you need to pay particular attention to changes in cooking times for foods that are boiled in water. If you like eggs that are boiled for 10 minutes near sea level, would you have to cook them for a longer or a shorter time at 3200 m to get the egg you like? Be sure to explain your answer.

Liquid State

Now we will look at some physical properties of liquids. After that, we will explain the experimental values of these properties in terms of intermolecular forces.

11.4 | Properties of Liquids; Surface Tension and Viscosity

You have seen that molecules tend to escape the liquid state and form a vapor. The vapor pressure is the equilibrium partial pressure of this vapor over the liquid; it increases with temperature. The boiling point is the temperature at which the vapor pressure equals the pressure applied to the liquid. Both vapor pressure and boiling point are important properties of a liquid. Values of the vapor pressure for some liquids at 20°C are listed in Table 11.2 (column 3). Two additional properties given in Table 11.2 are surface tension and viscosity. All of these properties, as you will see in the next section, depend on intermolecular forces, which are related to molecular structure.

Surface Tension

As Figure 11.16 illustrates, a molecule within the body of a liquid tends to be attracted equally in all directions, so that it experiences no net force. On the other hand, a molecule at the surface of a liquid experiences a net attraction by other molecules toward the interior of the liquid. As a result, there is a tendency for the surface area of a liquid to be reduced as much as possible. This explains why falling raindrops are nearly spherical. (The sphere has the smallest surface area for a given volume of any geometrical shape.)

Energy is needed to reverse the tendency toward reduction of surface area in liquids. **Surface tension** is *the energy required to increase the surface area of a liquid by a unit amount.* Column 4 in Table 11.2 lists values of the surface tension of some liquids at 20°C.

FIGURE 11.16 ▲

Explaining surface tension
Note that a molecule at the surface experiences a net force toward the interior of the liquid, whereas a molecule in the interior experiences no net force.

TABLE 11.2	Properties of Some Liquids at 20°C			
Substance	Molecular Weight (amu)	Vapor Pressure (mmHg)	Surface Tension (J/m^2)	Viscosity (kg/m·s)
Water, H_2O	18	1.8×10^1	7.3×10^{-2}	1.0×10^{-3}
Carbon dioxide, CO_2	44	4.3×10^4	1.2×10^{-3}	7.1×10^{-5}
Pentane, C_5H_{12}	72	4.4×10^2	1.6×10^{-2}	2.4×10^{-4}
Glycerol, $C_3H_8O_3$	92	1.6×10^{-4}	6.3×10^{-2}	1.5×10^0
Chloroform, $CHCl_3$	119	1.7×10^2	2.7×10^{-2}	5.8×10^{-4}
Carbon tetrachloride, CCl_4	154	8.7×10^1	2.7×10^{-2}	9.7×10^{-4}
Bromoform, $CHBr_3$	253	3.9×10^0	4.2×10^{-2}	2.0×10^{-3}

FIGURE 11.17 ▷

Water strider on a water surface
The water strider seems to skate on the surface "skin" of the water, which is actually a result of surface tension.

FIGURE 11.18 ▲

Demonstration of surface tension of water
A steel pin will float on the surface of water because of surface tension (*top*). The water surface is depressed and slightly stretched by the pin (*bottom*), but even more surface would have to be created for the pin to submerge, which takes more energy. The easiest way to float a pin is to place a square of tissue paper, with the pin on top of it, on the prongs of a fork. When the fork is lowered into the water, the tissue and pin float on the surface. The paper soon becomes water-logged and sinks, leaving the pin floating.

The surface tension of a liquid can be affected by dissolved substances. Soaps and detergents, in particular, drastically decrease the surface tension of water. An interesting but simple experiment shows the effect of soap on surface tension. Because of surface tension, a liquid behaves as though it had a skin. Water bugs (striders) seem to skitter across this skin as if ice-skating (Figure 11.17). You can actually float a pin on water, if you carefully lay it across the surface (Figure 11.18). If you then put a drop of soap solution onto the water, the soap spreads across the surface and the pin sinks. Water bugs also sink in soapy water.

Capillary rise is a phenomenon related to surface tension. When a small-diameter glass tube, or capillary, is placed upright in water, a column of the liquid rises in the tube (Figure 11.19A). This capillary rise can be explained in the following way: water molecules happen to be attracted to glass. Because of this attraction, a thin film of water starts to move up the inside of the glass capillary. But in order to reduce the

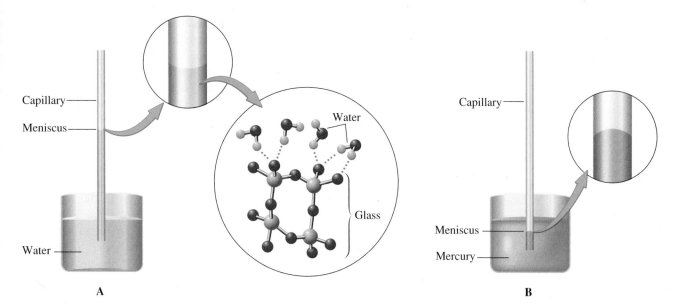

FIGURE 11.19 ▲

Liquid levels in capillaries
(*A*) Capillary rise, due to the attraction of water and glass. Hydrogen bonds between the water molecules and the gas are illustrated. The final water level in the capillary is a balance between the force of gravity and the surface tension of water.
(*B*) Depression, or lowering, of mercury level in a glass capillary. Unlike water, mercury is not attracted to glass.

FIGURE 11.20 ▲

Comparison of the viscosities of two liquids
Similar steel balls were dropped simultaneously into two graduated cylinders, the right one containing water and the left one glycerol. A steel ball takes considerably longer to fall through a column of glycerol than through a similar column of water, because glycerol has a greater viscosity than water.

surface area of this film, the water level begins to rise also. The final water level is a balance between the surface tension and the potential energy required to lift the water against gravity. Note that the *meniscus,* or liquid surface within the tube, has its edges curved upward; that is, it has a concave shape.

In the case of mercury, the liquid level in the capillary is lower than for the liquid outside (Figure 11.19B). Also, the meniscus has its edges curved downward; that is, it has a convex shape. The difference between Figures 11.19A and 11.19B results from the fact that the attraction between mercury atoms is greater than the attraction of mercury atoms for glass, in contrast to the situation for water and glass.

Viscosity

Viscosity is *the resistance to flow that is exhibited by all liquids and gases.* The viscosity of a liquid can be obtained by measuring the time it takes for a given quantity to flow through a capillary tube or, alternatively, by the time it takes for a steel ball of given radius to fall through a column of liquid (Figure 11.20). Even without such quantitative measurements, you know from experience that the viscosity of syrup is greater than that of water; syrup is a *viscous* liquid. Viscosity is an important characteristic of motor oils. In the United States, the Society of Automotive Engineers (SAE) has established numbers to indicate the viscosity of motor oils at a given temperature (0°F, or −18°C); higher numbers indicate greater viscosities at that temperature. The viscosity of a simple oil increases as the temperature decreases, so an SAE 40 oil that is appropriate for an auto engine in the summer would be too viscous in very cold weather. An oil designated as SAE 10W/40 is an oil mixture that behaves like an SAE 10 oil in the winter (W), but like an SAE 40 oil in the summer. Column 5 in Table 11.2 gives the viscosities (in SI units) of some liquids at 20°C.

11.5 | Intermolecular Forces; Explaining Liquid Properties

In the preceding section, we described a number of properties of liquids. Now we want to explain these properties. Many of the physical properties of liquids (and certain solids too) can be explained in terms of **intermolecular forces,** *the forces of interaction between molecules.* These forces are normally weakly attractive.

One of the most direct indications of the attraction between molecules is the heat of vaporization of liquids. Consider a substance like neon, which consists of molecules that are single atoms. (There is no tendency for these atoms to bond chemically.) Neon is normally a gas, but it liquefies when the temperature is lowered to −246°C at 1.00 atm pressure. The heat of vaporization of the liquid at this temperature is 1.77 kJ/mol. Some of this energy (0.23 kJ/mol) is needed to push back the atmosphere when the vapor forms. The remaining energy (1.54 kJ/mol) must be supplied to overcome intermolecular attractions. Because a molecule in a liquid is surrounded by several neighbor molecules, this remaining energy is some multiple of a single molecule–molecule interaction. Typically, this multiple is about 5, so we expect the neon–neon interaction energy to be about 0.3 kJ/mol. Other experiments yield a similar value. By comparison, the energy of attraction between two hydrogen atoms in the hydrogen molecule is 432 kJ/mol. Thus, the energy of attraction between neon atoms is about a thousand times smaller than that between atoms in a chemical bond.

Attractive intermolecular forces can be larger than those in neon. For example, chlorine, Cl_2, and bromine, Br_2, have intermolecular attractive energies of 3.0 kJ/mol and 4.3 kJ/mol, respectively. But even these values are much smaller than bond energies.

Three types of attractive forces are known to exist between neutral molecules: dipole–dipole forces, London (or dispersion) forces, and hydrogen bonding forces.

TABLE 11.3	
Types of Intermolecular and Chemical Bonding Interactions	
Type of Interaction	Approximate Energy (kJ/mol)
Intermolecular	
Van der Waals (dipole–dipole, London)	0.1 to 10
Hydrogen bonding	10 to 40
Chemical bonding	
Ionic	100 to 1000
Covalent	100 to 1000

The Dutch physicist Johannes van der Waals (1837–1923) was the first to suggest the importance of intermolecular forces and used the concept to derive his equation for gases. (See van der Waals equation, Section 5.8.)

Dipole moments were discussed in Section 10.2.

Each of these will be explained in this section. The term **van der Waals forces** is *a general term for those intermolecular forces that include dipole–dipole and London forces.* < Van der Waals forces are the weak attractive forces in a large number of substances, including Ne, Cl_2, and Br_2, which we just discussed. Hydrogen bonding occurs in substances containing hydrogen atoms bonded to certain very electronegative atoms. Approximate energies of intermolecular attractions are compared with those of chemical bonds in Table 11.3.

Dipole–Dipole Forces

Polar molecules can attract one another through dipole–dipole forces. The **dipole–dipole force** is *an attractive intermolecular force resulting from the tendency of polar molecules to align themselves such that the positive end of one molecule is near the negative end of another.* Recall that a polar molecule has a dipole moment as a result of the electronic structure of the molecule. < For example, hydrogen chloride, HCl, is a polar molecule because of the difference in electronegativities of the H and Cl atoms.

$$\overset{\delta+}{H}\!-\!\overset{\delta-}{Cl}$$

Figure 11.21 shows the alignment of polar molecules in the case of HCl. Note that this alignment creates a net attraction between molecules. This attractive force is partly responsible for the fact that hydrogen chloride, a gas at room temperature, becomes a liquid when cooled to −85°C. At this temperature, HCl molecules have slowed enough (that is, have a low enough kinetic energy) for the intermolecular forces to hold the molecules in the liquid state.

London (Dispersion) Forces

In nonpolar molecules, there can be no dipole–dipole force. Yet such substances liquefy, so there must be another type of attractive intermolecular force. Even in hydrogen chloride, calculations show that the dipole–dipole force accounts for less than 20% of the total energy of attraction. What is the nature of the additional attractive force?

In 1930 Fritz London found he could account for a weak attraction between any two molecules. Let us use neon to illustrate his argument. The electrons of this atom move about the nucleus so that over a period of time they have a spherical distribution. The electrons spend as much time on one side of the nucleus as on the other. Experimentally, you find that the atom has no dipole moment. However, at any instant,

FIGURE 11.21 ▼

Alignment of polar molecules of HCl

(A) Molecules tend to line up in the solid so that positive ends point to negative ends. *(B)* The normal random motion of molecules in a liquid only partially disrupts this alignment of polar molecules.

Solid

A

Liquid

B

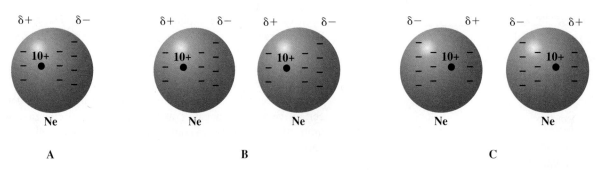

FIGURE 11.22 ▲

Origin of the London force
(A) At some instant, there are more electrons on one side of a neon atom than on the other. *(B)* If this atom is near another neon atom, the electrons on that atom are repelled. The result is two instantaneous dipoles, which give an attractive force. *(C)* Later the electrons on both atoms have moved, but they tend to move together, which gives an attractive force between the atoms.

more electrons may be on one side of the nucleus than on the other. The atom becomes a small, instantaneous dipole, with one side having a partial negative charge, δ^-, and the other side having a partial positive charge, δ^+ (see Figure 11.22*A*).

Now imagine that another neon atom is close to this first atom—say, next to the partial negative charge that appeared at that instant. This partial negative charge repels the electrons in the second atom, so at this instant it too becomes a small dipole (see Figure 11.22*B*). Note that these two dipoles are oriented with the partial negative charge of one atom next to the partial positive charge of the other atom. Therefore, an attractive force exists between the two atoms.

Electrons are in constant motion, but the motion of electrons on one atom affects the motion of electrons on the other atom. As a result, the *instantaneous dipoles* of the atoms tend to change together, maintaining a net attractive force (compare *B* and *C* of Figure 11.22). Such instantaneous changes of electron distributions occur in all molecules. For this reason, an attractive force always exists between any two molecules.

Thus, you see that **London forces** (also called **dispersion forces**) are *the weak attractive forces between molecules resulting from the small, instantaneous dipoles that occur because of the varying positions of the electrons during their motion about nuclei.*

London forces tend to increase with molecular mass. This is because molecules with larger molecular mass usually have more electrons, and London forces increase in strength with the number of electrons. Also, larger molecular mass often means larger atoms, which are more *polarizable* (more easily distorted to give instantaneous dipoles because the electrons are farther from the nuclei). The relationship of London forces to molecular mass is only approximate, however. For molecules of about the same molecular mass, the more compact one is probably less polarizable, so the London forces are smaller. Consider pentane, 2-methylbutane, and 2,2-dimethylpropane.

Name:	pentane	2-methylbutane	2,2-dimethylpropane
Boiling Point:	36°C	28°C	9.5°C
ΔH_{vap}:	25.8 kJ/mol	24.7 kJ/mol	22.8 kJ/mol

All have the same molecular formula, C_5H_{12}, and thus the same molecular mass, but they differ in the arrangement of the atoms. Pentane is a long chain of carbon atoms to which hydrogen atoms are attached. However, 2-methylbutane and neopentane have increasingly more compact arrangements of atoms. As a result, you expect London forces to decrease from pentane to 2-methylbutane and from 2-methylbutane to neopentane. This is confirmed in the heats of vaporization and boiling points listed above.

Intermolecular Forces and the Properties of Liquids

The vapor pressure of a liquid depends on intermolecular forces, because the ease or difficulty with which a molecule leaves the liquid depends on the strength of its attraction to other molecules. When the intermolecular forces in the liquid are strong, you expect the vapor pressure to be low.

Let us look again at Table 11.2, which lists vapor pressures as well as surface tensions and viscosities of some liquids at 20°C. The intermolecular attractions in these liquids (except for water and glycerol) are due entirely to van der Waals forces. Of the van der Waals forces, the London force is always present and usually dominant. The dipole–dipole force is usually appreciable only in small polar molecules or in large molecules having very large dipole moments. As noted earlier, the dipole–dipole attraction in the small, polar molecule HCl accounts for less than 20% of its interaction energy.

The liquids in Table 11.2 are listed in order of increasing molecular mass. Recall that London forces tend to increase with molecular mass. Therefore, London forces would be expected to increase for these liquids from the top to the bottom of the table. If London forces are the dominant attractive forces in these liquids, the vapor pressures should decrease from top to bottom in the table. And this is what you see, except for water and glycerol. (Their vapor pressures are relatively low, and an additional force, hydrogen bonding, is needed to explain them.)

The normal boiling point of a liquid must depend on intermolecular forces, because it is related to the vapor pressure. Normal boiling points are approximately proportional to the energy of intermolecular attraction. Thus, they are lowest for liquids with the weakest intermolecular forces.

Surface tension also depends on intermolecular forces. Surface tension is the energy needed to increase the surface area of a liquid. To increase the surface area, it is necessary to pull molecules apart against the intermolecular forces of attraction. Thus, surface tension would be expected to increase with the strength of attractive forces. If London forces are the dominant attractive forces in the liquid, surface tension should increase with molecular mass—that is, it should increase from top to bottom in Table 11.2. This is what you see, except for water and glycerol, which have relatively high surface tensions.

The viscosity of a liquid depends in part on intermolecular forces, because increasing the attractive forces between molecules increases the resistance to flow. If London forces are dominant, you should expect the viscosity of the liquids in Table 11.2 to increase from the top of the column to the bottom, which it does (again with the exception of water and glycerol; these liquids have relatively high viscosities). Note, however, that the viscosity also depends on other factors, such as the possibility of molecules tangling together. Liquids with long molecules that tangle together are expected to have high viscosities.

Hydrogen Bonding

It is interesting to compare fluoromethane, CH_3F, and methanol, CH_3OH (Figure 11.23). They have about the same molecular mass (34 for CH_3F and 32 for CH_3OH) and about the same dipole moment (1.81 D for CH_3F and 1.70 D for CH_3OH). You might expect these substances to have about the same intermolecular attractive forces

CH_3F

CH_3OH

FIGURE 11.23 ▲

Fluoromethane and methanol
Space-filling molecular models.
(Top) fluoromethane, CH_3F;
(bottom) methanol, CH_3OH.

and therefore about the same boiling points. In fact, the boiling points are quite different. Fluoromethane boils at −78°C and is a gas under normal conditions. Methanol boils at 65°C and is normally a liquid. We must conclude that there is an intermolecular attraction in methanol that is not present in fluoromethane.

We have already seen that the properties of water and glycerol cannot be explained in terms of van der Waals forces alone. What water, glycerol, and methanol have in common is one or more —OH groups.

$$H—O—H \qquad H—\underset{\underset{H}{\overset{|}{O}}}{\overset{\overset{H}{|}}{C}}—\underset{\underset{H}{\overset{|}{O}}}{\overset{\overset{H}{|}}{C}}—\underset{\underset{H}{\overset{|}{O}}}{\overset{\overset{H}{|}}{C}}—H \qquad H—\underset{\overset{|}{H}}{\overset{\overset{H}{|}}{C}}—O—H$$

Water   Glycerol   Methanol

Molecules that have the —OH group are subject to an additional attractive force called hydrogen bonding. **Hydrogen bonding** is *a weak to moderate attractive force that exists between a hydrogen atom covalently bonded to a very electronegative atom, X, and a lone pair of electrons on another small, electronegative atom, Y.* Hydrogen bonding is represented in structural drawings by a series of dots.

$$—X—H\cdots Y—$$

Usually, hydrogen bonding is seen in cases where X and Y are the atoms F, O, or N.

Figure 11.24A shows a plot of boiling point versus molecular mass for the hydrides (binary compounds with hydrogen) of the Group VIA elements. If London forces were the only intermolecular forces present in this series of compounds, the boiling points

FIGURE 11.24 ▶

Boiling point versus molecular mass for hydrides

(A) Plot for the Group VIA hydrides. Note that the boiling points of H_2S, H_2Se, and H_2Te increase fairly smoothly, as you would expect if London forces are dominant. H_2O has a much higher boiling point, indicating an additional intermolecular attraction.
(B) Plot for the hydrides of Groups VIIA, VA, and IVA.

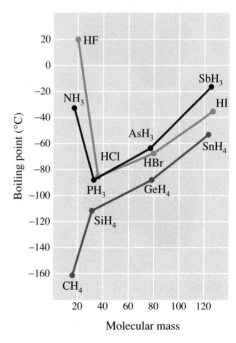

A   B

should increase regularly with molecular mass. You do see such a regular increase in boiling point for H_2S, H_2Se, and H_2Te. On the other hand, H_2O has a much higher boiling point than you would expect if only London forces were present. This is consistent with the view that hydrogen bonding exists in H_2O but is essentially absent in H_2S, H_2Se, and H_2Te.

Studies of the structure of H_2O in its different physical states show that hydrogen bonding is present. The hydrogen atom of one water molecule is attracted to the electron pair of another water molecule (Figure 11.25). Many H_2O molecules can be linked this way to form clusters of molecules. Similar hydrogen bonding is seen in other molecules containing —O—H groups.

Figure 11.24*B* shows plots of boiling point versus molecular mass for Groups VIIA, VA, and IVA hydrides. Hydrogen fluoride, HF, and ammonia, NH_3, have particularly high boiling points compared with other hydrides of their periodic group. Definite structural evidence has established hydrogen bonding in HF. In solid hydrogen fluoride, the structure shows a zigzag arrangement involving hydrogen bonding.

The hydrogen bonding attraction between two water molecules may be explained in part on the basis of the dipole moment of the —O—H bond.

$$\overset{\delta-}{-\text{O}}\overset{\delta+}{-\text{H}}$$

The partial positive charge on the hydrogen atom of one water molecule is attracted to the partial negative charge of a lone pair on another water molecule. In addition, however, a hydrogen atom covalently bonded to an electronegative atom appears to be special. The electrons in the —O—H bond are drawn to the O atom, leaving the concentrated positive charge of the proton partially exposed. This concentrated positive charge is strongly attracted to a lone pair of electrons on another O atom. Figure 11.26 shows the hydrogen bonding between two biologically important molecules.

FIGURE 11.25 ▲

Hydrogen bonding in water

Top: The electrons in the O—H bonds of H_2O molecules are attracted to the oxygen atoms, leaving the positively charged protons partially exposed. A proton on one water molecule is attracted to a lone pair on an oxygen atom in another water molecule. *Middle:* An electrostatic-potential map of two hydrogen-bonded water molecules, in which the electron density is shown by gradations of color from blue (low density) to green to yellow to red (high density). *Bottom:* Lewis structures of water with hydrogen bonding between molecules.

FIGURE 11.26 ▲

Hydrogen bonding between two biologically important molecules

These *electrostatic-potential maps* show the electron densities (relative to the nuclei) of two molecules (guanine and cytosine). The electron densities increase as the color changes from blue to green to yellow to red. Note the three H bonds between the two molecules. Each H bond is between an H atom with low electron density (exposing the positive charge on the atom) and the lone electron pair (high density) of either an O or N atom. (The molecules are guanine and cytosine, which are two of the four bases used as codes in DNA; this is explained in Chapter 24.)

Example 11.5 | Identifying Intermolecular Forces in a Substance

What kinds of intermolecular forces (London, dipole–dipole, hydrogen bonding) are expected in the following substances?

a. methane, CH_4

b. (see model at right)

c. butanol (butyl alcohol), $CH_3CH_2CH_2CH_2OH$

Problem Strategy Note that London forces are always present. Then ask yourself whether the molecule is polar—in which case, dipole–dipole forces exist. (Refer to Section 10.2 on dipole moment and molecular geometry.) Now note whether hydrogen bonding is present. (Is a hydrogen atom bonded to F, O, or N?)

Solution a. Methane is a nonpolar molecule. Hence, the only intermolecular attractions are **London forces.** b. Trichloromethane is an unsymmetrical molecule with polar bonds. Thus, we expect **dipole–dipole forces,** in addition to **London forces.** c. Butanol has a hydrogen atom attached to an oxygen atom. Therefore, you expect **hydrogen bonding.** Because the molecule is polar (from the O—H bond), you also expect **dipole–dipole forces. London forces** exist too, because such forces exist between all molecules.

Answer Check Remember that London forces are always present, even when other types of intermolecular forces exist.

Exercise 11.5   List the different intermolecular forces you would expect for each of the following compounds:

a. propanol, $CH_3CH_2CH_2OH$

b. (see model at right)

c. sulfur dioxide, SO_2

■ See Problems 11.63 and 11.64.

Example 11.6 | Determining Relative Vapor Pressures on the Basis of Intermolecular Attractions

For each of the following pairs, choose the substance you expect to have the lower vapor pressure at a given temperature: a. carbon dioxide (CO_2) or sulfur dioxide (SO_2); b. dimethyl ether (CH_3OCH_3) or ethanol (CH_3CH_2OH).

Problem Strategy There are a couple of basic ideas to keep in mind. First, London forces tend to increase with molecular mass. Second, hydrogen bonding tends to dominate other types of forces if it is present.

Solution a. The molecular weights for SO_2 and CO_2 are 64 amu and 44 amu, respectively. Therefore, the London forces between SO_2 molecules should be greater than between CO_2 molecules. Moreover, because SO_2 is polar but CO_2 is not, there are dipole–dipole forces between SO_2 molecules but not between CO_2 molecules.

You conclude that sulfur dioxide has the lower vapor pressure. Experimental values of the vapor pressure at 20°C are: CO_2, 56.3 atm; SO_2, 3.3 atm. b. Dimethyl ether and ethanol have the same molecular formulas but different structural formulas. The structural formulas are

$$
\begin{array}{cc}
\underset{\substack{|\\ \text{H}}}{\overset{\substack{\text{H}\\|}}{\text{H}-\text{C}}}-\text{O}-\underset{\substack{|\\ \text{H}}}{\overset{\substack{\text{H}\\|}}{\text{C}-\text{H}}} & \underset{\substack{|\\ \text{H}}}{\overset{\substack{\text{H}\\|}}{\text{H}-\text{C}}}-\underset{\substack{|\\ \text{H}}}{\overset{\substack{\text{H}\\|}}{\text{C}}}-\text{O}-\text{H}
\end{array}
$$

Dimethyl ether   Ethanol

The molecular masses are equal, and therefore the London forces are approximately the same. However, there will be strong hydrogen bonding in ethanol but not in dimethyl ether. **You expect ethanol to have the lower vapor pressure.** Experimental values of vapor pressure at 20°C are: CH_3OCH_3, 4.88 atm; CH_3CH_2OH, 0.056 atm.

(continued)

A Chemist Looks at . . .

frontiers

Gecko Toes, Sticky But Not Tacky

A gecko (Figure 11.27) can effortlessly climb a wall or walk across a glass ceiling. And like a superacrobat, it can catch itself by a toe while falling. How does it do this? Does the gecko have a gluey substance, or something like sticky tape, on its toes? But if so, how is it possible for the gecko to plant its feet and remove them 15 times a second, which it does when it scurries up a tree? Having a toe stick to a leaf is one thing; being able to remove it easily is another. Recently, the biologist Kellar Autumn at Lewis and Clark College, with other scientists, discovered that the gecko uses van der Waals forces to attach itself to surfaces and employs a special technique to disengage from that surface.

Van der Waals forces exist between any two surfaces, but they are extremely weak unless relatively large areas of the two surfaces come quite close together. The toe of a gecko is covered with fine hairs, each hair having over a thousand split ends. As the gecko walks across a surface, it presses these stalks of hairs against the surface. The intimate contact of a billion or so split ends of hairs with the surface results in a large, attractive force that holds the gecko fast. Just as easily, a gecko's foot comes cleanly away. As the gecko walks, its foot naturally bends so the hairs at the back edge of its toes disengage, row after row, until the toe is free. It is the mechanics of the gecko's walk that allows it to connect to and disengage easily from a surface.

It is interesting to compare gecko toes to adhesive tapes. These tapes are covered with a soft, tacky material that flows when pressure is applied. The tacky adhesive and a surface can then come in close contact, where intermolecular forces

FIGURE 11.27 ▲

A Tokay gecko
This is a common gecko, a small lizard of the type studied by Kellar Autumn.

provide effective attraction. The problem with a tacky adhesive is that it sticks to not only the surface but dirt as well. You can pull a Post-it Note off one surface and stick it to another surface several times. Eventually, the adhesive gets dirty, and the note loses its adhesive quality and refuses to stick. Gecko toes, though, are sticky but not tacky. The fine hairs do not continue to stick to dirt and can stick and unstick from surfaces indefinitely.

Materials scientists are busy trying to imitate the gecko by developing a "gecko tape," a plastic tape with the property that it can stick and unstick from surfaces many times. The plastic tape is covered in many hairs with split ends, like those on the gecko's toes. Other scientists are trying to design robots that mimic the way a gecko walks. Using gecko tape on the robot's feet might allow it to climb walls. Would we have tried to design such devices if no one had discovered how the gecko does it?

■ See Problems 11.125 and 11.126.

(continued)

Answer Check Make sure you have the correct molecular masses for the substances and that you have the correct molecular structures so that you will see hydrogen bonding if it is present.

Exercise 11.6 Arrange the following hydrocarbons in order of increasing vapor pressure: ethane, C_2H_6; propane, C_3H_8; and butane, C_4H_{10}. Explain your answer.

■ See Problems 11.67 and 11.68.

Exercise 11.7 At the same temperature, methyl chloride, CH_3Cl, has a vapor pressure of 1490 mmHg, and ethanol has a vapor pressure of 42 mmHg. Explain why you might expect methyl chloride to have a higher vapor pressure than ethanol, even though methyl chloride has a somewhat larger molecular weight.

■ See Problems 11.69 and 11.70.

Concept Check 11.3

A common misconception is that the following chemical reaction occurs when water is boiled:

$$2H_2O(l) \longrightarrow 2H_2(g) + O_2(g)$$

instead of

$$H_2O(l) \longrightarrow H_2O(g)$$

a. What evidence do you have that the second reaction is correct?

b. How would the enthalpy of the wrong reaction compare with that of the correct reaction?

c. How could you calculate the enthalpy change for the wrong reaction (Chapter 6)?

Solid State

A solid is a nearly incompressible state of matter with a well-defined shape, because the units (atoms, molecules, or ions) making up the solid are in close contact and in fixed positions or sites. In the next section, we will look at the kinds of forces holding the units together in different types of solids. In later sections, we will look at crystalline solids and their structure.

11.6 | Classification of Solids by Type of Attraction of Units

A solid consists of structural units—atoms, molecules, or ions—that are attracted to one another strongly enough to give a rigid substance. One way to classify solids is by the type of force holding the structural units together. In some cases, these forces are intermolecular and hold molecules together. In other cases, these forces are chemical bonds (metallic, ionic, or covalent) and hold atoms together. From this point of view, then, there are four different types of solids: molecular, metallic, ionic, and covalent. It should be noted, however, that a given ionic bond may have considerable covalent character, and vice versa, so the distinction between ionic and covalent solids is not a precise one.

Types of Solids

A **molecular solid** is *a solid that consists of atoms or molecules held together by intermolecular forces.* Many solids are of this type. Examples include solid neon, solid water (ice), and solid carbon dioxide (dry ice).

A **metallic solid** is *a solid that consists of positive cores of atoms held together by a surrounding "sea" of electrons (metallic bonding).* In this kind of bonding, positively charged atomic cores are surrounded by delocalized electrons. Examples include iron, copper, and silver.

An **ionic solid** is *a solid that consists of cations and anions held together by the electrical attraction of opposite charges (ionic bonds).* Examples are cesium chloride, sodium chloride, and zinc sulfide (but ZnS has considerable covalent character).

A **covalent network solid** is *a solid that consists of atoms held together in large networks or chains by covalent bonds.* Diamond is an example of a three-dimensional network solid. Every carbon atom in diamond is covalently bonded to four others, so an entire crystal might be considered an immense molecule. It is possible to have similar two-dimensional "sheet" and one-dimensional "chain" molecules, with atoms held together by covalent bonds. Examples are diamond (three-dimensional network), graphite (sheets), and asbestos (chains). Figure 11.28 shows the structures of diamond and graphite. Table 11.4 summarizes these four types of solids.

154 pm

335 pm

142 pm

Diamond

Graphite

FIGURE 11.28 ▲

Structures of diamond and graphite

Diamond is a three-dimensional network solid; every carbon atom is covalently bonded to four others. Graphite consists of sheets of carbon atoms covalently bonded to form a hexagonal pattern of atoms; the sheets are held together by van der Waals forces.

Example 11.7 | Identifying Types of Solids

Which of the four basic types of solids would you expect the following substances to be? a. solid ammonia, NH_3; b. cesium, Cs; c. cesium iodide, CsI; d. silicon, Si.

Problem Strategy Some general notions of bonding can be helpful, from which the type of solid formed follows. The metallic elements, of course, have metallic bonding. The nonmetallic elements in Groups VA to VIIA, which are rather reactive, are usually molecular, whereas those in Group VIIIA (the noble gases) are

atomic. The nonmetals in Groups IIIA (B) and IVA (C and Si) often occur with network bonding. A compound of two nonmetals is likely to be molecular, although in some cases network bonding occurs (involving Groups IIIA and IVA elements especially, such as BN, SiO_2, SiC, with strong single bonds). A compound of a metal and a nonmetal is likely to have ionic bonds.

Solution a. Ammonia has a molecular structure; therefore, it freezes as a **molecular solid.** b. Cesium is

(continued)

TABLE 11.4 | **Types of Solids**

Type of Solid	Structural Units	Attractive Forces Between Structural Units	Examples
Molecular	Atoms or molecules	Intermolecular forces	Ne, H_2O, CO_2
Metallic	Atoms (positive cores surrounded by electron "sea")	Metallic bonding (extreme delocalized bond)	Fe, Cu, Ag
Ionic	Ions	Ionic bonding	CsCl, NaCl, ZnS
Covalent network	Atoms	Covalent bonding	Diamond, graphite, asbestos

(continued)

a metal; it is a **metallic solid.** c. Cesium iodide is an ionic substance; it exists as an **ionic solid.** d. Silicon atoms might be expected to form covalent bonds to other silicon atoms, as carbon does in diamond. A **covalent network solid** would result.

Answer Check   Make sure you correctly understand the bonding involved in each case.

Exercise 11.8   Classify each of the following solids according to the forces of attraction that exist between the structural units: a. zinc, Zn; b. sodium iodide, NaI; c. silicon carbide, SiC; d. methane, CH_4.

■ See Problems 11.73, 11.74, 11.75, and 11.76.

Physical Properties

Many physical properties of a solid can be directly related to its structure. Let us look at several of these properties.

Melting Point and Structure   Table 11.1 lists the melting points for various solids and also gives the type of solid. For a solid to melt, the forces holding the structural units in their sites must be overcome, at least partially. In a molecular solid, these forces are weak intermolecular attractions. Thus, molecular solids tend to have low melting points (usually below 300°C). At room temperature, many molecular substances are either liquids (such as water and ethanol) or gases (such as carbon dioxide and ammonia). Note also that the melting points of molecular solids reflect the strengths of intermolecular attractions, just as boiling points do. This can be seen in the melting points of the molecular solids listed in Table 11.1.

For ionic solids and covalent network solids to melt, chemical bonds must be broken. For that reason, the melting points of these types of solids are relatively high. The melting point of the ionic solid sodium chloride is 801°C; that of magnesium oxide is 2800°C. Melting points of covalent network solids are generally quite high. Quartz, for example, melts at 1610°C; diamond, at 3550°C. See Table 11.1. <

> *Both molecular and covalent network solids have covalent bonds, but none of the covalent bonds are broken during the melting of a molecular solid.*

The difference between the melting points of sodium chloride (801°C) and magnesium oxide (2800°C) can be explained in terms of the charges on the ions. You expect the melting point to rise with lattice energy. < Lattice energies, however, depend on the product of the ionic charges (and inversely on the distance between charges). For sodium chloride (Na^+Cl^-) this ion-charge product is $(+1) \times (-1) = -1$, whereas for magnesium oxide ($Mg^{2+}O^{2-}$) it is $(+2) \times (-2) = -4$. Thus, the lattice energy is greater for magnesium oxide, and this is reflected in its much higher melting point.

> *Lattice energy is the energy needed to separate a crystal into isolated ions in the gaseous state. It represents the strength of attraction of ions in the solid.*

Metals often have high melting points, but there is considerable variability. Mercury, a liquid at room temperature, melts at −39°C. Tungsten melts at 3410°C, the highest melting point of any metallic element. In general, melting points are low for the Group IA and IIA elements but increase as you move right in the periodic table to the transition metals. The elements in the center of the transition series (such as tungsten) have high melting points. Then, as you move farther to the right, the melting points decrease and are again low for the Group IIB elements.

Example 11.8 | Determining Relative Melting Points Based on Types of Solids

---

Arrange the following elements in order of increasing melting point: silicon, hydrogen, lithium. Explain your reasoning.

Problem Strategy   You first need to decide the type of solid expected for each substance. Of these types, molecular substances tend to have relatively low melting

points. In comparing the melting points of two molecular solids, it is helpful to understand the intermolecular forces involved and their relative strengths. (Review Examples 11.5 and 11.6.) Stronger intermolecular forces result in higher melting points. Ionic solids and covalent network solids usually have relatively high melting points. Metals

(continued)

(*continued*)

have variable melting points, but roughly these increase in moving right through the periodic table.

Solution Hydrogen is a molecular substance (H_2) with a very low molecular mass (2 amu). You expect it to have a very low melting point. Lithium is a Group IA element and is expected to be a relatively low-melting metal. Except for mercury, however, all metals are solids below 25°C. So the melting point of lithium is well above that of hydrogen. Silicon might be expected to have a covalent network structure like carbon and to have a high melting point. Therefore, the list of these elements in order of increasing melting point is **hydrogen, lithium, silicon.**

Answer Check Make sure you understand the bonding and type of solid involved in each substance. Note that solving this problem draws on many skills, including your understanding of periodic behavior, bonding, polarity, and intermolecular forces and your ability to distinguish among types of solids.

Exercise 11.9 Decide what type of solid is formed for each of the following substances: C_2H_5OH, CH_4, CH_3Cl, $MgSO_4$. On the basis of the type of solid and the expected magnitude of intermolecular forces (for molecular crystals), arrange these substances in order of increasing melting point. Explain your reasoning.

■ See Problems 11.77 and 11.78.

FIGURE 11.29 ▲

Behavior of crystals when struck
Lead is malleable; rock salt cracks along crystal planes when struck.

Hardness and Structure Hardness depends on how easily the structural units of a solid can be moved relative to one another and therefore on the strength of attractive forces between the units. Thus, molecular crystals, with weak intermolecular forces, are rather soft compared with ionic crystals, in which the attractive forces are much stronger. A three-dimensional covalent network solid is usually quite hard because of the rigidity given to the structure by strong covalent bonds throughout it. Diamond and silicon carbide (SiC), three-dimensional covalent networks, are among the hardest substances known.

We should add that molecular and ionic crystals are generally brittle because they fracture easily along crystal planes. Metallic crystals, by contrast, are *malleable;* that is, they can be shaped by hammering (Figure 11.29).

Electrical Conductivity and Structure One of the characteristic properties of metals is good electrical conductivity. The delocalized valence electrons are easily moved by an electrical field and are responsible for carrying the electric current. By contrast, most covalent and ionic solids are nonconductors, because the electrons are localized to particular atoms or bonds. Ionic substances do become conducting in the liquid state, however, because the ions can move. In an ionic liquid, it is the ions that carry the electric current.

Table 11.5 summarizes the properties we discussed for the different types of solids.

TABLE 11.5	Properties of the Different Types of Solids		
Type of Solid	Melting Point	Hardness and Brittleness	Electrical Conductivity
Molecular	Low	Soft and brittle	Nonconducting
Metallic	Variable	Variable hardness; malleable	Conducting
Ionic	High to very high	Hard and brittle	Nonconducting solid (conducting liquid)
Covalent network	Very high	Very hard	Usually nonconducting

FIGURE 11.30 ▶

A two-dimensional pattern
(A) A pattern of A's. A point midway on the crossbar of each A has been selected for a lattice point. (B) The pattern of lattice points. (C) Division of the pattern into unit cells. (D) A single unit cell.

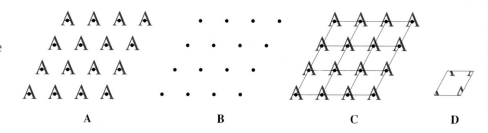

A   B   C   D

11.7 | Crystalline Solids; Crystal Lattices and Unit Cells

Solids can be crystalline or amorphous. A **crystalline solid** *is composed of one or more crystals; each crystal has a well-defined ordered structure in three dimensions.* Sodium chloride (table salt) and sucrose (table sugar) are examples of crystalline substances. Metals are usually compact masses of crystals. An **amorphous solid** *has a disordered structure; it lacks the well-defined arrangement of basic units (atoms, molecules, or ions) found in a crystal.* A glass is an amorphous solid obtained by cooling a liquid rapidly enough that its basic units are "frozen" in random positions before they can assume an ordered crystalline arrangement. Common window glass is an example, as is obsidian, a natural glass formed when molten rock from a volcanic eruption cools quickly. <

Crystal Lattices

When quartz crystals (SiO$_2$) are melted and then cooled rapidly, they form a glass called silica glass. Though ideal for some purposes, silica glass is difficult to work with because of its high temperature of softening. This temperature can be lowered by adding various oxides, such as Na$_2$O and CaO. In practice, ordinary glass is formed by melting sand (quartz crystals) with sodium carbonate and calcium carbonate. The carbonates decompose to the oxides plus carbon dioxide.

A crystal is a three-dimensional ordered arrangement of basic units. (The basic unit may be an atom, molecule, or ion, depending on the type of crystal.) The ordered structure of a crystal is conveniently described in terms of a *crystal lattice*. The idea of a crystal lattice is most easily grasped by looking at two-dimensional repeating patterns such as those seen on many fabrics or wallpapers. For simplicity, consider the pattern of A's shown in Figure 11.30A. This pattern consists of a repetition of basic units A. A lattice of points is obtained by choosing the same point in each basic unit. (The choice of this point is immaterial as long as the same point is chosen in each basic unit.) In the pattern of Figure 11.30, we have chosen the points to be midway on the crossbar of each A. The collection of these points constitutes the lattice of the pattern (Figure 11.30B). This lattice shows the essential arrangement of the basic units (A's) in the pattern. We could have chosen a different location for the point in each A, but we would have obtained the same lattice.

Similarly, we define a **crystal lattice** as *the geometric arrangement of lattice points of a crystal, in which we choose one lattice point at the same location within each of the basic units of the crystal.* Figure 11.31 shows the crystal structure of copper metal. If we place a point at the same location in each copper atom (say at the center of the atom), we obtain the crystal lattice for copper. The crystal lattice and crystal structure are not the same. We can imagine building the crystal structure for copper from its crystal lattice by placing a copper atom at each lattice point. Many different crystals have the same crystal lattice. For instance, the crystal lattice for solid methane, CH$_4$, is the same (except for the distances between points) as that for copper. We obtain the methane crystal structure by placing CH$_4$ molecules at the lattice points. The crystal lattice shows only the arrangement of basic units of the crystal.

You can imagine dividing a crystal into many equivalent cells, or *unit cells*, so that these cells become the "bricks" from which you mentally construct the crystal. Let us look at the two-dimensional pattern in Figure 11.30C, in which we have connected lattice points by straight lines. The parallelograms formed by the straight lines divide the pattern into small cells. These are the smallest possible cells from which you could imagine constructing the pattern by stacking the individual cells—they are the unit cells of the pattern (Figure 11.30D).

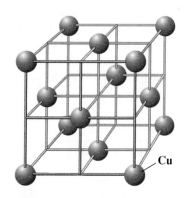

FIGURE 11.31 ▲

Crystal structure and crystal lattice of copper
The copper atoms have been shrunk so that the crystal structure is more visible. The crystal lattice is the geometric arrangement of lattice points, which you can take to be the centers of the atoms. Lines have been drawn to emphasize the geometry of the lattice.

Cu

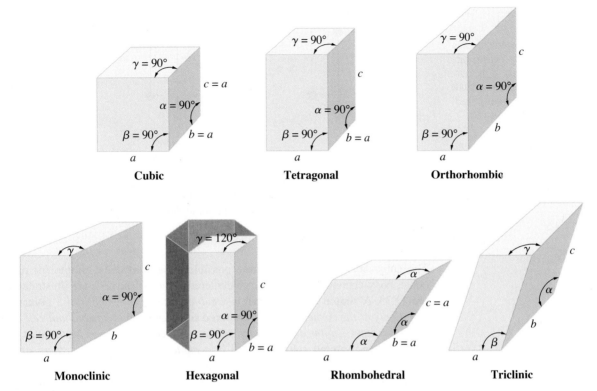

FIGURE 11.32 ▲

Unit-cell shapes of the different crystal systems

The unit cells of the seven different crystal systems are displayed, showing the relationships between edge lengths and angles (summarized in Table 11.6).

In the same way, you can divide any crystal lattice into boxlike cells, or unit cells. The **unit cell** of a crystal is *the smallest boxlike unit (each box having faces that are parallelograms) from which you can imagine constructing a crystal by stacking the units in three dimensions.*

There are seven basic shapes possible for unit cells, which give rise to the seven *crystal systems* used to classify crystals. A crystal belonging to a given crystal system has a unit cell with one of the seven shapes shown in Figure 11.32. Each unit-cell shape can be characterized by the angles between the edges of the unit cell and the relative lengths of those edges. A crystal belonging to the cubic system, for example, has 90° angles between the edges of the unit cell, and all edges are of equal length. Table 11.6 summarizes the relationships between the angles and edge lengths for the unit cell of each crystal system.

Most of the crystal systems have more than one possible crystal lattice. A *simple* (or *primitive*) lattice has a unit cell in which there are lattice points only at the corners

TABLE 11.6	The Seven Crystal Systems		
Crystal System	Edge Length	Angles	Examples
Cubic	$a = b = c$	$\alpha = \beta = \gamma = 90°$	NaCl, Cu
Tetragonal	$a = b \neq c$	$\alpha = \beta = \gamma = 90°$	TiO_2 (rutile), Sn (white tin)
Orthorhombic	$a \neq b \neq c$	$\alpha = \beta = \gamma = 90°$	$CaCO_3$ (aragonite), $BaSO_4$
Monoclinic	$a \neq b \neq c$	$\alpha = \beta = 90°, \gamma \neq 90°$	$PbCrO_4$
Hexagonal	$a = b \neq c$	$\alpha = \beta = 90°, \gamma = 120°$	C (graphite), ZnO
Rhombohedral	$a = b = c$	$\alpha = \beta = \gamma \neq 90°$	$CaCO_3$ (calcite), HgS (cinnabar)
Triclinic	$a \neq b \neq c$	$\alpha \neq \beta \neq \gamma \neq 90°$	$K_2Cr_2O_7$, $CuSO_4 \cdot 5H_2O$

FIGURE 11.33

Cubic unit cells
The simple cubic unit cell has lattice points only at the corners; the body-centered cubic unit cell also has a lattice point at the center of the cell; and the face-centered cubic unit cell has lattice points at the centers of each face in addition to those at the corners.

Simple cubic   Body-centered cubic   Face-centered cubic

of the unit cell. Other lattices in the same crystal system have additional lattice points either within the *body* of the unit cell or on *faces* of the unit cell. As an example, we will describe the cubic crystal system in some detail.

Cubic Unit Cells

The cubic crystal system has three possible cubic unit cells: simple (or primitive) cubic, body-centered cubic, and face-centered cubic. These cells are illustrated in Figure 11.33. A **simple cubic unit cell** is *a cubic unit cell in which lattice points are situated only at the corners*. A **body-centered cubic unit cell** is *a cubic unit cell in which there is a lattice point at the center of the cubic cell in addition to those at the corners*. A **face-centered cubic unit cell** is *a cubic unit cell in which there are lattice points at the centers of each face of the unit cell in addition to those at the corners*.

The simplest crystal structures are those in which there is only a single atom at each lattice point. Most metals are examples. Copper metal has a face-centered cubic unit cell with one copper atom at each lattice point (see Figure 11.31). The unit cells for this and other cubic cells of simple atomic crystals are shown in Figure 11.34. Note that only the portions of the atoms actually within the unit cell are shown. For certain applications, you will need to know the number of atoms in a unit cell of such an atomic crystal. The next example shows how you count atoms in a unit cell.

FIGURE 11.34

Space-filling representation of cubic unit cells
Only that portion of each atom belonging to a unit cell is shown. Note that a corner atom is shared with eight unit cells and a face atom is shared with two.

Simple cubic   Body-centered cubic   Face-centered cubic

Example 11.9 | Determining the Number of Atoms in a Unit Cell

How many atoms are there in the face-centered cubic unit cell of an atomic crystal having one atom at each lattice point?

Problem Strategy Remember that atoms at the corners and faces of a unit cell are shared with adjoining unit cells (see Figure 11.34). Each corner atom is shared

with eight unit cells (so there is only one-eighth of any corner atom in the unit cell), while each face is shared between two unit cells (giving one-half of a face atom per unit cell). Now add up the number of atoms for corners and faces, and then add the number of atoms totally within the unit cell (if any) to obtain the total number of atoms per unit cell.

(continued)

(*continued*)

Solution   There are six faces on a cube (each face giving one-half atom), yielding a total of three atoms from faces. Also, there are eight corners (each corner giving one-eighth atom), yielding one atom from corners. There are no atoms totally within the unit cell. Thus, there are a total of four atoms in a face-centered cubic unit cell. To summarize:

$$6 \text{ faces} \times \frac{\frac{1}{2} \text{ atom}}{\text{face}} = 3 \text{ atoms}$$

$$8 \text{ corners} \times \frac{\frac{1}{8} \text{ atom}}{\text{corner}} = 1 \text{ atom}$$

$$\text{Total} \quad \textbf{4 atoms}$$

Answer Check   Again, look at Figure 11.34, and see that your calculation agrees with it.

Exercise 11.10   Figure 11.35 shows solid dots ("atoms") forming a two-dimensional lattice. A unit cell is marked off by the black line. How many "atoms" are there in this unit cell in such a two-dimensional lattice?

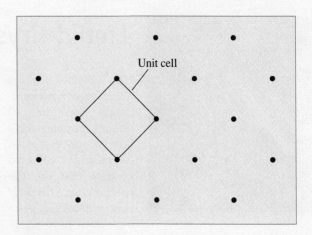

FIGURE 11.35 ▲
A two-dimensional lattice

■ See Problems 11.83 and 11.84.

Crystal Defects

So far we have assumed that crystals have perfect order. In fact, real crystals have various defects or imperfections. These are principally of two kinds: chemical impurities and defects in the formation of the lattice.

Ruby is an example of a crystal with a chemical impurity. The crystal is mainly colorless aluminum oxide, Al_2O_3, but occasional aluminum ions, Al^{3+}, are replaced by chromium(III) ions, Cr^{3+}, which give a red color.

Various lattice defects occur during crystallization. Crystal planes may be misaligned, or sites in the crystal lattice may remain vacant. For example, there might be an equal number of sodium ion vacancies and chloride ion vacancies in a sodium chloride crystal. It is also possible to have an unequal number of cation and anion vacancies in an ionic crystal. For example, iron(II) oxide, FeO, usually crystallizes with some iron(II) sites left unoccupied. Enough of the remaining iron atoms have 3+ charges to give an electrically balanced crystal. As a result, there are more oxygen atoms than iron atoms in the crystal. Moreover, the exact composition of the crystal can vary, so the formula FeO is only approximate. Such a compound whose composition varies slightly from its idealized formula is said to be *nonstoichiometric*. Other examples of nonstoichiometric compounds are Cu_2O and Cu_2S. Each usually has less copper than expected from the formula. The recently discovered ceramic materials having superconducting properties at relatively high temperatures (page 876) are nonstoichiometric compounds. An example is yttrium barium copper oxide, $YBa_2Cu_3O_{7-x}$, where x is approximately 0.1. It is a compound with oxygen atom vacancies.

11.8 | Structures of Some Crystalline Solids

We have described the structure of crystals in a general way. Now we want to look in detail at the structure of several crystalline solids that represent the different types: molecular, metallic, ionic, and covalent network.

A Chemist Looks at . . .

daily life

Liquid-Crystal Displays

Liquid-crystal displays (LCDs) are now commonly used in cell phones, portable computers, and flat-panel televisions. The liquid crystals that are the basis of these displays consist of rodlike, polar molecules in a phase that is intermediate in order between that of a liquid and that of a crystalline solid. The molecules tend to align or orient themselves in the same direction along their long axes, like matches in a matchbox, but they occupy random positions within the substance. This particular type of liquid crystal, having orientational order but no positional order, is referred to as *nematic* (Figure 11.36). The molecular order in a nematic liquid crystal, which results from weak intermolecular forces, is easily disrupted. And because these molecules are polar, they can be reoriented by the application of an electric field. A liquid-crystal display uses this ease of molecular reorientation by an electric field to change small areas, or *pixels*, of the display from light to dark.

An LCD display consists of many pixel cells arranged in rows and columns, from which an image is formed. Each pixel consists of liquid-crystal molecules contained between glass plates whose interior surfaces are covered with a transparent electrode material (Figure 11.37, *top*). Outside each glass plate is a *polarizer*. The polarizer is similar to a Polaroid lens in sunglasses. Only those light waves that are vibrating in a particular direction are allowed to pass—say, up and down at the left side. (We say that the light is *polarized*.) On the right, the polarizer is oriented so that only light vibrating at a 90° angle to that on the left can pass. Imagine light polarized in the up-and-down direction entering the glass plate at the left. Without liquid crystals between the glass plates, the polarized light passes to the right side, where it is blocked by the polarizer on that side. You can demonstrate this blocking effect (if you are willing to sacrifice a pair of sunglasses) by placing one Polaroid lens in front of the other, rotating one lens while holding the other fixed. The image you see varies from light to dark as you rotate.

Liquid-crystal molecules in an LCD cell can redirect polarized light so that it enters at the left vibrating up and down, but exits at the right vibrating at a 90° angle to that at the left. This is accomplished by treating the inner electrode surfaces so that the rodlike liquid-crystal molecules align themselves against the surface in a definite direction. At the left, these molecules are aligned up and down; at the right, they are aligned at a 90° angle to those on the left. From left to right, the molecules tend to line up one against the other, but they twist their orientations from up and down at the left to 90° at the right. Now, polarized light entering at the left is redirected by each molecule until it is vibrating so that it can exit the polarizer on the right. The light is no longer blocked.

Suppose we apply an electric charge to the electrodes. The rodlike, polar molecules of the liquid crystals now align themselves perpendicularly to the glass plates (Figure 11.37, *bottom*). The molecules can no longer reorient the polarized light; the light is blocked and the pixel is dark. By

FIGURE 11.36 ▲

Nematic liquid crystal
The rodlike molecules are aligned in the same direction, although the positions of the molecules are random.

Molecular Solids; Closest Packing

The simplest molecular solids are the frozen noble gases—for example, solid neon. In this case, the molecules are single atoms and the intermolecular interactions are London forces. These forces are nondirectional (in contrast to covalent bonding, which is directional), and the maximal attraction is obtained when each atom is surrounded by the largest possible number of other atoms. The problem, then, is simply to find how identical spheres can be packed as tightly as possible into a given space.

FIGURE 11.37 ▲

Liquid-crystal display

Top: Liquid crystals are sandwiched between glass plates. The rodlike molecules are aligned up and down at the left plate but gradually twist until, at the right plate, they are oriented at a 90° angle to the original direction. The polarizer at the left allows light to pass that is vibrating up and down. The liquid-crystal molecules turn the plane of polarization of the light so that it can exit at the right. The pixel is on (bright). *Bottom:* When an electric charge is placed on the electrodes, the molecules orient perpendicularly to the plates and can no longer twist the polarized light so that it can exit. The pixel is now off (dark). (From Joseph A. Castellano, "Modifying Light," *American Scientist,* September–October 2006: 442.)

turning the electrodes on or off, it is possible to make the pixels either dark or bright. An image is formed by turning various screen pixels on and others off by means of software.

A color display has each pixel subdivided into three subpixels. Each subpixel has a color filter in front of it, a filter that is red, green, or blue. The color image is obtained by turning appropriate subpixels on or off.

■ See Problems 11.127 and 11.128.

To form a layer of close-packed spheres, you place each row of spheres in the crevices of the adjoining rows. This is illustrated in Figure 11.38*A*. (You may find it helpful to stack identical coins in the manner described here for spheres.) Place the next layer of spheres in the hollows in the first layer. Only half of these hollows can be filled with spheres. Once you have placed a sphere in a given hollow, it partially covers three neighboring hollows (Figure 11.38*B*) and completely determines the pattern of the layer (Figure 11.38*C*).

When you come to fill the third layer, you find that you have a choice of sites for spheres, labeled *x* and *y* in Figure 11.38*C*. Note that each of the *x* sites has a sphere

A   B   C

FIGURE 11.38 ▲

Closest packing of spheres

(A) Each layer is formed by placing spheres in the crevices of the adjoining row. (B) When a sphere is placed in a hollow on top of a layer, three other hollows are partially covered. (C) There are two types of hollows on top of the second layer, labeled x and y. The x sites are directly above the spheres in the first layer; the y sites are not. Spheres of a third layer may occupy either all of the x sites or all of the y sites.

If you pack into a crate as many perfectly round oranges of the same size as possible, they will be close packed. However, they need not be either hexagonal or cubic close packed, because the A-, B-, and C-type layers can be placed at random (except that similar layers cannot be adjacent). A possible arrangement might be ABCABABABC · · · . It is the forces between structural units in a close-packed crystal that determine whether one of the ordered structures, either cubic or hexagonal, will occur.

in the first layer directly beneath it, but the y sites do not. When the spheres in the third layer are placed in the x sites, so that the third layer repeats the first layer, you label this stacking *ABA*. When successive layers are placed so that the spheres of each layer are directly over a layer that is one layer away, you get a stacking that you label *ABABABA · · · .* (This notation indicates that the A layers are directly over other A layers, whereas the B layers are directly over other B layers.) The result is a **hexagonal close-packed structure** (hcp), *a crystal structure composed of close-packed atoms (or other units) with the stacking* ABABABA · · · ; *the structure has a hexagonal unit cell.*

When the spheres in the third layer are placed in y sites, so that the third layer is over neither the first nor the second layer, you get a stacking that you label *ABC*. The fourth layer must be over either the A or the B layer. If subsequent layers are stacked so that they are over the layer two layers below, you get the stacking *ABCABCABCA · · ·,* which results in a **cubic close-packed structure** (ccp), *a crystal structure composed of close-packed atoms (or other units) with the stacking* ABCABCABCA · · · . <

The cubic close-packed lattice is identical to the lattice having a face-centered cubic unit cell. To see this, you take portions of four layers from the cubic close-packed array (Figure 11.39, *left*). When these are placed together, they form a cube, as shown in Figure 11.39, *right*.

In any close-packed arrangement, each interior atom is surrounded by 12 nearest-neighbor atoms. *The number of nearest-neighbor atoms of an atom* is called its **coordination number.** Thinking of atoms as hard spheres, one can calculate that the spheres occupy 74% of the space of the crystal. There is no way of packing identical spheres so that an atom has a coordination number greater than 12 or the spheres occupy more than 74% of the space of the crystal. All the noble-gas solids have cubic close-packed crystals except helium, which has a hexagonal close-packed crystal.

A substance composed of polyatomic molecules with approximately spherical shapes might be expected to crystallize in an approximately close-packed structure. Methane, CH_4, is an example. Solid methane has a face-centered cubic lattice with one CH_4 molecule at each lattice point.

A

C

B

A

FIGURE 11.39 ▲

The cubic close-packed structure has a face-centered cubic lattice

Left: An "exploded" view of portions of four layers of the cubic close-packed structure. *Right:* These layers form a face-centered cubic unit cell.

Metallic Solids

If you were to assume that metallic bonding is completely nondirectional, you would expect metals to crystallize in one of the close-packed structures, as the noble-gas elements do. Indeed, many of the metallic

FIGURE 11.40 ▶

Crystal structures of metals

Most metals have one of the close-packed structures (hcp = hexagonal close-packed; ccp = cubic close-packed) or a body-centered cubic structure (bcc; manganese has a complicated bcc lattice, with several atoms at each lattice point). Other structures are body-centered tetragonal (bct), orthorhombic (or), and rhombohedral (rh).

IA	IIA									IB	IIB	IIIA	IVA	VA
Li bcc	Be hcp													
Na bcc	Mg hcp	IIIB	IVB	VB	VIB	VIIB	VIIIB			IB	IIB	Al ccp		
K bcc	Ca ccp	Sc hcp	Ti hcp	V bcc	Cr bcc	Mn bcc	Fe bcc	Co hcp	Ni ccp	Cu ccp	Zn hcp	Ga or		
Rb bcc	Sr ccp	Y hcp	Zr hcp	Nb bcc	Mo bcc	Tc hcp	Ru hcp	Rh ccp	Pd ccp	Ag ccp	Cd hcp	In bct	Sn bct	
Cs bcc	Ba bcc	La hcp	Hf hcp	Ta bcc	W bcc	Re hcp	Os hcp	Ir ccp	Pt ccp	Au ccp	Hg rh	Tl hcp	Pb ccp	Bi rh

elements do have either cubic or hexagonal close-packed crystals. Copper and silver, for example, are cubic close packed (that is, face-centered cubic with one atom at each lattice point of a face-centered cubic lattice). However, a body-centered cubic arrangement of spheres (having one sphere at each lattice point of a body-centered cubic lattice) occupies almost as great a percentage of space as the close-packed ones. In a body-centered arrangement, 68% of the space is occupied by spheres, compared with the maximal value of 74% in the close-packed arrangement. Each atom in a body-centered lattice has a coordination number of 8, rather than the 12 of each atom in a close-packed lattice.

Figure 11.40 lists the structures of the metallic elements. With few exceptions, they have either a close-packed or a body-centered structure.

Ionic Solids

The description of ionic crystals is complicated by the fact that you must give the positions in the crystal structure of both the cations and the anions. We will look at the structures of three different cubic crystals with the general formula MX (where M is the metal and X is the nonmetal): cesium chloride (CsCl), sodium chloride (NaCl), and cubic zinc sulfide or zinc blende (ZnS). Many ionic substances of the general formula MX have crystal structures that are one of these types. Once you have learned these structures, you can relate the structures of many other compounds to them.

Cesium chloride consists of positive ions and negative ions of about equal size arranged in a cubic array. Figure 11.41 shows the unit cell of cesium chloride. It shows both a space-filling model (ions are shown as spheres of approximately the correct relative sizes) and a model in which the ions are shrunk in size in order to display more clearly their relative positions. Note that there are chloride ions at each corner of the cube and a cesium ion at the center. Alternatively, the unit cell may be taken to have cesium ions at the corners of a cube and a chloride ion at the center. In either case, the unit cell contains one Cs^+ ion and one Cl^- ion. (Figure 11.41 has $\frac{1}{8}$ Cl^- ion at each of eight corners plus one Cs^+ ion at the center of the unit cell.) Ammonium

FIGURE 11.41 ▶

Cesium chloride unit cell

Cesium chloride consists of interpenetrating simple cubic lattices of Cs^+ and Cl^- ions. The figure shows a unit cell with Cl^- ions at the corners of the unit cell and a Cs^+ ion at the center. (A space-filling model is on the left; a model with ions shrunk in size to emphasize the structure is on the right.) An alternative unit cell would have Cs^+ ions at the corners with a Cl^- ion at the center.

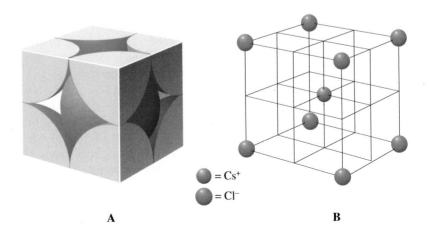

= Cs^+

= Cl^-

A   B

FIGURE 11.42 ▶

Sodium chloride unit cell

Sodium chloride has a face-centered cubic lattice. *(A)* The unit cell shown here (as a space-filling model) has Cl^- ions at the corners and at the centers of the faces of the cube. The Cl^- ions are much larger than Na^+ ions, so the Cl^- ions are nearly touching and have approximately a cubic close-packed structure; the Na^+ ions are in cavities in this structure. *(B)* The alternative unit cell shown here has Na^+ ions at the corners and the centers of the faces of the unit cell.

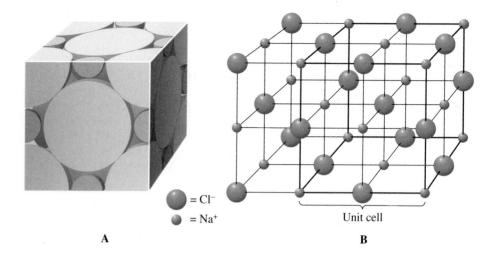

$\bullet = Cl^-$

$\bullet = Na^+$

Unit cell

A   **B**

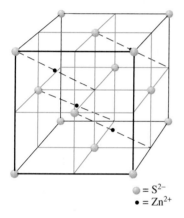

$\circ = S^{2-}$
$\bullet = Zn^{2+}$

FIGURE 11.43 ▲

Zinc blende (cubic ZnS) unit cell

Zinc sulfide, ZnS, crystallizes in two different forms, or polymorphs: a hexagonal form (wurtzite) and a face-centered cubic form (zinc blende, or sphalerite), which is shown here. Sulfide ions, S^{2-}, are at the corners and at the centers of the faces of the unit cell; Zn^{2+} ions are in alternate subcubes of the unit cell. The unit cell can also be described as having Zn^{2+} ions at each corner and at the center of each face, with S^{2-} ions in alternate subcubes.

chloride, NH_4Cl, and thallium chloride, $TlCl$, are examples of other ionic compounds having this "cesium chloride" structure.

Figure 11.42 shows the unit cell of sodium chloride. It has Cl^- ions at the corners as well as at the center of each cube face. Because the chloride ions are so much larger than the sodium ions, the Cl^- ions are nearly touching and form an approximate cubic close-packed structure of Cl^- ions. The Na^+ ions are arranged in cavities of this close-packed structure. Some other compounds that crystallize in this structure are potassium chloride, KCl; calcium oxide, CaO; and silver chloride, $AgCl$.

Zinc sulfide, ZnS, crystallizes in either of two structures. The zinc sulfide mineral having cubic structure is called zinc blende or sphalerite. Zinc sulfide also exists as hexagonal crystals. (The mineral is called wurtzite.) A solid substance that can occur in more than one crystal structure is said to be *polymorphic*. We will discuss only the zinc blende structure (cubic ZnS).

Figure 11.43 shows the unit cell of zinc blende. Sulfide ions are at the corners and at the center of each face of the unit cell. The positions of the zinc ions can be described if you imagine the unit cell divided into eight cubic parts, or subcubes. Zinc ions are at the centers of alternate subcubes. The number of S^{2-} ions per unit cell is four (8 corner ions $\times \frac{1}{8}$ + 6 face ions $\times \frac{1}{2}$), and the number of Zn^{2+} ions is four (all are completely within the unit cell). Thus, there are equal numbers of Zn^{2+} and S^{2-} ions, as expected by the formula ZnS.

The unit cell of zinc blende can also be taken to have zinc ions at the corners and face centers, with sulfide ions in alternate subcubes. Zinc oxide, ZnO, and beryllium oxide, BeO, also have the "zinc blende" structure.

Covalent Network Solids

The structures of covalent network solids are determined primarily by the directions of covalent bonds. Diamond is a simple example. It is one allotropic form of the element carbon, in which each carbon atom is covalently bonded to four other carbon atoms in tetrahedral directions to give a three-dimensional covalent network (see Figure 11.28). You can describe the bonding by assuming that every carbon atom is sp^3 hybridized. Each C—C bond forms by the overlap of one sp^3 hybrid orbital on one carbon atom with an sp^3 hybrid orbital on the other atom. The unit cell of diamond is similar to that of zinc blende (Figure 11.43); the Zn^{2+} and S^{2-} ions are replaced by carbon atoms, as in Figure 11.44. The crystal lattice, which is face-centered cubic, can be obtained by placing lattice points at the centers of alternate carbon atoms (either those shown in dark gray or those shown in light gray). Silicon, germanium, and gray tin (a nonmetallic allotrope) have "diamond" structures.

Graphite is another allotrope of carbon. It consists of large, flat sheets of carbon atoms covalently bonded to form hexagonal arrays, and these sheets are stacked one

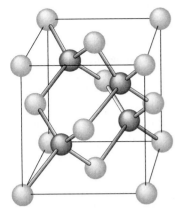

FIGURE 11.44 ▲

Diamond unit cell
The unit cell of diamond can be obtained from the unit cell of zinc blende by replacing Zn^{2+} ions by carbon atoms (shown here as dark spheres) and S^{2-} ions by carbon atoms (shown here as light spheres). Note that each carbon atom is bonded to four others.

FIGURE 11.45 ▲

Electron micrograph of graphite
Note the layer structure.

FIGURE 11.46 ▲

Demonstration of the electrical conductivity of graphite
The nonzero reading on the meter shows that the pencil lead (graphite) conducts electricity.

on top of the other (see Figure 11.27). You can describe each sheet in terms of resonance formulas such as the following:

(one resonance formula)

This is just one of many possible resonance formulas, because others can be drawn by moving the double bonds around. This means that the π electrons are delocalized over a plane of carbon atoms. You can also describe this delocalization in molecular orbital terms. You imagine that each carbon atom is sp^2 hybridized, so each atom has three sp^2 hybrid orbitals in the molecular plane and an additional $2p$ orbital perpendicular to this plane. A σ bond forms between two carbon atoms when an sp^2 hybrid orbital on one atom overlaps an sp^2 hybrid orbital on another. The result is a planar σ-bond framework. The $2p$ orbitals of all the atoms overlap to form π orbitals encompassing the entire plane of atoms.

Each carbon–carbon distance within a graphite sheet is 142 pm, which is almost midway between the length of a C—C bond (154 pm) and a C=C bond (134 pm) and which indicates an intermediate bond order (see Figure 11.28). The two-dimensional sheets, or layers, are stacked one on top of the other, and the attraction between sheets results from London forces. The distance between layers is 335 pm, which is greater than the carbon–carbon bond length, because London forces are weaker than covalent bonding forces.

You can explain several properties of graphite on the basis of its structure. The layer structure, which you see in electron micrographs (Figure 11.45), tends to separate easily, so that sheets of graphite slide over one another. The "lead" in a pencil is graphite. As you write with a pencil, layers of graphite rub off to form the pencil mark. Similarly, the use of graphite to lubricate locks and other closely fitting metal surfaces depends on the ability of graphite particles to move over one another as the layers slide. Another property of graphite is its electrical conductivity. Electrical conductivity is unusual in covalent network solids, because normally the electrons in such bonds are localized. Graphite is a moderately good conductor, however, because delocalization leads to mobile electrons within each carbon atom layer. Figure 11.46 shows a demonstration of the electrical conductivity of graphite.

Concept Check 11.4

Shown here is a representation of a unit cell for a crystal. The orange balls are atom A, and the grey balls are atom B.

a. What is the chemical formula of the compound that has this unit cell $(A_?B_?)$?

b. Consider the configuration of the A atoms. Is this a cubic unit cell? If so, which type?

11.9 | Calculations Involving Unit-Cell Dimensions

You can determine the structure and dimensions of a unit cell by diffraction methods, which we will describe briefly in the next section. Once you know the unit-cell dimensions and the structure of a crystal, however, some interesting calculations are possible. For instance, suppose you find that a metallic solid has a face-centered cubic unit cell with all atoms at lattice points, and you determine the edge length of the unit cell. From this unit-cell dimension, you can calculate the volume of the unit cell. Then, knowing the density of the metal, you can calculate the mass of the atoms in the unit cell. Because you know that the unit cell is face-centered cubic with all atoms at lattice points and that such a unit cell has four atoms, you can obtain the mass of an individual atom. This determination of the mass of a single atom gave one of the first accurate determinations of Avogadro's number. The calculations are shown in the next example.

| **Example 11.10** | Calculating Atomic Mass from Unit-Cell Dimension and Density |

X-ray diffraction from crystals provides one of the most accurate ways of determining Avogadro's number. Silver crystallizes in a face-centered cubic lattice with all atoms at the lattice points. The length of an edge of the unit cell was determined by x-ray diffraction to be 408.6 pm (4.086 Å). The density of silver is 10.50 g/cm^3. Calculate the mass of a silver atom. Then, using the known value of the atomic mass, calculate Avogadro's number.

408.6 pm

Silver
$d = 10.50$ g/cm^3

Problem Strategy Knowing the edge length of a unit cell, you can calculate the unit-cell volume. Then, from the density, you can find the mass of the unit cell and hence the mass of a silver atom.

Solution You obtain the volume, V, of the unit cell by cubing the length of an edge.

$$V = (4.086 \times 10^{-10} \text{ m})^3 = 6.822 \times 10^{-29} \text{ m}^3$$

The density, d, of silver in grams per cubic meter is

$$d = 10.50 \frac{\text{g}}{\text{cm}^3} \times \left(\frac{1 \text{ cm}}{10^{-2} \text{ m}}\right)^3 = 1.050 \times 10^7 \text{ g/m}^3$$

350.9 pm

Lithium
$d = 0.534$ g/cm^3

Density is mass per volume; hence, the mass of a unit cell equals the density times the volume of the unit cell.

$$m = dV$$
$$= 1.050 \times 10^7 \text{ g/m}^3 \times 6.822 \times 10^{-29} \text{ m}^3$$
$$= 7.163 \times 10^{-22} \text{ g}$$

Because there are four atoms in a face-centered unit cell having one atom at each lattice point (see Example 11.9), the mass of a silver atom is

$$\text{Mass of 1 Ag atom} = \tfrac{1}{4} \times 7.163 \times 10^{-22} \text{ g} = \textbf{1.791} \times \textbf{10}^{-22} \textbf{ g}$$

The known atomic mass of silver is 107.87 amu. Thus, the molar mass (Avogadro's number of atoms) is 107.87 g/mol, and Avogadro's number, N_A, is

$$N_A = \frac{107.87 \text{ g/mol}}{1.791 \times 10^{-22} \text{ g}} = \textbf{6.023} \times \textbf{10}^{23} \textbf{/mol}$$

(continued)

(*continued*)

Answer Check   In any problem of this type where you have to calculate the mass of an atom, you can always check the validity of your answer by calculating the mass of a mole of atoms (the molar mass). For example, because the calculated mass of the silver atom in this problem is 1.791×10^{-22} g, the molar mass is $(6.02 \times 10^{23}) \times (1.791 \times 10^{-22}) = 108$ g/mol, which is the expected molar mass of silver to three significant figures.

Exercise 11.11   Lithium metal has a body-centered cubic structure with all atoms at the lattice points and a unit-cell length of 350.9 pm (see art above). Calculate Avogadro's number. The density of lithium is 0.534 g/cm³.

■ See Problems 11.85 and 11.86.

If you know or assume the structure of an atomic crystal, you can calculate the length of the unit-cell edge from the density of the substance. This is illustrated in the next example. Agreement of this value with that obtained from x-ray diffraction confirms that your view of the structure of the crystal is correct.

Example 11.11 | Calculating Unit-Cell Dimension from Unit-Cell Type and Density

Platinum crystallizes in a face-centered cubic lattice with all atoms at the lattice points. It has a density of 21.45 g/cm³ and an atomic mass of 195.08 amu. From these data, calculate the length of a unit-cell edge. Compare this with the value of 392.4 pm obtained from x-ray diffraction.

Problem Strategy   The mass of an atom, and hence the mass of a unit cell, can be calculated from the atomic mass. Knowing the density and the mass of the unit cell, we can calculate the volume and the edge length of a unit cell.

Platinum
$d = 21.45$ g/cm³
atomic mass = 195.08 amu

Solution   You can use Avogadro's number (6.022×10^{23}/mol) to convert the molar mass of platinum (195.08 g/mol) to the mass per atom.

$$\frac{195.08 \text{ g Pt}}{1 \text{ mol Pt}} \times \frac{1 \text{ mol Pt}}{6.022 \times 10^{23} \text{ Pt atoms}} = \frac{3.239 \times 10^{-22} \text{ g Pt}}{1 \text{ Pt atom}}$$

Because there are four atoms per unit cell, the mass per unit cell can be calculated as follows:

$$\frac{3.239 \times 10^{-22} \text{ g Pt}}{1 \text{ Pt atom}} \times \frac{4 \text{ Pt atoms}}{1 \text{ unit cell}} = \frac{1.296 \times 10^{-21} \text{ g}}{1 \text{ unit cell}}$$

The volume of the unit cell is

$$V = \frac{m}{d} = \frac{1.296 \times 10^{-21} \text{ g}}{21.45 \text{ g/cm}^3} = 6.042 \times 10^{-23} \text{ cm}^3$$

Potassium
$d = 0.856$ g/cm³

(*continued*)

(*continued*)

If the edge length of the unit cell is denoted as l, the volume is $V = l^3$. Hence, the edge length is

$$
\begin{aligned}
l &= \sqrt[3]{V} \\
&= \sqrt[3]{6.042 \times 10^{-23} \text{ cm}^3} \\
&= 3.924 \times 10^{-8} \text{ cm (or } 3.924 \times 10^{-10} \text{ m)}
\end{aligned}
$$

Thus, the edge length is 392.4 pm, which is in excellent agreement with the x-ray diffraction value.

Answer Check   Note that the edge length for the unit cell will be greater by a small factor than the values you see for atomic diameters, so you should obtain something on the order of a few hundred picometers. You should suspect an error if you obtain anything much smaller or larger than this.

Exercise 11.12   Potassium metal has a body-centered cubic structure with all atoms at the lattice points (see art above). The density of the metal is 0.856 g/cm³. Calculate the edge length of a unit cell.

■ See Problems 11.87 and 11.88.

11.10 | Determining Crystal Structure by X-Ray Diffraction

The determination of crystal structure by x-ray diffraction is one of the most important ways of determining the structures of molecules. Because of its ordered structure, a crystal consists of repeating planes of the same kind of atom. These planes can act as reflecting surfaces for x rays. When x rays are reflected from these planes, they show a *diffraction pattern,* which can be recorded on a photographic plate as a series of spots (see Figure 11.47). By analyzing the diffraction pattern, you can determine the positions of the atoms in the unit cell of the crystal. Once you have determined the positions of each atom in the unit cell of a molecular solid, you have also found the positions of the atoms in the molecule. <

To understand how such a diffraction pattern occurs, let us look at the diffraction of two waves. Suppose two waves of the same wavelength come together in phase. By *in phase* we mean that the waves come together so that their peaks (maxima) and troughs (minima) match (see Figure 11.48A). Two waves that come together in phase form a wave with higher peaks and lower troughs than either wave. We say that the waves reinforce each other, or undergo *constructive interference.* The height of an x-ray wave (its *amplitude*) is related to the intensity of the x ray, so constructive interference gives a resultant wave having increased intensity.

Alternatively, suppose two waves of the same wavelength come together out of phase. By *out of phase* we mean that where one wave has its peaks, the other has its troughs (see Figure 11.48B). When two waves come together out of phase, each peak of one wave combines with a trough of the other so that the resultant wave amplitude is smaller than that of either wave (zero, if the two waves have the same amplitudes). We say that the waves undergo *destructive interference.* The resultant wave has decreased intensity.

Now consider the scattering, or reflection, of x rays from a crystal. Figure 11.49 shows two rays: one ray reflected from one plane, the other from another plane. The two rays start out in phase, but because one ray travels farther, they may end up out of phase after reflection. Only at certain angles of reflection do the rays remain in phase. At some angles the rays constructively interfere (giving dark areas on a

X-ray diffraction has been used to obtain the structure of proteins, which are large molecules essential to life. John Kendrew and Max Perutz received the Nobel Prize in chemistry in 1962 for their x-ray work in determining the structure of myoglobin (MM = 17,600 amu) and hemoglobin (MM = 66,000 amu). Hemoglobin is the oxygen-carrying protein of the red blood cells, and myoglobin is the oxygen-carrying protein in muscle tissue.

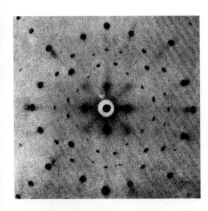

FIGURE 11.47 ▲

A crystal diffraction pattern
This diffraction pattern was obtained by
diffracting x rays from a sodium chloride
crystal and collecting the image on photographic film. The resulting negative shows
dark spots on a lighter background.

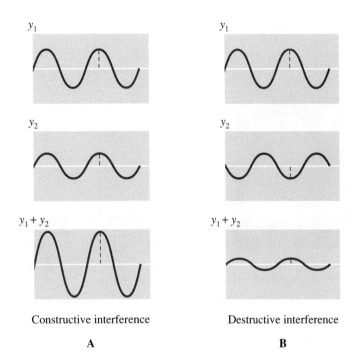

y_1

y_2

$y_1 + y_2$

Constructive interference

A

y_1

y_2

$y_1 + y_2$

Destructive interference

B

FIGURE 11.48 ▲

Wave interference
(A) Two waves constructively interfere when they are in phase (when their peaks and troughs match). The
two waves add to give a resultant wave with higher peaks and deeper troughs than either wave. (B) Two
waves destructively interfere when they are out of phase (when the peaks of one wave match the troughs
of the other wave). The two waves add to give a resultant wave with lower peaks and more shallow
troughs than either wave.

negative, corresponding to large x-ray intensity). At other angles the rays destructively interfere (giving light areas on a photographic plate, corresponding to low
x-ray intensity). Note the dark and light areas on the photographic negative of the
diffraction pattern shown in Figure 11.47.

You can relate the resulting pattern produced by the diffraction to the structure of
the crystal. You can determine the type of unit cell and its size; if the solid is composed of molecules, you can determine the position of each atom in the molecule.

FIGURE 11.49 ▶

Diffraction of x rays from crystal planes
(A) At most angles θ, reflected waves are
out of phase and destructively interfere.
(B) At certain angles θ, however, reflected
waves are in phase and constructively
interfere.

Instrumental Methods

Automated X-Ray Diffractometry

Max von Laue, a German physicist, was the first to suggest the use of x rays for the determination of crystal structure. Soon afterward, in 1913, the British physicists William Bragg and his son Lawrence developed the method on which modern crystal-structure determination is based. They realized that the atoms in a crystal form reflecting planes for x rays, and from this idea they derived the fundamental equation of crystal-structure determination.

$$n\lambda = 2d \sin \theta, \, n = 1, 2, 3, \ldots$$

The *Bragg equation* relates the wavelength of x rays, λ, to the distance between atomic planes, d, and the angle of reflection, θ. Note that reflections occur at several angles, corresponding to different integer values of n.

A molecular crystal has many different atomic planes, so that it reflects an x-ray beam in many different directions.

By analyzing the intensities and angular directions of the reflected beams, you can determine the exact positions of all the atoms in the unit cell of the crystal and therefore obtain the structure of the molecule. The problem of obtaining the x-ray data (intensities and angular directions of the reflections) and then analyzing them, however, is not trivial. Originally, the reflected x rays were recorded on photographic plates. After taking many pictures, the scientist would pore over the negatives, measuring the densities of the spots and their positions on the plates. Then he or she would work through lengthy and laborious calculations to analyze the data. Even with early computers, the determination of a molecular structure required a year or more.

With the development of electronic x-ray detectors and minicomputers, x-ray diffraction has become automated, so that the time and effort of determining the structure of a molecule have been substantially reduced. Now frequently the most difficult task is preparing a suitable crystal. The crystal should be several tenths of a millimeter in each dimension and without significant defects. Such crystals of protein molecules, for example, can be especially difficult to prepare.

Once a suitable crystal has been obtained, the structure of a molecule of moderate size can often be determined in a day or so. The crystal is mounted on a glass fiber (or in a glass capillary containing an inert gas, if the substance reacts with air) and placed on a pin or spindle within the circular assembly of the x-ray diffractometer (Figure 11.50). The crystal and x-ray detector (placed on the opposite side of the crystal from the x-ray tube) rotate under computer control, while the computer records the intensities and angles of thousands of x-ray reflection spots. After computer analysis of the data, the molecular structure is printed out.

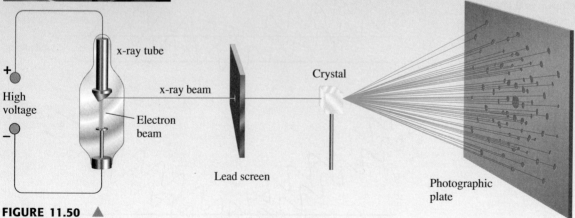

FIGURE 11.50 ▲

Automated x-ray diffractometer

(Top) The single-crystal specimen is mounted on a glass fiber, which is placed on a spindle within the circular assembly of the diffractometer. A new data collection system (left of specimen) reduces data collection time from several days to several hours. *(Bottom)* The schematic diagram shows the diffracted rays being detected by a photograph. In a modern diffractometer, the final data collection is done with a fixed electronic detector, and the crystal is rotated. The data are collected and analyzed by a computer accompanying the diffractometer.

■ See Problems 11.129 and 11.130.

A Chemist Looks at . . .

environment

Water (A Special Substance for Planet Earth)

Water is the only liquid substance (other than petroleum) to be found on earth in significant amounts. This liquid is also readily convertible under conditions on earth to the solid and gaseous forms. Water has several unusual properties that set it apart from other substances. For example, its solid phase, ice, is less dense than liquid water, whereas for most substances the solid phase is more dense than the liquid. In addition, water has an unusually large heat capacity. These are some of the properties that are important in determining conditions favorable to life. In fact, it is difficult to think of life without water.

The unusual properties of water are largely linked to its ability to form hydrogen bonds. For example, ice is less dense than liquid water because ice has an open, hydrogen-bonded structure (see Figure 11.51). Each oxygen atom in the structure of ice is surrounded tetrahedrally by four hydrogen atoms: two that are close and covalently bonded to give the H_2O molecule, and two others that are farther away and held by hydrogen bonds. The tetrahedral angles give rise to a three-dimensional structure that contains open space. When ice melts, hydrogen bonds break, the ice structure partially disintegrates, and the molecules become more compactly arranged, leading to a more dense liquid.

Even liquid water has significant hydrogen bonding. Only about 15% of the hydrogen bonds are broken when ice melts. You might view the liquid as composed of icelike clusters in which hydrogen bonds are continually breaking and forming, so clusters disappear and new ones appear. This is sometimes referred to as the "flickering cluster" model of liquid water.

As the temperature rises from 0°C, the clusters tend to break down further, giving an even more compact liquid. Thus, the density rises (see Figure 11.52). However, as is normal in any liquid when the temperature rises, the molecules begin to move and vibrate faster, and the space occupied by the average molecule increases. For most other liquids, this results in a continuous decrease in density with temperature increase. In water, this normal effect is countered by the density increase due to breaking of hydrogen bonds, but at 4°C the

FIGURE 11.51 ▲

The structure of ice

Oxygen atoms are represented by large red spheres; hydrogen atoms, by small spheres. Each oxygen atom is tetrahedrally surrounded by four hydrogen atoms. Two are close, giving the H_2O molecule. Two are farther away, held by hydrogen bonding (represented by three dots). The distribution of hydrogen atoms in these two types of positions is random.

FIGURE 11.52 ▲

Density of water versus temperature

Water has a maximum density at 4°C.

normal effect begins to predominate. Water shows a maximum density at 4°C and becomes less dense at higher temperatures.

The unusually large heat of vaporization of water has an important effect on the earth's weather. Evaporation of the surface waters absorbs over 30% of the solar energy reaching the earth's surface. This energy is released when the water vapor condenses, and thunderstorms and hurricanes may result. In the process, the waters of the earth are circulated and the freshwater sources are replenished. This natural cycle of water from the oceans to freshwater sources and its return to the ocean is called the *hydrologic cycle* (Figure 11.53).

Although evaporation and condensation of water play a dominant role in our weather, other properties are important as well. The exceptionally large heat capacity of bodies of water has an important moderating effect on the surrounding temperature by warming cold air masses in winter and cooling warm air masses in summer. Worldwide, the oceans are most important, but even inland lakes have a pronounced effect. For example, the Great Lakes give Detroit a more moderate winter than cities somewhat farther south but with no lakes nearby.

The fact that ice is less dense than water means that it forms on top of the liquid when freezing occurs. This has far-reaching effects, both for weather and for aquatic animals. When ice forms on a body of water, it insulates the underlying water from the cold air and limits further freezing. Fish depend on this for winter survival. Consider what would happen to a lake if ice were more dense than water. The ice would freeze from the bottom of the lake upward. Without the insulating effect at the surface, the lake could well freeze solid, killing the fish. Spring thaw would be prolonged, because the insulating effect of the surface water would make it take much longer for the ice at the bottom of a lake to melt.

The solvent properties of water are also unusual. Water is both a polar substance and a hydrogen-bonding molecule. As a result, water dissolves many substances, including ionic and polar compounds. These properties make water the premier solvent, biologically and industrially.

As a result of the solvent properties of water, the naturally occurring liquid always contains dissolved materials, particularly ionic substances. *Hard water* contains certain metal ions, such as Ca^{2+} and Mg^{2+}. These ions react with soaps, which are sodium salts of stearic acid and similar organic acids, to produce a curdy precipitate of calcium and magnesium salts. This precipitate adheres to clothing and bathtubs (as bathtub ring). Removing Ca^{2+} and Mg^{2+} ions from hard water is referred to as *water softening*.

Water is often softened by *ion exchange*. Ion exchange is a process whereby a water solution is passed through a column of a material that replaces one kind of ion in solution with another kind. Home and commercial water softeners contain cation-exchange resins, which are insoluble macromolecular substances (substances consisting of giant molecules) to which negatively charged groups are chemically bonded. The negative charges are counterbalanced by ions such as Na^+. When hard water containing the Ca^{2+} ion passes through a column of this resin, the Na^+ ion in the resin is replaced by Ca^{2+} ion.

$$2NaR(s) + Ca^{2+}(aq) \longrightarrow CaR_2(s) + 2Na^+(aq)$$
$$(R^- = \text{anion of exchange resin})$$

The water passing through the column now contains Na^+ in place of Ca^{2+} and has been softened. Once the resin has been completely converted to the calcium salt, it can be regenerated by flushing the column with a concentrated solution of NaCl to reverse the previous reaction.

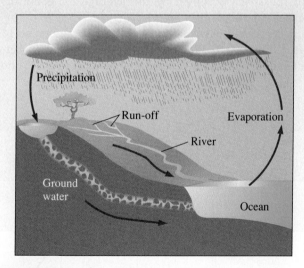

FIGURE 11.53 ▲

The hydrologic cycle

Ocean water evaporates to form clouds. Then, precipitation (rain and snow) from these clouds replenishes freshwater sources. Water from these sources eventually returns to the oceans via rivers, run-off, or groundwater.

■ See Problems 11.131 and 11.132.

A Checklist for Review

Important Terms

change of state (phase transition) (11.2)
melting (11.2)
freezing (11.2)
vaporization (11.2)
sublimation (11.2)
condensation (11.2)
vapor pressure (11.2)
boiling point (11.2)
freezing point (11.2)
melting point (11.2)
heat of fusion (11.2)
heat of vaporization (11.2)

phase diagram (11.3)
triple point (11.3)
critical temperature (11.3)
critical pressure (11.3)
surface tension (11.4)
viscosity (11.4)
intermolecular forces (11.5)
van der Waals forces (11.5)
dipole–dipole force (11.5)
London (dispersion) forces (11.5)
hydrogen bonding (11.5)
molecular solid (11.6)
metallic solid (11.6)

ionic solid (11.6)
covalent network solid (11.6)
crystalline solid (11.7)
amorphous solid (11.7)
crystal lattice (11.7)
unit cell (11.7)
simple cubic unit cell (11.7)
body-centered cubic unit cell (11.7)
face-centered cubic unit cell (11.7)
hexagonal close-packed
    structure (11.8)
cubic close-packed structure (11.8)
coordination number (11.8)

Key Equation

$$\ln \frac{P_2}{P_1} = \frac{\Delta H_{vap}}{R}\left(\frac{1}{T_1} - \frac{1}{T_2}\right)$$

Summary of Facts and Concepts

Gases are composed of molecules in constant random motion throughout mostly empty space. This explains why gases are compressible fluids. Liquids are also composed of molecules in constant random motion, but the molecules are more tightly packed. Thus, liquids are incompressible fluids. Solids are composed of atoms, molecules, or ions that are in close contact and oscillate about fixed sites. Thus, solids are incompressible and rigid rather than fluid.

Any state of matter may change to another state. Melting and freezing are examples of such changes of state, or *phase transitions.* Vapor pressure, boiling point, and melting point are properties of substances that involve phase transitions. Vapor pressure increases with temperature; according to the *Clausius–Clapeyron equation,* the logarithm of the vapor pressure varies inversely with the absolute temperature. The conditions under which a given state of a substance exists are graphically summarized in a *phase diagram.*

Like vapor pressure and boiling point, *surface tension* and *viscosity* are important properties of liquids. These properties can be explained in terms of intermolecular forces. The three kinds of attractive intermolecular forces are *dipole–dipole*

forces, London forces, and *hydrogen bonding.* London forces are weak attractive forces present in all molecules; London forces tend to increase with increasing molecular weight. Vapor pressure tends to decrease with increasing molecular weight, whereas boiling point, surface tension, and viscosity tend to increase (unless hydrogen bonding is present). Hydrogen bonding occurs in substances containing H atoms bonded to F, O, or N atoms. When hydrogen bonding is present, vapor pressure tends to be lower than otherwise expected, whereas boiling point, surface tension, and viscosity tend to be higher.

Solids can be classified in terms of the type of force between the structural units; there are molecular, metallic, ionic, and covalent network solids. Melting point, hardness, and electrical conductivity are properties that can be related to the structure of the solid.

Solids can be crystalline or amorphous. A crystalline solid has an ordered arrangement of structural units placed at *crystal lattice* points. We may think of a crystal as constructed from *unit cells.* Cubic unit cells are of three kinds: simple cubic, body-centered cubic, and face-centered cubic. One of the most important ways of determining the structure of a crystalline solid is by *x-ray diffraction.*

Media Summary

Visit the **student website at college.cengage.com/pic/ebbing9e** to help prepare for class, study for quizzes and exams, understand core concepts, and visualize molecular-level interactions. The following media activities are available for this chapter:

 Prepare for Class

■ **Video Lessons** *Mini lectures from chemistry experts*
    Vapor Pressure and Boiling Point

CIA Demonstration: Boiling Water at Reduced Pressure
CIA Demonstration: Boiling Water in a Paper Cup
Molecular Structure and Boiling Point
Phase Diagrams

Properties of Liquids
An Introduction to Intermolecular Forces and States of Matter
Intermolecular Forces
Types of Solids
CIA Demonstration: The Conductivity of Molten Salts
Crystal Structure
Crystal Packing
Calculating Atomic Mass and Radius from a Unit Cell

 Improve Your Grade

■ **Visualizations** *Molecular-level animations and lab demonstration videos*
Boiling Water with Ice Water
Changes of State
Intermolecular Forces: Dipole–Dipole Forces
Intermolecular Forces: London Dispersion Forces
Intermolecular Forces: Hydrogen Bonding Forces
Molecular Solids

Comparison of a Molecular Compound and an Ionic Compound
Structure of an Ionic Solid (NaCl)
Network Solids

■ **Tutorials** *Animated examples and interactive activities*
Hydrogen Bonding

■ **Flashcards** *Key terms and definitions*
Online Flashcards

■ **Self-Assessment Questions** *Additional questions with full worked-out solutions*
6 Self-Assessment Questions

 ACE the Test

Multiple-choice quizzes
3 ACE Practice Tests

Access these resources using the passkey available free with new texts or for purchase separately.

Learning Objectives

11.1 Comparison of Gases, Liquids, and Solids

■ Recall the definitions of *gas*, *liquid*, and *solid* given in Section 1.4.
■ Compare a gas, a liquid, and a solid using a kinetic-molecular theory description.
■ Recall the ideal gas law and the van der Waals equation for gases (there are no similar simple equations for liquids and solids).

11.2 Phase Transitions

■ Define *change of state (phase transition)*.
■ Define *melting, freezing, vaporization, sublimation,* and *condensation*.
■ Define *vapor pressure*.
■ Describe the process of reaching a dynamic equilibrium that involves the vaporization of a liquid and condensation of its vapor.
■ Define *boiling point*.
■ Describe the process of boiling.
■ Define *freezing point* and *melting point*.
■ Define *heat (enthalpy) of fusion* and *heat (enthalpy) of vaporization*.
■ Calculate the heat required for a phase change of a given mass of substance. Example 11.1
■ Describe the general dependence of the vapor pressure (ln *P*) on the temperature (*T*).
■ State the Clausius–Clapeyron equation (the two-point form).
■ Calculate the vapor pressure at a given temperature. Example 11.2
■ Calculate the heat of vaporization from vapor pressure. Example 11.3

11.3 Phase Diagrams

■ Define *phase diagram*.
■ Describe the melting-point curve and the vapor-pressure curves (for the liquid and the solid) in a phase diagram.
■ Define *triple point*.
■ Define *critical temperature* and *critical pressure*.
■ Relate the conditions for the liquefaction of a gas to its critical temperature. Example 11.4

11.4 Properties of Liquids; Surface Tension and Viscosity

■ Define *surface tension*.
■ Describe the phenomenon of capillary rise.
■ Define *viscosity*.

11.5 Intermolecular Forces; Explaining Liquid Properties

■ Define *intermolecular forces*.
■ Define *dipole–dipole force*.
■ Describe the alignment of polar molecules in a substance.
■ Define *London (dispersion) forces*.
■ Note that London forces tend to increase with molecular mass.
■ Relate the properties of liquids to the intermolecular forces involved.
■ Define *hydrogen bonding*.
■ Identify the intermolecular forces in a substance. Example 11.5
■ Determine relative vapor pressures on the basis of intermolecular attractions. Example 11.6

11.6 Classification of Solids by Type of Attraction of Units

- Define *molecular solid, metallic solid, ionic solid,* and *covalent network solid.*
- Identify types of solids. Example 11.7
- Relate the melting point of a solid to its structure.
- Determine relative melting points based on types of solids. Example 11.8
- Relate the hardness and electrical conductivity of a solid to its structure.

11.7 Crystalline Solids; Crystal Lattices and Unit Cells

- Define *crystalline solid* and *amorphous solid.*
- Define *crystal lattice* and *unit cell* of a crystal lattice.
- Define *simple cubic unit cell, body-centered cubic unit cell,* and *face-centered cubic unit cell.*
- Determine the number of atoms in a unit cell. Example 11.9
- Describe the two kinds of crystal defects.

11. 8 Structures of Some Crystalline Solids

- Define *hexagonal close-packed structure* and *cubic close-packed structure.*
- Define *coordination number.*

- Note the common structures (face-centered cubic and body-centered cubic) of metallic solids.
- Describe the three types of cubic structures of ionic solids.
- Describe the covalent network structure of diamond and graphite.

11.9 Calculations Involving Unit-Cell Dimensions

- Calculate atomic mass from unit-cell dimension and density. Example 11.10
- Calculate unit-cell dimension from unit-cell type and density. Example 11.11

11.10 Determining Crystal Structure by X-Ray Diffraction

- Describe how constructive and destructive interference give rise to a diffraction pattern.
- Note that diffraction of x rays from a crystal gives information about the positions of atoms in the crystal.

Self-Assessment and Review Questions

11.1   List the different phase transitions that are possible and give examples of each.

11.2   Describe how you could purify iodine by sublimation.

11.3   Describe vapor pressure in molecular terms. What do we mean by saying it involves a dynamic equilibrium?

11.4   Explain why 15 g of steam at 100°C melts more ice than 15 g of liquid water at 100°C.

11.5   Why is the heat of fusion of a substance smaller than its heat of vaporization?

11.6   Explain why evaporation leads to cooling of the liquid.

11.7   Describe the behavior of a liquid and its vapor in a closed vessel as the temperature increases.

11.8   Gases that cannot be liquefied at room temperature merely by compression are called "permanent" gases. How could you liquefy such a gas?

11.9   The pressure in a cylinder of nitrogen continuously decreases as gas is released from it. On the other hand, a cylinder of propane maintains a constant pressure as propane is released. Explain this difference in behavior.

11.10   Why does the vapor pressure of a liquid depend on the intermolecular forces?

11.11   Explain the surface tension of a liquid in molecular terms. How does the surface tension make a liquid act as though it had a "skin"?

11.12   Explain the origin of the London force that exists between two molecules.

11.13   Explain what is meant by hydrogen bonding. Describe the hydrogen bonding between two H_2O molecules.

11.14   Why do molecular substances have relatively low melting points?

11.15   Describe the distinguishing characteristics of a crystalline solid and an amorphous solid.

11.16   Describe the face-centered cubic unit cell.

11.17   Describe the structure of thallium(I) iodide, which has the same structure as cesium chloride.

11.18   What is the coordination number of Cs^+ in CsCl? of Na^+ in NaCl? of Zn^{2+} in ZnS?

11.19   Explain in words how Avogadro's number could be obtained from the unit-cell edge length of a cubic crystal. What other data are required?

11.20   Explain the production of an x-ray diffraction pattern by a crystal in terms of the interference of waves.

11.21   Which of the following would release the most heat? Assume the same mass of H_2O in each case.
   a. Cooling the H_2O sample from 20°C to −1.0°C
   b. Heating the H_2O sample from −15°C to 60°C
   c. Cooling the H_2O sample from 95°C to 74°C
   d. Cooling the H_2O sample from 123°C to 101°C
   e. Cooling the H_2O sample from 105°C to 84°C

11.22   The triple point of a solid is at 5.2 atm and −57°C. Under typical laboratory conditions of $P = 0.98$ atm and $T = 23$°C, this solid will
   a. remain solid indefinitely   b. boil
   c. melt   d. sublime
   e. condense

11.23   Under the right conditions, hydrogen gas, H_2, can be liquefied. Which is the most important intermolecular force that is responsible for allowing hydrogen molecules to be liquefied?
   a. hydrogen bonding
   b. dipole–dipole interactions
   c. London (dispersion) forces
   d. covalent bonds
   e. ion–dipole forces

11.24   An element crystallizes with a simple cubic lattice with atoms at all the lattice points. If the radius of the atom is 200. pm, what is the volume of the unit cell?
   a. 8.00×10^6 pm^3
   b. 6.40×10^7 pm^3
   c. 4.00×10^4 pm^3
   d. 1.60×10^5 pm^3
   e. 6.00×10^7 pm^3

Concept Explorations

11.25   Intermolecular Forces

The following picture represents atoms of hypothetical, non-metallic, monatomic elements A, B, and C in a container at a temperature of 4 K (the piston maintains the pressure at 1 atm). None of these elements reacts with the others.

= A
= B
= C

   a. What is the state (solid, liquid, or gas) of each of the elements represented in the container?

   b. Rank the elements in the container from greatest to least, in terms of intermolecular interactions. Explain your answer.

   c. What type(s) of intermolecular attractions are present in each of these elements?

   d. Explain which element has the greatest atomic mass.

   e. One of the elements in the container has a normal boiling point of 2 K. Which element would that be (A, B, or C)? How do you know?

   f. One of the elements has a melting point of 50 K. Which element would that be (A, B, or C)? Why?

   g. The remaining element (the one you have yet to choose) has a normal boiling point of 25 K. Identify the element. Could this element have a freezing point of 7 K? Explain.

   h. If you started heating the sample to 20 K, explain what you would observe with regard to the container and its contents during the heating.

   i. Describe the container and its contents at 20 K. Describe (include a drawing) how the container and its contents look at 20 K.

   j. Now you increase the temperature of the container to 30 K. Describe (include a drawing) how the container and its contents look at 30 K. Be sure to note any changes in going from 20 K to 30 K.

   k. Finally, you heat the container to 60 K. Describe (include a drawing) how the container and its contents look at this temperature. Be sure to note any changes in going from 30 K to 60 K.

11.26   Heat and Molecular Behavior

Part 1:

   a. Is it possible to add heat to a pure substance and not observe a temperature change? If so, provide examples.

   b. Describe, on a molecular level, what happens to the heat being added to a substance just before and during melting. Do any of these molecular changes cause a change in temperature?

Part 2: Consider two pure substances with equal molar masses: substance A, having very strong intermolecular attractions, and substance B, having relatively weak intermolecular attractions. Draw two separate heating curves for 0.25-mol samples of substance A and substance B in going from the solid to the vapor state. You decide on the freezing point and boiling point for each substance, keeping in mind the information provided in this problem. Here is some additional information for constructing the curves. In both cases, the rate at which you add heat is the same. Prior to heating, both substances are at $-50°C$, which is below their freezing points. The heat capacities of A and B are very similar in all states.

   a. As you were heating substances A and B, did they melt after equal quantities of heat were added to each substance? Explain how your heating curves support your answer.

   b. What were the boiling points you assigned to the substances? Are the boiling points the same? If not, explain how you decided to display them on your curves.

   c. According to your heating curves, which substance reached the boiling point first? Justify your answer.

   d. Is the quantity of heat added to melt substance A at its melting point the same as the quantity of heat required to convert all of substance A to a gas at its boiling point? Should these quantities be equal? Explain.

Conceptual Problems

11.27 Shown here is a curve of the distribution of kinetic energies of the molecules in a liquid at an arbitrary temperature T.

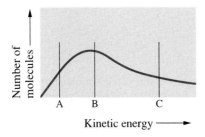

The lines marked A, B, and C represent the point where each of the molecules for three different liquids (liquid A, liquid B, and liquid C) has the minimum kinetic energy to escape into the gas phase (see Figure 11.5 for more information). Write a brief explanation for each of your answers to the following questions.

a. Which of the molecules—A, B, or C—would have the majority of the molecules in the gas phase at temperature T?

b. Which of the molecules—A, B, or C—has the strongest intermolecular attractions?

c. Which of the molecules would have the lowest vapor pressure at temperature T?

11.28 Consider a substance X with a $\Delta H_{vap} = 20.3$ kJ/mol and $\Delta H_{fus} = 9.0$ kJ/mol. The melting point, freezing point, and heat capacities of both the solid and liquid X are identical to those of water.

a. If you place one beaker containing 50 g of X at $-10°C$ and another beaker with 50 g of H_2O at $-10°C$ on a hot plate and start heating them, which material will reach the boiling point first?

b. Which of the materials from part a, X or H_2O, would completely boil away first?

c. On a piece of graph paper, draw the heating curve for H_2O and X. How do the heating curves reflect your answers from parts a and b?

11.29 Using the information presented in this chapter, explain why farmers spray water above and on their fruit trees on still nights when they know the temperature is going to drop below $0°C$. (*Hint:* Totally frozen fruit is what the farmers are trying to avoid.)

11.30 You are presented with three bottles, each containing a different liquid: bottle A, bottle B, and bottle C. Bottle A's label states that it is an ionic compound with a boiling point of $35°C$. Bottle B's label states that it is a molecular compound with a boiling point of $29.2°C$. Bottle C's label states that it is a molecular compound with a boiling point of $67.1°C$.

a. Which of the compounds is most likely to be incorrectly identified?

b. If Bottle A were a molecular compound, which of the compounds has the strongest intermolecular attractions?

c. If Bottle A were a molecular compound, which of the compounds would have the highest vapor pressure?

11.31 Shown here is a representation of a unit cell for a crystal. The orange balls are atom A, and the gray balls are atom B.

a. What is the chemical formula of the compound that has this unit cell ($A_?B_?$)?

b. Consider the configuration of the A atoms. Is this a cubic unit cell? If so, which type?

11.32 As a demonstration, an instructor had a block of ice suspended between two chairs. She then hung a wire over the block of ice, with weights attached to the ends of the wire:

Later, at the end of the lecture, she pointed out that the wire was lying on the floor, apparently having cut its way through the block of ice, although the ice block remained intact. Explain, by referring to the phase diagram for water (Figure 11.11), what has happened.

11.33 If you place water at room temperature in a well-insulated cup and allow some of the water to evaporate, the temperature of the water in the cup will drop lower than room temperature. Come up with an explanation for this observation.

11.34 The heats of vaporization for water and carbon disulfide are 40.7 kJ/mol and 26.8 kJ/mol, respectively. A vapor (steam) burn occurs when the concentrated vapor of a substance condenses on your skin. Which of these substances, water or carbon disulfide, will result in the most severe burn if identical quantities of each vapor at a temperature just above their boiling point came in contact with your skin?

11.35 When hypothetical element X forms a solid, it can crystallize in three ways: with unit cells being either simple cubic, face-centered cubic, or body-centered cubic.

a. Which crystalline form of solid X has the highest density?

b. Which crystalline form of solid X has the most empty space?

11.36 Consider two flasks that contain different pure liquids at $20°C$.

The liquid in one flask, substance A, has a molar mass of 100 g/mol and has hydrogen bonding. The liquid in the other flask, substance B, has a molar mass of 105 g/mol and has dipole–dipole interactions.

   a. If the molecular structures of the compounds are very similar, which flask probably contains substance A?

Practice Problems

Phase Transitions

11.37 Identify the phase transition occurring in each of the following.

   a. The water level in an aquarium tank falls continuously (the tank has no leak).

   b. A mixture of scrambled eggs placed in a cold vacuum chamber slowly turns to a powdery solid.

   c. Chlorine gas is passed into a very cold test tube where it turns to a yellow liquid.

   d. When carbon dioxide gas under pressure exits from a small orifice, it turns to a white "snow."

   e. Molten lava from a volcano cools and turns to solid rock.

11.38 Identify the phase transition occurring in each of the following.

   a. Mothballs slowly become smaller and eventually disappear.

   b. Rubbing alcohol spilled on the palm of the hand feels cool as the volume of liquid decreases.

   c. A black deposit of tungsten metal collects on the inside of a lightbulb whose filament is tungsten metal.

   d. Raindrops hit a cold metal surface, which becomes covered with ice.

   e. Candle wax turns to liquid under the heat of the candle flame.

11.39 Use Figure 11.7 to estimate the boiling point of diethyl ether, $(C_2H_5)_2O$, under an external pressure of 350 mmHg.

11.40 Use Figure 11.7 to estimate the boiling point of carbon tetrachloride, CCl_4, under an external pressure of 250 mmHg.

11.41 An electric heater coil provided heat to a 15.5-g sample of iodine, I_2, at the rate of 3.48 J/s. It took 4.54 min from the time the iodine began to melt until the iodine was completely melted. What is the heat of fusion per mole of iodine?

11.42 A 35.8-g sample of cadmium metal was melted by an electric heater providing 4.66 J/s of heat. If it took 6.92 min from the time the metal began to melt until it was completely melted, what is the heat of fusion per mole of cadmium?

11.43 Isopropyl alcohol, $CH_3CHOHCH_3$, is used in rubbing alcohol mixtures. Alcohol on the skin cools by evaporation. How much heat is absorbed by the alcohol if 2.25 g evaporates? The heat of vaporization of isopropyl alcohol is 42.1 kJ/mol.

11.44 Liquid butane, C_4H_{10}, is stored in cylinders to be used as a fuel. Suppose 39.3 g of butane gas is removed from a cylinder. How much heat must be provided to vaporize this much gas? The heat of vaporization of butane is 21.3 kJ/mol.

   b. If you were to increase the temperature of each of the flasks by 15°C, how would the pictures change (assume that you stay below the boiling points of the liquids)?

11.45 Water at 0°C was placed in a dish inside a vessel maintained at low pressure by a vacuum pump. After a quantity of water had evaporated, the remainder froze. If 9.31 g of ice at 0°C was obtained, how much liquid water must have evaporated? The heat of fusion of water is 6.01 kJ/mol and its heat of vaporization is 44.9 kJ/mol at 0°C.

11.46 A quantity of ice at 0.0°C was added to 33.6 g of water at 21.0°C to give water at 0.0°C. How much ice was added? The heat of fusion of water is 6.01 kJ/mol and the specific heat is 4.18 J/(g·°C).

11.47 A quantity of ice at 0°C is added to 64.3 g of water in a glass at 55°C. After the ice melted, the temperature of the water in the glass was 15°C. How much ice was added? The heat of fusion of water is 6.01 kJ/mol and the specific heat is 4.18 J/(g·°C).

11.48 Steam at 100°C was passed into a flask containing 275 g of water at 21°C, where the steam condensed. How many grams of steam must have condensed if the temperature of the water in the flask was raised to 83°C? The heat of vaporization of water at 100°C is 40.7 kJ/mol and the specific heat is 4.18 J/(g·°C).

11.49 Chloroform, $CHCl_3$, a volatile liquid, was once used as an anesthetic but has been replaced by safer compounds. Chloroform boils at 61.7°C and has a heat of vaporization of 31.4 kJ/mol. What is its vapor pressure at 36.2°C?

11.50 Methanol, CH_3OH, a colorless, volatile liquid, was formerly known as wood alcohol. It boils at 65.0°C and has a heat of vaporization of 37.4 kJ/mol. What is its vapor pressure at 22.0°C?

11.51 White phosphorus, P_4, is normally a white, waxy solid melting at 44°C to a colorless liquid. The liquid has a vapor pressure of 400.0 mmHg at 251.0°C and 760.0 mmHg at 280.0°C. What is the heat of vaporization of this substance?

11.52 Carbon disulfide, CS_2, is a volatile, flammable liquid. It has a vapor pressure of 400.0 mmHg at 28.0°C and 760.0 mmHg at 46.5°C. What is the heat of vaporization of this substance?

Phase Diagrams

11.53 Shown here is the phase diagram for compound Z. The triple point of Z is −5.1°C at 3.3 atm and the critical point is 51°C and 99.1 atm.

a. What is the state of Z at position A?

b. If we increase the temperature from the compound at position A to 60°C while holding the pressure constant, what is the state of Z?

c. If we take the compound starting under the conditions of part b and reduce the temperature to 20°C and increase the pressure to 65 atm, what is the state of Z?

d. Would it be possible to make the compound starting under the conditions of part c a solid by increasing just the pressure?

11.54 Shown here is the phase diagram for compound X. The triple point of X is −25.1°C at 0.50 atm and the critical point is 22°C and 21.3 atm.

a. What is the state of X at position A?

b. If we decrease the temperature from the compound at position A to −28.2°C while holding the pressure constant, what is the state of X?

c. If we take the compound starting under the conditions of part b and increase the temperature to 15.3°C and decrease the pressure to 0.002 atm, what is the state of X?

d. Would it be possible to make the compound starting under the conditions of part c a solid by increasing just the pressure?

11.55 Use graph paper and sketch the phase diagram of oxygen, O_2, from the following information: normal melting point, −218°C; normal boiling point, −183°C; triple point, −219°C, 1.10 mmHg; critical point, −118°C, 50.1 atm. Label each phase region on the diagram.

11.56 Use graph paper and sketch the phase diagram of argon, Ar, from the following information: normal melting point, −187°C; normal boiling point, −186°C; triple point, −189°C, 0.68 atm; critical point, −122°C, 48 atm. Label each phase region on the diagram.

11.57 Which of the following substances can be liquefied by applying pressure at 25°C? For those that cannot, describe the conditions under which they *can* be liquefied.

Substance	Critical Temperature	Critical Pressure
Sulfur dioxide, SO_2	158°C	78 atm
Acetylene, C_2H_2	36°C	62 atm
Methane, CH_4	−82°C	46 atm
Carbon monoxide, CO	−140°C	35 atm

11.58 A tank of gas at 21°C has a pressure of 1.0 atm. Using the data in the table, answer the following questions. Explain your answers.

a. If the tank contains carbon tetrafluoride, CF_4, is the liquid state also present?

b. If the tank contains butane, C_4H_{10}, is the liquid state also present?

Substance	Boiling Point at 1 atm	Critical Temperature	Critical Pressure
CF_4	− 128°C	−46°C	41 atm
C_4H_{10}	−0.5°C	152°C	38 atm

11.59 Bromine, Br_2, has a triple point at −7.3°C and 44 mmHg and a critical point at 315°C and 102 atm. The density of the solid is 3.4 g/cm³, and the density of the liquid is 3.1 g/cm³. Sketch a rough phase diagram of bromine, labeling all important features. Circle the correct word in each of the following sentences (and explain your answers).

a. Bromine vapor at 40 mmHg condenses to the (liquid, solid) when cooled sufficiently.

b. Bromine vapor at 400 mmHg condenses to the (liquid, solid) when cooled sufficiently.

11.60 Krypton, Kr, has a triple point at −169°C and 133 mmHg and a critical point at −63°C and 54 atm. The density of the solid is 2.8 g/cm³, and the density of the liquid is 2.4 g/cm³. Sketch a rough phase diagram of krypton. Circle the correct word in each of the following sentences (and explain your answers).

a. Solid krypton at 130 mmHg (melts, sublimes without melting) when the temperature is raised.

b. Solid krypton at 760 mmHg (melts, sublimes without melting) when the temperature is raised.

Intermolecular Forces and Properties of Liquids

11.61 The heats of vaporization of liquid Cl_2, liquid H_2, and liquid N_2 are 20.4 kJ/mol, 0.9 kJ/mol, and 5.6 kJ/mol, respectively. Are the relative values as you would expect? Explain.

11.62 The heats of vaporization of liquid O_2, liquid Ne, and liquid methanol, CH_3OH, are 6.8 kJ/mol, 1.8 kJ/mol, and 34.5 kJ/mol, respectively. Are the relative values as you would expect? Explain.

11.63 For each of the following substances, list the kinds of intermolecular forces expected.

a.

b. isopropyl alcohol, $CH_3CHOHCH_3$

c. hydrogen iodide, HI

d. krypton, Kr

11.64 Which of the following compounds would you expect to exhibit *only* London forces?

a. potassium chloride, KCl

b.

c. silicon tetrafluoride, SiF_4

d. phosphorus pentachloride, PCl_5

11.65 Arrange the following substances in order of increasing magnitude of the London forces: $SiCl_4$, CCl_4, $GeCl_4$.

11.66 Arrange the following substances in order of increasing magnitude of the London forces: Xe, Ne, Kr.

11.67 Methane, CH_4, reacts with chlorine, Cl_2, to produce a series of chlorinated hydrocarbons: methyl chloride (CH_3Cl), methylene chloride (CH_2Cl_2), chloroform ($CHCl_3$), and carbon tetrachloride (CCl_4). Which compound has the lowest vapor pressure at room temperature? Explain.

11.68 The halogens form a series of compounds with each other, which are called interhalogens. Examples are bromine chloride (BrCl), iodine bromide (IBr), bromine fluoride (BrF), and chlorine fluoride (ClF). Which compound is expected to have the lowest boiling point at any given pressure? Explain.

11.69 Predict the order of increasing vapor pressure at a given temperature for the following compounds:
  a. FCH_2CH_2F **b.** $HOCH_2CH_2OH$ **c.** FCH_2CH_2OH
Explain why you chose this order.

11.70 Predict the order of increasing vapor pressure at a given temperature for the following compounds:
  a. $CH_3CH_2CH_2CH_2OH$
  b. $CH_3CH_2OCH_2CH_3$
  c. $HOCH_2CH_2CH_2OH$
Explain why you chose this order.

11.71 List the following substances in order of increasing boiling point.

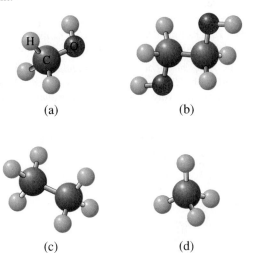

(a)   (b)

(c)   (d)

11.72 Arrange the following compounds in order of increasing boiling point.

(a)   (b)

(c)   (d)

Types of Solids

11.73 Classify each of the following by the type of solid it forms: (a) Na; (b) Fe; (c) B; (d) H_2O; (e) KF.

11.74 Classify each of the following by the type of solid it forms: (a) LiCl; (b) $BaCl_2$; (c) BCl_3; (d) CCl_4; (e) NCl_3.

11.75 Classify each of the following solid elements as molecular, metallic, ionic, or covalent network.
  a. tin, Sn
  b. germanium, Ge
  c. sulfur, S_8
  d. iodine, I_2

11.76 Which of the following do you expect to be molecular solids?
  a. solid silicon tetrachloride, $SiCl_4$
  b. lithium bromide, LiBr
  c. cadmium, Cd
  d. solid chlorine, Cl_2

11.77 Arrange the following compounds in order of increasing melting point.

(a)   (b)

(c)   (d)

11.78 Arrange the following substances in order of increasing melting point.

(a) (b) (c) (d)

11.79 Associate each type of solid in the left-hand column with two of the properties in the right-hand column. Each property may be used more than once.
  a. molecular solid   low-melting
  b. ionic solid   high-melting
  c. metallic solid   brittle
  d. covalent network   malleable
    solid   hard
        electrically conducting

11.80 On the basis of the description given, classify each of the following solids as molecular, metallic, ionic, or covalent network. Explain your answers.
  a. a lustrous, yellow solid that conducts electricity
  b. a hard, black solid melting at 2350°C to give a nonconducting liquid
  c. a nonconducting, pink solid melting at 650°C to give an electrically conducting liquid
  d. red crystals having a characteristic odor and melting at 171°C

11.81 Associate each of the solids Co, LiCl, SiC, and CHI_3 with one of the following sets of properties.
  a. A white solid melting at 613°C; the liquid is electrically conducting, although the solid is not.
  b. A very hard, blackish solid subliming at 2700°C.
  c. A yellow solid with a characteristic odor having a melting point of 120°C.
  d. A gray, lustrous solid melting at 1495°C; both the solid and liquid are electrical conductors.

11.82 Associate each of the solids BN, P_4S_3, Pb, and $CaCl_2$ with one of the following sets of properties.
  a. A bluish white, lustrous solid melting at 327°C; the solid is soft and malleable.
  b. A white solid melting at 772°C; the solid is an electrical nonconductor but dissolves in water to give a conducting solution.
  c. A yellowish green solid melting at 172°C.
  d. A very hard, colorless substance melting at about 3000°C.

Crystal Structure

11.83 How many atoms are there in a simple cubic unit cell of an atomic crystal in which all atoms are at lattice points?

11.84 How many atoms are there in a body-centered cubic unit cell of an atomic crystal in which all atoms are at lattice points?

11.85 Metallic iron has a body-centered cubic lattice with all atoms at lattice points and a unit cell whose edge length is 286.6 pm. The density of iron is 7.87 g/cm³. What is the mass of an iron atom? Compare this value with the value you obtain from the molar mass.

11.86 Nickel has a face-centered unit cell with all atoms at lattice points and an edge length of 352.4 pm. The density of metallic nickel is 8.91 g/cm³. What is the mass of a nickel atom? From the atomic mass, calculate Avogadro's number.

11.87 Copper metal has a face-centered cubic structure with all atoms at lattice points and a density of 8.93 g/cm³. Its atomic mass is 63.5 amu. Calculate the edge length of the unit cell.

11.88 Barium metal has a body-centered cubic lattice with all atoms at lattice points; its density is 3.51 g/cm³. From these data and the atomic weight, calculate the edge length of a unit cell.

11.89 Gold has cubic crystals whose unit cell has an edge length of 407.9 pm. The density of the metal is 19.3 g/cm³. From these data and the atomic mass, calculate the number of gold atoms in a unit cell, assuming all atoms are at lattice points. What type of cubic lattice does gold have?

11.90 Chromium forms cubic crystals whose unit cell has an edge length of 288.5 pm. The density of the metal is 7.20 g/cm³. Use these data and the atomic mass to calculate the number of atoms in a unit cell, assuming all atoms are at lattice points. What type of cubic lattice does chromium have?

11.91 Tungsten has a body-centered cubic lattice with all atoms at the lattice points. The edge length of the unit cell is 316.5 pm. The atomic mass of tungsten is 183.8 amu. Calculate its density.

11.92 Lead has a face-centered cubic lattice with all atoms at lattice points and a unit-cell edge length of 495.0 pm. Its atomic mass is 207.2 amu. What is the density of lead?

11.93 Metallic magnesium has a hexagonal close-packed structure and a density of 1.74 g/cm³. Assume magnesium atoms to be spheres of radius r. Because magnesium has a close-packed structure, 74.1% of the space is occupied by atoms. Calculate the volume of each atom; then find the atomic radius, r. The volume of a sphere is equal to $4\pi r^3/3$.

11.94 Metallic barium has a body-centered cubic structure (all atoms at the lattice points) and a density of 3.51 g/cm³. Assume barium atoms to be spheres. The spheres in a body-centered array occupy 68.0% of the total space. Find the atomic radius of barium. (See Problem 11.93.)

General Problems

11.95 If you leave your car parked outdoors in the winter, you may find frost on the windows in the morning. If you then start the car and let the heater warm the windows, after some minutes the windows will be dry. Describe all of the phase changes that have occurred.

11.96 Snow forms in the upper atmosphere in a cold air mass that is supersaturated with water vapor. When the snow later falls through a lower, warm air mass, rain forms. When this rain falls on a sunny spot, the drops evaporate. Describe all of the phase changes that have occurred.

11.97 The percent relative humidity of a sample of air is found as follows: (partial pressure of water vapor/vapor pressure of

water) × 100. A sample of air at 21°C was cooled to 15°C, where moisture began to condense as dew. What was the relative humidity of the air at 21°C?

11.98 A sample of air at 21°C has a relative humidity of 58%. At what temperature will water begin to condense as dew? (See Problem 11.97.)

11.99 The vapor pressure of benzene is 100.0 mmHg at 26.1°C and 400.0 mmHg at 60.6°C. What is the boiling point of benzene at 760.0 mmHg?

11.100 The vapor pressure of water is 17.5 mmHg at 20.0°C and 355.1 mmHg at 80.0°C. Calculate the boiling point of water at 760.0 mmHg.

11.101 Describe the behavior of carbon dioxide gas when compressed at the following temperatures:
   a. 20°C   **b.** −70°C   **c.** 40°C
The triple point of carbon dioxide is −57°C and 5.1 atm, and the critical point is 31°C and 73 atm.

11.102 Describe the behavior of iodine vapor when cooled at the following pressures:
   a. 120 atm   **b.** 1 atm   **c.** 50 mmHg
The triple point of iodine is 114°C and 90.1 mmHg, and the critical point is 512°C and 116 atm.

11.103 Describe the formation of hydrogen bonds in propanol, $CH_3CH_2CH_2OH$. Represent possible hydrogen bonding structures in propanol by using structural formulas and the conventional notation for a hydrogen bond.

11.104 Describe the formation of hydrogen bonds in hydrogen peroxide, H_2O_2. Represent possible hydrogen bonding structures in hydrogen peroxide by using structural formulas and the conventional notation for a hydrogen bond.

11.105 Ethylene glycol (CH_2OHCH_2OH) is a slightly viscous liquid that boils at 198°C. Pentane (C_5H_{12}), which has approximately the same molecular weight as ethylene glycol, is a nonviscous liquid that boils at 36°C. Explain the differences in physical characteristics of these two compounds.

11.106 Pentylamine, $CH_3CH_2CH_2CH_2CH_2NH_2$, is a liquid that boils at 104°C and has a viscosity of 10×10^{-4} kg/(m·s). Triethylamine, $(CH_3CH_2)_3N$, is a liquid that boils at 89°C and has a viscosity of about 4×10^{-4} kg/(m·s). Explain the differences in properties of these two compounds.

11.107 Consider the elements Al, Si, P, and S from the third row of the periodic table. In each case, identify the type of solid the element would form.

11.108 The elements in Problem 11.107 form the fluorides AlF_3, SiF_4, PF_3, and SF_4. In each case, identify the type of solid formed by the fluoride.

11.109 Decide which substance in each of the following pairs has the lower melting point. Explain how you made each choice.
   a. potassium chloride, KCl; or calcium oxide, CaO
   b. carbon tetrachloride,

   or hexachloroethane,

   c. zinc, Zn; or chromium, Cr
   d. acetic acid, CH_3COOH; or ethyl chloride, C_2H_5Cl

11.110 Decide which substance in each of the following pairs has the lower melting point. Explain how you made each choice.
   a. magnesium oxide, MgO; or hexane, C_6H_{14}
   b. 1-propanol,

   or ethylene glycol,

   c. silicon, Si; or sodium, Na
   d. methane, CH_4; or silane, SiH_4

11.111 Iridium metal, Ir, crystallizes in a face-centered cubic (close-packed) structure. The edge length of the unit cell was found by x-ray diffraction to be 383.9 pm. The density of iridium is 22.42 g/cm³. Calculate the mass of an iridium atom. Use Avogadro's number to calculate the atomic mass of iridium.

11.112 The edge length of the unit cell of tantalum metal, Ta, is 330.6 pm; the unit cell is body-centered cubic (one atom at each lattice point). Tantalum has a density of 16.69 g/cm³. What is the mass of a tantalum atom? Use Avogadro's number to calculate the atomic mass of tantalum.

11.113 Use your answer to Problem 11.87 to calculate the radius of the copper atom. Assume that copper atoms are spheres. Then note that the spheres on any face of a unit cell touch along the diagonal.

11.114 Rubidium metal has a body-centered cubic structure (with one atom at each lattice point). The density of the metal is 1.532 g/cm³. From this information and the atomic mass, calculate the edge length of the unit cell. Now assume that rubidium atoms are spheres. Each corner sphere of the unit cell touches the body-centered sphere. Calculate the radius of a rubidium atom.

11.115 Calculate the percent of volume that is actually occupied by spheres in a body-centered cubic lattice of identical spheres. You can do this by first relating the radius of a sphere, r, to the length of an edge of a unit cell, l. (Note that the spheres do not touch along an edge but do touch along a diagonal passing through the body-centered sphere.) Then calculate the volume of a unit cell in terms of r. The volume occupied by spheres equals the number of spheres per unit cell times the volume of a sphere ($4\pi r^3/3$).

11.116 Calculate the percent of volume that is actually occupied by spheres in a face-centered cubic lattice of identical spheres. You can do this by first relating the radius of a sphere, r, to the length of an edge of a unit cell, l. (Note that the spheres do not touch along an edge but do touch along the diagonal of a face.)

Then calculate the volume of a unit cell in terms of r. The volume occupied by spheres equals the number of spheres per unit cell times the volume of a sphere $(4\pi r^3/3)$.

11.117 For the hydrogen halides and the noble gases, we have the following boiling points:

Halogen Family, °C	Noble Gases, °C
HF, 19	Ne, −246
HCl, −115	Ar, −186
HBr, −67	Kr, −152
HI, −35	Xe, −108

Account for the following:
   a. The general trend in the boiling points of the hydrides and the noble gases.
   b. The unusual boiling point of hydrogen fluoride.
   c. The observation that the hydrogen halides have boiling points that are significantly higher than the noble gases.

11.118 For the carbon and nitrogen family hydrides, we have the following boiling points:

Carbon Family, °C	Nitrogen Family, °C
CH_4, −164	NH_3, −33
SiH_4, −112	PH_3, −88
GeH_4, −88	AsH_3, −55
SnH_4, −52	SbH_3, −17

Account for the following:
   a. The general trend in the boiling points of the binary hydrides.
   b. The unusual boiling point of ammonia.
   c. The observation that the nitrogen family hydrides have boiling points that are notably higher than those of the carbon family.

11.119 Account for the following observations:
   a. Both diamond and silicon carbide are very hard, whereas graphite is both soft and slippery.
   b. Carbon dioxide is a gas, whereas silicon dioxide is a high-melting solid.

11.120 Greater variation exists between the properties of the first and second members of a family in the periodic table than between other members. Discuss this observation for the oxygen family using the following data.

Element	Boiling Point, °C	Compound	Boiling Point, °C
O_2	−183	H_2O	100
S_8	445	H_2S	−61
Se_8	685	H_2Se	−42

11.121 Use chemical principles to discuss the following observations:
   a. CO_2 sublimes at −78°C, whereas SiO_2 boils at 2200°C.
   b. HF boils at 19°C, whereas HCl boils at −85°C.
   c. CF_4 boils at −128°C, whereas SiF_4 boils at −86°C.

11.122 a. Draw Lewis structures of each of the following compounds: LiH, NH_3, CH_4, CO_2.
   b. Which of these has the highest boiling point? Why?
   c. Which of these has the lowest boiling point? Why?
   d. Which of these has the next-to-highest boiling point? Why?

11.123 Describe the contents of a carbon dioxide fire extinguisher at 20°C. Then describe it at 35°C. Explain the difference.

11.124 Discuss why supercritical carbon dioxide is a nearly ideal solvent.

11.125 A gecko's toes have been shown to stick to walls through van der Waals forces. Van der Waals forces also exist between your finger and a wall. Why, then, doesn't your finger stick to the wall in the same way as the gecko's toes?

11.126 Although a gecko's toes stick easily to a wall, their toes lift off a surface just as easily. Explain.

11.127 Describe the structure of a nematic liquid crystal. How is it similar to a liquid? How is it similar to a crystalline solid?

11.128 What properties of nematic liquid crystals are employed in LCD displays?

11.129 Briefly describe what it is that the Bragg equation relates?

11.130 How is it possible to obtain the structure of a molecule using x-ray diffraction from the molecular crystal?

11.131 What properties of water are unusual? How does hydrogen bonding explain some of these unusual properties?

11.132 The fact that ice is less dense than the liquid is important to weather and aquatic life. Explain.

Strategy Problems

11.133 In an experiment, 20.00 L of dry nitrogen gas, N_2, at 20.0°C and 750.0 mmHg is slowly bubbled into water in a flask to determine its vapor pressure (see the figure below).

Dry N_2 →
→ Exiting gas
— Liquid water

The liquid water is weighed before and after the experiment, from which the experimenter determines that it loses 353.6 mg in mass. Answer the following questions.
   a. How many moles of nitrogen were bubbled into the water?
   b. The liquid water diminished by how many moles? What happened to the liquid?
   c. How many moles of gas exit the flask during the experiment? What is the partial pressure of nitrogen gas exiting? The total gas pressure is 750.0 mmHg.
   d. From these data, calculate the vapor pressure of water at 20°C. Does this agree with what you expect?

11.134 On a particular summer day, the temperature is 30.0°C and the relative humidity is 80.0% (which means that the partial pressure of water vapor in the ambient air is 80.0% of the equilibrium vapor pressure of water). A sample of this air is placed in a 1.00-L flask, which is then closed and cooled to 5.0°C. What is the mass (in grams) of water that still exists as vapor in the flask? How much liquid water (in grams) condenses out?

11.135 Look at the phase diagram for sulfur in Figure 11.12, *bottom*. What states of sulfur would you expect to see at each of the triple points? What solid phase would you expect to freeze out if you cooled liquid sulfur? Is this the phase that you usually see at room temperature? Explain your answers.

11.136 You may have seen the statement made that the liquid state is the stable state of water below 100°C (but above 0°C), whereas the vapor state is the stable state above 100°C. Yet you also know that a pan of water set out on a table at 20°C will probably evaporate completely in a few days, in which case, liquid water has changed to the vapor state. Explain what is happening here. What is wrong with the simple statement given at the beginning of this problem? Give a better statement.

11.137 Carbon dioxide is often sold in steel cylinders. Use the data given in Figure 11.12, *top,* to answer the following questions.

   a. Describe what you would expect to see in the cylinder if it were transparent and at room temperature. Explain.
   b. Suppose you have attached a pressure gauge to the cylinder to register the pressure within the cylinder. How would you expect the gauge to behave as you continue to use CO_2 from the cylinder until you can no longer obtain any CO_2 gas from it?

11.138 Consider the following two compounds:

   $CH_3CH_2CH_2CH_2CH_2OH$ 1-pentanol

   $CH_3CH_2CH_2CH_2CH_2CH_3$ hexane

   a. What are the different types of intermolecular forces that exist in each compound?
   b. One of these compounds has a normal boiling point of 69°C, and the other has a normal boiling point of 138°C. What is the normal boiling point of hexane? Explain.
   c. One of these compounds has a viscosity of 0.313 g/(cm·s), and the other has a viscosity of 2.987 g/(cm·s). Assign viscosities to 1-pentanol and to hexane.
   d. Consider the compound $CH_3CH_2CH_2CH_2CH_2Cl$. Where do you think the boiling point of this compound might lie: above both 1-pentanol and hexane, intermediate between these two compounds, or below both of these two compounds?

11.139 Consider the following three compounds:

$$CH_3CHO, CH_3CH_2CH_3, CH_3CH_2OH$$

   a. Describe the types of intermolecular forces that you expect to see in each. Explain how you arrived at these types.
   b. The heats of vaporization of these compounds are (in no particular order): 25.8 kJ/mol, 38.6 kJ/mol, and 19.0 kJ/mol. What is the heat of vaporization of CH_3CHO?
   c. If the normal boiling point of CH_3CHO is 21°C, what is its vapor pressure at 15°C?

11.140 Here is some information about a compound. It has a melting point of 33°C, a normal boiling point of 81°C, a heat of fusion of 11 kJ/mol, and a heat of vaporization of 32 kJ/mol. What is its vapor pressure at 15°C?

11.141 Rhenium forms a series of solid oxides: Re_2O_7 (yellow), ReO_3 (red), Re_2O_5 (blue), and ReO_2 (brown). One of them has a crystal structure with the following unit cell:

   a. How many rhenium atoms (gray spheres) are there in a unit cell? How many oxygen atoms are there in the unit cell?
   b. What is the color of the compound? Explain.

11.142 Shown below is the cubic unit cell of an ionic compound. Answer the questions by referring to this structure. Be careful to note that some atoms are hidden by those in front.

   a. One of the spheres (red or green) represents a monatomic, metallic ion. The other color sphere represents a monatomic, nonmetal ion. Which spheres probably represent the metal ion? Explain.
   b. How many red spheres are there in the unit cell? How many green ones?
   c. From the information you have, deduce the general formula of the compound, using M for the metallic element and X for the nonmetallic element. What are the formulas of the ions?
   d. Give an example of a compound that might have this structure. Explain why you think this compound might have this structure. Which ion of this compound would be represented by the red spheres?

Cumulative-Skills Problems

11.143 The vapor pressure of a volatile liquid can be determined by slowly bubbling a known volume of gas through the liquid at a given temperature and pressure. In an experiment, a 5.40-L sample of nitrogen gas, N_2, at 20.0°C and 745 mmHg is bubbled through liquid isopropyl alcohol, C_3H_8O, at 20.0°C. Nitrogen containing the vapor of C_3H_8O at its vapor pressure leaves the vessel at 20.0°C and 745 mmHg. It is found that 0.6149 g C_3H_8O has evaporated. How many moles of N_2 are in the gas leaving the liquid? How many moles of alcohol are in this gaseous mixture? What is the mole fraction of alcohol vapor in the gaseous mixture? What is the partial pressure of the alcohol in the gaseous mixture? What is the vapor pressure of C_3H_8O at 20.0°C?

11.144 In an experiment, a sample of 6.35 L of nitrogen at 25.0°C and 768 mmHg is bubbled through liquid acetone, C_3H_6O. The gas plus vapor at its equilibrium partial pressure leaves the liquid at the same temperature and pressure. If 6.550 g of acetone has evaporated, what is the vapor pressure of acetone at 25.0°C? See Problem 11.143.

11.145 How much heat is needed to vaporize 10.0 mL of liquid hydrogen cyanide, HCN, at 25.0°C? The density of the liquid is 0.687 g/mL. Use standard heats of formation, which are given in Appendix C.

11.146 How much heat is needed to vaporize 20.0 mL of liquid methanol, CH_3OH, at 25.0°C? The density of the liquid is 0.787 g/mL. Use standard heats of formation, which are given in Appendix C.

11.147 How much heat must be added to 12.5 g of solid white phosphorus, P_4, at 25.0°C to give the liquid at its melting point, 44.1°C? The heat capacity of solid white phosphorus is 95.4 J/(K·mol); its heat of fusion is 2.63 kJ/mol.

11.148 How much heat must be added to 25.0 g of solid sodium, Na, at 25.0°C to give the liquid at its melting point, 97.8°C? The heat capacity of solid sodium is 28.2 J/(K·mol), and its heat of fusion is 2.60 kJ/mol.

11.149 Acetic acid, CH_3COOH, forms stable pairs of molecules held together by two hydrogen bonds.

Such molecules—themselves formed by the association of two simpler molecules—are called dimers. The vapor over liquid acetic acid consists of a mixture of monomers (single acetic acid molecules) and dimers. At 100.6°C the total pressure of vapor over liquid acetic acid is 436 mmHg. If the vapor consists of 0.630 mole fraction of the dimer, what are the masses of monomer and dimer in 1.000 L of the vapor? What is the density of the vapor?

11.150 The total pressure of vapor over liquid acetic acid at 71.3°C is 146 mmHg. If the density of the vapor is 0.702 g/L, what is the mole fraction of dimer in the vapor? See Problem 11.149.

12

Solutions

Sugarcane produces a juice that is a solution containing sucrose (sugar). Soft drinks are flavored solutions of dissolved sucrose.

Contents and Concepts

Here you will have the opportunity to develop a more thorough understanding of the solution process and of what constitutes a solution.

We will explore how properties of solutions are affected by changes in concentration. You will also be introduced to several ways of expressing concentration.

When relatively large particles of a substance disperse throughout another substance, the result is called a colloid.

There are various practical reasons for preparing solutions. For instance, most chemical reactions are run in solution. Also, solutions have particular properties that are useful. When gold is used for jewelry, it is mixed, or alloyed, with a small amount of silver. Gold–silver alloys are not only harder than pure gold, but they also melt at lower temperatures and are therefore easier to cast.

Solubility, the amount of one substance that dissolves in another, varies with temperature and, in some cases, with pressure. The variation of solubility with pressure can be a useful property. Acetylene gas, C_2H_2, for example, is used as a fuel in welding torches. It can be transported safely under pressure in cylinders as a solution in acetone, CH_3COCH_3. Acetone is a liquid, and at 1 atm pressure 1 L of the liquid dissolves 27 g of acetylene. But at 12 atm, the pressure in a full cylinder, the same quantity of acetone dissolves 320 g of acetylene, so more can be transported. When the valve on a cylinder is opened, reducing the pressure, acetylene gas comes out of solution.

Another useful property of solutions is their lower melting, or freezing, points compared with those of the major component. We have already mentioned the lowering of the melting point of gold when a small amount of silver is added. The use of ethylene glycol, CH_2OHCH_2OH, as an automobile antifreeze depends on the same property. Water containing ethylene glycol freezes at temperatures below the freezing point of pure water.

What determines how much the freezing point of a solution is lowered? How does the solubility of a substance change when conditions such as pressure and temperature change? These are some of the questions we will address in this chapter.

■ **See page 515 for the Media Summary.**

Solution Formation

When sodium chloride dissolves in water, the resulting uniform dispersion of ions in water is called a solution. In general, a *solution* is a homogeneous mixture of two or more substances, consisting of ions or molecules. A *colloid* is similar in that it appears to be homogeneous like a solution. In fact, however, it consists of comparatively large particles of one substance dispersed throughout another substance or solution.

From the examples of solutions mentioned in the chapter opening, you see that they may be quite varied in their characteristics. To begin our discussion, let us look at the different types of solutions we might encounter. We will discuss colloids at the end of the chapter.

12.1 | Types of Solutions

Solutions may exist in any of the three states of matter; that is, they may be gases, liquids, or solids. Some examples are listed in Table 12.1. The terms *solute* and *solvent* refer to the components of a solution. The **solute,** *in the case of a solution of a gas or solid dissolved in a liquid, is the gas or solid; in other cases, the solute is the component in smaller amount.* The **solvent,** *in a solution of a gas or solid dissolved in a liquid, is the liquid; in other cases, the solvent is the component in greater amount.* Thus, when sodium chloride is dissolved in water, sodium chloride is the solute and water is the solvent.

Gaseous Solutions

In general, nonreactive gases or vapors can mix in all proportions to give a gaseous mixture. *Fluids that mix with or dissolve in each other in all proportions* are said

TABLE 12.1	Examples of Solutions	
Solution	State of Matter	Description
Air	Gas	Homogeneous mixture of gases (O_2, N_2, others)
Soda water	Liquid	Gas (CO_2) dissolved in a liquid (H_2O)
Ethanol in water	Liquid	Liquid solution of two completely miscible liquids
Brine	Liquid	Solid (NaCl) dissolved in a liquid (H_2O)
Potassium–sodium alloy	Liquid	Solution of two solids (K + Na)
Dental-filling alloy	Solid	Solution of a liquid (Hg) in a solid (Ag plus other metals)
Gold–silver alloy	Solid	Solution of two solids (Au + Ag)

to be **miscible fluids.** Gases are thus miscible. (If two fluids do not mix but, rather, form two layers, they are said to be *immiscible*.) Air, which is a mixture of oxygen, nitrogen, and smaller amounts of other gases, is an example of a gaseous solution.

Liquid Solutions

Sodium metal melts at 98°C and potassium metal melts at 63°C. When the two metals are mixed to give a solution that is 20% sodium, for example, the melting point is lowered to −10°C. This is another example of the lowering of the freezing, or melting, point of solutions, which we will discuss later in the chapter. Potassium–sodium alloy is used as a heat-transfer medium in nuclear reactors.

Most liquid solutions are obtained by dissolving a gas, liquid, or solid in some liquid. Soda water, for example, consists of a solution of carbon dioxide gas in water. Acetone, C_3H_6O, in water is an example of a liquid–liquid solution. (Immiscible and miscible liquids are shown in Figure 12.1.) Brine is water with sodium chloride (a solid) dissolved in it. Seawater contains both dissolved gases (from air) and solids (mostly sodium chloride).

It is also possible to make a liquid solution by mixing two solids together. Consider a potassium–sodium alloy. Both potassium and sodium are solid at room temperature, but a liquid solution results when the mixture contains 10% to 50% sodium. <

Solid Solutions

Solid solutions are also possible. In the chapter opening, we mentioned gold–silver alloys. Dental-filling alloy is a solution of mercury (a liquid) in silver (a solid), with small amounts of other metals.

FIGURE 12.1 ▼

Immiscible and miscible liquids
Left: Acetone and water are miscible liquids; that is, the two substances dissolve in each other in all proportions. *Right:* Water and methylene chloride are immiscible and form two layers.

Exercise 12.1 Give an example of a solid solution prepared from a liquid and a solid.

■ See Problems 12.37 and 12.38.

Concept Check 12.1

Identify the solute(s) and solvent(s) in the following solutions.

a. 80 g of Cr and 5 g of Mo
b. 5 g of $MgCl_2$ dissolved in 1000 g of H_2O
c. 39% N_2, 41% Ar, and the rest O_2

12.2 | Solubility and the Solution Process

The amount of substance that will dissolve in a solvent depends on both the substance and the solvent. We describe the amount that dissolves in terms of solubility.

Solubility; Saturated Solutions

To understand the concept of solubility, consider the process of dissolving sodium chloride in water. Sodium chloride is an ionic substance, and it dissolves in water as Na^+ and Cl^- ions. If you could view the dissolving of sodium chloride at the level of ions, you would see a dynamic process. Suppose you stir 40.0 g of sodium chloride crystals into 100 mL of water at 20°C. Sodium ions and chloride ions leave the surface of the crystals and enter the solution. The ions move about at random in the solution and may by chance collide with a crystal and stick, thus returning to the crystalline state. As the sodium chloride continues to dissolve, more ions enter the solution, and the rate at which they return to the crystalline state increases (the more ions in solution, the more likely ions are to collide with the crystals and stick). Eventually, a *dynamic equilibrium* is reached in which the rate at which ions leave the crystals equals the rate at which ions return to the crystals (see Figure 12.2). You write the dynamic equilibrium this way:

$$NaCl(s) \overset{H_2O}{\rightleftharpoons} Na^+(aq) + Cl^-(aq)$$

At equilibrium, no more sodium chloride appears to dissolve; 36.0 g has gone into solution, leaving 4.0 g of crystals at the bottom of the vessel. You have a **saturated solution**—that is, *a solution that is in equilibrium with respect to a given dissolved substance.* The solution is saturated with respect to NaCl, and no more NaCl can dissolve. The **solubility** of sodium chloride in water *(the amount that dissolves in a given quantity of water at a given temperature to give a saturated solution)* is 36.0 g/100 mL at 20°C. Note that if you had mixed 30.0 g of sodium chloride with 100 mL of water, all of the crystals would have dissolved. You would have an **unsaturated solution,** *a solution not in equilibrium with respect to a given dissolved substance and in which more of the substance can dissolve.* (Saturated and unsaturated solutions are compared in Figure 12.3.)

Sometimes it is possible to obtain a **supersaturated solution,** *a solution that contains more dissolved substance than a saturated solution does.* For example, the solubility of sodium thiosulfate, $Na_2S_2O_3$, in water at 100°C is 231 g/100 mL. But at room temperature, the solubility is much less—about 50 g/100 mL. Suppose you prepare a solution saturated with sodium thiosulfate at 100°C. You might expect that as

FIGURE 12.2 ▲

Solubility equilibrium
The solid crystalline phase is in dynamic equilibrium with species (ions or molecules) in a saturated solution. The rate at which species leave the crystals equals the rate at which species return to the crystals.

FIGURE 12.3 ▶

Comparison of unsaturated and saturated solutions

Top: The 30.0-g pile of NaCl will dissolve completely in 100 mL of water at 20°C, giving an unsaturated solution. *Bottom:* When 40.0 g NaCl is stirred into 100 mL H₂O, 36.0 g dissolves at 20°C, leaving 4.0 g of the crystalline solid on the bottom of the beaker. This solution is saturated.

30.0 g NaCl   100 mL H₂O

Unsaturated solution containing 100 mL H₂O and 30.0 g NaCl

40.0 g NaCl   100 mL H₂O

Saturated solution containing 100 mL H₂O and 36.0 g NaCl

The additional 4.0 g NaCl remains undissolved

the water solution was cooled, sodium thiosulfate would crystallize out. In fact, if the solution is slowly cooled to room temperature, this does not occur. Instead the result is a solution in which 231 g of sodium thiosulfate is dissolved in 100 mL of cold water, compared with the 50 g you would normally expect to find dissolved.

Supersaturated solutions are not in equilibrium with the solid substance. If a small crystal of sodium thiosulfate is added to a supersaturated solution, the excess immediately crystallizes out. Crystallization from a supersaturated solution is usually quite fast and dramatic (see Figure 12.4).

Factors in Explaining Solubility

FIGURE 12.4 ▼

Crystallization from a supersaturated solution of sodium acetate

Left: Crystallization begins to occur when a small crystal of sodium acetate is added. *Center, right:* Within seconds, crystal growth spreads from the original crystal throughout the solution.

The solubilities of substances in one another vary widely. You might find a substance miscible in one solvent but nearly insoluble in another. As a general rule, "like dissolves like." That is, similar substances dissolve one another. Oil is miscible in gasoline. Both are mixtures of hydrocarbon substances (compounds of hydrogen and carbon only). On the other hand, oil does not mix with water. Water is a polar substance, whereas hydrocarbons are not. Why do similar substances dissolve

FIGURE 12.5 ▶

The mixing of gas molecules
(A) A vessel is divided by a removable partition with oxygen gas on the left and nitrogen gas on the right. *(B)* When the partition is removed, molecules of the two gases begin to mix through their random motions.

in one another to greater extents than do dissimilar substances? What factors are involved in solubility?

The solubility of one substance in another can be explained in terms of two factors. One is the natural tendency of substances to mix. This is sometimes also referred to as the natural tendency toward disorder. Figure 12.5*A* shows a vessel divided into two parts, with oxygen gas on the left and nitrogen gas on the right. If you remove the partition, the molecules of the two gases begin to mix. Ultimately, the molecules become thoroughly mixed through their random motions (Figure 12.5*B*). You might expect a similar mixing of molecules or ions in other types of solutions.

If the process of dissolving one substance in another involved nothing more than simple mixing, you would expect substances to be completely soluble in one another; that is, you would expect substances to be miscible. You know that this is only sometimes the case. Usually, substances have limited solubility in one another. A factor that can limit solubility is the relative forces of attraction between species (molecules or ions). Suppose there are strong attractions between solute species and strong attractions between solvent species, but weak attractions between solute and solvent species. In that case, the strongest attractions are maintained so long as the solute and solvent species do not mix. The lowest energy of the solute–solvent system is obtained then also.

The solubility of a solute in a solvent (that is, the extent of the mixing of the solute and solvent species) depends on a balance between the natural tendency for the solute and solvent species to mix and the tendency for a system to have the lowest energy possible.

Molecular Solutions

The simplest example of a molecular solution is one gas dissolved in another gas. Air, essentially a solution of oxygen and nitrogen, is an example. The intermolecular forces in gases are weak. The only solubility factor of importance is the tendency for molecules to mix (this will be discussed in Chapter 18). Gases are therefore miscible.

Substances may be miscible even when the intermolecular forces are not negligible. Consider the solution of the two similar liquid hydrocarbons heptane, C_7H_{16}, and octane, C_8H_{18}, which are components of gasoline. The intermolecular attractions are due to London forces, and those between heptane and octane molecules are nearly equal to those between octane and octane molecules and heptane and heptane molecules. The different intermolecular attractions are about the same strength, so there are no favored attractions. Octane and heptane molecules tend to move freely through one another. Therefore, the tendency of molecules to mix results in miscibility of the substances.

As a counterexample, consider the mixing of octane with water. There are strong hydrogen bonding forces between water molecules. For octane to mix with water, hydrogen bonds must be broken and replaced by much weaker London forces between water and octane. In this case, the maximum forces of attraction among molecules (and therefore the lower energy) result if the octane and water remain unmixed. Therefore, octane and water are nearly immiscible. (See Figure 12.6.)

= A molecule

= B molecule

FIGURE 12.6 ▲

The immiscibility of liquids
Suppose an A molecule moves from liquid A into liquid B. If the intermolecular attraction between two A molecules is much stronger than the intermolecular attraction between an A molecule and a B molecule, the net force of attraction tends to pull the A molecule back into liquid A. Thus, liquid A will be immiscible with liquid B.

TABLE 12.2	Solubilities of Alcohols in Water	
Name	Formula	Solubility in H$_2$O (g/100 g H$_2$O at 20°C)
Methanol	CH$_3$OH	Miscible
Ethanol	CH$_3$CH$_2$OH	Miscible
1-Propanol	CH$_3$CH$_2$CH$_2$OH	Miscible
1-Butanol	CH$_3$CH$_2$CH$_2$CH$_2$OH	7.9
1-Pentanol	CH$_3$CH$_2$CH$_2$CH$_2$CH$_2$OH	2.7
1-Hexanol	CH$_3$CH$_2$CH$_2$CH$_2$CH$_2$CH$_2$OH	0.6

$$CH_3 - CH_2 - \overset{\overset{\displaystyle H}{\displaystyle |}}{O} \cdots H - O - CH_2 - CH_3$$

FIGURE 12.7 ▲

Hydrogen bonding between water and ethanol molecules

The dots depict the hydrogen bonding between the oxygen and hydrogen atoms on adjacent molecules.

The statement "like dissolves like" succinctly expresses these observations. That is, substances with similar intermolecular attractions are usually soluble in one another. The two similar hydrocarbons heptane and octane are completely miscible, whereas octane and water (with dissimilar intermolecular attractions) are immiscible.

For the series of alcohols (organic, or carbon-containing, compounds with an —OH group) listed in Table 12.2, the solubility in water decreases from miscible to slightly soluble. Water and alcohols are alike in having —OH groups through which strong hydrogen bonding attractions arise (see Figure 12.7).

The attraction between a methanol molecule, CH$_3$OH, and a water molecule is nearly as strong as that between two methanol molecules or between two water molecules. Methanol and water molecules tend to mix freely. Methanol and water are miscible, as are ethanol and water and 1-propanol and water. However, as the hydrocarbon end, R—, of the alcohol becomes the more prominent portion of the molecule, the alcohol becomes less like water. Now the forces of attraction between alcohol and water molecules are weaker than those between two alcohol molecules or between two water molecules. Therefore, the solubilities of alcohols decrease with increasing length of R.

Exercise 12.2 Which of the following compounds is likely to be more soluble in water: C$_4$H$_9$OH or C$_4$H$_9$SH? Explain.

■ See Problems 12.39, 12.40, 12.41, and 12.42.

Ionic Solutions

Ionic substances differ markedly in their solubilities in water. For example, sodium chloride, NaCl, has a solubility of 36 g per 100 mL of water at room temperature, whereas calcium phosphate, Ca$_3$(PO$_4$)$_2$, has a solubility of only 0.002 g per 100 mL of water. In most cases, these differences in solubility can be explained in terms of the different energies of attraction between ions in the crystal and between ions and water.

The energy of attraction between an ion and a water molecule is due to an *ion–dipole force*. Water molecules are polar, so they tend to orient with respect to nearby ions. In the case of a positive ion (Li$^+$, for example), water molecules orient with their oxygen atoms (the negative ends of the molecular dipoles) toward the

FIGURE 12.8 ▲

Attraction of water molecules to ions because of the ion–dipole force
The O end of H_2O orients toward the cation, whereas an H atom of H_2O orients toward the anion.

FIGURE 12.9 ▲

The dissolving of lithium fluoride in water
Ions on the surface of the crystal can hydrate—that is, associate with water molecules; ions at the corners are especially easy to remove because they are held by fewer lattice forces. Ions are completely hydrated in the aqueous phase and move off into the body of the liquid.

ion. In the case of a negative ion (for instance, F^-), water molecules orient with their hydrogen atoms (the positive ends of the molecular dipoles) toward the ion (see Figure 12.8).

The attraction of ions for water molecules is called **hydration.** Hydration of ions favors the dissolving of an ionic solid in water. Figure 12.9 illustrates the hydration of ions in the dissolving of a lithium fluoride crystal. Ions on the surface become hydrated and then move into the body of the solution as hydrated ions.

If the hydration of ions were the only factor in the solution process, you would expect all ionic solids to be soluble in water. The ions in a crystal, however, are very strongly attracted to one another. Therefore, the solubility of an ionic solid depends not only on the energy of hydration of ions (energy associated with the attraction between ions and water molecules) but also on *lattice energy,* the energy holding ions together in the crystal lattice. Lattice energy works against the solution process, so an ionic solid with relatively large lattice energy is usually insoluble (Figure 12.10). <

Hydration of ions also occurs in crystalline solids. For example, copper(II) sulfate pentahydrate, $CuSO_4 \cdot 5H_2O$, contains five water molecules for each $CuSO_4$ formula unit in the crystal. Substances like this, which are called hydrates, were discussed in Chapter 2.

According to Coulomb's law, the energy of attraction of two ions is proportional to the product of the ion charges and inversely proportional to the distance between the centers of the ions.

Lattice energies depend on the charges on the ions (as well as on the distance between the centers of neighboring positive and negative ions). The greater the magnitude of ion charge, the greater is the lattice energy. < For this reason, you might expect substances with singly charged ions to be comparatively soluble and those with multiply charged ions to be less soluble. This is borne out by the fact that compounds of the alkali metal ions (such as Na^+ and K^+) and ammonium ions (NH_4^+) are generally soluble, whereas those of phosphate ions (PO_4^{3-}), for example, are generally insoluble.

Lattice energy is also inversely proportional to the distance between neighboring ions, and this distance depends on the sum of the radii of the ions. For example, the lattice energy of magnesium hydroxide, $Mg(OH)_2$, is inversely proportional to the sum of the radii of Mg^{2+} and OH^-. In the series of alkaline earth hydroxides—$Mg(OH)_2$, $Ca(OH)_2$, $Sr(OH)_2$, $Ba(OH)_2$—the lattice energy decreases as the radius of the alkaline earth ion increases (from Mg^{2+} to Ba^{2+}). If the lattice energy alone determines the trend in solubilities, you should expect the solubility to increase from magnesium hydroxide to barium hydroxide. In fact, this is what you find. Magnesium hydroxide is insoluble in water, and barium hydroxide is soluble. But this is not the whole story. The energy of hydration also depends on ionic radius. A small ion has a concentrated electric charge and a strong electric field that attracts water molecules. Therefore, the energy of hydration is greatest for a small ion such as Mg^{2+} and least for a large ion such as Ba^{2+}. If the energy of hydration of ions alone determined the trend in solubilities, you would expect the solubilities to decrease from magnesium hydroxide to barium hydroxide, rather than to increase. (We should also add that the energy of hydration increases with the charge on the ion; energy of hydration is greater for Mg^{2+} than for Na^+. Magnesium ion has a larger charge, and also is a smaller ion than Na^+.)

The explanation for the observed solubility trend in the alkaline earth hydroxides is that the lattice energy decreases more rapidly in the series $Mg(OH)_2$, $Ca(OH)_2$, $Sr(OH)_2$, and $Ba(OH)_2$ than does the energy of hydration in the series of ions Mg^{2+}, Ca^{2+}, Sr^{2+}, and Ba^{2+}. For this reason, the lattice-energy factor dominates this solubility trend.

Hydration energy

Lattice energy

FIGURE 12.10 ▲

The effects of lattice energy and hydration energy on the solution process of ionic solids
Hydration energy pulls ions apart, whereas the lattice energy keeps the ions together. If the lattice energy is large relative to the hydration energy, the ions are likely to remain together, resulting in an insoluble compound.

A Chemist Looks at . . .

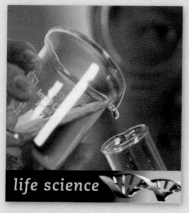

life science

Hemoglobin Solubility and Sickle-Cell Anemia

Sickle-cell anemia was the first inherited disease shown to have a specific molecular basis. In people with the disease, the red blood cells tend to become elongated (sickle-shaped) when the concentration of oxygen (O_2) is low, as it is, for example, in the venous blood supply (see Figure 12.11). Once the red blood cells have sickled, they can no longer function in their normal capacity as oxygen carriers, and they often break apart. Moreover, the sickled cells clog capillaries, interfering with the blood supply to vital organs.

In 1949 Linus Pauling showed that people with sickle-cell anemia have abnormal hemoglobin. Hemoglobin is the substance in red blood cells that carries oxygen. Hemoglobin is normally present in solution within the red blood cells. But in people with sickle-cell anemia, the unoxygenated hemoglobin readily comes out of solution. It produces a fibrous precipitate that deforms the cell, giving it the characteristic sickle shape.

Hemoglobins are large molecules (molecular weight about 64,000 amu) consisting of four protein chains, two of one kind (α chains) and two of another kind (β chains). Normal and sickle-cell hemoglobins are almost exactly alike, except that each β chain of the hemoglobin responsible for sickle-cell anemia differs from normal hemoglobin in one place. In this place, the normal hemoglobin has the group

$$
\begin{array}{c}
| \\
CH_2 \\
| \\
CH_2 \\
| \\
HO-C=O
\end{array}
$$

which helps confer water solubility on the molecule because of the polarity of the group and its ability to form hydrogen bonds. The abnormal hemoglobin has the following hydrocarbon group:

$$
\begin{array}{c}
| \\
H-C-CH_3 \\
| \\
CH_3
\end{array}
$$

Hydrocarbon groups are nonpolar. This small change makes the molecule less water-soluble.

FIGURE 12.11 ▲

Red blood cells

Scanning electron micrographs of normal (*left*) and sickled (*right*) red blood cells. The color is added by computer.

■ See Problems 12.111 and 12.112.

You see the opposite solubility trend when the energy of hydration decreases more rapidly so that it dominates the trend. Consider the alkaline earth sulfates. Here the lattice energy depends on the sum of the radius of the cation and the radius of the sulfate ion. Because the sulfate ion, SO_4^{2-}, is much larger than the hydroxide ion, OH^-, the percent change in lattice energy in going through the series of sulfates from $MgSO_4$ to $BaSO_4$ is smaller than in the hydroxides. The lattice energy changes less, and the energy of hydration of the cation decreases by a greater amount. Now the energy of hydration dominates the solubility trend, and the solubility decreases from magnesium sulfate to barium sulfate. Magnesium sulfate is soluble in water, and barium sulfate is insoluble.

Exercise 12.3 Which ion has the larger hydration energy, Na^+ or K^+?

■ See Problems 12.43 and 12.44.

Concept Check 12.2

The hypothetical ionic compound AB_2 is very soluble in water. Another hypothetical ionic compound, CB_2, is only slightly soluble in water. The lattice energies for these compounds are about the same. Provide an explanation for the solubility difference between these compounds.

12.3 | Effects of Temperature and Pressure on Solubility

In general, the solubility of a substance depends on temperature. For example, the solubility of ammonium nitrate in 100 mL of water is 118 g at 0°C and 811 g at 100°C. Pressure may also have an effect on solubility, as you will see.

Temperature Change

Most gases become less soluble in water at higher temperatures. The first bubbles that appear when tap water is heated are bubbles of air released as the increasing temperature reduces the solubility of air in water. In contrast, most ionic solids become more soluble in water with rising temperature.

The variations of the solubilities of the salts KNO_3, $CuSO_4$, $NaCl$, and $Ce_2(SeO_4)_3$ are shown in Figure 12.12. Three of the salts show the usual behavior; their solubilities

FIGURE 12.12

Solubility of some ionic salts at different temperatures
The solubilities of the salts $NaCl$, KNO_3, and $CuSO_4$ rise with increasing temperature, as is the case with most ionic solids. The solubility of $Ce_2(SeO_4)_3$, however, falls with increasing temperature.

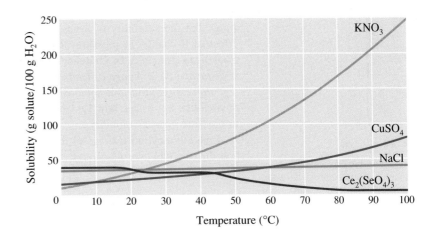

FIGURE 12.13 ▶

Instant hot and cold compress packs
The inner bag of the instant hot compress contains calcium chloride, $CaCl_2$. When the inner bag is broken, the $CaCl_2$ dissolves exothermically in water (heat is released). The instant cold compress contains an inner bag of ammonium nitrate, NH_4NO_3, which when broken apart allows the NH_4NO_3 to dissolve in the water in the outer bag. The solution process is endothermic (heat is absorbed), so the bag feels cold.

increase with rising temperature. For example, potassium nitrate, KNO_3, changes solubility dramatically from 14 g/100 g H_2O at 0°C to 245 g/100 g H_2O at 100°C. Copper(II) sulfate, $CuSO_4$, shows a moderate increase in solubility over this temperature interval. Sodium chloride, $NaCl$, increases only slightly in solubility with temperature.

A number of ionic compounds decrease in solubility with increasing temperature. Calcium sulfate, $CaSO_4$, and calcium hydroxide, $Ca(OH)_2$, are common examples. They are slightly soluble compounds that become even less soluble at higher temperatures. Cerium selenate, $Ce_2(SeO_4)_3$, shown in Figure 12.12, is very soluble at 0°C but much less soluble at 100°C.

Heat can be released or absorbed when ionic substances are dissolved in water. In some cases, this *heat of solution* is quite noticeable. When sodium hydroxide is dissolved in water, the solution becomes hot (the solution process is exothermic). On the other hand, when ammonium nitrate is dissolved in water, the solution becomes very cold (the solution process is endothermic). This cooling effect from the dissolving of ammonium nitrate in water is exploited in instant cold packs used in hospitals and elsewhere. An instant cold pack consists of a bag of NH_4NO_3 crystals inside a bag of water (Figure 12.13). When the inner bag is broken, NH_4NO_3 dissolves in the water. Heat is absorbed, so the bag feels cold. Hot packs, by contrast, containing either $CaCl_2$ or $MgSO_4$, dissolve in water with the evolution of heat.

Pressure Change

In general, pressure change has little effect on the solubility of a liquid or solid in water, but the solubility of a gas is very much affected by pressure. The qualitative effect of a change in pressure on the solubility of a gas can be predicted from Le Châtelier's principle. **Le Châtelier's principle** *states that when a system in equilibrium is disturbed by a change of temperature, pressure, or concentration variable, the system shifts in equilibrium composition in a way that tends to counteract this change of variable.* Let us see how Le Châtelier's principle can predict the effect of a change in pressure on gas solubility.

Imagine a cylindrical vessel that is fitted with a movable piston and contains carbon dioxide gas over its saturated water solution (Figure 12.14). The equilibrium is

$$CO_2(g) \rightleftharpoons CO_2(aq)$$

Suppose you increase the partial pressure of CO_2 gas by pushing the piston down. This change of partial pressure, according to Le Châtelier's principle, shifts the equilibrium

FIGURE 12.14 ▲

Effect of pressure on gas solubility
When the piston is pushed down, increasing the partial pressure of carbon dioxide, more gas dissolves (which tends to reduce the carbon dioxide partial pressure).

composition in a way that tends to counteract the pressure increase. From the preceding equation, you see that the partial pressure of CO_2 gas decreases if more CO_2 dissolves.

$$CO_2(g) \longrightarrow CO_2(aq)$$

The system comes to a new equilibrium, in which more CO_2 has dissolved. So you can predict that carbon dioxide is more soluble at higher pressures. Conversely, when the partial pressure of carbon dioxide gas is reduced, its solubility is decreased. A bottle of carbonated beverage fizzes when the cap is removed: as the partial pressure of carbon dioxide is reduced, gas comes out of solution (Figure 12.15). The argument given here for carbon dioxide holds for any gas:

> All gases become more soluble in a liquid at a given temperature when the partial pressure of the gas over the solution is increased.

Henry's Law: Relating Pressure to the Solubility of a Gas in a Liquid

The effect of pressure on the solubility of a gas in a liquid can be predicted quantitatively. According to **Henry's law,** *the solubility of a gas is directly proportional to the partial pressure of the gas above the solution.* Expressed mathematically, the law is

$$S = k_H P$$

where S is the solubility of the gas (expressed as mass of solute per unit volume of solvent), k_H is Henry's law constant for the gas for a particular liquid at a given temperature, and P is the partial pressure of the gas. The next example shows how this formula is used.

FIGURE 12.15 ▲

Sudden release of pressure from a carbonated beverage
A carbonated beverage is produced by dissolving carbon dioxide in beverage solution under pressure. More carbon dioxide dissolves at the higher pressure than otherwise. When this pressure is suddenly released, carbon dioxide is less soluble, and the excess bubbles from the solution.

| **Example 12.1** | Applying Henry's Law |

In the chapter opening, we noted that 27 g of acetylene, C_2H_2, dissolves in 1 L of acetone at 1.0 atm pressure. If the partial pressure of acetylene is increased to 12 atm, what is its solubility in acetone?

Problem Strategy Because we are trying to determine the solubility of a gas in a liquid, this problem is an application of the Henry's law equation: $S = k_H P$. Let S_1 be the solubility of the gas at partial pressure P_1, and let S_2 be the solubility at partial pressure P_2. Then you can write Henry's law for both pressures.

$$S_1 = k_H P_1$$
$$S_2 = k_H P_2$$

Dividing the second equation by the first, you get

$$\frac{S_2}{S_1} = \frac{k_H P_2}{k_H P_1} \quad \text{or} \quad \frac{S_2}{S_1} = \frac{P_2}{P_1}$$

You can use this relation to find the solubility at one pressure given the solubility at another.

Solution At 1.0 atm partial pressure of acetylene (P_1), the solubility S_1 is 27 g C_2H_2 per liter of acetone. For a partial pressure of 12 atm (P_2),

$$\frac{S_2}{27 \text{ g } C_2H_2/\text{L acetone}} = \frac{12 \text{ atm}}{1.0 \text{ atm}}$$

Then

$$S_2 = \frac{27 \text{ g } C_2H_2}{\text{L acetone}} \times \frac{12}{1.0} = \frac{3.2 \times 10^2 \text{ g } C_2H_2}{\text{L acetone}}$$

At 12 atm partial pressure of acetylene, 1 L of acetone dissolves **3.2×10^2 g of acetylene.**

Answer Check Because the solubility of a gas is directly proportional to the pressure of the gas above the solution, check your answer to make certain that the gas at higher pressure has the greater solubility.

(continued)

(continued)

Exercise 12.4 A liter of water at 25°C dissolves 0.0404 g O$_2$ when the partial pressure of the oxygen is 1.00 atm. What is the solubility of oxygen from air, in which the partial pressure of O$_2$ is 159 mmHg?

■ See Problems 12.47 and 12.48.

Concept Check 12.3

Most fish have a very difficult time surviving at elevations much above 3500 m. How could Henry's law be used to account for this fact?

Colligative Properties

In the chapter opening, we mentioned that the addition of ethylene glycol, CH$_2$OHCH$_2$OH, to water lowers the freezing point of water below 0°C. For example, if 0.010 mol of ethylene glycol is added to 1 kg of water, the freezing point is lowered to −0.019°C. The magnitude of freezing-point lowering is directly proportional to the number of ethylene glycol molecules added to a quantity of water. Thus, if you add 0.020 (= 0.010 × 2) mol of ethylene glycol to 1 kg of water, the freezing point is lowered to −0.038°C (= −0.019°C × 2). The same lowering is observed with the addition of other nonelectrolyte substances. For example, an aqueous solution of 0.020 mol of urea, (NH$_2$)$_2$CO, in 1 kg of water also freezes at −0.038°C.

Freezing-point lowering is a colligative property. **Colligative properties** of solutions are *properties that depend on the concentration of solute molecules or ions in solution but not on the chemical identity of the solute* (whether it is ethylene glycol or urea, for instance). In the next sections, we will discuss several colligative properties, which are expressed quantitatively in terms of various concentration units. We will first look into ways of expressing the concentration of a solution.

12.4 | Ways of Expressing Concentration

The *concentration* of a solute is the amount of solute dissolved in a given quantity of solvent or solution. The quantity of solvent or solution can be expressed in terms of volume or in terms of mass or molar amount. Thus, there are several ways of expressing the concentration of a solution.

Recall that the *molarity* of a solution is the moles of solute in a liter of solution. <

Molarity was discussed in Section 4.7.

$$\text{Molarity} = \frac{\text{moles of solute}}{\text{liters of solution}}$$

For example, 0.20 mol of ethylene glycol dissolved in enough water to give 2.0 L of solution has a molarity of

$$\frac{0.20 \text{ mol ethylene glycol}}{2.0 \text{ L solution}} = 0.10 \, M \text{ ethylene glycol}$$

The solution is 0.10 molar (denoted *M*). This unit is especially useful when you wish to dispense a given amount of solute, because the unit directly relates the amount of solute to the volume of solution.

Some other concentration units are defined in terms of the mass or molar amount of solvent or solution. The most important of these are mass percentage of solute, molality, and mole fraction.

Mass Percentage of Solute

Solution concentration is sometimes expressed in terms of the **mass percentage of solute**—that is, *the percentage by mass of solute contained in a solution.*

$$\text{Mass percentage of solute} = \frac{\text{mass of solute}}{\text{mass of solution}} \times 100\%$$

For example, an aqueous solution that is 3.5% sodium chloride by mass contains 3.5 g of NaCl in 100.0 g of solution. It could be prepared by dissolving 3.5 g of NaCl in 96.5 g of water ($100.0 - 3.5 = 96.5$).

Example 12.2 | Calculating with Mass Percentage of Solute

How would you prepare 425 g of an aqueous solution containing 2.40% by mass of sodium acetate, $NaC_2H_3O_2$?

Problem Strategy In order to know how to prepare this solution, we need to know the mass of solute ($NaC_2H_3O_2$) and the mass of solution. The mass percent given in the problem (2.40%) will enable us to determine the mass of solute present in the 425-g sample. Keeping in mind that the total mass of solution equals the sum of the mass of solute and the mass of solvent (mass solution = mass solute + mass solvent), we will be able to determine the mass of H_2O needed to prepare the solution.

Solution The mass of sodium acetate (solute) in 425 g of solution is

$$\text{Mass of } NaC_2H_3O_2 = 425 \text{ g} \times 0.0240 = 10.2 \text{ g}$$

We have the relationship

$$\text{Mass of solution} = \text{mass } NaC_2H_3O_2 + \text{mass } H_2O$$

Therefore, the quantity of water in the solution is

$$\text{Mass of } H_2O = \text{mass of solution} - \text{mass of } NaC_2H_3O_2 = 425 \text{ g} - 10.2 \text{ g} = 415 \text{ g}$$

You would prepare the solution by dissolving 10.2 g of sodium acetate in 415 g of water.

Answer Check A quick way to check your work is to substitute the values you determined into the formula for mass percentage of solute; make sure that the calculated value agrees with that given in the problem.

Exercise 12.5 An experiment calls for 35.0 g of hydrochloric acid that is 20.2% HCl by mass. How many grams of HCl is this? How many grams of water?

■ See Problems 12.49, 12.50, 12.51, and 12.52.

Molality

The **molality** of a solution is *the moles of solute per kilogram of solvent.*

$$\text{Molality} = \frac{\text{moles of solute}}{\text{kilograms of solvent}}$$

For example, 0.20 mol of ethylene glycol dissolved in 2.0×10^3 g (= 2.0 kg) of water has a molality of

$$\frac{0.20 \text{ mol ethylene glycol}}{2.0 \text{ kg solvent}} = 0.10 \text{ } m \text{ ethylene glycol}$$

That is, the solution is 0.10 molal (denoted *m*). The units of molality and molarity are sometimes confused. Note that molality is defined in terms of *mass of solvent*, and molarity is defined in terms of *volume of solution*.

Example 12.3	Calculating the Molality of Solute

Glucose, $C_6H_{12}O_6$, is a sugar that occurs in fruits. It is also known as "blood sugar" because it is found in blood and is the body's main source of energy (see Figure 12.16). What is the molality of a solution containing 5.67 g of glucose dissolved in 25.2 g of water?

Problem Strategy Recall that the definition of *molality* is moles of solute per kilogram of solvent. Therefore, we need to determine these two quantities to solve this problem. Start by converting mass of solute (glucose) to moles, and next determine the mass of solvent (water) in kilograms. Then use these quantities to calculate the solution molality.

Solution The moles of glucose (MM = 180.2 amu) in 5.67 g are found as follows:

$$5.67 \text{ g } C_6H_{12}O_6 \times \frac{1 \text{ mol } C_6H_{12}O_6}{180.2 \text{ g } C_6H_{12}O_6} = 0.0315 \text{ mol } C_6H_{12}O_6$$

The mass of water is 25.2 g, or 25.2×10^{-3} kg.

$$\text{Molality} = \frac{0.0315 \text{ mol } C_6H_{12}O_6}{25.2 \times 10^{-3} \text{ kg solvent}} = \textbf{1.25 } \textit{m} \textbf{ } C_6H_{12}O_6$$

Answer Check Any time you calculate a molality that is greater than about 15 *m*, unless it is a very concentrated solution or a pure solvent, you probably made an error.

Exercise 12.6 Toluene, $C_6H_5CH_3$, is a liquid compound similar to benzene, C_6H_6. It is the starting material for other substances, including trinitrotoluene (TNT). Find the molality of toluene in a solution that contains 35.6 g of toluene and 125 g of benzene.

FIGURE 12.16 ▶

Intravenous feeding of glucose
Glucose, $C_6H_{12}O_6$, is the principal energy substance of the body and is transported to various cells by the blood. Here a glucose solution is being prepared for administration to a patient.

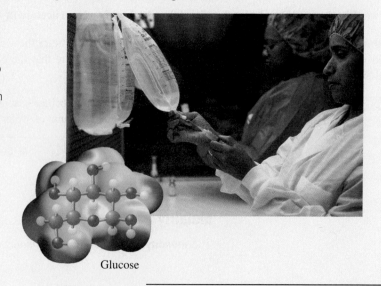

Glucose

■ See Problems 12.53, 12.54, 12.55, and 12.56.

Mole Fraction

The **mole fraction** of a component substance A (X_A) in a solution is defined as *the moles of component substance divided by the total moles of solution* (that is, moles of solute plus solvent).

$$X_A = \frac{\text{moles of substance } A}{\text{total moles of solution}}$$

For example, if a solution is made up of 1 mol of ethylene glycol and 9 mol of water, the total moles of solution are 1 mol + 9 mol = 10 mol. The mole fraction of ethylene glycol is 1/10 = 0.1, and the mole fraction of water is 9/10 = 0.9. Multiplying mole fractions by 100 gives *mole percent*. Hence, this solution is 10 mole percent ethylene glycol and 90 mole percent water. You can also say that 10% of the molecules in the solution are ethylene glycol and 90% are water. The sum of the mole fractions of all the components of a solution equals 1.

Example 12.4 | Calculating the Mole Fractions of Components

What are the mole fractions of glucose and water in a solution containing 5.67 g of glucose, $C_6H_{12}O_6$, dissolved in 25.2 g of water?

Problem Strategy The mole fraction of a solution is the moles of the substance of interest divided by the total number of moles of solution. For this problem, the total number of moles of solution is the sum of the moles of glucose and the moles of water. The moles of glucose and water can be calculated directly from their masses. Add these mole quantities together to obtain the total moles of the solution. Divide each substance by the total moles to obtain the mole fractions.

Solution This is the glucose solution described in Example 12.3. There you found that 5.67 g of glucose equals 0.0315 mol of glucose. The moles of water in the solution are

$$25.2 \text{ g } H_2O \times \frac{1 \text{ mol } H_2O}{18.0 \text{ g } H_2O} = 1.40 \text{ mol } H_2O$$

Hence, the total moles of solution are

$$1.40 \text{ mol} + 0.0315 \text{ mol} = 1.432 \text{ mol}$$

(You retain an extra figure in the answer for further computation.) Finally, you get

$$\textbf{Mole fraction glucose} = \frac{0.0315 \text{ mol}}{1.432 \text{ mol}} = \textbf{0.0220}$$

$$\textbf{Mole fraction water} = \frac{1.40 \text{ mol}}{1.432 \text{ mol}} = \textbf{0.978}$$

Answer Check Note that the sum of the mole fractions is 1.00. Whenever you calculate mole fractions, you can check your answer by making sure that they sum to 1.

Exercise 12.7   Calculate the mole fractions of toluene and benzene in the solution described in Exercise 12.6.

Toluene   Benzene

■ See Problems 12.57 and 12.58.

Conversion of Concentration Units

It is relatively easy to interconvert concentration units when they are expressed in terms of mass or moles of solute and solvent, as the following examples show.

Example 12.5 | Converting Molality to Mole Fractions

An aqueous solution is 0.120 m glucose, $C_6H_{12}O_6$. What are the mole fractions of each component in the solution?

Problem Strategy   Because molality is the moles of solute per kilogram of solvent, a 0.120 m glucose solution contains 0.120 mol of glucose in 1.00 kg of water. After converting 1.00 kg H_2O to moles, you can calculate the mole fraction using its definition.

Solution   The moles of H_2O in 1.00 kg of water are

$$1.00 \times 10^3 \text{ g } H_2O \times \frac{1 \text{ mol } H_2O}{18.0 \text{ g } H_2O} = 55.6 \text{ mol } H_2O$$

Hence,

$$\text{Mole fraction glucose} = \frac{0.120 \text{ mol}}{(0.120 + 55.6) \text{ mol}} = \textbf{0.00215}$$

$$\text{Mole fraction water} = \frac{55.6 \text{ mol}}{(0.120 + 55.6) \text{ mol}} = \textbf{0.998}$$

Answer Check   Check to see that the mole fractions of each substance sum to 1.

Exercise 12.8   A solution is 0.120 m methanol dissolved in ethanol. Calculate the mole fractions of methanol, CH_3OH, and ethanol, C_2H_5OH, in the solution.

■ See Problems 12.59 and 12.60.

Example 12.6 | Converting Mole Fractions to Molality

A solution is 0.150 mole fraction glucose, $C_6H_{12}O_6$, and 0.850 mole fraction water. What is the molality of glucose in the solution?

Problem Strategy   The molality of the solution is the moles of solute (glucose) per kilogram of solvent (H_2O). Given the mole fraction information in the problem, we know that each mole of solution contains 0.150 mol of glucose and 0.850 mol of water. If we convert the moles of water (0.850 mol H_2O) to mass of water, in kilograms, we can then calculate the molality.

Solution   The mass of this amount of water is

$$0.850 \text{ mol } H_2O \times \frac{18.0 \text{ g } H_2O}{1 \text{ mol } H_2O} = 15.3 \text{ g } H_2O \, (= 0.0153 \text{ kg } H_2O)$$

The molality of glucose, $C_6H_{12}O_6$, in the solution is

$$\text{Molality of } C_6H_{12}O_6 = \frac{0.150 \text{ mol } C_6H_{12}O_6}{0.0153 \text{ kg solvent}} = \textbf{9.80 } \boldsymbol{m} \textbf{ } \mathbf{C_6H_{12}O_6}$$

Glucose

Answer Check   When calculating molality of solutions, always make certain that the mass of solvent is expressed in kilograms.

Exercise 12.9   A solution is 0.250 mole fraction methanol, CH_3OH, and 0.750 mole fraction ethanol, C_2H_5OH. What is the molality of methanol in the solution?

■ See Problems 12.61 and 12.62.

To convert molality to molarity, and vice versa, you must know the density of the solution. The calculations are described in the next two examples. As the first example shows, molality and molarity are approximately equal in dilute aqueous solutions.

Example 12.7 | Converting Molality to Molarity

An aqueous solution is 0.273 m KCl. What is the molar concentration of potassium chloride, KCl? The density of the solution is 1.011×10^3 g/L.

Problem Strategy   You are asked to determine the molarity of the solution, which is the moles of solute (KCl) per liter of solution (volume of H_2O and KCl). The molality tells you that the solution contains 0.273 mol KCl in 1 kg of water. If we determine the volume of solution that contains 0.273 mol KCl, we should be able to calculate the molarity. Because the solution is made up of only KCl and water, the solution mass is the mass of 0.273 mol KCl plus the mass of 1.000 kg of water. Knowing the total mass of solution, we then can use the solution density to convert from the mass of solution to the volume of solution. The molarity is obtained by dividing the moles of solute by the volume of solution in liters.

Solution   The first step in determining the volume of solution is to find the mass of potassium chloride in this quantity of solution:

$$0.273 \ \text{mol KCl} \times \frac{74.6 \ \text{g KCl}}{1 \ \text{mol KCl}} = 20.4 \ \text{g KCl}$$

The total mass of the solution equals the mass of water plus the mass of potassium chloride.

$$1.000 \times 10^3 \ \text{g} + 20.4 \ \text{g} = 1.020 \times 10^3 \ \text{g}$$

The volume of the solution can be calculated using the inverse of the density of the solution.

$$\text{Volume of solution} = 1.020 \times 10^3 \ g \times \frac{1 \ \text{L}}{1.011 \times 10^3 \ g} = 1.009 \ \text{L}$$

There is 0.273 mol KCl in every 1.000 L of solution. Hence, the molarity of the solution is

$$\frac{0.273 \ \text{mol KCl}}{1.009 \ \text{L solution}} = \textbf{0.271 } \textbf{\textit{M}} \textbf{ KCl}$$

Note that the molarity and the molality of this solution are approximately equal. This happens in cases where the solutions are dilute and the density is about 1 g/mL.

Answer Check   If you are converting between molarity and molality of an aqueous solution, the concentrations expressed either way generally do not differ greatly. You can see that is the case here: 0.271 M KCl versus 0.273 m KCl. Use this fact to check your answers for this type of problem.

Exercise 12.10   Urea, $(NH_2)_2CO$, is used as a fertilizer (see the accompanying molecular model). What is the molar concentration of an aqueous solution that is 3.42 m urea? The density of the solution is 1.045 g/mL.

Urea

■ See Problems 12.63 and 12.64.

Example 12.8 | Converting Molarity to Molality

An aqueous solution is 0.907 M $Pb(NO_3)_2$. What is the molality of lead(II) nitrate, $Pb(NO_3)_2$, in this solution? The density of the solution is 1.252 g/mL.

(continued)

(continued)

Problem Strategy   You are asked to calculate the molality of the solution, which is the moles of solute ($Pb(NO_3)_2$) per kilogram of solvent (H_2O). From the molarity, we know that there are 0.907 mol $Pb(NO_3)_2$ per liter of solution. If we consider a 1-L sample of this solution, we can use the density to determine the mass of solution. Because the mass of solution is the mass of lead(II) nitrate and the mass of water, you can calculate the mass of lead(II) nitrate by difference (mass H_2O = mass of solution − mass of $Pb(NO_3)_2$). Now you can calculate the molality.

Solution   Assuming 1.000 L (1.000×10^3 mL) of solution,

$$\text{Mass of solution} = \text{density} \times \text{volume}$$
$$= 1.252 \text{ g/mL} \times 1.000 \times 10^3 \text{ mL}$$
$$= 1.252 \times 10^3 \text{ g}$$

The mass of lead nitrate is

$$0.907 \text{ mol Pb(NO}_3)_2 \times \frac{331.2 \text{ g Pb(NO}_3)_2}{1 \text{ mol Pb(NO}_3)_2} = 3.00 \times 10^2 \text{ g Pb(NO}_3)_2$$

The mass of water in 1.000 L of solution is

$$\text{Mass of H}_2\text{O} = \text{mass of solution} - \text{mass of Pb(NO}_3)_2$$
$$= 1.252 \times 10^3 \text{ g} - 3.00 \times 10^2 \text{ g}$$
$$= 9.52 \times 10^2 \text{ g} (= 0.952 \text{ kg})$$

Hence, the molality of lead(II) nitrate in this solution is

$$\frac{0.907 \text{ mol Pb(NO}_3)_2}{0.952 \text{ kg solvent}} = \textbf{0.953 } \textbf{\textit{m}} \textbf{ Pb(NO}_3)_2$$

Answer Check   A very common error that you want to avoid when doing this kind of problem is to forget that the solution density is typically the mass of solute per volume of *solution*, not the mass of solute per volume of solvent.

Exercise 12.11   An aqueous solution is 2.00 *M* urea. The density of the solution is 1.029 g/mL. What is the molal concentration of urea in the solution?

■ See Problems 12.65 and 12.66.

12.5 | Vapor Pressure of a Solution

During the nineteenth century, chemists observed that the vapor pressure of a volatile solvent was lowered by addition of a nonvolatile solute. **Vapor-pressure lowering** of a solvent is *a colligative property equal to the vapor pressure of the pure solvent minus the vapor pressure of the solution.* For example, water at 20°C has a vapor pressure of 17.54 mmHg. Ethylene glycol, CH_2OHCH_2OH, is a liquid whose vapor pressure at 20°C is relatively low; it can be considered to be nonvolatile compared with water. An aqueous solution containing 0.0100 mole fraction of ethylene glycol has a vapor pressure of 17.36 mmHg. Thus, the vapor-pressure lowering, ΔP, of water is

$$\Delta P = 17.54 \text{ mmHg} - 17.36 \text{ mmHg} = 0.18 \text{ mmHg}$$

Figure 12.17 shows a demonstration of vapor-pressure lowering.

FIGURE 12.17 ▶

Demonstration of vapor-pressure lowering
Initially, two beakers, both containing water solutions of the same solute, are placed under a bell jar. The solution in the left beaker is less concentrated than that in the right beaker, so its vapor pressure is greater. The partial pressure of vapor in the bell jar is an intermediate value. It is less than the vapor pressure of the solution on the left, but more than that of the solution on the right. As a result, vapor leaves the solution on the left (which becomes more concentrated) and condenses on the solution on the right (which becomes less concentrated). After some time, the two solutions become equal in concentration and in vapor pressure.

In about 1886, the French chemist François Marie Raoult observed that the partial vapor pressure of solvent over a solution of a nonelectrolyte solute depends on the mole fraction of solvent in the solution. Consider a solution of volatile solvent, A, and nonelectrolyte solute, B, which may be volatile or nonvolatile. According to **Raoult's law,** *the partial pressure of solvent, P_A, over a solution equals the vapor pressure of the pure solvent, P_A°, times the mole fraction of solvent, X_A, in the solution.*

$$P_A = P_A^\circ X_A$$

If the solute is nonvolatile, P_A is the total vapor pressure of the solution. Because the mole fraction of solvent in a solution is always less than 1, the vapor pressure of the solution of a nonvolatile solute is less than that for the pure solvent; the vapor pressure is lowered. In general, Raoult's law is observed to hold for dilute solutions—that is, solutions in which X_A is close to 1. If the solvent and solute are chemically similar, Raoult's law may hold for all mole fractions. Raoult's law is displayed graphically for two solutions in Figure 12.18.

You can obtain an explicit expression for the vapor-pressure lowering of a solvent in a solution, assuming that Raoult's law holds and that the solute is a nonvolatile nonelectrolyte. The vapor-pressure lowering, ΔP, is

$$\Delta P = P_A^\circ - P_A$$

Substituting Raoult's law gives

$$\Delta P = P_A^\circ - P_A^\circ X_A = P_A^\circ (1 - X_A)$$

But the sum of the mole fractions of the components of a solution must equal 1; that is, $X_A + X_B = 1$. So $X_B = 1 - X_A$. Therefore,

$$\Delta P = P_A^\circ X_B$$

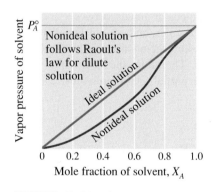

FIGURE 12.18 ▲

Plot of vapor pressures of solutions showing Raoult's law
Vapor pressures of solvent A for two solutions have been plotted against mole fraction of solvent. In one case (labeled "ideal solution"), the vapor pressure is proportional to the mole fraction of solvent for all mole fractions; it follows Raoult's law for all concentrations of solute. For the "nonideal solution," Raoult's law is followed for low solute concentrations (mole fraction of solvent near 1), but the vapor pressure deviates at other concentrations.

From this equation, you can see that the vapor-pressure lowering is a colligative property—one that depends on the concentration, but not on the nature, of the solute. Thus, if the mole fraction of ethylene glycol, X_B, in an aqueous solution is doubled from 0.010 to 0.020, the vapor-pressure lowering is doubled from 0.18 mmHg to 0.36 mmHg. Also, because the previous equation does not depend on the characteristics of the solute (other than its being nonvolatile and a nonelectrolyte), a solution that is 0.010 mole fraction urea, $(NH_2)_2CO$, has the same vapor-pressure lowering as one that is 0.010 mole fraction ethylene glycol. The next example illustrates the use of the previous equation.

Example 12.9 | Calculating Vapor-Pressure Lowering

Calculate the vapor-pressure lowering of water when 5.67 g of glucose, $C_6H_{12}O_6$, is dissolved in 25.2 g of water at 25°C. The vapor pressure of water at 25°C is 23.8 mmHg. What is the vapor pressure of the solution?

Problem Strategy In order to calculate the vapor-pressure lowering of the solution described in this problem, we need to determine the amount that the vapor pressure of the pure solvent is changed (ΔP of water) with the addition of a solute (glucose). We can use Raoult's law to calculate this quantity, noting that we need to know the mole fraction of the solute (glucose). The vapor pressure of the solution is found by subtracting the vapor-pressure change of the pure solvent from the vapor pressure of the pure solvent.

Solution This is the glucose solution described in Example 12.4. According to the calculations performed

there, the solution is 0.0220 mole fraction glucose. Therefore, the vapor-pressure lowering is

$$\Delta P = P_A^\circ X_B = 23.8 \text{ mmHg} \times 0.0220 = \textbf{0.524 mmHg}$$

The vapor pressure of the solution is

$$P_A = P_A^\circ - \Delta P = (23.8 - 0.524) \text{ mmHg} = \textbf{23.3 mmHg}$$

Answer Check In this type of calculation, a correct answer will always have the vapor pressure of the solution lower than the vapor pressure of the pure solvent.

Exercise 12.12 Naphthalene, $C_{10}H_8$, is used to make mothballs. Suppose a solution is made by dissolving 0.515 g of naphthalene in 60.8 g of chloroform, $CHCl_3$. Calculate the vapor-pressure lowering of chloroform at 20°C from the naphthalene. The vapor pressure of chloroform at 20°C is 156 mmHg. Naphthalene can be assumed to be nonvolatile compared with chloroform. What is the vapor pressure of the solution?

■ See Problems 12.67 and 12.68.

Benzene

Toluene

FIGURE 12.19 ▲

Molecular models of benzene and toluene

Top: Benzene. *Bottom:* Toluene, which differs from benzene, where one hydrogen is replaced by a CH_3 group.

An *ideal solution* of substances A and B is one in which both substances follow Raoult's law for all values of mole fractions. Such solutions occur when the substances are chemically similar so that the intermolecular forces between A and B molecules are similar to those between two A molecules or between two B molecules. In this case, we are not restricted to the solute being nonvolatile: both the solute and solvent have significant vapor pressure. Therefore, the total vapor pressure over an ideal solution equals the sum of the partial vapor pressures, each of which is given by Raoult's law:

$$P = P_A^\circ X_A + P_B^\circ X_B$$

Solutions of benzene, C_6H_6, and toluene, $C_6H_5CH_3$, are ideal. Note the similarity in their structures (see Figure 12.19).

Suppose a solution is 0.70 mole fraction benzene and 0.30 mole fraction toluene. The vapor pressures of pure benzene and pure toluene are 75 mmHg and 22 mmHg, respectively. Hence, the total vapor pressure is

$$P = (75 \text{ mmHg} \times 0.70) + (22 \text{ mmHg} \times 0.30) = 59 \text{ mmHg}$$

You can easily see that the vapor over this solution is richer in the more volatile component (benzene). The partial vapor pressure of benzene over the solution is

$$75 \text{ mmHg} \times 0.70 = 53 \text{ mmHg}$$

Because the total vapor pressure is 59 mmHg, the mole fraction of benzene in the vapor is

$$\frac{53 \text{ mmHg}}{59 \text{ mmHg}} = 0.90$$

FIGURE 12.20 ▶

Fractional distillation

This is a typical laboratory apparatus for the fractional distillation of a liquid solution to obtain pure liquid components. The fractionating column contains a packing material, such as glass beads, on which vapor condenses and liquid redistills. The stopper on the receiver is loosely fitted to allow ventilation to the atmosphere.

The vapor is 0.90 mole fraction benzene, whereas the liquid solution is 0.70 mole fraction benzene. This is a general principle: the vapor over a solution is richer in the more volatile component.

Use is made of this principle to separate a more volatile component from a liquid mixture. If you distill a mixture of benzene and toluene, the vapor and the resulting liquid that distills over (the distillate) will be richer in benzene, the more volatile component. If you then take this distillate and distill *it*, the vapor and the resulting liquid that comes over will be even richer in benzene. After many such distillations, you can obtain nearly pure benzene. <

Simple distillation was discussed in Section 1.4.

In practice, instead of actually performing a series of simple distillations to separate the volatile components of a mixture, you perform a single *fractional distillation* using a fractionating column, such as the one shown in Figure 12.20. Vapor from the liquid in the flask condenses on cooler packing material (which might be glass beads) in the lower part of the column. In turn, this liquid (which is slightly richer in benzene) vaporizes and condenses farther up the column, where it is even cooler. The liquid that results is even richer in benzene. The distillation process continues up the column, so the composition of the liquid varies continuously from a mixture of benzene and toluene at the bottom of the column to pure benzene at the top. The temperature also varies continuously up the column, being cooler at the top than at the bottom. The liquid that distills over at first is pure benzene. As the liquid in the distillation flask becomes richer in the less volatile component (toluene), the boiling point of the liquid in the flask increases. Fractional distillation is a common procedure in the laboratory and in industrial processing. For example, it is used to separate the components of petroleum into gasoline, diesel fuel, and so forth. <

Table 23.4 lists the various fractions obtained from petroleum, along with their boiling-point ranges.

Concept Check 12.4

Suppose you need to boil a water-based solution at a temperature lower than 100°C. What kind of liquid could you add to the water to make this happen?

FIGURE 12.21 ▶

Phase diagram showing the effect of a nonvolatile solute on freezing point and boiling point

Note that the freezing point (T_f) is lowered and the boiling point (T_b) is elevated.

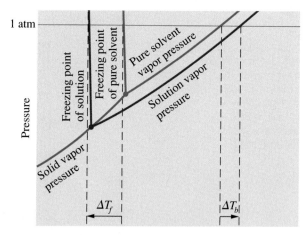

12.6 | Boiling-Point Elevation and Freezing-Point Depression

The *normal* boiling point of a liquid is the temperature at which its vapor pressure equals 1 atm. Because the addition of a nonvolatile solute to a liquid reduces its vapor pressure, the temperature must be increased to a value greater than the normal boiling point to achieve a vapor pressure of 1 atm. Figure 12.21 shows the vapor-pressure curve of a solution. The curve is below the vapor-pressure curve of the pure liquid solvent. The **boiling-point elevation,** ΔT_b, is *a colligative property of a solution equal to the boiling point of the solution minus the boiling point of the pure solvent.*

The boiling-point elevation, ΔT_b, is found to be proportional to the molal concentration, c_m, of the solution (for dilute solutions).

$$\Delta T_b = K_b c_m$$

The constant of proportionality, K_b (called the *boiling-point-elevation constant*), depends only on the solvent. Table 12.3 lists values of K_b, as well as boiling points, for some solvents. Benzene, for example, has a boiling-point-elevation constant of 2.61°C/m. This means that a 0.100 *m* solution of a nonvolatile, undissociated solute in benzene boils at 0.261°C above the boiling point of pure benzene. Pure benzene boils at 80.2°C, so a 0.100 *m* solution boils at 80.2°C + 0.261°C = 80.5°C.

TABLE 12.3	Boiling-Point-Elevation Constants (K_b) and Freezing-Point-Depression Constants (K_f)				
Solvent	Formula	Boiling Point (°C)	Freezing Point (°C)	K_b (°C/m)	K_f (°C/m)
Acetic acid	$HC_2H_3O_2$	118.5	16.60	3.08	3.59
Benzene	C_6H_6	80.2	5.455	2.61	5.065
Camphor	$C_{10}H_{16}O$	—	179.5	—	40
Carbon disulfide	CS_2	46.3	—	2.40	—
Cyclohexane	C_6H_{12}	80.74	6.55	2.79	20.0
Ethanol	C_2H_5OH	78.3	—	1.07	—
Water	H_2O	100.000	0.000	0.512	1.858

Data are taken from Landolt-Börnstein, 6th ed., *Zahlenwerte und Functionen aus Physik, Chemie, Astronomie, Geophysik, und Technik*, Vol. II, Part IIa (Heidelberg: © Springer-Verlag, 1960), pp. 844–849 and pp. 918–919.

Figure 12.21 also shows the effect of a dissolved solute on the freezing point of a solution. Usually it is the pure solvent that freezes out of solution. Sea ice, for example, is almost pure water. For that reason, the vapor-pressure curve for the solid is unchanged. Therefore, the freezing point shifts to a lower temperature. The **freezing-point depression,** ΔT_f, is *a colligative property of a solution equal to the freezing point of the pure solvent minus the freezing point of the solution.* (ΔT_f is shown in Figure 12.21.)

Freezing-point depression, ΔT_f, like boiling-point elevation, is proportional to the molal concentration, c_m (for dilute solutions).

$$\Delta T_f = K_f c_m$$

Here K_f is the *freezing-point-depression constant* and depends only on the solvent. Table 12.3 gives values of K_f for some solvents. The freezing-point-depression constant for benzene is 5.07°C/m. Thus a 0.100 m solution freezes at 0.507°C below the freezing point of pure benzene. Pure benzene freezes at 5.46°C; the freezing point of the solution is 5.46°C − 0.507°C = 4.95°C.

Example 12.10 | Calculating Boiling-Point Elevation and Freezing-Point Depression

An aqueous solution is 0.0222 m glucose. What are the boiling point and the freezing point of this solution?

Problem Strategy In this problem we will need to use the equations for both boiling-point elevation and freezing-point depression. To use these equations, we need solution molality and the appropriate constants. The constants are found in Table 12.3.

Solution Table 12.3 gives K_b and K_f for water as 0.512°C/m and 1.86°C/m, respectively. Therefore,

$\Delta T_b = K_b c_m = 0.512°C/m \times 0.0222\ m = 0.0114°C$

$\Delta T_f = K_f c_m = 1.86°C/m \times 0.0222\ m = 0.0413°C$

The boiling point of the solution is 100.000°C + 0.0114°C = **100.011°C,** and the freezing point is 0.000°C − 0.0413°C = **−0.041°C.** Note that ΔT_b is added and ΔT_f is subtracted.

Answer Check When reporting the final answer for either freezing-point depression or boiling-point elevation, always make sure that the final answer makes sense. For example, a solvent that contains a nonvolatile solute will always boil at a higher than normal boiling-point temperature and freeze at a lower than normal freezing-point temperature, as is the case here. If you find a solution like the one in this problem that has water as the solvent boiling at less than 100°C or freezing above 0°C, you will know that you have made an error.

Exercise 12.13 How many grams of ethylene glycol, CH_2OHCH_2OH, must be added to 37.8 g of water to give a freezing point of −0.150°C?

■ See Problems 12.69 and 12.70

The boiling-point elevation and the freezing-point depression of solutions have a number of practical applications. We mentioned in the chapter opening that ethylene glycol is used in automobile radiators as an antifreeze because it lowers the freezing point of the coolant (Figure 12.22). The same substance also helps prevent the radiator coolant from boiling away by elevating the boiling point. Sodium chloride and calcium chloride are spread on icy roads in the winter to lower the melting point of ice and snow below the temperature of the surrounding air. Salt–ice mixtures are used as freezing mixtures in home ice cream makers. Melting ice cools the ice cream mixture to the freezing point of the solution, which is well below the freezing point of pure water.

FIGURE 12.22 ▶

Automobile antifreeze mixtures
The main ingredient of automobile antifreeze mixtures is ethylene glycol, CH_2OHCH_2OH. This substance has low vapor pressure, so it does not easily vaporize away. It is relatively cheap, being manufactured from ethylene, C_2H_4, which is obtained from petroleum. Ethylene glycol is also used to produce polyester fibers and plastics. The substance has a sweet taste (the name glycol derives from the Greek word *glukus*, meaning "sweet") but is poisonous.

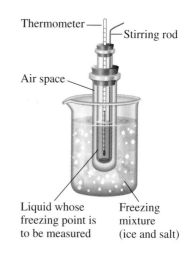

FIGURE 12.23 ▲

Determination of the freezing point of a liquid
The liquid is cooled by means of a freezing mixture. To control the rate of temperature decrease, the liquid is separated from the freezing mixture by an air space.

Colligative properties are also used to obtain molecular masses. Although the mass spectrometer is now often used for routine determinations of the molecular mass of pure substances, colligative properties are still employed to obtain information about the species in solution. Freezing-point depression is often used because it is simple to determine a melting point or a freezing point (Figure 12.23). From the freezing-point lowering, you can calculate the molal concentration, and from the molality, you can obtain the molecular mass. The next two examples illustrate these calculations.

Example 12.11 | Calculating the Molecular Mass of a Solute from Molality

A solution is prepared by dissolving 0.131 g of a substance in 25.4 g of water. The molality of the solution is determined by freezing-point depression to be 0.056 *m*. What is the molecular mass of the substance?

Problem Strategy The key to this problem is to determine the moles of substance in the sample. Recall that if you know the molality of a substance (given in the problem), you can determine the moles of substance present in 1 kg of solvent (0.056 mol substance/1.0 kg H_2O). You then can use this ratio to determine the moles of substance present in the mass of water used to prepare the sample solution (moles of substance/25.4×10^{-3} kg H_2O). Now you know the moles of substance, its molar mass equals mass of substance (0.131 g) divided by moles of substance. The molecular mass (in amu) has the same numerical value as molar mass in g/mol.

Solution The molality of an aqueous solution is

$$\text{Molality} = \frac{\text{moles of substance}}{\text{kg H}_2\text{O}}$$

Hence, for the given solution,

$$0.056 \, \frac{\text{mol}}{\text{kg H}_2\text{O}} = \frac{\text{moles of substance}}{25.4 \times 10^{-3} \, \text{kg H}_2\text{O}}$$

(*continued*)

(*continued*)

Rearranging this equation, you get

$$\text{Moles of substance} = 0.056 \ \frac{\text{mol}}{\text{kg H}_2\text{O}} \times 25.4 \times 10^{-3} \ \text{kg H}_2\text{O} = 1.42 \times 10^{-3} \ \text{mol}$$

(An extra digit is retained for further computation.) The molar mass of substance equals

$$\text{Molar mass} = \frac{0.131 \ \text{g}}{1.42 \times 10^{-3} \ \text{mol}} = 92.3 \ \text{g/mol}$$

You round the answer to two significant figures. The molecular mass is **92 amu.**

Answer Check   Mistakes often give unreasonable values. For example, if you calculated the molality by dividing moles of substance by g H_2O (instead of kg H_2O), you would have obtained a molecular mass of 0.092 amu. Because the atomic mass of H (the lightest element) is 1.01 amu, a value of 0.092 amu is not possible. Very large molecular masses, like 92,000 amu, should also set off alarm bells (unless you have reason to believe the material is polymeric or biological). Typical molecular substances have molecular masses that range from tens up to hundreds of amu.

Exercise 12.14   A 0.930-g sample of ascorbic acid (vitamin C) was dissolved in 95.0 g of water. The concentration of ascorbic acid, as determined by freezing-point depression, was 0.0555 *m*. What is the molecular mass of ascorbic acid?

■ See Problems 12.73 and 12.74.

Example 12.12 | Calculating the Molecular Mass from Freezing-Point Depression

Camphor is a white solid that melts at 179.5°C. It has been used to determine the molecular masses of organic compounds because of its unusually large freezing-point-depression constant (40°C/*m*), which allows ordinary thermometers to be used. The organic substance is dissolved in melted camphor, and then the melting point of the solution is determined. a. A 1.07-mg sample of a compound was dissolved in 78.1 mg of camphor. The solution melted at 176.0°C. What is the molecular mass of the compound? b. If the empirical formula of the compound is CH, what is the molecular formula?

Problem Strategy   a. The key to this problem is to determine the molality of the solution. Given the information in the problem, the equation for freezing-point depression provides a path for determining the solution molality. From the melting point of the solution, calculate the freezing-point depression, ΔT_f; then solve the equation $\Delta T_f = K_f c_m$ for the molality, *m*. Use the method of the preceding example to obtain the molecular mass, given the mass of the sample and the molality of the solution.   b. See Example 3.12 for the relation between number of empirical formula units *n*, empirical formula mass, and molecular mass.

Solution   a. The freezing-point lowering is

$$\Delta T_f = (179.5 - 176.0)°\text{C} = 3.5°\text{C}$$

so the molality of the solution is

$$\frac{\Delta T_f}{K_f} = \frac{3.5°\text{C}}{40°\text{C}/m} = 0.088 \ m$$

From this you compute the moles of the compound that are dissolved in 78.1 mg of camphor (see Example 12.11).

$$0.088 \ \text{mol/kg} \times 78.1 \times 10^{-6} \ \text{kg} = 6.9 \times 10^{-6} \ \text{mol}$$

Camphor

(*continued*)

(*continued*)

The molar mass of the compound is

$$M_m = \frac{1.07 \times 10^{-3}\ \text{g}}{6.9 \times 10^{-6}\ \text{mol}} = 1.6 \times 10^2\ \text{g/mol}$$

The molecular mass is **160 amu** (two significant figures).

b. The empirical formula mass of CH is 13 amu. Therefore, the number of CH units in the molecule is

$$n = \frac{\text{molecular mass}}{\text{empirical formula mass}} = \frac{1.6 \times 10^2\ \text{amu}}{13\ \text{amu}} = 12$$

The molecular formula is $C_{12}H_{12}$.

Answer Check   In calculations like this, which focus on molecular mass determinations, the concentrations (molality) of the solutions are typically on the order of that in this problem. If you calculate a concentration of solute that is very large, check for errors.

Exercise 12.15   A 0.205-g sample of white phosphorus was dissolved in 25.0 g of carbon disulfide, CS_2. The boiling-point elevation of the carbon disulfide solution was found to be 0.159°C. What is the molecular mass of the phosphorus in solution? What is the formula of molecular phosphorus?

■ See Problems 12.75 and 12.76.

12.7 | Osmosis

Certain membranes allow solvent molecules to pass through them but not solute molecules, particularly not those of large molecular mass. Such a membrane is called *semipermeable* and might be an animal bladder, a vegetable tissue, or a piece of cellophane. Figure 12.24 depicts the operation of a semipermeable membrane. **Osmosis** is *the phenomenon of solvent flow through a semipermeable membrane to equalize the solute concentrations on both sides of the membrane.* When two solutions of the same solvent are separated by a semipermeable membrane, solvent molecules migrate through the membrane in both directions. However, the solvent migration is faster from the solution of low concentration to the solution of high concentration.

Figure 12.25 shows an experiment that demonstrates osmosis. A concentrated glucose solution is placed in an inverted funnel whose mouth is sealed with a semipermeable membrane. The funnel containing the glucose solution is then placed in a beaker of pure water. As water flows from the beaker through the membrane into the funnel, the liquid level rises in the stem of the funnel.

The glucose solution continues to rise up the funnel stem until the downward pressure exerted by the solution above the membrane eventually stops the upward flow of solvent (water). In general, **osmotic pressure** is *a colligative property of a solution equal to the pressure that, when applied to the solution, just stops osmosis.*

The osmotic pressure, π, of a solution is related to the molar concentration of solute, M:

$$\pi = MRT$$

Here R is the gas constant and T is the absolute temperature. There is a formal similarity between this equation for osmotic pressure and the equation for an ideal gas:

$$PV = nRT$$

The molar concentration M of a gas equals n/V; therefore, $P = (n/V)RT = MRT$.

Water molecule

Glucose

Semipermeable membrane

FIGURE 12.24 ▲

A semipermeable membrane separating water and an aqueous solution of glucose
Here the membrane is depicted as being similar to a sieve—the pores are too small to allow the glucose molecules to pass. The actual mechanism in particular cases may be more complicated. For example, water may be absorbed on one side of the membrane and diffuse through it to the other side.

FIGURE 12.25 ▲

An experiment in osmosis

Left: Before reaching equilibrium, water molecules pass through the membrane into the glucose solution in the inverted funnel at a greater rate than they return (osmosis). This causes the liquid level in the funnel to rise. *Right:* The column of liquid in the funnel eventually reaches sufficient height to exert a downward pressure, π (the osmotic pressure), causing the rates of water molecules entering and leaving the glucose solution to become equal. Once the osmotic pressure, π, has been reached, osmosis stops, and the liquid level in the funnel has reached its maximum height.

To see the order of magnitude of the osmotic pressure of a solution, consider the aqueous solution described in Example 12.10. There you found that a solution that is about 0.02 m has a freezing-point depression of about 0.04°C. The molarity and molality of a dilute aqueous solution are approximately equal (see Example 12.7). Therefore, this solution will also be about 0.02 M. Hence, the osmotic pressure at 25°C (298 K) is

$$\begin{aligned} \pi &= MRT \\ &= 0.02 \ \cancel{mol}/\cancel{L} \times 0.082 \ \cancel{L}\cdot atm/(\cancel{K}\cdot\cancel{mol}) \times 298 \ \cancel{K} \\ &= 0.5 \ atm \end{aligned}$$

If this pressure were to be exerted by a column of a water solution, as in Figure 12.25, the column would have to be more than 4.5 m high.

In most osmotic-pressure experiments, much more dilute solutions are employed. Often osmosis is used to determine the molecular masses of macromolecular or polymeric substances. Polymers are very large molecules generally made up from a simple, repeating unit. A typical molecule of polyethylene, for instance, might have the formula $CH_3(CH_2CH_2)_{2000}CH_3$. Although polymer solutions can be fairly concentrated in terms of grams per liter, on a mole-per-liter basis they may be quite dilute. The freezing-point depression is usually too small to measure, although the osmotic pressure may be appreciable.

Example 12.13	Calculating Osmotic Pressure

The formula for low-molecular-mass starch is $(C_6H_{10}O_5)_n$, where n averages 2.00×10^2. When 0.798 g of starch is dissolved in 100.0 mL of water solution, what is the osmotic pressure, in mmHg, at 25°C?

(continued)

(continued)

Problem Strategy Calculations of osmotic pressure involve the formula $\pi = MRT$. In order to employ this equation here, we need to determine the molarity (M) of the solution. If we obtain the molecular mass of the starch, we can determine the number of moles of starch in the 0.798-g sample used to prepare the solution. Then, knowing the moles of starch and the volume of the solution (100.0 mL), we can calculate the molarity. After using the formula to determine osmotic pressure, convert the pressure from units of atm to mmHg.

Solution The molecular mass of $(C_6H_{10}O_5)_{200}$ is 32,400 amu. The number of moles in 0.798 g of starch is

$$0.798 \text{ g starch} \times \frac{1 \text{ mol starch}}{32,400 \text{ g starch}} = 2.46 \times 10^{-5} \text{ mol starch}$$

The molarity of the solution is

$$\frac{2.46 \times 10^{-5} \text{ mol}}{0.1000 \text{ L solution}} = 2.46 \times 10^{-4} \text{ mol/L solution}$$

and the osmotic pressure at 25°C is

$$\pi = MRT$$
$$= 2.46 \times 10^{-4} \text{ mol/L} \times 0.0821 \text{ L·atm/(K·mol)} \times 298 \text{ K}$$
$$= 6.02 \times 10^{-3} \text{ atm} = 6.02 \times 10^{-3} \text{ atm} \times \frac{760 \text{ mmHg}}{1 \text{ atm}}$$
$$= \mathbf{4.58 \text{ mmHg}}$$

For comparison, you can calculate the freezing-point depression. Assume that the molality is equal to the molarity (this is in effect the case for very dilute aqueous solutions). Then,

$$\Delta T_f = 1.86°C/m \times 2.46 \times 10^{-4} m = 4.58 \times 10^{-4} °C$$

which is barely detectable with generally available equipment.

Answer Check When performing calculations that involve the formula for osmotic pressure, always make certain that your temperature is in kelvins and that you use the correct value of the ideal gas constant, R.

Exercise 12.16 Calculate the osmotic pressure at 20°C of an aqueous solution containing 5.0 g of sucrose, $C_{12}H_{22}O_{11}$, in 100.0 mL of solution.

■ See Problems 12.77 and 12.78.

Osmotic pressure appears to be important for the rising of sap in a tree. During the day, water evaporates from the leaves of the tree, so the aqueous solution in the leaves becomes more concentrated and the osmotic pressure increases. Sap flows upward to dilute the water solution in the leaves.

Osmosis is important in many biological processes. < A cell might be thought of (simplistically) as an aqueous solution enclosed by a semipermeable membrane. The solution surrounding the cell must have an osmotic pressure equal to that within the cell. Otherwise, water would either leave the cell, dehydrating it, or enter the cell and possibly burst the membrane. For intravenous feeding (adding a nutrient solution to the venous blood supply of a patient), it is necessary that the nutrient solution have exactly the same osmotic pressure as blood plasma. If it does not, the blood cells may collapse or burst as a result of osmosis (Figure 12.26).

The body has portions of organs that are at different osmotic pressures, and an active pumping mechanism is required to offset osmosis. For example, cells of the transparent tissue of the exterior eye, the cornea, have a more concentrated optical fluid than does the aqueous humor, a solution just behind the cornea (Figure 12.27). To prevent the cornea from taking up additional water from the aqueous humor, cells

FIGURE 12.26 ▲

The importance of osmotic pressure to cells
Shown here are color-enhanced electron micrographs of red blood cells in solutions of various osmotic pressures. *(A)* The osmotic pressure of the solution is greater than that of the cell; the cell has collapsed. *(B)* The osmotic pressure of the solution is equal to that of the cell; the cell has its normal round shape with depressed center. *(C)* The osmotic pressure of the solution is less than that of the cell; the cell has a bloated shape.

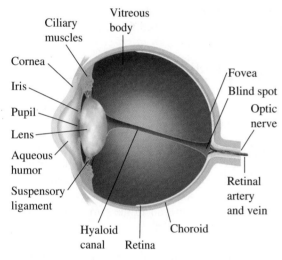

FIGURE 12.27 ▲

Parts of the eye
Certain cells in the cornea act as pumps to prevent osmosis of water from the aqueous humor.

that pump water are located in the corneal tissue adjacent to the aqueous humor. Corneas that are to be stored and used for transplants must be removed from the globe of the eye soon after the donor's death. This prevents the clouding that occurs when the pumping mechanism fails (as its energy supply is depleted at death).

The process of *reverse osmosis* has been applied to the problem of purifying water. In particular, the method has been used to *desalinate* ocean water (that is, remove salts from seawater to make drinkable or industrially usable water). In normal osmosis, the solvent flows from a dilute solution through a membrane to a more concentrated solution. By applying a pressure equal to the osmotic pressure to the more concentrated solution, it is possible to stop the process of osmosis. By application of an even greater pressure, the osmotic process can be reversed. Then, solvent flows from the concentrated solution (which could be ocean water) through a membrane to the more dilute solution (which could be more or less pure water).

Concept Check 12.5

Explain why pickles are stored in a brine (salt) solution. What would the pickles look like if they were stored in water?

12.8 | Colligative Properties of Ionic Solutions

To explain the colligative properties of ionic solutions, you must realize that it is the total concentration of ions, rather than the concentration of ionic substance, that is important. For example, the freezing-point depression of 0.100 *m* sodium chloride solution is nearly twice that of 0.100 *m* glucose solution. You can explain this by saying that sodium chloride dissolves in water to form the ions Na^+ and Cl^-. Each formula unit of NaCl gives two particles. You can write the freezing-point lowering more generally as

$$\Delta T_f = iK_f c_m$$

where *i* is the number of ions resulting from each formula unit and c_m is the molality computed on the basis of the formula of the ionic compound. With ionic solutions, the equations for the other colligative properties must be modified in a similar fashion to include the factor i.

Vapor-pressure lowering: $\Delta P = iP_A^\circ X_B$

Boiling-point elevation: $\Delta T_b = iK_b c_m$

Osmotic pressure: $\pi = iMRT$

The actual values for the colligative properties of ionic solutions agree with the previous equations only when the solutions are quite dilute. For example, the i values calculated from the freezing-point depression are usually smaller than the number of ions obtained from the formula unit. For example, a 0.029 m aqueous solution of potassium sulfate, K_2SO_4, has a freezing point of $-0.14°C$. Hence,

$$i = \frac{\Delta T_f}{K_f c_m} = \frac{0.14°C}{1.86°C/m \times 0.029\,m} = 2.6$$

The value of i equal to $\Delta T_f/K_f c_m$ is often called the van't Hoff factor. Thus, the van't Hoff factor for 0.029 m K_2SO_4 is 2.6.

You might have expected a value of 3, on the basis of the fact that K_2SO_4 ionizes to give three ions. < At first, this was taken as evidence that salts were not completely ionized in solution. In 1923, however, Peter Debye and Erich Hückel were able to show that the colligative properties of salt solutions could be explained by assuming that the salt is completely ionized in solution but that the *activities*, or effective concentrations, of the ions are less than their actual concentrations as a result of the electrical interactions of the ions in solution. The *Debye–Hückel theory* allows us to calculate these activities. When this is done, excellent agreement is obtained for dilute solutions.

Example 12.14 | Determining Colligative Properties of Ionic Solutions

Estimate the freezing point of a 0.010 m aqueous solution of aluminum sulfate, $Al_2(SO_4)_3$. Assume the value of i based on the formula of the compound.

Problem Strategy Because aluminum sulfate is a soluble ionic compound, we need to use a modified form of the freezing-point depression formula, $\Delta T_f = iK_f c_m$. To obtain i, we need to determine the number of ions produced when $Al_2(SO_4)_3$ dissolves in water.

Solution When aluminum sulfate, $Al_2(SO_4)_3$, dissolves in water, it dissociates into five ions.

$$Al_2(SO_4)_3(s) \xrightarrow{H_2O} 2Al^{3+}(aq) + 3SO_4^{2-}(aq)$$

Therefore, you assume $i = 5$. The freezing-point depression is

$$\Delta T_f = iK_f c_m = 5 \times 1.86°C/m \times 0.010\,m = 0.093°C$$

The estimated freezing point of the solution is 0.000°C $- 0.093°C = \mathbf{-0.093°C}$.

Answer Check Whenever you have to solve a problem involving the colligative properties of aqueous solutions, always make your first step a determination of whether the solute is an ionic or a molecular compound. This information will point you to the correct form of the equation.

Exercise 12.17 Estimate the boiling point of a 0.050 m aqueous $MgCl_2$ solution. Assume a value of i based on the formula.

■ See Problems 12.79 and 12.80.

Concept Check 12.6

Each of the following substances is dissolved in a separate 10.0-L container of water: 1.5 mol NaCl, 1.3 mol Na_2SO_4, 2.0 mol $MgCl_2$, and 2.0 mol KBr. Without doing extensive calculations, rank the boiling points of the solutions from highest to lowest.

Colloid Formation

As we noted at the beginning of the chapter, colloids appear homogeneous like solutions, but they consist of comparatively large particles of one substance dispersed throughout another substance. We will look at colloids in the following section.

12.9 | Colloids

A **colloid** is *a dispersion of particles of one substance (the dispersed phase) throughout another substance or solution (the continuous phase).* Fog is an example of a colloid: it consists of very small water droplets (dispersed phase) in air (continuous phase). A colloid differs from a true solution in that the dispersed particles are larger than normal molecules, though they are too small to be seen with a microscope. The particles range from about 1×10^3 pm to about 2×10^5 pm in size.

Tyndall Effect

Although a colloid appears to be homogeneous because the dispersed particles are quite small, it can be distinguished from a true solution by its ability to scatter light. *The scattering of light by colloidal-size particles* is known as the **Tyndall effect.** < For example, the atmosphere appears to be a clear gas, but a ray of sunshine against a dark background shows up many fine dust particles by light scattering. Similarly, when a beam of light is directed through clear gelatin (a colloid, not a true solution), the beam becomes visible by the scattering of light from colloidal gelatin particles. The beam appears as a ray passing through the solution (Figure 12.28). When the same experiment is performed with a true solution, such as an aqueous solution of sodium chloride, the beam of light is not visible.

Although all gases and liquids scatter light, the scattering from a pure substance or true solution is quite small and usually not detectable. However, because of the considerable depth of the atmosphere, the scattering of light by air molecules can be seen. The blue color of the sky is due to the fact that blue light is scattered more easily than red light.

FIGURE 12.28 ▲

A demonstration of the Tyndall effect by a colloid
A light beam is visible perpendicular to its path only if light is scattered toward the viewer. The vessel on the left contains a colloid, which scatters light. The vessel on the right contains a true solution, which scatters negligible light.

Types of Colloids

Colloids are characterized according to the state (solid, liquid, or gas) of the dispersed phase and of the continuous phase. Table 12.4 lists various types of colloids and some examples of each. Fog and smoke are **aerosols,** which are *liquid droplets or solid particles dispersed throughout a gas.* An **emulsion** consists of *liquid droplets dispersed throughout another liquid* (as particles of butterfat are dispersed through homogenized milk). A **sol** consists of *solid particles dispersed in a liquid.*

Hydrophilic and Hydrophobic Colloids

Colloids in which the continuous phase is water are divided into two major classes: hydrophilic colloids and hydrophobic colloids. A **hydrophilic colloid** is *a colloid in which there is a strong attraction between the dispersed phase and the continuous phase (water).* Many such colloids consist of macromolecules (very large molecules) dispersed in water. Except for the large size of the dispersed molecules, these colloids are like normal solutions. Protein solutions, such as gelatin in water, are hydrophilic

TABLE 12.4	Types of Colloids		
Continuous Phase	Dispersed Phase	Name	Example
Gas	Liquid	Aerosol	Fog, mist
Gas	Solid	Aerosol	Smoke
Liquid	Gas	Foam	Whipped cream
Liquid	Liquid	Emulsion	Mayonnaise (oil dispersed in water)
Liquid	Solid	Sol	AgCl(s) dispersed in H_2O
Solid	Gas	Foam	Pumice, plastic foams
Solid	Liquid	Gel	Jelly, opal (mineral with liquid inclusions)
Solid	Solid	Solid sol	Ruby glass (glass with dispersed metal)

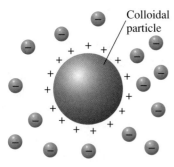

Fe(OH)₃ particle surrounded
by Cl⁻ ions

A

Fe(OH)₃ particle surrounded
by PO₄³⁻ ions

B

FIGURE 12.29 ▲

Layers of ions surrounding charged colloidal particles

(A) A positively charged colloidal particle of iron(III) hydroxide surrounded by chloride ions. *(B)* The same colloidal particle surrounded by phosphate ions. Because these ions gather more closely to the colloidal particles, coagulation is more likely to occur.

colloids. Gelatin molecules are attracted to water molecules by London forces and hydrogen bonding.

A **hydrophobic colloid** is *a colloid in which there is a lack of attraction between the dispersed phase and the continuous phase (water)*. Hydrophobic colloids are basically unstable. Given sufficient time, the dispersed phase aggregates into larger particles. In this behavior, they are quite unlike true solutions and hydrophilic colloids. The time taken to separate may be extremely long, however. A colloid of gold particles in water prepared by Michael Faraday in 1857 is still preserved in the British Museum in London. This colloid is hydrophobic as well as a sol (solid particles dispersed in water).

Hydrophobic sols are often formed when a solid crystallizes rapidly from a chemical reaction or a supersaturated solution. When crystallization occurs rapidly, many centers of crystallization (called *nuclei*) form at the same time. Ions are attracted to these nuclei, and very small crystals form. These small crystals are prevented from settling out by the random thermal motion of the solvent molecules, which continue to buffet them.

You might expect these very small crystals to aggregate into larger crystals because the aggregation would bring ions of opposite charge into contact. However, sol formation appears to happen when, for some reason, each of the small crystals gets a preponderance of one kind of charge on its surface. For example, iron(III) hydroxide forms a colloid because an excess of iron(III) ion (Fe^{3+}) is present on the surface, giving each crystal an excess of positive charge. These positively charged crystals repel one another, so aggregation to larger particles is prevented.

Coagulation

An iron(III) hydroxide sol can be made to aggregate by the addition of an ionic solution, particularly if the solution contains anions with multiple charges (such as phosphate ions, PO_4^{3-}). **Coagulation** is *the process by which the dispersed phase of a colloid is made to aggregate and thereby separate from the continuous phase.* You can picture what happens in the following way: A positively charged colloidal particle of iron(III) hydroxide gathers a layer of anions around it. The thickness of this layer is determined by the charge on the anions. The greater the magnitude of the negative charge, the more compact is the layer of charge. Phosphate ions, for example, gather more closely to the positively charged colloidal particles than do chloride ions (see Figure 12.29). If the ion layer is gathered close to the colloidal particle, the overall charge is effectively neutralized. In that case, two colloidal particles can approach close enough to aggregate.

The curdling of milk when it sours is another example of coagulation. Milk is a colloidal suspension in which the particles are prevented from aggregating because they have electric charges of the same sign. The ions responsible for the coagulation (curdling) are formed when lactose (milk sugar) ferments to lactic acid. A third example is the coagulation of a colloidal suspension of soil in river water when the water meets the concentrated ionic solution of an ocean. The Mississippi Delta was formed in this way.

Exercise 12.18   Colloidal sulfur particles are negatively charged with thiosulfate ions, $S_2O_3^{2-}$, and other ions on the surface of the sulfur. Indicate which of the following would be most effective in coagulating colloidal sulfur: $NaCl$, $MgCl_2$, or $AlCl_3$.

■ See Problems 12.85 and 12.86.

Association Colloids

When molecules or ions that have both a hydrophobic and a hydrophilic end are dispersed in water, they associate, or aggregate, to form colloidal-sized particles, or micelles. A **micelle** is *a colloidal-sized particle formed in water by the association of molecules or ions that each have a hydrophobic end and a hydrophilic end.* The hydrophobic ends point inward toward one another, and the hydrophilic ends are on the outside of the micelle facing the water. *A colloid in which the dispersed phase consists of micelles* is called an **association colloid.**

Ordinary soap in water provides an example of an association colloid. Soap consists of compounds such as sodium stearate, $C_{17}H_{35}COONa$. The stearate ion has a long hydrocarbon end that is hydrophobic (because it is nonpolar) and a carboxyl group (COO^-) at the other end that is hydrophilic (because it is ionic).

$$CH_3CH_2CH_2CH_2CH_2CH_2CH_2CH_2CH_2CH_2CH_2CH_2CH_2CH_2CH_2CH_2CH_2C \overset{O}{\underset{O^-}{}}$$

hydrophobic end   hydrophilic end

Stearate ion

In water solution, the stearate ions associate into micelles in which the hydrocarbon ends point inward toward one another and away from the water, and ionic carboxyl groups are on the outside of the micelle facing the water (Figure 12.30).

The cleansing action of soap occurs because oil and grease can be absorbed into the hydrophobic centers of soap micelles and washed away (Figures 12.31 and 12.32).

FIGURE 12.30 ▷

A stearate micelle in a water solution
Stearate ions associate in groups (micelles), with their hydrocarbon ends pointing inward. The ionic ends, on the outside of the micelle, point into the water solution.

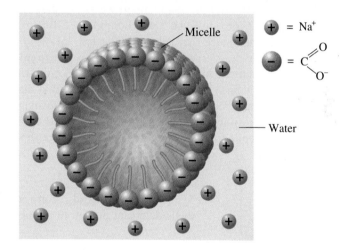

FIGURE 12.31 ▷

The cleansing action of soap
The hydrocarbon ends of soap ions gather around an oil spot, forming a micelle that can be washed away in the water.

A Chemist Looks at . . .

frontiers

The World's Smallest Test Tubes

Phospholipids are the main constituents of the membranes of living cells. These membranes enclose the chemical substances of a cell and allow these substances to carry on the reactions needed for life processes unimpeded by random events external to the membrane. Recently, chemists have prepared cell-like structures—*lipid vesicles*—from phospholipids and have used them to carry out chemical reactions by combining the contents of two lipid vesicles, with diameters from about 50 nanometers (billionths of a meter) to several micrometers (millionths of a meter). Richard Zare, at Stanford University, who was one of those who described these experiments, has called these lipid vesicles "the world's smallest test tubes."

Like the soap ions, phospholipids have the intriguing property of self-assembly into groups. Soap ions in water naturally group themselves into micelles. Phospholipids, however, have a chemical structure that, while similar to that of soap ions, precludes their assembly into micelles. Rather, they form layer structures. And under the right circumstances, a layer may fold back on itself like the skin of a basketball to enclose a space, forming a vesicle.

Lecithins are typical phospholipids. Lipids are biological substances like fats and oils that are soluble in organic solvents; phospholipids contain phosphate groups. (If you are a label reader, you may have seen soy lecithin listed as an ingredient in food products such as bakery goods.) Here is the general structure of a lecithin:

$$
\begin{array}{c}
O \\
\| \\
R-C-O-CH_2 \\
R'-C-O-CH O \\
\| | \| \\
O H_2C-O-P-O-CH_2-CH_2-\overset{+}{N}(CH_3)_3 \\
 | \\
 O^-
\end{array}
$$

R and R′ denote long hydrocarbon groups, with perhaps 14 to 18 carbon atoms.

Note that, like a soap ion, a phospholipid has a hydrophobic end (the two hydrocarbon groups) and a hydrophilic end (an ionic portion containing a phosphate group, $-PO_4^-$). Like soap ions, phospholipid molecules in water tend to associate so that their hydrophilic (or ionic) "heads" dip into the water, with their hydrophobic (or hydrocarbon) "tails" pointing away. However, the hydrocarbon tails of a phospholipid molecule are too bulky to associate into micelles and instead form a *bilayer*, a layer two molecules thick. Figure 12.34 shows a model of a cell membrane that displays this bilayer structure, with two phospholipid layers, their hydrocarbon tails pointing inward toward each other. The hydrophilic heads are rendered in blue; the hydrophobic tails are in green. Note that the interior of a

FIGURE 12.32 ▲

Formation of an association colloid with soap

Left: Vegetable oil floating on water (dyed green). *Right:* When the mixture is shaken with soap, an emulsion forms as the oil droplets are absorbed into soap micelles.

Synthetic detergents also form association colloids. Sodium lauryl sulfate is a synthetic detergent present in toothpastes and shampoos.

$$CH_3CH_2CH_2CH_2CH_2CH_2CH_2CH_2CH_2CH_2CH_2CH_2OSO_3^- Na^+$$

Sodium lauryl sulfate

It has a hydrophilic sulfate group ($-OSO_3^-$) and a hydrophobic dodecyl group ($C_{12}H_{25}-$, the hydrocarbon end).

The detergent molecules we have discussed so far are classified in the trade as "anionics," because they have a negative charge at the hydrophilic end. Other detergent

FIGURE 12.34 ▶

A model of a cell membrane
The membrane consists of a phospholipid bilayer with protein molecules inserted in it.

Specific proteins associated with the membrane surface

Specific proteins embedded in phospholipid bilayer

Protein extending fully through the membrane

Phospholipid bilayer composed of polar head groups and hydrophobic tails of phospholipid molecules

membrane (shown in pale green) is "oily" from the hydrocarbon groups and therefore repels molecules or ions dissolved in the water solutions outside and inside a cell. (A cell, though, must interact with its environment. Protein molecules embedded in the cell membrane form channels or active pumps to transport specific molecules and ions across the cell membrane.)

In one of their experiments, Zare and his colleagues brought two phospholipid vesicles, each about a micrometer in diameter and containing different reactant substances, together under a special microscope. When the

vesicles just touched, the researchers delivered an electrical pulse to them that opened a small pore in each vesicle. The two vesicles coalesced into one, and their contents reacted. The scientists detected the product molecules from the orange fluorescence they gave off when radiated with ultraviolet light. The techniques these researchers are developing should allow scientists to mimic the conditions in biological cells. And lipid vesicles might one day be designed to deliver drugs to specific cells, say cancer cells.

■ See Problems 12.113 and 12.114.

FIGURE 12.33 ▲

Commercial preparations containing cationic detergents
Many cationic detergents exhibit germicidal properties. For that reason, they are used in certain hospital antiseptics, mouthwashes, and eye-wetting solutions.

molecules are "cationics," because they have a positive charge at the hydrophilic end. An example is

$$H_3C \quad CH_2CH_2CH_2CH_2CH_2CH_2CH_2CH_2CH_2CH_2CH_2CH_2CH_2CH_2CH_3$$
$$\overset{+}{N}$$
$$H_3C \quad CH_2CH_2CH_2CH_2CH_2CH_2CH_2CH_2CH_2CH_2CH_2CH_2CH_2CH_2CH_3$$

hydrophilic end   hydrophobic end

Many cationic detergents also have germicidal properties and are used in hospital disinfectants and in mouthwashes (Figure 12.33).

Concept Check 12.7

If electrodes that are connected to a direct current (DC) source are dipped into a beaker of collodial iron(III) hydroxide, a precipitate collects at the negative electrode. Explain why this happens.

A Checklist for Review

Important Terms

solute (12.1)
solvent (12.1)
miscible fluids (12.1)
saturated solution (12.2)
solubility (12.2)
unsaturated solution (12.2)
supersaturated solution (12.2)
hydration (of ions) (12.2)
Le Châtelier's principle (12.3)
Henry's law (12.3)

colligative properties (12.4)
mass percentage of solute (12.4)
molality (12.4)
mole fraction (12.4)
vapor-pressure lowering (12.5)
Raoult's law (12.5)
boiling-point elevation (12.6)
freezing-point depression (12.6)
osmosis (12.7)
osmotic pressure (12.7)

colloid (12.9)
Tyndall effect (12.9)
aerosols (12.9)
emulsion (12.9)
sol (12.9)
hydrophilic colloid (12.9)
hydrophobic colloid (12.9)
coagulation (12.9)
micelle (12.9)
association colloid (12.9)

Key Equations

$$S = k_H P$$

$$\text{Mass percentage of solute} = \frac{\text{mass of solute}}{\text{mass of solution}} \times 100\%$$

$$\text{Molality} = \frac{\text{moles of solute}}{\text{kilograms of solvent}}$$

$$X_A = \frac{\text{moles of substance } A}{\text{total moles of solution}}$$

$$P_A = P_A^\circ X_A$$

$$\Delta P = P_A^\circ X_B$$

$$\Delta T_b = K_b c_m$$

$$\Delta T_f = K_f c_m$$

$$\pi = MRT$$

Summary of Facts and Concepts

Solutions are homogeneous mixtures and can be gases, liquids, or solids. Two gases, for example, will mix in all proportions to give a gaseous solution, because gases are *miscible* in one another. Often one substance will dissolve in another only to a limited extent. The maximum amount that dissolves at equilibrium is the *solubility* of that substance. Solubility is explained in terms of the natural tendency toward disorder (say, by the mixing of two substances) and by the tendency to result in the strongest forces of attraction between species. The dissolving of one molecular substance in another is limited when intermolecular forces strongly favor the unmixed substances. When two substances have similar types of intermolecular forces, they tend to be soluble ("like dissolves like"). Ionic substances differ greatly in their solubilities in water, because solubility depends on the relative values of *lattice energy* and *hydration energy.*

Solubilities usually vary with temperature. At higher temperatures, most gases will become less soluble in water, whereas most ionic solids will become more soluble. Pressure has a significant effect on the solubility only of a gas. A gas is more soluble in a liquid if the partial pressure of the gas is increased, which is in agreement with *Le Châtelier's principle.* According to *Henry's law,* the solubility of a gas is directly proportional to the partial pressure of the gas.

Colligative properties of solutions depend only on the concentration of solute particles. The concentration may be defined by the *molarity, mass percentage of solute, molality,* or *mole fraction.* One example of a colligative property is the *vapor-pressure lowering* of a volatile solvent by the addition of a nonvolatile solute. According to *Raoult's law,* the vapor pressure of this solution depends on the mole fraction of solvent. Because adding a nonvolatile solute lowers the vapor pressure, the boiling point must be raised to bring the vapor pressure back to 1 atm *(boiling-point elevation).* Such a solution also exhibits a *freezing-point depression.* Boiling-point elevation and freezing-point depression are colligative properties. *Osmosis* is another colligative property. In osmosis, there is a flow of solvent through a semipermeable membrane in order to equalize the concentrations of solutions on the two sides of the membrane. Colligative properties may be used to measure solute concentration. In this way, one can determine the molecular mass of the solute. The colligative properties of an ionic solution depend on the concentration of ions, which you can obtain from the concentration of ionic compound and its formula. Interactions of ions in solution do affect the properties significantly, however.

A *colloid* is a dispersion of particles of one substance (about 1×10^3 pm to 2×10^5 pm in size) throughout another. Colloids can be detected by the *Tyndall effect* (the scattering of light by colloidal-size particles). Colloids are characterized by the state of the dispersed phase and the state of the continuous phase. An aerosol, for example, consists of liquid droplets or solid particles dispersed in a gas. Colloids in water are hydrophilic or hydrophobic. A *hydrophilic colloid* consists of a dispersed phase that is attracted to the water. Many of these colloids have macromolecules dissolved in water. In *hydrophobic colloids,* there is little attraction between the dispersed phase and the water. The colloidal particles may be electrically charged and repel one another, preventing aggregation to larger particles. An ionic solution can neutralize this charge so that the colloid will *coagulate*—that is, aggregate. An *association colloid* consists of molecules with a hydrophobic end and a hydrophilic end dispersed in water. These molecules associate into colloidal-size groups, or *micelles*.

Media Summary

Visit the **student website at college.cengage.com/pic/ebbing9e** to help prepare for class, study for quizzes and exams, understand core concepts, and visualize molecular-level interactions. The following media activities are available for this chapter:

 Prepare for Class

■ **Video Lessons** *Mini lectures from chemistry experts*

Types of Solutions
Factors Determining Solubility
Energy and the Solution Process
Extractions
Temperature Change and Solubility
Pressure Change and Solubility
Molality
Molality and the Mole Fraction
Vapor-Pressure Lowering
Boiling-Point Elevation and Freezing-Point Depression
Boiling-Point-Elevation Problem
Osmosis
Colligative Properties of Ionic Solutions
CIA Demonstration: The Tyndall Effect
Colloid Formulation and Flocculation

 Improve Your Grade

■ **Visualizations** *Molecular-level animations and lab demonstration videos*

Saturated Solution Equilibrium
Dissolution of a Solid in a Liquid

Supersaturated Sodium Acetate
Vapor-Pressure Lowering: Liquid/Vapor Equilibrium
Vapor-Pressure Lowering: Addition of a Solute
Vapor-Pressure Lowering: Solution/Vapor Equilibrium
Boiling-Point Elevation: Liquid/Vapor Equilibrium
Boiling-Point Elevation: Addition of a Solute
Boiling-Point Elevation: Solution/Vapor Equilibrium
Freezing-Point Depression: Solid/Liquid Equilibrium
Freezing-Point Depression: Addition of Solute
Freezing-Point Depression: Solid/Solution Equilibrium
Osmosis
Micelle Formation: The Cleansing Action of Soap

■ **Flashcards** *Key terms and definitions*
Online Flashcards

■ **Self-Assessment Questions** *Additional questions with full worked-out solutions*
6 Self-Assessment Questions

 ACE the Test

Multiple-choice quizzes
3 ACE Practice Tests

Access these resources using the passkey available free with new texts or for purchase separately.

Learning Objectives

12.1 Types of Solutions

■ Define *solute* and *solvent.*
■ Define *miscible fluid.*
■ Provide examples of *gaseous solutions, liquid solutions,* and *solid solutions.*

12.2 Solubility and the Solution Process

■ List the conditions that must be present to have a *saturated solution,* to have an *unsaturated solution,* and to have a *supersaturated solution.*
■ Describe the factors that make one substance soluble in another.

■ Determine when a *molecular solution* will form when substances are mixed.
■ Learn what conditions must be met in order to create an *ionic solution.*

12.3 Effects of Temperature and Pressure on Solubility

■ State the general trends of the solubility of gases and solids with temperature.
■ Explain how the solubility of a gas changes with temperature.
■ Apply Henry's law. **Example 12.1**

12.4 Ways of Expressing Concentration

- Define *colligative property.*
- Define *molarity.*
- Define *mass percentage of solute.*
- Calculate with mass percentage of solute. **Example 12.2**
- Define *molality.*
- Calculate the molality of solute. **Example 12.3**
- Define *mole fraction.*
- Calculate the mole fraction of components. **Example 12.4**
- Convert molality to mole fractions. **Example 12.5**
- Convert mole fractions to molality. **Example 12.6**
- Convert molality to molarity. **Example 12.7**
- Convert molarity to molality. **Example 12.8**

12.5 Vapor Pressure of a Solution

- Explain *vapor-pressure lowering* of a solvent.
- State *Raoult's law.*
- Calculate vapor-pressure lowering. **Example 12.9**
- Describe an *ideal solution.*

12.6 Boiling-Point Elevation and Freezing-Point Depression

- Define *boiling-point elevation* and *freezing-point depression.*
- Calculate boiling-point elevation and freezing-point depression. **Example 12.10**

- Calculate the molecular mass of a solute from molality. **Example 12.11**
- Calculate the molecular mass from freezing-point depression. **Example 12.12**

12.7 Osmosis

- Describe a system where *osmosis* will take place.
- Calculate osmotic pressure. **Example 12.13**

12.8 Colligative Properties of Ionic Solutions

- Determine the colligative properties of ionic solutions. **Example 12.14**

12.9 Colloids

- Define *colloid.*
- Explain the *Tyndall effect.*
- Give examples of *hydrophilic colloids* and *hydrophobic colloids.*
- Describe *coagulation.*
- Explain how *micelles* can form an *association colloid.*

Self-Assessment and Review Questions

12.1 Give one example of each: a gaseous solution, a liquid solution, a solid solution.

12.2 What are the two factors needed to explain the differences in solubilities of substances?

12.3 Explain in terms of intermolecular attractions why octane is immiscible in water.

12.4 Explain why ionic substances show a wide range of solubilities in water.

12.5 Using the concept of hydration, describe the process of dissolving a sodium chloride crystal in water.

12.6 What is the usual solubility behavior of an ionic compound in water when the temperature is raised? Give an example of an exception to this behavior.

12.7 Give one example of each: a salt whose heat of solution is exothermic and a salt whose heat of solution is endothermic.

12.8 What do you expect to happen to a concentration of dissolved gas in a solution as the solution is heated?

12.9 Explain why a carbonated beverage must be stored in a closed container.

12.10 Pressure has an effect on the solubility of oxygen in water but a negligible effect on the solubility of sugar in water. Why?

12.11 Four ways were discussed to express the concentration of a solute in solution. Identify them and define each concentration unit.

12.12 When two beakers containing different concentrations of a solute in water are placed in a closed cabinet for a time, one

beaker gains solvent and the other loses it, so that the concentrations of solute in the two beakers become equal. Explain what is happening.

12.13 Explain the process of fractional distillation to separate a solution of two liquids into pure components.

12.14 Explain why the boiling point of a solution containing a nonvolatile solute is higher than the boiling point of a pure solvent.

12.15 List two applications of freezing-point depression.

12.16 Explain the process of reverse osmosis to produce drinkable water from ocean water.

12.17 One can often see "sunbeams" passing through the less dense portions of clouds. What is the explanation for this?

12.18 Give an example of an aerosol, a foam, an emulsion, a sol, and a gel.

12.19 Explain on the basis that "like dissolves like" why glycerol, $CH_2OHCHOHCH_2OH$, is miscible in water but benzene, C_6H_6, has very limited solubility in water.

12.20 Explain how soap removes oil from a fabric.

12.21 Calculate the number of moles of barium chloride in 427 g of a 3.17% by mass barium chloride solution?
  a. 6.50×10^{-02} mol
  b. 7.83×10^{-02} mol
  c. 4.31×10^{-02} mol
  d. 7.81×10^{-02} mol
  e. 4.27×10^{-02} mol

12.22 The mole fraction of copper(II) nitrate in an aqueous copper(II) nitrate solution is 0.135. What is the molality of the copper(II) nitrate solution?
  a. 7.49 m **b.** 8.01 m
  c. 8.66 m **d.** 9.34 m
  e. 8.09 m

12.23 If 291g of a compound is added to 1.02 kg of water to increase the boiling point by 5.77°C, what is the molar mass of the added compound? (Assume a van't Hoff factor of 1.)
  a. 31.1 g/mol   **b.** 30.3 g/mol
  c. 28.5 g/mol   **d.** 18.3 g/mol
  e. 25.3 g/mol

12.24 A 5.1-g sample of $CaCl_2$ is dissolved in a beaker of water. Which of the following statements is true of this solution?
  a. The solution will freeze at a lower temperature than pure water.
  b. The solution has a higher vapor pressure than pure water.
  c. The solution will boil at a lower temperature than pure water.
  d. Water is the solute in this solution.
  e. None of the other statements (a–d) are true.

Concept Explorations

Colligative Properties I

12.25 Consider two hypothetical pure substances, $AB(s)$ and $XY(s)$. When equal molar amounts of these substances are placed in separate 500-mL samples of water, they undergo the following reactions:

$$AB(s) \longrightarrow A^+(aq) + B^-(aq)$$
$$XY(s) \longrightarrow XY(aq)$$

  a. Which solution would you expect to have the lower boiling point? Why?
  b. Would you expect the vapor pressures of the two solutions to be equal? If not, which one would you expect to have the higher vapor pressure?
  c. Describe a procedure that would make the two solutions have the same boiling point.
  d. If you took 250 mL of the $AB(aq)$ solution prepared above, would it have the same boiling point as the original solution? Be sure to explain your answer.
  e. The container of $XY(aq)$ is left out on the bench top for several days, which allows some of the water to evaporate from the solution. How would the melting point of this solution compare to the melting point of the original solution?

Colligative Properties II

12.26 Equal numbers of moles of two soluble, substances, substance A and substance B, are placed into separate 1.0-L samples of water.
  a. The water samples are cooled. Sample A freezes at −0.50°C, and Sample B freezes at −1.00°C. Explain how the solutions can have different freezing points.
  b. You pour 500 mL of the solution containing substance B into a different beaker. How would the freezing point of this 500-mL portion of solution B compare to the freezing point of the 1.0-L sample of solution A?
  c. Calculate the molality of the solutions of A and B. Assume that $i = 1$ for substance A.
  d. If you were to add an additional 1.0 kg of water to solution B, what would be the new freezing point of the solution? Try to write an answer to this question without using a mathematical formula.
  e. What concentration (molality) of substances A and B would result in both solutions having a freezing point of −0.25°C?
  f. Compare the boiling points, vapor pressure, and osmotic pressure of the original solutions of A and B. Don't perform the calculations; just state which is the greater in each case.

Conceptual Problems

12.27 Even though the oxygen demands of trout and bass are different, they can exist in the same body of water. However, if the temperature of the water in the summer gets above about 23°C, the trout begin to die, but not the bass. Why is this the case?

12.28 You want to purchase a salt to melt snow and ice on your sidewalk. Which one of the following salts would best accomplish your task using the least amount: KCl, $CaCl_2$, PbS_2, $MgSO_4$, or AgCl?

12.29 Ten grams of the hypothetical ionic compounds XZ and YZ are each placed in a separate 2.0-L beaker of water. XZ completely dissolves, whereas YZ is insoluble. The energy of hydra-

tion of the Y^+ ion is greater than the X^+ ion. Explain this difference in solubility.

12.30 Small amounts of a nonvolatile, nonelectrolyte solute and a volatile solute are each dissolved in separate beakers containing 1 kg of water. If the number of moles of each solute is equal:
  a. Which solution will have the higher vapor pressure?
  b. Which solution will boil at a higher temperature?

12.31 A Cottrell precipitator consists of a column containing electrodes that are connected to a high-voltage direct current (DC) source. The Cottrell precipitator is placed in smokestacks to remove smoke particles from the gas discharged from an industrial plant. Explain how you think this works.

12.32 Consider the following dilute NaCl(*aq*) solutions.

A   B

a. Which one will boil at a higher temperature?
b. Which one will freeze at a lower temperature?
c. If the solutions were separated by a semipermeable membrane that allowed only water to pass, which solution would you expect to show an increase in the concentration of NaCl?

12.33 A green leafy salad wilts if left too long in a salad dressing containing vinegar and salt. Explain what happens.

12.34 People have proposed towing icebergs to arid parts of the earth as a way to deliver freshwater. Explain why icebergs do not contain salts although they are formed by the freezing of ocean water (i.e., saltwater).

12.35 If 1-mol samples of urea, a nonelectrolyte, sodium chloride, and calcium chloride are each dissolved in equal volumes of water in separate containers:
 a. Which solution would have the highest boiling point?
 b. Which solution would have the highest freezing point?

12.36 Consider the following three beakers that contain water and a non-volatile solute. The solute is represented by the orange spheres.

A   B   C

 a. Which solution would have the highest vapor pressure?
 b. Which solution would have the lowest boiling point?
 c. What could you do in the laboratory to make each solution have the same freezing point?

Practice Problems

Types of Solutions

12.37 Give an example of a liquid solution prepared by dissolving a gas in a liquid.

12.38 Give an example of a solid solution prepared from two solids.

Solubility

12.39 Would boric acid, $B(OH)_3$, be more soluble in ethanol, C_2H_5OH, or in benzene, C_6H_6?

12.40 Would naphthalene, $C_{10}H_8$, be more soluble in ethanol, C_2H_5OH, or in benzene, C_6H_6?

12.41 Arrange the following substances in order of increasing solubility in hexane, C_6H_{14}: CH_2OHCH_2OH, $C_{10}H_{22}$, H_2O.

12.42 Indicate which of the following is more soluble in ethanol, C_2H_5OH: acetic acid, CH_3COOH, or stearic acid, $C_{17}H_{35}COOH$.

12.43 Which of the following ions would be expected to have the greater energy of hydration, Mg^{2+} or Al^{3+}?

12.44 Which of the following ions would be expected to have the greater energy of hydration, F^- or Cl^-?

12.45 Arrange the following alkaline-earth-metal iodates in order of increasing solubility in water; explain your reasoning: $Ba(IO_3)_2$, $Ca(IO_3)_2$, $Sr(IO_3)_2$, $Mg(IO_3)_2$. Note that IO_3^- is a large anion.

12.46 Explain the trends in solubility (grams per 100 mL of water) of the alkali-metal fluorides and permanganates.

	Li^+	Na^+	K^+	Rb^+	Cs^+
F^-	0.27	4.2	92	131	367
MnO_4^-	71	Very soluble	6.4	0.5	0.097

12.47 The solubility of carbon dioxide in water is 0.161 g CO_2 in 100 mL of water at 20°C and 1.00 atm. A soft drink is carbonated with carbon dioxide gas at 5.50 atm pressure. What is the solubility of carbon dioxide in water at this pressure?

12.48 Nitrogen, N_2, is soluble in blood and can cause intoxication at sufficient concentration. For this reason, the U.S. Navy advises divers using compressed air not to go below 125 feet. The total pressure at this depth is 4.79 atm. If the solubility of nitrogen at 1.00 atm is 1.75×10^{-3} g/100 mL of water, and the mole percent of nitrogen in air is 78.1, what is the solubility of nitrogen in water from air at 4.79 atm?

Solution Concentration

12.49 How would you prepare 72.5 g of an aqueous solution that is 5.00% potassium iodide, KI, by mass?

12.50 How would you prepare 455 g of an aqueous solution that is 6.50% sodium sulfate, Na_2SO_4, by mass?

12.51 What mass of solution containing 5.00% potassium iodide, KI, by mass contains 258 mg KI?

12.52 What mass of solution containing 6.50% sodium sulfate, Na_2SO_4, by mass contains 1.50 g Na_2SO_4?

12.53 Vanillin, $C_8H_8O_3$, occurs naturally in vanilla extract and is used as a flavoring agent. A 39.1-mg sample of vanillin was dissolved in 168.5 mg of diphenyl ether, $(C_6H_5)_2O$. What is the molality of vanillin in the solution?

12.54 Lauryl alcohol, $C_{12}H_{25}OH$, is prepared from coconut oil; it is used to make sodium lauryl sulfate, a synthetic detergent. What is the molality of lauryl alcohol in a solution of 17.1 g lauryl alcohol dissolved in 165 g ethanol, C_2H_5OH?

12.55 Fructose, $C_6H_{12}O_6$, is a sugar occurring in honey and fruits. The sweetest sugar, it is nearly twice as sweet as sucrose (cane or beet sugar). How much water should be added to 1.75 g of fructose to give a 0.125 *m* solution?

Fructose

12.56 Caffeine, $C_8H_{10}N_4O_2$, is a stimulant found in tea and coffee. A sample of the substance was dissolved in 45.0 g of chloroform, $CHCl_3$, to give a 0.0946 *m* solution. How many grams of caffeine were in the sample?

Caffeine

12.57 A 100.0-g sample of a brand of rubbing alcohol contains 65.0 g of isopropyl alcohol, C_3H_7OH, and 35.0 g of water. What is the mole fraction of isopropyl alcohol in the solution? What is the mole fraction of water?

12.58 An automobile antifreeze solution contains 2.50 kg of ethylene glycol, CH_2OHCH_2OH, and 2.00 kg of water. Find the mole fraction of ethylene glycol in this solution. What is the mole fraction of water?

12.59 A bleaching solution contains sodium hypochlorite, NaClO, dissolved in water. The solution is 0.650 *m* NaClO. What is the mole fraction of sodium hypochlorite?

12.60 An antiseptic solution contains hydrogen peroxide, H_2O_2, in water. The solution is 0.600 *m* H_2O_2. What is the mole fraction of hydrogen peroxide?

12.61 Concentrated hydrochloric acid contains 1.00 mol HCl dissolved in 3.31 mol H_2O. What is the mole fraction of HCl in concentrated hydrochloric acid? What is the molal concentration of HCl?

12.62 Concentrated aqueous ammonia contains 1.00 mol NH_3 dissolved in 2.44 mol H_2O. What is the mole fraction of NH_3 in concentrated aqueous ammonia? What is the molal concentration of NH_3?

12.63 Oxalic acid, $H_2C_2O_4$, occurs as the potassium or calcium salt in many plants, including rhubarb and spinach. An aqueous solution of oxalic acid is 0.580 *m* $H_2C_2O_4$. The density of the solution is 1.022 g/mL. What is the molar concentration?

12.64 Citric acid, $H_3C_6H_5O_7$, occurs in plants. Lemons contain 5% to 8% citric acid by mass. The acid is added to beverages and candy. An aqueous solution is 0.688 *m* citric acid. The density is 1.049 g/mL. What is the molar concentration?

12.65 A solution of vinegar is 0.763 *M* acetic acid, $HC_2H_3O_2$. The density of the vinegar is 1.004 g/mL. What is the molal concentration of acetic acid?

12.66 A beverage contains tartaric acid, $H_2C_4H_4O_6$, a substance obtained from grapes during wine making. If the beverage is 0.265 *M* tartaric acid, what is the molal concentration? The density of the solution is 1.016 g/mL.

Colligative Properties

12.67 Calculate the vapor pressure at 35°C of a solution made by dissolving 20.2 g of sucrose, $C_{12}H_{22}O_{11}$, in 70.1 g of water. The vapor pressure of pure water at 35°C is 42.2 mmHg. What is the vapor-pressure lowering of the solution? (Sucrose is nonvolatile.)

12.68 What is the vapor pressure at 23°C of a solution of 1.20 g of naphthalene, $C_{10}H_8$, in 25.6 g of benzene, C_6H_6? The vapor pressure of pure benzene at 23°C is 86.0 mmHg; the vapor pressure of naphthalene can be neglected. Calculate the vapor-pressure lowering of the solution.

12.69 What is the boiling point of a solution of 0.150 g of glycerol, $C_3H_8O_3$, in 20.0 g of water? What is the freezing point?

12.70 A solution was prepared by dissolving 0.834 g of sulfur, S_8, in 100.0 g of acetic acid, $HC_2H_3O_2$. Calculate the freezing point and boiling point of the solution.

12.71 An aqueous solution of a molecular compound freezes at −0.086°C. What is the molality of the solution?

12.72 Urea, $(NH_2)_2CO$, is dissolved in 100.0 g of water. The solution freezes at −0.085°C. How many grams of urea were dissolved to make this solution?

12.73 A 0.0182-g sample of an unknown substance was dissolved in 2.135 g of benzene. The molality of this solution, determined by freezing-point depression, was 0.0698 *m*. What is the molecular mass of the unknown substance?

12.74 A solution contains 0.0653 g of a compound in 8.31 g of ethanol. The molality of the solution is 0.0368 *m*. Calculate the molecular mass of the compound.

12.75 Safrole is contained in oil of sassafras and was once used to flavor root beer. A 2.39-mg sample of safrole was dissolved in 103.0 mg of diphenyl ether. The solution had a melting point of 25.70°C. Calculate the molecular mass of safrole. The freezing point of pure diphenyl ether is 26.84°C, and the freezing-point-depression constant, K_f, is 8.00°C/m.

12.76 Butylated hydroxytoluene (BHT) is used as an antioxidant in processed foods. (It prevents fats and oils from becoming rancid.) A solution of 2.500 g of BHT in 100.0 g of benzene had a freezing point of 4.880°C. What is the molecular mass of BHT?

12.77 Dextran is a polymeric carbohydrate produced by certain bacteria. It is used as a blood plasma substitute. An aqueous solution contains 0.582 g of dextran in 106 mL of solution at 21°C. It has an osmotic pressure of 1.47 mmHg. What is the average molecular mass of the dextran?

12.78 Arginine vasopressin is a pituitary hormone. It helps regulate the amount of water in the blood by reducing the flow of urine from the kidneys. An aqueous solution containing 21.6 mg of vasopressin in 100.0 mL of solution has an osmotic pressure at 25°C of 3.70 mmHg. What is the molecular mass of the hormone?

12.79 What is the freezing point of 0.0075 m aqueous calcium chloride, $CaCl_2$? Use the formula of the salt to obtain i.

12.80 What is the freezing point of 0.0091 m aqueous sodium phosphate, Na_3PO_4? Use the formula of the salt to obtain i.

12.81 A 0.0140-g sample of an ionic compound with the formula $Cr(NH_3)_5Cl_3$ was dissolved in water to give 25.0 mL of solution at 25°C. The osmotic pressure was determined to be

119 mmHg. How many ions are obtained from each formula unit when the compound is dissolved in water?

12.82 In a mountainous location, the boiling point of pure water is found to be 95°C. How many grams of sodium chloride must be added to 1 kg of water to bring the boiling point back to 100°C? Assume that $i = 2$.

Colloids

12.83 Give the type of colloid (aerosol, foam, emulsion, sol, or gel) that each of the following represents.
 a. rain cloud   **b.** milk of magnesia
 c. soapsuds   **d.** silt in water

12.84 Give the type of colloid (aerosol, foam, emulsion, sol, or gel) that each of the following represents.
 a. ocean spray   **b.** beaten egg white
 c. dust cloud   **d.** salad dressing

12.85 Arsenic(III) sulfide forms a sol with a negative charge. Which of the following ionic substances should be most effective in coagulating the sol?
 a. KCl   **b.** $MgCl_2$ **c.** $Al_2(SO_4)_3$ **d.** Na_3PO_4

12.86 Aluminum hydroxide forms a positively charged sol. Which of the following ionic substances should be most effective in coagulating the sol?
 a. NaCl   **b.** $CaCl_2$ **c.** $Fe_2(SO_4)_3$ **d.** K_3PO_4

General Problems

12.87 A gaseous mixture consists of 80.0 mole percent N_2 and 20.0 mole percent O_2 (the approximate composition of air). Suppose water is saturated with the gas mixture at 25°C and 1.00 atm total pressure, and then the gas is expelled from the water by heating. What is the composition in mole fractions of the gas mixture that is expelled? The solubilities of N_2 and O_2 at 25°C and 1.00 atm are 0.0175 g/L H_2O and 0.0393 g/L H_2O, respectively.

12.88 A natural gas mixture consists of 90.0 mole percent CH_4 (methane) and 10.0 mole percent C_2H_6 (ethane). Suppose water is saturated with the gas mixture at 20°C and 1.00 atm total pressure, and the gas is then expelled from the water by heating. What is the composition in mole fractions of the gas mixture that is expelled? The solubilities of CH_4 and C_2H_6 at 20°C and 1.00 atm are 0.023 g/L H_2O and 0.059 g/L H_2O, respectively.

12.89 An aqueous solution is 8.50% ammonium chloride, NH_4Cl, by mass. The density of the solution is 1.024 g/mL. What are the molality, mole fraction, and molarity of NH_4Cl in the solution?

12.90 An aqueous solution is 27.0% lithium chloride, LiCl, by mass. The density of the solution is 1.127 g/mL. What are the molality, mole fraction, and molarity of LiCl in the solution?

12.91 A 55-g sample of a gaseous fuel mixture contains 0.51 mole fraction propane, C_3H_8; the remainder of the mixture is butane, C_4H_{10}. What are the masses of propane and butane in the sample?

12.92 The diving atmosphere used by the U.S. Navy in its undersea Sea-Lab experiments consisted of 0.036 mole fraction O_2 and 0.056 mole fraction N_2, with helium (He) making up the remainder. What are the masses of nitrogen, oxygen, and helium in a 8.32-g sample of this atmosphere?

12.93 A liquid solution consists of 0.25 mole fraction ethylene dibromide, $C_2H_4Br_2$, and 0.75 mole fraction propylene dibromide, $C_3H_6Br_2$. Both ethylene dibromide and propylene dibromide are volatile liquids; their vapor pressures at 85°C are 173 mmHg and 127 mmHg, respectively. Assume that each compound follows Raoult's law in the solution. Calculate the total vapor pressure of the solution.

12.94 What is the total vapor pressure at 20°C of a liquid solution containing 0.30 mole fraction benzene, C_6H_6, and 0.70 mole fraction toluene, $C_6H_5CH_3$? Assume that Raoult's law holds for each component of the solution. The vapor pressure of pure benzene at 20°C is 75 mmHg; that of toluene at 20°C is 22 mmHg.

12.95 A sample of potassium aluminum sulfate 12-hydrate, $KAl(SO_4)_2 \cdot 12H_2O$, containing 118.6 mg is dissolved in 1.000 L of solution. Calculate the following for the solution:
 a. The molarity of $KAl(SO_4)_2$.
 b. The molarity of SO_4^{2-}.
 c. The molality of $KAl(SO_4)_2$, assuming that the density of the solution is 1.00 g/mL.

12.96 A sample of aluminum sulfate 18-hydrate, $Al_2(SO_4)_3 \cdot 18H_2O$, containing 159.3 mg is dissolved in 1.000 L of solution. Calculate the following for the solution:
   a. The molarity of $Al_2(SO_4)_3$.
   b. The molarity of SO_4^{2-}.
   c. The molality of $Al_2(SO_4)_3$, assuming that the density of the solution is 1.00 g/mL.

12.97 Urea, $(NH_2)_2CO$, has been used to melt ice from sidewalks, because the use of salt is harmful to plants. If the saturated aqueous solution contains 41% urea by mass, what is the freezing point? (The answer will be approximate, because the equation in the text applies accurately only to dilute solutions.)

12.98 Calcium chloride, $CaCl_2$, has been used to melt ice from roadways. Given that the saturated solution is 32% $CaCl_2$ by mass, estimate the freezing point.

12.99 The osmotic pressure of blood at 37°C is 7.7 atm. A solution that is given intravenously must have the same osmotic pressure as the blood. What should be the molarity of a glucose solution to give an osmotic pressure of 7.7 atm at 37°C?

12.100 Maltose, $C_{12}H_{22}O_{11}$, is a sugar produced by malting (sprouting) grain. A solution of maltose at 25°C has an osmotic pressure of 5.50 atm. What is the molar concentration of maltose?

12.101 Which aqueous solution has the lower freezing point, 0.10 m $CaCl_2$ or 0.10 m glucose?

12.102 Which aqueous solution has the lower boiling point, 0.10 m KCl or 0.10 m $CaCl_2$?

12.103 Commercially, sulfuric acid is obtained as a 98% solution. If this solution is 18 M, what is its density? What is its molality?

12.104 Phosphoric acid is usually obtained as an 85% phosphoric acid solution. If it is 15 M, what is the density of this solution? What is its molality?

12.105 A compound of manganese, carbon, and oxygen contains 28.17% Mn and 30.80% C. When 0.125 g of this compound is dissolved in 5.38 g of cyclohexane, the solution freezes at 5.28°C. What is the molecular formula of this compound?

12.106 A compound of cobalt, carbon, and oxygen contains 28.10% C and 34.47% Co. When 0.147 g of this compound is dissolved in 6.72 g of cyclohexane, the solution freezes at 5.23°C. What is the molecular formula of this compound?

12.107 The carbohydrate digitoxose contains 48.64% carbon and 8.16% hydrogen. The addition of 18.0 g of this compound to 100. g of water gives a solution that has a freezing point of −2.2°C.
   a. What is the molecular formula of the compound?
   b. What is the molar mass of this compound to the nearest tenth of a gram?

12.108 Analysis of a compound gave 39.50% C, 2.21% H, and 58.30% Cl. When 0.855 g of this solid was dissolved in 7.50 g of naphthalene, the solution had a freezing point of 78.0°C. The pure solvent freezes at 80.0°C; its molal freezing point constant is 6.8°C/m.
   a. What is the molecular formula of the compound?
   b. What is its molecular mass to the nearest 0.1 g?

12.109 Fish blood has an osmotic pressure equal to that of seawater. If seawater freezes at −2.3°C, what is the osmotic pressure of the blood at 25°C? To solve this problem, what assumptions must be made?

12.110 A salt solution has an osmotic pressure of 17 atmospheres at 22°C. What is the freezing point of this solution? What assumptions must be made to solve this problem?

12.111 What is the difference between normal hemoglobin and the hemoglobin associated with sickle-cell anemia? How does this affect the solubility of the hemoglobin?

12.112 What tends to happen to the hemoglobin in a blood cell of a person who has sickle-cell anemia? How does this affect the shape and oxygen-carrying capacity of the cell?

12.113 How are phospholipids similar in structure to a soap molecule? What structural difference accounts for the fact that phospholipids form lipid bilayers rather than the micelles that soaps form?

12.114 How have chemists used these phospholipids to form "the world's smallest test tubes"? Describe how these phospholipid vesicles might be used.

Strategy Problems

12.115 When 79.3 g of a particular compound is dissolved in 0.878 kg of water at 1 atm pressure, the solution freezes at −1.34°C. If the compound does not undergo ionization in solution and is nonvolatile, determine the molecular mass of the compound.

12.116 What is the boiling point of a solution made by adding 6.69 g of magnesium chloride to 243.3 g of water? Use the formula of the salt to obtain i.

12.117 At 15°C and a partial pressure of 2.14 atm, the solubility of an unknown gas in a liquid is 15.6 g/L. What is the solubility of the gas in the liquid when the partial pressure of the gas is

24.6 atm? What would happen to the solubility of the gas if the temperature of the liquid were increased?

12.118 Methanol, CH_3OH, is a compound that is used in car windshield washer fluid to lower the freezing point of the solution. If an aqueous solution of windshield washer fluid has a mole fraction of methanol of 0.520, what is the mass percentage of water in this solution?

12.119 How many grams of potassium chloride must be added to 372 g of water in order to prepare a 0.110 m potassium chloride solution?

12.120 Although somewhat toxic, barium chloride has been used as a cardiac stimulant. Calculate the number of moles of barium chloride in 427 g of a 3.17% by mass barium chloride solution?

12.121 Ethanol, CH_3CH_2OH, is known as grain alcohol and is the alcohol found in alcoholic beverages. Calculate the mole fraction of ethanol in a solution that contains 4.76 g of ethanol dissolved in 50.0 g of water.

12.122 A starch has a molar mass of 3.20×10^{04} g/mol. If 0.759 g of this starch is dissolved in 112 mL of solution, what is the osmotic pressure, *in torr*, at 25.00°C?

12.123 An aqueous solution is 0.797 *M* magnesium chloride. Given that the density of the solution is 1.108 g/mL, what is the molality of magnesium chloride in this solution?

12.124 A $CaCl_2$ solution at 25°C has an osmotic pressure of 16 atm and a density of 1.108 g/mL. What is the freezing point of this solution?

Cumulative-Skills Problems

12.125 An experimenter makes up a solution of 0.375 mol Na_2CO_3, 0.125 mol $Ca(NO_3)_2$, and 0.200 mol $AgNO_3$ in 2.000 L of water solution. Note any precipitations that occur, writing a balanced equation for each. Then, calculate the molarities of each ion in the solution.

12.126 An experimenter makes up a solution of 0.310 mol Na_3PO_4, 0.100 mol $Ca(NO_3)_2$, and 0.150 mol $AgNO_3$ in 4.000 L of water solution. Note any precipitations that occur, writing a balanced equation for each. Then, calculate the molarities of each ion in the solution.

12.127 The lattice enthalpy of sodium chloride, $\Delta H°$ for

$$NaCl(s) \longrightarrow Na^+(g) + Cl^-(g)$$

is 787 kJ/mol; the heat of solution in making up 1 *M* NaCl(*aq*) is +4.0 kJ/mol. From these data, obtain the sum of the heats of hydration of Na^+ and Cl^-. That is, obtain the sum of $\Delta H°$ values for

$$Na^+(g) \longrightarrow Na^+(aq)$$
$$Cl^+(g) \longrightarrow Cl^-(aq)$$

If the heat of hydration of Cl^- is -338 kJ/mol, what is the heat of hydration of Na^+?

12.128 The lattice enthalpy of potassium chloride is 717 kJ/mol; the heat of solution in making up 1 *M* KCl(*aq*) is +18.0 kJ/mol. Using the value for the heat of hydration of Cl^- given in Problem 12.125, obtain the heat of hydration of K^+. Compare this with the value you obtained for Na^+ in Problem 12.127. Explain the relative values of Na^+ and K^+.

12.129 A solution is made up by dissolving 15.0 g $MgSO_4 \cdot 7H_2O$ in 100.0 g of water. What is the molality of $MgSO_4$ in this solution?

12.130 A solution is made up by dissolving 15.0 g $Na_2CO_3 \cdot 10H_2O$ in 100.0 g of water. What is the molality of Na_2CO_3 in this solution?

12.131 An aqueous solution is 15.0% by mass of copper(II) sulfate pentahydrate, $CuSO_4 \cdot 5H_2O$. What is the molarity of $CuSO_4$ in this solution at 20°C? The density of this solution at 20°C is 1.167 g/mL.

12.132 An aqueous solution is 20.0% by mass of sodium thiosulfate pentahydrate, $Na_2S_2O_3 \cdot 5H_2O$. What is the molarity of $Na_2S_2O_3$ in this solution at 20°C? The density of this solution at 20°C is 1.174 g/mL.

12.133 The freezing point of 0.0830 *m* aqueous acetic acid is -0.159°C. Acetic acid, $HC_2H_3O_2$, is partially dissociated according to the equation

$$HC_2H_3O_2(aq) \rightleftharpoons H^+(aq) + C_2H_3O_2^-(aq)$$

Calculate the percentage of $HC_2H_3O_2$ molecules that are dissociated, assuming the equation for the freezing-point depression holds for the total concentration of molecules and ions in the solution.

12.134 The freezing point of 0.109 *m* aqueous formic acid is -0.210°C. Formic acid, $HCHO_2$, is partially dissociated according to the equation

$$HCHO_2(aq) \rightleftharpoons H^+(aq) + CHO_2^-(aq)$$

Calculate the percentage of $HCHO_2$ molecules that are dissociated, assuming the equation for the freezing-point depression holds for the total concentration of molecules and ions in the solution.

12.135 A compound of carbon, hydrogen, and oxygen was burned in oxygen, and 1.000 g of the compound produced 1.434 g CO_2 and 0.783 g H_2O. In another experiment, 0.1107 g of the compound was dissolved in 25.0 g of water. This solution had a freezing point of -0.0894°C. What is the molecular formula of the compound?

12.136 A compound of carbon, hydrogen, and oxygen was burned in oxygen, and 1.000 g of the compound produced 1.418 g CO_2 and 0.871 g H_2O. In another experiment, 0.1103 g of the compound was dissolved in 45.0 g of water. This solution had a freezing point of -0.0734°C. What is the molecular formula of the compound?

13

Rates of Reaction

The bombardier beetle and the rocket belt use hydrogen peroxide (H_2O_2) to fuel energetic reactions. In both reactions, a catalyst rapidly breaks down the H_2O_2, releasing oxygen, heat, and water vapor. The pressure from these hot gas mixtures being released is enough to expel a caustic chemical defense or propel a person into the air.

Contents and Concepts

We will investigate how to determine the rate of chemical reactions and identify the factors that influence this rate.

We continue to look at reaction rate; however, the focus has shifted to an atomic and molecular perspective.

C hemical reactions require varying lengths of time for completion, depending on the characteristics of the reactants and products and the conditions under which the reaction is run (Figure 13.1). Many reactions are over in a fraction of a second, whereas others can take much longer. If you add barium ion to an aqueous solution of sulfate ion, a precipitate of barium sulfate forms almost immediately. On the other hand, the reactions that occur in a cement mixture as it hardens to concrete require years for completion.

The study of the rate, or speed, of a reaction has important applications. In the manufacture of ammonia from nitrogen and hydrogen, you may wish to know what conditions will help the reaction proceed in a commercially feasible length of time. You may also wish to know whether the nitrogen monoxide, NO, in the exhaust gases of high-altitude aircraft will destroy the ozone in the stratosphere faster than the ozone is produced. Answering these questions requires knowledge of the rates of reactions.

Another reason for studying reaction rates is to understand how chemical reactions occur. By noting how the rate of a reaction is affected by changing conditions, you can sometimes learn the details of what is happening at the molecular level.

A reaction whose rate has been extensively studied under various conditions is the decomposition of dinitrogen pentoxide, N_2O_5. When this substance is heated in the gas phase, it decomposes to nitrogen dioxide and oxygen:

$$2N_2O_5(g) \longrightarrow 4NO_2(g) + O_2(g)$$

We will look at this reaction in some detail. The questions we will pose include: How is the rate of a reaction like this measured? What conditions affect the rate of a reaction? How do you express the relationship of rate of a reaction to the variables that affect rate? What happens at the molecular level when N_2O_5 decomposes to NO_2 and O_2?

■ See page 566 for the Media Summary.

FIGURE 13.1 ▲
Reaction time
A chemical reaction takes time. Some reactions are complete in a fraction of a second; others take years. The reaction shown here is complete in less than a minute. The reaction is the formation of a product of formaldehyde with hydrogen sulfite ion: $H_2C{=}O(aq) + HSO_3^-(aq) \longrightarrow H_2C(OH)SO_3^-(aq)$. As the hydrogen sulfite ion is used up, the solution becomes less acidic and then changes to basic. Bromthymol-blue indicator marks the change from acidic to basic by changing from yellow to blue.

Reaction Rates

Chemical kinetics is the study of reaction rates, how reaction rates change under varying conditions, and what molecular events occur during the overall reaction. In the first part of this chapter, we will look at reaction rates and the variables that affect them.

What variables affect reaction rates? As we noted in the chapter opening, the rate depends on the characteristics of the reactants in a particular reaction. Some reactions are fast and others are slow, but the rate of any given reaction may be affected by the following factors:

1. *Concentrations of reactants.* Often the rate of reaction increases when the concentration of a reactant is increased. A piece of steel wool burns with some difficulty in air (20% O_2) but bursts into a dazzling white flame in pure oxygen. The

FIGURE 13.2 ▶

Catalytic decomposition of hydrogen peroxide
The hydrogen peroxide decomposes rapidly when hydrobromic acid is added to an aqueous solution. One of the products is oxygen gas, which bubbles vigorously from the solution. In addition, some HBr is oxidized to Br_2, as can be seen from the red color of the liquid and vapor.

FIGURE 13.3 ▲

Effect of large surface area on the rate of reaction
Lycopodium powder (from the tiny spores of a club moss) ignites easily to produce a yellow flame. The powder has a large surface area per volume and burns rapidly in air.

rate of burning increases with the concentration of O_2. In some reactions, however, the rate is unaffected by the concentration of a particular reactant, as long as it is present at some concentration.

2. *Concentration of catalyst.* A **catalyst** is *a substance that increases the rate of reaction without being consumed in the overall reaction.* Because the catalyst is not consumed by the reaction, it does not appear in the balanced chemical equation (although its presence may be indicated by writing its formula over the arrow). A solution of pure hydrogen peroxide, H_2O_2, is stable, but when hydrobromic acid, HBr(*aq*), is added, H_2O_2 decomposes rapidly into H_2O and O_2 (Figure 13.2).

$$2H_2O_2(aq) \xrightarrow{\text{HBr}(aq)} 2H_2O(l) + O_2(g)$$

Here HBr acts as a catalyst to speed decomposition.

3. *Temperature at which the reaction occurs.* Usually reactions speed up when the temperature increases. It takes less time to boil an egg at sea level than on a mountaintop, where water boils at a lower temperature. Reactions during cooking go faster at higher temperature.

4. *Surface area of a solid reactant or catalyst.* If a reaction involves a solid with a gas or liquid, the surface area of the solid affects the reaction rate. Because the reaction occurs at the surface of the solid, the rate increases with increasing surface area. A wood fire burns faster if the logs are chopped into smaller pieces. Similarly, the surface area of a solid catalyst is important to the rate of reaction. The greater the surface area per unit volume, the faster the reaction (Figure 13.3).

In the first sections of this chapter, we will look primarily at reactions in the gas phase and in liquid solution where factors 1 to 3 are important. Thus, we will look at the effect of *concentrations* and *temperature* on reaction rates. Before we can explore these factors, however, we need a precise definition of reaction rate.

13.1 | Definition of Reaction Rate

The rate of a reaction is the amount of product formed or the amount of reactant used up per unit of time. So that a rate calculation does not depend on the total quantity of reaction mixture used, you express the rate for a unit volume of the mixture. Therefore, the **reaction rate** is *the increase in molar concentration of product of a reaction per unit time or the decrease in molar concentration of reactant per unit time.* The usual unit of reaction rate is moles per liter per second, mol/(L·s).

Consider the gas-phase reaction discussed in the chapter opening:

$$2N_2O_5(g) \longrightarrow 4NO_2(g) + O_2(g)$$

The rate for this reaction could be found by observing the increase in molar concentration of O_2 produced. You denote the molar concentration of a substance by enclosing

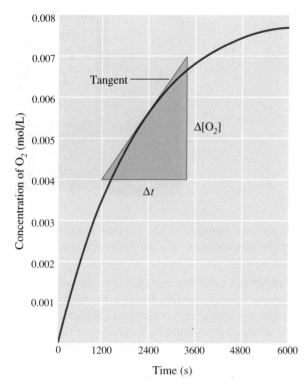

FIGURE 13.4 ▲

The instantaneous rate of reaction
In the reaction $2N_2O_5(g) \longrightarrow 4NO_2(g) + O_2(g)$, the concentration of O_2 increases over time. You obtain the instantaneous rate at a given time from the slope of the tangent at the point on the curve corresponding to that time. In this diagram, the slope equals $\Delta[O_2]/\Delta t$ obtained from the tangent.

| In calculus, the rate at a given moment (the instantaneous rate) is given by the derivative $d\,[O_2]/dt$.

its formula in square brackets. Thus, $[O_2]$ is the molar concentration of O_2. In a given time interval Δt, the molar concentration of oxygen, $[O_2]$, in the reaction vessel increases by the amount $\Delta[O_2]$. The symbol Δ (capital Greek delta) means "change in"; you obtain the change by subtracting the initial value from the final value. The rate of the reaction is given by

$$\text{Rate of formation of oxygen} = \frac{\Delta[O_2]}{\Delta t}$$

This equation gives the *average* rate over the time interval Δt. If the time interval is very short, the equation gives the *instantaneous* rate—that is, the rate at a particular instant of time. The instantaneous rate is also the value of $\Delta[O_2]/\Delta t$ for the tangent at a given instant (the straight line that just touches the curve of concentration versus time at a given point). See Figure 13.4. <

To understand the difference between average rate and instantaneous rate, it may help to think of the speed of an automobile. Speed can be defined as the rate of change of position, x; that is, speed equals $\Delta x/\Delta t$, where Δx is the distance traveled. If an automobile travels 84 miles in 2.0 hours, the average speed over this time interval is 84 mi/2.0 hr = 42 mi/hr. However, at any instant during this interval, the speedometer, which registers instantaneous speed, may read more or less than 42 mi/hr. At some moment on the highway, it may read 55 mi/hr, whereas on a congested city street it may read only 20 mi/hr. The quantity $\Delta x/\Delta t$ becomes more nearly an instantaneous speed as the time interval Δt is made smaller.

Figure 13.5 shows the increase in concentration of O_2 during the decomposition of N_2O_5. It shows the calculation of average rates at two positions on the curve. For

FIGURE 13.5 ▶

Calculation of the average rate
The average rate of formation of O_2 during the decomposition of N_2O_5 was calculated during two different time intervals. When the time changes from 600 s to 1200 s, the average rate is 2.5×10^{-6} mol/(L·s). Later, when the time changes from 4200 s to 4800 s, the average rate has slowed to 5×10^{-7} mol/(L·s). Thus, the rate of the reaction decreases as the reaction proceeds.

Time	$[O_2]$
0	0.0000
600	0.0021
1200	0.0036
1800	0.0048
2400	0.0057
3000	0.0063
3600	0.0068
4200	0.0072
4800	0.0075
5400	0.0077
6000	0.0078

example, when the time changes from 600 s to 1200 s ($\Delta t = 600$ s), the O_2 concentration increases by 0.0015 mol/L ($= \Delta[O_2]$). Therefore, the average rate $= \Delta[O_2]/\Delta t = (0.0015 \text{ mol/L})/600$ s $= 2.5 \times 10^{-6}$ mol/(L·s). Later, during the time interval from 4200 s to 4800 s, the average rate is 5×10^{-7} mol/(L·s). Note that the rate decreases as the reaction proceeds.

Because the amounts of products and reactants are related by stoichiometry, any substance in the reaction can be used to express the rate of reaction. In the case of the decomposition of N_2O_5 to NO_2 and O_2, we gave the rate in terms of the rate of formation of oxygen, $\Delta[O_2]/\Delta t$. However, you can also express it in terms of the rate of decomposition of N_2O_5.

$$\text{Rate of decomposition of } N_2O_5 = -\frac{\Delta[N_2O_5]}{\Delta t}$$

Note the negative sign. It always occurs in a rate expression for a reactant in order to indicate a decrease in concentration and to give a positive value for the rate. Thus, because $[N_2O_5]$ decreases, $\Delta[N_2O_5]$ is negative and $-\Delta[N_2O_5]/\Delta t$ is positive.

The rate of decomposition of N_2O_5 and the rate of formation of oxygen are easily related. Two moles of N_2O_5 decompose for each mole of oxygen formed, so the rate of decomposition of N_2O_5 is twice the rate of formation of oxygen. To equate the rates, you must divide the rate of decomposition of N_2O_5 by 2 (its coefficient in the balanced chemical equation).

$$\text{Rate of formation of } O_2 = \tfrac{1}{2}(\text{rate of decomposition of } N_2O_5)$$

or

$$\frac{\Delta[O_2]}{\Delta t} = -\tfrac{1}{2}\frac{\Delta[N_2O_5]}{\Delta t}$$

Example 13.1 Relating the Different Ways of Expressing Reaction Rates

Consider the reaction of nitrogen dioxide with fluorine to give nitryl fluoride, NO_2F.

$$2NO_2(g) + F_2(g) \longrightarrow 2NO_2F(g)$$

How is the rate of formation of NO_2F related to the rate of reaction of fluorine?

Problem Strategy We need to express the rate of this reaction in terms of concentration changes with time of the product, NO_2F, and reactant, F_2, and then relate these two rates. The rate of disappearance of reactants is expressed as a negative quantity of concentration change per some time interval. The rate of formation of products is expressed as a positive quantity of concentration change per some time interval. In order to equate rate expressions, we need to divide each by the coefficient of the corresponding substance in the chemical equation.

Solution You write

$$\text{Rate of formation of } NO_2F = \frac{\Delta[NO_2F]}{\Delta t}$$

and

$$\text{Rate of reaction of } F_2 = -\frac{\Delta[F_2]}{\Delta t}$$

You divide each rate by the corresponding coefficient and then equate them:

$$\frac{1}{2}\frac{\Delta[NO_2F]}{\Delta t} = -\frac{\Delta[F_2]}{\Delta t}$$

NO_2

(continued)

Answer Check   When solving problems such as this, always make sure that you have expressed the rates with the correct sign: negative for reactants, positive for products.

Exercise 13.1   For the reaction given in Example 13.1, how is the rate of formation of NO_2F related to the rate of reaction of NO_2?

■ See Problems 13.39 and 13.40.

Example 13.2 | Calculating the Average Reaction Rate

Calculate the average rate of decomposition of N_2O_5, $-\Delta[N_2O_5]/\Delta t$, by the reaction

$$2N_2O_5(g) \longrightarrow 4NO_2(g) + O_2(g)$$

during the time interval from $t = 600$ s to $t = 1200$ s (regard all time figures as significant). Use the following data:

Time	$[N_2O_5]$
600 s	$1.24 \times 10^{-2}\ M$
1200 s	$0.93 \times 10^{-2}\ M$

Problem Strategy   An average reaction rate is the change in concentration of a reactant or product over a time interval; in this case it's the rate of decomposition of the reactant N_2O_5 $(-\Delta[N_2O_5]/\Delta t)$. The $\Delta[N_2O_5]$ in the equation is the change in concentration of N_2O_5 (final value minus initial value). The Δt is the time interval (final minus initial) over which the concentration change occurred.

Solution   Average rate of decomposition of $N_2O_5 = -\dfrac{\Delta[N_2O_5]}{\Delta t} =$

$$-\frac{(0.93 - 1.24) \times 10^{-2}\ M}{(1200 - 600)\ \text{s}} = -\frac{-0.31 \times 10^{-2}\ M}{600\ \text{s}} = \mathbf{5.2 \times 10^{-6}\ \textit{M/s}}$$

Note that this rate is twice the rate of formation of O_2 in the same time interval (within the experimental error of the value given in the preceding text discussion).

Answer Check   Always make sure that your reaction rates are expressed as a positive number. If you end up with a negative rate, it is likely that you did not treat Δ quantities as a final value minus an initial value.

Exercise 13.2   Iodide ion is oxidized by hypochlorite ion in basic solution.

$$I^-(aq) + ClO^-(aq) \longrightarrow Cl^-(aq) + IO^-(aq)$$

In 1.00 M NaOH at 25°C, the iodide-ion concentration (equal to the ClO^- concentration) at different times was as follows:

Time	$[I^-]$
2.00 s	0.00169 M
8.00 s	0.00101 M

Calculate the average rate of reaction of I^- during this time interval.

■ See Problems 13.46 and 13.47.

Concept Check 13.1

Shown here is a plot of the concentration of a reactant D versus time.

a. How do the instantaneous rates at points A and B compare?

b. Is the rate for this reaction constant at all points in time?

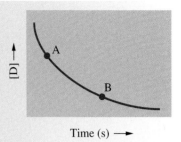

13.2 | Experimental Determination of Rate

Ethyl acetate is a liquid with a fruity odor that belongs to a class of organic (carbon-containing) compounds called esters.

To obtain the rate of a reaction, you must determine the concentration of a reactant or product during the course of the reaction. One way to do this for a slow reaction is to withdraw samples from the reaction vessel at various times and analyze them. The rate of the reaction of ethyl acetate with water in acidic solution was one of the first to be determined this way. <

$$CH_3CH_2OCCH_3 + H_2O \xrightarrow{H^+} CH_3CH_2OH + HOCCH_3$$

Ethyl acetate   Ethanol   Ecetic acid

This reaction is slow, so the amount of acetic acid produced is easily obtained by titration before any significant further reaction occurs.

More convenient are techniques that can continuously follow the progress of a reaction by observing the change in some physical property of the system. These physical methods are often adaptable to fast reactions as well as slow ones. For example, if a gas reaction involves a change in the number of molecules, the pressure of the system changes when the volume and temperature are held constant. By following the pressure change as the reaction proceeds, you can obtain the reaction rate. The decomposition of dinitrogen pentoxide in the gas phase, which we mentioned earlier, has been studied this way. Dinitrogen pentoxide crystals are sealed in a vessel equipped with a manometer (a pressure-measuring device; see Figure 13.6). The vessel is then plunged into a water bath at 45°C, at which temperature the solid vaporizes and the gas decomposes.

$$2N_2O_5(g) \longrightarrow 4NO_2(g) + O_2(g)$$

FIGURE 13.6 ▶

An experiment to follow the concentration of N_2O_5 as the decomposition proceeds

The total pressure is measured during the reaction at 45°C. Pressure values can be related to the concentrations of N_2O_5, NO_2, and O_2 in the flask.

Manometer readings are taken at regular time intervals, and the pressure values are converted to partial pressures or concentrations of N_2O_5. The rates of reaction during various time intervals can be calculated as described in the previous section.

Another physical property used to follow the progress of a reaction is color, or the absorption of light by some species. Consider the reaction

$$ClO^-(aq) + I^-(aq) \longrightarrow IO^-(aq) + Cl^-(aq)$$

The hypoiodite ion, IO^-, absorbs at the blue end of the spectrum near 400 nm. The intensity of this absorption is proportional to $[IO^-]$, and you can use the absorption to determine the reaction rate. You can also follow the decomposition of N_2O_5 from the intensity of the red-brown color of the product NO_2.

In these experiments, the intensity of absorption at a particular wavelength is measured by a spectrometer appropriate for the visible region of the spectrum. You are not limited to the use of visible-region spectrometers for the determination of reaction rates, however. Depending on the reaction, other types of instruments are used, including infrared (IR) and nuclear magnetic resonance (NMR) spectrometers, which are described briefly in Instrumental Methods essays in earlier chapters.

13.3 | Dependence of Rate on Concentration

Experimentally, it has been found that a reaction rate depends on the concentrations of certain reactants as well as the concentration of catalyst, if there is one (Figure 13.7). Consider the reaction of nitrogen dioxide with fluorine to give nitryl fluoride, NO_2F.

$$2NO_2(g) + F_2(g) \longrightarrow 2NO_2F(g)$$

FIGURE 13.7 ▼

Effect of reactant concentrations on rate of reaction

(A) Both beakers contain the same amounts of reactants: sodium thiosulfate, $Na_2S_2O_3$, in acidic solution and sodium arsenite, Na_3AsO_3. However, the beaker on the right contains more water and thus lower concentrations of reactants. *(B)* $Na_2S_2O_3$ decomposes slowly in acidic solution to yield H_2S, which reacts quickly with Na_3AsO_3 to give a bright yellow precipitate of As_2S_3. The time it takes the precipitate to form depends on the decomposition rate of $Na_2S_2O_3$. *(C)* Note that the precipitate forms more slowly in the solution of lower concentrations (the beaker on the right).

The rate of this reaction is observed to be proportional to the concentration of nitrogen dioxide. When the concentration of nitrogen dioxide is doubled, the rate doubles. The rate is also proportional to the concentration of fluorine; doubling the concentration of fluorine also doubles the rate.

A **rate law** is *an equation that relates the rate of a reaction to the concentrations of reactants (and catalyst) raised to various powers.* The following equation is the rate law for the foregoing reaction:

$$\text{Rate} = k[NO_2][F_2]$$

Note that in this rate law both reactant concentrations have an exponent of 1. Here k, called the **rate constant**, is *a proportionality constant in the relationship between rate and concentrations.* It has a fixed value at any given temperature, but it varies with

Time = 0	Time = 20 seconds	Time = 40 seconds
A	B	C

temperature. Whereas the units of rate are usually given as mol/(L·s), the units of k depend on the form of the rate law. For the previous rate law,

$$k = \frac{\text{rate}}{[NO_2][F_2]}$$

from which you get the following unit for k:

$$\frac{\text{mol/(L·s)}}{(\text{mol/L})^2} = \text{L/(mol·s)}$$

As a more general example, consider the reaction of substances A and B to give D and E, according to the balanced equation

$$a\text{A} + b\text{B} \xrightarrow{\text{C}} d\text{D} + e\text{E} \qquad \text{C} = \text{catalyst}$$

You could write the rate law in the form

$$\text{Rate} = k[\text{A}]^m[\text{B}]^n[\text{C}]^p$$

The exponents m, n, and p are frequently, but not always, integers. *They must be determined experimentally* and they cannot be obtained simply by looking at the balanced equation. For example, note that the exponents in the equation Rate = $k[NO_2][F_2]$ have no relationship to the coefficients in the balanced equation $2NO_2 + F_2 \longrightarrow 2NO_2F$.

Once you know the rate law for a reaction and have found the value of the rate constant, you can calculate the rate of a reaction for any values of reactant concentrations. As you will see later, knowledge of the rate law is also useful in understanding how the reaction occurs at the molecular level.

Reaction Order

You can classify a reaction by its orders. The **reaction order** with respect to a given reactant species equals *the exponent of the concentration of that species in the rate law, as determined experimentally*. For the reaction of NO_2 with F_2 to give NO_2F, the reaction is first order with respect to the NO_2 because the exponent of $[NO_2]$ in the rate law is 1. Similarly, the reaction is first order with respect to F_2.

The **overall order of a reaction** equals *the sum of the orders of the reactant species in the rate law*. In this example, the overall order is 2; that is, the reaction is second order overall.

Reactions display a variety of reaction orders. Some examples follow.

1. Cyclopropane, C_3H_6, has the molecular structure

$$\begin{array}{c} \text{CH}_2 \\ \diagup \quad \diagdown \\ \text{H}_2\text{C} \!\!-\!\!\!-\!\! \text{CH}_2 \end{array}$$

When heated, the carbon ring (the triangle) opens up to give propylene, $CH_2{=}CHCH_3$. Because the compounds are isomers (different compounds with the same molecular formula), the reaction is called an *isomerization*.

$$C_3H_6(g) \longrightarrow CH_2{=}CHCH_3(g)$$

Cyclopropane   Propylene

The reaction has the experimentally determined rate law

$$\text{Rate} = k[\text{C}_3\text{H}_6]$$

The reaction is first order in cyclopropane and first order overall.

2. Nitrogen monoxide, NO, reacts with hydrogen according to the equation

$$2\text{NO}(g) + 2\text{H}_2(g) \longrightarrow \text{N}_2 + 2\text{H}_2\text{O}(g)$$

The experimentally determined rate law is

$$\text{Rate} = k[\text{NO}]^2[\text{H}_2]$$

Thus, the reaction is second order in NO, first order in H_2, and third order overall.

3. Acetone, CH_3COCH_3, reacts with iodine in acidic solution.

$$\text{CH}_3\text{COCH}_3(aq) + \text{I}_2(aq) \xrightarrow{\text{H}^+} \text{CH}_3\text{COCH}_2\text{I}(aq) + \text{HI}(aq)$$

The experimentally determined rate law is

$$\text{Rate} = k[\text{CH}_3\text{COCH}_3][\text{H}^+]$$

The reaction is first order in acetone. It is zero order in iodine; that is, the rate law contains the factor $[\text{I}_2]^0 = 1$. Therefore, the rate does not depend on the concentration of I_2, as long as some concentration of I_2 is present. Note that the reaction is first order in the catalyst, H^+. Thus, the overall order is 2.

Although reaction orders frequently have whole-number values (particularly 1 or 2), they can be fractional. Zero and negative orders are also possible.

Example 13.3 | Determining the Order of Reaction from the Rate Law

Bromide ion is oxidized by bromate ion in acidic solution.

$$5\text{Br}^-(aq) + \text{BrO}_3^-(aq) + 6\text{H}^+(aq) \longrightarrow 3\text{Br}_2(aq) + 3\text{H}_2\text{O}(l)$$

The experimentally determined rate law is

$$\text{Rate} = k[\text{Br}^-][\text{BrO}_3^-][\text{H}^+]^2$$

What is the order of reaction with respect to each reactant species? What is the overall order of the reaction?

Problem Strategy   The exponent of each of the reactants given in the experimentally determined rate law is the reaction order of that reactant. The overall order of the reaction is the sum of the orders of the reactant species in the rate law.

Solution   The reaction is **first order with respect to Br^-** and **first order with respect to BrO_3^-**; it is **second order with respect to H^+. The reaction is fourth order overall** $(= 1 + 1 + 2)$.

Answer Check   Whenever you are determining the order of reactions or of reactant species, never rely on the stoichiometry of the reaction. You must use the experimentally determined rate law.

(continued)

(*continued*)

Exercise 13.3   What are the reaction orders with respect to each reactant species for the following reaction?

$$NO_2(g) + CO(g) \longrightarrow NO(g) + CO_2(g)$$

Assume the rate law is

$$Rate = k[NO_2]^2$$

What is the overall order?

■ See Problems 13.47, 13.48, 13.49, and 13.50.

Concept Check 13.2

Consider the reaction $Q + R \longrightarrow S + T$ and the rate law for the reaction:

$$Rate = k[Q]^0[R]^2$$

a. You run the reaction three times, each time starting with $[R] = 2.0\ M$. For each run you change the starting concentration of $[Q]$: run 1, $[Q] = 0.0\ M$; run 2, $[Q] = 1.0\ M$; run 3, $[Q] = 2.0\ M$. Rank the rate of the three reactions using each of these concentrations.

b. The way the rate law is written in this problem is not typical for expressions containing reactants that are zero order in the rate law. Write the rate law in the more typical fashion.

Determining the Rate Law

The experimental determination of the rate law for a reaction requires that you find the order of the reaction with respect to each reactant and any catalyst. The *initial-rate method* is a simple way to obtain reaction orders. It consists of doing a series of experiments in which the initial, or starting, concentrations of reactants are varied. Then the initial rates are compared, from which the reaction orders can be deduced.

To see how this method works, again consider the reaction

$$2N_2O_5(g) \longrightarrow 4NO_2(g) + O_2(g)$$

You observe this reaction in two experiments. In Experiment 2, the initial concentration of N_2O_5 is twice that in Experiment 1. You then note the initial rate of disappearance of N_2O_5 in each case. The initial concentrations and corresponding initial rates for the two experiments are given in the following table: <

In Figure 13.4, the slope of the tangent to the curve at t = 0 equals the initial rate of appearance of O_2, which equals one-half the initial rate of disappearance of N_2O_5.

	Initial N_2O_5 Concentration	*Initial Rate of Disappearance of N_2O_5*
Experiment 1	1.0×10^{-2} mol/L	4.8×10^{-6} mol/(L·s)
Experiment 2	2.0×10^{-2} mol/L	9.6×10^{-6} mol/(L·s)

TABLE 13.1

Effect on Rate of Doubling the Initial Concentration of Reactant

m	Rate Is Multiplied by:
-1	$\frac{1}{2}$
0	1
1	2
2	4

The rate law for this reaction will have the concentration of reactant raised to a power m.

$$\text{Rate} = k[N_2O_5]^m$$

The value of m (the reaction order) must be determined from the experimental data. Note that when the N_2O_5 concentration is doubled, you get a new rate, Rate′, given by the following equation:

$$\text{Rate}' = k(2[N_2O_5])^m = 2^m k[N_2O_5]^m$$

This rate is 2^m times the original rate.

You can now see how the rate is affected when the concentration is doubled for various choices of m. Suppose $m = 2$. You get $2^m = 2^2 = 4$. That is, when the initial concentration is doubled, the rate is multiplied by 4. We summarize the results for various choices of m in Table 13.1.

Suppose you divide the initial rate of reaction of N_2O_5 from Experiment 2 by the initial rate from Experiment 1.

$$\frac{9.6 \times 10^{-6}\,\text{mol/(L·s)}}{4.8 \times 10^{-6}\,\text{mol/(L·s)}} = 2.0$$

You see that when the N_2O_5 concentration is doubled, the rate is doubled. This corresponds to the case $m = 1$. The rate law must have the form

$$\text{Rate} = k[N_2O_5]$$

You can determine the value of the rate constant k by substituting values of the rate and N_2O_5 concentrations from any of the experiments into the rate law. Using values from Experiment 2, you get

$$9.6 \times 10^{-6}\,\text{mol/(L·s)} = k \times 2.0 \times 10^{-2}\,\text{mol/L}$$

Hence,

$$k = \frac{9.6 \times 10^{-6}/\text{s}}{2.0 \times 10^{-2}} = 4.8 \times 10^{-4}/\text{s}$$

Example 13.4 | Determining the Rate Law from Initial Rates

Iodide ion is oxidized in acidic solution to triiodide ion, I_3^-, by hydrogen peroxide.

$$H_2O_2(aq) + 3I^-(aq) + 2H^+(aq) \longrightarrow I_3^-(aq) + 2H_2O(l)$$

A series of four experiments was run at different concentrations, and the initial rates of I_3^- formation were determined (see table). a. From these data, obtain the reaction orders with respect to H_2O_2, I^-, and H^+. b. Then find the rate constant.

	Initial Concentrations (mol/L)			Initial Rate
	H_2O_2	I^-	H^+	[mol/(L·s)]
Exp. 1	0.010	0.010	0.00050	1.15×10^{-6}
Exp. 2	0.020	0.010	0.00050	2.30×10^{-6}
Exp. 3	0.010	0.020	0.00050	2.30×10^{-6}
Exp. 4	0.010	0.010	0.00100	1.15×10^{-6}

H_2O_2

(continued)

(continued)

Problem Strategy a. In order to know the reaction orders of the reactants, you need to know the rate law. Using the reactants in the chemical equation, you assume the rate law has the following form:

$$\text{Rate} = k[H_2O_2]^m[I^-]^n[H^+]^p$$

You can determine each of the reaction orders (exponents m, n, and p) by choosing experiments in which all concentrations of reactants except one are held constant. Solving for each exponent will require comparing different experiments. Once you know the reaction orders, you will know the rate law. b. To determine the rate constant, you can take the data from one of the experiments and substitute them into the rate law; the only unknown in the equation will be the rate constant, k.

Solution a. Comparing Experiment 1 and Experiment 2, you see that when the H_2O_2 concentration is doubled (with other concentrations constant), the rate is doubled. From Table 13.1, you see that $m = 1$. The reaction is first order in H_2O_2.

To solve a problem such as this in a general way, you approach it algebraically. You write the rate law for two experiments. (The subscripts denote the experiments.)

$$(\text{Rate})_1 = k[H_2O_2]_1^m[I^-]_1^n[H^+]_1^p$$

$$(\text{Rate})_2 = k[H_2O_2]_2^m[I^-]_2^n[H^+]_2^p$$

Now you divide the second equation by the first.

$$\frac{(\text{Rate})_2}{(\text{Rate})_1} = \frac{k[H_2O_2]_2^m[I^-]_2^n[H^+]_2^p}{k[H_2O_2]_1^m[I^-]_1^n[H^+]_1^p}$$

The rate constant cancels. Grouping the terms, you obtain

$$\frac{(\text{Rate})_2}{(\text{Rate})_1} = \left(\frac{[H_2O_2]_2}{[H_2O_2]_1}\right)^m\left(\frac{[I^-]_2}{[I^-]_1}\right)^n\left(\frac{[H^+]_2}{[H^+]_1}\right)^p$$

Now you substitute values from Experiment 1 and Experiment 2. (In a ratio the units cancel and can be omitted.)

$$\frac{2.30 \times 10^{-6}}{1.15 \times 10^{-6}} = \left[\frac{0.020}{0.010}\right]^m\left[\frac{0.010}{0.010}\right]^n\left[\frac{0.00050}{0.00050}\right]^p$$

This gives $2 = 2^m$, from which you obtain $m = 1$. That is, doubling the H_2O_2 concentration doubles the rate.

The exponents n and p are obtained in the same way. Comparing Experiment 1 and Experiment 3, you see that doubling the I^- concentration (with the other concentrations constant) doubles the rate. Therefore, $n = 1$ (the reaction is first order in I^-). Finally, comparing Experiment 1 and Experiment 4, you see that doubling the H^+ concentration (holding other concentrations constant) has no effect on the rate. Therefore, $p = 0$ (the reaction is zero order in H^+). Because $[H^+]^0 = 1$, the rate law is

$$\text{Rate} = k[H_2O_2][I^-]$$

The reaction orders with respect to H_2O_2, I^-, and H^+, are **1, 1, and 0,** respectively. Note that the orders are *not* related to the coefficients of the overall equation.

b. You calculate the rate constant by substituting values from any of the experiments into the rate law. Using Experiment 1, you obtain

$$1.15 \times 10^{-6}\frac{\text{mol}}{\text{L·s}} = k \times 0.010\frac{\text{mol}}{\text{L}} \times 0.010\frac{\text{mol}}{\text{L}}$$

$$k = \frac{1.15 \times 10^{-6}/s}{0.010 \times 0.010 \times \text{mol/L}} = \mathbf{1.2 \times 10^{-2}\ L/(mol·s)}$$

(continued)

(continued)

Answer Check   Although reaction orders of greater than 2 are certainly possible, they are not nearly as common as those less than or equal to 2. If you keep this fact in mind when solving problems of this type, a reaction order greater than 2 should be looked at carefully to make sure that a calculation error wasn't made.

Exercise 13.4   The initial-rate method was applied to the decomposition of nitrogen dioxide.

$$2NO_2(g) \longrightarrow 2NO(g) + O_2(g)$$

It yielded the following results:

	Initial NO_2 Concentration	Initial Rate of Formation of O_2
Exp.1	0.010 mol/L	7.1×10^{-5} mol/(L·s)
Exp.2	0.020 mol/L	28×10^{-5} mol/(L·s)

Find the rate law and the value of the rate constant with respect to O_2 formation.

■ See Problems 13.51, 13.52, 13.53, 13.54, 13.55, and 13.56.

Concept Check 13.3

Rate laws are not restricted to chemical systems; they are used to help describe many "everyday" events. For example, a rate law for tree growth might look something like this:

$$\text{Rate of growth} = (\text{soil type})^w(\text{temperature})^x(\text{light})^y(\text{fertilizer})^z$$

In this equation, like chemical rate equations, the exponents need to be determined by experiment. (Can you think of some other factors?)

a. Say you are a famous physician trying to determine the factors that influence the rate of aging in humans. Develop a rate law, like the one above, that would take into account at least four factors that affect the rate of aging.

b. Explain what you would need to do in order to determine the exponents in your rate law.

c. Consider smoking to be one of the factors in your rate law. You conduct an experiment and find that a person smoking two packs of cigarettes a day quadruples (4×) the rate of aging over that of a one-pack-a-day smoker. Assuming that you could hold all other factors in your rate law constant, what would be the exponent of the smoking term in your rate law?

13.4 | Change of Concentration with Time

A rate law tells you how the rate of a reaction depends on reactant concentrations at a particular moment. But often you would like to have a mathematical relationship showing how a reactant concentration changes over a period of time. Such an equation would be directly comparable to the experimental data, which are usually obtained as concentrations at various times. In addition to summarizing the experimental data, this equation would predict concentrations for all times. Using it, you could answer questions such as: How long does it take for this reaction to be 50% complete? to be 90% complete?

Moreover, as you will see, knowing exactly how the concentrations change with time for different rate laws suggests ways of plotting the experimental data on a graph. Graphical plotting provides an alternative to the initial-rate method for determining the rate law.

Using calculus, we can transform a rate law into a *mathematical relationship between concentration and time* called an **integrated rate law.** Because we will work only with the final equations, we need not go into the derivations here. We will look in some depth at first-order reactions and briefly at second-order and zero-order reactions.

Integrated Rate Laws (Concentration—Time Equations)

First-Order Rate Law   Let us first look at first-order rate laws. The decomposition of dinitrogen pentoxide,

$$2N_2O_5(g) \longrightarrow 4NO_2(g) + O_2(g)$$

has the following rate law:

$$\text{Rate} = -\frac{\Delta[N_2O_5]}{\Delta t} = k[N_2O_5]$$

Using calculus, one can show that such a first-order rate law leads to the following relationship between N_2O_5 concentration and time: <

$$\ln \frac{[N_2O_5]_t}{[N_2O_5]_0} = -kt$$

Here $[N_2O_5]_t$ is the concentration at time t, and $[N_2O_5]_0$ is the initial concentration of N_2O_5 (that is, the concentration at $t = 0$). The symbol "ln" denotes the natural logarithm (base $e = 2.718 \ldots$).

This equation enables you to calculate the concentration of N_2O_5 at any time, once you are given the initial concentration and the rate constant. Also, you can find the time it takes for the N_2O_5 concentration to decrease to a particular value.

More generally, let A be a substance that reacts to give products according to the equation

$$a\text{A} \longrightarrow \text{products}$$

where a is the stoichiometric coefficient of reactant A. Suppose that this reaction has a first-order rate law

$$\text{Rate} = -\frac{\Delta[\text{A}]}{\Delta t} = k[\text{A}]$$

Using calculus, you get the following integrated rate law equation:

$$\ln \frac{[\text{A}]_t}{[\text{A}]_0} = -kt \quad \text{(first-order integrated rate law)}$$

Here $[\text{A}]_t$ is the concentration of reactant A at time t, and $[\text{A}]_0$ is the initial concentration. The ratio $[\text{A}]_t/[\text{A}]_0$ is the fraction of reactant remaining at time t.

Second-Order Rate Law   Consider the reaction

$$a\text{A} \longrightarrow \text{products}$$

and suppose it has the second-order rate law

$$\text{Rate} = -\frac{\Delta[\text{A}]}{\Delta t} = k[\text{A}]^2$$

The general derivation using calculus is as follows: Substituting [A] for [N_2O_5], the rate law becomes

$$\frac{-d[\text{A}]}{dt} = k[\text{A}]$$

You rearrange this to give

$$\frac{-d[\text{A}]}{[\text{A}]} = k\, dt$$

Integrating from time = 0 to time = t,

$$-\int_{[\text{A}]_0}^{[\text{A}]_t} \frac{d[\text{A}]}{[\text{A}]} = k \int_0^t dt$$

gives

$$-\{\ln[\text{A}]_t - \ln[\text{A}]_0\} = k(t - 0)$$

This can be rearranged to give the equation in the text.

An example is the decomposition of nitrogen dioxide at moderately high temperatures (300°C to 400°C).

$$2NO_2(g) \longrightarrow 2NO(g) + O_2(g)$$

Using calculus, you can obtain the following relationship between the concentration of A and the time.

$$\frac{1}{[A]_t} = kt + \frac{1}{[A]_0} \quad \text{(second-order integrated rate law)}$$

Using this equation, you can calculate the concentration of NO_2 at any time during its decomposition if you know the rate constant and the initial concentration. At 330°C, the rate constant for the decomposition of NO_2 is 0.775 L/(mol·s). Suppose the initial concentration is 0.0030 mol/L. What is the concentration of NO_2 after 645 s? By substituting into the previous equation, you get

$$\frac{1}{[NO_2]_t} = 0.775 \text{ L/(mol·s)} \times 645 \text{ s} + \frac{1}{0.0030 \text{ mol/L}} = 8.3 \times 10^2 \text{ L/mol}$$

If you invert both sides of the equation, you find that $[NO_2]_t = 0.0012$ mol/L. Thus, after 645 s, the concentration of NO_2 decreased from 0.0030 mol/L to 0.0012 mol/L.

Zero-Order Reactions

There are instances where reactions are zero-order. An example includes the decomposition of ethyl alcohol in the liver in the presence of the enzyme liver alcohol dehydrogenase. Once again, consider the reaction with the general form

$$aA \longrightarrow \text{products}$$

which has a zero-order rate law of

$$\text{Rate} = k[A]^0$$

Keeping in mind that any real number raised to the zero power is 1, the expression for zero-order rate law is usually written as

$$\text{Rate} = k$$

This rate law indicates that the rate of a zero-order reaction does not change with concentration. For example, if you have a zero-order reaction

$$A \longrightarrow B + C$$

the rate of this reaction has no dependence upon the concentration of A; however, there must be some A present for the reaction to occur. Many zero-order reactions also require some minimum reactant concentration for the reaction to behave as zero-order. This is true in the case of enzyme reactions like that mentioned above as well as in reactions that are catalyzed by a metal surface, such as the decomposition reaction of N_2O in the presence of platinum metal.

$$2N_2O(g) \xrightarrow{\text{Pt}} 2N_2(g) + O_2(g)$$

As long as this reaction is run at a high enough pressure of N_2O to saturate the metal surface, it will behave as a zero-order reaction.

The relationship between concentration and time for a zero-order reaction is

$$[A]_t = -kt + [A]_0 \quad \text{(zero-order integrated rate law)}$$

Below is an example of a calculation that requires an integrated rate law.

Example 13.5   Using an Integrated Rate Law

The decomposition of N_2O_5 to NO_2 and O_2 is first order, with a rate constant of 4.80×10^{-4}/s at 45°C. a. If the initial concentration is 1.65×10^{-2} mol/L, what is the concentration after 825 s?   b. How long would it take for the concentration of N_2O_5 to decrease to 1.00×10^{-2} mol/L from its initial value, given in a?

Problem Strategy   Part a of this problem wants us to determine the concentration of a reactant (N_2O_5) after some period of time has elapsed. Part b of the problem asks us to determine the amount of time that has elapsed for a certain change in concentration of the reactant. An integrated rate law (first-order here), which relates concentration changes to time, will enable us to complete both of these problems.

Solution   a. In this case, you need to use the equation relating concentration to time for a first-order reaction, which is

$$\ln \frac{[A]_t}{[A]_0} = -kt$$

N_2O_5

Substituting the appropriate values, you get

$$\ln \frac{[N_2O_5]_t}{1.65 \times 10^{-2} \text{ mol/L}} = -4.80 \times 10^{-4}/\text{s} \times 825 \text{ s} = -0.396$$

To solve for $[N_2O_5]_t$, you take the antilogarithm (antiln) of both sides. This removes the ln from the left and gives antiln(-0.396), or $e^{-0.396}$, on the right, which equals 0.673.

$$\frac{[N_2O_5]_t}{1.65 \times 10^{-2} \text{ mol/L}} = 0.673$$

Hence,

$$[N_2O_5]_t = 1.65 \times 10^{-2} \text{ mol/L} \times 0.673 = \textbf{0.0111 mol/L}$$

b. You substitute into the same first-order equation relating concentration to time.

$$\ln \frac{1.00 \times 10^{-2} \text{ mol/L}}{1.65 \times 10^{-2} \text{ mol/L}} = -4.80 \times 10^{-4}/\text{s} \times t$$

The left side equals -0.501; the right side equals -4.80×10^{-4}/s $\times t$. Hence,

$$0.501 = 4.80 \times 10^{-4}/\text{s} \times t$$

or

$$t = \frac{0.501}{4.80 \times 10^{-4}/\text{s}} = \textbf{1.04} \times \textbf{10}^{\textbf{3}} \textbf{ s} \qquad \textbf{(17.4 min)}$$

Answer Check   It is easy to make calculation errors when working with exponents and logarithms. Because of this, it is a good idea to check whether your final answer yields expected results when placed into a starting equation. For example, the first step of part *a* of this calculation involved the equation

$$\ln \frac{[N_2O_5]_t}{1.65 \times 10^{-2} \text{ mol/L}} = -0.396$$

If you plug the answer that you obtained for $[N_2O_5]_t$ into the left-hand side of this equation, it should yield -0.396.

(continued)

(continued)

Exercise 13.5   a. What would be the concentration of dinitrogen pentoxide in the experiment described in Example 13.5 after 6.00×10^2 s? b. How long would it take for the concentration of N_2O_5 to decrease to 10.0% of its initial value?

■ See Problems 13.57, 13.58, 13.59, 13.60, 13.61, and 13.62.

Half-Life of a Reaction

The concept of half-life is also used to characterize a radioactive nucleus, whose radioactive decay is a first-order process. This is discussed in Chapter 20.

As a reaction proceeds, the concentration of a reactant decreases, because it is being consumed. The **half-life,** $t_{1/2}$, of a reaction is *the time it takes for the reactant concentration to decrease to one-half of its initial value.* <

For a first-order reaction, such as the decomposition of dinitrogen pentoxide, the half-life is independent of the initial concentration. To see this, substitute into the equation

$$\ln \frac{[N_2O_5]_t}{[N_2O_5]_0} = -kt$$

In one half-life, the N_2O_5 concentration decreases by one-half, from its initial value, $[N_2O_5]_0$, to the value $[N_2O_5]_t = \frac{1}{2}[N_2O_5]_0$. After substituting, the equation becomes

$$\ln \frac{\frac{1}{2}[N_2O_5]_0}{[N_2O_5]_0} = -kt_{1/2}$$

The expression on the left equals $\ln \frac{1}{2} = -0.693$. Hence,

$$0.693 = kt_{1/2}$$

Solving for the half-life, $t_{1/2}$, you get

$$t_{1/2} = \frac{0.693}{k}$$

Because the rate constant for the decomposition of N_2O_5 at 45°C is 4.80×10^{-4}/s, the half-life is

$$t_{1/2} = \frac{0.693}{4.80 \times 10^{-4}/s} = 1.44 \times 10^3 \text{ s}$$

Thus, the half-life is 1.44×10^3 s, or 24.0 min.

You see that the half-life of N_2O_5 does not depend on the initial concentration of N_2O_5. This means that the half-life is the same at any time during the reaction. If the initial concentration is 0.0165 mol/L, after one half-life (24.0 min) the concentration decreases to $\frac{1}{2} \times 0.0165$ mol/L = 0.0083 mol/L. After another half-life (another 24.0 min), the N_2O_5 concentration decreases to $\frac{1}{2} \times 0.0083$ mol/L = 0.0042 mol/L. Every time one half-life passes, the N_2O_5 concentration decreases by one-half again (see Figure 13.8).

The foregoing result for the half-life for the first-order decomposition of N_2O_5 is perfectly general. That is, for the general first-order rate law

$$\text{Rate} = -\frac{\Delta[A]}{\Delta t} = k[A]$$

the half-life is related to the rate constant but is independent of concentration of A.

$$t_{1/2} = \frac{0.693}{k} \quad \text{(first-order)}$$

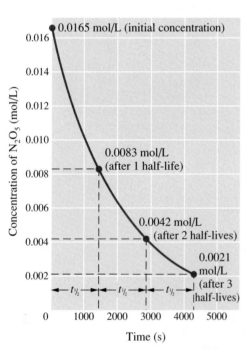

FIGURE 13.8 ▲

A graph illustrating that the half-life of a first-order reaction is independent of initial concentration

In one half-life (1440 s, or 24.0 min), the concentration decreases by one-half, from 0.0165 mol/L to $\frac{1}{2} \times 0.0165$ mol/L = 0.0083 mol/L. After each succeeding half-life (24.0 min), the concentration decreases by one-half again, from 0.0083 mol/L to $\frac{1}{2} \times 0.0083$ mol/L = 0.0042 mol/L, then to $\frac{1}{2} \times 0.0042$ mol/L = 0.0021 mol/L, and so forth.

Example 13.6 | Relating the Half-Life of a Reaction to the Rate Constant

Sulfuryl chloride, SO_2Cl_2, is a colorless, corrosive liquid whose vapor decomposes in a first-order reaction to sulfur dioxide and chlorine.

$$SO_2Cl_2(g) \longrightarrow SO_2(g) + Cl_2(g)$$

At 320°C, the rate constant is 2.20×10^{-5}/s. a. What is the half-life of SO_2Cl_2 vapor at this temperature? b. How long (in hours) would it take for 50.0% of the SO_2Cl_2 to decompose? How long would it take for 75.0% of the SO_2Cl_2 to decompose?

Problem Strategy In part a of this problem we are asked about the half-life of a first-order reaction, so a logical starting point is to use the appropriate half-life equation. For part b, consider that each half-life reduces the amount of material by 50.0%; thus two half-lives will reduce a starting amount of material by 75%, three half lives by 87.5%, and so on.

Solution

a. $t_{1/2} = \dfrac{0.693}{k} = \dfrac{0.693}{2.20 \times 10^{-5}/s} = \textbf{3.15} \times \textbf{10}^4 \textbf{ s}$

b. The half-life is the time required for one-half (50.0%) of the SO_2Cl_2 to decompose. This is 3.15×10^4 s, or **8.75 hr.** After another half-life, one-half of the remaining SO_2Cl_2 decomposes. The total decomposed is $\frac{1}{2} + (\frac{1}{2} \times \frac{1}{2}) = \frac{3}{4}$, or 75.0%. The time required is two half-lives, or 2×8.75 hr = **17.5 hr.**

An alternative approach is to use the integrated rate law for a first-order reaction:

$$\ln\frac{[SO_2Cl_2]_t}{[SO_2Cl_2]_0} = -kt$$

Given the data in the problem statement, we can let $[SO_2Cl_2]_0 = 1.00$ and $[SO_2Cl_2]_t = 0.250$ (the 0.250 represents how much would be remaining at time t after 75% of the SO_2Cl_2 had decomposed). Using these values and the given rate constant, solve for t.

Answer Check In a problem such as this, where the initial concentration of reactant is not given, the alternative approach works *only* for first-order reactions.

Exercise 13.6 The isomerization of cyclopropane, C_3H_6, to propylene, $CH_2{=}CHCH_3$, is first order in cyclopropane and first order overall. At 1000°C, the rate constant is 9.2/s. What is the half-life of cyclopropane at 1000°C? How long would it take for the concentration of cyclopropane to decrease to 50% of its initial value? to 25% of its initial value?

■ See Problems 13.63 and 13.64.

It can be shown by reasoning similar to that given previously that the half-life of a second-order rate law, Rate = $k[A]^2$, is

$$t_{1/2} = \frac{1}{k[A]_0} \quad \text{(second-order)}$$

In this case, the half-life depends on initial concentration and each subsequent half-life becomes larger as time goes on. Consider the decomposition of NO_2 at 330°C. It takes 430 s for the concentration to decrease by one-half from 0.0030 mol/L to 0.0015 mol/L. However, it takes 860 s (twice as long) for the concentration to decrease by one-half again. The fact that the half-life decreases with time is evidence that the reaction is not first order.

For zero-order reactions, the half-life is dependent upon the initial concentration of the reactant. However, in contrast to the second-order reaction, as a zero-order reaction proceeds, each half-life gets shorter.

$$t_{1/2} = \frac{[A]_0}{2k} \quad \text{(zero-order)}$$

Graphing of Kinetic Data

Earlier you saw that the order of a reaction can be determined by comparing initial rates for several experiments in which different initial concentrations are used (initial-rate method). It is also possible to determine the order of a reaction by graphical plotting of the data for a particular experiment. The experimental data are plotted in several different ways, first assuming a first-order reaction, then a second-order reaction, and so forth. The order of the reaction is determined by which graph gives the best fit to the experimental data. To illustrate, we will look at how the plotting is done for first-order and second-order reactions and then compare graphs for a specific reaction.

You have seen that the first-order rate law, $-\Delta[A]/\Delta t = k[A]$, gives the following relationship between concentration of A and time:

$$\ln\frac{[A]_t}{[A]_0} = -kt$$

This equation can be rewritten in a slightly different form, which you can identify with the equation of a straight line. Using the property of logarithms that $\ln(A/B) = \ln A - \ln B$, you get

$$\ln[A]_t = -kt + \ln[A]_0$$

A straight line has the mathematical form $y = mx + b$, when y is plotted on the vertical axis against x on the horizontal axis. < Let us now make the following identifications:

$$\underbrace{\ln[A]_t}_{\downarrow} = \underbrace{-k}_{\downarrow} \ \underbrace{t}_{\downarrow} + \underbrace{\ln[A]_0}_{\downarrow}$$
$$\quad y \quad = \quad mx \quad + \quad b$$

See Appendix A for a discussion of the mathematics of a straight line.

This means that if you plot $\ln[A]_t$ on the vertical axis against the time t on the horizontal axis, you will get a straight line for a first-order reaction. Figure 13.9 shows a plot of $\ln[N_2O_5]$ at various times during the decomposition reaction. The fact that the points lie on a straight line is confirmation that the rate law is first order.

You can obtain the rate constant for the reaction from the slope, m, of the straight line.

$$-k = m \quad \text{or} \quad k = -m$$

You calculate the slope of this curve in the same way you obtained the average rate of reaction from kinetic data (Example 13.2). You select two points far enough apart

FIGURE 13.9 ▶

Plot of ln[N₂O₅] versus time
A straight line can be drawn through the experimental points (colored dots). The fact that the straight line fits the experimental data so well confirms that the rate law is first order.

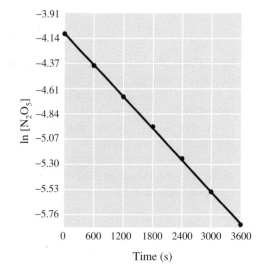

Time	$[N_2O_5]$	$\ln[N_2O_5]$
0	0.0165	−4.104
600	0.0124	−4.390
1200	0.0093	−4.678
1800	0.0071	−4.948
2400	0.0053	−5.240
3000	0.0039	−5.547
3600	0.0029	−5.843

that when you subtract to obtain Δx and Δy for the slope, you do not lose significant figures. Using the first and last points in Figure 13.9, you get

$$m = \frac{\Delta y}{\Delta x} = \frac{(-5.843) - (-4.104)}{(3600 - 0)\ s} = \frac{-1.739}{3600\ s} = -4.83 \times 10^{-4}/s$$

Therefore, $k = 4.84 \times 10^{-4}/s$. (Two points were selected directly from the experimental data. In precise work, you would first draw the straight line that best fits the experimental data points and then calculate the slope of this line.)

The second-order rate law, $-\Delta[A]/\Delta t = k[A]^2$, gives the following relationship between concentration of A and time:

$$\underbrace{\frac{1}{[A]_t}}_{} = \underbrace{kt}_{} + \underbrace{\frac{1}{[A]_0}}_{}$$

$$y\ \ = mx +\ \ b$$

In this case, you get a straight line if you plot $1/[A]_t$ on the vertical axis against the time t on the horizontal axis for a second-order reaction.

As an illustration of the determination of reaction order by graphical plotting, consider the following data for the decomposition of NO_2 at 330°C.

$$2NO_2(g) \longrightarrow 2NO(g) + O_2(g)$$

The concentrations of NO_2 for various times are given in the table of data in Figure 13.10. In Figure 13.10A we have plotted $\ln[NO_2]$ against t, and in Figure 13.10B we

FIGURE 13.10 ▼

Plotting the data for the decomposition of nitrogen dioxide at 330°C
(A) Plot of $\ln[NO_2]$ against time. Note that a straight line does not fit the points well. (B) Plot of $1/[NO_2]$ against time. Note how closely the points follow the straight line, indicating that the decomposition is second order.

A

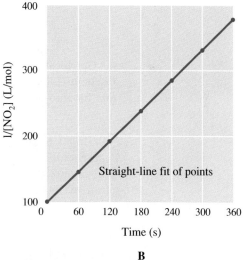

B

Time (s)	[NO₂] (mol/L)	(A) ln [NO₂]	(B) l/[NO₂]
0	1.00×10^{-2}	−4.605	100
60	0.683×10^{-2}	−4.984	146
120	0.518×10^{-2}	−5.263	193
180	0.418×10^{-2}	−5.476	239
240	0.350×10^{-2}	−5.656	286
300	0.301×10^{-2}	−5.805	332
360	0.264×10^{-2}	−5.938	379

		Integrated		Straight-
Order	Rate Law	Rate Law	Half-Life	Line Plot
0	Rate $= k$	$[A]_t = -kt + [A]_0$	$\dfrac{[A]_0}{2k}$	$[A]$ vs t
1	Rate $= k[A]$	$\ln\dfrac{[A]_t}{[A]_0} = -kt$	$0.693/k$	$\ln[A]$ vs t
2	Rate $= k[A]^2$	$\dfrac{1}{[A]_t} = kt + \dfrac{1}{[A]_0}$	$1/(k[A]_0)$	$\dfrac{1}{[A]}$ vs t

TABLE 13.2 | Relationships for Zero-Order, First-Order, and Second-Order Reactions

have plotted $1/[NO_2]$ against t. Only in Figure 13.10B do the points closely follow a straight line, indicating that the rate law is second order. That is,

$$\text{Rate of disappearance of } NO_2 = -\frac{\Delta[NO_2]}{\Delta t} = k[NO_2]^2$$

You can obtain the rate constant, k, for a second-order reaction from the slope of the line, similar to the way you did for a first-order reaction. In this case, however, the slope equals k, as you can see from the preceding equation. Choosing the first and last points in Figure 13.10B, you get

$$k = \frac{\Delta y}{\Delta x} = \frac{(379 - 100)\ \text{L/mol}}{(360 - 0)\ \text{s}} = 0.775\ \text{L/(mol·s)}$$

Graphical methods can also be used to determine the rate constant for zero-order reactions. Table 13.2 summarizes this and the other relationships discussed in this section for zero-order, first-order, and second-order reactions.

Concept Check 13.4

A reaction believed to be either first or second order has a half-life of 20 s at the beginning of the reaction but a half-life of 40 s sometime later. What is the order of the reaction?

13.5 | Temperature and Rate; Collision and Transition-State Theories

As we noted earlier, the rate of reaction depends on temperature. This shows up in the rate law through the rate constant, which is found to vary with temperature. In most cases, the rate increases with temperature (Figure 13.11). Consider the reaction of nitrogen monoxide, NO, with chlorine, Cl_2, to give nitrosyl chloride, NOCl, and chlorine atoms.

$$NO(g) + Cl_2(g) \longrightarrow NOCl(g) + Cl(g)$$

The rate constant k for this reaction is 4.9×10^{-6} L/(mol·s) at 25°C and 1.5×10^{-5} L/(mol·s) at 35°C. In this case the rate constant and therefore the rate are more than tripled for a 10°C rise in temperature. The change in rate constant with temperature varies considerably from one reaction to another. In many cases, the rate of reaction approximately doubles for a 10°C rise, and this is often given as an approximate rule.

FIGURE 13.11 ▲

Effect of temperature on reaction rate
Top: Each test tube contains potassium permanganate, KMnO$_4$, and oxalic acid, H$_2$C$_2$O$_4$, at the same concentrations. Permanganate ion oxidizes oxalic acid to CO$_2$ and H$_2$O. One test tube was placed in a beaker of warm water (40°C); the other was kept at room temperature (20°C). *Bottom:* After 10 minutes, the test tube at 40°C showed a noticeable reaction, whereas the other did not.

| According to the kinetic theory of gases, the *rms* molecular speed equals $\sqrt{3RT/M_m}$ (see Section 5.6).

How do you explain this strong dependence of reaction rate on temperature? To understand it, you need to look at a simple theoretical explanation of reaction rates.

Collision Theory

Why the rate constant depends on temperature can be explained by collision theory. **Collision theory** of reaction rates is *a theory that assumes that, for reaction to occur, reactant molecules must collide with an energy greater than some minimum value and with the proper orientation. The minimum energy of collision required for two molecules to react* is called the **activation energy,** E_a. The value of E_a depends on the particular reaction.

In collision theory, the rate constant for a reaction is given as a product of three factors: (1) Z, the collision frequency, (2) f, the fraction of collisions having energy greater than the activation energy, and (3) p, the fraction of collisions that occur with the reactant molecules properly oriented. Thus,

$$k = Zfp$$

We will discuss each of these factors in turn.

To have a specific reaction to relate the concepts to, consider the gas-phase reaction of NO with Cl$_2$, mentioned previously. This reaction is believed to occur in a single step. An NO molecule collides with a Cl$_2$ molecule. If the collision has sufficient energy and if the molecules are properly oriented, they react to produce NOCl and Cl.

Collision frequency Z, the frequency with which the reactant molecules collide, depends on temperature. As you will see, however, this dependence of collision frequency on temperature does not explain why reaction rates usually change greatly with small temperature increases. You can easily explain why the collision frequency depends on temperature. As the temperature rises, the gas molecules move faster and therefore collide more frequently. Thus, collision frequency is proportional to the root-mean-square (rms) molecular speed, which in turn is proportional to the square root of the absolute temperature, according to the kinetic theory of gases. < From kinetic theory, one can show that at 25°C, a 10°C rise in temperature increases the collision frequency by about 2%. If you were to assume that each collision of reactant molecules resulted in reaction, you would conclude that the rate would increase with temperature at the same rate as the collision frequency—that is, by 2% for a 10°C rise in temperature. This clearly does not explain the tripling of the rate (a 300% increase) that you see in the reaction of NO with Cl$_2$ when the temperature is raised from 25°C to 35°C.

You see that the collision frequency varies only slowly with temperature. However, f, the fraction of molecular collisions having energy greater than the activation energy, changes rapidly in most reactions with even small temperature changes. It can be shown that f is related to the activation energy, E_a, this way:

$$f = e^{-E_a/RT}$$

Here $e = 2.718 \ldots$, and R is the gas constant, which equals 8.31 J/(mol·K). For the reaction of NO with Cl$_2$, the activation energy is 8.5×10^4 J/mol. At 25°C (298 K), the fraction of collisions with sufficient energy for reaction is 1.2×10^{-15}. Thus, the number of collisions of reactant molecules that actually result in reaction is extremely small. But the frequency of collisions is very large, so the reaction rate, which depends on the product of these quantities, is not small. If the temperature is raised by 10°C to 35°C, the fraction of collisions of NO and Cl$_2$ molecules with sufficient energy for reaction is 3.8×10^{-15}, over three times larger than the value at 25°C! The tripling of the reaction rate is explained by the temperature dependence of f.

From the previous equation relating f to E_a, you see that f decreases with increasing values of E_a. Because the rate constant depends on f, this means that reactions

FIGURE 13.12

Importance of molecular orientation in the reaction of NO and Cl_2
(A) NO approaches with its N atom toward Cl_2, and an N—Cl bond forms. Also, the angle of approach is close to that in the product NOCl. *(B)* NO approaches with its O atom toward Cl_2. No N—Cl bond can form, so NO and Cl_2 collide and then fly apart.

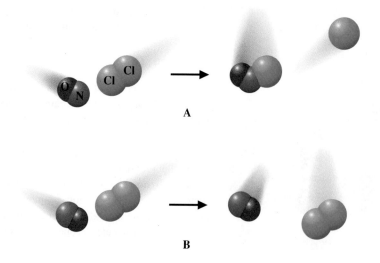

with large activation energies have small rate constants and that reactions with small activation energies have large rate constants.

The reaction rate also depends on p, the proper orientation of the reactant molecules when they collide. This factor is independent of temperature changes. You can see why it is important that the reactant molecules be properly oriented by looking in some detail at the reaction of NO with Cl_2. Figure 13.12 shows two possible molecular collisions. In Figure 13.12*A*, the NO and Cl_2 molecules collide properly oriented for reaction. The NO molecule approaches with its N atom toward the Cl_2 molecule. In addition, the angle of approach is about that expected for the formation of bonds in the product molecule NOCl. In Figure 13.12*B*, an NO molecule approaches with its O atom toward the Cl_2 molecule. Because this orientation does not allow the formation of a bond between the N atom and a Cl atom, it is ineffective for reaction. The NO and Cl_2 molecules come together and then fly apart. All orientations except those close to that shown in *(A)* are ineffective.

Transition-State Theory

Collision theory explains some important features of a reaction, but it is limited in that it does not explain the role of activation energy. **Transition-state theory** *explains the reaction resulting from the collision of two molecules in terms of an activated complex.* An **activated complex** (transition state) is *an unstable grouping of atoms that can break up to form products.* We can represent the formation of the activated complex this way:

$$O{=}N + Cl{-}Cl \longrightarrow [O{=}N\text{---}Cl\text{---}Cl]$$

When the molecules come together with proper orientation, an N—Cl bond begins to form. At the same time, the kinetic energy of the collision is absorbed by the activated complex as a vibrational motion of the atoms. This energy becomes concentrated in the bonds denoted by the dashed lines and can flow between them. If, at some moment, sufficient energy becomes concentrated in one of the bonds of the activated complex, that bond breaks or falls apart. Depending on whether the N----Cl or Cl----Cl bond breaks, the activated complex either reverts to the reactants or yields the products.

Reactants   Activated complex   Products

$$O{=}N + Cl_2 \longleftarrow [O{=}N\text{---}Cl\text{---}Cl] \longrightarrow O{=}N{-}Cl + Cl$$

Potential-Energy Diagrams for Reactions

It is instructive to consider a potential-energy diagram for the reaction of NO with Cl_2. We can represent this reaction by the equation

$$NO + Cl_2 \longrightarrow NOCl_2^{\ddagger} \longrightarrow NOCl + Cl$$

Here $NOCl_2^{\ddagger}$ denotes the activated complex. Figure 13.13 shows the change in potential energy (indicated by the solid curve) that occurs during the progress of the reaction. The potential-energy curve starts at the left with the potential energy of the reactants, $NO + Cl_2$. Moving along the curve toward the right, the potential energy increases to a maximum, corresponding to the activated complex. Farther to the right, the potential energy decreases to that of the products, $NOCl + Cl$.

At the start, the NO and Cl_2 molecules have a certain quantity of kinetic energy. The total energy of these molecules equals their potential energy plus their kinetic energy, and it remains constant throughout the reaction (according to the law of conservation of energy). As the reaction progresses (going from left to right in the diagram), the reactants come together. The potential energy increases because the outer electrons of the two molecules repel. The kinetic energy decreases, and the molecules slow down. Only if the reactant molecules have sufficient kinetic energy is it possible for the potential energy to increase to the value for the activated complex. This kinetic energy must be equal to or greater than the difference in energy between the activated complex and the reactant molecules (85 kJ/mol). The energy difference is the activation energy for the forward reaction.

At the maximum in the potential-energy curve, the reactant molecules have come together as the activated complex. When the activated complex breaks up into products, the products go to lower potential energy (by 2 kJ/mol) and gain in kinetic energy. Note that the energy of the products is higher than the energy of the reactants. The difference in energy equals the heat of reaction, ΔH. Because the energy increases, ΔH is positive and the reaction is endothermic.

Now look at the reverse reaction:

$$NOCl + Cl \longrightarrow NO + Cl_2$$

The activation energy is 2 kJ/mol, the difference in energy of the initial species, $NOCl + Cl$, and the activated complex. This is a smaller quantity than that for the forward reaction, so the rate constant for the reverse reaction is larger.

FIGURE 13.13 ▶

Potential-energy curve (not to scale) for the endothermic reaction NO + Cl$_2$ ⟶ NOCl + Cl

For NO and Cl_2 to react, at least 85 kJ/mol of energy must be supplied by the collision of reactant molecules. Once the activated complex forms, it may break up to products, releasing 2 kJ/mol of energy. The difference, (85 − 2) kJ/mol = 83 kJ/mol, is the heat energy absorbed, ΔH.

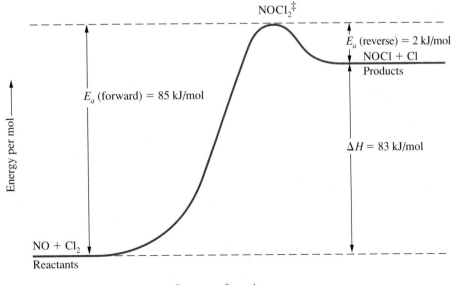

FIGURE 13.14 ▶

Potential-energy curve for an exothermic reaction
The energy of the reactants is higher than that of the products, so heat energy is released when the reaction goes in the forward direction.

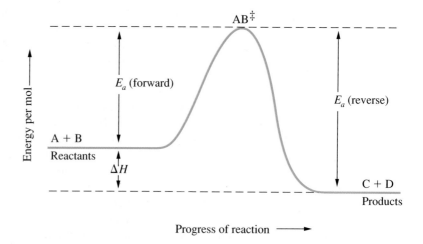

Figure 13.14 shows the potential-energy curve for an exothermic reaction. In this case, the energy of the reactants is higher than that of the products, so heat energy is released when the reaction goes in the forward direction.

Concept Check 13.5

Consider the following potential-energy curves for two different reactions:

a. Which reaction has a higher activation energy for the forward reaction?

b. If both reactions were run at the same temperature and have the same orientation requirements to react, which one would have the larger rate constant?

c. Are these reactions exothermic or endothermic?

13.6 | Arrhenius Equation

Rate constants for most chemical reactions closely follow an equation of the form

$$k = Ae^{-E_a/RT}$$

The mathematical equation $k = Ae^{-E_a/RT}$, *which expresses the dependence of the rate constant on temperature,* is called the **Arrhenius equation,** after its formulator, the Swedish chemist Svante Arrhenius. < Here e is the base of natural logarithms, 2.718 . . . ; E_a is the activation energy; R is the gas constant, 8.31 J/(K·mol); and T is the absolute temperature. *The symbol A in the Arrhenius equation, which is assumed to be a constant,* is called the **frequency factor.** The frequency factor is related to the frequency of collisions with proper orientation (pZ). (The frequency factor does have a slight dependence on temperature, as you see from collision theory, but usually it can be ignored.)

Arrhenius published this equation in 1889 and suggested that molecules must be given enough energy to become "activated" before they could react. Collision and transition-state theories, which enlarged on this concept, were developed later (1920s and 1930s, respectively).

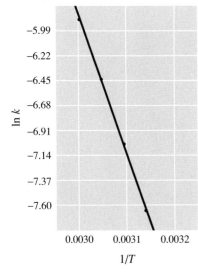

FIGURE 13.15 ▲

Plot of ln *k* versus 1/*T*
The logarithm of the rate constant for the decomposition of N_2O_5 (data from Table 13.3) is plotted versus 1/*T*. A straight line is then fitted to the points; the slope equals $-E_a/R$.

TABLE 13.3	
Rate Constant for the Decomposition of N_2O_5 at Various Temperatures	
Temperature (°C)	*k* (/s)
45.0	4.8×10^{-4}
50.0	8.8×10^{-4}
55.0	1.6×10^{-3}
60.0	2.8×10^{-3}

It is useful to recast Arrhenius's equation in logarithmic form. Taking the natural logarithm of both sides of the Arrhenius equation gives

$$\ln k = \ln A - \frac{E_a}{RT}$$

Let us make the following identification of symbols:

$$\underbrace{\ln k}_{y} = \underbrace{\ln A}_{b} + \underbrace{\left(\frac{-E_a}{R}\right)}_{m}\underbrace{\left(\frac{1}{T}\right)}_{x}$$

$$y = b + mx$$

This shows that if you plot ln *k* against 1/*T*, you should get a straight line. The slope of this line is $-E_a/R$, from which you can obtain the activation energy E_a. The intercept is ln *A*. Figure 13.15 shows a plot of ln *k* versus 1/*T* for the data given in Table 13.3. It demonstrates that the points do lie on a straight line.

You can put the previous equation into a form that is useful for computation. First you write the equation for two different absolute temperatures T_1 and T_2. You write k_1 for the rate constant at temperature T_1 and k_2 for the rate constant at temperature T_2.

$$\ln k_2 = \ln A - \frac{E_a}{RT_2}$$

$$\ln k_1 = \ln A - \frac{E_a}{RT_1}$$

You eliminate ln *A* by subtracting the equations.

$$\ln k_2 - \ln k_1 = -\frac{E_a}{RT_2} + \frac{E_a}{RT_1}$$

or

$$\ln \frac{k_2}{k_1} = \frac{E_a}{R}\left(\frac{1}{T_1} - \frac{1}{T_2}\right)$$

The next example illustrates the use of the Arrhenius equation in this form.

Example 13.7 | Using the Arrhenius Equation

The rate constant for the formation of hydrogen iodide from the elements

$$H_2(g) + I_2(g) \longrightarrow 2HI(g)$$

is 2.7×10^{-4} L/(mol·s) at 600 K and 3.5×10^{-3} L/(mol·s) at 650 K. a. Find the activation energy E_a. b. Then calculate the rate constant at 700 K.

Problem Strategy a. Substitute the data given in the problem statement into the equation noted just before this example, then solve for E_a. b. Use the same equation, but substitute for k_1, T_1, T_2, and E_a obtained in a, and solve for k_2.

(continued)

(continued)

Solution a.
$$\ln \frac{3.5 \times 10^{-3}}{2.7 \times 10^{-4}} = \frac{E_a}{8.31 \text{ J/(mol·K)}} \left(\frac{1}{600 \text{ K}} - \frac{1}{650 \text{ K}} \right)$$

$$\ln 1.30 \times 10^{1} = 2.56 = \frac{E_a}{8.31 \text{ J/mol}} \times (1.28 \times 10^{-4})$$

Hence,

$$E_a = \frac{2.56 \times 8.31 \text{ J/mol}}{1.28 \times 10^{-4}} = \mathbf{1.66 \times 10^5 \text{ J/mol}}$$

b. Substitute $E_a = 1.66 \times 10^5$ J/mol and

$$k_1 = 2.7 \times 10^{-4} \text{ L/(mol·s)} \quad (T_1 = 600 \text{ K})$$
$$k_2 = \text{unknown as yet} \quad (T_2 = 700 \text{ K})$$

You get

$$\ln \frac{k_2}{2.7 \times 10^{-4} \text{ L/(mol·s)}} = \frac{1.66 \times 10^5 \text{ J/mol}}{8.31 \text{ J/(mol·K)}} \times \left(\frac{1}{600 \text{ K}} - \frac{1}{700 \text{ K}} \right) = 4.77$$

Taking antilogarithms,

$$\frac{k_2}{2.7 \times 10^{-4} \text{ L/(mol·s)}} = e^{4.77} = 1.2 \times 10^2$$

Hence,

$$k_2 = (1.2 \times 10^2) \times (2.7 \times 10^{-4}) \text{ L/(mol·s)} = \mathbf{3.2 \times 10^{-2} \text{ L/(mol·s)}}$$

Answer Check Activation energies are typically in the range of 10–100 kJ, as is true here. Anything outside that range should be suspect.

Exercise 13.7 Acetaldehyde, CH_3CHO, decomposes when heated.

$$CH_3CHO(g) \longrightarrow CH_4(g) + CO(g)$$

The rate constant for the decomposition is $1.05 \times 10^{-3}/(M^{1/2} \cdot \text{s})$ at 759 K and $2.14 \times 10^{-2}/(M^{1/2} \cdot \text{s})$ at 836 K. What is the activation energy for this decomposition? What is the rate constant at 865 K?

■ See Problems 13.77, 13.78, 13.79, and 13.80.

Reaction Mechanisms

A balanced chemical equation is a description of the overall result of a chemical reaction. However, what actually happens at the molecular level may be more involved than is represented by this single equation. The reaction may take place in several steps. In the next sections, we will examine some reactions and see how the rate law can give us information about these steps, or *elementary reactions*.

13.7 | Elementary Reactions

Consider the reaction of nitrogen dioxide with carbon monoxide.

$$NO_2(g) + CO(g) \longrightarrow NO(g) + CO_2(g) \quad \text{(net chemical equation)}$$

At temperatures below 500 K, this gas-phase reaction is believed to take place in two steps.

$$NO_2 + NO_2 \longrightarrow NO_3 + NO \qquad \text{(elementary reaction)}$$
$$NO_3 + CO \longrightarrow NO_2 + CO_2 \qquad \text{(elementary reaction)}$$

Each step, called an **elementary reaction,** is *a single molecular event, such as a collision of molecules, resulting in a reaction. The set of elementary reactions whose overall effect is given by the net chemical equation* is called the **reaction mechanism.**

According to the reaction mechanism just given, two NO_2 molecules collide and react to give the product molecule NO and the reaction intermediate NO_3. A **reaction intermediate** is *a species produced during a reaction that does not appear in the net equation because it reacts in a subsequent step in the mechanism.* Often the reaction intermediate has a fleeting existence and cannot be isolated from the reaction mixture. The NO_3 molecule is known only from its visible light spectrum. It reacts quickly with CO to give the product molecules NO_2 and CO_2.

The overall chemical equation, which represents the net result of these two elementary reactions in the mechanism, is obtained by adding the steps and canceling species that occur on both sides.

$$NO_2 + NO_2 \longrightarrow NO_3 + NO \qquad \text{(elementary reaction)}$$
$$NO_3 + CO \longrightarrow NO_2 + CO_2 \qquad \text{(elementary reaction)}$$
$$\overline{NO_2 + \cancel{NO_2} + \cancel{NO_3} + CO \longrightarrow \cancel{NO_3} + NO + \cancel{NO_2} + CO_2} \qquad \text{(overall equation)}$$

Example 13.8 | Writing the Overall Chemical Equation from a Mechanism

Carbon tetrachloride, CCl_4, is obtained by chlorinating methane or an incompletely chlorinated methane such as chloroform, $CHCl_3$. The mechanism for the gas-phase chlorination of $CHCl_3$ is

$$Cl_2 \rightleftharpoons 2Cl \qquad \text{(elementary reaction)}$$
$$Cl + CHCl_3 \longrightarrow HCl + CCl_3 \qquad \text{(elementary reaction)}$$
$$Cl + CCl_3 \longrightarrow CCl_4 \qquad \text{(elementary reaction)}$$

Obtain the net, or overall, chemical equation from this mechanism.

Problem Strategy To obtain the overall chemical equation, we need to add up the steps of the mechanism and cancel the species that occur on both sides.

Solution The first step produces two Cl atoms (a reaction intermediate). One Cl atom is used in the second step and another is used in the third step. Thus all Cl atoms cancel. Similarly, the intermediate CCl_3, produced in the second step, is used up in the third step. You can cancel all Cl and CCl_3 species.

$$Cl_2 \rightleftharpoons 2\cancel{Cl}$$
$$\cancel{Cl} + CHCl_3 \longrightarrow HCl + \cancel{CCl_3}$$
$$\cancel{Cl} + \cancel{CCl_3} \longrightarrow CCl_4$$
$$\overline{\mathbf{Cl_2 + CHCl_3 \longrightarrow HCl + CCl_4}} \qquad \text{(overall equation)}$$

Answer Check As a final check of the overall equation, make sure that it is balanced. If it is not balanced, you probably missed a reaction intermediate and/or canceled a species that was not a reaction intermediate.

(continued)

(continued)

Exercise 13.8   The iodide ion catalyzes the decomposition of aqueous hydrogen peroxide, H_2O_2. This decomposition is believed to occur in two steps.

$$H_2O_2 + I^- \longrightarrow H_2O + IO^- \qquad \text{(elementary reaction)}$$
$$H_2O_2 + IO^- \longrightarrow H_2O + O_2 + I^- \qquad \text{(elementary reaction)}$$

What is the overall equation representing this decomposition? Note that IO^- is a reaction intermediate. The iodide ion is not an intermediate; it was added to the reaction mixture.

■ See Problems 13.83 and 13.84.

Molecularity

Elementary reactions are classified according to their molecularity. The **molecularity** is *the number of molecules on the reactant side of an elementary reaction. A unimolecular reaction* is *an elementary reaction that involves one reactant molecule;* a **bimolecular reaction** is *an elementary reaction that involves two reactant molecules.* Bimolecular reactions are the most common. Unimolecular reactions are best illustrated by decomposition of some previously excited species. Some gas-phase reactions are thought to occur in a **termolecular reaction,** *an elementary reaction that involves three reactant molecules.* Higher molecularities are not encountered, presumably because the chance of the correct four molecules coming together at once is extremely small.

As an example of a unimolecular reaction, consider the elementary process in which an energetically excited ozone molecule (symbolized by O_3^*) spontaneously decomposes.

$$O_3^* \longrightarrow O_2 + O$$

Normally, a molecule in a sample of ozone gas is in a lower energy level. But such a molecule may be excited to a higher level if it collides with another molecule or absorbs a photon. The energy of the excited molecule is distributed among its three nuclei as vibrational energy. After a period of time, this energy becomes redistributed. If by chance most of the energy finds its way to one end oxygen atom, that atom will fly off. In other words, the excited ozone molecule decomposes into an oxygen molecule and an oxygen atom.

All of the steps in the mechanism of the reaction of NO_2 with CO, given earlier in this section, are bimolecular. Consider the first step, which involves the reaction of two NO_2 molecules.

$$NO_2 + NO_2 \longrightarrow NO_3 + NO$$

When these two NO_2 molecules come together, they form an activated complex of the six atoms, $(NO_2)_2$, which immediately breaks into two new molecules, NO_3 and NO.

The overall reaction of two atoms—say, two Br atoms—to form a diatomic molecule (Br_2) is normally a termolecular process. When two bromine atoms collide, they form an excited bromine molecule, Br_2^*. This excited molecule immediately flies apart, re-forming the atoms, unless another atom or molecule is present just at the moment of molecule formation to take away the excess energy. Suppose an argon atom and the two bromine atoms all collide at the same moment.

$$Br + Br + Ar \longrightarrow Br_2 + Ar^*$$

Energy that would have been left with the bromine molecule is now picked up by the argon atom (giving the energized atom Ar^*). The bromine molecule is stabilized by being left in a lower energy level.

Example 13.9 | Determining the Molecularity of an Elementary Reaction

What is the molecularity of each step in the mechanism described in Example 13.8?

$$Cl_2 \rightleftharpoons 2Cl$$
$$Cl + CHCl_3 \longrightarrow HCl + CCl_3$$
$$Cl + CCl_3 \longrightarrow CCl_4$$

Problem Strategy The molecularity of any elementary reaction equals the number of reactant molecules.

Solution Counting the reactant molecules, the forward part of the first step is **unimolecular;** the reverse

of the first step, the second step, and the third step are each **bimolecular.**

Answer Check If you end up with a molecularity of a reaction greater than 3, you have made a mistake.

Exercise 13.9   The following is an elementary reaction that occurs in the decomposition of ozone in the stratosphere by nitrogen monoxide.

$$O_3 + NO \longrightarrow O_2 + NO_2$$

What is the molecularity of this reaction? That is, is the reaction unimolecular, bimolecular, or termolecular?

■ See Problems 13.85 and 13.86.

Rate Equation for an Elementary Reaction

There is no necessarily simple relationship between the overall reaction and the rate law that you observe for it. As we stressed before, the rate law must be obtained experimentally. However, when you are dealing with an elementary reaction, the rate does have a simple, predictable form.

> For an elementary reaction, the rate is proportional to the product of the concentration of each reactant molecule.

To understand this, let us look at the different possibilities. Consider the unimolecular elementary reaction

$$A \longrightarrow B + C$$

For each A molecule there is a definite probability, or chance, that it will decompose into B and C molecules. The more A molecules there are in a given volume, the more A molecules that can decompose in that volume per unit time. In other words, the rate of reaction is proportional to the concentration of A.

$$\text{Rate} = k[A]$$

Now consider a bimolecular elementary reaction, such as

$$A + B \longrightarrow C + D$$

For the reaction to occur, the reactant molecules A and B must collide. Reaction does not occur with every collision. Nevertheless, the rate of formation of product is proportional to the frequency of molecular collisions, because a definite fraction of the collisions produces reaction. Within a given volume, the frequency of collisions is proportional to the number of A molecules, n_A, times the number of B molecules, n_B. Furthermore, the concentration of A is proportional to n_A, and the concentration of B is proportional to n_B. Therefore, the rate of this elementary reaction is proportional to [A][B].

$$\text{Rate} = k[A][B]$$

A termolecular elementary reaction has a rate equation that is obtained by similar reasoning. For the elementary reaction

$$A + B + C \longrightarrow D + E$$

the rate is proportional to the concentrations of A, B, and C.

$$\text{Rate} = k[\text{A}][\text{B}][\text{C}]$$

Any reaction you observe is likely to consist of several elementary steps, and the rate law that you find is the combined result of these steps. This is why you cannot predict the rate law by looking at the overall equation.

Example 13.10 | Writing the Rate Equation for an Elementary Reaction

Write rate equations for each of the following elementary reactions.

a. Ozone is converted to O_2 by NO in a single step.

$$O_3 + NO \longrightarrow O_2 + NO_2$$

b. The recombination of iodine atoms occurs as follows:

$$I + I + M \longrightarrow I_2 + M^*$$

where M is some atom or molecule that absorbs energy from the reaction.

c. An H_2O molecule absorbs energy; some time later enough of this energy flows into one O—H bond to break it.

$$H_2O \longrightarrow H + O-H$$

Problem Strategy The rate equation can be written directly from the elementary reaction (but *only* for an elementary reaction).

Solution
a. **Rate = $k[O_3][NO]$**
b. **Rate = $k[I]^2[M]$**
c. **Rate = $k[H_2O]$**

Answer Check Keep in mind that writing the rate equation of the reaction works *only* for an elementary reaction.

Exercise 13.10 Write the rate equation, showing the dependence of rate on concentrations, for the elementary reaction

$$NO_2 + NO_2 \longrightarrow N_2O_4$$

■ See Problems 13.87 and 13.88.

In the next section, we look at the relationship between a reaction mechanism and the observed rate law.

13.8 | The Rate Law and the Mechanism

The mechanism of a reaction cannot be observed directly. A mechanism is devised to explain the experimental observations. It is like the explanation provided by a detective to explain a crime in terms of the clues found. Other explanations may be possible, and further clues may make one of these other explanations seem more plausible than the currently accepted one. So it is with reaction mechanisms. They are accepted provisionally, with the understanding that further experiments may lead you to accept another mechanism as the more probable explanation. <

You see the scientific method in operation here, which recalls the discussion in Chapter 1. Experiments have been made from which you determine the rate law. Then a mechanism is devised to explain the rate law. This mechanism in turn suggests more experiments. These may confirm the explanation or may disagree with it. If they disagree, a new mechanism must be devised that explains all of the experimental evidence.

An important clue in understanding the mechanism of a reaction is the rate law. The reason for its importance is that once you assume a mechanism, you can predict the rate law. If this prediction does not agree with the experimental rate law, the assumed mechanism must be wrong. Take, for example, the overall equation

$$2NO_2(g) + F_2(g) \longrightarrow 2NO_2F(g)$$

If you follow the rate of disappearance of F_2, you observe that it is directly proportional to the concentration of NO_2 and F_2.

$$\text{Rate} = k[NO_2][F_2] \qquad \text{(experimental rate law)}$$

This rate law is a summary of the experimental data. Assume that the reaction occurs in a single elementary reaction.

$$NO_2 + NO_2 + F_2 \longrightarrow NO_2F + NO_2F \qquad \text{(elementary reaction)}$$

This, then, is your assumed mechanism. Because this is an elementary reaction, you can immediately write the rate law predicted by it.

$$\text{Rate} = k[NO_2]^2[F_2] \qquad \text{(predicted rate law)}$$

However, this does not agree with experiment, and your assumed mechanism must be discarded. You conclude that the reaction occurs in more than one step.

Rate-Determining Step

The reaction of NO_2 with F_2 is believed to occur in the following steps (elementary reactions).

$$NO_2 + F_2 \xrightarrow{k_1} NO_2F + F \qquad \text{(slow step)}$$
$$F + NO_2 \xrightarrow{k_2} NO_2F \qquad \text{(fast step)}$$

The rate constant for each step has been written over the arrow. The net result of the mechanism must be equivalent to the net result of the overall equation. By adding the two steps together, you can see that this is the case.

$$
\begin{array}{l}
NO_2 + F_2 \longrightarrow NO_2F + F \\
\underline{F + NO_2 \longrightarrow NO_2F} \\
2NO_2 + F_2 \longrightarrow 2NO_2F
\end{array}
$$

The F atom is a reaction intermediate.

The mechanism must also be in agreement with the experimental rate law. Let us look at that. Note that the second step is assumed to be much faster than the first, so that as soon as NO_2 and F_2 react, the F atom that is formed reacts with an NO_2 molecule to give another NO_2F molecule. Therefore, the rate of disappearance of F_2 (and therefore the rate law) is determined completely by the slow step, or rate-determining step. The **rate-determining step** is *the slowest step in the reaction mechanism.*

To understand better the significance of the rate-determining step, suppose you and a friend want to start a study group. You and your friend decide to send invitation cards to some students in your class. You write a lengthy note on each card explaining the study group, taking an average of 2.0 minutes per card. Your friend puts the card in an envelope, affixes a computer-printed address label, seals the envelope, and stamps it, taking 0.5 minute per card. How long does it take to do 100 cards? What is the average time taken per card (*rate* of completing the cards)?

Because you take longer than your friend to do each card, your friend can complete the task for one card while you are working on another. It takes you a total of (100 cards $\times$ 2.0 min/card) to do your step in the task. When you have finished the last card, your friend still has to place the card in the envelope, and so forth. Therefore, you have to add an additional 0.5 min to the total time.

$$
\begin{aligned}
\text{Total time for 100 cards} &= (100 \text{ cards} \times 2.\underline{0} \text{ min/card}) + 0.\underline{5} \text{ min} \\
&= 2\underline{0}0.5 \text{ min}
\end{aligned}
$$

We have underlined the last significant figure.

The rate of completing the invitation cards is

$$\text{Rate} = 2\underline{0}0.5 \text{ min}/100 \text{ cards} = 2.0 \text{ min/card}$$

The rate is essentially the time it takes you to compose a note. The time for your friend to finish the task is insignificant compared with the total time. The rate for the task equals the rate for the slower step (the rate-determining step).

The rate-determining step in the reaction of NO_2 and F_2 is the first step in the mechanism, in which NO_2 reacts with F_2 to produce NO_2F and an F atom. The rate equation for this rate-determining step of the mechanism is

$$\text{Rate} = k_1[NO_2][F_2]$$

This should equal the experimental rate law (otherwise the mechanism cannot be correct), which it does if you equate k_1 to k (the experimental rate constant). This agreement is not absolute evidence that the mechanism is correct. However, one can perform experiments to see whether fluorine atoms react very quickly with nitrogen dioxide. Such experiments show that they do.

Example 13.11   Determining the Rate Law from a Mechanism with an Initial Slow Step

Ozone reacts with nitrogen dioxide to produce oxygen and dinitrogen pentoxide.

$$O_3(g) + 2NO_2(g) \longrightarrow O_2(g) + N_2O_5(g)$$

The proposed mechanism is

$$O_3 + NO_2 \longrightarrow NO_3 + O_2 \qquad \text{(slow)}$$
$$NO_3 + NO_2 \longrightarrow N_2O_5 \qquad \text{(fast)}$$

What is the rate law predicted by this mechanism?

Ozone
O_3

Problem Strategy   Consider the mechanism of the reaction and look to see whether the first step is slow compared to the other steps. If this is the case, then the rate law can be written on the basis of this first step.

Solution   The rate law from the first step is

$$\textbf{Rate} = k[\textbf{O}_3][\textbf{NO}_2]$$

Answer Check   Keep in mind that writing the rate law as we have done in this problem works when the first step of the mechanism is much slower than the other steps. Reaction mechanisms that are not structured like this one will require different approaches to determine the mechanism.

Exercise 13.11   The iodide-ion-catalyzed decomposition of hydrogen peroxide, H_2O_2, is believed to follow the mechanism

$$H_2O_2 + I^- \xrightarrow{k_1} H_2O + IO^- \qquad \text{(slow)}$$
$$H_2O_2 + IO^- \xrightarrow{k_2} H_2O + O_2 + I^- \qquad \text{(fast)}$$

What rate law is predicted by this mechanism? Explain.

■ See Problems 13.89 and 13.90.

Mechanisms with an Initial Fast Step

A somewhat more complicated situation occurs when the rate-determining step follows an initial fast, equilibrium step. The decomposition of dinitrogen pentoxide,

$$2N_2O_5(g) \longrightarrow 4NO_2(g) + O_2(g) \qquad \text{(overall equation)}$$

which we discussed in the chapter opening section, is believed to follow this type of mechanism.

$$N_2O_5 \underset{k_{-1}}{\overset{k_1}{\rightleftharpoons}} NO_2 + NO_3 \qquad \text{(fast, equilibrium)}$$

$$NO_2 + NO_3 \xrightarrow{k_2} NO + NO_2 + O_2 \qquad \text{(slow)}$$
$$NO_3 + NO \xrightarrow{k_3} 2NO_2 \qquad \text{(fast)}$$

FIGURE 13.16 ▶

Representation of the mechanism of decomposition of N_2O_5, using molecular models
Note that little atomic rearrangement occurs during each step.

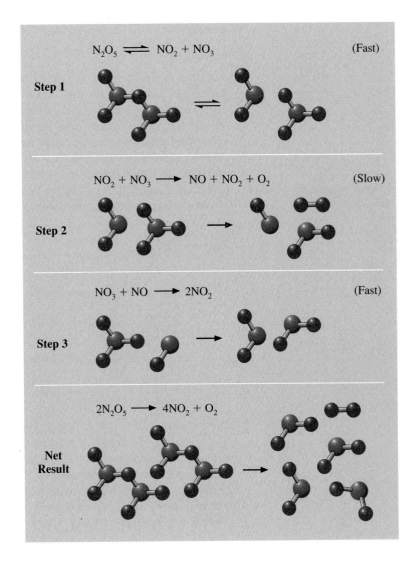

$N_2O_5 \rightleftharpoons NO_2 + NO_3$ (Fast)

Step 1

$NO_2 + NO_3 \longrightarrow NO + NO_2 + O_2$ (Slow)

Step 2

$NO_3 + NO \longrightarrow 2NO_2$ (Fast)

Step 3

$2N_2O_5 \longrightarrow 4NO_2 + O_2$

Net Result

To give the overall stoichiometry, you need to multiply the first step by two. Note that there are two reaction intermediates, NO_3 and NO. Figure 13.16 represents the mechanism by means of molecular models. Let us show that this mechanism is consistent with the experimentally determined rate law,

$$\text{Rate} = k[N_2O_5]$$

The second step in the mechanism is assumed to be much slower than the other steps and is therefore rate-determining. Hence, the rate law predicted from this mechanism is

$$\text{Rate} = k_2[NO_2][NO_3]$$

However, this equation cannot be compared directly with experiment because it is written in terms of the reaction intermediate, NO_3. The experimental rate law will be written in terms of substances that occur in the chemical equation, not of reaction intermediates. For purposes of comparison, it is necessary to re-express the rate equation, eliminating $[NO_3]$. To do this, you must look at the first step in the mechanism.

This step is fast and reversible. That is, N_2O_5 dissociates rapidly into NO_2 and NO_3, and these products in turn react to re-form N_2O_5. The rate of the forward reaction (dissociation of N_2O_5) is

$$\text{Forward rate} = k_1[N_2O_5]$$

and the rate of the reverse reaction (formation of N_2O_5 from NO_2 and NO_3) is

$$\text{Reverse rate} = k_{-1}[NO_2][NO_3]$$

When the reaction first begins, there are no NO_2 or NO_3 molecules, and the reverse rate is zero. But as N_2O_5 dissociates, the concentration of N_2O_5 decreases and the concentrations of NO_2 and NO_3 increase. Therefore, the forward rate decreases and the reverse rate increases. Soon the two rates become equal, such that N_2O_5 molecules form as often as other N_2O_5 molecules dissociate. The first step has reached *dynamic equilibrium.* Because these elementary reactions are much faster than the second step, this equilibrium is reached before any significant reaction by the second step occurs. Moreover, this equilibrium is maintained throughout the reaction. <

| *Chemical equilibrium is discussed in detail in the next chapter.*

At equilibrium, the forward and reverse rates are equal, so you can write

$$k_1[N_2O_5] = k_{-1}[NO_2][NO_3]$$

$$[NO_3] = \frac{k_1}{k_{-1}} \frac{[N_2O_5]}{[NO_2]}$$

Substituting into the rate law, you get

$$\text{Rate} = k_2[NO_2][NO_3] = k_2[\cancel{NO_2}] \times \frac{k_1}{k_{-1}} \frac{[N_2O_5]}{[\cancel{NO_2}]}$$

or

$$\text{Rate} = k_2 \frac{k_1}{k_{-1}} [N_2O_5]$$

Thus, if you identify $k_1 k_2 / k_{-1}$ as k, you reproduce the experimental rate law.

In addition to correctly predicting the experimental rate law, the mechanism must also be in agreement with the overall equation for the reaction. Although the first step is essentially in equilibrium, the products of this step (NO_2 and NO_3) are being continuously used in the subsequent steps. Note that each of these subsequent steps uses up a molecule of NO_3. For these steps to proceed, the first step must effectively produce two molecules of NO_3. Thus, the net result of the mechanism is as follows:

$$2(N_2O_5 \longrightarrow NO_2 + \cancel{NO_3})$$
$$\cancel{NO_2} + \cancel{NO_3} \longrightarrow \cancel{NO} + \cancel{NO_2} + O_2$$
$$\cancel{NO_3} + \cancel{NO} \longrightarrow 2NO_2$$
$$\overline{2N_2O_5 \longrightarrow 4NO_2 + O_2}$$

The net result of the mechanism is equivalent to the overall equation for the reaction, as it should be.

Example 13.12 | Determining the Rate Law from a Mechanism with an Initial Fast, Equilibrium Step

Nitrogen monoxide can be reduced with hydrogen gas to give nitrogen and water vapor.

$$2NO(g) + 2H_2(g) \longrightarrow N_2(g) + 2H_2O(g) \qquad \text{(overall equation)}$$

A proposed mechanism is

$$2NO \underset{k_{-1}}{\overset{k_1}{\rightleftharpoons}} N_2O_2 \qquad \text{(fast, equilibrium)}$$

$$N_2O_2 + H_2 \xrightarrow{k_2} N_2O + H_2O \qquad \text{(slow)}$$
$$N_2O + H_2 \xrightarrow{k_3} N_2 + H_2O \qquad \text{(fast)}$$

What rate law is predicted by this mechanism?

(continued)

(continued)

Problem Strategy Examining the reaction mechanism, you can see that it has an initial fast, equilibrium step, followed by a slow step. You write the rate equation for the rate-determining (slow) step, just as in the previous example. In this case, however, the equation contains a species, N_2O_2, that does not appear in the overall equation for the reaction. You need to eliminate it from the final form of the rate law. Note that the first step is fast and reaches equilibrium. You use this fact to write an expression for $[N_2O_2]$. Then you substitute this expression for $[N_2O_2]$ into the rate equation.

Solution According to the rate-determining step,

$$\text{Rate} = k_2[N_2O_2][H_2]$$

You try to eliminate N_2O_2 from the rate law by looking at the first step, which is fast and reaches equilibrium. At equilibrium, the forward rate and the reverse rate are equal.

$$k_1[NO]^2 = k_{-1}[N_2O_2]$$

Therefore, $[N_2O_2] = (k_1/k_{-1})[NO]^2$, so

$$\text{Rate} = \frac{k_2 k_1}{k_{-1}} [NO]^2[H_2]$$

Experimentally, you should observe the rate law

$$\textbf{Rate} = k[NO]^2[H_2]$$

where we have replaced the constants $k_2 k_1/k_{-1}$ with k, which represents the experimentally observed rate constant.

Answer Check Always examine your answer to make certain that the rate law is expressed in terms of the concentrations of the reactants in the overall equation. However, keep in mind that the exponents do not necessarily reflect the stoichiometry of the overall equation.

Exercise 13.12 Nitrogen monoxide, NO, reacts with oxygen to produce nitrogen dioxide.

$$2NO(g) + O_2(g) \longrightarrow 2NO_2(g) \qquad \text{(overall equation)}$$

If the mechanism is

$$NO + O_2 \underset{k_{-1}}{\overset{k_1}{\rightleftharpoons}} NO_3 \qquad \text{(fast, equilibrium)}$$

$$NO_3 + NO \overset{k_2}{\longrightarrow} NO_2 + NO_2 \qquad \text{(slow)}$$

what is the predicted rate law? Remember to express this in terms of substances in the chemical equation.

■ See Problems 13.91 and 13.92.

Concept Check 13.6

You are a chemist in charge of a research laboratory that is trying to increase the reaction rate for the balanced chemical reaction

$$X + 2Y \longrightarrow Z$$

a. One of your researchers comes into your office and states that she has found a material that significantly lowers the activation energy of the reaction. Explain the effect this will have on the rate of the reaction.

b. Another researcher states that after doing some experiments, he has determined that the rate law is

$$\text{Rate} = k[X][Y]$$

Is this possible?

c. Yet another person in the lab reports that the mechanism for the reaction is:

$$2Y \longrightarrow I \qquad \text{(slow)}$$
$$X + I \longrightarrow Z \qquad \text{(fast)}$$

Is the rate law from part b consistent with this mechanism? If not, what should the rate law be?

13.9 | Catalysis

A catalyst is a substance that has the seemingly miraculous power of speeding up a reaction without being consumed by it. In theory, you could add a catalyst to a reaction mixture and, after the reaction, separate that catalyst and use it over and over again. In practice, there is often some loss of catalyst through other reactions that can occur at the same time. **Catalysis** is *the increase in rate of a reaction that results from the addition of a catalyst.*

Catalysts are of enormous importance to the chemical industry, because they allow a reaction to occur with a reasonable rate at a much lower temperature than otherwise; lower temperatures translate into lower energy costs. Moreover, catalysts are often quite specific—they increase the rate of certain reactions, but not others. For instance, an industrial chemist can start with a mixture of carbon monoxide and hydrogen and produce methane gas using one catalyst or produce gasoline using another catalyst. The most remarkable catalysts are enzymes. *Enzymes* are the marvelously selective catalysts employed by biological organisms. A biological cell contains thousands of different enzymes that in effect direct all of the chemical processes that occur in the cell.

How can we explain how a catalyst can influence a reaction without being consumed by it? Briefly, the catalyst must participate in at least one step of a reaction and be regenerated in a later step. Consider the commercial preparation of sulfuric acid, H_2SO_4, from sulfur dioxide, SO_2. The first step involves the reaction of SO_2 with O_2 to produce sulfur trioxide, SO_3. For this reaction to occur at an economical rate, it requires a catalyst. An early industrial process employed nitrogen monoxide, NO, as the catalyst.

$$2SO_2(g) + O_2(g) \xrightarrow{\ \text{NO}\ } 2SO_3(g)$$

Nitrogen monoxide does not appear in the overall equation but must participate in the reaction mechanism. Here is a proposed mechanism:

$$2NO + O_2 \longrightarrow 2NO_2$$
$$NO_2 + SO_2 \longrightarrow NO + SO_3$$

To obtain the overall reaction, the last step must occur twice each time the first step occurs once. As you can see from the mechanism, two molecules of NO are used up in the first step and are regenerated in the second step.

Note that the catalyst is an active participant in the reaction. But how does this participation explain the increase in speed of the catalyzed reaction over the uncatalyzed reaction? The Arrhenius equation (given at the beginning of Section 13.6) provides an answer. The catalyzed reaction mechanism makes available a reaction path having an increased overall rate of reaction. It increases this rate either by increasing the frequency factor A or, more commonly, by decreasing the activation energy E_a. The most dramatic effect comes from decreasing the activation energy, because it occurs as an exponent in the Arrhenius equation.

FIGURE 13.17 ▶

Comparison of activation energies in the uncatalyzed and catalyzed decompositions of ozone
The uncatalyzed reaction is $O_3 + O \longrightarrow O_2 + O_2$. Catalysis by Cl atoms provides an alternative pathway with lower activation energy, and therefore a faster reaction.

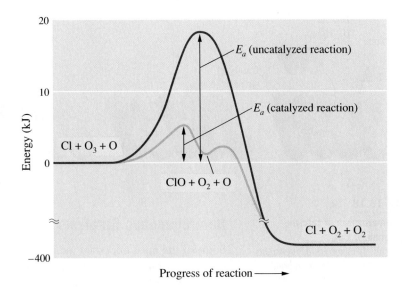

The depletion of ozone in the stratosphere by Cl atoms provides an example of the lowering of activation energy by a catalyst. Ozone is normally present in the stratosphere and provides protection against biologically destructive, short-wavelength ultraviolet radiation from the sun. Some recent ozone depletion in the stratosphere is believed to result from the Cl-catalyzed decomposition of O_3. Cl atoms in the stratosphere originate from the decomposition of chlorofluorocarbons (CFCs), which are compounds manufactured as refrigerants, aerosol propellants, and so forth. These Cl atoms react with ozone to form ClO and O_2, and the ClO reacts with O atoms (normally in the stratosphere) to produce Cl and O_2.

$$\begin{array}{c} Cl(g) + O_3(g) \longrightarrow ClO(g) + O_2(g) \\ \underline{ClO(g) + O(g) \longrightarrow Cl(g) + O_2(g)} \\ O_3(g) + O(g) \longrightarrow 2O_2(g) \end{array}$$

The net result is the decomposition of ozone with O atoms to produce O_2. Figure 13.17 shows the potential-energy curves for the uncatalyzed and the catalyzed reactions. The uncatalyzed reaction has such a large activation energy that its rate is extremely low. The addition of chlorine atoms provides an alternative pathway to the same overall reaction, but has a much lower activation energy and therefore an increased rate. <

Ozone depletion in the stratosphere was discussed in an essay at the end of Chapter 10.

Homogeneous Catalysis

The oxidation of sulfur dioxide using nitrogen monoxide as a catalyst is an example of **homogeneous catalysis,** which is *the use of a catalyst in the same phase as the reacting species.* The catalyst NO and the reacting species SO_2 and O_2 are all in the gas phase. Another example occurs in the oxidation of thallium(I) to thallium(III) by cerium(IV) in aqueous solution.

$$2Ce^{4+}(aq) + Tl^+(aq) \longrightarrow 2Ce^{3+}(aq) + Tl^{3+}(aq)$$

The uncatalyzed reaction is very slow; presumably it involves the collision of three positive ions. The reaction can be catalyzed by manganese(II) ion, however. The mechanism is thought to be

$$\begin{array}{c} Ce^{4+} + Mn^{2+} \longrightarrow Ce^{3+} + Mn^{3+} \\ Ce^{4+} + Mn^{3+} \longrightarrow Ce^{3+} + Mn^{4+} \\ Mn^{4+} + Tl^+ \longrightarrow Tl^{3+} + Mn^{2+} \end{array}$$

Each step is bimolecular.

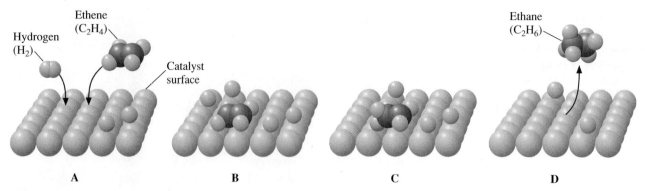

A   B   C   D

FIGURE 13.18 ▲

Proposed mechanism of catalytic hydrogenation of C₂H₄

(A) C_2H_4 and H_2 molecules diffuse to the catalyst. *(B)* The molecules form bonds to the catalyst surface. (The H_2 molecules dissociate to atoms in the process.) *(C)* H atoms migrate to the C_2H_4 molecule, where they react to form C_2H_6. *(D)* C_2H_6 diffuses away from the catalyst.

> *Understanding the chemical processes occurring at surfaces is being advanced by new techniques, including x-ray photoelectron spectroscopy and scanning tunneling microscopy.*

Heterogeneous Catalysis

Some of the most important industrial reactions involve **heterogeneous catalysis**—that is, *the use of a catalyst that exists in a different phase from the reacting species, usually a solid catalyst in contact with a gaseous or liquid solution of reactants.* Such surface, or heterogeneous, catalysis is thought to occur by chemical adsorption of the reactants onto the surface of the catalyst. *Adsorption* is the attraction of molecules to a surface. In *physical adsorption,* the attraction is provided by weak intermolecular forces. **Chemisorption,** by contrast, is *the binding of a species to a surface by chemical bonding forces.* It may happen that bonds in the species are broken during chemisorption, and this may provide the basis of catalytic action in certain cases. <

An example of heterogeneous catalysis involving chemisorption is provided by *catalytic hydrogenation.* This is the addition of H_2 to a compound, such as one with a carbon–carbon double bond, using a catalyst of platinum or nickel metal. Vegetable oils, which contain carbon–carbon double bonds, are changed to solid fats (shortening) when the bonds are catalytically hydrogenated. In the case of ethylene, C_2H_4, the equation is

$$
\begin{array}{c}
\underset{\text{Ethylene}}{\overset{\displaystyle \mathrm{H}\diagdown\quad\diagup\mathrm{H}}{\underset{\mathrm{H}\diagup\quad\diagdown\mathrm{H}}{\mathrm{C}=\mathrm{C}}}} + \mathrm{H}_2 \xrightarrow{\text{Pt}} \underset{\text{Ethane}}{\overset{\displaystyle \mathrm{H}\ \ \mathrm{H}}{\mathrm{H}-\underset{\mathrm{H}\ \ \mathrm{H}}{\mathrm{C}-\mathrm{C}}-\mathrm{H}}}
\end{array}
$$

A mechanism for this reaction is represented by the four steps shown in Figure 13.18. In *(A),* ethylene and hydrogen molecules diffuse to the catalyst surface, where, as shown in *(B),* they undergo chemisorption. The pi electrons of ethylene form bonds to the metal, and hydrogen molecules break into H atoms that bond to the metal. In *(C),* two H atoms migrate to an ethylene molecule bonded to the catalyst, where they react to form ethane. Then, in *(D),* because ethane does not bond to the metal, it diffuses away. Note that the catalyst surface that was used in *(B)* is regenerated in *(D).*

At the beginning of this section, we described the catalytic oxidation of SO_2 to SO_3, the anhydride of sulfuric acid. In an early process, the homogeneous catalyst NO was used. Today, in the *contact process,* a heterogeneous catalyst, Pt or V_2O_5, is used. Surface catalysts are used in the catalytic converters of automobiles to convert substances that would be atmospheric pollutants, such as CO and NO, into harmless substances, such as CO_2 and N_2 (Figure 13.19).

Enzyme Catalysis

Almost all enzymes, the catalysts of biological organisms, are protein molecules with molecular masses ranging to over a million amu. An enzyme has enormous catalytic activity, converting a thousand or so reactant molecules to products in a second. Enzymes are also highly specific, each enzyme acting only on a specific substance,

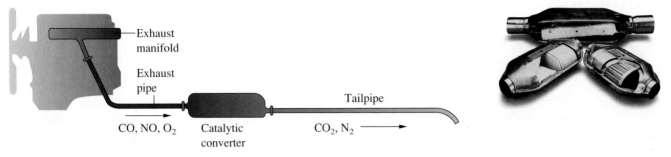

FIGURE 13.19 ▲

Automobile catalytic converter
Left: Exhaust gases from the automobile engine pass to the exhaust manifold and then to the catalytic converter, where pollutants CO and NO are converted to CO_2 and N_2. *Right:* Cross-sectional views of some automobile catalytic converters, showing the packing material with catalyst on its surface.

FIGURE 13.20 ▲

Enzyme action (lock-and-key model)
The enzyme has an active site to which the substrate binds to form an enzyme–substrate complex. The active site of the enzyme acts like a lock into which the substrate (key) fits. While bound to the enzyme, the substrate may have bonds weakened or new bonds formed to yield the products, which leave the enzyme.

or a specific type of substance, catalyzing it to undergo a particular reaction. For example, the enzyme sucrase, which is present in the digestive fluid of the small intestine, catalyzes the reaction of sucrose (table sugar) with water to form the simpler sugars glucose and fructose. *The substance whose reaction the enzyme catalyzes* is called the **substrate.** Thus, the enzyme sucrase acts on the substrate sucrose.

Figure 13.20 shows schematically how an enzyme acts. The enzyme molecule is a protein chain that tends to fold into a roughly spherical form with an *active site* at which the substrate molecule binds and the catalysis takes place. The substrate molecule, S, fits into the active site on the enzyme molecule, E, somewhat in the way a key fits into a lock, forming an enzyme–substrate complex, ES. (The lock-and-key model is only a rough approximation, because the active site on an enzyme deforms somewhat to fit the substrate molecule.) In effect, the active site "recognizes" the substrate and gives the enzyme its specificity. On binding to the enzyme, the substrate may have bonds weakened or new bonds formed that help yield the products, P.

$$E + S \longrightarrow ES \longrightarrow E + P$$

The formation of the enzyme–substrate complex provides a new pathway to products with a lower activation energy. Figure 13.21 compares the potential-energy curves of the uncatalyzed and catalyzed reactions. Note the lower activation energy of the catalyzed reaction.

FIGURE 13.21 ▲

Potential-energy curves for the reaction of substrate, S, to products, P
(A) The uncatalyzed reaction of substrate to product. *(B)* The enzyme-catalyzed reaction of substrate to product. Note that the catalyzed reaction provides a pathway with lower activation energy than does the uncatalyzed reaction.

A Chemist Looks at . . .

frontiers

Seeing Molecules React

Exactly what happens when molecules react? Transition-state theory and, more recently, calculations from quantum-mechanical theory have given us insight into how molecules behave in elementary reactions. But can we actually observe *through experiment* how molecules react? Until fairly recently, this seemed an impossible dream. Molecules are so small, the distances that atoms in molecules move to break bonds and form new ones are so minuscule, and the time that it takes a reaction to occur is so short that to be able to observe molecules while they react seemed well beyond human ability.

Within the last couple of decades, however, chemistry has progressed enormously in its quest to deal with substances at the molecular level. In 1987, Ahmed H. Zewail, professor of chemistry at California Institute of Technology, managed to devise an experimental technique that can follow molecules while they are reacting. In effect, Zewail developed "the world's smallest camera." In the process, he founded an area of research that has come to be called "femtochemistry," because reactions between molecules happen on the scale of femtoseconds. A femtosecond (fs)

FIGURE 13.22 ▲

Two possible potential-energy curves for the decomposition of cyclobutane to ethylene
Left: The cyclobutane molecule goes to a transition state in which two carbon–carbon bonds are stretched. When the transition state goes over to products, these stretched bonds break. *Right:* The cyclobutane molecule goes to an intermediate molecule in which one carbon–carbon bond has broken. When this intermediate goes over to products, the other carbon–carbon bond breaks. Experiments show that this is what actually happens. (Reprinted with the permission of The Nobel e-Museum from wysiwyg://26/http://www.nobel.se/chemistry/laureates/1999/press.html.)

A Checklist for Review

Important Terms

catalyst (13.1)
reaction rate (13.1)
rate law (13.3)
rate constant (13.3)
reaction order (13.3)
overall order of a
    reaction (13.3)
integrated rate
    law (13.4)
half-life (13.4)

collision theory (13.5)
activation energy (13.5)
transition-state theory (13.5)
activated complex (13.5)
Arrhenius equation (13.6)
frequency factor (13.6)
elementary reaction (13.7)
reaction mechanism (13.7)
reaction intermediate (13.7)
molecularity (13.7)

unimolecular reaction (13.7)
bimolecular reaction (13.7)
termolecular reaction (13.7)
rate-determining step (13.8)
catalysis (13.9)
homogeneous catalysis (13.9)
heterogeneous catalysis (13.9)
chemisorption (13.9)
substrate (13.9)

is 10^{-15} s, which is a million times smaller than a billionth of a second!

The experiment involves using a laser, first to send a *pump pulse* to excite a reactant molecule to a higher energy state. (See the essay on lasers at the end of Section 7.3.) Then, a weaker laser pulse or *probe pulse* of properly chosen wavelength is used to detect the molecule as it transforms to products. By varying the time between the pump pulse and the probe pulse, the experimenter can follow a molecule throughout the course of its reaction. The change of wavelength of the probe pulse tells the experimenter something about the change in character of the molecule as it reacts.

As an example of a reaction, Zewail looked at the decomposition of cyclobutane to ethylene:

H—C—C—H
H—C—C—H   ⟶ 2   C=C

Cyclobutane   Ethylene

FIGURE 13.23 ▲
Ahmed H. Zewail
The chemist is shown here with his laser apparatus.

Figure 13.22 shows two possible potential-energy diagrams for this reaction. The left diagram shows the cyclobutane molecule passing through a transition state (at the peak of the potential curve) in which two carbon–carbon bonds have simultaneously stretched. When the transition state goes over to products, these stretched bonds break. The right diagram shows the cyclobutane molecule going first to an intermediate molecule (between the two peaks). In this intermediate molecule, one carbon–carbon bond is broken. When the intermediate molecule goes over to products, another bond breaks, giving two ethylene molecules. Zewail and his coworkers were able to show that cyclobutane decomposed to ethylene by first going to an intermediate molecule (that is, the reaction actually goes by the potential curve on the right in Figure 13.22). The total time of the reaction was 700 fs! In 1999, Zewail (Figure 13.23) won the Nobel Prize in chemistry for his work in femtochemistry.

■ See Problems 13.129 and 13.130.

Key Equations

$$\ln\frac{[A]_t}{[A]_0} = -kt \text{ (first-order)}$$

$$t_{1/2} = \frac{0.693}{k} \text{ (first-order)}$$

$$\frac{1}{[A]_t} = kt + \frac{1}{[A]_0} \text{ (second-order)}$$

$$t_{1/2} = \frac{1}{k[A]_0} \text{ (second-order)}$$

$$[A]_t = -kt + [A]_0 \text{ (zero-order)}$$

$$t_{1/2} = \frac{[A]_0}{2k} \text{ (zero-order)}$$

$$\ln\frac{k_2}{k_1} = \frac{E_a}{R}\left(\frac{1}{T_1} - \frac{1}{T_2}\right)$$

Summary of Facts and Concepts

The *reaction rate* is defined as the increase in moles of product per liter per second (or as the decrease in moles of reactant per liter per second). Rates of reaction are determined by following the change of concentration of a reactant or product, either by chemical analysis or by observing a physical property. It is found that reaction rates are proportional to concentrations of reactants raised to various powers (usually 1 or 2, but they can be fractional or negative). The *rate law* mathematically expresses the relationship between rates and concentrations for a chemical reaction. Although the rate law tells you how the rate of a reaction depends on concentrations at a given moment, it is possible to transform a rate law to show how concentrations change with time, producing the *integrated rate law*. The *half-life* of a reaction is the time it takes for the reaction concentration to decrease to one-half of its original concentration.

Reaction rates can often double or triple with a 10°C rise in temperature. The effect of temperature on the rate can be explained by *collision theory*. According to this theory, two molecules react after colliding only when the energy of collision is greater than the *activation energy* and when the molecules are properly oriented. It is the rapid increase in the fraction of collisions having energy greater than the activation energy that explains the large temperature dependence of reaction rates. *Transition-state theory* explains reaction rates in terms of the formation of an *activated complex* of the colliding molecules.

The *Arrhenius equation* is a mathematical relationship showing the dependence of a rate constant on temperature.

A chemical equation describes the overall result of a chemical reaction that may take place in one or more steps. The steps are called *elementary reactions,* and the set of elementary reactions that describes what is happening at the molecular level in an overall reaction is called the *reaction mechanism.* In some cases, the overall reaction involves a *reaction intermediate*—a species produced in one step but used up in a subsequent one. The rate of the overall reaction depends on the rate of the slowest step (the *rate-determining step*). This rate is proportional to the product of the concentrations of the reactant molecules in that step. If this step involves a reaction intermediate, its concentration can be eliminated by using the relationship of the concentrations in the preceding fast, *equilibrium* step.

A *catalyst* is a substance that speeds up a chemical reaction without being consumed by it. The catalyst is used up in one step of the reaction mechanism but regenerated in a later step. Catalytic activity operates by providing a reaction mechanism that has lower activation energy. Catalysis is classified as *homogeneous catalysis* if the substances react within one phase and as *heterogeneous catalysis* if the substances in a gas or liquid phase react at the surface of a solid catalyst. Many industrial reactions involve heterogeneous catalysis. Enzymes are biological catalysts (usually proteins). *Enzyme catalysis* is highly specific, so each enzyme acts on a particular kind of *substrate.*

Media Summary

Visit the **student website at college.cengage.com/pic/ebbing9e** to help prepare for class, study for quizzes and exams, understand core concepts, and visualize molecular-level interactions. The following media activities are available for this chapter:

 Prepare for Class

■ **Video Lessons** *Mini lectures from chemistry experts*
An Introduction to Reaction Rates
Rate Laws: How the Reaction Rate Depends on Concentration
CIA Demonstration: Shifting the Equilibrium of $Fe(SCN)_2{}^-$
Determining the Form of a Rate Law
First-Order Reactions
Second-Order Reactions
A Kinetics Problem
The Collision Model
The Arrhenius Equation
Using the Arrhenius Equation
Defining the Molecularity of a Reaction
Determining the Rate Laws of Elementary Reactions
Calculating the Rate Laws of Multistep Reactions
Catalysts and Types of Catalysts
CIA Demonstration: The Copper-Catalyzed Decomposition of Acetone
CIA Demonstration: Elephant Snot
CIA Demonstration: The Cobalt(II)-Catalyzed Decomposition of Potassium Sodium Tartrate

 Improve Your Grade

■ **Visualizations** *Molecular-level animations and lab demonstration videos*
Surface Area and Reaction Rate: Coffee Creamer Flammability
Reaction Rate and Concentration
Rate Laws
Half-Life of Reactions
The Gas–Phase Reaction of NO and Cl_2
Transition States and Activation Energy
Decomposition of N_2O_5
Homogeneous Catalysis
Heterogeneous Catalysis

■ **Flashcards** *Key terms and definitions*
Online Flashcards

■ **Self-Assessment Questions** *Additional questions with full worked-out solutions*
6 Self-Assessment Questions

 ACE the Test

Multiple-choice quizzes
3 ACE Practice Tests

Access these resources using the passkey available free with new texts or for purchase separately.

Learning Objectives

13.1 Definition of a Reaction Rate

- Define *reaction rate*.
- Explain *instantaneous* rate and *average* rate of a reaction.
- Explain how the different ways of expressing reaction rates are related. **Example 13.1**
- Calculate average reaction rate. **Example 13.2**

13.2 Experimental Determination of Rate

- Describe how reaction rates may be experimentally determined.

13.3 Dependence of Rate on Concentration

- Define and provide examples of a *rate law*, *rate constant*, and *reaction order*.
- Determine the order of reaction from the rate law. **Example 13.3**
- Determine the rate law from initial rates. **Example 13.4**

13.4 Change of Concentration with Time

- Learn the *integrated rate laws* for *first-order*, *second-order*, and *zero-order* reactions.
- Use an integrated rate law. **Example 13.5**
- Define *half-life* of a reaction.
- Learn the half-life equations for first-order, second-order, and zero-order reactions.
- Relate the half-life of a reaction to the rate constant. **Example 13.6**
- Plot kinetic data to determine the order of a reaction.

13.5 Temperature and Rate; Collision and Transition-State Theories

- State the postulates of *collision theory*.
- Explain *activation energy* (E_a).
- Describe how temperature, activation energy, and molecular orientation influence reaction rates.

- State the *transition-state theory*.
- Define *activated complex*.
- Describe and interpret *potential-energy curves* for endothermic and exothermic reactions.

13.6 Arrhenius Equation

- Use the *Arrhenius equation*. **Example 13.7**

13.7 Elementary Reactions

- Define *elementary reaction, reaction mechanism*, and *reaction intermediate*.
- Write the overall chemical equation from a mechanism. **Example 13.8**
- Define *molecularity*.
- Give examples of *unimolecular, bimolecular,* and *termolecular* reactions.
- Determine the molecularity of an elementary reaction. **Example 13.9**
- Write the rate equation for an elementary reaction. **Example 13.10**

13.8 The Rate Law and the Mechanism

- Explain the *rate-determining* step of a mechanism.
- Determine the rate law from a mechanism with an initial slow step. **Example 13.11**
- Determine the rate law from a mechanism with an initial fast, equilibrium step. **Example 13.12**

13.9 Catalysis

- Describe how a *catalyst* influences the rate of a reaction.
- Indicate how a catalyst changes the potential-energy curve of a reaction.
- Define *homogeneous catalysis* and *heterogeneous catalysis*.
- Explain *enzyme catalysis*.

Self-Assessment and Review Questions

13.1 List the four variables or factors that can affect the rate of reaction.

13.2 Define the rate of reaction of HBr in the following reaction. How is this related to the rate of formation of Br_2?

$$4HBr(g) + O_2(g) \longrightarrow 2Br_2(g) + 2H_2O(g)$$

13.3 Give at least two physical properties that might be used to determine the rate of a reaction.

13.4 A rate of reaction depends on four variables (Question 13.1). Explain by means of an example how the rate law deals with each of these variables.

13.5 The exponents in a rate law have no relationship to the coefficients in the overall balanced equation for the reaction. Give an example of a balanced equation and the rate law for a reaction that clearly demonstrates this.

13.6 The reaction

$$3I^-(aq) + H_3AsO_4(aq) + 2H^+(aq) \longrightarrow$$
$$I_3^-(aq) + H_3AsO_3(aq) + H_2O(l)$$

is found to be first order with respect to each of the reactants. Write the rate law. What is the overall order?

13.7 The rate of a reaction is quadrupled when the concentration of one reactant is doubled. What is the order of the reaction with respect to this reactant?

13.8 A rate law is one-half order with respect to a reactant. What is the effect on the rate when the concentration of this reactant is doubled?

13.9 The reaction $A(g) \longrightarrow B(g) + C(g)$ is known to be first order in $A(g)$. It takes 25 s for the concentration of $A(g)$ to decrease by one-half of its initial value. How long does it take for the concentration of A(g) to decrease to one-fourth of its initial value? to one-eighth of its initial value?

13.10 Compare the half-life equations for a first-order and a second-order reaction. For which reaction order is the value of the half-life independent of the reactant concentration?

13.11 What two factors determine whether a collision between two reactant molecules will result in reaction?

13.12 Sketch a potential-energy diagram for the exothermic, elementary reaction

$$A + B \longrightarrow C + D$$

and on it denote the activation energies for the forward and reverse reactions. Also indicate the reactants, products, and activated complex.

13.13 Draw a structural formula for the activated complex in the following reaction:

$$NO_2 + NO_3 \longrightarrow NO + NO_2 + O_2$$

Refer to Figure 13.16, Step 2, for details of this reaction. Use dashed lines for bonds about to form or break. Use a single line for all other bonds.

13.14 Rate constants for reactions often follow the Arrhenius equation. Write this equation and then identify each term in it with the corresponding factor or factors from collision theory. Give a physical interpretation of each of those factors.

13.15 By means of an example, explain what is meant by the term *reaction intermediate*.

13.16 Why is it generally impossible to predict the rate law for a reaction on the basis of the chemical equation only?

13.17 The rate law for the reaction

$$2NO_2Cl(g) \longrightarrow 2NO_2(g) + Cl_2(g) \quad \text{(overall equation)}$$

is first order in nitryl chloride, NO_2Cl.

$$\text{Rate} = k[NO_2Cl]$$

Explain why the mechanism for this reaction cannot be the single elementary reaction

$$2NO_2Cl \longrightarrow 2NO_2 + Cl_2 \quad \text{(elementary reaction)}$$

13.18 There is often one step in a reaction mechanism that is rate-determining. What characteristic of such a step makes it rate-determining? Explain.

13.19 The dissociation of N_2O_4 into NO_2,

$$N_2O_4(g) \rightleftharpoons 2NO_2(g)$$

is believed to occur in one step. Obtain the concentration of N_2O_4 in terms of the concentration of NO_2 and the rate constants for the forward and reverse reactions, when the reactions have come to equilibrium.

13.20 How does a catalyst speed up a reaction? How can a catalyst be involved in a reaction without being consumed by it?

13.21 Compare physical adsorption and chemisorption (chemical adsorption).

13.22 Describe the steps in the catalytic hydrogenation of ethylene.

13.23 You are running the reaction $2A + B \longrightarrow C + 3D$. Your lab partner has conducted the first two experiments to determine the rate law for the reaction by the method of initial rates.

Experiment Number	Concentration of A (M)	Concentration of B (M)
1	0.0250	0.0330
2	0.0500	0.0330
3		

Presuming that you can measure the initial rate of each experiment, which of the following concentrations for Experiment 3 would help you to determine the rate law easily?

  a. [A] = 0.0330 M, [B] = 0.0330 M
  b. [A] = 0.0125 M, [B] = 0.0500 M
  c. [A] = 0.0250 M, [B] = 0.0400 M
  d. [A] = 0.0250 M, [B] = 0.0330 M
  e. [A] = 0.0500 M, [B] = 0.0330 M

13.24 At a constant temperature, which of the following would be expected to affect the rate of a given chemical reaction, A + B $\longrightarrow$ C + D?
  I. The reaction temperature
  II. The concentration of the products
  III. A catalyst
  a. I only   **b.** II only
  c. III only   **d.** I and II only
  e. I and III only

13.25 Consider the reaction E + F $\longrightarrow$ G + H, which has the following reaction coordinate diagram.

E + F $\longrightarrow$ G + H

Which one of the following statements is true?
  a. The activation energy is greatest for the forward reaction.
  b. The reactants are at a lower energy than the products.
  c. The reaction is endothermic.
  d. The rate of the forward reaction would be slowed by an increase in temperature.
  e. If the rate law for the reaction is Rate = $k[E]^2[F]$, then doubling the concentration of E will cause the rate to increase by a factor of 4 (that is, the reaction will proceed four times faster).

13.26 The hypothetical reaction

$$A + B + C \longrightarrow D + E$$

has the rate law Rate = $k[A]^2[B]$. Which of the following changes would have the *least* effect on increasing the rate of this reaction?
  a. Doubling $[A]_0$ while keeping $[B]_0$ and $[C]_0$ constant.
  b. Doubling $[B]_0$ while keeping $[A]_0$ and $[C]_0$ constant.
  c. Doubling $[C]_0$ while keeping $[A]_0$ and $[B]_0$ constant.
  d. Increasing the rate constant by running the reaction at a higher temperature.
  e. Adding a catalyst to the reaction mixture.

Concept Explorations

13.27   Kinetics I

Consider the hypothetical reaction $A(g) + 2B(g) \longrightarrow C(g)$. The four containers below represent this reaction being run with different initial amounts of A and B. Assume that the volume of each container is 1.0 L. The reaction is second order with respect to A and first order with respect to B.

● = A
● = B

W   X   Y   Z

a. Based on the information presented in the problem, write the rate law for the reaction.

b. Which of the containers, W, X, Y, or Z, would have the greatest reaction rate? Justify your answer.

c. Which of the containers would have the lowest reaction rate? Explain

d. If the volume of the container X were increased to 2.0 L, how would the rate of the reaction in this larger container compare to the rate of reaction run in the 1.0-L container X? (Assume that the number of A and B atoms is the same in each case.)

e. If the temperature in container W were increased, what impact would this probably have on the rate of reaction? Why?

f. If you want to double the rate of reaction in container X, what are some things that you could do to the concentration(s) of A and B?

g. In which container would you observe the slowest rate of formation of C?

h. Assuming that A and B are not in great excess, which would have the greater impact on the rate of reaction in container W: removing a unit of B or removing a unit of A? Explain.

i. Describe how the rate of consumption of A compares to the rate of consumption of B. If you cannot answer this question, what additional information do you need to provide an answer?

j. If the product C were removed from the container as it formed, what effect would this have on the rate of the reaction?

13.28   Kinetics II

You and a friend are working together in order to obtain as much kinetic information as possible about the reaction $A(g) \longrightarrow B(g) + C(g)$. One thing you know before performing the experiments is that the reaction is zero order, first order, or second order with respect to A. Your friend goes off, runs the experiment, and brings back the following graph.

Time (s) →

a. After studying the curve of the graph, she declares that the reaction is second order, with a corresponding rate law of Rate $= k[A]^2$. Judging solely on the basis of the information presented in this plot, is she correct in her statement that the reaction must be second order?

Here are some data collected from her experiment:

Time (s)	[A]
0.0	1.0
1.0	0.14
3.0	2.5×10^{-3}
5.0	4.5×10^{-5}
7.0	8.3×10^{-7}

b. The half-life of the reaction is 0.35 s. Do these data support the reaction being second order, or is it something else? Try to reach a conclusive answer without graphing the data.

c. What is the rate constant for the reaction?

d. The mechanism for this reaction is found to be a two-step process, with intermediates X and Y. The first step of the reaction is the rate-determining step. Write a possible mechanism for the reaction.

e. You perform additional experiments and find that the rate constant doubles in value when you increase the temperature by 10°C. Your lab partner doesn't understand why the rate constant changes in this manner. What could you say to your partner to help her understand? Feel free to use figures and pictures as part of your explanation.

Conceptual Problems

13.29   Consider the reaction $3A \longrightarrow 2B + C$.

a. One rate expression for the reaction is

$$\text{Rate of formation of C} = +\frac{\Delta[C]}{\Delta t}$$

Write two other rate expressions for this reaction in this form.

b. Using your two rate expressions, if you calculated the average rate of the reaction over the same time interval, would the rates be equal?

c. If your answer to part b was no, write two rate expressions that would give an equal rate when calculated over the same time interval.

13.30 Given the reaction 2A + B ⟶ C + 3D, can you write the rate law for this reaction? If so, write the rate law; if not, why?

13.31 The reaction 2A(g) ⟶ A₂(g) is being run in each of the following containers. The reaction is found to be second-order with respect to A.

a. Write the rate law for the reaction.
b. Which reaction container will have a greater reaction rate?
c. In which container will the reaction have a shorter half-life?
d. What are the relative rates of the reactions in each container?
e. After a set amount of time has elapsed, which container will contain fewer A atoms?

13.32 When viewed from a molecular perspective, a particular reaction is written as

AB ⟶ A + B

a. If the reaction is first-order with a half-life of 10 seconds, complete the following pictures after 10 and 20 seconds have elapsed.

$t = 0$ s $t = 10$ s $t = 20$ s

b. How would the pictures from part a change if the reaction were second-order with the same half-life?
c. For the first-order case, what are the relative reaction rates at the start of the reaction and after 10 seconds have elapsed?
d. For the second-order case, what are the relative reaction rates at the start of the reaction and after 10 seconds have elapsed?

13.33 You perform some experiments for the reaction A ⟶ B + C and determine the rate law has the form

Rate = $k[A]^x$

Calculate the value of exponent x for each of the following.
a. [A] is tripled and you observe no rate change.
b. [A] is doubled and the rate doubles.
c. [A] is tripled and the rate goes up by a factor of 27.

13.34 A friend of yours runs a reaction and generates the following plot. She explains that in following the reaction, she measured the concentration of a compound that she calls "E."

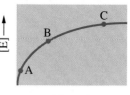

a. Your friend tells you that E is either a reactant or a product. Which is it and why?
b. Is the average rate faster between points A and B or B and C? Why?

13.35 Given the hypothetical plot shown here for the concentration of compound Y versus time, answer the following questions.

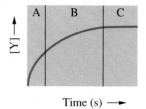

a. In which region of the curve does the rate have a constant value (A, B, or C)?
b. In which region of the curve is the rate the fastest (A, B, or C)?

13.36 You carry out the following reaction by introducing N₂O₄ into an evacuated flask and observing the concentration change of the product over time.

$$N_2O_4(g) \longrightarrow 2NO_2(g)$$

Which one of the curves shown here reflects the data collected for this reaction?

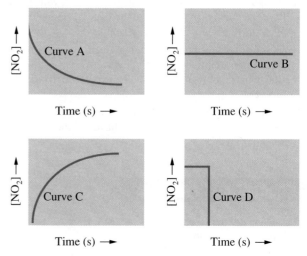

13.37 You are running the reaction 2A + B ⟶ C + 3D. Your lab partner has conducted the first two experiments to determine the rate law for the reaction. He has recorded the initial rates for these experiments in another data table. Come up with some reactant concentrations for Experiment 3 that will allow you to determine the rate law by measuring the initial rate.

Experiment Number	Concentration of A (M)	Concentration of B (M)
1	1.0	1.0
2	2.0	1.0
3		

13.38 The chemical reaction A $\longrightarrow$ B + C has a rate constant that obeys the Arrhenius equation. Predict what happens to both the rate constant k and the rate of the reaction if the following were to occur.
  a. a decrease in temperature
  b. an increase in the activation energy of the forward and reverse reactions
  c. an increase in both activation energy and temperature

Practice Problems

Reaction Rates

13.39 Relate the rate of decomposition of NO_2 to the rate of formation of O_2 for the following reaction:

$$2NO_2(g) \longrightarrow 2NO(g) + O_2(g)$$

13.40 For the reaction of hydrogen with iodine

$$H_2(g) + I_2(g) \longrightarrow 2HI(g)$$

relate the rate of disappearance of hydrogen gas to the rate of formation of hydrogen iodide.

13.41 To obtain the rate of the reaction

$$5Br^-(aq) + BrO_3^-(aq) + 6H^+(aq) \longrightarrow 3Br_2(aq) + 3H_2O(l)$$

you might follow the Br^- concentration or the BrO_3^- concentration. How are the rates in terms of these species related?

13.42 To obtain the rate of the reaction

$$3I^-(aq) + H_3AsO_4(aq) + 2H^+(aq) \longrightarrow I_3^-(aq) + H_3AsO_3(aq) + H_2O(l)$$

you might follow the I^- concentration or the I_3^- concentration. How are the rates in terms of these species related?

13.43 Ammonium nitrite, NH_4NO_2, decomposes in solution, as shown here.

$$NH_4NO_2(aq) \longrightarrow N_2(g) + 2H_2O(l)$$

The concentration of NH_4^+ ion at the beginning of an experiment was 0.500 M. After 3.00 hours, it was 0.432 M. What is the average rate of decomposition of NH_4NO_2 in this time interval?

13.44 Iron(III) chloride is reduced by tin(II) chloride.

$$2FeCl_3(aq) + SnCl_2(aq) \longrightarrow 2FeCl_2(aq) + SnCl_4(aq)$$

The concentration of Fe^{3+} ion at the beginning of an experiment was 0.03586 M. After 4.00 min, it was 0.02638 M. What is the average rate of reaction of $FeCl_3$ in this time interval?

13.45 Azomethane, CH_3NNCH_3, decomposes according to the following equation:

$$CH_3NNCH_3(g) \longrightarrow C_2H_6(g) + N_2(g)$$

The initial concentration of azomethane was 1.50×10^{-2} mol/L. After 7.00 min, this concentration decreased to 1.01×10^{-2} mol/L. Obtain the average rate of reaction during this time interval. Express the answer in units of mol/(L·s).

13.46 Nitrogen dioxide, NO_2, decomposes upon heating to form nitric oxide and oxygen according to the following equation:

$$2NO_2(g) \longrightarrow 2NO(g) + O_2(g)$$

At the beginning of an experiment, the concentration of nitrogen dioxide in a reaction vessel was 0.1103 mol/L. After 60.0 s, the concentration decreased to 0.1076 mol/L. What is the average rate of decomposition of NO_2 during this time interval, in mol/(L·s)?

Rate Laws

13.47 Hydrogen sulfide is oxidized by chlorine in aqueous solution.

$$H_2S(aq) + Cl_2(aq) \longrightarrow S(s) + 2HCl(aq)$$

The experimental rate law is

$$Rate = k[H_2S][Cl_2]$$

What is the reaction order with respect to H_2S? with respect to Cl_2? What is the overall order?

13.48 For the reaction of nitrogen monoxide, NO, with chlorine, Cl_2,

$$2NO(g) + Cl_2(g) \longrightarrow 2NOCl(g)$$

the observed rate law is

$$Rate = k[NO]^2[Cl_2]$$

What is the reaction order with respect to nitrogen monoxide? with respect to Cl_2? What is the overall order?

13.49 Oxalic acid, $H_2C_2O_4$, is oxidized by permanganate ion to CO_2 and H_2O.

$$2MnO_4^-(aq) + 5H_2C_2O_4(aq) + 6H^+(aq) \longrightarrow 2Mn^{2+}(aq) + 10CO_2(g) + 8H_2O(l)$$

The rate law is

$$Rate = k[MnO_4^-][H_2C_2O_4]$$

What is the order with respect to each reactant? What is the overall order?

13.50 Iron(II) ion is oxidized by hydrogen peroxide in acidic solution.

$$H_2O_2(aq) + 2Fe^{2+}(aq) + 2H^+(aq) \longrightarrow 2Fe^{3+}(aq) + 2H_2O(l)$$

The rate law is

$$\text{Rate} = k[H_2O_2][Fe^{2+}]$$

What is the order with respect to each reactant? What is the overall order?

13.51   In experiments on the decomposition of azomethane,

$$CH_3NNCH_3(g) \longrightarrow C_2H_6(g) + N_2(g)$$

the following data were obtained:

	Initial Concentration of Azomethane	Initial Rate
Exp. 1	$1.13 \times 10^{-2}\ M$	$2.8 \times 10^{-6}\ M/s$
Exp. 2	$2.26 \times 10^{-2}\ M$	$5.6 \times 10^{-6}\ M/s$

What is the rate law? What is the value of the rate constant?

13.52   Ethylene oxide, C_2H_4O, decomposes when heated to give methane and carbon monoxide.

$$C_2H_4O(g) \longrightarrow CH_4(g) + CO(g)$$

The following kinetic data were observed for the reaction at 688 K:

	Initial Concentration of Ethylene Oxide	Initial Rate
Exp. 1	$0.00272\ M$	$5.57 \times 10^{-7}\ M/s$
Exp. 2	$0.00544\ M$	$1.11 \times 10^{-6}\ M/s$

Find the rate law and the value of the rate constant for this reaction.

13.53   Nitrogen monoxide, NO, reacts with hydrogen to give nitrous oxide, N_2O, and water.

$$2NO(g) + H_2(g) \longrightarrow N_2O(g) + H_2O(g)$$

In a series of experiments, the following initial rates of disappearance of NO were obtained:

	Initial Concentration		Initial Rate of Reaction of NO
	NO	H_2	
Exp. 1	$6.4 \times 10^{-3}\ M$	$2.2 \times 10^{-3}\ M$	$2.6 \times 10^{-5}\ M/s$
Exp. 2	$12.8 \times 10^{-3}\ M$	$2.2 \times 10^{-3}\ M$	$1.0 \times 10^{-4}\ M/s$
Exp. 3	$6.4 \times 10^{-3}\ M$	$4.5 \times 10^{-3}\ M$	$5.1 \times 10^{-5}\ M/s$

Find the rate law and the value of the rate constant for the reaction of NO.

13.54   In a kinetic study of the reaction

$$2NO(g) + O_2(g) \longrightarrow 2NO_2(g)$$

the following data were obtained for the initial rates of disappearance of NO:

	Initial Concentrations		Initial Rate of Reaction of NO
	NO	O_2	
Exp. 1	$0.0125\ M$	$0.0253\ M$	$0.0281\ M/s$
Exp. 2	$0.0250\ M$	$0.0253\ M$	$0.112\ M/s$
Exp. 3	$0.0125\ M$	$0.0506\ M$	$0.0561\ M/s$

Obtain the rate law. What is the value of the rate constant?

13.55   Chlorine dioxide, ClO_2, is a reddish-yellow gas that is soluble in water. In basic solution it gives ClO_3^- and ClO_2^- ions.

$$2ClO_2(aq) + 2OH^-(aq) \longrightarrow$$
$$ClO_3^-(aq) + ClO_2^-(aq) + H_2O$$

To obtain the rate law for this reaction, the following experiments were run and, for each, the initial rate of reaction of ClO_2 was determined. Obtain the rate law and the value of the rate constant.

	Initial Concentrations (mol/L)		Initial Rate (mol/(L·s))
	ClO_2	OH^-	
Exp. 1	0.060	0.030	0.0248
Exp. 2	0.020	0.030	0.00276
Exp. 3	0.020	0.090	0.00828

13.56   Iodide ion is oxidized to hypoiodite ion, IO^-, by hypochlorite ion, ClO^-, in basic solution. The equation is

$$I^-(aq) + ClO^-(aq) \xrightarrow{OH^-} IO^-(aq) + Cl^-(aq)$$

The following initial-rate experiments were run and, for each, the initial rate of formation of IO^- was determined. Find the rate law and the value of the rate constant.

	Initial Concentrations (mol/L)			Initial Rate (mol/(L·s))
	I^-	ClO^-	OH^-	
Exp. 1	0.010	0.020	0.010	12.2×10^{-2}
Exp. 2	0.020	0.010	0.010	12.2×10^{-2}
Exp. 3	0.010	0.010	0.010	6.1×10^{-2}
Exp. 4	0.010	0.010	0.020	3.0×10^{-2}

Integrated Rate Laws (Change of Concentration with Time); Half-Life

13.57   Sulfuryl chloride, SO_2Cl_2, decomposes when heated.

$$SO_2Cl_2(g) \longrightarrow SO_2(g) + Cl_2(g)$$

In an experiment, the initial concentration of SO_2Cl_2 was 0.0248 mol/L. If the rate constant is 2.2×10^{-5}/s, what is the concentration of SO_2Cl_2 after 2.0 hr? The reaction is first order.

13.58   Cyclopropane, C_3H_6, is converted to its isomer propylene, $CH_2{=}CHCH_3$, when heated. The rate law is first order in cyclopropane, and the rate constant is 6.0×10^{-4}/s at 500°C. If the initial concentration of cyclopropane is 0.0226 mol/L, what is the concentration after 899 s?

13.59   A reaction of the form $aA \longrightarrow$ Products is second-order with a rate constant of 0.225 L/(mol·s). If the initial concentration of A is 0.293 mol/L, what is the molar concentration of A after 35.4 s?

13.60 A reaction of the form $aA \longrightarrow$ Products is second order with a rate constant of 0.169 L/(mol·s). If the initial concentration of A is 0.159 mol/L, how many seconds would it take for the concentration of A to decrease to 6.07×10^{-3} mol/L?

13.61 Ethyl chloride, CH_3CH_2Cl, used to produce tetraethyllead gasoline additive, decomposes, when heated, to give ethylene and hydrogen chloride.

$$CH_3CH_2Cl(g) \longrightarrow C_2H_4(g) + HCl(g)$$

The reaction is first order. In an experiment, the initial concentration of ethyl chloride was 0.00100 M. After heating at 500°C for 155 s, this was reduced to 0.00067 M. What was the concentration of ethyl chloride after a total of 256 s?

13.62 Cyclobutane, C_4H_8, consisting of molecules in which four carbon atoms form a ring, decomposes, when heated, to give ethylene.

$$C_4H_8(g) \longrightarrow 2C_2H_4(g)$$

The reaction is first order. In an experiment, the initial concentration of cyclobutane was 0.00150 M. After heating at 450°C for 455 s, this was reduced to 0.00119 M. What was the concentration of cyclobutane after a total of 750 s?

13.63 Methyl isocyanide, CH_3NC, isomerizes, when heated, to give acetonitrile (methyl cyanide), CH_3CN.

$$CH_3NC(g) \longrightarrow CH_3CN(g)$$

The reaction is first order. At 230°C, the rate constant for the isomerization is 6.3×10^{-4}/s. What is the half-life? How long would it take for the concentration of CH_3NC to decrease to 50.0% of its initial value? to 25.0% of its initial value?

13.64 Dinitrogen pentoxide, N_2O_5, decomposes when heated in carbon tetrachloride solvent.

$$N_2O_5 \longrightarrow 2NO_2 + \tfrac{1}{2}O_2(g)$$

If the rate constant for the decomposition of N_2O_5 is 6.2×10^{-4}/min, what is the half-life? (The rate law is first order in N_2O_5.) How long would it take for the concentration of N_2O_5 to decrease to 25% of its initial value? to 12.5% of its initial value?

13.65 In the presence of excess thiocyanate ion, SCN^-, the following reaction is first order in chromium(III) ion, Cr^{3+}; the rate constant is 2.0×10^{-6}/s.

$$Cr^{3+}(aq) + SCN^-(aq) \longrightarrow Cr(SCN)^{2+}(aq)$$

What is the half-life in hours? How many hours would be required for the initial concentration of Cr^{3+} to decrease to each

of the following values: 25.0% left, 12.5% left, 6.25% left, 3.125% left?

13.66 In the presence of excess thiocyanate ion, SCN^-, the following reaction is first order in iron(III) ion, Fe^{3+}; the rate constant is 1.27/s.

$$Fe^{3+}(aq) + SCN^-(aq) \longrightarrow Fe(SCN)^{2+}(aq)$$

What is the half-life in seconds? How many seconds would be required for the initial concentration of Fe^{3+} to decrease to each of the following values: 25.0% left, 12.5% left, 6.25% left, 3.125% left? What is the relationship between these times and the half-life?

13.67 A reaction of the form $aA \longrightarrow$ Products is second order with a rate constant of 0.413 L/(mol·s). What is the half-life, in seconds, of the reaction if the initial concentration of A is 5.25×10^{-3} mol/L?

13.68 A reaction of the form $aA \longrightarrow$ Products is second order with a half-life of 425 s. What is the rate constant of the reaction if the initial concentration of A is 5.99×10^{-3} mol/L?

13.69 In the presence of excess thiocyanate ion, SCN^-, the following reaction is first order in chromium(III) ion, Cr^{3+}; the rate constant is 2.0×10^{-6}/s.

$$Cr^{3+}(aq) + SCN^-(aq) \longrightarrow Cr(SCN)^{2+}(aq)$$

If 85.0% reaction is required to obtain a noticeable color from the formation of the $Cr(SCN)^{2+}$ ion, how many hours are required?

13.70 In the presence of excess thiocyanate ion, SCN^-, the following reaction is first order in iron(III) ion, Fe^{3+}; the rate constant is 1.27/s.

$$Fe^{3+}(aq) + SCN^-(aq) \longrightarrow Fe(SCN)^{2+}(aq)$$

If 90.0% reaction is required to obtain a noticeable color from the formation of the $Fe(SCN)^{2+}$ ion, how many seconds are required?

13.71 It is found that a gas undergoes a zero-order decomposition reaction in the presence of a nickel catalyst. If the rate constant for this reaction is 8.1×10^{-2} mol/(L·s), how long will it take for the concentration of the gas to change from an initial concentration of 0.10 M to 1.0×10^{-2} M?

13.72 The reaction A $\longrightarrow$ B + C is found to be zero order. If it takes 4.3×10^2 seconds for an initial concentration of A to go from 0.50 M to 0.25 M, what is the rate constant for the reaction?

13.73 Chlorine dioxide oxidizes iodide ion in aqueous solution to iodine; chlorine dioxide is reduced to chlorite ion.

$$2ClO_2(aq) + 2I^-(aq) \longrightarrow 2ClO_2^-(aq) + I_2(aq)$$

The order of the reaction with respect to ClO_2 was determined by starting with a large excess of I^-, so that its concentration was essentially constant. Then

$$\text{Rate} = k[ClO_2]^m[I^-]^n = k'[ClO_2]^m$$

where $k' = k[I^-]^n$. Determine the order with respect to ClO_2 and the rate constant k' by plotting the following data assuming first- and then second-order kinetics. [Data from H. Fukutomi and G. Gordon, *J. Am. Chem. Soc.*, 89, 1362 (1967).]

Time (s)	$[ClO_2]$ (mol/L)
0.00	4.77×10^{-4}
1.00	4.31×10^{-4}
2.00	3.91×10^{-4}
3.00	3.53×10^{-4}
5.00	2.89×10^{-4}
10.00	1.76×10^{-4}
30.00	2.4×10^{-5}
50.00	3.2×10^{-6}

13.74 Methyl acetate, CH_3COOCH_3, reacts in basic solution to give acetate ion, CH_3COO^-, and methanol, CH_3OH.

$$CH_3COOCH_3(aq) + OH^-(aq) \longrightarrow$$
$$CH_3COO^-(aq) + CH_3OH(aq)$$

The overall order of the reaction was determined by starting with methyl acetate and hydroxide ion at the same concentrations, so $[CH_3COOCH_3] = [OH^-] = x$. Then

$$\text{Rate} = k[CH_3COOCH_3]^m[OH^-]^n = kx^{m+n}$$

Determine the overall order and the value of the rate constant by plotting the following data assuming first- and then second-order kinetics.

Time (min)	$[CH_3COOCH_3]$ (mol/L)
0.00	0.01000
3.00	0.00740
4.00	0.00683
5.00	0.00634
10.00	0.00463
20.00	0.00304
30.00	0.00224

Rate and Temperature

13.75 Sketch a potential-energy diagram for the reaction of nitric oxide with ozone.

$$NO(g) + O_3(g) \longrightarrow NO_2(g) + O_2(g)$$

The activation energy for the forward reaction is 10 kJ; the $\Delta H°$ is -200 kJ. What is the activation energy for the reverse reaction? Label your diagram appropriately.

13.76 Sketch a potential-energy diagram for the decomposition of nitrous oxide.

$$N_2O(g) \longrightarrow N_2(g) + O(g)$$

The activation energy for the forward reaction is 251 kJ; the $\Delta H°$ is $+167$ kJ. What is the activation energy for the reverse reaction? Label your diagram appropriately.

13.77 In a series of experiments on the decomposition of dinitrogen pentoxide, N_2O_5, rate constants were determined at two different temperatures. At 35°C, the rate constant was 1.4×10^{-4}/s; at 45°C, the rate constant was 5.0×10^{-4}/s. What is the activation energy for this reaction? What is the value of the rate constant at 55°C?

13.78 The reaction

$$2NOCl(g) \longrightarrow 2NO(g) + Cl_2(g)$$

has rate-constant values for the reaction of NOCl of 9.3×10^{-6}/s at 350 K and 6.9×10^{-4}/s at 400 K. Calculate activation energy for the reaction. What is the rate constant at 435 K?

13.79 The rate of a particular reaction triples when the temperature is increased from 25°C to 35°C. Calculate the activation energy for this reaction.

13.80 The rate of a particular reaction quadruples when the temperature is increased from 25°C to 35°C. Calculate the activation energy for this reaction.

13.81 The following values of the rate constant were obtained for the decomposition of nitrogen dioxide at various temperatures. Plot the logarithm of k versus $1/T$ and from the graph obtain the energy of activation.

Temperature (°C)	k (L/mol·s)
320	0.527
330	0.776
340	1.121
350	1.607

13.82 The following values of the rate constant were obtained for the decomposition of hydrogen iodide at various temperatures. Plot the logarithm of k versus $1/T$ and from the graph obtain the energy of activation.

Temperature (°C)	k (L/mol·s)
440	2.69×10^{-3}
460	6.21×10^{-3}
480	1.40×10^{-2}
500	3.93×10^{-2}

Reaction Mechanisms; Catalysis

13.83 Nitrogen monoxide, NO, is believed to react with chlorine according to the following mechanism:

$NO + Cl_2 \rightleftharpoons NOCl_2$	(elementary reaction)
$NOCl_2 + NO \longrightarrow 2NOCl$	(elementary reaction)

Identify any reaction intermediate. What is the overall equation?

13.84 The decomposition of ozone is believed to occur in two steps:

$O_3 \rightleftharpoons O_2 + O$	(elementary reaction)
$O_3 + O \longrightarrow 2O_2$	(elementary reaction)

Identify any reaction intermediate. What is the overall reaction?

13.85 Identify the molecularity of each of the following elementary reactions.
  a. $NO + O_3 \longrightarrow NO_2 + O_2$
  b. $NOCl_2 + NO \longrightarrow 2NOCl$
  c. $O_3 \longrightarrow O_2 + O$
  d. $H + H + N_2 \longrightarrow H_2 + N_2^*$

13.86 What is the molecularity of each of the following elementary reactions?
  a. $O + O_2 + N_2 \longrightarrow O_3 + N_2^*$
  b. $NO_2Cl + Cl \longrightarrow NO_2 + Cl_2$
  c. $Cl + H_2 \longrightarrow HCl + H$
  d. $CS_2 \longrightarrow CS + S$

13.87 Write a rate equation, showing the dependence of rate on reactant concentrations, for each of the following elementary reactions.

a. $O_3 \longrightarrow O_2 + O$
b. $NOCl_2 + NO \longrightarrow 2NOCl$

13.88 Write a rate equation, showing the dependence of rate on reactant concentrations, for each of the following elementary reactions.

a. $CS_2 \longrightarrow CS + S$
b. $CH_3Br + OH^- \longrightarrow CH_3OH + Br^-$

13.89 The isomerization of cyclopropane, C_3H_6, is believed to occur by the mechanism shown in the following equations:

$$C_3H_6 + C_3H_6 \xrightarrow{k_1} C_3H_6 + C_3H_6^* \quad \text{(Step 1)}$$
$$C_3H_6^* \xrightarrow{k_2} CH_2{=}CHCH_3 \quad \text{(Step 2)}$$

Here $C_3H_6^*$ is an excited cyclopropane molecule. At low pressure, Step 1 is much slower than Step 2. Derive the rate law for this mechanism at low pressure. Explain.

13.90 The thermal decomposition of nitryl chloride, NO_2Cl,

$$2NO_2Cl(g) \longrightarrow 2NO_2(g) + Cl_2(g)$$

is thought to occur by the mechanism shown in the following equations:

$$NO_2Cl \xrightarrow{k_1} NO_2 + Cl \quad \text{(slow step)}$$
$$NO_2Cl + Cl \xrightarrow{k_2} NO_2 + Cl_2 \quad \text{(fast step)}$$

What rate law is predicted by this mechanism?

13.91 The reaction

$$H_2(g) + I_2(g) \longrightarrow 2HI(g)$$

may occur by the following mechanism:

$$I_2 \underset{k_{-1}}{\overset{k_1}{\rightleftharpoons}} 2I \quad \text{(fast, equilibrium)}$$
$$I + I + H_2 \xrightarrow{k_2} 2HI \quad \text{(slow)}$$

What rate law is predicted by the mechanism?

13.92 Ozone decomposes to oxygen gas.

$$2O_3(g) \longrightarrow 3O_2(g)$$

A proposed mechanism for this decomposition is

$$O_3 \underset{k_{-1}}{\overset{k_1}{\rightleftharpoons}} O_2 + O \quad \text{(fast, equilibrium)}$$
$$O_3 + O \xrightarrow{k_2} 2O_2 \quad \text{(slow)}$$

What is the rate law derived from this mechanism?

13.93 The following is a possible mechanism for a reaction involving hydrogen peroxide in aqueous solution; only a small amount of sodium bromide was added to the reaction mixture.

$$H_2O_2 + Br^- \longrightarrow BrO^- + H_2O$$
$$H_2O_2 + BrO^- \longrightarrow Br^- + H_2O + O_2$$

What is the overall reaction? What species is acting as a catalyst? Are there any reaction intermediates?

13.94 Consider the following mechanism for a reaction in aqueous solution and indicate the species acting as a catalyst:

$$NH_2NO_2 + OH^- \rightleftharpoons H_2O + NHNO_2^-$$
$$NHNO_2^- \longrightarrow N_2O(g) + OH^-$$

Explain why you believe this species is a catalyst. What is the overall reaction? What substance might be added to the reaction mixture to give the catalytic activity?

General Problems

13.95 A study of the decomposition of azomethane,

$$CH_3NNCH_3(g) \longrightarrow C_2H_6(g) + N_2(g)$$

gave the following concentrations of azomethane at various times:

Time	$[CH_3NNCH_3]$
0 min	$1.50 \times 10^{-2}\,M$
10 min	$1.29 \times 10^{-2}\,M$
20 min	$1.10 \times 10^{-2}\,M$
30 min	$0.95 \times 10^{-2}\,M$

Obtain the average rate of decomposition in units of M/s for each time interval.

13.96 Nitrogen dioxide decomposes when heated.

$$2NO_2(g) \longrightarrow 2NO(g) + O_2(g)$$

During an experiment, the concentration of NO_2 varied with time in the following way:

Time	$[NO_2]$
0.0 min	$0.1103\,M$
1.0 min	$0.1076\,M$
2.0 min	$0.1050\,M$
3.0 min	$0.1026\,M$

Obtain the average rate of decomposition of NO_2 in units of M/s for each time interval.

13.97 You can write the rate law for the decomposition of azomethane as

$$\text{Rate} = k[CH_3NNCH_3]^n \quad \text{or} \quad k = \frac{\text{rate}}{[CH_3NNCH_3]^n}$$

when n is the order of the reaction. Note that when you divide the rates at various times by the concentrations raised to the correct power n, you should get the same number (the rate constant k). Verify that the decomposition of azomethane is first order by dividing each average rate in a time interval (obtained in Problem 13.95) by the average concentration in that interval. Note that each calculation gives nearly the same value. Take the average of these values to obtain the rate constant.

13.98 Use the technique described in Problem 13.97 to verify that the decomposition of nitrogen dioxide is second order. That is, divide each average rate in a time interval (obtained in Problem 13.96) by the square of the average concentration in that interval. Note that each calculation gives nearly the same value. Take the average of these calculated values to obtain the rate constant.

13.99   Methyl acetate reacts in acidic solution.

$$CH_3COOCH_3 + H_2O \xrightarrow{H^+} CH_3OH + CH_3COOH$$

methyl acetate   methanol   acetic acid

The rate law is first order in methyl acetate in acidic solution, and the rate constant at 25°C is 1.26×10^{-4}/s. How long will it take for 65% of the methyl acetate to react?

13.100   Benzene diazonium chloride, C_6H_5NNCl, decomposes by a first-order rate law.

$$C_6H_5NNCl \longrightarrow C_6H_5Cl + N_2(g)$$

If the rate constant at 20°C is 4.3×10^{-5}/s, how long will it take for 75% of the compound to decompose?

13.101   What is the half-life of methyl acetate at 25°C in the acidic solution described in Problem 13.99?

13.102   What is the half-life of benzene diazonium chloride at 20°C? See Problem 13.98 for data.

13.103   A compound decomposes by a first-order reaction. If the concentration of the compound is 0.0250 M after 65 s when the initial concentration was 0.0350 M, what is the concentration of the compound after 88 s?

13.104   A compound decomposes by a first-order reaction. The concentration of compound decreases from 0.1180 M to 0.0950 M in 5.2 min. What fraction of the compound remains after 7.1 min?

13.105   Butadiene can undergo the following reaction to form a dimer (two butadiene molecules hooked together).

$$2C_4H_8(g) \longrightarrow C_8H_{12}(g)$$

The half-life for the reaction at a given temperature is 5.92×10^{-2} s. The reaction is second order.
   a. If the initial concentration of C_4H_8 is 0.50 M, what is the rate constant for the reaction?
   b. If the initial concentration of C_4H_8 is 0.010 M, what will be the concentration of C_4H_8 after 3.6×10^2 s?

13.106   A plot of 1/[A] versus time for the hypothetical reaction A $\longrightarrow$ B + C yields a straight line.
   a. What is the order of the reaction?
   b. If it took 57 s for the concentration to drop 40 percent from its initial value of 0.50 M, what is the rate constant for the reaction?

13.107   At 330°C, the rate constant for the decomposition of NO_2 is 0.775 L/(mol·s). If the reaction is second order, what is the concentration of NO_2 after 2.5×10^2 seconds if the starting concentration was 0.050 M? What is the half-life of this reaction under these conditions?

13.108   A second-order decomposition reaction run at 550°C has a rate constant of 3.1×10^{-2} L/(mol·s). If the initial concentration of the reactant is 0.10 M, what is the concentration of this reactant after 1.0×10^2 s? What is the half-life of this reaction under these conditions?

13.109   Plot the data given in Problem 13.95 to verify that the decomposition of azomethane is first order. Determine the rate constant from the slope of the straight-line plot of log [CH_3NNCH_3] versus time.

13.110   The decomposition of aqueous hydrogen peroxide in a given concentration of catalyst yielded the following data:

Time	0.0 min	5.0 min	10.0 min	15.0 min
[H_2O_2]	0.1000 M	0.0804 M	0.0648 M	0.0519 M

Verify that the reaction is first order. Determine the rate constant for the decomposition of H_2O_2 (in units of /s) from the slope of the straight-line plot of ln [H_2O_2] versus time.

13.111   In the presence of a tungsten catalyst at high temperatures, the decomposition of ammonia to nitrogen and hydrogen is a zero-order process. If the rate constant at a particular temperature is 3.7×10^{-6} mol/(L·s), how long will it take for the ammonia concentration to drop from an initial concentration of 5.0×10^{-4} M to 5.0×10^{-5} M? What is the half-life of the reaction under these conditions?

13.112   The reaction 2B $\longrightarrow$ C + 2D is found to be zero-order when run at 990°C. If it takes 3.3×10^2 s for an initial concentration of B to go from 0.50 M to 0.20 M, what is the rate constant for the reaction? What is the half-life of the reaction under these conditions?

13.113   The decomposition of nitrogen dioxide,

$$2NO_2(g) \longrightarrow 2NO(g) + O_2(g)$$

has a rate constant of 0.498 M/s at 319°C and a rate constant of 1.81 M/s at 354°C. What are the values of the activation energy and the frequency factor for this reaction? What is the rate constant at 420°C?

13.114   A second-order reaction has a rate constant of 8.7×10^{-4}/(M·s) at 30°C. At 40°C, the rate constant is 1.8×10^{-3}/(M·s). What are the activation energy and frequency factor for this reaction? Predict the value of the rate constant at 45°C.

13.115   At high temperature, the reaction

$$NO_2(g) + CO(g) \longrightarrow NO(g) + CO_2(g)$$

is thought to occur in a single step. What should be the rate law in that case?

13.116   Methyl chloride, CH_3Cl, reacts in basic solution to give methanol.

$$CH_3Cl + OH^- \longrightarrow CH_3OH + Cl^-$$

This reaction is believed to occur in a single step. If so, what should be the rate law?

13.117   Nitryl bromide, NO_2Br, decomposes into nitrogen dioxide and bromine.

$$2NO_2Br(g) \longrightarrow 2NO_2(g) + Br_2(g)$$

A proposed mechanism is

$$NO_2Br \longrightarrow NO_2 + Br \qquad \text{(slow)}$$
$$NO_2Br + Br \longrightarrow NO_2 + Br_2 \qquad \text{(fast)}$$

Write the rate law predicted by this mechanism.

13.118   Tertiary butyl chloride reacts in basic solution according to the equation

$$(CH_3)_3CCl + OH^- \longrightarrow (CH_3)_3COH + Cl^-$$

The accepted mechanism for this reaction is

$$(CH_3)_3CCl \longrightarrow (CH_3)_3C^+ + Cl^- \quad \text{(slow)}$$
$$(CH_3)_3C^+ + OH^- \longrightarrow (CH_3)_3COH \quad \text{(fast)}$$

What should be the rate law for this reaction?

13.119 Urea, $(NH_2)_2CO$, can be prepared by heating ammonium cyanate, NH_4OCN.

$$NH_4OCN \longrightarrow (NH_2)_2CO$$

This reaction may occur by the following mechanism:

$$NH_4^+ + OCN^- \underset{k_{-1}}{\overset{k_1}{\rightleftharpoons}} NH_3 + HOCN \quad \text{(fast, equilibrium)}$$

$$NH_3 + HOCN \overset{k_2}{\longrightarrow} (NH_2)_2CO \quad \text{(slow)}$$

What is the rate law predicted by this mechanism?

13.120 Acetone reacts with iodine in acidic aqueous solution to give monoiodoacetone.

$$CH_3COCH_3 + I_2 \overset{H^+}{\longrightarrow} CH_3COCH_2I + HI$$
$$\text{acetone} \qquad\qquad\qquad \text{monoiodoacetone}$$

A possible mechanism for this reaction is

Write the rate law that you derive from this mechanism.

13.121 A study of the gas-phase oxidation of nitrogen monoxide at 25°C and 1.00 atm pressure gave the following results:

$$2NO(g) + O_2(g) \longrightarrow NO_2(g)$$

	Conc. NO, mol/L	Conc. O₂, mol/L	Initial Rate
Exp. 1	4.5×10^{-2}	2.2×10^{-2}	0.80×10^{-2} mol/(L·s)
Exp. 2	4.5×10^{-2}	4.5×10^{-2}	1.60×10^{-2} mol/(L·s)
Exp. 3	9.0×10^{-2}	9.0×10^{-2}	1.28×10^{-1} mol/(L·s)
Exp. 4	3.8×10^{-1}	4.6×10^{-3}	?

a. What is the experimental rate law for the reaction above?
b. What is the initial rate of the reaction in Experiment 4?

13.122 The reaction of water with CH_3Cl in acetone as a solvent is represented by the equation

$$CH_3Cl + H_2O \longrightarrow CH_3OH + HCl$$

The rate of the reaction doubles when the concentration of CH_3Cl is doubled and it quadruples when the concentration of H_2O is doubled.

a. What is the unit for k?
b. Calculate k if CH_3OH is formed at a rate of 1.50 M/s when $[CH_3Cl] = [H_2O] = 0.40\ M$.

13.123 The reaction of thioacetamide with water is shown by the equation below:

$$CH_3C(S)NH_2(aq) + H_2O \longrightarrow H_2S(aq) + CH_3C(O)NH_2(aq)$$

The rate of reaction is given by the rate law:

$$\text{Rate} = k[H_3O^+][CH_3C(S)NH_2]$$

Consider one liter of solution that is 0.20 M in $CH_3C(S)NH_2$ and 0.15 M in HCl at 25°C.

a. For each of the changes listed below, state whether the rate of reaction increases, decreases, or remains the same. Why?
  i. A 4-g sample of NaOH is added to the solution.
  ii. 500 mL of water is added to the solution.
b. For each of the changes listed below, state whether the value of k will increase, decrease, or remain the same. Why?
  i. A catalyst is added to the solution.
  ii. The reaction is carried out at 15°C instead of 25°C.

13.124 The reaction of methylacetate with water is shown by the equation below:

$$CH_3COOCH_3(aq) + H_2O \longrightarrow$$
$$CH_3COOH(aq) + CH_3OH(aq)$$

The rate of the reaction is given by the rate law:

$$\text{Rate} = k[H_3O^+][CH_3COOCH_3]$$

Consider one liter of solution that is 0.15 M in CH_3COOCH_3 and 0.015 M in H_3O^+ at 25°C.

a. For each of the changes listed below, state whether the rate of reaction increases, decreases, or remains the same. Why?
  i. Some concentrated sulfuric acid is added to the solution.
  ii. Water is added to the solution.
b. For each of the changes listed below, state whether the value of k will increase, decrease, or remain the same. Why?
  i. Some concentrated sulfuric acid is added to the solution.
  ii. The reaction is carried out at 35°C instead of 25°C.

13.125 Draw a potential-energy diagram for an uncatalyzed exothermic reaction. On the same diagram, indicate the change that results on the addition of a catalyst. Discuss the role of a catalyst in changing the rate of reaction.

13.126 Draw and label the potential-energy curve for the reaction

$$N_2O_4(g) \rightleftharpoons 2NO_2(g); \Delta H = 57\ \text{kJ}$$

The activation energy for the reverse reaction is 23 kJ. Note ΔH and E_a on the diagram. What is the activation energy for the forward reaction? For which reaction (forward or reverse) will the reaction rate be most sensitive to a temperature increase? Explain.

13.127 What is meant by the term *rate of a chemical reaction*? Why does the rate of a reaction normally change with time?

When does the rate of a chemical reaction equal the rate constant?

13.128 Briefly discuss the factors that affect the rates of chemical reactions. Which of the factors affect the magnitude of the rate constant? Which factor(s) do not affect the magnitude of the rate constant? Why?

13.129 Describe in general terms how chemists can follow the character of a reacting molecule using lasers.

13.130 Describe the potential-energy curve for the decomposition of cyclobutane to ethylene.

Strategy Problems

13.131 The rate constant for a certain reaction is 1.4×10^{-05} M^{-1} min^{-1} at 483 K. The activation energy for the reaction is 2.11×10^{03} J/mol. What is the rate constant for the reaction at 611 K?

13.132 The decomposition of hydrogen peroxide is a first-order reaction:

$$H_2O_2(aq) \longrightarrow H_2O(l) + \tfrac{1}{2}O_2(g)$$

The half-life of the reaction is 17.0 minutes.
  a. What is the rate constant of the reaction?
  b. If you had a bottle of H_2O_2, how long would it take for 86.0% to decompose?
  c. If you started the reaction with $[H_2O_2] = 0.100$ M, what would be the hydrogen peroxide concentration after 15.0 minutes?

13.133 A reaction of the form $aA \longrightarrow$ Products is second order with a half-life of 307 s. What is the rate constant of the reaction if the initial concentration of A is 1.87×10^{-02} mol/L?

13.134 What is the rate law for the following gas-phase elementary reaction?

$$2I + H_2 \longrightarrow 2HI$$

13.135 A possible mechanism for a gas-phase reaction is given below. What is the rate law predicted by this mechanism?

$$NO + Cl_2 \underset{k_r}{\overset{k_f}{\rightleftharpoons}} NOCl_2 \qquad \text{(fast equilibrium)}$$

$$NOCl_2 + NO \overset{k_2}{\longrightarrow} 2NOCl \qquad \text{(slow)}$$

13.136 Say you run the following elementary, termolecular reaction:

$$2A + B \longrightarrow D$$

Using the starting concentrations $[A] = 2.0$ M and $[B] = 1.0$ M, you measure the rate to be 16 $M^{-2} \cdot s^{-1}$. What is the value of the rate constant?

13.137 The hypothetical reaction A + 2B $\longrightarrow$ Products has the rate law Rate $= k[A]^2[B]^3$. If the reaction is run two separate times, holding the concentration of A constant while doubling the concentration of B from one run to the next, how would the rate of the second run compare to the rate of the first run?

13.138 For the decomposition of one mole of nitrosyl chloride, $\Delta H = 38$ kJ.

$$NOCl(g) \longrightarrow NO(g) + \tfrac{1}{2}Cl_2(g)$$

The activation energy for this reaction is 100 kJ.
  a. Is this reaction exothermic or endothermic?
  b. What is the activation energy for the reverse reaction?
  c. If a catalyst were added to the reaction, how would this affect the activation energy?

13.139 Given the following mechanism for a chemical reaction:

$$H_2O_2 + I^- \longrightarrow H_2O + IO^-$$
$$H_2O_2 + IO^- \longrightarrow H_2O + O_2 + I^-$$

  a. Write the overall reaction.
  b. Identify the catalyst and the reaction intermediate.
  c. With the information given in this problem, can you write the rate law? Explain.

13.140 The following data were collected for the reaction $A(g) + B(g) \longrightarrow$ Products.

Experiment	$[A]_0$ (M)	$[B]_0$ (M)	Rate (M/s)
1	0.0100	0.100	1.0×10^{-03}
2	0.0300	0.100	3.0×10^{-03}
3	0.0300	0.300	2.7×10^{-02}

  a. Determine the rate law for this reaction.
  b. Calculate the rate constant.
  c. Calculate the rate when $[A] = 0.200$ M and $[B] = 0.200$ M.

Cumulative-Skills Problems

13.141 Dinitrogen pentoxide, N_2O_5, undergoes first-order decomposition in chloroform solvent to yield NO_2 and O_2. The rate constant at 45°C is 6.2×10^{-4}/min. Calculate the volume of O_2 obtained from the reaction of 1.00 mol N_2O_5 at 45°C and 770 mmHg after 20.0 hr.

13.142 Hydrogen peroxide undergoes a first-order decomposition to water and O_2 in aqueous solution. The rate constant at 25°C is 7.40×10^{-4}/s. Calculate the volume of O_2 obtained from the decomposition reaction of 1.00 mol H_2O_2 at 25°C and 740 mmHg after 20.0 min.

13.143 Hydrogen peroxide in aqueous solution decomposes by a first-order reaction to water and oxygen. The rate constant for this decomposition is 7.40×10^{-4}/s. What quantity of heat energy is initially liberated per second from 2.00 L of solution that is 1.50 M H_2O_2? See Appendix C for data.

13.144 Nitrogen dioxide reacts with carbon monoxide by the overall equation

$$NO_2(g) + CO(g) \longrightarrow NO(g) + CO_2(g)$$

At a particular temperature, the reaction is second order in NO_2 and zero order in CO. The rate constant is 0.515 L/(mol·s). How much heat energy evolves per second initially from 3.50 L of reaction mixture containing 0.0250 M NO_2? See Appendix C for data. Assume the enthalpy change is constant with temperature.

13.145 Nitrogen monoxide reacts with oxygen to give nitrogen dioxide.

$$2NO(g) + O_2(g) \longrightarrow 2NO_2(g)$$

The rate law is $-\Delta[NO]/\Delta t = k[NO]^2[O_2]$, where the rate constant is 1.16×10^{-5} L^2/(mol^2·s) at 339°C. A vessel contains NO

and O_2 at 339°C. The initial partial pressures of NO and O_2 are 155 mmHg and 345 mmHg, respectively. What is the rate of decrease of partial pressure of NO (in mmHg per second)? (*Hint:* From the ideal gas law, obtain an expression for the molar concentration of a particular gas in terms of its partial pressure.)

13.146 Nitrogen monoxide reacts with hydrogen as follows:

$$2NO(g) + H_2(g) \longrightarrow N_2O(g) + H_2O(g)$$

The rate law is $-\Delta[H_2]/\Delta t = k[NO]^2[H_2]$, where k is 1.10×10^{-7} L^2/(mol^2·s) at 826°C. A vessel contains NO and H_2 at 826°C. The partial pressures of NO and H_2 are 144 mmHg and 324 mmHg, respectively. What is the rate of decrease of partial pressure of NO? See Problem 13.145.

14

Chemical Equilibrium

Nitrogen dioxide, NO_2 (a reddish brown gas), is in equilibrium with dinitrogen tetroxide, N_2O_4 (a colorless gas). Nitrogen dioxide is present in many urban smogs, giving them a characteristic reddish brown color.

Contents and Concepts

Many chemical reactions can be made to go in either the forward or the reverse direction, depending on the conditions of the reaction. In the next few sections, we will look at this reversibility.

The various possible equilibrium compositions of a reaction mixture at a given temperature are characterized by the equilibrium constant for the reaction. In the next sections, we look at how we can use this equilibrium constant to answer important questions.

We obtain the maximum product from a reaction by properly selecting the reaction conditions. We look at the various ways to do this in the last sections of the chapter.

hemical reactions often seem to stop before they are complete. Such reactions are *reversible*. That is, the original reactants form products, but then the products react with themselves to give back the original reactants. Actually two reactions are occurring, and the eventual result is a mixture of reactants and products, rather than simply a mixture of products.

Consider the gaseous reaction in which carbon monoxide and hydrogen react to produce methane and steam:

$$CO(g) + 3H_2(g) \longrightarrow CH_4(g) + H_2O(g)$$
$$\text{methane}$$

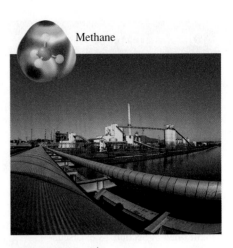
Methane

FIGURE 14.1 ▲

Coal gasification plant
Gaseous fuels can be made from coal in a number of ways. One way (described in the text) is to react coal with steam to produce a mixture of CO and H_2, which then reacts by catalytic methanation to yield CH_4, the major component of natural gas.

This reaction, which requires a catalyst to occur at a reasonable rate, is called *catalytic methanation*. It is a potentially useful reaction because it can be used to produce methane from coal or organic wastes from which carbon monoxide can be obtained (Figure 14.1). Methane, in turn, can be used as a fuel and as a starting material for the production of organic chemicals. Although, at the moment, natural gas (which is mostly methane) is plentiful, analysts predict that oil and natural gas production will peak sometime in the early part of this century. Then the demand for other sources of fuels and organic chemicals, such as coal and organic wastes, will rise.

Catalytic methanation is a reversible reaction, and depending on the reaction conditions, the final reaction mixture will have varying amounts of the products methane and steam, as well as the starting substances carbon monoxide and hydrogen. It is also possible to start with methane and steam and, under the right conditions, form a mixture that is predominantly carbon monoxide and hydrogen. The process is called *steam reforming*.

$$CH_4(g) + H_2O(g) \longrightarrow CO(g) + 3H_2(g)$$

The product mixture of CO and H_2 (synthesis gas) is used to prepare a number of industrial chemicals.

The processes of catalytic methanation and steam reforming illustrate the reversibility of chemical reactions. Starting with CO and H_2 and using the right conditions, you can form predominantly CH_4 and H_2O. Starting with CH_4 and H_2O and using different conditions, you can obtain a reaction mixture that is predominantly CO and H_2. An important question is, What conditions favor the production of CH_4 and H_2O, and what conditions favor the production of CO and H_2?

As noted earlier, certain reactions (such as catalytic methanation) appear to stop before they are complete. The reaction mixture ceases to change in any of its properties and consists of both reactants and products in definite concentrations. Such a reaction mixture is said to have reached *chemical equilibrium*. In earlier chapters, we discussed other types of equilibria, including the equilibrium between a liquid and its vapor and the equilibrium between a solid and its saturated solution. In this chapter, we will see how to determine the composition of a reaction mixture at equilibrium and how to alter this composition by changing the conditions for the reaction.

■ **See page 611 for the Media Summary.**

Describing Chemical Equilibrium

Many chemical reactions are like the catalytic methanation reaction. Such reactions can be made to go predominantly in one direction or the other, depending on the conditions. Let us look more closely at this reversibility and see how to characterize it quantitatively.

14.1 | Chemical Equilibrium—A Dynamic Equilibrium

The concept of dynamic equilibrium in chemical reactions was briefly mentioned in Section 13.8. Discussions on vapor pressure (Section 11.2) and solubility (Section 12.2) give detailed explanations of the role of dynamic equilibria.

When substances react, they eventually form a mixture of reactants and products in *dynamic equilibrium.* < This dynamic equilibrium consists of a forward reaction, in which substances react to give products, and a reverse reaction, in which products react to give the original reactants. Both forward and reverse reactions occur at the same rate, or speed.

Consider the catalytic methanation reaction discussed in the chapter opening. It consists of forward and reverse reactions, as represented by the chemical equation

$$CO(g) + 3H_2(g) \rightleftharpoons CH_4(g) + H_2O(g)$$

Suppose you put 1.000 mol CO and 3.000 mol H_2 into a 10.00-L vessel at 1200 K (927°C). The rate of the reaction of CO and H_2 depends on the concentrations of CO and H_2. At first these concentrations are large, but as the substances react their concentrations decrease (Figure 14.2). The rate of the forward reaction, which depends on reactant concentrations, is large at first but steadily decreases. On the other hand, the concentrations of CH_4 and H_2O, which are zero at first, increase with time. The rate of the reverse reaction starts at zero and steadily increases. The forward rate decreases and the reverse rate increases until eventually the rates become equal. When that happens, CO and H_2 molecules are formed as fast as they react. The concentrations of reactants and products no longer change, and the reaction mixture has reached *equilibrium.* Figure 14.3 shows how the amounts of substances in the reaction mixture become constant when equilibrium is reached.

Chemical equilibrium is *the state reached by a reaction mixture when the rates of forward and reverse reactions have become equal.* If you observe the reaction mixture, you see no net change, although the forward and reverse reactions are continuing. The continuing forward and reverse reactions make the equilibrium a *dynamic* process.

Suppose you place known amounts of reactants in a vessel and let the mixture come to equilibrium. To obtain the composition of the equilibrium mixture, you need to determine the amount of only one of the substances. The amounts of the others can be calculated from the amounts originally placed in the vessel and the equation that

FIGURE 14.2 ▶

Change of rates as reaction proceeds
(A) Initially, only the reaction CO + 3H₂ ⟶ occurs, because the concentrations of CH₄ and H₂O are zero. *(B)* Later, as this reaction proceeds, the concentrations of CH₄ and H₂O increase, and the reaction CH₄ + H₂O ⟶ begins. The rate of the reaction CH₄ + H₂O ⟶ steadily increases, whereas the rate of the reaction CO + 3H₂ ⟶ decreases. Eventually, the two rates become equal.

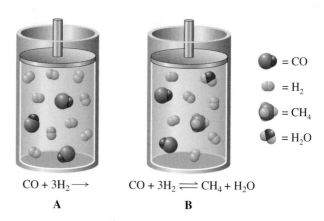

= CO
= H₂
= CH₄
= H₂O

CO + 3H₂ ⟶
A

CO + 3H₂ ⇌ CH₄ + H₂O
B

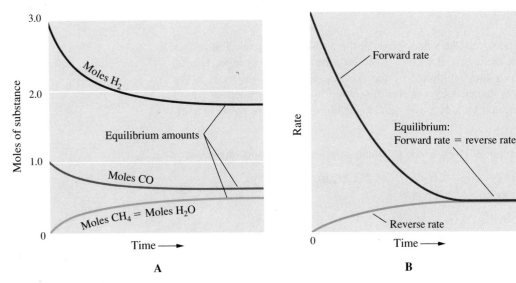

FIGURE 14.3 ▲

Catalytic methanation reaction approaches equilibrium
(A) The experiment begins with 1.000 mol CO and 3.000 mol H_2 in a 10.00-L vessel. Note that the amounts of substances become constant at equilibrium. *(B)* The forward rate is large at first but steadily decreases, whereas the reverse rate starts at zero and steadily increases. Eventually both rates become equal (at equilibrium).

represents the reaction. For example, suppose you place 1.000 mol CO and 3.000 mol H_2 in a reaction vessel at 1200 K. After equilibrium is reached, you chill the reaction mixture quickly to condense the water vapor to liquid, which you then weigh and find to be 0.387 mol. You calculate the other substances from the stoichiometry of the reaction, as shown in the following example.

Example 14.1 | **Applying Stoichiometry to an Equilibrium Mixture**

Carbon monoxide and hydrogen react according to the following equation:

$$CO(g) + 3H_2(g) \rightleftharpoons CH_4(g) + H_2O(g)$$

When 1.000 mol CO and 3.000 mol H_2 are placed in a 10.00-L vessel at 927°C (1200 K) and allowed to come to equilibrium, the mixture is found to contain 0.387 mol H_2O. What is the molar composition of the equilibrium mixture? That is, how many moles of each substance are present?

Problem Strategy The problem is essentially one of stoichiometry. It involves initial, or *starting,* amounts of reactants. These amounts *change* as reaction occurs. Later, the reaction comes to *equilibrium,* and you analyze the reaction mixture for the amount of one of the reactants or products. It is convenient to solve this problem by first setting up a table in which you write the starting, change, and equilibrium values of each substance under the balanced equation. This way you can easily see what you have to calculate.

Amount (mol)   *CO(g) + 3H₂(g) ⇌ CH₄(g) + H₂O(g)*

Starting

Change

Equilibrium

(continued)

(continued)

You fill in the starting amounts from the values given in the problem statement. You are not given explicit values for the changes that occur, so you let x be the molar change. That is, each product increases by x moles multiplied by the coefficients of the substances in the balanced equation. Reactants decrease by x moles multiplied by the corresponding coefficients. The decrease is indicated by a negative sign. Equilibrium values are equal to starting values plus the changes.

Solution   Using the information given in the problem, you set up the following table:

Amount (mol)	$CO(g)$	+	$3H_2(g)$	$\rightleftharpoons$	$CH_4(g)$	+	$H_2O(g)$
Starting	1.000		3.000		0		0
Change	$-x$		$-3x$		$+x$		$+x$
Equilibrium	$1.000 - x$		$3.000 - 3x$		x		$x = 0.387$

The problem statement gives the equilibrium amount for H_2O. This tells you that $x = 0.387$ mol. You calculate equilibrium amounts for other substances from the expressions given in the table, using this value of x.

$$\begin{aligned}
\text{Equilibrium amount CO} &= (1.000 - x) \text{ mol} \\
&= (1.000 - 0.387) \text{ mol} \\
&= 0.613 \text{ mol}
\end{aligned}$$

$$\begin{aligned}
\text{Equilibrium amount } H_2 &= (3.000 - 3x) \text{ mol} \\
&= (3.000 - 3 \times 0.387) \text{ mol} \\
&= 1.839 \text{ mol}
\end{aligned}$$

$$\text{Equilibrium amount } CH_4 = x \text{ mol} = 0.387 \text{ mol}$$

Therefore, the amounts of substances in the equilibrium mixture are **0.613 mol CO, 1.839 mol H_2, 0.387 mol CH_4, and 0.387 mol H_2O.**

Answer Check   You start with 4.000 mol reactants (1.000 mol CO + 3.000 mol H_2). If the reaction were to go to completion, you would obtain 2.000 mol products (1.000 mol CH_4 + 1.000 mol H_2O). The equilibrium quantities will be intermediate. Check that this is the case.

Exercise 14.1   Synthesis gas (a mixture of CO and H_2) is increased in concentration of hydrogen by passing it with steam over a catalyst. This is the so-called water–gas shift reaction. Some of the CO is converted to CO_2, which can be removed:

$$CO(g) + H_2O(g) \rightleftharpoons CO_2(g) + H_2(g)$$

Suppose you start with a gaseous mixture containing 1.00 mol CO and 1.00 mol H_2O. When equilibrium is reached at 1000°C, the mixture contains 0.43 mol H_2. What is the molar composition of the equilibrium mixture?

■ See Problems 14.29, 14.30, 14.31, 14.32, 14.33, and 14.34.

Concept Check 14.1

Two substances A and B react to produce substance C. When reactant A decreases by molar amount x, product C increases by molar amount x. When reactant B decreases by molar amount x, product C increases by molar amount $2x$. Write the chemical equation for the reaction.

14.2 | The Equilibrium Constant

In the preceding example, we found that when 1.000 mol CO and 3.000 mol H_2 react in a 10.00-L vessel by catalytic methanation at 1200 K, they give an equilibrium mixture containing 0.613 mol CO, 1.839 mol H_2, 0.387 mol CH_4, and 0.387 mol H_2O. Let us call this Experiment 1. Now consider a similar experiment, Experiment 2, in which you start with an additional mole of carbon monoxide. That is, you place 2.000 mol CO and 3.000 mol H_2 in a 10.00-L vessel at 1200 K. At equilibrium, you find that the vessel contains 1.522 mol CO, 1.566 mol H_2, 0.478 mol CH_4, and 0.478 mol H_2O. What you observe from the results of Experiments 1 and 2 is that the equilibrium composition depends on the amounts of starting substances. Nevertheless, you will see that all of the equilibrium compositions for a reaction at a given temperature are related by a quantity called the *equilibrium constant*.

Definition of the Equilibrium Constant K_c

Consider the reaction

$$a\text{A} + b\text{B} \rightleftharpoons c\text{C} + d\text{D}$$

where A, B, C, and D denote reactants and products, and a, b, c, and d are coefficients in the balanced chemical equation. The **equilibrium-constant expression** for a reaction is *an expression obtained by multiplying the concentrations of products, dividing by the concentrations of reactants, and raising each concentration term to a power equal to the coefficient in the chemical equation.* The **equilibrium constant K_c** is *the value obtained for the equilibrium-constant expression when equilibrium concentrations are substituted.* < For the previous reaction, you have

In Section 14.3, you will see that you ignore concentrations of pure liquids and solids when you write the equilibrium-constant expression. The concentrations of these substances are constant and are incorporated into the value of K_c.

$$K_c = \frac{[\text{C}]^c[\text{D}]^d}{[\text{A}]^a[\text{B}]^b}$$

Here you denote the molar concentration of a substance by writing its formula in square brackets. The subscript c on the equilibrium constant means that it is defined in terms of molar concentrations. The **law of mass action** is *a relation that states that the values of the equilibrium-constant expression K_c are constant for a particular reaction at a given temperature, whatever equilibrium concentrations are substituted.* <

"Active mass" was an early term for concentration—hence the term mass action.

As the following example illustrates, the equilibrium-constant expression is defined in terms of the balanced chemical equation. If the equation is rewritten with different coefficients, the equilibrium-constant expression will be changed.

Example 14.2 | Writing Equilibrium-Constant Expressions

a. Write the equilibrium-constant expression K_c for catalytic methanation.

$$CO(g) + 3H_2(g) \rightleftharpoons CH_4(g) + H_2O(g)$$

b. Write the equilibrium-constant expression K_c for the reverse of the previous reaction.

$$CH_4(g) + H_2O(g) \rightleftharpoons CO(g) + 3H_2(g)$$

c. Write the equilibrium-constant expression K_c for the synthesis of ammonia.

$$N_2(g) + 3H_2(g) \rightleftharpoons 2NH_3(g)$$

d. Write the equilibrium-constant expression K_c when the equation for the previous reaction is written

$$\tfrac{1}{2}N_2(g) + \tfrac{3}{2}H_2(g) \rightleftharpoons NH_3(g)$$

Problem Strategy Write the concentrations of products in the top (numerator) of the equilibrium-constant expression, and write the concentrations of reactants in the bottom (denominator). Raise each concentration term to the power equal to the coefficient of the substance in the chemical equation.

(continued)

(continued)

Solution a. The expression for the equilibrium constant is

$$K_c = \frac{[CH_4][H_2O]}{[CO][H_2]^3}$$

Note that concentrations of products are on the top and concentrations of reactants are on the bottom. Also note that each concentration term is raised to a power equal to the coefficient of the substance in the chemical equation.

b. When the equation is written in reverse order, the expression for K_c is inverted:

$$K_c = \frac{[CO][H_2]^3}{[CH_4][H_2O]}$$

c. The equilibrium constant for $N_2 + 3H_2 \rightleftharpoons 2NH_3$ is

$$K_c = \frac{[NH_3]^2}{[N_2][H_2]^3}$$

d. When the coefficients in the equation in part c are multiplied by $\frac{1}{2}$ to give

$$\tfrac{1}{2}N_2 + \tfrac{3}{2}H_2 \rightleftharpoons NH_3$$

the equilibrium-constant expression becomes

$$K_c = \frac{[NH_3]}{[N_2]^{1/2}[H_2]^{3/2}}$$

which is the square root of the previous expression.

Answer Check Check your answers. Make sure that the products are on top and the reactants are on the bottom of each equilibrium-constant expression. Then check that each reactant and product term is raised to the correct power (equal to the stoichiometric coefficient in the chemical equation).

Exercise 14.2 a. Write the equilibrium-constant expression K_c for the equation

$$2NO_2(g) + 7H_2(g) \rightleftharpoons 2NH_3(g) + 4H_2O(g)$$

b. Write the equilibrium-constant expression K_c when this reaction is written

$$NO_2(g) + \tfrac{7}{2}H_2(g) \rightleftharpoons NH_3(g) + 2H_2O(g)$$

■ See Problems 14.35 and 14.36.

Equilibrium: A Kinetics Argument

The law of mass action was first stated by the Norwegian chemists Cato Guldberg and Peter Waage in 1867. They were led to this law by a kinetics argument. To understand the argument, consider the decomposition of dinitrogen tetroxide, N_2O_4.

Dinitrogen tetroxide is a colorless substance that decomposes, when warmed, to give nitrogen dioxide, NO_2, a brown substance (see Figure 14.4). Suppose you start with dinitrogen tetroxide gas and heat it above room temperature. At this higher temperature, N_2O_4 decomposes to NO_2, which can be noted by the increasing intensity of the brown color of the reaction mixture.

$$N_2O_4(g) \longrightarrow 2NO_2(g)$$

Once some NO_2 is produced, it can react to re-form N_2O_4. Call the decomposition of N_2O_4 the forward reaction and the formation of N_2O_4 the reverse reaction. These are elementary reactions, and you can immediately write the rate equations. The rate of the forward reaction is $k_f[N_2O_4]$, where k_f is the rate constant for the forward reaction. The rate of the reverse reaction is $k_r[NO_2]^2$, where k_r is the rate constant for the reverse reaction.

At first, the reaction vessel contains mostly N_2O_4, so the concentration of NO_2 is very small. Therefore, the rate of the forward reaction is relatively large, and the rate of the reverse reaction is relatively small. However, as the decomposition proceeds, the concentration of N_2O_4 decreases, so the forward rate decreases. At the same time, the concentration of NO_2 increases, so the reverse rate increases. Eventually the two

FIGURE 14.4 ▲

Temperature effect on NO₂–N₂O₄ equilibrium

The temperature in the test tubes increases from left to right. N₂O₄ (colorless) predominates at cooler temperatures, whereas NO₂ (reddish brown) predominates at higher temperatures.

rates become equal. After that, on average, every time an N_2O_4 molecule decomposes, two NO_2 molecules recombine. Overall, the concentrations of N_2O_4 and NO_2 no longer change, although forward and reverse reactions are still occurring. The reaction has reached a dynamic equilibrium.

At equilibrium, you can write: Rate of forward reaction = rate of reverse reaction, or

$$k_f[N_2O_4] = k_r[NO_2]^2$$

Rearranging gives

$$\frac{k_f}{k_r} = \frac{[NO_2]^2}{[N_2O_4]}$$

The right side is the equilibrium-constant expression for the decomposition of dinitrogen tetroxide. The left side is the ratio of rate constants. Thus, the equilibrium-constant expression is constant for a given temperature, and you can identify the equilibrium constant K_c as the ratio of rate constants for the forward and reverse reactions.

$$K_c = \frac{k_f}{k_r}$$

If the overall reaction occurs by a multistep mechanism, one can show that the equilibrium constant equals a product of ratios of rate constants—one ratio for each step in the mechanism.

Obtaining Equilibrium Constants for Reactions

At the beginning of this section, we gave data from the results of two experiments, Experiments 1 and 2, involving catalytic methanation. By substituting the molar concentrations from these two experiments into the equilibrium-constant expression for the reaction, you can show that you get the same value for both experiments, as you expect from the law of mass action. This value equals K_c for methanation at 1200 K. Thus, besides verifying the validity of the law of mass action in this case, you can see how an equilibrium constant can be obtained from concentration data. <

It is also possible to determine equilibrium constants from thermochemical data, as described in Section 18.6.

Experiment 1   The equilibrium composition is 0.613 mol CO, 1.839 mol H_2, 0.387 mol CH_4, and 0.387 mol H_2O. The volume of the reaction vessel is 10.00 L, so the equilibrium concentration of CO is

$$[CO] = \frac{0.613 \text{ mol}}{10.00 \text{ L}} = 0.0613 \ M$$

Similarly, the other equilibrium concentrations are $[H_2] = 0.1839 \ M$, $[CH_4] = 0.0387 \ M$, and $[H_2O] = 0.0387 \ M$.

Substitute these values into the equilibrium expression for catalytic methanation. (The expression was obtained in Example 14.2.) Although until now we have consistently carried units along with numbers in calculations, it is the usual practice to write equilibrium constants without units. We will follow that practice here. < Substitution of concentrations into the equilibrium-constant expression gives

In thermodynamics, the equilibrium constant is defined in terms of activities, rather than concentrations. For an ideal mixture, the activity of a substance is the ratio of its concentration (or partial pressure if a gas) to a standard concentration of 1 M (or partial pressure of 1 atm), so that units cancel. Thus, activities have numerical values but no units.

$$K_c = \frac{[CH_4][H_2O]}{[CO][H_2]^3} = \frac{(0.0387)(0.0387)}{(0.0613)(0.1839)^3} = 3.93$$

Experiment 2   The equilibrium composition is 1.522 mol CO, 1.566 mol H_2, 0.478 mol CH_4, and 0.478 mol H_2O. Therefore, the concentrations, which are obtained by dividing by 10.00 L, are $[CO] = 0.1522 \ M$, $[H_2] = 0.1566 \ M$, $[CH_4] =$

FIGURE 14.5 ▶

Some equilibrium compositions for the methanation reaction
Different starting concentrations have been used in each experiment (all at 1200 K). Experiments 1 and 2 start with different concentrations of reactants CO and H_2. Experiment 3 starts with the products CH_4 and H_2O. All three experiments yield essentially the same value of K_c.

	Starting Concentrations	Equilibrium Concentrations	Calculated Value of K_c
Experiment 1	0.1000 M CO 0.3000 M H_2	0.0613 M CO 0.1839 M H_2 0.0387 M CH_4 0.0387 M H_2O	$K_c = 3.93$
Experiment 2	0.2000 M CO 0.3000 M H_2	0.1522 M CO 0.1566 M H_2 0.0478 M CH_4 0.0478 M H_2O	$K_c = 3.91$
Experiment 3	0.1000 M CH_4 0.1000 M H_2O	0.0613 M CO 0.1839 M H_2 0.0387 M CH_4 0.0387 M H_2O	$K_c = 3.93$

0.0478 M, and $[H_2O] = 0.0478$ M. Substituting into the equilibrium-constant expression gives

$$K_c = \frac{[CH_4][H_2O]}{[CO][H_2]^3} = \frac{(0.0478)(0.0478)}{(0.1522)(0.1566)^3} = 3.91$$

Within the precision of the data, these values (3.93 and 3.91) of the equilibrium expression for different starting mixtures of these gases at 1200 K are the same. Moreover, experiment shows that when you start with CH_4 and H_2O, instead of CO and H_2, an equilibrium mixture is again reached that yields the same value of K_c (see Experiment 3, Figure 14.5). You can take the equilibrium constant for catalytic methanation at 1200 K to be 3.92, the average of these values.

The reaction described here is used industrially to adjust the ratio of H_2 to CO in synthesis gas (mixture of CO and H_2). In this process, CO reacts with H_2O to give H_2, so the ratio of H_2 to CO is increased.

The following exercise provides additional practice in evaluating an equilibrium constant from equilibrium compositions that are experimentally determined. Example 14.3 gives the detailed solution of a more complicated problem of this type.

Exercise 14.3 When 1.00 mol each of carbon monoxide and water reach equilibrium at 1000°C in a 10.0-L vessel, the equilibrium mixture contains 0.57 mol CO, 0.57 mol H_2O, 0.43 mol CO_2, and 0.43 mol H_2. Write the chemical equation for the equilibrium. What is the value of K_c? <

■ See Problems 14.43 and 14.44.

Example 14.3 | Obtaining an Equilibrium Constant from Reaction Composition

Hydrogen iodide, HI, decomposes at moderate temperatures according to the equation

$$2HI(g) \rightleftharpoons H_2(g) + I_2(g)$$

The amount of I_2 in the reaction mixture can be determined from the intensity of the violet color of I_2; the more intense the color, the more I_2 in the reaction vessel. When 4.00 mol HI was placed in a 5.00-L vessel at 458°C, the equilibrium mixture was found to contain 0.442 mol I_2. What is the value of K_c for the decomposition of HI at this temperature?

(continued)

(*continued*)

Problem Strategy You will first need to calculate the molar concentrations of substances, because the equilibrium constant is stated in terms of these quantities. The problem statement gives the starting amount of HI and the equilibrium amount of I_2. As in Example 14.1, it is convenient to set up a table of starting, change, and equilibrium concentrations. You use the equilibrium values to calculate the equilibrium constant K_c.

Solution To obtain the concentrations of HI and I_2, you divide the molar amounts by the volume of the reaction vessel (5.00 L).

$$\text{Starting concentration of HI} = \frac{4.00 \text{ mol}}{5.00 \text{ L}} = 0.800 \ M$$

$$\text{Equilibrium concentration of } I_2 = \frac{0.442 \text{ mol}}{5.00 \text{ L}} = 0.0884 \ M$$

From these values, you set up the following table:

Concentration (M)	*2HI*(g) ⇌	*H₂*(g) +	*I₂*(g)
Starting	0.800	0	0
Change	$-2x$	x	x
Equilibrium	$0.800 - 2x$	x	$x = 0.0884$

The equilibrium concentrations of substances can be evaluated from the expressions given in the last line of this table. You know that the equilibrium concentration of I_2 is 0.0884 M and that this equals x. Therefore,

$$[\text{HI}] = (0.800 - 2x) \, M = (0.800 - 2 \times 0.0884) \, M = 0.623 \ M$$

$$[\text{H}_2] = x = 0.0884 \ M$$

Now you substitute into the equilibrium-constant expression for the reaction. From the chemical equation, you write

$$K_c = \frac{[\text{H}_2][\text{I}_2]}{[\text{HI}]^2}$$

Substituting yields

$$K_c = \frac{(0.0884)(0.0884)}{(0.623)^2} = \mathbf{0.0201}$$

Answer Check Arithmetic mistakes are frequent sources of error. If you can obtain even a rough estimate of the answer, you can often spot such errors. For example, suppose the decomposition of HI could go completely to products; then, 4 mol HI would give 2 mol I_2. The reaction actually gives only a little over 0.4 mol I_2, which suggests that K_c is small, probably much less than 1. (Remember, K_c has products over reactants.) If your calculation gives you something greater than 1, you probably made an arithmetic error. Recheck your calculations.

Exercise 14.4 Hydrogen sulfide, a colorless gas with a foul odor, dissociates on heating:

$$2H_2S(g) \rightleftharpoons 2H_2(g) + S_2(g)$$

When 0.100 mol H_2S was put into a 10.0-L vessel and heated to 1132°C, it gave an equilibrium mixture containing 0.0285 mol H_2. What is the value of K_c at this temperature?

■ See Problems 14.45, 14.46, 14.47, and 14.48.

FIGURE 14.6 ▶

The concentration of a gas at a given temperature is proportional to the pressure

When the gas is compressed, the pressure increases (as noted from the pressure gauge) and the concentration of the gas (molecules per unit volume) increases.

Pressure gauge

The Equilibrium Constant K_p

In discussing gas-phase equilibria, it is often convenient to write the equilibrium constant in terms of partial pressures of gases rather than concentrations. Note that the concentration of a gas is proportional to its partial pressure at a fixed temperature (Figure 14.6). You can see this by looking at the ideal gas law, $PV = nRT$, and solving for n/V, which is the molar concentration of the gas. You get $n/V = P/RT$. In other words, the molar concentration of a gas equals its partial pressure divided by RT, which is constant at a given temperature.

When you express *an equilibrium constant for a gaseous reaction in terms of partial pressures,* you call it the **equilibrium constant K_p.** For catalytic methanation,

$$CO(g) + 3H_2(g) \rightleftharpoons CH_4(g) + H_2O(g)$$

the equilibrium expression in terms of partial pressures becomes

$$K_p = \frac{P_{CH_4}P_{H_2O}}{P_{CO}P_{H_2}^3}$$

In general, the value of K_p is different from that of K_c. From the relationship for molar concentration $n/V = P/RT$, one can show that

$$K_p = K_c(RT)^{\Delta n}$$

where Δn is the sum of the coefficients of *gaseous* products in the chemical equation minus the sum of the coefficients of *gaseous* reactants. For the methanation reaction ($K_c = 3.92$), in which 2 mol of gaseous products ($CH_4 + H_2O$) are obtained from 4 mol of gaseous reactants ($CO + 3H_2$), Δn equals $2 - 4 = -2$. The usual unit of partial pressures in K_p is atmospheres; therefore, the value of R is 0.0821 L·atm/(K·mol). Hence,

$$K_p = 3.92 \times (0.0821 \times 1200)^{-2} = 4.04 \times 10^{-4}$$

Exercise 14.5   Phosphorus pentachloride dissociates on heating:

$$PCl_5(g) \rightleftharpoons PCl_3(g) + Cl_2(g)$$

If K_c equals 3.26×10^{-2} at 191°C, what is K_p at this temperature?

■ See Problems 14.51, 14.52, 14.53, and 14.54.

Equilibrium Constant for the Sum of Reactions

It is possible to determine the equilibrium constants for various chemical reactions and then use them to obtain the equilibrium constants of other reactions. A useful rule is as follows: *If a given chemical equation can be obtained by taking the sum of other equations, the equilibrium constant for the given equation equals the product of the equilibrium constants of the other equations.*

As an application of this rule, consider the following reactions at 1200 K:

$$CO(g) + 3H_2(g) \rightleftharpoons CH_4(g) + H_2O(g); K_1 = 3.92 \qquad \text{(Reaction 1)}$$

$$CH_4(g) + 2H_2S(g) \rightleftharpoons CS_2(g) + 4H_2(g); K_2 = 3.3 \times 10^4 \quad \text{(Reaction 2)}$$

When you take the sum of these two equations, you get

$$CO(g) + 2H_2S(g) \rightleftharpoons CS_2(g) + H_2O(g) + H_2(g) \qquad \text{(Reaction 3)}$$

According to the rule, the equilibrium constant for this reaction, K_3, is $K_3 = K_1K_2$. This result is easy to verify. Substituting the expressions for K_1 and K_2 in the product K_1K_2 gives

$$K_1K_2 = \frac{[CH_4][H_2O]}{[CO][H_2]^3} \times \frac{[CS_2][H_2]^4}{[CH_4][H_2S]^2} = \frac{[CS_2][H_2O][H_2]}{[CO][H_2S]^2}$$

which is the equilibrium-constant expression for Reaction 3. The value of the equilibrium constant is $K_1K_2 = 3.92 \times (3.3 \times 10^4) = 1.3 \times 10^5$. <

You may also use equilibrium expressions in terms of pressures in this calculation.

Concept Check 14.2

Consider the following hypothetical reactions. The equilibrium constants K given for each reaction are defined in terms of a concentration unit of molecules per liter.

$$
\begin{array}{ll}
A(g) \rightleftharpoons B(g) & K = 2 \\
X(g) \rightleftharpoons 2Y(g) & K = 6 \\
2C(g) \rightleftharpoons D(g) & K = 1
\end{array}
$$

Assume that the reactions have reached equilibrium. Match each of these reactions with one of the containers **I** to **IV** (each of which has a volume of 1 L). Identify the "color" of each molecule (that is, is A red or blue?).

| I | II | III | IV |

14.3 | Heterogeneous Equilibria; Solvents in Homogeneous Equilibria

A **homogeneous equilibrium** is *an equilibrium that involves reactants and products in a single phase.* Catalytic methanation is an example of a homogeneous equilibrium; it involves only gaseous reactants and products. On the other hand, a **heterogeneous equilibrium** is *an equilibrium involving reactants and products in more than one phase.* For example, the reaction of iron metal filings with steam to produce iron oxide, Fe_3O_4, and hydrogen involves solid phases, Fe and Fe_3O_4, in addition to a gaseous phase.

$$3Fe(s) + 4H_2O(g) \rightleftharpoons Fe_3O_4(s) + 4H_2(g)$$

In writing the equilibrium-constant expression for a heterogeneous equilibrium, you omit concentration terms for pure solids and liquids. For the reaction of iron with steam, you would write

$$K_c = \frac{[H_2]^4}{[H_2O]^4}$$

A Chemist Looks at . . .

Slime Molds and Leopards' Spots

daily life

A bright yellow splotch highlights a patch of wood chips in a garden. It looks as if a prankster has poured yellow paint over the chips. Next day the yellow splotch has moved a few inches, and now appears to be climbing up the base of a wall by the garden! A biologist would tell you the yellow splotch is a slime mold (Figure 14.7).

Less noticeable are the cellular slime molds. Much of the time they consist of a group of single-celled amoebas searching for bacteria to eat. But when their food supply is gone, the amoebas release a chemical that signals them to clump together, forming a multicelled slug that moves to a dry, sunlit patch where it forms spores that can be blown to better feeding grounds. During the initial stages of aggregation, the amoebas form a distinctive pattern reminiscent of that seen by chemists in an *oscillating reaction,* which occurs as substances diffuse through a gel (Figure 14.8).

The Russian chemist Boris P. Belousov reported one of the first oscillating reactions in 1958, in which the reaction cycled back and forth over time from one color to another. At first, his work was ignored. You might expect a reaction to form products of a given color, with the reaction gradually slowing as it comes to equilibrium, but how could a chemical reaction oscillate, say, from red to blue and back,

over a period of hours? Another Russian chemist, Anatol Zhabotinsky, improved the experiment, leaving no doubt that some chemical reactions do oscillate. And when the chemicals are placed in a gel in a flat dish, the colors appear as a pattern of waves in space rather than as oscillations in time. Chemists have since shown that the Belousov–Zhabotinsky reaction occurs by two different mechanisms, first by one, then by the other. These mechanisms are repeated in space or time, depending on the concentrations of intermediate substances. During the reaction, an indicator changes color depending on which mechanism is active. Although the complete set of elementary steps of the Belousov–Zhabotinsky reaction is complicated, the overall reaction occurs just as you would expect. The initial reactants continue to decrease over time and the final products increase as the substances come to equilibrium.

An oscillating mechanism also appears to be at work in the aggregation phase of cellular slime molds. And these are not the only biological examples of chemical oscillations. One theory of the formation of fur patterns in animals, such as a leopard's spots, assumes that an oscillating reaction occurs in the skin of the embryo, which eventually generates the fur pattern you see in the adult. A similar theory has been used to explain striped patterns on seashells. The rhythmic beat of your heart is an example where the concentrations of substances oscillate in time. Who would have thought that slime molds, leopards' spots, and cardiac rhythm had anything in common?

FIGURE 14.7 ▲
A slime mold
The fruiting body (yellow) of the slime mold *Fuligo septica* appears on a patch of leaves.

FIGURE 14.8 ▲
An oscillating reaction
This is a plate showing the wave patterns of the Belousov–Zhabotinsky reaction (in a gel).

■ See Problems 14.113 and 14.114.

Concentrations of Fe and Fe_3O_4 are omitted, because whereas the concentration of a gas can have various values, the concentration of a pure solid or a pure liquid is a constant at a given temperature.

To understand why such constant concentrations are omitted in writing K_c, write the equilibrium-constant expression for the reaction of iron with steam, but include [Fe] and [Fe_3O_4]. Call this K'_c.

$$K'_c = \frac{[Fe_3O_4][H_2]^4}{[Fe]^3[H_2O]^4}$$

You can rearrange the above equation, putting all of the constant factors on the left side.

$$\underbrace{\frac{[Fe]^3}{[Fe_3O_4]}}_{\substack{\text{constant} \\ \text{factors}}} \times K'_c = \underbrace{\frac{[H_2]^4}{[H_2O]^4}}_{\substack{\text{variable} \\ \text{factors}}}$$

If you use the thermodynamic equilibrium constant, which is defined in terms of activities, you find that the activity of a pure solid or liquid is 1. Therefore, when you write the equilibrium constant, the activities of pure solids and liquids need not be given explicitly.

Note that all terms on the left are constant but that those on the right (the concentrations of H_2 and H_2O) are variable. The left side equals K_c. Thus, in effect, concentrations of pure solids or pure liquids are incorporated in the value of K_c. Following similar reasoning, you also omit the concentration of solvent from K_c for a homogeneous reaction, as long as the concentration of solvent remains essentially constant during reaction. <

The fact that the concentrations of both Fe and Fe_3O_4 do not appear in the equilibrium-constant expression means that the equilibrium is not affected by the amounts of these substances, *as long as some of each is present.*

Example 14.4 | Writing K_c for a Reaction with Pure Solids or Liquids

a. Quicklime (calcium oxide, CaO) is prepared by heating a source of calcium carbonate, $CaCO_3$, such as limestone or seashells.

$$CaCO_3(s) \rightleftharpoons CaO(s) + CO_2(g)$$

Write the expression for K_c.

b. You can write the equilibrium-constant expression for a physical equilibrium, such as vaporization, as well as for a chemical equilibrium. Write the expression for K_c for the vaporization of water.

$$H_2O(l) \rightleftharpoons H_2O(g)$$

Problem Strategy Write the equilibrium-constant expression excluding terms for pure solids and liquids.

Solution In writing the equilibrium expressions, you ignore pure liquid and solid phases.
a. $K_c = [CO_2]$; b. $K_c = [H_2O(g)]$.

Answer Check The equilibrium-constant expressions should include all reactants and products, except those of pure solids and liquids. Note that the equilibrium between liquid water and water vapor depends only on the vapor (the vapor pressure).

Exercise 14.6 The Mond process for purifying nickel involves the formation of nickel tetracarbonyl, $Ni(CO)_4$, a volatile liquid, from nickel metal and carbon monoxide. Carbon monoxide is passed over impure nickel to form nickel carbonyl vapor, which, when heated, decomposes and deposits pure nickel.

$$Ni(s) + 4CO(g) \rightleftharpoons Ni(CO)_4(g)$$

Write the expression for K_c for this reaction.

$Ni(CO)_4$

■ See Problems 14.55 and 14.56.

Using the Equilibrium Constant

In the preceding sections, we described how a chemical reaction reaches equilibrium and how you can characterize this equilibrium by the equilibrium constant. Now we want to see the ways in which an equilibrium constant can be used to answer important questions. We will look at the following uses:

1. *Qualitatively interpreting the equilibrium constant.* By merely looking at the magnitude of K_c, you can tell whether a particular equilibrium favors products or reactants.

2. *Predicting the direction of reaction.* Consider a reaction mixture that is not at equilibrium. By substituting the concentrations of substances that exist in a reaction mixture into an expression similar to the equilibrium constant and comparing with K_c, you can predict whether the reaction will proceed toward products or toward reactants (as defined by the way you write the chemical equation).

3. *Calculating equilibrium concentrations.* Once you know the value of K_c for a reaction, you can determine the composition at equilibrium for any set of starting concentrations.

Let us see what meaning we can attach to the value of K_c.

14.4 | Qualitatively Interpreting the Equilibrium Constant

If the value of the equilibrium constant is large, you know immediately that the products are favored at equilibrium. Consider the synthesis of ammonia from its elements.

$$N_2(g) + 3H_2(g) \rightleftharpoons 2NH_3(g)$$

At 25°C the equilibrium constant K_c equals 4.1×10^8. This means that the numerator (product concentrations) is 4.1×10^8 times larger than the denominator (reactant concentrations). In other words, at this temperature the reaction favors the formation of ammonia at equilibrium.

You can verify this by calculating one possible equilibrium composition for this reaction. Suppose the equilibrium mixture is 0.010 *M* in N_2 and 0.010 *M* in H_2. From these concentrations you can calculate the concentration of ammonia necessary to give equilibrium. Substitute the concentrations of N_2 and H_2 and the value of K_c into the equilibrium expression

$$K_c = \frac{[NH_3]^2}{[N_2][H_2]^3}$$

You get

$$\frac{[NH_3]^2}{(0.010)(0.010)^3} = 4.1 \times 10^8$$

Now you can solve for the concentration of ammonia.

$$[NH_3]^2 = 4.1 \times 10^8 \times (0.010)(0.010)^3 = 4.1$$

After you take the square root of both sides of this equation, you find that $[NH_3] = 2.0$ *M*. The concentrations of N_2 and H_2 are both 0.010 *M*, so the amount of ammonia formed at equilibrium is 200 times that of any one reactant. Figure 14.9 shows the burning of methane, another reaction with an enormously large equilibrium constant.

FIGURE 14.9 ▲

Methane (natural gas) reacts with oxygen
The equilibrium mixture is almost entirely carbon dioxide and water. The equilibrium constant K_c for the reaction $CH_4 + 2O_2 \rightleftharpoons CO_2 + 2H_2O$ is 10^{140} at 25°C.

If the value of the equilibrium constant is small, the reactants are favored at equilibrium. As an example, consider the reaction of nitrogen and oxygen to give nitrogen monoxide, NO:

$$N_2(g) + O_2(g) \rightleftharpoons 2NO(g)$$

The equilibrium constant K_c equals 4.6×10^{-31} at 25°C. If you assume that the concentrations of N_2 and O_2 are 1.0 M, you find that the concentration of NO is 6.8×10^{-16} M. In this case the equilibrium constant is very small, and the concentration of product is not detectable. Reaction occurs to only a very limited extent. <

When the equilibrium constant is neither large nor small (around 1), neither reactants nor products are strongly favored. The equilibrium mixture contains significant amounts of all substances in the reaction. For example, in the case of the methanation reaction, the equilibrium constant K_c equals 3.92 at 1200 K. You found that if you start with 1.000 mol CO and 3.000 mol H_2 in a 10.00-L vessel, the equilibrium composition is 0.613 mol CO, 1.839 mol H_2, 0.387 mol CH_4, and 0.387 mol H_2O. Neither the reactants nor the products are predominant.

The equilibrium constant does become large enough at higher temperatures (about 2000°C) to give appreciable amounts of nitrogen monoxide (nitric oxide). This is why air ($N_2 + O_2$) in flames and in auto engines becomes a source of the pollutant NO.

> If K_c for a reaction,
>
> $$\underbrace{aA + bB}_{\text{reactants}} \rightleftharpoons \underbrace{cC + dD}_{\text{products}}$$
>
> is large, the equilibrium mixture is mostly products. If K_c is small, the equilibrium mixture is mostly reactants. When K_c is around 1, the equilibrium mixture contains appreciable amounts of both reactants and products.

Exercise 14.7 The equilibrium constant K_c for the reaction

$$2NO(g) + O_2(g) \rightleftharpoons 2NO_2(g)$$

equals 4.0×10^{13} at 25°C. Does the equilibrium mixture contain predominantly reactants or products? If [NO] = [O_2] = 2.0×10^{-6} M at equilibrium, what is the equilibrium concentration of NO_2?

■ See Problems 14.57, 14.58, 14.59, and 14.60.

14.5 | Predicting the Direction of Reaction

Suppose a gaseous mixture from an industrial plant has the following composition at 1200 K: 0.0200 M CO, 0.0200 M H_2, 0.00100 M CH_4, and 0.00100 M H_2O. If the mixture is passed over a catalyst at 1200 K, would the reaction

$$CO(g) + 3H_2(g) \rightleftharpoons CH_4(g) + H_2O(g)$$

go toward the right or the left? That is, would the mixture form more CH_4 and H_2O in going toward equilibrium, or more CO and H_2?

To answer this question, you substitute the concentrations of substances into the *reaction quotient* and compare its value to K_c. The **reaction quotient**, Q_c, is *an expression that has the same form as the equilibrium-constant expression but whose concentration values are not necessarily those at equilibrium*. For catalytic methanation, the reaction quotient is

$$Q_c = \frac{[CH_4]_i[H_2O]_i}{[CO]_i[H_2]_i^3}$$

where the subscript i indicates concentrations at a particular instant i. When you substitute the concentrations of the gaseous mixture described earlier, you get

$$Q_c = \frac{(0.00100)(0.00100)}{(0.0200)(0.0200)^3} = 6.25$$

Recall that the equilibrium constant K_c for catalytic methanation is 3.92 at 1200 K. For the reaction mixture to go to equilibrium, the value of Q_c must decrease from 6.25 to 3.92. This will happen if the reaction goes to the left. In that case, the numerator of Q_c ($[CH_4]_i[H_2O]_i$) will decrease, and the denominator ($[CO]_i[H_2]_i^3$) will increase. Thus, the gaseous mixture will give more CO and H_2.

Consider the problem more generally. You are given a reaction mixture that is not yet at equilibrium. You would like to know in what direction the reaction will go as it approaches equilibrium. To answer this, you substitute the concentrations of substances from the mixture into the reaction quotient Q_c. Then, you compare Q_c to the equilibrium constant K_c.

For the general reaction $aA + bB \rightleftharpoons cC + dD$,

$$Q_c = \frac{[C]_i^c[D]_i^d}{[A]_i^a[B]_i^b}$$

Then

> If $Q_c > K_c$, the reaction will go to the left.
> If $Q_c < K_c$, the reaction will go to the right.
> If $Q_c = K_c$, the reaction mixture is at equilibrium.

(See Figure 14.10.)

FIGURE 14.10 ▶

Direction of reaction
The figure shows the relative sizes of Q_c and K_c. Reaction proceeds in the direction of the arrows. Thus, on the left, $Q_c < K_c$, so the reaction goes to the right, from reactants to products.

Equilibrium

Example 14.5 | Using the Reaction Quotient

A 50.0-L reaction vessel contains 1.00 mol N_2, 3.00 mol H_2, and 0.500 mol NH_3. Will more ammonia, NH_3, be formed or will it dissociate when the mixture goes to equilibrium at 400°C? The equation is

$$N_2(g) + 3H_2(g) \rightleftharpoons 2NH_3(g)$$

K_c is 0.500 at 400°C.

Problem Strategy First, write the reaction quotient, Q_c, which has the same form as the equilibrium-constant

expression, but whose concentrations are those for a reaction mixture. Then, compare the value of Q_c with that of K_c. If Q_c is less than K_c, the reaction goes in the direction written; otherwise it goes in the opposite direction (unless $Q_c = K_c$, in which case the reaction is at equilibrium).

Solution The composition of the gas has been given in terms of moles. You convert these to molar concentrations by dividing by the volume (50.0 L). This gives 0.0200 M N_2, 0.0600 M H_2, and 0.0100 M NH_3.

(continued)

(continued)

Substituting these concentrations into the reaction quotient gives

$$Q_c = \frac{[NH_3]_i^2}{[N_2]_i[H_2]_i^3} = \frac{(0.0100)^2}{(0.0200)(0.0600)^3} = 23.1$$

Because $Q_c = 23.1$ is greater than $K_c = 0.500$, the reaction will go to the left as it approaches equilibrium. Therefore, **ammonia will dissociate.**

Answer Check   Here is a check on your result. A reaction tends to go toward equilibrium. This means that Q goes toward K_c. If Q is larger than K_c, it must become smaller; the top values in Q (products) need to get smaller, and the bottom values (reactants) need to get larger. Thus, the reaction goes from right to left.

Exercise 14.8   A 10.0-L vessel contains 0.0015 mol CO_2 and 0.10 mol CO. If a small amount of carbon is added to this vessel and the temperature raised to 1000°C, will more CO form? The reaction is

$$CO_2(g) + C(s) \rightleftharpoons 2CO(g)$$

The value of K_c is 1.17 at 1000°C. Assume that the volume of gas in the vessel is 10.0 L.

■ See Problems 14.61 and 14.62.

Concept Check 14.3

Carbon monoxide and hydrogen react in the presence of a catalyst to form methanol, CH_3OH:

$$CO(g) + 2H_2(g) \rightleftharpoons CH_3OH(g)$$

An equilibrium mixture of these three substances is suddenly compressed so that the concentrations of all substances initially double. In what direction does the reaction go as a new equilibrium is attained?

14.6 | Calculating Equilibrium Concentrations

Once you have determined the equilibrium constant for a reaction, you can use it to calculate the concentrations of substances in an equilibrium mixture. The next example illustrates a simple type of equilibrium problem.

Example 14.6 | Obtaining One Equilibrium Concentration Given the Others

A gaseous mixture contains 0.30 mol CO, 0.10 mol H_2, and 0.020 mol H_2O, plus an unknown amount of CH_4, in each liter. This mixture is at equilibrium at 1200 K.

$$CO(g) + 3H_2(g) \rightleftharpoons CH_4(g) + H_2O(g)$$

What is the concentration of CH_4 in this mixture? The equilibrium constant K_c equals 3.92.

Problem Strategy   Calculate concentrations from moles of substances. Substitute these concentrations into the equilibrium-constant equation and solve for the unknown concentration.

Solution   The equilibrium-constant equation is

$$K_c = \frac{[CH_4][H_2O]}{[CO][H_2]^3}$$

(continued)

(continued)

Substituting the known concentrations and the value of K_c gives

$$3.92 = \frac{[CH_4](0.020)}{(0.30)(0.10)^3}$$

You can now solve for $[CH_4]$.

$$[CH_4] = \frac{(3.92)(0.30)(0.10)^3}{(0.020)} = 0.059$$

The concentration of CH_4 in the mixture is **0.059 mol/L.**

Answer Check   A simple check is to put the equilibrium concentrations you have calculated into the equilibrium-constant expression. You should obtain the correct value of K_c (within rounding error).

Exercise 14.9   Phosphorus pentachloride gives an equilibrium mixture of PCl_5, PCl_3, and Cl_2 when heated.

$$PCl_5(g) \rightleftharpoons PCl_3(g) + Cl_2(g)$$

A 1.00-L vessel contains an unknown amount of PCl_5 and 0.020 mol each of PCl_3 and Cl_2 at equilibrium at 250°C. How many moles of PCl_5 are in the vessel if K_c for this reaction is 0.0415 at 250°C?

■ See Problems 14.65 and 14.66.

Usually you begin a reaction with known starting quantities of substances and want to calculate the quantities at equilibrium. The next example illustrates the steps used to solve this type of problem.

Example 14.7	Solving an Equilibrium Problem (Involving a Linear Equation in *x*)

The reaction

$$CO(g) + H_2O(g) \rightleftharpoons CO_2(g) + H_2(g)$$

is used to increase the ratio of hydrogen in synthesis gas (mixtures of CO and H_2). Suppose you start with 1.00 mol each of carbon monoxide and water in a 50.0-L vessel. How many moles of each substance are in the equilibrium mixture at 1000°C? The equilibrium constant K_c at this temperature is 0.58.

Problem Strategy   The solution of an equilibrium problem involves three steps. In Step 1, you use the given information to set up a table of starting, change, and equilibrium concentrations. In this problem, you are given starting amounts of reactants. You use these to obtain the starting concentrations. Express the change concentrations in terms of *x*, as we did in Example 14.1. In Step 2, you substitute the equilibrium concentrations in the table into the equilibrium-constant expression and equate this to the value of the equilibrium constant. In Step 3, you solve this equilibrium-constant equation. This example gives an equation that is a perfect square; taking the square root of it gives a linear equation, which is easy to solve. (More generally, an equilibrium equation involves solving an *n*th-order equation for its roots. For $n = 2$, you can use the quadratic formula, as illustrated in Example 14.8. For $n > 2$, it is time to think about using a computer.) >

See the "Equilibrium Calculator (Equilib)," by Robert Allendorfer, JCE: Software, Madison, WI (requires MS Windows).

(continued)

(continued)

Solution

Step 1: The *starting concentrations* of CO and H_2O are

$$[CO] = [H_2O] = \frac{1.00 \text{ mol}}{50.0 \text{ L}} = 0.0200 \text{ mol/L}$$

The starting concentrations of the products, CO_2 and H_2, are 0. The *changes in concentrations* when the mixture goes to equilibrium are not given. However, you can write them all in terms of a single unknown. If you let x be the moles of CO_2 formed per liter, then the moles of H_2 formed per liter is also x. Similarly, x moles each of CO and H_2O are consumed. You write the changes for CO and H_2O as $-x$. You obtain the *equilibrium concentrations* by adding the change in concentrations to the starting concentrations, as shown in the following table:

Concentration (M)	CO(g)	+	H₂O(g)	⇌	CO₂(g)	+	H₂(g)
Starting	0.0200		0.0200		0		0
Change	$-x$		$-x$		$+x$		$+x$
Equilibrium	$0.0200 - x$		$0.0200 - x$		x		x

Step 2: You then substitute the values for the equilibrium concentrations into the equilibrium-constant equation,

$$K_c = \frac{[CO_2][H_2]}{[CO][H_2O]}$$

and you get

$$0.58 = \frac{(x)(x)}{(0.0200 - x)(0.0200 - x)}$$

or

$$0.58 = \frac{x^2}{(0.0200 - x)^2}$$

Step 3: You now solve this equilibrium equation for the value of x. Note that the right-hand side is a perfect square. If you take the square root of both sides, you get

$$\pm 0.76 = \frac{x}{0.0200 - x}$$

We have written $\pm$ to indicate that you should consider both positive and negative values, because both are mathematically possible. Rearranging the equation gives

$$x = \frac{0.0200 \times 0.76}{1.76} = 0.0086 \quad \text{and} \quad x = \frac{-0.0200 \times 0.76}{0.24} = -0.063$$

You can dismiss the negative value as physically impossible (x can be only positive; it represents the concentration of CO_2 formed). If you substitute for x in the last line of the table, the equilibrium concentrations are 0.0114 M CO, 0.0114 M H_2O, 0.0086 M CO_2, and 0.0086 M H_2. To find the moles of each substance in the 50.0-L vessel, you multiply the concentrations by the volume of the vessel. For example, the amount of CO is

$$0.0114 \text{ mol/L} \times 50.0 \text{ L} = 0.570 \text{ mol}$$

The equilibrium composition of the reaction mixture is **0.570 mol CO, 0.570 mol H_2O, 0.43 mol CO_2, and 0.43 mol H_2.**

(continued)

(continued)

Answer Check A rough estimate of the answer can sometimes save you from giving the wrong answer. If this reaction could go completely to products, 1 mol CO could give only 1 mol CO_2. (Is the molar amount that you obtained for CO_2 less than 1?) The magnitude of K_c suggests that the reaction will give a mixture of approximately similar molar amounts of reactants and products. (Does your answer agree with this?)

Exercise 14.10 What is the equilibrium composition of a reaction mixture if you start with 0.500 mol each of H_2 and I_2 in a 1.0-L vessel? The reaction is

$$H_2(g) + I_2(g) \rightleftharpoons 2HI(g) \qquad K_c = 49.7 \text{ at } 458°C$$

■ See Problems 14.67 and 14.68.

The preceding example illustrates the three steps used to solve for equilibrium concentrations, as summarized in the following list:

1. Set up a table of concentrations (starting, change, and equilibrium expressions in x).

2. Substitute the expressions in x for equilibrium concentrations into the equilibrium-constant equation.

3. Solve the equilibrium-constant equation for the values of the equilibrium concentrations.

In the previous example, if you had not started with the same number of moles of reactants, you would not have gotten an equation with a perfect square. In that case you would have had to solve a quadratic equation. The next example illustrates how to solve such an equation. <

A quadratic equation of the form
$$ax^2 + bx + c = 0$$
has the solutions
$$x = \frac{-b \pm \sqrt{b^2 - 4ac}}{2a}$$
This equation for x is called the quadratic formula. (See Appendix A.)

Example 14.8 | Solving an Equilibrium Problem (Involving a Quadratic Equation in x)

Hydrogen and iodine react according to the equation

$$H_2(g) + I_2(g) \rightleftharpoons 2HI(g)$$

Suppose 1.00 mol H_2 and 2.00 mol I_2 are placed in a 1.00-L vessel. How many moles of substances are in the gaseous mixture when it comes to equilibrium at 458°C? The equilibrium constant K_c at this temperature is 49.7.

Problem Strategy You follow the three-step approach outlined just before this example. The equilibrium equation will be a quadratic equation, which you can solve by the quadratic formula. (See Appendix A for a discussion of this equation and formula.)

Solution

Step 1: The concentrations of substances are as follows:

Concentration (M)	$H_2(g)$ +	$I_2(g)$ $\rightleftharpoons$	$2HI(g)$
Starting	1.00	2.00	0
Change	$-x$	$-x$	$2x$
Equilibrium	$1.00 - x$	$2.00 - x$	$2x$

Note that the changes in concentrations equal x multiplied by the coefficient of that substance in the balanced chemical equation. The change is negative for a reactant

(continued)

(*continued*)

and positive for a product. Equilibrium concentrations equal starting concentrations plus the changes in concentrations.

Step 2: Substituting into the equilibrium-constant equation,

$$K_c = \frac{[HI]^2}{[H_2][I_2]}$$

you get

$$49.7 = \frac{(2x)^2}{(1.00 - x)(2.00 - x)}$$

Step 3: Because the right-hand side is not a perfect square, you must use the quadratic formula to solve for x. The equation rearranges to give

$$(1.00 - x)(2.00 - x) = (2x)^2/49.7 = 0.0805x^2$$

or

$$0.920x^2 - 3.00x + 2.00 = 0$$

Hence,

$$x = \frac{3.00 \pm \sqrt{9.00 - 7.36}}{1.84} = 1.63 \pm 0.70$$

A quadratic equation has two mathematical solutions. You obtain one solution by taking the upper (positive) sign in $\pm$ and the other by taking the lower (negative) sign. You get

$$x = 2.33 \quad \text{and} \quad x = 0.93$$

However, $x = 2.33$ gives a negative value to $1.00 - x$ (the equilibrium concentration of H_2), which is physically impossible. Only $x = 0.93$ remains. You substitute this value of x into the last line of the table in Step 1 to get the equilibrium concentrations and then multiply these by the volume of the vessel (1.00 L) to get the amounts of substances. The last line of the table is rewritten

Concentration (M)	$H_2(g)$	+	$I_2(g)$	$\rightleftharpoons$	$2HI(g)$
Equilibrium	$1.00 - x = 0.07$		$2.00 - x = 1.07$		$2x = 1.86$

The equilibrium composition is **0.07 mol H_2, 1.07 mol I_2, and 1.86 mol HI.**

Answer Check If you substitute the equilibrium concentrations of reactants and product into the equilibrium-constant expression, you should get the value of K_c. Check that you do.

Exercise 14.11 Phosphorus pentachloride, PCl_5, decomposes when heated.

$$PCl_5(g) \rightleftharpoons PCl_3(g) + Cl_2(g)$$

If the initial concentration of PCl_5 is 1.00 mol/L, what is the equilibrium composition of the gaseous mixture at 160°C? The equilibrium constant K_c at 160°C is 0.0211.

See Problems 14.69 and 14.70.

Concept Check 14.4

A and B react to produce C according to the following chemical equation:

$$A + B \longrightarrow C$$

Amounts of A and B are added to an equilibrium reaction mixture of A, B, and C such that when equilibrium is again attained, the amounts of A and B are doubled in the same volume. How is the amount of C changed?

Changing the Reaction Conditions; Le Châtelier's Principle

Obtaining the maximum amount of product from a reaction depends on the proper selection of reaction conditions. By changing these conditions, you can increase or decrease the yield of product. There are three ways to alter the equilibrium composition of a gaseous reaction mixture and possibly increase the yield of product:

1. Changing the concentrations by removing products or adding reactants to the reaction vessel.

2. Changing the partial pressure of gaseous reactants and products by changing the volume.

3. Changing the temperature.

Note that a catalyst cannot alter equilibrium composition, although it can change the rate at which a product is formed and affect the result.

14.7 | Removing Products or Adding Reactants

One way to increase the yield of a desired product is to change concentrations in a reaction mixture by removing a product or adding a reactant. Consider the methanation reaction,

$$CO(g) + 3H_2(g) \rightleftharpoons CH_4(g) + H_2O(g)$$

If you place 1.000 mol CO and 3.000 mol H_2 in a 10.00-L reaction vessel, the equilibrium composition at 1200 K is 0.613 mol CO, 1.839 mol H_2, 0.387 mol CH_4, and 0.387 mol H_2O. Can you alter this composition by removing or adding one of the substances to improve the yield of methane?

To answer this question, you can apply **Le Châtelier's principle,** which states that *when a system in chemical equilibrium is disturbed by a change of temperature, pressure, or a concentration, the system shifts in equilibrium composition in a way that tends to counteract this change of variable.* < Suppose you remove a substance from or add a substance to the equilibrium mixture in order to alter the concentration of the substance. Chemical reaction then occurs to partially restore the initial concentration of the removed or added substance. (However, if the concentration of substance cannot be changed, as in the case of a pure solid or liquid reactant or product, changes in amount will have no effect on the equilibrium composition.)

For example, suppose that water vapor is removed from the reaction vessel containing the equilibrium mixture for methanation. Le Châtelier's principle predicts that net chemical change will occur to partially reinstate the original concentration of water vapor. This means that the methanation reaction momentarily goes in the forward direction,

$$CO(g) + 3H_2(g) \longrightarrow CH_4(g) + H_2O(g)$$

until equilibrium is re-established. Going in the forward direction, the concentrations of both water vapor and methane increase.

A practical way to remove water vapor in this reaction would be to cool the reaction mixture quickly to condense the water. Liquid water could be removed and the gases reheated until equilibrium is again established. The concentration of water vapor would build up as the concentration of methane increases. Table 14.1 lists the amounts of each substance at each stage of this process (carried out in a 10.00-L reaction vessel). Note how the yield of methane has been improved.

It is often useful to add an excess of a cheap reactant in order to force the reaction toward more products. In this way, the more expensive reactant is made to react to a greater extent than it would otherwise.

Le Châtelier's principle was introduced in Section 12.3, where it was used to determine the effect of pressure on solubility of gases in liquids.

TABLE 14.1	Effect of Removing Water Vapor from a Methanation Mixture (in a 10.00-L Vessel)			
Stage of Process	Mol CO	Mol H_2	Mol CH_4	Mol H_2O
Original reaction mixure	0.613	1.839	0.387	0.387
After removing water (before equilibrium)	0.613	1.839	0.387	0
When equilibrium is reestablished	0.491	1.473	0.509	0.122

Consider the ammonia synthesis

$$N_2(g) + 3H_2(g) \rightleftharpoons 2NH_3(g)$$

If you wished to convert as much hydrogen to ammonia as possible, you might increase the concentration of nitrogen. To understand the effect of this, first suppose that a mixture of nitrogen, hydrogen, and ammonia is at equilibrium. If nitrogen is now added to this mixture, the equilibrium is disturbed. According to Le Châtelier's principle, the reaction will now go in the direction that will use up some of the added nitrogen.

$$N_2(g) + 3H_2(g) \longrightarrow 2NH_3(g)$$

Consequently, adding more nitrogen has the effect of converting a greater quantity of hydrogen to ammonia. Figure 14.11 illustrates the effect of adding or removing a reactant on another chemical equilibrium.

You can look at these situations in terms of the reaction quotient, Q_c. Consider the methanation reaction, in which

$$Q_c = \frac{[CH_4]_i[H_2O]_i}{[CO]_i[H_2]_i^3}$$

If the reaction mixture is at equilibrium, $Q_c = K_c$. Suppose you remove some H_2O from the equilibrium mixture. Now $Q_c < K_c$, and from what we said in Section 14.5, you know the reaction will proceed in the forward direction to restore equilibrium.

A

B

C

FIGURE 14.11 ▲

Effect on a chemical equilibrium of changing the concentration of a substance
The concentration is changed by adding or removing a substance. *(A)* The center beaker contains a reddish orange precipitate of HgI_2 in equilibrium with I^- (colorless) and HgI_4^{2-} (pale yellow): $HgI_2(s) + 2I^-(aq) \rightleftharpoons HgI_4^{2-}(aq)$. *(B)* The solution of NaI (right beaker) is added to the equilibrium mixture in the center beaker. By adding I^-, the reaction is forced to the right: $HgI_2(s) + 2I^-(aq) \longrightarrow HgI_4^{2-}(aq)$. The orange precipitate of HgI_2 disappears. *(C)* A solution of NaClO (left beaker) is now added to the reaction mixture; the NaClO removes I^- by oxidizing it to IO^-. By removing I^-, the reaction shifts to the left: $HgI_2(s) + 2I^-(aq) \longleftarrow HgI_4^{2-}(aq)$. An orange precipitate of HgI_2 appears.

We can now summarize the conclusions from this section:

> When more reactant is added to, or some product is removed from, an equilibrium mixture, thereby changing the concentration of reactant or product, net reaction occurs left to right (that is, in the forward direction) to give a new equilibrium, and more products are produced.

> When more product is added to, or some reactant is removed from, an equilibrium mixture, thereby changing the concentration of reactant or product, net reaction occurs right to left (that is, in the reverse direction) to give a new equilibrium, and more reactants are produced.

Example 14.9 | Applying Le Châtelier's Principle When a Concentration Is Altered

Predict the direction of reaction when H_2 is removed from a mixture (lowering its concentration) in which the following equilibrium has been established:

$$H_2(g) + I_2(g) \rightleftharpoons 2HI(g)$$

Problem Strategy According to Le Châtelier's principle, when you remove a component from an equilibrium mixture, the reaction goes in the direction that tends to restore this component.

Solution When H_2 is removed from the reaction mixture, lowering its concentration, the reaction goes in the **reverse direction** (more HI dissociates to H_2 and I_2) to partially restore the H_2 that was removed.

$$H_2(g) + I_2(g) \longleftarrow 2HI(g)$$

Answer Check Make sure that your answer is consistent with Le Châtelier's principle: the component

removed (hydrogen in this case) is partially restored by the reaction.

Exercise 14.12 Consider each of the following equilibria, which are disturbed as indicated. Predict the direction of reaction.

a. The equilibrium

$$CaCO_3(s) \rightleftharpoons CaO(s) + CO_2(g)$$

is disturbed by increasing the pressure (that is, concentration) of carbon dioxide.

b. The equilibrium

$$2Fe(s) + 3H_2O(g) \rightleftharpoons Fe_2O_3(s) + 3H_2(g)$$

is disturbed by increasing the concentration of hydrogen.

■ See Problems 14.73 and 14.74.

A reaction whose equilibrium constant is extremely small remains almost completely as reactants and cannot be shifted to products by adding an excess of one reactant. For example, the reaction

$$CO_2(g) + 2H_2O(g) \rightleftharpoons CH_4(g) + 2O_2(g)$$

has an equilibrium constant K_c equal to 10^{-140} at 25°C. This value is so small that the equilibrium mixture practically consists only of carbon dioxide and water. Adding more carbon dioxide has no appreciable effect.

14.8 | Changing the Pressure and Temperature

The optimum conditions for catalytic methanation involve moderately elevated temperatures and normal to moderately high pressures.

$$CO(g) + 3H_2(g) \xrightleftharpoons[\text{1 atm–100 atm}]{\text{230°C–450°C}} CH_4(g) + H_2O(g)$$

Let us see whether we can gain insight into why these might be the optimum conditions for the reaction.

Effect of Pressure Change

A pressure change *obtained by changing the volume* can affect the yield of product in a gaseous reaction if the reaction involves a change in total moles of gas. The methanation reaction, $CO + 3H_2 \rightleftharpoons CH_4 + H_2O$, is an example of a change in moles of gas. When the reaction goes in the forward direction, four moles of reactant gas ($CO + 3H_2$) become two moles of product gas ($CH_4 + H_2O$).

To see the effect of such a pressure change, consider what happens when an equilibrium mixture from the methanation reaction is compressed to one-half of its original volume at a fixed temperature (see Figure 14.12). The total pressure is doubled (PV = constant at a fixed temperature, according to Boyle's law, so halving V requires that P double). Because the partial pressures and therefore the concentrations of reactants and products have changed, the mixture is no longer at equilibrium. The direction in which the reaction goes to re-establish equilibrium can be predicted by applying Le Châtelier's principle. Reaction should go in the forward direction, because then the moles of gas decrease, and the pressure (which is proportional to moles of gas) decreases. In this way, the initial pressure increase is partially reduced.

You find the same result by looking at the reaction quotient Q_c. Let [CO], [H_2], [CH_4], and [H_2O] be the molar concentrations at equilibrium for the methanation reaction. When the volume of an equilibrium mixture is halved, the partial pressures and therefore the concentrations are doubled. You obtain the reaction quotient at that moment by replacing each equilibrium concentration by double its value.

$$Q_c = \frac{(2[CH_4])(2[H_2O])}{(2[CO])(2[H_2])^3} = \frac{K_c}{4}$$

Because $Q_c < K_c$, the reaction proceeds in the forward direction.

You can see the quantitative effect of the pressure change by solving the equilibrium problem. Recall that if you put 1.000 mol CO and 3.000 mol H_2 into a 10.00-L vessel, the equilibrium composition at 1200 K, where K_c equals 3.92, is 0.613 mol CO, 1.839 mol H_2, 0.387 mol CH_4, and 0.387 mol H_2O. Suppose the volume of the

FIGURE 14.12

Effect on chemical equilibrium of changing the pressure
The effect on the methanation reaction is shown; the approximate composition is represented by the proportion of different "molecules" (see key at right). The actual arrangement of molecules in a gas is random. *(A)* The original equilibrium mixture of CO, H_2, CH_4, and H_2O molecules. *(B)* The gases are compressed to one-half their initial volume, increasing their partial pressures, so that the mixture is no longer at equilibrium. *(C)* Equilibrium is re-established when the reaction goes in the forward direction: $CO + 3H_2 \longrightarrow CH_4 + H_2O$. In this way, the total number of molecules is reduced, which reduces the initial pressure increase.

Key

CO

H_2

CH_4

H_2O

Gases at equilibrium

After compression, but before equilibrium

Compressed gases at equilibrium

A **B** **C**

reaction gases is halved so that the initial concentrations are doubled. The temperature remains at 1200 K, so K_c is still 3.92. But if you solve for the new equilibrium composition (following the method of Example 14.8), you obtain 0.495 mol CO, 1.485 mol H_2, 0.505 mol CH_4, and 0.505 mol H_2O. Note that the amount of CH_4 has increased from 0.387 mol to 0.505 mol. You conclude that high pressure of reaction gases favors high yields of methane.

To decide the direction of reaction when the pressure of the reaction mixture is increased (say, by decreasing the volume), you ignore liquids and solids. They are not much affected by pressure changes, because they are nearly incompressible. Consider the reaction

$$C(s) + CO_2(g) \rightleftharpoons 2CO(g)$$

The moles *of gas* increase when the reaction goes in the forward direction (1 mol CO_2 goes to 2 mol CO). Therefore, when you increase the pressure of the reaction mixture by decreasing its volume, the reaction goes in the reverse direction. The moles of gas decrease, and the initial increase of pressure is partially reduced, as Le Châtelier's principle leads you to expect.

It is important to note that an increase or a decrease in pressure of a gaseous reaction must result in changes of partial pressures of substances in the chemical equation if it is to have an effect on the equilibrium composition. Only changes in partial pressures, or concentrations, of these substances can affect the reaction quotient. Consider the effect of increasing the pressure in the methanation reaction by adding helium gas. Although the total pressure increases, the partial pressures of CO, H_2, CH_4, and H_2O do not change. Thus, the equilibrium composition is not affected. However, changing the pressure by changing the volume of this system changes the partial pressures of all gases, so the equilibrium composition is affected.

We can summarize these conclusions:

> If the pressure is increased by decreasing the volume of a reaction mixture, the reaction shifts in the direction of fewer moles of gas.

Example 14.10 | Applying Le Châtelier's Principle When the Pressure Is Altered

Look at each of the following equations and decide whether an increase of pressure obtained by decreasing the volume will increase, decrease, or have no effect on the amounts of products.

a. $CO(g) + Cl_2(g) \rightleftharpoons COCl_2(g)$

b. $2H_2S(g) \rightleftharpoons 2H_2(g) + S_2(g)$

c. $C(\text{graphite}) + S_2(g) \rightleftharpoons CS_2(g)$

Problem Strategy According to Le Châtelier's principle, if you apply pressure to an equilibrium mixture, the reaction goes in the direction to partially offset this applied pressure. Ask whether the molecules of *gas* increase or decrease during reaction from left to right. If they decrease, this should partially offset any increase in applied pressure; the reaction should go

from left to right. Otherwise, the reaction should go from right to left.

Solution

a. Reaction decreases the number of molecules of gas (from two to one). According to Le Châtelier's principle, an increase of pressure **increases** the amount of product.

b. Reaction increases the number of molecules of gas (from two to three); hence, an increase of pressure **decreases** the amounts of products.

c. Reaction does not change the number of molecules of gas. (You ignore the change in volume due to consumption of solid carbon, because the change in volume of a solid is insignificant. Look only at gas

(continued)

(continued)

volumes when deciding the effect of pressure change on equilibrium composition.) Pressure change has **no effect.**

Answer Check You look only at the gaseous components when deciding the direction of reaction from an applied pressure. Make sure you have done this correctly.

Exercise 14.13 Can you increase the amount of product in each of the following reactions by increasing the pressure? Explain.

a. $CO_2(g) + H_2(g) \rightleftharpoons CO(g) + H_2O(g)$

b. $4CuO(s) \rightleftharpoons 2Cu_2O(s) + O_2(g)$

c. $2SO_2(g) + O_2(g) \rightleftharpoons 2SO_3(g)$

■ See Problems 14.75 and 14.76.

Effect of Temperature Change

Temperature has a profound effect on most reactions. In the first place, reaction rates usually increase with an increase in temperature, meaning that equilibrium is reached sooner. Many gaseous reactions are sluggish or have imperceptible rates at room temperature but speed up enough at higher temperature to become commercially feasible processes.

Second, equilibrium constants vary with temperature. Table 14.2 gives values of K_c for methanation at various temperatures. Note that K_c equals 4.9×10^{27} at 298 K. Therefore, an equilibrium mixture at room temperature is mostly methane and water.

Whether you should raise or lower the temperature of a reaction mixture to increase the equilibrium amount of product can be shown by Le Châtelier's principle. Again, consider the methanation reaction,

$$CO(g) + 3H_2(g) \rightleftharpoons CH_4(g) + H_2O(g); \Delta H° = -206.2 \text{ kJ}$$

The value of $\Delta H°$ shows this reaction to be quite exothermic. As products are formed, considerable heat is released. According to Le Châtelier's principle, as the temperature is raised, the reaction shifts to form more reactants, thereby absorbing heat and "attempting" to counter the increase in temperature.

$$CO(g) + 3H_2(g) \longleftarrow CH_4(g) + H_2O(g) + \text{heat}$$

You predict that the equilibrium constant will be smaller for higher temperatures, in agreement with the values of K_c given in Table 14.2. Figure 14.13 illustrates the effect of temperature on another chemical equilibrium. <

The conclusions from Le Châtelier's principle regarding temperature effects on an equilibrium can be summarized this way:

> For an endothermic reaction ($\Delta H°$ positive), the amounts of products are increased at equilibrium by an increase in temperature (K_c is larger at higher T). For an exothermic reaction ($\Delta H°$ negative), the amounts of products are increased at equilibrium by a decrease in temperature (K_c is larger at lower T).

TABLE 14.2

Equilibrium Constant for Methanation at Different Temperatures

Temperature (K)	K_c
298	4.9×10^{27}
800	1.38×10^5
1000	2.54×10^2
1200	3.92

The quantitative effect of temperature on the equilibrium constant is discussed in Chapter 18.

Example 14.11 | Applying Le Châtelier's Principle When the Temperature Is Altered

Carbon monoxide is formed when carbon dioxide reacts with solid carbon (graphite).

$$CO_2(g) + C(\text{graphite}) \rightleftharpoons 2CO(g); \Delta H° = 172.5 \text{ kJ}$$

Is a high or low temperature more favorable to the formation of carbon monoxide?

Problem Strategy Decide in which direction you want the reaction to go in. (If you want more product, then you want to shift the reaction to the right.) Is this endothermic or exothermic? According to Le Châtelier's principle, if you raise the temperature of an equilibrium mixture, reaction goes in the direction that absorbs heat

(continued)

(continued)

(that is, it goes in the endothermic direction), to partially offset the heat added for the temperature increase. (Similarly, if you lower the temperature, the reaction goes in the exothermic direction.) Now you can determine whether you must increase or decrease the temperature.

Solution You want to increase the yield of CO, so you need to shift the equilibrium toward the right, which is endothermic (absorbs heat). You need to raise the temperature (add heat).

Alternatively, you can look at the problem this way. Write the chemical equation with heat on the left or right, depending on whether the heat is absorbed (consumed) or given off. The reaction to produce CO absorbs heat, so you write the equation with heat on the left.

$$\text{Heat} + CO_2(g) + C(\text{graphite}) \longrightarrow 2CO(g)$$

If you add heat (increasing the temperature), you push the reaction to the right, using up some of that heat.

Thus, **high temperature** is more favorable to the formation of carbon monoxide. This explains why combustion of carbon, or of materials containing carbon, can produce significant amounts of carbon monoxide, in addition to carbon dioxide.

Answer Check Check that your answer is consistent with Le Châtelier's principle. If you increase the temperature of the reaction (add heat), the reaction shifts in a direction to use up some of that added heat.

Exercise 14.14 Consider the possibility of converting carbon dioxide to carbon monoxide by the endothermic reaction

$$CO_2(g) + H_2(g) \rightleftharpoons CO(g) + H_2O(g)$$

Is a high or a low temperature more favorable to the production of carbon monoxide? Explain.

■ See Problems 14.77 and 14.78.

FIGURE 14.13 ▲

Effect on chemical equilibrium of changing the temperature
The reaction shown is endothermic: $Co(H_2O)_6^{2+}(aq) + 4Cl^-(aq) \rightleftharpoons$ $CoCl_4^{2-}(aq) + 6H_2O(l)$. At room temperature, the equilibrium mixture is blue, from $CoCl_4^{2-}$. When cooled by the ice bath, the equilibrium mixture turns pink, from $Co(H_2O)_6^{2+}$.

Concept Check 14.5

Given the hypothetical exothermic reaction $A_2(g) + 2B(g) \longrightarrow 2AB(g)$ at equilibrium, decide which of the following containers represents the reaction mixture at the higher temperature? (The other container represents the reaction at a lower temperature.)

I   II

Choosing the Optimum Conditions for Reaction

You are now in a position to understand the optimum conditions for the methanation reaction. Because the reaction is exothermic, low temperatures should favor high yields of methane; that is, the equilibrium constant is large for low temperature. But gaseous reactions are often very slow at room temperature. In practice, the methanation reaction is run at moderately elevated temperatures (230°C–450°C) in the presence of a nickel catalyst. Under these conditions, the rate of reaction is sufficiently fast, but the equilibrium constant is not too small. Because the methanation reaction involves a decrease in moles of gas, the yield of methane should increase as the pressure increases. However, the equilibrium constant is large at the usual operating temperatures, so very high pressures are not needed to obtain economical yields of methane. Pressures of 1 atm to 100 atm are usual for this reaction.

As another example, consider the Haber process for the synthesis of ammonia:

$$N_2(g) + 3H_2(g) \xrightleftharpoons{\text{Fe catalyst}} 2NH_3(g); \Delta H° = -91.8 \text{ kJ}$$

This technological problem has stimulated a great deal of basic research into understanding how certain bacteria "fix" nitrogen at atmospheric pressure to make NH_3. An enzyme called nitrogenase is responsible for N_2 fixation in these bacteria. This enzyme contains Fe and Mo, which may play a catalytic role.

Because the reaction is exothermic, the equilibrium constant is larger for lower temperatures. But the reaction proceeds too slowly at room temperature to be practical, even in the presence of the best available catalysts. < The optimum choice of temperature, found experimentally to be about 450°C, is a compromise between an increased rate of reaction at higher temperature and an increased yield of ammonia at lower temperature. Because the formation of ammonia decreases the moles of gases, the yield of product is improved by high pressures. The equilibrium constant K_c is only 0.159 at 450°C, so higher pressures (up to 600 atm) are required for an economical yield of ammonia. Ammonia from the Haber reactor is removed from the reaction mixture by cooling the compressed gases until NH_3 liquefies. Unreacted N_2 and H_2 circulate back to the reactor.

Exercise 14.15 Consider the reaction

$$2CO_2(g) \rightleftharpoons 2CO(g) + O_2(g); \Delta H° = 566 \text{ kJ}$$

Discuss the temperature and pressure conditions that would give the best yield of carbon monoxide.

■ See Problems 14.81 and 14.82.

14.9 | Effect of a Catalyst

A *catalyst* is a substance that increases the rate of a reaction but is not consumed by it. The significance of a catalyst can be seen in the reaction of sulfur dioxide with oxygen to give sulfur trioxide.

$$2SO_2(g) + O_2(g) \rightleftharpoons 2SO_3(g)$$

The equilibrium constant K_c for this reaction is 1.7×10^{26}, which indicates that for all practical purposes the reaction should go almost completely to products. Yet when sulfur is burned in air or oxygen, it forms predominantly SO_2 and very little SO_3. Oxidation of SO_2 to SO_3 is simply too slow to give a significant amount of product. However, the rate of the reaction is appreciable in the presence of a platinum or divanadium pentoxide catalyst. The oxidation of SO_2 in the presence of a catalyst is the main step in the *contact process* for the industrial production of sulfuric acid, H_2SO_4. Sulfur trioxide reacts with water to form sulfuric acid. (In the industrial process, SO_3 is dissolved in concentrated H_2SO_4, which is then diluted.) <

Sulfur dioxide from the combustion of coal and from other sources appears to be a major cause of the marked increase in acidity of rain in the eastern United States in the past few decades. This acid rain has been shown to contain sulfuric and nitric acids. The SO_2 is oxidized in moist, polluted air to H_2SO_4. Acid rain is discussed in the essay on acid rain at the end of Section 16.2.

It is important to understand that *a catalyst has no effect on the equilibrium composition of a reaction mixture. A catalyst merely speeds up the attainment of equilibrium.* For example, suppose you mix 2.00 mol SO_2 and 1.00 mol O_2 in a 100.0-L vessel. In the absence of a catalyst, these substances appear unreactive. Much later, if you analyze the mixture, you find essentially the same amounts of SO_2 and O_2. But when a catalyst is added, the rates of both forward and reverse reactions are very much increased. As a result, the reaction mixture comes to equilibrium in a short time. The amounts of SO_2, O_2, and SO_3 can be calculated from the equilibrium constant. You find that the mixture is mostly SO_3 (2.00 mol), with only 1.7×10^{-8} mol SO_2 and 8.4×10^{-9} mol O_2.

A catalyst is useful for a reaction, such as $2SO_2 + O_2 \rightleftharpoons 2SO_3$, that is normally slow but has a large equilibrium constant. However, if the reaction has an exceedingly small equilibrium constant, a catalyst is of little help. The reaction

$$N_2(g) + O_2(g) \rightleftharpoons 2NO(g)$$

Time = 0
A

Time = 45 minutes
B

FIGURE 14.14 ▲

An example of how rates of reaction can affect the kind of product

(A) Mercury(II) ion reacts with iodide ion to precipitate mercury(II) iodide. In concentrated solutions, HgI_2 precipitates as tetragonal crystals, which are orange (see left beaker). In dilute solution (in the right beaker), however, rhombic crystals of HgI_2, which are yellow, form faster, giving an initial yellow precipitate. (B) The yellow form of HgI_2 is unstable, though, and in about an hour is replaced by the orange tetragonal form. Both beakers then contain the more stable orange form.

has been considered for the industrial production of nitric acid. (NO reacts with O_2 and H_2O to give nitric acid.) At 25°C, however, the equilibrium constant K_c equals 4.6×10^{-31}. An equilibrium mixture would contain an extremely small concentration of NO. A catalyst would not provide a significant yield at this temperature; a catalyst merely speeds up the attainment of equilibrium. The equilibrium constant increases as the temperature is raised, so that at 2000°C, air (a mixture of N_2 and O_2) forms about 0.4% NO at equilibrium. An industrial plant was set up in Norway in 1905 to prepare nitrate fertilizers using this reaction. The plant was eventually made obsolete by the *Ostwald process* for making nitric acid, in which NO is prepared by the oxidation of ammonia. This latter reaction is more economical than the direct reaction of N_2 and O_2, in part because the equilibrium constant is larger at moderate temperatures.

Although a catalyst cannot affect the composition at true equilibrium, in some cases it can affect the product in a reaction because it affects the rate of one reaction out of several possible reactions. The importance of rate for determining the product in a reaction is illustrated by a simple example in Figure 14.14. Mercury(II) ion reacts with iodide ion to form a precipitate of mercury(II) iodide.

$$Hg^{2+}(aq) + 2I^-(aq) \longrightarrow HgI_2(s)$$

In concentrated solutions, orange tetragonal crystals of HgI_2 form. In dilute solution, however, yellow rhombic crystals form faster and are the initial product. Later, when true equilibrium is attained, the orange crystals appear.

The Ostwald process presents an interesting example of the effect of a catalyst in determining a product when several possibilities exist. Two reactions of ammonia with oxygen are possible. The reaction used in the Ostwald process is

$$4NH_3(g) + 5O_2(g) \rightleftharpoons 4NO(g) + 6H_2O(g)$$

However, nitrogen monoxide dissociates to its elements,

$$2NO(g) \rightleftharpoons N_2(g) + O_2(g)$$

and the equilibrium constant for this is quite large (2.2×10^{30} at 25°C), so at true equilibrium the products of the reaction of ammonia with oxygen might be expected to be nitrogen and water.

$$4NH_3(g) + 3O_2(g) \rightleftharpoons 2N_2(g) + 6H_2O(g)$$

FIGURE 14.15 ▲

Oxidation of ammonia using a copper catalyst

The products (formed on the glowing copper coil) are N_2 and H_2O, whereas a platinum catalyst results in NO and H_2O as products.

Ammonia can be made to burn in oxygen, and N_2 and H_2O are the products. (The reaction occurs most readily in the presence of a copper catalyst; see Figure 14.15.) However, what Ostwald discovered was that the first reaction, to form NO from NH_3 and O_2, is catalyzed by platinum. Therefore, by using this catalyst at moderate temperatures, nitric oxide can be selectively formed. The dissociation of nitric oxide to its elements is normally too slow at moderate temperatures to be significant. Many other examples could be cited in which the products of given reactants depend on the catalyst.

A Checklist for Review

Important Terms

chemical equilibrium (14.1)
equilibrium-constant
  expression (14.2)
equilibrium constant K_c (14.2)

equilibrium constant K_p (14.2)
law of mass action (14.2)
homogeneous
  equilibrium (14.3)

heterogeneous
  equilibrium (14.3)
reaction quotient (14.5)
Le Châtelier's principle (14.7)

Key Equations

$$K_c = \frac{[C]^c[D]^d}{[A]^a[B]^b} \qquad Q_c = \frac{[C]_i^c[D]_i^d}{[A]_i^a[B]_i^b}$$

Summary of Facts and Concepts

Chemical equilibrium can be characterized by the *equilibrium constant K_c*. In the expression for K_c, the concentration of products is in the numerator and the concentration of reactants is in the denominator. Pure liquids and solids are ignored in writing the equilibrium-constant expression. When K_c is very large, the equilibrium mixture is mostly products, and when K_c is very small, the equilibrium mixture is mostly reactants. The reaction quotient Q_c takes the form of the equilibrium-constant expression. If you substitute the concentrations of substances in a reaction mixture into Q_c, you can predict the direction the reaction

must go to attain equilibrium. You can use K_c to calculate the composition of the reaction mixture at equilibrium, starting from various initial compositions.

The *choice of conditions,* including *catalysts,* can be very important to the success of a reaction. Removing a product from the reaction mixture, for example, shifts the equilibrium composition to give more product. Changing the pressure and temperature can also affect the product yield. *Le Châtelier's principle* is useful in predicting the effect of such changes.

Media Summary

Visit the **student website at college.cengage.com/pic/ebbing9e** to help prepare for class, study for quizzes and exams, understand core concepts, and visualize molecular-level interactions. The following media activities are available for this chapter:

 Prepare for Class

■ **Video Lessons** *Mini lectures from chemistry experts*
The Concept of Equilibrium
The Law of Mass Action and Types of Equilibrium
CIA Demonstration: $NO_2N_2O_4$
Converting Between K_c and K_p
Approaching Chemical Equilibrium
Predicting the Direction of a Reaction
Strategies for Solving Equilibrium Problems
Solving Problems Far from Equilibrium
An Equilibrium Problem Using the Quadratic Equation
Le Châtelier's Principle
The Effect of Changing Amounts on Equilibrium
CIA Demonstration: Silver Chloride and Ammonia
The Effect of Pressure and Volume on Equilibrium
The Effect of Temperature and Catalysts on Equilibrium
Common Mathematical Functions

 Improve Your Grade

■ **Visualizations** *Molecular-level animations and lab demonstration videos*
Equilibrium Decomposition of N_2O_4

Oscillating Reaction
Le Châtelier's Principle
Ostwald Process

■ **Tutorials** *Animated examples and interactive activites*
The Equilibrium Condition and Equilibrium Constant
Le Châtelier's Principle

■ **Flashcards** *Key terms and definitions*
Online Flashcards

■ **Self-Assessment Questions** *Additional questions with full worked-out solutions*
6 Self-Assessment Questions

 ACE the Test

Multiple-choice quizzes
3 ACE Practice Tests

Access these resources using the passkey available free with new texts or for purchase separately.

Learning Objectives

14.1 Chemical Equilibrium—A Dynamic Equilibrium

- Define *dynamic equilibrium* and *chemical equilibrium*.
- Apply stoichiometry to an equilibrium mixture. **Example 14.1**

14.2 The Equilibrium Constant

- Define *equilibrium-constant expression* and *equilibrium constant*.
- State the *law of mass action*.
- Write equilibrium-constant expressions. **Example 14.2**
- Describe the kinetics argument for the approach to chemical equilibrium.
- Obtain an equilibrium constant from reaction composition. **Example 14.3**
- Describe the equilibrium constant K_p; indicate how K_p and K_c are related.
- Obtain K_c for a reaction that can be written as a sum of other reactions of known K_c values.

14.3 Heterogeneous Equilibria; Solvents in Homogeneous Equilibria

- Define *homogeneous equilibrium* and *heterogeneous equilibrium*.
- Write K_c for a reaction with pure solids or liquids. **Example 14.4**

14.4 Qualitatively Interpreting the Equilibrium Constant

- Give a qualitative interpretation of the equilibrium constant based on its value.

14.5 Predicting the Direction of Reaction

- Define *reaction quotient, Q*.
- Describe the direction of reaction after comparing Q with K_c.
- Use the reaction quotient. **Example 14.5**

14.6 Calculating Equilibrium Concentrations

- Obtain one equilibrium concentration given the others. **Example 14.6**
- Solve an equilibrium problem (involving a linear equation in x). **Example 14.7**
- Solve an equilibrium problem (involving a quadratic equation in x). **Example 14.8**

14.7 Removing Products or Adding Reactants

- State *Le Châtelier's principle*.
- State what happens to an equilibrium when a reactant or product is added or removed.
- Apply Le Châtelier's principle when a concentration is altered. **Example 14.9**

14.8 Changing the Pressure and Temperature

- Describe the effect of a pressure change on chemical equilibrium.
- Apply Le Châtelier's principle when the pressure is altered. **Example 14.10**
- Describe the effect of a temperature change on chemical equilibrium.
- Apply Le Châtelier's principle when the temperature is altered. **Example 14.11**
- Describe how the optimum conditions for a reaction are chosen.

14.9 Effect of a Catalyst

- Define *catalyst*.
- Compare the effect of a catalyst on rate of reaction with its effect on equilibrium.
- Describe how a catalyst can affect the product formed.

Self-Assessment and Review Questions

14.1 Consider the reaction $N_2O_4(g) \rightleftharpoons 2NO_2(g)$. Draw a graph illustrating the changes of concentrations of N_2O_4 and NO_2 as equilibrium is approached. Describe how the rates of the forward and reverse reactions change as the mixture approaches dynamic equilibrium. Why is this called a *dynamic* equilibrium?

14.2 When 1.0 mol each of $H_2(g)$ and $I_2(g)$ are mixed at a certain high temperature, they react to give a final mixture consisting of 0.5 mol each of $H_2(g)$ and $I_2(g)$ and 1.0 mol HI(g). Why do you obtain the same final mixture when you bring 2.0 mol HI(g) to the same temperature?

14.3 Explain why the equilibrium constant for a gaseous reaction can be written in terms of partial pressures instead of concentrations.

14.4 Obtain the equilibrium constant for the reaction

$$HCN(aq) \rightleftharpoons H^+(aq) + CN^-(aq)$$

from the following

$$HCN(aq) + OH^-(aq) \rightleftharpoons CN^-(aq) + H_2O(l); K_1 = 4.9 \times 10^4$$
$$H_2O(l) \rightleftharpoons H^+(aq) + OH^-(aq); K_2 = 1.0 \times 10^{-14}$$

14.5 Which of the following reactions involve homogeneous equilibria and which involve heterogeneous equilibria? Explain the difference.
  a. $2NO(g) + O_2(g) \rightleftharpoons 2NO_2(g)$
  b. $2Cu(NO_3)_2(s) \rightleftharpoons 2CuO(s) + 4NO_2(g) + O_2(g)$
  c. $2N_2O(g) \rightleftharpoons 2N_2(g) + O_2(g)$
  d. $2NH_3(g) + 3CuO(s) \rightleftharpoons 3H_2O(g) + N_2(g) + 3Cu(s)$
14.6 Explain why pure liquids and solids can be ignored when writing the equilibrium-constant expression.
14.7 What qualitative information can you get from the magnitude of the equilibrium constant?
14.8 What is the reaction quotient? How is it useful?
14.9 List the possible ways in which you can alter the equilibrium composition of a reaction mixture.
14.10 Two moles of H_2 are mixed with 1 mol O_2 at 25°C. No observable reaction takes place, although K_c for the reaction to form water is very large at this temperature. When a piece of platinum is added, however, the gases react rapidly. Explain the role of platinum in this reaction. How does it affect the equilibrium composition of the reaction mixture?
14.11 How is it possible for a catalyst to give products from a reaction mixture that are different from those obtained when no catalyst or a different catalyst is used? Give an example.
14.12 List four ways in which the yield of ammonia in the reaction

$$N_2(g) + 3H_2(g) \rightleftharpoons 2NH_3(g); \Delta H° < 0$$

can be improved for a given amount of H_2. Explain the principle behind each way.
14.13 A chemist put 1.18 mol of substance A and 2.85 mol of substance B into a 10.0-L flask, which she then closed. A and B react by the following equation:

$$A(g) + 2B(g) \rightleftharpoons 3C(g) + D(g)$$

She found that the equilibrium mixture at 25°C contained 0.376 mol of D. How many moles of B are in the flask at equilibrium at 25°C?
  a. 2.47 mol
  b. 3.60 mol
  c. 2.52 mol
  d. 2.10 mol
  e. 2.41 mol

14.14 The reaction $3A(g) + B(s) \rightleftharpoons 2C(aq) + D(aq)$ occurs at 25°C in a flask, which has 1.87 L available for gas. After the reaction attains equilibrium, the amounts (mol) *or* concentrations (M) of substances are as follows:

2.48 mol A	1.13 M C
2.41 mol B	2.27 M D

What is the equilibrium constant K_c for this reaction at 25°C?
  a. 1.24
  b. 0.190
  c. 0.516
  d. 1.15
  e. 0.939
14.15 A graduate student places 0.272 mol of $PCl_3(g)$ and 8.56×10^{-4} mol of $PCl_5(g)$ into a 0.718-L flask at a certain temperature. $PCl_5(g)$ is known to dissociate as follows:

$$PCl_5(g) \rightleftharpoons PCl_3(g) + Cl_2(g)$$

After the reaction attains equilibrium, the student finds that the flask contains 2.51×10^{-4} mol of Cl_2. Calculate the equilibrium constant K_c for the reaction at this temperature.
  a. 0.114
  b. 8.51×10^{-2}
  c. 0.157
  d. 8.88×10^4
  e. 2.40×10^4
14.16 An experimenter places the following concentrations of gases in a closed container: $[NOBr] = 7.13 \times 10^{-2} M$, $[NO] = 1.58 \times 10^{-2} M$, $[Br_2] = 1.29 \times 10^{-2} M$. These gases then react:

$$2NOBr(g) \rightleftharpoons 2NO(g) + Br_2(g)$$

At the temperature of the reaction, the equilibrium constant K_c is 3.07×10^{-4}. Calculate the reaction quotient, Q_c, from the initial concentrations and determine whether the concentration of NOBr increases or decreases as the reaction approaches equilibrium.
  a. $Q_c = 6.33 \times 10^{-4}$; the concentration of NOBr decreases
  b. $Q_c = 6.33 \times 10^{-4}$; the concentration of NOBr increases
  c. $Q_c = 1.58 \times 10^4$; the concentration of NOBr increases
  d. $Q_c = 4.65 \times 10^{-4}$; the concentration of NOBr decreases
  e. $Q_c = 4.65 \times 10^{-4}$; the concentration of NOBr increases

Concept Explorations

14.17 Chemical Equilibrium I
Part 1: You run the chemical reaction $C(aq) + D(aq) \rightleftharpoons 2E(aq)$ at 25°C. The equilibrium constant K_c for the reaction at this temperature is 2.0.

  a. Write the equilibrium-constant expression for the reaction.
  b. Can you come up with some possible concentrations of C, D, and E that you might observe when the reaction has reached equilibrium at 25°C? What are these values?

  c. A student says that only a very limited number of concentrations for C, D, and E are possible at equilibrium. Is this true? State why you think this is true or is not true.
  d. If you start with 1.0 M concentrations of both C and D and allow the reaction to come to equilibrium, would you expect the concentration of C to have decreased to zero? If not, what would you expect for the concentration of C? (An approximate value is fine.)

Part 2: Consider the reaction A(*aq*) + B(*aq*) $\rightleftharpoons$ F(*aq*) + G(*aq*), whose equilibrium constant is 1.0×10^{-5} at 20°C. For each of the situations described below, indicate whether any reaction occurs. If reaction does occur, then indicate the direction of that reaction and describe how the concentrations of A, B, F, and G change during this reaction.

  a. A(*aq*) and B(*aq*) are mixed together in a container.

  b. F(*aq*) and G(*aq*) are mixed together in a container.

  c. A(*aq*) and F(*aq*) are mixed together in a container.

  d. B(*aq*) and G(*aq*) are mixed together in a container.

  e. Just B(*aq*) is placed into a container.

  f. Just G(*aq*) is placed into a container.

Consider any one of these situations in which a reaction does occur. At equilibrium, does the reaction mixture have appreciably more products than reactants? If not, how would you describe the equilibrium composition of the reaction mixture? How did you arrive at this answer?

14.18   Chemical Equilibrium II

Magnesium hydroxide, $Mg(OH)_2$, is a white, partially soluble solid that is used in many antacids. The chemical equation for the dissolving of $Mg(OH)_2(s)$ in water is

$$Mg(OH)_2(s) \rightleftharpoons Mg^{2+}(aq) + 2OH^-(aq)$$

  a. Describe a simple experimental procedure that you could use to study this solubility equilibrium. In your experiment, how would determine when the solution process has attained equilibrium?

  b. Write the equilibrium-constant expression for this dissolving of magnesium hydroxide.

  c. Suppose equilibrium has been established in container of magnesium hydroxide in water, and you decide to add more solid $Mg(OH)_2$. What would you expect to observe? What effect will this addition of $Mg(OH)_2$ have on the concentrations of $Mg^{2+}(aq)$ and $OH^-(aq)$?

  d. Say you have prepared an equilibrium solution of $Mg(OH)_2$ by adding pure solid $Mg(OH)_2$ to water. If you know the concentration of $OH^-(aq)$, can you determine the concentration of $Mg^{2+}(aq)$? If not, what information do you need that will allow you to determine the answer?

  e. You slowly add OH^- from another source (say, NaOH) to an equilibrium mixture of $Mg(OH)_2$ and water. How do you expect the concentration of the $Mg^{2+}(aq)$ to change? What might you be able to observe happening to the $Mg(OH)_2(s)$ as you add the OH^-?

  f. Next you remove some, but not all, of the $Mg(OH)_2(s)$ from the mixture. How will this affect the concentrations of the $Mg^{2+}(aq)$ and $OH^-(aq)$

  g. If someone hands you a container of $Mg(OH)_2(aq)$ and there is no solid $Mg(OH)_2$ present, is this solution at equilibrium? If it is not at equilibrium, what could you add to or remove from the container that would give an equilibrium system?

  h. Consider an individual $OH^-(aq)$ ion in an $Mg(OH)_2$ solution at equilibrium. If you could follow this ion over a long period of time, would you expect it always to remain as an $OH^-(aq)$ ion, or could it change in some way?

Conceptual Problems

14.19   During an experiment with the Haber process, a researcher put 1 mol N_2 and 1 mol H_2 into a reaction vessel to observe the equilibrium formation of ammonia, NH_3.

$$N_2(g) + 3H_2(g) \rightleftharpoons 2NH_3(g)$$

When these reactants come to equilibrium, assume that x mol H_2 react. How many moles of ammonia form?

14.20   Suppose liquid water and water vapor exist in equilibrium in a closed container. If you add a small amount of liquid water to the container, how does this affect the amount of water vapor in the container? If, instead, you add a small amount of water vapor to the container, how does this affect the amount of liquid water in the container?

14.21   A mixture initially consisting of 2 mol CO and 2 mol H_2 comes to equilibrium with methanol, CH_3OH, as the product:

$$CO(g) + 2H_2(g) \rightleftharpoons CH_3OH(g)$$

At equilibrium, the mixture will contain which of the following?

  a. less than 1 mol CH_3OH

  b. 1 mol CH_3OH

  c. more than 1 mol CH_3OH but less than 2 mol

  d. 2 mol CH_3OH

  e. more than 2 mol CH_3OH

14.22   When a continuous stream of hydrogen gas, H_2, passes over hot magnetic iron oxide, Fe_3O_4, metallic iron and water vapor form. When a continuous stream of water vapor passes over hot metallic iron, the oxide Fe_3O_4 and H_2 form. Explain why the reaction goes in one direction in one case but in the reverse direction in the other.

14.23   For the reaction $2HI(g) \rightleftharpoons H_2(g) + I_2(g)$ carried out at some fixed temperature, the equilibrium constant is 2.0.

  a. Which of the following pictures correctly depicts the reaction mixture at equilibrium?

  b. For the pictures that represent nonequilibrium situations, describe which way the reaction will shift to attain equilibrium.

I   II   III

= HI
= H_2
= I_2

14.24 An experimenter introduces 4.0 mol of gas A into a 1.0-L container at 200 K to form product B according to the reaction

$$2A(g) \rightleftharpoons B(g)$$

Using the experimenter's data (one curve is for A, the other is for B), calculate the equilibrium constant at 200 K.

14.25 The following reaction is carried out at 500 K in a container equipped with a movable piston.

$$A(g) + B(g) \rightleftharpoons C(g); \quad K_c = 10 \text{ (at 500 K)}$$

After the reaction has reached equilibrium, the container has the composition depicted here.

Suppose the container volume is doubled.
  a. How does the equilibrium composition shift?
  b. How does the concentration of each of the reactants and the product change? (That is, does the concentration increase, decrease, or stay the same?)

14.26 For the endothermic reaction $AB(g) \rightleftharpoons A(g) + B(g)$, the following represents a reaction container at two different temperatures. Which one (I or II) is at the lower temperature?

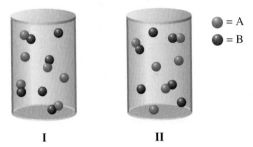

14.27 During the commercial preparation of sulfuric acid, sulfur dioxide reacts with oxygen in an exothermic reaction to produce sulfur trioxide. In this step, sulfur dioxide mixed with oxygen-enriched air passes into a reaction tower at about 420°C, where reaction occurs on a vanadium(V) oxide catalyst. Discuss the conditions used in this reaction in terms of its effect on the yield of sulfur trioxide. Are there any other conditions that you might explore in order to increase the yield of sulfur trioxide?

14.28 At some temperature, a 100-L reaction vessel contains a mixture that is initially 1.00 mol CO and 2.00 mol H_2. The vessel also contains a catalyst so that the following equilibrium is attained:

$$CO(g) + 2H_2(g) \rightleftharpoons CH_3OH(g)$$

At equilibrium, the mixture contains 0.100 mol CH_3OH. In a later experiment in the same vessel, you start with 1.00 mol CH_3OH. How much methanol is there at equilibrium? Explain.

Practice Problems

Reaction Stoichiometry

14.29 A 2.500-mol sample of phosphorus pentachloride, PCl_5, dissociates at 160°C and 1.00 atm to give 0.338 mol of phosphorus trichloride, PCl_3, at equilibrium.

$$PCl_5(g) \rightleftharpoons PCl_3(g) + Cl_2(g)$$

What is the composition of the final reaction mixture?

14.30 You place 3.00 mol of dinitrogen trioxide, N_2O_3, into a flask, where it decomposes at 25.0°C and 1.00 atm:

$$N_2O_3(g) \rightleftharpoons NO_2(g) + NO(g)$$

What is the composition of the reaction mixture at equilibrium if it contains 0.90 mol of nitrogen dioxide, NO_2?

14.31 You place 0.600 mol of nitrogen, N_2, and 1.800 mol of hydrogen, H_2, into a reaction vessel at 450°C and 10.0 atm. The reaction is

$$N_2(g) + 3H_2(g) \rightleftharpoons 2NH_3(g)$$

What is the composition of the equilibrium mixture if you obtain 0.048 mol of ammonia, NH_3, from it?

14.32 Nitrogen monoxide, NO, reacts with bromine, Br_2, to give nitrosyl bromide, NOBr.

$$2NO(g) + Br_2(g) \rightleftharpoons 2NOBr(g)$$

A sample of 0.0524 mol NO with 0.0262 mol Br_2 gives an equilibrium mixture containing 0.0311 mol NOBr. What is the composition of the equilibrium mixture?

14.33 In the contact process, sulfuric acid is manufactured by first oxidizing SO_2 to SO_3, which is then reacted with water. The reaction of SO_2 with O_2 is

$$2SO_2(g) + O_2(g) \rightleftharpoons 2SO_3(g)$$

A 2.000-L flask was filled with 0.0400 mol SO_2 and 0.0200 mol O_2. At equilibrium at 900 K, the flask contained 0.0296 mol SO_3. How many moles of each substance were in the flask at equilibrium?

14.34 Methanol, CH_3OH, formerly known as wood alcohol, is manufactured commercially by the following reaction:

$$CO(g) + 2H_2(g) \rightleftharpoons CH_3OH(g)$$

A 1.500-L vessel was filled with 0.1500 mol CO and 0.3000 mol H_2. When this mixture came to equilibrium at 500 K, the vessel contained 0.1187 mol CO. How many moles of each substance were in the vessel?

The Equilibrium Constant and Its Evaluation

14.35 Write equilibrium-constant expressions K_c for each of the following reactions.
 a. $N_2O_3(g) \rightleftharpoons NO_2(g) + NO(g)$
 b. $2H_2S(g) \rightleftharpoons 2H_2(g) + S_2(g)$
 c. $2NO(g) + O_2(g) \rightleftharpoons 2NO_2(g)$
 d. $PCl_3(g) + 3NH_3(g) \rightleftharpoons P(NH_2)_3(g) + 3HCl(g)$

14.36 Write equilibrium-constant expressions K_c for each of the following reactions.
 a. $N_2(g) + 2H_2(g) \rightleftharpoons N_2H_4(g)$
 b. $2NOCl(g) \rightleftharpoons 2NO(g) + Cl_2(g)$
 c. $2NO(g) + 2H_2(g) \rightleftharpoons N_2(g) + 2H_2O(g)$
 d. $2HCl(g) + \frac{1}{2}O_2(g) \rightleftharpoons Cl_2(g) + H_2O(g)$

14.37 The equilibrium-constant expression for a gas reaction is

$$K_c = \frac{[H_2O]^2[SO_2]^2}{[H_2S]^2[O_2]^3}$$

Write the balanced chemical equation corresponding to this expression.

14.38 The equilibrium-constant expression for a gas reaction is

$$K_c = \frac{[CO_2]^3[H_2O]^4}{[C_3H_8][O_2]^5}$$

Write the balanced chemical equation corresponding to this expression.

14.39 The equilibrium-constant expression for a reaction is

$$K_c = \frac{[NO_2]^4[O_2]}{[N_2O_5]^2}$$

What is the equilibrium-constant expression when the equation for this reaction is halved and then reversed?

14.40 The equilibrium-constant expression for a reaction is

$$K_c = \frac{[NH_3]^4[O_2]^5}{[NO]^4[H_2O]^6}$$

What is the equilibrium-constant expression when the equation for this reaction is halved and then reversed?

14.41 The equilibrium constant K_c for the equation

$$2HI(g) \rightleftharpoons H_2(g) + I_2(g)$$

at 425°C is 1.84. What is the value of K_c for the following equation?

$$H_2(g) + I_2(g) \rightleftharpoons 2HI(g)$$

14.42 The equilibrium constant K_c for the equation

$$CS_2(g) + 4H_2(g) \rightleftharpoons CH_4(g) + 2H_2S(g)$$

at 900°C is 27.8. What is the value of K_c for the following equation?

$$\frac{1}{2}CH_4(g) + H_2S(g) \rightleftharpoons \frac{1}{2}CS_2(g) + 2H_2(g)$$

14.43 A 6.00-L reaction vessel at 491°C contained 0.488 mol H_2, 0.206 mol I_2, and 2.250 mol HI. Assuming that the substances are at equilibrium, find the value of K_c at 491°C for the reaction of hydrogen and iodine to give hydrogen iodide. The equation is

$$H_2(g) + I_2(g) \rightleftharpoons 2HI(g)$$

14.44 A 4.00-L vessel contained 0.0148 mol of phosphorus trichloride, 0.0126 mol of phosphorus pentachloride, and 0.0870 mol of chlorine at 230°C in an equilibrium mixture. Calculate the value of K_c for the reaction

$$PCl_3(g) + Cl_2(g) \rightleftharpoons PCl_5(g)$$

14.45 Obtain the value of K_c for the following reaction at 900 K:

$$2SO_2(g) + O_2(g) \rightleftharpoons 2SO_3(g)$$

Use the data given in Problem 14.33.

14.46 Obtain the value of K_c for the following reaction at 500 K:

$$CO(g) + 2H_2(g) \rightleftharpoons CH_3OH(g)$$

Use the data given in Problem 14.34.

14.47 At 77°C, 2.00 mol of nitrosyl bromide, NOBr, placed in a 1.00-L flask dissociates to the extent of 9.4%; that is, for each mole of NOBr before reaction, $(1.000 - 0.094)$ mol NOBr remains after dissociation. Calculate the value of K_c for the dissociation reaction

$$2NOBr(g) \rightleftharpoons 2NO(g) + Br_2(g)$$

14.48 A 2.00-mol sample of nitrogen dioxide was placed in an 80.0-L vessel. At 200°C, the nitrogen dioxide was 6.0% decomposed according to the equation

$$2NO_2(g) \rightleftharpoons 2NO(g) + O_2(g)$$

Calculate the value of K_c for this reaction at 200°C. (See Problem 14.47.)

14.49 Write equilibrium-constant expressions K_p for each of the following reactions:
 a. $H_2(g) + Br_2(g) \rightleftharpoons 2HBr(g)$
 b. $CS_2(g) + 4H_2(g) \rightleftharpoons CH_4(g) + 2H_2S(g)$
 c. $4HCl(g) + O_2(g) \rightleftharpoons 2H_2O(g) + 2Cl_2(g)$
 d. $CO(g) + 2H_2(g) \rightleftharpoons CH_3OH(g)$

14.50 Write equilibrium-constant expressions K_p for each of the following reactions:
 a. $N_2O_4(g) \rightleftharpoons 2NO_2(g)$
 b. $2NO(g) + Br_2(g) \rightleftharpoons 2NOBr(g)$
 c. $2SO_2(g) + O_2(g) \rightleftharpoons 2SO_3(g)$
 d. $4NH_3(g) + 5O_2(g) \rightleftharpoons 4NO(g) + 6H_2O(g)$

14.51 The value of K_c for the following reaction at 900°C is 0.28.

$$CS_2(g) + 4H_2(g) \rightleftharpoons CH_4(g) + 2H_2S(g)$$

What is K_p at this temperature?

14.52 The equilibrium constant K_c equals 0.0952 for the following reaction at 227°C.

$$CH_3OH(g) \rightleftharpoons CO(g) + 2H_2(g)$$

What is the value of K_p at this temperature?

14.53 The reaction

$$SO_2(g) + \tfrac{1}{2}O_2(g) \rightleftharpoons SO_3(g)$$

has K_p equal to 6.55 at 627°C. What is the value of K_c at this temperature?

14.54 Fluorine, F_2, dissociates into atoms on heating.

$$\tfrac{1}{2}F_2(g) \rightleftharpoons F(g)$$

The value of K_p at 842°C is 7.55×10^{-2}. What is the value of K_c at this temperature?

14.55 Write the expression for the equilibrium constant K_c for each of the following equations:
a. $C(s) + CO_2(g) \rightleftharpoons 2CO(g)$
b. $FeO(s) + CO(g) \rightleftharpoons Fe(s) + CO_2(g)$
c. $Na_2CO_3(s) + SO_2(g) + \tfrac{1}{2}O_2(g) \rightleftharpoons Na_2SO_4(s) + CO_2(g)$
d. $PbI_2(s) \rightleftharpoons Pb^{2+}(aq) + 2I^-(aq)$

14.56 For each of the following equations, give the expression for the equilibrium constant K_c:
a. $NH_4Cl(s) \rightleftharpoons NH_3(g) + HCl(g)$
b. $2N_2(g) + CO_2(g) \rightleftharpoons 2N_2O(g) + C(s)$
c. $2NaHCO_3(s) \rightleftharpoons Na_2CO_3(s) + H_2O(g) + CO_2(g)$
d. $Fe^{3+}(aq) + 3OH^-(aq) \rightleftharpoons Fe(OH)_3(s)$

Using the Equilibrium Constant

14.57 On the basis of the value of K_c, decide whether or not you expect nearly complete reaction at equilibrium for each of the following:
a. $N_2(g) + O_2(g) \rightleftharpoons 2NO(g)$; $K_c = 4.6 \times 10^{-31}$
b. $C_2H_4(g) + H_2(g) \rightleftharpoons C_2H_6(g)$; $K_c = 1.3 \times 10^{21}$

14.58 Would either of the following reactions go almost completely to product at equilibrium?
a. $2NO(g) + 2H_2(g) \rightleftharpoons N_2(g) + 2H_2O(g)$; $K_c = 6.5 \times 10^{113}$
b. $N_2(g) + 2O_2(g) \rightleftharpoons 2NO_2(g)$; $K_c = 3 \times 10^{-17}$

14.59 Hydrogen fluoride decomposes according to the following equation:

$$2HF(g) \rightleftharpoons H_2(g) + F_2(g)$$

The value of K_c at room temperature is 1.0×10^{-95}. From the magnitude of K_c, do you think the decomposition occurs to any great extent at room temperature? If an equilibrium mixture in a 1.0-L vessel contains 1.0 mol HF, what is the amount of H_2 formed? Does this result agree with what you expect from the magnitude of K_c?

14.60 Suppose sulfur dioxide reacts with oxygen at 25°C.

$$2SO_2(g) + O_2(g) \rightleftharpoons 2SO_3(g)$$

The equilibrium constant K_c equals 8.0×10^{35} at this temperature. From the magnitude of K_c, do you think this reaction occurs to any great extent when equilibrium is reached at room temperature? If an equilibrium mixture is 1.0 M SO_3 and has equal concentrations of SO_2 and O_2, what is the concentration of SO_2

in the mixture? Does this result agree with what you expect from the magnitude of K_c?

14.61 The following reaction has an equilibrium constant K_c equal to 3.07×10^{-4} at 24°C.

$$2NOBr(g) \rightleftharpoons 2NO(g) + Br_2(g)$$

For each of the following compositions, decide whether the reaction mixture is at equilibrium. If it is not, decide which direction the reaction should go.
a. $[NOBr] = 0.0720$ M, $[NO] = 0.0162$ M, $[Br_2] = 0.0123$ M
b. $[NOBr] = 0.121$ M, $[NO] = 0.0159$ M, $[Br_2] = 0.0139$ M
c. $[NOBr] = 0.103$ M, $[NO] = 0.0134$ M, $[Br_2] = 0.0181$ M
d. $[NOBr] = 0.0472$ M, $[NO] = 0.0121$ M, $[Br_2] = 0.0105$ M

14.62 The following reaction has an equilibrium constant K_c equal to 3.59 at 900°C.

$$CH_4(g) + 2H_2S(g) \rightleftharpoons CS_2(g) + 4H_2(g)$$

For each of the following compositions, decide whether the reaction mixture is at equilibrium. If it is not, decide which direction the reaction should go.
a. $[CH_4] = 1.26$ M, $[H_2S] = 1.32$ M, $[CS_2] = 1.43$ M, $[H_2] = 1.12$ M
b. $[CH_4] = 1.25$ M, $[H_2S] = 1.52$ M, $[CS_2] = 1.15$ M, $[H_2] = 1.73$ M
c. $[CH_4] = 1.30$ M, $[H_2S] = 1.41$ M, $[CS_2] = 1.10$ M, $[H_2] = 1.20$ M
d. $[CH_4] = 1.56$ M, $[H_2S] = 1.43$ M, $[CS_2] = 1.23$ M, $[H_2] = 1.91$ M

14.63 Methanol, CH_3OH, is manufactured industrially by the reaction

$$CO(g) + 2H_2(g) \rightleftharpoons CH_3OH(g)$$

A gaseous mixture at 500 K is 0.020 M CH_3OH, 0.10 M CO, and 0.10 M H_2. What will be the direction of reaction if this mixture goes to equilibrium? The equilibrium constant K_c equals 10.5 at 500 K.

14.64 Sulfur trioxide, used to manufacture sulfuric acid, is obtained commercially from sulfur dioxide.

$$2SO_2(g) + O_2(g) \rightleftharpoons 2SO_3(g)$$

The equilibrium constant K_c for this reaction is 4.17×10^{-2} at 727°C. What is the direction of reaction when a mixture that is 0.20 M SO_2, 0.10 M O_2, and 0.40 M SO_3 approaches equilibrium?

14.65 Phosgene, $COCl_2$, used in the manufacture of polyurethane plastics, is prepared from CO and Cl_2.

$$CO(g) + Cl_2(g) \rightleftharpoons COCl_2(g)$$

An equilibrium mixture at 395°C contains 0.012 mol CO and 0.025 mol Cl_2 per liter, as well as $COCl_2$. If K_c at 395°C is 1.23×10^3, what is the concentration of $COCl_2$?

14.66 Nitrogen monoxide, NO, is formed in automobile exhaust by the reaction of N_2 and O_2 (from air).

$$N_2(g) + O_2(g) \rightleftharpoons 2NO(g)$$

The equilibrium constant K_c is 0.0025 at 2127°C. If an equilibrium mixture at this temperature contains 0.023 mol N_2 and 0.031 mol O_2 per liter, what is the concentration of NO?

14.67 Iodine and bromine react to give iodine monobromide, IBr.

$$I_2(g) + Br_2(g) \rightleftharpoons 2IBr(g)$$

What is the equilibrium composition of a mixture at 150°C that initially contained 0.0015 mol each of iodine and bromine in a 5.0-L vessel? The equilibrium constant K_c for this reaction at 150°C is 1.2×10^2.

14.68 Initially a mixture contains 0.795 mol each of N_2 and O_2 in an 8.00-L vessel. Find the composition of the mixture when equilibrium is reached at 3900°C. The reaction is

$$N_2(g) + O_2(g) \rightleftharpoons 2NO(g)$$

and $K_c = 0.0123$ at 3900°C.

14.69 Calculate the composition of the gaseous mixture obtained when 1.25 mol of carbon dioxide is exposed to hot carbon at 800°C in a 1.25-L vessel. The equilibrium constant K_c at 800°C is 14.0 for the reaction

$$CO_2(g) + C(s) \rightleftharpoons 2CO(g)$$

14.70 The equilibrium constant K_c for the reaction

$$PCl_3(g) + Cl_2(g) \rightleftharpoons PCl_5(g)$$

equals 49 at 230°C. If 0.400 mol each of phosphorus trichloride and chlorine are added to a 4.0-L reaction vessel, what is the equilibrium composition of the mixture at 230°C?

14.71 Suppose 1.000 mol CO and 3.000 mol H_2 are put in a 10.00-L vessel at 1200 K. The equilibrium constant K_c for

$$CO(g) + 3H_2(g) \rightleftharpoons CH_4(g) + H_2O(g)$$

equals 3.92. Find the equilibrium composition of the reaction mixture.

14.72 The equilibrium constant K_c for the reaction

$$N_2(g) + 3H_2(g) \rightleftharpoons 2NH_3(g)$$

at 450°C is 0.159. Calculate the equilibrium composition when 1.00 mol N_2 is mixed with 3.00 mol H_2 in a 5.00-L vessel.

Le Châtelier's Principle

14.73 Consider the equilibrium

$$FeO(s) + CO(g) \rightleftharpoons Fe(s) + CO_2(g)$$

When carbon dioxide is removed from the equilibrium mixture (say, by passing the gases through water to absorb CO_2), what is the direction of net reaction as the new equilibrium is achieved?

14.74 (a) Predict the direction of reaction when chlorine gas is added to an equilibrium mixture of $COCl_2$, CO, and Cl_2. The reaction is

$$COCl_2(g) \rightleftharpoons CO(g) + Cl_2(g)$$

(b) What is the direction of reaction when chlorine gas is removed from an equilibrium mixture of these gases?

14.75 What would you expect to be the effect of an increase of pressure on each of the following reactions? Would the pressure change cause the reaction to go to the right or left?
 a. $CH_4(g) + 2S_2(g) \rightleftharpoons CS_2(g) + 2H_2S(g)$
 b. $H_2(g) + Br_2(g) \rightleftharpoons 2HBr(g)$
 c. $CO_2(g) + C(s) \rightleftharpoons 2CO(g)$

14.76 Indicate whether either an increase or a decrease of pressure obtained by changing the volume would increase the amount of product in each of the following reactions.
 a. $CO(g) + 2H_2(g) \rightleftharpoons CH_3OH(g)$
 b. $2SO_2(g) + O_2(g) \rightleftharpoons 2SO_3(g)$
 c. $COCl_2(g) \rightleftharpoons CO(g) + Cl_2(g)$

14.77 Methanol is prepared industrially from synthesis gas (CO and H_2).

$$CO(g) + 2H_2(g) \rightleftharpoons CH_3OH(g); \Delta H° = -21.7 \text{ kcal}$$

Would the fraction of methanol obtained at equilibrium be increased by raising the temperature? Explain.

14.78 One way of preparing hydrogen is by the decomposition of water.

$$2H_2O(g) \rightleftharpoons 2H_2(g) + O_2(g); \Delta H° = 484 \text{ kJ}$$

Would you expect the decomposition to be favorable at high or low temperature? Explain.

14.79 Use thermochemical data (Appendix C) to decide whether the equilibrium constant for the following reaction will increase or decrease with temperature.

$$2NO_2(g) + 7H_2(g) \rightleftharpoons 2NH_3(g) + 4H_2O(g)$$

14.80 Use thermochemical data (Appendix C) to decide whether the equilibrium constant for the following reaction will increase or decrease with temperature.

$$CH_4(g) + 2H_2S(g) \rightleftharpoons CS_2(g) + 4H_2(g)$$

14.81 What would you expect to be the general temperature and pressure conditions for an optimum yield of nitrogen monoxide, NO, by the oxidation of ammonia?

$$4NH_3(g) + 5O_2(g) \rightleftharpoons 4NO(g) + 6H_2O(g); \Delta H° < 0$$

14.82 Predict the general temperature and pressure conditions for the optimum conversion of ethylene (C_2H_4) to ethane (C_2H_6).

$$C_2H_4(g) + H_2(g) \rightleftharpoons C_2H_6(g); \Delta H° < 0$$

General Problems

14.83 A mixture of carbon monoxide, hydrogen, and methanol, CH_3OH, is at equilibrium according to the equation

$$CO(g) + 2H_2(g) \rightleftharpoons CH_3OH(g)$$

At 250°C, the mixture is 0.096 M CO, 0.191 M H_2, and 0.015 M CH_3OH. What is K_c for this reaction at 250°C?

14.84 An equilibrium mixture of SO_3, SO_2, and O_2 at 727°C is 0.0160 M SO_3, 0.0056 M SO_2, and 0.0021 M O_2. What is the value of K_c for the following reaction?

$$SO_2(g) + \tfrac{1}{2}O_2(g) \rightleftharpoons SO_3(g)$$

14.85 At 850°C and 1.000 atm pressure, a gaseous mixture of carbon monoxide and carbon dioxide in equilibrium with solid carbon is 90.55% CO by mass.

$$C(s) + CO_2(g) \rightleftharpoons 2CO(g)$$

Calculate K_c for this reaction at 850°C.

14.86 An equilibrium mixture of dinitrogen tetroxide, N_2O_4, and nitrogen dioxide, NO_2, is 65.8% NO_2 by mass at 1.00 atm pressure and 25°C. Calculate K_c at 25°C for the reaction

$$N_2O_4(g) \rightleftharpoons 2NO_2(g)$$

14.87 A 2.00-L vessel contains 1.00 mol N_2, 1.00 mol H_2, and 2.00 mol NH_3. What is the direction of reaction (forward or reverse) needed to attain equilibrium at 400°C? The equilibrium constant K_c for the reaction

$$N_2(g) + 3H_2(g) \rightleftharpoons 2NH_3(g)$$

is 0.51 at 400°C.

14.88 A vessel originally contained 0.200 mol iodine monobromide (IBr), 0.0010 mol I_2, and 0.0010 mol Br_2. The equilibrium constant K_c for the reaction

$$I_2(g) + Br_2(g) \rightleftharpoons 2IBr(g)$$

is 1.2×10^2 at 150°C. What is the direction (forward or reverse) needed to attain equilibrium at 150°C?

14.89 A gaseous mixture containing 1.00 mol each of CO, H_2O, CO_2, and H_2 is exposed to a zinc oxide–copper oxide catalyst at 1000°C. The reaction is

$$CO(g) + H_2O(g) \rightleftharpoons CO_2(g) + H_2(g)$$

and the equilibrium constant K_c is 0.58 at 1000°C. What is the direction of reaction (forward or reverse) as the mixture attains equilibrium?

14.90 A 2.0-L reaction flask initially contains 0.10 mol CO, 0.20 mol H_2, and 0.50 mol CH_3OH (methanol). If this mixture is brought in contact with a zinc oxide–chromium(III) oxide catalyst, the equilibrium

$$CO(g) + 2H_2(g) \rightleftharpoons CH_3OH(g)$$

is attained. The equilibrium constant K_c for this reaction at 300°C is 1.1×10^{-2}. What is the direction of reaction (forward or reverse) as the mixture attains equilibrium?

14.91 Hydrogen bromide dissociates when heated according to the equation

$$2HBr(g) \rightleftharpoons H_2(g) + Br_2(g)$$

The equilibrium constant K_c equals 1.6×10^{-2} at 200°C. What are the moles of substances in the equilibrium mixture at 200°C if we start with 0.010 mol HBr in a 1.0-L vessel?

14.92 Iodine monobromide, IBr, occurs as brownish-black crystals that vaporize with decomposition:

$$2IBr(g) \rightleftharpoons I_2(g) + Br_2(g)$$

The equilibrium constant K_c at 100°C is 0.026. If 0.010 mol IBr is placed in a 1.0-L vessel at 100°C, what are the moles of substances at equilibrium in the vapor?

14.93 Phosgene, $COCl_2$, is a toxic gas used in the manufacture of urethane plastics. The gas dissociates at high temperature.

$$COCl_2(g) \rightleftharpoons CO(g) + Cl_2(g)$$

At 400°C, the equilibrium constant K_c is 8.05×10^{-4}. Find the percentage of phosgene that dissociates at this temperature when 1.00 mol of phosgene is placed in a 25.0-L vessel.

14.94 Dinitrogen tetroxide, N_2O_4, is a colorless gas (boiling point, 21°C), which dissociates to give nitrogen dioxide, NO_2, a reddish brown gas.

$$N_2O_4(g) \rightleftharpoons 2NO_2(g)$$

The equilibrium constant K_c at 25°C is 0.125. What percentage of dinitrogen tetroxide is dissociated when 0.0300 mol N_2O_4 is placed in a 1.00-L flask at 25°C?

14.95 Suppose you start with a mixture of 1.00 mol CO and 4.00 mol H_2 in a 10.00-L vessel. Find the moles of substances present at equilibrium at 1200 K for the reaction

$$CO(g) + 3H_2(g) \rightleftharpoons CH_4(g) + H_2O(g); K_c = 3.92$$

You will get an equation of the form

$$f(x) = 3.92$$

where $f(x)$ is an expression in the unknown x (the amount of CH_4). Solve this equation by guessing values of x, then computing values of $f(x)$. Find values of x such that the values of $f(x)$ bracket 3.92. Then choose values of x to get a smaller bracket around 3.92. Obtain x to two significant figures.

14.96 What are the moles of substances present at equilibrium at 450°C if 1.00 mol N_2 and 4.00 mol H_2 in a 10.0-L vessel react according to the following equation?

$$N_2(g) + 3H_2(g) \rightleftharpoons 2NH_3(g)$$

The equilibrium constant K_c is 0.153 at 450°C. Use the numerical procedure described in Problem 14.95.

14.97 The amount of nitrogen dioxide formed by dissociation of dinitrogen tetroxide,

$$N_2O_4(g) \rightleftharpoons 2NO_2(g)$$

increases as the temperature rises. Is the dissociation of N_2O_4 endothermic or exothermic?

14.98 The equilibrium constant K_c for the synthesis of methanol, CH_3OH,

$$CO(g) + 2H_2(g) \rightleftharpoons CH_3OH(g)$$

is 4.3 at 250°C and 1.8 at 275°C. Is this reaction endothermic or exothermic?

14.99 For the reaction

$$N_2(g) + 3H_2(g) \rightleftharpoons 2NH_3(g)$$

show that $K_c = K_p(RT)^2$

Do not use the formula $K_p = K_c(RT)^{\Delta n}$ given in the text. Start from the fact that $P_i = [i]RT$, where P_i is the partial pressure of substance i and $[i]$ is its molar concentration. Substitute into K_c.

14.100 For the reaction

$$COCl_2(g) \rightleftharpoons CO(g) + Cl_2(g)$$

show that $K_c = K_p/(RT)$

Do not use the formula $K_p = K_c(RT)^{\Delta n}$ given in the text. See Problem 14.99.

14.101 At high temperatures, a dynamic equilibrium exists between carbon monoxide, carbon dioxide, and solid carbon.

$$C(s) + CO_2(g) \rightleftharpoons 2CO(g); \Delta H° = 172.5 \text{ kJ}$$

At 850°C, K_c is 0.153.
 a. What is the value of K_p?
 b. If the original reaction system consisted of just carbon and 1.50 atm of CO_2, what are the pressures of CO_2 and CO when equilibrium has been established?
 c. How will the equilibrium pressure of CO change if the temperature is decreased?

14.102 At high temperatures, a dynamic equilibrium exists between carbon monoxide, carbon dioxide, and solid carbon.

$$C(s) + CO_2(g) \rightleftharpoons 2CO(g); \Delta H° = 172.5 \text{ kJ}$$

At 900°C, K_c is 0.238.
 a. What is the value of K_p?
 b. Some carbon dioxide is added to the hot carbon and the system is brought to equilibrium at 900°C. If the total pressure in the system is 6.40 atm, what are the partial pressures of CO and CO_2?
 c. How will the equilibrium system respond if additional carbon at 900°C is added to the reaction system? Why?

14.103 The equilibrium constant K_c for the reaction

$$PCl_3(g) + Cl_2(g) \rightleftharpoons PCl_5(g)$$

equals 4.1 at 300°C.
 a. A sample of 35.8 g of PCl_5 is placed in a 5.0-L reaction vessel and heated to 300°C. What are the equilibrium concentrations of all of the species?
 b. What fraction of PCl_5 has decomposed?
 c. If 35.8 g of PCl_5 were placed in a 1.0-L vessel, what qualitative effect would this have on the fraction of PCl_5 that has decomposed (give a qualitative answer only; do not do the calculation)? Why?

14.104 At 25°C in a closed system, ammonium hydrogen sulfide exists as the following equilibrium:

$$NH_4HS(s) \rightleftharpoons NH_3(g) + H_2S(g)$$

 a. When a sample of pure $NH_4HS(s)$ is placed in an evacuated reaction vessel and allowed to come to equilibrium at 25°C, total pressure is 0.660 atm. What is the value of K_p?
 b. To this system, sufficient $H_2S(g)$ is injected until the pressure of H_2S is three times that of the ammonia at equilibrium. What are the partial pressures of NH_3 and H_2S?
 c. In a different experiment, 0.750 atm of NH_3 and 0.500 atm of H_2S are introduced into a 1.00-L vessel at 25°C. How many moles of NH_4HS are present when equilibrium is established?

14.105 At moderately high temperatures, $SbCl_5$ decomposes into $SbCl_3$ and Cl_2 as follows:

$$SbCl_5(g) \rightleftharpoons SbCl_3(g) + Cl_2(g)$$

A 65.4-g sample of $SbCl_5$ is placed in an evacuated 5.00-L vessel and it is raised to 195°C and the system comes to equilibrium. If at this temperature 35.8% of the $SbCl_5$ is decomposed, what is the value of K_p?

14.106 The following reaction is important in the manufacture of sulfuric acid.

$$SO_2(g) + \tfrac{1}{2}O_2(g) \rightleftharpoons SO_3(g)$$

At 900 K, 0.0216 mol of SO_2 and 0.0148 mol of O_2 are sealed in a 1.00-L reaction vessel. When equilibrium is reached, the concentration of SO_3 is determined to be 0.0175 M. Calculate K_c for this reaction.

14.107 Sulfuryl chloride is used in organic chemistry as a chlorinating agent. At moderately high temperatures it decomposes as follows:

$$SO_2Cl_2(g) \rightleftharpoons SO_2(g) + Cl_2(g)$$

with $K_c = 0.045$ at 650 K.
 a. A sample of 8.25 g of SO_2Cl_2 is placed in a 1.00-L reaction vessel and heated to 650 K. What are the equilibrium concentrations of all of the species?
 b. What fraction of SO_2Cl_2 has decomposed?
 c. If 5 g of chlorine is inserted into the reaction vessel, what qualitative effect would this have on the fraction of SO_2Cl_2 that has decomposed?

14.108 Phosgene was used as a poisonous gas in World War I. At high temperatures it decomposes as follows:

$$COCl_2(g) \rightleftharpoons CO(g) + Cl_2(g)$$

with $K_c = 4.6 \times 10^{-3}$ at 800 K.
 a. A sample of 6.55 g of $COCl_2$ is placed in a 1.00-L reaction vessel and heated to 800 K. What are the equilibrium concentrations of all of the species?
 b. What fraction of $COCl_2$ has decomposed?
 c. If 3 g of carbon monoxide is inserted into the reaction vessel, what qualitative effect would this have on the fraction of $COCl_2$ that has decomposed?

14.109 Gaseous acetic acid molecules have a certain tendency to form dimers. (A *dimer* is a molecule formed by the association of two identical, simpler molecules.) The equilibrium constant K_c at 25°C for this reaction is 3.2×10^4.
 a. If the initial concentration of CH_3COOH monomer (the simpler molecule) is 4.0×10^{-4} M, what are the concentrations of monomer and dimer when the system comes to equilibrium? (The simpler quadratic equation is obtained by assuming that all of the acid molecules have dimerized and then some of it dissociates to monomer.)
 b. Why do acetic acid molecules dimerize? What type of structure would you draw for the dimer?
 c. As the temperature increases, would you expect the percentage of dimer to increase or decrease? Why?

14.110 Gaseous acetic acid molecules have a certain tendency to form dimers. (A *dimer* is a molecule formed by the association of two identical, simpler molecules.) The equilibrium constant K_p at 25°C for this reaction is 1.3×10^3.
 a. If the initial pressure of CH_3COOH monomer (the simpler molecule) is 7.5×10^{-3} atm, what are the pressures of monomer and dimer when the system comes to equilibrium? (The simpler quadratic equation is obtained by assuming that all of the acid molecules have dimerized and then some of it dissociates to monomer.)

b. Why do acetic acid molecules dimerize? What type of structure would you draw for the dimer?

c. As the temperature decreases, would you expect the percentage of dimer to increase or decrease? Why?

14.111 When 0.112 mol of NO and 18.22 g of bromine are placed in a 1.00-L reaction vessel and sealed, the mixture is heated to 350 K and the following equilibrium is established:

$$2NO(g) + Br_2(g) \rightleftharpoons 2NOBr(g)$$

If the equilibrium concentration of nitrosyl bromide is 0.0824 M, what is K_c?

Strategy Problems

14.115 A chemist placed a mixture of $CO_2(g)$ and $CF_4(g)$ into a flask at a particular temperature. These gases react:

$$CO_2(g) + CF_4(g) \rightleftharpoons 2COF_2(g)$$

After this mixture came to equilibrium, she found that it contained 0.40 mole fraction of CF_4 and 0.20 mole fraction of COF_2. Calculate K_p at this temperature for this reaction.

14.116 You mix equal moles of N_2, O_2, and NO and place them into a container fitted with a movable piston. Then you heat the mixture to 2127°C, compressing the mixture with the piston to 10.0 atm, where the following reaction may occur:

$$N_2(g) + O_2(g) \rightleftharpoons 2NO(g)$$

K_p for this reaction at 2127°C is 0.0025. Is the mixture of gases initially at equilibrium at this temperature and pressure, or does it undergo reaction to the left or to the right? Do you have enough information to answer this question? Explain your answer.

14.117 Consider the mixture described in the previous problem, but suppose it is heated to 3900°C and compressed to 15.0 atm. K_p at this temperature is 0.0123. What is the equilibrium composition of the mixture? Would it be best to describe this composition in moles or in mole fractions?

14.118 The equilibrium constant K_c for the equation

$$2HI(g) \rightleftharpoons H_2(g) + I_2(g)$$

is 1.84 at 425°C. The equilibrium constant K_c for the equation

$$H_2(g) + I_2(g) \rightleftharpoons 2HI(g)$$

is 49.7 at 458°C. Is this second equation endothermic or exothermic? How do you know? Describe the effect on this second equation of an increase in temperature. What would be the effect of an increase in pressure?

14.119 Consider the reaction $N_2O_4(g) \rightleftharpoons 2NO_2(g)$. Would you expect this reaction to be endothermic or exothermic? Why? N_2O_4 is a colorless gas; NO_2 is red-brown. Would you expect a mixture of these gases to become more or less red-brown as you raise the temperature? Explain.

14.120 A researcher put 0.400 mol PCl_3 and 0.600 mol Cl_2 into a 5.00-L vessel at a given temperature to produce phosphorus pentachloride, PCl_5:

$$PCl_3(g) + Cl_2(g) \rightleftharpoons PCl_5(g)$$

What will be the composition of this gaseous mixture at equilibrium? $K_c = 25.6$ at the temperature of this experiment.

14.112 When 0.0322 mol of NO and 1.52 g of bromine are placed in a 1.00-L reaction vessel and sealed, the mixture reacts and the following equilibrium is established:

$$2NO(g) + Br_2(g) \rightleftharpoons 2NOBr(g)$$

At 25°C the equilibrium pressure of nitrosyl bromide is 0.438 atm. What is K_p?

14.113 Oscillating reactions were first reported in 1958. How is it possible for a reaction to oscillate from one color to another?

14.114 In what way are slime molds and leopards' spots related?

14.121 Ammonium hydrogen sulfide, NH_4HS, is unstable at room temperature and decomposes:

$$NH_4HS(s) \rightleftharpoons NH_3(g) + H_2S(g)$$

You have placed some solid ammonium hydrogen sulfide in a closed flask. Which of the following would produce less hydrogen sulfide, H_2S, which is a poisonous gas?

a. Removing some NH_3 from the flask
b. Adding some NH_3 to the flask
c. Removing some of the NH_4HS
d. Increasing the pressure in the flask by adding helium gas
Explain each of your answers.

14.122 A chemist wants to prepare phosgene, $COCl_2$, by the following reaction:

$$CO(g) + Cl_2(g) \rightleftharpoons COCl_2(g)$$

He places 4.00 g of chlorine, Cl_2, and an equal molar amount of carbon monoxide, CO, into a 10.00-L reaction vessel at 395°C. After the reaction comes to equilibrium, he adds another 4.00 g of chlorine to the vessel in order to push the reaction to the right to get more product. What is the partial pressure of phosgene when the reaction again comes to equilibrium? $K_c = 1.23 \times 10^3$.

14.123 Iodine, I_2, is a blue-black solid, but it easily vaporizes to give a violet vapor. At high temperatures, this molecular substance dissociates to atoms:

$$I_2(g) \rightleftharpoons 2I(g)$$

An absent-minded professor measured equilibrium constants for this dissociation at two temperatures, 700°C and 800°C. He obtained the K_p values 0.01106 and 0.001745, but he couldn't remember which value went with what temperature. Can you please help him assign temperatures to the equilibrium constants? State your argument carefully.

14.124 Nitrogen dioxide, NO_2, is a red-brown gas that reacts with itself to produce N_2O_4, a colorless gas:

$$2NO_2(g) \rightleftharpoons N_2O_4(g)$$

A flask of "nitrogen dioxide" gas is actually a mixture of NO_2 and N_2O_4. It is possible to obtain the equilibrium constant K_p for this reaction from the density of an equilibrium mixture at a given temperature and total pressure. To see how to do that, answer the following questions. (You might find it helpful to refer to the derivation of the equation relating molar mass and density at the end of Section 5.3, on ideal gases.)

a. Use the ideal gas law to obtain an equation at a given T and P for the mass of a gas, m, in terms of its molar mass, M_m.

b. Suppose you have a mixture of two gases, A and B. Write an equation for the mass of gas A (m_A) in terms of the molar mass of A, M_{mA}, and its partial pressure P_A. Write a similar equation for B. Now write an equation for the total mass of gas, $m = m_A + m_B$. Finally, obtain an equation for the density of the gas mixture, d, in terms of the partial pressures and molar masses of the components A and B.

c. Let A be NO_2 and B be N_2O_4. Express the equation you just obtained for the density, d, in terms of the molar mass, M_{mA}, eliminating M_{mB}. Also, eliminate P_B by expressing it in terms of P_A and P (total pressure). Now solve this to obtain an equation for P_A.

d. In an experiment, a chemist discovered that the density of nitrogen dioxide in equilibrium with dinitrogen tetroxide at 1.00 atm and 35.0°C is 2.86 g/L. What is the equilibrium constant K_p for the reaction as written at the beginning of this problem?

Cumulative-Skills Problems

14.125   The following equilibrium was studied by analyzing the equilibrium mixture for the amount of H_2S produced.

$$Sb_2S_3(s) + 3H_2(g) \rightleftharpoons 2Sb(s) + 3H_2S(g)$$

A vessel whose volume was 2.50 L was filled with 0.0100 mol of antimony(III) sulfide, Sb_2S_3, and 0.0100 mol H_2. After the mixture came to equilibrium in the closed vessel at 440°C, the gaseous mixture was removed, and the hydrogen sulfide was dissolved in water. Sufficient lead(II) ion was added to react completely with the H_2S to precipitate lead(II) sulfide, PbS. If 1.029 g PbS was obtained, what is the value of K_c at 440°C?

14.126   The following equilibrium was studied by analyzing the equilibrium mixture for the amount of HCl produced.

$$LaCl_3(s) + H_2O(g) \rightleftharpoons LaOCl(s) + 2HCl(g)$$

A vessel whose volume was 1.25 L was filled with 0.0125 mol of lanthanum(III) chloride, $LaCl_3$, and 0.0250 mol H_2O. After the mixture came to equilibrium in the closed vessel at 619°C, the gaseous mixture was removed and dissolved in more water.

Sufficient silver(I) ion was added to precipitate the chloride ion completely as silver chloride. If 3.59 g AgCl was obtained, what is the value of K_c at 619°C?

14.127   Phosphorus(V) chloride, PCl_5, dissociates on heating to give phosphorus(III) chloride, PCl_3, and chlorine.

$$PCl_5(g) \rightleftharpoons PCl_3(g) + Cl_2(g)$$

A closed 2.00-L vessel initially contains 0.0100 mol PCl_5. What is the total pressure at 250°C when equilibrium is achieved? The value of K_c at 250°C is 4.15×10^{-2}.

14.128   Antimony(V) chloride, $SbCl_5$, dissociates on heating to give antimony(III) chloride, $SbCl_3$, and chlorine.

$$SbCl_5(g) \rightleftharpoons SbCl_3(g) + Cl_2(g)$$

A closed 3.50-L vessel initially contains 0.0125 mol $SbCl_5$. What is the total pressure at 248°C when equilibrium is achieved? The value of K_c at 248°C is 2.50×10^{-2}.

15
Acids and Bases

Red cabbage juice is green in basic solution (left beaker) but turns red when dry ice, solid CO_2, is added (center) to give an acidic solution (right). The colors of red cabbage and many fruits, such as blueberries, result from compounds called *anthocyanins* (see model of the one present in red cabbage), which are important in human nutrition.

Contents and Concepts

Svante Arrhenius was the first to explain that acids were substances that produce hydrogen ion, $H^+(aq)$ when dissolved in water. Later, Johannes Brønsted and Thomas Lowry explained that acid–base reactions are proton-transfer reactions. We look at these ideas in the first sections of this chapter.

From the Brønsted–Lowry view, it is useful to think of acid–base reactions as a competition between different species for protons. Then you can order acids (and bases) by their relative strengths. This idea is expanded on in the next two sections.

The dominant ions in water solution are the hydronium ion H_3O^+ (also described as the hydrogen ion H^+) and the hydroxide ion OH^-, which result from the dissociation or self-ionization of water. This self-ionization is characterized in terms of the concept of pH. The self-ionization of water and the concept of pH are discussed in the next sections.

A cids and bases were first recognized by simple properties, such as taste. Acids have a sour taste; bases are bitter. Also, acids and bases change the color of certain dyes called indicators, such as litmus and phenolphthalein. Acids change litmus from blue to red and basic phenolphthalein from red to colorless. Bases change litmus from red to blue and phenolphthalein from colorless to pink. As you can see from these color changes, acids and bases neutralize, or reverse, the action of one another. During neutralization, acids and bases react with each other to produce ionic substances called salts. Acids react with active metals, such as magnesium and zinc, to release hydrogen.

FIGURE 15.1 ▲

Reaction of $HCl(g)$ and $NH_3(g)$ to form $NH_4Cl(s)$
Gases from the concentrated solutions diffuse from their watch glasses (shallow dishes) and react to give a smoke of ammonium chloride.

The Swedish chemist Svante Arrhenius framed the first successful concept of acids and bases. He defined acids and bases in terms of the effect these substances have on water. According to Arrhenius, acids are substances that increase the concentration of H^+ ion in aqueous solution, and bases increase the concentration of OH^- ion in aqueous solution. But many reactions that have characteristics of acid–base reactions in aqueous solution occur in other solvents or without a solvent. For example, hydrochloric acid reacts with aqueous ammonia, which in the Arrhenius view is a base because it increases the concentration of OH^- ion in aqueous solution. The reaction can be written

$$HCl(aq) + NH_3(aq) \longrightarrow NH_4Cl(aq)$$

The product is a solution of NH_4Cl—that is, a solution of NH_4^+ and Cl^- ions. A very similar reaction occurs between hydrogen chloride and ammonia dissolved in benzene, C_6H_6. The product is again NH_4Cl, which in this case precipitates from the solution.

$$HCl(benzene) + NH_3(benzene) \longrightarrow NH_4Cl(s)$$

Hydrogen chloride and ammonia react even in the gas phase. If watch glasses (shallow glass dishes) of concentrated hydrochloric acid and concentrated ammonia are placed next to each other, dense, white fumes of NH_4Cl form where HCl gas and NH_3 gas come into contact (Figure 15.1).

$$HCl(g) + NH_3(g) \longrightarrow NH_4Cl(s)$$

These reactions of HCl and NH_3, in benzene and in the gas phase, are similar to the reaction in aqueous solution but cannot be explained by the Arrhenius concept. Broader acid–base concepts are needed.

In the first part of this chapter, we will discuss the Arrhenius, the Brønsted–Lowry, and the Lewis concepts of acids and bases. The Brønsted–Lowry and Lewis concepts apply to nonaqueous as well as aqueous solutions and also enlarge on the Arrhenius concept in other ways. This chapter expands on what you learned in Chapter 4 about acids and bases.

■ See page 644 for the Media Summary.

Acid–Base Concepts

Antoine Lavoisier was one of the first chemists to try to explain what makes a substance acidic. In 1777 he proposed that oxygen was an essential element in acids. (*Oxygen,* which he named, means "acid-former" in Greek.) But in 1808 Humphry Davy showed that hydrogen chloride, which dissolves in water to give hydrochloric acid, contains only hydrogen and chlorine. Although some chemists argued that chlorine was a compound of oxygen, chlorine was eventually proved to be an element. Chemists then noted that hydrogen, not oxygen, must be the essential constituent of acids. The cause of acidity and basicity was first explained in 1884 by Svante Arrhenius.

15.1 | Arrhenius Concept of Acids and Bases

We can state the Arrhenius concept of an acid as follows: *An acid is a substance that, when dissolved in water, increases the concentration of hydronium ion, $H_3O^+(aq)$.* For simplicity, chemists frequently use the notation $H^+(aq)$ for the $H_3O^+(aq)$ ion and call it the hydrogen ion. Remember, however, that the aqueous hydrogen ion is not a bare proton in water, but a proton chemically bonded to water—that is, $H_3O^+(aq)$. The $H_3O^+(aq)$ ion is itself associated through hydrogen bonding with a variable number of water molecules. One such species is shown in Figure 15.2. *A base, in the Arrhenius concept, is a substance that, when dissolved in water, increases the concentration of hydroxide ion, $OH^-(aq)$.* <

The special role of the hydronium ion (or hydrogen ion) and the hydroxide ion in aqueous solutions arises from the following reaction:

$$H_2O(l) + H_2O(l) \rightleftharpoons H_3O^+(aq) + OH^-(aq)$$

The addition of acids and bases alters the concentrations of these ions in water.

In Arrhenius's theory, a *strong acid* is a substance that completely ionizes in aqueous solution to give $H_3O^+(aq)$ and an anion. An example is perchloric acid, $HClO_4$.

$$HClO_4(aq) + H_2O(l) \longrightarrow H_3O^+(aq) + ClO_4^-(aq)$$

Other examples of strong acids are H_2SO_4, HI, HBr, HCl, and HNO_3. A *strong base* completely ionizes in aqueous solution to give OH^- and a cation. Sodium hydroxide is an example of a strong base.

$$NaOH(s) \xrightarrow{H_2O} Na^+(aq) + OH^-(aq)$$

The principal strong bases are the hydroxides of Group IA elements and Group IIA elements (except Be). See Table 15.1. <

Most of the other acids and bases you encounter are *weak*. They are not completely ionized in solution and exist in reversible reaction with the corresponding ions. Consider acetic acid, $HC_2H_3O_2$. The reaction is

$$HC_2H_3O_2(aq) + H_2O(l) \rightleftharpoons H_3O^+(aq) + C_2H_3O_2^-(aq)$$

Evidence for the Arrhenius theory comes from the heat of reaction, $\Delta H°$, for the neutralization of a strong acid by a strong base. This neutralization is essentially the reaction of $H_3O^+(aq)$ with $OH^-(aq)$ and should therefore always give the same $\Delta H°$ per mole of water formed. For example, if you write the neutralization of $HClO_4$ with NaOH in ionic form, you have

$$H_3O^+(aq) + \cancel{ClO_4^-(aq)} + \cancel{Na^+(aq)} + OH^-(aq) \longrightarrow \cancel{Na^+(aq)} + \cancel{ClO_4^-(aq)} + 2H_2O(l)$$

After canceling, you get the net ionic equation

$$H_3O^+(aq) + OH^-(aq) \longrightarrow 2H_2O(l)$$

Experimentally, it is found that all neutralizations involving strong acids and bases have the same $\Delta H°$: -55.90 kJ per mole of H^+. This indicates that the same reaction occurs in each neutralization, as Arrhenius's theory predicts.

Despite its successes, the Arrhenius concept is limited. In addition to looking at acid–base reactions only in aqueous solutions, it singles out the OH^- ion as the source of base character, when other species can play a similar role. Broader definitions of acids and bases are described in the next sections.

15.2 | Brønsted–Lowry Concept of Acids and Bases

In 1923 the Danish chemist Johannes N. Brønsted (1879–1947) and, independently, the British chemist Thomas M. Lowry (1874–1936) pointed out that acid–base reactions can be seen as proton-transfer reactions and that acids and bases can be defined

---

This section summarizes the discussion in Section 4.4.

FIGURE 15.2 ▲

The hydronium ion, H_3O^+
The species is shown here hydrogen-bonded to three water molecules. The positive charge shown is actually distributed over the ion.

We introduced strong and weak acids and bases in Section 4.4.

TABLE 15.1

Common Strong Acids and Bases

Strong Acids	Strong Bases*
$HClO_4$	LiOH
H_2SO_4	NaOH
HI	KOH
HBr	$Ca(OH)_2$
HCl	$Sr(OH)_2$
HNO_3	$Ba(OH)_2$

*In general, the Group IA and Group IIA hydroxides (except beryllium hydroxide) are strong bases.

FIGURE 15.3 ▶

Representation of the reaction
$H_3O^+ + NH_3 \rightleftharpoons H_2O + NH_4^+$
Note the transfer of a proton, H^+, from H_3O^+ to NH_3. The charges indicated for ions are *overall* charges. They are not to be associated with specific locations on the ions.

H_3O^+ NH_3 H_2O NH_4^+

> *To be precise, we should say* hydrogen nucleus *instead of* proton *(because natural hydrogen contains some ^2H as well as ^1H). The term* proton *is conventional in this context, however.*

in terms of this proton (H^+) transfer. According to the Brønsted–Lowry concept, an **acid** is *the species donating a proton in a proton-transfer reaction.* A **base** is *the species accepting the proton in a proton-transfer reaction.* <

Consider, for example, the reaction of hydrochloric acid with ammonia, which was mentioned in the chapter opening. Writing it as an ionic equation, you have

$$H_3O^+(aq) + Cl^-(aq) + NH_3(aq) \longrightarrow H_2O(l) + NH_4^+(aq) + Cl^-(aq)$$

After canceling Cl^-, you obtain the net ionic equation.

$$H_3O^+(aq) + NH_3(aq) \longrightarrow H_2O(l) + NH_4^+(aq)$$

In this reaction in aqueous solution, a proton, H^+, is transferred from the H_3O^+ ion to the NH_3 molecule, giving H_2O and NH_4^+ (Figure 15.3). Here H_3O^+ is the proton donor, or acid, and NH_3 is the proton acceptor, or base. Note that in the Brønsted–Lowry concept, acids (and bases) can be ions as well as molecular substances.

You can also apply the Brønsted–Lowry concept to the reaction of HCl and NH_3 dissolved in benzene, C_6H_6, which was mentioned in the chapter opening. In benzene, HCl and NH_3 are not ionized. The equation is

$$HCl(benzene) + NH_3(benzene) \longrightarrow NH_4Cl(s)$$
       acid   base

Here the HCl molecule is the proton donor, or acid, and the NH_3 molecule is the proton acceptor, or base.

In any reversible acid–base reaction, both forward and reverse reactions involve proton transfers. Consider the reaction of NH_3 with H_2O.

$$NH_3(aq) + H_2O(l) \rightleftharpoons NH_4^+(aq) + OH^-(aq)$$
    base   acid   acid   base

In the forward reaction, NH_3 accepts a proton from H_2O. Thus, NH_3 is a base and H_2O is an acid. In the reverse reaction, NH_4^+ donates a proton to OH^-. NH_4^+ ion is the acid and OH^- is the base.

Note that NH_3 and NH_4^+ differ by a proton. That is, NH_3 becomes the NH_4^+ ion by gaining a proton, whereas the NH_4^+ ion becomes the NH_3 molecule by losing a proton. The species NH_4^+ and NH_3 are a conjugate acid–base pair. A **conjugate acid–base pair** consists of *two species in an acid–base reaction, one acid and one base, that differ by the loss or gain of a proton.* The acid in such a pair is called the *conjugate acid* of the base, whereas the base is the *conjugate base* of the acid. Here NH_4^+ is the conjugate acid of NH_3, and NH_3 is the conjugate base of NH_4^+.

Example 15.1 | Identifying Acid and Base Species

In the following equations, label each species as an acid or a base. Show the conjugate acid–base pairs.

a. $HCO_3^-(aq) + HF(aq) \rightleftharpoons H_2CO_3(aq) + F^-(aq)$

b. $HCO_3^-(aq) + OH^-(aq) \rightleftharpoons CO_3^{2-}(aq) + H_2O(l)$

(continued)

(*continued*)

Problem Strategy Recall that a Brønsted–Lowry acid is a proton donor, and the base is a proton acceptor. Examine each equation to find the proton donor on each side. Then label the acids and bases.

Solution a. On the left, HF is the proton donor; on the right, H_2CO_3 is the proton donor. The proton acceptors are HCO_3^- and F^-. Once the proton donors and acceptors are identified, the acids and bases can be labeled.

$$HCO_3^-(aq) + HF(aq) \rightleftharpoons H_2CO_3(aq) + F^-(aq)$$
$$\text{base} \qquad \text{acid} \qquad\qquad \text{acid} \qquad \text{base}$$

In this reaction, H_2CO_3 and HCO_3^- are a conjugate acid–base pair, as are HF and F^-.

b. You have

$$HCO_3^-(aq) + OH^-(aq) \rightleftharpoons CO_3^{2-}(aq) + H_2O(l)$$
$$\text{acid} \qquad\quad \text{base} \qquad\qquad \text{base} \qquad \text{acid}$$

Here HCO_3^- and CO_3^{2-} are a conjugate acid–base pair, as are H_2O and OH^-. Note that although HCO_3^- functions as an acid in this reaction, it functions as a base in part a.

Answer Check Check that each conjugate acid–base pair consists of one species from the left side of the equation and one species from the right side, and that the two species differ by only a proton.

Exercise 15.1 For the reaction

$$H_2CO_3(aq) + CN^-(aq) \rightleftharpoons HCN(aq) + HCO_3^-(aq)$$

label each species as an acid or a base. For the base on the left, what is the conjugate acid?

■ See Problems 15.35 and 15.36.

The Brønsted–Lowry concept defines a species as an acid or a base according to its function in the acid–base, or proton-transfer, reaction. As you saw in Example 15.1, some species can act as either an acid or a base. An **amphiprotic species** is *a species that can act as either an acid or a base (it can lose or gain a proton)*, depending on the other reactant. < For example, HCO_3^- acts as an acid in the presence of OH^- but as a base in the presence of HF. Anions with ionizable hydrogens, such as HCO_3^-, and certain solvents, such as water, are amphiprotic.

Amphoteric is a general term referring to a species that can act as an acid or a base. The species need not be amphiprotic, however. For example, aluminum oxide is an amphoteric oxide, because it reacts with acids and bases. It is not amphiprotic, because it has no protons.

The amphiprotic characteristic of water is important in the acid–base properties of aqueous solutions. Consider, for example, the reactions of water with the base NH_3 and with the acid $HC_2H_3O_2$ (acetic acid).

$$NH_3(aq) + H_2O(l) \rightleftharpoons NH_4^+(aq) + OH^-(aq)$$
$$\text{base} \qquad \text{acid} \qquad\qquad \text{acid} \qquad \text{base}$$

$$HC_2H_3O_2(aq) + H_2O(aq) \rightleftharpoons C_2H_3O_2^-(aq) + H_3O^+(aq)$$
$$\text{acid} \qquad\qquad \text{base} \qquad\qquad \text{base} \qquad \text{acid}$$

In the first case, water reacts as an acid with the base NH_3. In the second case, water reacts as a base with the acid $HC_2H_3O_2$.

You have now seen several ways in which the Brønsted–Lowry concept of acids and bases has greater scope than the Arrhenius concept. In the Brønsted–Lowry concept:

1. A base is a species that accepts protons; OH^- is only one example of a base.

2. Acids and bases can be ions as well as molecular substances.

3. Acid–base reactions are not restricted to aqueous solution.

4. Some species can act as either acids or bases, depending on what the other reactant is.

Concept Check 15.1

Chemists in the seventeenth century discovered that the substance that gives red ants their irritating bite is an acid with the formula $HCHO_2$. They called this substance formic acid after the ant, whose Latin name is *formica rufus*. Formic acid has the following structural formula and molecular model:

Write the acid–base equilibria connecting all components in the aqueous solution. Now list all of the species present.

Acidic and basic oxides were discussed in Section 8.7.

15.3 | Lewis Concept of Acids and Bases

Certain reactions have the characteristics of acid–base reactions but do not fit the Brønsted–Lowry concept. An example is the reaction of the basic oxide Na_2O with the acidic oxide SO_3 to give the salt Na_2SO_4. <

$$Na_2O(s) + SO_3(g) \longrightarrow Na_2SO_4(s)$$

G. N. Lewis, who proposed the electron-pair theory of covalent bonding, realized that the concept of acids and bases could be generalized to include reactions of acidic and basic oxides and many other reactions, as well as proton-transfer reactions. According to this concept, a **Lewis acid** is *a species that can form a covalent bond by accepting an electron pair from another species;* a **Lewis base** is *a species that can form a covalent bond by donating an electron pair to another species.* The Lewis and the Brønsted–Lowry concepts are simply different ways of looking at certain chemical reactions. Such different views are often helpful in devising new reactions.

Consider again the neutralization of NH_3 by HCl in aqueous solution, mentioned earlier. It consists of the reaction of a proton from H_3O^+ with NH_3:

$$H^+ \quad + \quad :N:H \quad \longrightarrow \quad \left[H:N:H \right]^+$$

electron-pair   electron-pair
acceptor   donor

Here the red arrow shows the proton accepting an electron pair from NH_3 and an H—N bond being formed. The proton is an electron-pair acceptor, so it is a Lewis acid. Ammonia, NH_3, which has a lone pair of electrons, is an electron-pair donor and therefore a Lewis base.

Now let us look at the reaction of Na_2O with SO_3. It involves the reaction of the oxide ion, O^{2-}, from the ionic solid, Na_2O, with SO_3.

$$:O:^{2-} \quad + \quad S::O \quad \longrightarrow \quad \left[:O:S:O: \right]^{2-}$$

Lewis   Lewis
base   acid

Here SO_3 accepts the electron pair from the O^{2-} ion. At the same time, an electron pair from the $S{=}O$ bond moves to the O atom. Thus, O^{2-} is the Lewis base and SO_3 is the Lewis acid.

The Lewis concept embraces many reactions that we might not think of as acid–base reactions. The reaction of boron trifluoride with ammonia is an example.

$$\text{(Lewis acid)} \quad \text{(Lewis base)}$$

In this reaction, the NH_3 molecule donates the lone pair of electrons on the nitrogen atom to the boron atom of BF_3. Boron trifluoride accepts the electron pair and so is a Lewis acid. Ammonia donates the electron pair and so is a Lewis base. The electron pair originally on the nitrogen atom is now shared between the nitrogen and boron atoms, forming a B–N bond.

The formation of *complex ions* can also be looked at as Lewis acid–base reactions. Complex ions are formed when a metal ion bonds to electron pairs from molecules such as H_2O or NH_3 or from anions such as $:C{\equiv}N{:}^-$. An example of a complex ion is $Al(H_2O)_6^{3+}$. Hydrated ions like $Al(H_2O)_6^{3+}$ are present in compounds (hydrates) and in aqueous solution. The formation of a hydrated metal ion, such as $Al(H_2O)_6^{3+}$, involves a Lewis acid–base reaction.

$$Al^{3+} + 6(:\overset{..}{O}{-}H) \longrightarrow Al(:\overset{..}{O}{-}H)_6^{3+}$$

$$\quad\quad\quad\quad\quad\; \underset{\text{Lewis acid}}{\;} \;\; \underset{\text{Lewis base}}{\;}$$

$Al(OH_2)_6{}^{3+}$

Example 15.2 | Identifying Lewis Acid and Base Species

In the following reactions, identify the Lewis acid and the Lewis base.

a. $Ag^+ + 2NH_3 \rightleftharpoons Ag(NH_3)_2{}^+$

b. $B(OH)_3 + H_2O \rightleftharpoons B(OH)_4{}^- + H^+$

Problem Strategy Write the equations using Lewis electron-dot formulas. Then identify the electron-pair acceptor, or Lewis acid, and the electron-pair donor, or Lewis base.

Solution a. The silver ion, Ag^+, forms a complex ion with two NH_3 molecules.

$$Ag^+ + 2:NH_3 \rightleftharpoons Ag(:NH_3)_2{}^+$$

$$\underset{\text{Lewis acid}}{\;}\quad \underset{\text{Lewis base}}{\;}$$

b. The reaction is

$$\text{(Lewis acid)} \quad \text{(Lewis base)}$$

Answer Check Check the electron-dot formulas of the species in each acid–base reaction. The Lewis base donates an electron pair to the Lewis acid, which accepts that pair.

(*continued*)

A Chemist Looks at . . .

life science

Taking Your Medicine

The expressions "take your medicine" and "a bitter pill to swallow" are metaphors that refer to doing whatever is necessary to solve a difficult personal problem. Taking medicine might be unpleasant if the medicine is bitter—and medicines frequently taste bitter. Why?

A bitter taste appears to be a common feature of a base. It is a fact that many medicinal substances are nitrogen bases, substances that organic chemists call *amines*. Such substances are considered derivatives of ammonia, in which one or more hydrogen atoms have been substituted by carbon-containing groups. Here, for example, are the structures of some amines:

$$H-\underset{..}{\overset{\overset{\displaystyle CH_3}{|}}{N}}-H \qquad H_3C-\underset{..}{\overset{\overset{\displaystyle CH_3}{|}}{N}}-H \qquad H_3C-\underset{..}{\overset{\overset{\displaystyle CH_3}{|}}{N}}-CH_3$$

The nitrogen atom in an amine has a lone pair of electrons that can be donated to form a covalent bond, so an amine is a Lewis base. But like ammonia, an amine accepts a hydrogen ion from an acid to form an amine ion, so it is also a Brønsted–Lowry base:

$$H-\underset{..}{\overset{\overset{\displaystyle CH_3}{|}}{N}}-H + H_3O^+ \rightleftharpoons \left[H-\underset{\overset{\displaystyle |}{H}}{\overset{\overset{\displaystyle CH_3}{|}}{N}}-H\right]^+ + H_2O$$

Some of our most important medicinal drugs have originated from plants. Lewis and Clark took Peruvian bark, or cinchona bark, with them as a medicine on their 1804 expedition from the eastern United States to the Pacific Coast and back. The bitter essence of cinchona bark is quinine, an amine drug that has been used to combat malaria. Quinine is responsible for the bitter taste of tonic water, a carbonated beverage (Figure 15.4). Some other amines that come from plants are caffeine (from coffee, a stimulant), atropine (from the deadly nightshade, used to dilate the pupil of the eye for eye exams), and codeine (from the opium poppy, used as a painkiller).

FIGURE 15.4 ▶

Tonic water
Left: This carbonated beverage contains quinine, which accounts for its bitter taste.
Right: Structural formula of quinine.

Quinine (antimalarial)

■ See Problems 15.109 and 15.110.

(continued)

Exercise 15.2   Identify the Lewis acid and the Lewis base in each of the following reactions. Write the chemical equations using electron-dot formulas.

a. $BF_3 + CH_3OH \longrightarrow F_3B\!:\!\underset{..}{\overset{\overset{\displaystyle H}{|}}{O}}CH_3$

b. $O^{2-} + CO_2 \longrightarrow CO_3^{2-}$

■ See Problems 15.39, 15.40, 15.41, and 15.42.

Acid and Base Strengths

The Brønsted–Lowry concept considers an acid–base reaction as a proton-transfer reaction. It is useful to consider such acid–base reactions as a competition between species for protons. From this point of view, you can order acids by their relative strengths as proton donors. The stronger acids are those that lose their protons more easily than other acids. Similarly, the stronger bases are those that hold on to protons more strongly than other bases.

15.4 | Relative Strengths of Acids and Bases

By comparing various acid–base reactions, you can construct a table of relative strengths of acids and bases (see Table 15.2). To see how you might do this, look again at what we have called a strong acid. Recall that an acid is strong if it completely ionizes in water. In the reaction of hydrogen chloride with water, for example, water acts as a base, accepting the proton from HCl.

$$HCl(aq) + H_2O(l) \longrightarrow Cl^-(aq) + H_3O^+(aq)$$

acid   base   base   acid

TABLE 15.2	Relative Strengths of Acids and Bases		
	Acid	Base	
Strongest acids	$HClO_4$	ClO_4^-	Weakest bases
	H_2SO_4	HSO_4^-	
	HI	I^-	
	HBr	Br^-	
	HCl	Cl^-	
	HNO_3	NO_3^-	
	H_3O^+	H_2O	
	HSO_4^-	SO_4^{2-}	
	H_2SO_3	HSO_3^-	
	H_3PO_4	$H_2PO_4^-$	
	HNO_2	NO_2^-	
	HF	F^-	
	$HC_2H_3O_2$	$C_2H_3O_2^-$	
	$Al(H_2O)_6^{3+}$	$Al(H_2O)_5OH^{2+}$	
	H_2CO_3	HCO_3^-	
	H_2S	HS^-	
	HClO	ClO^-	
	HBrO	BrO^-	
	NH_4^+	NH_3	
	HCN	CN^-	
	HCO_3^-	CO_3^{2-}	
	H_2O_2	HO_2^-	
	HS^-	S^{2-}	
Weakest acids	H_2O	OH^-	Strongest bases

The reverse reaction occurs only to an extremely small extent. Because the reaction goes almost completely to the right, you say that HCl is a strong acid. However, even though the reaction goes almost completely to products, you can consider the reverse reaction. In it, the Cl^- ion acts as the base, accepting a proton from the acid H_3O^+.

Look at this reaction in terms of the relative strengths of the two acids, HCl and H_3O^+. Because HCl is a strong acid, it must lose its proton readily, more readily than H_3O^+ does. You would say that HCl is a stronger acid than H_3O^+, or that, of the two, H_3O^+ is the weaker acid.

$$HCl(aq) + H_2O(l) \rightleftharpoons Cl^-(aq) + H_3O^+(aq)$$

stronger   weaker

acid   acid

It is important to understand that the terms *stronger* and *weaker* are used here only in a comparative sense. The H_3O^+ ion is a relatively strong acid.

An acid–base reaction normally goes in the direction of the weaker acid. You can use this fact to compare the relative strengths of any two acids, as we did in comparing the relative strengths of HCl and H_3O^+. As another example, look at the ionization of acetic acid, $HC_2H_3O_2$, in water.

$$HC_2H_3O_2(aq) + H_2O(l) \rightleftharpoons C_2H_3O_2^-(aq) + H_3O^+(aq)$$

Experiment reveals that in a 0.1 *M* acetic acid solution, only about 1% of the acetic acid molecules have ionized by this reaction. This implies that $HC_2H_3O_2$ is a weaker acid than H_3O^+. If you look at the similar situation for 0.1 *M* HF, you find that about 3% of the HF molecules have dissociated. Thus, HF is a weaker acid than H_3O^+ but a stronger acid than $HC_2H_3O_2$. You have already seen that HCl is stronger than H_3O^+. Thus, you have determined that the acid strengths for these four acids are in the order $HCl > H_3O^+ > HF > HC_2H_3O_2$.

This procedure of determining the relative order of acid strengths by comparing their relative ionizations in water cannot be used to obtain the relative strengths of two strong acids such as HCl and HI. When these acids are dissolved in water, they are essentially 100% ionized. However, if you look at solutions of equal concentrations of these acids in another solvent that is less basic than water—say, pure acetic acid—you do see a difference. Neither acid is completely ionized, but a greater fraction of HI molecules is found to be ionized. Thus, HI is a stronger acid than HCl. In water, the acid strengths of the strong acids appear to be the same; that is, they are "leveled out." We say that water exhibits a *leveling effect* on the strengths of the strong acids.

The first column of Table 15.2 lists acids by their strength; the strongest is at the top of the table. Note that the arrow down the left side of the table points toward the weaker acid and is in the direction the reaction goes. For example, in the reaction involving HCl and H_3O^+, the arrow points from HCl toward H_3O^+ (the weaker acid) and is in the direction in which the reaction occurs.

You can also view this same reaction in terms of the bases, H_2O and Cl^-. A stronger base picks up a proton more readily than does a weaker one. Water has greater base strength than the Cl^- ion; that is, H_2O picks up protons more readily than Cl^- does. In fact, Cl^- has little attraction for protons. (If it had more, HCl would not lose its proton so readily.) Because H_2O molecules compete more successfully for protons than Cl^- ions do, the reaction goes almost completely to the right. (Note that the arrow on the right in Table 15.2 points from H_2O to Cl^-.) That is, at the completion of the reaction, concentrations of product species (Cl^- and H_3O^+) are much greater than concentrations of reactant species.

$$HCl(aq) + H_2O(l) \longrightarrow Cl^-(aq) + H_3O^+(aq)$$

stronger   weaker

base   base

The reaction goes in the direction of the weaker base.

By comparing reactions between different pairs of bases, you can arrive at a relative order for base strengths, just as for acids. A definite relationship exists between acid and base strengths. When you say an acid loses its proton readily, you can also say that its conjugate base does not hold the proton very tightly. *The strongest acids have the weakest conjugate bases, and the strongest bases have the weakest conjugate acids.* This means that a list of conjugate bases of the acids in Table 15.2 will be in order of increasing base strength. The weakest bases will be at the top of the table and the strongest at the bottom.

You can use Table 15.2 to predict the direction of an acid–base reaction. The direction for an acid–base reaction always favors the weaker acid and weaker base; that is, the normal direction of reaction is from the stronger acid and base to the weaker acid and base. For the reaction we have been discussing, you have

$$HCl(aq) + H_2O(l) \longrightarrow Cl^-(aq) + H_3O^+(aq)$$

| stronger acid | stronger base | weaker base | weaker acid |

The reaction follows the direction of the arrows at the left and right of Table 15.2.

Example 15.3 | Deciding Whether Reactants or Products Are Favored in an Acid–Base Reaction

For the following reaction, decide which species (reactants or products) are favored at the completion of the reaction.

$$SO_4^{2-}(aq) + HCN(aq) \rightleftharpoons HSO_4^-(aq) + CN^-(aq)$$

Problem Strategy Use Table 15.2 to compare the relative strengths of acids and bases.

Solution If you compare the relative strengths of the two acids HCN and HSO_4^-, you see that HCN is weaker. Or, comparing the bases SO_4^{2-} and CN^-, you see that SO_4^{2-} is weaker. Hence, the reaction would normally go from right to left.

$$SO_4^{2-}(aq) + HCN(aq) \longleftarrow HSO_4^-(aq) + CN^-(aq)$$

| weaker base | weaker acid | stronger acid | stronger base |

The reactants are favored.

Answer Check Check that the stronger acid has a weaker conjugate base, and vice versa. The reaction goes from stronger acid and base to weaker acid and base.

Exercise 15.3 Determine the direction of the following reaction from the relative strengths of acids and bases.

$$H_2S(aq) + C_2H_3O_2^-(aq) \rightleftharpoons HC_2H_3O_2(aq) + HS^-(aq)$$

■ See Problems 15.45, 15.46, 15.47, and 15.48.

Concept Check 15.2

Formic acid, $HCHO_2$, is a stronger acid than acetic acid, $HC_2H_3O_2$. Which is the stronger base, formate ion, CHO_2^-, or acetate ion, $C_2H_3O_2^-$?

15.5 | Molecular Structure and Acid Strength

The strength of an acid depends on how easily the proton, H^+, is lost or removed from an H—X bond in the acid species. By understanding the factors that determine the ease of proton loss, you will be able to predict the relative strengths of similar acids.

Acetic acid

Sulfuric acid

FIGURE 15.5 ▲

Electrostatic-potential maps of acetic acid and sulfuric acid molecules
High electron densities are shown in red and low densities are shown in blue, with intermediate colors of the spectrum for intermediate densities. Note the hydrogen atoms at the right end of each molecule (blue colors, indicating low electron densities). These atoms have partial positive charges and thus are acidic.

Two factors are important in determining relative acid strengths. One is the polarity of the bond to which the H atom is attached. The H atom should have a positive partial charge:

$$\overset{\delta+}{H}\text{—}\overset{\delta-}{X}$$

The more polarized the bond is in this direction, the more easily the proton is removed and the greater the acid strength. Figure 15.5 dramatically illustrates this idea. The figure shows *electrostatic-potential maps* of acetic acid, $HC_2H_3O_2$ or CH_3COOH, and sulfuric acid, H_2SO_4. These drawings show the distribution of electron density in the molecules.

$$\underset{\text{Acetic acid}}{\overset{\displaystyle H-\overset{\displaystyle \overset{H}{|}}{\underset{\displaystyle \underset{H}{|}}{C}}-\overset{\displaystyle \overset{O}{\|}}{C}-O-H}{}} \qquad \underset{\text{Sulfuric acid}}{\overset{\displaystyle H-O-\overset{\displaystyle \overset{O}{\|}}{\underset{\displaystyle \underset{O}{\|}}{S}}-O-H}{}}$$

$$CH_3COOH \qquad\qquad H_2SO_4$$

High electron densities are shown in red (giving a partial negative charge, $\delta-$) and low densities are shown in blue (giving a partial positive charge, $\delta+$). Intermediate densities are shown in colors between red and blue. A hydrogen atom bonded to an oxygen atom generally has a partial positive charge, but in comparing such an atom in acetic acid (light blue atom at the right end of the molecule) and sulfuric acid (dark blue atom at the right end of the molecule), you can see that the hydrogen atom in sulfuric acid is much more positive. You would expect the hydrogen atom in sulfuric acid to be more acidic—and it certainly is.

The second factor determining acid strength is the strength of the bond—that is, how tightly the proton is held. This, in turn, depends on the size of atom X. The larger atom X, the weaker the bond and the greater the acid strength.

Consider a series of binary acids, HX, formed from a given column of elements of the periodic table. The acids would be compounds of these elements with hydrogen, such as the binary acids of the Group VIIA elements: HF, HCl, HBr, and HI. As you go down the column of elements, each time adding a shell of electrons to the atom, the radius increases markedly. For this reason, the size of atom X is the dominant factor in determining the acid strength. *In going down a column of elements of the periodic table, the size of atom X increases, the H—X bond strength decreases, and the strength of the binary acid increases.* You predict the following order of acid strength:

$$HF < HCl < HBr < HI$$

This is the same order shown in Table 15.2.

As you go across a row of elements of the periodic table, the atomic radius decreases slowly. For this reason, the relative strengths of the binary acids of these elements are less dependent on the size of atom X. Now the polarity of the H—X bond becomes the dominant factor in determining acid strength. *Going across a row of elements of the periodic table, the electronegativity increases, the H—X bond polarity increases, and the acid strength increases.* For example, the binary acids of the last two elements of the second period are H_2O and HF. The acid strengths are

$$H_2O < HF$$

HClO   HBrO

FIGURE 15.6 ▲

Effect of atom Y on the acid strengths of acids H—O—Y

Electronegative atoms tend to pull electrons toward themselves. Thus, the O atom in the H—O bond of an oxoacid pulls the bonding electrons toward itself, giving the H atom a positive polarity (δ^+) compared with that of the O atom (δ^-). Other electronegative atoms attached to this O atom increase its effective electronegativity. (The arrow indicates the resulting movement of electrons in each molecule.) Thus, in a series of acids H—O—Y, the acidity increases with the electronegativity of Y. Here H—O—Cl is more acidic than H—O—Br.

The formulas of these acids may be written HXO or HOX, depending on the convention used. Formulas of oxoacids are generally written with the acidic H atoms first, followed by the characteristic element (X), then O atoms. However, the formulas of molecules composed of three atoms are often written in the order in which the atoms are bonded, which in this case is HOX.

This again is the order shown in Table 15.2. Hydrogen fluoride, HF, is a weak acid, and H_2O is a very weak acid.

Now consider the oxoacids. An oxoacid has the structure

$$H—O—Y—$$

The acidic H atom is always attached to an O atom, which, in turn, is attached to an atom Y. Other groups, such as O atoms or O—H groups, may also be attached to Y. Bond polarity appears to be the dominant factor determining relative strengths of the oxoacids. This, in turn, depends on the electronegativity of atom Y (see Figure 15.6). If the electronegativity of atom Y is large, the H—O bond is relatively polar and the acid strength large. *For a series of oxoacids of the same structure, differing only in the atom Y, the acid strength increases with the electronegativity of Y.* Consider, for example, the acids HClO, HBrO, and HIO. < The structures are

$$H—\overset{..}{\underset{..}{O}}—\overset{..}{\underset{..}{Cl}}: \qquad H—\overset{..}{\underset{..}{O}}—\overset{..}{\underset{..}{Br}}: \qquad H—\overset{..}{\underset{..}{O}}—\overset{..}{\underset{..}{I}}:$$

The electronegativity of Group VIIA elements decreases going down the column of elements, so the electronegativity decreases from Cl to Br to I. The order of acid strengths is

$$HIO < HBrO < HClO$$

For a series of oxoacids, $(HO)_m YO_n$, the acid strength increases with n, the number of O atoms bonded to Y (excluding O atoms in OH groups). The oxoacids of chlorine provide an example:

$$H—\overset{..}{\underset{..}{O}}—\overset{..}{\underset{..}{Cl}}: \qquad H—\overset{..}{\underset{..}{O}}—\overset{..}{\underset{..}{Cl}}—\overset{..}{\underset{..}{O}}: \qquad H—\overset{..}{\underset{..}{O}}—\overset{\overset{\displaystyle ..}{\overset{\displaystyle O}{|}}}{\underset{..}{Cl}}—\overset{..}{\underset{..}{O}}: \qquad H—\overset{..}{\underset{..}{O}}—\overset{\overset{\displaystyle ..}{\overset{\displaystyle O}{|}}}{\underset{\underset{\displaystyle :O:}{\displaystyle |}}{Cl}}—\overset{..}{\underset{..}{O}}:$$

With each additional O atom, the Cl atom becomes effectively more electronegative (see Figure 15.7). As a result, the H atom becomes more acidic. The acid strengths increase in the following order:

$$HClO < HClO_2 < HClO_3 < HClO_4$$

Before we leave the subject of molecular structure and acid strength, let us look at the relative acid strengths of a polyprotic acid and its corresponding acid anions. For example, H_2SO_4 ionizes by losing a proton to give HSO_4^-, which, in turn, ionizes to give SO_4^{2-}. HSO_4^- can lose a proton, so it is acidic. However, because of the negative charge of the ion, which tends to attract protons, its acid strength is reduced from that of the uncharged species. That is, the acid strengths are in the order

$$HSO_4^- < H_2SO_4$$

FIGURE 15.7 ▶

Acid strengths of a series of oxoacids $(HO)_m YO_n$

Consider the acids where Y is Cl. The Cl atom becomes effectively more electronegative as more O atoms are attached to it. As a result, the O atom bonded to the H atom becomes effectively more electronegative and so attracts electrons more easily; the H atom then becomes more acidic. Thus, $HClO_4$ has the greatest acid strength of this series of oxoacids.

We conclude that *the acid strength of a polyprotic acid and its anions decreases with increasing negative charge* (see Table 15.2).

HClO   HClO₂   HClO₃   HClO₄

a. NH_3, PH_3; b. HI, H_2Te; c. HSO_3^-, H_2SO_3; d. H_3AsO_4, H_3AsO_3; e. HSO_4^-, $HSeO_4^-$

■ See Problems 15.51 and 15.52.

Self-Ionization of Water and pH

In aqueous solutions, two ions have dominant roles. These ions, the hydronium ion H_3O^+ (or hydrogen ion, H^+) and the hydroxide ion OH^-, are available in any aqueous solution as a result of the *self-ionization* of water, a reaction of water with itself, which we will describe in the next section. This will also give us some background to acid–base equilibrium calculations, which we will discuss in Chapter 16.

15.6 | Self-Ionization of Water

Although pure water is often considered a nonelectrolyte (nonconductor of electricity), precise measurements do show a very small conduction. This conduction results from **self-ionization** (or **autoionization**), *a reaction in which two like molecules react to give ions.* In the case of water, a proton from one H_2O molecule is transferred to another H_2O molecule, leaving behind an OH^- ion and forming a hydronium ion, $H_3O^+(aq)$.

$$H_2O(l) + H_2O(l) \rightleftharpoons H_3O^+(aq) + OH^-(aq)$$

You can see the slight extent to which the self-ionization of water occurs by noting the small value of its equilibrium constant K_c.

$$K_c = \frac{[H_3O^+][OH^-]}{[H_2O]^2}$$

Because the concentration of ions formed is very small, the concentration of H_2O remains essentially constant, about 56 M at 25°C. If you rearrange this equation, placing $[H_2O]^2$ with K_c, the ion product $[H_3O^+][OH^-]$ equals a constant.

$$\underbrace{[H_2O]^2 K_c}_{\text{constant}} = [H_3O^+][OH^-]$$

We call *the equilibrium value of the ion product* $[H_3O^+][OH^-]$ the **ion-product constant for water,** which is written K_w. ◄ At 25°C, the value of K_w is 1.0×10^{-14}. Like any equilibrium constant, K_w varies with temperature. At body temperature (37°C), K_w equals 2.5×10^{-14}.

$$K_w = [H_3O^+][OH^-] = 1.0 \times 10^{-14} \text{ at 25°C}$$

Because we often write $H^+(aq)$ for $H_3O^+(aq)$, the ion-product constant for water can be written $K_w = [H^+][OH^-]$.

Using K_w, you can calculate the concentrations of H_3O^+ and OH^- ions in pure water. These ions are produced in equal numbers in pure water, so their concentrations are equal. Let $x = [H_3O^+] = [OH^-]$. Then, substituting into the equation for the ion-product constant,

$$K_w = [H_3O^+][OH^-]$$

you get, at 25°C,

$$1.0 \times 10^{-14} = x^2$$

The thermodynamic equilibrium constant is defined in terms of activities. The activity of water is essentially 1, so we do not include water explicitly in the equilibrium expression.

Hence, x equals 1.0×10^{-7}. Thus, the concentrations of H_3O^+ and OH^- are both 1.0×10^{-7} M in pure water.

If you add an acid or a base to water, the concentrations of H_3O^+ and OH^- will no longer be equal. The equilibrium-constant equation $K_w = [H_3O^+][OH^-]$ will still hold, however, as we will discuss in the next section.

15.7   Solutions of a Strong Acid or Base

Consider an aqueous solution of a strong acid or base. Suppose you dissolve 0.10 mol HCl in 1.0 L of aqueous solution, giving 0.10 M HCl. You would like to know the concentration of H_3O^+ ion in this solution. In addition to the self-ionization of water, you have the reaction of HCl with water, which also produces H_3O^+ ion. A strong acid such as hydrochloric acid, HCl(aq), essentially reacts completely with water.

$$HCl(aq) + H_2O(l) \longrightarrow H_3O^+(aq) + Cl^-(aq)$$

Because you started with 0.10 mol HCl in 1.0 L of solution, the reaction will produce 0.10 mol H_3O^+, so the concentration of H_3O^+ ion from HCl is 0.10 M.

Now consider the concentration of H_3O^+ ion produced by the self-ionization of water. In pure water, the concentration of H_3O^+ produced is 1.0×10^{-7} M; in an acid solution, the contribution of H_3O^+ from water will be even smaller. You can see this by applying Le Châtelier's principle to the self-ionization reaction. When you increase the concentration of H_3O^+ in water by adding an acid, the self-ionization of water reverses until a new equilibrium is obtained.

$$H_2O(l) + H_2O(l) \longleftarrow H_3O^+(aq) + OH^-(aq)$$

Consequently, the concentration of H_3O^+ produced by the self-ionization of water ($< 1 \times 10^{-7}$ M) is negligible in comparison with that produced from HCl (0.10 M). So, 0.10 M HCl has a concentration of H_3O^+ ion equal to 0.10 M.

In a solution of a strong acid, you can normally ignore the self-ionization of water as a source of H_3O^+. The H_3O^+ concentration is usually determined by the strong acid concentration. (This is not true when the acid solution is extremely dilute, however. In a solution that is 1.0×10^{-7} M HCl, the self-ionization of water produces an amount of H_3O^+ comparable with that produced by HCl.)

Although you normally ignore the self-ionization of water in calculating the H_3O^+ concentration in a solution of a strong acid, the self-ionization equilibrium still exists and is responsible for a small concentration of OH^- ion. You can use the ion-product constant for water to calculate this concentration. As an example, calculate the concentration of OH^- ion in 0.10 M HCl. You substitute $[H_3O^+] = 0.10$ M into the equilibrium equation for K_w (for 25°C).

$$K_w = [H_3O^+][OH^-]$$
$$1.0 \times 10^{-14} = 0.10 \times [OH^-]$$

Solving for $[OH^-]$,

$$[OH^-] = \frac{1.0 \times 10^{-14}}{0.10} = 1.0 \times 10^{-13}$$

The OH^- concentration is 1.0×10^{-13} M.

Now consider a solution of a strong base, such as 0.010 M NaOH. What are the OH^- and H_3O^+ concentrations in this solution? Because NaOH is a strong base, all of the NaOH is present in the solution as ions. One mole of NaOH dissolves in water as one mole of Na^+ and one mole of OH^-. Therefore, the concentration of OH^- obtained from NaOH in 0.010 M NaOH solution is 0.010 M. The concentration of OH^- produced from the self-ionization of water in this solution ($< 1 \times 10^{-7}$ M) is negligible and can be ignored. Therefore, the concentration of OH^- ion in the solution is 0.010 M. Hydronium ion, H_3O^+, is produced by the self-ionization of water. To obtain its concentration, you substitute into the equilibrium equation for K_w (for 25°C).

$$K_w = [H_3O^+][OH^-]$$
$$1.0 \times 10^{-14} = [H_3O^+] \times 0.010$$

Solving for H_3O^+ concentration,

$$[H_3O^+] = \frac{1.0 \times 10^{-14}}{0.010} = 1.0 \times 10^{-12}$$

The H_3O^+ concentration is 1.0×10^{-12} M.

The following example further illustrates the calculation of H_3O^+ and OH^- concentrations in solutions of a strong acid or base.

Example 15.4 | Calculating Concentrations of H_3O^+ and OH^- in Solutions of a Strong Acid or Base

Calculate the concentrations of hydronium ion and hydroxide ion at 25°C in: a. 0.15 M HNO_3, b. 0.010 M $Ca(OH)_2$.

Problem Strategy A strong acid (or base) is fully ionized in solution, so you can use its formula and molar concentration to determine the H_3O^+ (or OH^-) ion concentration. (Any contribution to this ion concentration from the self-ionization of water is negligible.) K_w relates the H_3O^+ and OH^- ion concentrations; therefore, you use this relation to obtain the OH^- concentration, given the H_3O^+ concentration, or vice versa.

Solution   a. Every mole of HNO_3 contributes one mole of H_3O^+ ion, so the H_3O^+ concentration is **0.15 M.** The OH^- concentration is obtained from the equation for K_w.

$$K_w = [H_3O^+][OH^-]$$
$$1.0 \times 10^{-14} = 0.15 \times [OH^-]$$

so

$$[OH^-] = \frac{1.0 \times 10^{-14}}{0.15} = 6.7 \times 10^{-14}$$

The concentration of OH^- in 0.15 M HNO_3 is **6.7 × 10⁻¹⁴ M.**

b. $Ca(OH)_2(s) \xrightarrow{H_2O} Ca^{2+}(aq) + 2OH^-(aq)$

Every mole of $Ca(OH)_2$ that dissolves yields two moles of OH^-. Therefore, 0.010 M $Ca(OH)_2$ contains 2 × 0.010 M OH^- = **0.020 M OH^-.** The H_3O^+ concentration is obtained from

$$K_w = [H_3O^+][OH^-]$$
$$1.0 \times 10^{-14} = [H_3O^+] \times 0.020$$

so

$$[H^+] = \frac{1.0 \times 10^{-14}}{0.020} = 5.0 \times 10^{-13}$$

The hydronium-ion concentration is **5.0 × 10⁻¹³ M.**

Answer Check The hydronium-ion concentration of a solution of an acid should be greater than that in pure water (1.0×10^{-7} M); the hydroxide-ion concentration of a solution of an acid should be less than that in pure water (1.0×10^{-7} M). The hydroxide-ion concentration of a solution of a base should be greater than that in pure water; the hydronium-ion concentration of a solution of a base should be less than that in pure water. Always check your calculations to see that this is true.

Exercise 15.5   A solution of barium hydroxide at 25°C is 0.125 M $Ba(OH)_2$. What are the concentrations of hydronium ion and hydroxide ion in the solution?

■ See Problems 15.53 and 15.54.

By dissolving substances in water, you can alter the concentrations of H_3O^+ and OH^- ions. In a *neutral* solution, the concentrations of H_3O^+ and OH^- remain equal, as they are in pure water. In an *acidic* solution, the concentration of H_3O^+ is greater than that of OH⁻. In a *basic* solution, the concentration of OH⁻ is greater than that of H_3O^+. At 25°C, you observe the following conditions:

In an acidic solution, $[H_3O^+] > 1.0 \times 10^{-7} M$.

In a neutral solution, $[H_3O^+] = 1.0 \times 10^{-7} M$.

In a basic solution, $[H_3O^+] < 1.0 \times 10^{-7} M$.

Exercise 15.6   A solution has a hydroxide-ion concentration of $1.0 \times 10^{-5} M$ at 25°C. Is the solution acidic, neutral, or basic?

■ See Problems 15.59 and 15.60.

Concept Check 15.3

Rank the following solutions from most acidic to most basic (water molecules have been omitted for clarity).

A   B   C

● = H_3O^+
● = OH⁻

15.8 | The pH of a Solution

You see that whether an aqueous solution is acidic, neutral, or basic depends on the hydronium-ion concentration. You can quantitatively describe the acidity by giving the hydronium-ion concentration. But because these concentration values may be very small, it is often more convenient to give the acidity in terms of **pH**, which is defined as *the negative of the logarithm of the molar hydronium-ion concentration:* <

The Danish biochemist S. P. L. Sørensen devised the pH scale while working on the brewing of beer.

$$pH = -\log [H_3O^+]$$

(You can also write $pH = -\log [H^+]$.) For a solution in which the hydronium-ion concentration is $1.0 \times 10^{-3} M$, the pH is

$$pH = -\log(1.0 \times 10^{-3}) = 3.00$$

Note that the number of places after the decimal point in the pH equals the number of significant figures reported in the hydronium-ion concentration. <

See Appendix A for a discussion of logarithms.

A neutral solution, whose hydronium-ion concentration at 25°C is $1.0 \times 10^{-7} M$, has a pH of 7.00. For an acidic solution, the hydronium-ion concentration is greater than $1.0 \times 10^{-7} M$, so the pH is less than 7.00. Similarly, a basic solution has a pH greater than 7.00. Figure 15.8 shows a diagram of the pH scale and lists pH values of some common solutions.

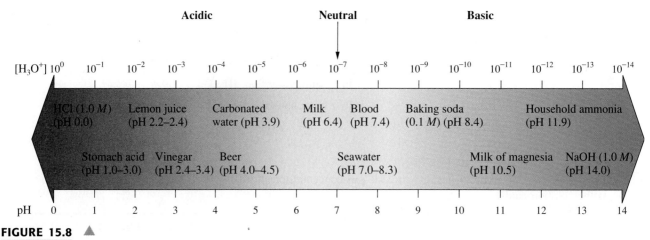

FIGURE 15.8 ▲

The pH scale   Solutions having pH less than 7 are acidic; those having pH more than 7 are basic.

Example 15.5 | Calculating the pH from the Hydronium-Ion Concentration

A sample of orange juice has a hydronium-ion concentration of 2.9×10^{-4} M. What is the pH? Is the solution acidic?

Problem Strategy   pH is the negative logarithm of the molar hydronium-ion concentration. Determine the log by using either an electronic calculator or log tables (see Appendix A for a discussion of logarithms). On a calculator, enter the H_3O^+ concentration, press *log*, and change the sign of the result. You should write the pH with the same number of decimal places as there are significant figures in $[H_3O^+]$.

Solution

$$pH = -\log [H_3O^+] = -\log(2.9 \times 10^{-4}) = \mathbf{3.54}$$

The pH is less than 7.00, so the solution is **acidic** (as you expect for orange juice).

Answer Check   Having obtained the pH, you should check the result by calculating 10^{-pH}, which should give you back the hydronium-ion concentration of the solution. Remember that a pH greater than 7 is basic and a pH less than 7 is acidic.

Exercise 15.7   What is the pH of a sample of gastric juice (digestive juice in the stomach) whose hydronium-ion concentration is 0.045 M?

■ See Problems 15.67 and 15.68.

You can find the pH of a solution of known hydroxide-ion concentration by first solving for the hydronium-ion concentration, as shown in Example 15.4 b. However, you can also find the pH simply from the pOH, a measure of hydroxide-ion concentration similar to the pH:

$$pOH = -\log [OH^-]$$

Then, because $K_w = [H_3O^+][OH^-] = 1.0 \times 10^{-14}$ at 25°C, you can show that <

$$pH + pOH = 14.00$$

You can rearrange this equation to obtain the pH from the value of pOH. For example, suppose you wish to find the pH of an ammonia solution whose hydroxide-ion concentration is 1.9×10^{-3} M. You first calculate the pOH.

$$pOH = -\log(1.9 \times 10^{-3}) = 2.72$$

Then the pH is

$$pH = 14.00 - pOH$$
$$= 14.00 - 2.72 = 11.28$$

Taking the logarithm of both sides of the equation

$[H_3O^+][OH^-] = 1.0 \times 10^{-14}$

you get

$\log [H_3O^+] + \log [OH^-] = -14.00$

or

$(-\log [H_3O^+]) + (-\log [OH^-])$
$\qquad = 14.00$

Hence, pH + pOH = 14.00.

Exercise 15.8   A saturated solution of calcium hydroxide has a hydroxide-ion concentration of 0.025 *M*. What is the pH of the solution?

■ See Problems 15.73 and 15.74.

The usefulness of the pH scale depends on the ease with which you can interconvert pH and hydronium-ion concentrations. In the next example, you will find the hydronium-ion concentration, given the pH value.

Example 15.6 | Calculating the Hydronium-Ion Concentration from the pH

The pH of human arterial blood is 7.40. What is the hydronium-ion concentration?

Problem Strategy   The hydronium-ion concentration is

$$[H_3O^+] = \text{antilog}(-\text{pH}) = 10^{-\text{pH}}$$

On some calculators, you obtain the antilogarithm by taking the *inverse* of the logarithm. On others, you use a 10^x key.

Solution   The result is

$$[H_3O^+] = \text{antilog}(-7.40) = 10^{-7.40} = \mathbf{4.0 \times 10^{-8}}\, \textit{M}$$

Because the pH was given to two decimal places, you write the hydronium-ion concentration with two significant figures.

Answer Check   Check your result by using your answer (the hydronium-ion concentration) to obtain the pH ($= -\log [H_3O^+]$).

Exercise 15.9   A brand of carbonated beverage has a pH of 3.16. What is the hydronium-ion concentration of the beverage?

■ See Problems 15.75 and 15.76.

Exercise 15.10   A 0.010 *M* solution of ammonia, NH_3, has a pH of 10.6 at 25°C. What is the concentration of hydroxide ion? (One way to solve this problem is to find the pOH first and then calculate the hydroxide-ion concentration.)

■ See Problems 15.77 and 15.78.

FIGURE 15.9 ▲

A digital pH meter
The experimenter places a probe containing electrodes into the solution and reads the pH on the meter.

Litmus contains several substances and changes color over a broader range, from about pH 5 to pH 8.

The pH of a solution can be accurately measured by a pH meter (Figure 15.9). This instrument consists of specially designed electrodes that are dipped into the solution. A voltage, which depends on the pH, is generated between the electrodes and is read on a meter calibrated directly in pH. (The principle behind the operation of a pH meter is discussed in Chapter 19.)

Although less precise, acid–base indicators are often used to measure pH, because they usually change color within a small pH range. The color change of an indicator involves establishment of an equilibrium between an acid form and a base form that have different colors. If we denote the acid form as HIn, then the base form is In⁻ and the equilibrium is

$$HIn(aq) + H_2O(l) \rightleftharpoons H_3O^+(aq) + In^-(aq)$$

Consider the case of phenolphthalein. The acid form is colorless and the base form is pink. When a base is added to an acidic solution of phenolphthalein, OH^- ion from the base reacts with H_3O^+ in the solution. According to Le Châtelier's principle, the equilibrium is shifted to the right (to replenish H_3O^+). Thus, the colorless acid form of the indicator, HIn, is converted to the pink base form, In⁻. A solution of phenolphthalein begins to turn pink at about pH 8.0. By pH 9.7, the color change is essentially complete. < Figure 15.10 shows the color changes for

FIGURE 15.10 ▶

Color changes of some acid–base indicators

Acid–base indicators are dyes whose acid form has one color and whose base form has another color. Thymol blue is a diprotic acid and has two different color changes (listed here in the acidic range and the basic range).

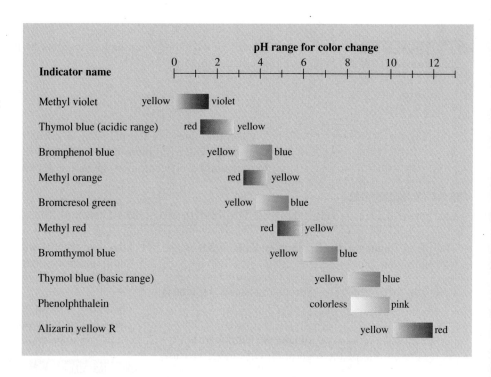

various acid–base indicators. (See also Figure 15.11.) Paper strips impregnated with several indicators are often used to measure pH values. Such "pH paper" gives a definite color for different pH ranges and can give the pH to the nearest integer value or better.

Concept Check 15.4

You have solutions of NH_3, HCl, NaOH, and $HC_2H_3O_2$ (acetic acid), all with the same solute concentrations. Rank these solutions in order of pH, from the highest to the lowest.

FIGURE 15.11 ▶

Some acid–base indicators in solutions of different H_3O^+ concentrations.

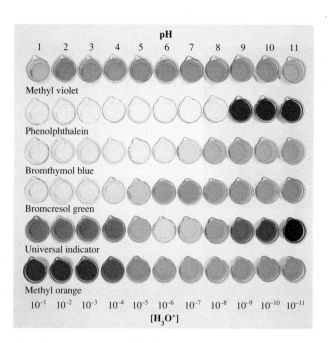

A Chemist Looks at . . .

daily life

Unclogging the Sink and Other Chores

When the sink drain is clogged, you might need a strong arm, but a strong base might work just as well. Drain cleaner solutions, available in grocery stores, are simply solutions of sodium hydroxide, a strong base.

Such solutions work by chemically reacting with fat and with hair, the usual ingredients of a stopped drain. When fat reacts with a strong base such as sodium hydroxide, it forms the salt of a fatty acid, a product otherwise known as soap. Hair is a protein material, and in the presence of a strong base, the protein breaks up into the salts of its constituent amino acids. So a wad of greasy hair packed in a drain, in the presence of sodium hydroxide, becomes a soapy solution of amino acid salts. That solution washes easily down the drain. Oven cleaner is a paste made of sodium hydroxide. It cleans by reacting with the fatty deposits and other residues in the oven.

Sodium hydroxide is produced commercially by sending a direct current through an aqueous solution of sodium chloride, a process referred to as electrolysis (Figure 15.12). Hydrogen gas is released at the negative pole and chlorine gas is released at the positive pole. At the end of the electrolysis, the solution contains sodium hydroxide. The overall reaction is

$$2NaCl(aq) + 2H_2O(l) \xrightarrow{\text{electrolysis}} H_2(g) + Cl_2(g) + 2NaOH(aq)$$

Chlorine is prepared commercially in this same process.

FIGURE 15.12 ▲

Preparation of sodium hydroxide by hydrolysis
A solution of sodium chloride is electrolyzed. Note the pink color at the negative electrode. Phenolphthalein indicator turns pink from the hydroxide ion formed at the electrode. Later, if we evaporate the solution, sodium hydroxide crystallizes out.

■ See Problems 15.111 and 15.112.

A Checklist for Review

Important Terms

acid (Brønsted–Lowry) (15.2)
base (Brønsted–Lowry) (15.2)
conjugate acid–base pair (15.2)
amphiprotic species (15.2)

Lewis acid (15.3)
Lewis base (15.3)
self-ionization
   (autoionization) (15.6)

ion-product constant for water
   (**K_w**) (15.6)
pH (15.8)

Key Equations

$K_w = [H_3O^+][OH^-]$
   $= 1.0 \times 10^{-14}$ at 25°C

$pH = -\log[H_3O^+]$
$pH + pOH = 14.00$

Summary of Facts and Concepts

The *Arrhenius concept* was the first successful theory of acids and bases. Then, in 1923, Brønsted and Lowry characterized acid–base reactions as proton-transfer reactions. According to the *Brønsted–Lowry concept,* an acid is a proton donor and a base is a proton acceptor. The *Lewis concept* is even more general than the Brønsted–Lowry concept. A Lewis acid is an electron-pair acceptor and a Lewis base is an electron-pair donor. Reactions of acidic and basic oxides and the formation of complex ions, as well as proton-transfer reactions, can be described in terms of the Lewis concept.

Acid–base reactions can be viewed as a competition for protons. Using this idea, you can construct a table of *relative strengths of acids and bases.* Reaction favors the weaker acid

and the weaker base. Acid strength depends on the polarity and the strength of the bond involving the acidic hydrogen atom. Therefore, you can *relate molecular structure and acid strength.* The text gives a number of rules that allow you to predict the relative strengths of similar acids based on molecular structure.

Water ionizes to give hydronium ion and hydroxide ion. The concentrations of these ions in aqueous solution are related by the *ion-product constant for water* (K_w). Thus, you can describe the acidity or basicity of a solution by the hydronium-ion concentration. You often use the pH, which is the negative logarithm of the hydronium-ion concentration, as a measure of acidity.

Media Summary

Visit the **student website at college.cengage.com/pic/ebbing9e** to help prepare for class, study for quizzes and exams, understand core concepts, and visualize molecular-level interactions. The following media activities are available for this chapter:

 Prepare for Class

■ **Video Lessons** *Mini lectures from chemistry experts*
Arrhenius/Brønsted–Lowry Definitions of Acids and Bases
Lewis Acids and Bases
Strong Acids and Bases
Weak Acids
Weak Bases
Trends in Acid and Base Strengths
Examining Polyprotic Acids
Hydronium, Hydroxide, and the pH Scale
Common Mathematical Functions

 Improve Your Grade

■ **Visualizations** *Molecular-level animations and lab demonstration videos*
Proton Transfer
Brønsted–Lowry Reaction

Self-Ionization of Water
pH Scale

■ **Tutorials** *Animated examples and interactive activities*
Brønsted–Lowry Acid–Base Reactions
Acid Strength
The pH Scale
Calculating pH of Strong Acid and Base Solutions

■ **Flashcards** *Key terms and definitions*
Online Flashcards

■ **Self-Assessment Questions** *Additional questions with full worked-out solutions*
6 Self-Assessment Questions

 ACE the Test

Multiple-choice quizzes
3 ACE Practice Tests

Access these resources using the passkey available free with new texts or for purchase separately.

Learning Objectives

15.1 Arrhenius Concept of Acids and Bases

■ Define *acid* and *base* according to the Arrhenius concept.

■ Identify acid and base species. Example 15.1
■ Define *amphiprotic species.*

15.2 Brønsted–Lowry Concept of Acids and Bases

■ Define *acid* and *base* according to the Brønsted–Lowry concept.
■ Define the term *conjugate acid–base pair.*

15.3 Lewis Concept of Acids and Bases

■ Define *Lewis acid* and *Lewis base.*
■ Identify Lewis acid and Lewis base species. Example 15.2

15.4 Relative Strengths of Acids and Bases

■ Understand the relationship between the strength of an acid and that of its conjugate base.
■ Decide whether reactants or products are favored in an acid–base reaction. **Example 15.3**

15.5 Molecular Structure and Acid Strength

■ Note the two factors that determine relative acid strengths.
■ Understand the periodic trends in the strengths of the binary acids HX.
■ Understand the rules for determining the relative strengths of oxoacids.
■ Understand the relative acid strengths of a polyprotic acid and its anions.

15.6 Self-Ionization of Water

■ Define *self-ionization* (or *autoionization*).
■ Define the *ion-product constant for water*.

15.7 Solutions of a Strong Acid or Base

■ Calculate the concentrations of H_3O^+ and OH^- in solutions of a strong acid or base. **Example 15.4**

15.8 The pH of a Solution

■ Define *pH*.
■ Calculate the pH from the hydronium-ion concentration. **Example 15.5**
■ Calculate the hydronium-ion concentration from the pH. **Example 15.6**
■ Describe the determination of pH by a pH meter and by acid–base indicators.

Self-Assessment and Review Questions

15.1 Which of the following are strong acids? Which are weak acids? (a) $HC_2H_3O_2$; (b) $HClO$; (c) HCl; (d) HNO_3; (e) HNO_2; (f) HCN

15.2 Describe any thermochemical (heat of reaction) evidence for the Arrhenius concept.

15.3 Define an acid and a base according to the Brønsted–Lowry concept. Give an acid–base equation and identify each species as an acid or a base.

15.4 What is meant by the conjugate acid of a base?

15.5 Write an equation in which $H_2PO_3^-$ acts as an acid and another in which it acts as a base.

15.6 Describe four ways in which the Brønsted–Lowry concept enlarges on the Arrhenius concept.

15.7 Define an acid and a base according to the Lewis concept. Give a chemical equation to illustrate.

15.8 Explain why an acid–base reaction favors the weaker acid.

15.9 Give two important factors that determine the strength of an acid. How does an increase in each factor affect the acid strength?

15.10 What is meant by the self-ionization of water? Write the expression for K_w. What is its value at 25°C?

15.11 What is meant by the pH of a solution? Describe two ways of measuring pH.

15.12 Which is more acidic, a solution having a pH of 4 or one having a pH of 5?

15.13 What is the pH of a neutral solution at 37°C, where K_w equals 2.5×10^{-14}?

15.14 What is the sum of the pH and the pOH for a solution at 37°C, where K_w equals 2.5×10^{-14}?

15.15 The conjugate base of hydrofluoric acid dissolved in water is:
   a. F^- **b.** OH^-
   c. H_3O^+ **d.** HF
   e. F_2

15.16 In the following reaction, identify the Lewis acid.

$$Fe^{3+}(aq) + 6CN^-(aq) \rightleftharpoons Fe(CN)_6^{3-}(aq)$$

   a. CN^- **b.** $Fe(CN)_6^{3-}$
   c. H^+ **d.** Fe^{3+}
   e. OH^-

15.17 Calculate the hydronium-ion concentration at 25°C in a $1.3 \times 10^{-2}\ M$ $Ba(OH)_2$ solution.
   a. $1.3 \times 10^{-2}\ M$ **b.** $7.7 \times 10^{-13}\ M$
   c. $2.6 \times 10^{-2}\ M$ **d.** $3.8 \times 10^{-13}\ M$
   e. $1.5 \times 10^2\ M$

15.18 The pH of a solution is 9.55 at 25°C. What is the hydroxide-ion concentration in the solution?
   a. $2.8 \times 10^{-10}\ M$ **b.** $3.5 \times 10^{-5}\ M$
   c. $3.1 \times 10^{-10}\ M$ **d.** $3.2 \times 10^{-5}\ M$
   e. $3.8 \times 10^{-5}\ M$

Concept Explorations

15.19 Acids

You make a solution by dissolving 0.0010 mol of HCl in enough water to make 1.0 L of solution.

   a. Write the chemical equation for the reaction of HCl(*aq*) and water.

   b. Without performing calculations, give a rough estimate of the pH of the HCl solution. Justify your answer.

   c. Calculate the H_3O^+ concentration and the pH of the solution.

   d. Is there any concentration of the base OH^- present in this solution of HCl(*aq*)? If so, where did it come from?

   e. If you increase the OH^- concentration of the solution by adding NaOH, does the H_3O^+ concentration change? If you think it does, explain why this change occurs and whether the H_3O^+ concentration increases or decreases.

f. If you were to measure the pH of 10 drops of the original HCl solution, would you expect it to be different from the pH of the entire sample? Explain.

g. Explain how two different volumes of your original HCl solution can have the same pH yet contain different moles of H_3O^+.

h. If 1.0 L of pure water were added to the HCl solution, would this have any impact on the pH? Explain.

15.20 Strong Acids, Weak Acids, and pH

Two 0.10-mol samples of the hypothetical monoprotic acids HA(*aq*) and HB(*aq*) are used to prepare 1.0-L stock solutions of each acid.

a. Write the chemical reactions for these acids in water. What are the concentrations of the two acid solutions?

b. One of these acids is a strong acid, and one is weak. What could you measure that would tell you which acid was strong and which was weak?

c. Say that the HA(*aq*) solution has a pH of 3.7. Is this the stronger of the two acids? How did you arrive at your answer?

d. What is the concentration of $A^-(aq)$ in the HA solution described in part c?

e. If HB(*aq*) is a strong acid, what is the hydronium-ion concentration?

f. In the solution of HB(*aq*), which of the following would you expect to be in the greatest concentration: $H_3O^+(aq)$, $B^-(aq)$, HB(*aq*), or $OH^-(aq)$? How did you decide?

g. In the solution of HA(*aq*), which of the following would you expect to be in the greatest concentration: $H_3O^+(aq)$, $A^-(aq)$, HA(*aq*), or $OH^-(aq)$? How did you decide?

h. Say you add 1.0 L of pure water to a solution of HB. Would this water addition make the solution more acidic, make it less acidic, or not change the acidity of the original solution? Be sure to fully justify your answer.

i. You prepare a 1.0-L solution of HA. You then take a 200-mL sample of this solution and place it into a separate container. Would this 200 mL sample be more acidic, be less acidic, or have the same acidity as the original 1.0-L solution of HA (*aq*)? Be sure to support your answer.

Conceptual Problems

15.21 Aqueous solutions of ammonia, NH_3, were once thought to be solutions of an ionic compound (ammonium hydroxide, NH_4OH) in order to explain how the solutions could contain hydroxide ion. Using the Brønsted–Lowry concept, show how NH_3 yields hydroxide ion in aqueous solution without involving the species NH_4OH.

15.22 Blood contains several substances that minimize changes in its acidity by reacting with either an acid or a base. One of these is the hydrogen phosphate ion, HPO_4^{2-}. Write one equation showing this species acting as a Brønsted–Lowry acid and another in which the species acts as a Brønsted–Lowry base.

15.23 Self-contained environments, such as that of a space station, require that the carbon dioxide exhaled by people be continuously removed. This can be done by passing the air over solid alkali hydroxide, in which carbon dioxide reacts with hydroxide ion. What ion is produced by the addition of OH^- ion to CO_2? Use the Lewis concept to explain this.

15.24 Compare the structures of HNO_2 and H_2CO_3. Which would you expect to be the stronger acid? Explain your choice.

15.25 The value of the ion-product constant for water, K_w, increases with temperature. What will be the effect of lowering the temperature on the pH of pure water?

15.26 You make solutions of ammonia and sodium hydroxide by adding the same moles of each solute to equal volumes of water. Which solution would you expect to have the higher pH?

15.27 A strong monoprotic acid, with the molecular structure ⬤, is dissolved in a beaker of water. Which of the following pictures best represents the acid solution (water molecules have been omitted for clarity)?

⬤ = H_3O^+
⬤ = acid anion
⬤ = monoprotic acid

15.28 A weak acid, HA, is dissolved in water. Which one of the following beakers represents the resulting solution? (Water molecules have been omitted for clarity.)

⬤ = H_3O^+
⬤ = OH^-
⬤ = acid anion

A **B** **C**

Practice Problems

Brønsted-Lowry Concept

15.29 Write the balanced reaction of hydroxide ion with hydrofluoric acid, HF, to form fluoride ion and water. Identify each species as either an acid or a base.

15.30 Write the balanced reaction of hypochlorous acid, HOCl, with water to form hydronium ion and the conjugate base of HOCl. Identify each species as either an acid or a base.

15.31 Give the conjugate base to each of the following species regarded as acids.
a. HPO_4^{2-} b. H_2S
c. HNO_2 d. $H_2AsO_4^-$

15.32 Give the conjugate base to each of the following species regarded as acids.
a. $HSeO_4^-$ b. PH_4^+
c. HS^- d. HOCl

15.33 Give the conjugate acid to each of the following species regarded as bases.
a. ClO^- b. AsH_3
c. $H_2PO_4^-$ d. TeO_3^{2-}

15.34 Give the conjugate acid to each of the following species regarded as bases.
a. HSe^- b. NH_2^-
c. ClO_2^- d. N_2H_4

15.35 For the following reactions, label each species as an acid or a base. Indicate the species that are conjugates of one another.
a. $HSO_4^- + NH_3 \rightleftharpoons SO_4^{2-} + NH_4^+$
b. $HPO_4^{2-} + NH_4^+ \rightleftharpoons H_2PO_4^- + NH_3$
c. $Al(H_2O)_6^{3+} + H_2O \rightleftharpoons Al(H_2O)_5OH^{2+} + H_3O^+$
d. $SO_3^{2-} + NH_4^+ \rightleftharpoons HSO_3^- + NH_3$

15.36 For the following reactions, label each species as an acid or a base. Indicate the species that are conjugates of one another.
a. $HPO_4^{2-} + HCO_3^- \rightleftharpoons PO_4^{3-} + H_2CO_3$
b. $F^- + HSO_4^- \rightleftharpoons HF + SO_4^{2-}$
c. $HSO_4^- + H_2O \rightleftharpoons SO_4^{2-} + H_3O^+$
d. $HS^- + CN^- \rightleftharpoons S^{2-} + HCN$

Lewis Acid–Base Concept

15.37 The following shows ball-and-stick models of the reactants in a Lewis acid–base reaction.

Write the complete equation for the reaction, including the product. Identify each reactant as a Lewis acid or a Lewis base.

15.38 The following shows ball-and-stick models of the reactants in a Lewis acid–base reaction.

Write the complete equation for the reaction, including the product. Identify each reactant as a Lewis acid or a Lewis base.

15.39 Complete each of the following equations. Then write the Lewis formulas of the reactants and products and identify each reactant as a Lewis acid or a Lewis base.
a. $AlCl_3 + Cl^- \longrightarrow$
b. $I^- + I_2 \longrightarrow$

15.40 Complete each of the following equations. Then write the Lewis formulas of the reactants and products and identify each reactant as a Lewis acid or a Lewis base.
a. $GaBr_3 + Br^- \longrightarrow$
b. $BF_3 + F^- \longrightarrow$

15.41 In the following reactions, identify each reactant as a Lewis acid or a Lewis base.
a. $Cu^{2+} + 6H_2O \longrightarrow Cu(H_2O)_6^{2+}$
b. $BBr_3 + :AsH_3 \longrightarrow Br_3B:AsH_3$

15.42 In the following reactions, label each reactant as a Lewis acid or a Lewis base.
a. $BeF_2 + 2F^- \longrightarrow BeF_4^{2-}$
b. $SnCl_4 + 2Cl^- \longrightarrow SnCl_6^{2-}$

15.43 Natural gas frequently contains hydrogen sulfide, H_2S. H_2S is removed from natural gas by passing it through aqueous ethanolamine, $HOCH_2CH_2NH_2$ (an ammonia derivative), which reacts with the hydrogen sulfide. Write the equation for the reaction. Identify each reactant as either a Lewis acid or a Lewis base. Explain how you arrived at your answer.

15.44 Coal and other fossil fuels usually contain sulfur compounds that produce sulfur dioxide, SO_2, when burned. One possible way to remove the sulfur dioxide is to pass the combustion gases into a tower packed with calcium oxide, CaO. Write the equation for the reaction. Identify each reactant as either a Lewis acid or a Lewis base. Explain how you arrived at your answer.

Acid and Base Strengths

15.45 Complete the following equation. Using Table 15.2, predict whether you would expect the reaction to occur to any significant extent or whether the reaction is more likely to occur in the opposite direction.

$$HSO_4^-(aq) + ClO^-(aq) \longrightarrow$$

15.46 Complete the following equation. Using Table 15.2, predict whether you would expect the reaction to occur to any significant extent or whether the reaction is more likely to occur in the opposite direction.

$$HCN(aq) + SO_4^{2-}(aq) \longrightarrow$$

15.47 Use Table 15.2 to decide whether the species on the left or those on the right are favored by the reaction.
a. $NH_4^+ + H_2PO_4^- \rightleftharpoons NH_3 + H_3PO_4$
b. $HCN + HS^- \rightleftharpoons CN^- + H_2S$
c. $HCO_3^- + OH^- \rightleftharpoons CO_3^{2-} + H_2O$
d. $Al(H_2O)_6^{3+} + OH^- \rightleftharpoons Al(H_2O)_5OH^{2+} + H_2O$

15.48 Use Table 15.2 to decide whether the species on the left or those on the right are favored by the reaction.
a. $NH_4^+ + HCO_3^- \rightleftharpoons NH_3 + H_2CO_3$
b. $HCO_3^- + H_2S \rightleftharpoons H_2CO_3 + HS^-$
c. $CN^- + H_2O \rightleftharpoons HCN + OH^-$
d. $CN^- + HCO_3^- \rightleftharpoons HCN + CO_3^{2-}$

15.49 In the following reaction of trichloroacetic acid, $HC_2Cl_3O_2$, with formate ion, CHO_2^-, the formation of trichloroacetate ion, $C_2Cl_3O_2^-$, and formic acid, $HCHO_2$ is favored.

$$HC_2Cl_3O_2 + CHO_2^- \longrightarrow C_2Cl_3O_2^- + HCHO_2$$

Which is the stronger acid, trichloroacetic acid or formic acid? Explain.

15.50 In the following reaction of tetrafluoroboric acid, HBF_4, with the acetate ion, $C_2H_3O_2^-$, the formation of tetrafluoroborate ion, BF_4^-, and acetic acid, $HC_2H_3O_2$ is favored.

$$HBF_4 + C_2H_3O_2^- \longrightarrow BF_4^- + HC_2H_3O_2$$

Which is the weaker base, BF_4^- or acetate ion?

15.51 For each of the following pairs, give the stronger acid. Explain your answer.
a. H_2S, HS^- b. H_2SO_3, H_2SeO_3 c. HBr, H_2Se
d. HIO_4, HIO_3 e. H_2S, H_2O

15.52 Order each of the following pairs by acid strength, giving the weaker acid first. Explain your answer.
a. $HBrO_4, HBrO_3$ b. HCO_3^-, H_2CO_3 c. H_2S, H_2Te
d. HBr, H_2Se e. H_3PO_4, H_3AsO_4

Solutions of a Strong Acid or Base

15.53 What are the concentrations of H_3O^+ and OH^- in each of the following?
a. $1.2 \, M \, HBr$ b. $0.32 \, M \, KOH$
c. $0.085 \, M \, Ca(OH)_2$ d. $0.38 \, M \, HNO_3$

15.54 What are the concentrations of H_3O^+ and OH^- in each of the following?
a. $1.65 \, M \, NaOH$ b. $0.35 \, M \, Sr(OH)_2$
c. $0.045 \, M \, HClO_4$ d. $0.58 \, M \, HCl$

15.55 A solution of hydrochloric acid is $0.050 \, M \, HCl$. What is the hydronium-ion concentration at 25°C? What is the hydroxide-ion concentration at 25°C?

15.56 A solution is $0.020 \, M \, HNO_3$ (nitric acid). What is the hydronium-ion concentration at 25°C? What is the hydroxide-ion concentration at 25°C?

15.57 What are the hydronium-ion and the hydroxide-ion concentrations of a solution at 25°C that is $0.0085 \, M$ barium hydroxide, $Ba(OH)_2$?

15.58 A saturated solution of magnesium hydroxide is $3.2 \times 10^{-4} \, M \, Mg(OH)_2$. What are the hydronium-ion and hydroxide-ion concentrations in the solution at 25°C?

15.59 The following are solution concentrations. Indicate whether each solution is acidic, basic, or neutral.
a. $5 \times 10^{-6} \, M \, H_3O^+$ b. $5 \times 10^{-9} \, M \, OH^-$
c. $1 \times 10^{-7} \, M \, OH^-$ d. $2 \times 10^{-9} \, M \, H_3O^+$

15.60 The following are solution concentrations. Indicate whether each solution is acidic, basic, or neutral.
a. $2 \times 10^{-11} \, M \, OH^-$ b. $2 \times 10^{-9} \, M \, H_3O^+$
c. $6 \times 10^{-5} \, M \, OH^-$ d. $6 \times 10^{-3} \, M \, H_3O^+$

15.61 A shampoo solution at 25°C has a hydroxide-ion concentration of $1.5 \times 10^{-9} \, M$. Is the solution acidic, neutral, or basic?

15.62 An antiseptic solution at 25°C has a hydroxide-ion concentration of $8.4 \times 10^{-5} \, M$. Is the solution acidic, neutral, or basic?

Calculations Involving pH

15.63 Which of the following pH values indicate an acidic solution at 25°C? Which are basic and which are neutral?
a. 4.6   b. 7.0   c. 1.6   d. 10.5

15.64 Which of the following pH values indicate an acidic solution at 25°C? Which are basic and which are neutral?
a. 5.6   b. 2.5   c. 13.2   d. 9.3

15.65 For each of the following, state whether the solution at 25°C is acidic, neutral, or basic: (a) A beverage solution has a pH of 3.5. (b) A $0.50 \, M$ solution of potassium bromide, KBr, has a pH of 7.0. (c) A $0.050 \, M$ solution of pyridine, C_5H_5N, has a pH of 9.0. (d) A solution of iron(III) chloride has a pH of 5.5.

15.66 For each of the following, state whether the solution at 25°C is acidic, neutral, or basic: (a) A $0.1 \, M$ solution of trisodium phosphate, Na_3PO_4, has a pH of 12.0. (b) A $0.1 \, M$ solution of calcium chloride, $CaCl_2$, has a pH of 7.0. (c) A $0.2 \, M$ solution of copper(II) sulfate, $CuSO_4$, has a pH of 4.0. (d) A sample of rainwater has a pH of 5.7.

15.67 Obtain the pH corresponding to the following hydronium-ion concentrations.
a. $1.0 \times 10^{-8} \, M$ b. $5.0 \times 10^{-12} \, M$
c. $7.5 \times 10^{-3} \, M$ d. $6.35 \times 10^{-9} \, M$

15.68 Obtain the pH corresponding to the following hydronium-ion concentrations.
a. $2.5 \times 10^{-4} \, M$ b. $5.7 \times 10^{-10} \, M$
c. $4.6 \times 10^{-5} \, M$ d. $2.91 \times 10^{-11} \, M$

15.69 A sample of vinegar has a hydronium-ion concentration of $7.5 \times 10^{-3} \, M$. What is the pH of the vinegar?

15.70 Some lemon juice has a hydronium-ion concentration of $5.0 \times 10^{-3} \, M$. What is the pH of the lemon juice?

15.71 Obtain the pH corresponding to the following hydroxide-ion concentrations.
a. $5.25 \times 10^{-9} \, M$ b. $8.3 \times 10^{-3} \, M$
c. $3.6 \times 10^{-12} \, M$ d. $2.1 \times 10^{-8} \, M$

15.72 Obtain the pH corresponding to the following hydroxide-ion concentrations.
a. $6.74 \times 10^{-11}\ M$ b. $5.8 \times 10^{-5}\ M$
c. $3.4 \times 10^{-10}\ M$ d. $7.1 \times 10^{-4}\ M$

15.73 A solution of washing soda (sodium carbonate, Na_2CO_3) has a hydroxide-ion concentration of $0.0040\ M$. What is the pH at 25°C?

15.74 A solution of lye (sodium hydroxide, NaOH) has a hydroxide-ion concentration of $0.050\ M$. What is the pH at 25°C?

15.75 The pH of a cup of coffee (at 25°C) was found to be 5.12. What is the hydronium-ion concentration?

15.76 A wine was tested for acidity, and its pH was found to be 3.85 at 25°C. What is the hydronium-ion concentration?

15.77 A detergent solution has a pH of 11.63 at 25°C. What is the hydroxide-ion concentration?

15.78 Morphine is a narcotic that is used to relieve pain. A solution of morphine has a pH of 9.61 at 25°C. What is the hydroxide-ion concentration?

15.79 A 1.00-L aqueous solution contained 5.80 g of sodium hydroxide, NaOH. What was the pH of the solution at 25°C?

15.80 A 1.00-L aqueous solution contained 6.78 g of barium hydroxide, $Ba(OH)_2$. What was the pH of the solution at 25°C?

15.81 A certain sample of rainwater gives a yellow color with methyl red and a yellow color with bromthymol blue. What is the approximate pH of the water? Is the rainwater acidic, neutral, or basic? (See Figure 15.10.)

15.82 A drop of thymol blue gave a yellow color with a solution of aspirin. A sample of the same aspirin solution gave a yellow color with bromphenol blue. What was the pH of the solution? Was the solution acidic, neutral, or basic? (See Figure 15.10.)

General Problems

15.83 Identify each of the following as an acid or a base in terms of the Arrhenius concept. Give the chemical equation for the reaction of the substance with water, showing the origin of the acidity or basicity.
a. BaO   b. H_2S c. CH_3NH_2 d. SO_2

15.84 Which of the following substances are acids in terms of the Arrhenius concept? Which are bases? Show the acid or base character by using chemical equations.
a. P_4O_{10} b. K_2O c. N_2H_4 d. H_2Se

15.85 Write a reaction for each of the following in which the species acts as a Brønsted acid. The equilibrium should favor the product side.
a. H_2O_2 b. HCO_3^- c. NH_4^+ d. $H_2PO_4^-$

15.86 Write a reaction for each of the following in which the species acts as a Brønsted base. The equilibrium should favor the product side.
a. H_2O b. HCO_3^- c. NH_3 d. $H_2PO_4^-$

15.87 For each of the following, write the complete chemical equation for the acid–base reaction that occurs. Describe each using Brønsted language (if appropriate) and then using Lewis language (show electron-dot formulas).
a. The ClO^- ion reacts with water.
b. The reaction of NH_4^+ and NH_2^- in liquid ammonia to produce NH_3.

15.88 For each of the following, write the complete chemical equation for the acid–base reaction that occurs. Describe each using Brønsted language (if appropriate) and then using Lewis language (show electron-dot formulas).
a. The HS^- ion reacts in water to produce H_2S.
b. Cyanide ion, CN^-, reacts with Fe^{3+}.

15.89 Complete the following proton-transfer reaction. Decide on the basis of relative acid strengths whether the reaction is more likely to go in the direction written or in the opposite direction.

$$HNO_2 + F^- \rightleftharpoons$$

15.90 Complete the following reaction. Decide on the basis of relative acid strengths whether the reaction is more likely to go in the direction written or in the opposite direction.

$$HS^- + HCN \rightleftharpoons$$

15.91 List the following compounds in order of increasing acid strength: HBr, H_2Se, H_2S.

15.92 List the following compounds in order of increasing acid strength: $HBrO_2$, $HClO_2$, HBrO.

15.93 A solution is $0.25\ M$ KOH. What are the concentrations of H_3O^+ and OH^- in this solution?

15.94 A solution is $0.35\ M$ $Sr(OH)_2$. What are the concentrations of H_3O^+ and OH^- in this solution?

15.95 A wine has a hydronium-ion concentration equal to $1.5 \times 10^{-3}\ M$. What is the pH of this wine?

15.96 A sample of lemon juice has a hydronium-ion concentration equal to $2.5 \times 10^{-2}\ M$. What is the pH of this sample?

15.97 A sample of apple cider has a pH of 3.15. What is the hydroxide-ion concentration of this solution?

15.98 A sample of grape juice has a pH of 4.05. What is the hydroxide-ion concentration of this solution?

15.99 A 2.500-g sample of a mixture of sodium hydrogen carbonate and potassium chloride is dissolved in 25.00 mL of $0.437\ M$ H_2SO_4. Some acid remains after treatment of the sample.
a. Write both the net ionic and the molecular equations for the complete reaction of sodium hydrogen carbonate with sulfuric acid.
b. If 35.4-mL of $0.108\ M$ NaOH were required to titrate the excess sulfuric acid, how many moles of sodium hydrogen carbonate were present in the original sample?
c. What is the percent composition of the original sample?

15.100 A 2.500-g sample of a mixture of sodium carbonate and sodium chloride is dissolved in 25.00 mL of 0.798 M HCl. Some acid remains after the treatment of the sample.
  a. Write the net ionic equation for the complete reaction of sodium carbonate with hydrochloric acid.
  b. If 28.7 mL of 0.108 M NaOH were required to titrate the excess hydrochloric acid, how many moles of sodium carbonate were present in the original sample?
  c. What is the percent composition of the original sample?

15.101 The bicarbonate ion has the ability to act as an acid in the presence of a base and as a base in the presence of an acid, so it is said to be amphiprotic. Illustrate this behavior with water by writing Brønsted–Lowry acid–base reactions. Also illustrate this property by selecting a common strong acid and base to react with the bicarbonate ion.

15.102 The dihydrogen phosphate ion has the ability to act as an acid in the presence of a base and as a base in the presence of an acid. What is this property called? Illustrate this behavior with water by writing Brønsted–Lowry acid–base reactions. Also illustrate this property by selecting a common acid and base to react with the dihydrogen phosphate ion.

15.103 The hydride ion does not exist in water because it has a greater attraction for the hydronium ion than the hydroxide ion does. Write the equation for the reaction that occurs when calcium hydride is added to water. Which is the stronger base, the hydride ion or the hydroxide ion? What is the meaning of the statement that the strongest base that can exist in water is the hydroxide ion?

15.104 The nitride ion and the amide ion, NH_2^-, have greater attractions for the hydronium ion than the hydroxide ion does. Write the equations for the reactions that occur when calcium nitride and sodium amide are added to water (each gives NH_3). Which is the stronger base, the nitride ion or the amide ion? Why? What is the meaning of the statement that the hydroxide ion is the strongest base that can exist in water?

15.105 Pure liquid hydrogen fluoride ionizes in a way similar to that of water.
  a. Write the equilibrium reaction for the self-ionization of liquid hydrogen fluoride.
  b. Will sodium fluoride be an acid or a base in liquid hydrogen fluoride? Why?
  c. Perchloric acid is a strong acid in liquid hydrogen fluoride. Write the chemical equation for the ionization reaction. What is the conjugate acid in this medium?

15.106 Pure liquid ammonia ionizes in a way similar to that of water.
  a. Write the equilibrium reaction of liquid ammonia.
  b. Will sodium amide, $NaNH_2$, be an acid or a base in liquid ammonia? Why?
  c. Ammonium chloride can be used to titrate sodium amide in liquid ammonia. Write the chemical equation for the titration of sodium amide with ammonium chloride in liquid ammonia.

15.107 A solution contains 4.25 g of ammonia per 250.0 mL of solution. Electrical conductivity measurements at 25°C show that 0.42% of the ammonia has reacted with water. Write the equation for this reaction and calculate the pH of the solution.

15.108 A solution contains 0.675 g of ethylamine, $C_2H_5NH_2$, per 100.0 mL of solution. Electrical conductivity measurements at 20°C show that 0.98% of the ethylamine has reacted with water. Write the equation for this reaction. Calculate the pH of the solution.

15.109 Why do medicines frequently taste bitter?

15.110 Show how methylamine, CH_3NH_2, is a Bronsted–Lowry base. Is methylamine also a Lewis base? Explain.

15.111 Explain how sodium hydroxide dissolves grease and hair from a stopped drain.

15.112 How is sodium hydroxide prepared commercially?

Strategy Problems

15.113 Ethanol (ethyl alcohol), CH_3CH_2OH, can act as a Brønsted–Lowry acid. Write the chemical equation for the reaction of ethanol as an acid with hydroxide ion, OH^-. Ethanol can also react as a Brønsted–Lowry base. Write the chemical equation for the reaction of ethanol as a base with hydronium ion, H_3O^+. Explain how you arrived at these chemical equations. Both of these reactions can also be considered Lewis acid–base reactions. Explain this.

15.114 Ethanol, CH_3CH_2OH, can undergo self-ionization. Write the chemical equation for this self-ionization. Explain how you arrived at this equation. At room temperature, the ion product for this self-ionization is 1.0×10^{-20}. What is the concentration of each ion at this temperature? Show how you arrived at these concentrations.

15.115 Aluminum chloride, $AlCl_3$, reacts with trimethylamine, $N(CH_3)_3$. What would you guess to be the product of this reac-

tion? Explain why you think so. Describe the reaction in terms of one of the acid–base concepts. Write an appropriate equation to go with this description. Which substance is the acid according to this acid–base concept? Explain.

15.116 Consider each of the following pairs of compounds, and indicate which one of each pair is the stronger Lewis acid. Explain how you arrived at your answers.
  a. Fe^{2+}, Fe^{3+} **b.** BF_3, BCl_3

15.117 Arrange each of the following in order of increasing acidity. You may need to use a couple of rules to decide the order for a given series. Explain the reasoning you use in each case.
  a. $HBrO_2$, $HBrO_3$, $HBrO$
  b. H_2TeO_3, H_2SO_3, H_2SeO_3
  c. HI, SbH_3, H_2Te
  d. H_2S, HBr, H_2Se
  e. $HClO_2$, $HClO_3$, $HBrO_2$

15.118 The following is a table of some of the oxoacids of the halogens. Which acid in the table is the strongest? Which is the weakest? Explain how you arrived at your answers.

Chlorine	Bromine	Iodine
HOCl	HOBr	HOI
HOClO	HOBrO	HOIO
HOClO$_2$	HOBrO$_2$	HOIO$_2$

15.119 Suppose you have 557 mL of 0.0300 M HCl, and you want to make up a solution of HCl that has a pH of 1.831. What is the maximum volume (in liters) that you can make of this solution?

15.120 How many grams of water are in dissociated form (as H$^+$ and OH$^-$ ions) in 1.00 L of pure water? How many hydrogen ions, H$^+$(aq), are there in 1.00 L of pure water?

15.121 You want to make up 3.00 L of aqueous hydrochloric acid, HCl(aq), that has a pH of 2.00. How many grams of concentrated hydrochloric acid will you need? Concentrated hydrochloric acid contains 37.2 mass percent of HCl.

15.122 You can obtain the pH of a 0.100 M HCl solution by assuming that all of the H$_3$O$^+$ ion comes from the HCl, in which case the pH equals $-$ log 0.100 = 1.00. But if you want the pH of a solution that is 1.00 × 10^{-7} M HCl, you need to account for any H$_3$O$^+$ ion coming from water. (Why?) Note that the self-ionization of water is the only equilibrium you need to account for. What is the pH of 1.00 × 10^{-7} M HCl?

Cumulative-Skills Problems

15.123 Phosphorous acid, H$_3$PO$_3$, and phosphoric acid, H$_3$PO$_4$, have approximately the same acid strengths. From this information, and noting the possibility that one or more hydrogen atoms may be directly bonded to the phosphorus atom, draw the structural formula of phosphorous acid. How many grams of sodium hydroxide would be required to completely neutralize 1.00 g of this acid?

15.124 Hypophosphorous acid, H$_3$PO$_2$, and phosphoric acid, H$_3$PO$_4$, have approximately the same acid strengths. From this information, and noting the possibility that one or more hydrogen atoms may be directly bonded to the phosphorus atom, draw the structural formula of hypophosphorous acid. How many grams of sodium hydroxide would be required to completely neutralize 1.00 g of this acid?

15.125 Boron trifluoride, BF$_3$, and ammonia, NH$_3$, react to produce BF$_3$·NH$_3$. A coordinate covalent bond is formed between the boron atom on BF$_3$ and the nitrogen atom on NH$_3$. Write the equation for this reaction, using Lewis electron-dot formulas. Label the Lewis acid and the Lewis base. Determine how many grams of BF$_3$·NH$_3$ are formed when 10.0 g BF$_3$ and 10.0 g NH$_3$ are placed in a reaction vessel, assuming that the reaction goes to completion.

15.126 Boron trifluoride, BF$_3$, and diethyl ether, (C$_2$H$_5$)$_2$O, react to produce a compound with the formula BF$_3$·(C$_2$H$_5$)$_2$O. A coordinate covalent bond is formed between the boron atom on BF$_3$ and the oxygen atom on (C$_2$H$_5$)$_2$O. Write the equation for this reaction, using Lewis electron-dot formulas. Label the Lewis acid and the Lewis base. Determine how many grams of BF$_3$·(C$_2$H$_5$)$_2$O are formed when 10.0 g BF$_3$ and 20.0 g (C$_2$H$_5$)$_2$O are placed in a reaction vessel, assuming that the reaction goes to completion.

16
Acid–Base Equilibria

Limestone, which is mainly $CaCO_3$, is slightly soluble in acidic solution, so these limestone gargoyles are easily damaged by acid rain. The basic property of limestone makes the powdered form useful as a soil conditioner, to adjust soil pH. Sulfuric acid is a component of acid rain; a major commercial use of this acid is to produce fertilizers, such as ammonium phosphate, from phosphate rock.

Contents and Concepts

We will investigate the reactions and equilibrium calculations of weak acids, weak bases, and salts in aqueous solution.

We now take the opportunity to see how the pH of weak acids and weak bases is affected by the addition of a solute.

M any well-known substances are weak acids or bases. The following are weak acids: aspirin (acetylsalicylic acid, a headache remedy), phenobarbital (a sedative), saccharin (a sweetener), and niacin (nicotinic acid, a B vitamin). That these are *weak* acids means that their reactions with water do not go to completion. To discuss such acid–base reactions, you need to look at the equilibria involved and be able to calculate the concentrations of species in a reaction mixture.

Consider, for example, how you could answer the following questions: What is the hydronium-ion concentration of 0.10 M niacin (nicotinic acid)? What is the hydronium-ion concentration of the solution obtained by dissolving one 5.00-grain tablet of aspirin (acetylsalicylic acid) in 0.500 L of water? If these were solutions of strong acids, the calculations would be simple; 0.10 M monoprotic acid would yield 0.10 M H_3O^+ ion. However, because niacin is a weak monoprotic acid, the H_3O^+ concentration is less than 0.10 M. To find the concentration, you need the equilibrium constant for the reaction involved, and you need to solve an equilibrium problem.

A similar process is involved in finding the hydronium-ion concentration of 0.10 M sodium nicotinate (sodium salt of niacin). In this case, you need to look at the acid–base equilibrium of the nicotinate ion. Let us see how you answer questions of this sort.

■ **See page 689 for the Media Summary.**

Solutions of a Weak Acid or Base

The simplest acid–base equilibria are those in which a single acid or base solute reacts with water. We will look first at solutions of weak acids, next at solutions of weak bases. Then we will consider solutions of salts, which can have acidic or basic properties as a result of reactions of their ions with water.

16.1 | Acid-Ionization Equilibria

An acid reacts with water to produce hydronium ion (hydrogen ion) and the conjugate base ion. The process is called *acid ionization* or *acid dissociation*. Consider an aqueous solution of the weak acid acetic acid, $HC_2H_3O_2$, the sour constituent of vinegar (Figure 16.1). When the acid is added to water, it reacts according to the equation

$$HC_2H_3O_2(aq) + H_2O(l) \rightleftharpoons H_3O^+(aq) + C_2H_3O_2^-(aq)$$

Because acetic acid is a weak electrolyte, the acid *ionizes* to a small extent in water (about 1% or less, depending on the concentration of acid).

FIGURE 16.1 ▶

The structure of acetic acid
Left: Structural formula. Only the hydrogen atom (in color) attached to the oxygen atom is acidic. The hydrogen atoms attached to carbon atoms are not acidic. The acidic group

$$-\overset{\displaystyle O}{\underset{\displaystyle \|}{C}}-O-H$$

(often written —COOH and called the carboxylic acid group) occurs in many organic acids. *Right:* Electrostatic potential map of acetic acid.

For a strong acid, which ionizes completely in solution, the concentrations of ions are determined by the stoichiometry of the reaction from the initial concentration of acid. However, for a weak acid such as acetic acid, the concentrations of ions in solution are determined from the **acid-ionization constant** (also called the acid-dissociation constant), which is *the equilibrium constant for the ionization of a weak acid*.

To find the acid-ionization constant, write HA for the general formula of a weak, monoprotic acid. The acid-ionization equilibrium in aqueous solution is

$$HA(aq) + H_2O(l) \rightleftharpoons H_3O^+(aq) + A^-(aq)$$

In terms of the thermodynamic equilibrium constant, the activity of H_2O is nearly constant and essentially 1, so it does not appear explicitly in the equilibrium constant.

The corresponding equilibrium constant is

$$K_c = \frac{[H_3O^+][A^-]}{[HA][H_2O]}$$

Assuming that this is a dilute solution and that the reaction occurs to only a small extent, the concentration of water will be nearly constant. Rearranging this equation gives

$$K_a = [H_2O]K_c = \frac{[H_3O^+][A^-]}{[HA]}$$

Thus, K_a, the acid-ionization constant, equals the constant $[H_2O]K_c$. <

$$K_a = \frac{[H_3O^+][A^-]}{[HA]}$$

FIGURE 16.2 ▲

The structure of nicotinic acid
Top: The structural formula of nicotinic acid (niacin); note the acidic hydrogen atom (in color). Nicotinic acid was first prepared by oxidizing nicotine, a basic substance present in tobacco. *Bottom:* Electrostatic potential map of nicotinic acid.

Experimental Determination of K_a

The ionization constant for a weak acid is usually determined experimentally by one of two methods. In one method, the electrical conductivity or some colligative property of a solution of the acid is measured to obtain its degree of ionization. The **degree of ionization** of a weak electrolyte is *the fraction of molecules that react with water to give ions*. This may also be expressed as a percentage, giving the *percent ionization*. In the other method, the pH of a solution of the weak acid is determined. From the pH one finds the concentration of H_3O^+ ion and then the concentrations of other ions. The following example shows how to calculate K_a from the pH of a solution of nicotinic acid (Figure 16.2). It also shows how to calculate the degree of ionization and the percent ionization.

Example 16.1	Determining K_a from the Solution pH

Nicotinic acid (niacin) is a monoprotic acid with the formula $HC_6H_4NO_2$. A solution that is 0.012 M in nicotinic acid has a pH of 3.39 at 25°C. What is the acid-ionization constant, K_a, for this acid at 25°C? What is the degree of ionization of nicotinic acid in this solution?

Problem Strategy   It is important to realize that when we say the solution is 0.012 M, this refers to *how the solution is prepared*. The solution is made up by adding 0.012 mol of substance to enough water to give a liter of solution. Once the solution is prepared, some molecules ionize, so the actual concentration is somewhat less than 0.012 M. To solve for K_a, you follow the three steps outlined in Chapter 14 for solving equilibrium problems.

Solution

Step 1:   Abbreviate the formula for nicotinic acid as HNic. Then 1 L of solution contains 0.012 mol HNic and 0 mol Nic⁻, the acid anion, before ionization. The H_3O^+

(continued)

(continued)

concentration at the start is that from the self-ionization of water. It is usually much smaller than that obtained from the acid (unless the solution is extremely dilute or K_a is quite small), so you can write $[H_3O^+] = {\sim}0$ (meaning approximately zero). If x mol HNic ionizes, x mol each of H_3O^+ and Nic^- is formed, leaving $(0.012 - x)$ mol HNic in solution. You can summarize the situation as follows:

Concentration (M)	$HNic(aq) + H_2O(l) \rightleftharpoons H_3O^+(aq) + Nic^-(aq)$		
Starting	0.012	~0	0
Change	$-x$	$+x$	$+x$
Equilibrium	$0.012 - x$	x	x

Thus, the molar concentrations of HNic, H_3O^+, and Nic^- at equilibrium are $(0.012 - x)$, x, and x, respectively.

Step 2: The equilibrium-constant equation is

$$K_a = \frac{[H_3O^+][Nic^-]}{[HNic]}$$

When you substitute the expressions for the equilibrium concentrations, you get

$$K_a = \frac{x^2}{(0.012 - x)}$$

Step 3: The value of x equals the numerical value of the molar hydronium-ion concentration and can be obtained from the pH of the solution.

$$x = [H_3O^+] = \text{antilog}(-pH) = \text{antilog}(-3.39) = 4.1 \times 10^{-4} = 0.00041$$

You can substitute this value of x into the equation obtained in Step 2. Note first, however, that

$$0.012 - x = 0.012 - 0.00041 = 0.01159 \approx 0.012 \quad \text{(to two significant figures)}$$

This means that the concentration of undissolved acid is equal to the original concentration of the acid within the precision of the data. (We will make use of this type of observation in later problem solving.) Therefore,

$$K_a = \frac{x^2}{(0.012 - x)} \approx \frac{x^2}{0.012} \approx \frac{(0.00041)^2}{0.012} = \mathbf{1.4 \times 10^{-5}}$$

To obtain the degree of ionization, note that x mol out of 0.012 mol of nicotinic acid ionizes. Hence,

$$\text{Degree of ionization} = \frac{x}{0.012} = \frac{0.00041}{0.012} = \mathbf{0.034}$$

The percent ionization is obtained by multiplying this by 100, which gives 3.4%.

Answer Check In order to be a weak acid, the K_a value must be very small, as it is here. Therefore, if you calculate a K_a for a weak acid that is greater than 10^{-1}, you should check for errors in your work.

Exercise 16.1 Lactic acid, $HC_3H_5O_3$, is found in sour milk, where it is produced by the action of lactobacilli on lactose, or milk sugar. A 0.025 M solution of lactic acid has a pH of 2.75. What is the ionization constant K_a for this acid? What is the degree of ionization? >

Lactic acid has the structural formula

H–C–C–C–O–H with H H O on top and H O below

and the electrostatic potential map

■ See Problems 16.35 and 16.36.

TABLE 16.1	Acid-Ionization Constants at 25°C*	
Substance	Formula	K_a
Acetic acid	$HC_2H_3O_2$	1.7×10^{-5}
Benzoic acid	$HC_7H_5O_2$	6.3×10^{-5}
Boric acid	H_3BO_3	5.9×10^{-10}
Carbonic acid	H_2CO_3	4.3×10^{-7}
	HCO_3^-	4.8×10^{-11}
Cyanic acid	$HOCN$	3.5×10^{-4}
Formic acid	$HCHO_2$	1.7×10^{-4}
Hydrocyanic acid	HCN	4.9×10^{-10}
Hydrofluoric acid	HF	6.8×10^{-4}
Hydrogen sulfate ion	HSO_4^-	1.1×10^{-2}
Hydrogen sulfide	H_2S	8.9×10^{-8}
	HS^-	$1.2 \times 10^{-13\dagger}$
Hypochlorous acid	$HClO$	3.5×10^{-8}
Nitrous acid	HNO_2	4.5×10^{-4}
Oxalic acid	$H_2C_2O_4$	5.6×10^{-2}
	$HC_2O_4^-$	5.1×10^{-5}
Phosphoric acid	H_3PO_4	6.9×10^{-3}
	$H_2PO_4^-$	6.2×10^{-8}
	HPO_4^{2-}	4.8×10^{-13}
Phosphorous acid	H_2PHO_3	1.6×10^{-2}
	$HPHO_3^-$	7×10^{-7}
Propionic acid	$HC_3H_5O_2$	1.3×10^{-5}
Pyruvic acid	$HC_3H_3O_3$	1.4×10^{-4}
Sulfurous acid	H_2SO_3	1.3×10^{-2}
	HSO_3^-	6.3×10^{-8}

*The ionization constants for polyprotic acids are for successive ionizations. For example, for H_3PO_4, the equilibrium is $H_3PO_4 + H_2O \rightleftharpoons H_3O^+ + H_2PO_4^-$. For $H_2PO_4^-$, the equilibrium is $H_2PO_4^- + H_2O \rightleftharpoons H_3O^+ + HPO_4^{2-}$.

†This value is in doubt. Some evidence suggests that it is about 10^{-19}. See R. J. Myers, *J. Chem. Educ.*, **63**, 687 (1986).

Table 16.1 lists acid-ionization constants for various weak acids. The weakest acids have the smallest values of K_a.

Calculations with K_a

Once you know the value of K_a for an acid HA, you can calculate the equilibrium concentrations of species HA, A^-, and H_3O^+ for solutions of different molarities. The general method for doing this was discussed in Chapter 14. Here we illustrate the use of a simplifying approximation that can often be used for weak acids. In the next example, we will look at an amplification of the first question posed in the chapter opening.

Example 16.2 | Calculating Concentrations of Species in a Weak Acid Solution Using K_a (Approximation Method)

What are the concentrations of nicotinic acid, hydrogen ion, and nicotinate ion in a solution of 0.10 *M* nicotinic acid, $HC_6H_4NO_2$, at 25°C? What is the pH of the solution? What

(continued)

(continued)

is the degree of ionization of nicotinic acid? The acid-ionization constant, K_a, was determined in the previous example to be 1.4×10^{-5}.

Problem Strategy You follow the three steps for solving equilibrium problems that were introduced in Example 14.7. In the last step, you solve the equilibrium-constant equation for the equilibrium concentrations. The resulting equation is quadratic, but because the equilibrium concentration of a weak acid is usually negligibly different from its starting value, the equation simplifies so that it involves only the square of the unknown, which is easily solved by taking the square root. (You will need to check that this assumption is valid.)

Solution

Step 1: At the start (before ionization), the concentration of nicotinic acid, HNic, is 0.10 M and that of its conjugate base, Nic^-, is 0. The concentration of H_3O^+ is essentially zero ($\sim$0), assuming that the contribution from the self-ionization of water can be neglected. In 1 L of solution, the nicotinic acid ionizes to give x mol H_3O^+ and x mol Nic^-, leaving $(0.10 - x)$ mol of nicotinic acid. These data are summarized in the following table:

Concentration (M)	$HNic(aq) + H_2O(l) \rightleftharpoons H_3O^+(aq) + Nic^-(aq)$		
Starting	0.10	$\sim$0	0
Change	$-x$	$+x$	$+x$
Equilibrium	$0.10 - x$	x	x

The equilibrium concentrations of HNic, H_3O^+, and Nic^- are $(0.10 - x)$, x, and x, respectively.

Step 2: Now substitute these concentrations and the value of K_a into the equilibrium-constant equation for acid ionization:

$$\frac{[H_3O^+][Nic^-]}{[HNic]} = K_a$$

You get

$$\frac{x^2}{(0.10 - x)} = 1.4 \times 10^{-5}$$

Step 3: Now solve this equation for x. This is actually a quadratic equation, but it can be simplified so that the value of x is easily found. Because the acid-ionization constant is small, the value of x is small. Assume that x is much smaller than 0.10, so that

$$0.10 - x \simeq 0.10$$

You will need to check that this assumption is valid after you obtain a value for x. The equilibrium-constant equation becomes

$$\frac{x^2}{0.10} \simeq 1.4 \times 10^{-5}$$

or

$$x^2 \simeq 1.4 \times 10^{-5} \times 0.10 = 1.4 \times 10^{-6}$$

Hence,

$$x \simeq 1.2 \times 10^{-3} = 0.0012$$

(continued)

(continued)

At this point, you should check to make sure that the assumption $0.10 - x \simeq 0.10$ is valid. You substitute the value obtained for x into $0.10 - x$.

$$0.10 - x = 0.10 - 0.0012 = 0.10 \qquad \text{(to two significant figures)}$$

The assumption is indeed valid.

Now you can substitute the value of x into the last line of the table written in Step 1 to find the concentrations of species. The concentrations of nicotinic acid, hydronium ion, and nicotinate ion are **0.10 M, 0.0012 M, and 0.0012 M,** respectively.

The pH of the solution is

$$\text{pH} = -\log [H_3O^+] = -\log (0.0012) = \textbf{2.92}$$

The degree of ionization equals the amount per liter of nicotinic acid that ionizes ($x = 0.0012$) divided by the total amount per liter of nicotinic acid initially present (0.10). Thus, the degree of ionization is $0.0012/0.10 = \textbf{0.012}$.

Answer Check   As a quick check on your work, substitute the concentrations that you calculated for the acid (nicotinic), acid ion (nicotinate), and hydronium ion into the equilibrium expression for K_a. You should get the value of K_a given in the problem.

$$K_a = \frac{[H_3O^+][\text{Nic}^-]}{[\text{HNic}]} = \frac{0.0012 \times 0.0012}{0.10} = 1.4 \times 10^{-5}$$

The pH, of course, should be in the acid range, below 7. Check that this is the case.

Exercise 16.2   What are the concentrations of hydrogen ion and acetate ion in a solution of 0.10 M acetic acid, $HC_2H_3O_2$? What is the pH of the solution? What is the degree of ionization? See Table 16.1 for the value of K_a.

■ See Problems 16.37 and 16.38.

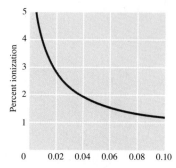

FIGURE 16.3 ▲

Variation of percent ionization of a weak acid with concentration

On this curve for nicotinic acid, note that the percent ionization is greatest for the most dilute solutions.

In Example 16.2, the degree of ionization of nicotinic acid (0.012) is relatively small in a 0.10 M solution. That is, only 1.2% of the molecules ionize. It is the small value of the degree of ionization that allows you to neglect x in the term $0.10 - x$ and thereby simplify the calculation.

The degree of ionization of a weak acid depends on both K_a and the concentration of the acid solution. For a given concentration, the larger the K_a, the greater is the degree of ionization. For a given value of K_a, however, the more dilute the solution, the greater is the degree of ionization. Figure 16.3 shows how the percent ionization (degree of ionization $\times$ 100) varies with the concentration of solution.

How do you know when you can use the simplifying assumption of Example 16.2, where you neglected x in the denominator of the equilibrium equation? *It can be shown that this simplifying assumption gives an error of less than 5% if the concentration of acid, C_a, divided by K_a equals 100 or more.* For example, for an acid concentration of 10^{-2} M and K_a of 10^{-5}, $C_a/K_a = 10^{-2}/10^{-5} = 10^3$, so the assumption is valid. It would not be valid, however, if the concentration of the same acid were 10^{-4} M.

If the simplifying assumption of Example 16.2 is not valid, you can solve the equilibrium equation exactly by using the *quadratic formula*. We illustrate this in the next example with a solution of aspirin, $HC_9H_7O_4$, a common headache remedy. (Figure 16.4 shows the structural formula.)

Example 16.3	Calculating Concentrations of Species in a Weak Acid Solution Using K_a (Quadratic Formula)

What is the pH at 25°C of the solution obtained by dissolving a 5.00-grain tablet of aspirin (acetylsalicylic acid) in 0.500 L of water? The tablet contains 5.00 grains, or 0.325 g, of acetylsalicylic acid, $HC_9H_7O_4$. The acid is monoprotic, and K_a equals 3.3×10^{-4} at 25°C.

Problem Strategy You follow the three steps for equilibrium problems. However, the approximation used in the previous example to solve the equilibrium-constant equation is not valid here. Verify this by calculating C_a/K_a; it is not greater than 100. You solve the equation exactly using the quadratic formula.

Solution The molar mass of $HC_9H_7O_4$ is 180.2 g. From this you find that an aspirin tablet contains 0.00180 mol of the acid. Hence, the concentration of the aspirin solution is 0.00180 mol/0.500 L, or 0.0036 M. (Retain two significant figures, the number of significant figures in K_a.) $C_a/K_a = 0.0036/3.3 \times 10^{-4} = 11$, which is less than 100, so we must solve the equilibrium equation exactly.

FIGURE 16.4 ▲

The structure of aspirin
Top: Structural formula of aspirin (acetylsalicylic acid), a well-known headache remedy. Note the acidic hydrogen atom (in color). *Bottom:* Electrostatic potential map of aspirin.

Step 1: Abbreviate the formula for acetylsalicylic acid as HAcs and let x be the amount of H_3O^+ ion formed in 1 L of solution. The amount of acetylsalicylate ion formed is also x mol; the amount of nonionized acetylsalicylic acid is $(0.0036 - x)$ mol. These data are summarized in the following table:

Concentration (M)	$HAcs(aq) + H_2O(l) \rightleftharpoons H_3O^+(aq) + Acs^-(aq)$		
Starting	0.0036	~0	0
Change	$-x$	$+x$	$+x$
Equilibrium	$0.0036 - x$	x	x

Step 2: If you substitute the equilibrium concentrations and the value of K_a into the equilibrium-constant equation, you get

$$\frac{[H_3O^+][Acs^-]}{[HAcs]} = K_a$$

$$\frac{x^2}{0.0036 - x} = 3.3 \times 10^{-4}$$

Step 3: You can solve the equation exactly using the quadratic formula. Rearrange the preceding equation to put it in the form $ax^2 + bx + c = 0$. You get

$$x^2 = (0.0036 - x) \times 3.3 \times 10^{-4} = 1.2 \times 10^{-6} - 3.3 \times 10^{-4} x$$

or

$$x^2 + 3.3 \times 10^{-4} x - 1.2 \times 10^{-6} = 0$$

Now substitute into the quadratic formula.

$$x = \frac{-b \pm \sqrt{b^2 - 4ac}}{2a}$$

$$= \frac{-3.3 \times 10^{-4} \pm \sqrt{(3.3 \times 10^{-4})^2 + 4(1.2 \times 10^{-6})}}{2}$$

$$= \frac{-3.3 \times 10^{-4} \pm 2.2 \times 10^{-3}}{2}$$

(continued)

(*continued*)

If you take the lower sign in ±, you will get a negative value for x. But x equals the concentration of H_3O^+ ion, so it must be positive. Therefore, you ignore the negative solution. Taking the upper sign, you get

$$x = [H_3O^+] = 9.4 \times 10^{-4}$$

Now you can calculate the pH.

$$pH = -\log [H_3O^+] = -\log(9.4 \times 10^{-4}) = \textbf{3.03}$$

Answer Check As in the previous example, you can do a quick check of your work by essentially reversing the problem, calculating K_a from the equilibrium concentrations of acid, acid ion, and hydronium ion. You can obtain this from the last line of the equilibrium table, now that you have the value of x.

$$[HAcs] = 0.0036 - x = 0.0036 - 9.4 \times 10^{-4} = 0.0027$$
$$[Acs^-] = [H_3O^+] - x = 9.4 \times 10^{-4}$$

Substituting these values into the expression for K_a gives the value of the equilibrium constant.

$$K_a = \frac{[H_3O^+][Acs^-]}{[HAcs]} = \frac{(9.4 \times 10^{-4})^2}{0.0027} = 3.3 \times 10^{-4}$$

Exercise 16.3   What is the pH of an aqueous solution that is 0.0030 M pyruvic acid, $HC_3H_3O_3$? (Pyruvic acid forms during the breakdown of glucose in a cell.) >

Exercise 16.3 mentions that pyruvic acid is formed in biological cells. In muscle tissue, glucose is broken down to pyruvic acid, which is eventually oxidized to carbon dioxide and water. The structural formula of pyruvic acid is

$$\begin{array}{ccc} H & O & O \\ | & \| & \| \\ H-C-C-C-O-H \\ | \\ H \end{array}$$

and the electrostatic potential map is

■ See Problems 16.43 and 16.44.

Concept Check 16.1

You have prepared dilute solutions of equal molar concentrations of $HC_2H_3O_2$ (acetic acid), HNO_2, HF, and HCN. Rank the solutions from the highest pH to the lowest pH. (Refer to Table 16.1.)

16.2 | Polyprotic Acids

In the preceding section, we dealt only with acids releasing one H_3O^+ ion or proton. Some acids, however, have two or more such protons; these acids are called *polyprotic acids*. Sulfuric acid, for example, can lose two protons in aqueous solution. One proton is lost completely to form H_3O^+ (sulfuric acid is a strong acid).

$$H_2SO_4(aq) + H_2O(l) \longrightarrow H_3O^+(aq) + HSO_4^-(aq)$$

The hydrogen sulfate ion, HSO_4^-, may then lose the other proton. In this case, an equilibrium exists.

$$HSO_4^-(aq) + H_2O(l) \rightleftharpoons H_3O^+(aq) + SO_4^{2-}(aq)$$

For a weak diprotic acid like carbonic acid, H_2CO_3, there are two simultaneous equilibria to consider.

$$H_2CO_3(aq) + H_2O(l) \rightleftharpoons H_3O^+(aq) + HCO_3^-(aq)$$
$$HCO_3^-(aq) + H_2O(l) \rightleftharpoons H_3O^+(aq) + CO_3^{2-}(aq)$$

Carbonic acid is in equilibrium with the hydrogen carbonate ion, HCO_3^-, which is in turn in equilibrium with the carbonate ion, CO_3^{2-}. Each equilibrium has an associated acid-ionization constant. For the loss of the first proton,

$$K_{a1} = \frac{[H_3O^+][HCO_3^-]}{[H_2CO_3]} = 4.3 \times 10^{-7}$$

and for the loss of the second proton,

$$K_{a2} = \frac{[H_3O^+][CO_3^{2-}]}{[HCO_3^-]} = 4.8 \times 10^{-11}$$

Note that K_{a1} for carbonic acid is much larger than K_{a2} (by a factor of about 1×10^4). This indicates that carbonic acid loses the first proton more easily than the second one, because the first proton separates from an ion of single negative charge, whereas the second proton separates from an ion of double negative charge. This double negative charge strongly attracts the proton back to it.

> In general, the second ionization constant, K_{a2}, of a polyprotic acid is much smaller than the first ionization constant, K_{a1}. In the case of a triprotic acid, the third ionization constant, K_{a3}, is much smaller than the second one, K_{a2}.

See the values for phosphoric acid, H_3PO_4, in Table 16.1.

Calculating the concentrations of various species in a solution of a polyprotic acid might appear complicated, because several equilibria occur at once. However, reasonable assumptions can be made that simplify the calculation, as we show in the next example.

Example 16.4 | Calculating Concentrations of Species in a Solution of a Diprotic Acid

Ascorbic acid (vitamin C) is a diprotic acid, $H_2C_6H_6O_6$ (Figure 16.5). What is the pH of a 0.10 M solution? What is the concentration of ascorbate ion, $C_6H_6O_6^{2-}$? The acid ionization constants are $K_{a1} = 7.9 \times 10^{-5}$ and $K_{a2} = 1.6 \times 10^{-12}$.

Problem Strategy Diprotic acids have two ionization constants, one for the loss of each proton. To be exact, you should account for both reactions. However, K_{a2} is so much smaller than K_{a1} that the smaller amount of hydronium ion produced in the second reaction can be neglected. Follow the three steps for solving equilibrium problems.

Considering only the first ionization, set up a table of concentrations (starting, change, and equilibrium). Substitute these values into the equilibrium equation for K_{a1}, solve for $x = [H_3O^+]$, and then solve for pH (as in Example 16.2). Ascorbate ion is produced in the second ionization; its concentration, as we show, equals K_{a2}.

Solution **CALCULATION OF PH** Abbreviate the formula for ascorbic acid as H_2Asc. Hydronium ions are produced by two successive acid ionizations.

$$H_2Asc(aq) + H_2O(l) \rightleftharpoons H_3O^+(aq) + HAsc^-(aq); \quad K_{a1} = 7.9 \times 10^{-5}$$

$$HAsc^-(aq) + H_2O(l) \rightleftharpoons H_3O^+(aq) + Asc^{2-}(aq); \quad K_{a2} = 1.6 \times 10^{-12}$$

FIGURE 16.5 ▲

The structure of ascorbic acid
Top: Structural formula of ascorbic acid (vitamin C); note the acidic hydrogen atoms (in color). *Bottom:* Electrostatic potential map of ascorbic acid.

(continued)

A Chemist Looks at . . .

Acid Rain

environment

Acid rain means rain having a pH lower than that of natural rain (pH 5.6). Natural rain dissolves carbon dioxide from the atmosphere to give a slightly acidic solution. The pH of rain in eastern North America and western Europe, however, is approximately 4 and sometimes lower. This acidity is primarily the result of the dissolving in rainwater of sulfur oxides and nitrogen oxides from human activities. In the northeastern United States, the strong acid components in acid rain are about 62% sulfuric acid, 32% nitric acid, and 6% hydrochloric acid.

The sulfuric acid in acid rain has been traced to the burning of fossil fuels and to the burning of sulfide ores in the production of metals, such as zinc and copper. Coal, for example, contains some sulfur mainly as pyrite, or iron(II) disulfide, FeS_2. When this burns in air, it produces sulfur dioxide.

$$4FeS_2(s) + 11O_2(g) \longrightarrow 2Fe_2O_3(s) + 8SO_2(g)$$

In the presence of dust particles and other substances in polluted air, the sulfur dioxide oxidizes further to give sulfur trioxide, which reacts with water to form sulfuric acid.

$$2SO_2(g) + O_2(g) \longrightarrow 2SO_3(g)$$
$$SO_3(g) + H_2O(l) \longrightarrow H_2SO_4(aq)$$

Almost all of the sulfuric acid dissociates into the ions H_3O^+, HSO_4^-, and SO_4^{2-}. The first ionization of H_2SO_4 is complete; the second ionization (that of HSO_4^-) is partial ($K_{a2} = 1.1 \times 10^{-2}$).

Acid rain can be harmful to some plants, to fish (by changing the pH of lake water), and to structural materials and monuments (Figure 16.6). Marble, for example, is composed of calcium carbonate, $CaCO_3$, which dissolves in water of low pH.

$$H_3O^+(aq) + CaCO_3(s) \longrightarrow$$
$$Ca^{2+}(aq) + HCO_3^-(aq) + H_2O(l)$$

It is instructive to calculate the pH of natural rain—that is, water saturated with carbon dioxide from the atmosphere. For this, you need to solve two equilibrium problems. First, you need the equilibrium for the solution of CO_2 in water.

$$CO_2(g) + H_2O(l) \rightleftharpoons H_2CO_3(aq)$$

$$K = \frac{[H_2CO_3]}{P_{CO_2}} = 3.5 \times 10^{-2}$$

Here $[H_2CO_3]$ represents the concentration of the molecular species formed when CO_2 dissolves in water. The partial pressure of CO_2 in the atmosphere is 0.00033 atm. If you substitute this for P_{CO_2} and solve for $[H_2CO_3]$, you obtain 1.2×10^{-5} M. (Note that the equilibrium-constant equation involving P_{CO_2} is essentially Henry's law, discussed in Section 12.3.) Now you need to account for the

(continued)

If you let x be the amount of H_3O^+ formed in the first ionization, you get the following results:

Concentration (M)	$H_2Asc(aq) + H_2O(l) \rightleftharpoons H_3O^+(aq) + Hasc^-(aq)$		
Starting	0.10	~0	0
Change	$-x$	$+x$	$+x$
Equilibrium	$0.10 - x$	x	x

Now substitute into the equilibrium-constant equation for the first ionization.

$$\frac{[H_3O^+][HAsc^-]}{[H_2Asc]} = K_{a1}$$

$$\frac{x^2}{0.10 - x} = 7.9 \times 10^{-5}$$

(continued)

acid ionization of H_2CO_3. You look only at the first ionization, which produces almost all of the H_3O^+.

$$H_2CO_3(aq) + H_2O(l) \rightleftharpoons H_3O^+(aq) + HCO_3^-(aq)$$

$$K_{a1} = \frac{[H_3O^+][HCO_3^-]}{[H_2CO_3]} = 4.3 \times 10^{-7}$$

Denoting $[H_3O^+] = [HCO_3^-]$ by x, you can write the equilibrium equation

$$\frac{x^2}{1.2 \times 10^{-5} - x} = 4.3 \times 10^{-7}$$

Making the usual assumption about neglecting x in the denominator, you obtain $x = [H_3O^+] = 2.3 \times 10^{-6}$. This assumption and the neglect of the self-ionization of water affect the answer in the second significant figure. Retaining one significant figure, pH = $-\log(2 \times 10^{-6}) = 5.7$, which is essentially what we gave earlier for the pH of natural rain.

FIGURE 16.6 ▲

Effect of acid rain on marble

These photographs of a marble statue of George Washington, located in New York, were taken 60 years apart. The more recent photograph (*right*) shows that much of the detail of the statue has been dissolved by acid rain. Marble ($CaCO_3$) reacts with H_3O^+ ion to form soluble $Ca(HCO_3)_2$.

■ See Problems 16.133 and 16.134.

(*continued*)

Assuming x to be much smaller than 0.10, you get

$$\frac{x^2}{0.10} \simeq 7.9 \times 10^{-5}$$

or

$$x^2 \simeq 7.9 \times 10^{-5} \times 0.10$$
$$x \simeq 2.8 \times 10^{-3} = 0.0028$$

(Note that $0.10 - x = 0.10 - 0.0028 = 0.10$, correct to two significant figures. Therefore, the assumption that $0.10 - x \simeq 0.10$ is correct.)

The hydronium-ion concentration is 0.0028 M, so

$$pH = -\log [H_3O^+] = -\log(0.0028) = \mathbf{2.55}$$

ASCORBATE-ION CONCENTRATION Ascorbate ion, Asc^{2-}, which we will call y, is produced only in the second reaction. Assume the starting concentrations of H_3O^+ and $HAsc^-$

(*continued*)

(*continued*)

for this reaction to be those from the first equilibrium. The amounts of the species in 1 L of solution are as follows:

Concentration (M)	$HAsc^-(aq) + H_2O(l) \rightleftharpoons H_3O^+(aq) + Asc^{2-}(aq)$		
Starting	0.0028	0.0028	0
Change	$-y$	$+y$	$+y$
Equilibrium	$0.0028 - y$	$0.0028 + y$	y

Now substitute into the equilibrium-constant equation for the second ionization.

$$\frac{[H_3O^+][Asc^{2-}]}{[HAsc^-]} = K_{a2}$$

$$\frac{(0.0028 + y)y}{0.0028 - y} = 1.6 \times 10^{-12}$$

This equation can be simplified if you assume that y is much smaller than 0.0028. (Again, this assumes that the reaction occurs to only a small extent, as you expect from the magnitude of the equilibrium constant.) That is,

$$0.0028 + y \simeq 0.0028$$

$$0.0028 - y \simeq 0.0028$$

Then the equilibrium equation reads

$$\frac{(0.0028)y}{0.0028} \simeq 1.6 \times 10^{-12}$$

Hence, $$y \simeq 1.6 \times 10^{-12}$$

(Note that 1.6×10^{-12} is indeed much smaller than 0.0028, as you assumed.) The concentration of ascorbate ion equals K_{a2}, or **1.6×10^{-12} M.**

Answer Check   Because the second ionization constant of an acid, K_{a2} is always smaller than the first ionization constant, K_{a1}, you should expect any species produced during the second ionization to be in lower concentration than those from the first ionization.

Exercise 16.4   Sulfurous acid, H_2SO_3, is a diprotic acid with $K_{a1} = 1.3 \times 10^{-2}$ and $K_{a2} = 6.3 \times 10^{-8}$. The acid forms when sulfur dioxide (a gas with a suffocating odor) dissolves in water. What is the pH of a 0.25 M solution of sulfurous acid? What is the concentration of sulfite ion, SO_3^{2-}, in the solution? Note that K_{a1} is relatively large.

■ See Problems 16.47 and 16.48.

Example 16.4 shows that $[H_3O^+]$ and $[HA^-]$ in a solution of a diprotic acid H_2A can be calculated from the first ionization constant, K_{a1}.

The concentration of the ion A^{2-} equals the second ionization constant, K_{a2}.

16.3 | Base-Ionization Equilibria

Equilibria involving weak bases are treated similarly to those for weak acids. Ammonia, for example, ionizes in water as follows:

$$NH_3(aq) + H_2O(l) \rightleftharpoons NH_4^+(aq) + OH^-(aq)$$

TABLE 16.2	Base-Ionization Constants at 25°C	
Substance	Formula	K_b
Ammonia	NH_3	1.8×10^{-5}
Aniline	$C_6H_5NH_2$	4.2×10^{-10}
Dimethylamine	$(CH_3)_2NH$	5.1×10^{-4}
Ethylamine	$C_2H_5NH_2$	4.7×10^{-4}
Hydrazine	N_2H_4	1.7×10^{-6}
Hydroxylamine	NH_2OH	1.1×10^{-8}
Methylamine	CH_3NH_2	4.4×10^{-4}
Pyridine	C_5H_5N	1.4×10^{-9}
Urea	NH_2CONH_2	1.5×10^{-14}

The corresponding equilibrium constant is

$$K_c = \frac{[NH_4^+][OH^-]}{[NH_3][H_2O]}$$

In terms of the thermodynamic equilibrium constant, the activity of H_2O is nearly constant and essentially 1, so it does not appear explicitly in the equilibrium constant.

Because the concentration of H_2O is nearly constant, you can rearrange this equation as you did for acid ionization. <

$$K_b = [H_2O]K_c = \frac{[NH_4^+][OH^-]}{[NH_3]}$$

In general, a weak base B with the *base ionization*

$$B(aq) + H_2O(l) \rightleftharpoons HB^+(aq) + OH^-(aq)$$

has a **base-ionization constant,** K_b (*the equilibrium constant for the ionization of a weak base*), equal to

$$K_b = \frac{[HB^+][OH^-]}{[B]}$$

Table 16.2 lists ionization constants for some weak bases. All of these bases are similar to ammonia in that they have an N atom with a lone pair of electrons that accepts an H^+ ion from water. For example, the base ionization of methylamine, CH_3NH_2, is

FIGURE 16.7 ▲

Many over-the-counter drugs are salts of bases

These salts are often chlorides (frequently called hydrochlorides) and are analogous to ammonium chloride. You might find it instructive to read the ingredients from the labels for these products.

Some other well-known alkaloids and their plant sources are nicotine (tobacco), cocaine (coca bush), mescaline (species of cactus), and caffeine (coffee and tea).

$$
\begin{array}{ccc}
\underset{\underset{H}{|}}{\overset{\overset{H}{|}}{H-C}} - \underset{\underset{H}{|}}{\overset{\overset{H}{|}}{N:}} + H_2O & \rightleftharpoons & \underset{\underset{H}{|}}{\overset{\overset{H}{|}}{H-C}} - \underset{\underset{H}{|}}{\overset{\overset{H}{|}}{N^+}} - H + OH^-
\end{array}
$$

Many drugs and plant substances such as caffeine are bases. Often a prescription or over-the-counter drug is a salt of a base, because the salt is more soluble in water (Figure 16.7). These salts are analogous to the salts of ammonia, such as NH_4Cl. Other common bases are anions of weak acids. Examples are F^- and $C_2H_3O_2^-$ (acetate ion). We will discuss these in the next section.

In the following exercise, you will determine the K_b of a molecular base from the pH of a solution. Note that this is essentially the problem you looked at in Example 16.1.

Exercise 16.5 Quinine is an alkaloid, or naturally occurring base, used to treat malaria. A 0.0015 *M* solution of quinine has a pH of 9.84. The basicity of alkaloids is due to a nitrogen atom that picks up protons from water in the same manner as ammonia does. < What is K_b?

■ See Problems 16.51 and 16.52.

Example 16.5 | Calculating Concentrations of Species in a Weak Base Solution Using K_b

Morphine, $C_{17}H_{19}NO_3$, is administered medically to relieve pain. It is a naturally occurring base, or alkaloid. What is the pH of a 0.0075 M solution of morphine at 25°C? The base-ionization constant, K_b, is 1.6×10^{-6} at 25°C.

Problem Strategy First of all, you need to be aware that the compound $C_{17}H_{19}NO_3$ is a weak base. The calculation for the ionization of a weak base parallels that used with weak acids in Examples 16.2 and 16.3: you write the equation, make a table of concentrations (Step 1), set up the equilibrium-constant equation for K_b (Step 2), and solve for $x = [OH^-]$ (Step 3). Assume the self-ionization of water can be neglected. You obtain $[H_3O^+]$, and then the pH, by solving $K_w = [H_3O^+][OH^-]$.

Solution Morphine, which we abbreviate as Mor, ionizes by picking up a proton from water (as does ammonia).

$$Mor(aq) + H_2O \rightleftharpoons HMor^+(aq) + OH^-(aq)$$

Step 1: Summarize the concentrations in a table. For the *change* values, note that the morphine in 1 L of solution ionizes to give x mol $HMor^+$ and x mol OH^-.

Concentration (M)	*Mor*(aq) + H_2O(l) $\rightleftharpoons$	$HMor^+$(aq) +	OH^-(aq)
Starting	0.0075	0	~0
Change	$-x$	$+x$	$+x$
Equilibrium	$0.0075 - x$	x	x

Step 2: Substituting into the equilibrium equation

$$\frac{[HMor^+][OH^-]}{[Mor]} = K_b$$

gives

$$\frac{x^2}{0.0075 - x} = 1.6 \times 10^{-6}$$

Step 3: If you assume that x is small enough to neglect compared with 0.0075, you have

$$0.0075 - x \approx 0.0075$$

and you can write the equilibrium-constant equation as

$$\frac{x^2}{0.0075} \approx 1.6 \times 10^{-6}$$

Hence,

$$x^2 \approx 1.6 \times 10^{-6} \times 0.0075 = 1.2 \times 10^{-8}$$

$$x = [OH^-] \approx 1.1 \times 10^{-4}$$

You can now calculate the hydronium-ion concentration. The product of the hydronium-ion concentration and the hydroxide-ion concentration equals 1.0×10^{-14} at 25°C:

$$[H_3O^+][OH^-] = 1.0 \times 10^{-14}$$

Substituting into this equation gives

$$[H_3O^+] \times 1.1 \times 10^{-4} = 1.0 \times 10^{-14}$$

(continued)

(*continued*)

Hence,

$$[H_3O^+] = \frac{1.0 \times 10^{-14}}{1.1 \times 10^{-4}} = 9.1 \times 10^{-11}$$

The pH of the solution is

$$pH = -\log\,[H_3O^+] = -\log(9.1 \times 10^{-11}) = \mathbf{10.04}$$

Note that you could also calculate the pH using the formula pH + pOH = 14.00. You would first calculate the pOH; then pH = 14.00 − pOH.

Answer Check   A reasonable answer for the pH of a weak base in aqueous solution is greater than 7.

Exercise 16.6   What is the hydronium-ion concentration of a 0.20 *M* solution of ammonia in water? See Table 16.2 for K_b.

■ See Problems 16.53 and 16.54.

Concept Check 16.2

A base B is placed into a beaker of water with the result depicted below (water molecules have been omitted for clarity). Write the ionization reaction for this base and classify the base as being strong or weak.

= B
= BH$^+$
= OH$^-$

16.4 | Acid–Base Properties of Salt Solutions

A salt may be regarded as an ionic compound obtained by a neutralization reaction in aqueous solution. The resulting salt solution may be neutral, but often it is acidic or basic (Figure 16.8). One of the successes of the Brønsted–Lowry concept of acids and bases was in pointing out that some ions can act as acids or bases. The acidity or basicity of a salt solution is explained in terms of the acidity or basicity of individual ions in the solution.

Consider a solution of sodium cyanide, NaCN. A 0.1 *M* solution has a pH of 11.1 and is therefore fairly basic. Sodium cyanide dissolves in water to give Na$^+$ and CN$^-$ ions.

$$NaCN(s) \xrightarrow{\text{H}_2\text{O}} Na^+(aq) + CN^-(aq)$$

Sodium ion, Na$^+$, is unreactive with water, but the cyanide ion, CN$^-$, reacts to produce HCN and OH$^-$.

$$CN^-(aq) + H_2O(l) \rightleftharpoons HCN(aq) + OH^-(aq)$$

From the Brønsted–Lowry point of view, the CN$^-$ ion acts as a base, because it accepts a proton from H$_2$O. You can also see, however, that OH$^-$ ion is a product, so you expect the solution to have a basic pH. This explains why solutions of NaCN are basic.

NH₄Cl

NaCl

Na₂CO₃

FIGURE 16.8 ▲

Salt solutions are acidic, neutral, or basic
A pH meter measures the pH of solutions
of the salts NH₄Cl, NaCl, and Na₂CO₃.

The reaction of the CN^- ion with water is referred to as the *hydrolysis* of CN^-. The **hydrolysis** of an ion is *the reaction of an ion with water to produce the conjugate acid and hydroxide ion or the conjugate base and hydronium ion.* The CN^- ion hydrolyzes to give the conjugate acid and OH^- ion. As another example, consider the ammonium ion, NH_4^+, which hydrolyzes as follows:

$$NH_4^+(aq) + H_2O(l) \rightleftharpoons NH_3(aq) + H_3O^+(aq)$$

The ammonium ion acts as an acid, donating a proton to H_2O and forming NH_3. Note that this equation has the form of an acid ionization, so you could write the K_a expression for it. Similarly, the hydrolysis reaction for the CN^- ion has the form of a base ionization, so you could write the K_b expression for it.

Two questions become apparent. First, how can you predict whether a particular salt solution will be acidic, basic, or neutral? Then, how can you calculate the concentrations of H_3O^+ ion and OH^- ion in the salt solution (or, equivalently, how do you predict the pH of the salt solution)? We will now look at the first of these questions.

Prediction of Whether a Salt Solution Is Acidic, Basic, or Neutral

When the CN^- ion hydrolyzes, it produces the conjugate acid, HCN. Hydrogen cyanide, HCN, is a weak acid. That means that it tends to hold on to the proton strongly (does not ionize readily). In other words, the cyanide ion, CN^-, tends to pick up a proton easily, so it acts as a base. This argument can be generalized: *The anions of weak acids are basic.* On the other hand, the anions of strong acids have hardly any basic character; that is, these ions do not hydrolyze. For example, the Cl^- ion, which is conjugate to the strong acid HCl, shows no appreciable reaction with water.

$$Cl^-(aq) + H_2O(l) \longrightarrow \text{no reaction}$$

Now consider a cation conjugate to a weak base. The simplest example is the NH_4^+ ion, which we just discussed. It behaves like an acid. *The cations of weak bases are acidic.* On the other hand, the cations of strong bases (metal ions of Groups IA and IIA elements—except Be) have hardly any acidic character; that is, these ions do not hydrolyze. For example,

$$Na^+(aq) + H_2O(l) \longrightarrow \text{no reaction}$$

Aqueous metal ions, other than the cations of the strong bases, usually hydrolyze by acting as acids. These ions usually form hydrated metal ions. For example, the aluminum ion Al^{3+} forms the hydrated ion $Al(H_2O)_6^{3+}$. The bare Al^{3+} ion acts as a Lewis acid, forming bonds to the electron pairs on O atoms of H_2O molecules. Because the electrons are drawn away from the O atoms by the Al atom, the O atoms in turn tend to draw electrons from the O—H bonds, making them highly polar. As a result, the H_2O molecules in $Al(H_2O)_6^{3+}$ are acidic. The $Al(H_2O)_6^{3+}$ ion hydrolyzes in aqueous solution by donating a proton (from one of the acidic H_2O molecules on the ion) to water molecules in the solvent. After the proton leaves the hydrated metal ion, the ion charge is reduced by 1 and an H_2O molecule on the ion becomes a hydroxide ion bonded to the metal. Thus, the formula of the ion becomes $Al(H_2O)_5(OH)^{2+}$.

$$Al(H_2O)_6^{3+}(aq) + H_2O(l) \rightleftharpoons Al(H_2O)_5(OH)^{2+}(aq) + H_3O^+(aq)$$

To predict the acidity or basicity of a salt solution, you need to examine the acidity or basicity of the ions composing the salt. Consider potassium acetate, $KC_2H_3O_2$. The ions are K^+ and $C_2H_3O_2^-$ (acetate ion). Potassium is a Group IA element, so K^+ does not hydrolyze. However, the acetate ion is the conjugate of acetic acid, a weak acid. Therefore, the acetate ion is basic.

$$K^+(aq) + H_2O(l) \longrightarrow \text{no reaction}$$

$$C_2H_3O_2^-(aq) + H_2O(l) \rightleftharpoons HC_2H_3O_2(aq) + OH^-(aq)$$

A solution of potassium acetate is predicted to be basic.

From this discussion, we can derive a set of rules for deciding whether a salt solution will be neutral, acidic, or basic. These rules apply to normal salts (those in which the anion has no acidic hydrogen atoms).

1. **A salt of a strong base and a strong acid.** The salt has no hydrolyzable ions and so gives a neutral aqueous solution. An example is NaCl.

2. **A salt of a strong base and a weak acid.** The anion of the salt is the conjugate of the weak acid. It hydrolyzes to give a basic solution. An example is NaCN.

3. **A salt of a weak base and a strong acid.** The cation of the salt is the conjugate of the weak base. It hydrolyzes to give an acidic solution. An example is NH_4Cl.

4. **A salt of a weak base and a weak acid.** Both ions hydrolyze. Whether the solution is acidic or basic depends on the relative acid–base strengths of the two ions. To determine this, you need to compare the K_a of the cation with the K_b of the anion. If the K_a is larger, the solution is acidic. If the K_b is larger, the solution is basic. Consider solutions of ammonium formate, NH_4CHO_2. These solutions are slightly acidic, because the K_a for NH_4^+ ($= 5.6 \times 10^{-10}$) is somewhat larger than the K_b for formate ion, CHO_2^- ($= 5.9 \times 10^{-11}$).

The next example illustrates the application of these rules.

Example 16.6 | Predicting Whether a Salt Solution Is Acidic, Basic, or Neutral

Decide whether aqueous solutions of the following salts are acidic, basic, or neutral: a. KCl; b. NaF; c. $Zn(NO_3)_2$; d. NH_4CN.

Problem Strategy Start by determining what type of acid–base reaction occurred to make the salt. Once you know this, you can apply the rules above to predict whether a solution will be acidic, basic, or neutral.

Solution a. KCl is a salt of a strong base (KOH) and a strong acid (HCl), so none of the ions hydrolyze, and a solution of KCl is **neutral.**

b. NaF is a salt of a strong base (NaOH) and a weak acid (HF), so a solution of NaF is **basic** because of the hydrolysis of F^-. (You assume HF is a weak acid, because it is not one of the common strong acids listed in Table 15.1.)

c. $Zn(NO_3)_2$ is the salt of a weak base $(Zn(OH)_2)$ and a strong acid (HNO_3), so a solution of $Zn(NO_3)_2$ is **acidic.** Note also that Zn^{2+} is not an ion of a Group IA or Group IIA element, so you can expect it to form a metal hydrate ion that hydrolyzes to give an acidic solution.

d. NH_4CN is a salt of a weak base (NH_3) and a weak acid (HCN). Therefore, to answer the question, you would need the K_a for NH_4^+ and the K_b for CN^-. Although these are listed in some tables, more frequently they are not. However, as you will see later in this section, values are easily calculated from the molecular substances that are conjugates (NH_3 and HCN). The K_a for NH_4^+ is 5.6×10^{-10}, and the K_b for CN^- is 2.0×10^{-5}. From these values, you conclude that a solution of NH_4CN is **basic.**

Answer Check You can check your answers by writing hydrolysis reactions for each of the ions in solution. If either or both of these reactions produce a weak acid or base, the solution will not be neutral. You then can analyze the products of these reactions for OH^- and/or H_3O^+ to check your final answer (keep in mind you may have to look at the K_a and K_b information as well). For example, using NaF from part b, the hydrolysis reactions for the ions that make up this salt are

$$Na^+(aq) + H_2O(l) \longrightarrow \text{no reaction}$$
$$F^-(aq) + H_2O(l) \longrightarrow HF(aq) + OH^-(aq)$$

(continued)

(continued)

Because there was no reaction for the Na^+, and OH^- was produced by the hydrolysis of F^-, the solution containing the NaF salt is basic.

Exercise 16.7 Consider solutions of the following salts: a. NH_4NO_3; b. KNO_3; c. $Al(NO_3)_3$. For each, state whether the solution is acidic, basic, or neutral.

■ See Problems 16.59 and 16.60.

The pH of a Salt Solution

Suppose you wish to calculate the pH of 0.10 *M* NaCN. As you have seen, the solution is basic because of the hydrolysis of the CN^- ion. The calculation is essentially the same as that for any weak base (Example 16.5). You would require the base-ionization constant of the cyanide ion. However, frequently the ionization constants for ions are not listed directly in tables, because the values are easily related to those for the conjugate molecular species. Thus, the K_b for CN^- is related to the K_a for HCN.

To see this relationship between K_a and K_b for conjugate acid–base pairs, consider the acid ionization of HCN and the base ionization of CN^-. When these two reactions are added, you get the ionization of water.

$$\begin{array}{ll} HCN(aq) + H_2O(l) \rightleftharpoons H_3O^+(aq) + CN^-(aq) & K_a \\ CN^-(aq) + H_2O(l) \rightleftharpoons HCN(aq) + OH^-(aq) & K_b \\ \hline 2H_2O(l) \rightleftharpoons H_3O^+(aq) + OH^-(aq) & K_w \end{array}$$

Another way to obtain this result is by multiplying the expression for K_b by $[H_3O^+]/[H_3O^+]$ and rearranging.

$$K_b = \frac{[HCN][OH^-]}{[CN^-]} \times \frac{[H_3O^+]}{[H_3O^+]}$$

$$= [H_3O^+][OH^-] \Big/ \frac{[H_3O^+][CN^-]}{[HCN]}$$

This is equivalent to

$$K_b = K_w/K_a \quad or \quad K_aK_b = K_w$$

The equilibrium constants for the reactions are shown symbolically at the right. In Section 14.2, it was shown that when two reactions are added, their equilibrium constants are multiplied. Therefore, <

$$K_aK_b = K_w$$

This relationship is general and shows that the product of acid- and base-ionization constants in aqueous solution for conjugate acid–base pairs equals the ion-product constant for water, K_w.

Example 16.7	Obtaining K_a from K_b or K_b from K_a

Use Tables 16.1 and 16.2 to obtain the following at 25°C: a. K_b for CN^-; b. K_a for NH_4^+.

Problem Strategy Keeping in mind that K_w is known, we can apply the formula $K_aK_b = K_w$ to find the unknown ionization constant (K_a or K_b).

Solution a. The conjugate acid of CN^- is HCN, whose K_a is 4.9×10^{-10} (Table 16.1). Hence,

$$K_b = \frac{K_w}{K_a} = \frac{1.0 \times 10^{-14}}{4.9 \times 10^{-10}} = \mathbf{2.0 \times 10^{-5}}$$

Note that K_b is approximately equal to K_b for ammonia (1.8×10^{-5}). This means that the base strength of CN^- is comparable to that of NH_3.

b. The conjugate base of NH_4^+ is NH_3, whose K_b is 1.8×10^{-5} (Table 16.2). Hence,

$$K_a = \frac{K_w}{K_b} = \frac{1.0 \times 10^{-14}}{1.8 \times 10^{-5}} = \mathbf{5.6 \times 10^{-10}}$$

NH_4^+ is a relatively weak acid. Acetic acid, by way of comparison, has K_a equal to 1.7×10^{-5}.

Answer Check Be aware that the values of K_a, K_b, and K_w are all temperature dependent, so make sure that you are using the appropriate values when performing calculations.

Exercise 16.8 Calculate the following, using Tables 16.1 and 16.2: a. K_b for F^-; b. K_a for $C_6H_5NH_3^+$ (conjugate acid of aniline, $C_6H_5NH_2$).

■ See Problems 16.63 and 16.64.

For a solution of a salt in which only one of the ions hydrolyzes, the calculation of the concentrations of species present follows that for solutions of weak acids or bases. The only difference is that you must first obtain K_a or K_b for the ion that hydrolyzes. The next example illustrates the reasoning and calculations involved.

Example 16.8 | Calculating Concentrations of Species in a Salt Solution

What is the pH of 0.10 M sodium nicotinate at 25°C (a problem posed in the chapter opening)? The K_a for nicotinic acid was determined in Example 16.1 to be 1.4×10^{-5} at 25°C.

Problem Strategy   We first need to determine the relevant reactions of sodium nicotinate in water. If there is a reaction, we need to write it down and determine whether the reaction is that of an acid or of a base. If the reaction is that of an acid, we will need to use K_a in our calculations; for a base, we will need K_b. If necessary, we can use the equation $K_a K_b = K_w$ to find the needed ionization constant. We then can perform the equilibrium calculation in the usual manner.

Solution   Sodium nicotinate gives Na^+ and nicotinate ions in solution. Only the nicotinate ion hydrolyzes. Write HNic for nicotinic acid and Nic$^-$ for the nicotinate ion. The hydrolysis of nicotinate ion is

$$Nic^-(aq) + H_2O(l) \rightleftharpoons HNic(aq) + OH^-(aq)$$

Nicotinate ion acts as a base, and you can calculate the concentration of species in solution as in Example 16.5. First, however, you need K_b for the nicotinate ion. This is related to K_a for nicotinic acid by the equation $K_a K_b = K_w$. Substituting, you get

$$K_b = \frac{K_w}{K_a} = \frac{1.0 \times 10^{-14}}{1.4 \times 10^{-5}} = 7.1 \times 10^{-10}$$

Now you can proceed with the equilibrium calculation. We will only sketch this calculation, because it is similar to that in Example 16.5. You let $x = [HNic] = [OH^-]$ and then substitute into the equilibrium-constant equation.

$$\frac{[HNic][OH^-]}{[Nic^-]} = K_b$$

This gives

$$\frac{x^2}{0.10 - x} = 7.1 \times 10^{-10}$$

Solving this equation, you find that $x = [OH^-] = 8.4 \times 10^{-6}$. Hence,

$$pH = 14.00 - pOH = 14.00 + \log(8.4 \times 10^{-6}) = \mathbf{8.92}$$

Answer Check   Use the rules for predicting whether a salt is acidic, basic, or neutral to assess your answer. In this case, the solution was prepared by dissolving the salt of a strong base and a weak acid, so we should expect the correct answer to have a pH greater than 7.

Exercise 16.9   Benzoic acid, $HC_7H_5O_2$, and its salts are used as food preservatives. What is the concentration of benzoic acid in an aqueous solution of 0.015 M sodium benzoate? What is the pH of the solution? K_a for benzoic acid is 6.3×10^{-5}.

■ See Problems 16.65, 16.66, 16.67, and 16.68.

Concept Check 16.3
Which of the following aqueous solutions has the highest pH and which has the lowest? a. $0.1\ M$ NH_3; b. $0.1\ M$ NH_4Br; c. $0.1\ M$ NaF; d. $0.1\ M$ NaCl

Solutions of a Weak Acid or Base with Another Solute

In the preceding sections, we looked at solutions that contained a weak acid, a weak base, or a salt of a weak acid or base. In the remaining sections of this chapter, we will look at the effect of adding another solute to a solution of a weak acid or base. The solutes we will look at are those that significantly affect acid or base ionization— that is, strong acids and bases, and salts that contain an ion that is produced in the acid or base ionization. These solutes affect the equilibrium through the *common-ion effect*.

16.5 | Common-Ion Effect

The **common-ion effect** is *the shift in an ionic equilibrium caused by the addition of a solute that provides an ion that takes part in the equilibrium.* Consider a solution of acetic acid, $HC_2H_3O_2$, in which you have the following acid-ionization equilibrium:

$$HC_2H_3O_2(aq) + H_2O(l) \rightleftharpoons C_2H_3O_2^-(aq) + H_3O^+(aq)$$

Suppose you add HCl(aq) to this solution. What is the effect on the acid-ionization equilibrium? Because HCl(aq) is a strong acid, it provides H_3O^+ ion, which is present on the right side of the equation for acetic acid ionization. According to Le Châtelier's principle, the equilibrium composition should shift to the left. <

Le Châtelier's principle was applied in Section 14.7 to the problem of adding substances to an equilibrium mixture.

$$HC_2H_3O_2(aq) + H_2O(l) \longleftarrow \underset{\text{added}}{C_2H_3O_2^-(aq) + H_3O^+(aq)}$$

The degree of ionization of acetic acid is decreased by the addition of a strong acid. This repression of the ionization of acetic acid by HCl(aq) is an example of the common-ion effect.

Example 16.9 | Calculating the Common-Ion Effect on Acid Ionization (Effect of a Strong Acid)

The degree of ionization of acetic acid, $HC_2H_3O_2$, in a $0.10\ M$ aqueous solution at 25°C is 0.013. K_a at this temperature is 1.7×10^{-5}. Calculate the degree of ionization of $HC_2H_3O_2$ in a $0.10\ M$ solution at 25°C to which sufficient HCl is added to make it $0.010\ M$ HCl. How is the degree of ionization affected?

Problem Strategy This is an acid-ionization problem, but it differs from the simple ionization illustrated by Example 16.2. Here you have a starting concentration of H_3O^+ ($= 0.010\ M$) from the addition of a strong acid (HCl). This gives a different type of equation in Step 2, but you solve it in Step 3 by using a similar approximation method. You assume that x is small compared with starting concentrations of acid and H_3O^+, so that the resulting equation is linear, rather than quadratic. The calculation of degree of ionization follows that in Example 16.2.

(continued)

(*continued*)

Solution

Step 1: Starting concentrations are $[HC_2H_3O_2] = 0.10\ M$, $[H_3O^+] = 0.010\ M$ (from HCl), and $[C_2H_3O_2^-] = 0$. The acetic acid ionizes to give an additional x mol/L of H_3O^+ and x mol/L of $C_2H_3O_2^-$. The table is

Concentration (M)	$HC_2H_3O_2(aq)$	$+ H_2O(l)$	$\rightleftharpoons$	$H_3O^+(aq)$	$+ C_2H_3O_2^-(aq)$
Starting	0.10			0.010	0
Change	$-x$			$+x$	$+x$
Equilibrium	$0.10 - x$			$0.010 + x$	x

Step 2: You substitute into the equilibrium-constant equation

$$\frac{[H_3O^+][C_2H_3O_2^-]}{[HC_2H_3O_2]} = K_a$$

obtaining

$$\frac{(0.010 + x)x}{0.10 - x} = 1.7 \times 10^{-5}$$

Step 3: To solve this equation, assume that x is small compared with 0.010. Then

$$0.010 + x \simeq 0.010$$
$$0.10 - x \simeq 0.10$$

The equation becomes

$$\frac{0.010x}{0.10} \simeq 1.7 \times 10^{-5}$$

Solving for x, you get

$$x = 1.7 \times 10^{-5} \times \frac{0.10}{0.010} = 1.7 \times 10^{-4}$$

The degree of ionization of $HC_2H_3O_2$ is $x/0.10 = $ **0.0017.** This is much smaller than the value for $0.10\ M\ HC_2H_3O_2$ (0.013), because **the addition of HCl represses the ionization of $HC_2H_3O_2$.**

Answer Check As with all problems of this type, check to see that all approximations that you made are valid. In this case, make certain that x can be neglected in the $0.010 + x$ and $0.10 - x$ terms.

Exercise 16.10 What is the concentration of formate ion, CHO_2^-, in a solution at 25°C that is $0.10\ M\ HCHO_2$ and $0.20\ M$ HCl? What is the degree of ionization of formic acid, $HCHO_2$?

■ See Problems 16.69 and 16.70.

As you will see in the following section, solutions that contain a weak acid or a weak base and a corresponding salt are especially important. Therefore, you will need to be able to calculate the concentrations of species present in such solutions. A solution of acetic acid and sodium acetate is an example. From Le Châtelier's principle, you can see that the addition of acetate ion (from sodium acetate) represses the ionization of the acetic acid by the common-ion effect:

$$HC_2H_3O_2(aq) + H_2O(l) \longleftarrow C_2H_3O_2^-\ (aq) + H_3O^+(aq)$$
$$\text{added}$$

The next example illustrates the calculation of pH, which is similar to that of the previous example.

Example 16.10 | Calculating the Common-Ion Effect on Acid Ionization (effect of a Conjugate Base)

A solution is prepared to be 0.10 M acetic acid, $HC_2H_3O_2$, and 0.20 M sodium acetate, $NaC_2H_3O_2$. What is the pH of this solution at 25°C? K_a for acetic acid at 25°C is 1.7×10^{-5}.

Problem Strategy   First you need to identify the relevant reaction for the acid or base in solution. In this case,

$$HC_2H_3O_2(aq) + H_2O(l) \longrightarrow C_2H_3O_2^-(aq) + H_3O^+(aq)$$

Once you have the reaction, you need to see whether there are any ions in solution from the added salt ($NaC_2H_3O_2$) that will affect the chemical reaction (a common ion). If there is a common ion, as there is here ($C_2H_3O_2^-$), you need to take into account its concentration when creating your table and performing calculations.

Solution

Step 1:   Consider the equilibrium

$$HC_2H_3O_2(aq) + H_2O(l) \rightleftharpoons H_3O^+(aq) + C_2H_3O_2^-(aq)$$

Initially, 1 L of solution contains 0.10 mol of acetic acid. Sodium acetate is a strong electrolyte, so 1 L of solution contains 0.20 mol of acetate ion (a common ion). When the acetic acid ionizes, it gives x mol of hydronium ion and x mol of acetate ion. This is summarized in the following table:

Concentration (M)	$HC_2H_3O_2$(aq) + H_2O(l) $\rightleftharpoons$	H_3O^+(aq) +	$C_2H_3O_2^-$(aq)
Starting	0.10	~0	0.20
Change	$-x$	$+x$	$+x$
Equilibrium	$0.10 - x$	x	$0.20 + x$

Step 2:   The equilibrium-constant equation is

$$\frac{[H_3O^+][C_2H_3O_2^-]}{[HC_2H_3O_2]} = K_a$$

Substituting into this equation gives

$$\frac{x(0.20 + x)}{0.10 - x} = 1.7 \times 10^{-5}$$

Step 3:   To solve the equation, assume that x is small compared with 0.10 and 0.20. Then

$$0.20 + x \simeq 0.20$$

$$0.10 - x \simeq 0.10$$

The equilibrium equation becomes

$$\frac{x(0.20)}{0.10} \simeq 1.7 \times 10^{-5}$$

Hence,

$$x \simeq 1.7 \times 10^{-5} \times \frac{0.10}{0.20} = 8.5 \times 10^{-6}$$

(continued)

(continued)

(Note that x is indeed much smaller than 0.10 or 0.20.) The hydronium-ion concentration is $8.5 \times 10^{-6}\ M$, and

$$\mathrm{pH} = -\log\,[\mathrm{H_3O^+}] = -\log(8.5 \times 10^{-6}) = \mathbf{5.07}$$

For comparison, the pH of 0.10 M acetic acid is 2.88.

Answer Check Always make sure that the ions in solution will have an effect on the equilibrium. For example, if the solution were 0.20 M NaCl instead of 0.20 M $HC_2H_3O_2$, there would have been no common ion, and therefore the calculated pH would be the same as that of a solution of only 0.20 M $HC_2H_3O_2$.

Exercise 16.11   One liter of solution was prepared by dissolving 0.025 mol of formic acid, $HCHO_2$, and 0.018 mol of sodium formate, $NaCHO_2$, in water. What was the pH of the solution? K_a for formic acid is 1.7×10^{-4}.

■ See Problems 16.71 and 16.72.

The previous examples considered the common-ion effect in solutions of weak acids. You also encounter the common-ion effect in solutions of weak bases. For example, the base ionization of NH_3 is

$$\mathrm{NH_3}(aq) + \mathrm{H_2O}(l) \rightleftharpoons \mathrm{NH_4^+}(aq) + \mathrm{OH^-}(aq)$$

This suggests that you could repress, or decrease the effect of, the base ionization by adding an ammonium salt (providing NH_4^+ ion) or a strong base (providing OH^- ion). The calculations are similar to those for acid ionization, except that you use the appropriate base ionization.

16.6 | Buffers

A **buffer** is *a solution characterized by the ability to resist changes in pH when limited amounts of acid or base are added to it.* If 0.01 mol of hydrochloric acid is added to 1 L of pure water, the pH changes from 7.0 to 2.0—a pH change of 5.0 units. By contrast, the addition of this amount of hydrochloric acid to 1 L of buffered solution might change the pH by only 0.1 unit. Biological fluids, such as blood, are usually buffer solutions; the control of pH is vital to proper functioning of these fluids. The oxygen-carrying function of blood depends on its being maintained very near a pH of 7.4. If the pH were to change by a tenth of a unit, the capacity of the blood to carry oxygen would be lost.

Buffers contain either a weak acid and its conjugate base or a weak base and its conjugate acid. Thus, a buffer solution contains both an acid species and a base species in equilibrium. To understand the action of a buffer, consider one that contains approximately equal molar amounts of a weak acid HA and its conjugate base A^-. When a strong acid is added to the buffer, it supplies hydronium ions that react with the base A^-.

$$\mathrm{H_3O^+}(aq) + \mathrm{A^-}(aq) \longrightarrow \mathrm{HA}(aq) + \mathrm{H_2O}(l)$$

On the other hand, when a strong base is added to the buffer, it supplies hydroxide ions. These react with the acid HA.

$$\mathrm{OH^-}(aq) + \mathrm{HA}(aq) \longrightarrow \mathrm{H_2O}(l) + \mathrm{A^-}(aq)$$

A buffer solution resists changes in pH through its ability to combine with both H_3O^+ and OH^- ions. Figure 16.9 depicts this buffer action.

FIGURE 16.9 ▲

Buffer action

A buffer is a solution of about equal molar amounts of a weak acid, HA, and its conjugate base, A⁻, in equilibrium (center beaker). When an acid, such as HCl, is added to the buffer, H_3O^+ from this acid reacts with A⁻ in the buffer to produce HA (left beaker). However, when a base, such as NaOH, is added to the buffer, OH⁻ from this base reacts with HA in the buffer to produce A⁻ (right beaker). The buffer pH changes only slightly in both cases.

Blood, as a buffer solution, contains H_2CO_3 and HCO_3^-, as well as other conjugate acid–base pairs. A buffer frequently used in the laboratory contains varying proportions of the conjugate acid–base pair $H_2PO_4^-$ and HPO_4^{2-} (Figure 16.10).

Buffers also have commercial applications. For example, the label on a package of artificial fruit juice mix says that it contains "citric acid to provide tartness (acidity) and sodium citrate to regulate tartness." A solution of citric acid and its conjugate base, citrate ion (provided by sodium citrate), functions as an acid–base buffer, which is what "to regulate tartness" means. The pH of the buffer is in the acid range.

Two important characteristics of a buffer are its pH and its *buffer capacity*, which is the amount of acid or base the buffer can react with before giving a significant pH change. Buffer capacity depends on the amount of acid and conjugate base in the solution. Figure 16.11 illustrates the change in pH of a buffer solution containing 1.0 mol of acetic acid and 1.0 mol of acetate ion to which varying amounts of H_3O^+ and OH⁻ are added. This buffer changes less than 0.5 pH unit as long as no more than 0.5 mol H_3O^+ or OH⁻ ion is added. Note that this is one-half (or less than one-half) the amounts of acid and conjugate base in the solution. The ratio of amount of acid to amount of conjugate base is also important. Unless this ratio is close to 1 (between 1:10 and 10:1), the buffer capacity will be too low to be useful.

The other important characteristic of a buffer is its pH. Let us now look at how to calculate the pH of a buffer.

FIGURE 16.10 ▲

Some laboratory buffers

These commercially prepared buffer solutions have different proportions of the same conjugate acid and base.

FIGURE 16.11 ▶

Effect of added acid or base on a buffer solution

The buffer contains 1.0 mol of acetic acid and 1.0 mol of acetate ion in 1.00 L of solution. Note that the addition of 0.5 mol or less of strong acid or base gives only a small change of pH.

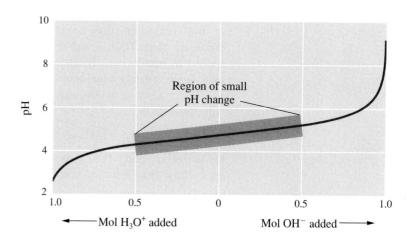

The pH of a Buffer

The solution described in Example 16.10 is a buffer, because it is a solution of a weak acid (0.10 M acetic acid) and its conjugate base (0.20 M acetate ion from sodium acetate). The example described how to calculate the pH of such a buffer (we obtained a pH of 5.07). The next example is similar, except now you are given a recipe for making up a buffer from volumes of solutions and are asked to calculate the pH. In this example, the buffer consists of a molecular base (NH_3) and its conjugate acid (NH_4^+).

Example 16.11	Calculating the pH of a Buffer from Given Volumes of Solution

Instructions for making up a buffer say to mix 60. mL (0.060 L) of 0.100 M NH_3 with 40. mL (0.040 L) of 0.100 M NH_4Cl. What is the pH of this buffer?

Problem Strategy The buffer contains a base and its conjugate acid in equilibrium. The equation is

$$NH_3(aq) + H_2O(l) \rightleftharpoons NH_4^+(aq) + OH^-(aq)$$

The problem is to obtain the concentration of H_3O^+ or OH^- in this equilibrium mixture. To do the equilibrium calculation, you need the starting concentrations in the solution obtained by mixing the NH_3 and NH_4Cl solutions. For this, you calculate the moles of NH_3 and moles of NH_4^+ added to the buffer solution, and divide by the total volume of buffer. Then you are ready to do the equilibrium calculation.

Solution How many moles of NH_3 are added? Recall that

$$\text{Molarity } NH_3 = \frac{\text{moles } NH_3}{\text{liters } NH_3 \text{ solution}}$$

Note that the instructions say to add 60. mL (or 0.060 L) of 0.100 M NH_3. So

$$\text{Moles } NH_3 = \text{molarity } NH_3 \times \text{liters } NH_3 \text{ solution}$$
$$= 0.100 \frac{\text{mol}}{\text{L}} \times 0.060 \text{ L} = 0.0060 \text{ mol } NH_3$$

In the same way, you find that you have added 0.0040 mol NH_4^+ (from NH_4Cl). Assume that the total volume of buffer equals the sum of the volumes of the two solutions.

$$\text{Total volume buffer} = 60. \text{ mL} + 40. \text{ mL} = 100. \text{ mL (0.100 L)}$$

Therefore, the concentrations of base and conjugate acid are

$$[NH_3] = \frac{0.0060 \text{ mol}}{0.100 \text{ L}} = 0.060 \, M$$

$$[NH_4^+] = \frac{0.0040 \text{ mol}}{0.100 \text{ L}} = 0.040 \, M$$

Step 1: Fill in the concentration table for the acid–base equilibrium (base ionization of NH_3).

Concentration (M)	$NH_3(aq)$	$+ H_2O(l)$	$\rightleftharpoons$	$NH_4^+(aq)$	$+ OH^-(aq)$
Starting	0.060			0.040	0
Change	$-x$			$+x$	$+x$
Equilibrium	$0.060 - x$			$0.040 + x$	x

(continued)

(*continued*)

Step 2: You substitute the equilibrium concentrations into the equilibrium-constant equation.

$$\frac{[NH_4^+][OH^-]}{[NH_3]} = K_b$$

$$\frac{(0.040 + x)x}{0.060 - x} = 1.8 \times 10^{-5}$$

Step 3: To solve this equation, you assume that x is small compared with 0.040 and 0.060. So this equation becomes

$$\frac{0.040x}{0.060} = 1.8 \times 10^{-5}$$

Therefore, $x = (0.060/0.040) \times (1.8 \times 10^{-5}) = 2.7 \times 10^{-5}$. (Check that x can be neglected in $0.040 + x$ and $0.060 - x$.) Thus, the hydroxide-ion concentration is 2.7×10^{-5} M. The pH of the buffer is

$$pH = 14.00 - pOH = 14.00 + \log(2.7 \times 10^{-5}) = \mathbf{9.43}$$

(If you have 2.7×10^{-5} in your calculator from the previous calculation, you obtain the pH by pressing the *log* button, then adding 14.)

Answer Check To avoid a very common mistake, prior to setting up the equilibrium problem, always make sure that you first take into account the total volume of solution and then calculate the concentrations.

Exercise 16.12   What is the pH of a buffer prepared by adding 30.0 mL of 0.15 M $HC_2H_3O_2$ (acetic acid) to 70.0 mL of 0.20 M $NaC_2H_3O_2$ (sodium acetate)?

■ See Problems 16.75 and 16.76.

Adding an Acid or a Base to a Buffer

We noted earlier that a buffer resists changes in pH, and we also described qualitatively how this occurs. What we want to do here is to show quantitatively that a buffer does indeed tend to resist pH change when a small quantity of an acid or a base is added to it.

All of the previous acid–base examples dealt with situations in which an acid and its conjugate base were close to equilibrium. In the following example, we consider the addition of a strong acid to an acetic acid/acetate ion buffer. Hydronium ion reacts with the conjugate base (acetate ion) in the buffer, so that the concentrations of species in solution change markedly from their initial value. (If you add a strong base to this buffer, hydroxide ion reacts with acetic acid in the buffer.)

Example 16.12 | Calculating the pH of a Buffer When a Strong Acid or Strong Base Is Added

Calculate the pH of 75 mL of the buffer solution described in Example 16.10 (0.10 M $HC_2H_3O_2$ and 0.20 M $NaC_2H_3O_2$) to which 9.5 mL of 0.10 M hydrochloric acid is added. Compare the pH change with what would occur if this amount of acid were added to pure water.

Problem Strategy Do the problem in two parts. To get started, you assume that the H_3O^+ ion from the strong acid and the conjugate base from the buffer react completely. This is a

(continued)

stoichiometric calculation. Next, you need to refine the assumption from the stoichiometric calculation that you started with, because in reality the H_3O^+ ion and the base from the buffer reach equilibrium just before complete reaction. So you now solve the equilibrium problem using concentrations from the stoichiometric calculation. Because these concentrations are not far from equilibrium, you can use the usual simplifying assumption about *x*.

Solution When hydronium ion (from hydrochloric acid) is added to the buffer, it reacts with acetate ion.

$$H_3O^+(aq) + C_2H_3O_2{}^-(aq) \longrightarrow HC_2H_3O_2(aq) + H_2O(l)$$

Because acetic acid is a weak acid, you can assume as a first approximation that the reaction goes to completion. This part of the problem is simply a stoichiometric calculation. Then you assume that the acetic acid ionizes slightly. This part of the problem involves an acid-ionization equilibrium.

STOICHIOMETRIC CALCULATION You must first calculate the amounts of hydrogen ion, acetate ion, and acetic acid present in the solution before reaction. The molar amount of hydrogen ion will equal the molar amount of hydrochloric acid added, which you obtain by converting the volume of hydrochloric acid, HCl, to moles of HCl. To do this, you note for 0.10 *M* HCl that 1 L HCl is equivalent to 0.10 mol HCl. Hence, to convert 9.5 mL ($= 9.5 \times 10^{-3}$ L) of hydrochloric acid, you have

$$9.5 \times 10^{-3} \; \text{L HCl} \times \frac{0.10 \; \text{mol HCl}}{1 \; \text{L HCl}} = 0.00095 \; \text{mol HCl}$$

Hydrochloric acid is a strong acid, so it exists in solution as the ions H_3O^+ and Cl^-. Therefore, the amount of H_3O^+ added is 0.00095 mol.

The amounts of acetate ion and acetic acid in the 75-mL sample are found in a similar way. The buffer in Example 16.10 contains 0.20 mol of acetate ion and 0.10 mol of acetic acid in 1 L of solution. The amounts in 75 mL ($= 0.075$ L) of solution are obtained by converting to moles.

$$0.075 \; \text{L soln} \times \frac{0.20 \; \text{mol} \; C_2H_3O_2{}^-}{1 \; \text{L soln}} = 0.015 \; \text{mol} \; C_2H_3O_2{}^-$$

$$0.075 \; \text{L soln} \times \frac{0.10 \; \text{mol} \; HC_2H_3O_2}{1 \; \text{L soln}} = 0.0075 \; \text{mol} \; HC_2H_3O_2$$

You now assume that all of the hydronium ion added (0.00095 mol) reacts with acetate ion. Therefore, 0.00095 mol of acetic acid is produced and 0.00095 mol of acetate ion is used up. Hence, after reaction you have

Moles of acetate ion $= (0.015 - 0.00095)$ mol $C_2H_3O_2{}^- = 0.014$ mol $C_2H_3O_2{}^-$

Moles of acetic acid $= (0.0075 + 0.00095)$ mol $HC_2H_3O_2 = 0.0085$ mol $HC_2H_3O_2$

EQUILIBRIUM CALCULATION You first calculate the concentrations of $HC_2H_3O_2$ and $C_2H_3O_2{}^-$ present in the solution before you consider the acid-ionization equilibrium. Note that the total volume of solution (buffer plus hydrochloric acid) is 75 mL $+$ 9.5 mL, or 85 mL (0.085 L). Hence, the starting concentrations are

$$[HC_2H_3O_2] = \frac{0.0085 \; \text{mol}}{0.085 \; \text{L}} = 0.10 \; M$$

$$[C_2H_3O_2{}^-] = \frac{0.014 \; \text{mol}}{0.085 \; \text{L}} = 0.16 \; M$$

(continued)

(*continued*)

From this, you construct the following table:

Concentration (M)	$HC_2H_3O_2(aq) + H_2O(l) \rightleftharpoons$	$H_3O^+(aq) +$	$C_2H_3O_2^-(aq)$
Starting	0.10	~0	0.16
Change	$-x$	$+x$	$+x$
Equilibrium	$0.10 - x$	x	$0.16 + x$

The equilibrium-constant equation is

$$\frac{[H_3O^+][C_2H_3O_2^-]}{[HC_2H_3O_2]} = K_a$$

Substituting, you get

$$\frac{x(0.16 + x)}{0.10 - x} = 1.7 \times 10^{-5}$$

If you assume that x is small enough that $0.16 + x \simeq 0.16$ and $0.10 - x \simeq 0.10$, this equation becomes

$$\frac{x(0.16)}{0.10} = 1.7 \times 10^{-5}$$

or

$$x = 1.7 \times 10^{-5} \times \frac{0.10}{0.16} = 1.1 \times 10^{-5}$$

Note that x is indeed small, so the assumptions you made earlier are correct. The H_3O^+ concentration is 1.1×10^{-5} M. The pH is

$$pH = -\log [H_3O^+] = -\log(1.1 \times 10^{-5}) = \textbf{4.96}$$

Because the pH of the buffer was 5.07 (see Example 16.10), the pH has changed by $5.07 - 4.96 = 0.11$ unit.

ADDING HCL TO PURE WATER   If 9.5 mL of 0.10 M hydrochloric acid were added to 75 mL of pure water, the hydronium-ion concentration would change to

$$[H_3O^+] = \frac{\text{amount of } H_3O^+ \text{ added}}{\text{total volume of solution}}$$

$$[H_3O^+] = \frac{0.00095 \text{ mol } H_3O^+}{0.085 \text{ L solution}} = 0.011 \text{ M}$$

(The total volume is 75 mL of water plus 9.5 mL HCl, assuming no change of volume on mixing.) The pH is

$$pH = -\log [H_3O^+] = -\log(0.011) = 1.96$$

The pH of pure water is 7.00, so the change in pH is $7.00 - 1.96 = 5.04$ units, compared with 0.11 unit for the buffered solution.

Answer Check   Generally speaking, buffer solutions will not undergo large changes in pH by the addition of small amounts of a strong acid or strong base, so this is something to look for in your answers. However, if the buffer capacity of the solution is exceeded, you will see significant changes in pH.

Exercise 16.13   Suppose you add 50.0 mL of 0.10 M sodium hydroxide to 1 L of the solution described in Exercise 16.11. What would be the pH of the result?

■ See Problems 16.77 and 16.78.

Henderson–Hasselbalch Equation

How do you prepare a buffer of given pH? We can show that the buffer must be prepared from a conjugate acid–base pair in which the acid-ionization constant is approximately equal to the desired H_3O^+ concentration. To illustrate, consider a buffer made up of a weak acid HA and its conjugate base A^-. The acid-ionization equilibrium is

$$HA(aq) + H_2O(l) \rightleftharpoons H_3O^+(aq) + A^-(aq)$$

and the acid-ionization constant is

$$K_a = \frac{[H_3O^+][A^-]}{[HA]}$$

By rearranging, you get an equation for the H_3O^+ concentration.

$$[H_3O^+] = K_a \times \frac{[HA]}{[A^-]}$$

This equation expresses the H_3O^+ concentration in terms of the K_a for the acid and the ratio of concentrations of HA and A^-. This equation was derived from the equilibrium constant, so the concentrations of HA and A^- should be equilibrium values. But because the presence of A^- represses the ionization of HA, these concentrations do not differ significantly from the values used to prepare the buffer. If [HA] and $[A^-]$ are approximately equal, the hydronium-ion concentration of the buffer is approximately equal to K_a.

You can use the preceding equation to derive an equation for the pH of a buffer. Take the negative logarithm of both sides of the equation. That is,

$$-\log [H_3O^+] = -\log\left(K_a \times \frac{[HA]}{[A^-]}\right) = -\log K_a - \log\frac{[HA]}{[A^-]}$$

The left side equals the pH. You can also simplify the right side. The pK_a of a weak acid is defined in a manner similar to pH and pOH. <

$$pK_a = -\log K_a$$

The previous equation can be written

$$pH = pK_a - \log\frac{[HA]}{[A^-]} = pK_a + \log\frac{[A^-]}{[HA]}$$

More generally, you can write

$$pH = pK_a + \log\frac{[base]}{[acid]}$$

This is *an equation relating the pH of a buffer for different concentrations of conjugate acid and base;* it is known as the **Henderson–Hasselbalch equation.** By substituting the value of pK_a for the conjugate acid and the ratio [base]/[acid], you obtain the pH of the buffer.

The question we asked earlier was how to prepare a buffer of a given pH—for example, pH 4.90. You can see that you need to find a conjugate acid–base pair in which the pK_a of the acid is close to the desired pH. K_a for acetic acid is 1.7×10^{-5}, and its pK_a is $-\log(1.7 \times 10^{-5}) = 4.77$. You can get a pH somewhat higher by increasing the ratio [base]/[acid].

Consider the calculation of the pH of a buffer containing 0.10 M NH_3 and 0.20 M NH_4Cl. The conjugate acid is NH_4^+, whose K_a you can calculate from K_b for NH_3

Acid- and base-ionization constants are often listed as pK_as and pK_bs ($pK_b = -\log K_b$).

$(= 1.8 \times 10^{-5})$. K_a for NH_4^+ is 5.6×10^{-10}, and the pK_a is $-\log(5.6 \times 10^{-10}) = 9.25$. Hence,

$$pH = 9.25 + \log \frac{0.10}{0.20} = 8.95$$

The solution is basic, as you could have guessed, because the buffer contains the weak base NH_3 and the very weak acid NH_4^+.

Concept Check 16.4

You add 1.5 mL of 1 *M* HCl to each of the following solutions. Which one will show the least change of pH?

a. 15 mL of 0.1 *M* NaOH

b. 15 mL of 0.1 *M* $HC_2H_3O_2$

c. 30 mL of 0.1 *M* NaOH and 30 mL of 0.1 *M* $HC_2H_3O_2$

d. 30 mL of 0.1 *M* NaOH and 60 mL of 0.1 *M* $HC_2H_3O_2$

Concept Check 16.5

The beaker on the left below represents a buffer solution of a weak acid HA and its conjugate base, A^-. (Water molecules and spectator ions have been omitted for clarity.)

a. Which beaker on the right, X or Y, depicts the solution after the addition of two formula units of NaOH?

b. How many HCl molecules can be added to the original buffer solution before the buffer capacity is exceeded?

c. Draw a picture of the solution where the buffer capacity has been exceeded by the addition of HCl.

X   Y

● = HA
● = A^-

16.7 | Acid–Base Titration Curves

An acid–base titration is a procedure for determining the amount of acid (or base) in a solution by determining the volume of base (or acid) of known concentration that will completely react with it. < An **acid–base titration curve** is *a plot of the pH of a solution of acid (or base) against the volume of added base (or acid)*. Such curves are used to gain insight into the titration process. You can use the titration curve to choose an indicator that will show when the titration is complete.

The technique of titration was discussed in Section 4.10.

Titration of a Strong Acid by a Strong Base

Figure 16.12 shows a curve for the titration of 25.0 mL of 0.100 *M* HCl by 0.100 *M* NaOH. Note that the pH changes slowly at first until the molar amount of base added

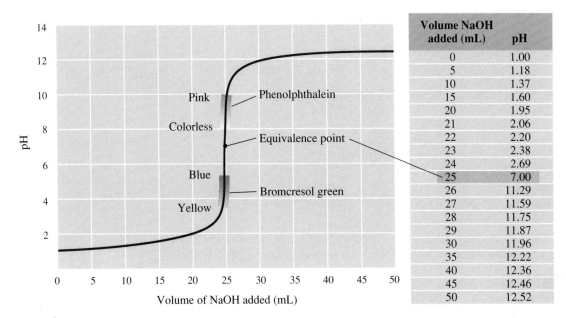

Volume NaOH added (mL)	pH
0	1.00
5	1.18
10	1.37
15	1.60
20	1.95
21	2.06
22	2.20
23	2.38
24	2.69
25	7.00
26	11.29
27	11.59
28	11.75
29	11.87
30	11.96
35	12.22
40	12.36
45	12.46
50	12.52

FIGURE 16.12 ▲

Curve for the titration of a strong acid by a strong base

Here 25.0 mL of 0.100 M HCl is titrated by 0.100 M NaOH. The portions of the curve where indicators bromcresol green and phenolphthalein change color are shown. Note that both indicators change color where the pH changes rapidly (the nearly vertical part of the curve).

nearly equals that of the acid—that is, until the titration is near the equivalence point. The **equivalence point** is *the point in a titration when a stoichiometric amount of reactant has been added.* At the equivalence point, the pH of this solution of NaOH and HCl is 7.0, because it contains a salt, NaCl, that does not hydrolyze. However, the pH changes rapidly near the equivalence point, from a pH of about 3 to a pH of about 11. To detect the equivalence point, you add an indicator that changes color within the pH range 3–11. Phenolphthalein can be used, because it changes from colorless to pink in the pH range 8.2–10.0. (Figure 15.10 showed the pH ranges for the color changes of indicators.) Even though this color change occurs on the basic side, only a fraction of a drop of base is required to change the pH several units when the titration is near the equivalence point. The indicator bromcresol green, whose color changes in the pH range 3.8–5.4, would also work. Because the pH change is so large, many other indicators could be used.

The following example shows how to calculate a point on the titration curve of a strong acid and a strong base.

Example 16.13 | Calculating the pH of a Solution of a Strong Acid and a Strong Base

Calculate the pH of a solution in which 10.0 mL of 0.100 M NaOH is added to 25.0 mL of 0.100 M HCl.

Problem Strategy   Whenever we are performing calculations that involve titrations, we need to write down the balanced chemical equation and determine the extent of the reaction. In this case, the reaction is between a strong acid and strong base, so we assume that the reaction is complete. Therefore, we will be performing a stoichiometric calculation.

Solution   The equation is

$$H_3O^+(aq) + OH^-(aq) \longrightarrow H_2O(l) + H_2O(l)$$

You get the amounts of reactants by multiplying the volume (in liters) of each solution by its molar concentration.

$$\text{Mol } H_3O^+ = 0.0250 \text{ L} \times 0.100 \text{ mol/L} = 0.00250 \text{ mol}$$

$$\text{Mol } OH^- = 0.0100 \text{ L} \times 0.100 \text{ mol/L} = 0.00100 \text{ mol}$$

(continued)

(continued)

All of the OH^- reacts, leaving an excess of H_3O^+.

$$\text{Excess } H_3O^+ = (0.00250 - 0.00100) \text{ mol} = 0.00150 \text{ mol } H_3O^+$$

You obtain the concentration of H_3O^+ by dividing this amount of H_3O^+ by the total volume of solution (= 0.0250 L + 0.0100 L = 0.0350 L).

$$[H_3O^+] = \frac{0.00150 \text{ mol}}{0.0350 \text{ L}} = 0.0429$$

Hence,

$$pH = -\log [H_3O^+] = -\log(0.0429) = \mathbf{1.368}$$

Answer Check A quick check of the concentrations and volumes of the HCl and NaOH being reacted indicates that we would expect the answer to have a pH less than 7.

Exercise 16.14 What is the pH of a solution in which 15 mL of 0.10 M NaOH has been added to 25 mL of 0.10 M HCl?

■ See Problems 16.85 and 16.86.

Titration of a Weak Acid by a Strong Base

The titration of a weak acid by a strong base gives a somewhat different curve. Figure 16.13 shows the curve for the titration of 25.0 mL of 0.100 M nicotinic acid,

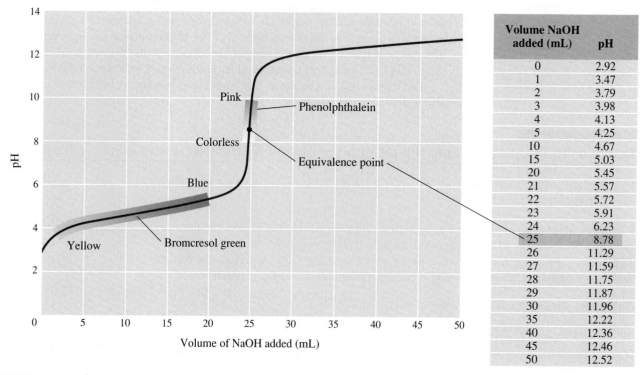

Volume NaOH added (mL)	pH
0	2.92
1	3.47
2	3.79
3	3.98
4	4.13
5	4.25
10	4.67
15	5.03
20	5.45
21	5.57
22	5.72
23	5.91
24	6.23
25	8.78
26	11.29
27	11.59
28	11.75
29	11.87
30	11.96
35	12.22
40	12.36
45	12.46
50	12.52

FIGURE 16.13 ▲

Curve for the titration of a weak acid by a strong base

Here 25.0 mL of 0.100 M nicotinic acid, a weak acid, is titrated by 0.100 M NaOH. Note that bromcresol green changes color during the early part of the titration, well before the equivalence point. Phenol-phthalein changes color where the pH changes rapidly (near the equivalence point). Thus, phenolphthalein could be used as an indicator for the titration, whereas bromcresol green could not.

$HC_6H_4NO_2$, by 0.100 M NaOH. The titration starts at a higher pH than the titration of HCl, because nicotinic acid is a weak acid. As before, the pH changes slowly at first, then rapidly near the equivalence point. The pH range in which the rapid change is seen occurs from about pH 7 to pH 11. Note that the pH range is shorter than that for the titration of a strong acid by a strong base. This means that the choice of an indicator is more critical. Phenolphthalein would work; it changes color in the range 8.2–10.0. Bromcresol green would not work because it changes color in the range 3.8–5.4, which occurs before the titration curve rises steeply.

Note also that the equivalence point for the titration curve of nicotinic acid occurs on the basic side. This happens because at the equivalence point the solution is that of the salt, sodium nicotinate, which is basic from the hydrolysis of the nicotinate ion. The optimum choice of indicator would be one that changes color over a range that includes the pH of the equivalence point.

The following example shows how to calculate the pH at the equivalence point in the titration of a weak acid and a strong base.

Example 16.14 | Calculating the pH at the Equivalence Point in the Titration of a Weak Acid by a Strong Base

---

Calculate the pH of the solution at the equivalence point when 25 mL of 0.10 M nicotinic acid is titrated by 0.10 M sodium hydroxide. K_a for nicotinic acid equals 1.4×10^{-5}.

Problem Strategy Because the titration is at the equivalence point, we know that equal molar amounts of nicotinic acid and sodium hydroxide have been reacted. From the chemical reaction we can determine that 1 mol of nicotinic acid reacts with 1 mol of sodium hydroxide to produce 1 mol of sodium nicotinate and 1 mol of water. We now can perform the stoichiometric calculation to determine the moles of nicotinate ion. Using this quantity and the total volume of solution, we can calculate the nicontinate ion concentration. We then can find the pH of this solution by treating it as a hydrolysis problem.

Solution CONCENTRATION OF NICOTINATE ION: Because the reaction is at the equivalence point, we assume that the reaction of the base with the acid is complete. The chemical equation for the titration is

$$HNic(aq) + NaOH(aq) \longrightarrow H_2O(aq) + NaNic(aq)$$

Therefore, the calculation of the moles of nicotinate ion is

$$2.5 \times 10^{-3} \text{ L HNic} \times \frac{0.10 \text{ mol HNic}}{1 \text{ L HNic}} \times \frac{1 \text{ mol NaNic}}{1 \text{ mol HNic}} \times \frac{1 \text{ mol Nic}^-}{1 \text{ mol NaNic}} = 2.5 \times 10^{-4} \text{ mol Nic}^-$$

From the reaction stoichiometry, we know that 25 mL of 0.10 M sodium hydroxide is needed to completely react with 25 mL of 0.10 M nicotinic acid, so the total volume of solution is 50 mL (assuming there is no volume change on mixing). Dividing the molar amount of nicotinate ion by the volume of solution in liters gives the molar concentration of nicotinate ion.

$$\text{Molar concentration} = \frac{2.5 \times 10^{-3} \text{ mol}}{50 \times 10^{-3} \text{ L}} = 0.050 \, M$$

HYDROLYSIS OF NICOTINATE ION This portion of the calculation follows the method given in Example 16.8. You find that K_b for nicotinate ion is 7.1×10^{-10} and that the concentration of hydroxide ion is 6.0×10^{-6} M. The pH is **8.78**.

Answer Check One bad assumption that is often made concerning acid–base titrations is that the pH is always 7 at the equivalence point. Although this is true when strong acids

(continued)

(continued)

and bases are used, it is not the case here. Note that you can predict whether the solution will be acidic or basic at the equivalence point by examining the products of the chemical reaction to see if an acid or base was produced. Here, the weak base Nic⁻ was produced; therefore, we would expect a correct answer to be a pH greater than 7.

Exercise 16.15   What is the pH at the equivalence point when 25 mL of 0.10 M HF is titrated by 0.15 M NaOH?

■ See Problems 16.87 and 16.88.

Titration of a Weak Base by a Strong Acid

When you titrate a weak base by a strong acid, you get a titration curve similar to that obtained when a weak acid is titrated by a strong base. Figure 16.14 shows the pH changes during the titration of 25.0 mL of 0.100 M NH₃ by 0.100 M HCl. In this case, the pH declines slowly at first, then falls abruptly from about pH 7 to pH 3. Methyl red, which changes color from yellow at pH 6.0 to red at pH 4.8, is a possible indicator for this titration. Note that phenolphthalein could not be used to find the equivalence point.

This last section covering acid–base titrations is an ideal place to illustrate how titration problems can be configured to encompass many of the ideas and problem-solving approaches encountered in this chapter. Although Example 16.5 is focused on the titration of a weak base by a strong acid, the concepts and operational skills apply to the other types of acid–base titrations.

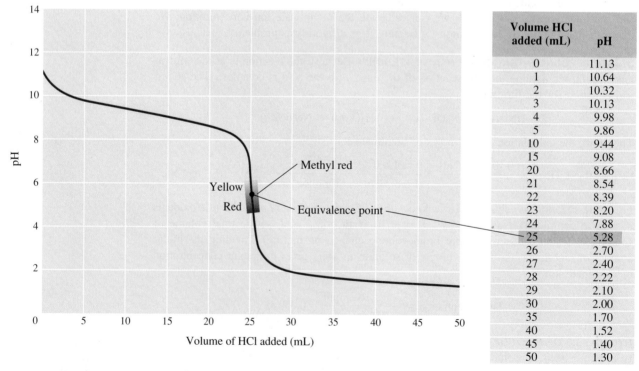

Volume HCl added (mL)	pH
0	11.13
1	10.64
2	10.32
3	10.13
4	9.98
5	9.86
10	9.44
15	9.08
20	8.66
21	8.54
22	8.39
23	8.20
24	7.88
25	5.28
26	2.70
27	2.40
28	2.22
29	2.10
30	2.00
35	1.70
40	1.52
45	1.40
50	1.30

FIGURE 16.14 ▲

Curve for the titration of a weak base by a strong acid

Here 25.0 mL of 0.100 M NH₃ is titrated by 0.100 M HCl. Methyl red can be used as an indicator for the titration.

Example 16.15 | Calculation of the pH of a Solution at Several Points of a Titration of a Weak Base by a Strong Acid

Figure 16.14 is the curve for the titration of a 25-mL sample of 0.100 M NH_3 by 0.100 M HCl. Calculate the pH of the NH_3 solution at the following points during the titration: a. Prior to the addition of any HCl. b. After the addition of 12 mL of 0.100 M HCl. c. At the equivalence point. d. After the addition of 31 mL of 0.100 M HCl.

Problem Strategy The key to solving this problem is to relate each part to a problem that you have already encountered. Part a involves a weak base (NH_3) in water, which was done in Example 16.5. For part b, you need to recognize that all of the H_3O^+ from the strong acid (HCl) will completely react with the NH_3, creating a buffer solution. This is similar to Example 16.12. Part c is at the equivalence point, so you know that the moles of HCl added to the solution are equal to the moles of NH_3. As in Example 16.14, you will need to perform a stoichiometry problem followed by an equilibrium calculation, only this time it is for a weak base with a strong acid. Finally, in part d, the titration is past the equivalence point. Because you are adding a strong acid beyond the equivalence point, the pH of the solution can be calculated based *only* on the moles of unreacted HCl (H_3O^+) that remain in the solution.

Solution a. NH_3, a weak base, undergoes the hydrolysis reaction

$$NH_3(aq) + H_2O(aq) \longrightarrow NH_4^+(aq) + OH^-(aq) \qquad K_b = 1.8 \times 10^{-5}$$

Starting with the initial concentration of NH_3 of 0.100 M, you perform an equilibrium calculation by setting up a table and solving for the concentration of OH^-. Then calculate the pH.

The pH prior to the start of the titration is **11.13.**

b. When HCl is added to the NH_3 solution, it undergoes the reaction

$$H_3O^+(aq) + NH_3(aq) \longrightarrow NH_4^+(aq) + H_2O(l)$$

During the reaction all of the added HCl is consumed. (When looking at the reaction, keep in mind that because HCl is a strong acid, we represent it as H_3O^+ in aqueous solution.) Solving this stoichiometry problem, you can determine the moles of NH_3 that remain and the number of moles of NH_4^+ that were produced. Accounting for the volume of the solution, you calculate the following concentrations:

$$[NH_3] = 3.5 \times 10^{-2} \, M$$
$$[NH_4^+] = 3.2 \times 10^{-2} \, M$$

Recognizing that this is a buffer solution, you can use the Henderson–Hasselbalch equation (K_a for $NH_4^+ = 5.6 \times 10^{-10}$) to solve for the pH, which is **9.29.** If you don't recognize that this is a buffer solution, you can solve this as an equilibrium problem based on the hydrolysis reaction of NH_3.

c. This part is solved in nearly the same manner as part b, only now the number of moles of H_3O^+ is equal to the number of moles of NH_3. Using the reaction stoichiometry and keeping track of the total solution volume (50 mL), you determine

$$[NH_4^+] = 5.0 \times 10^{-2} \, M$$
$$[NH_3] = 0 \, M$$

This is not a buffer solution because the $[NH_3] = 0 \, M$; therefore, we need to solve an equilibrium problem of the hydrolysis of NH_4^+, which indicates pH = **5.28.** Note how this agrees with Figure 16.14.

(continued)

(continued)

d. Finally, you need to calculate the concentration of H_3O^+ that is due to the excess HCl added beyond the equivalence point. Remembering the titration reaction

$$H_3O^+ (aq) + NH_3(aq) \longrightarrow NH_4^+(aq) + H_2O(l)$$

You perform the stoichiometry calculation by first determing the moles of H_3O^+ that reacted with the NH_3. Then you use this quantity to determine the amount of unreacted H_3O^+ that remains in solution.

$$\text{Mol } H_3O^+ \text{ reacted} = 2.5 \times 10^{-3} \text{ mol}$$

$$\text{Mol } H_3O^+ \text{ remaining} = (3.1 \times 10^{-3} \text{ mol} - 2.5 \times 10^{-3} \text{ mol}) = 6.0 \times 10^{-4} \text{ mol}$$

In order to calculate the pH, you first need to know the concentration of the H_3O^+. Taking into account the total volume of solution (56 mL), you determine the concentration of H_3O^+.

$$[H_3O^+] = \frac{6.0 \times 10^{-4} \text{ mol}}{0.056 \text{ L}} = 1.1 \times 10^{-2} M$$

Therefore, the pH = **1.96**.

Answer Check   If you know the general attributes of the different titration curves, you can make sure that your numerical answers fall on the curve. Compare the answers in this problem with the curve in Figure 16.14.

Exercise 16.16   An 80.0-mL sample of 0.200 M ammonia is titrated with 0.100 M hydrochloric acid. K_b for ammonia is 1.8×10^{-5}. Calculate the pH of the solution at each of the following points of the titration: a. before the addition of any HCl; b. halfway to the equivalence point; c. at the equivalence point; d. after the addition of 175 mL of 0.100 M HCl.

■ See Problems 16.91 and 16.92.

A Checklist for Review

Important Terms

acid-ionization constant (16.1)
degree of ionization (16.1)
base-ionization constant (16.3)
hydrolysis (16.4)

common-ion effect (16.5)
buffer (16.6)
Henderson–Hasselbalch equation (16.6)

acid–base titration curve (16.7)
equivalence point (16.7)

Key Equations

$$K_a = \frac{[H_3O^+][A^-]}{[HA]}$$

$$K_b = \frac{[HB^+][OH^-]}{[B]}$$

$$K_a K_b = K_w$$

$$pH = pK_a + \log \frac{[\text{base}]}{[\text{acid}]}$$

Summary of Facts and Concepts

When a weak acid dissolves in water, it ionizes to give hydronium ions and the conjugate base ions. The equilibrium constant for this *acid ionization* is $K_a = [H_3O^+][A^-]/[HA]$, where HA is the general formula for the acid. The constant K_a can be determined from the pH of an acid solution of known concentration. Once obtained, the acid-ionization constant can be used to find the concentrations of species in any solution of the acid.

In the case of a *diprotic* acid, H_2A, the concentration of H_3O^+ and HA^- are calculated from K_{a1}, and the concentration of A^{2-} equals K_{a2}. Similar considerations apply to *base ionizations*.

Solutions of salts may be acidic or basic because of *hydrolysis* of the ions. The equilibrium constant for hydrolysis equals K_a for a cation or K_b for an anion. Calculation of the pH of a solution of a salt in which one ion hydrolyzes is fundamentally the same as calculation of the pH of a solution of an acid or base. However, K_a or K_b for an ion is usually obtained from the conjugate base or acid by applying the equation $K_aK_b = K_w$.

A *buffer* is a solution that can resist changes in pH when small amounts of acid or base are added to it. A buffer contains either a weak acid and its conjugate base or a weak base and its conjugate acid. The concentrations of acid and base conjugates are approximately equal. Different pH ranges are possible for acid–base conjugates, depending on their ionization constants.

An *acid–base titration curve* is a plot of the pH of the solution against the volume of reactant added. During the titration of a strong acid by a strong base, the pH changes slowly at first. Then, as the amount of base nears the stoichiometric value—that is, nears the *equivalence point*—the pH rises abruptly, changing by several units. The pH at the equivalence point is 7.0. A similar curve is obtained when a weak acid is titrated by a strong base. However, the pH changes less at the equivalence point. Moreover, the pH at the equivalence point is greater than 7.0 because of hydrolysis of the salt produced. An indicator must be chosen that changes color within a pH range near the equivalence point, where the pH changes rapidly.

Media Summary

Visit the **student website at college.cengage.com/pic/ebbing9e** to help prepare for class, study for quizzes and exams, understand core concepts, and visualize molecular-level interactions. The following media activities are available for this chapter:

 Prepare for Class

■ **Video Lessons** *Mini lectures from chemistry experts*
   CIA Demonstration: Creating Acid Rain
   Acid–Base Properties of Salt Solutions
   The Common-Ion Effect
   An Introduction to Buffers
   CIA Demonstration: Buffers in Action
   Acidic Buffers
   Basic Buffers
   The Henderson–Hasselbach Equation
   Acid–Base Indicators
   Strong Acid–Strong Base Titration
   CIA Demonstration: Barium Hydroxide–Sulfuric Acid
      Titration
   Weak Acid–Strong Base Titration
   Weak Base–Strong Acid Titration
   Common Mathematical Functions

 Improve Your Grade

■ **Visualizations** *Molecular-level animations and lab demonstration videos*

   Acid-Ionization Equilibrium
   Buffers
   Adding an Acid to a Buffer
   Neutralization of a Strong Acid by a Strong Base

■ **Tutorials** *Animated examples and interactive activities*
   Calculating pH of Weak Acid and Base Solutions
   Buffered Solutions

■ **Flashcards** *Key terms and definitions*
   Online Flashcards

■ **Self-Assessment Questions** *Additional questions with full worked-out solutions*
   6 Self-Assessment Questions

 ACE the Test

Multiple-choice quizzes
3 ACE Practice Tests

Access these resources using the passkey available free with new texts or for purchase separately.

Learning Objectives

16.1 Acid-Ionization Equilibria

■ Write the chemical equation for a weak acid undergoing *acid ionization* in aqueous solution.
■ Define *acid-ionization constant* and *degree of ionization*.
■ Determine K_a from the solution pH. **Example 16.1**
■ Calculate concentrations of species in a weak acid solution using K_a (approximation method). **Example 16.2**
■ State the assumption that allows for using approximations when solving problems.
■ Calculate concentrations of species in a weak acid solution using K_a (quadratic formula). **Example 16.3**

16.2 Polyprotic Acids

■ State the general trend in the ionization constants of a polyprotic acid.
■ Calculate concentrations of species in a solution of a diprotic acid. **Example 16.4**

16.3 Base-Ionization Equilibria

■ Write the chemical equation for a weak base undergoing ionization in aqueous solution.
■ Define *base-ionization constant*.

■ Calculate concentrations of species in a weak base solution using K_b. **Example 16.5**

16.4 Acid–Base Properties of Salt Solutions

■ Write the *hydrolysis* reaction of an ion to form an acidic solution.
■ Write the hydrolysis reaction of an ion to form a basic solution.
■ Predict whether a salt solution is acidic, basic, or neutral. **Example 16.6**
■ Obtain K_a from K_b or K_b from K_a. **Example 16.7**
■ Calculating concentrations of species in a salt solution. **Example 16.8**

16.5 Common-Ion Effect

■ Explain the common-ion effect.
■ Calculate the common-ion effect on acid ionization (effect of a strong acid). **Example 16.9**
■ Calculate the common-ion effect on acid ionization (effect of a conjugate base). **Example 16.10**

16.6 Buffers

■ Define *buffer* and *buffer capacity.*
■ Describe the pH change of a buffer solution with the addition of acid or base.

■ Calculate the pH of a buffer from given volumes of solution. **Example 16.11**
■ Calculate the pH of a buffer when a strong acid or a strong base is added. **Example 16.12**
■ Learn the *Henderson–Hasselbalch* equation.
■ State when the Henderson–Hasselbalch equation can be applied

16.7 Acid–Base Titration Curves

■ Define *equivalence point.*
■ Describe the curve for the titration of a strong acid by a strong base.
■ Calculate the pH of a solution of a strong acid and a strong base. **Example 16.13**
■ Describe the curve for the titration of a weak acid by a strong base.
■ Calculate the pH at the equivalence point in the titration of a weak acid by a strong base. **Example 16.14**
■ Describe the curve for the titration of a weak base by a strong acid.
■ Calculate the pH of a solution at several points of a titration of weak base by a strong acid. **Example 16.15**

Self-Assessment and Review Questions

16.1 Write an equation for the ionization of hydrogen cyanide, HCN, in aqueous solution. What is the equilibrium expression K_a for this acid ionization?

16.2 Which of the following is the weakest acid: $HClO_4$, HCN, or $HC_2H_3O_2$? See Table 15.1 and Table 16.1.

16.3 Briefly describe two methods for determining K_a for a weak acid.

16.4 Describe how the degree of ionization of a weak acid changes as the concentration increases.

16.5 Consider a solution of 0.0010 M HF ($K_a = 6.8 \times 10^{-4}$). In solving for the concentrations of species in this solution, could you use the simplifying assumption in which you neglect x in the denominator of the equilibrium equation? Explain.

16.6 Phosphorous acid, H_2PHO_3, is a diprotic acid. Write equations for the acid ionizations. Write the expressions for K_{a1} and K_{a2}.

16.7 What is the concentration of oxalate ion, $C_2O_4^{2-}$, in 0.10 M oxalic acid, $H_2C_2O_4$? K_{a1} is 5.6×10^{-2}, and K_{a2} is 5.1×10^{-5}.

16.8 Write the equation for the ionization of aniline, $C_6H_5NH_2$, in aqueous solution. Write the expression for K_b.

16.9 Which of the following is the strongest base: NH_3, $C_6H_5NH_2$, or CH_3NH_2? See Table 16.2.

16.10 Do you expect a solution of anilinium chloride (aniline hydrochloride), $C_6H_5NH_3Cl$, to be acidic or basic? (Anilinium chloride is the salt of aniline and hydrochloric acid.) Write the equation for the reaction involved. What is the equilibrium expression? How would you obtain the value for the equilibrium constant from Table 16.2?

16.11 What is meant by the common-ion effect? Give an example.

16.12 The pH of 0.10 M CH_3NH_2 (methylamine) is 11.8. When the chloride salt of methylamine, CH_3NH_3Cl, is added to this solution, does the pH increase or decrease? Explain, using Le Châtelier's principle and the common-ion effect.

16.13 Define the term *buffer.* Give an example.

16.14 What is meant by the capacity of a buffer? Describe a buffer with low capacity and the same buffer with greater capacity.

16.15 Describe the pH changes that occur during the titration of a weak base by a strong acid. What is meant by the term *equivalence point?*

16.16 If the pH is 8.0 at the equivalence point for the titration of a certain weak acid with sodium hydroxide, what indicator might you use? (See Figure 15.10.) Explain your choice.

16.17 Which of the following salts would produce the most basic aqueous solution?
   a. NaF   **b.** KBr   **c.** NH_4Cl
   d. $MgCl_2$ **e.** $LiNO_3$

16.18 If you mix 0.10 mol of NH_3 and 0.10 mol of HCl in a bucket of water, you would expect the resulting solution to be
   a. very basic   **b.** slightly basic   **c.** neutral
   d. slightly acidic   **e.** very acidic

16.19 Hydrogen sulfide, H_2S, is a very weak diprotic acid. In a 0.10 M solution of this acid, which of the following would you expect to find in the *highest* concentration?
   a. H_2S **b.** H_3O^+ **c.** HS^- **d.** S^{2-} **e.** OH^-

16.20 If 20.0 mL of a 0.10 M NaOH solution is added to a 30.0-mL sample of a 0.10 M weak acid, HA, what is the pH of the resulting solution? ($K_a = 1.8 \times 10^{-5}$ for HA)
   a. 2.87   **b.** 2.74   **c.** 4.74   **d.** 5.05   **e.** 8.73

Concept Explorations

16.21 Aqueous Solutions of Acids, Bases, and Salts

a. For each of the following salts, write the reaction that occurs when it dissociates in water: $NaCl(s)$, $NaCN(s)$, $KClO_2(s)$, $NH_4NO_3(s)$, $KBr(aq)$, and $NaF(s)$.

b. Consider each of the reactions that you wrote above, and identify the aqueous ions that *could* be proton donors (acids) or proton acceptors (bases). Briefly explain how you decided which ions to choose.

c. For each of the acids and bases that you identified in part b, write the chemical reaction it can undergo in aqueous solution (its reaction with water).

d. Are there any reactions that you have written above that you anticipate will occur to such an extent that the pH of the solution will be affected? As part of your answer, be sure to explain how you decided.

e. Assume that in each case above, 0.01 mol of the salt was dissolved in enough water at 25°C to make 1.0 L of solution. In each case, what additional information would you need in order to calculate the pH? If there are cases where no additional information is required, be sure to state that as well.

f. Say you take 0.01 mol of NH_4CN and dissolve it in enough water at 25°C to make 1.0 L of solution. Using chemical reactions and words, explain how you would go about determining what effect this salt will have on the pH of the solution. Be sure to list any additional information you would need to arrive at an answer.

16.22 The pH of Mixtures of Acid, Base, and Salt Solutions

a. When 0.10 mol of the ionic solid NaX, where X is an unknown anion, is dissolved in enough water to make 1.0 L of solution, the pH of the solution is 9.12. When 0.10 mol of the ionic solid ACl, where A is an unknown cation, is dissolved in enough water to make 1.0 L of solution, the pH of the solution is 7.00. What would be the pH of 1.0 L of solution that contained 0.10 mol of AX? Be sure to document how you arrived at your answer.

b. In the AX solution prepared above, is there any OH^- present? If so, compare the $[OH^-]$ in the solution to the $[H_3O^+]$.

c. From the information presented in part a, calculate K_b for the $X^-(aq)$ anion and K_a for the conjugate acid of $X^-(aq)$.

d. To 1.0 L of solution that contains 0.10 mol of AX, you add 0.025 mol of HCl. How will the pH of this solution compare to that of the solution that contained only NaX? Use chemical reactions as part of your explanation; you do not need to solve for a numerical answer.

e. Another 1.0 L sample of solution is prepared by mixing 0.10 mol of AX and 0.10 mol of HCl. The pH of the resulting solution is found to be 3.12. Explain why the pH of this solution is 3.12.

f. Finally, consider a different 1.0-L sample of solution that contains 0.10 mol of AX and 0.1 mol of NaOH. The pH of this solution is found to be 13.00. Explain why the pH of this solution is 13.00.

g. Some students mistakenly think that a solution that contains 0.10 mol of AX and 0.10 mol of HCl should have a pH of 1.00. Can you come up with a reason why students have this misconception? Write an approach that you would use to help these students understand what they are doing wrong.

Conceptual Problems

16.23 Which of the following beakers best represents a container of a weak acid, HA, in water? (Water molecules have been omitted for clarity.)

⬤ = H_3O^+

⬤ = A^-

⬤ = HA

A

B

C

16.24 You have 0.10-mol samples of three acids identified simply as HX, HY, and HZ. For each acid, you make up 0.10 M solutions by adding sufficient water to each of the acid samples. When you measure the pH of these samples, you find that the pH of HX is greater than the pH of HY, which in turn is greater than the pH of HZ.

a. Which of the acids is the least ionized in its solution?

b. Which acid has the largest K_a?

16.25 What reaction occurs when each of the following is dissolved in water?

a. HF

b. NaF

c. $C_6H_5NH_2$

d. $C_6H_5NH_3Cl$

16.26 You have the following solutions, all of the same molar concentration: KBr, HBr, CH_3NH_2, and NH_4Cl. Rank them from the lowest to the highest hydroxide-ion concentration.

16.27 Rantidine is a nitrogen base that is used to control stomach acidity by suppressing the stomach's production of hydrochloric acid. The compound is present in Zantac® as the chloride salt (rantidinium chloride; also called rantidine hydrochloride). Do you expect a solution of rantidine hydrochloride to be acidic, basic, or neutral? Explain by means of a general chemical equation.

16.28 A chemist prepares dilute solutions of equal molar concentrations of NH_3, NH_4Br, NaF, and $NaCl$. Rank these solutions from highest pH to lowest pH.

16.29 You want to prepare a buffer solution that has a pH equal to the pKa of the acid component of the buffer. If you have 100 mL of a 0.10 M solution of the acid HA, what volume and concentration of NaA solution could you use in order to prepare the buffer?

16.30 A friend of yours has performed three titrations: strong acid with a strong base, weak acid with a strong base, and weak base with a strong acid. He hands you the three titration curves, saying he has forgotten which is which. What attributes of the curves would you look at to identify each curve correctly?

16.31 You are given the following acid–base titration data, where each point on the graph represents the pH after adding a given volume of titrant (the substance being added during the titration).

a. What substance is being titrated, a strong acid, strong base, weak acid, or weak base?
b. What is the pH at the equivalence point of the tiration?
c. What indicator might you use to perform this titration? Explain.

16.32 The three flasks shown below depict the titration of an aqueous NaOH solution with HCl at different points. One represents the titration prior to the equivalence point, another represents the titration at the equivalence point, and the other represents the titration past the equivalence point. (Sodium ions and solvent water molecules have been omitted for clarity.)

a. Write the balanced chemical equation for the titration.
b. Label each of the beakers shown to indicate which point in the titration they represent.
c. For each solution, indicate whether you expect it to be acidic, basic, or neutral.

Practice Problems

Note: For values of K_a and K_b that are not given in the following problems, see Tables 16.1 and 16.2.

Acid Ionization

16.33 Write chemical equations for the acid ionizations of each of the following weak acids (express these in terms of H_3O^+).
a. HBrO (hypobromous acid)   **b.** $HClO_2$ (chlorous acid)
c. HNO_2 (nitrous acid)   **d.** HCN (hydrocyanic acid)

16.34 Write chemical equations for the acid ionizations of each of the following weak acids (express these in terms of H_3O^+).
a. HCO_2H (formic acid)
b. HF (hydrofluoric acid)
c. HN_3 (hydrazoic acid)
d. HOCN (cyanic acid)

16.35 Acrylic acid, whose formula is $HC_3H_3O_2$ or $HO_2CCH{=}CH_2$, is used in the manufacture of plastics. A 0.10 M aqueous solution of acrylic acid has a pH of 2.63. What is K_a for acrylic acid?

16.36 Heavy metal azides, which are salts of hydrazoic acid, HN_3, are used as explosive detonators. A solution of 0.20 M hydrazoic acid has a pH of 3.21. What is the K_a for hydrazoic acid?

16.37 Boric acid, $B(OH)_3$, is used as a mild antiseptic. What is the pH of a 0.021 M aqueous solution of boric acid? What is the degree of ionization of boric acid in this solution? The hydronium ion arises principally from the reaction

$$B(OH)_3(aq) + 2H_2O(l) \rightleftharpoons B(OH)_4^-(aq) + H_3O^+(aq)$$

The equilibrium constant for this reaction is 5.9×10^{-10}.

16.38 Formic acid, $HCHO_2$, is used to make methyl formate (a fumigant for dried fruit) and ethyl formate (an artificial rum flavor). What is the pH of a 0.10 M solution of formic acid? What is the degree of ionization of $HCHO_2$ in this solution? See Table 16.1 for K_a.

16.39 $C_6H_4NH_2COOH$, *para*-aminobenzoic acid (PABA), is used in some sunscreen agents. Calculate the concentrations of hydronium ion and *para*-aminobenzoate ion, $C_6H_4NH_2COO^-$, in a 0.055 M solution of the acid. The value of K_a is 2.2×10^{-5}.

16.40 Barbituric acid, $HC_4H_3N_2O_3$, is used to prepare various barbiturate drugs (used as sedatives). Calculate the concentrations of hydronium ion and barbiturate ion in a 0.10 M solution of the acid. The value of K_a is 9.8×10^{-5}.

16.41 A solution of acetic acid, $HC_2H_3O_2$, on a laboratory shelf was of undetermined concentration. If the pH of the solution was found to be 2.68, what was the concentration of the acetic acid?

16.42 A chemist wanted to determine the concentration of a solution of lactic acid, $HC_3H_5O_3$. She found that the pH of the solution was 2.51. What was the concentration of the solution? The K_a of lactic acid is 1.4×10^{-4}.

16.43 Hydrofluoric acid, HF, unlike hydrochloric acid, is a weak electrolyte. What is the hydronium-ion concentration and the pH of a 0.040 M aqueous solution of HF?

16.44 Chloroacetic acid, $HC_2H_2ClO_2$, has a greater acid strength than acetic acid, because the electronegative chlorine atom pulls electrons away from the O—H bond and thus weakens it. Calculate the hydronium-ion concentration and the pH of a 0.0020 M solution of chloroacetic acid. K_a is 1.3×10^{-3}.

16.45 What is the hydronium-ion concentration of a 2.00 M solution of 2,6-dinitrobenzoic acid, $(NO_2)_2C_6H_3COOH$, for which $K_a = 7.94 \times 10^{-2}$?

16.46 What is the hydronium-ion concentration of a 2.00×10^{-4} M solution of p-bromobenzoic acid, BrC_6H_4COOH, for which $K_a = 1.00 \times 10^{-4}$?

16.47 Phthalic acid, $H_2C_8H_4O_4$, is a diprotic acid used in the synthesis of phenolphthalein indicator. $K_{a1} = 1.2 \times 10^{-3}$, and $K_{a2} = 3.9 \times 10^{-6}$. (a) Calculate the hydronium-ion concentration of a 0.015 M solution. (b) What is the concentration of the $C_8H_4O_4^{2-}$ ion in the solution?

16.48 Carbonic acid, H_2CO_3, can be found in a wide variety of body fluids (from dissolved CO_2). (a) Calculate the hydronium-ion concentration of a 5.45×10^{-4} M H_2CO_3 solution. (b) What is the concentration of CO_3^{2-}?

Base Ionization

16.49 Write the chemical equation for the base ionization of methylamine, CH_3NH_2. Write the K_b expression for methylamine.

16.50 Write the chemical equation for the base ionization of aniline, $C_6H_5NH_2$. Write the K_b expression for aniline.

16.51 Ethanolamine, $HOC_2H_4NH_2$, is a viscous liquid with an ammonialike odor; it is used to remove hydrogen sulfide from natural gas. A 0.15 M aqueous solution of ethanolamine has a pH of 11.34. What is K_b for ethanolamine?

16.52 Trimethylamine, $(CH_3)_3N$, is a gas with a fishy, ammonialike odor. An aqueous solution that is 0.25 M trimethylamine has a pH of 11.63. What is K_b for trimethylamine?

16.53 What is the concentration of hydroxide ion in a 0.060 M aqueous solution of methylamine, CH_3NH_2? What is the pH?

16.54 What is the concentration of hydroxide ion in a 0.18 M aqueous solution of hydroxylamine, NH_2OH? What is the pH?

Acid–Base Properties of Salt Solutions; Hydrolysis

16.55 Note whether hydrolysis occurs for each of the following ions. If hydrolysis does occur, write the chemical equation for it. Then write the equilibrium expression for the acid or base ionization (whichever occurs).
  a. NO_3^- **b.** OCl^-
  c. $NH_2NH_3^+$ **d.** Br^-

16.56 Note whether hydrolysis occurs for each of the following ions. If hydrolysis does occur, write the chemical equation for it. Then write the equilibrium expression for the acid or base ionization (whichever occurs).
  a. $CH_3NH_3^+$
  b. I^-
  c. ClO_2^-
  d. PO_4^{3-}

16.57 Write the equation for the acid ionization of the $Zn(H_2O)_6^{2+}$ ion.

16.58 Write the equation for the acid ionization of the $Cu(H_2O)_6^{2+}$ ion.

16.59 For each of the following salts, indicate whether the aqueous solution will be acidic, basic, or neutral.
  a. $Fe(NO_3)_3$
  b. Na_2CO_3
  c. $Ca(CN)_2$
  d. NH_4ClO_4

16.60 Note whether the aqueous solution of each of the following salts will be acidic, basic, or neutral.
  a. Na_2S
  b. $Cu(NO_3)_2$
  c. $KClO_4$
  d. CH_3NH_3Cl

16.61 Decide whether solutions of the following salts are acidic, neutral, or basic.
  a. ammonium acetate
  b. anilinium acetate

16.62 Decide whether solutions of the following salts are acidic, neutral, or basic.
  a. ammonium cyanate
  b. anilinium cyanate

16.63 Obtain (a) the K_b value for NO_2^-; (b) the K_a value for $C_5H_5NH^+$ (pyridinium ion).

16.64 Obtain (a) the K_b value for ClO^-; (b) the K_a value for NH_3OH^+ (hydroxylammonium ion).

16.65 What is the pH of a 0.025 M aqueous solution of sodium propionate, $NaC_3H_5O_2$? What is the concentration of propionic acid in the solution?

16.66 Calculate the OH^- concentration and pH of a 0.0020 M aqueous solution of sodium cyanide, NaCN. Finally, obtain the hydronium-ion, CN^-, and HCN concentrations.

16.67 Calculate the concentration of pyridine, C_5H_5N, in a solution that is 0.15 M pyridinium bromide, C_5H_5NHBr. What is the pH of the solution?

16.68 What is the pH of a 0.35 M solution of methylammonium chloride, CH_3NH_3Cl? What is the concentration of methylamine in the solution?

Common-Ion Effect

16.69 Calculate the degree of ionization of (a) 0.75 M HF (hydrofluoric acid); (b) the same solution that is also 0.12 M HCl.

16.70 Calculate the degree of ionization of (a) 0.22 M $HCHO_2$ (formic acid); (b) the same solution that is also 0.12 M HCl.

16.71 What is the pH of a solution that is 0.10 M KNO_2 and 0.15 M HNO_2 (nitrous acid)?

16.72 What is the pH of a solution that is 0.20 M KOCN and 0.10 M HOCN (cyanic acid)?

16.73 What is the pH of a solution that is 0.10 M CH_3NH_2 (methylamine) and 0.15 M CH_3NH_3Cl (methylammonium chloride)?

16.74 What is the pH of a solution that is 0.15 M $C_2H_5NH_2$ (ethylamine) and 0.10 M $C_2H_5NH_3Br$ (ethylammonium bromide)?

Buffers

16.75 A buffer is prepared by adding 45.0 mL of 0.15 M NaF to 35.0 mL of 0.10 M HF. What is the pH of the final solution?

16.76 A buffer is prepared by adding 115 mL of 0.30 M NH_3 to 145 mL of 0.15 M NH_4NO_3. What is the pH of the final solution?

16.77 What is the pH of a buffer solution that is 0.10 M NH_3 and 0.10 M NH_4^+? What is the pH if 12 mL of 0.20 M hydrochloric acid is added to 125 mL of buffer?

16.78 A buffer is prepared by mixing 525 mL of 0.50 M formic acid, $HCHO_2$, and 475 mL of 0.50 M sodium formate, $NaCHO_2$. Calculate the pH. What would be the pH of 85 mL of the buffer to which 8.6 mL of 0.15 M hydrochloric acid had been added?

16.79 What is the pH of a buffer solution that is 0.15 M chloroacetic acid and 0.10 M sodium chloroacetate? $K_a = 1.3 \times 10^{-3}$.

16.80 What is the pH of a buffer solution that is 0.10 M propionic acid and 0.20 M sodium propionate?

16.81 What is the pH of a buffer solution that is 0.15 M pyridine and 0.10 M pyridinium bromide?

16.82 What is the pH of a buffer solution that is 0.15 M methylamine and 0.20 M methylammonium chloride?

16.83 How many moles of sodium acetate must be added to 2.0 L of 0.10 M acetic acid to give a solution that has a pH equal to 5.00? Ignore the volume change due to the addition of sodium acetate.

16.84 How many moles of hydrofluoric acid, HF, must be added to 500.0 mL of 0.25 M sodium fluoride to give a buffer of pH 3.50? Ignore the volume change due to the addition of hydrofluoric acid.

Titration Curves

16.85 What is the pH of a solution in which 15 mL of 0.10 M NaOH is added to 25 mL of 0.10 M HCl?

16.86 What is the pH of a solution in which 40 mL of 0.10 M NaOH is added to 25 mL of 0.10 M HCl?

16.87 A 1.24-g sample of benzoic acid was dissolved in water to give 50.0 mL of solution. This solution was titrated with 0.180 M NaOH. What was the pH of the solution when the equivalence point was reached?

16.88 A 0.400-g sample of propionic acid was dissolved in water to give 50.0 mL of solution. This solution was titrated with 0.150 M NaOH. What was the pH of the solution when the equivalence point was reached?

16.89 Find the pH of the solution obtained when 32 mL of 0.087 M ethylamine is titrated to the equivalence point with 0.15 M HCl.

16.90 What is the pH at the equivalence point when 22 mL of 0.20 M hydroxylamine is titrated with 0.15 M HCl?

16.91 A 50.0-mL sample of a 0.100 M solution of NaCN is titrated by 0.200 M HCl. K_b for CN^- is 2.0×10^{-5}. Calculate the pH of the solution: a. prior to the start of the titration; b. after the addition of 15.0 mL of 0.100 M HCl; c. at the equivalence point; d. after the addition of 30.0 mL of 0.200 M HCl.

16.92 Sodium benzoate, $NaC_7H_5O_2$, is used as a preservative in foods. Consider a 50.0-mL sample of 0.250 M $NaC_7H_5O_2$ being titrated by 0.200 M HBr. Calculate the pH of the solution: a. when no HBr has been added; b. after the addition of 50.0 mL of the HBr solution; c. at the equivalence point; d. after the addition of 75.00 mL of the HBr solution. The K_b value for $NaC_7H_5O_2$ is 1.6×10^{-10}.

16.93 Calculate the pH of a solution obtained by mixing 500.0 mL of 0.10 M NH_3 with 200.0 mL of 0.15 M HCl.

16.94 Calculate the pH of a solution obtained by mixing 35.0 mL of 0.15 M acetic acid with 25.0 mL of 0.10 M sodium acetate.

General Problems

16.95 Salicylic acid, $C_6H_4OHCOOH$, is used in the manufacture of acetylsalicylic acid (aspirin) and methyl salicylate (wintergreen flavor). A saturated solution of salicylic acid contains 2.2 g of the acid per liter of solution and has a pH of 2.43. What is the value of K_a?

16.96 Cyanoacetic acid, $CH_2CNCOOH$, is used in the manufacture of barbiturate drugs. An aqueous solution containing 5.0 g in a liter of solution has a pH of 1.89. What is the value of K_a?

16.97 A 0.050 M aqueous solution of sodium hydrogen sulfate, $NaHSO_4$, has a pH of 1.73. Calculate K_{a2} for sulfuric acid. Sulfuric acid is a strong electrolyte, so you can ignore hydrolysis of the HSO_4^- ion.

16.98 A 0.10 M aqueous solution of sodium dihydrogen phosphate, NaH_2PO_4, has a pH of 4.10. Calculate K_{a2} for phosphoric acid. You can ignore hydrolysis of the $H_2PO_4^-$ ion.

16.99 Calculate the base-ionization constants for CN^- and CO_3^{2-}. Which ion is the stronger base?

16.100 Calculate the base-ionization constants for PO_4^{3-} and SO_4^{2-}. Which ion is the stronger base?

16.101 Calculate the pH of a 0.15 M aqueous solution of aluminum chloride, $AlCl_3$. The acid ionization of hydrated aluminum ion is

$$Al(H_2O)_6^{3+}(aq) + H_2O(l) \rightleftharpoons$$
$$Al(H_2O)_5OH^{2+}(aq) + H_3O^+(aq)$$

and K_a is 1.4×10^{-5}.

16.102 Calculate the pH of a 0.15 M aqueous solution of zinc chloride, $ZnCl_2$. The acid ionization of hydrated zinc ion is

$$Zn(H_2O)_6^{2+}(aq) + H_2O(l) \rightleftharpoons$$
$$Zn(H_2O)_5OH^+(aq) + H_3O^+(aq)$$

and K_a is 2.5×10^{-10}.

16.103 An artificial fruit beverage contains 11.0 g of tartaric acid, $H_2C_4H_4O_6$, and 20.0 g of its salt, potassium hydrogen tartrate, per liter. What is the pH of the beverage? $K_{a1} = 1.0 \times 10^{-3}$.

16.104 A buffer is made by dissolving 13.0 g of sodium dihydrogen phosphate, NaH_2PO_4, and 15.0 g of disodium hydrogen phosphate, Na_2HPO_4, in a liter of solution. What is the pH of the buffer?

16.105 Blood contains several acid–base systems that tend to keep its pH constant at about 7.4. One of the most important buffer systems involves carbonic acid and hydrogen carbonate ion. What must be the ratio of $[HCO_3^-]$ to $[H_2CO_3]$ in the blood if the pH is 7.40?

16.106 Codeine, $C_{18}H_{21}NO_3$, is an alkaloid ($K_b = 6.2 \times 10^{-9}$) used as a painkiller and cough suppressant. A solution of codeine is acidified with hydrochloric acid to pH 4.60. What is the ratio of the concentration of the conjugate acid of codeine to that of the base codeine?

16.107 Calculate the pH of a solution obtained by mixing 456 mL of 0.10 M hydrochloric acid with 285 mL of 0.15 M sodium hydroxide. Assume the combined volume is the sum of the two original volumes.

16.108 Calculate the pH of a solution made up from 2.0 g of potassium hydroxide dissolved in 115 mL of 0.19 M perchloric acid. Assume the change in volume due to adding potassium hydroxide is negligible.

16.109 Find the pH of the solution obtained when 25 mL of 0.065 M benzylamine, $C_7H_7NH_2$, is titrated to the equivalence point with 0.050 M hydrochloric acid. K_b for benzylamine is 4.7×10^{-10}.

16.110 What is the pH of the solution obtained by titrating 1.24 g of sodium hydrogen sulfate, $NaHSO_4$, dissolved in 50.0 mL of water with 0.175 M sodium hydroxide until the equivalence point is reached? Assume that any volume change due to adding the sodium hydrogen sulfate or to mixing the solutions is negligible.

16.111 Ionization of the first proton from H_2SO_4 is complete (H_2SO_4 is a strong acid); the acid-ionization constant for the second proton is 1.1×10^{-2}. (a) What would be the approximate hydronium-ion concentration in 0.100 M H_2SO_4 if ionization of the second proton were ignored? (b) The ionization of the second proton must be considered for a more exact answer, however. Calculate the hydronium-ion concentration in 0.100 M H_2SO_4, accounting for the ionization of both protons.

16.112 Ionization of the first proton from H_2SeO_4 is complete (H_2SeO_4 is a strong acid); the acid-ionization constant for the second proton is 1.2×10^{-2}. (a) What would be the approximate hydronium-ion concentration in 0.150 M H_2SeO_4 if ionization of the second proton were ignored? (b) The ionization of the second proton must be considered for a more exact answer, however. Calculate the hydronium-ion concentration in 0.150 M H_2SeO_4, accounting for the ionization of both protons.

16.113 Methylammonium chloride is a salt of methylamine, CH_3NH_2. A 0.10 M solution of this salt has a pH of 5.82.
  a. Calculate the value for the equilibrium constant for the reaction
$$CH_3NH_3^+ + H_2O \rightleftharpoons CH_3NH_2 + H_3O^+$$
  b. What is the K_b value for methylamine?
  c. What is the pH of a solution in which 0.450 mol of solid methylammonium chloride is added to 1.00 L of a 0.250 M solution of methylamine? Assume no volume change.

16.114 Sodium benzoate is a salt of benzoic acid, C_6H_5COOH. A 0.15 M solution of this salt has a pOH of 5.31 at room temperature.
  a. Calculate the value for the equilibrium constant for the reaction
$$C_6H_5COO^- + H_2O \rightleftharpoons C_6H_5COOH + OH^-$$
  b. What is the K_a value for benzoic acid?

c. Benzoic acid has a low solubility in water. What is its molar solubility if a saturated solution has a pH of 2.83 at room temperature?

16.115 Each of the following statements concerns a 0.010 M solution of a weak acid, HA. Briefly describe why each statement is either true or false.
   a. [HA] is approximately equal to 0.010 M.
   b. [HA] is much greater than [A$^-$].
   c. [OH$^-$] is approximately equal to [H$_3$O$^+$].
   d. The pH is 2.
   e. The H$_3$O$^+$ concentration is 0.010 M.
   f. [H$_3$O$^+$] is approximately equal to [A$^-$].

16.116 Each of the following statements concerns a 0.10 M solution of a weak organic base, B. Briefly describe why each statement is either true or false.
   a. [B] is approximately equal to 0.10 M.
   b. [B] is much greater than [HB$^+$].
   c. [H$_3$O$^+$] is greater than [HB$^+$].
   d. The pH is 13.
   e. [HB$^+$] is approximately equal to [OH$^-$].
   f. [OH$^-$] equals 0.10 M.

16.117 A 0.288-g sample of an unknown monoprotic organic acid is dissolved in water and titrated with a 0.115 M sodium hydroxide solution. After the addition of 17.54 mL of base, a pH of 4.92 is recorded. The equivalence point is reached when a total of 33.83 mL of NaOH is added.
   a. What is the molar mass of the organic acid?
   b. What is the K_a value for the acid? The K_a value could have been determined very easily if a pH measurement had been made after the addition of 16.92 mL of NaOH. Why?

16.118 A 0.239-g sample of unknown organic base is dissolved in water and titrated with a 0.135 M hydrochloric acid solution. After the addition of 18.35 mL of acid, a pH of 10.73 is recorded. The equivalence point is reached when a total of 39.24 mL of HCl is added. The base and acid combine in a 1:1 ratio.
   a. What is the molar mass of the organic base?
   b. What is the K_b value for the base? The K_b value could have been determined very easily if a pH measurement had been made after the addition of 19.62 mL of HCl. Why?

16.119 (a) Draw a pH titration curve that represents the titration of 50.0 mL of 0.10 M NH$_3$ by the addition of 0.10 M HCl from a buret. Label the axes and put a scale on each axis. Show where the equivalence point and the buffer region are on the titration curve. You should do calculations for the 0%, 30%, 50%, and 100% titration points.
(b) Is the solution neutral, acidic, or basic at the equivalence point? Why?

16.120 (a) Draw a pH titration curve that represents the titration of 25.0 mL of 0.15 M propionic acid, CH$_3$CH$_2$COOH, by the addition of 0.15 M KOH from a buret. Label the axes and put a scale on each axis. Show where the equivalence point and the buffer region are on the titration curve. You should do calculations for the 0%, 50%, 60%, and 100% titration points.
(b) Is the solution neutral, acidic, or basic at the equivalence point? Why?

16.121 The equilibrium equations and K_a values for three reaction systems are given below.

$$H_2C_2O_4(aq) + H_2O \rightleftharpoons$$
$$H_3O^+(aq) + HC_2O_4^-(aq); K_a = 5.6 \times 10^{-2}$$
$$H_3PO_4(aq) + H_2O \rightleftharpoons$$
$$H_3O^+(aq) + H_2PO_4^-(aq); K_a = 6.9 \times 10^{-3}$$
$$HCOOH(aq) + H_2O \rightleftharpoons$$
$$H_3O^+(aq) + HCOO^-(aq); K_a = 1.7 \times 10^{-4}$$

   a. Which conjugate pair would be best for preparing a buffer with a pH of 2.88?
   b. How would you prepare 50 mL of a buffer with a pH of 2.88 assuming that you had available 0.10 M solutions of each pair?

16.122 The equilibrium equations and K_a values for three reaction systems are given below.

$$NH_4^+(aq) + H_2O \rightleftharpoons H_3O^+ + NH_3(aq); K_a = 5.6 \times 10^{-10}$$
$$H_2CO_3(aq) + H_2O \rightleftharpoons$$
$$H_3O^+(aq) + HCO_3^-(aq); K_a = 4.3 \times 10^{-7}$$
$$H_2PO_4^-(aq) + H_2O \rightleftharpoons$$
$$H_3O^+(aq) + HPO_4^{2-}(aq); K_a = 6.2 \times 10^{-8}$$

   a. Which conjugate pair would be best for preparing a buffer with a pH of 6.96? Why?
   b. How would you prepare 100 mL of a buffer with a pH of 6.96 assuming that you had available 0.10 M solutions of each pair?

16.123 A 25.0-mL sample of hydroxylamine is titrated to the equivalence point with 35.8 mL of 0.150 M HCl.
   a. What was the concentration of the original hydroxylamine solution?
   b. What is the pH at the equivalence point?
   c. Which indicators, bromphenol blue, methyl red, or phenolphthalein, should be used to detect the end point of the titration? Why?

16.124 A 25.00-mL sample contains 0.562 g of NaHCO$_3$. This sample is used to standardize an NaOH solution. At the equivalence point, 42.36 mL of NaOH has been added.
   a. What was the concentration of the NaOH?
   b. What is the pH at the equivalence point?
   c. Which indicator, bromthymol blue, methyl violet, or alizarin yellow R, should be used in the titration? Why?

16.125 A solution made up of 1.0 M NH$_3$ and 0.50 M (NH$_4$)$_2$SO$_4$ has a pH of 9.26.
   a. Write the net ionic equation that represents the reaction of this solution with a strong acid.
   b. Write the net ionic equation that represents the reaction of this solution with a strong base.
   c. To 100. mL of this solution, 10.0 mL of 1.00 M HCl is added. How many moles of NH$_3$ and NH$_4^+$ are present in the reaction system before and after the addition of the HCl? What is the pH of the resulting solution?
   d. Why did the pH change only slightly upon the addition of HCl?

16.126 A solution is prepared from 0.150 mol of formic acid and enough water to make 0.425 L of solution.
  a. Determine the concentrations of H_3O^+ and $HCOO^-$ in this solution.
  b. Determine the H_3O^+ concentration that would be necessary to decrease the $HCOO^-$ concentration above by a factor of 10. How many milliliters of 2.00 M HCl would be required to produce this solution? Consider that the solution was made by combining the HCl, the HCOOH, and enough water to make 0.425 L of solution.
  c. Qualitatively, how can you account for the differences in the percentage dissociation of formic acid in parts a and b of this problem?

16.127 An important component of blood is the buffer combination of dihydrogen phosphate ion and the hydrogen phosphate ion. Consider blood with a pH of 7.44.
  a. What is the ratio of $[H_2PO_4^-]$ to $[HPO_4^{2-}]$?
  b. What does the pH become if 25% of the hydrogen phosphate ions are converted to dihydrogen phosphate ion?
  c. What does the pH become if 15% of the dihydrogen phosphate ions are converted to hydrogen phosphate ions?

16.128 An important component of blood is the buffer combination of bicarbonate ion and carbonic acid. Consider blood with a pH of 7.42.
  a. What is the ratio of $[H_2CO_3]$ to $[HCO_3^-]$?
  b. What does the pH become if 15% of the bicarbonate ions are converted to carbonic acid?
  c. What does the pH become if 25% of the carbonic acid molecules are converted to bicarbonate ions?

16.129 Tartaric acid is a weak diprotic fruit acid with $K_{a1} = 1.0 \times 10^{-3}$ and $K_{a2} = 4.6 \times 10^{-5}$.
  a. Letting the symbol H_2A represent tartaric acid, write the chemical equations that represent K_{a1} and K_{a2}. Write the chemical equation that represents $K_{a1} \times K_{a2}$.
  b. Qualitatively describe the relative concentrations of H_2A, HA^-, A^{2-}, and H_3O^+ in a solution that is about 0.5 M in tartaric acid.

  c. Calculate the pH of a 0.0250 M tartaric acid solution and the equilibrium concentration of $[H_2A]$.
  d. What is the A^{2-} concentration?

16.130 Malic acid is a weak diprotic organic acid with $K_{a1} = 4.0 \times 10^{-4}$ and $K_{a2} = 9.0 \times 10^{-6}$.
  a. Letting the symbol H_2A represent malic acid, write the chemical equations that represent K_{a1} and K_{a2}. Write the chemical equation that represents $K_{a1} \times K_{a2}$.
  b. Qualitatively describe the relative concentrations of H_2A, HA^-, A^{2-}, and H_3O^+ in a solution that is about one molar in malic acid.
  c. Calculate the pH of a 0.0150 M malic acid solution and the equilibrium concentration of $[H_2A]$.
  d. What is the A^{2-} concentration?

16.131 A quantity of 0.25 M sodium hydroxide is added to a solution containing 0.15 mol of acetic acid. The final volume of the solution is 375 mL and the pH of this solution is 4.45.
  a. What is the molar concentration of the sodium acetate?
  b. How many milliliters of sodium hydroxide were added to the original solution?
  c. What was the original concentration of the acetic acid?

16.132 A quantity of 0.15 M hydrochloric acid is added to a solution containing 0.10 mol of sodium acetate. Some of the sodium acetate is converted to acetic acid, resulting in a final volume of 650 mL of solution. The pH of the final solution is 4.56.
  a. What is the molar concentration of the acetic acid?
  b. How many milliliters of hydrochloric acid were added to the original solution?
  c. What was the original concentration of the sodium acetate?

16.133 How can you account for the fact that normal rain is slightly acidic?

16.134 How is acid rain defined? What is the source of the low pH of acid rain?

Strategy Problems

16.135 A 30.0-mL sample of 0.05 M HClO is titrated by a 0.0250 M KOH solution. K_a for HClO is 3.5×10^{-8}. Calculate (a) the pH when no base has been added; (b) the pH when 30.00 mL of the base has been added; (c) the pH at the equivalence point; (d) the pH when an additional 4.00 mL of the KOH solution has been added beyond the equivalence point.

16.136 A 0.108 M sample of a weak acid is 4.16% ionized in solution. What is the hydroxide concentration of this solution?

16.137 A generic base, B^-, is added to 2.25 L of water. The pH of the solution is found to be 10.10. What is the concentration of the base B^- in this solution? K_a for the acid HB at 25°C is 1.99×10^{-9}.

16.138 Calculate the pH of a solution made by mixing 0.60 L of 0.10 M NH_4Cl with 0.50 L of 0.10 M NaOH. K_b for NH_3 is 1.8×10^{-5}.

16.139 Cyanic acid, HOCN, is a weak acid with a K_a value of 3.5×10^{-04} at 25°C. In a 0.293 M solution of the acid, the degree of ionization is 3.5×10^{-02}. Calculate the degree of ionization in a 0.293 M solution to which sufficient HCl is added to make it 4.19×10^{-2} M HCl in the given volume.

16.140 The K_b for NH_3 is 1.8×10^{-5} at 25°C. Calculate the pH of a buffer solution made by mixing 65.1 mL of 0.142 M NH_3 with 39.2 mL of 0.172 M NH_4Cl at 25°C. Assume that the volumes of the solutions are additive.

16.141 K_a for formic acid is 1.7×10^{-4} at 25°C. A buffer is made by mixing 529 mL of 0.465 M formic acid, $HCHO_2$, and 494 mL of 0.524 M sodium formate, $NaCHO_2$. Calculate the pH of this solution at 25°C after 110. mL of 0.152 M HCl has been added to this buffer.

16.142 K_a for acetic acid is 1.7×10^{-5} at 25°C. A buffer solution is made by mixing 52.1 mL of 0.122 M acetic acid with 46.1 mL of 0.182 M sodium acetate. Calculate the pH of this solution at 25°C after the addition of 5.82 mL of 0.125 M NaOH.

16.143 Calculate the pH of a solution made by mixing 7.52 mL of 4.9×10^{-2} M Ca(OH)$_2$ with 22.5 mL of 0.11 M HCl.

16.144 A 0.150 M solution of NaClO is prepared by dissolving NaClO in water. A 50.0-mL sample of this solution is titrated with 0.100 M HCl. Calculate the pH of the solution at each of the following points of the titration: (a) prior to the addition of any HCl; (b) halfway to the equivalence point; (c) at the equivalence point; (d) after 5.00 mL of HCl has been added beyond the equivalence point. K_a for HClO is 3.5×10^{-8}.

Cumulative-Skills Problems

16.145 The pH of a white vinegar solution is 2.45. This vinegar is an aqueous solution of acetic acid with a density of 1.09 g/mL. What is the mass percentage of acetic acid in the solution?

16.146 The pH of a household cleaning solution is 11.87. This cleanser is an aqueous solution of ammonia with a density of 1.00 g/mL. What is the mass percentage of ammonia in the solution?

16.147 What is the freezing point of 0.92 M aqueous acetic acid? The density of this solution is 1.008 g/cm³.

16.148 What is the freezing point of 0.87 M aqueous ammonia? The density of this solution is 0.992 g/cm³.

16.149 A chemist needs a buffer with pH 4.35. How many milliliters of pure acetic acid (density = 1.049 g/mL) must be added to 465 mL of 0.0941 M NaOH solution to obtain such a buffer?

16.150 A chemist needs a buffer with pH 3.50. How many milliliters of pure formic acid (density = 1.220 g/mL) must be added to 325 mL of 0.0857 M NaOH solution to obtain such a buffer?

17

Solubility and Complex-Ion Equilibria

Formation of the dark blue copper–ammonia complex ion. A number of household products employ complexes: rust stain remover (contains oxalic acid to complex iron ions in rust), chromium picolinate (a neutral complex used to supply nutritional chromium), and mayonnaise (uses a complexing agent to bind metal ions that lead to spoilage).

Contents and Concepts

In these sections, we look at the equilibria of slightly soluble (or nearly insoluble) ionic compounds. We first show how you can determine their equilibrium constants. Then we show how to use these equilibrium constants to answer questions about solubility and precipitation.

Metal ions, especially transition-metal ions, form coordinate covalent bonds with molecules or anions that have lone pairs of electrons. The result is a complex ion. In these sections, we look at the formation of complex ions and their effect on solubility of slightly soluble ionic compounds.

In this last section, we look at the sulfide scheme of qualitative analysis to illustrate concepts of solubility, buffers, and complex-ion equilibria.

M any natural processes depend on the precipitation or the dissolving of a slightly soluble salt. For example, caves form in limestone (calcium carbonate) over thousands of years as groundwater seeps through cracks, dissolving out cavities in the rock. Kidney stones form when salts such as calcium phosphate or calcium oxalate slowly precipitate in the kidney (Figure 17.1). Poisoning by oxalic acid is also explained by the precipitation of the calcium salt. If oxalic acid is accidentally ingested, the oxalate-ion concentration in the blood may increase sufficiently to precipitate calcium oxalate. Calcium ion, which is needed for proper muscle control, is then removed from the blood, and muscle tissues go into spasm.

FIGURE 17.1 ▲

A kidney stone
Kidney stones are usually calcium phosphate or calcium oxalate that precipitates as a crystalline mass.

   To understand such phenomena quantitatively, you must be able to solve problems in solubility equilibria. Calcium oxalate kidney stones form when the concentrations of calcium ion and oxalate ion are sufficiently great. What is the relationship between the concentrations of ions and the solubility of a salt? What is the minimum concentration of oxalate ion that gives a precipitate of the calcium salt from a 0.0025 M solution of Ca^{2+} (the approximate concentration of calcium ion in blood plasma)? What is the effect of pH on the solubility of this salt? We will look at questions such as these in this chapter.

■ **See page 723 for the Media Summary.**

Solubility Equilibria

To deal quantitatively with an equilibrium, you must know the equilibrium constant. In the next section, we will look at the equilibria of slightly soluble (or nearly insoluble) ionic compounds and show how you can determine their equilibrium constants. Once you find these values for various ionic compounds, you can use them to answer questions about solubility or precipitation.

17.1 | The Solubility Product Constant

When an ionic compound is dissolved in water, it usually goes into solution as the ions. When an excess of a slightly soluble ionic compound is mixed with water, an equilibrium occurs between the solid compound and the ions in the saturated solution. For the salt calcium oxalate, CaC_2O_4, you have the following equilibrium:

$$CaC_2O_4(s) \xrightleftharpoons{H_2O} Ca^{2+}(aq) + C_2O_4^{2-}(aq)$$

The equilibrium constant for this solubility process is called the *solubility product constant* of CaC_2O_4. It is written

$$K_{sp} = [Ca^{2+}][C_2O_4^{2-}]$$

In general, the **solubility product constant (K_{sp})** is *the equilibrium constant for the solubility equilibrium of a slightly soluble (or nearly insoluble) ionic compound.* It equals the product of the equilibrium concentrations of the ions in the compound, each concentration raised to a power equal to the number of such ions in the formula of the compound. Like any equilibrium constant, K_{sp} depends on the temperature, but at a given temperature it has a constant value for various concentrations of the ions. <

An ionic equilibrium is affected to a small extent by the presence of ions not directly involved in the equilibrium. We will ignore this effect here.

   Lead(II) iodide, PbI_2, is another slightly soluble salt. The equilibrium in water is

$$PbI_2(s) \rightleftharpoons Pb^{2+}(aq) + 2I^-(aq)$$

and the expression for the equilibrium constant, or solubility product constant, is

$$K_{sp} = [Pb^{2+}][I^-]^2$$

| Example 17.1 | Writing Solubility Product Expressions |

Write the solubility product expressions for the following salts: a. AgCl; b. Hg_2Cl_2; c. $Pb_3(AsO_4)_2$.

Problem Strategy The equilibrium constant for a slightly soluble ionic compound is simply the product of the concentrations of the ions, each raised to a power equal to the number of such ions in the formula of the compound.

Solution The equilibria and solubility product expressions are

a. $AgCl(s) \rightleftharpoons Ag^+(aq) + Cl^-(aq)$; $K_{sp} = [Ag^+][Cl^-]$

b. $Hg_2Cl_2(s) \rightleftharpoons Hg_2^{2+}(aq) + 2Cl^-(aq)$; $K_{sp} = [Hg_2^{2+}][Cl^-]^2$

Note that the mercury(I) ion is Hg_2^{2+}. (Mercury also has salts with the mercury(II) ion, Hg^{2+}.)

c. $Pb_3(AsO_4)_2(s) \rightleftharpoons 3Pb^{2+}(aq) + 2AsO_4^{3-}(aq)$; $K_{sp} = [Pb^{2+}]^3[AsO_4^{3-}]^2$

Answer Check Make sure that you have the correct formula of the compound and that you understand the ions that are present. For example, Hg_2Cl_2 is made up of the ions Hg_2^{2+} and Cl^- (not Hg^+ and Cl^-).

Exercise 17.1 Give solubility product expressions for the following: a. barium sulfate; b. iron(III) hydroxide; c. calcium phosphate.

■ See Problems 17.27 and 17.28.

The solubility product constant, K_{sp}, of a slightly soluble ionic compound is expressed in terms of the molar concentrations of ions in the saturated solution. These ion concentrations are in turn related to the *molar solubility* of the ionic compound, which is the moles of compound that dissolve to give a liter of saturated solution. The next two examples show how to determine the solubility product constant from the solubility of a slightly soluble ionic compound.

| Example 17.2 | Calculating K_{sp} from the Solubility (Simple Example) |

A liter of a solution saturated at 25°C with calcium oxalate, CaC_2O_4, is evaporated to dryness, giving a 0.0061-g residue of CaC_2O_4. Calculate the solubility product constant for this salt at 25°C.

Problem Strategy The grams of residue from a liter of saturated solution equals the solubility in grams per liter. Convert this to molar solubility (solubility in moles per liter). Then follow the steps similar to those for an equilibrium calculation: set up a table of ion concentrations (starting, change, and equilibrium) and calculate K_{sp} from the concentrations. The starting concentrations are those before any solid has dissolved (= 0), and the change values are obtained from the molar solubility.

Solution The solubility of calcium oxalate is 0.0061 g/L of *solution*, and the formula mass of CaC_2O_4 is 128 amu. Convert grams per liter to moles per liter:

$$\text{Molar solubility of } CaC_2O_4 = 0.0061 \text{ g } CaC_2O_4/L \times \frac{1 \text{ mol } CaC_2O_4}{128 \text{ g } CaC_2O_4}$$
$$= 4.8 \times 10^{-5} \text{ mol } CaC_2O_4/L$$

Now look at the equilibrium problem.

(continued)

(continued)

Step 1: Suppose you mix solid CaC_2O_4 in a liter of solution. Of this solid, 4.8×10^{-5} mol will dissolve to form 4.8×10^{-5} mol of each ion. The results are summarized in the following table. (Because the concentration of the solid does not appear in K_{sp}, we do not include it in the table.)

Concentration (M)	$CaC_2O_4(s) \rightleftharpoons$	$Ca^{2+}(aq)$ +	$C_2O_4{}^{2-}(aq)$
Starting		0	0
Change		$+4.8 \times 10^{-5}$	$+4.8 \times 10^{-5}$
Equilibrium		4.8×10^{-5}	4.8×10^{-5}

Step 2: You now substitute into the equilibrium-constant equation:

$$K_{sp} = [Ca^{2+}][C_2O_4{}^{2-}] = (4.8 \times 10^{-5})(4.8 \times 10^{-5}) = \mathbf{2.3 \times 10^{-9}}$$

Answer Check   Often, the most effective way to check your work is to invert the problem, using your answer to calculate the information given in the problem statement; the actual steps often involve different operations. Here, you would first calculate the ion concentrations by taking the square root of the K_{sp} that you obtained. This ion concentration is, in this case, equal to the molar solubility. Multiplying the molar solubility by the formula mass gives the solubility of the compound, which should match the value given in the problem.

Exercise 17.2   Silver ion may be recovered from used photographic fixing solution by precipitating it as silver chloride. The solubility of silver chloride is 1.9×10^{-3} g/L. Calculate K_{sp}.

■ See Problems 17.29 and 17.30.

Example 17.3 │ Calculating K_{sp} from the Solubility (More Complicated Example)

By experiment, it is found that 1.2×10^{-3} mol of lead(II) iodide, PbI_2, dissolves in 1 L of aqueous solution at 25°C. What is the solubility product constant at this temperature?

Problem Strategy   This is similar to the previous example, except that every mole of the compound (PbI_2) dissolves to form *two* moles of the anion (I^-). This difference affects the calculation in two places: it affects the molar concentration of the ion (the molar concentration of the anion is *twice* that of the molar solubility), and it affects the equilibrium-constant expression (which contains the anion concentration *squared*).

Solution

Step 1: Suppose the solid lead(II) iodide is mixed into 1 L of solution. You find that 1.2×10^{-3} mol dissolves to form 1.2×10^{-3} mol Pb^{2+} and $2 \times (1.2 \times 10^{-3})$ mol I^-, as summarized in the following table:

Concentration (M)	$PbI_2(s) \rightleftharpoons$	$Pb^{2+}(aq)$ +	$2I^-(aq)$
Starting		0	0
Change		$+1.2 \times 10^{-3}$	$+2 \times (1.2 \times 10^{-3})$
Equilibrium		1.2×10^{-3}	$2 \times (1.2 \times 10^{-3})$

Lead(II) iodide

Step 2: You substitute into the equilibrium-constant equation:

$$K_{sp} = [Pb^{2+}][I^-]^2 = (1.2 \times 10^{-3}) \times (2 \times 1.2 \times 10^{-3})^2 = \mathbf{6.9 \times 10^{-9}}$$

(continued)

(continued)

Answer Check As in the previous example, an effective check is simply to reverse the calculation to see whether you do get the value given in the problem statement. Suppose you let the molar solubility be x (which is the value given in the problem statement). Then x is the concentration of Pb^{2+}, and $2x$ is the concentration of I^- (because there are twice as many I^- ions as Pb^{2+} ions). Thus, $K_{sp} = [Pb^{2+}][I^-] = x \times (2x)^2 = 4x^3$, and

$$x = \sqrt[3]{K_{sp}/4} = \sqrt[3]{6.9 \times 10^{-9}/4} = 1.2 \times 10^{-3}$$

Exercise 17.3 Lead(II) arsenate, $Pb_3(AsO_4)_2$, has been used as an insecticide. It is only slightly soluble in water. If the solubility is 3.0×10^{-5} g/L, what is the solubility product constant? Assume that the solubility equilibrium is the only important one.

■ See Problems 17.31 and 17.32.

Table 17.1 lists the solubility product constants for various ionic compounds. If the solubility product constant is known, the solubility of the compound can be calculated.

TABLE 17.1 | **Solubility Product Constants, K_{sp}, at 25°C**

Substance	Formula	K_{sp}	Substance	Formula	K_{sp}
Aluminum hydroxide	$Al(OH)_3$	4.6×10^{-33}	Lead(II) sulfide	PbS	2.5×10^{-27}
Barium chromate	$BaCrO_4$	1.2×10^{-10}	Magnesium arsenate	$Mg_3(AsO_4)_2$	2×10^{-20}
Barium fluoride	BaF_2	1.0×10^{-6}	Magnesium carbonate	$MgCO_3$	1.0×10^{-5}
Barium sulfate	$BaSO_4$	1.1×10^{-10}	Magnesium hydroxide	$Mg(OH)_2$	1.8×10^{-11}
Cadmium oxalate	CdC_2O_4	1.5×10^{-8}	Magnesium oxalate	MgC_2O_4	8.5×10^{-5}
Cadmium sulfide	CdS	8×10^{-27}	Manganese(II) sulfide	MnS	2.5×10^{-10}
Calcium carbonate	$CaCO_3$	3.8×10^{-9}	Mercury(I) chloride	Hg_2Cl_2	1.3×10^{-18}
Calcium fluoride	CaF_2	3.4×10^{-11}	Mercury(II) sulfide	HgS	1.6×10^{-52}
Calcium oxalate	CaC_2O_4	2.3×10^{-9}	Nickel(II) hydroxide	$Ni(OH)_2$	2.0×10^{-15}
Calcium phosphate	$Ca_3(PO_4)_2$	1×10^{-26}	Nickel(II) sulfide	NiS	3×10^{-19}
Calcium sulfate	$CaSO_4$	2.4×10^{-5}	Silver acetate	$AgC_2H_3O_2$	2.0×10^{-3}
Cobalt(II) sulfide	CoS	4×10^{-21}	Silver bromide	AgBr	5.0×10^{-13}
Copper(II) hydroxide	$Cu(OH)_2$	2.6×10^{-19}	Silver chloride	AgCl	1.8×10^{-10}
Copper(II) sulfide	CuS	6×10^{-36}	Silver chromate	Ag_2CrO_4	1.1×10^{-12}
Iron(II) hydroxide	$Fe(OH)_2$	8×10^{-16}	Silver iodide	AgI	8.3×10^{-17}
Iron(II) sulfide	FeS	6×10^{-18}	Silver sulfide	Ag_2S	6×10^{-50}
Iron(III) hydroxide	$Fe(OH)_3$	2.5×10^{-39}	Strontium carbonate	$SrCO_3$	9.3×10^{-10}
Lead(II) arsenate	$Pb_3(AsO_4)_2$	4×10^{-36}	Strontium chromate	$SrCrO_4$	3.5×10^{-5}
Lead(II) chloride	$PbCl_2$	1.6×10^{-5}	Strontium sulfate	$SrSO_4$	2.5×10^{-7}
Lead(II) chromate	$PbCrO_4$	1.8×10^{-14}	Zinc hydroxide	$Zn(OH)_2$	2.1×10^{-16}
Lead(II) iodide	PbI_2	6.5×10^{-9}	Zinc sulfide	ZnS	1.1×10^{-21}
Lead(II) sulfate	$PbSO_4$	1.7×10^{-8}			

Example 17.4 | Calculating the Solubility from K_{sp}

The mineral fluorite is calcium fluoride, CaF_2. Calculate the solubility (in grams per liter) of calcium fluoride in water from the solubility product constant (3.4×10^{-11}).

Problem Strategy This problem is the reverse of the preceding ones; instead of finding K_{sp} from the solubility, here you calculate solubility from the K_{sp}. You follow the three steps for equilibrium problems, but since the molar solubility is not immediately known, you assign it the value x. For Step 1, you obtain the concentration of each ion by multiplying x by the coefficient of the ion in the chemical equation. In Step 2, you obtain K_{sp} as a cubic in x. In Step 3, you solve the equilibrium-constant equation for x, which will involve taking a cube root.

The mineral fluorite (CaF_2)

Solution

Step 1: Let x be the molar solubility of CaF_2. When solid CaF_2 is mixed into a liter of solution, x mol dissolves, forming x mol Ca^{2+} and $2x$ mol F^-.

Concentration (M)	$CaF_2(s) \rightleftharpoons Ca^{2+}(aq) +$	$2F^-(aq)$
Starting	0	0
Change	$+x$	$+2x$
Equilibrium	x	$2x$

Step 2: You substitute into the equilibrium-constant equation.

$$[Ca^{2+}][F^-]^2 = K_{sp}$$
$$(x) \times (2x)^2 = 3.4 \times 10^{-11}$$
$$4x^3 = 3.4 \times 10^{-11}$$

Step 3: You now solve for x.

$$x = \sqrt[3]{\frac{3.4 \times 10^{-11}}{4}} = 2.0 \times 10^{-4}$$

The molar solubility is 2.0×10^{-4} mol CaF_2 per liter. To get the solubility in grams per liter, you convert, using the molar mass of CaF_2 (78.1 g/mol).

$$\text{Solubility} = 2.0 \times 10^{-4} \text{ mol } CaF_2/L \times \frac{78.1 \text{ g } CaF_2}{1 \text{ mol } CaF_2} = \mathbf{1.6 \times 10^{-2} \text{ g } CaF_2/L}$$

Answer Check As a quick check of your work, calculate K_{sp} for CaF_2 from the values you obtained for the molar concentrations of ions:

$$[Ca^{2+}] = x = 2.0 \times 10^{-4}$$
$$[F^-] = 2x = 4.0 \times 10^{-4}$$
$$K_{sp} = [Ca^{2+}][F^-]^2 = (2.0 \times 10^{-4})(4.0 \times 10^{-4})^2 = 3.2 \times 10^{-11}$$

Note the agreement (within computational error) with the value given in the problem (3.4×10^{-11}).

Exercise 17.4   Anhydrite is a calcium sulfate mineral deposited when seawater evaporates. What is the solubility of calcium sulfate, in grams per liter? Table 17.1 gives the solubility product constant for calcium sulfate.

■ See Problems 17.35, 17.36, 17.37, and 17.38.

These examples illustrate the relationship between the solubility of a slightly soluble ionic compound in pure water and its solubility product constant. In the next section, you will see how the solubility product constant can be used to calculate the solubility in the presence of other ions. K_{sp} is also useful in deciding whether to expect precipitation under given conditions.

Before leaving this section, we need to add a note of caution. We have calculated the solubility product of calcium oxalate, CaC_2O_4, and the solubility of calcium fluoride, CaF_2, assuming that only the solubility equilibrium is important. You need to be aware, however, that hydrolysis of the anion can be important, too, particularly if the anion is quite basic, which will be the case if the conjugate acid is rather weak. In the two examples given in this section, hydrolysis is relatively unimportant. (You may want to look at Problem 17.117, which examines this issue.)

Concept Check 17.1

Lead compounds have been used as paint pigments, but because the lead(II) ion is toxic, the use of lead paints in homes is now prohibited. Which of the following lead(II) compounds would yield the greatest number of lead(II) ions when added to the same quantity of water (assuming that some undissolved solid always remains): $PbCrO_4$, $PbSO_4$, or PbS?

17.2

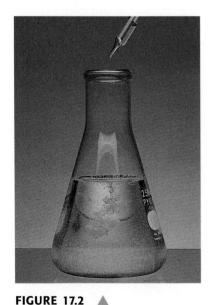

FIGURE 17.2 ▲

Demonstration of the common-ion effect When the experimenter adds lead(II) nitrate solution (colorless) from the dropper to the saturated solution of lead(II) chromate (pale yellow), a yellow precipitate of lead chromate forms.

Solubility and the Common-Ion Effect

The importance of the solubility product constant becomes apparent when you consider the solubility of one salt in the solution of another salt having the same cation or anion. For example, suppose you wish to know the solubility of calcium oxalate in a solution of calcium chloride. Each salt contributes the same cation (Ca^{2+}). The effect of the calcium ion provided by the calcium chloride is to make calcium oxalate less soluble than it would be in pure water.

You can explain this decrease in solubility in terms of Le Châtelier's principle. Suppose you first mix crystals of calcium oxalate in a quantity of pure water to establish the equilibrium

$$CaC_2O_4(s) \rightleftharpoons Ca^{2+}(aq) + C_2O_4^{2-}(aq)$$

Now imagine that you add some calcium chloride. Calcium chloride is a soluble salt, so it dissolves to give an increase in calcium-ion concentration. You can regard this increase as a stress on the original equilibrium. According to Le Châtelier's principle, the ions will react to remove some of the added calcium ion.

$$CaC_2O_4(s) \longleftarrow Ca^{2+}(aq) + C_2O_4^{2-}(aq)$$

In other words, some calcium oxalate precipitates from the solution. The solution now contains less calcium oxalate. You conclude that calcium oxalate is less soluble in a solution of calcium chloride than in pure water.

A solution of soluble calcium chloride has an ion *in common* with the slightly soluble calcium oxalate. The decrease in solubility of calcium oxalate in a solution of calcium chloride is an example of the *common-ion effect* (first discussed in Section 16.5). In general, any ionic equilibrium is affected by a substance producing an ion involved in the equilibrium, as you would predict from Le Châtelier's principle. Figure 17.2 illustrates the principle of the common-ion effect for lead(II) chromate, $PbCrO_4$, which is only slightly soluble in water at 25°C. When the very soluble $Pb(NO_3)_2$ is added to a saturated solution of $PbCrO_4$, the concentration of the common ion, Pb^{2+}, increases and $PbCrO_4$ precipitates. The equilibrium is

$$PbCrO_4(s) \rightleftharpoons Pb^{2+}(aq) + CrO_4^{2-}(aq)$$

The next example shows how you can calculate the solubility of a slightly soluble salt in a solution containing a substance with a common ion.

Example 17.5 | Calculating the Solubility of a Slightly Soluble Salt in a Solution of a Common Ion

What is the molar solubility of calcium oxalate in 0.15 M calcium chloride? Compare this molar solubility with that found earlier (Example 17.2) for CaC_2O_4 in pure water (4.8 × 10^{-5} M). The solubility product constant for calcium oxalate is 2.3 × 10^{-9}.

Problem Strategy The two salts have a common ion (Ca^{2+}): one salt ($CaCl_2$) is soluble and provides Ca^{2+} ion that suppresses the solubility of the slightly soluble salt (CaC_2O_4). You solve the solubility equilibrium for the slightly soluble salt, noting that when you set up the concentration table, you have a starting concentration of Ca^{2+} ion from $CaCl_2$. The equilibrium-constant equation you obtain is a quadratic, which you can reduce to a linear equation using the same approximation used in Chapter 16; you assume x is small compared with the number you add it to. (That is, the starting Ca^{2+} concentration is not much affected by the dissolution of the slightly soluble salt.) The value of x equals the molar solubility of the slightly soluble salt in the presence of the common ion.

Solution

Step 1: Suppose solid CaC_2O_4 is mixed into 1 L of 0.15 M $CaCl_2$ and that the molar solubility of the CaC_2O_4 is x M. At the start (before CaC_2O_4 dissolves), there is 0.15 mol Ca^{2+} in the solution. Of the solid CaC_2O_4, x mol dissolves to give x mol of additional Ca^{2+} and x mol $C_2O_4^{2-}$. The following table summarizes these results:

Concentration (M)	$CaC_2O_4(s) \rightleftharpoons Ca^{2+}(aq) +$	$C_2O_4^{2-}(aq)$
Starting	0.15	0
Change	$+x$	$+x$
Equilibrium	$0.15 + x$	x

Step 2: You substitute into the equilibrium-constant equation:

$$[Ca^{2+}][C_2O_4^{2-}] = K_{sp}$$

$$(0.15 + x)x = 2.3 \times 10^{-9}$$

Step 3: Now rearrange this equation to give

$$x = \frac{2.3 \times 10^{-9}}{0.15 + x}$$

Because calcium oxalate is only slightly soluble, you might expect x to be negligible compared with 0.15. In that case,

$$0.15 + x \simeq 0.15$$

and the previous equation becomes

$$x \simeq \frac{2.3 \times 10^{-9}}{0.15} = 1.5 \times 10^{-8}$$

Note that x is indeed much smaller than 0.15, so your assumption was correct. Therefore, the molar solubility of calcium oxalate in 0.15 M $CaCl_2$ is **1.5 × 10^{-8}** **M.** In pure water, the molar solubility is 4.8 × 10^{-5} M, which is over **3000 times greater.**

(continued)

(continued)

Answer Check   Calculate K_{sp} from the calculated molar solubility of calcium oxalate (1.5×10^{-8}). The concentration of Ca^{2+} ion is 0.15 M from $CaCl_2$ (plus 1.5×10^{-8} M from dissolved calcium oxalate, which is negligible), and the concentration of oxalate ion is 1.5×10^{-8} M. Therefore,

$$K_{sp} = [Ca^{2+}][C_2O_4^{2-}] = (0.15)(1.5 \times 10^{-8}) = 2.3 \times 10^{-9}$$

which agrees with the value given in the problem statement.

Exercise 17.5   a. Calculate the molar solubility of barium fluoride, BaF_2, in water at 25°C. The solubility product constant for BaF_2 at this temperature is 1.0×10^{-6}.

b. What is the molar solubility of barium fluoride in 0.15 M NaF at 25°C? Compare the solubility in this case with that of BaF_2 in pure water.

■ See Problems 17.39, 17.40, 17.41, and 17.42.

FIGURE 17.3 ▲

Formation of a precipitate
Silver chromate, Ag_2CrO_4, precipitates when a demonstrator adds aqueous potassium chromate, $K_2CrO_4(aq)$, to aqueous silver nitrate, $AgNO_3(aq)$.

Concept Check 17.2

Suppose you have equal volumes of saturated solutions of $NaNO_3$, Na_2SO_4, and PbS. Which solution would dissolve the most lead(II) sulfate, $PbSO_4$?

Concept Check 17.3

Consider the beaker below, which represents a saturated solution of AgCl(aq). Draw a picture of the solution in the beaker after the addition of NaCl(aq).

● = Ag^+
● = Cl^-

+ NaCl(aq) ⟶

17.3 | Precipitation Calculations

In the chapter opening, we mentioned that calcium oxalate precipitates to form kidney stones. The same salt would precipitate in the body if oxalic acid (a poison) were accidentally ingested, because Ca^{2+} ion is present in the blood. (See Figure 17.3 for another example of a precipitation.) To understand processes such as these, you must understand the conditions under which precipitation occurs. Precipitation is merely another way of looking at a solubility equilibrium. Rather than ask how much of a substance will dissolve in a solution, you ask: Will precipitation occur for given starting ion concentrations?

Criterion for Precipitation

The question just asked can be stated more generally: Given the concentrations of substances in a reaction mixture, will the reaction go in the forward or the reverse direction? To answer this, you evaluate the *reaction quotient* Q_c and compare it with the equilibrium constant K_c. < The reaction quotient has the same form as the equilibrium-constant expression, but the concentrations of substances are not

The reaction quotient was discussed in Section 14.5.

necessarily equilibrium values. Rather, they are concentrations at the start of a reaction. To predict the direction of reaction, you compare Q_c with K_c.

If $Q_c < K_c$, the reaction should go in the forward direction.
If $Q_c = K_c$, the reaction mixture is at equilibrium.
If $Q_c > K_c$, the reaction should go in the reverse direction.

Suppose you add lead(II) nitrate, $Pb(NO_3)_2$, and sodium chloride, $NaCl$, to water to give a solution that is $0.050\ M\ Pb^{2+}$ and $0.10\ M\ Cl^-$. Will lead(II) chloride, $PbCl_2$, precipitate? To answer this, you first write the solubility equilibrium.

$$PbCl_2(s) \underset{}{\overset{H_2O}{\rightleftharpoons}} Pb^{2+}(aq) + 2Cl^-(aq)$$

The reaction quotient has the form of the equilibrium-constant expression, which in this case is the K_{sp} expression, but the concentrations of the products are starting values, denoted by the subscript i.

$$Q_c = [Pb^{2+}]_i[Cl^-]_i^2$$

Here Q_c for a solubility reaction is often called the **ion product** (rather than reaction quotient), because it is *the product of ion concentrations in a solution, each concentration raised to a power equal to the number of ions in the formula of the ionic compound.*

To evaluate the ion product Q_c, you substitute the concentrations of Pb^{2+} and Cl^- ions in the solution at the start of the reaction. You have $0.050\ M\ Pb^{2+}$ and $0.10\ M\ Cl^-$. Substituting, you find that

$$Q_c = (0.050)(0.10)^2 = 5.0 \times 10^{-4}$$

K_{sp} for $PbCl_2$ is 1.6×10^{-5} (Table 17.1), so Q_c is greater than K_{sp}. Therefore, the reaction goes in the reverse direction. That is,

$$PbCl_2(s) \longleftarrow Pb^{2+}(aq) + 2Cl^-(aq)$$

In other words, Pb^{2+} and Cl^- react to precipitate $PbCl_2$. As precipitation occurs, the ion concentrations, and hence the ion product, decrease. Precipitation ceases when the ion product equals K_{sp}. The reaction mixture is then at equilibrium.

We can summarize our conclusions in terms of the following criterion for precipitation.

Precipitation may not occur even though the ion product has been exceeded. In such a case, the solution is supersaturated. Usually a small crystal forms after a time, and then precipitation occurs rapidly.

Precipitation is expected to occur if the ion product for a solubility reaction is greater than K_{sp}. If the ion product is less than K_{sp}, precipitation will not occur (the solution is unsaturated with respect to the ionic compound). If the ion product equals K_{sp}, the reaction is at equilibrium (the solution is saturated with the ionic compound). <

Example 17.6 | Predicting Whether Precipitation Will Occur (Given Ion Concentrations)

The concentration of calcium ion in blood plasma is $0.0025\ M$. If the concentration of oxalate ion is $1.0 \times 10^{-7}\ M$, do you expect calcium oxalate to precipitate? K_{sp} for calcium oxalate is 2.3×10^{-9}.

Problem Strategy Precipitation is simply another way of looking at solubility equilibrium.

$$CaC_2O_4(s) \rightleftharpoons Ca^{2+}(aq) + C_2O_4^{2-}(aq)$$

(continued)

(*continued*)

Going to the right, calcium oxalate dissolves, but going to the left, Ca^{2+} and $C_2O_4^{2-}$ react to precipitate calcium oxalate. The reaction quotient, Q_c, for this equation as written is the ion product $[Ca^{2+}]_i[C_2O_4^{2-}]_i$. This ion product decreases as precipitation occurs (and the ion concentrations decrease). As the reaction approaches equilibrium, it approaches the equilibrium constant (the solubility product) K_{sp}. This means that Q_c should be greater than K_{sp} for precipitation to occur; otherwise, precipitation cannot occur. Thus, you calculate Q_c and compare it with K_{sp}.

Solution The ion product for calcium oxalate is

$$\text{Ion product} = [Ca^{2+}]_i[C_2O_4^{2-}]_i = (0.0025) \times (1.0 \times 10^{-7}) = 2.5 \times 10^{-10}$$

This value is smaller than the solubility product constant, so **you do not expect precipitation to occur.**

Answer Check Be sure that you have the correct expression for the reaction quotient and that you correctly compare the reaction quotient to the solubility product.

Exercise 17.6 Anhydrite is a mineral composed of $CaSO_4$ (calcium sulfate). An inland lake has Ca^{2+} and SO_4^{2-} concentrations of 0.0052 M and 0.0041 M, respectively. If these concentrations were doubled by evaporation, would you expect calcium sulfate to precipitate?

■ See Problems 17.47 and 17.48.

Precipitation is an important industrial and laboratory process. Figure 17.4 (next page) shows the vats used to precipitate magnesium ion from seawater, which is a source of magnesium metal. The following example is a typical problem in precipitation. You are given the volumes and concentrations of two solutions and asked whether a precipitate will form when the solutions are mixed.

Example 17.7 | Predicting Whether Precipitation Will Occur (Given Solution Volumes and Concentrations)

Sulfate ion, SO_4^{2-}, in solution is often determined quantitatively by precipitating it as barium sulfate, $BaSO_4$. The sulfate ion may have been formed from a sulfur compound. Analysis for the amount of sulfate ion then indicates the percentage of sulfur in the compound. Is a precipitate expected to form at equilibrium when 50.0 mL of 0.0010 M $BaCl_2$ is added to 50.0 mL of 0.00010 M Na_2SO_4? The solubility product constant for barium sulfate is 1.1×10^{-10}. Assume that the total volume of solution, after mixing, equals the sum of the volumes of the separate solutions.

Problem Strategy You need to calculate Q_c, the ion product, to compare it with K_{sp}, the solubility product. For Q_c, you need to obtain the concentrations of ions in the solution just after mixing, but before precipitation, if any occurs. First, calculate the moles of each ion added. Then, using the total volume of solution (assumed to equal the sum of the two added solutions), calculate the molar concentration of each ion present. Finally, calculate Q_c and compare it with K_{sp}.

Solution The molar amount of Ba^{2+} present in 50.0 mL (0.0500 L) of 0.0010 M $BaCl_2$ is

$$\text{Amount of } Ba^{2+} = \frac{0.0010 \text{ mol } Ba^{2+}}{1 \text{ L soln}} \times 0.050 \text{ L soln} = 5.0 \times 10^{-5} \text{ mol } Ba^{2+}$$

(*continued*)

(continued)

The molar concentration of Ba^{2+} in the total solution equals the molar amount of Ba^{2+} divided by the total volume (0.0500 L $BaCl_2$ + 0.0500 L Na_2SO_4 = 0.1000 L).

$$[Ba^{2+}] = \frac{5.0 \times 10^{-5}\ mol}{0.1000\ L\ soln} = 5.0 \times 10^{-4}\ M$$

Similarly, you find $\qquad [SO_4^{2-}] = 5.0 \times 10^{-5}\ M$

(Try the calculations for SO_4^{2-}.) The ion product is

$$Q_c = [Ba^{2+}]_i[SO_4^{2-}]_i = (5.0 \times 10^{-4}) \times (5.0 \times 10^{-5}) = 2.5 \times 10^{-8}$$

Because the ion product is greater than the solubility product constant (1.1 × 10^{-10}), **you expect barium sulfate to precipitate.**

Answer Check Note that you calculate the *amount* of barium ion added using the volume of barium chloride solution added (0.050 L). Similarly, you calculate the amount of sulfate ion present from the *initial* volume of sodium sulfate (0.050 L). But to calculate the *concentrations* of these ions when both solutions are present together, you use the total volume of the two solutions (0.1000 L).

Exercise 17.7 A solution of 0.00016 M lead(II) nitrate, $Pb(NO_3)_2$, was poured into 456 mL of 0.00023 M sodium sulfate, Na_2SO_4. Would a precipitate of lead(II) sulfate, $PbSO_4$, be expected to form if 255 mL of the lead nitrate solution were added?

An x-ray photograph of a patient's colon (large intestine)
The colon shows up after the patient has ingested an aqueous suspension of barium sulfate, which is opaque to x rays. Even though free barium ion is toxic, barium sulfate is harmless because it is so insoluble. (Color enhanced by computer for contrast.)

■ See Problems 17.49 and 17.50.

FIGURE 17.4 ▲

Vats for the precipitation of magnesium hydroxide from seawater
Seawater contains magnesium ion (in addition to other ions). When base is added, magnesium hydroxide precipitates. This is the source of magnesium metal.

Fractional Precipitation

Fractional precipitation is *the technique of separating two or more ions from a solution by adding a reactant that precipitates first one ion, then another, and so forth.* For example, suppose a solution is 0.10 M Ba^{2+} and 0.10 M Sr^{2+}. As we will show in the following paragraphs, when you slowly add a concentrated solution of potassium chromate, K_2CrO_4, to the solution of Ba^{2+} and Sr^{2+} ions, barium chromate precipitates first. After most of the Ba^{2+} ion has precipitated, strontium chromate begins to come out of solution. It is therefore possible to separate Ba^{2+} and Sr^{2+} ions from a solution by fractional precipitations using K_2CrO_4.

To understand why Ba^{2+} and Sr^{2+} ions can be separated in this way, calculate (1) the concentration of CrO_4^{2-} necessary to just begin the precipitation of $BaCrO_4$, and (2) the concentration of CrO_4^{2-} necessary to just begin the precipitation of $SrCrO_4$. Ignore any volume change in the solution of Ba^{2+} and Sr^{2+} ions resulting from the addition of the concentrated K_2CrO_4 solution. To calculate the CrO_4^{2-} concentration when $BaCrO_4$ begins to precipitate, you substitute the initial Ba^{2+} concentration into the solubility product equation. K_{sp} for $BaCrO_4$ is 1.2 × 10^{-10}.

$$[Ba^{2+}][CrO_4^{2-}] = K_{sp}\ (for\ BaCrO_4)$$
$$(0.10)[CrO_4^{2-}] = 1.2 \times 10^{-10}$$
$$[CrO_4^{2-}] = \frac{1.2 \times 10^{-10}}{0.10} = 1.2 \times 10^{-9}\ M$$

In the same way, you can calculate the CrO_4^{2-} concentration when $SrCrO_4$ begins to precipitate. K_{sp} for $SrCrO_4$ is 3.5×10^{-5}.

$$[Sr^{2+}][CrO_4^{2-}] = K_{sp} \text{ (for } SrCrO_4)$$

$$(0.10)[CrO_4^{2-}] = 3.5 \times 10^{-5}$$

$$[CrO_4^{2-}] = \frac{3.5 \times 10^{-5}}{0.10} = 3.5 \times 10^{-4} \, M$$

Note that $BaCrO_4$ precipitates first, because the CrO_4^{2-} concentration necessary to form the $BaCrO_4$ precipitate is smaller.

These results reveal that as the solution of K_2CrO_4 is slowly added to the solution of Ba^{2+} and Sr^{2+}, barium chromate begins to precipitate when the CrO_4^{2-} concentration reaches $1.2 \times 10^{-9} \, M$. Barium chromate continues to precipitate as K_2CrO_4 is added. When the concentration of CrO_4^{2-} reaches $3.5 \times 10^{-4} \, M$, strontium chromate begins to precipitate.

What is the percentage of Ba^{2+} ion remaining just as $SrCrO_4$ begins to precipitate? First calculate the concentration of Ba^{2+} at this point. You write the solubility product equation and substitute $[CrO_4^{2-}] = 3.5 \times 10^{-4}$, the concentration of chromate ion when $SrCrO_4$ begins to precipitate.

$$[Ba^{2+}][CrO_4^{2-}] = K_{sp} \text{ (for } BaCrO_4)$$

$$[Ba^{2+}](3.5 \times 10^{-4}) = 1.2 \times 10^{-10}$$

$$[Ba^{2+}] = \frac{1.2 \times 10^{-10}}{3.5 \times 10^{-4}} = 3.4 \times 10^{-7} \, M$$

To calculate the percentage of Ba^{2+} ion remaining, you divide this concentration of Ba^{2+} by the initial concentration (0.10 M) and multiply by 100%.

$$\frac{3.4 \times 10^{-7}}{0.10} \times 100\% = 0.00034\%$$

The percentage of Ba^{2+} ion remaining in solution is quite low, so most of the Ba^{2+} ion has precipitated by the time $SrCrO_4$ begins to precipitate. You conclude that Ba^{2+} and Sr^{2+} can indeed be separated by fractional precipitation. (Another application of fractional precipitation is shown in Figure 17.5.)

FIGURE 17.5 ▶

Titration of chloride ion by silver nitrate using potassium chromate as an indicator
Left: A small amount of K_2CrO_4 (yellow) has been added to a solution containing an unknown amount of Cl^- ion. *Center:* The solution is titrated by $AgNO_3$ solution, giving a white precipitate of AgCl. *Right:* When nearly all of the Cl^- ion has precipitated as AgCl, silver chromate begins to precipitate. Silver chromate, Ag_2CrO_4, has a red-brown color, and the appearance of this color signals the end of the titration. An excess of Ag^+ was added to show the color of Ag_2CrO_4 more clearly.

17.4 | Effect of pH on Solubility

In discussing solubility, we have assumed that the only equilibrium of interest was the one between the solid ionic compound and its ions in solution. Sometimes, however, it is necessary to account for other reactions the ions might undergo. For example, if the anion is the conjugate base of a weak acid, the anion reacts with H_3O^+ ion. You should expect the solubility to be affected by pH. We will look into this possibility now.

Qualitative Effect of pH

Consider the equilibrium between solid calcium oxalate, CaC_2O_4, and its ions in aqueous solution:

$$CaC_2O_4(s) \rightleftharpoons Ca^{2+}(aq) + C_2O_4^{2-}(aq)$$

Because the oxalate ion is conjugate to a weak acid (hydrogen oxalate ion, $HC_2O_4^-$), you would expect it to react with any H_3O^+ ion that is added—say, from a strong acid:

$$C_2O_4^{2-}(aq) + H_3O^+(aq) \rightleftharpoons HC_2O_4^-(aq) + H_2O(l)$$

According to Le Châtelier's principle, as $C_2O_4^{2-}$ ion is removed by reaction with H_3O^+ ion, more calcium oxalate dissolves to replenish some of the $C_2O_4^{2-}$ ion.

$$CaC_2O_4(s) \longrightarrow Ca^{2+}(aq) + C_2O_4^{2-}(aq)$$

Therefore, you expect calcium oxalate to be more soluble in acidic solution (low pH) than in pure water.

In general, salts of weak acids should be expected to be more soluble in acidic solutions. As an example, consider the process of tooth decay. Bacteria on the teeth produce an acidic medium as a result of the metabolism of sugar. Teeth are normally composed of a calcium phosphate mineral hydroxyapatite, which you can denote as either $Ca_5(PO_4)_3OH$ or $3Ca_3(PO_4)_2 \cdot Ca(OH)_2$. This mineral salt of the weak acid H_2O (conjugate to OH^-) dissolves in the presence of the acid medium, producing cavities in the teeth. Fluoride toothpastes provide F^- ion, which gradually replaces the OH^- ion in the teeth to produce fluorapatite, $Ca_5(PO_4)_3F$ or $3Ca_3(PO_4)_2 \cdot CaF_2$, which is much less soluble than hydroxyapatite.

Example 17.8 | Determining the Qualitative Effect of pH on Solubility

Consider two slightly soluble salts, calcium carbonate and calcium sulfate. Which of these would have its solubility more affected by the addition of HCl, a strong acid? Would the solubility of the salt increase or decrease?

Problem Strategy A strong acid affects the solubility of a salt of a weak acid by providing hydronium ion that reacts with the anion of the salt in the solution. As the anion is removed by this reaction, more salt dissolves to replenish the anion concentration. You need to determine which salt has the anion corresponding to the weaker acid.

Solution Calcium carbonate gives the solubility equilibrium

$$CaCO_3(s) \rightleftharpoons Ca^{2+}(aq) + CO_3^{2-}(aq)$$

When a strong acid is added, the hydrogen ion reacts with carbonate ion, because it is conjugate to a weak acid (HCO_3^-).

$$H_3O^+(aq) + CO_3^{2-}(aq) \rightleftharpoons H_2O(l) + HCO_3^-(aq)$$

(continued)

(continued)

As carbonate ion is removed, calcium carbonate dissolves. Moreover, the hydrogen carbonate ion itself is removed in further reaction.

$$H_3O^+(aq) + HCO_3^-(aq) \longrightarrow H_2O(l) + H_2CO_3(aq) \longrightarrow 2H_2O(l) + CO_2(g)$$

Bubbles of carbon dioxide gas appear as more calcium carbonate dissolves.

For calcium sulfate, the corresponding equilibria are

$$CaSO_4(s) \rightleftharpoons Ca^{2+}(aq) + SO_4^{2-}(aq)$$

$$H_3O^+(aq) + SO_4^{2-}(aq) \rightleftharpoons H_2O(l) + HSO_4^-(aq)$$

Again, the anion of the insoluble salt is removed by reaction with hydronium ion. You would expect calcium sulfate to become more soluble in strong acid. However, HSO_4^- is a much stronger acid than HCO_3^-, as you can see by comparing acid-ionization constants. (The values K_{a2} for H_2CO_3 and K_a for HSO_4^- in Table 16.1 are 4.8×10^{-11} and 1.1×10^{-2}, respectively.) **Thus, calcium carbonate is much more soluble in acidic solution, whereas the solubility of calcium sulfate is only slightly affected.**

Answer Check Make sure you compare the correct acid-ionization constants. For each salt, you look at the acid corresponding to the anion plus a hydrogen ion. For $CaCO_3$, you look at CO_3^{2-} plus H^+ (HCO_3^-, not H_2CO_3). For $CaSO_4$, you look at SO_4^{2-} plus H^+ (HSO_4^-, not H_2SO_4).

Exercise 17.8   Which salt would have its solubility more affected by changes in pH, silver chloride or silver cyanide?

■ See Problems 17.59 and 17.60.

Concept Check 17.4

If you add a dilute acidic solution to a mixture containing magnesium oxalate and calcium oxalate, which of the two compounds is more likely to dissolve?

Separation of Metal Ions by Sulfide Precipitation

Many metal sulfides are insoluble in water but dissolve in acidic solution. The sulfide scheme discussed later, in Section 17.7, uses this change in solubility of the metal sulfides with pH, or hydronium-ion concentration, to separate a mixture of metal ions. Here is how the separation scheme works.

Consider a solution that is 0.10 M in zinc ion and in lead(II) ion. You add hydrogen sulfide, H_2S, to this solution. Hydrogen sulfide ionizes in water as a diprotic acid:

$$H_2S(aq) + H_2O(l) \rightleftharpoons H_3O^+(aq) + HS^-(aq)$$

$$HS^-(aq) + H_2O(l) \rightleftharpoons H_3O^+(aq) + S^{2-}(aq)$$

The ionization forms sulfide ion, S^{2-}, which can combine with the metal ions to precipitate the sulfides. Note that by increasing the hydronium-ion concentration, you can reverse both of the previous equilibria and in that way reduce the sulfide-ion concentration. This allows you to control the sulfide-ion concentration of a hydrogen sulfide solution by varying its pH; the lower the pH, the lower the sulfide-ion concentration.

Whether lead(II) sulfide and zinc sulfide precipitate from the hydrogen sulfide solution depends on the solubility product constants of the sulfides and on the sulfide-ion concentration, which in turn depends on the pH of the solution. Here are the solubility equilibria:

$$Zn^{2+}(aq) + S^{2-}(aq) \rightleftharpoons ZnS(s); K_{sp} = 1.1 \times 10^{-21}$$

$$Pb^{2+}(aq) + S^{2-}(aq) \rightleftharpoons PbS(s); K_{sp} = 2.5 \times 10^{-27}$$

A Chemist Looks at . . .

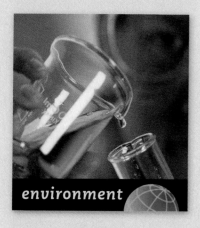

environment

Limestone Caves

On the side of a hill, covered by tall grass and shrubs, the cave entrance might easily be missed. It is barely large enough for a person to enter, even if hunched over, but the space soon expands into a chamber that one can easily stand in. Rock columns rise to an arched ceiling, and there are caverns leading mysteriously away on both sides of the chamber. Limestone caves, like the one described here, which is in Tennessee, dot the landscapes of the eastern and southwestern United States and of Europe and other places as well. Though many limestone caves are inaccessible, a few, like Mammouth Cave in Kentucky and Carlsbad Caverns in New Mexico, are spectacular tourist attractions with multicolored rock draperies and icicles hanging from the ceilings of large underground rooms (Figure 17.6). How do such caves form?

Limestone itself formed millions of years ago. Seashells accumulated on ocean floors, and then layers of these shells were subsequently compacted by great pressure from overlying sediment. Later movements of the earth's crust pushed the limestone layers out of the sea, often leaving them well inland.

Seashells and limestone are primarily calcium carbonate. Calcium carbonate is fairly insoluble, as you would expect from its solubility product constant (3.8×10^{-9}). But it dissolves readily in acidic solution. Water that has filtered through decomposing vegetation contains carbonic acid, as well as other acids. When such an acidic solution comes into contact with limestone, it carves out caverns. The water is now a solution of calcium hydrogen carbonate.

$$CaCO_3(s) + H_2O(l) + CO_2(aq) \longrightarrow$$
$$Ca^{2+}(aq) + 2HCO_3^-(aq)$$

FIGURE 17.6 ▲

A limestone cave (Luray Caverns, Virginia)
Such caves are formed by the action of acidic groundwater on limestone deposits. The icicle-like formations (stalagmites and stalactites) in the caves are caused by the reprecipitation of calcium carbonate as carbon dioxide in the solution equilibrates with the surrounding air.

This process is reversible, which you would predict from Le Châtelier's principle. As the calcium hydrogen carbonate solution percolates through holes in the limestone and drips into caverns, water evaporates and carbon dioxide gas escapes; calcium carbonate precipitates onto icicle-shaped *stalactites*.

$$Ca^{2+}(aq) + 2HCO_3^-(aq) \longrightarrow$$
$$CaCO_3(s) + H_2O(l) + CO_2(g)$$

Excess solution drips onto the cavern floor, where calcium carbonate precipitates on upward-growing *stalagmites*. Iron compounds in the solution add yellow and brown colors to the columns of rock. Stalactites and stalagmites grow at the rate of about a centimeter every 300 years.

■ See Problems 17.107 and 17.108.

By adjusting the pH of the solution, you adjust the sulfide-ion concentration in order to precipitate the least soluble metal sulfide while maintaining the other metal ion in solution. The solubility product constant of lead(II) sulfide is much smaller than that of zinc sulfide, so it is the least soluble sulfide. When a solution that is 0.10 M in each metal ion and 0.30 M in hydronium ion is saturated with hydrogen sulfide, lead(II) sulfide precipitates, but zinc ion remains in solution, You can now filter off the precipitate of lead(II) sulfide, leaving a solution containing the zinc ion.

Complex-Ion Equilibria

Many metal ions, especially those of the transition elements, form coordinate covalent bonds with molecules or anions having lone pairs of electrons. For example, the silver ion, Ag^+, can react with NH_3 to form the $Ag(NH_3)_2^+$ ion. The lone pair of electrons on the N atom of NH_3 forms a coordinate covalent bond to the silver ion to form what is called a complex ion. (See Figure 17.7.)

$$Ag^+ + 2(:NH_3) \longrightarrow (H_3N:Ag:NH_3)^+$$

Note that the metal ion acts as a Lewis acid, and the molecule or anion having the lone pair of electrons acts as a Lewis base. <

| *The Lewis concept of acids and bases was discussed in Section 15.3.*

A **complex ion** is an *ion formed from a metal ion with a Lewis base attached to it by a coordinate covalent bond.* A *complex* is a compound containing complex ions. A **ligand** is *a Lewis base that bonds to a metal ion to form a complex ion.* For example, $Ag(NH_3)_2^+$ is a complex ion formed from the Ag^+ ion and two NH_3 molecules. The NH_3 molecules are the ligands.

17.5 | Complex-Ion Formation

The aqueous silver ion forms a complex ion with ammonia by reacting with NH_3 in steps.

$$Ag^+(aq) + NH_3(aq) \rightleftharpoons Ag(NH_3)^+(aq)$$

$$Ag(NH_3)^+(aq) + NH_3(aq) \rightleftharpoons Ag(NH_3)_2^+(aq)$$

When you add these equations, you get the overall equation for the formation of the complex ion $Ag(NH_3)_2^+$.

$$Ag^+(aq) + 2NH_3(aq) \rightleftharpoons Ag(NH_3)_2^+(aq)$$

The **formation constant,** or **stability constant, Kf,** of a complex ion is *the equilibrium constant for the formation of the complex ion from the aqueous metal ion and the ligands.* The formation constant of $Ag(NH_3)_2^+$ is

$$K_f = \frac{[Ag(NH_3)_2^+]}{[Ag^+][NH_3]^2}$$

The value of K_f for $Ag(NH_3)_2^+$ is 1.7×10^7. Its large value means that the complex ion is quite stable. When a large amount of NH_3 is added to a solution of Ag^+, you expect most of the Ag^+ ion to react to form the complex ion. Table 17.2 on the following page lists values for the formation constants of some complex ions.

The **dissociation constant (K_d)** for a complex ion is *the reciprocal, or inverse, value of K_f.* The equation for the dissociation of $Ag(NH_3)_2^+$ is

$$Ag(NH_3)_2^+(aq) \rightleftharpoons Ag^+(aq) + 2NH_3(aq)$$

and its equilibrium constant is

$$K_d = \frac{1}{K_f} = \frac{[Ag^+][NH_3]^2}{[Ag(NH_3)_2^+]}$$

FIGURE 17.7 ▲

Complex ions of nickel(II)
The test tube on the left contains a solution of $Ni(H_2O)_6^{2+}$ ion (green). Adding ammonia to a similar test tube containing this ion, on the right, yields the ammonia complex ion $Ni(NH_3)_6^{2+}$ (purple).

Equilibrium Calculations with K_f

The next example shows how to calculate the concentration of an aqueous metal ion in equilibrium with a complex ion.

Example 17.9 | Calculating the Concentration of a Metal Ion in Equilibrium with a Complex Ion

What is the concentration of $Ag^+(aq)$ ion in 0.010 M $AgNO_3$ that is also 1.00 M NH_3? K_f for $Ag(NH_3)_2^+$ ion is 1.7×10^7.

Problem Strategy The formation constant for $Ag(NH_3)_2^+$ is large, so silver exists primarily as this ion. This suggests that you do this problem in two parts. First you do the *stoichiometry calculation*, in which you assume that $Ag^+(aq)$ reacts completely to form $Ag(NH_3)_2^+(aq)$. Then you do the *equilibrium calculation*, in which this complex ion dissociates to give a small amount of $Ag^+(aq)$.

Solution STOICHIOMETRY CALCULATION In 1 L of solution, you initially have 0.010 mol $Ag^+(aq)$ from $AgNO_3$. This reacts to give 0.010 mol $Ag(NH_3)_2^+$, leaving $(1.00 - 2 \times 0.010)$ mol NH_3, which equals 0.98 mol NH_3 to two significant figures. You now look at the equilibrium for the dissociation of $Ag(NH_3)_2^+$.

EQUILIBRIUM CALCULATION

Step 1: One liter of the solution contains 0.010 mol $Ag(NH_3)_2^+$ and 0.98 mol NH_3. The complex ion dissociates slightly, so that 1 L of solution contains x mol Ag^+. These data are summarized in the following table:

Concentration (M)	$Ag(NH_3)_2^+(aq)$	$\rightleftharpoons$	$Ag^+(aq)$	+	$2NH_3(aq)$
Starting	0.010		0		0.98
Change	$-x$		$+x$		$+2x$
Equilibrium	$0.010 - x$		x		$0.98 + 2x$

Step 2: The formation constant is

$$K_f = \frac{[Ag(NH_3)_2^+]}{[Ag^+][NH_3]^2} = 1.7 \times 10^7$$

From this you can write the dissociation constant, which corresponds to the reaction as shown in the table.

$$\frac{[Ag^+][NH_3]^2}{[Ag(NH_3)_2^+]} = K_d = \frac{1}{K_f}$$

Substituting into this equation gives

$$\frac{x(0.98 + 2x)^2}{(0.010 - x)} = \frac{1}{1.7 \times 10^7}$$

Step 3: The right-hand side of the equation equals 5.9×10^{-8}. If you assume x to be small compared with 0.010,

$$\frac{x(0.98)^2}{0.010} \approx 5.9 \times 10^{-8}$$

and

$$x \approx 5.9 \times 10^{-8} \times 0.010/(0.98)^2 = 6.1 \times 10^{-10}$$

The silver-ion concentration is $\mathbf{6.1 \times 10^{-10}}$ M (over 10 million times smaller than its value in 0.010 M $AgNO_3$ that does not contain ammonia).

TABLE 17.2 |

Formation Constants of Complex Ions at 25°C

Complex Ion	K_f
$Ag(CN)_2^-$	5.6×10^{18}
$Ag(NH_3)_2^+$	1.7×10^7
$Ag(S_2O_3)_2^{3-}$	2.9×10^{13}
$Cd(NH_3)_4^{2+}$	1.0×10^7
$Cu(CN)_2^-$	1.0×10^{16}
$Cu(NH_3)_4^{2+}$	4.8×10^{12}
$Fe(CN)_6^{4-}$	1.0×10^{35}
$Fe(CN)_6^{3-}$	9.1×10^{41}
$Ni(CN)_4^{2-}$	1.0×10^{31}
$Ni(NH_3)_6^{2+}$	5.6×10^8
$Zn(NH_3)_4^{2+}$	2.9×10^9
$Zn(OH)_4^{2-}$	2.8×10^{15}

Formation of copper(II)–ammonia complex ion, $Cu(NH_3)_4^{2+}$ (dark blue) Ammonia is being added to copper sulfate solution (light blue), giving a precipitate of copper(II) hydroxide, which dissolves as the copper(II) ion complexes with more ammonia.

(continued)

(continued)

Answer Check Calculate the value of K_f from the equilibrium concentrations of species, using the value of x (6.1×10^{-10}) that you just obtained.

$$K_f = \frac{[Ag(NH_3)^{2+}]}{[Ag^+][NH_3]^2} = \frac{(0.010 - x)}{x(0.98 + 2x)^2} = \frac{0.010}{6.1 \times 10^{-10}(0.98)^2} = 1.7 \times 10^7$$

Exercise 17.9   What is the concentration of $Cu^{2+}(aq)$ in a solution that was originally 0.015 M $Cu(NO_3)_2$ and 0.100 M NH_3? The Cu^{2+} ion forms the complex ion $Cu(NH_3)_4^{2+}$. Its formation constant is given in Table 17.2.

■ See Problems 17.64 and 17.65.

Amphoteric Hydroxides

An **amphoteric hydroxide** is *a metal hydroxide that reacts with both bases and acids.* Zinc is an example of a metal that forms such a hydroxide. Zinc hydroxide, $Zn(OH)_2$, is an insoluble hydroxide, as are most of the metal hydroxides except those of Groups IA and IIA elements. Zinc hydroxide reacts with a strong acid, as you would expect of a base, and the metal hydroxide dissolves.

$$Zn(OH)_2(s) + 2H_3O^+(aq) \longrightarrow Zn^{2+}(aq) + 4H_2O(l)$$

With a base, however, $Zn(OH)_2$ reacts to form the complex ion $Zn(OH)_4^{2-}$.

$$Zn(OH)_2(s) + 2OH^-(aq) \longrightarrow Zn(OH)_4^{2-}(aq)$$

In this way the hydroxide also dissolves in a strong base.

When a strong base is slowly added to a solution of $ZnCl_2$, a white precipitate of $Zn(OH)_2$ first forms.

$$Zn^{2+}(aq) + 2OH^-(aq) \longrightarrow Zn(OH)_2(s)$$

But as more base is added, the white precipitate dissolves, forming the complex ion $Zn(OH)_4^{2-}$. (See Figure 17.8.)

Other common amphoteric hydroxides are those of aluminum, chromium(III), lead(II), tin(II), and tin(IV). The amphoterism of $Al(OH)_3$ is commercially used to separate aluminum oxide from the aluminum ore bauxite. Bauxite contains hydrated

FIGURE 17.8 ▲

Demonstration of the amphoteric behavior of zinc hydroxide

Left: The beaker on the left contains $ZnCl_2$; the one on the right contains NaOH. *Center:* As some of the solution of NaOH is added to the solution of $ZnCl_2$, a white precipitate of $Zn(OH)_2$ forms. *Right:* After more NaOH is added, the precipitate dissolves by forming the hydroxo complex $Zn(OH)_4^{2-}$.

Al_2O_3 plus impurities, such as silica sand (SiO_2) and iron oxide (Fe_2O_3). The aluminum oxide dissolves in NaOH solution as the $Al(OH)_4^-$ ion. After the insoluble impurities are filtered off, the solution of $Al(OH)_4^-$ can be slightly acidified to precipitate pure $Al(OH)_3$.

$$Al(OH)_4^-(aq) + H_3O^+(aq) \longrightarrow Al(OH)_3(s) + 2H_2O(l)$$

17.6 | Complex Ions and Solubility

Example 17.9 demonstrates that the formation of the complex ion $Ag(NH_3)_2^+$ reduces the concentration of silver ion, $Ag^+(aq)$, in solution. The solution was initially 0.010 M AgNO$_3$, or 0.010 M $Ag^+(aq)$. When this solution is made 1.00 M in NH_3, the $Ag^+(aq)$ ion concentration decreases to 6.1×10^{-10} M. You can see that the ion product for a slightly soluble silver salt could be decreased to below K_{sp}. Then the slightly soluble salt might not precipitate in a solution containing ammonia, whereas it otherwise would.

Example 17.10 | Predicting Whether a Precipitate Will Form in the Presence of the Complex Ion

---

a. Will silver chloride precipitate from a solution that is 0.010 M AgNO$_3$ and 0.010 M NaCl? b. Will silver chloride precipitate from this solution if it is also 1.00 M NH_3?

Problem Strategy Part a is a simple precipitation problem in which you compare Q_c with K_{sp}. See Example 17.6. Part b differs only in that you need to know the Ag^+ concentration in equilibrium with a complex ion.

Solution   a. To determine whether a precipitate should form, you calculate the ion product and compare it with K_{sp} for AgCl (1.8×10^{-10}).

$$\text{Ion product} = [Ag^+]_i[Cl^-]_i = (0.010)(0.010) = 1.0 \times 10^{-4}$$

This is greater than $K_{sp} = 1.8 \times 10^{-10}$, so **a precipitate should form.**

b. You first need to calculate the concentration of $Ag^+(aq)$ in a solution containing 1.00 M NH_3. We did this in Example 17.9 and found that $[Ag^+]$ equals 6.1×10^{-10}. Hence,

$$\text{Ion product} = [Ag^+]_i[Cl^-]_i = (6.1 \times 10^{-10})(0.010) = 6.1 \times 10^{-12}$$

Because the ion product is smaller than $K_{sp} = 1.8 \times 10^{-10}$, **no precipitate should form.**

Answer Check   Check your arithmetic in calculating the ion product. Then note that when a precipitate forms, the ion product decreases as it approaches the solubility product. Therefore, the ion product, Q_c, should be larger than K_{sp} if a precipitate is to form.

Exercise 17.10   Will silver iodide precipitate from a solution that is 0.0045 M AgNO$_3$, 0.15 M NaI, and 0.20 M KCN?

■ See Problems 17.65 and 17.66.

In Example 17.10, we determined whether a precipitate of AgCl is expected to form from a solution made up with given concentrations of Ag^+, Cl^-, and NH_3. The problem involved the $Ag(NH_3)_2^+$ complex in equilibrium. From it, we determined the concentration of free $Ag^+(aq)$ and then calculated the ion product of AgCl.

Suppose you want to find the solubility of AgCl in a solution of aqueous ammonia of given concentration. This problem involves the solubility equilibrium for AgCl, in addition to the complex-ion equilibrium. As silver chloride dissolves to give ions, the Ag^+ ion reacts with NH_3 to give the complex ion $Ag(NH_3)_2^+$. The equilibria are

$$AgCl(s) \rightleftharpoons Ag^+(aq) + Cl^-(aq)$$

$$Ag^+(aq) + 2NH_3(aq) \rightleftharpoons Ag(NH_3)_2^+(aq)$$

When $Ag^+(aq)$ reacts to give the complex ion, more AgCl dissolves to partially replenish the $Ag^+(aq)$ ion, according to Le Châtelier's principle. Therefore, silver chloride is more soluble in aqueous ammonia than in pure water. The next example shows how you can calculate this solubility.

Example 17.11	Calculating the Solubility of a Slightly Soluble Ionic Compound in a Solution of the Complex Ion

Calculate the molar solubility of AgCl in 1.0 M NH_3.

Problem Strategy If you add the solubility equilibrium and the complex-ion equilibrium (the two equations just before this example), you obtain the overall equilibrium for the dissolving of AgCl in NH_3. The equilibrium constant for this reaction equals the product of the equilibrium constants for solubility and complex-ion formation. (We will show that in the solution to this example; however, we discussed the general principle at the end of Section 14.2.) Once you have the equilibrium constant, you can solve the equilibrium problem.

Solution You obtain the overall equation for the process by adding the solubility and complex-ion equilibria.

$$AgCl(s) \rightleftharpoons \cancel{Ag^+(aq)} + Cl^-(aq)$$
$$\underline{\cancel{Ag^+(aq)} + 2NH_3(aq) \rightleftharpoons Ag(NH_3)_2^+(aq)}$$
$$AgCl(s) + 2NH_3(aq) \rightleftharpoons Ag(NH_3)_2^+(aq) + Cl^-(aq)$$

The equilibrium constant for the overall equation is

$$K_c = \frac{[Ag(NH_3)_2^+][Cl^-]}{[NH_3]^2}$$

Because the overall equation is the sum of the solubility and complex-ion equilibria, the equilibrium constant K_c equals the product of the equilibrium constants for the solubility and complex-ion equilibria. You can easily verify this.

$$K_c = K_{sp}K_f = [\cancel{Ag^+}][Cl^-]\frac{[Ag(NH_3)_2^+]}{[\cancel{Ag^+}][NH_3]^2}$$

The value of $K_c = K_{sp}K_f$ can be obtained from K_{sp} for AgCl in Table 17.1 and K_f for $Ag(NH_3)_2^+$ in Table 17.2.

$$K_{sp}K_f = (1.8 \times 10^{-10})(1.7 \times 10^7) = 3.1 \times 10^{-3}$$

You now solve the equilibrium problem. The concentration table follows:

Concentration (M)	$AgCl(s) +$	$2NH_3(aq) \rightleftharpoons$	$Ag(NH_3)_2^+(aq) +$	$Cl^-(aq)$
Starting		1.0	0	0
Change		$-2x$	$+x$	$+x$
Equilibrium		$1.0 - 2x$	x	x

(continued)

(*continued*)

Substituting into the equilibrium-constant equation

$$\frac{[Ag(NH_3)_2^+][Cl^-]}{[NH_3]^2} = K_{sp}K_f$$

gives

$$\frac{x^2}{(1.0 - 2x)^2} = 3.1 \times 10^{-3}$$

You solve this equation by taking the square root of both sides.

$$\frac{x}{1.0 - 2x} = 0.056$$

Rearranging yields

$$x = 0.056(1.0 - 2x) = 0.056 - 0.11x$$

Hence,

$$x = \frac{0.056}{1.11} = 0.050$$

Note that the molar solubility of AgCl equals the molar concentration of silver in the solution. Because of the stability of $Ag(NH_3)_2^+$, most of the silver in solution will be in the form of this complex ion. Therefore, because x equals the concentration of $Ag(NH_3)_2^+$, the molar solubility of AgCl equals **0.050 *M*.**

Answer Check Check that you have the correct overall equilibrium for the problem and that you have then done the arithmetic correctly for the equilibrium constant. Once you have the molar solubility of the compound, x, you can put x back into the equilibrium-constant expression and calculate the value of K_c as a final check.

Exercise 17.11   What is the molar solubility of AgBr in 1.0 *M* $Na_2S_2O_3$ (sodium thiosulfate)? Silver ion forms the complex ion $Ag(S_2O_3)_2^{3-}$. See Tables 17.1 and 17.2 for data.

■ See Problems 17.67 and 17.68.

An Application of Solubility Equilibria

Qualitative analysis involves *the determination of the identity of the substances present in a mixture.* One scheme for the qualitative analysis of a solution of metal ions is based on the relative solubilities of the metal sulfides. This scheme is no longer widely used in practical analysis, having been largely replaced by modern instrumental methods. But it is still taught in general chemistry laboratory as a way of imparting some knowledge of inorganic chemistry while illustrating the concepts of solubility, buffers, and so forth. We will look at the main outline of the sulfide scheme.

17.7 | Qualitative Analysis of Metal Ions

In the qualitative analysis scheme for metal ions, a cation is usually detected by the presence of a characteristic precipitate. For example, silver ion gives a white precipitate with chloride ion. But other ions also give a white precipitate with chloride ion. Therefore, you must first subject a mixture to a procedure that separates individual ions before applying a precipitation test to any particular ion.

FIGURE 17.9 ▶

Flowchart of the qualitative analysis scheme for the separation of metal ions
The first group of ions consists of those precipitated by HCl. The separation of the next two groups is based on the differences in solubilities of the metal sulfides. The fourth group consists of ions of the alkaline earth elements, which are precipitated as carbonates or phosphates. The final group of ions is in the filtrate after these precipitations.

Figure 17.9 shows a flowchart illustrating how the metal ions in an aqueous solution are first separated into five analytical groups. The Analytical Group I ions, Ag^+, Hg_2^{2+}, and Pb^{2+}, are separated from a solution of other ions by adding dilute hydrochloric acid. The ions are precipitated as the chlorides $AgCl$, Hg_2Cl_2, and $PbCl_2$, which are removed by filtering.

The other metal ions remain in the filtrate, the solution that passes through the filter. Many of these ions can be separated by precipitating them as metal sulfides with H_2S. This separation takes advantage of the fact that only the least soluble metal sulfides precipitate in acidic solution. After these are removed and the solution is made basic, other metal sulfides precipitate. <

Analytical Group II consists of metal ions precipitated as metal sulfides from a solution that is 0.3 M H_3O^+ and is saturated with H_2S. < The ions are As^{3+}, Bi^{3+}, Cd^{2+}, Cu^{2+}, Hg^{2+}, Pb^{2+}, Sb^{3+}, and Sn^{4+}. Lead(II) ion can appear in Analytical Group II as well as in Group I, because $PbCl_2$ is somewhat soluble and therefore Pb^{2+} may not be completely precipitated by HCl.

Analytical Group III consists of the metal ions in the filtrate from Group II that are precipitated in weakly basic solution with H_2S. The ions Co^{2+}, Fe^{2+}, Mn^{2+}, Ni^{2+}, and Zn^{2+} are precipitated as the sulfides. The ions Al^{3+} and Cr^{3+} are precipitated as hydroxides.

The filtrate obtained after the Group III metal ions have precipitated contains the alkali metal ions and the alkaline earth ions. The Analytical Group IV ions, Ba^{2+}, Ca^{2+}, Mg^{2+}, and Sr^{2+}, are precipitated as carbonates or phosphates by adding $(NH_4)_2CO_3$ or $(NH_4)_2HPO_4$. The filtrate from this separation contains the Analytical Group V ions, K^+ and Na^+.

The solubility of the metal sulfides at different pH was discussed in Section 17.4.

Hydrogen sulfide is often prepared in the solution by adding thioacetamide, CH_3CSNH_2, and warming.

$$CH_3CSNH_2 + H_2O \longrightarrow CH_3CONH_2 + H_2S$$

To illustrate the separation scheme, suppose you have a solution containing the metal cations Ag^+, Cu^{2+}, Zn^{2+}, Ca^{2+}, and Na^+. When you add dilute $HCl(aq)$ to this solution, Ag^+ precipitates as AgCl.

$$Ag^+(aq) + Cl^-(aq) \longrightarrow \underset{\text{white}}{AgCl(s)}$$

You filter off the precipitate of AgCl. The filtrate contains the remaining ions.

When you make the filtrate 0.3 M H_3O^+ and then saturate it with H_2S, the Cu^{2+} ion precipitates as CuS.

$$Cu^{2+}(aq) + S^{2-}(aq) \longrightarrow \underset{\text{black}}{CuS(s)}$$

Zinc(II) ion also forms a sulfide, but it is soluble in acidic solution. After removal of the precipitate of CuS, the solution is made weakly basic with $NH_3(aq)$. This increases the S^{2-} concentration sufficiently to precipitate ZnS.

$$Zn^{2+}(aq) + S^{2-}(aq) \longrightarrow \underset{\text{white}}{ZnS(s)}$$

The filtrate from this separation contains Ca^{2+} and Na^+. Calcium ion can be precipitated as the phosphate or the carbonate. For example, by adding $(NH_4)_2CO_3$, you get the reaction

$$Ca^{2+}(aq) + CO_3^{2-}(aq) \longrightarrow \underset{\text{white}}{CaCO_3(s)}$$

The filtrate from this solution contains Na^+ ion. Now the five ions have been separated.

In the complete analysis, once the ions are separated into analytical groups, these are further separated into the individual ions. We can illustrate this with Analytical Group I, which is precipitated as a mixture of the chlorides AgCl, Hg_2Cl_2, and $PbCl_2$. Of these, only $PbCl_2$ is significantly soluble in hot water. Thus, if the Analytical Group I precipitate is mixed with hot water, lead chloride dissolves and the silver and mercury(I) chlorides can be filtered off. Any lead(II) ion is in the filtrate and can be revealed by adding potassium chromate. Lead(II) ion gives a bright yellow precipitate of lead(II) chromate, $PbCrO_4$.

$$Pb^{2+}(aq) + CrO_4^{2-}(aq) \longrightarrow \underset{\text{yellow}}{PbCrO_4(s)}$$

If there is precipitate remaining after the extraction with hot water, it consists of AgCl, Hg_2Cl_2, or both. However, only silver ion forms a stable ammonia complex ion. Therefore, silver chloride dissolves in ammonia.

$$AgCl(s) + 2NH_3(aq) \longrightarrow Ag(NH_3)_2^+(aq) + Cl^-(aq)$$

Mercury(I) chloride is simultaneously oxidized and reduced in ammonia solution, giving a precipitate of mercury(II) amido chloride, $HgNH_2Cl$, and mercury metal, which appears black because of its finely divided state.

$$Hg_2Cl_2(s) + 2NH_3(aq) \longrightarrow \underset{\text{black or gray}}{\underbrace{HgNH_2Cl(s) + Hg(l)}} + NH_4^+(aq) + Cl^-(aq)$$

The presence of silver ion in the filtrate is revealed by adding hydrochloric acid, which combines with the NH_3, releasing $Ag^+(aq)$ ion. The $Ag^+(aq)$ ion reacts with $Cl^-(aq)$ to give a white precipitate of AgCl.

$$Ag(NH_3)_2^+(aq) + 2H_3O^+(aq) + Cl^-(aq) \longrightarrow AgCl(s) + 2NH_4^+(aq) + 2H_2O(l)$$

The other analytical groups are separated in similar fashion. Once a given ion has been separated, its presence is usually confirmed by a particular reactant—perhaps one that gives a distinctive precipitate.

A Checklist for Review

Important Terms

solubility product constant (K_sp) (17.1)
ion product (17.3)
fractional precipitation (17.3)

complex ion (17.5)
ligand (17.5)
formation (stability) constant (K_f) (17.5)

dissociation constant (of a complex ion) (K_d) (17.5)
amphoteric hydroxide (17.5)
qualitative analysis (17.7)

Summary of Facts and Concepts

The equilibrium constant for the equilibrium between a slightly soluble ionic solid and its ions in solution is called the *solubility product constant, K_{sp}*. Its value can be determined from the solubility of the solid. Conversely, when the solubility product constant is known, the solubility of the solid can be calculated. The solubility is decreased by the addition of a soluble salt that supplies a common ion. Qualitatively, this can be seen to follow from Le Châtelier's principle. Quantitatively, the *common-ion effect* on solubility can be obtained from the solubility product constant.

Rather than look at the solubility process as the dissolving of a solid in a solution, you can look at it as the *precipitation* of the solid from the solution. You can decide whether precipitation will occur by computing the *ion product*. Precipitation occurs when the ion product is greater than K_{sp}.

Solubility is affected by the pH if the compound supplies an anion conjugate to a weak acid. As the pH decreases (H_3O^+ ion concentration increases), the anion concentration decreases because the anion forms the weak acid. Therefore, the ion product decreases and the solubility increases.

The concentration of a metal ion in solution is decreased by *complex-ion formation*. The equilibrium constant for the formation of the complex ion from the aqueous metal ion and the ligands is called the *formation constant* (or *stability constant*), K_f. Because complex-ion formation reduces the concentration of aqueous metal ion, an ionic compound of the metal is more soluble in a solution of the ligand.

The sulfide scheme of *qualitative analysis* separates the metal ions in a mixture by using precipitation reactions. Variation of solubility with pH and with complex-ion formation is used to aid in the separation.

Media Summary

Visit the **student website at college.cengage.com/pic/ebbing9e** to help prepare for class, study for quizzes and exams, understand core concepts, and visualize molecular-level interactions. The following media activities are available for this chapter:

Prepare for Class

■ **Video Lessons** *Mini lectures from chemistry experts*
The Solubility Product Constant
Solubility and the Common-Ion Effect
Fraction Precipitation
The Effect of pH on Solubility
The Formation of Complex Ions
Amphoteric Metal Hydroxides

Improve Your Grade

■ **Visualizations** *Molecular-level animations and lab demonstration videos*
Nickel(II) Complexes
Reactions of Silver(I)

■ **Flashcards** *Key terms and definitions*
Online Flashcards

■ **Self-Assessment Questions** *Additional questions with full worked-out solutions*
6 Self-Assessment Questions

ACE the Test

Multiple-choice quizzes
3 ACE Practice Tests

Access these resources using the passkey available free with new texts or for purchase separately.

Learning Objectives

17.1 The Solubility Product Constant

- Define the *solubility product constant, K_{sp}.*
- Write solubility product expressions. **Example 17.1**
- Define *molar solubility.*
- Calculate K_{sp} from the solubility (simple example). **Example 17.2**
- Calculate K_{sp} from the solubility (more complicated example). **Example 17.3**
- Calculate the solubility from K_{sp}. **Example 17.4**

17.2 Solubility and the Common-Ion Effect

- Explain how the solubility of a salt is affected by another salt that has the same cation or anion. (*common ion*)
- Calculate the solubility of a slightly soluble salt in a solution of a common ion. **Example 17.5**

17.3 Precipitation Calculations

- Define *ion product.*
- State the criterion for precipitation.
- Predict whether precipitation will occur, given ion concentrations. **Example 17.6**
- Predict whether precipitation will occur, given solution volumes and concentrations. **Example 17.7**
- Define *fractional precipitation.*
- Explain how two ions can be separated using fractional precipitation.

17.4 Effect of pH on Solubility

- Explain the qualitative effect of pH on solubility of a slightly soluble salt.
- Determine the qualitative effect of pH on solubility. **Example 17.8**
- Explain the basis for the sulfide scheme to separate a mixture of metal ions.

17.5 Complex-Ion Formation

- Define *complex ion* and *ligand.*
- Define *formation constant* or *stability constant, K_f,* and *dissociation constant, K_d.*
- Calculate the concentration of a metal ion in equilibrium with a complex ion. **Example 17.9**
- Define *amphoteric hydroxide.*

17.6 Complex Ions and Solubility

- Predict whether a precipitate will form in the presence of the complex ion. **Example 17.10**
- Calculate the solubility of a slightly soluble ionic compound in a solution of the complex ion. **Example 17.11**

17.7 Qualitative Analysis of Metal Ions

- Define *qualitative analysis.*
- Describe the main outline of the sulfide scheme for qualitative analysis.

Self-Assessment and Review Questions

17.1 Suppose the molar solubility of nickel hydroxide, $Ni(OH)_2$, is x M. Show that K_{sp} for nickel hydroxide equals $4x^3$.

17.2 Explain why calcium sulfate is less soluble in sodium sulfate solution than in pure water.

17.3 What must be the concentration of silver ion in a solution that is in equilibrium with solid silver chloride and that is 0.10 M in Cl^-?

17.4 Discuss briefly how you could predict whether a precipitate will form when solutions of lead nitrate and potassium iodide are mixed. What information do you need to have?

17.5 Explain why barium fluoride dissolves in dilute hydrochloric acid but is insoluble in water.

17.6 Explain how metal ions such as Pb^{2+} and Zn^{2+} are separated by precipitation with hydrogen sulfide.

17.7 Lead chloride at first precipitates when sodium chloride is added to a solution of lead nitrate. Later, when the solution is made more concentrated in chloride ion, the precipitate dissolves. Explain what is happening. What equilibria are involved? Note that lead ion forms the complex ion $PbCl_4^{2-}$.

17.8 A precipitate forms when a small amount of sodium hydroxide is added to a solution of aluminum sulfate. This precipitate dissolves when more sodium hydroxide is added. Explain what is happening.

17.9 Describe how you would separate the metal ions in a solution containing silver ion, copper(II) ion, and nickel(II) ion, using the sulfide scheme of qualitative analysis.

17.10 A solution containing calcium ion and magnesium ion is buffered with ammonia–ammonium chloride. When carbonate ion is added to the solution, calcium carbonate precipitates but magnesium carbonate does not. Explain.

17.11 The solubility of the hypothetical salt A_3B_2 is 6.1×10^{-9} mol/L at a certain temperature. What is K_{sp} for the salt? A_3B_2 dissolves according to the equation

$$A_3B_2(s) \rightleftharpoons 3A^{2+}(aq) + 2B^{3-}(aq)$$

- **a.** 3.7×10^{-17}
- **b.** 9.1×10^{-25}
- **c.** 9.1×10^{-40}
- **d.** 3.7×10^{-32}
- **e.** 1.4×10^{-33}

17.12 Write the solubility product expression for the salt Ag_3PO_4.

- **a.** $K_{sp} = 3[Ag^+] \times [PO_4^{3-}]$
- **b.** $K_{sp} = [Ag^+][PO_4^{3-}]^3$
- **c.** $K_{sp} = [Ag^+]^3[P^{3-}][O^{2-}]^4$
- **d.** $K_{sp} = [Ag^{3+}][PO_4^-]^3$
- **e.** $K_{sp} = [Ag^+]^3[PO_4^{3-}]$

17.13 What is the molar solubility of calcium oxalate, CaC_2O_4, in a 0.203 M calcium chloride solution? The solubility product constant for calcium oxalate is 2.3×10^{-9}.

   a. 4.8×10^{-5} M
   b. 6.6×10^{-6} M
   c. 8.0×10^{-6} M
   d. 1.1×10^{-8} M
   e. 1.2×10^{-5} M

17.14 Suppose the K_a values for the hypothetical acids HX, HY, and HZ are 9.5×10^{-5}, 7.6×10^{-4}, and 1.2×10^{-2}, respectively. Assuming that "A" is a cation that produces a slightly soluble salt with all three acids, which of the following salts would have its solubility most affected (compared with its solubility in pure water) when it is dissolved in a 0.10 M solution of HCl?

   a. AX
   b. AY
   c. AZ
   d. The solubility of all the salts would be affected by the same amount.
   e. There is not enough information given in the problem to determine the answer.

Concept Explorations

17.15 Solubility and Solubility Product

You put 0.10-mol samples of KNO_3, $(NH_4)_2S$, K_2S, MnS, AgCl, and $BaSO_4$ into separate flasks and add 1.0 L of water to each one. Then you stir the solutions for 5 minutes at room temperature. Assume that you have 1.0 L of solution in each case.

   a. Are there any beakers where you would observe solid still present? How do you know?

   b. Can you calculate the potassium ion concentration, K^+, for the solutions of KNO_3 and K_2S? If so, do the calculations, and then compare these K^+ concentrations.

   c. For the solutions of $(NH_4)_2S$, K_2S, and MnS, how do the concentrations of sulfide ion, S^{2-}, compare? (You don't need to calculate an answer at this point; just provide a rough comparison.) Be sure to justify your answer.

   d. Are there any cases where you need more information to calculate the sulfide-ion concentration for the solutions of $(NH_4)_2S$, K_2S, and MnS from part c? If so, what additional information do you need?

   e. Consider all of the solutions listed at the beginning of this problem. For which ones do you need more information than is given in the question to determine the concentrations of the ions present? Where can you find this information?

   f. How is the solubility of an ionic compound related to the concentrations of the ions of the dissolved compound in solution?

17.16 Solubility Equilibria

Consider three hypothetical ionic solids: AX, AX_2, and AX_3 (each X forms X^-). Each of these solids has the same K_{sp} value, 5.5×10^{-7}. You place 0.25 mol of each compound in a separate container and add enough water to bring the volume to 1.0 L in each case.

   a. Write the chemical equation for each of the solids dissolving in water.

   b. Would you expect the concentration of each solution to be 0.25 M in the compound? Explain, in some detail, why or why not.

   c. Would you expect the concentrations of the A cations (A^+, A^{2+}, and A^{3+}) in the three solutions to be the same? Does just knowing the stoichiometry of each reaction help you determine the answer, or do you need something else? Explain your answer in detail, but without doing any arithmetic calculations.

   d. Of the three solids, which one would you expect to have the greatest molar solubility? Explain in detail, but without doing any arithmetic calculations.

   e. Calculate the molar solubility of each compound.

Conceptual Problems

17.17 Which compound in each of the following pairs of compounds is the more soluble one?

   a. silver chloride or silver iodide
   b. magnesium hydroxide or copper(II) hydroxide

17.18 You are given two mineral samples: halite, which is NaCl, and fluorite, which is CaF_2. Describe a simple test you could use to discover which mineral is fluorite.

17.19 You are given a saturated solution of lead(II) chloride. Which one of the following solutions would be most effective in yielding a precipitate when added to the lead(II) chloride solution?

   a. 0.1 M NaCl(aq)
   b. saturated PbS(aq)
   c. 0.1 M Na_2SO_4(aq)

17.20 Which of the following pictures best represents a solution made by adding 10 g of silver chloride, AgCl, to a liter of water?

In these pictures, the gray spheres represent Ag^+ ions and the green spheres represent chloride ions. For clarity, water molecules are not shown.

17.21 Which of the following pictures best represents an unsaturated solution of sodium chloride, NaCl? In these pictures, the dark gray spheres represent Na^+ ions and the green spheres represent chloride ions. For clarity, water molecules are not shown.

17.22 When ammonia is first added to a solution of copper(II) nitrate, a pale blue precipitate of copper(II) hydroxide forms. As more ammonia is added, however, this precipitate dissolves. Describe what is happening.

17.23 You are given a solution of the ions Mg^{2+}, Ca^{2+}, and Ba^{2+}. Devise a scheme to separate these ions using sodium sulfate. Note that magnesium sulfate is soluble.

17.24 You add dilute hydrochloric acid to a solution containing a metal ion. No precipitate forms. After the acidity is adjusted to 0.3 M hydronium ion, you bubble hydrogen sulfide into the solution. Again no precipitate forms. Is it possible that the original solution contained silver ion? Could it have contained copper(II) ion?

Practice Problems

Solubility and K_{sp}

17.25 Use the solubility rules (Table 4.1) to decide which of the following compounds are expected to be soluble and which insoluble.
  a. NaBr **b.** PbI_2 **c.** $BaCO_3$ **d.** $(NH_4)_2SO_4$

17.26 Use the solubility rules (Table 4.1) to decide which of the following compounds are expected to be soluble and which insoluble.
  a. $Ca(NO_3)_2$ **b.** AgBr **c.** MgI_2 **d.** $PbSO_4$

17.27 Write solubility product expressions for the following compounds.
  a. $Mg(OH)_2$ **c.** $Ca_3(AsO_4)_2$
  b. $SrCO_3$ **d.** $Fe(OH)_3$

17.28 Write solubility product expressions for the following compounds.
  a. $Ba_3(PO_4)_2$ **c.** PbI_2
  b. $FePO_4$ **d.** Ag_2S

17.29 The solubility of silver bromate, $AgBrO_3$, in water is 0.0072 g/L. Calculate $K_{sp.}$

17.30 The solubility of magnesium oxalate, MgC_2O_4, in water is 0.0093 mol/L. Calculate $K_{sp.}$

17.31 Calculate the solubility product constant for copper(II) iodate, $Cu(IO_3)_2$. The solubility of copper(II) iodate in water is 0.13 g/100 mL.

17.32 The solubility of silver dichromate, $Ag_2Cr_2O_7$, in water is 1.59 g/L. Calculate $K_{sp.}$

17.33 The pH of a saturated solution of magnesium hydroxide (milk of magnesia) was found to be 10.52. From this, find K_{sp} for magnesium hydroxide.

17.34 A solution saturated in calcium hydroxide (limewater) has a pH of 12.35. What is K_{sp} for calcium hydroxide?

17.35 Strontianite (strontium carbonate) is an important mineral of strontium. Calculate the solubility of strontium carbonate, $SrCO_3$, from the solubility product constant (see Table 17.1).

17.36 Magnesite (magnesium carbonate, $MgCO_3$) is a common magnesium mineral. From the solubility product constant (Table 17.1), find the solubility of magnesium carbonate in grams per liter of water.

17.37 What is the solubility of PbF_2 in water? The K_{sp} for PbF_2 is 2.7×10^{-8}.

17.38 What is the solubility of MgF_2 in water? The K_{sp} for MgF_2 is 7.4×10^{-11}.

Common-Ion Effect

17.39 What is the solubility (in grams per liter) of strontium sulfate, $SrSO_4$, in 0.23 M sodium sulfate, Na_2SO_4? See Table 17.1.

17.40 What is the solubility (in grams per liter) of lead(II) chromate, $PbCrO_4$, in 0.13 M potassium chromate, K_2CrO_4? See Table 17.1.

17.41 The solubility of magnesium fluoride, MgF_2, in water is 0.016 g/L. What is the solubility (in grams per liter) of magnesium fluoride in 0.020 M sodium fluoride, NaF?

17.42 The solubility of silver sulfate, Ag_2SO_4, in water has been determined to be 8.0 g/L. What is the solubility in 0.45 M sodium sulfate, Na_2SO_4?

17.43 What is the solubility (in grams per liter) of magnesium oxalate, MgC_2O_4, in 0.020 M sodium oxalate, $Na_2C_2O_4$? Solve the equation exactly. See Table 17.1 for K_{sp}.

17.44 Calculate the molar solubility of strontium sulfate, $SrSO_4$, in 0.0015 M sodium sulfate, Na_2SO_4. Solve the equation exactly. See Table 17.1 for K_{sp}.

Precipitation

17.45 From each of the following ion concentrations in a solution, predict whether a precipitate will form in the solution.
  a. $[Ba^{2+}] = 0.020\ M$, $[F^-] = 0.015\ M$
  b. $[Pb^{2+}] = 0.035\ M$, $[Cl^-] = 0.15\ M$

17.46 From each of the following ion concentrations in a solution, predict whether a precipitate will form in the solution.
  a. $[Sr^{2+}] = 0.012\ M$, $[CO_3^{2-}] = 0.0015\ M$
  b. $[Pb^{2+}] = 0.0012\ M$, $[Cl^-] = 0.041\ M$

17.47 Lead(II) chromate, $PbCrO_4$, was used as a yellow paint pigment ("chrome yellow"). When a solution is prepared that is

5.0×10^{-4} M in lead ion, Pb^{2+}, and 5.0×10^{-5} M in chromate ion, CrO_4^{2-}, would you expect some of the lead(II) chromate to precipitate? See Table 17.1.

17.48 Lead sulfate, $PbSO_4$, was used as a white paint pigment. When a solution is prepared that is 5.0×10^{-4} M in lead ion, Pb^{2+}, and 1.0×10^{-5} M in sulfate ion, SO_4^{2-}, would you expect some of the lead sulfate to precipitate? See Table 17.1.

17.49 The following solutions are mixed: 1.0 L of 0.00010 M NaOH and 1.0 L of 0.0020 M $MgSO_4$. Is a precipitate expected? Explain.

17.50 A 45-mL sample of 0.015 M calcium chloride, $CaCl_2$, is added to 55 mL of 0.010 M sodium sulfate, Na_2SO_4. Is a precipitate expected? Explain.

17.51 A 45.0-mL sample of 0.0015 M $BaCl_2$ was added to a beaker containing 75.0 mL of 0.0025 M KF. Will a precipitate form?

17.52 A 65.0-mL sample of 0.010 M $Pb(NO_3)_2$ was added to a beaker containing 40.0 mL of 0.035 M KCl. Will a precipitate form?

17.53 How many moles of calcium chloride, $CaCl_2$, can be added to 1.5 L of 0.020 M potassium sulfate, K_2SO_4, before a precipitate is expected? Assume that the volume of the solution is not changed significantly by the addition of calcium chloride.

17.54 Magnesium sulfate, $MgSO_4$, is added to 456 mL of 0.040 M sodium hydroxide, NaOH, until a precipitate just forms. How many grams of magnesium sulfate were added? Assume that the volume of the solution is not changed significantly by the addition of magnesium sulfate.

17.55 What is the I^- concentration just as AgCl begins to precipitate when 1.0 M $AgNO_3$ is slowly added to a solution containing 0.015 M Cl^- and 0.015 M I^-?

17.56 What is the Cl^- concentration just as Ag_2CrO_4 begins to precipitate when 1.0 M $AgNO_3$ is slowly added to a solution containing 0.015 M Cl^- and 0.015 M CrO_4^{2-}?

Effect of pH on Solubility

17.57 Write the net ionic equation in which the slightly soluble salt barium fluoride, BaF_2, dissolves in dilute hydrochloric acid.

17.58 Write the net ionic equation in which the slightly soluble salt lead(II) carbonate, $PbCO_3$, dissolves in dilute hydrochloric acid.

17.59 Which salt would you expect to dissolve more readily in acidic solution, barium sulfate or barium fluoride? Explain.

17.60 Which salt would you expect to dissolve more readily in acidic solution, calcium phosphate, $Ca_3(PO_4)_2$, or calcium sulfate, $CaSO_4$? Explain.

General Problems

17.73 Lead(II) sulfate is often used as a test for lead(II) ion in qualitative analysis. Using the solubility product constant (Table 17.1), calculate the molar solubility of lead(II) sulfate in water.

17.74 Mercury(II) ion is often precipitated as mercury(II) sulfide in qualitative analysis. Using the solubility product constant (Table 17.1), calculate the molar solubility of mercury(II) sulfide in water, assuming that no other reactions occur.

Complex Ions

17.61 Write the chemical equation for the formation of the $Cu(CN)_2^-$ ion. Write the K_f expression.

17.62 Write the chemical equation for the formation of the $Ni(NH_3)_6^{2+}$ ion. Write the K_f expression.

17.63 Sufficient sodium cyanide, NaCN, was added to 0.015 M silver nitrate, $AgNO_3$, to give a solution that was initially 0.100 M in cyanide ion, CN^-. What is the concentration of silver ion, Ag^+, in this solution after $Ag(CN)_2^-$ forms? The formation constant K_f for the complex ion $Ag(CN)_2^-$ is 5.6×10^{18}.

17.64 The formation constant K_f for the complex ion $Zn(OH)_4^{2-}$ is 2.8×10^{15}. What is the concentration of zinc ion, Zn^{2+}, in a solution that is initially 0.20 M in $Zn(OH)_4^{2-}$?

17.65 Predict whether cadmium oxalate, CdC_2O_4, will precipitate from a solution that is 0.0020 M $Cd(NO_3)_2$, 0.010 M $Na_2C_2O_4$, and 0.10 M NH_3. Note that cadmium ion forms the $Cd(NH_3)_4^{2+}$ complex ion.

17.66 Predict whether nickel(II) hydroxide, $Ni(OH)_2$, will precipitate from a solution that is 0.0020 M $NiSO_4$, 0.010 M NaOH, and 0.10 M NH_3. Note that nickel(II) ion forms the $Ni(NH_3)_6^{2+}$ complex ion.

17.67 What is the molar solubility of CdC_2O_4 in 0.10 M NH_3?

17.68 What is the molar solubility of NiS in 0.10 M NH_3?

Qualitative Analysis

17.69 Describe how you could separate the following mixture of metal ions: Cd^{2+}, Pb^{2+}, and Sr^{2+}.

17.70 Describe how you could separate the following mixture of metal ions: Na^+, Hg^{2+}, and Ca^{2+}.

17.71 A student dissolved a compound in water and added hydrochloric acid. No precipitate formed. Next she bubbled H_2S into this solution, but again no precipitate formed. However, when she made the solution basic with ammonia and bubbled in H_2S, a precipitate formed. Which of the following are possible as the cation in the compound?
  a. Ag^+ **b.** Ca^{2+} **c.** Mn^{2+} **d.** Cd^{2+}

17.72 A student was asked to identify a compound. In an effort to do so, he first dissolved the compound in water. He found that no precipitate formed when hydrochloric acid was added, but when H_2S was bubbled into this acidic solution, a precipitate formed. Which one of the following could be the precipitate?
  a. $PbCl_2$ **b.** CbS **c.** MnS **d.** Ag_2S

17.75 Mercury(I) chloride, Hg_2Cl_2, is an unusual salt in that it dissolves to form Hg_2^{2+} and $2Cl^-$. Use the solubility product constant (Table 17.1) to calculate the following: (a) the molar solubility of Hg_2Cl_2; (b) the solubility of Hg_2Cl_2 in grams per liter.

17.76 Magnesium ammonium phosphate is an unusual salt in that it dissolves to form Mg^{2+}, NH_4^+, and PO_4^{3-} ions. K_{sp} for magnesium ammonium phosphate equals 2.5×10^{-13}. Calculate: (a) its molar solubility; (b) its solubility in grams per liter.

17.77 For cerium(III) hydroxide, $Ce(OH)_3$, K_{sp} equals 2.0×10^{-20}. Calculate: (a) its molar solubility (recall that taking the square root twice gives the fourth root); (b) the pOH of the saturated solution.

17.78 Copper(II) ferrocyanide, $Cu_2Fe(CN)_6$, dissolves to give Cu^{2+} and $[Fe(CN)_6]^{4-}$ ions; K_{sp} for $Cu_2Fe(CN)_6$ equals 1.3×10^{-16}. Calculate: (a) the molar solubility, and (b) the solubility in grams per liter of copper(II) ferrocyanide.

17.79 What is the solubility of magnesium hydroxide in a solution buffered at pH 8.80?

17.80 What is the solubility of silver oxide, Ag_2O, in a solution buffered at pH 10.50? The equilibrium is $Ag_2O(s) + H_2O(l) \rightleftharpoons 2Ag^+(aq) + 2OH^-(aq)$; $K_c = 2.0 \times 10^{-8}$.

17.81 What is the molar solubility of $Mg(OH)_2$ in a solution containing 1.0×10^{-1} M NaOH? See Table 17.1 for K_{sp}.

17.82 What is the molar solubility of $Al(OH)_3$ in a solution containing 1.0×10^{-3} M NaOH? See Table 17.1 for K_{sp}.

17.83 What must be the concentration of sulfate ion in order to precipitate calcium sulfate, $CaSO_4$, from a solution that is 0.0030 M Ca^{2+}?

17.84 What must be the concentration of chromate ion in order to precipitate strontium chromate, $SrCrO_4$, from a solution that is 0.0025 M Sr^{2+}? K_{sp} for strontium chromate is 3.5×10^{-5}.

17.85 A 3.20-L solution of 1.25×10^{-3} M $Pb(NO_3)_2$ is mixed with a 0.80-L solution of 5.0×10^{-1} M NaCl. Calculate Q_c for the dissolution of $PbCl_2$. No precipitate has formed. Is the solution supersaturated, saturated, or unsaturated?

17.86 A 0.150-L solution of 2.4×10^{-5} M $MgCl_2$ is mixed with 0.050 L of 4.0×10^{-3} M NaOH. Calculate Q_c for the dissolution of $Mg(OH)_2$. No precipitate has formed. Is the solution supersaturated, saturated, or unsaturated?

17.87 How many grams of sodium chloride can be added to 785 mL of 0.0015 M silver nitrate before a precipitate forms?

17.88 How many grams of sodium sulfate can be added to 435 mL of 0.0028 M barium chloride before a precipitate forms?

17.89 Solid KSCN was added to a 2.00 M Fe^{3+} solution so that it was also initially 2.00 M SCN^-. These ions then reacted to give the complex ion $Fe(SCN)^{2+}$, whose formation constant was 9.0×10^2. What is the concentration of $Fe^{3+}(aq)$ at equilibrium? Be sure to check any simplifying assumption you make.

17.90 Solid KSCN was added to a 2.00 M Co^{2+} solution so that it was also initially 2.00 M SCN^-. These ions then reacted to give the complex ion $Co(SCN)^+$, whose formation constant was 1.0×10^2. What is the concentration of $Co^{2+}(aq)$ at equilibrium? Be sure to check any simplifying assumption you make.

17.91 Calculate the molar solubility of silver bromide, AgBr, in 5.0 M NH_3.

17.92 Calculate the molar solubility of silver iodide, AgI, in 2.0 M NH_3.

17.93 The solubility of zinc oxalate, ZnC_2O_4, in 0.0150 M ammonia is 3.6×10^{-4} mol/L. What is the oxalate-ion concentration in the saturated solution? If the solubility product constant for zinc oxalate is 1.5×10^{-9}, what must be the zinc-ion concentration in the solution? Now calculate the formation constant for the complex ion $Zn(NH_3)_4^{2+}$.

17.94 The solubility of cadmium oxalate, CdC_2O_4, in 0.150 M ammonia is 6.1×10^{-3} mol/L. What is the oxalate-ion concentration in the saturated solution? If the solubility product constant for cadmium oxalate is 1.5×10^{-8}, what must be the cadmium-ion concentration in the solution? Now calculate the formation constant for the complex ion $Cd(NH_3)_4^{2+}$.

17.95 Ammonia, NH_3, is a base that ionizes to give NH_4^+ and OH^- ($K_b = 1.8 \times 10^{-5}$). You add magnesium sulfate to an ammonia solution. Calculate the concentration of Mg^{2+} ion when magnesium hydroxide, $Mg(OH)_2$, just begins to precipitate from 0.10 M NH_3. K_{sp} for $Mg(OH)_2$ is 1.8×10^{-11}.

17.96 Hydrazine, N_2H_4, is a base that ionizes to give $N_2H_5^+$ and OH^- ($K_b = 1.7 \times 10^{-6}$). You add magnesium sulfate to a hydrazine solution. Calculate the concentration of Mg^{2+} ion when magnesium hydroxide, $Mg(OH)_2$, just begins to precipitate from 0.20 M N_2H_4. K_{sp} for $Mg(OH)_2$ is 1.8×10^{-11}.

17.97 A saturated solution of copper(II) iodate in pure water has a copper-ion concentration of 2.7×10^{-3} M.
  a. What is the molar solubility of copper iodate in a 0.35 M potassium iodate solution?
  b. What is the molar solubility of copper iodate in a 0.35 M copper nitrate solution?
  c. Should there be a difference in the answers to parts a and b? Why?

17.98 A saturated solution of lead iodate in pure water has an iodate-ion concentration of 8.0×10^{-5} M.
  a. What is the molar solubility of lead iodate in a 0.15 M lead nitrate solution at the same temperature?
  b. Should the molar solubility of lead iodate in part a be the same as, greater than, or less than that of lead iodate in pure water? Why?

17.99 A solution contains 0.0150 M lead(II) ion. A concentrated sodium iodide solution is added to precipitate lead iodide (assume no volume change).
  a. At what concentration of I^- does precipitate start to form?
  b. When $[I^-] = 2.0 \times 10^{-3}$ M, what is the lead-ion concentration? What percentage of the lead(II) originally present remains in solution?

17.100 A solution contains 0.00750 M calcium ion. A concentrated sodium fluoride solution is added to precipitate calcium fluoride (assume no volume change).
  a. At what concentration of F^- does precipitate start to form?
  b. When $[F^-] = 9.5 \times 10^{-4}$ M, what is the calcium-ion concentration? What percentage of the calcium ion has precipitated?

17.101 a. If the molar solubility of cobalt(II) hydroxide is 5.4×10^{-6} mol/L in pure water, what is its K_{sp} value?
  b. What is the molar solubility of $Co(OH)_2$ in a buffered solution that has a pH of 10.43?
  c. Account for the differences in molar solubility in parts a and b.

17.102 a. If the molar solubility of beryllium(II) hydroxide is 8.6×10^{-7} M in pure water, what is its K_{sp} value?
  b. What is the molar solubility of beryllium(II) hydroxide in a solution that is 1.50 M in NH_3 and 0.25 M in NH_4Cl?
  c. Account for the differences in molar solubility in parts a and b.

17.103 Although silver chloride is insoluble in water, it readily dissolves upon the addition of ammonia.

$$AgCl(s) + 2NH_3(aq) \rightleftharpoons Ag(NH_3)_2{}^+ (aq) + Cl^- (aq)$$

  a. What is the equilibrium constant for this dissolving process?
  b. Ammonia is added to a solution containing excess $AgCl(s)$. The final volume is 1.00 L and the resulting equilibrium concentration of NH_3 is 0.80 M. Calculate the number of moles of AgCl dissolved, the molar concentration of $Ag(NH_3)_2{}^+$, and the number of moles of NH_3 added to the original solution.

17.104 Crystals of AgBr can be removed from black-and-white photographic film by reacting the AgBr with sodium thiosulfate.

$$AgBr(s) + 2S_2O_3{}^{2-}(aq) \rightleftharpoons [Ag(S_2O_3)_2]^{3-}(aq) + Br^-(aq)$$

  a. What is the equilibrium constant for this dissolving process?
  b. In order to dissolve 2.5 g of AgBr in 1.0 L of solution how many moles of $Na_2S_2O_3$ must be added?

17.105 A 1.0-L solution that is 4.2 M in ammonia is mixed with 26.7 g of ammonium chloride.
  a. What is the hydroxide-ion concentration of this solution?
  b. 0.075 mol of $MgCl_2$ is added to the above solution. Assume that there is no volume change. After $Mg(OH)_2$ has precipitated, what is the molar concentration of magnesium ion? What percent of the Mg^{2+} is removed from solution?

17.106 A 1.0-L solution that is 1.6 M in ammonia is mixed with 75.8 g of ammonium sulfate.
  a. What is the hydroxide-ion concentration of this solution?
  b. 0.058 mol of $MnCl_2$ is added to the above solution. Assume that there is no volume change. After $Mn(OH)_2$ has precipitated, what is the molar concentration of manganese ion? What percent of the Mn^{2+} is removed from solution (K_{sp} of $Mn(OH)_2$ is 4.6×10^{-14})?

17.107 What chemical reaction is responsible for the dissolving out of caverns in limestone caves?

17.108 What chemical reaction is responsible for the formation of stalactites and stalagmites in limestone caves? How is this reaction related to the one involved in the dissolving out of caverns?

Strategy Problems

17.109 You add 50.0 mL of 0.100 M HCl to 50.0 mL of 0.100 M $AgNO_3$. What are the final concentrations of H_3O^+ and Cl^- in the solution?

17.110 A chemist mixes 1.00 L each of 0.100 M Na_2CO_3 and 0.200 M $CaCl_2$ in a beaker. What is the concentration of carbonate ion, $CO_3{}^{2-}$, in the final solution?

17.111 A researcher found the solubility of lead(II) bromide in 0.100 M NaBr to be 1.31 g/L. What is the solubility product of lead(II) bromide?

17.112 Gout is a painful inflammation of the joints caused by an excess of uric acid in the blood and its precipitation as sodium urate (the sodium salt of uric acid), $NaC_5H_3N_4O_3$, in tissues of the joints. The solubility of sodium urate in aqueous solution is 7.0 mg per 100 mL at body temperature, 37°C. The normal level of sodium ion in blood plasma is 3.2 g per liter. What would be the concentration of urate ion in blood plasma if it were saturated with sodium urate?

Uric acid

17.113 An analytical chemist has a solution containing chloride ion, Cl^-. She decides to determine the amount of chloride ion in the solution by titrating 50.0 mL of this solution by 0.100 M $AgNO_3$. As a way to indicate the endpoint of the titration, she added 1.00 g of potassium chromate, K_2CrO_4 (see Figure 17.5). As she slowly added the silver nitrate to the solution, a white precipitate formed. She continued the titration, with more white precipitate forming. Finally, the solution turned red, from another precipitate. The volume of the solution at this point was 60.3 mL. How many moles of chloride ion were there in the original solution? How many moles of chloride ion were there in the final solution? You may make any reasonable approximations.

17.114 How would the solubility of calcium fluoride be affected by the presence of fluoride ion from another source? What is the solubility of calcium fluoride in a saturated solution of barium fluoride? How does this compare with the value of the solubility of calcium fluoride found in Example 17.4? Is this what you expect?

17.115 A scientist was interested in how soluble rust is in acidic soils, so she set up an idealized problem to get an initial feel for the situation. A fairly acidic soil has a pH of 4.50. Also, rust is essentially $Fe(OH)_3$. Therefore, she considered the following problem: Suppose a 1.00-g sample of iron(III) hydroxide is exposed to 1.00 L of a buffer with a pH of 4.50. She then calculated the nanograms of Fe^{3+} that dissolve in a liter of this buffer. Show how you would do this problem. Explain your work.

17.116 A 1.00-g sample of solid barium sulfate and a similar 1.00-g sample of solid calcium sulfate were added to water at 25°C to give 1.00 L of solution. Calculate the concentrations of Ba^{2+}, Ca^{2+}, and $SO_4{}^{2-}$ ions present in the solution.

17.117 Calcium fluoride, CaF_2, is a very slightly soluble salt. In Example 17.4, we calculated its solubility from the solubility constant, assuming that the solubility equilibrium represented by

K_{sp} was the only important one. However, a solution of the salt does contain the species HF. Where does this come from? Would you expect this to increase or decrease the solubility as we calculated it in the example? Using the fluoride-ion concentration that we calculated in the example, obtain the concentration of HF in the solution. From this, decide how important the formation of fluoride ion is in determining the solubility of calcium fluoride. Without doing any calculations, decide how important you think a similar effect would be in determining the solubility of calcium carbonate. Explain.

17.118 You slowly add ammonia, NH_3, to 1.00 L of water containing 5.00 g of solid nickel(II) iodate, $Ni(IO_3)_2$. How much ammonia (in moles) would you have to add to just dissolve the nickel(II) iodate? What would be the molar concentration of ammonia in the solution at that point? K_{sp} for nickel iodate is 1.4×10^{-8}.

Cumulative-Skills Problems

17.119 A solution is 1.5×10^{-4} M Zn^{2+} and 0.20 M $HSO_4{}^{-}$. The solution also contains Na_2SO_4. What should be the minimum molarity of Na_2SO_4 to prevent the precipitation of zinc sulfide when the solution is saturated with hydrogen sulfide (0.10 M H_2S)?

17.120 A solution is 1.8×10^{-4} M Co^{2+} and 0.20 M $HSO_4{}^{-}$. The solution also contains Na_2SO_4. What should be the minimum molarity of Na_2SO_4 to prevent the precipitation of cobalt(II) sulfide when the solution is saturated with hydrogen sulfide (0.10 M H_2S)?

17.121 What is the solubility of calcium fluoride in a buffer solution containing 0.45 M $HCHO_2$ (formic acid) and 0.20 M $NaCHO_2$? (*Hint:* Consider the equation $CaF_2(s) + 2H^+(aq) \rightleftharpoons Ca^{2+}(aq) + 2HF(aq)$, and solve the equilibrium problem.)

17.122 What is the solubility of magnesium fluoride in a buffer solution containing 0.45 M $HC_2H_3O_2$ (acetic acid) and 0.20 M $NaC_2H_3O_2$? The K_{sp} for magnesium fluoride is 6.5×10^{-9}. (See the hint for Problem 17.121.)

17.123 A 67.0-mL sample of 0.350 M $MgSO_4$ is added to 45.0 mL of 0.250 M $Ba(OH)_2$. What is the net ionic equation for the reaction that occurs? What are the concentrations of ions in the mixture at equilibrium?

17.124 A 50.0-mL sample of 0.0150 M Ag_2SO_4 is added to 25.0 mL of 0.0100 M $PbCl_2$. What is the net ionic equation for the reaction that occurs? What are the concentrations of ions in the mixture at equilibrium?

18

Thermodynamics and Equilibrium

The spontaneous reaction of iron with oxygen in air produces a coating of rust, a form of iron(III) oxide. Hematite, a mineral form of iron(III) oxide, is a commercial source of iron metal (produced from a spontanous reaction with carbon and oxygen).

Contents and Concepts

A spontaneous process is one that occurs by itself. As we will see, the entropy of a system and its surroundings increases in a spontaneous process.

In Section 18.2, we showed that the quantity $\Delta H - T\Delta S$ can function as a criterion for the spontaneity of a reaction at constant temperature, T, and pressure, P. By defining a quantity called the free energy $G = H - TS$, we find that ΔG equals this quantity $\Delta H - T\Delta S$, so the free energy gives us a thermodynamic criterion of spontaneity.

The total free energy of the substances in a reaction mixture decreases as the reaction proceeds. As we discuss, the standard free-energy change for a reaction is related to its equilibrium constant.

731

Urea, NH_2CONH_2, is an important industrial chemical. It is used to make synthetic resins for adhesives and melamine plastics (Figure 18.1). Its major use, however, is as a nitrogen fertilizer for plants. Urea is produced by reacting ammonia with carbon dioxide.

$$2NH_3(g) + CO_2(g) \longrightarrow NH_2CONH_2(aq) + H_2O(l)$$

Suppose you want to determine whether this or some other reaction could be useful for the industrial preparation of urea. Some of your immediate questions might be the following: Does the reaction naturally go in the direction it is written? Will the reaction mixture contain a sufficient amount of the product at equilibrium? We addressed these questions in the preceding chapters by looking at the equilibrium constant. Now we want to discuss these questions from the point of view of thermodynamics.

Thermodynamics is the study of the relationship between heat and other forms of energy involved in a chemical or physical process. With only heat measurements of substances, you can answer the questions just posed. You can predict the natural direction of a chemical reaction, and you can also determine the composition of a reaction mixture at equilibrium. Consider, then, the possibility of reacting NH_3 and CO_2 to give urea. Just how do you apply thermodynamics to such a reaction?

■ **See pages 759–760 for the Media Summary.**

FIGURE 18.1 ▲
Urea
Top: Urea is used as a plant fertilizer because it slowly decomposes in the soil to provide ammonia. *Bottom:* A molecular model of urea.

18.1 | First Law of Thermodynamics; Enthalpy

We introduced the thermodynamic property of enthalpy, H, in Chapter 6. There we noted that the change in enthalpy equals the heat of reaction at constant pressure. Now we want to look at this property again, but define it more precisely, in terms of the energy of the system. We begin by discussing the first law of thermodynamics.

First Law of Thermodynamics

Thermodynamics is normally described in terms of three laws. The first law of thermodynamics is essentially the law of conservation of energy applied to thermodynamic systems. < To state the law, you need to understand what the internal energy of a system is and how you can change the internal energy.

The **internal energy, U,** is *the sum of the kinetic and potential energies of the particles making up the system.* The kinetic energy includes the energy of motion of electrons, nuclei, and molecules. The potential energy results from the chemical bonding of atoms and from the attractions between molecules.

Internal energy is a **state function.** That is, it is *a property of a system that depends only on its present state, which is completely determined by variables such as temperature and pressure.* Thus, 1 mol of water at 0°C and 1 atm pressure has a definite quantity of energy. When a system changes from one state to another, its internal energy changes from one definite value to another. You can calculate the change in internal energy, ΔU, from the initial value of the internal energy, U_i, and the final value of the internal energy, U_f.

$$\Delta U = U_f - U_i$$

Normally you are interested in changes in internal energy rather than in absolute values. You measure these changes for a thermodynamic system by noting the exchanges of energy between the system and its surroundings. These exchanges of

According to the law of conservation of energy, the total energy remains constant; energy is neither created nor destroyed.

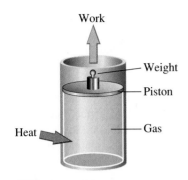

Work

Weight

Piston

Heat

Gas

FIGURE 18.2 ▲

Exchanges of heat and work with the surroundings
A gas is enclosed in a vessel with a piston. Heat flows into the vessel from the surroundings, which are at a higher temperature. As the temperature of the gas increases, the gas expands, lifting the weight (doing work).

The convention given here is that adopted by IUPAC (International Union of Pure and Applied Chemistry).

energy are of two kinds: heat and work. Heat, you will recall, is energy that moves into or out of the system because of a temperature difference between the system and its surroundings. **Work,** on the other hand, is *the energy exchange that results when a force F moves an object through a distance d; work (w) equals F × d.*

The distinction between heat and work is illustrated in the system shown in Figure 18.2. This system consists of a gas in a vessel equipped with a movable piston. On top of the piston is a weight, which you can consider as part of the surroundings. You momentarily fix the position of the piston so it does not move. Suppose the temperature of the surroundings is raised, and as a result, heat passes from the surroundings to the vessel. If you find that the energy of the surroundings decreases by 165 J in this way, you know from the law of conservation of energy that the internal energy of the system must have increased by just this quantity. You write $q = +165$ J, using the sign convention that heat (denoted by the symbol q) absorbed by the system is positive (energy is added to the system) and that heat evolved by the system is negative (energy is subtracted from the system).

As the temperature of the gas in the vessel increases, the gas pressure increases at fixed volume. You now allow the piston to move, so the gas expands and lifts the piston and the weight on top of it. In lifting the weight, the system does work. The energy gained by the weight equals the force of gravity on the weight times the height to which the weight was raised (the distance it was moved). Suppose this energy is 92 J. Because the surroundings, which include the weight, have gained 92 J of energy, the system must have lost 92 J of energy (energy cannot be created or destroyed). You write $w = -92$ J, adhering to the sign convention that work done *on* the system is positive (energy is added to the system) and work done *by* the system is negative (energy is subtracted from the system). <

The system in Figure 18.2 gains internal energy from the heat absorbed and loses internal energy via the work done. In general, the net change of internal energy equals heat plus work.

$$\Delta U = q + w$$

The **first law of thermodynamics** states that *the change in internal energy of a system, ΔU, equals $q + w$.* For the system shown in Figure 18.2,

$$\Delta U = (+165 \text{ J}) + (-92 \text{ J}) = +73 \text{ J}$$

Exercise 18.1   A gas is enclosed in a system similar to that shown in Figure 18.2. More weights are added to the piston, giving a total mass of 2.20 kg. As a result, the gas is compressed and the weights are lowered 0.250 m. At the same time, 1.50 J of heat evolves from (leaves) the system. What is the change in internal energy of the system, ΔU? The force of gravity on a mass m is mg, where g is the constant acceleration of gravity ($g = 9.80$ m/s²).

■ See Problems 18.31 and 18.32.

Heat of Reaction and Internal Energy

Now consider a chemical system—for example, the reaction of zinc metal with hydrochloric acid. The reaction is

$$Zn(s) + 2H_3O^+(aq) \longrightarrow Zn^{2+}(aq) + 2H_2O(l) + H_2(g)$$

When this reaction is carried out in a beaker open to the atmosphere, the reaction is exothermic, evolving 152.4 kJ of heat per mole of zinc consumed. You write $q_p = -152.4$ kJ, where the subscript p indicates that the process occurs at constant pressure (the pressure of the atmosphere).

FIGURE 18.3 ▲

Reaction of zinc metal with hydrochloric acid at constant pressure
(A) The beginning of the reaction. The constant pressure of the atmosphere has been replaced by a piston and weight to give an equivalent pressure. (B) The reaction produces hydrogen gas. This increases the volume of the system, so that the piston and weight are lifted upward. Work is done by the system on the piston and weight.

The hydrogen gas that is produced increases the volume of the system. As hydrogen is evolved, work must be done by the system to push back the atmosphere. How can you calculate this work? Imagine for the moment that the atmosphere is replaced by a piston and weights, whose downward force from gravity F creates a pressure on the gas equivalent to that of the atmosphere. The pressure P equals F divided by the cross-sectional area of the piston, A. (See Figure 18.3.)

Suppose the increase in volume of the system due to the production of hydrogen is ΔV. Because the volume of a cylinder equals its height h times its cross-sectional area A, the change in volume is $\Delta V = A \times h$, and $h = \Delta V/A$. The work done by the system in expanding equals the force of gravity times the distance the piston moves.

$$w = -F \times h = -F \times \frac{\Delta V}{A} = -\frac{F}{A} \times \Delta V$$

The negative sign is given because w is work done by the system and represents energy lost by it. Note that F/A is the pressure, P, which equals that of the atmosphere. Therefore,

$$w = -P\Delta V$$

This formula tells you that you can calculate the work done by a chemical reaction carried out in an open vessel by multiplying the atmospheric pressure P by the change in volume of the chemical system, ΔV. For example, when 1.00 mol Zn reacts with excess hydrochloric acid, 1.00 mol H_2 is produced. At 25°C and 1.00 atm ($= 1.01 \times 10^5$ Pa), this amount of H_2 occupies 24.5 L ($= 24.5 \times 10^{-3}$ m³). The work done by the chemical system in pushing back the atmosphere is

$$w = -P\Delta V = -(1.01 \times 10^5 \text{ Pa}) \times (24.5 \times 10^{-3} \text{ m}^3)$$
$$= -2.47 \times 10^3 \text{ J, or } -2.47 \text{ kJ}$$

If you apply the first law to this chemical system, you can relate the change in internal energy of the system to the heat of reaction. You have

$$\Delta U = q_p + w = q_p - P\Delta V$$

For the reaction of Zn with HCl, $q_p = -152.4$ kJ and $w = -P\Delta V = -2.47$ kJ, so

$$\Delta U = -152.4 \text{ kJ} - 2.47 \text{ kJ} = -154.9 \text{ kJ}$$

We can now summarize what happens when 1.00 mol Zn reacts with excess hydrochloric acid. When the reaction occurs, the internal energy changes as the kinetic and potential energies change in going from reactants to products. This energy change, ΔU, equals -154.9 kJ. Energy leaves the system mostly as heat ($q_p = -152.4$ kJ) but partly as expansion work ($w = -2.47$ kJ).

Exercise 18.2   Consider the combustion (burning) of methane, CH_4, in oxygen.

$$CH_4(g) + 2O_2(g) \longrightarrow CO_2(g) + 2H_2O(l)$$

The heat of reaction at 25°C and 1.00 atm is -890.2 kJ. What is the change in volume when 1.00 mol CH_4 reacts with 2.00 mol O_2? (You can ignore the volume of liquid water, which is insignificant compared with volumes of gases.) What is w for this change? Calculate ΔU for the change indicated by the chemical equation.

■ See Problems 18.33 and 18.34.

Enthalpy and Enthalpy Change

In Chapter 6, we defined enthalpy tentatively in terms of the relationship of ΔH to the heat of reaction at constant pressure, q_p. We now define **enthalpy, H,** precisely as *the quantity $U + PV$*. Because U, P, and V are state functions, H is also a state function. This means that for a given temperature and pressure, a given amount of a substance has a definite enthalpy. Therefore, if you know the enthalpies of substances, you can calculate the change of enthalpy, ΔH, for a reaction.

Let us now show the relationship of ΔH to the heat of reaction q_p. Note that ΔH is the final enthalpy H_f minus the initial enthalpy H_i.

$$\Delta H = H_f - H_i$$

Now, substitute defining expressions for H_f and H_i, using the subscripts f and i to indicate *final* and *initial*, respectively. Note, however, that the pressure is constant.

$$\Delta H = (U_f + PV_f) - (U_i + PV_i) = (U_f - U_i) + P(V_f - V_i) = \Delta U + P\Delta V$$

Earlier we found that $\Delta U = q_p - P\Delta V$. Hence,

$$\Delta H = (q_p - P\Delta V) + P\Delta V = q_p$$

This shows that $\Delta H = q_p$, as noted in Chapter 6.

In practice, what you do is measure certain heats of reaction and use them to tabulate enthalpies of formation, ΔH_f°. The standard enthalpy change for a reaction is

$$\Delta H^\circ = \Sigma\, n\Delta H_f^\circ(\text{products}) - \Sigma\, m\Delta H_f^\circ(\text{reactants})$$

Standard enthalpies of formation for selected substances and ions are listed in Table 6.2 and in Appendix C.

Suppose you would like to know how much heat is absorbed or evolved in the reaction between NH_3 and CO_2 to produce urea and water, which is the reaction given in the chapter opening. The following are standard enthalpies of formation at 25°C for the substances indicated (in kJ/mol): $NH_3(g)$, -45.9; $CO_2(g)$, -393.5; $NH_2CONH_2(aq)$, -319.2; $H_2O(l)$, -285.8. Substituting into the previous equation yields

$$\Delta H^\circ = [(-319.2 - 285.8) - (-2 \times 45.9 - 393.5)]\ \text{kJ} = -119.7\ \text{kJ}$$

From the minus sign in the value of ΔH°, you conclude that heat is evolved. The reaction is exothermic.

Spontaneous process

Nonspontaneous process

FIGURE 18.4 ▲

Examples of a spontaneous and a nonspontaneous process
Top: The rolling of a rock downhill is a spontaneous process. The rock eventually comes to equilibrium at the bottom of the hill. *Bottom:* The rolling of a rock uphill is a nonspontaneous process.

Spontaneous Processes and Entropy

Why does a chemical reaction go naturally in a particular direction? To answer this question, we need to look at spontaneous processes. A **spontaneous process** is *a physical or chemical change that occurs by itself*. It requires no continuing outside agency to make it happen. A rock at the top of a hill rolls down (Figure 18.4, *top*). Heat flows from a hot object to a cold one. An iron object rusts in moist air (Figure 18.5). These processes occur spontaneously, or naturally, without requiring an outside force or agency. They continue until equilibrium is reached. If these processes were to go in the opposite direction, they would be *nonspontaneous*. The rolling of a rock uphill by itself is not a natural process; it is nonspontaneous (see Figure 18.4, *bottom*). The rock could be moved to the top of the hill, but work would have to be expended. Heat can be made to flow from a cold to a hot object, but a heat pump or refrigerator is needed. Rust can be converted to iron, but the process requires chemical reactions used in the manufacture of iron from its ore (iron oxide).

FIGURE 18.5 ▲

The rusting of iron in moist air is a spontaneous reaction

This sculpture by Picasso in Chicago (Daley Plaza) was allowed to rust to give a pleasing effect.

18.2 | Entropy and the Second Law of Thermodynamics

When you ask whether a chemical reaction goes in the direction in which it is written, as we did in the chapter opening, you are asking whether the reaction is spontaneous in this direction. The first law of thermodynamics cannot help you answer such a question. It does help you keep track of the various forms of energy in a chemical change, using the constancy of total energy (conservation of energy). But although at one time it was thought that spontaneous reactions must be exothermic ($\Delta H < 0$), many spontaneous reactions are now known to be endothermic ($\Delta H > 0$); recall the reaction shown in Figure 6.1.

The second law of thermodynamics, which we will discuss in this section, provides a way to answer questions about the spontaneity of a reaction. The second law is expressed in terms of a quantity called *entropy*.

Entropy

Entropy, S, is *a thermodynamic quantity that is a measure of how dispersed the energy of a system is among the different possible ways that system can contain energy.* When the energy of a thermodynamic system is concentrated in a relatively few energy states, the entropy of the system is low. When that same energy, however, is dispersed or spread out over a great many energy states, the entropy of the system is high. What you will see is that the entropy (energy dispersal) of a system plus its surroundings increases in a spontaneous process.

Let's look at some simple spontaneous processes. Suppose you place a hot cup of coffee on the table. Heat energy from the hot coffee flows slowly to the table and to the air surrounding the cup. In this process, energy spreads out or disperses. The entropy of the system (coffee cup) and its surroundings (table and surrounding air) increases in this spontaneous process.

As a slightly more complicated example, consider a rock at the top of a hill. The rock has potential energy relative to what it would have at the bottom of the hill. Imagine the rock rolling downhill. As it does so, its potential energy changes to kinetic energy, and during its descent atoms of the rock collide with those of the hillside and surrounding air, dispersing energy from the rock to its surroundings. The entropy of the system (rock) plus its surroundings (hillside and surrounding air) increases in this spontaneous process.

As a final example, imagine a flask containing a gas connected to an evacuated flask by a valve or stopcock (Figure 18.6). When the valve is opened, gas in the flask flows into the space of the evacuated flask. In this case, the kinetic energy of the gas molecules spreads out or disperses over the volumes of both flasks. The entropy of this system (both flasks) increases in this spontaneous process. In this case, we assume that the surroundings do not participate in the overall change (there is no entropy change in the surroundings); the entropy change occurs entirely within the system.

In each of these spontaneous processes, energy has been dispersed, or spread out. The entropy of the system plus surroundings has increased.

As we will discuss later, the SI unit of entropy is joules per kelvin (J/K). Entropy, like enthalpy, is a state function. That is, the quantity of entropy in a given amount of substance depends only on variables, such as temperature and pressure, that determine the state of the substance. If these variables are fixed, the quantity of entropy is fixed. For example, 1 mol of ice at 0°C and 1 atm pressure has an entropy that has been determined experimentally to be 41 J/K. One mole of liquid water at 0°C and 1 atm has an entropy of 63 J/K. (In the next section, we will describe how you measure

FIGURE 18.6 ▶

Expansion of a gas into a vacuum

Initially, the flask on the left contains a gas, whereas the flask on the right is evacuated. Then the valve is opened and gas spontaneously flows into the evacuated flask (the vacuum).

Stopcock closed

Vacuum

Stopcock open

these values.) Why is the entropy of liquid water higher than that of solid water (ice)? In an ice crystal, water molecules occupy regular fixed positions in the crystal lattice. Molecules can vibrate or oscillate about these fixed positions, but otherwise are restricted in their motions, and therefore the energies available to them. In the liquid state, water molecules can rotate as well as vibrate internally and can move around somewhat (though not as freely as molecules can move in the gaseous state). Thus, the entropy of liquid water is expected to be higher than that of ice—the energy is dispersed over more available energy states in the liquid.

You calculate the entropy change, ΔS, for a process similarly to the way you calculate ΔH. If S_i is the initial entropy and S_f is the final entropy, the change in entropy is

$$\Delta S = S_f - S_i$$

For the melting of ice to liquid water,

$$H_2O(s) \longrightarrow H_2O(l)$$
$$\Delta S = (63 - 41) \text{ J/K} = 22 \text{ J/K}$$

When 1 mol of ice melts at 0°C, the water increases in entropy by 22 J/K. The entropy increases, as you expect, because the energy of water becomes more dispersed when it melts.

Concept Check 18.1

You have a sample of 1.0 mg of solid iodine at room temperature. Later, you notice that the iodine has sublimed (passed into the vapor state). What can you say about the change of entropy of the iodine?

Second Law of Thermodynamics

A process occurs naturally as a result of the dispersal of energy in the system plus surroundings. We can state this precisely in terms of the **second law of thermodynamics,** which states that *the total entropy of a system and its surroundings always increases for a spontaneous process.* Note that entropy (energy dispersal) is quite different from energy itself. Energy can be neither created nor destroyed during a spontaneous, or natural, process—its total amount remains fixed. But energy is dispersed in a spontaneous process, which means that entropy is produced (or created) during such a process.

For a spontaneous process carried out at a given temperature, the second law can be restated in a form that refers only to the system (and not to the system plus surroundings, as in the previous statement of the second law). We will find this new statement particularly useful in analyzing chemical problems.

Suppose a spontaneous process occurs within a system that is in thermal contact with its surroundings at a given temperature T—say, a chemical reaction in a flask. As the chemical reaction occurs, entropy is produced (or created) within the system (the flask) as a result of this spontaneous process. At the same time, heat might flow into or out of the system as a result of the thermal contact. (In other words, the reaction may be endothermic or exothermic.) *Heat flow is also a flow of entropy, because it is a dispersal of energy,* either into the flask or outside of it. In general, the entropy change associated with a flow of heat q at an absolute temperature T can be shown to equal q/T. The *net change* of entropy in the system (in the flask) is the entropy created during the spontaneous chemical reaction that occurs plus the entropy change that is associated with the heat flow (entropy flow).

$$\Delta S = \text{entropy created} + \frac{q}{T}$$

It might be helpful to consider an analogy. A baker makes (creates) cookies at her store (the system). She also buys cookies from a wholesaler and sells cookies at her store. The change in number of cookies in her store in any given interval of time equals the number made (number created) plus the number bought minus the number sold (flow of cookies into or out of her store). We obtain an equation similar to the one we wrote for the entropy change, ΔS.

Change of cookies in store = cookies created + flow of cookies into or out of store

However, our analogy breaks down if someone eats cookies in the store. Whereas entropy can only be created, cookies can be created and destroyed (eaten).

The quantity of entropy created during a spontaneous process is a positive quantity—the entropy increases as it is created. If we delete "entropy created" from the right side of the equation for ΔS, we know that the left side is then greater than the right side:

$$\Delta S > \frac{q}{T}$$

We can now restate the second law as follows:

Second Law of Thermodynamics: *For a spontaneous process at a given temperature T, the change in entropy of the system is greater than the heat divided by the absolute temperature, q/T.*

Entropy and Molecular Disorder

Fundamentally, entropy is related to energy dispersal. The energy of a molecular system may at first be concentrated in a few energy states and then later dispersed among many more energy states. In such a case, the entropy of the system increases. You might also say that the molecular system has increased in "disorder," in the sense that the energy is strewn or distributed over many energy states, rather than concentrated in a few energy states.

Consider the pendulum depicted in Figure 18.7. Suppose you start the pendulum by moving it up and releasing it. The pendulum begins to swing to and fro.

FIGURE 18.7 ▶

Motion of a pendulum
A to *C* depicts the spontaneous motion of the pendulum. (*A*) A pendulum is placed in motion. Molecules of the pendulum (red spheres) move in the same direction (but with thermal motions superimposed on this concerted motion). (*B*) As a result of collisions of the pendulum with air molecules (blue spheres), some of the concerted motion is degraded to random motion of surrounding air molecules. (*C*) Eventually, the pendulum comes to rest with its energy dispersed. *D* to *F* depicts the nonspontaneous motion of a pendulum. (*D*) The pendulum at rest is surrounded by air molecules in random motion. (*E*) By chance, a group of air molecules gather together to buffet the pendulum on one side. (*F*) The pendulum starts moving. Although *E* to *F* is not impossible, it is highly unlikely.

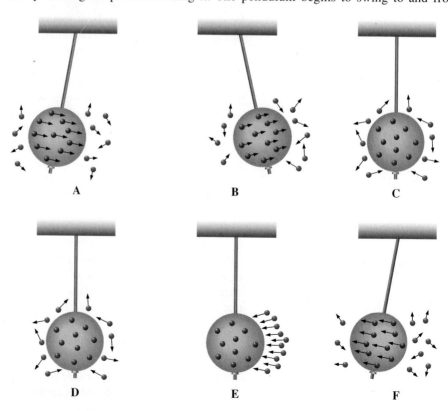

A   B   C

D   E   F

On each swing, it moves through a smaller and smaller arc, eventually coming to rest. While the pendulum is moving, its atoms have a concerted motion, which is the kinetic energy of the pendulum (Figure 18.7A). All of the atoms of the pendulum are moving in the same direction, though with small oscillational motions (or thermal motions) superimposed on this concerted motion. As these atoms collide with molecules of the surrounding air, however, some of this concerted motion is transferred to the random motion of air molecules (Figure 18.7B). Air molecules buffeted by the pendulum begin to move with it, but soon, their motions become random as they collide with many other air molecules. The molecular motion becomes more disordered. Eventually, the pendulum comes to rest with its energy dispersed, partly to the surrounding air (Figure 18.7C). Entropy has increased.

Imagine that you had captured this motion on film or video, and later you show this film in reverse. The pendulum, initially at rest, begins to swing through larger and larger arcs. This motion is clearly not what you would expect to see. A pendulum at rest does not spontaneously begin to move to and fro. Let's look at this process in molecular detail. At first the pendulum is at rest with surrounding molecules of air in random motion (Figure 18.7D). Then, by chance a large number of air molecules gather together to buffet the stationary pendulum (Figure 18.7E). Molecules of air, at first moving randomly, begin to move together, and start the pendulum moving upward (Figure 18.7F). What does thermodynamics have to say about this process? Note that this process does not violate the first law; energy remains constant; it merely exchanges from one molecule to another. This process does violate the second law, however. Energy dispersed over many energy states (molecules moving randomly) becomes more concentrated in those states in which the molecules move together. A disordered state becomes ordered, and entropy decreases. This process is nonspontaneous.

Let's look at a few other examples. Earlier we considered the cooling of a cup of coffee. Heat moves from the hot coffee to its surroundings. Molecular motion becomes more disordered, in the sense that it is dispersed over a larger volume. Similarly, when a gas flows from a flask into a connected evacuated flask, molecules become more disordered in the sense that they are strewn over a larger volume. When ice melts, water molecules leave an ordered crystal and enter a more disordered liquid state. As a final example, consider the chemical reaction in which dinitrogen tetroxide, N_2O_4, dissociates into two nitrogen dioxide molecules, NO_2:

$$N_2O_4(g) \longrightarrow 2NO_2(g)$$

The reaction, in breaking one molecule into two smaller ones, creates more disorder in the sense that the two NO_2 molecules can now move independently. In each of these changes, molecular disorder increases, as does entropy.

Unfortunately, the picture of entropy as a measure of disorder has been misapplied to situations that are not molecular. For example, imagine your desk with books and papers placed carefully to give an "orderly" arrangement. Later, as you work, your books and papers become strewn about—your desk becomes disordered. This has sometimes been described as a spontaneous process in which entropy increases. Of course, the books and papers do not move spontaneously—you move them. In fact, there is essentially no difference between the thermodynamic entropies of the ordered and disordered desks. All that has happened is that normal-sized objects (books and papers) have been moved by you from human-defined order to human-defined disorder.

Again, fundamentally entropy is related to the dispersal of energy. The entropy of a system can be defined rigorously by the methods of *statistical thermodynamics* in terms of a sum over the energy levels available to the system. The picture of thermodynamic entropy as disorder may sometimes be useful, but it should be applied carefully to molecular systems.

Entropy Change for a Phase Transition

Certain processes occur at equilibrium or, more precisely, very close to equilibrium. For example, ice at 0°C is in equilibrium with liquid water at 0°C. If heat is slowly absorbed by the system, it remains very near equilibrium, but the ice melts. Under these essentially equilibrium conditions, no significant amount of entropy is created. The entropy change results entirely from the absorption of heat. Therefore,

$$\Delta S = \frac{q}{T} \quad \text{(equilibrium process)}$$

When a system is at equilibrium, a small change in a condition can make the process go in one direction or the other. The process is said to be reversible. Think of a two-pan balance in which the weight on each pan has been adjusted to make the balance beam level—that is, so the beam is at equilibrium. A small weight on either pan will tip the scale one way or the other.

Other phase changes, such as the vaporization of a liquid, also occur under equilibrium conditions. <

You can use the previous equation to obtain the entropy change for a phase change. Consider the melting of ice. The heat absorbed is the heat of fusion, ΔH_{fus}, which is known from experiment to be 6.0 kJ for 1 mol of ice. You get the entropy change for melting by dividing ΔH_{fus} by the absolute temperature of the phase transition, 273 K (0°C). Because entropy changes are usually expressed in joules per kelvin, you convert ΔH_{fus} to 6.0×10^3 J.

$$\Delta S = \frac{\Delta H_{fus}}{T} = \frac{6.0 \times 10^3 \text{ J}}{273 \text{ K}} = 22 \text{ J/K}$$

Note that this is the ΔS value we obtained earlier for the conversion of ice to water.

Example 18.1 | Calculating the Entropy Change for a Phase Transition

The heat of vaporization, ΔH_{vap}, of carbon tetrachloride, CCl_4, at 25°C is 39.4 kJ/mol.

$$CCl_4(l) \longrightarrow CCl_4(g); \Delta H_{vap} = 39.4 \text{ kJ/mol}$$

If 1 mol of liquid carbon tetrachloride at 25°C has an entropy of 216 J/K, what is the entropy of 1 mol of the vapor in equilibrium with the liquid at this temperature?

Problem Strategy The entropy change for this equilibrium vaporization is $\Delta H_{vap}/T$. The entropy of the vapor equals the entropy of the liquid plus the entropy change.

Solution When liquid CCl_4 evaporates, it absorbs heat: $\Delta H_{vap} = 39.4$ kJ/mol (39.4×10^3 J/mol) at 25°C, or 298 K. The entropy change, ΔS, is

$$\Delta S = \frac{\Delta H_{vap}}{T} = \frac{39.4 \times 10^3 \text{ J/mol}}{298 \text{ K}} = 132 \text{ J/(mol·K)}$$

In other words, 1 mol of carbon tetrachloride increases in entropy by 132 J/K when it vaporizes. The entropy of

1 mol of the vapor equals the entropy of 1 mol of liquid (216 J/K) plus 132 J/K.

Entropy of vapor = (216 + 132)J/(mol·K) = **348 J/(mol·K)**

Note: This is the entropy at the equilibrium vapor pressure, which differs from $S°$ (entropy at 1 atm).

Answer Check A simple check is to reverse the problem. At equilibrium, the enthalpy change, ΔH, equals $T\Delta S$.

$$\Delta H = 298 \text{ K} \times 132 \text{ J/(mol·K)} = 39.3 \times 10^3 \text{ J/mol}$$

This is the enthalpy of vaporization given in the problem statement (within rounding error).

Exercise 18.3 Liquid ethanol, $C_2H_5OH(l)$, at 25°C has an entropy of 161 J/(mol·K). If the heat of vaporization, ΔH_{vap}, at 25°C is 42.6 kJ/mol, what is the entropy of the vapor in equilibrium with the liquid at 25°C?

■ See Problems 18.35 and 18.36.

Criterion for a Spontaneous Reaction

Now you can see how thermodynamics is applied to the question of whether a reaction is spontaneous. Suppose that you propose a chemical reaction for the preparation of a substance. You also assume that the reaction occurs at constant temperature and pressure. For urea, you propose the reaction

$$2NH_3(g) + CO_2(g) \longrightarrow NH_2CONH_2(aq) + H_2O(l)$$

Is this a spontaneous reaction? That is, does it go left to right as written? You can use the second law in the form $\Delta S > q/T$ to answer this question if you know both ΔH and ΔS for the reaction.

Recall that the heat of reaction at constant pressure, q_p, equals the enthalpy change ΔH. The second law for a spontaneous reaction at constant temperature and pressure becomes

$$\Delta S > \frac{q_p}{T} = \frac{\Delta H}{T} \qquad \text{(spontaneous reaction, constant } T \text{ and } P\text{)}$$

ΔS is greater than $\Delta H/T$ for a spontaneous reaction at constant temperature and pressure. Therefore, if you subtract ΔS from $\Delta H/T$, you get a negative quantity. That is,

$$\frac{\Delta H}{T} - \Delta S < 0 \qquad \text{(spontaneous reaction, constant } T \text{ and } P\text{)}$$

Multiplying each term of this inequality by the positive quantity T, you get

$$\Delta H - T\Delta S < 0 \qquad \text{(spontaneous reaction, constant } T \text{ and } P\text{)}$$

This inequality is important. If you have a table of entropies of substances, you can calculate ΔS for the proposed reaction. From Table 6.2, you can also calculate ΔH. If $\Delta H - T\Delta S$ is negative for the reaction, you would predict that it is spontaneous left to right, as written. However, if $\Delta H - T\Delta S$ is positive, you would predict that the reaction is nonspontaneous in the direction written but spontaneous in the opposite direction. If $\Delta H - T\Delta S$ is zero, the reaction is at equilibrium.

18.3

Standard Entropies and the Third Law of Thermodynamics

Heat capacity was discussed in Section 6.6.

To determine experimentally the entropy of a substance, you first measure the heat absorbed by the substance by warming it at various temperatures. That is, you find the heat capacity at different temperatures. < You then calculate the entropy as we will describe. This determination of the entropy is based on the third law of thermodynamics.

Third Law of Thermodynamics

The **third law of thermodynamics** states that *a substance that is perfectly crystalline at 0 K has an entropy of zero*. This seems reasonable. A perfectly crystalline substance at 0 K should have perfect order. When the temperature is raised, however, the substance increases in entropy as it absorbs heat and energy disperses through it.

You can determine the entropy of a substance at a temperature other than 0 K—say, at 298 K (25°C)—by slowly heating the substance from near 0 K to 298 K. Recall that the entropy change ΔS that occurs when heat is absorbed at a temperature T is q/T. Suppose you heat the substance from near 0.0 K to 2.0 K, and the heat absorbed is 0.19J. You find the entropy change by dividing the heat absorbed by the average absolute temperature $[\frac{1}{2}(0.0 + 2.0)K = 1.0 \text{ K}]$. Therefore, ΔS equals 0.19 J/1.0 K = 0.19 J/K. This gives you the entropy of the substance at 2.0 K. Now you heat the substance from 2.0 K to 4.0 K, and this time 0.88 J of heat is absorbed. The average temperature is $\frac{1}{2}(2.0 + 4.0)K = 3.0 \text{ K}$, and the entropy change is 0.88 J/3.0 K = 0.29 J/K.

FIGURE 18.8 ▶

Standard entropy of bromine, Br₂, at various temperatures
The entropy rises gradually as the temperature increases, but it jumps sharply at each phase transition.

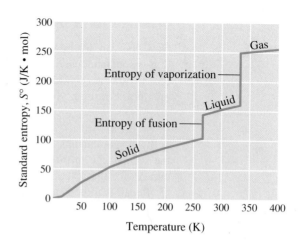

The process just described is essentially the numerical evaluation of an integral, which you can obtain as follows: The heat absorbed for temperature change dT is $C_p(T)dT$, and the entropy change is $C_p(T)dT/T$. The standard entropy at temperature T is

$$\int_0^T \frac{C_p(T)dT}{T}$$

Entropies of substances must be positive. Those for ions, however, can be negative because they are derived in a different way by arbitrarily setting S° for $H_3O^+(aq)$ equal to zero.

The entropy of the substance at 4.0 K is $(0.19 + 0.29)$ J/K = 0.48 J/K. Proceeding this way, you can eventually get the entropy at 298 K. <

Figure 18.8 shows how the entropy of a substance changes with temperature. Note that the entropy increases gradually as the temperature increases. But when there is a phase change (for example, from solid to liquid), the entropy increases sharply. The entropy change for the phase transition is calculated from the enthalpy of the phase transition, as described earlier (see Example 18.1). The **standard entropy** of a substance or ion (Table 18.1), also called its **absolute entropy,** $S°$, is *the entropy value for the standard state of the species* (indicated by the superscript degree sign). For a substance, the standard state is the pure substance at 1 atm pressure. For a species in solution, the standard state is the 1 M solution. Table 18.1 gives standard entropies of various substances at 25°C and 1 atm. Note that the elements have nonzero values, unlike standard enthalpies of formation, $\Delta H_f°$, which by convention are zero. The symbol $S°$, rather than $\Delta S°$, is chosen for standard entropies to emphasize that they originate from the third law. <

Entropy Change for a Reaction

Once you determine the standard entropies of all substances in a reaction, you can calculate the change of entropy, $\Delta S°$, for the reaction. A sample calculation is described in Example 18.3. Even without knowing values for the entropies of substances, you can sometimes predict the sign of $\Delta S°$ for a reaction. The entropy usually increases in the following situations:

1. A reaction in which a molecule is broken into two or more smaller molecules.

2. A reaction in which there is an increase in moles of gas. (This may result from a molecule breaking up, in which case Rules 1 and 2 are related.)

3. A process in which a solid changes to liquid or gas or a liquid changes to a gas.

Example 18.2 | Predicting the Sign of the Entropy Change of a Reaction

a. The following equation represents the essential change that takes place during the fermentation of glucose (grape sugar) to ethanol (ethyl alcohol).

$$C_6H_{12}O_6(s) \longrightarrow 2C_2H_5OH(l) + 2CO_2(g)$$
glucose   ethanol

Is $S°$ positive or negative? Explain.

b. Do you expect the entropy to increase or decrease in the preparation of urea from NH_3 and CO_2?

$$2NH_3(g) + CO_2(g) \longrightarrow NH_2CONH_2(aq) + H_2O(l)$$

Explain.

(continued)

TABLE 18.1	**Standard Entropies (at 25°C)***				
Substance or Ion	S_f° J/(mol·K)	Substance or Ion	S_f° J/(mol·K)	Substance or Ion	S_f° J/(mol·K)
$e^-(g)$	20.87	*Aldehydes (continued)*		**Nitrogen** *(continued)*	
Bromine		$CH_3CHO(g)$	246.4	$NO_2(g)$	239.9
$Br(g)$	174.9	$CH_3CHO(l)$	160.4	$HNO_3(aq)$	146.4
$Br^-(aq)$	82.4	**Chlorine**		**Oxygen**	
$Br^-(g)$	163.4	$Cl(g)$	165.1	$O(g)$	160.9
$Br_2(g)$	245.3	$Cl^-(aq)$	56.5	$O_2(g)$	205.0
$Br_2(l)$	152.2	$Cl^-(g)$	153.2	$O_3(g)$	238.8
$HBr(g)$	198.6	$Cl_2(g)$	223.0	$OH^-(aq)$	−10.75
Calcium		$HCl(g)$	186.8	$H_2O(g)$	188.7
$Ca(s)$	41.59	**Fluorine**		$H_2O(l)$	69.95
$Ca^{2+}(aq)$	−53.1	$F(g)$	158.6	**Silicon**	
$CaCO_3(s, \text{calcite})$	92.9	$F^-(g)$	145.5	$Si(s)$	18.82
$CaO(s)$	38.21	$F^-(aq)$	−13.8	$SiCl_4(l)$	239.7
Carbon		$F_2(g)$	202.7	$SiF_4(g)$	282.7
$C(g)$	158.0	$HF(g)$	173.7	$SiO_2(s, \text{quartz})$	41.46
$C(s, \text{diamond})$	2.377	**Hydrogen**		**Silver**	
$C(s, \text{graphite})$	5.740	$H(g)$	114.6	$Ag(s)$	42.55
$CCl_4(g)$	309.7	$H^+(aq)$	0	$Ag^+(aq)$	72.68
$CCl_4(l)$	216.4	$H^+(g)$	108.8	$AgBr(s)$	107.1
$CO(g)$	197.5	$H_2(g)$	130.6	$AgCl(s)$	96.2
$CO_2(g)$	213.7	**Iodine**		$AgF(s)$	83.7
$CO_3^{2-}(aq)$	−56.9	$I(g)$	180.7	$AgI(s)$	115.5
$CS_2(g)$	237.9	$I^-(aq)$	109.6	**Sodium**	
$CS_2(l)$	151.3	$I^-(g)$	169.2	$Na(g)$	153.6
$HCN(g)$	201.7	$I_2(s)$	116.1	$Na(s)$	51.46
$HCN(l)$	112.8	$HI(g)$	206.5	$Na^+(aq)$	59.1
$HCO_3^-(aq)$	91.2	**Lead**		$Na^+(g)$	147.8
Hydrocarbons		$Pb(s)$	64.78	$Na_2CO_3(s)$	138.8
$CH_4(g)$	186.1	$Pb^{2+}(aq)$	10.5	$NaCl(s)$	72.12
$C_2H_4(g)$	219.2	$PbO(s)$	66.32	$NaHCO_3(s)$	101.7
$C_2H_6(g)$	229.5	$PbS(s)$	91.34	**Sulfur**	
$C_6H_6(l)$	173.4	**Nitrogen**		$S(g)$	167.7
Alcohols		$N(g)$	153.2	$S(s, \text{monoclinic})$	33.03
$CH_3OH(l)$	126.8	$N_2(g)$	191.6	$S(s, \text{rhombic})$	32.06
$C_2H_5OH(l)$	160.7	$NH_3(g)$	192.7	$S_2(g)$	228.1
Aldehydes		$NH_4^+(aq)$	113.4	$SO_2(g)$	248.1
$HCHO(g)$	219.0	$NO(g)$	210.6	$H_2S(g)$	205.6

*See Appendix C for additional values.

(continued)

c. What is the sign of $\Delta S°$ for the following reaction?

$$CO(g) + H_2O(g) \longrightarrow CO_2(g) + H_2(g)$$

Problem Strategy Compare the reactants and products in each reaction. Look for the following: molecules breaking into smaller parts or aggregrating into larger parts, moles of gas increasing or decreasing, and changes of state. Then apply the three rules preceding this example.

Solution a. A molecule (glucose) breaks into smaller molecules (C_2H_5OH and CO_2). Moreover, this results in a gas being released. You predict that $\Delta S°$ for this reaction is **positive.** That is, the entropy increases.

b. In this reaction, the moles of gas decrease (by 3 mol), which would decrease the entropy. You predict that the entropy should **decrease.** That is, $\Delta S°$ is negative.

c. Because there is no change in the number of moles of gas, **you cannot predict the sign of $\Delta S°$ from the rules given.**

Answer Check Review the situations listed before this example, and note that the entropy increases whenever a molecule breaks up, moles of gas increase, or a phase change occurs from solid to liquid or from liquid to gas.

Exercise 18.4 Predict the sign of $\Delta S°$ for each of the following reactions.

a. $CaCO_3(s) \longrightarrow CaO(s) + CO_2(g)$
b. $CS_2(l) \longrightarrow CS_2(g)$
c. $2Hg(l) + O_2(g) \longrightarrow 2HgO(s)$
d. $2Na_2O_2(s) + 2H_2O(l) \longrightarrow 4NaOH(aq) + O_2(g)$

■ See Problems 18.39 and 18.40.

It is useful to be able to predict the sign of $\Delta S°$. You gain some understanding of the reaction, and you can use the prediction for qualitative work. For quantitative work, however, you need to find the value of $\Delta S°$. You can find the standard change of entropy, $\Delta S°$, for a reaction by subtracting the standard entropies of reactants from the standard entropies of products, similar to the way you obtained $\Delta H°$.

$$\Delta S° = \Sigma \, nS°(\text{products}) - \Sigma \, mS°(\text{reactants})$$

The next example illustrates the calculations.

Example 18.3 | Calculating $\Delta S°$ for a Reaction

Calculate the change of entropy, $\Delta S°$, at 25°C for the reaction in which urea is formed from NH_3 and CO_2.

$$2NH_3(g) + CO_2(g) \longrightarrow NH_2CONH_2(aq) + H_2O(l)$$

The standard entropy of $NH_2CONH_2(aq)$ is 174 J/(mol·K). See Table 18.1 for other values.

Problem Strategy The calculation is similar to that used to obtain $\Delta H°$ from $\Delta H_f°$ values.

Solution It is convenient to put the standard entropy values multiplied by stoichiometric coefficients below the formulas in the balanced equation.

$$2NH_3(g) + CO_2(g) \longrightarrow NH_2CONH_2(aq) + H_2O(l)$$
$$S°: 2 \times 193 \quad 214 \qquad\qquad 174 \qquad\quad 70$$

You calculate the entropy change by subtracting the entropy of the reactants from the entropy of the products.

$$\Delta S° = \Sigma \, nS°(\text{products}) - \Sigma \, mS°(\text{reactants})$$
$$= [(174 + 70) - (2 \times 193 + 214)] \text{ J/K} = -356 \text{ J/K}$$

Answer Check Carefully review your arithmetic. Also, note that moles of gas decrease, so we expect that the entropy decreases (and, thus, the sign should be negative; see Example 18.2b).

Exercise 18.5 Calculate the change of entropy, $\Delta S°$, for the reaction given in Example 18.2a. The standard entropy of glucose, $C_6H_{12}O_6(s)$, is 212 J/(mol·K). See Table 18.1 for other values.

■ See Problems 18.41 and 18.42.

Free-Energy Concept

At the end of Section 18.2, you saw that the quantity $\Delta H - T\Delta S$ can serve as a criterion for spontaneity of a reaction at constant temperature and pressure. If the value of this quantity is negative, the reaction is spontaneous. If it is positive, the reaction is nonspontaneous. If it equals zero, the reaction is at equilibrium.

As an application of this criterion, consider the reaction described in the chapter opening, in which urea is prepared from NH_3 and CO_2. The heat of reaction $\Delta H°$ was calculated from enthalpies of formation in Section 18.1, where we obtained -119.7 kJ. Then, in Example 18.3, we calculated the entropy of reaction $\Delta S°$ and found a value of -356 J/K, or -0.356 kJ/K. Substitute these values and $T = 298$ K (25°C) into the expression $\Delta H° - T\Delta S°$.

$$\Delta H° - T\Delta S° = (-119.7 \text{ kJ}) - (298 \text{ K})(-0.356 \text{ kJ/K}) = -13.6 \text{ kJ}$$

We see that $\Delta H° - T\Delta S°$ is a negative quantity, from which we conclude that the reaction is spontaneous under standard conditions.

18.4 | Free Energy and Spontaneity

It is very convenient to define a new thermodynamic quantity in terms of H and S that will be directly useful as a criterion of spontaneity. For this purpose, the American physicist J. Willard Gibbs (1839–1903) introduced the concept of **free energy, G,** which is *a thermodynamic quantity defined by the equation* $G = H - TS$. This quantity gives a direct criterion for spontaneity of reaction. <

As a reaction proceeds at a given temperature and pressure, reactants form products and the enthalpy H and entropy S change. These changes in H and S, denoted ΔH and ΔS, result in a change in free energy, ΔG, given by the equation

$$\Delta G = \Delta H - T\Delta S$$

The quantity G is called Gibbs energy, Gibbs free energy, or the Gibbs function—hence the symbol G.

Note that the change in free energy, ΔG, equals the quantity $\Delta H - T\Delta S$ that you just saw serves as a criterion for spontaneity of a reaction. Thus, if you can show that ΔG for a reaction at a given temperature and pressure is negative, you can predict that the reaction will be spontaneous.

Standard Free-Energy Change

Recall that for purposes of tabulating thermodynamic data, certain *standard states* are chosen, which are indicated by a superscript degree sign on the symbol of the quantity. The standard states are as follows: for pure liquids and solids, 1 atm pressure; for gases, 1 atm partial pressure; for solutions, 1 M concentration. The temperature is the temperature of interest, usually 25°C (298 K).

The standard free-energy change, $\Delta G°$, is the free-energy change that occurs when reactants in their standard states are converted to products in their standard states. Example 18.4 illustrates the calculation of the standard free-energy change, $\Delta G°$, from $\Delta H°$ and $\Delta S°$.

$$\Delta G° = \Delta H° - T\Delta S°$$

Example 18.4 | Calculating $\Delta G°$ from $\Delta H°$ and $\Delta S°$

What is the standard free-energy change, $\Delta G°$, for the following reaction at 25°C?

$$N_2(g) + 3H_2(g) \longrightarrow 2NH_3(g)$$

Use values of $\Delta H_f°$ and $S°$, from Tables 6.2 and 18.1.

(continued)

(continued)

Problem Strategy   Calculate $\Delta H°$ and $\Delta S°$, then substitute these values into $\Delta H° - T\Delta S°$ to obtain $\Delta G°$.

Solution   Write the balanced equation and place below each formula the values of $\Delta H_f°$ and $S°$ multiplied by stoichiometric coefficients.

$$N_2(g) \; + \; 3H_2(g) \; \longrightarrow \; 2NH_3(g)$$

$\Delta H_f°$: 0	0	$2 \times (-45.9)$ kJ
$S°$: 191.6	3×130.6	2×192.7 J/K

You calculate $\Delta H°$ and $\Delta S°$ by taking values for products and subtracting values for reactants.

$$\Delta H° = \Sigma \, n\Delta H_f°(\text{products}) - \Sigma \, m\Delta H_f°(\text{reactants})$$

$$= [2 \times (-45.9) - 0] \text{ kJ} = -91.8 \text{ kJ}$$

$$\Delta S° = \Sigma \, nS°(\text{products}) - \Sigma \, mS°(\text{reactants})$$

$$= [2 \times 192.7 - (191.6 + 3 \times 130.6)] \text{ J/K} = -198.0 \text{ J/K}$$

You now substitute into the equation for $\Delta G°$ in terms of $\Delta H°$ and $\Delta S°$. Note that you substitute $\Delta S°$ in units of kJ/K.

$$\Delta G° = \Delta H° - T\Delta S° = -91.8 \text{ kJ} - (298 \text{ K})(-0.1980 \text{ kJ/K}) = \mathbf{-32.8 \text{ kJ}}$$

Answer Check   Check your arithmetic. You need to be careful about the signs, especially when calculating ΔH. Individual enthalpies of formation may be positive or negative. Also, you will be subtracting reactants from products.

Exercise 18.6   Calculate $\Delta G°$ for the following reaction at 25°C. Use data given in Tables 6.2 and 18.1.

$$CH_4(g) + 2O_2(g) \longrightarrow CO_2(g) + 2H_2O(g)$$

■ See Problems 18.45 and 18.46.

Standard Free Energies of Formation

The **standard free energy of formation, $\Delta G_f°$,** of a substance is defined similarly to the standard enthalpy of formation. That is, $\Delta G_f°$ is *the free-energy change that occurs when 1 mol of substance is formed from its elements in their stablest states at 1 atm and at a specified temperature* (usually 25°C). (For a species in solution, the standard state is the 1 M solution.) For example, the standard free energy of formation of $NH_3(g)$ is the free-energy change for the reaction

$$\tfrac{1}{2}N_2(g) + \tfrac{3}{2}H_2(g) \longrightarrow NH_3(g)$$

The reactants, N_2 and H_2, each at 1 atm, are converted to the product, NH_3, at 1 atm pressure. In Example 18.4, you found $\Delta G°$ for the formation of 2 mol NH_3 from its elements to be -32.8 kJ. Hence, $\Delta G_f°$ (NH_3) $= -32.8$ kJ/2 mol $= -16.4$ kJ/mol.

As in the case of standard enthalpies of formation, the standard free energies of formation of elements in their stablest states are assigned the value zero. By tabulating $\Delta G_f°$ for substances, as in Table 18.2, you can easily calculate $\Delta G°$ for any reaction involving those substances. You simply subtract the standard free energies of reactants from the standard free energies of products:

$$\Delta G° = \Sigma \, n\Delta G_f°(\text{products}) - \Sigma \, m\Delta G_f°(\text{reactants})$$

The next example illustrates the calculations.

TABLE 18.2	Standard Free Energies of Formation (at 25°C)*

Substance or Ion	ΔG_f° (kJ/mol)	Substance or Ion	ΔG_f° (kJ/mol)	Substance or Ion	ΔG_f° (kJ/mol)
$e^-(g)$	0	*Aldehydes (continued)*		**Nitrogen** *(continued)*	
Bromine		$CH_3CHO(l)$	−128.3	$HNO_3(aq)$	−111.3
$Br(g)$	82.40	**Chlorine**		**Oxygen**	
$Br^-(aq)$	−104.0	$Cl(g)$	105.3	$O(g)$	231.8
$Br^-(g)$	−238.8	$Cl^-(aq)$	−131.3	$O_2(g)$	0
$Br_2(g)$	3.159	$Cl^-(g)$	−240.2	$O_3(g)$	163.2
$Br_2(l)$	0	$Cl_2(g)$	0	$OH^-(aq)$	−157.3
$HBr(g)$	−53.50	$HCl(g)$	−95.30	$H_2O(g)$	−228.6
Calcium		**Fluorine**		$H_2O(l)$	−237.1
$Ca(s)$	0	$F(g)$	62.31	**Silicon**	
$Ca^{2+}(aq)$	−553.5	$F^-(g)$	−262.0	$Si(s)$	0
$CaCO_3(s, \text{calcite})$	−1128.8	$F^-(aq)$	−278.8	$SiCl_4(l)$	−619.9
$CaO(s)$	−603.5	$F_2(g)$	0	$SiF_4(g)$	−1572.7
Carbon		$HF(g)$	−274.6	$SiO_2(s, \text{quartz})$	−856.4
$C(g)$	671.3	**Hydrogen**		**Silver**	
$C(s, \text{diamond})$	2.900	$H(g)$	203.3	$Ag(s)$	0
$C(s, \text{graphite})$	0	$H^+(aq)$	0	$Ag^+(aq)$	77.12
$CCl_4(g)$	−53.65	$H^+(g)$	1517.0	$AgBr(s)$	−96.90
$CCl_4(l)$	−65.27	$H_2(g)$	0	$AgCl(s)$	−109.8
$CO(g)$	−137.2	**Iodine**		$AgF(s)$	—
$CO_2(g)$	−394.4	$I(g)$	70.21	$AgI(s)$	−66.19
$CO_3^{2-}(aq)$	−527.9	$I^-(aq)$	−51.59	**Sodium**	
$CS_2(g)$	66.85	$I^-(g)$	−221.5	$Na(g)$	76.86
$CS_2(l)$	65.27	$I_2(s)$	0	$Na(s)$	0
$HCN(g)$	124.7	$HI(g)$	1.576	$Na^+(aq)$	−261.9
$HCN(l)$	124.9	**Lead**		$Na^+(g)$	574.4
$HCO_3^-(aq)$	−586.8	$Pb(s)$	0	$Na_2CO_3(s)$	−1048.0
Hydrocarbons		$Pb^{2+}(aq)$	−24.39	$NaCl(s)$	−384.0
$CH_4(g)$	−50.80	$PbO(s)$	−189.3	$NaHCO_3(s)$	−851.0
$C_2H_4(g)$	68.39	$PbS(s)$	−96.68		
$C_2H_6(g)$	−32.89	**Nitrogen**		**Sulfur**	
$C_6H_6(l)$	124.4	$N(g)$	455.6	$S(g)$	236.5
Alcohols		$N_2(g)$	0	$S(s, \text{monoclinic})$	0.070
$CH_3OH(l)$	−166.4	$NH_3(g)$	−16.40	$S(s, \text{rhombic})$	0
$C_2H_5OH(l)$	−174.9	$NH_4^+(aq)$	−79.37	$S_2(g)$	79.7
Aldehydes		$NO(g)$	86.60	$SO_2(g)$	−300.1
$HCHO(g)$	−113	$NO_2(g)$	51.24	$H_2S(g)$	−33.33
$CH_3CHO(g)$	−133.4				

*See Appendix C for additional values.

Example 18.5 | **Calculating $\Delta G°$ from Standard Free Energies of Formation**

Calculate $\Delta G°$ for the combustion of 1 mol of ethanol, C_2H_5OH, at 25°C.

$$C_2H_5OH(l) + 3O_2(g) \longrightarrow 2CO_2(g) + 3H_2O(g)$$

Use the standard free energies of formation given in Table 18.2.

Problem Strategy Calculate $\Delta G°$ from $\Delta G_f°$ values, similar to the way you calculate $\Delta H°$ from $\Delta H_f°$.

Solution Write the balanced equation with values of $\Delta G_f°$ multiplied by stoichiometric coefficients below each formula.

$$C_2H_5OH(l) + 3O_2(g) \longrightarrow 2CO_2(g) + 3H_2O(g)$$
$$\Delta G_f°: \quad -174.9 \qquad 0 \qquad 2(-394.4) \quad 3(-228.6)\ kJ$$

The calculation is

$$\Delta G° = \Sigma\, n\Delta G_f°(\text{products}) - \Sigma\, m\Delta G_f°(\text{reactants})$$
$$= [2(-394.4) + 3(-228.6) - (-174.9)]\ kJ$$
$$= \mathbf{-1299.7\ kJ}$$

Answer Check As in calculating ΔH values, you need to be careful of signs. Also, note that you can obtain standard free energies from Appendix C. Just be careful to use the correct column for $\Delta G°$ values.

Exercise 18.7 Calculate $\Delta G°$ at 25°C for the following reaction, using values of $\Delta G_f°$.

$$CaCO_3(s) \longrightarrow CaO(s) + CO_2(g)$$

■ See Problems 18.49 and 18.50.

$\Delta G°$ as a Criterion for Spontaneity

You have already seen that the quantity $\Delta G = \Delta H - T\Delta S$ can be used as a criterion for the spontaneity of a reaction. The change of free energy, ΔG, should be calculated for the conditions at which the reaction occurs. If the reactants are at standard conditions and give products at standard conditions, the free-energy change you need to look at is $\Delta G°$. The calculation is simple, as shown in Example 18.5. For other conditions, you should look at the appropriate ΔG value. This would be a more complicated calculation. Nevertheless, the standard free-energy change $\Delta G°$ is still a useful guide to the spontaneity of reaction in these cases. The following rules are useful in judging the spontaneity of a reaction:

1. When $\Delta G°$ is a large negative number (more negative than about -10 kJ), the reaction is spontaneous as written, and reactants transform almost entirely to products when equilibrium is reached.

2. When $\Delta G°$ is a large positive number (larger than about 10 kJ), the reaction is nonspontaneous as written, and reactants do not give significant amounts of products at equilibrium.

3. When $\Delta G°$ has a small negative or positive value (less than about 10 kJ), the reaction gives an equilibrium mixture with significant amounts of both reactants and products.

Example 18.6	Interpreting the Sign of $\Delta G°$

Calculate $\Delta H°$ and $\Delta G°$ for the reaction

$$2KClO_3(s) \longrightarrow 2KCl(s) + 3O_2(g)$$

Interpret the signs obtained for $\Delta H°$ and $\Delta G°$. Values of $\Delta H_f°$ (in kJ/mol) are as follows: $KClO_3(s)$, -397.7; $KCl(s)$, -436.7. Similarly, values of $\Delta G_f°$ (in kJ/mol) are as follows: $KClO_3(s)$, -296.3; $KCl(s)$, -408.8. Note that $O_2(g)$ is the reference form of the element, so $\Delta H_f° = \Delta G_f° = 0$ for it.

Problem Strategy Calculate $\Delta H°$ and $\Delta G°$; then interpret the signs of these quantities. The interpretation of the sign of ΔH was discussed in Chapter 6. As long as $\Delta G°$ is not close to zero, you can interpret its sign as follows: a negative $\Delta G°$ means the reactants tend to go mostly to products; a positive $\Delta G°$ means that the reaction is nonspontaneous as written. When the value of $\Delta G°$ is close to zero, the reaction gives an equilibrium mixture.

Solution The problem is set up as follows:

	$2KClO_3(s)$	$\longrightarrow$	$2KCl(s)$	$+ 3O_2(g)$
$\Delta H_f°$:	$2 \times (-397.7)$		$2 \times (-436.7)$	$0\,kJ$
$\Delta G_f°$:	$2 \times (-296.3)$		$2 \times (-408.8)$	$0\,kJ$

Then,

$$\Delta H° = [2 \times (-436.7) - 2 \times (-397.7)]\ kJ = \mathbf{-78.0\ kJ}$$

$$\Delta G° = [2 \times (-408.8) - 2 \times (-296.3)]\ kJ = \mathbf{-225.0\ kJ}$$

The reaction is exothermic, liberating 78.0 kJ of heat. The large negative value for $\Delta G°$ indicates that the equilibrium composition is mostly potassium chloride and oxygen.

Answer Check Check your arithmetic. Then remember that a negative sign for $\Delta H°$ means that heat was lost from the system; a large negative sign for $\Delta G°$ means that products predominate.

Exercise 18.8 Which of the following reactions are spontaneous in the direction written? See Table 18.2 for data.

a. $C(graphite) + 2H_2(g) \longrightarrow CH_4(g)$

b. $2H_2(g) + O_2(g) \longrightarrow 2H_2O(l)$

c. $4HCN(g) + 5O_2(g) \longrightarrow 2H_2O(l) + 4CO_2(g) + 2N_2(g)$

d. $Ag^+(aq) + I^-(aq) \longrightarrow AgI(s)$

■ See Problems 18.53 and 18.54.

Concept Check 18.2

Consider the reaction of nitrogen, N_2, and oxygen, O_2, to form nitrogen monoxide, NO:

$$N_2(g) + O_2(g) \longrightarrow 2NO(g)$$

From the standard free energy of formation of NO, what can you say about this reaction?

18.5 | Interpretation of Free Energy

You have seen that the free-energy change serves as a criterion for spontaneity of a chemical reaction. This gives you some idea of what free energy is and how you interpret it. In this section, we will look more closely at the meaning of free energy.

Maximum Work

Theoretically, spontaneous reactions can be used to obtain useful work. By useful work, we mean energy that can be used directly to move objects of normal size. We use the combustion of gasoline to move an automobile, and we use a reaction in a battery to generate electricity to drive a motor. Similarly, biochemical reactions in muscle tissue occur in such a way as to contract muscle fibers and lift a weight.

A Chemist Looks at . . .

Coupling of Reactions

life science

Many important processes are thermodynamically unfavorable, or *nonspontaneous*. Assembling many small amino acid molecules into a large protein molecule is an example of a nonspontaneous process. Yet biological organisms do assemble proteins from amino acids. Biological organisms accomplish many similar nonspontaneous processes. How do they do this?

Let's look at a simpler example. We would like to obtain iron metal from iron ore. Here is the equation for the direct decomposition of iron(III) oxide, the iron-containing substance in the iron ore hematite:

$$2Fe_2O_3(s) \longrightarrow 4Fe(s) + 3O_2(g); \quad \Delta G° = +1487 \text{ kJ}$$

This reaction is clearly nonspontaneous, because $\Delta G°$ is a large positive quantity. The nonspontaneity of this reaction is in agreement with common knowledge. Iron tends to rust (forms iron oxide) in air, by combining with oxygen. You do not expect a rusty wrench to turn spontaneously into shiny iron and oxygen. But this does not mean you cannot change iron(III) oxide to iron metal. It merely means that you have to do work on the iron(III) oxide to reduce it to the metal. You must, in effect, find a way to couple this nonspontaneous reaction to one that is sufficiently spontaneous; that is, you must couple this reaction to one having a more negative $\Delta G°$.

Consider the spontaneous reaction of carbon monoxide with oxygen (the burning of CO):

$$2CO(g) + O_2(g) \longrightarrow 2CO_2(g); \quad \Delta G° = -514.4 \text{ kJ}$$

For 3 mol O_2, $\Delta G°$ is -1543 kJ, which is more negative than for the direct decomposition of 2 mol Fe_2O_3 to its elements. Let us add the two reactions:

$$2Fe_2O_3(s) \longrightarrow 4Fe(s) + 3O_2(g);$$
$$\Delta G° = 1487 \text{ kJ}$$
$$6CO(g) + 3O_2(g) \longrightarrow 6CO_2(g);$$
$$\Delta G° = -1543 \text{ kJ}$$
$$\overline{2Fe_2O_3(s) + 6CO(g) \longrightarrow 4Fe(s) + 6CO_2(g);}$$
$$\Delta G° = -56 \text{ kJ}$$

The net result is to reduce iron(III) oxide to the metal by reacting the oxide with carbon monoxide. This is the reaction that occurs in a blast furnace, where iron ore is commercially reduced to iron.

The concept of the coupling of two chemical reactions, a nonspontaneous reaction with a spontaneous one, to give an overall spontaneous change is a very useful one, especially in biochemistry. Adenosine triphosphate, or ATP, is a molecule containing a triphosphate group. It reacts with water, in the presence of an enzyme (biochemical catalyst), to give adenosine diphosphate, ADP, and a phosphate ion. (Figure 18.9 shows the structure of ATP and ADP.) The reaction has a negative $\Delta G°$ (and is a spontaneous reaction.)

$$ATP + H_2O \longrightarrow ADP + \text{phosphate ion}; \quad \Delta G° = -31 \text{ kJ}$$

ATP is first synthesized in a living organism; the energy for this synthesis is obtained from food. The spontaneous reaction of ATP to give ADP is then coupled to various nonspontaneous reactions in the organism to accomplish necessary life processes (see Figure 18.10).

Often reactions are not carried out in a way that does useful work. The reactants are simply poured together in a reaction vessel, and products are separated from the mixture. As the reaction occurs, the free energy of the system decreases and entropy is produced, but no useful work is obtained.

In principle, if a reaction is carried out to obtain the maximum useful work, no entropy is produced. It can be shown that the maximum useful work, w_{max}, for a spontaneous reaction is ΔG.

$$w_{max} = \Delta G$$

The term *free energy* comes from this result. *The free-energy change is the maximum energy available, or free, to do useful work.* As a reaction occurs in such a way as to

Adenosine triphosphate
(ATP)

Adenosine diphosphate
(ADP)

FIGURE 18.9 ▲

Molecular models of ATP and ADP
The phosphate groups are on the left, with the phosphorus atoms shown in orange, oxygen atoms in red, nitrogen atoms in blue, carbon atoms in gray, and hydrogen atoms in light blue.

FIGURE 18.10 ▶

Coupling of reactions in a biological cell
The mitochondria are parts of a cell that obtain energy in the form of ATP from glucose (from food), $C_6H_{12}O_6$. ATP molecules are used in various cell processes, such as protein synthesis from amino acids, which occurs in the ribosomes.

Ribosomes
(dots)

Mitochondria

In the mitochondria:

Glucose + O_2

ADP

ATP

CO_2 + H_2O

In the ribosomes:

Protein

ADP

ATP

Amino acids

■ See Problems 18.105 and 18.106.

The sign of w (work) is defined so that a negative value means work obtained from the system (that is, energy is subtracted from the system). You can obtain work from a reaction if its ΔG is negative.

give the maximum useful work, the free energy decreases and a corresponding quantity of useful work is obtained. <

The concept of maximum work from a chemical reaction is an idealization. In any real situation, less than this maximum work is obtained and some entropy is created. When this work is eventually expended, it appears in the environment as additional entropy.

Free-Energy Change During Reaction

You have seen that the free-energy change is related to the work done during a chemical reaction. Consider the combustion of gasoline in O_2. The reaction is spontaneous,

FIGURE 18.11 ▲

Free-energy change during a spontaneous reaction (combustion of gasoline)
The free energy decreases as the reaction proceeds. At equilibrium, the free energy becomes a minimum, and the equilibrium mixture is mostly products.

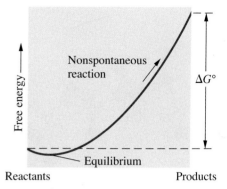

FIGURE 18.12 ▲

Free-energy change during a nonspontaneous reaction
The free energy decreases until equilibrium, at which the minimum value is reached. There is very little reaction, however, because the equilibrium mixture is mostly reactants. To change reactants to mostly products is to undergo a nonspontaneous reaction.

What happens in the gasoline engine is complicated, but you need look at only the initial and final states. Reactants at the surrounding temperature and pressure go into the engine, which produces work and heat, and the products leave the engine, eventually reaching the initial temperature and pressure of the reactants.

so the free-energy change is negative. That is, the free energy of the system changes to a lower value as the reactants are converted to products. Figure 18.11 shows the free-energy change that occurs during this reaction. When the gasoline is burned in a gasoline stove, the decrease in free energy shows up as an increase in entropy of the system and the surroundings. However, when the gasoline is burned in an automobile engine, some of the decrease in free energy shows up as work done. Theoretically, all of the free-energy decrease can be used to do work. This gives the maximum work. In practice, less work is obtained, and the difference appears as an increase of entropy. Ultimately, the work is itself used up—that is, changed to entropy. <

Look at Figure 18.11 again. At the start of the reaction, the system contains only reactants: gasoline and O_2. The free energy has a relatively high value. This decreases as the reaction proceeds. The decrease in free energy appears either as an increase in entropy or as work done. Eventually, the free energy of the system reaches its minimum value. Then the net reaction stops; it comes to equilibrium.

Before we leave this section, consider a reaction in which $\Delta G°$ is positive. You would predict that the reaction is nonspontaneous. Figure 18.12 shows the free-energy change as the reaction proceeds. Note that there is a small decrease in free energy as the system goes to equilibrium. Some reaction occurs in order to give the equilibrium mixture. But this mixture consists primarily of reactants, because the reaction does not go very far before coming to equilibrium. To change reactants completely to products is a nonspontaneous reaction (shown by the arrow along the curve in Figure 18.12).

Free Energy and Equilibrium Constants

In the previous section, you saw that for any spontaneous reaction, the total free energy of the substances in the reaction mixture decreases as the reaction proceeds (that is, the free-energy change is negative). Earlier, you saw that the standard free-energy change, $\Delta G°$, can be used as a criterion for the spontaneity of a reaction. When $\Delta G°$ is negative, the reaction is spontaneous. We will now describe how the standard free-energy change is related to the equilibrium constant.

18.6 | Relating Δ*G*° to the Equilibrium Constant

One of the most important results of chemical thermodynamics is an equation relating the standard free-energy change for a reaction to the equilibrium constant. Before we look at this equation, we must discuss the thermodynamic form of the equilibrium constant that occurs in that equation.

The **thermodynamic equilibrium constant, *K*,** is *the equilibrium constant in which the concentrations of gases are expressed in partial pressures in atmospheres, whereas the concentrations of solutes in liquid solutions are expressed in molarities.* For a reaction involving only solutes in liquid solution, *K* is identical to *K*c; for reactions involving only gases, *K* equals *K*p. <

To be precise, K is defined in terms of activities, which are dimensionless quantities numerically equal to "effective" concentrations and pressures.

Example 18.7 | Writing the Expression for a Thermodynamic Equilibrium Constant

Write expressions for the thermodynamic equilibrium constants for each of the following reactions:

a. The reaction given in the chapter opening,

$$2NH_3(g) + CO_2(g) \rightleftharpoons NH_2CONH_2(aq) + H_2O(l)$$

b. The solubility process

$$AgCl(s) \rightleftharpoons Ag^+(aq) + Cl^-(aq)$$

Problem Strategy The thermodynamic equilibrium constant, *K*, is an amalgam of *K*p and *K*c. All gases appear in *K* as partial pressures; all solutes appear as concentrations. Pure solids and liquids do not appear in the equilibrium constant.

Solution a. Note that H_2O is a solvent, so it does not appear explicitly in *K*. The gases appear in *K* as partial pressures, and the solute appears as a molar concentration.

$$K = \frac{[NH_2CONH_2]}{P^2_{NH_3}P_{CO_2}}$$

b. Note that AgCl is a solid, so it does not appear explicitly in *K*. The solutes appear as molar concentrations.

$$K = [Ag^+][Cl^-]$$

This is identical to K_{sp}.

Answer Check Make sure that the products are on top and the reactants are on the bottom of each equilibrium-constant expression. Then check that each reactant and product term is raised to the correct power (equal to the stoichiometric coefficient in the chemical equation).

Exercise 18.9 Give the expression for *K* for each of the following reactions.

a. $CaCO_3(s) \rightleftharpoons CaO(s) + CO_2(g)$
b. $PbI_2(s) \rightleftharpoons Pb^{2+}(aq) + 2I^-(aq)$
c. $H^+(aq) + HCO_3^-(aq) \rightleftharpoons H_2O(l) + CO_2(g)$

■ See Problems 18.59 and 18.60.

The standard free-energy change, Δ*G*°, for a reaction can be calculated using data from thermodynamic tables. If you want the free-energy change when reactants under nonstandard conditions are changed to products under nonstandard conditions (Δ*G*), you can obtain it from the standard free-energy change Δ*G*° using the following equation:

$$\Delta G = \Delta G^\circ + RT \ln Q$$

Here *Q* is the thermodynamic form of the reaction quotient. It has the same general appearance as the thermodynamic equilibrium constant *K*, but the concentrations and partial pressures are those for a mixture at some instant, perhaps at the beginning of a reaction. You obtain Δ*G* from Δ*G*° by adding *RT* ln *Q*, where ln *Q* is the natural logarithm of *Q* (ln *Q* = 2.303 log *Q*). Note that Δ*G* is the change

Strictly speaking, because the composition changes with reaction, ΔG is for an infinitesimal change in G per infinitesimal change in reaction amounts; that is, ΔG equals the slope of the reaction curve (like the curve in Figure 18.12).

of free energy that occurs when the reaction mixture has the composition expressed by Q. <

You can derive the equation relating $\Delta G°$ to the equilibrium constant K from the preceding equation. In the previous section, you saw that as a chemical reaction approaches equilibrium, the free energy decreases and continues to decrease until equilibrium is reached. At equilibrium, the free energy ceases to change; then $\Delta G = 0$. Also, the reaction quotient Q becomes equal to the equilibrium constant K. If you substitute $\Delta G = 0$ and $Q = K$ into the preceding equation, you obtain

$$0 = \Delta G° + RT \ln K$$

This result is easily rearranged to give the basic equation relating the standard free-energy change to the equilibrium constant.

$$\Delta G° = -RT \ln K$$

The next example illustrates the calculation of a thermodynamic equilibrium constant from the standard free-energy change, $\Delta G°$.

Example 18.8 | Calculating K from the Standard Free-Energy Change (Molecular Equation)

Find the value of the equilibrium constant K at 25°C (298 K) for the reaction

$$2NH_3(g) + CO_2(g) \rightleftharpoons NH_2CONH_2(aq) + H_2O(l)$$

The standard free-energy change, $\Delta G°$, at 25°C equals -13.6 kJ. (We calculated this value of $\Delta G° = \Delta H° - T\Delta S°$ just before Section 18.4.)

Problem Strategy Rearrange the equation $\Delta G° = -RT \ln K$ to give

$$\ln K = \frac{\Delta G°}{-RT}$$

$\Delta G°$ and R must be in compatible units. You normally express $\Delta G°$ in joules and set R equal to 8.31 J/(K·mol).

Solution Substituting numerical values into this equation,

$$\ln K = \frac{-13.6 \times 10^3}{-8.31 \times 298} = 5.49$$

Hence,

$$K = e^{5.49} = \textbf{2.4} \times \textbf{10}^2$$

Note that although the value of K indicates that products predominate at equilibrium, K is only moderately large. You would expect that the composition could be easily shifted toward reactants if you could remove either NH_3 or CO_2 (according to Le Châtelier's principle). This is what happens when urea is used as a fertilizer. As NH_3 is used up, more NH_3 is produced by the decomposition of urea.

Answer Check Make sure that you have expressed $\Delta G°$ and R in similar units. If $\Delta G°$ is given in kJ/mol, whereas R is given in J/(K·mol), express both in joules or both in kilojoules. (If you always carry units in your calculations, you will not make a mistake in units.) Also, note that ln is the natural logarithm, and its inverse or antilogarithm is the exponential function. Thus, the inverse of ln x is e^x.

Exercise 18.10 Use the data from Table 18.2 to obtain the equilibrium constant K_p at 25°C for the reaction

$$CaCO_3(s) \rightleftharpoons CaO(s) + CO_2(g)$$

Note that values of $\Delta G°_f$ are needed for $CaCO_3$ and CaO, even though the substances do not appear in $K_p = P_{CO_2}$.

■ See Problems 18.61, 18.62, 18.63, and 18.64.

The method of calculating K from $\Delta G°$ also works for net ionic equations. In Example 18.9, you obtain a solubility product constant from thermodynamic data.

Example 18.9 | Calculating K from the Standard Free-Energy Change (Net Ionic Equation)

Calculate the equilibrium constant K_{sp} at 25°C for the reaction

$$AgCl(s) \rightleftharpoons Ag^+(aq) + Cl^-(aq)$$

using standard free energies of formation.

Problem Strategy This is similar to the preceding example, except that you must first calculate ΔG_f° for the ionic equation. Note that K_{sp} equals K, the thermodynamic equilibrium constant.

Solution You first calculate ΔG°. Writing ΔG_f° values below the formulas in the equation gives

$$AgCl(s) \rightleftharpoons Ag^+(aq) + Cl^-(aq)$$
$$\Delta G_f^\circ: \quad -109.8 \qquad 77.1 \qquad -131.3 \text{ kJ}$$

Hence,

$$\Delta G^\circ = [(77.1 - 131.3) - (-109.8)] \text{ kJ}$$
$$= 55.6 \text{ kJ (or } 55.6 \times 10^3 \text{ J)}$$

You now substitute numerical values into the equation relating $\ln K$ and ΔG°.

$$\ln K = \frac{\Delta G^\circ}{-RT} = \frac{55.6 \times 10^3}{-8.31 \times 298} = -22.45$$

Therefore,

$$K = e^{-22.45} = 2 \times 10^{-10}$$

Answer Check When you calculate ΔG°, be careful of signs. In this example, note that the last term in calculating ΔG° has a minus sign before -109.8, which gives $+109.8$.

Exercise 18.11 Calculate the solubility product constant for $Mg(OH)_2$ at 25°C. The ΔG_f° values (in kJ/mol) are as follows: $Mg^{2+}(aq)$, -454.8; $OH^-(aq)$, -157.3; $Mg(OH)_2(s)$, -833.7.

■ See Problems 18.65 and 18.66.

You can understand the use of ΔG° as a criterion for spontaneity by looking at its relationship to the equilibrium constant, $\Delta G^\circ = -RT \ln K$. When the equilibrium constant is greater than 1, $\ln K$ is positive and ΔG° is negative. Similarly, when the equilibrium constant is less than 1, $\ln K$ is negative and ΔG° is positive. This agrees with the first two rules listed at the end of Section 18.4. You can get the third rule by substituting $\Delta G^\circ = \pm 10 \times 10^3$ J into $\Delta G^\circ = -RT \ln K$ and solving for K. You find that K is between 0.018 and 57. In this range, the equilibrium mixture contains significant amounts of reactants as well as products.

Concept Check 18.3

The following reaction is spontaneous in the direction given.

$$A(g) + B(g) \longrightarrow C(g) + D(g)$$

Suppose you are given a vessel containing an equilibrium mixture of A, B, C, and D, and you increase the concentration of C by increasing its partial pressure.

a. How is the value of ΔG° affected by the addition of C to the vessel?

b. How is the value of ΔG affected by the addition of C to the vessel?

18.7 | Change of Free Energy with Temperature

In the previous sections, you obtained the free-energy change and equilibrium constant for a reaction at 25°C, the temperature at which the thermodynamic data were given. How do you find ΔG° or K at another temperature? Precise calculations are possible but are rather involved. Instead, we will look at a simple method that gives approximate results.

In this method, you assume that ΔH° and ΔS° are essentially constant with respect to temperature. (This is only approximately true.) You get the value of ΔG_T° at any

This approximation is most accurate for temperatures not too different from the temperature for which the $\Delta H°$ and $\Delta S°$ values are obtained. Much different temperatures give greater error.

temperature T by substituting values of $\Delta H°$ and $\Delta S°$ at 25°C (obtained from appropriate tables) into the following equation. <

$$\Delta G_T° = \Delta H° - T\Delta S° \quad \text{(approximation for } \Delta G_T°)$$

Remember that the superscript degree sign (°) refers to substances in standard states, that is, at 1 atm and at the *specified temperature*. Although until now this was 25°C (298 K), we now consider other temperatures. Note that in general, $\Delta G°$ depends strongly on temperature.

Spontaneity and Temperature Change

All of the four possible choices of signs for $\Delta H°$ and $\Delta S°$, listed in Table 18.3, give different temperature behaviors for $\Delta G°$. Consider the case in which $\Delta H°$ is negative and $\Delta S°$ is positive. An example is the reaction

$$\underset{\text{glucose}}{C_6H_{12}O_6(s)} \longrightarrow \underset{\text{ethanol}}{2C_2H_5OH(l)} + 2CO_2(g)$$

This represents the overall change of glucose (grape sugar) to ethanol (ethyl alcohol). The signs of $\Delta H°$ and $\Delta S°$ are easily explained. The formation of more stable bonds, such as occur in CO_2, releases energy as heat. The reaction is exothermic and $\Delta H°$ is negative. As explained in Example 18.2, the breaking up of a molecule ($C_6H_{12}O_6$) into smaller ones and the formation of a gas are expected to increase the entropy, so $\Delta S°$ is positive.

When $\Delta H°$ is negative and $\Delta S°$ is positive, both terms in $\Delta G°$ (that is, $\Delta H°$ and $-T\Delta S°$) are negative. Therefore, $\Delta G°$ is always negative and the reaction is spontaneous whatever the temperature.

If the signs of $\Delta H°$ and $\Delta S°$ are reversed (that is, if $\Delta H°$ is positive, or endothermic, and $\Delta S°$ is negative), $\Delta G°$ is always positive. Thus, the reaction is nonspontaneous at all temperatures. An example is the reaction in which oxygen gas is converted to ozone.

$$3O_2(g) \longrightarrow 2O_3(g)$$

To accomplish this conversion, oxygen is passed through a tube in which an electrical discharge occurs. The electrical discharge supplies the necessary free energy for this otherwise nonspontaneous change.

In the reaction described in the chapter opening,

$$2NH_3(g) + CO_2(g) \longrightarrow NH_2CONH_2(aq) + H_2O(l)$$

both $\Delta H°$ and $\Delta S°$ are negative. In this case, the sign of $\Delta G°$ depends on the relative magnitudes of the terms $\Delta H°$ and $-T\Delta S°$, which have opposite signs. At some temperature,

TABLE 18.3		Effect of Temperature on the Spontaneity of Reactions		
$\Delta H°$	$\Delta S°$	$\Delta G°$	Description*	Example
−	+	−	Spontaneous at all T	$C_6H_{12}O_6(s) \longrightarrow 2C_2H_5OH(l) + 2CO_2(g)$
+	−	+	Nonspontaneous at all T	$3O_2(g) \longrightarrow 2O_3(g)$
−	−	+ or −	Spontaneous at low T; nonspontaneous at high T	$2NH_3(g) + CO_2(g) \longrightarrow NH_2CONH_2(aq) + H_2O(l)$
+	+	+ or −	Nonspontaneous at low T; spontaneous at high T	$Ba(OH)_2 \cdot 8H_2O(s) + 2NH_4NO_3(s) \longrightarrow$ $Ba(NO_3)_2(aq) + 2NH_3(g) + 10H_2O(l)$

*The terms *low temperature* and *high temperature* are relative. For a particular reaction, *high temperature* could mean room temperature.

these terms just cancel and $\Delta G°$ equals zero. Below this temperature, $\Delta G°$ is negative. Above it, $\Delta G°$ is positive. Therefore, this reaction is spontaneous at low temperatures but nonspontaneous at sufficiently high temperatures. This particular reaction is spontaneous at 25°C but nonspontaneous at about 60°C.

A reaction in which both $\Delta H°$ and $\Delta S°$ are positive is the one described in the opening to Chapter 6. <

The reaction mixture spontaneously cools enough to freeze water. See Figure 6.1.

$$Ba(OH)_2 \cdot 8H_2O(s) + 2NH_4NO_3(s) \longrightarrow Ba(NO_3)_2(aq) + 2NH_3(g) + 10H_2O(l)$$

The reaction is endothermic, and because crystalline solids change to a solution and a gas, the entropy increases. Again, the sign of $\Delta G°$ depends on the relative magnitudes of the terms $\Delta H°$ and $-T\Delta S°$. The reaction is spontaneous at room temperature but would be nonspontaneous at a sufficiently low temperature. Table 18.3 summarizes this discussion.

Concept Check 18.4

Consider the decomposition of dinitrogen tetroxide, N_2O_4, to nitrogen dioxide, NO_2:

$$N_2O_4(g) \longrightarrow 2NO_2(g)$$

How would you expect the spontaneity of the reaction to behave with temperature change?

Calculation of $\Delta G°$ at Various Temperatures

As an application of the method of calculating $\Delta G°$ at various temperatures, assuming $\Delta H°$ and $\Delta S°$ are constant, look at the following reaction:

$$CaCO_3(s) \longrightarrow CaO(s) + CO_2(g)$$

At 25°C, $\Delta G°$ equals +130.9 kJ, and the equilibrium partial pressure of CO_2 calculated from this is 1.1×10^{-23} atm. The very small value of this partial pressure shows that $CaCO_3$ is quite stable at room temperature. In the next example, you will see how $\Delta G°$ and K_p for this reaction change at higher temperature.

Example 18.10 | Calculating $\Delta G°$ and K at Various Temperatures

a. What is $\Delta G°$ at 1000°C for the following reaction?

$$CaCO_3(s) \rightleftharpoons CaO(s) + CO_2(g)$$

Is this reaction spontaneous at 1000°C and 1 atm?

b. What is the value of K_p at 1000°C for this reaction? What is the partial pressure of CO_2?

Problem Strategy a. Calculate $\Delta H°$ and $\Delta S°$ at 25°C using standard enthalpies of formation and standard entropies. Then substitute into the equation for $\Delta G_T°$.

b. Use the value of $\Delta G_T°$ to find K ($= K_p$), as in Example 18.8.

Solution a. From Tables 6.2 and 18.1, you have

$$CaCO_3(s) \rightleftharpoons CaO(s) + CO_2(g)$$

	$CaCO_3(s)$	$CaO(s)$	$CO_2(g)$
$\Delta H_f°$:	−1206.9	−635.1	−393.5 kJ
$S°$:	92.9	38.2	213.7 J/K

(continued)

(continued)

You calculate $\Delta H°$ and $\Delta S°$ from these values.

$$\Delta H° = [(-635.1 - 393.5) - (-1206.9)] \text{ kJ} = 178.3 \text{ kJ}$$

$$\Delta S° = [(38.2 + 213.7) - (92.9)] \text{ J/K} = 159.0 \text{ J/K}$$

Now you substitute $\Delta H°$, $\Delta S°$ ($= 0.1590$ kJ/K), and T ($= 1273$ K) into the equation for $\Delta G°_T$.

$$\Delta G°_T = \Delta H° - T\Delta S° = 178.3 \text{ kJ} - (1273 \text{ K})(0.1590 \text{ kJ/K}) = \mathbf{-24.1 \text{ kJ}}$$

Because $\Delta G°_T$ is negative, the reaction should be **spontaneous** at 1000°C and 1 atm

b. Substitute the value of $\Delta G°$ at 1273 K, which equals -24.1×10^3 J, into the equation relating ln K and $\Delta G°$.

$$\ln K = \frac{\Delta G°}{-RT} = \frac{-24.1 \times 10^3}{-8.31 \times 1273} = 2.278$$

$$K = K_p = e^{2.278} = \mathbf{9.8}$$

$K_p = P_{CO_2}$, so the partial pressure of CO_2 is **9.76 atm.**

Answer Check The things to be careful of have been noted before: watch the signs in calculating $\Delta H°$ and $\Delta S°$, and always use compatible units. Usually, $\Delta H°$ is given in kJ, whereas $\Delta S°$ is given in J/K. Here, we converted the units for $\Delta S°$ to kJ/K. As long as you carry units in your calculations, you will detect any error in choice of units that you might make.

Exercise 18.12 The thermodynamic equilibrium constant for the vaporization of water,

$$H_2O(l) \rightleftharpoons H_2O(g)$$

is $K_p = P_{H_2O}$. Use thermodynamic data to calculate the vapor pressure of water at 45°C. Compare your answer with the value given in Appendix B.

■ See Problems 18.67 and 18.68.

You can use the ideas described in this section to find the temperature at which a reaction such as the decomposition of $CaCO_3$ changes from nonspontaneous to spontaneous under standard conditions (1 atm for reactants and products). At this temperature, $\Delta G°$ equals zero.

$$\Delta G° = 0 = \Delta H° - T\Delta S°$$

Solving for T gives

$$T = \frac{\Delta H°}{\Delta S°}$$

For the decomposition of $CaCO_3$, using values obtained in Example 18.10, you get

$$T = \frac{178.3 \text{ kJ}}{0.1590 \text{ kJ/K}} = 1121 \text{ K } (848°C)$$

Thus, $CaCO_3$ should be stable to thermal decomposition to CaO and CO_2 at 1 atm until heated to 848°C. This is only approximate, of course, because you assumed that $\Delta H°$ and $\Delta S°$ are constant with temperature.

Exercise 18.13 To what temperature must magnesium carbonate be heated to decompose it to MgO and CO_2 at 1 atm? Is this higher or lower than the temperature required to decompose $CaCO_3$? Values of $\Delta H°_f$ (in kJ/mol) are as follows: MgO(s), -601.2; $MgCO_3(s)$, -1111.7. Values of $S°$ (in J/K) are as follows: MgO(s), 26.9; $MgCO_3(s)$, 65.9. Data for CO_2 are given in Tables 6.2 and 18.1.

■ See Problems 18.69 and 18.70.

A Checklist for Review

Important Terms

internal energy, U (18.1)
state function (18.1)
work (18.1)
first law of thermodynamics (18.1)
enthalpy, H (18.1)

spontaneous process (18.2)
entropy, S (18.2)
second law of thermodynamics (18.2)
third law of thermodynamics (18.3)
standard (absolute) entropy (18.3)

free energy, G (18.4)
standard free energy of formation,
 ΔG_f° (18.4)
thermodynamic equilibrium
 constant, K (18.6)

Key Equations

$\Delta U = q + w$

$w = -P\Delta V$

$\Delta S > \dfrac{q}{T}$ (spontaneous process)

$\Delta S = \dfrac{q}{T}$ (equilibrium process)

$\Delta S^\circ = \Sigma\, nS^\circ(\text{products}) - \Sigma\, mS^\circ(\text{reactants})$

$\Delta G^\circ = \Delta H^\circ - T\Delta S^\circ$

$\Delta G^\circ = \Sigma\, n\Delta G_f^\circ(\text{products}) - \Sigma\, m\Delta G_f^\circ(\text{reactants})$

$\Delta G = \Delta G^\circ + RT \ln Q$

$\Delta G^\circ = -RT \ln K$

$\Delta G_T^\circ = \Delta H^\circ - T\Delta S^\circ$ (approximation for ΔG_T°)

Summary of Facts and Concepts

The *first law of thermodynamics* states that $\Delta U = q + w$. For a chemical reaction at constant pressure, this becomes $\Delta U = q_p - P\Delta V$. If you define *enthalpy, H,* as $U + PV$, you can show that for a reaction at constant pressure, $\Delta H = \Delta U + P\Delta V = q_p$. *Entropy, S,* is a thermodynamic measure of energy dispersal in a system. According to the *second law of thermodynamics,* the total entropy of a system and its surroundings increases for a *spontaneous process,* one that occurs of its own accord. For a spontaneous reaction at constant T and P, you can show that the entropy change ΔS is greater than $\Delta H/T$. For an equilibrium process, such as a phase transition, $\Delta S = \Delta H/T$. The standard entropy S° of a substance is determined by measuring the heat absorbed in warming it at increasing temperatures at 1atm. The method depends on the *third law of thermodynamics,* which states that perfectly crystalline substances at 0 K have zero entropy.

Free energy, G, is defined as $H - TS$. The change in free energy, ΔG, for a reaction at constant T and P equals $\Delta H - T\Delta S$, which is negative for a spontaneous change. *Standard free-energy changes, ΔG°,* can be calculated from ΔH_f° and S° values or from *standard free energies of formation, ΔG_f°. ΔG_f°* for a substance is the standard free-energy change for the formation of the substance from the elements in their stablest states. The standard free-energy change, ΔG°, serves as a *criterion for spontaneity* of a reaction. A negative value means the reaction is spontaneous. A value of zero means the reaction is at equilibrium. A positive value means the reaction is nonspontaneous.

The free-energy change, ΔG, is related to the *maximum work* that can be done by a reaction. This maximum work equals ΔG. A nonspontaneous reaction can be made to go by coupling it with a reaction that has a negative ΔG, so that ΔG for the overall result is negative. The reaction with the negative ΔG does work on the nonspontaneous reaction.

The *thermodynamic equilibrium constant, K,* can be calculated from the standard free-energy change by the relationship $\Delta G^\circ = -RT \ln K$. ΔG° at various temperatures can be obtained by using the approximation that ΔH° and ΔS° are constant. Therefore, ΔG°, which equals $\Delta H^\circ - T\Delta S^\circ$, can be easily calculated for any T.

Media Summary

Visit the **student website at college.cengage.com/pic/ebbing9e** to help prepare for class, study for quizzes and exams, understand core concepts, and visualize molecular-level interactions. The following media activities are available for this chapter:

 Prepare for Class

■ **Video Lessons** *Mini lectures from chemistry experts*
 Heat
 Work

First Law of Thermodynamics
Heats of Reaction: Enthalpy
Spontaneous Processes
Entropy and the Second Law of Thermodynamics
Entropy and Temperature

Gibbs Free Energy
Standard Free-Energy Changes of Formation
Enthalpy and Entropy Contributions to K
The Temperature Dependence of K

 Improve Your Grade

■ **Visualizations** *Molecular-level animations and lab demonstration videos*
Work Versus Energy Flow
Spontaneous Reactions
Spontaneous Reaction of Phosphorus (Barking Dogs)
Entropy

■ **Tutorials** *Animated examples and interactive activities*
Work, Heat, and Energy Flow

■ **Flashcards** *Key terms and definitions*
Online Flashcards

■ **Self-Assessment Questions** *Additional questions with full worked-out solutions*
6 Self-Assessment Questions

 ACE the Test

Multiple-choice quizzes
3 ACE Practice Tests

Access these resources using the passkey available free with new texts or for purchase separately.

Learning Objectives

18.1 First Law of Thermodynamics; Enthalpy

■ Define *internal energy, state function, work,* and *first law of thermodynamics.*
■ Explain why the work done by the system as a result of expansion or contraction during a chemical reaction is $-P\Delta V$.
■ Relate the change of internal energy, ΔU, and heat of reaction, q.
■ Define *enthalpy,* H.
■ Show how heat of reaction at constant pressure, q_p, equals the change of enthalpy, ΔH.

18.2 Entropy and the Second Law of Thermodynamics

■ Define *spontaneous process.*
■ Define *entropy.*
■ Relate entropy to disorder in a molecular system (energy dispersal).
■ State the *second law of thermodynamics* in terms of system plus surroundings.
■ State the second law of thermodynamics in terms of the system only.
■ Calculate the entropy change for a phase transition. **Example 18.1**
■ Describe how $\Delta H - T\Delta S$ functions as a criterion of a spontaneous reaction.

18.3 Standard Entropies and the Third Law of Thermodynamics

■ State the *third law of thermodynamics.*
■ Define *standard entropy (absolute entropy).*
■ State the situations in which the entropy usually increases.
■ Predict the sign of the entropy change of a reaction. **Example 18.2**
■ Express the standard change of entropy of a reaction in terms of standard entropies of products and reactants.
■ Calculate $\Delta S°$ for a reaction. **Example 18.3**

18.4 Free Energy and Spontaneity

■ Define *free energy, G.*
■ Define the *standard free-energy change.*
■ Calculate $\Delta G°$ from $\Delta H°$ and $\Delta S°$. **Example 18.4**
■ Define the *standard free energy of formation, $\Delta G°$.*
■ Calculate $\Delta G°$ from standard free energies of formation. **Example 18.5**
■ State the rules for using $\Delta G°$ as a criterion for spontaneity.
■ Interpret the sign of $\Delta G°$. **Example 18.6**

18.5 Interpretation of Free Energy

■ Relate the free-energy change to maximum useful work.
■ Describe how the free energy changes during a chemical reaction.

18.6 Relating $\Delta G°$ to the Equilibrium Constant

■ Define the *thermodynamic equilibrium constant, K.*
■ Write the expression for a thermodynamic equilibrium constant. **Example 18.7**
■ Indicate how the free-energy change of a reaction and the reaction quotient are related.
■ Relate the standard free-energy change to the thermodynamic equilibrium constant.
■ Calculate K from the standard free-energy change (molecular equation). **Example 18.8**
■ Calculate K from the standard free-energy change (net ionic equation). **Example 18.9**

18.7 Change of Free Energy with Temperature

■ Describe how $\Delta G°$ at a given temperature ($\Delta G_T°$) is approximately related to $\Delta H°$ and $\Delta S°$ at that temperature.
■ Describe how the spontaneity or nonspontaneity of a reaction is related to each of the four possible combinations of signs of $\Delta H°$ and $\Delta S°$.
■ Calculate $\Delta G°$ and K at various temperatures. **Example 18.10**

Self-Assessment and Review Questions

18.1 What is a spontaneous process? Give three examples of spontaneous processes. Give three examples of nonspontaneous processes.

18.2 Which contains greater entropy, a quantity of frozen benzene or the same quantity of liquid benzene at the same temperature? Explain in terms of the dispersal of energy in the substance.

18.3 State the second law of thermodynamics.

18.4 The entropy change ΔS for a phase transition equals $\Delta H/T$, where ΔH is the enthalpy change. Why is it that the entropy change for a system in which a chemical reaction occurs spontaneously does not equal $\Delta H/T$?

18.5 Describe how the standard entropy of hydrogen gas at 25°C can be obtained from heat measurements.

18.6 Describe what you would look for in a reaction involving gases in order to predict the sign of $\Delta S°$. Explain.

18.7 Define the free energy G. How is ΔG related to ΔH and ΔS?

18.8 What is meant by the standard free-energy change $\Delta G°$ for a reaction? What is meant by the standard free energy of formation $\Delta G_f°$ of a substance?

18.9 Explain how $\Delta G°$ can be used to decide whether a chemical equation is spontaneous in the direction written.

18.10 What is the useful work obtained in the ideal situation in which a chemical reaction with free-energy change ΔG is run so that it produces no entropy?

18.11 Give an example of a chemical reaction used to obtain useful work.

18.12 How is the concept of coupling of reactions useful in explaining how a nonspontaneous change could be made to occur?

18.13 Explain how the free energy changes as a spontaneous reaction occurs. Show by means of a diagram how G changes with the extent of reaction.

18.14 Explain how an equilibrium constant can be obtained from thermal data alone (that is, from measurements of heat only).

18.15 Discuss the different sign combinations of $\Delta H°$ and $\Delta S°$ that are possible for a process carried out at constant temperature and pressure. For each combination, state whether the process must be spontaneous or not, or whether both situations are possible. Explain.

18.16 Consider a reaction in which $\Delta H°$ and $\Delta S°$ are positive. Suppose the reaction is nonspontaneous at room temperature.

How would you estimate the temperature at which the reaction becomes spontaneous?

18.17 Which of the following are true about the process of water making the transition from the liquid to the gaseous state at 110°C?
   a. $\Delta G > 0$, $\Delta H < 0$, and $\Delta S = 0$
   b. $\Delta G < 0$, $\Delta H > 0$, and $\Delta S < 0$
   c. $\Delta G > 0$, $\Delta H > 0$, and $\Delta S > 0$
   d. $\Delta G < 0$, $\Delta H < 0$, and $\Delta S > 0$
   e. $\Delta G < 0$, $\Delta H > 0$, and $\Delta S > 0$

18.18 You run a reaction that has a negative entropy change and is exothermic. Assuming that the entropy and enthalpy do not change with temperature, you could predict that as you increase the temperature:
   I.   the equilibrium shifts to favor the reaction products.
   II. the reaction becomes more spontaneous.
   III. ΔG for the reaction increases (becomes more positive).
   a. I only
   b. II only
   c. III only
   d. I and III only
   e. II and III only

18.19 A reaction has a $\Delta G = -10.0$ kJ and a $\Delta H = -20.0$ kJ. If $\Delta S = -1.82 \times 10^3$ J/K, what was the temperature at which the reaction occurred?
   a. 6.04 K
   b. 6.04×10^{-3} K
   c. 5.49×10^{-3} K
   d. 5.49 K
   e. 8.55 K

18.20 Given the following information at 25°C, calculate $\Delta G°$ at 25°C for the reaction

$$2A(g) + B(g) \longrightarrow 3C(g)$$

Substance	$\Delta H_f°$ (kJ/mol)	S°(J/mol·K)
A(g)	191	244
B(g)	70.8	300
C(g)	−197	164

   a. −956 kJ   **b.** 956 kJ   **c.** −346 kJ
   d. 346 kJ   **e.** -1.03×10^3 kJ

Concept Explorations

18.21 Thermodynamics and Spontaneous Processes

Consider a sample of water at 25°C in a beaker in a room at 50°C.

   a. What change do you expect to observe in the water sample? Would this be a spontaneous process or not?

   b. What are the enthalpy and entropy changes for this change in the water sample? (Just indicate the sign of the changes.) Explain your answers.

   c. Does the entropy of the water increase or decrease during the change? How do you know?

   d. Is there a change in free energy for the water sample? If so, indicate the sign of the free-energy change and explain how you arrived at your answer.

Consider the same sample of water, but starting at 75°C in a room at 50°C.

   e. What change would you observe in the water sample? Would this change be a spontaneous process or not?

   f. What are the enthalpy and entropy changes for the water sample? (Just indicate the sign of the changes.) Explain your answers.

g. Does the entropy of the water increase or decrease during the change? How do you know?

h. Is there a change in free energy for the water sample? If so, indicate the sign of the free-energy change and explain how you arrived at your answer.

Finally, consider the same sample of water, starting at 50°C in a room at 50°C.

i. What would you observe in the water sample? Is this a spontaneous process?

j. What are the enthalpy and entropy changes for the water sample? (Just indicate the sign of the changes.) Be sure to justify your answer.

k. Did the entropy of the water increase or decrease during the change? How do you know?

l. Can you determine the exact free-energy change of the water in this case? If you can make this determination, what is the significance of this value?

18.22   Free Energy and the Equilibrium Constant

You place the substance A(g) in a container. Consider the following reaction under standard conditions to produce the substance B(g):

$$A(g) \rightleftharpoons B(g)$$

For this reaction as written, the equilibrium constant is a very large, positive number.

a. When A(g) reacts to give B(g), does the standard free energy ($G°$) of the reaction change as the reaction proceeds or does it remain constant? Explain.

b. When A(g) reacts to give B(g), does the free energy (G) of the reaction change as the reaction proceeds, or does it remain constant? Explain.

c. Is this reaction spontaneous? How do you know?

d. When the reaction reaches equilibrium, is the following statement true: $\Delta G° = \Delta G = 0$? If not, what can you say about the values of $\Delta G°$ and ΔG when equilibrium has been reached?

e. When the reaction has reached equilibrium, what can you say about the composition of the reaction mixture? Is it mostly A(g), is it mostly B(g), or is it something close to equal amounts of A(g) and B(g)?

f. Now consider running the reaction in reverse: B(g) $\longrightarrow$ A(g). For the reaction as written, what can you say about $\Delta G°$, ΔG, the equilibrium constant, and the composition of the reaction mixture at equilibrium? Also, is the reaction spontaneous in this direction?

Conceptual Problems

18.23   For each of the following statements, indicate whether it is true or false.

a. A spontaneous reaction always releases heat.

b. A spontaneous reaction is always a fast reaction.

c. The entropy of a system always increases for a spontaneous change.

d. The entropy of a system and its surroundings always increases for a spontaneous change.

e. The energy of a system always increases for a spontaneous change.

18.24   Which of the following are spontaneous processes?

a. A cube of sugar dissolves in a cup of hot tea.

b. A rusty crowbar turns shiny.

c. Butane from a lighter burns in air.

d. A clock pendulum, initially stopped, begins swinging.

e. Hydrogen and oxygen gases bubble out from a glass of pure water.

18.25   For each of the following series of pairs, indicate which one of the pair has the greater quantity of entropy.

a. 1.0 mol of carbon dioxide gas at 20°C, 1 atm, or 2.0 mol of carbon dioxide gas at 20°C, 1 atm

b. 1.0 mol of butane liquid at 20°C, 10 atm, or 1.0 mol of butane gas at 20°C, 10 atm

c. 1.0 mol of solid carbon dioxide at −80°C, 1 atm, or 1.0 mol of solid carbon dioxide at −90°C, 1 atm

d. 25 g of solid bromine at −7°C, 1 atm, or 25 g of bromine vapor at −7°C, 1 atm

18.26   Predict the sign of the entropy change for each of the following processes.

a. A drop of food coloring diffuses throughout a glass of water.

b. A tree leafs out in the spring.

c. Flowers wilt and stems decompose in the fall.

d. A lake freezes over in the winter.

e. Rainwater on the pavement evaporates.

18.27   Hypothetical elements A(g) and B(g) are introduced into a container and allowed to react according to the reaction A(g) + 2B(g) $\longrightarrow$ AB$_2$(g). The container depicts the reaction mixture after equilibrium has been attained.

a. Is the value of ΔS for the reaction positive, negative, or zero?

b. Is the value of ΔH for the reaction positive, negative, or zero?

c. Prior to equilibrium, is the value of ΔG for the reaction positive, negative, or zero?

d. At equilibrium, is the value of ΔG for the reaction positive, negative, or zero?

18.28   Here is a simple experiment. Take a rubber band and stretch it. (Is this a spontaneous process? How does the Gibbs free energy change?) Place the rubber band against your lips; note how warm the rubber band has become. (How does the enthalpy change?) According to polymer chemists, the rubber band consists of long, coiled molecules. On stretching the rubber band, these long molecules uncoil and align themselves in a more ordered state. Show how the experiment given here is in accord with this molecular view of the rubber band.

18.29 Hypothetical elements X(g) and Y(g) are introduced into a container and allowed to react according to the reaction: X(g) + Y(g) ⟶ XY(g). The container depicts the reaction mixture after equilibrium has been attained.

● = X
● = Y

Next, the volume of the container is doubled by rapidly moving the plunger upward.

Practice Problems

First Law of Thermodynamics

18.31 A gas is cooled and loses 82 J of heat. The gas contracts as it cools, and work done on the system equal to 29 J is exchanged with the surroundings. What are q, w, and ΔU?

18.32 An ideal gas is cooled isothermally (at constant temperature). The internal energy of an ideal gas remains constant during an isothermal change. If q is −76 J, what are ΔU and w?

18.33 What is ΔU when 1.00 mol of liquid water vaporizes at 100°C? The heat of vaporization, ΔH°_{vap}, of water at 100°C is 40.66 kJ/mol.

18.34 What is ΔU for the following reaction at 25°C?

$$2H_2(g) + O_2(g) \longrightarrow 2H_2O(l)$$

Entropy Changes

18.35 Chloroform, $CHCl_3$, is a solvent and has been used as an anesthetic. The heat of vaporization of chloroform at its boiling point (61.2°C) is 29.6 kJ/mol. What is the entropy change when 1.20 mol $CHCl_3$ vaporizes at its boiling point?

18.36 Diethyl ether (known simply as ether), $(C_2H_5)_2O$, is a solvent and anesthetic. The heat of vaporization of diethyl ether at its boiling point (35.6°C) is 26.7 kJ/mol. What is the entropy change when 1.34 mol $(C_2H_5)_2O$ vaporizes at its boiling point?

18.37 The enthalpy change when liquid methanol, CH_3OH, vaporizes at 25°C is 38.0 kJ/mol. What is the entropy change when 1.00 mol of vapor in equilibrium with liquid condenses to liquid at 25°C? The entropy of this vapor at 25°C is 255 J/(mol·K). What is the entropy of the liquid at this temperature?

18.38 The heat of vaporization of carbon disulfide, CS_2, at 25°C is 27.2 kJ/mol. What is the entropy change when 1.00 mol

of vapor in equilibrium with liquid condenses to liquid at 25°C? The entropy of this vapor at 25°C is 243 J/(mol·K). What is the entropy of the liquid at this temperature?

18.39 Predict the sign of ΔS°, if possible, for each of the following reactions. If you cannot predict the sign for any reaction, state why.
a. $C_2H_2(g) + 2H_2(g) \longrightarrow C_2H_6(g)$
b. $N_2(g) + O_2(g) \longrightarrow 2NO(g)$
c. $2C_2H_2(g) + 3O_2(g) \longrightarrow 4CO(g) + 2H_2O(g)$
d. $2C(s) + O_2(g) \longrightarrow 2CO(g)$

18.40 Predict the sign of ΔS°, if possible, for each of the following reactions. If you cannot predict the sign for any reaction, state why.
a. $N_2H_4(l) \longrightarrow N_2(g) + 2H_2O(g)$
b. $C_2H_5OH(l) + 3O_2(g) \longrightarrow 2CO_2(g) + 3H_2O(l)$
c. $P_4(s) + 5O_2(g) \longrightarrow P_4O_{10}(s)$
d. $2NaHCO_3(s) \longrightarrow Na_2CO_3(s) + H_2O(g) + CO_2(g)$

18.41 Calculate ΔS° for the following reactions, using standard entropy values.
a. $2Na(s) + Cl_2(g) \longrightarrow 2NaCl(s)$
b. $Ag(s) + \frac{1}{2}Cl_2(g) \longrightarrow AgCl(s)$
c. $CS_2(l) + 3O_2(g) \longrightarrow CO_2(g) + 2SO_2(g)$
d. $2CH_3OH(l) + 3O_2(g) \longrightarrow 2CO_2(g) + 4H_2O(g)$

18.42 Calculate ΔS° for the following reactions, using standard entropy values.
a. $Pb(s) + \frac{1}{2}O_2(g) \longrightarrow PbO(s)$
b. $CS_2(g) + 4H_2(g) \longrightarrow CH_4(g) + 2H_2S(g)$
c. $C_2H_4(g) + 3O_2(g) \longrightarrow 2CO_2(g) + 2H_2O(g)$
d. $Ca(s) + 2HCl(aq) \longrightarrow CaCl_2(aq) + H_2(g)$

18.43 Calculate ΔS° for the reaction

$$C_2H_4(g) + 3O_2(g) \longrightarrow 2CO_2(g) + 2H_2O(l)$$

a. How will this volume change affect the equilibrium constant of the reaction?
b. Immediately after the volume change, how does Q compare to the equilibrium constant and which way will the reaction proceed?
c. Immediately after the volume change, are the values of ΔG and ΔS positive, negative, or zero for the forward reaction?

18.30 Describe how you would expect the spontaneity (ΔG°) for each of the following reactions to behave with a change of temperature.
a. Phosgene, $COCl_2$, the starting material for the preparation of polyurethane plastics, decomposes as follows:

$$COCl_2(g) \longrightarrow CO(g) + Cl_2(g)$$

b. Chlorine adds to ethylene to produce dichloroethane, a solvent:

$$Cl_2(g) + C_2H_4(g) \longrightarrow C_2H_4Cl_2(l)$$

See Table 18.1 for values of standard entropies. Does the entropy of the chemical system increase or decrease as you expect? Explain.

18.44 What is the change in entropy, $\Delta S°$, for the reaction

$$CaCO_3(s) + 2H^+(aq) \longrightarrow Ca^{2+}(aq) + H_2O(l) + CO_2(g)$$

See Table 18.1 for values of standard entropies. Does the entropy of the chemical system increase or decrease as you expect? Explain.

Free-Energy Change and Spontaneity

18.45 Using enthalpies of formation (Appendix C), calculate $\Delta H°$ for the following reaction at 25°C. Also calculate $\Delta S°$ for this reaction from standard entropies at 25°C. Use these values to calculate $\Delta G°$ for the reaction at this temperature.

$$2CH_3OH(l) + 3O_2(g) \longrightarrow 2CO_2(g) + 4H_2O(l)$$

18.46 Using enthalpies of formation (Appendix C), calculate $\Delta H°$ for the following reaction at 25°C. Also calculate $\Delta S°$ for this reaction from standard entropies at 25°C. Use these values to calculate $\Delta G°$ for the reaction at this temperature.

$$C_3H_8(g) + 5O_2(g) \longrightarrow 3CO_2(g) + 4H_2O(g)$$

18.47 The free energy of formation of one mole of compound refers to a particular chemical equation. For each of the following, write that equation.
 a. KBr(s) **b.** $CH_3Cl(l)$ **c.** $H_2S(g)$ **d.** $AsH_3(g)$

18.48 The free energy of formation of one mole of compound refers to a particular chemical equation. For each of the following, write that equation.
 a. MgO(s) **b.** $COCl_2(g)$ **c.** $CF_4(g)$ **d.** $PCl_5(g)$

18.49 Calculate the standard free energy of the following reactions at 25°C, using standard free energies of formation.
 a. $C_2H_4(g) + 3O_2(g) \longrightarrow 2CO_2(g) + 2H_2O(l)$
 b. $CaCO_3(s) + 2H^+(aq) \longrightarrow Ca^{2+}(aq) + H_2O(l) + CO_2(g)$

18.50 Calculate the standard free energy of the following reactions at 25°C, using standard free energies of formation.
 a. $C_2H_4(g) + 3O_2(g) \longrightarrow 2CO_2(g) + 2H_2O(g)$
 b. $Na_2CO_3(s) + H^+(aq) \longrightarrow 2Na^+(aq) + HCO_3^-(aq)$

18.51 On the basis of $\Delta G°$ for each of the following reactions, decide whether the reaction is spontaneous or nonspontaneous as written. Or, if you expect an equilibrium mixture with significant amounts of both reactants and products, say so.
 a. $SO_2(g) + 2H_2S(g) \longrightarrow 3S(s) + 2H_2O(g)$; $\Delta G° = -91$ kJ
 b. $2H_2O_2(aq) \longrightarrow O_2(g) + 2H_2O(l)$; $\Delta G° = -211$ kJ
 c. $HCOOH(l) \longrightarrow CO_2(g) + H_2(g)$; $\Delta G° = 119$ kJ
 d. $I_2(s) + Br_2(l) \longrightarrow 2IBr(g)$; $\Delta G° = 7.5$ kJ
 e. $NH_4Cl(s) \longrightarrow NH_3(g) + HCl(g)$; $\Delta G° = 92$ kJ

18.52 For each of the following reactions, state whether the reaction is spontaneous or nonspontaneous as written or is easily reversible (that is, is a mixture with significant amounts of reactants and products).
 a. $HCN(g) + 2H_2(g) \longrightarrow CH_3NH_2(g)$; $\Delta G° = -92$ kJ
 b. $2NO(g) \longrightarrow N_2(g) + O_2(g)$; $\Delta G° = -173$ kJ
 c. $2NO(g) + 3H_2O(g) \longrightarrow 2NH_3(g) + \frac{5}{2}O_2(g)$; $\Delta G° = 479$ kJ
 d. $2HBr(g) \longrightarrow H_2(g) + Br_2(g)$; $\Delta G° = 110$ kJ
 e. $H_2(g) + I_2(s) \longrightarrow 2HI(g)$; $\Delta G° = 2.6$ kJ

18.53 Calculate $\Delta H°$ and $\Delta G°$ for the following reactions at 25°C, using thermodynamic data from Appendix C; interpret the signs of $\Delta H°$ and $\Delta G°$.
 a. $Al_2O_3(s) + 2Fe(s) \longrightarrow Fe_2O_3(s) + 2Al(s)$
 b. $COCl_2(g) + H_2O(l) \longrightarrow CO_2(g) + 2HCl(g)$

18.54 Calculate $\Delta H°$ and $\Delta G°$ for the following reactions at 25°C, using thermodynamic data from Appendix C; interpret the signs of $\Delta H°$ and $\Delta G°$.
 a. $2PbO(s) + N_2(g) \longrightarrow 2Pb(s) + 2NO(g)$
 b. $CS_2(l) + 2H_2O(l) \longrightarrow CO_2(g) + 2H_2S(g)$

Maximum Work

18.55 Consider the reaction of 2 mol $H_2(g)$ at 25°C and 1 atm with 1 mol $O_2(g)$ at the same temperature and pressure to produce liquid water at these conditions. If this reaction is run in a controlled way to generate work, what is the maximum useful work that can be obtained? How much entropy is produced in this case?

18.56 Consider the reaction of 1 mol $H_2(g)$ at 25°C and 1 atm with 1 mol $Br_2(l)$ at the same temperature and pressure to produce gaseous HBr at these conditions. If this reaction is run in a controlled way to generate work, what is the maximum useful work that can be obtained? How much entropy is produced in this case?

18.57 What is the maximum work that could be obtained from 4.85 g of zinc metal in the following reaction at 25°C?

$$Zn(s) + Cu^{2+}(aq) \longrightarrow Zn^{2+}(aq) + Cu(s)$$

18.58 What is the maximum work that could be obtained from 3.65 g of zinc metal in the following reaction at 25°C?

$$Zn(s) + 2H^+(aq) \longrightarrow Zn^{2+}(aq) + H_2(g)$$

Calculation of Equilibrium Constants

18.59 Give the expression for the thermodynamic equilibrium constant for each of the following reactions.
 a. $CO(g) + H_2O(g) \rightleftharpoons CO_2(g) + H_2(g)$
 b. $Mg(OH)_2(s) \rightleftharpoons Mg^{2+}(aq) + 2OH^-(aq)$
 c. $2Li(s) + 2H_2O(l) \rightleftharpoons 2Li^+(aq) + 2OH^-(aq) + H_2(g)$

18.60 Write the expression for the thermodynamic equilibrium constant for each of the following reactions.
 a. $CO(g) + 2H_2(g) \rightleftharpoons CH_3OH(g)$
 b. $2Ag^+(aq) + CrO_4^{2-}(aq) \rightleftharpoons Ag_2CrO_4(s)$
 c. $CaCO_3(s) + 2H^+(aq) \rightleftharpoons Ca^{2+}(aq) + H_2O(l) + CO_2(g)$

18.61 What is the standard free-energy change $\Delta G°$ at 25°C for the following reaction? Obtain necessary information from Appendix C.

$$H_2(g) + Br_2(l) \longrightarrow 2HBr(g)$$

What is the value of the thermodynamic equilibrium constant K?

18.62 What is the standard free-energy change $\Delta G°$ at 25°C for the following reaction? See Table 18.2 for data.

$$H_2(g) + S(\text{rhombic}) \longrightarrow H_2S(g)$$

Calculate the value of the thermodynamic equilibrium constant K.

18.63 Calculate the standard free-energy change and the equilibrium constant K_p for the following reaction at 25°C. See Table 18.2 for data.

$$CO(g) + 3H_2(g) \rightleftharpoons CH_4(g) + H_2O(g)$$

18.64 Calculate the standard free-energy change and the equilibrium constant K_p for the following reaction at 25°C. See Appendix C for data.

$$CO(g) + 2H_2(g) \rightleftharpoons CH_3OH(g)$$

18.65 Obtain the equilibrium constant K_c at 25°C from the free-energy change for the reaction

$$Fe(s) + Cu^{2+}(aq) \rightleftharpoons Fe^{2+}(aq) + Cu(s)$$

See Appendix C for data.

18.66 Calculate the equilibrium constant K_c at 25°C from the free-energy change for the following reaction:

$$Zn(s) + 2Ag^+(aq) \rightleftharpoons Zn^{2+}(aq) + Ag(s)$$

See Appendix C for data.

Free Energy and Temperature Change

18.67 Use data given in Tables 6.2 and 18.1 to obtain the value of K_p at 1000°C for the reaction

$$C(graphite) + CO_2(g) \rightleftharpoons 2CO(g)$$

Carbon monoxide is known to form during combustion of carbon at high temperatures. Do the data agree with this? Explain.

18.68 Use data given in Tables 6.2 and 18.1 to obtain the value of K_p at 2100°C for the reaction

$$N_2(g) + O_2(g) \rightleftharpoons 2NO(g)$$

Nitric oxide is known to form in hot flames in air, which is a mixture of N_2 and O_2. It is present in auto exhaust from this reaction. Are the data in agreement with this result? Explain.

18.69 Sodium carbonate, Na_2CO_3, can be prepared by heating sodium hydrogen carbonate, $NaHCO_3$.

$$2NaHCO_3(s) \longrightarrow Na_2CO_3(s) + H_2O(g) + CO_2(g)$$

Estimate the temperature at which $NaHCO_3$ decomposes to products at 1 atm. See Appendix C for data.

18.70 Oxygen was first prepared by heating mercury(II) oxide, HgO.

$$2HgO(s) \longrightarrow 2Hg(g) + O_2(g)$$

Estimate the temperature at which HgO decomposes to O_2 at 1 atm. See Appendix C for data.

General Problems

18.71 Find the sign of $\Delta S°$ for the reaction

$$2N_2O_5(s) \longrightarrow 4NO_2(g) + O_2(g)$$

The reaction is endothermic and spontaneous at 25°C. Explain the spontaneity of the reaction in terms of enthalpy and entropy changes.

18.72 The combustion of acetylene, C_2H_2, is a spontaneous reaction given by the equation

$$2C_2H_2(g) + 5O_2(g) \longrightarrow 4CO_2(g) + 2H_2O(l)$$

As expected for a combustion, the reaction is exothermic. What is the sign of $\Delta H°$? What do you expect for the sign of $\Delta S°$? Explain the spontaneity of the reaction in terms of the enthalpy and entropy changes.

18.73 Estimate the value of $\Delta H°$ for the following reaction from bond energies (Table 9.5).

$$H_2(g) + Cl_2(g) \longrightarrow 2HCl(g)$$

Is the reaction exothermic or endothermic? Note that the reaction involves the breaking of symmetrical molecules (H_2 and Cl_2) and the formation of a less symmetrical product (HCl). From this, would you expect $\Delta S°$ to be positive or negative? Comment on the spontaneity of the reaction in terms of the changes in enthalpy and entropy.

18.74 Compare the energies of the bonds broken and those formed (see Table 9.5) for the reaction

$$HCN(g) + 2H_2(g) \longrightarrow CH_3NH_2(g)$$

From this, conclude whether the reaction is exothermic or endothermic. What is the sign of $\Delta S°$? Explain. The reaction is spontaneous at 25°C. Explain this in terms of the enthalpy and entropy changes.

18.75 Acetic acid, CH_3COOH, freezes at 16.6°C. The heat of fusion, ΔH_{fus}, is 69.0 J/g. What is the change of entropy, ΔS, when 1 mol of liquid acetic acid freezes to the solid?

18.76 Acetone, CH_3COCH_3, boils at 56°C. The heat of vaporization of acetone at this temperature is 29.1 kJ/mol. What is the entropy change when 1 mol of liquid acetone vaporizes at 56°C?

18.77 Without doing any calculations, decide what the sign of $\Delta S°$ will be for each of the following reactions.
  a. $2LiOH(aq) + CO_2(g) \longrightarrow Li_2CO_3(aq) + H_2O(l)$
  b. $(NH_4)_2Cr_2O_7(s) \longrightarrow N_2(g) + 4H_2O(g) + Cr_2O_3(s)$
  c. $2N_2O_5(g) \longrightarrow 4NO_2(g) + O_2(g)$
  d. $O_2(g) + 2F_2(g) \longrightarrow 2OF_2(g)$

18.78 For each of the following reactions, decide whether there is an increase or a decrease in entropy. Why do you think so? (No calculations are needed.)
  a. $N_2(g) + 3H_2(g) \longrightarrow 2NH_3(g)$
  b. $NH_4Cl(s) \longrightarrow NH_3(g) + HCl(g)$
  c. $CO(g) + 2H_2(g) \longrightarrow CH_3OH(l)$
  d. $Li_3N(s) + 3H_2O(l) \longrightarrow 3LiOH(aq) + NH_3(g)$

18.79 The following equation shows how nitrogen dioxide reacts with water to produce nitric acid:

$$3NO_2(g) + H_2O(l) \longrightarrow 2HNO_3(l) + NO(g)$$

Predict the sign of $\Delta S°$ for this reaction.

18.80 Ethanol burns in air or oxygen according to the equation

$$C_2H_5OH(l) + 3O_2(g) \longrightarrow 2CO_2(g) + 3H_2O(g)$$

Predict the sign of $\Delta S°$ for this reaction.

18.81 Acetic acid in vinegar results from the bacterial oxidation of ethanol.

$$C_2H_5OH(l) + O_2(g) \longrightarrow CH_3COOH(l) + H_2O(l)$$

What is $\Delta S°$ for this reaction? Use standard entropy values. (See Appendix C for data.)

18.82 Methanol is produced commercially from carbon monoxide and hydrogen.

$$CO(g) + 2H_2(g) \longrightarrow CH_3OH(l)$$

What is $\Delta S°$ for this reaction? Use standard entropy values.

18.83 Is the following reaction spontaneous as written? Explain. Do whatever calculation is needed to answer the question.

$$SO_2(g) + H_2(g) \longrightarrow H_2S(g) + O_2(g)$$

18.84 Is the following reaction spontaneous as written? Explain. Do whatever calculation is needed to answer the question.

$$CH_4(g) + N_2(g) \longrightarrow HCN(g) + NH_3(g)$$

18.85 The reaction

$$CO_2(g) + H_2(g) \longrightarrow CO(g) + H_2O(g)$$

is nonspontaneous at room temperature but becomes spontaneous at a much higher temperature. What can you conclude from this about the signs of $\Delta H°$ and $\Delta S°$, assuming that the enthalpy and entropy changes are not greatly affected by the temperature change? Explain your reasoning.

18.86 The reaction

$$N_2(g) + 3H_2(g) \longrightarrow 2NH_3(g)$$

is spontaneous at room temperature but becomes nonspontaneous at a much higher temperature. From this fact alone, obtain the signs of $\Delta H°$, and $\Delta S°$, assuming that $\Delta H°$ and $\Delta S°$ do not change much with temperature. Explain your reasoning.

18.87 Calculate $\Delta G°$ at 25°C for the reaction

$$CaF_2(s) \rightleftharpoons Ca^{2+}(aq) + 2F^-(aq)$$

See Appendix C for values of $\Delta G_f°$. What is the value of the solubility product constant, K_{sp}, for this reaction at 25°C?

18.88 Calculate $\Delta G°$ at 25°C for the reaction

$$BaSO_4(s) \rightleftharpoons Ba^{2+}(aq) + SO_4^{2-}(aq)$$

See Appendix C for values of $\Delta G_f°$. What is the value of the solubility product constant, K_{sp}, for this reaction at 25°C?

18.89 Consider the decomposition of phosgene, $COCl_2$.

$$COCl_2(g) \longrightarrow CO(g) + Cl_2(g)$$

Calculate $\Delta H°$, and $\Delta S°$, at 25°C for this reaction. See Appendix C for data. What is $\Delta G°$ at 25°C? Assume that $\Delta H°$ and $\Delta S°$ are constant with respect to a change of temperature. Now calculate $\Delta G°$ at 800°C. Compare the two values of $\Delta G°$. Briefly discuss the spontaneity of the reaction at 25°C and at 800°C.

18.90 Consider the reaction

$$CS_2(g) + 4H_2(g) \rightleftharpoons CH_4(g) + 2H_2S(g)$$

Calculate $\Delta H°$, $\Delta S°$, and $\Delta G°$ at 25°C for this reaction. Assume $\Delta H°$ and $\Delta S°$ are constant with respect to a change of temperature. Now calculate $\Delta G°$ at 650°C. Compare the two values of $\Delta G°$. Briefly discuss the spontaneity of the reaction at 25°C and at 650°C.

18.91 **a.** From a consideration of the following reactions, calculate $\Delta H_f°$ for methane, $CH_4(g)$.

$$CO_2(g) + 2H_2(g) \longrightarrow HCHO(g) + H_2O(g); \Delta H°(kJ) = 35$$

$$CO_2(g) \longrightarrow C(s) + O_2(g); \Delta H°(kJ) = 393$$

$$HCHO(g) + 2H_2(g) \longrightarrow CH_4(g) + H_2O(g); \Delta H°(kJ) = -201$$

$$2H_2(g) + O_2(g) \longrightarrow 2H_2O(g); \Delta H°(kJ) = -484$$

b. From appropriate entropy data, calculate $\Delta S°$ for the formation of methane from the elements.
c. Using the information from above, calculate $\Delta G_f°$ for methane at 25°C.

18.92 **a.** From a consideration of the following reactions, calculate $\Delta H_f°$ for ethane, $C_2H_6(g)$.

$$CH_3CHO(g) + 2H_2(g) \longrightarrow C_2H_6(g) + H_2O(l); \Delta H°(kJ) = -204$$

$$2H_2(g) + O_2(g) \longrightarrow 2H_2O(g); \Delta H°(kJ) = -484$$

$$2C_2H_5OH(l) + O_2(g) \longrightarrow 2CH_3CHO(g) + 2H_2O(l); \Delta H°(kJ) = -348$$

$$H_2O(l) \longrightarrow H_2O(g); \Delta H°(kJ) = 44$$

$$2C_2H_5OH(l) \longrightarrow 4C(s) + 6H_2(g) + O_2(g); \Delta H°(kJ) = 555$$

b. From appropriate entropy data, calculate $\Delta S°$ for the formation of ethane from the elements.
c. Using the information from above, calculate $\Delta G_f°$ for ethane at 25°C.

18.93 For the reaction

$$CH_3OH(l) + \tfrac{3}{2}O_2(g) \longrightarrow 2H_2O(l) + CO_2(g)$$

the value of $\Delta G°$ is -702.2 kJ at 25°C. Other data are as follows:

	$\Delta H_f°$ (kJ/mol) at 25°C	$S°(J/mol \cdot K)$ at 25°C
$CH_3OH(l)$	-238.7	126.8
$H_2O(l)$	-285.8	70.0
$CO_2(g)$	-393.5	213.7

Calculate the absolute entropy, $S°$, per mole of $O_2(g)$.

18.94 For the reaction

$$HCHO(g) + \tfrac{2}{3}O_3(g) \longrightarrow CO_2(g) + H_2O(g)$$

the value of $\Delta G°$ is -618.8 kJ/mol at 25°C. Other data are as follows:

	$\Delta H_f°$ (kJ/mol) at 25°C	$S°(J/mol \cdot K)$ at 25°C
HCHO	-117.0	219.0
$H_2O(g)$	-241.8	188.7
$CO_2(g)$	-393.5	213.7
$O_3(g)$	142.7	?

Calculate the absolute entropy, $S°$, per mole of $O_3(g)$.

18.95 Tin(IV) oxide can be reacted with either hydrogen or carbon to form tin and water vapor or carbon dioxide, respectively. See Appendix C for data.
a. Calculate $\Delta H°$ and $\Delta S°$ at 25°C for the reaction of SnO_2 with H_2 and for the reaction of SnO_2 with C.
b. At what temperature will each of these processes become spontaneous?
c. Industrially, which process is preferred? Why?

18.96 Tungsten is usually produced by the reduction of WO_3 with hydrogen

$$WO_3(s) + 3H_2(g) \longrightarrow W(s) + 3H_2O(g)$$

Consider the following data:

	$WO_3(s)$	$H_2O(g)$
$\Delta H_f°$ (kJ/mol)	−839.9	−241.8
$\Delta G_f°$ (kJ/mol)	−763.1	−228.6

a. Is $K > 1$ or < 1 at 25°C? Explain your answer.
b. What is the value of $\Delta S°$ at 25°C?
c. What is the temperature at which $\Delta G°$ equals zero for this reaction at 1 atm pressure?
d. What is the driving force of this reaction?

18.97 For the decomposition of formic acid,

$$HCOOH(l) \longrightarrow H_2O(l) + CO(g)$$

$\Delta H° = +29$ kJ/mol at 25°C.
a. Does the tendency of this reaction to proceed to a state of minimum energy favor the formation of water and carbon monoxide or formic acid? Explain.
b. Does the tendency of this reaction to proceed to a state of maximum entropy favor the formation of products or reactants? Explain.

18.98 **a.** Why are some reactions exothermic and others endothermic?
b. Discuss the driving force in a spontaneous reaction that is highly exothermic and in one that is endothermic.

18.99 For the reaction

$$2Cu(s) + S(s) \longrightarrow Cu_2S(s)$$

$\Delta H°$ and $\Delta G°$ are negative and $\Delta S°$ is positive.
a. At equilibrium, will reactants or products predominate? Why?
b. Why must the reaction system be heated in order to produce copper(I) sulfide?

18.100 For the reaction

$$C_6H_6(l) + Br_2(l) \longrightarrow C_6H_5Br(l) + HBr(g)$$

the products have a lower energy than the reactants.
a. Predict the sign of the entropy change for this reaction. Explain.
b. Predict whether reactants or products would predominate in an equilibrium mixture. Why?
c. How can you account for the fact that a mixture of the reactants must be heated in the presence of a catalyst in order to produce products?

18.101 When 1.000 g of gaseous butane, C_4H_{10}, is burned at 25°C and 1.00 atm pressure, $H_2O(l)$ and $CO_2(g)$ are formed with the evolution of 49.50 kJ of heat.
a. Calculate the molar enthalpy of formation of butane. (Use enthalpy of formation data for H_2O and CO_2.)
b. $\Delta G_f°$ of butane is −17.2 kJ/mol. What is $\Delta G°$ for the combustion of 1 mol butane?
c. From a and b, calculate $\Delta S°$ for the combustion of 1 mol butane.

18.102 When 1.000 g of ethylene glycol, $C_2H_6O_2$, is burned at 25°C and 1.00 atmosphere pressure, $H_2O(l)$ and $CO_2(g)$ are formed with the evolution of 19.18 kJ of heat.
a. Calculate the molar enthalpy of formation of ethylene glycol. (It will be necessary to use data from Appendix C.)
b. $\Delta G_f°$ of ethylene glycol is −322.5 kJ/mol. What is $\Delta G°$ for the combustion of 1 mol ethylene glycol?
c. What is $\Delta S°$ for the combustion of 1 mol ethylene glycol?

18.103 **a.** Calculate K_1 at 25°C for phosphoric acid:

$$H_3PO_4(aq) \rightleftharpoons H^+(aq) + H_2PO_4{}^-(aq)$$

	$H_3PO_4(aq)$	$H^+(aq)$	$H_2PO_4{}^-(aq)$
$\Delta H_f°$ (kJ/mol)	−1288.3	0	−1285
$S°$ (J/mol·K)	158.2	0	89

b. Which thermodynamic factor is the most significant in accounting for the fact that phosphoric acid is a weak acid? Why?

18.104 **a.** Calculate K_1 at 25°C for sulfurous acid:

$$H_2SO_3(aq) \rightleftharpoons H^+(aq) + HSO_3{}^-(aq)$$

	$H_2SO_3(aq)$	$H^+(aq)$	$HSO_3{}^-(aq)$
$\Delta H_f°$ (kJ/mol)	−608.8	0	−626.2
$S°$ (J/mol·K)	232.2	0	139.8

b. Which thermodynamic factor is the most significant in accounting for the fact that sulfurous acid is a weak acid? Why?

18.105 The direct reaction of iron(III) oxide, Fe_2O_3, to give iron and oxygen gas is a nonspontaneous reaction; normally, iron combines with oxygen to give rust (the oxide). Yet we do change iron(III) oxide, as iron ore, into iron metal. How is this possible? Explain.

18.106 Adenosine triphosphate (ATP) is often referred to as a biological "energy" source. What does this mean? Explain how ATP is used in biological organisms to produce proteins from amino acids.

Strategy Problems

18.107 Consider the reaction in which hydrazine vapor decomposes to its elements:

$$N_2H_4(g) \rightleftharpoons N_2(g) + 2H_2(g)$$

Use data from Appendix C to answer the following questions.
  a. What is the standard enthalpy change for this reaction at 25°C?
  b. Calculate the standard entropy change at 25°C. Does the sign of the entropy change agree with what you would expect? Explain.
  c. Describe the spontaneity or nonspontaneity of the reaction at various temperatures.
  d. What happens to $\Delta G°$ as you lower the temperature? Would this reaction give greater product at higher or at lower temperature? Explain.

18.108 Consider the reaction for the formation of $H_2O(g)$ from its elements. Use the data in Appendix C to answer the following questions.
  a. What is the standard enthalpy of formation of $H_2O(g)$ at 25°C?
  b. What is the standard entropy of formation of $H_2O(g)$ at 25°C?
  c. Use these values to calculate the standard free energy of formation of $H_2O(g)$ at 25°C. Check this value against the one given in Appendix C.
  d. A student obtained $\Delta G_f°$ for $H_2O(g)$ by calculating $\Delta H_f° - TS°$, using $\Delta H_f°$ and $S°$ for $H_2O(g)$ from Appendix C. Is this correct? Explain.

18.109 Acetone, CH_3COCH_3, is a fragrant liquid that is used as a solvent for lacquers, paint removers, and nail polish remover. It burns in oxygen to give carbon dioxide and water:

$$CH_3COCH_3(l) + 4O_2(g) \longrightarrow 3CO_2(g) + 3H_2O(l)$$

If the standard free-energy change for this reaction is -1739 kJ/mol, what is the standard free energy of formation of acetone? Use data from Appendix C.

18.110 Cobalt chloride hexahydrate, $CoCl_2\cdot6H_2O$, is a bright pink compound, but in the presence of very dry air it loses water vapor to the air to produce the light blue anhydrous salt $CoCl_2$. Calculate the standard free-energy change for the reaction at 25°C:

$$CoCl_2\cdot6H_2O(s) \rightleftharpoons CoCl_2(s) + 6H_2O(g)$$

Here are some thermodynamic data at 25°C:

	$\Delta H_f°$ (kJ/mol)	$\Delta G_f°$ (kJ/mol)	$S°$ (J/mol·K)
$CoCl_2(s)$	$-313.$	$-270.$	109.
$CoCl_2\cdot6H_2O(s)$	$-2115.$	$-1725.$	343.

What is the partial pressure of water vapor in equilibrium with the anhydrous salt and the hexahydrate at 25°C? (Give the value in mmHg.) What is the relative humidity of air that has this partial pressure of water? The relative humidity of a sample of air is

$$\text{Relative humidity} = \frac{\text{partial pressure of } H_2O(g) \text{ in air}}{\text{vapor pressure of water}} \times 100\%$$

What do you expect to happen to the equilibrium partial pressure over the hexahydrate as the temperature is raised? Explain.

18.111 An experimenter placed 1.000 mol of H_2 and 1.000 mol of I_2 in a 1.000-L flask. The substances reacted to produce hydrogen iodide:

$$H_2(g) + I_2(g) \rightleftharpoons 2HI(g)$$

When the contents of the flask came to equilibrium at 458°C, the experimenter found that it contained 0.225 mol H_2, 0.225 mol I_2, and 1.550 mol HI.
  a. Calculate the standard free-energy change for the reaction at 458°C.
  b. Assume that the standard enthalpy change for the reaction at 458°C is the same as it is at 298°C. Calculate the standard entropy change for the reaction at 458°C.

18.112 Hydrogen gas and iodine vapor react to produce hydrogen iodide gas:

$$H_2(g) + I_2(g) \rightleftharpoons 2HI(g)$$

Calculate the free-energy change ΔG for the following two conditions, at 25°C. Which one is closer to equilibrium? Explain.
  a. The partial pressures of $H_2(g)$, $I_2(g)$, and $HI(g)$ are each $\frac{1}{3}$ atm.
  b. The partial pressures of $H_2(g)$ and $I_2(g)$ are each $\frac{1}{3}$ atm; the partial pressure of $HI(g)$ is $\frac{1}{90}$ atm.

18.113 Silver carbonate, Ag_2CO_3, is a light yellow compound that decomposes when heated to give silver oxide and carbon dioxide:

$$Ag_2CO_3(s) \rightleftharpoons Ag_2O(s) + CO_2(g)$$

A researcher measured the partial pressure of carbon dioxide over a sample of silver carbonate at 220°C and found that it was 1.37 atm. Calculate the partial pressure of carbon dioxide at 25°C. The standard enthalpies of formation of silver carbonate and silver oxide at 25°C are -505.9 kJ/mol and -31.05 kJ/mol, respectively. Make any reasonable assumptions in your calculations. State the assumptions that you make, and note why you think they are reasonable.

18.114 Sulfur is produced in volcanic gases by the reaction of hydrogen sulfide with sulfur dioxide:

$$2H_2S(g) + SO_2(g) \rightleftharpoons 3S(s, \text{rhombic}) + 2H_2O(g)$$

A particular sample of volcanic gas at 1.00 atm has a partial pressure of sulfur dioxide of 89 mmHg. If this gas at 1170°C also contains hydrogen sulfide and water vapor in equilibrium with rhombic sulfur, what is the ratio of the partial pressure of water vapor to the partial pressure of hydrogen sulfide? Use any reasonable approximations.

18.115 Adenosine triphosphate, ATP, is used as a free-energy source by biological cells. (See the essay on page 750.) ATP hydrolyzes in the presence of enzymes to give ADP:

$$ATP(aq) + H_2O(l) \longrightarrow ADP(aq) + H_2PO_4^-(aq);$$
$$\Delta G° = -30.5 \text{ kJ/mol at } 25°C$$

Consider a hypothetical biochemical reaction of molecule A to give molecule B:

$$A(aq) \longrightarrow B(aq); \Delta G° = +15.0 \text{ kJ/mol at } 25°C$$

a. Calculate the ratio [B]/[A] at 25°C at equilibrium.

b. Now consider this reaction "coupled" to the reaction for the hydrolysis of ATP:

$$A(aq) + ATP(aq) + H_2O(l) \longrightarrow$$
$$B(aq) + ADP(aq) + H_2PO_4^-(aq)$$

If a cell maintains a high ratio of ATP to ADP and $H_2PO_4^-$ by continuously making ATP, the conversion of A to B can be made highly spontaneous. A characteristic value of this ratio is

$$\frac{[ATP]}{[ADP][H_2PO_4]} = 500.$$

Calculate the ratio [B][A] in this case and compare it with the uncoupled reaction. Compared with the uncoupled reaction, how much larger is this ratio when coupled to the hydrolysis of ATP?

Cumulative-Skills Problems

18.117 Hydrogen bromide dissociates into its gaseous elements, H_2 and Br_2, at elevated temperatures. Calculate the percent dissociation at 375°C and 1.00 atm. What would be the percent dissociation at 375°C and 10.0 atm? Use data from Appendix C and any reasonable approximation to obtain K.

18.118 Hydrogen gas and iodine gas react to form hydrogen iodide. If 0.500 mol H_2 and 1.00 mol I_2 are placed in a closed 10.0-L vessel, what is the mole fraction of HI in the mixture when equilibrium is reached at 205°C? Use data from Appendix C and any reasonable approximations to obtain K.

18.119 A 20.0-L vessel is filled with 1.00 mol of ammonia, NH_3. What percent of ammonia dissociates to the elements if equilibrium is reached at 345°C? Use data from Appendix C and make any reasonable approximation to obtain K.

18.116 A car has been fitted with an internal combustion engine that uses propane as a fuel.

$$C_3H_8(g) + 5O_2(g) \longrightarrow 3CO_2(g) + 4H_2O(g)$$

What is the maximum work that you can obtain from 1.00 kg of propane, C_3H_8? Suppose the car is driving uphill. What is the maximum height, in miles, that the car could go to, assuming that the car's mass is 4000. lb? The work done in moving a mass, m, up to a height h is mgh, where g is the constant acceleration of gravity (equal to 9.81 m/s^2).

18.120 A 25.0-L vessel is filled with 0.0100 mol CO and 0.0300 mol H_2. How many moles of CH_4 and how many moles of H_2O are produced when equilibrium is reached at 785°C? Use data from Appendix C and make any reasonable approximation to obtain K.

18.121 K_a for acetic acid at 25.0°C is 1.754×10^{-5}. At 50.0°C, K_a is 1.633×10^{-5}. What are $\Delta H°$ and $\Delta S°$ for the ionization of acetic acid?

18.122 K_{sp} for silver chloride at 25.0°C is 1.782×10^{-10}. At 35.0°C, K_{sp} is 4.159×10^{-10}. What are $\Delta H°$ and $\Delta S°$ for the reaction?

19

Electrochemistry

Electrolysis of a potassium iodide solution producing iodine and hydrogen gas. Potassium iodide pills can be used to protect against thyroid cancer that results from heavy exposure to nuclear fallout by blocking the absorption of radioactive iodine by the thyroid gland.

Contents and Concepts

We start by furthering our understanding of oxidation–reduction reactions, which are the foundation of electrochemistry.

Now we apply our understanding of oxidation–reduction reactions to the study of voltaic cells (commonly called batteries), which spontaneously produce current.

Unlike voltaic cells, electrolytic cells require an electric current to drive a nonspontaneous reaction.

The first battery was invented by Alessandro Volta about 1800. He assembled a pile consisting of pairs of zinc and silver disks separated by paper disks soaked in salt water. With a tall pile, he could detect a weak electric shock when he touched the two ends of the pile. Later Volta showed that any two different metals could be used to make such a voltaic pile (Figure 19.1).

A battery cell that became popular during the nineteenth century was constructed in 1836 by the English chemist John Frederick Daniell. This cell used zinc and copper. The basic principle was that of Volta's battery pile, but each metal was surrounded by a solution of the metal ion, and the solutions were kept separate by a porous ceramic barrier. Each metal with its solution was a half-cell; a zinc half-cell and a copper half-cell made up one voltaic cell. This construction became the standard form of such cells, which exploit the spontaneous chemical reaction

FIGURE 19.1 ▲
Lemon battery
Zinc and copper strips in a lemon generate a voltage.

$$Zn(s) + Cu^{2+}(aq) \longrightarrow Zn^{2+}(aq) + Cu(s)$$

to generate electrical energy.

Today many different kinds of batteries are in use. They include miniature button batteries for pocket calculators and watches, as well as larger batteries to power electric cars or to store the energy from the solar collectors of communications satellites. But all such batteries operate on the same general principles of Volta's pile or Daniell's cell. In this chapter, we will look at the general principles involved in setting up a chemical reaction as a battery. We will answer such questions as the following: What voltage can you expect from a particular battery? How can you relate the battery voltage to the equilibrium constant for the reaction?

■ **See pages 809–810 for the Media Summary.**

Half-Reactions

You may wish to review Sections 4.5 and 4.6.

A voltaic cell employs a spontaneous oxidation–reduction reaction as a source of energy. It is constructed to separate the reaction physically into two half-reactions, one involving oxidation and the other reduction, with electrons moving from the oxidation half-reaction through the external circuit to the reduction half-reaction. <

19.1 | Balancing Oxidation–Reduction Reactions in Acidic and Basic Solutions

In Chapter 4 (Section 4.6) we introduced the *half-reaction method* of balancing simple oxidation–reduction reactions. We now extend this method to reactions that occur in acidic or basic solution. The steps used to balance these equations successfully are built upon those presented in Chapter 4. Keep in mind that oxidation–reduction reactions involve a transfer of electrons from one species to another. For example, in the reaction described in the chapter opener, zinc metal becomes zinc(II) ion: each zinc atom loses two electrons, and copper(II) ion becomes copper metal (each copper ion gains two electrons).

In this chapter, we will represent the hydronium ion, $H_3O^+(aq)$, by its simpler notation $H^+(aq)$, which chemists call the hydrogen ion. In the chapters that focused on acid–base reactions, we stressed proton transfer in solution, so we adopted the hydronium-ion notation. Here, we shift our focus to the electron-transfer aspect of certain reactions, so we adopt the simpler hydrogen-ion notation. Remember, however, that this is simply a notation change. It does not change the chemistry.

Skeleton Oxidation–Reduction Equations

To tackle more complex oxidation–reduction reactions in acidic and basic solutions, we need to review and discuss the essential information required to describe an oxidation–reduction reaction, which is called a *skeleton equation*. To set up the skeleton equation and then balance it, you need answers to the following questions:

1. What species is being oxidized (or, what is the reducing agent)? What species is being reduced (or, what is the oxidizing agent)?
2. What species result from the oxidation and reduction?
3. Does the reaction occur in acidic or basic solution?

For example, iron(II) ion may be oxidized easily by a number of oxidizing agents to yield the iron(III) ion. Permanganate ion in acidic, aqueous solution is a strong oxidizing agent and can oxidize Fe^{2+} to Fe^{3+}. In the process of oxidizing the iron(II) ion, the permanganate ion (MnO_4^-) is reduced to manganese(II) ion (Mn^{2+}). We can express these facts in the following skeleton equation:

$$\overset{+2}{Fe^{2+}}(aq) + \overset{+7}{MnO_4^-}(aq) \longrightarrow \overset{+3}{Fe^{3+}}(aq) + \overset{+2}{Mn^{2+}}(aq) \qquad \text{(acidic solution)}$$

We have written oxidation numbers over the appropriate atoms. Note that the skeleton equation is not balanced. Nor is it complete; in an acidic, aqueous solution, $H^+(aq)$ and $H_2O(l)$ may be possible reactants or products in the equation. (If this were a basic solution, OH^- ion would replace the H^+ ion.)

Half-Reaction Method in Acidic and Basic Solutions

Although the preceding skeleton equation is not complete, it does give the essential information about the oxidation–reduction reaction. Moreover, given the skeleton equation, you can complete and balance the equation using the half-reaction method. Let us see how to do that. We first look at balancing oxidation–reduction equations in acidic solution. To balance such equations in basic solution requires additional steps.

Steps in Balancing Oxidation–Reduction Equations in Acidic Solution

Step 1: Assign oxidation numbers to each atom so you know what is oxidized and what is reduced.

Step 2: Split the skeleton equation into two half-reactions, proceeding as follows. Note the species containing the element that increases in oxidation number, and write those species to give the oxidation half-reaction. Similarly, note the species containing the element that decreases in oxidation number, and write the reduction half-reaction.

Step 3: Complete and balance each half-reaction.

    a. Balance all atoms except O and H.

    b. Balance O atoms by adding H_2O's to one side of the equation.

    c. Balance H atoms by adding H^+ ions to one side of the equation.

    d. Balance electric charge by adding electrons (e^-) to the more positive side.

Step 4: Combine the two half-reactions to obtain the final balanced oxidation–reduction equation.

    a. Multiply each half-reaction by a factor such that when the half-reactions are added, the electrons cancel. (Electrons cannot appear in the final equation.)

    b. Simplify the balanced equation by canceling species that occur on both sides, and reduce the coefficients to smallest whole numbers. Check that the equation is indeed balanced.

Let us see how we would apply this method to the skeleton equation we wrote for the oxidation of iron(II) ion by permanganate ion in acidic solution. We have already determined the elements that change oxidation number (Step 1). We now write the incomplete equation representing the oxidation half-reaction. Iron(II) is oxidized to iron(III) ion. Therefore, following Step 2, we write

$$\overset{+2}{Fe^{2+}}(aq) \longrightarrow \overset{+3}{Fe^{3+}}(aq)$$

Note that the equation is balanced in Fe as it stands (Step 3a). Steps 3b and 3c require that the half-reaction be balanced in O and H. However, since these atoms do not appear in the half-reaction, we can ignore those steps. Then (Step 3d) you need to balance the half-reaction in electric charge. You do that by adding one electron to the more positive side.

$$Fe^{2+}(aq) \longrightarrow Fe^{3+}(aq) + e^- \qquad \text{(oxidation half-reaction)}$$

Check that the half-reaction is balanced in Fe and in electric charge. Note that electrons are lost, as you expect for oxidation.

Now let us look at the reduction half-reaction. From the skeleton equation, you write the species containing the atom for which the oxidation number decreases (Step 2):

$$\overset{+7}{MnO_4^-}(aq) \longrightarrow \overset{+2}{Mn^{2+}}(aq)$$

The equation is balanced in Mn as it stands (Step 3a). For Step 3b, you add four H_2O's to the right side of the equation to balance the O atoms. (Water is present, since this is an aqueous solution.)

$$MnO_4^-(aq) \longrightarrow Mn^{2+}(aq) + 4H_2O(l)$$

Step 3c says to balance the H atoms by adding H^+ ions. (Hydrogen ions are present, since this is an acidic solution.) You add eight H^+ ions to the left side of the equation.

$$MnO_4^-(aq) + 8H^+(aq) \longrightarrow Mn^{2+}(aq) + 4H_2O(l)$$

Finally, you balance the half-reaction in electric charge by adding electrons to the more positive side of the equation (Step 3d). Note that the left side has a charge of $(-1 + 8) = +7$, whereas the right side has a charge of $+2$. So you add five electrons to the left side:

$$MnO_4^-(aq) + 8H^+(aq) + 5e^- \longrightarrow Mn^{2+}(aq) + 4H_2O(l) \qquad \text{(reduction half-reaction)}$$

Check that this half-reaction is balanced in the different kinds of atoms and in electric charge. Note that electrons are gained, as you expect for reduction.

In Step 4a, you need to multiply each half-reaction by a factor such that when the two half-reactions are added, the electrons cancel. You multiply the oxidation half-reaction by 5 (the number of electrons in the reduction half-reaction) and multiply the reduction half-reaction by 1 (the number of electrons in the oxidation half-reaction). Then you add the two half-reactions:

$$
\begin{array}{l}
5 \times (Fe^{2+} \longrightarrow Fe^{3+} + e^-) \\
\underline{1 \times (MnO_4^- + 8H^+ + 5e^- \longrightarrow Mn^{2+} + 4H_2O)} \\
5Fe^{2+} + MnO_4^- + 8H^+ + \cancel{5e^-} \longrightarrow 5Fe^{3+} + Mn^{2+} + 4H_2O + \cancel{5e^-}
\end{array}
$$

After canceling electrons, the equation is in simplest form (Step 4b). The final balanced equation is

$$5Fe^{2+}(aq) + MnO_4^-(aq) + 8H^+(aq) \longrightarrow 5Fe^{3+}(aq) + Mn^{2+}(aq) + 4H_2O(l)$$

You can write this equation in terms of the hydronium-ion notation, $H_3O^+(aq)$, if you wish, by changing $8H^+(aq)$ to $8H_3O^+(aq)$ and adding $8H_2O(l)$ to the other side of the equation to give a total of $12H_2O(l)$.

The following example further illustrates the half-reaction method.

| Example 19.1 | Balancing Equations by the Half-Reaction Method (Acidic Solution) |

Zinc metal reacts with nitric acid, HNO_3, to produce a number of products, depending on how dilute the acid solution is. In a concentrated solution, zinc reduces nitrate ion to ammonium ion; zinc is oxidized to zinc ion, Zn^{2+}. Write the net ionic equation for this reaction.

Problem Strategy From the word statement of the problem, you write the skeleton equation representing the essential features of the oxidation–reduction reaction. Then, assign oxidation numbers to the atoms (Step 1) and separate the skeleton equation into two incomplete half-reactions (Step 2). Now complete and balance each half-reaction (Step 3). (Balance the half-reaction in all elements except O and H; then balance O atoms, then H atoms, and finally electric charge.) In Step 4, you combine the half-reactions to eliminate electrons and simplify the result.

Solution Note that nitric acid is a strong acid, so it exists in solution as H^+ and NO_3^- ions. For the skeleton equation, write just the NO_3^- ion, because you will be adding H^+ later as needed to balance the equation. The skeleton equation, with oxidation numbers for those atoms that change values (following Step 1), is

$$\overset{0}{Zn}(s) + \overset{+5}{N}O_3^-(aq) \longrightarrow \overset{+2}{Zn}^{2+}(aq) + \overset{-3}{N}H_4^+(aq)$$

Now you separate this equation into two incomplete half-reactions (Step 2). Note that zinc is oxidized (increases in oxidation number), and nitrogen is reduced (decreases in oxidation number). The two incomplete half-reactions are

$$Zn(s) \longrightarrow Zn^{2+}(aq)$$
$$NO_3^-(aq) \longrightarrow NH_4^+(aq)$$

The oxidation half-reaction is balanced in Zn, as it stands (Step 3a). There are no O or H atoms, so you can ignore Steps 3b and 3c. Following Step 3d, you add electrons to the more positive side to balance the charge.

$$Zn(s) \longrightarrow Zn^{2+}(aq) + 2e^- \qquad \text{(oxidation half-reaction)}$$

The reduction half-reaction is balanced in N (Step 3a) but is not complete in either O or H. Therefore, you add three H_2O's to the right side to balance O atoms (Step 3b) and add ten H^+ ions to the left side to balance the four H atoms in the NH_4^+ ion and the six H atoms in the H_2O's you just added (Step 3c).

$$10H^+(aq) + NO_3^-(aq) \longrightarrow NH_4^+(aq) + 3H_2O(l)$$

Now, you add electrons to the more positive side to balance the charge.

$$10H^+(aq) + NO_3^-(aq) + 8e^- \longrightarrow NH_4^+(aq) + 3H_2O(l) \qquad \text{(reduction half-reaction)}$$

Check that the half-reaction is balanced in charge, as well as in the different kinds of atoms.

Finally (Step 4a), you multiply the two half-reactions by factors so that when added, the electrons cancel. You multiply the oxidation half-reaction by 4 and the reduction half-reaction by 1:

$$4 \times (Zn \longrightarrow Zn^{2+} + 2e^-)$$
$$\underline{10H^+ + NO_3^- + 8e^- \longrightarrow NH_4^+ + 3H_2O}$$
$$4Zn + 10H^+ + NO_3^- + \cancel{8e^-} \longrightarrow 4Zn^{2+} + NH_4^+ + 3H_2O + \cancel{8e^-}$$

(continued)

(continued)

The equation requires no further simplification beyond canceling electrons (Step 4b). The net ionic equation is

$$4Zn(s) + 10H^+(aq) + NO_3^-(aq) \longrightarrow 4Zn^{2+}(aq) + NH_4^+(aq) + 3H_2O(l)$$

Answer Check After you have completed the process for balancing this type of equation, you can perform a final check of your answer by making sure that you have both mass and charge balance.

Exercise 19.1   Iodic acid, HIO_3, can be prepared by reacting iodine, I_2, with concentrated nitric acid. The skeleton equation is

$$I_2(s) + NO_3^-(aq) \longrightarrow IO_3^-(aq) + NO_2(g)$$

Balance this equation.

■ See Problems 19.35 and 19.36.

You can apply Steps 5 and 6 to the individual half-reactions, rather than to the overall equation. Although this is more work, it does yield the complete half-reactions, which can be useful in discussing batteries (later in this chapter).

To balance an oxidation–reduction equation in basic solution, you begin by balancing the equation *as if it were a reaction in acidic solution*. Then, you add the following steps. <

Additional Steps for Balancing Oxidation–Reduction Equations in Basic Solution

Step 5: Note the number of H^+ ions in the equation. Add this number of OH^- ions to both sides of the equation.

Step 6: Simplify the equation by noting that H^+ reacts with OH^- to give H_2O. Cancel any H_2O's that occur on both sides of the equation and reduce the equation to simplest terms.

The following example illustrates how to apply these rules.

Example 19.2 | Balancing Equations by the Half-Reaction Method (Basic Solution)

Permanganate ion oxidizes sulfite ion in basic solution according to the following skeleton equation:

$$MnO_4^-(aq) + SO_3^{2-}(aq) \longrightarrow MnO_2(s) + SO_4^{2-}(aq)$$

Use the half-reaction method to complete and balance this equation.

Problem Strategy First complete and balance this equation as if it were in acid solution, as in the previous example. Then, following Step 5, add as many OH^- ions to both sides of the equation as there are H^+ ions. After noting that each H^+ ion reacts with an OH^- ion to give H_2O, simplify the equation (Step 6).

Solution After balancing the equation as if it were in acid solution, you obtain the following:

$$2MnO_4^- + 3SO_3^{2-} + 2H^+ \longrightarrow 2MnO_2 + 3SO_4^{2-} + H_2O$$

(continued)

(continued)

Following Step 5, you add 2OH⁻ to both sides of the equation.

$$2MnO_4^- + 3SO_3^{2-} + \underbrace{2H^+ + 2OH^-}_{2H_2O} \longrightarrow 2MnO_2 + 3SO_4^{2-} + H_2O + 2OH^-$$

You replace $2H^+ + 2OH^-$ by $2H_2O$ on the left side, then cancel one of these with the H_2O on the right side. The balanced equation for the reaction in basic solution is

$$2MnO_4^-(aq) + 3SO_3^{2-}(aq) + H_2O(l) \longrightarrow 2MnO_2(s) + 3SO_4^{2-}(aq) + 2OH^-(aq)$$

Answer Check Just as in balancing oxidation–reduction reactions in acidic solution, as a final check, be certain that the masses and charges balance in the equation.

Exercise 19.2 Balance the following equation using the half-reaction method.

$$H_2O_2 + ClO_2 \longrightarrow ClO_2^- + O_2 \qquad \text{(basic solution)}$$

■ See Problems 19.36 and 19.37.

Voltaic Cells

The next several sections describe battery cells, or voltaic cells (also called galvanic cells). These are a kind of electrochemical cell. An **electrochemical cell** is *a system consisting of electrodes that dip into an electrolyte and in which a chemical reaction either uses or generates an electric current.* A **voltaic,** or **galvanic, cell** is *an electrochemical cell in which a spontaneous reaction generates an electric current.* An **electrolytic cell** is *an electrochemical cell in which an electric current drives an otherwise nonspontaneous reaction.* In the next sections, we will discuss the basic principles behind voltaic cells and then explore some of their commercial uses.

19.2 | Construction of Voltaic Cells

A voltaic cell consists of two *half-cells* that are electrically connected. Each **half-cell** is *the portion of an electrochemical cell in which a half-reaction takes place.* A simple half-cell can be made from a metal strip that dips into a solution of its metal ion. An example is the zinc–zinc ion half-cell (often called simply a zinc electrode), which consists of a zinc metal strip dipping into a solution of a zinc salt. Another simple half-cell consists of a copper metal strip dipping into a solution of a copper salt (copper electrode).

In a voltaic cell, two half-cells are connected in such a way that electrons flow from one metal electrode to another through an external circuit, and ions flow from one half-cell to another through an internal cell connection. Figure 19.2 illustrates an atomic view of a voltaic cell consisting of a zinc electrode and a copper electrode. As long as there is an external circuit, electrons can flow through it from one electrode to another. Because zinc tends to lose electrons more readily than copper, zinc atoms in the zinc electrode lose electrons to produce zinc ions. These electrons flow through the external circuit to the copper electrode, where they react with the copper ions in that half-cell to deposit copper metal atoms. The net result is that zinc metal reacts with copper ions to produce zinc ions and copper metal, and an electric current flows through the external circuit.

The two half-cells must be connected internally to allow ions to flow between them. As zinc ions continue to be produced, the zinc ion solution begins to build up

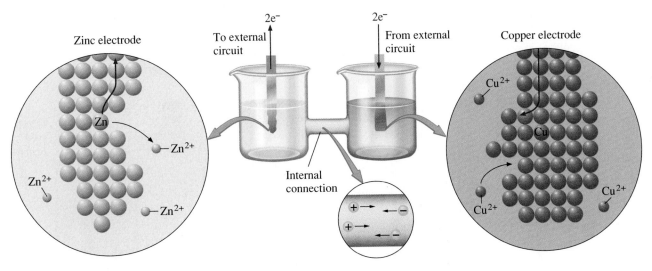

FIGURE 19.2 ▲

Atomic view of a voltaic cell

In the half-cell on the left, a zinc metal atom loses two electrons. These flow through the zinc electrode to the external circuit, then to the copper electrode in the half-cell on the right. Negative charge on the copper electrode (from the electrons) attracts a copper ion, which reacts with the electrons on the electrode to form a copper metal atom. The internal connection, discussed later in the text, allows ions to flow between the two half-cells; it is required to maintain charge balance.

a positive charge. Similarly, as copper ions plate out as copper, the solution builds up a negative charge. The half-cell reactions will stop unless positive ions can move from the zinc half-cell to the copper half-cell, and negative ions from the copper half-cell can move to the zinc half-cell. It is necessary that these ion flows occur without mixing of the zinc ion and copper ion solutions. If copper ion were to come in contact with the zinc metal, for example, direct reaction would occur without an electric current being generated. The voltage would drop, and the battery would run down quickly.

Figure 19.3*A* shows the two half-cells of a voltaic cell connected by a salt bridge. A **salt bridge** is *a tube of an electrolyte in a gel that is connected to the two half-cells of a voltaic cell; the salt bridge allows the flow of ions but prevents the mixing of the different solutions that would allow direct reaction of the cell reactants.* In Figure 19.3*B*, the half-cells are connected externally so that an electric current flows. Figure 19.3*C* shows an actual setup of the zinc–copper cell.

The two half-cell reactions, as noted earlier, are

$$Zn(s) \longrightarrow Zn^{2+}(aq) + 2e^- \qquad \text{(oxidation half-reaction)}$$
$$Cu^{2+}(aq) + 2e^- \longrightarrow Cu(s) \qquad \text{(reduction half-reaction)}$$

The first half-reaction, in which a species loses electrons, is the oxidation half-reaction. *The electrode at which oxidation occurs* is called the **anode.** The second half-reaction, in which a species gains electrons, is the reduction half-reaction. *The electrode at which reduction occurs* is called the **cathode.** These definitions of anode and cathode hold for all electrochemical cells, including electrolytic cells.

Note that the sum of the two half-reactions

$$Zn(s) + Cu^{2+}(aq) \longrightarrow Zn^{2+}(aq) + Cu(s)$$

is *the net reaction that occurs in the voltaic cell;* it is called the **cell reaction.**

Once you know which electrode is the anode and which is the cathode, you can determine the direction of electron flow in the external portion of the circuit. Electrons are given up by the anode (from the oxidation half-reaction) and thus flow from

A

B

Zn → Zn²⁺ + 2e⁻   Cu²⁺ + 2e⁻ → Cu

$$Zn \rightarrow Zn^{2+} + 2e^-$$ $$Cu^{2+} + 2e^- \rightarrow Cu$$

C

FIGURE 19.3 ▶

A zinc–copper voltaic cell
(A) A zinc electrode and a copper electrode, without an external circuit; there is no cell reaction. *(B)* When the two electrodes are connected by an external circuit (with a lightbulb), chemical reaction occurs. *(C)* A similar cell, with the bulb replaced by a voltmeter. Note the blue color of $Cu^{2+}(aq)$.

it, whereas electrons are used up by the cathode (by the reduction half-reaction) and so flow into this electrode. The anode in a voltaic cell has a negative sign, because electrons flow from it. The cathode in a voltaic cell has a positive sign. Look again at Figure 19.3*B* and note the labeling of the electrodes as anode and cathode; also note the direction of electron flow in the external circuit and the signs of the electrodes. Note too the migration of ions in the solutions. The following example further illustrates these points about a voltaic cell.

Example 19.3 | Sketching and Labeling a Voltaic Cell

A voltaic cell is constructed from a half-cell in which a cadmium rod dips into a solution of cadmium nitrate, $Cd(NO_3)_2$, and another half-cell in which a silver rod dips into a solution of silver nitrate, $AgNO_3$. The two half-cells are connected by a salt bridge. Silver ion is reduced during operation of the voltaic cell. Draw a sketch of the cell. Label the anode and cathode, showing the corresponding half-reactions at these electrodes. Indicate the electron flow in the external circuit (with a lightbulb), the signs of the electrodes, and the direction of cation migration in the half-cells.

Problem Strategy   The problem states that silver ion is reduced during the cell operation, so we know that silver is the cathode. If silver is the cathode, then cadmium must be the anode. With this information we can then write the half-reactions. The

(continued)

(continued)

half-reactions provide all of the information we need to draw a complete sketch of the cell.

Solution   Because silver ion is reduced at the silver electrode, the silver electrode is the cathode. The half-reaction is

$$Ag^+(aq) + e^- \longrightarrow Ag(s)$$

The cadmium electrode must be the anode (the electrode at which oxidation occurs); the half-reaction is

$$Cd(s) \longrightarrow Cd^{2+}(aq) + 2e^-$$

Now that you have labeled the electrodes, you can see that the electron flow in the external circuit is from the cadmium electrode (anode) to the silver electrode (cathode). Positive ions will flow in the solution portion of the circuit opposite to the direction of the electrons. **The sketch for this cell, including the labeling, is given in Figure 19.4.**

Answer Check   Make sure that the direction of electron flow is consistent with the half-reactions; the electrons always flow *from* the material undergoing oxidation.

$$Cd \rightarrow Cd^{2+} + 2e^- \qquad Ag^+ + e^- \rightarrow Ag$$

FIGURE 19.4 ▲

Cell described in the example
A voltaic cell consisting of cadmium and silver electrodes.

Exercise 19.3   A voltaic cell consists of a silver–silver ion half-cell and a nickel–nickel(II) ion half-cell. Silver ion is reduced during operation of the cell. Sketch the cell, labeling the anode and cathode and indicating the corresponding electrode reactions. Show the direction of electron flow in the external circuit and the direction of cation movement in the half-cells.

■ See Problems 19.43 and 19.44.

Concept Check 19.1

If you were to construct a wet cell and decided to replace the salt bridge with a piece of copper wire, would the cell produce a sustainable current? Explain your answer.

19.3 | Notation for Voltaic Cells

It is convenient to have a shorthand way of designating particular voltaic cells. The cell described earlier, consisting of a zinc metal–zinc ion half-cell and a copper metal–copper ion half-cell, is written

$$Zn(s) \,|\, Zn^{2+}(aq) \,\|\, Cu^{2+}(aq) \,|\, Cu(s)$$

In this notation, the anode, or oxidation half-cell, is always written on the left; the cathode, or reduction half-cell, is written on the right. The two electrodes are electrically connected by means of a salt bridge, denoted by two vertical bars.

$$\underset{\text{anode}}{Zn(s)|Zn^{2+}(aq)} \quad \underset{\text{salt bridge}}{\|} \quad \underset{\text{cathode}}{Cu^{2+}(aq)|Cu(s)}$$

The cell terminals are at the extreme ends in this cell notation, and a single vertical bar indicates a phase boundary—say, between a solid terminal and the electrode solution. For the anode of the same cell, you have

$$\underset{\text{anode terminal}}{Zn(s)} \quad \underset{\text{phase boundary}}{|} \quad \underset{\text{anode electrolyte}}{Zn^{2+}(aq)}$$

FIGURE 19.5 ▲

A hydrogen electrode
Hydrogen gas bubbles over a platinum surface, where the half-reaction $2H^+(aq) + 2e^- \rightleftharpoons H_2(g)$ occurs.

When the half-reaction involves a gas, an inert material such as platinum serves as a terminal and as an electrode surface on which the half-reaction occurs. The platinum catalyzes the half-reaction but otherwise is not involved in it. Figure 19.5 shows a hydrogen electrode; hydrogen bubbles over a platinum plate that is immersed in an acidic solution. The cathode half-reaction is

$$2H^+(aq) + 2e^- \rightleftharpoons H_2(g)$$

The notation for the hydrogen electrode, written as a cathode, is

$$H^+(aq) \,|\, H_2(g) \,|\, Pt$$

To write such an electrode as an anode, you simply reverse the notation:

$$Pt \,|\, H_2(g) \,|\, H^+(aq)$$

Here are several additional examples of this notation for electrodes (written as cathodes). A comma separates ions present in the same solution. We will write the cathode with oxidized species before reduced species, in the same order as in the half-reaction.

Cathode	Cathode Reaction
$Cl_2(g) \,|\, Cl^-(aq) \,|\, Pt$	$Cl_2(g) + 2e^- \rightleftharpoons 2Cl^-(aq)$
$Fe^{3+}(aq), Fe^{2+}(aq) \,|\, Pt$	$Fe^{3+}(aq) + e^- \rightleftharpoons Fe^{2+}(aq)$
$Cd^{2+}(aq) \,|\, Cd(s)$	$Cd^{2+}(aq) + 2e^- \rightleftharpoons Cd(s)$

Exercise 19.4 Write the notation for a cell in which the electrode reactions are

$$2H^+(aq) + 2e^- \longrightarrow H_2(g)$$
$$Zn(s) \longrightarrow Zn^{2+}(aq) + 2e^-$$

■ See Problems 19.49 and 19.50.

You can write the overall cell reaction from the cell notation by first writing the appropriate half-cell reactions, multiplying as necessary, and then summing so that the electrons cancel. Example 19.4 shows how this is done.

Example 19.4 | Writing the Cell Reaction from the Cell Notation

a. Write the cell reaction for the voltaic cell

$$Tl(s) \,|\, Tl^+(aq) \,\|\, Sn^{2+}(aq) \,|\, Sn(s)$$

b. Write the cell reaction for the voltaic cell

$$Zn(s) \,|\, Zn^{2+}(aq) \,\|\, Fe^{3+}(aq), Fe^{2+}(aq) \,|\, Pt$$

Problem Strategy The cell notation gives the species involved in each half-reaction. Complete and balance each half-reaction, and then multiply by factors so that when you add the half-reactions, the electrons cancel. The result is the cell reaction.

Solution a. The half-cell reactions are

$$Tl(s) \longrightarrow Tl^+(aq) + e^-$$
$$Sn^{2+}(aq) + 2e^- \longrightarrow Sn(s)$$

(continued)

(*continued*)

Multiplying the anode reaction by 2 and then summing the half-cell reactions give

$$2Tl(s) + Sn^{2+}(aq) \longrightarrow 2Tl^+(aq) + Sn(s)$$

b. The half-cell reactions are

$$Zn(s) \longrightarrow Zn^{2+}(aq) + 2e^-$$
$$Fe^{3+}(aq) + e^- \longrightarrow Fe^{2+}(aq)$$

and the cell reaction is

$$Zn(s) + 2Fe^{3+}(aq) \longrightarrow Zn^{2+}(aq) + 2Fe^{2+}(aq)$$

Answer Check Always make sure that you multiplied the half-reactions by the correct coefficients to ensure that the electrons cancel.

Exercise 19.5 Give the overall cell reaction for the voltaic cell

$$Cd(s)\,|\,Cd^{2+}(aq)\,\|\,H^+(aq)\,|\,H_2(g)\,|\,Pt$$

■ See Problems 19.53 and 19.54.

To fully specify a voltaic cell, it is necessary to give the concentrations of solutions or ions and the pressure of gases. In the cell notation, these are written within parentheses for each species. For example,

$$Zn(s)\,|\,Zn^{2+}(1.0\,M)\,\|\,H^+(1.0\,M)\,|\,H_2(1.0\,atm)\,|\,Pt$$

19.4 | Cell Potential

Work is needed to move electrons in a wire or to move ions through a solution to an electrode. The situation is analogous to pumping water from one point to another. Work must be expended to pump the water. The analogy may be extended. Water moves from a point at high pressure to a point at low pressure. Thus, a pressure difference is required. The work expended in moving water through a pipe depends on the volume of water and the pressure difference. The situation with electricity is similar. An electric charge moves from a point at high electric potential (high electrical pressure) to a point at low electric potential (low electrical pressure). The work needed to move an electric charge through a conductor depends on the total charge moved and the potential difference. **Potential difference** is *the difference in electric potential (electrical pressure) between two points.* You measure this quantity in volts. The **volt, V,** is *the SI unit of potential difference.* The electrical work expended in moving a charge through a conductor is

Electrical work = charge × potential difference

Corresponding SI units for the terms in this equation are

Joules = coulombs × volts

The **Faraday constant, F,** is *the magnitude of charge on one mole of electrons; it equals 9.6485×10^4 C per mole of electrons* (96,485 C/mol e⁻). The *faraday* is a unit of charge equal to 9.6485×10^4 C. In moving this quantity of charge (1 faraday of charge) from one electrode to another, the numerical value of the work done by a voltaic cell is the product of the faraday constant F times the potential difference between the electrodes. The work w is the negative of this, because the voltaic cell loses energy as it does work on the surroundings.

$$w = -F \times \text{potential difference}$$

In the normal operation of a voltaic cell, the potential difference (voltage) across the electrodes is less than the maximum possible voltage of the cell. One reason for this is that it takes energy or work to drive a current through the cell itself. The decrease in cell voltage as current is drawn reflects this energy expenditure within the cell; and the greater the current, the lower the voltage. Thus, the cell voltage has its maximum value only when no current flows. The situation is analogous to measuring the difference between the pressure of water in a faucet and that of the outside atmosphere. You expect this difference to be higher if you measure it by a device that does not require you to run water from the faucet. When you do run water, the pressure difference drops.

The maximum potential difference between the electrodes of a voltaic cell is referred to as the **cell potential** or **electromotive force (emf)** of the cell, or E_{cell}. It can be measured by an electronic digital voltmeter (Figure 19.6).

You can also determine which electrode of a cell is the anode and which is the cathode from this measurement. The digital voltmeter gives the reading with a sign attached, from which you can deduce the sign, or polarity, of each electrode. The anode of a voltaic cell has negative polarity, and the cathode has positive polarity.

We can now write an expression for the maximum work obtainable from a voltaic cell. Let n be the number of moles of electrons transferred in the overall cell equation. The maximum electrical work of a voltaic cell for molar amounts of reactants (according to the cell equation *as written*) is

$$w_{max} = -nFE_{cell}$$

Here E_{cell} is the cell potential, and F is the Faraday constant, 9.6485×10^4 C/mol e⁻.

FIGURE 19.6 ▲

A digital voltmeter

A digital voltmeter draws negligible current, so it can be used to measure cell potential.

Example 19.5 | Calculating the Quantity of Work from a Given Amount of Cell Reactant

The cell potential of a particular voltaic cell with the cell reaction

$$Hg_2^{2+}(aq) + H_2(g) \rightleftharpoons 2Hg(l) + 2H^+(aq)$$

is 0.650 V. Calculate the maximum electrical work of this cell when 0.500 g H_2 is consumed.

Problem Strategy We can determine the maximum work of a cell by using the formula $w_{max} = -nFE_{cell}$, where E_{cell} is given in the problem, F is the Faraday constant, and n is the number of moles of electrons transferred in the overall cell equation. To get n, you split the cell reaction into half-reactions, multiplying each by a factor so that when added together, they give the cell reaction. Then n equals the number of moles of electrons in either half-reaction.

Solution The half-reactions are

$$Hg_2^{2+}(aq) + 2e^- \rightleftharpoons 2Hg(l)$$
$$H_2(g) \rightleftharpoons 2H^+(aq) + 2e^-$$

n equals 2, and the maximum work for the reaction as written is

$$w_{max} = -nFE_{cell} = -2 \text{ mol e}^- \times 96{,}485 \text{ C/mol e}^- \times 0.650 \text{ V}$$
$$= -1.25 \times 10^5 \text{ V·C}$$
$$= -1.25 \times 10^5 \text{ J}$$

(continued)

(*continued*)

(Remember that a joule is equal to a volt-coulomb. Also, note that the negative sign means work is done by the cell—that is, energy is lost by the cell.) For 0.500 g H_2, the maximum work is

$$0.500 \; \text{g} \, H_2 \times \frac{1 \; \text{mol} \, H_2}{2.02 \; \text{g} \, H_2} \times \frac{-1.25 \times 10^5 \; \text{J}}{1 \; \text{mol} \, H_2} = \mathbf{-3.09 \times 10^4 \; J}$$

Note that the conversion factor -1.25×10^5 J/1 mol H_2 is determined by the chemical equation as written. In the equation, 1 mol H_2 reacts, and the maximum work produced is -1.25×10^5 J.

Answer Check   The maximum work per mole should be in the range of values expected for ΔG, which is on the order of tens to hundreds of kilojoules per mole, as it is here. You should be suspicious of any values that you obtain that lie outside this range.

Exercise 19.6   What is the maximum electrical work that can be obtained from 6.54 g of zinc metal that reacts in a Daniell cell, described in the chapter opening, whose cell potential is 1.10 V? The overall cell reaction is

$$Zn(s) + Cu^{2+}(aq) \longrightarrow Zn^{2+}(aq) + Cu(s)$$

■ See Problems 19.57, 19.58, 19.59, and 19.60.

19.5 | Standard Cell Potentials and Standard Electrode Potentials

A cell potential is a measure of the driving force of the cell reaction. This reaction occurs in the cell as separate half-reactions: an oxidation half-reaction and a reduction half-reaction. The general forms of these half-reactions are

Reduced species $\longrightarrow$ oxidized species + ne^- (oxidation/anode)

Oxidized species + $ne^- \longrightarrow$ reduced species   (reduction/cathode)

You can imagine that the cell potential is composed of a contribution from the anode (whose value depends on the ability of the oxidation half-reaction to lose electrons) and a contribution from the cathode (whose value depends on the ability of the reduction half-reaction to gain electrons). We call these contributions the *oxidation potential* and the *reduction potential,* respectively. Then

$$E_{\text{cell}} = \text{oxidation potential} + \text{reduction potential}$$

A reduction potential is a measure of the tendency for an oxidized species to gain electrons in the reduction half-reaction (in other words, a measure of the ability of the species to act as an oxidizing agent). If you can construct a table of reduction potentials, you will have a list of strengths of oxidizing agents, in addition to having a way of calculating cell potentials.

You can look at an oxidation half-reaction as the reverse of a corresponding reduction half-reaction. The oxidation potential for an oxidation half-reaction equals the negative of the reduction potential for the reverse half-reaction (which is a reduction).

Oxidation potential for a half-reaction = −reduction potential for the reverse half-reaction

This means that in practice you need to tabulate only oxidation potentials or reduction potentials. The choice, by convention, is to tabulate reduction potentials. We call these *electrode potentials,* and we denote them by the symbol E (without the subscript cell, as in E_{cell}).

Consider the zinc–copper cell described earlier.

$$Zn(s)\,|\,Zn^{2+}(aq)\,\|\,Cu^{2+}(aq)\,|\,Cu(s)$$

The half-reactions are

$$Zn(s) \longrightarrow Zn^{2+}(aq) + 2e^-$$
$$Cu^{2+}(aq) + 2e^- \longrightarrow Cu(s)$$

The first half-reaction is an oxidation. If you write E_{Zn} for the electrode potential corresponding to the reduction half-reaction $Zn^{2+}(aq) + 2e^- \longrightarrow Zn(s)$, then $-E_{Zn}$ is the potential for the oxidation half-reaction $Zn(s) \longrightarrow Zn^{2+}(aq) + 2e^-$. The copper half-reaction is a reduction. Write E_{Cu} for the electrode potential.

The cell potential is the sum of the potentials for the reduction and oxidation half-reactions. For the cell we have been describing, the cell potential is the sum of the reduction potential (electrode potential) for the copper half-cell and the oxidation potential (negative of the electrode potential) for the zinc half-cell.

$$E_{cell} = E_{Cu} + (-E_{Zn}) = E_{Cu} - E_{Zn}$$

Note that the cell potential equals the difference between the two electrode potentials. You can think of the electrode potential as the electric potential on the electrode, and you obtain the cell potential as a potential difference in which you subtract the anode potential from the cathode potential.

$$E_{cell} = E_{cathode} - E_{anode}$$

The electrode potential is an *intensive property*. This means that its value is independent of the amount of species in the reaction. Thus, the electrode potential for the half-reaction

$$2Cu^{2+}(aq) + 4e^- \longrightarrow 2Cu(s)$$

is the same as for

$$Cu^{2+}(aq) + 2e^- \longrightarrow Cu(s)$$

Tabulating Standard Electrode Potentials

The cell potential of a voltaic cell depends on the concentrations of substances and the temperature of the cell. For purposes of tabulating electrochemical data, it is usual to choose thermodynamic standard-state conditions for voltaic cells. The **standard cell potential**, E°_{cell}, is *the emf of a voltaic cell operating under standard-state conditions (solute concentrations are each 1 M, gas pressures are each 1 atm, and the temperature has a specified value—usually 25°C)*. Note the superscript degree sign (°), which signifies standard-state conditions. <

To be precise, the standard-state conditions are those in which the activities (ideal concentrations) of solutes and gases equal 1. This is equivalent to 1 M only for ideal solutions. Because of the strong attractions between ions, substantial deviations from ideal conditions exist in electrolyte solutions, except when very dilute. We will ignore these deviations here.

If you can derive a table of electrode potentials, you can calculate cell potentials from them. This provides a great advantage over tabulating cell potentials. From a small table of electrode potentials, you can obtain all the cell potentials you could construct from pairs of electrodes. For instance, a table of 40 electrode potentials would give the cell potentials of nearly 800 voltaic cells.

However, it is not possible to measure the potential of a single electrode; only the cell potentials of cells can be measured. What you can do is measure the cell potentials of cells constructed from various electrodes connected in turn to one particular electrode, which you choose as a reference. You arbitrarily assign this reference electrode a potential equal to zero and obtain the potentials for the other electrodes by measuring the cell potentials. By convention, the reference chosen for comparing electrode potentials is the *standard hydrogen electrode*, and it is assigned a potential of 0.00 V. This is an electrode like that pictured earlier in Figure 19.5 operating under standard-state conditions.

The **standard electrode potential,** $E°$, is *the electrode potential when the concentrations of solutes are 1 M, the gas pressures are 1 atm, and the temperature has a specified value (usually 25°C).* The superscript degree sign (°) signifies standard-state conditions.

To understand how standard electrode potentials are obtained, look at how you would find the standard electrode potential, $E°$, for the zinc electrode. You connect a standard zinc electrode to a standard hydrogen electrode. When you measure the cell potential with a voltmeter, you obtain 0.76 V, with the zinc electrode acting as the anode.

Now write the cell potential in terms of the electrode potentials. The cell is

$$Zn(s) \,|\, Zn^{2+}(aq) \,\|\, H^+(aq) \,|\, H_2(g) \,|\, Pt$$

and the half-reactions with corresponding half-cell potentials (oxidation or reduction potentials) are

$$Zn(s) \longrightarrow Zn^{2+}(aq) + 2e^-; \; -E°_{Zn}$$
$$2H^+(aq) + 2e^- \longrightarrow H_2(g); \; E°_{H_2}$$

The cell potential is the sum of the half-cell potentials.

$$E_{cell} = E°_{H_2} + (-E°_{Zn})$$

Substitute 0.76 V for the cell potential and 0.00 V for the standard hydrogen electrode potential. This gives $E°_{Zn} = -0.76$ V.

Proceeding in this way, you can obtain the electrode potential for a series of half-cell reactions. Table 19.1 lists standard electrode potentials for selected half-cells at 25°C.

Strengths of Oxidizing and Reducing Agents

Standard electrode potentials are useful in determining the strengths of oxidizing and reducing agents under standard-state conditions. Because electrode potentials are reduction potentials, those reduction half-reactions in Table 19.1 with the larger (that is, more positive) electrode potentials have the greater tendency to go left to right as written. A reduction half-reaction has the general form

$$\text{Oxidized species} + ne^- \longrightarrow \text{reduced species}$$

The oxidized species acts as an oxidizing agent. Consequently, *the strongest oxidizing agents in a table of standard electrode potentials are the oxidized species corresponding to half-reactions with the largest (most positive) $E°$ values.*

Those reduction half-reactions with lower (that is, more negative) electrode potentials have a greater tendency to go right to left. That is,

$$\text{Reduced species} \longrightarrow \text{oxidized species} + ne^-$$

The reduced species acts as a reducing agent. Consequently, *the strongest reducing agents in a table of standard electrode potentials are the reduced species corresponding to half-reactions with the smallest (most negative) $E°$ values.*

The first two and the last two entries in Table 19.1 are as follows:

$$Li^+(aq) + e^- \longrightarrow Li(s)$$
$$Na^+(aq) + e^- \longrightarrow Na(s)$$

$$\cdots$$

$$\cdots$$

$$S_2O_8^{2-}(aq) + 2e^- \longrightarrow 2SO_4^{2-}(aq)$$
$$F_2(g) + 2e^- \longrightarrow 2F^-(aq)$$

The strongest oxidizing agents are the species on the left side in the last two entries in the table (given here in red). The strongest reducing agents are the species on the right side in the first two entries in the table (given here in blue).

TABLE 19.1	Standard Electrode (Reduction) Potentials in Aqueous Solution at 25°C*
Cathode (Reduction) Half-Reaction	Standard Potential, $E°$(V)
$Li^+(aq) + e^- \rightleftharpoons Li(s)$	−3.04
$Na^+(aq) + e^- \rightleftharpoons Na(s)$	−2.71
$Mg^{2+}(aq) + 2e^- \rightleftharpoons Mg(s)$	−2.38
$Al^{3+}(aq) + 3e^- \rightleftharpoons Al(s)$	−1.66
$2H_2O(l) + 2e^- \rightleftharpoons H_2(g) + 2OH^-(aq)$	−0.83
$Zn^{2+}(aq) + 2e^- \rightleftharpoons Zn(s)$	−0.76
$Cr^{3+}(aq) + 3e^- \rightleftharpoons Cr(s)$	−0.74
$Fe^{2+}(aq) + 2e^- \rightleftharpoons Fe(s)$	−0.41
$Cd^{2+}(aq) + 2e^- \rightleftharpoons Cd(s)$	−0.40
$Ni^{2+}(aq) + 2e^- \rightleftharpoons Ni(s)$	−0.23
$Sn^{2+}(aq) + 2e^- \rightleftharpoons Sn(s)$	−0.14
$Pb^{2+}(aq) + 2e^- \rightleftharpoons Pb(s)$	−0.13
$Fe^{3+}(aq) + 3e^- \rightleftharpoons Fe(s)$	−0.04
$2H^+(aq) + 2e^- \rightleftharpoons H_2(g)$	0.00
$Sn^{4+}(aq) + 2e^- \rightleftharpoons Sn^{2+}(aq)$	0.15
$Cu^{2+}(aq) + e^- \rightleftharpoons Cu^+(aq)$	0.16
$Cu^{2+}(aq) + 2e^- \rightleftharpoons Cu(s)$	0.34
$IO^-(aq) + H_2O(l) + 2e^- \rightleftharpoons I^-(aq) + 2OH^-(aq)$	0.49
$Cu^+(aq) + e^- \rightleftharpoons Cu(s)$	0.52
$I_2(s) + 2e^- \rightleftharpoons 2I^-(aq)$	0.54
$Fe^{3+}(aq) + e^- \rightleftharpoons Fe^{2+}(aq)$	0.77
$Hg_2^{2+}(aq) + 2e^- \rightleftharpoons 2Hg(l)$	0.80
$Ag^+(aq) + e^- \rightleftharpoons Ag(s)$	0.80
$Hg^{2+}(aq) + 2e^- \rightleftharpoons Hg(l)$	0.85
$ClO^-(aq) + H_2O(l) + 2e^- \rightleftharpoons Cl^-(aq) + 2OH^-(aq)$	0.90
$2Hg^{2+}(aq) + 2e^- \rightleftharpoons Hg_2^{2+}(aq)$	0.90
$NO_3^-(aq) + 4H^+(aq) + 3e^- \rightleftharpoons NO(g) + 2H_2O(l)$	0.96
$Br_2(l) + 2e^- \rightleftharpoons 2Br^-(aq)$	1.07
$O_2(g) + 4H^+(aq) + 4e^- \rightleftharpoons 2H_2O(l)$	1.23
$Cr_2O_7^{2-}(aq) + 14H^+(aq) + 6e^- \rightleftharpoons 2Cr^{3+}(aq) + 7H_2O(l)$	1.33
$Cl_2(g) + 2e^- \rightleftharpoons 2Cl^-(aq)$	1.36
$MnO_4^-(aq) + 8H^+(aq) + 5e^- \rightleftharpoons Mn^{2+}(aq) + 4H_2O(l)$	1.49
$H_2O_2(aq) + 2H^+(aq) + 2e^- \rightleftharpoons 2H_2O(l)$	1.78
$S_2O_8^{2-}(aq) + 2e^- \rightleftharpoons 2SO_4^{2-}(aq)$	2.01
$F_2(g) + 2e^- \rightleftharpoons 2F^-(aq)$	2.87

*See Appendix I for a more extensive table.

Example 19.6 | Determining the Relative Strengths of Oxidizing and Reducing Agents

a. Order the following oxidizing agents by increasing strength under standard-state conditions: $Cl_2(g)$, $H_2O_2(aq)$, $Fe^{3+}(aq)$.

b. Order the following reducing agents by increasing strength under standard-state conditions: $H_2(g)$, $Al(s)$, $Cu(s)$.

Problem Strategy a. Read down the table of electrode potentials, picking out the reduction half-reactions in which the species of interest occur as reactants. The order from *top to bottom* in which these species occur in the table is the order of increasing oxidizing power.

b. Read down the table of electrode potentials, picking out the reduction half-reactions in which the species of interest occur as products. The order from *bottom to top* in which these species occur in the table is the order of increasing reducing strength.

Solution a. The half-reactions and corresponding electrode potentials are as follows:

$$Fe^{3+}(aq) + e^- \longrightarrow Fe^{2+}(aq) \qquad 0.77 \text{ V}$$
$$Cl_2(g) + 2e^- \longrightarrow 2Cl^-(aq) \qquad 1.36 \text{ V}$$
$$H_2O_2(aq) + 2H^+(aq) + 2e^- \longrightarrow 2H_2O(l) \qquad 1.78 \text{ V}$$

The order by increasing oxidizing strength is $\mathbf{Fe^{3+}(aq)}$, $\mathbf{Cl_2(g)}$, $\mathbf{H_2O_2(aq)}$.

b. The half-reactions and corresponding electrode potentials are

$$Al^{3+}(aq) + 3e^- \longrightarrow Al(s) \qquad -1.66 \text{ V}$$
$$2H^+(aq) + 2e^- \longrightarrow H_2(g) \qquad 0.00 \text{ V}$$
$$Cu^{2+}(aq) + 2e^- \longrightarrow Cu(s) \qquad 0.34 \text{ V}$$

The order by increasing reducing strength is $\mathbf{Cu(s)}$, $\mathbf{H_2(g)}$, $\mathbf{Al(s)}$.

Answer Check To consistently get this type of problem right, make certain that you understand that the strongest oxidizing agents are those species that are most likely to undergo reduction, and the strongest reducing agents are the least likely to undergo reduction.

Exercise 19.7 Which is the stronger oxidizing agent, $NO_3^-(aq)$ in acidic solution (to NO) or $Ag^+(aq)$?

■ See Problems 19.61, 19.62, 19.63, and 19.64.

You can use a table of electrode potentials to predict the direction of spontaneity of an oxidation–reduction reaction. You need note only the relative strengths of the oxidizing agents on the left and right sides of the equation. The stronger oxidizing agent will be on the reactant side when the equation is written as a spontaneous reaction. (Alternatively, you can look at the reducing agents; the stronger reducing agent will be on the reactant side of the spontaneous reaction.)

Example 19.7 | Determining the Direction of Spontaneity from Electrode Potentials

Consider the reaction

$$Zn^{2+}(aq) + 2Fe^{2+}(aq) \longrightarrow Zn(s) + 2Fe^{3+}(aq)$$

Does the reaction go spontaneously in the direction indicated, under standard conditions?

Problem Strategy Find the oxidizing agents in the equation; one is on the left side and the other on the right side. Locate these oxidizing agents in a table of electrode potentials. (The oxidizing agent is on the left side of the reduction half-reaction.) The stronger oxidizing agent is the one involved in the

half-reaction with the more positive standard electrode potential.

Solution In this reaction, Zn^{2+} is the oxidizing agent on the left side; Fe^{3+} is the oxidizing agent on the right side. The corresponding standard electrode potentials are

$$Zn^{2+}(aq) + 2e^- \longrightarrow Zn(s); E^\circ = -0.76 \text{ V}$$
$$Fe^{3+}(aq) + e^- \longrightarrow Fe^{2+}(aq); E^\circ = 0.77 \text{ V}$$

The stronger oxidizing agent is the one involved in the half-reaction with the more positive standard electrode

(continued)

(continued)

potential, so Fe^{3+} is the stronger oxidizing agent. The reaction is **nonspontaneous** as written.

Answer Check When writing the half-reactions for comparison, make sure that you have noted the correct sign of $E°$ for each reaction.

Exercise 19.8 Does the following reaction occur spontaneously in the direction indicated, under standard conditions?

$$Cu^{2+}(aq) + 2I^-(aq) \longrightarrow Cu(s) + I_2(s)$$

■ See Problems 19.65 and 19.66.

Calculating Cell Potentials

When calculating cell potential values, chemists employ two approaches, both of which rely on using standard reduction potential values. One approach requires that you combine half-reactions and their standard potential values (reduction and oxidation); the other involves using an equation to calculate the difference between standard reduction potentials. The advantage of the first approach is that while determining a cell potential value, you will develop a complete understanding of the half-reactions that are taking place in the cell, identification of the species that are undergoing oxidation and reduction, as well as the number of electrons involved in the balanced oxidation–reduction reaction. The second approach involves determination of the anode and cathode in the reaction and using an equation with the appropriate reduction potentials. The advantage of this approach is that you can quickly calculate the cell potential from tabulated standard reduction potential values and that you are calculating the cell potential by difference.

Calculating Cell Potentials by Addition of Half-Reactions and Standard Potentials Consider a voltaic cell constructed from a cadmium electrode and a silver electrode having the following reduction half-reactions and corresponding standard electrode potentials (reduction potentials):

$$Cd^{2+}(aq) + 2e^- \longrightarrow Cd(s); \quad E°_{Cd} = -0.40 \text{ V}$$
$$Ag^+(aq) + e^- \longrightarrow Ag(s); \quad E°_{Ag} = 0.80 \text{ V}$$

You will need to reverse one of these half-reactions to obtain the oxidation part of the cell reaction. The cell reaction is spontaneous, with the stronger reducing agent on the left. This will be Cd, because it is the reactant in the half-reaction with the more negative electrode potential. Therefore, you reverse the first half-reaction, as well as the sign of the half-cell potential (to obtain the oxidation potential, which equals $-E°_{Cd}$).

$$Cd(s) \longrightarrow Cd^{2+}(aq) + 2e^-; \quad -E°_{Cd} = 0.40 \text{ V}$$
$$Ag^+(aq) + e^- \longrightarrow Ag(s); \quad E°_{Ag} = 0.80 \text{ V}$$

To obtain the cell reaction, you must multiply the half-reactions by factors so that when the half-reactions are added together, the electrons cancel. This does not affect the half-cell potentials, which do not depend on amount of substance. You multiply the second half-reaction by 2 and then add.

$$\begin{array}{ll} Cd(s) \longrightarrow Cd^{2+}(aq) + 2e^- & -E°_{Cd} = 0.40 \text{ V} \\ 2Ag^+(aq) + 2e^- \longrightarrow 2Ag(s) & E°_{Ag} = 0.80 \text{ V} \\ \hline Cd(s) + 2Ag^+(aq) \longrightarrow Cd^{2+}(aq) + 2Ag(s) & E°_{Ag} - E°_{Cd} = 1.20 \text{ V} \end{array}$$

The cell potential, $E°_{cell}$, is 1.20 V. The cell diagram is

$$Cd(s) \,|\, Cd^{2+}(aq) \,\|\, Ag^+(aq) \,|\, Ag(s)$$

Suppose that at the beginning of this problem, you had mistakenly reversed the silver half-reaction, instead of correctly reversing the cadmium half-reaction. Then your work would have looked like the following:

$$Cd^{2+}(aq) + 2e^- \longrightarrow Cd(s) \qquad\qquad E^\circ_{Cd} = -0.40 \text{ V}$$
$$\underline{2Ag(s) \longrightarrow 2Ag^+(aq) + 2e^- \qquad\qquad -E^\circ_{Ag} = -0.80 \text{ V}}$$
$$Cd^{2+}(aq) + 2Ag(s) \longrightarrow Cd(s) + 2Ag^+(aq) \qquad E^\circ_{Cd} - E^\circ_{Ag} = -1.20 \text{ V}$$

The corresponding cell notation would have been

$$Ag(s)\,|\,Ag^+(aq)\,\|\,Cd^{2+}(aq)\,|\,Cd(s)$$

Everything is simply the reverse of the correct result. At this point, you realize your mistake, because the cell potential is found to be negative. A negative potential merely indicates that the cell reaction is nonspontaneous as written. To obtain the spontaneous reaction and a positive cell potential, you simply reverse both half-reactions and corresponding half-cell potentials. (You would also reverse the cell notation.) This changes the sign of the cell potential.

Calculation of Cell Potentials Using Standard Reduction Potentials   Note that in the case of the cadmium–silver cell above, the cell potential equals the standard electrode potential of the cathode minus the standard electrode potential of the anode. Thus, alternatively, you can calculate any cell potential using the equation

$$E^\circ_{cell} = E^\circ_{cathode} - E^\circ_{anode}$$

Applying this equation to our example, you obtain

$$E^\circ_{cell} = E^\circ_{Ag} - E^\circ_{Cd} = 0.80 \text{ V} - (-0.40 \text{ V}) = 1.20 \text{ V}$$

Example 19.8	Calculating the Cell Potential from Standard Potentials

Calculate the standard cell potential of the following voltaic cell at 25°C using standard electrode potentials.

$$Al(s)\,|\,Al^{3+}(aq)\,\|\,Fe^{2+}(aq)\,|\,Fe(s)$$

What is the cell reaction?

Problem Strategy   From a table of electrode potentials, write the two reduction half-reactions and standard electrode potentials for the cell. The cell notation assumes that the anode (the oxidation half-cell) is on the left. Change the direction of this half-reaction and the sign of its electrode potential. (Assuming that the cell notation was written correctly, you change the direction of the half-reaction corresponding to the smaller, or more negative, electrode potential.) Multiply the half-reactions (but not the electrode potentials) by factors so that when the half-reactions are added, the electrons cancel. The sum of the half-reactions is the cell reaction. Add the electrode potentials to get the cell potential.
   An alternative strategy is to apply the equation

$$E^\circ_{cell} = E^\circ_{cathode} - E^\circ_{anode}$$

Solution (Both Approaches)   The reduction half-reactions and standard electrode potentials are

$$Al^{3+}(aq) + 3e^- \longrightarrow Al(s); \; E^\circ_{Al} = -1.66 \text{ V}$$
$$Fe^{2+}(aq) + 2e^- \longrightarrow Fe(s); \; E^\circ_{Fe} = -0.41 \text{ V}$$

(continued)

(continued)

You reverse the first half-reaction and its half-cell potential to obtain

$$Al(s) \longrightarrow Al^{3+}(aq) + 3e^-; \; -E^\circ_{Al} = 1.66 \text{ V}$$

$$Fe^{2+}(aq) + 2e^- \longrightarrow Fe(s); \; E^\circ_{Fe} = -0.41 \text{ V}$$

You obtain the cell potential by adding the half-cell potentials. Because you also want the cell reaction, you multiply the first half-reaction by 2 and the second half-reaction by 3, so that when the half-reactions are added, the electrons cancel. The addition of half-reactions is displayed below. The cell potential is **1.25 V.**

$$
\begin{array}{ll}
2Al(s) \longrightarrow 2Al^{3+}(aq) + 6e^- & -E^\circ_{Al} = 1.66 \text{ V} \\
\underline{3Fe^{2+}(aq) + 6e^- \longrightarrow 3Fe(s)} & \underline{E^\circ_{Fe} = -0.41 \text{ V}} \\
\mathbf{2Al(s) + 3Fe^{2+}(aq) \longrightarrow 2Al^{3+}(aq) + 3Fe(s)} & E^\circ_{Fe} - E^\circ_{Al} = 1.25 \text{ V}
\end{array}
$$

Alternatively, you can calculate the cell potential from the formula

$$E^\circ_{cell} = E^\circ_{cathode} - E^\circ_{anode}$$

to obtain

$$
\begin{aligned}
E^\circ_{cell} &= E^\circ_{Fe} - E^\circ_{Al} \\
&= -0.41 \text{ V} - (-1.66 \text{ V}) \\
&= 1.25 \text{ V}
\end{aligned}
$$

Answer Check If the problem states that the cell is voltaic, the cell potential should always be positive as it is here. If you calculate a negative cell potential for a voltaic cell, it is likely that you reversed the half-reactions or mislabeled the anode and cathode.

Exercise 19.9 Using standard electrode potentials, calculate E°_{cell} at 25°C for the following cell.

$$Zn(s) | Zn^{2+}(aq) \| Cu^{2+}(aq) | Cu(s)$$

■ See Problems 19.69 and 19.70.

Concept Check 19.2

Let us define the reduction of I_2 to I^- ions, $I_2(s) + 2e^- \longrightarrow 2I^-(aq)$, as the standard reduction reaction with $E^\circ = 0.00$ V. We then construct a new standard reduction table based on this definition.

a. What would be the new standard reduction potential of H^+?

b. Would using a new standard reduction table change the *measured* value of a freshly prepared voltaic cell made from Cu and Zn? (Assume you have the appropriate solutions and equipment to construct the cell.)

c. Would the calculated voltage for the cell in part b be different if you were using the values presented in Table 19.1? Do the calculations to justify your answer.

19.6 | Equilibrium Constants from Cell Potentials

Some of the most important results of electrochemistry are the relationships among cell potential, free-energy change, and equilibrium constant. Recall that the free-energy change ΔG for a reaction equals the maximum useful work of the reaction (Section 18.5).

$$\Delta G = w_{max}$$

For a voltaic cell, this work is the electrical work, $-nFE_{cell}$ (where n is the number of moles of electrons transferred in a reaction), so when the reactants and products are in their standard states, you have

$$\Delta G° = -nFE°_{cell}$$

With this equation, cell potential measurements become an important source of thermodynamic information. Alternatively, thermodynamic data can be used to calculate cell potentials. These calculations are shown in the following examples.

Example 19.9 | Calculating the Free-Energy Change from Electrode Potentials

Using standard electrode potentials, calculate the standard free-energy change at 25°C for the reaction

$$Zn(s) + 2Ag^+(aq) \longrightarrow Zn^{2+}(aq) + 2Ag(s)$$

Problem Strategy Substitute into $\Delta G° = -nFE°_{cell}$. Use a table of standard electrode potentials to obtain $E°_{cell}$. The cell reaction equals the sum of the half-reactions after they have been multiplied by factors so that the electrons cancel in the summation. Note that n is the number of moles of electrons involved in each half-reaction.

Solution The half-reactions, corresponding half-cell potentials, and their sums are displayed below.

$$
\begin{array}{ll}
Zn(s) \longrightarrow Zn^{2+}(aq) + 2e^- & -E° = 0.76 \text{ V} \\
\underline{2Ag^+(aq) + 2e^- \longrightarrow 2Ag(s)} & \underline{E° = 0.80 \text{ V}} \\
Zn(s) + 2Ag^+(aq) \longrightarrow Zn^{2+}(aq) + 2Ag(s) & E°_{cell} = 1.56 \text{ V}
\end{array}
$$

Note that each half-reaction involves the transfer of two moles of electrons; hence, $n = 2$. Also, $E°_{cell} = 1.56$ V, and the faraday constant, F, is 9.6485×10^4 C/mol e$^-$. Therefore,

$$\Delta G° = -nFE°_{cell} = -2 \text{ mol e}^- \times 96{,}485 \text{ C/mol e}^- \times 1.56 \text{ V} = -3.01 \times 10^5 \text{ J}$$

Recall that (coulombs) $\times$ (volts) = joules. Thus, the standard free-energy change is **−301 kJ.**

Answer Check Free energies of reaction are generally of the order of tens to hundreds of kilojoules, as shown in this answer. Values outside of this range would indicate that you probably made a calculation error.

Exercise 19.10 What is $\Delta G°$ at 25°C for the reaction

$$Sn^{2+}(aq) + 2Hg^{2+}(aq) \longrightarrow Sn^{4+}(aq) + Hg_2^{2+}(aq)$$

For data, see Table 19.1.

■ See Problems 19.73 and 19.74.

Example 19.10 | Calculating the Cell Potential from Free-Energy Change

Suppose the reaction of zinc metal and chlorine gas is utilized in a voltaic cell in which zinc ions and chloride ions are formed in aqueous solution.

$$Zn(s) + Cl_2(g) \xrightarrow{\text{H}_2\text{O}} Zn^{2+}(aq) + 2Cl^-(aq)$$

Calculate the standard potential for this cell at 25°C from standard free energies of formation (see Appendix C).

(continued)

(*continued*)

Problem Strategy Calculate $\Delta G°$ and substitute it and the value of n into the equation $\Delta G° = -nFE°_{cell}$. Solve for $E°_{cell}$.

Solution Write the equation with $\Delta G°_f$'s beneath.

$$Zn(s) + Cl_2(g) \longrightarrow Zn^{2+}(aq) + 2Cl^-(aq)$$
$$\Delta G°_f: \quad 0 \qquad 0 \qquad -147.0 \qquad 2 \times (-131.3) \text{ kJ}$$

Hence,

$$\Delta G° = \Sigma n\Delta G°_f(\text{products}) - \Sigma m\Delta G°_f(\text{reactants})$$
$$= [-147.0 + 2 \times (-131.3)] \text{ kJ}$$
$$= -410 \text{ kJ} = -4.10 \times 10^5 \text{ J}$$

You obtain n by splitting the reaction into half-reactions.

$$Zn(s) \longrightarrow Zn^{2+}(aq) + 2e^-$$
$$Cl_2(g) + 2e^- \longrightarrow 2Cl^-(aq)$$

Each half-reaction involves the transfer of two moles of electrons, so $n = 2$. Now you substitute into

$$\Delta G° = -nFE°_{cell}$$
$$-4.10 \times 10^5 \text{ J} = -2 \text{ mol } e^- \times 96,485 \text{ C/mol } e^- \times E°_{cell}$$

Solving for $E°_{cell}$, you get $E°_{cell} = \textbf{2.12 V.}$

Answer Check Because this problem describes a voltaic cell, we should expect the value of $E°_{cell}$ to be positive.

Exercise 19.11 Use standard free energies of formation (Appendix C) to obtain the standard cell potential of a cell at 25°C with the reaction

$$Mg(s) + Cu^{2+}(aq) \longrightarrow Mg^{2+}(aq) + Cu(s)$$

■ See Problems 19.77 and 19.78.

The measurement of cell potentials gives you yet another way to obtain equilibrium constants. Combining the previous equation, $\Delta G° = -nFE°_{cell}$, with the equation $\Delta G° = -RT \ln K$ from Section 18.6, you get

$$nFE°_{cell} = RT \ln K$$

or

$$E°_{cell} = \frac{RT}{nF} \ln K = \frac{2.303 \, RT}{nF} \log K$$

Substituting values for the constants R and F at 25°C gives the equation

This formula is typically written using the common logarithm (base 10) function as it is shown here. The factor 2.303 allows for conversion between the common logarithm and base e logarithm (2.303 log x = ln x).

$$E°_{cell} = \frac{0.0592}{n} \log K \qquad \text{(values in volts at 25°C)}$$

Figure 19.7 summarizes the various relationships among K, $\Delta G°$, and $E°_{cell}$. <

The next example illustrates calculation of the thermodynamic equilibrium constant from the cell potential.

FIGURE 19.7 ▶

The relationships among K, $\Delta G°$, and $E°_{cell}$

The diagram shows how composition data, calorimetric data, and electrochemical data are related.

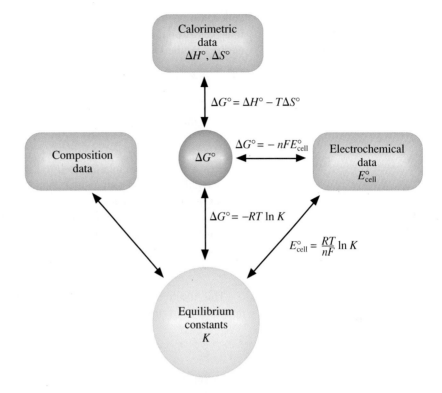

Example 19.11 | Calculating the Equilibrium Constant from Cell Potential

The standard cell potential for the following voltaic cell is 1.10 V:

$$Zn(s)\,|\,Zn^{2+}(aq)\,\|\,Cu^{2+}(aq)\,|\,Cu(s)$$

Calculate the equilibrium constant K_c for the reaction

$$Zn(s) + Cu^{2+}(aq) \rightleftharpoons Zn^{2+}(aq) + Cu(s)$$

Problem Strategy Substitute the standard cell potential into the equation relating this quantity to the thermodynamic equilibrium constant, K. Solve for K. Note that $K = K_c$.

Solution The reaction corresponds to the one for the voltaic cell. Note that $n = 2$. Substituting into the equation relating $E°_{cell}$ and K gives

$$1.10 = \frac{0.0592}{2}\,\log K_c$$

Solving for $\log K_c$, you find

$$\log K_c = 37.2$$

Now take the antilog of both sides:

$$K_c = \text{antilog}\,(37.2) = 1.6 \times 10^{37}$$

The number of significant figures in the answer equals the number of decimal places in 37.2 (one). Thus

$$\boldsymbol{K_c = 2 \times 10^{37}}$$

Answer Check Whenever the cell potential is a positive number (voltaic cell), you should calculate an equilibrium constant greater than 1.

Exercise 19.12   Calculate the equilibrium constant K_c for the following reaction from standard electrode potentials.

$$Fe(s) + Sn^{4+}(aq) \rightleftharpoons Fe^{2+}(aq) + Sn^{2+}(aq)$$

■ See Problems 19.81 and 19.82.

19.7 | Dependence of Cell Potential on Concentration

The cell potential of a cell depends on the concentrations of ions and on gas pressures. For that reason, cell potentials provide a way to measure ion concentrations. The pH meter, for example, depends on the variation of cell potential with hydrogen-ion

Nernst also formulated the third law of thermodynamics, for which he received the Nobel Prize in 1920.

concentration. You can relate cell potentials for various concentrations of ions and various gas pressures to standard electrode potentials by means of an equation first derived by the German chemist Walther Nernst (1864–1941). <

Nernst Equation

Recall that the free-energy change, ΔG, is related to the standard free-energy change, $\Delta G°$, by the following equation (Section 18.6):

$$\Delta G = \Delta G° + RT \ln Q$$

Here Q is the thermodynamic reaction quotient. The reaction quotient has the form of the equilibrium constant, except that the concentrations and gas pressures are those that exist in a reaction mixture at a given instant. You can apply this equation to a voltaic cell. In that case, the concentrations and gas pressures are those that exist in the cell at a particular instant. If you substitute $\Delta G = -nFE_{cell}$ and $\Delta G° = -nFE°_{cell}$ into this equation, you obtain

$$-nFE_{cell} = -nFE°_{cell} + RT \ln Q$$

This result rearranges to give the **Nernst equation,** *an equation relating the cell potential to its standard cell potential and the reaction quotient.*

$$E_{cell} = E°_{cell} - \frac{RT}{nF} \ln Q \quad \text{or} \quad E_{cell} = E°_{cell} - \frac{2.303\, RT}{nF} \log Q$$

If you substitute 298 K (25°C) for the temperature in the Nernst equation and put in values for R and F, you get (using common logarithms)

$$E_{cell} = E°_{cell} - \frac{0.0592}{n} \log Q \quad \text{(values in volts at 25°C)}$$

You can show from the Nernst equation that the cell potential, E_{cell}, decreases as the cell reaction proceeds. As the reaction occurs in the voltaic cell, the concentrations of products increase and the concentrations of reactants decrease. Therefore, Q and $\log Q$ increase. The second term in the Nernst equation, $(0.0592/n) \log Q$, increases, so that the difference $E°_{cell} - (0.0592/n) \log Q$ decreases. Thus, the cell potential, E_{cell}, becomes smaller. Eventually the cell potential goes to zero, and the cell reaction comes to equilibrium.

As an example of the computation of the reaction quotient, consider the following voltaic cell:

$$Cd(s)|Cd^{2+}(0.0100\ M)\|H^{+}(1.00\ M)|H_2(1.00\ atm)|Pt$$

The cell reaction is

$$Cd(s) + 2H^{+}(aq) \rightleftharpoons Cd^{2+}(aq) + H_2(g)$$

and the expression for the equilibrium constant is

$$K = \frac{[Cd^{2+}]P_{H_2}}{[H^{+}]^2}$$

Note that the hydrogen-gas concentration is given here in terms of the pressure (in atmospheres). The expression for the reaction quotient has the same form as K, except that the values for the ion concentrations and hydrogen-gas pressures are those that exist in the cell. < Hence,

We have omitted subscript i's on the concentrations and pressures in Q to simplify the notation.

$$Q = \frac{[Cd^{2+}]P_{H_2}}{[H^{+}]^2} = \frac{0.0100 \times 1.00}{(1.00)^2} = 0.0100$$

The next example illustrates a complete calculation of cell potential from the ion concentrations in a voltaic cell.

| **Example 19.12** | Calculating the Cell Potential for Nonstandard Conditions |

What is the cell potential of the following voltaic cell at 25°C?

$$Zn(s)|Zn^{2+}(1.00 \times 10^{-5}M)\|Cu^{2+}(0.100\ M)|Cu(s)$$

The standard cell potential of this cell is 1.10 V.

Problem Strategy   From the cell reaction, deduce the value of n; then calculate Q. Now substitute n, Q, and E°_{cell} into the Nernst equation to obtain E_{cell}.

Solution   The cell reaction is

$$Zn(s) + Cu^{2+}(aq) \rightleftharpoons Zn^{2+}(aq) + Cu(s)$$

The number of moles of electrons transferred is two; hence, $n = 2$. The reaction quotient is

$$Q = \frac{[Zn^{2+}]}{[Cu^{2+}]} = \frac{1.00 \times 10^{-5}}{0.100} = 1.00 \times 10^{-4}$$

The standard cell potential is 1.10 V, so the Nernst equation becomes

$$E_{cell} = E^\circ_{cell} - \frac{0.0592}{n} \log Q$$

$$= 1.10 - \frac{0.0592}{2} \log (1.0 \times 10^{-4})$$

$$= 1.10 - (-0.12) = 1.22\ V$$

The cell potential is **1.22 V.**

Answer Check   Whenever you perform a calculation involving nonstandard cell concentrations, you can use Le Châtelier's principle to see if your answer is reasonable. Recall that standard cell concentrations are equivalent and are 1.00 M. At standard concentrations the cell potential is 1.10 V. In this problem, the concentration of the product (Zn^{2+}) is 1.0×10^{-5} M, whereas the concentration of the reactant (Cu^{2+}) is 0.100 M. With these concentrations we would expect this spontaneous reaction to be shifted toward products, thereby resulting in a value of E_{cell} greater than the standard value, which is what we observe.

| **Exercise 19.13** | What is the cell potential of the following voltaic cell at 25°C? |

$$Zn(s)|Zn^{2+}(0.200\ M)\|Ag^+(0.00200\ M)|Ag(s)$$

■ See Problems 19.85 and 19.86.

Determination of pH

The pH of a solution can be obtained very accurately from cell potential measurements, using the Nernst equation to relate cell potential to pH. To see how this is done, suppose you have a test solution whose pH you would like to determine. You set up a voltaic cell as follows: You use the test solution as the electrolyte for a hydrogen electrode and bubble in hydrogen gas at 1 atm. (The hydrogen electrode is shown in Figure 19.5.) Now connect this hydrogen electrode to a standard zinc electrode to give the following cell:

$$Zn|Zn^{2+}(1\ M)\|H^+(test\ solution)|H_2(1\ atm)|Pt$$

The cell reaction is

$$Zn(s) + 2H^+(test\ solution) \longrightarrow Zn^{2+}(1\ M) + H_2(1\ atm)$$

The cell potential depends on the hydrogen-ion concentration of the test solution, according to the Nernst equation. The standard cell potential of the cell equals 0.76 V, and

$$Q = \frac{[Zn^{2+}]P_{H_2}}{[H^+]^2} = \frac{1}{[H^+]^2}$$

Keeping in mind that H^+ is a shorthand representation of H_3O^+, the equation for pH used here is the same as presented in Chapter 15 ($pH = -\log [H_3O^+]$).

FIGURE 19.8

A glass electrode
Left: A small, commercial glass electrode.
Right: A sketch showing the construction of a glass electrode for measuring hydrogen-ion concentrations.

(labels: Ag–AgCl electrode; HCl; Thin glass membrane)

Substituting into the Nernst equation, you obtain

$$E_{cell} = 0.76 - \frac{0.0592}{2} \log \frac{1}{[H^+]^2} = 0.76 + 0.0592 \log [H^+]$$

where $[H^+]$ is the hydrogen-ion concentration of the test solution.

To obtain the relationship between the cell potential (E_{cell}) and pH, you substitute the following into the preceding equation: <

$$pH = -\log [H^+]$$

The result is

$$E_{cell} = 0.76 - 0.0592 \ pH$$

Which you can rearrange to give the pH directly in terms of the cell potential:

$$pH = \frac{0.76 - E_{cell}}{0.0592}$$

In this way, measurement of the cell potential gives you the pH of the solution.

The hydrogen electrode is seldom employed in routine laboratory work, because it is awkward to use. It is often replaced by a *glass electrode*. This compact electrode (see Figure 19.8) consists of a silver wire coated with silver chloride immersed in a solution of dilute hydrochloric acid. The electrode solution is separated from the test solution by a thin glass membrane, which develops a potential across it depending on the hydrogen-ion concentrations on its inner and outer surfaces. A mercury–mercury(I) chloride (calomel) electrode is often used as the other electrode. The cell potential depends linearly on the pH. In a common arrangement, the cell potential is measured with a voltmeter that reads pH directly (see Figure 15.7).

The glass electrode is an example of an *ion-selective electrode.* Many electrodes have been developed that are sensitive to a particular ion, such as K^+, NH_4^+, Ca^{2+}, or Mg^{2+}. They can be used to monitor solutions of that ion. It is even possible to measure the concentration of a nonelectrolyte. To measure urea, NH_2CONH_2, in solution, you can use an electrode selective to NH_4^+ that is coated with a gel containing the enzyme urease. (An enzyme is a biochemical catalyst.) The gel is held in place around the electrode by means of a nylon net. Urease catalyzes the decomposition of urea to ammonium ion, whose concentration is measured.

$$NH_2CONH_2(aq) + 2H_2O(l) + H^+(aq) \xrightarrow{\text{urease}} 2NH_4^+(aq) + HCO_3^-(aq)$$

Exercise 19.14   What is the nickel(II)-ion concentration in the voltaic cell

$$Zn(s)|Zn^{2+}(1.00\ M)\|Ni^{2+}(aq)|Ni(s)$$

if the cell potential is 0.34 V at 25°C?

■ See Problems 19.89 and 19.90.

Concept Check 19.3

Consider a voltaic cell, $Fe(s)|Fe^{2+}(aq)\|Cu^{2+}(aq)|Cu(s)$, being run under standard conditions.

a. Is $\Delta G°$ positive or negative for this process?

b. Change the concentrations from their standard values in such a way that E_{cell} is reduced. Write your answer using the shorthand notation of Section 19.3.

Positive terminal

Air space

Asphalt seal

Porous paper

Paste of MnO$_2$, ZnCl$_2$, NH$_4$Cl, and C

Graphite rod (cathode)

Zinc can (anode)

Metal jacket

Insulator

Negative terminal

FIGURE 19.9 ▲

Leclanché dry cell
The cell has a zinc anode and a graphite rod with a paste of MnO$_2$, ZnCl$_2$, NH$_4$Cl, and C as the cathode.

19.8 Some Commercial Voltaic Cells

We commonly use voltaic cells as convenient, portable sources of energy. Flashlights and radios are examples of devices that are often powered by the **zinc–carbon,** or **Leclanché, dry cell** (Figure 19.9). *This voltaic cell has a zinc can as the anode; a graphite rod in the center, surrounded by a paste of manganese dioxide, ammonium and zinc chlorides, and carbon black, is the cathode.* The electrode reactions are complicated but are approximately these:

$$Zn(s) \longrightarrow Zn^{2+}(aq) + 2e^- \qquad \text{(anode)}$$

$$2NH_4^+(aq) + 2MnO_2(s) + 2e^- \longrightarrow Mn_2O_3(s) + H_2O(l) + 2NH_3(aq) \qquad \text{(cathode)}$$

The voltage of this dry cell is initially about 1.5 V, but it decreases as current is drawn off. The voltage also deteriorates rapidly in cold weather.

An **alkaline dry cell** (Figure 19.10) is *similar to the Leclanché cell, but it has potassium hydroxide in place of ammonium chloride.* This cell performs better under current drain and in cold weather. The half-reactions are

$$Zn(s) + 2OH^-(aq) \longrightarrow Zn(OH)_2(s) + 2e^- \qquad \text{(anode)}$$

$$2MnO_2(s) + H_2O(l) + 2e^- \longrightarrow Mn_2O_3(s) + 2OH^-(aq) \qquad \text{(cathode)}$$

A dry cell is not truly "dry," because the electrolyte is an aqueous paste. Solid-state batteries have been developed, however. One of these is a **lithium–iodine battery,** *a voltaic cell in which the anode is lithium metal and the cathode is an I$_2$ complex.* These solid-state electrodes are separated by a thin crystalline layer of lithium iodide (Figure 19.11). Current is carried through the crystal by diffusion of Li$^+$ ions. Although the cell has high resistance and therefore low current, the battery is very reliable and is used to power heart pacemakers. The battery is implanted within the patient's chest and lasts about ten years before it has to be replaced.

Once a dry cell is completely discharged (has come to equilibrium), the cell is not easily reversed, or recharged, and is normally discarded. Some types of cells are rechargeable after use, however. An important example is the **lead storage cell.** *This voltaic cell consists of electrodes of lead alloy grids; one electrode is packed with a spongy lead to form the anode, and the other electrode is packed with lead dioxide to form the cathode* (see Figure 19.12). Both are bathed in an aqueous solution of

Anode (negative): Zn powder + KOH electrolyte

Anode cap

Gasket

Cell can

Separator

Cathode (positive): MnO$_2$ + KOH electrolyte

FIGURE 19.10 ▲

A small alkaline dry cell
The anode is zinc powder and the cathode is MnO$_2$, as in the Leclanché cell; however, the electrolyte is KOH.

Negative pole

Li metal anode

Nickel mesh

I$_2$ complex cathode

LiI crystals

FIGURE 19.11 ▲

A solid-state lithium–iodine battery
The anode is lithium metal and the cathode is a complex of iodine, I$_2$; the electrodes are separated by a thin crystalline layer of lithium iodide. The battery consists of two cells enclosed in a titanium shell.

Anode (negative): lead grids filled with spongy lead

Cathode (positive): lead grids filled with PbO$_2$

H$_2$SO$_4$ electrolyte fills the battery case

FIGURE 19.12 ▲

A lead storage battery
Each cell delivers about 2 V, and a battery consisting of six cells in series gives about 12 V.

FIGURE 19.13 ▲

A maintenance-free battery
This lead storage battery contains calcium–lead alloy grids for electrodes. This alloy resists the decomposition of water, so the battery can be sealed.

FIGURE 19.14 ▲

NiCad storage batteries
These rechargeable cells have a cadmium anode and a hydrated nickel oxide cathode.

sulfuric acid, H_2SO_4. The half-cell reactions during discharge are

$$Pb(s) + HSO_4^-(aq) \longrightarrow PbSO_4(s) + H^+(aq) + 2e^- \qquad \text{(anode)}$$

$$PbO_2(s) + 3H^+(aq) + HSO_4^-(aq) + 2e^- \longrightarrow PbSO_4(s) + 2H_2O(l) \qquad \text{(cathode)}$$

White lead(II) sulfate coats each electrode during discharge, and sulfuric acid is consumed. Each cell delivers about 2 V, and a battery consisting of six cells in series gives about 12 V.

After the lead storage battery is discharged, it is recharged from an external electric current. The previous half-reactions are reversed. Some water is decomposed into hydrogen and oxygen gas during this recharging, so more water may have to be added at intervals. However, newer batteries use lead electrodes containing some calcium metal; the calcium–lead alloy resists the decomposition of water. These *maintenance-free* batteries are sealed (Figure 19.13).

The **nickel–cadmium cell** (nicad cell) is a common storage battery. It is *a voltaic cell consisting of an anode of cadmium and a cathode of hydrated nickel oxide (approximately NiOOH) on nickel; the electrolyte is potassium hydroxide.* Nicad batteries are used in calculators, portable power tools, shavers, and toothbrushes. The half-cell reactions during discharge are

$$Cd(s) + 2OH^-(aq) \longrightarrow Cd(OH)_2(s) + 2e^- \qquad \text{(anode)}$$

$$NiOOH(s) + H_2O(l) + e^- \longrightarrow Ni(OH)_2(s) + OH^-(aq) \qquad \text{(cathode)}$$

These half-reactions are reversed when the cell is recharged. Nicad batteries can be recharged and discharged many times (see Figure 19.14). Recently, *nickel metal hydride* (NiMH) and *lithium* batteries have been replacing nicad batteries in many applications that require rechargeable batteries. The NiMH batteries use a metal hydride for the anode instead of the more toxic cadmium. NiHM batteries are currently used to supply electric power for hybrid-electric vehicles. Lithium batteries typically use a carbon anode and lithium cobalt dioxide or a lithium manganese compound as the cathode. Lithium batteries are commonly used to power consumer electronics.

A **fuel cell** is *essentially a battery, but it differs in operating with a continuous supply of energetic reactants, or fuel.* Figure 19.15 shows a proton-exchange membrane (PEM) fuel cell that uses hydrogen and oxygen. On one side of the cell, the anode, hydrogen passes through a porous material containing a platinum catalyst, allowing the following reaction to occur:

$$H_2(g) \longrightarrow 2H^+(aq) + 2e^- \qquad \text{(anode)}$$

The $H^+(aq)$ ions then migrate through a proton-exchange membrane to the other side of the cell to participate in the cathode reaction with $O_2(g)$:

$$O_2(g) + 4H^+(aq) + 4e^- \longrightarrow 2H_2O(l) \qquad \text{(cathode)}$$

The sum of the half-reactions (note that the anode reaction must be multiplied by 2 prior to adding) is

$$2H_2(g) + O_2(g) \longrightarrow 2H_2O(l)$$

which is the net reaction in the fuel cell. The first applications of PEM fuel cells were in space, but more recently, they have provided power for lighting, emergency power generators, communications equipment, automobiles, and buses. Other types of cells using other materials and fuels such as hydrocarbons or methanol are either in commercial production or under development.

Another use of voltaic cells is to control the corrosion of underground pipelines and tanks. Such pipelines and tanks are usually made of steel, an alloy of iron, and their corrosion or rusting is an electrochemical process.

Consider the rusting that occurs when a drop of water is in contact with iron. The edge of the water drop exposed to the air becomes one pole of a voltaic cell (see Figure 19.16). At this edge, molecular oxygen from air is reduced to hydroxide ion in solution.

$$O_2(g) + 2H_2O(l) + 4e^- \longrightarrow 4OH^-(aq)$$

FIGURE 19.15 ▶

A hydrogen–oxygen fuel cell

At the anode, hydrogen gas enters a chamber where a porous platinum catalyst oxidizes the hydrogen to $H^+(aq)$ ions at the anode. The H^+ ions then migrate through a special proton-exchange membrane (PEM) and move to the cathode; the proton-exchange membrane allows only the very small $H^+(aq)$ ions to pass from the anode to the cathode. At the cathode, oxygen gas enters the cell, where it comes into contact with a platinum catalyst that facilitates the reduction of $O_2(g)$ in the presence of the $H^+(aq)$ and the electrons from the oxidation reaction to produce water. The net chemical change is the reaction of hydrogen with oxygen to produce water. This fuel cell has a measured potential of 0.7 V and, unlike many other types of fuel cells, can run at temperatures under 100°C. (Reprinted by permission of Ballard.)

FIGURE 19.16 ▶

The electrochemical process involved in the rusting of iron

Here a single drop of water containing ions forms a voltaic cell in which iron is oxidized to iron(II) ion at the center of the drop (this is the anode). Oxygen gas from air is reduced to hydroxide ion at the periphery of the drop (the cathode). Hydroxide ions and iron(II) ions migrate together and react to form iron(II) hydroxide. This is oxidized to iron(III) hydroxide by more O_2 that dissolves at the surface of the drop. Iron(III) hydroxide precipitates, and this settles to form rust on the surface of the iron.

FIGURE 19.17 ▲

Cathodic protection of a buried steel pipe

Iron in the steel becomes the cathode in an iron–magnesium voltaic cell. Magnesium is then oxidized in preference to iron.

The electrons for this reduction are supplied by the oxidation of metallic iron at the center of the drop, which acts as the other pole of the voltaic cell.

$$Fe(s) \longrightarrow Fe^{2+}(aq) + 2e^-$$

These electrons flow from the center of the drop through the metallic iron to the edge of the drop. The metallic iron functions as the external circuit between the cell poles.

Ions move within the water drop, completing the electric circuit. Iron(II) ions move outward from the center of the drop, and hydroxide ions move inward from the edge. The two ions meet in a doughnut-shaped region, where they react to precipitate iron(II) hydroxide.

$$Fe^{2+}(aq) + 2OH^-(aq) \longrightarrow Fe(OH)_2(s)$$

This precipitate is quickly oxidized by oxygen to rust (approximated by the formula $Fe_2O_3 \cdot H_2O$).

$$4Fe(OH)_2(s) + O_2(g) \longrightarrow 2Fe_2O_3 \cdot H_2O(s) + 2H_2O(l)$$

If a buried steel pipeline (Figure 19.17) is connected to an active metal (that is, a highly electropositive substance) such as magnesium, a voltaic cell is formed; the active metal is the anode and iron becomes the cathode. Wet soil forms the electrolyte,

FIGURE 19.18 ▶

A demonstration of cathodic protection
The nails are in a gel containing phenol-phthalein indicator and potassium ferricyanide. Iron corrosion yields Fe^{2+}, which reacts with ferricyanide ion to give a dark blue precipitate. Where OH^- forms, phenolphthalein appears pink. *Left:* The unprotected nail. *Right:* The nail has magnesium wrapped around the center. Note that no corrosion (dark blue or black region) appears on it.

and the electrode reactions are

$$Mg(s) \longrightarrow Mg^{2+}(aq) + 2e^- \qquad \text{(anode)}$$

$$O_2(g) + 2H_2O(l) + 4e^- \longrightarrow 4OH^-(aq) \qquad \text{(cathode)}$$

As the cathode, the iron-containing steel pipe is protected from oxidation. Of course, the magnesium rod is eventually consumed and must be replaced, but this is cheaper than digging up the pipeline. This use of an active metal to protect iron from corrosion is called *cathodic protection*. See Figure 19.18 for a laboratory demonstration of cathodic protection.

Concept Check 19.4

Keeping in mind that seawater contains a number of ions, explain why seawater corrodes iron much faster than freshwater.

Electrolytic Cells

An *electrolytic cell,* you may recall, is an electrochemical cell in which an electric current drives an otherwise nonspontaneous reaction. *The process of producing a chemical change in an electrolytic cell* is called **electrolysis.** Many important substances, including aluminum and chlorine, are produced commercially by electrolysis. We will begin by looking at the electrolysis of molten salts.

19.9 | Electrolysis of Molten Salts

Figure 19.19 shows a simple electrolytic cell. Wires from a battery are connected to electrodes that dip into molten sodium chloride. (NaCl melts at 801°C.) At the electrode connected to the negative pole of the battery, globules of sodium metal form; chlorine gas evolves from the other electrode. The half-reactions are

$$Na^+(l) + e^- \longrightarrow Na(l)$$

$$Cl^-(l) \longrightarrow \tfrac{1}{2}Cl_2(g) + e^-$$

As noted earlier (Section 19.2), the *anode* is the electrode at which oxidation occurs, and the *cathode* is the electrode at which reduction occurs (these definitions hold for electrolytic cells as well as for voltaic cells). Thus, during the electrolysis of molten NaCl, the reduction of Na^+ to Na occurs at the cathode, and the oxidation of Cl^- to Cl_2 occurs at the anode (note the labeling of electrodes in Figure 19.19).

This electrolysis of molten NaCl is used commercially to obtain sodium metal from sodium chloride. A **Downs cell** is *a commercial electrochemical cell used to obtain sodium metal by the electrolysis of molten sodium chloride* (Figure 19.20). The cell is constructed to keep the products of the electrolysis separate, because they would otherwise react. Calcium chloride is added to the sodium chloride to lower the melting point from 801°C for NaCl to about 580°C for the mixture. (Remember that the

FIGURE 19.19 ▷

Electrolysis of molten sodium chloride
Sodium metal forms at the cathode from the reduction of Na^+ ion; chlorine gas forms at the anode from the oxidation of Cl^- ion. Sodium metal is produced commercially this way, although the commercial cell must be designed to collect the products and to keep them away from one another.

Chlorine gas evolves at anode

$$2Cl^-(l) \longrightarrow Cl_2(g) + 2e^-$$

Sodium metal forms at cathode

$$Na^+(l) + e^- \longrightarrow Na(l)$$

FIGURE 19.20 ▷

A Downs cell for the preparation of sodium metal
In this commercial cell, sodium is produced by the electrolysis of molten sodium chloride. The salt contains calcium chloride, which is added to lower the melting point of the mixture. Liquid sodium forms at the cathode, where it rises to the top of the molten salt and collects in a tank. Chlorine gas is a by-product.

Chlorine gas

Add sodium chloride

Molten sodium chloride

Iron cathode

Liquid sodium

Graphite anode ——— +

melting point, or freezing point, of a substance is lowered by the addition of a solute.) You obtain the cell reaction by adding the half-reactions.

$$
\begin{aligned}
Na^+(l) + e^- &\longrightarrow Na(l) \\
Cl^-(l) &\longrightarrow \tfrac{1}{2}Cl_2(g) + e^- \\
\hline
Na^+(l) + Cl^-(l) &\longrightarrow Na(l) + \tfrac{1}{2}Cl_2(g)
\end{aligned}
$$

A number of other reactive metals are obtained by the electrolysis of a molten salt or ionic compound. Lithium, magnesium, and calcium metals are all obtained by the electrolysis of the chlorides. The first commercial preparation of sodium metal adapted the method used by Humphry Davy when he discovered the element in 1807. Davy electrolyzed molten sodium hydroxide, NaOH, whose melting point (318°C) is relatively low for an ionic compound. The half-reactions are

$$Na^+(l) + e^- \longrightarrow Na(l) \qquad \text{(cathode)}$$

$$4OH^-(l) \longrightarrow O_2(g) + 2H_2O(g) + 4e^- \qquad \text{(anode)}$$

Many of the commercial uses of electrolysis involve aqueous solutions. We will look at electrolysis in aqueous solution in the next section.

Exercise 19.15   Write the half-reactions for the electrolysis of the following molten compounds: a. KCl;   b. KOH.

■ See Problems 19.91 and 19.92.

19.10 | Aqueous Electrolysis

In the electrolysis of a molten salt, the possible half-reactions are usually limited to those involving ions from the salt. When you electrolyze an aqueous solution of an ionic compound, however, you must consider the possibility that water is involved at one or both electrodes. Let us look at the possible half-reactions involving water.

Water can be reduced or oxidized in half-reactions, and you can easily obtain these half-reactions. To do this, first note the species likely to be involved. In addition to H_2O, these are H_2, O_2, H^+, and OH^-. Only H_2 and O_2 involve a change of oxidation state. Hydrogen has a lower oxidation state in H_2 (0) than in H_2O (+1), whereas the oxygen in has a higher oxidation state O_2 (0) than in H_2O (−2). Therefore, you can reduce water to H_2 or oxidize it to O_2.

Consider the reduction half-reaction. It must involve the reduction of H_2O to H_2. You need to balance the half-reaction by putting an oxygen-containing species on the right. The only species in which there are no changes in oxidation states from those in H_2O is OH^-. The balanced half-reaction is

$$2H_2O(l) + 2e^- \longrightarrow H_2(g) + 2OH^-(aq)$$

You can obtain the oxidation half-reaction for water in a similar way. It involves the oxidation of H_2O to O_2. You need to put a hydrogen-containing species on the right side of the equation to balance it. The only species in which there is no change in oxidation state is H^+. The balanced half-reaction is

$$2H_2O(l) \longrightarrow O_2(g) + 4H^+(aq) + 4e^-$$

Now let us consider the electrolysis of different aqueous solutions and try to decide what the half-reactions might be. Once you have the half-reactions, you can obtain the overall chemical change due to the electrolysis.

Electrolysis of Sulfuric Acid Solutions

To decide what is likely to happen during the electrolysis of a solution of sulfuric acid, H_2SO_4, you must consider the half-reactions involving ionic species from H_2SO_4, in addition to those involving water. Sulfuric acid is a strong acid and ionizes completely into H^+ and HSO_4^-. The HSO_4^- ion is relatively strong and for the most part ionizes into H^+ and SO_4^{2-}. Therefore, the species you have to look at are H^+, SO_4^{2-}, and H_2O.

At the cathode, the possible reduction half-reactions are

$$2H^+(aq) + 2e^- \longrightarrow H_2(g)$$
$$2H_2O(l) + 2e^- \longrightarrow H_2(g) + 2OH^-(aq)$$

At the anode, the possible oxidation half-reactions are

$$2SO_4^{2-}(aq) \longrightarrow S_2O_8^{2-}(aq) + 2e^-$$
$$2H_2O(l) \longrightarrow O_2(g) + 4H^+(aq) + 4e^-$$

In the first half-reaction, the sulfate ion, SO_4^{2-}, is oxidized to the peroxydisulfate ion, $S_2O_8^{2-}$. The $S_2O_8^{2-}$ ion contains the peroxy group —O—O— and therefore has O in the −1 oxidation state. Oxygen in this half-reaction is oxidized from oxidation state −2 to −1.

$$2H_2O(l) \longrightarrow O_2(g) + 2H_2(g)$$

Consider the cathode reaction. As you can easily show, the two reduction half-reactions (reduction of H^+ and reduction of H_2O) in acidic solution are essentially equivalent, although this is not immediately obvious. Consider the reduction of water to give H_2 and OH^-. In acidic solution, OH^- reacts with H^+ to give H_2O. The net result is obtained by adding the two reactions.

$$2H_2O(l) + 2e^- \longrightarrow H_2(g) + 2OH^-(aq)$$
$$\underline{2H^+(aq) + 2OH^-(aq) \longrightarrow 2H_2O(l)}$$
$$2H^+(aq) + 2e^- \longrightarrow H_2(g)$$

You can consider the cathode reaction to be the reduction of H^+.

For the anode, consider the oxidation half-reactions and their oxidation potentials (which equal the electrode potentials with signs reversed).

$$2SO_4^{2-}(aq) \longrightarrow S_2O_8^{2-}(aq) + 2e^-; \ -E^\circ = -2.01 \text{ V}$$
$$2H_2O(l) \longrightarrow O_2(g) + 4H^+(aq) + 4e^-; \ -E^\circ = -1.23 \text{ V}$$

The species whose oxidation half-reaction has the larger (less negative) oxidation potential is the more easily oxidized. Therefore, under standard conditions, you expect H_2O to be oxidized in preference to SO_4^{2-}.

A note of caution must be added here. Electrode potentials are measured under conditions in which the half-reactions are at or very near equilibrium. In electrolysis, in which the half-reactions can be far from equilibrium, you may have to supply a larger voltage than predicted from electrode potentials. This additional voltage, called *overvoltage*, can be fairly large (several tenths of a volt), particularly for forming a gas. This means that in trying to predict which of two half-reactions is the one that actually occurs at an electrode, you must be especially careful if the electrode potentials are within several tenths of a volt of one another. For example, the standard oxidation potential for O_2 is -1.23 V, but because of overvoltage, the effective oxidation potential may be several tenths of a volt lower (more negative). The sulfate ion is so difficult to oxidize ($-E^\circ = -2.01$ V), however, that the previous conclusion about the anode half-reaction in electrolyzing aqueous sulfuric acid is unaltered.

You obtain the cell reaction by adding the half-reactions that occur at the electrodes.

$$2 \times [2H^+(aq) + 2e^- \longrightarrow H_2(g)] \qquad \text{(cathode)}$$
$$\underline{2H_2O(l) \longrightarrow O_2(g) + 4H^+(aq) + 4e^-} \qquad \text{(anode)}$$
$$2H_2O(l) \longrightarrow 2H_2(g) + O_2(g)$$

The net cell reaction is simply the *electrolysis of water.* Where electricity is cheap, hydrogen can be prepared commercially by the electrolysis of water. Here H_2SO_4 was used as an electrolyte; however, various electrolytes can be used, including NaCl.

Electrolysis of Sodium Chloride Solutions

When you electrolyze an aqueous solution of sodium chloride, NaCl, the possible species involved in half-reactions are Na^+, Cl^-, and H_2O. The possible cathode half-reactions are

$$Na^+(aq) + e^- \longrightarrow Na(s); \ E^\circ = -2.71 \text{ V}$$
$$2H_2O(l) + 2e^- \longrightarrow H_2(g) + 2OH^-(aq); \ E^\circ = -0.83 \text{ V}$$

Under standard conditions, you expect H_2O to be reduced in preference to Na^+, which agrees with what you observe. Hydrogen gas evolves at the cathode. <

The possible anode half-reactions are

$$2Cl^-(aq) \longrightarrow Cl_2(g) + 2e^-; \ -E^\circ = -1.36 \text{ V}$$
$$2H_2O(l) \longrightarrow O_2(g) + 4H^+(aq) + 4e^-; \ -E^\circ = -1.23 \text{ V}$$

The OH^- concentration is actually 1×10^{-7} M. From Nernst's equation, E for the reduction of H_2O is -0.41 V, so you still conclude that H_2O is reduced in preference to Na^+.

FIGURE 19.21 ▲

Electrolysis of aqueous potassium iodide
Iodine forms at the anode by the oxidation of I⁻ ion. Iodine reacts with iodide ion to form I_3^- ion, which is red-brown. Hydrogen bubbles and hydroxide ion form at the cathode by the reduction of water.

Under standard-state conditions, you might expect H_2O to be oxidized in preference to Cl^-. However, the potentials are close and overvoltages at the electrodes could alter this conclusion.

It is possible, nevertheless, to give a general statement about the product expected at the anode. Electrode potentials, as you have seen, depend on concentrations. It turns out that when the solution is concentrated enough in Cl^-, Cl_2 is the product, but in dilute solution, O_2 is the product. To see this, you would simply apply the Nernst equation to the $Cl^-|Cl_2$ half-reaction.

$$2Cl^-(aq) \longrightarrow Cl_2(g) + 2e^-$$

Starting with very dilute NaCl solutions, you would find that the oxidation potential of Cl^- is very negative, so H_2O is reduced in preference to Cl^-. But as you increased the NaCl concentration, you would find that the oxidation potential of Cl^- increases until eventually Cl^- is oxidized in preference to H_2O. The product changes from O_2 to Cl_2.

The half-reactions and cell reaction for the electrolysis of aqueous sodium chloride to chlorine and hydroxide ion are as follows:

$$
\begin{array}{ll}
2H_2O(l) + 2e^- \longrightarrow H_2(g) + 2OH^-(aq) & \text{(cathode)} \\
\underline{2Cl^-(aq) \longrightarrow Cl_2(g) + 2e^-} & \text{(anode)} \\
2H_2O(l) + 2Cl^-(aq) \longrightarrow H_2(g) + Cl_2(g) + 2OH^-(aq) &
\end{array}
$$

Because the electrolysis started with sodium chloride, the cation in the electrolyte solution is Na^+. When you evaporate the electrolyte solution at the cathode, you obtain sodium hydroxide, NaOH. Figure 19.21 shows the similar electrolysis of aqueous potassium iodide, KI.

The electrolysis of aqueous sodium chloride is the basis of the *chlor-alkali industry,* the major commercial source of chlorine and sodium hydroxide. Commercial cells are of several types, but in each the main problem is to keep the products separate, because chlorine reacts with aqueous sodium hydroxide.

Figure 19.22 shows a modern **chlor-alkali membrane cell,** *a cell for the electrolysis of aqueous sodium chloride in which the anode and cathode compartments are separated by a special plastic membrane that allows only cations to pass through it.* Sodium chloride solution is added to the anode compartment, where chloride ion is oxidized to chlorine. The sodium ions carry the current from the anode to the cathode by passing through the membrane. Water is added at the top of the cathode compartment, where it is reduced to hydroxide ion, and sodium hydroxide solution is removed at the bottom of the cathode compartment.

FIGURE 19.22 ▶

A chlor-alkali membrane cell
Sodium chloride solution enters the anode compartment, where Cl^- ion is oxidized to Cl_2. Sodium ion migrates from the anode compartment through the membrane to the cathode compartment. Here water is reduced to hydrogen and OH^- ion. Sodium hydroxide solution is removed at the bottom of the cathode compartment.

FIGURE 19.23 ▶

A chlor-alkali mercury cell
Chloride ion oxidizes to chlorine gas at the graphite anodes (+ electrodes), and sodium deposits at the mercury cathode. Sodium amalgam (a liquid sodium–mercury alloy) circulates to the amalgam decomposer, where sodium reacts with water to form NaOH(aq) and H_2.

The older **chlor-alkali mercury cell** is *a cell for the electrolysis of aqueous sodium chloride in which mercury metal is used as the cathode* (Figure 19.23). At the mercury cathode, sodium ion is reduced in preference to water. Sodium ion is reduced to sodium to form a liquid sodium–mercury alloy called sodium amalgam. (An *amalgam* is an alloy of mercury with any of various other metals.)

$$Na^+(aq) + e^- \longrightarrow Na(amalgam)$$

Sodium amalgam circulates from the electrolytic cell to the amalgam decomposer. The amalgam and graphite particles in the decomposer form the electrodes of many voltaic cells, in which sodium reacts with water to give sodium hydroxide solution and hydrogen gas. Historically, loss of mercury from these cells has been a source of mercury pollution of waterways.

Electroplating of Metals

Many metals are protected from corrosion by plating them with other metals. Zinc coatings are often used to protect steel, because the coat protects the steel by cathodic protection even when the zinc coat is scratched (see end of Section 19.8). A thin zinc coating can be applied to steel by *electrogalvanizing,* or zinc electroplating. (Galvanized steel has a thick zinc coating obtained by dipping the object in molten zinc.) The steel object is placed in a bath of zinc salts and made the cathode in an electrolytic cell. The cathode half-reaction is

$$Zn^{2+}(aq) + 2e^- \longrightarrow Zn(s)$$

Electrolysis is also used to purify some metals. For example, copper for electrical use, which must be very pure, is purified by electrolysis. Slabs of impure copper serve as anodes, and pure copper sheets serve as cathodes; the electrolyte bath is copper(II) sulfate, $CuSO_4$ (Figure 19.24). During the electrolysis, copper(II) ions leave the anode slabs and plate out on the cathode sheets. Less reactive metals, such as gold, silver, and platinum, that were present in the impure copper form a valuable mud that collects on the bottom of the electrolytic cell. Metals more reactive than copper remain as ions in the electrolytic bath. After about a month in the electrolytic cell, the pure copper cathodes are much enlarged and are removed from the cell bath.

FIGURE 19.24 ▲

Purification of copper by electrolysis

Left: Copper(II) ion leaves the anode and plates out on the cathode. Reactive ions, such as Zn^{2+}, remain in solution, and unreactive substances (including gold) collect as a mud under the anode. *Right:* Very pure copper sheets alternate with impure copper slabs in this electrolytic tank. The pure copper sheets grow in size and are removed in about a month.

Example 19.13 | Predicting the Half-Reactions in an Aqueous Electrolysis

What do you expect to be the half-reactions in the electrolysis of aqueous copper(II) sulfate?

Problem Strategy From the problem, determine which species might be involved in the electrolysis. Write the half-reactions for these species, identifying those that could undergo reduction (cathode) and those that could undergo oxidation (anode). Using the electrode potentials of the half-reactions, determine which are most likely to occur.

Solution The species you should consider for half-reactions are $Cu^{2+}(aq)$, $SO_4{}^{2-}(aq)$, and H_2O.
Possible cathode half-reactions are

$$Cu^{2+}(aq) + 2e^- \longrightarrow Cu(s); \; E° = 0.34 \text{ V}$$
$$2H_2O(l) + 2e^- \longrightarrow H_2(g) + 2OH^-(aq); \; E° = -0.83 \text{ V}$$

Because the copper electrode potential is much larger than the reduction potential of water, you expect Cu^{2+} to be reduced.

Possible anode half-reactions are

$$2SO_4{}^{2-}(aq) \longrightarrow S_2O_8{}^{2-}(aq) + 2e^-; \; -E° = -2.01 \text{ V}$$
$$2H_2O(l) \longrightarrow O_2(g) + 4H^+(aq) + 4e^-; \; -E° = -1.23 \text{ V}$$

You expect H_2O to be oxidized.
The expected half-reactions are

$$Cu^{2+}(aq) + 2e^- \longrightarrow Cu(s)$$
$$2H_2O(l) \longrightarrow O_2(g) + 4H^+(aq) + 4e^-$$

Answer Check For aqueous electrolysis, always make sure that you consider the possibility of water undergoing oxidation at the anode or reduction at the cathode.

Exercise 19.16 Give the half-reactions that occur when aqueous silver nitrate is electrolyzed. Nitrate ion is not oxidized during the electrolysis.

■ See Problems 19.93 and 19.94.

19.11 | Stoichiometry of Electrolysis

In 1831 and 1832, the British chemist and physicist Michael Faraday showed that the amounts of substances released at the electrodes during electrolysis are related to the total charge that has flowed in the electric circuit. < If you look at the electrode reactions, you see that the relationship is stoichiometric.

| *See note at the top of page 807.*

Faraday's results were summarized in two laws: (1) The quantity of a substance liberated at an electrode is directly proportional to the quantity of electric charge that has flowed in the circuit. (2) For a given quantity of electric charge, the amount of any metal deposited is proportional to its equivalent mass (atomic mass divided by the charge on the metal ion). These laws follow directly from the stoichiometry of electrolysis.

When molten sodium chloride is electrolyzed, sodium ions migrate to the cathode, where they react with electrons.

$$Na^+ + e^- \longrightarrow Na(l)$$

Similarly, chloride ions migrate to the anode and release electrons.

$$Cl^- \longrightarrow \tfrac{1}{2}Cl_2(g) + e^-$$

Therefore, when one mole of electrons reacts with sodium ions, one faraday of charge (the magnitude of charge on one mole of electrons) passes through the circuit. One mole of sodium metal is deposited at one electrode, and one-half mole of chlorine gas evolves at the other electrode.

What is new in this type of stoichiometric problem is the measurement of numbers of electrons. You do not weigh them as you do substances. Rather, you measure the quantity of electric charge that has passed through the circuit. You use the following fact:

One faraday (9.6485×10^4 C) is equivalent to the charge on one mole of electrons.

If you know the current in a circuit and the length of time it has been flowing, you can calculate the electric charge.

$$Electric\ charge = electric\ current \times time\ lapse$$

Corresponding units are

$$Coulombs = amperes \times seconds$$

The **ampere (A)** is *the base unit of current in the International System (SI)*. The coulomb (C), the SI unit of electric charge, is equivalent to an ampere-second. Thus, a current of 0.50 amperes flowing for 84 seconds gives a charge of 0.50 A × 84 s = 42 A·s, or 42 C.

If you are given the amount of substance produced at an electrode and the time of electrolysis, you can determine the current. If you are given the current and the time of electrolysis, you can calculate the amount of substance produced at an electrode. The next two examples illustrate these calculations.

Example 19.14 | Calculating the Amount of Charge from the Amount of Product in an Electrolysis

When an aqueous solution of copper(II) sulfate, $CuSO_4$, is electrolyzed, copper metal is deposited.

$$Cu^{2+}(aq) + 2e^- \longrightarrow Cu(s)$$

(The other electrode reaction gives oxygen: $2H_2O \longrightarrow O_2 + 4H^+ + 4e^-$.) If a constant current was passed for 5.00 h and 404 mg of copper metal was deposited, what was the current?

Problem Strategy The electrode equation for copper says that 1 mol Cu is equivalent to 2 mol e⁻. You can use this in the conversion of grams of Cu to moles of electrons needed to deposit this amount of copper. The Faraday constant (which says that one mole of electrons is equivalent to 9.6485×10^4 C) converts moles of electrons to coulombs. The conversions are

$$g\ Cu \longrightarrow mol\ Cu \longrightarrow mol\ e^- \longrightarrow coulombs\ (C)$$

The current in amperes (A) equals the charge in coulombs divided by the time in seconds.

(continued)

(continued)

Solution   The conversion of grams of Cu to coulombs required to deposit 404 mg of copper is

$$0.404 \text{ g Cu} \times \frac{1 \text{ mol Cu}}{63.6 \text{ g Cu}} \times \frac{2 \text{ mol e}^-}{1 \text{ mol Cu}} \times \frac{9.6485 \times 10^4 \text{ C}}{1 \text{ mol e}^-} = 1.2\underline{2}6 \times 10^3 \text{ C}$$

The time lapse, 5.00 h, equals 1.80×10^4 s. Thus,

$$\text{Current} = \frac{\text{charge}}{\text{time}} = \frac{1.226 \times 10^3 \text{ C}}{1.80 \times 10^4 \text{ s}} = \mathbf{6.81 \times 10^{-2} \text{ A}}$$

Answer Check   A common mistake that you want to avoid when you work this type of problem is thinking that the coulomb (C) is the current. Therefore, always make sure that when a problem asks for the current, you convert from coulombs to amps (A).

Exercise 19.17   A constant electric current deposits 365 mg of silver in 216 min from an aqueous silver nitrate solution. What is the current?

■ See Problems 19.95 and 19.96.

Example 19.15 | Calculating the Amount of Product from the Amount of Charge in an Electrolysis

When an aqueous solution of potassium iodide is electrolyzed using platinum electrodes, the half-reactions are

$$2\text{I}^-(aq) \longrightarrow \text{I}_2(aq) + 2\text{e}^-$$
$$2\text{H}_2\text{O}(l) + 2\text{e}^- \longrightarrow \text{H}_2(g) + 2\text{OH}^-(aq)$$

How many grams of iodine are produced when a current of 8.52 mA flows through the cell for 10.0 min?

Problem Strategy   The current in amperes multiplied by the time in seconds equals the charge in coulombs. Convert the charge in coulombs to moles of electrons. Then, noting that each mole of iodine produced requires 2 mol e$^-$, convert mol e$^-$ to mol I$_2$. Finally, convert mol I$_2$ to g I$_2$.

$$\text{Coulombs} \longrightarrow \text{mol e}^- \longrightarrow \text{mol I}_2 \longrightarrow \text{g I}_2$$

Solution   When the current flows for 6.00×10^2 s (10.0 min), the amount of charge is

$$8.52 \times 10^{-3} \text{ A} \times 6.00 \times 10^2 \text{ s} = 5.11 \text{ C}$$

Note that two moles of electrons are equivalent to one mole of I$_2$. Hence,

$$5.11 \text{ C} \times \frac{1 \text{ mol e}^-}{9.6485 \times 10^4 \text{ C}} \times \frac{1 \text{ mol I}_2}{2 \text{ mol e}^-} \times \frac{254 \text{ g I}_2}{1 \text{ mol I}_2} = \mathbf{6.73 \times 10^{-3} \text{ g I}_2}$$

Answer Check   It is wise to see whether the calculated amount of material deposited during electrolysis is consistent with the amount and duration of the current. In this problem, where a small amount of current (8.52 mA) flows for a short period of time (10.0 min), we should not expect a large mass of product (I$_2$) to be deposited.

Exercise 19.18   How many grams of oxygen are liberated by the electrolysis of water with a current of 0.0565 A after 1.85×10^4 s?

■ See Problems 19.97 and 19.98.

A Checklist for Review

Important Terms

electrochemical cell (19.1)
voltaic (galvanic) cell (19.1)
electrolytic cell (19.1)
half-cell (19.2)
salt bridge (19.2)
anode (19.2)
cathode (19.2)
cell reaction (19.2)
potential difference (19.4)

volt (V) (19.4)
Faraday constant (*F*) (19.4)
cell potential or electromotive
   force (emf) (19.4)
standard cell potential (19.5)
standard electrode potential (19.5)
Nernst equation (19.7)
zinc–carbon (Leclanché) dry cell (19.8)
alkaline dry cell (19.8)

lithium–iodine battery (19.8)
lead storage cell (19.8)
nickel–cadmium cell (19.8)
fuel cell (19.8)
electrolysis (19.9)
Downs cell (19.9)
chlor-alkali membrane cell (19.10)
chlor-alkali mercury cell (19.10)
ampere (A) (19.11)

Key Equations

$$w_{max} = -nFE_{cell}$$

$$E°_{cell} = E°_{cathode} - E°_{anode}$$

$$\Delta G° = -nFE°_{cell}$$

$$E°_{cell} = \frac{0.0592}{n} \log K \quad \text{(values in volts at 25°C)}$$

$$E_{cell} = E°_{cell} - \frac{0.0592}{n} \log Q \quad \text{(values in volts at 25°C)}$$

Summary of Facts and Concepts

Oxidation–reduction reactions involve a transfer of electrons from one species to another. The *half-reaction method* can be applied to balancing oxidation–reduction reactions in acidic and basic solutions. Many of the principles required for balancing these reactions were presented in Chapter 4.

Electrochemical cells are of two types: voltaic and electrolytic. A *voltaic cell* uses a spontaneous chemical reaction to generate an electric current. It does this by physically separating the reaction into its oxidation and reduction half-reactions. These half-reactions take place in *half-cells*. The half-cell in which reduction occurs is called the *cathode;* the half-cell in which oxidation occurs is called the *anode.* Electrons flow in the external circuit from the anode to the cathode.

The *cell potential* is the maximum voltage of a voltaic cell. It can be directly related to the maximum work that can be done by the cell. A *standard electrode potential,* or reduction potential, refers to the potential of an electrode in which molar concentrations and gas pressures (in atmospheres) have unit values. A table of standard electrode potentials is useful for establishing the direction of spontaneity of an oxidation–reduction reaction and for calculating the *standard cell potential* of a cell.

The standard free-energy change, standard cell potential, and equilibrium constant are all related. Knowing one, you can calculate the others. Electrochemical measurements can therefore provide equilibrium or thermodynamic information.

An electrode potential depends on concentrations of the electrode substances, according to the *Nernst equation.* Because of this relationship, cell potentials can be used to measure ion concentrations. This is the basic principle of a pH meter, a device that measures the hydrogen-ion concentration.

Voltaic cells are used commercially as portable energy sources (batteries). In addition, the basic principle of the voltaic cell is employed in the *cathodic protection* of buried pipelines and tanks.

Electrolytic cells represent another type of electrochemical cell. They use an external voltage source to push a reaction in a nonspontaneous direction. The electrolysis of an aqueous solution often involves the oxidation or reduction of water at the electrodes. Electrolysis of concentrated sodium chloride solution, for example, gives hydrogen at the cathode. The amounts of substances released at an electrode are related to the amount of charge passed through the cell. This relationship is stoichiometric and follows from the electrode reactions.

Media Summary

Visit the **student website at college.cengage.com/pic/ebbing9e** to help prepare for class, study for quizzes and exams, understand core concepts, and visualize molecular-level interactions. The following media activities are available for this chapter:

 Prepare for Class

■ **Video Lessons** *Mini lectures from chemistry experts*
  CIA Demonstration: Fruit-Powered Clock

Reviewing Oxidation–Reduction Reactions
Electrochemical Cells
Electromotive Force
Standard Reduction Potentials

Using Standard Reduction Principles
The Nernst Equation
Electrochemical Determina of Equilibria
Batteries
Corrosion and the Prevention of Corrosion
Electrolytic Cells
The Stoichiometry of Electrolysis

Electrochemical Half-Reactions in a Galvanic Cell
Electrolysis of Water

■ **Tutorials:** *Animated examples and interactive activities*
Galvanic Cells

■ **Flashcards** *Key terms and definitions*
Online Flashcards

■ **Self-Assessment Questions** *Additional questions with full worked-out solutions*
6 Self-Assessment Questions

Improve Your Grade

■ **Visualizations** *Molecular-level animations and lab demonstration videos*
Zinc/Copper Cells (Lemon Battery)
Voltaic Cell: Anode Reaction
Voltaic Cell: Cathode Reaction
Galvanic (Voltaic) Cells

ACE the Test

Multiple-choice quizzes
3 ACE Practice Tests

Access these resources using the passkey available free with new texts or for purchase separately.

Learning Objectives

19.1 Balancing Oxidation–Reduction Reactions in Acidic and Basic Solutions

■ Learn the steps for balancing oxidation–reduction reactions in acidic solution using the half-reaction method.
■ Balance equations by the half-reaction method (acidic solution). **Example 19.1**
■ Learn the additional steps for balancing oxidation–reduction reactions in basic solution using the half-reaction method.
■ Balancing equations by the half-reaction method (basic solution). **Example 19.2**

19.2 Construction of Voltaic Cells

■ Define *electrochemical cell, voltaic (galvanic) cell, electrolytic cell,* and *half-cell.*
■ Describe the function of the *salt bridge* in a voltaic cell.
■ State the reactions that occurs at the *anode* and the *cathode* in an electrochemical cell.
■ Define *cell reaction.*
■ Sketch and label a voltaic cell. **Example 19.3**

19.3 Notation for Voltaic Cells

■ Write the cell reaction from the cell notation. **Example 19.4**

19.4 Cell Potential

■ Define *cell potential* and *volt.*
■ Calculate the quantity of work from a given amount of cell reactant. **Example 19.5**

19.5 Standard Cell Potentials and Standard Electrode Potentials

■ Explain how the electrode potential of a cell is an *intensive property.*

■ Define *standard cell potential* and *standard electrode potential.*
■ Interpret the table of standard reduction potentials.
■ Determine the relative strengths of oxidizing and reducing agents. **Example 19.6**
■ Determine the direction of spontaneity from electrode potentials. **Example 19.7**
■ Calculate cell potential from standard potentials. **Example 19.8**

19.6 Equilibrium Constants from Cell Potentials

■ Calculate the free-energy change from electrode potentials. **Example 19.9**
■ Calculate the cell potential from free-energy change. **Example 19.10**
■ Calculate the equilibrium constant from cell potential. **Example 19.11**

19.7 Dependence of Cell Potential on Concentration

■ Calculate the cell potential for nonstandard conditions. **Example 19.12**
■ Describe how pH can be determined using a glass electrode.

19.8 Some Commercial Voltaic Cells

■ Describe the construction and reactions of a *zinc–carbon dry cell,* a *lithium–iodine battery,* a *lead storage cell,* and a *nickel-cadmium cell.*
■ Explain the operation of a proton-exchange membrane *fuel cell.*
■ Explain the electrochemical process of the rusting of iron.
■ Define *cathodic protection.*

19.9 Electrolysis of Molten Salts

■ Define *electrolysis*.

19.10 Aqueous Electrolysis

■ Learn the half-reactions for water undergoing oxidation and reduction.
■ Predict the half-reactions in an aqueous electrolysis. Example 19.13

19.11 Stoichiometry of Electrolysis

■ Calculate the amount of charge from the amount of product in an electrolysis. Example 19.14
■ Calculate the amount of product from the amount of charge in an electrolysis. Example 19.15

Self-Assessment and Review Questions

19.1 Describe the difference between a voltaic cell and an electrolytic cell.
19.2 Define *cathode* and *anode*.
19.3 What is the SI unit of electrical potential?
19.4 Define the *faraday*.
19.5 Why is it necessary to measure the voltage of a voltaic cell when no current is flowing to obtain the cell potential?
19.6 How are standard electrode potentials defined?
19.7 Express the SI unit of energy as the product of two electrical units.
19.8 Give the mathematical relationships between the members of each possible pair of the three quantities $\Delta G°$, $E°_{cell}$, and K.
19.9 Using the Nernst equation, explain how the corrosion of iron would be affected by the pH of a water drop.
19.10 Describe the zinc–carbon, or Leclanché, dry cell and the lead storage battery.
19.11 What is a fuel cell? Describe an example.
19.12 Explain the electrochemistry of rusting.
19.13 Iron may be protected by coating with tin (tin cans) or with zinc (galvanized iron). Galvanized iron does not corrode as long as zinc is present. By contrast, when a tin can is scratched, the exposed iron underneath corrodes rapidly. Explain the difference between zinc and tin as protective coatings against iron corrosion.
19.14 The electrolysis of water is often done by passing a current through a dilute solution of sulfuric acid. What is the function of the sulfuric acid?
19.15 Describe a method for the preparation of sodium metal from sodium chloride.
19.16 Potassium was discovered by the British chemist Humphry Davy when he electrolyzed molten potassium hydroxide. What would be the anode reaction?
19.17 Briefly explain why different products are obtained from the electrolysis of molten NaCl and the electrolysis of a dilute aqueous solution of NaCl.
19.18 Write the Nernst equation for the electrode reaction $2Cl^-(aq) \longrightarrow Cl_2(g) + 2e^-$. With this equation, explain why the electrolysis of concentrated sodium chloride solution might be expected to release chlorine gas rather than oxygen gas at the anode.

19.19 The following oxidation–reduction reaction occurs in acidic solution. When the equation is balanced using the smallest set of whole-number stoichiometric coefficients possible, what is the stoichiometric coefficient for water? (*Hint:* In addition to the species shown in the original equation, $H^+(aq)$ and $H_2O(l)$ can also appear in the balanced equation.)

$$MnO_4^-(aq) + CH_3OH(aq) \longrightarrow Mn^{2+}(aq) + HCO_2H(aq)$$

a. 13   **b.** 19   **c.** 11   **d.** 7   **e.** 4

19.20 What half-reaction would be expected to occur at the cathode in the electrolysis of aqueous sodium fluoride?
a. $2F^-(aq) \longrightarrow F_2(g) + 2e^-$
b. $2H_2O(l) \longrightarrow O_2(g) + 4H^+(aq) + 4e^-$
c. $2H_2O(l) + 2e^- \longrightarrow H_2(g) + 2OH^-(aq)$
d. $Na^+(aq) + e^- \longrightarrow Na(s)$
e. $NaF(aq) \longrightarrow NaF(s)$

19.21 Electrolysis of an aqueous solution of sodium chloride produces chlorine, $Cl_2(g)$. The reaction that occurs at the anode is

$$2Cl^-(aq) \longrightarrow Cl_2(g) + 2e^-$$

A constant electric current deposits 152 g Cl_2 in 56.1 min from an aqueous solution of sodium chloride. What is the current?

a. 123 A
b. 61.5 A
c. 30.7 A
d. 6.18×10^5 A
e. 4.36×10^3 A

19.22 The voltaic cell is represented as

$$Zn(s)\,|\,Zn^{2+}(1.0\ M)\,\|\,Cu^{2+}(1.0\ M)\,|\,Cu(s)$$

Which of the following statements is *not* true of this cell?
a. The mass of the zinc electrode, $Zn(s)$, decreases as the cell runs.
b. The copper electrode is the anode.
c. Electrons flow through the external circuit from the zinc electrode to the copper electrode.
d. Reduction occurs at the copper electrode as the cell runs.
e. The concentration of Cu^{2+} decreases as the cell runs.

Concept Explorations

19.23　Electrochemical Cells I

You have the following setup to construct a cell under standard conditions. The anode and cathode are iron and silver rods. Using cell notation, the cell is

$$Fe(s)\,|\,Fe^{2+}(aq)\,\|\,Ag^{+}(aq)\,|\,Ag(s).$$

a. Complete the figure of the cell by labeling the anode and cathode and showing the corresponding reactions at the electrodes. Indicate the electron flow in the external circuit, the signs of the electrodes, and the direction of cation migration in the half-cells.

b. What is the cell potential, E°_{cell}? Is this a voltaic or an electrolytic cell? How do you know?

c. You send your lab partner to find the solutions for the beakers. What would you tell him to look for? Provide specific examples of solutions as part of your answer.

d. When you are constructing the cell, what impact does the volume of solution in each of the beakers have on the cell potential? (Assume that there is enough volume to cover at least one-third of the anode and cathode rods.)

e. If you were to add dionized (distilled) water to the solution that contains the $Ag^{+}(aq)$, would this have any effect on the cell voltage? If so, explain how the cell voltage would change.

f. When constructing the cell, you decide to swap the silver rod that is used as an anode for a copper rod, $Cu(s)$. Will this change have any effect on the cell potential or the operation of the cell? Explain.

g. Starting with the original cell, this time you swap the iron rod used as the cathode for a copper rod, $Cu(s)$. How will this change affect the cell potential and the operation of the cell?

19.24　Electrochemical Cells II

Consider this cell running under standard conditions:

$$Ni(s)\,|\,Ni^{2+}(aq)\,\|\,Cu^{+}(aq)\,|\,Cu(s)$$

a. Is this cell a voltaic or an electrolytic cell? How do you know?

b. Does current flow in this cell spontaneously?

c. What is the maximum cell potential for this cell?

d. Say the cell is connected to a voltmeter. Describe what you might see for an initial voltage and what voltage changes, if any, you would observe as time went by.

e. What is the free energy of this cell when it is first constructed?

e. Does the free energy of the cell change over time as the cell runs? If so, how does it change?

Conceptual Problems

19.25　Keeping in mind that aqueous Cu^{2+} is blue and aqueous Zn^{2+} is colorless, predict what you would observe over a several-day period if you performed the following experiments.

a. A strip of Zn is placed into a beaker containing aqueous Zn^{2+}.

b. A strip of Cu is placed into a beaker containing aqueous Cu^{2+}.

c. A strip of Zn is placed into a beaker containing aqueous Cu^{2+}.

d. A strip of Cu is placed into a beaker containing aqueous Zn^{2+}.

19.26　You are working at a plant that manufactures batteries. A client comes to you and asks for a 6.0-V battery that is made from silver and cadmium. Assuming that you are running the battery under standard conditions, how should it be constructed?

19.27　The composition of the hull of a submarine is mostly iron. Pieces of zinc, called "zincs," are placed in contact with the hull throughout the inside of the submarine. Why is this done?

19.28　You place a battery in a flashlight in which all of the electrochemical reactions have reached equilibrium. What do you expect to observe when you turn on the flashlight? Explain your answer.

19.29　The difference between a "heavy-duty" and a regular zinc–carbon battery is that the zinc can in the heavy-duty battery has thicker walls. What makes this battery heavy-duty in terms of output?

19.30　From an electrochemical standpoint, what metal, other than zinc, would be a reasonable candidate to coat a piece of iron to prevent corrosion (oxidation)?

19.31　Pick a combination of two metals from the Standard Reduction Potential table (Table 19.1 or Appendix I) that would result in a cell with a potential of about +0.90 V. For your answer, write both the half-reactions, write the overall balanced reaction, and calculate the cell potential for your choice.

19.32　You have 1.0 M solutions of $Al(NO_3)_3$ and $AgNO_3$ along with Al and Ag electrodes to construct a voltaic cell. The salt bridge contains a saturated solution of KCl. Complete the picture associated with this problem by

a. writing the symbols of the elements and ions in the appropriate areas (both solutions and electrodes).

b. identifying the anode and cathode.
c. indicating the direction of electron flow through the external circuit.
d. indicating the cell potential (assume standard conditions, with no current flowing).
e. writing the appropriate half-reaction under each of the containers.
f. indicating the direction of ion flow in the salt bridge.
g. identifying the species undergoing oxidation and reduction.
h. writing the balanced overall reaction for the cell.

19.33 The zinc–copper voltaic cell shown with this problem is currently running under standard conditions. How would the intensity of light from the bulb change if you were to
   a. dissolve some additional $CuSO_4(s)$ in the $CuSO_4$ solution?
   b. dissolve some additional $Zn(NO_3)_2(s)$ in the $Zn(NO_3)_2$ solution?

c. add H_2O to the $CuSO_4$ solution?
d. remove the salt bridge?

1.0 M $Zn(NO_3)_2$ 1.0 M $CuSO_4$

19.34 The development of lightweight batteries is an ongoing research effort combining many of the physical sciences. You are a member of an engineering team trying to develop a lightweight battery that will effectively react with $O_2(g)$ from the atmosphere as an oxidizing agent. A reducing agent must be chosen for this battery that will be lightweight, have nontoxic products, and react spontaneously with oxygen. Using data from Appendix I, suggest a likely reducing agent, being sure the above conditions are met. Are there any drawbacks to your selection?

Practice Problems

Balancing Oxidation–Reduction Equations

19.35 Balance the following oxidation–reduction equations. The reactions occur in acidic solution.
   a. $Cr_2O_7^{2-} + C_2O_4^{2-} \longrightarrow Cr^{3+} + CO_2$
   b. $Cu + NO_3^- \longrightarrow Cu^{2+} + NO$
   c. $MnO_2 + HNO_2 \longrightarrow Mn^{2+} + NO_3^-$
   d. $PbO_2 + Mn^{2+} + SO_4^{2-} \longrightarrow PbSO_4 + MnO_4^-$
   e. $HNO_2 + Cr_2O_7^{2-} \longrightarrow Cr^{3+} + NO_3^-$

19.36 Balance the following oxidation–reduction equations. The reactions occur in acidic solution.
   a. $Mn^{2+} + BiO_3^- \longrightarrow MnO_4^- + Bi^{3+}$
   b. $Cr_2O_7^{2-} + I^- \longrightarrow Cr^{3+} + IO_3^-$
   c. $MnO_4^- + H_2SO_3 \longrightarrow Mn^{2+} + SO_4^{2-}$
   d. $Cr_2O_7^{2-} + Fe^{2+} \longrightarrow Cr^{3+} + Fe^{3+}$
   e. $As + ClO_3^- \longrightarrow H_3AsO_3 + HClO$

19.37 Balance the following oxidation–reduction equations. The reactions occur in basic solution.
   a. $Mn^{2+} + H_2O_2 \longrightarrow MnO_2 + H_2O$
   b. $MnO_4^- + NO_2^- \longrightarrow MnO_2 + NO_3^-$
   c. $Mn^{2+} + ClO_3^- \longrightarrow MnO_2 + ClO_2$
   d. $MnO_4^- + NO_2 \longrightarrow MnO_2 + NO_3^-$
   e. $Cl_2 \longrightarrow Cl^- + ClO_3^-$

19.38 Balance the following oxidation–reduction equations. The reactions occur in basic solution.
   a. $Cr(OH)_4^- + H_2O_2 \longrightarrow CrO_4^{2-} + H_2O$
   b. $MnO_4^- + Br^- \longrightarrow MnO_2 + BrO_3^-$

c. $Co^{2+} + H_2O_2 \longrightarrow Co(OH)_3 + H_2O$
d. $Pb(OH)_4^{2-} + ClO^- \longrightarrow PbO_2 + Cl^-$
e. $Zn + NO_3^- \longrightarrow NH_3 + Zn(OH)_4^{2-}$

19.39 Balance the following oxidation–reduction equations. The reactions occur in acidic or basic aqueous solution, as indicated.
   a. $H_2S + NO_3^- \longrightarrow NO_2 + S_8$ (acidic)
   b. $NO_3^- + Cu \longrightarrow NO + Cu^{2+}$ (acidic)
   c. $MnO_4^- + SO_2 \longrightarrow SO_4^{2-} + Mn^{2+}$ (acidic)
   d. $Bi(OH)_3 + Sn(OH)_3^- \longrightarrow Sn(OH)_6^{2-} + Bi$ (basic)

19.40 Balance the following oxidation–reduction equations. The reactions occur in acidic or basic aqueous solution, as indicated.
   a. $Hg_2^{2+} + H_2S \longrightarrow Hg + S_8$ (acidic)
   b. $S^{2-} + I_2 \longrightarrow SO_4^{2-} + I^-$ (basic)
   c. $Al + NO_3^- \longrightarrow Al(OH)_4^- + NH_3$ (basic)
   d. $MnO_4^- + C_2O_4^{2-} \longrightarrow MnO_2 + CO_2$ (basic)

19.41 Balance the following oxidation–reduction equations. The reactions occur in acidic or basic aqueous solution, as indicated.
   a. $MnO_4^- + I^- \longrightarrow MnO_2 + IO_3^-$ (basic)
   b. $Cr_2O_7^{2-} + Cl^- \longrightarrow Cr^{3+} + Cl_2$ (acidic)
   c. $S_8 + NO_3^- \longrightarrow SO_2 + NO$ (acidic)
   d. $H_2O_2 + MnO_4^- \longrightarrow O_2 + MnO_2$ (basic)
   e. $Zn + NO_3^- \longrightarrow Zn^{2+} + N_2$ (acidic)

19.42 Balance the following oxidation–reduction equations. The reactions occur in acidic or basic aqueous solution, as indicated.

a. $Cr_2O_7^{2-} + H_2O_2 \longrightarrow Cr^{3+} + O_2$ (acidic)
b. $CN^- + MnO_4^- \longrightarrow CNO^- + MnO_2$ (basic)
c. $Cr(OH)_4^- + OCl^- \longrightarrow CrO_4^{2-} + Cl^-$ (basic)
d. $Br_2 + SO_2 \longrightarrow Br^- + SO_4^{2-}$ (acidic)
e. $CuS + NO_3^- \longrightarrow Cu^{2+} + NO + S_8$ (acidic)

Electrochemical Cells

19.43 A voltaic cell is constructed from the following half-cells: a magnesium electrode in magnesium sulfate solution and a nickel electrode in nickel sulfate solution. The half-reactions are

$$Mg(s) \longrightarrow Mg^{2+}(aq) + 2e^-$$
$$Ni^{2+}(aq) + 2e^- \longrightarrow Ni(s)$$

Sketch the cell, labeling the anode and cathode (and the electrode reactions), and show the direction of electron flow and the movement of cations.

19.44 Half-cells were made from a nickel rod dipping in a nickel sulfate solution and a copper rod dipping in a copper sulfate solution. The half-reactions in a voltaic cell using these half-cells were

$$Cu^{2+}(aq) + 2e^- \longrightarrow Cu(s)$$
$$Ni(s) \longrightarrow Ni^{2+}(aq) + 2e^-$$

Sketch the cell and label the anode and cathode, showing the corresponding electrode reactions. Give the direction of electron flow and the movement of cations.

19.45 Zinc reacts spontaneously with silver ion.

$$Zn(s) + 2Ag^+(aq) \longrightarrow Zn^{2+}(aq) + 2Ag(s)$$

Describe a voltaic cell using this reaction. What are the half-reactions?

19.46 Iron reacts spontaneously with copper(II) ion.

$$Fe(s) + Cu^{2+}(aq) \longrightarrow Fe^{2+}(aq) + Cu(s)$$

Obtain half-reactions for this, and then describe a voltaic cell using these half-reactions.

19.47 A silver oxide–zinc cell maintains a fairly constant voltage during discharge (1.60 V). The button form of this cell is used in watches, hearing aids, and other electronic devices. The half-reactions are

$$Zn(s) + 2OH^-(aq) \longrightarrow Zn(OH)_2(s) + 2e^-$$
$$Ag_2O(s) + H_2O(l) + 2e^- \longrightarrow 2Ag(s) + 2OH^-(aq)$$

Identify the anode and the cathode reactions. What is the overall reaction in the voltaic cell?

19.48 A mercury battery, used for hearing aids and electric watches, delivers a constant voltage (1.35 V) for long periods. The half-reactions are

$$HgO(s) + H_2O(l) + 2e^- \longrightarrow Hg(l) + 2OH^-(aq)$$
$$Zn(s) + 2OH^-(aq) \longrightarrow Zn(OH)_2(s) + 2e^-$$

Which half-reaction occurs at the anode and which occurs at the cathode? What is the overall cell reaction?

Voltaic Cell Notation

19.49 Write the cell notation for a voltaic cell with the following half-reactions.

$$Ni(s) \longrightarrow Ni^{2+}(aq) + 2e^-$$
$$Pb^{2+}(aq) + 2e^- \longrightarrow Pb(s)$$

19.50 Write the cell notation for a voltaic cell with the following half-reactions.

$$Al(s) \longrightarrow Al^{3+}(aq) + 3e^-$$
$$2H^+(aq) + 2e^- \longrightarrow H_2(g)$$

19.51 Give the notation for a voltaic cell constructed from a hydrogen electrode (cathode) in 1.0 M HCl and a nickel electrode (anode) in 1.0 M $NiSO_4$ solution. The electrodes are connected by a salt bridge.

19.52 A voltaic cell has an iron rod in 0.30 M iron(III) chloride solution for the cathode and a zinc rod in 0.20 M zinc sulfate solution for the anode. The half-cells are connected by a salt bridge. Write the notation for this cell.

19.53 Write the overall cell reaction for the following voltaic cell.

$$Fe(s)\,|\,Fe^{2+}(aq)\,\|\,Ag^+(aq)\,|\,Ag(s)$$

19.54 Write the overall cell reaction for the following voltaic cell.

$$Pt\,|\,H_2(g)\,|\,H^+(aq)\,\|\,Br_2(l)\,|\,Br^-(aq)\,|\,Pt$$

19.55 Consider the voltaic cell

$$Cd(s)\,|\,Cd^{2+}(aq)\,\|\,Ni^{2+}(aq)\,|\,Ni(s)$$

Write the half-cell reactions and the overall cell reaction. Make a sketch of this cell and label it. Include labels showing the anode, cathode, and direction of electron flow.

19.56 Consider the voltaic cell

$$Zn(s)\,|\,Zn^{2+}(aq)\,\|\,Cr^{3+}(aq)\,|\,Cr(s)$$

Write the half-cell reactions and the overall cell reaction. Make a sketch of this cell and label it. Include labels showing the anode, cathode, and direction of electron flow.

Electrode Potentials and Cell Potentials

19.57 A voltaic cell whose cell reaction is

$$2Fe^{3+}(aq) + Zn(s) \longrightarrow 2Fe^{2+}(aq) + Zn^{2+}(aq)$$

has a cell potential of 0.72 V. What is the maximum electrical work that can be obtained from this cell per mole of iron(III) ion?

19.58 A particular voltaic cell operates on the reaction

$$Zn(s) + Cl_2(g) \longrightarrow Zn^{2+}(aq) + 2Cl^-(aq)$$

giving a cell potential of 0.853 V. Calculate the maximum electrical work generated when 20.0 g of zinc metal is consumed.

19.59 What is the maximum work you can obtain from 30.0 g of nickel in the following cell when the cell potential is 0.97 V?

$$Ni(s)\,|\,Ni^{2+}(aq)\,\|\,Ag^+(aq)\,|\,Ag(s)$$

19.60 Calculate the maximum work available from 50.0 g of aluminum in the following cell when the cell potential is 1.15 V.

$$Al(s)\,|\,Al^{3+}(aq)\,\|\,H^+(aq)\,|\,O_2(g)\,|\,Pt$$

Note that O_2 is reduced to H_2O.

19.61 Order the following oxidizing agents by increasing strength under standard-state conditions: $O_2(g)$; $MnO_4^-(aq)$; $NO_3^-(aq)$ (in acidic solution).

19.62 Order the following oxidizing agents by increasing strength under standard-state conditions: $Ag^+(aq)$; $I_2(aq)$; $MnO_4^-(aq)$ (in acidic solution).

19.63 Consider the reducing agents $Cu^+(aq)$, $Zn(s)$, and $Fe(s)$. Which is strongest? Which is weakest?

19.64 Consider the reducing agents $Sn^{2+}(aq)$, $Cu(s)$, and $I^-(aq)$. Which is strongest? Which is weakest?

19.65 Consider the following reactions. Are they spontaneous in the direction written, under standard conditions at 25°C?
a. $Sn^{4+}(aq) + 2Fe^{2+}(aq) \longrightarrow Sn^{2+}(aq) + 2Fe^{3+}(aq)$
b. $4MnO_4^-(aq) + 12H^+(aq) \longrightarrow$
$\qquad\qquad 4Mn^{2+}(aq) + 5O_2(g) + 6H_2O(l)$

19.66 Answer the following questions by referring to standard electrode potentials at 25°C.
a. Will dichromate ion, $Cr_2O_7^{2-}$, oxidize iron(II) ion in acidic solution under standard conditions?
b. Will copper metal reduce $1.0\ M\ Ni^{2+}(aq)$ to metallic nickel?

19.67 What would you expect to happen when chlorine gas, Cl_2, at 1 atm pressure is bubbled into a solution containing $1.0\ M\ F^-$ and $1.0\ M\ Br^-$ at 25°C? Write a balanced equation for the reaction that occurs.

19.68 Dichromate ion, $Cr_2O_7^{2-}$, is added to an acidic solution containing Br^- and Mn^{2+}. Write a balanced equation for any reaction that occurs. Assume standard conditions at 25°C.

19.69 Calculate the standard cell potential of the following cell at 25°C.

$$Cr(s)\,|\,Cr^{3+}(aq)\,\|\,Hg_2^{2+}(aq)\,|\,Hg(l)$$

19.70 Calculate the standard cell potential of the following cell at 25°C.

$$Sn(s)\,|\,Sn^{2+}(aq)\,\|\,Cu^{2+}(aq)\,|\,Cu(s)$$

19.71 What is the standard cell potential you would obtain from a cell at 25°C using an electrode in which $I^-(aq)$ is in contact with $I_2(s)$ and an electrode in which a chromium strip dips into a solution of $Cr^{3+}(aq)$?

19.72 What is the standard cell potential you would obtain from a cell at 25°C using an electrode in which $Hg_2^{2+}(aq)$ is in contact with mercury metal and an electrode in which an aluminum strip dips into a solution of $Al^{3+}(aq)$?

Relationships Among $E°_{cell}$, $\Delta G°$, and K

19.73 Calculate the standard free-energy change at 25°C for the following reaction.

$3Cu(s) + 2NO_3^-(aq) + 8H^+(aq) \longrightarrow$
$\qquad\qquad 3Cu^{2+}(aq) + 2NO(g) + 4H_2O(l)$

Use standard electrode potentials.

19.74 Calculate the standard free-energy change at 25°C for the following reaction.

$$4Al(s) + 3O_2(g) + 12H^+(aq) \longrightarrow 4Al^{3+}(aq) + 6H_2O(l)$$

Use standard electrode potentials.

19.75 What is $\Delta G°$ for the following reaction?

$$2I^-(aq) + Cl_2(g) \longrightarrow I_2(s) + 2Cl^-(aq)$$

Use data given in Table 19.1.

19.76 Using electrode potentials, calculate the standard free-energy change for the reaction

$$Na(s) + \tfrac{1}{2}Br_2(g) \xrightarrow{\text{H}_2\text{O}} Na^+(aq) + Br^-(aq)$$

19.77 Calculate the standard cell potential at 25°C for the following cell reaction from standard free energies of formation (Appendix C).

$$Mg(s) + 2Ag^+(aq) \longrightarrow Mg^{2+}(aq) + 2Ag(s)$$

19.78 Calculate the standard cell potential at 25°C for the following cell reaction from standard free energies of formation (Appendix C).

$$2Al(s) + 3Cu^{2+}(aq) \longrightarrow 2Al^{3+}(aq) + 3Cu(s)$$

19.79 Calculate the standard cell potential of the lead storage cell whose overall reaction is

$PbO_2(s) + 2HSO_4^-(aq) + 2H^+(aq) + Pb(s) \longrightarrow$
$\qquad\qquad 2PbSO_4(s) + 2H_2O(l)$

See Appendix C for free energies of formation.

19.80 Calculate the standard cell potential of the cell corresponding to the oxidation of oxalic acid, $H_2C_2O_4$, by permanganate ion, MnO_4^-.

$5H_2C_2O_4(aq) + 2MnO_4^-(aq) + 6H^+(aq) \longrightarrow$
$\qquad\qquad 10CO_2(g) + 2Mn^{2+}(aq) + 8H_2O(l)$

See Appendix C for free energies of formation; $\Delta G°_f$ for $H_2C_2O_4(aq)$ is -698 kJ.

19.81 Calculate the equilibrium constant K for the following reaction at 25°C from standard electrode potentials.

$$Fe^{3+}(aq) + Cu(s) \longrightarrow Fe^{2+}(aq) + Cu^{2+}(aq)$$

The equation is not balanced.

19.82 Calculate the equilibrium constant K for the following reaction at 25°C from standard electrode potentials.

$$Sn^{4+}(aq) + 2Hg(l) \longrightarrow Sn^{2+}(aq) + Hg_2^{2+}(aq)$$

The equation is not balanced.

19.83 Copper(I) ion can act as both an oxidizing agent and a reducing agent. Hence, it can react with itself.

$$2Cu^+(aq) \longrightarrow Cu(s) + Cu^{2+}(aq)$$

Calculate the equilibrium constant at 25°C for this reaction, using appropriate values of electrode potentials.

19.84 Use electrode potentials to calculate the equilibrium constant at 25°C for the reaction

$$ClO_4^-(aq) + ClO_2^-(aq) \rightleftharpoons 2ClO_3^-(aq)$$

See Appendix I for data.

Nernst Equation

19.85 Calculate the cell potential of the following cell at 25°C.

$$Cr(s)\,|\,Cr^{3+}(1.0 \times 10^{-3}\ M)\,\|\,Ni^{2+}(1.5\ M)\,|\,Ni(s)$$

19.86 What is the cell potential of the following cell at 25°C?

$$Ni(s)\,|\,Ni^{2+}(1.0\ M)\,\|\,Sn^{2+}(1.0 \times 10^{-4}\ M)\,|\,Sn(s)$$

19.87 Calculate the cell potential of a cell operating with the following reaction at 25°C, in which $[MnO_4^-] = 0.010\ M$, $[Br^-] = 0.010\ M$, $[Mn^{2+}] = 0.15\ M$, and $[H^+] = 1.0\ M$.

$$2MnO_4^-(aq) + 10Br^-(aq) + 16H^+(aq) \longrightarrow$$
$$2Mn^{2+}(aq) + 5Br_2(l) + 8H_2O(l)$$

19.88 Calculate the cell potential of a cell operating with the following reaction at 25°C, in which $[Cr_2O_7^{2-}] = 0.020\ M$, $[I^-] = 0.015\ M$, $[Cr^{3+}] = 0.40\ M$, and $[H^+] = 0.50\ M$.

$$Cr_2O_7^{2-}(aq) + 6I^-(aq) + 14H^+(aq) \longrightarrow$$
$$2Cr^{3+}(aq) + 3I_2(s) + 7H_2O(l)$$

19.89 The voltaic cell

$$Cd(s)\,|\,Cd^{2+}(aq)\,\|\,Ni^{2+}(1.0\ M)\,|\,Ni(s)$$

has a cell potential of 0.240 V at 25°C. What is the concentration of cadmium ion? $(E^\circ_{cell} = 0.170\ V.)$

19.90 The cell potential of the following cell at 25°C is 0.475 V.

$$Zn\,|\,Zn^{2+}(1\ M)\,\|\,H^+(\text{test solution})\,|\,H_2(1\ atm)\,|\,Pt$$

What is the pH of the test solution?

Electrolysis

19.91 What are the half-reactions in the electrolysis of (a) CaS(l); (b) CsOH(l)?

19.92 What are the half-reactions in the electrolysis of (a) $MgBr_2(l)$; (b) $Ca(OH)_2(l)$?

19.93 Describe what you expect to happen when the following solutions are electrolyzed: (a) aqueous Na_2SO_4; (b) aqueous KBr. That is, what are the electrode reactions? What is the overall reaction?

19.94 Describe what you expect to happen when the following solutions are electrolyzed: (a) aqueous $CuCl_2$; (b) aqueous $Cu(NO_3)_2$. That is, what are the electrode reactions? What is the overall reaction? Nitrate ion is not oxidized.

19.95 In the commercial preparation of aluminum, aluminum oxide, Al_2O_3, is electrolyzed at 1000°C. (The mineral cryolite is added as a solvent.) Assume that the cathode reaction is

$$Al^{3+} + 3e^- \longrightarrow Al$$

How many coulombs of electricity are required to give 3.61 kg of aluminum?

19.96 Chlorine, Cl_2, is produced commercially by the electrolysis of aqueous sodium chloride. The anode reaction is

$$2Cl^-(aq) \longrightarrow Cl_2(g) + 2e^-$$

How long will it take to produce 1.18 kg of chlorine if the current is 5.00×10^2 A?

19.97 When molten lithium chloride, LiCl, is electrolyzed, lithium metal is liberated at the cathode. How many grams of lithium are liberated when 5.00×10^3 C of charge passes through the cell?

19.98 How many grams of cadmium are deposited from an aqueous solution of cadmium sulfate, $CdSO_4$, when an electric current of 1.51 A flows through the solution for 221 min?

General Problems

19.99 Some metals, such as iron, can be oxidized to more than one oxidation state. Obtain the balanced net ionic equations for the following oxidation–reduction reactions, in which nitric acid is reduced to nitric oxide, NO.

  a. Oxidation of iron metal to iron(II) ion by nitric acid.
  b. Oxidation of iron(II) ion to iron(III) ion by nitric acid.
  c. Oxidation of iron metal to iron(III) by nitric acid. [Consider adding the a and b equations.]

19.100 Some metals, such as thallium, can be oxidized to more than one oxidation state. Obtain the balanced net ionic equations for the following oxidation–reduction reactions, in which nitric acid is reduced to nitric oxide, NO.

  a. Oxidation of thallium metal to thallium(I) ion by nitric acid.
  b. Oxidation of thallium(I) ion to thallium(III) ion by nitric acid.
  c. Oxidation of thallium metal to thallium(III) by nitric acid. [Consider adding the a and b equations.]

19.101 Balance the following skeleton equations. The reactions occur in acidic or basic aqueous solution, as indicated.

  a. $MnO_4^- + S^{2-} \longrightarrow MnO_2 + S_8$ (basic)
  b. $IO_3^- + HSO_3^- \longrightarrow I^- + SO_4^{2-}$ (acidic)

  c. $Fe(OH)_2 + CrO_4^{2-} \longrightarrow Fe(OH)_3 + Cr(OH)_4^-$ (basic)
  d. $Cl_2 \longrightarrow Cl^- + ClO^-$ (basic)

19.102 Balance the following skeleton equations. The reactions occur in acidic or basic aqueous solution, as indicated.

  a. $MnO_4^- + H_2S \longrightarrow Mn^{2+} + S_8$ (acidic)
  b. $Zn + NO_3^- \longrightarrow Zn^{2+} + N_2O$ (acidic)
  c. $MnO_4^{2-} \longrightarrow MnO_4^- + MnO_2$ (basic)
  d. $Br_2 \longrightarrow Br^- + BrO_3^-$ (basic)

19.103 Iron(II) hydroxide is a greenish precipitate that is formed from iron(II) ion by the addition of a base. This precipitate gradually turns to the yellowish-brown iron(III) hydroxide from oxidation by O_2 in the air. Write a balanced equation for this oxidation by O_2.

19.104 A sensitive test for bismuth(III) ion consists of shaking a solution suspected of containing the ion with a basic solution of sodium stannite, Na_2SnO_2. A positive test consists of the formation of a black precipitate of bismuth metal. Stannite ion is oxidized by bismuth(III) ion to stannate ion, SnO_3^{2-}. Write a balanced equation for the reaction.

19.105 Give the notation for a voltaic cell that uses the reaction

$$Ca(s) + Cl_2(g) \longrightarrow Ca^{2+}(aq) + 2Cl^-(aq)$$

What is the half-cell reaction for the anode? for the cathode? What is the standard cell potential of the cell?

19.106 Give the notation for a voltaic cell whose overall cell reaction is

$$Mg(s) + 2Ag^+(aq) \longrightarrow Mg^{2+}(aq) + 2Ag(s)$$

What are the half-cell reactions? Label them as anode or cathode reactions. What is the standard cell potential of this cell?

19.107 Use electrode potentials to answer the following questions. (a) Is the oxidation of nickel by iron(III) ion a spontaneous reaction under standard conditions?

$$Ni(s) + 2Fe^{3+}(aq) \longrightarrow Ni^{2+}(aq) + 2Fe^{2+}(aq)$$

(b) Will iron(III) ion oxidize tin(II) ion to tin(IV) ion under standard conditions?

$$2Fe^{3+}(aq) + Sn^{2+}(aq) \longrightarrow 2Fe^{2+}(aq) + Sn^{4+}(aq)$$

19.108 Use electrode potentials to answer the following questions, assuming standard conditions. (a) Do you expect permanganate ion (MnO_4^-) to oxidize chloride ion to chlorine gas in acidic solution? (b) Will dichromate ion ($Cr_2O_7^{2-}$) oxidize chloride ion to chlorine gas in acidic solution?

19.109 Determine the cell potential of the following cell.

$$Pb\,|\,PbSO_4(s), SO_4^{2-}(1.0\ M)\,\|\,H^+(1.0\ M)\,|\,H_2(1.0\ atm)\,|\,Pt$$

The anode is essentially a lead electrode, $Pb\,|\,Pb^{2+}(aq)$. However, the anode solution is saturated with lead sulfate, so that the lead(II)-ion concentration is determined by the solubility product of $PbSO_4$ ($K_{sp} = 1.7 \times 10^{-8}$).

19.110 Determine the cell potential of the following cell.

$$Pt\,|\,H_2(1.0\ atm)\,|\,H^+(1.0\ M)\,\|\,Cl^-(1.0\ M), AgCl(s)\,|\,Ag$$

The cathode is essentially a silver electrode, $Ag^+(aq)\,|\,Ag$. However, the cathode solution is saturated with silver chloride, so that the silver-ion concentration is determined by the solubility product of AgCl ($K_{sp} = 1.8 \times 10^{-10}$).

19.111 (a) Calculate the equilibrium constant for the following reaction at 25°C.

$$Sn(s) + Pb^{2+}(aq) \rightleftharpoons Sn^{2+}(aq) + Pb(s)$$

The standard cell potential of the corresponding voltaic cell is 0.010 V. (b) If an excess of tin metal is added to 1.0 M Pb^{2+}, what is the concentration of Pb^{2+} at equilibrium?

19.112 (a) Calculate the equilibrium constant for the following reaction at 25°C.

$$Ag^+(aq) + Fe^{2+}(aq) \rightleftharpoons Ag(s) + Fe^{3+}(aq)$$

The standard cell potential of the corresponding voltaic cell is 0.030 V. (b) When equal volumes of 1.0 M solutions of Ag^+ and Fe^{2+} are mixed, what is the equilibrium concentration of Fe^{2+}?

19.113 How many faradays are required for each of the following processes? How many coulombs are required?
  a. Reduction of 1.0 mol Na^+ to Na
  b. Reduction of 1.0 mol Cu^{2+} to Cu

  c. Oxidation of 1.0 g H_2O to O_2
  d. Oxidation of 1.0 g Cl^- to Cl_2

19.114 How many faradays are required for each of the following processes? How many coulombs are required?
  a. Reduction of 1.0 mol Fe^{3+} to Fe^{2+}
  b. Reduction of 1.0 mol Fe^{3+} to Fe
  c. Oxidation of 1.0 g Sn^{2+} to Sn^{4+}
  d. Reduction of 1.0 g Au^{3+} to Au

19.115 In an analytical determination of arsenic, a solution containing arsenious acid, H_3AsO_3, potassium iodide, and a small amount of starch is electrolyzed. The electrolysis produces free iodine from iodide ion, and the iodine immediately oxidizes the arsenious acid to hydrogen arsenate ion, $HAsO_4^{2-}$.

$$I_2(aq) + H_3AsO_3(aq) + H_2O(l) \longrightarrow$$
$$2I^-(aq) + HAsO_4^{2-}(aq) + 4H^+(aq)$$

When the oxidation of arsenic is complete, the free iodine combines with the starch to give a deep blue color. If, during a particular run, it takes 65.4 s for a current of 10.5 mA to give an endpoint (indicated by the blue color), how many grams of arsenic are present in the solution?

19.116 The amount of lactic acid, $HC_3H_5O_3$, produced in a sample of muscle tissue was analyzed by reaction with hydroxide ion. Hydroxide ion was produced in the sample mixture by electrolysis. The cathode reaction was

$$2H_2O(l) + 2e^- \longrightarrow H_2(g) + 2OH^-(aq)$$

Hydroxide ion reacts with lactic acid as soon as it is produced. The endpoint is detected with an acid–base indicator. It required 115 s for a current of 15.6 mA to reach the endpoint. How many grams of lactic acid (a monoprotic acid) were present in the sample?

19.117 A standard electrochemical cell is made by dipping a silver electrode into a 1.0 M Ag^+ solution and a cadmium electrode into a 1.0 M Cd^{2+} solution.
  a. What is the spontaneous chemical reaction, and what is the maximum potential produced by this cell?
  b. What would be the effect on the potential of this cell if sodium sulfide were added to the Cd^{2+} half-cell and CdS were precipitated? Why?
  c. What would be the effect on the potential of the cell if the size of the silver electrode were doubled?

19.118 A standard electrochemical cell is made by dipping an iron electrode into a 1.0 M Fe^{2+} solution and a copper electrode into a 1.0 M Cu^{2+} solution.
  a. What is the spontaneous chemical reaction, and what is the maximum potential produced by this cell?
  b. What would be the effect on the potential of this cell if sodium carbonate were added to the Cu^{2+} half-cell and $CuCO_3$ were precipitated? Why?
  c. What would be the effect on the potential of the cell if the size of the iron electrode were halved?

19.119 A solution of copper(II) sulfate is electrolyzed by passing a current through the solution using inert electrodes. Consequently, there is a decrease in the Cu^{2+} concentration and an increase in the hydronium ion concentration. Also, one electrode increases in mass and a gas evolves at the other electrode. Write half-reactions that occur at the anode and at the cathode.

19.120   A potassium chloride solution is electrolyzed by passing a current through the solution using inert electrodes. A gas evolves at each electrode, and there is a large increase in pH of the solution. Write the half-reactions that occur at the anode and at the cathode.

19.121   A constant current of 1.50 amp is passed through an electrolytic cell containing a 0.10 M solution of $AgNO_3$ and a silver anode and a platinum cathode until 2.48 g of silver is deposited.
a. How long does the current flow to obtain this deposit?
b. What mass of chromium would be deposited in a similar cell containing 0.10 M Cr^{3+} if the same amount of current were used?

19.122   A constant current of 1.25 amp is passed through an electrolytic cell containing a 0.050 M solution of $CuSO_4$ and a copper anode and a platinum cathode until 2.20 g of copper is deposited.
a. How long does the current flow to obtain this deposit?
b. What mass of silver would be deposited in a similar cell containing 0.10 M Ag^+ if the same amount of current were used?

19.123   An aqueous solution of an unknown salt of gold is electrolyzed by a current of 2.75 amps for 3.50 hours. The electroplating is carried out with an efficiency of 90.0%, resulting in a deposit of 21.221 g of gold.
a. How many faradays are required to deposit the gold?
b. What is the charge on the gold ions (based on your calculations)?

19.124   An aqueous solution of an unknown salt of vanadium is electrolyzed by a current of 2.50 amps for 1.90 hours. The electroplating is carried out with an efficiency of 95.0%, resulting in a deposit of 2.850 g of vanadium.

a. How many faradays are required to deposit the vanadium?
b. What is the charge on the vanadium ions (based on your calculations)?

19.125   An electrochemical cell is made by placing a zinc electrode in 1.00 L of 0.200 M $ZnSO_4$ solution and a copper electrode in 1.00 L of 0.0100 M $CuCl_2$ solution.
a. What is the initial voltage of this cell when it is properly constructed?
b. Calculate the final concentration of Cu^{2+} in this cell if it is allowed to produce an average current of 1.00 amp for 225 s.

19.126   An electrochemical cell is made by placing an iron electrode in 1.00 L of 0.15 M $FeSO_4$ solution and a copper electrode in 1.00 L of 0.036 M $CuSO_4$ solution.
a. What is the initial voltage of this cell when it is properly constructed?
b. Calculate the final concentration of Cu^{2+} in this cell if it is allowed to produce an average current of 1.25 amp for 335 s.

19.127   (a) Calculate $\Delta G°$ for the following cell reaction:
$$Cd(s)\,|\,Cd^{2+}(aq)\,\|\,Co^{2+}(aq)\,|\,Co(s)$$
The $\Delta G_f°$ for $Cd^{2+}(aq)$ is -77.6 kJ/mol.
(b) From $\Delta G°$, calculate the standard cell potential for the cell reaction and from this, determine the standard potential for $Co^{2+}(aq) + 2e^- \longrightarrow Co(s)$.

19.128   (a) Calculate $\Delta G°$ for the following cell reaction:
$$Tl(s)\,|\,Tl^+(aq)\,\|\,Pb^{2+}(aq)\,|\,Pb(s)$$
The $\Delta G_f°$ for $Tl^+(aq)$ is -32.4 kJ/mol.
(b) From $\Delta G°$, calculate the standard cell potential for the cell reaction and from this, determine the standard potential for $Tl^+(aq) + e^- \longrightarrow Tl(s)$.

Strategy Problems

19.129   A voltaic cell is constructed from a half-cell in which a chromium rod dips into a solution of chromium(III) nitrate, $Cr(NO_3)_3$, and another half-cell in which a lead rod dips into a solution of lead(II) nitrate, $Pb(NO_3)_2$. The two half-cells are connected by a salt bridge. Chromium metal is oxidized during operation of the voltaic cell. What is the half-reaction that occurs at the cathode?
19.130   What are the overall cell reaction and the cell potential for this voltaic cell?
$$Mg(s)\,|\,Mg^{2+}(aq)\,\|\,Fe^{3+}(aq)\,|\,Fe(s)$$

19.131   The cell potential of a particular voltaic cell with the cell reaction
$$2Cr(s) + 3Cu^{2+}(aq) \longrightarrow 2Cr^{3+}(aq) + 3\,Cu(s)$$
is 1.14 V. What is the maximum electrical work, per mole, that can be obtained from 6.61 g of chromium metal?
19.132   Order the following oxidizing agents by increasing strength under standard-state conditions: $Mg^{2+}(aq)$, $Hg^{2+}(aq)$, $Pb^{2+}(aq)$.
19.133   What is the cell potential (E_{cell}) of a spontaneous cell that is run at 25°C and contains $[Cr^{3+}] = 0.10\ M$ and $[Ag^+] = 1.0 \times 10^{-4}\ M$?

19.134   A strip of aluminum metal is placed into a beaker containing 1.0 M $CuSO_4$. (a) Will a spontaneous reaction occur? (b) If a spontaneous reaction does occur, write the half-reactions and describe what you would observe.
19.135   Which of the following reactions occur spontaneously *as written*, with the production of a measurable electric current?
a. $I_2 + NaBr \longrightarrow Br_2 + 2NaI$
b. $Li + NaCl \longrightarrow LiCl + Na$
c. $Li^+ + Na^+ \longrightarrow NaLi$
d. $Ag + Li \longrightarrow Ag^+ + Li^+$
e. $2Li^+ + F_2 \longrightarrow 2LiF$
19.136   How many grams of hydrogen can be produced by the electrolysis of water with a current of 0.325 A running for 5.00 min?
19.137   The following two half-reactions are involved in a voltaic cell. At standard conditions, what species is produced at each electrode?
$$Ag^+ + e^- \longrightarrow Ag \qquad E° = 0.80\ V$$
$$Ni^{2+} + 2e^- \longrightarrow Ni \qquad E° = -0.25\ V$$

19.138 Consider the following reaction run at standard conditions:

$$Al(s) + Fe^{2+}(aq) \longrightarrow Fe(s) + Al^{3+}(aq)$$

a. Calculate the standard cell potential for this cell from standard free energies of formation (see Appendix C).

Cumulative-Skills Problems

19.139 Consider the following cell reaction at 25°C.

$$2Cr^{3+}(aq) + 3Zn(s) \longrightarrow 3Zn^{2+}(aq) + 2Cr(s)$$

Calculate the standard cell potential of this cell from the standard electrode potentials, and from this obtain $\Delta G°$ for the cell reaction. Use data in Appendix C to calculate $\Delta H°$; note that $Cr(H_2O)_6{}^{3+}(aq)$ equals $Cr^{3+}(aq)$. Use these values of $\Delta H°$ and $\Delta G°$ to obtain $\Delta S°$ for the cell reaction.

19.140 Consider the following cell reaction at 25°C.

$$2Cr(s) + 3Fe^{2+}(aq) \longrightarrow 2Cr^{3+}(aq) + 3Fe(s)$$

Calculate the standard cell potential of this cell from the standard electrode potentials, and from this obtain $\Delta G°$ for the cell reaction. Use data in Appendix C to calculate $\Delta H°$; note that $Cr(H_2O)_6{}^{3+}(aq)$ equals $Cr^{3+}(aq)$. Use these values of $\Delta H°$ and $\Delta G°$ to obtain $\Delta S°$ for the cell reaction.

19.141 Under standard conditions for all concentrations, the following reaction is spontaneous at 25°C.

$$O_2(g) + 4H^+(aq) + 4Br^-(aq) \longrightarrow 2H_2O(l) + 2Br_2(l)$$

If $[H^+]$ is decreased so that the pH = 3.60, what value will E_{cell} have, and will the reaction be spontaneous at this $[H^+]$?

19.142 Under standard conditions for all concentrations, the following reaction is spontaneous at 25°C.

$$O_3(g) + 2H^+(aq) + 2Co^{2+}(aq) \longrightarrow$$
$$O_2(g) + H_2O(l) + 2Co^{3+}(l)$$

If $[H^+]$ is decreased so that the pH = 9.10, what value will E_{cell} have, and will the reaction be spontaneous at this $[H^+]$?

b. Calculate the equilibrium constant for the reaction.
c. How would the value of the equilibrium constant be affected if the concentration of $Fe^{2+}(aq)$ were changed to 1.1 M?

19.143 Under standard conditions for all concentrations, the following reaction is spontaneous at 25°C.

$$O_2(g) + 4H^+(aq) + 4Br^-(aq) \longrightarrow 2H_2O(l) + 2Br_2(l)$$

If $[H^+]$ is adjusted by adding a buffer of 0.10 M NaOCN and 0.10 M HOCN ($K_a = 3.5 \times 10^{-4}$), what value will E_{cell} have, and will the reaction be spontaneous at this $[H^+]$?

19.144 Under standard conditions for all concentrations, the following reaction is spontaneous at 25°C.

$$O_3(g) + 2H^+(aq) + 2Co^{2+}(aq) \longrightarrow$$
$$O_2(g) + H_2O(l) + 2Co^{3+}(aq)$$

If $[H^+]$ is adjusted by adding a buffer of 0.10 M NaClO and 0.10 M HClO ($K_a = 3.5 \times 10^{-8}$), what value will E_{cell} have, and will the reaction be spontaneous at this $[H^+]$?

19.145 An electrode is prepared by dipping a silver strip into a solution saturated with silver thiocyanate, AgSCN, and containing 0.10 M SCN$^-$. The cell potential of the voltaic cell constructed by connecting this electrode as the cathode to the standard hydrogen half-cell as the anode is 0.45 V. What is the solubility product of silver thiocyanate?

19.146 An electrode is prepared from liquid mercury in contact with a saturated solution of mercury(I) chloride, Hg$_2$Cl$_2$, containing 1.00 M Cl$^-$. The cell potential of the voltaic cell constructed by connecting this electrode as the cathode to the standard hydrogen half-cell as the anode is 0.268 V. What is the solubility product of mercury(I) chloride?

1

Chemistry and Measurement

One of the forms of SiO_2 in nature is the quartz crystal. Optical fibers that employ light for data transmission use ultrapure SiO_2 that is produced synthetically.

Contents and Concepts

We start by defining the science called chemistry and introducing some fundamental concepts.

Making and recording measurements of the properties and chemical behavior of matter is the foundation of chemistry.

1

In 1964 Barnett Rosenberg and his coworkers at Michigan State University were studying the effects of electricity on bacterial growth. They inserted platinum wire electrodes into a live bacterial culture and allowed an electric current to pass. After 1 to 2 hours, they noted that cell division in the bacteria stopped. The researchers were very surprised by this result, but even more surprised by the explanation. They were able to show that cell division was inhibited by a substance containing platinum, produced from the platinum electrodes by the electric current. A substance such as this one, the researchers thought, might be useful as an anticancer drug, because cancer involves runaway cell division. Later research confirmed this view, and today the platinum-containing substance *cisplatin* is a leading anticancer drug (Figure 1.1).

FIGURE 1.1 ▲
Barnett Rosenberg
Discoverer of the anticancer activity of cisplatin.

This story illustrates three significant reasons to study chemistry. First, chemistry has important practical applications. The development of lifesaving drugs is one, and a complete list would touch upon most areas of modern technology.

Second, chemistry is an intellectual enterprise, a way of explaining our material world. When Rosenberg and his coworkers saw that cell division in the bacteria had ceased, they systematically looked for the chemical substance that caused it to cease. They sought a chemical explanation for the occurrence.

Finally, chemistry figures prominently in other fields. Rosenberg's experiment began as a problem in biology; through the application of chemistry, it led to an advance in medicine. Whatever your career plans, you will find that your knowledge of chemistry is a useful intellectual tool for making important decisions.

■ See page 30 for the Media Summary.

An Introduction to Chemistry

Because the material of this chapter is likely to be more or less familiar to students, you might wish to confine your lecture to a few main points, while stressing to students that they should read the chapter carefully.

All of the objects around you—this book, your pen or pencil, and the things of nature such as rocks, water, and plant and animal substances—constitute the *matter* of the universe. Each of the particular kinds of matter, such as a certain kind of paper or plastic or metal, is referred to as a *material*. We can define chemistry as the science of the composition and structure of materials and of the changes that materials undergo.

One chemist may hope that by understanding certain materials, he or she will be able to find a cure for a disease or a solution for an environmental ill. Another chemist may simply want to understand a phenomenon. Because chemistry deals with all materials, it is a subject of enormous breadth. It would be difficult to exaggerate the influence of chemistry on modern science and technology or on our ideas about our planet and the universe. In the section that follows, we will take a brief glimpse at modern chemistry and see some of the ways it has influenced technology, science, and modern thought.

1.1   Modern Chemistry: A Brief Glimpse

Tyrian purple is one of the few known natural compounds of bromine; it is a bromine derivative of indigo, another natural dye. The bromine atoms are the large red-brown atoms in Figure 1.2.

For thousands of years, human beings have fashioned natural materials into useful products. Modern chemistry certainly has its roots in this endeavor. After the discovery of fire, people began to notice changes in certain rocks and minerals exposed to high temperatures. From these observations came the development of ceramics, glass, and metals, which today are among our most useful materials. Dyes and medicines were other early products obtained from natural substances. For example, the ancient

Phoenicians extracted a bright purple dye, known as Tyrian purple, from a species of sea snail. One ounce of Tyrian purple required over 200,000 snails. Because of its brilliant hue and scarcity, the dye became the choice of royalty.

Although chemistry has its roots in early technology, chemistry as a field of study based on scientific principles came into being only in the latter part of the eighteenth century. Chemists began to look at the precise quantities of substances they used in their experiments. From this work came the central principle of modern chemistry: the materials around us are composed of exceedingly small particles called *atoms*, and the precise arrangement of these atoms into *molecules* or more complicated structures accounts for the many different characteristics of materials. Once chemists understood this central principle, they could begin to fashion molecules to order. They could *synthesize* molecules; that is, they could build large molecules from small ones. Tyrian purple, for example, was eventually synthesized from the simpler molecule aniline; see Figure 1.2. Chemists could also correlate molecular structure with the characteristics of materials and so begin to fashion materials with special characteristics.

The liquid-crystal displays (LCDs) that are used on everything from watches and cell phones to computer monitors and televisions are an example of an application that depends on the special characteristics of materials (Figure 1.3). The liquid crystals used in these displays are a form of matter intermediate in characteristics between those of liquids and those of solid crystals—hence the name. Many of these liquid crystals are composed of rodlike molecules that tend to align themselves something like the wood matches in a matchbox. The liquid crystals are held in alignment in layers by plates that have microscopic grooves. The molecules are attached to small electrodes or transistors. When the molecules are subjected to an electric charge from the transistor or electrode, they change alignment to point in a new direction. When they change direction, they change how light passes through their layer. When the liquid-crystal layer is combined with a light source and color filters, incremental changes of alignment of the molecules throughout the display allow for images that have high contrast and millions of colors. Figure 1.4 shows a model of one of the molecules that forms a liquid crystal; note the rodlike shape of the molecule. Chemists have designed many similar molecules for liquid-crystal applications. <

FIGURE 1.2

Molecular models of Tyrian purple and aniline

Tyrian purple *(top)* is a dye that was obtained by the early Phoenicians from a species of sea snail. The dye was eventually synthesized from aniline *(bottom)*.

> *Liquid crystals and liquid-crystal displays are described in the essay at the end of Section 11.7.*

FIGURE 1.3 ▶

A cell phone that uses a liquid-crystal display

These liquid-crystal displays are used in a variety of electronic devices.

FIGURE 1.4 ▼

Model of a molecule that forms a liquid crystal

Note that the molecule has a rodlike shape.

NOT FOR SALE OR INSTRUCTOR—FOR INSTRUCTOR REVIEW USE ONLY—NOT FOR SALE—FOR INSTRUCTOR REVIEW USE ONLY—NOT FOR SALE—FOR INSTRUCTOR REVIEW USE ONLY—NOT FOR SALE—FOR INSTRUCTOR REVIEW USE ONLY

FIGURE 1.5 ▲
Optical fibers
A bundle of optical fibers that can be used to transmit data via pulses of light.

Chemists continue to develop new materials and to discover new properties of old ones. Electronics and communications, for example, have been completely transformed by technological advances in materials. Optical-fiber cables have replaced long-distance telephone cables made of copper wire. Optical fibers are fine threads of extremely pure glass. Because of their purity, these fibers can transmit laser light pulses for miles compared with only a few inches in ordinary glass. Not only is optical-fiber cable cheaper and less bulky than copper cable carrying the same information, but through the use of different colors of light, optical-fiber cable can carry voice, data, and video information at the same time (Figure 1.5). At the ends of an optical-fiber cable, devices using other new materials convert the light pulses to electrical signals and back, while computer chips constructed from still other materials process the signals.

Chemistry has also affected the way we think of the world around us. For example, biochemists and molecular biologists—scientists who study the molecular basis of living organisms—have made a remarkable finding: all forms of life appear to share many of the same molecules and molecular processes. Consider the information of inheritance, the genetic information that is passed on from one generation of organism to the next. Individual organisms, whether bacteria or human beings, store this information in a particular kind of molecule called deoxyribonucleic acid, or DNA (Figure 1.6).

DNA consists of two intertwined molecular chains; each chain consists of links of four different types of molecular pieces, or bases. Just as you record information on a page by stringing together characters (letters, numbers, spaces, and so on), an organism stores the information for reproducing itself in the order of these bases in its DNA. In a multicellular organism, such as a human being, every cell contains the same DNA.

One of our first projects will be to look at this central concept of chemistry, the atomic theory of matter. We will do that in the next chapter, but first we must lay the groundwork for this discussion. We will need some basic vocabulary to talk about science and to describe materials; then we will need to discuss measurement and units, because measurement is critical for quantitative work.

1.2 | Experiment and Explanation

Experiment and explanation are the heart of chemical research. A chemist makes observations under circumstances in which variables, such as temperature and amounts of substances, can be controlled. An **experiment** is *an observation of natural phenomena carried out in a controlled manner so that the results can be duplicated and rational conclusions obtained.* In the chapter opening it was mentioned that Rosenberg studied the effects of electricity on bacterial growth. Temperature and amounts of nutrients in a given volume of bacterial medium are important variables in such experiments. Unless these variables are controlled, the work cannot be duplicated, nor can any reasonable conclusion be drawn.

After a series of experiments, perhaps a researcher sees some relationship or regularity in the results. For instance, Rosenberg noted that in each experiment in which an electric current was passed through a bacterial culture by means of platinum wire electrodes, the bacteria ceased dividing. If the regularity or relationship is fundamental and we can state it simply, we call it a law. A **law** is *a concise statement or mathematical equation about a fundamental relationship or regularity of nature.* An example is the law of conservation of mass, which says that the mass, or quantity of matter, remains constant during any chemical change.

At some point in a research project, a scientist tries to make sense of the results by devising an explanation. Explanations help us organize knowledge and predict future events. A **hypothesis** is *a tentative explanation of some regularity of nature.* Having seen that bacteria ceased to divide when an electric current from platinum wire electrodes passed through the culture, Rosenberg was eventually able to propose the hypothesis that certain platinum compounds were responsible. If a hypothesis is

FIGURE 1.6 ▲
A side view of a fragment of a DNA molecule
DNA contains the hereditary information of an organism that is passed on from one generation to the next.

A Chemist Looks at . . .

The Birth of the Post-it Note®

daily life

Have you ever used a Post-it and wondered where the idea for those little sticky notes came from? You have a chemist to thank for their invention. The story of the Post-it Note illustrates how the creativity and insights of a scientist can result in a product that is as common in the office as the stapler or pen.

In the early 1970s, Art Fry, a 3M scientist, was standing in the choir at his church trying to keep track of all the little bits of paper that marked the music selections for the service. During the service, a number of the markers fell out of the music, making him lose his place. While standing in front of the congregation, he realized that he needed a bookmark that would stick to the book, wouldn't hurt the book, and could be easily detached. To make his plan work, he required an adhesive that would not *permanently* stick things together. Finding the appropriate adhesive was not as simple as it may seem, because most adhesives at that time were created to stick things together permanently.

Still thinking about his problem the next day, Fry consulted a colleague, Spencer Silver, who was studying adhesives at the 3M research labs. That study consisted of conducting a series of tests on a range of adhesives to determine the strength of the bond they formed. One of the adhesives that Silver created for the study was an adhesive that always remained sticky. Fry recognized that this adhesive was just what he needed for his bookmark. His first bookmark, invented the day after the initial idea, consisted of a strip of Silver's tacky adhesive applied to the edge of a piece of paper.

Part of Fry's job description at 3M was to spend time working on creative ideas such as his bookmark. As a result, he continued to experiment with the bookmark to improve its properties of sticking, detaching, and not hurting the surface to which it was attached. One day, while doing some paperwork, he wrote a question on one of his experimental strips of paper and sent it to his boss stuck to the top of a file folder. His boss then answered the question on the note and returned it attached to some other documents. During a later discussion over coffee, Fry and his boss realized that they had invented a new way for people to communicate: the Post-it Note was born. Today the Post-it Note is one of the top-selling office products in the United States.

■ See Problems 1.43 and 1.44.

---

to be useful, it should suggest new experiments that become tests of the hypothesis. Rosenberg could test his hypothesis by looking for the platinum compound and testing for its ability to inhibit cell division.

If a hypothesis successfully passes many tests, it becomes known as a theory. A **theory** is *a tested explanation of basic natural phenomena*. An example is the molecular theory of gases—the theory that all gases are composed of very small particles called molecules. This theory has withstood many tests and has been fruitful in suggesting many experiments. Note that we cannot prove a theory absolutely. It is always possible that further experiments will show the theory to be limited or that someone will develop a better theory. For example, the physics of the motion of objects devised by Isaac Newton withstood experimental tests for more than two centuries, until physicists discovered that the equations do not hold for objects moving near the speed of light. Later physicists showed that very small objects also do not follow Newton's equations. Both discoveries resulted in revolutionary developments in physics. The first led to the theory of relativity, the second to quantum mechanics, which has had an immense impact on chemistry.

The two aspects of science, experiment and explanation, are closely related. A scientist performs experiments and observes some regularity; someone explains this regularity and proposes more experiments; and so on. From his experiments, Rosenberg explained that certain platinum compounds inhibit cell division. This explanation led him to do new experiments on the anticancer activity of these compounds.

FIGURE 1.7 ▶

A representation of the scientific method
This flow diagram shows the general steps in the scientific method. At the right, Rosenberg's work on the development of an anticancer drug illustrates the steps.

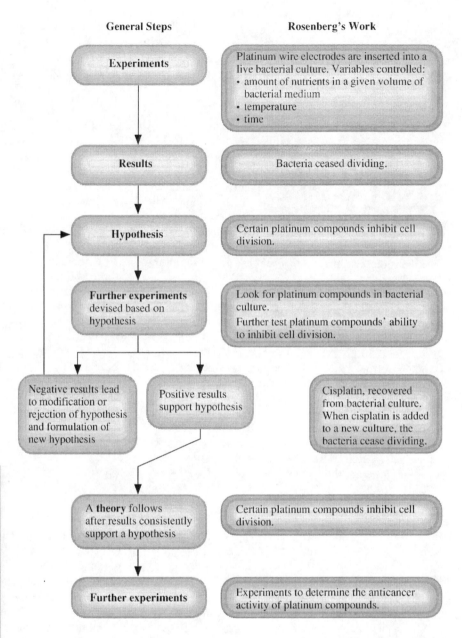

General Steps | Rosenberg's Work

Experiments → Platinum wire electrodes are inserted into a live bacterial culture. Variables controlled:
- amount of nutrients in a given volume of bacterial medium
- temperature
- time

Results → Bacteria ceased dividing.

Hypothesis → Certain platinum compounds inhibit cell division.

Further experiments devised based on hypothesis → Look for platinum compounds in bacterial culture.
Further test platinum compounds' ability to inhibit cell division.

Negative results lead to modification or rejection of hypothesis and formulation of new hypothesis

Positive results support hypothesis

Cisplatin, recovered from bacterial culture. When cisplatin is added to a new culture, the bacteria cease dividing.

A **theory** follows after results consistently support a hypothesis → Certain platinum compounds inhibit cell division.

Further experiments → Experiments to determine the anticancer activity of platinum compounds.

FIGURE 1.8 ▲

Laboratory balance
A modern single-pan balance. The mass of the material on the pan appears on the digital readout.

Demonstrating the conservation of matter: A trilogy of experiments (TD). *J. Chem. Educ.* 69 (1992): 925.

The *general* process of advancing scientific knowledge through observation; the framing of laws, hypotheses, or theories; and the conducting of more experiments is called the *scientific method* (Figure 1.7). It is not a method for carrying out a *specific* research program, because the design of experiments and the explanation of results draw on the creativity and individuality of a researcher.

1.3 | Law of Conservation of Mass

Modern chemistry emerged in the eighteenth century, when chemists began to use the balance systematically as a tool in research. Balances measure **mass,** which is *the quantity of matter in a material* (Figure 1.8). **Matter** is the general term for the material things around us; we can define it as *whatever occupies space and can be perceived by our senses.*

FIGURE 1.9 ▷

Heating mercury metal in air
Mercury metal reacts with oxygen to yield mercury(II) oxide. The color of the oxide varies from red to yellow, depending on the particle size.

Mercury   Mercury(II) oxide

FIGURE 1.10 ▷

Heated mercury(II) oxide
When you heat mercury(II) oxide, it decomposes to mercury and oxygen gas.

Antoine Lavoisier (1743–1794), a French chemist, was one of the first to insist on the use of the balance in chemical research. By weighing substances before and after chemical change, he demonstrated the **law of conservation of mass,** which states that *the total mass remains constant during a chemical change (chemical reaction).* <

In a series of experiments, Lavoisier applied the law of conservation of mass to clarify the phenomenon of burning, or combustion. He showed that when a material burns, a component of air (which he called oxygen) combines chemically with the material. For example, when the liquid metal mercury is heated in air, it burns or combines with oxygen to give a red-orange substance, whose modern name is mercury(II) oxide. We can represent the chemical change as follows:

$$\text{Mercury + oxygen} \longrightarrow \text{mercury(II) oxide}$$

Chemical reactions may involve a gain or loss of heat and other forms of energy. According to Einstein, mass and energy are equivalent. Thus, when energy is lost as heat, mass is also lost, but changes of mass in chemical reactions (billionths of a gram) are too small to detect.

The arrow means "is changed to." See Figure 1.9.

By strongly heating the red-orange substance, Lavoisier was able to decompose it to yield the original mercury and oxygen gas (Figure 1.10). The following example illustrates how the law of conservation of mass can be used to study this reaction.

Example 1.1	Using the Law of Conservation of Mass

You heat 2.53 grams of metallic mercury in air, which produces 2.73 grams of a red-orange residue. Assume that the chemical change is the reaction of the metal with oxygen in air.

An alternative example is provided in the Instructor's Resource Manual.

$$\text{Mercury + oxygen} \longrightarrow \text{red-orange residue}$$

What is the mass of oxygen that reacts? When you strongly heat the red-orange residue, it decomposes to give back the mercury and release the oxygen, which you collect. What is the mass of oxygen you collect?

Problem Strategy   You apply the law of conservation of mass to the reaction. According to this law, the total mass remains constant during a chemical reaction; that is,

Mass of substances before reaction = mass of substances after reaction

(continued)

(continued)

Solution   From the law of conservation of mass,

Mass of mercury + mass of oxygen = mass of red-orange residue

Substituting, you obtain

2.53 grams + mass of oxygen = 2.73 grams

or

Mass of oxygen = (2.73 − 2.53) grams = **0.20 grams**

The mass of oxygen collected when the red-orange residue decomposes equals the mass of oxygen that originally reacted **(0.20 grams).**

Answer Check   Arithmetic errors account for many mistakes. You should always check your arithmetic, either by carefully redoing the calculation or, if possible, by doing the arithmetic in a slightly different way. Here, you obtained the answer by subtracting numbers. You can check the result by addition: the sum of the masses of mercury and oxygen, 2.53 + 0.20 grams, should equal the mass of the residue, 2.73 grams.

Exercise 1.1   You place 1.85 grams of wood in a vessel with 9.45 grams of air and seal the vessel. Then you heat the vessel strongly so that the wood burns. In burning, the wood yields ash and gases. After the experiment, you weigh the ash and find that its mass is 0.28 gram. What is the mass of the gases in the vessel at the end of the experiment?

■ See Problems 1.37, 1.38, 1.39, and 1.40.

Lavoisier set out his views on chemistry in his *Traité Élémentaire de Chimie* (*Basic Treatise on Chemistry*) in 1789. The book was very influential, especially among younger chemists, and set the stage for modern chemistry.

Before leaving this section, you should note the distinction between the terms *mass* and *weight* in precise usage. The weight of an object is the force of gravity exerted on it. The weight is proportional to the mass of the object divided by the square of the distance between the center of mass of the object and that of the earth. < Because the earth is slightly flattened at the poles, an object weighs more at the North Pole, where it is closer to the center of the earth, than at the equator. The mass of an object is the same wherever it is measured.

The force of gravity F between objects whose masses are m_1 and m_2 is Gm_1m_2/r^2, where G is the gravitational constant and r is the distance between the centers of mass of the two objects.

1.4 | Matter: Physical State and Chemical Constitution

Experiments in General Chemistry, 1A, "Identification of an Unknown Compound."

We describe iron as a silvery-colored metal that melts at 1535°C (2795°F). Once we have collected enough descriptive information about many different kinds of matter, patterns emerge that suggest ways of classifying it. There are two principal ways of classifying matter: by its physical state as a solid, liquid, or gas and by its chemical constitution as an element, compound, or mixture.

Solids, Liquids, and Gases

ChemWork: Classifying Matter

Commonly, a given kind of matter exists in different physical forms under different conditions. Water, for example, exists as ice (solid water), as liquid water, and as steam

Solid

Liquid

Gas

FIGURE 1.11 ▲

Molecular representations of solid, liquid, and gas
The top beaker contains a solid with a molecular view of the solid; the molecular view depicts the closely packed, immobile atoms that make up the solid structure. The middle beaker contains a liquid with a molecular view of the liquid; the molecular view depicts atoms that are close together but moving freely. The bottom beaker contains a gas with a molecular view of the gas; the molecular view depicts atoms that are far apart and moving freely.

ChemWork: Identifying Physical Changes

Demonstration of reaction of hydrogen with oxygen: Summerlin and Ealy, *Chemical Demonstrations,* Vol. 1 (Washington, D.C.: Am. Chem. Soc., 1985), no. 108, p. 173.

(gaseous water) (Figure 1.11). The main identifying characteristic of solids is their rigidity: they tend to maintain their shapes when subjected to outside forces. Liquids and gases, however, are *fluids;* that is, they flow easily and change their shapes in response to slight outside forces.

What distinguishes a gas from a liquid is the characteristic of *compressibility* (and its opposite, *expansibility*). A gas is easily compressible, whereas a liquid is not. You can put more and more air into a tire, which increases only slightly in volume. In fact, a given quantity of gas can fill a container of almost any size. A small quantity would expand to fill the container; a larger quantity could be compressed to fill the same space. By contrast, if you were to try to force more liquid water into a closed glass bottle that was already full of water, it would burst.

These two characteristics, rigidity (or fluidity) and compressibility (or expansibility), can be used to frame definitions of the three common states of matter:

solid *the form of matter characterized by rigidity;* a solid is relatively incompressible and has fixed shape and volume.

liquid *the form of matter that is a relatively incompressible fluid;* a liquid has a fixed volume but no fixed shape.

gas *the form of matter that is an easily compressible fluid;* a given quantity of gas will fit into a container of almost any size and shape.

The term *vapor* is often used to refer to the gaseous state of any kind of matter that normally exists as a liquid or a solid.

*These three forms of matter—solid, liquid, gas—*comprise the common **states of matter.**

Elements, Compounds, and Mixtures

To understand how matter is classified by its chemical constitution, we must first distinguish between physical and chemical changes and between physical and chemical properties. A **physical change** is *a change in the form of matter but not in its chemical identity.* Changes of physical state are examples of physical changes. The process of dissolving one material in another is a further example of a physical change. For instance, you can dissolve sodium chloride (table salt) in water. The result is a clear liquid, like pure water, though many of its other characteristics are different from those of pure water. The water and sodium chloride in this liquid retain their chemical identities and can be separated by some method that depends on physical changes.

Distillation is one way to separate the sodium chloride and water components of this liquid. You place the liquid in a flask to which a device called a *condenser* is attached (see Figure 1.12 on page 10). The liquid in the flask is heated to bring it to a boil. (Boiling entails the formation of bubbles of the vapor in the body of the liquid.) Water vapor forms and passes from the flask into the cooled condenser, where the vapor changes back to liquid water. The liquid water is collected in another flask, called a *receiver.* The original flask now contains the solid sodium chloride. Thus, by means of physical changes (the change of liquid water to vapor and back to liquid), you have separated the sodium chloride and water that you had earlier mixed together.

A **chemical change,** or **chemical reaction,** is *a change in which one or more kinds of matter are transformed into a new kind of matter or several new kinds of matter.* The rusting of iron, during which iron combines with oxygen in the air to form a new material called rust, is a chemical change. The original materials (iron and oxygen) combine chemically and cannot be separated by any physical means. To recover the iron and oxygen from rust requires a chemical change or a series of chemical changes.

FIGURE 1.12 ▶

Separation by distillation
You can separate an easily vaporized liquid from another substance by distillation.

ChemWork: Identifying Chemical Properties

FIGURE 1.13 ▲

Reaction of sodium with water
Sodium metal flits around the water surface as it reacts briskly, giving off hydrogen gas. The other product is sodium hydroxide, which changes a substance added to the water (phenolphthalein) from colorless to pink.

We characterize or identify a material by its various properties, which may be either physical or chemical. A **physical property** is *a characteristic that can be observed for a material without changing its chemical identity.* Examples are physical state (solid, liquid, or gas), melting point, and color. A **chemical property** is *a characteristic of a material involving its chemical change.* A chemical property of iron is its ability to react with oxygen to produce rust.

Substances   The various materials we see around us are either substances or mixtures of substances. A **substance** is *a kind of matter that cannot be separated into other kinds of matter by any physical process.* Earlier you saw that when sodium chloride is dissolved in water, it is possible to separate the sodium chloride from the water by the physical process of distillation. However, sodium chloride is itself a substance and cannot be separated by physical processes into new materials. Similarly, pure water is a substance.

No matter what its source, a substance always has the same characteristic properties. Sodium is a solid metal having a melting point of 98°C. The metal also reacts vigorously with water (Figure 1.13). No matter how sodium is prepared, it always has these properties. Similarly, whether sodium chloride is obtained by burning sodium in chlorine or from seawater, it is a white solid melting at 801°C.

Exercise 1.2   Potassium is a soft, silvery-colored metal that melts at 64°C. It reacts vigorously with water, with oxygen, and with chlorine. Identify all of the physical properties given in this description. Identify all of the chemical properties given.

■ See Problems 1.47, 1.48, 1.49, and 1.50.

FIGURE 1.14

Some elements

Center: Sulfur. *From upper right, clockwise:* Arsenic, iodine, magnesium, bismuth, mercury.

Demonstration of separating iron from cereal: Summerlin et al., *Chemical Demonstrations,* Vol. 2 (Washington, D.C.: Am. Chem. Soc., 1987), no. 34, p. 62. (Alternatively, magnetically separate a mixture of sulfur and iron filings.)

In Chapter 2, we will redefine an element in terms of atoms.

Elements   Millions of substances have been characterized by chemists. Of these, a very small number are known as elements, from which all other substances are made. Lavoisier was the first to establish an experimentally useful definition of an element. He defined an **element** as *a substance that cannot be decomposed by any chemical reaction into simpler substances.* In 1789 Lavoisier listed 33 substances as elements, of which more than 20 are still so regarded. Today 116 elements are known. Some elements are shown in Figure 1.14. <

Compounds   Most substances are compounds. A **compound** is *a substance composed of two or more elements chemically combined.* By the end of the eighteenth century, Lavoisier and others had examined many compounds and showed that all of them were composed of the elements in definite proportions by mass. Joseph Louis Proust (1754–1826), by his painstaking work, convinced the majority of chemists of the general validity of the **law of definite proportions** (also known as the **law of constant composition**): *a pure compound, whatever its source, always contains definite or constant proportions of the elements by mass.* For example, 1.0000 gram of sodium chloride always contains 0.3934 gram of sodium and 0.6066 gram of chlorine, chemically combined. Sodium chloride has definite proportions of sodium and chlorine; that is, it has constant or definite composition. <

It is now known that some compounds do not follow the law of definite proportions. These nonstoichiometric compounds, as they are called, are described briefly in Chapter 11.

Chromatography, another example of a physical method used to separate mixtures, is described in the essay at the end of this section.

Mixtures   Most of the materials around us are mixtures. A **mixture** is *a material that can be separated by physical means into two or more substances.* Unlike a pure compound, a mixture has variable composition. When you dissolve sodium chloride in water, you obtain a mixture; its composition depends on the relative amount of sodium chloride dissolved. You can separate the mixture by the physical process of distillation. <

Mixtures are classified into two types. A **heterogeneous mixture** is *a mixture that consists of physically distinct parts, each with different properties.* Figure 1.15 shows a heterogeneous mixture of potassium dichromate and iron filings. Another example is salt and sugar that have been stirred together. If you were to look closely, you would see the separate crystals of sugar and salt. A **homogeneous mixture** (also known as a **solution**) is *a mixture that is uniform in its properties throughout given samples.* When sodium chloride is dissolved in water, you obtain a homogeneous mixture, or solution. Air is a gaseous solution, principally of two

FIGURE 1.15

A heterogeneous mixture
Left: The mixture on the watch glass consists of potassium dichromate (orange crystals) and iron filings. *Right:* A magnet separates the iron filings from the mixture.

Experiments in General Chemistry, 1B, "Separation of a Mixture by Paper Chromatography."

elementary substances, nitrogen and oxygen, which are physically mixed but not chemically combined.

A **phase** is *one of several different homogeneous materials present in the portion of matter under study.* A heterogeneous mixture of salt and sugar is said to be composed of two different phases: one of the phases is salt; the other is sugar. Similarly, ice cubes in water are said to be composed of two phases: one phase is ice; the other is liquid water. Ice floating in a solution of sodium chloride in water also consists of two phases, ice and the liquid solution. Note that a phase may be either a pure substance in a particular state or a solution in a particular state (solid, liquid, or gaseous). Also, the portion of matter under consideration may consist of several phases of the same substance or several phases of different substances.

Figure 1.16 summarizes the relationships among elements, compounds, and mixtures. Materials are either substances or mixtures. Substances can be mixed by physical processes, and other physical processes can be used to separate the mixtures into substances. Substances are either elements or compounds. Elements may react chemically to yield compounds, and compounds may be decomposed by chemical reactions into elements.

Concept Check 1.1

Matter can be represented as being composed of individual units. For example, the smallest individual unit of matter can be represented as a single circle, ●, and chemical combinations of these units of matter as connected circles, ●●, with each element represented by a different color. Using this model, place the appropriate label—element, compound, or mixture—on each container.

A   B   C

FIGURE 1.16 ▲ ◧

Relationships among elements, compounds, and mixtures
Mixtures can be separated by physical processes into substances, and substances can be combined physically into mixtures. Compounds can be separated by chemical reactions into their elements, and elements can be combined chemically to form compounds.

Physical Measurements

Chemists characterize and identify substances by their particular properties. To determine many of these properties requires physical measurements. Cisplatin, the substance featured in the chapter opening, is a yellow substance whose solubility in water (the amount that dissolves in a given quantity of water) is 0.252 gram in 100 grams of water. You can use the solubility, as well as other physical properties, to identify cisplatin. In a modern chemical laboratory, measurements often are complex, but many experiments begin with simple measurements of mass, volume, time, and so forth. In the next few sections, we will look at the measurement process. We first consider the concept of *precision* of a measurement.

1.5   Measurement and Significant Figures

Measurement is the comparison of a physical quantity to be measured with a **unit** of measurement—that is, with *a fixed standard of measurement*. On a centimeter scale, the centimeter unit is the standard of comparison. < A steel rod that measures 9.12 times the centimeter unit has a length of 9.12 centimeters. To record the measurement, you must be careful to give both the *measured number* (9.12) and the *unit* (centimeters).

If you repeat a particular measurement, you usually do not obtain precisely the same result, because each measurement is subject to experimental error. The measured values vary slightly from one another. Suppose you perform a series of identical measurements of a quantity. The term **precision** refers to *the closeness of the set of values obtained from identical measurements of a quantity.* **Accuracy** is a related term; it refers to *the closeness of a single measurement to its true value.* To illustrate

| 2.54 *centimeters* = 1 *inch*

Significant figures: A classroom demonstration (TD). *J. Chem. Educ.* 69 (1992): 497.

Separation of Mixtures by Chromatography

Chromatography is a group of similar separation techniques. Each depends on how fast a substance moves, in a stream of gas or liquid, past a stationary phase to which the substance may be slightly attracted. An example is provided by a simple experiment in *paper chromatography* (see Figure 1.17). In this experiment, a line of ink is drawn near one edge of a sheet of paper, and the paper is placed upright with this edge in a solution of methanol and water. As the solution creeps up the paper, the ink moves upward, separating into a series of different-colored bands that correspond to the different dyes in the ink. All the dyes are attracted to the wet paper fibers, but with different strengths of attraction. As the solution moves upward, the dyes less strongly attracted to the paper fibers move more rapidly.

The Russian botanist Mikhail Tswett was the first to understand the basis of chromatography and to apply it systematically as a method of separation. In 1906 Tswett separated pigments in plant leaves by *column chromatography*. He first dissolved the pigments from the leaves in petroleum ether, a liquid similar to gasoline. After packing a glass tube or column with powdered chalk, he poured the solution of pigments into the top of the column (see Figure 1.18). When he washed the column by pouring in more petroleum ether, it began to show distinct yellow and green bands. These bands, each containing a pure pigment, became well separated as they moved down the column, so that the pure pigments could be obtained. The name *chromatography* originates from this early separation of colored substances (the stem *chromato-* means "color"), although the technique is not limited to colored substances.

Gas chromatography (GC) is a more recent separation method. Here the moving stream is a gaseous mixture of vaporized substances plus a gas such as helium, which is called the *carrier*. The stationary material is either a solid or a liquid adhering to a solid, packed in a column. As the gas passes through the column, substances in the mixture are attracted differently to the stationary column packing and thus are separated. Gas chromatography is a rapid, small-scale method of separating mixtures. It is also important in the analysis of mixtures because the time it takes for a substance at a given temperature to travel through the column to a detector (called the *retention time*) is fixed. You can therefore use retention times to help identify substances. Figure 1.19 shows a gas chromatograph and a portion of a computer plot (*chromatogram*). Each peak on the chromatogram corresponds to a specific substance. The peaks were automatically recorded by the instrument as the different substances in the mixture passed the detector. Chemists have analyzed complicated mixtures by gas chromatography. Analysis of chocolate, for example, shows that it contains over 800 flavor compounds.

FIGURE 1.17 ▶

An illustration of paper chromatography
A line of ink has been drawn along the lower edge of a sheet of paper. The dyes in the ink separate as a solution of methanol and water creeps up the paper.

FIGURE 1.18

Column chromatography

(A) A solution containing substances to be separated is poured into the top of a column, which contains powdered chalk. *(B)* Pure liquid is added to the column, and the substances begin to separate into bands. *(C)* The substances separate further on the column. Each substance is collected in a separate flask as it comes off the column.

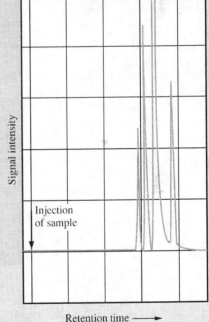

FIGURE 1.19

Gas chromatography

Top: A modern gas chromatograph. *Bottom:* This is a chromatogram of a hexane mixture, showing its separation into four different substances. Such hexane mixtures occur in gasoline; hexane is also used as a solvent to extract the oil from certain vegetable seeds.

■ See Problems 1.145 and 1.146.

FIGURE 1.20

Precision of measurement with a centimeter ruler
The length of the rod is just over 9.1 cm. On successive measurements, we estimate the length by eye at 9.12, 9.11, and 9.13 cm. We record the length as between 9.11 cm and 9.13 cm.

Steel rod
Centimeters

the idea of precision, consider a simple measuring device, the centimeter ruler. In Figure 1.20, a steel rod has been placed near a ruler subdivided into tenths of a centimeter. You can see that the rod measures just over 9.1 cm (cm = centimeter). With care, it is possible to estimate by eye to hundredths of a centimeter. Here you might give the measurement as 9.12 cm. Suppose you measure the length of this rod twice more. You find the values to be 9.11 cm and 9.13 cm. Thus, you record the length of the rod as being somewhere between 9.11 cm and 9.13 cm. The spread of values indicates the precision with which a measurement can be made by this centimeter ruler. <

To indicate the precision of a measured number (or result of calculations on measured numbers), we often use the concept of significant figures. **Significant figures** are *those digits in a measured number (or in the result of a calculation with measured numbers) that include all certain digits plus a final digit having some uncertainty.* When you measured the rod, you obtained the values 9.12 cm, 9.11 cm, and 9.13 cm. You could report the result as the average, 9.12 cm. The first two digits (9.1) are certain; the next digit (2) is estimated, so it has some uncertainty. It would be incorrect to write 9.120 cm for the length of the rod. This would say that the last digit (0) has some uncertainty but that the other digits (9.12) are certain, which is not true.

Measurements that are of high precision are usually accurate. It is possible, however, to have a systematic error in a measurement. Suppose that, in calibrating a ruler, the first centimeter is made too small by 0.1 cm. Then, although the measurements of length on this ruler are still precise to 0.01 cm, they are accurate to only 0.1 cm.

ChemWork: Identifying Significant Figures

Number of Significant Figures

The term **number of significant figures** refers to *the number of digits reported for the value of a measured or calculated quantity, indicating the precision of the value.* Thus, there are three significant figures in 9.12 cm, whereas 9.123 cm has four. To count the number of significant figures in a given measured quantity, you observe the following rules:

1. All digits are significant except zeros at the beginning of the number and possibly terminal zeros (one or more zeros at the end of a number). Thus, 9.12 cm, 0.912 cm, and 0.00912 cm all contain three significant figures.

2. Terminal zeros ending at the right of the decimal point are significant. Each of the following has three significant figures: 9.00 cm, 9.10 cm, 90.0 cm.

3. Terminal zeros in a number without an explicit decimal point may or may not be significant. If someone gives a measurement as 900 cm, you do not know whether one, two, or three significant figures are intended. If the person writes 900. cm (note the decimal point), the zeros are significant. More generally, you can remove any uncertainty in such cases by expressing the measurement in scientific notation.

Scientific notation is *the representation of a number in the form $A \times 10^n$, where A is a number with a single nonzero digit to the left of the decimal point and n is an integer, or whole number.* In scientific notation, the measurement 900 cm precise to two significant figures is written 9.0×10^2 cm. If precise to three significant figures, it is written 9.00×10^2 cm. Scientific notation is also convenient for expressing very large or very small quantities. It is much easier (and simplifies calculations) to write the speed of light as 3.00×10^8 (rather than as 300,000,000) meters per second. <

See Appendix A for a review of scientific notation.

FIGURE 1.21 ▲

Significant figures and calculators
Not all of the figures that appear on a calculator display are significant. In performing the calculation 100.0 × 0.0634 ÷ 25.31, the calculator display shows 0.250493875. We would report the answer as 0.250, however, because the factor 0.0634 has the least number of significant figures (three).

ChemWork: Using Significant Figures in Calculations

Significant Figures in Calculations

Measurements are often used in calculations. How do you determine the correct number of significant figures to report for the answer to a calculation? The following are two rules that we use:

1. **Multiplication and division.** When multiplying or dividing measured quantities, give as many significant figures in the answer as there are in the measurement with *the least number of significant figures.*

2. **Addition and subtraction.** When adding or subtracting measured quantities, give the same number of decimal places in the answer as there are in the measurement with *the least number of decimal places.*

Let us see how you apply these rules. Suppose you have a substance believed to be cisplatin, and, in an effort to establish its identity, you measure its solubility (the amount that dissolves in a given quantity of water). You find that 0.0634 gram of the substance dissolves in 25.31 grams of water. The amount dissolving in 100.0 grams is

$$100.0 \text{ grams of water} \times \frac{0.0634 \text{ gram cisplatin}}{25.31 \text{ grams of water}}$$

Performing the arithmetic on a pocket calculator (Figure 1.21), you get 0.250493875 for the numerical part of the answer (100.0 × 0.0634 ÷ 25.31). It would be incorrect to give this number as the final answer. The measurement 0.0634 gram has the least number of significant figures (three). Therefore, you report the answer to three significant figures—that is, 0.250 gram.

Now consider the addition of 184.2 grams and 2.324 grams. On a calculator, you find that 184.2 + 2.324 = 186.524. But because the quantity 184.2 grams has the least number of decimal places—one, whereas 2.324 grams has three—the answer is 186.5 grams.

Exact Numbers

So far we have discussed only numbers that involve uncertainties. However, you will also encounter exact numbers. An **exact number** is *a number that arises when you count items or sometimes when you define a unit.* For example, when you say there are 9 coins in a bottle, you mean exactly 9, not 8.9 or 9.1. Also, when you say there are 12 inches to a foot, you mean exactly 12. Similarly, the inch is defined to be exactly 2.54 centimeters. The conventions of significant figures do not apply to exact numbers. Thus, the 2.54 in the expression "1 inch equals 2.54 centimeters" should not be interpreted as a measured number with three significant figures. In effect, the 2.54 has an infinite number of significant figures, but of course it would be impossible to write out an infinite number of digits. You should make a mental note of any numbers in a calculation that are exact, because they have no effect on the number of significant figures in a calculation. The number of significant figures in a calculation result depends only on the numbers of significant figures in quantities having uncertainties. For example, suppose you want the total mass of 9 coins when each coin has a mass of 3.0 grams. The calculation is

$$3.0 \text{ grams} \times 9 = 27 \text{ grams}$$

You report the answer to two significant figures because 3.0 grams has two significant figures. The number 9 is exact and does not determine the number of significant figures.

Rounding

In reporting the solubility of your substance in 100.0 grams of water as 0.250 gram, you *rounded* the number you read off the calculator (0.2504938). **Rounding** is *the* *procedure of dropping nonsignificant digits in a calculation result and adjusting the last digit reported.* The general procedure is as follows: Look at the leftmost digit to be dropped. Then . . .

1. If this digit is 5 or greater, add 1 to the last digit to be retained and drop all digits farther to the right. Thus, rounding 1.2151 to three significant figures gives 1.22.

2. If this digit is less than 5, simply drop it and all digits farther to the right. Rounding 1.2143 to three significant figures gives 1.21.

In doing a calculation of two or more steps, it is desirable to retain nonsignificant digits for intermediate answers. This ensures that accumulated small errors from rounding do not appear in the final result. If you use a calculator, you can simply enter numbers one after the other, performing each arithmetic operation and rounding only the final answer. < To keep track of the correct number of significant figures, you may want to record intermediate answers with a line under the last significant figure, as shown in the solution to part d of the following example.

The answers for Exercises and Problems will follow this practice. For most Example Problems where intermediate answers are reported, all answers, intermediate and final, will be rounded.

Example 1.2 | Using Significant Figures in Calculations

Perform the following calculations and round the answers to the correct number of significant figures (units of measurement have been omitted).

a. $\dfrac{2.568 \times 5.8}{4.186}$ b. $5.41 - 0.398$

c. $3.38 - 3.01$ d. $4.18 - 58.16 \times (3.38 - 3.01)$

Problem Strategy Parts a, b, and c are relatively straightforward; use the rule for significant figures that applies in each case. In a multistep calculation as in d, proceed step by step, applying the relevant rule to each step. First, do the operations within parentheses. By convention, you perform multiplications and divisions before additions and subtractions. Do not round intermediate answers, but do keep track of the least significant digit—say, by underlining it.

Solution a. The factor 5.8 has the fewest significant figures; therefore, the answer should be reported to two significant figures. Round the answer to **3.6.** b. The number with the least number of decimal places is 5.41. Therefore, round the answer to two decimal places, to **5.01.** c. The answer is **0.37.** Note how you have lost one significant figure in the subtraction. d. You first do the subtraction within parentheses, underlining the least significant digits.

$4.1\underline{8} - 58.1\underline{6} \times (3.3\underline{8} - 3.0\underline{1}) = 4.1\underline{8} - 58.1\underline{6} \times 0.3\underline{7}$

Following convention, you do the multiplication before the subtraction.

$4.1\underline{8} - 58.1\underline{6} \times 0.3\underline{7} = 4.1\underline{8} - 21.5192 = -17.3392$

The final answer is **−17.**

Answer Check When performing any calculation, you should always report answers to the correct number of significant figures. If a set of calculations involves *only* multiplication and division, it is not necessary to track the significant figures through intermediate calculations; you just need to use the measurement with the least number of significant figures as the guide. However, when addition or subtraction is involved, make sure that you have noted the correct number of significant figures in each calculated step in order to ensure that your answer is correctly reported.

Exercise 1.3   Give answers to the following arithmetic setups. Round to the correct number of significant figures.

a. $\dfrac{5.61 \times 7.891}{9.1}$ b. $8.91 - 6.435$

c. $6.81 - 6.730$ d. $38.91 \times (6.81 - 6.730)$

An alternative example is provided in the Instructor's Resource Manual.   ■ See Problems 1.61 and 1.62.

Concept Check 1.2

a. When you report your weight to someone, how many significant figures do you typically use?

b. What is your weight with two significant figures?

c. Indicate your weight and the number of significant figures you would obtain if you weighed yourself on a truck scale that can measure in 50 kg or 100 lb increments.

ChemWork: Using Metric System Definitions

A simple demonstration for introducing the metric system to introductory chemistry classes. *J. Chem. Educ.* 76 (1999): 1215.

In the system of units that Lavoisier used in the eighteenth century, there were 9216 grains to the pound (the livre). English chemists of the same period used a system in which there were 7000 grains to the pound—unless they were trained as apothecaries, in which case there were 5760 grains to the pound!

The amount of substance is discussed in Chapter 3, and the electric current (ampere) is introduced in Chapter 19. Luminous intensity will not be used in this book.

1.6   SI Units

The first measurements were probably based on the human body (the length of the foot, for example). In time, fixed standards developed, but these varied from place to place. Each country or government (and often each trade) adopted its own units. As science became more quantitative in the seventeenth and eighteenth centuries, scientists found that the lack of standard units was a problem. < They began to seek a simple, international system of measurement. In 1791 a study committee of the French Academy of Sciences devised such a system. Called the *metric system*, it became the official system of measurement for France and was soon used by scientists throughout the world. Most nations have since adopted the metric system or, at least, have set a schedule for changing to it.

SI Base Units and SI Prefixes

In 1960 the General Conference of Weights and Measures adopted the **International System of units** (or **SI**, after the French *le Système International d'Unités*), which is *a particular choice of metric units*. This system has seven **SI base units,** *the SI units from which all others can be derived*. Table 1.1 lists these base units and the symbols used to represent them. In this chapter, we will discuss four base quantities: length, mass, time, and temperature. <

One advantage of any metric system is that it is a decimal system. In SI, a larger or smaller unit for a physical quantity is indicated by an **SI prefix,** which is *a prefix used in the International System to indicate a power of 10*. For example, the base unit of length in SI is the meter (somewhat longer than a yard), and 10^{-2} meter is called a *centi*meter. Thus 2.54 centimeters equals 2.54×10^{-2} meters. The SI prefixes used in this book are presented in Table 1.2.

TABLE 1.2	Selected SI Prefixes	
Prefix	Multiple	Symbol
mega	10^{6}	M
kilo	10^{3}	k
deci	10^{-1}	d
centi	10^{-2}	c
milli	10^{-3}	m
micro	10^{-6}	μ^{*}
nano	10^{-9}	n
pico	10^{-12}	p

*Greek letter mu, pronounced "mew."

TABLE 1.1	SI Base Units	
Quantity	Unit	Symbol
Length	meter	m
Mass	kilogram	kg
Time	second	s
Temperature	kelvin	K
Amount of substance	mole	mol
Electric current	ampere	A
Luminous intensity	candela	cd

Length, Mass, and Time

The meter was originally defined in terms of a standard platinum–iridium bar kept at Sèvres, France. In 1983, the meter was defined as the distance traveled by light in a vacuum in 1/299,792,458 seconds.

The **meter (m)** is *the SI base unit of length.* < By combining it with one of the SI prefixes, you can get a unit of appropriate size for any length measurement. For the very small lengths used in chemistry, the nanometer (nm; 1 nanometer = 10^{-9} m) or the picometer (pm; 1 picometer = 10^{-12} m) is an acceptable SI unit. *A non-SI unit of length* traditionally used by chemists is the **angstrom (Å)**, which equals 10^{-10} m. (An oxygen atom, one of the minute particles of which the substance oxygen is composed, has a diameter of about 1.3 Å. If you could place oxygen atoms adjacent to one another, you could line up over 75 million of them in 1 cm.)

The present standard of mass is the platinum–iridium kilogram mass kept at the International Bureau of Weights and Measures in Sèvres, France.

The **kilogram (kg)** is *the SI base unit of mass*, equal to about 2.2 pounds. < This is an unusual base unit in that it contains a prefix. In forming other SI mass units, prefixes are added to the word *gram* (g) to give units such as the *milli*gram (mg; 1 mg = 10^{-3} g).

The **second (s)** is *the SI base unit of time* (Figure 1.22). Combining this unit with prefixes such as *milli-, micro-, nano-,* and *pico-,* you create units appropriate for measuring very rapid events. The time required for the fastest chemical processes is about a picosecond, which is on the order of how fast supercomputers can perform a single calculation. When you measure times much longer than a few hundred seconds, you revert to *minutes* and *hours,* an obvious exception to the prefix–base format of the International System.

Exercise 1.4   Express the following quantities using an SI prefix and a base unit. For instance, 1.6×10^{-6} m = 1.6 μm. A quantity such as 0.000168 g could be written 0.168 mg or 168 μg.

a. 1.84×10^{-9} m   b. 5.67×10^{-12} s   c. 7.85×10^{-3} g

d. 9.7×10^{3} m   e. 0.000732 s   f. 0.000000000154 m

■ See Problems 1.65 and 1.66.

ChemWork: Temperature Conversions

FIGURE 1.22 ▲

NIST F-1 cesium fountain clock

First put into service in 1999 at the National Institute of Standards and Technology (NIST) in Boulder, Colorado, this clock represents a new generation of super-accurate atomic clocks. The clock is so precise that it loses only one second every 20 million years.

ChemWork: Changing Temperature Scales

Temperature

Temperature is difficult to define precisely, but we all have an intuitive idea of what we mean by it. It is a measure of "hotness." A hot object placed next to a cold one becomes cooler, while the cold object becomes hotter. Heat energy passes from a hot object to a cold one, and the quantity of heat passed between the objects depends on the difference in temperature between the two. Therefore, temperature and heat are different, but related, concepts.

A thermometer is a device for measuring temperature. The common type consists of a glass capillary containing a column of liquid whose length varies with temperature. A scale alongside the capillary gives a measure of the temperature. The **Celsius scale** (formerly the centigrade scale) is *the temperature scale in general scientific use.* On this scale, the freezing point of water is 0°C and the boiling point of water at normal barometric pressure is 100°C. However, *the SI base unit of temperature* is the **kelvin (K),** a unit on an *absolute temperature* scale. (See the first margin note on the next page.) On any absolute scale, the lowest temperature that can be attained theoretically is zero. The Celsius and the Kelvin scales have equal-size units (that is, a change of 1°C is equivalent to a change of 1 K), where 0°C is a temperature equivalent to 273.15 K. Thus, it is easy to convert from one scale to the other, using the formula

$$T_K = \left(t_C \times \frac{1\ K}{1°C} \right) + 273.15\ K$$

where T_K is the temperature in kelvins and t_C is the temperature in degrees Celsius. A temperature of 20°C (about room temperature) equals 293 K.

FIGURE 1.23 ▷ 🏴

Comparison of temperature scales
Room temperature is about 68°F, 20°C, and
293 K. Water freezes at 32°F, 0°C, and
273.15 K. Water boils under normal pressure
at 212°F, 100°C, and 373.15 K.

*Note that the degree sign (°) is not
used with the Kelvin scale, and the
unit of temperature is simply the
kelvin (not capitalized).*

*These two temperature conversion
formulas are often written K = °C +
273.15 and °F = (1.8 × °C) + 32.
Although these yield the correct
number, they do not take into
account the units.*

The Fahrenheit scale is at present the common temperature scale in the United
States. Figure 1.23 compares Kelvin, Celsius, and Fahrenheit scales. As the figure
shows, 0°C is the same as 32°F (both exact), and 100°C corresponds to 212°F (both
exact). Therefore, there are $212 - 32 = 180$ Fahrenheit degrees in the range of 100
Celsius degrees. That is, there are exactly 9 Fahrenheit degrees for every 5 Celsius
degrees. Knowing this, and knowing that 0°C equals 32°F, we can derive a formula
to convert degrees Celsius to degrees Fahrenheit. <

$$t_F = \left(t_C \times \frac{9°F}{5°C}\right) + 32°F$$

where t_F is the temperature in Fahrenheit and t_C is the temperature in Celsius. By
rearranging this, we can obtain a formula for converting degrees Fahrenheit to degrees
Celsius:

$$t_C = \frac{5°C}{9°F} \times (t_F - 32°F)$$

Example 1.3 | Converting from One Temperature Scale to Another

The hottest place on record in North America is Death Valley in California. It reached
a temperature of 134°F in 1913. What is this temperature reading in degrees Celsius?
in kelvins?

An alternative example is
provided in the Instructor's
Resource Manual.

(continued)

(*continued*)

Problem Strategy   This calculation involves conversion of a temperature in degrees Fahrenheit (°F) to degrees Celsius (°C) and kelvins (K). This is a case where using formulas is the most reliable method for arriving at the answer.

Solution   Substituting, we find that

$$t_C = \frac{5°C}{9°F} \times (t_F - 32°F) = \frac{5°C}{9°F} \times (134°F - 32°F) = \mathbf{56.7°C}$$

In kelvins,

$$T_K = \left(t_C \times \frac{1\,K}{1°C}\right) + 273.15\,K = \left(56.7°C \times \frac{1\,K}{1°C}\right) + 273.15\,K = \mathbf{329.9\,K}$$

Answer Check   An easy way to check temperature conversions is to use the appropriate equation and convert your answer back to the original temperature to see whether it matches.

Exercise 1.5   a. A person with a fever has a temperature of 102.5°F. What is this temperature in degrees Celsius? b. A cooling mixture of dry ice and isopropyl alcohol has a temperature of −78°C. What is this temperature in kelvins?

■ See Problems 1.69, 1.70, 1.71, and 1.72.

Concept Check 1.3

a. Estimate and express the length of your leg in an appropriate metric unit.

b. What would be a reasonable height, in meters, of a three-story building?

c. How would you be feeling if your body temperature was 39°C?

d. Would you be comfortable sitting in a room at 23°C in a short-sleeved shirt?

1.7 | Derived Units

Experiments in General Chemistry, 1C, "Some Measurements of Mass and Volume."

Once base units have been defined for a system of measurement, you can derive other units from them. You do this by using the base units in equations that define other physical quantities. For example, *area* is defined as length times length. Therefore,

SI unit of area = (SI unit of length) × (SI unit of length)

From this, you see that the SI unit of area is meter × meter, or m². Similarly, *speed* is defined as the rate of change of distance with time; that is, speed = distance/time. Consequently,

$$\text{SI unit of speed} = \frac{\text{SI unit of distance}}{\text{SI unit of time}}$$

The SI unit of speed is meters per second (that is, meters divided by seconds). The unit is symbolized m/s or m · s⁻¹. The unit of speed is an example of an **SI derived unit**, which is *a unit derived by combining SI base units*. Table 1.3 defines a number of derived units. Volume and density are discussed in this section; pressure and energy are discussed later (in Sections 5.1 and 6.1, respectively).

Volume

Volume is defined as length cubed and has the SI unit of cubic meter (m³). This is too large a unit for normal laboratory work, so we use either cubic decimeters (dm³)

TABLE 1.3	Derived Units	
Quantity	Definition of Quantity	SI Unit
Area	Length squared	m^2
Volume	Length cubed	m^3
Density	Mass per unit volume	kg/m^3
Speed	Distance traveled per unit time	m/s
Acceleration	Speed changed per unit time	m/s^2
Force	Mass times acceleration of object	$kg \cdot m/s^2$ (= newton, N)
Pressure	Force per unit area	$kg/(m \cdot s^2)$ (= pascal, Pa)
Energy	Force times distance traveled	$kg \cdot m^2/s^2$ (= joule, J)

or cubic centimeters (cm^3, also written cc). Traditionally, chemists have used the **liter (L),** which is *a unit of volume equal to a cubic decimeter* (approximately one quart). In fact, most laboratory glassware (Figure 1.24) is calibrated in liters or milliliters (1000 mL = 1 L). Because 1 dm equals 10 cm, a cubic decimeter, or one liter, equals $(10 \text{ cm})^3 = 1000 \text{ cm}^3$. Therefore, a milliliter equals a cubic centimeter. In summary

$$1 \text{ L} = 1 \text{ dm}^3 \quad \text{and} \quad 1 \text{ mL} = 1 \text{ cm}^3$$

Density

The **density** of an object is its *mass per unit volume*. You can express this as

$$d = \frac{m}{V}$$

where d is the density, m is the mass, and V is the volume. Suppose an object has a mass of 15.0 g and a volume of 10.0 cm^3. Substituting, you find that

$$d = \frac{15.0 \text{ g}}{10.0 \text{ cm}^3} = 1.50 \text{ g/cm}^3$$

The density of the object is 1.50 g/cm^3 (or 1.50 $g \cdot cm^{-3}$).

Density is an important characteristic property of a material. Water, for example, has a density of 1.000 g/cm^3 at 4°C and a density of 0.998 g/cm^3 at 20°C. Lead has

Demonstration of relative liquid densities, Bassam Z. Shakhashiri, *Chemical Demonstrations*, Vol. 3 (Madison: University of Wisconsin Press, 1989), no. 9.2, pp. 229–233.

Demonstration of relative gas densities, Summerlin and Ealy, *Chemical Demonstrations*, Vol. 1 (Washington, D.C.: Am. Chem. Soc., 1985), no. 2, p. 7.

Density visualization. *J. Chem. Educ.* 83 (2006): 1629.

ChemWork: Density of Atoms

ChemWork: Density for Osmium

ChemWork: Finding the Density of a Liquid

FIGURE 1.24

Some laboratory glassware
Left to right: A 600-mL beaker; a 100-mL graduated cylinder; a 250-mL volumetric flask; a 250-mL Erlenmeyer flask. *Front:* A 5-mL pipet.

FIGURE 1.25 ▷ (*left*)

The relative densities of copper and mercury
Copper floats on mercury because the density of copper is less than that of mercury. (This is a copper penny; recently minted pennies are copper-clad zinc.)

FIGURE 1.26 ▷ (*right*)

Relative densities of some liquids
Shown are three liquids (dyed so that they will show up clearly): *ortho*-xylene, water, and 1,1,1-trichloroethane. Water (blue layer) is less dense than 1,1,1-trichloroethane (colorless) and floats on it. *Ortho*-xylene (top, golden layer) is less dense than water and floats on it.

The density of solid materials on earth ranges from about 1 g/cm³ to 22.5 g/cm³ (osmium metal). In the interior of certain stars, the density of matter is truly staggering. Black neutron stars—stars composed of neutrons, or atomic cores compressed by gravity to a superdense state—have densities of about 10¹⁵ g/cm³.

a density of 11.3 g/cm³ at 20°C. (Figures 1.25 and 1.26 dramatically show some relative densities.) < Oxygen gas has a density of 1.33×10^{-3} g/cm³ at normal pressure and 20°C. (Like other gases under normal conditions, oxygen has a density that is about 1000 times smaller than those of liquids and solids.) Because the density is characteristic of a substance, it can be helpful in identifying it. Example 1.4 illustrates this point. Density can also be useful in determining whether a substance is pure. Consider a gold bar whose purity is questioned. The metals likely to be mixed with gold, such as silver or copper, have lower densities than gold. Therefore, an adulterated (impure) gold bar can be expected to be far less dense than pure gold.

Example 1.4 | Calculating the Density of a Substance

A colorless liquid, used as a solvent (a liquid that dissolves other substances), is believed to be one of the following:

Substance	Density (in g/mL)
n-butyl alcohol	0.810
ethylene glycol	1.114
isopropyl alcohol	0.785
toluene	0.866

To identify the substance, a chemist determined its density. By pouring a sample of the liquid into a graduated cylinder, she found that the volume was 35.1 mL. She also found that the sample weighed 30.5 g. What was the density of the liquid? What was the substance?

Problem Strategy The solution to this problem lies in finding the density of the unknown substance. Once the density of the unknown substance is known, you can compare it to the list of known substances presented in the problem and look for a match. Density is the relationship of the mass of a substance per volume of that substance.

An alternative example is provided in the Instructor's Resource Manual.

Expressed as an equation, density is the mass divided by the volume: $d = m/v$.

Solution You substitute 30.5 g for the mass and 35.1 mL for the volume into the equation.

$$d = \frac{m}{V} = \frac{30.5 \text{ g}}{35.1 \text{ mL}} = \textbf{0.869 g/mL}$$

The density of the liquid equals that of **toluene** (within experimental error).

Answer Check Always be sure to report the density in the units used when performing the calculation. Density is not always reported in units of g/ml or g/cm³, for example; gases are often reported with the units of g/L.

Exercise 1.6   A piece of metal wire has a volume of 20.2 cm³ and a mass of 159 g. What is the density of the metal? We know that the metal is manganese, iron, or nickel, and these have densities of 7.21 g/cm³, 7.87 g/cm³, and 8.90 g/cm³, respectively. From which metal is the wire made?

■ See Problems 1.73, 1.74, 1.75, and 1.76.

In addition to characterizing a substance, the density provides a useful relationship between mass and volume. For example, suppose an experiment calls for a certain mass of liquid. Rather than weigh the liquid on a balance, you might instead measure out the corresponding volume. Example 1.5 illustrates this idea.

Example 1.5 | Using the Density to Relate Mass and Volume

An experiment requires 43.7 g of isopropyl alcohol. Instead of measuring out the sample on a balance, a chemist dispenses the liquid into a graduated cylinder. The density of isopropyl alcohol is 0.785 g/mL. What volume of isopropyl alcohol should he use?

Problem Strategy The formula that defines density provides a relationship between the density of a substance and the mass and volume of the substance: $d = m/V$. Because this relationship is an equation, it can be used to solve for one variable when the other two are known. Examining this problem reveals that the mass (m) and density (d) of the substance are known, so the equation can be used to solve for the volume (V) of the liquid.

Solution You rearrange the formula defining the density to obtain the volume.

$$V = \frac{m}{d}$$

An alternative example is provided in the Instructor's Resource Manual.

Then you substitute into this formula:

$$V = \frac{43.7 \text{ g}}{0.785 \text{ g/mL}} = \textbf{55.7 mL}$$

Answer Check Note that the density of the alcohol is close to 1 g/mL, which is common for many substances. In cases like this, you can perform a very quick check of your answer, because the numerical value for the volume of the liquid should not be much different from the numerical value of the mass of the liquid.

Exercise 1.7 Ethanol (grain alcohol) has a density of 0.789 g/cm^3. What volume of ethanol must be poured into a graduated cylinder to equal 30.3 g?

■ See Problems 1.77, 1.78, 1.79, and 1.80.

Concept Check 1.4

You are working in the office of a precious metals buyer. A miner brings you a nugget of metal that he claims is gold. You suspect that the metal is a form of "fool's gold," called marcasite, that is composed of iron and sulfur. In the back of your office, you have a chunk of pure gold. What simple experiments could you perform to determine whether the miner's nugget is gold?

1.8 | Units and Dimensional Analysis (Factor-Label Method)

In performing numerical calculations with physical quantities, it is good practice to enter each quantity as a number with its associated unit. Both the numbers and the units are then carried through the indicated algebraic operations. The advantages of this are twofold:

ChemWork: Unit Conversions

ChemWork: Length Conversions

ChemWork: Speed Conversions

ChemWork: Metric Mileage

1. The units for the answer will come out of the calculations.

2. If you make an error in arranging factors in the calculation (for example, if you use the wrong formula), this will become apparent because the final units will be nonsense.

Dimensional analysis (or the **factor-label method**) is *the method of calculation in which one carries along the units for quantities.* As an illustration, suppose you want to find the volume V of a cube, given s, the length of a side of the cube. Because

$V = s^3$, if $s = 5.00$ cm, you find that $V = (5.00 \text{ cm})^3 = 5.00^3 \text{ cm}^3$. There is no guess-work about the unit of volume here; it is cubic centimeters (cm^3).

Suppose, however, that you wish to express the volume in liters (L), a metric unit that equals 10^3 cubic centimeters (approximately one quart). You can write this equality as

$$1 \text{ L} = 10^3 \text{ cm}^3$$

If you divide both sides of the equality by the right-hand quantity, you get

$$\frac{1 \text{ L}}{10^3 \text{ cm}^3} = \frac{10^3 \text{ cm}^3}{10^3 \text{ cm}^3} = 1$$

Observe that you treat units in the same way as algebraic quantities. Note too that the right-hand side now equals 1 and no units are associated with it. Because it is always possible to multiply any quantity by 1 without changing that quantity, you can multiply the previous expression for the volume by the factor $1 \text{ L}/10^3 \text{ cm}^3$ without changing the actual volume. You are changing only the way you express this volume:

$$V = 5.00^3 \text{ cm}^3 \times \underbrace{\frac{1 \text{ L}}{10^3 \text{ cm}^3}}_{\substack{\text{converts} \\ \text{cm}^3 \text{ to L}}} = 125 \times 10^{-3} \text{ L} = 0.125 \text{ L}$$

It takes more room to explain conversion factors than it does to use them. With practice, you will be able to write the final conversion step without the intermediate algebraic manipulations outlined here.

The ratio $1 \text{ L}/10^3 \text{ cm}^3$ is called a **conversion factor** because it is *a factor equal to 1 that converts a quantity expressed in one unit to a quantity expressed in another unit.* < Note that the numbers in this conversion factor are *exact*, because 1 L equals exactly 1000 cm^3. Such exact conversion factors do not affect the number of significant figures in an arithmetic result. In the previous calculation, the quantity 5.00 cm (the measured length of the side) does determine or limit the number of significant figures.

The next two examples illustrate how the conversion-factor method may be used to convert one metric unit to another.

Example 1.6 | Converting Units: Metric Unit to Metric Unit

Nitrogen gas is the major component of air. A sample of nitrogen gas in a glass bulb weighs 243 mg. What is this mass in SI base units of mass (kilograms)?

An alternative example is provided in the Instructor's Resource Manual.

Problem Strategy   This problem requires converting a mass in milligrams to kilograms. Finding the correct relationship for performing such a conversion directly in one step might be more difficult than doing the conversion in multiple steps. In this case, conversion factors for converting milligrams to grams and from grams to kilograms are relatively easy to derive, so it makes sense to do this conversion in two steps. First convert milligrams to grams; then convert grams to kilograms. To convert from milligrams to grams, note that the prefix *milli-* means 10^{-3}. To convert from grams to kilograms, note that the prefix *kilo-* means 10^3.

Solution   Since 1 mg $= 10^{-3}$ g, you can write

$$243 \text{ mg} \times \frac{10^{-3} \text{ g}}{1 \text{ mg}} = 2.43 \times 10^{-1} \text{ g}$$

Then, because the prefix *kilo-* means 10^3, you write

$$1 \text{ kg} = 10^3 \text{ g}$$

and

$$2.43 \times 10^{-1} \text{ g} \times \frac{1 \text{ kg}}{10^3 \text{ g}} = \mathbf{2.43 \times 10^{-4} \text{ kg}}$$

Nitrogen molecular model

(continued)

(*continued*)

Note, however, that you can do the two conversions in one step, as follows:

$$243 \; \text{mg} \times \underbrace{\frac{10^{-3} \; \text{g}}{1 \; \text{mg}}}_{\substack{\text{converts} \\ \text{mg to g}}} \times \underbrace{\frac{1 \; \text{kg}}{10^{3} \; \text{g}}}_{\substack{\text{converts} \\ \text{g to kg}}} = 2.43 \times 10^{-4} \; \text{kg}$$

Answer Check Often, mistakes lead to answers that are easily detected by giving them a *reasonableness check*. For example, if while solving this problem you mistakenly write the conversion factors in inverted order (although this should not happen if you use units in your calculation), the final answer will be very large. Or perhaps you inadvertently copy the exponent from your calculator with the wrong sign, giving the answer as 2.43×10^{4} kg. A large answer is not reasonable, given that you are converting from small mass units (mg) to relatively large mass units (kg). Both of these errors can be caught simply by taking the time to make sure that your answer is reasonable. After completing any calculations, be sure to check for reasonableness in your answers.

Exercise 1.8   The oxygen molecule (the smallest particle of oxygen gas) consists of two oxygen atoms a distance of 121 pm apart. How many millimeters is this distance?

121 pm

Oxygen molecular model

■ See Problems 1.81, 1.82, 1.83, and 1.84.

Example 1.7 | Converting Units: Metric Volume to Metric Volume

The world's oceans contain approximately $1.35 \times 10^{9} \; \text{km}^{3}$ of water. What is this volume in liters?

An alternative example is provided in the Instructor's Resource Manual.

Problem Strategy This problem requires several conversions. A relationship that will prove helpful here is the definition of the liter: $1 \; \text{dm}^{3} = 1 \; \text{L}$. This provides a clue that if we can convert cubic kilometers (km^{3}) to cubic decimeters (dm^{3}), we can use this relationship to convert to liters. When solving problems that involve cubic units such as this one, it is often helpful to think of the conversion factors that you would use if the units were not cubed. In this case, convert from kilometers to meters and then from meters to decimeters. Next, think about how these conversion factors would look if they were cubed. For example, $10^{3} \; \text{m} = 1 \; \text{km}$, so $(10^{3} \; \text{m})^{3} = (1 \; \text{km})^{3}$ is the cubic relationship. Likewise, $10^{-1} \; \text{m} = 1 \; \text{dm}$, so $(10^{-1} \; \text{m})^{3} = (1 \; \text{dm})^{3}$ is the cubic relationship. Now these cubic conversion factors can be combined into three steps to solve the problem.

Solution

$$1.35 \times 10^{9} \; \text{km}^{3} \times \underbrace{\left(\frac{10^{3} \; \text{m}}{1 \; \text{km}}\right)^{3}}_{\substack{\text{converts} \\ \text{km}^{3} \text{ to m}^{3}}} \times \underbrace{\left(\frac{1 \; \text{dm}}{10^{-1} \; \text{m}}\right)^{3}}_{\substack{\text{converts} \\ \text{m}^{3} \text{ to dm}^{3}}} = 1.35 \times 10^{21} \; \text{dm}^{3}$$

Because a cubic decimeter is equal to a liter, the volume of the oceans is

$$\mathbf{1.35 \times 10^{21} \; L}$$

Answer Check One of the most common errors made with this type of problem is a failure to cube both the numerator and the denominator in the conversion factors. For example, $(10^{3} \; \text{m}/1 \; \text{km})^{3} = 10^{9} \; \text{m}^{3}/1 \; \text{km}^{3}$.

(*continued*)

(continued)

Exercise 1.9   A large crystal is constructed by stacking small, identical pieces of crystal, much as you construct a brick wall by stacking bricks. A unit cell is the smallest such piece from which a crystal can be made. The unit cell of a crystal of gold metal has a volume of 67.6 Å^3. What is this volume in cubic decimeters?

■ See Problems 1.85 and 1.86.

The conversion-factor method can be used to convert any unit to another unit, provided a conversion equation exists between the two units. Relationships between certain U.S. units and metric units are given in Table 1.4. You can use these to convert between U.S. and metric units. Suppose you wish to convert 0.547 lb to grams. From Table 1.4, note that 1 lb = 0.4536 kg, or 1 lb = 453.6 g, so the conversion factor from pounds to grams is 453.6 g/1 lb. Therefore,

$$0.547 \cancel{\text{lb}} \times \frac{453.6 \text{ g}}{1 \cancel{\text{lb}}} = 248 \text{ g}$$

The next example illustrates a conversion requiring several steps.

TABLE 1.4	Relationships of Some U.S. and Metric Units		
Length		**Mass**	**Volume**
1 in. = 2.54 cm (exact)		1 lb = 0.4536 kg	1 qt = 0.9464 L
1 yd = 0.9144 m (exact)		1 lb = 16 oz (exact)	4 qt = 1 gal (exact)
1 mi = 1.609 km		1 oz = 28.35 g	
1 mi = 5280 ft (exact)			

Example 1.8   Converting Units: Any Unit to Another Unit

How many centimeters are there in 6.51 miles? Use the exact definitions 1 mi = 5280 ft, 1 ft = 12 in., and 1 in. = 2.54 cm.

Problem Strategy This problem involves converting from U.S. to metric units: specifically, from miles to centimeters. One path to a solution is using three conversions: miles to feet, feet to inches, and inches to centimeters. Table 1.4 has the information you need to develop the conversion factors.

Solution From the definitions, you obtain the following conversion factors:

$$1 = \frac{5280 \text{ ft}}{1 \text{ mi}} \qquad 1 = \frac{12 \text{ in.}}{1 \text{ ft}} \qquad 1 = \frac{2.54 \text{ cm}}{1 \text{ in.}}$$

Then,

$$6.51 \cancel{\text{mi}} \times \underbrace{\frac{5280 \cancel{\text{ft}}}{1 \cancel{\text{mi}}}}_{\substack{\text{converts} \\ \text{mi to ft}}} \times \underbrace{\frac{12 \cancel{\text{in.}}}{1 \cancel{\text{ft}}}}_{\substack{\text{converts} \\ \text{ft to in.}}} \times \underbrace{\frac{2.54 \text{ cm}}{1 \cancel{\text{in.}}}}_{\substack{\text{converts} \\ \text{in. to cm}}} = \mathbf{1.05 \times 10^6 \text{ cm}}$$

All of the conversion factors are exact, so the number of significant figures in the result is determined by the number of significant figures in 6.51 mi.

Two alternative examples are provided in the Instructor's Resource Manual.

(continued)

(continued)

Answer Check Because miles are a relatively large unit of length and centimeters are a relatively small unit of length, one would expect that converting from miles to centimeters would yield a very large number. This is the case here, so the answer is reasonable.

Exercise 1.10   Using the definitions 1 in. = 2.54 cm and 1 yd = 36 in. (both exact), obtain the conversion factor for yards to meters. How many meters are there in 3.54 yd?

██ See Problems 1.87, 1.88, 1.89, and 1.90.

A Checklist for Review

Important Terms

Note: The number in parentheses denotes the section in which the term is defined.

experiment (1.2)
law (1.2)
hypothesis (1.2)
theory (1.2)
mass (1.3)
matter (1.3)
law of conservation of mass (1.3)
solid (1.4)
liquid (1.4)
gas (1.4)
states of matter (1.4)
physical change (1.4)
chemical change
  (chemical reaction) (1.4)
physical property (1.4)
chemical property (1.4)
substance (1.4)

element (1.4)
compound (1.4)
law of definite proportions (law of
  constant composition) (1.4)
mixture (1.4)
heterogeneous mixture (1.4)
homogeneous mixture
  (solution) (1.4)
phase (1.4)
unit (1.5)
precision (1.5)
accuracy (1.5)
significant figures (1.5)
number of significant
  figures (1.5)
scientific notation (1.5)
exact number (1.5)

rounding (1.5)
International System
  of units (SI) (1.6)
SI base units (1.6)
SI prefix (1.6)
meter (m) (1.6)
angstrom (Å) (1.6)
kilogram (kg) (1.6)
second (s) (1.6)
Celsius scale (1.6)
kelvin (K) (1.6)
SI derived unit (1.7)
liter (L) (1.7)
density (1.7)
dimensional analysis
  (factor-label method) (1.8)
conversion factor (1.8)

Key Equations

$$T_K = \left(t_C \times \frac{1\text{ K}}{1°\text{C}}\right) + 273.15\text{ K}$$

$$t_C = \frac{5°\text{C}}{9°\text{F}} \times (t_F - 32°\text{F})$$

$$d = m/V$$

Summary of Facts and Concepts

Chemistry is an experimental science in that the facts of chemistry are obtained by *experiment*. These facts are systematized and explained by *theory*, and theory suggests more experiments. The *scientific method* involves this interplay, in which the body of accepted knowledge grows as it is tested by experiment.

Chemistry emerged as a *quantitative science* with the work of the eighteenth-century French chemist Antoine Lavoisier. He made use of the idea that the mass, or quantity of matter, remains constant during a chemical reaction *(law of conservation of mass)*.

Matter may be classified by its physical state as a *gas, liquid,* or *solid*. Matter may also be classified by its chemical constitution as an *element, compound,* or *mixture*. Materials are either substances or mixtures of substances. Substances are either elements or compounds, which are composed of two or more elements. Mixtures can be separated into substances by physical processes, but compounds can be separated into elements only by chemical reactions.

A quantitative science requires the making of measurements. Any measurement has limited *precision*, which you convey by writing the measured number to a certain number of *significant figures*. There are many different systems of measurement, but scientists generally use the metric system. The International System (SI) uses a particular selection of metric units. It employs seven *base units* combined with *prefixes* to obtain units of various size. Units for other quantities are derived from these. To obtain a *derived unit* in SI for a quantity such as the volume or

density, you merely substitute base units into a defining equation for the quantity.

Dimensional analysis is a technique of calculating with physical quantities in which units are included and treated in the same way as numbers. You can thus obtain the *conversion factor* needed to express a quantity in new units.

Media Summary

Visit the **student website at college.hmco.com/pic/ebbing9e** to help prepare for class, study for quizzes and exams, understand core concepts, and visualize molecular-level interactions. The following media activities are available for this chapter:

 Prepare for Class

■ **Video Lessons** *Mini lectures from chemistry experts*
An Introduction to Chemistry
The Scientific Method
States of Matter
CIA Demonstration: Distillation
Properties of Matter
CIA Demonstration: Chromatography
Precision and Accuracy
CIA Demonstration: Precision and Accuracy with Glassware
Significant Figures
Scientific (Exponential) Notation
The Measurement of Matter
CIA Demonstration: Differences in Density Due to Temperature
Dimensional Analysis

 Improve Your Grade

■ **Visualizations** *Molecular-level animations and lab demonstration videos*
Structure of a Solid
Structure of a Liquid

Structure of a Gas
Comparison of a Compound and a Mixture
Comparison of a Solution and a Mixture
Homogeneous Mixtures: Air and Brass

■ **Tutorials** *Animated examples and interactive activities*
Unit Conversions

■ **Flashcards** *Key terms and definitions*
Online Flashcards

■ **Self-Assessment Questions** *Additional questions with full worked-out solutions*
6 Self-Assessment Questions

 ACE the Test

Multiple-choice quizzes
3 ACE Practice Tests

Access these resources using the passkey available free with new texts or for purchase separately.

Learning Objectives

1.1 Modern Chemistry: A Brief Glimpse

■ Provide examples of the contributions of chemistry to humanity.

1.2 Experiment and Explanation

■ Describe how chemistry is an experimental science.
■ Understand how the scientific method is an approach to performing science.

1.3 Law of Conservation of Mass

■ Explain the law of conservation of mass.
■ Apply the law of the conservation of mass. Example 1.1

1.4 Matter: Physical State and Chemical Constitution

■ Compare and contrast the three common states of matter: solid, liquid, and gas.
■ Describe the classifications of matter: elements, compounds, and mixtures (heterogeneous and homogeneous).
■ Understand the difference between chemical changes (chemical reactions) and physical changes.
■ Distinguish between chemical properties and physical properties.

1.5 Measurement and Significant Figures

■ Define and use the terms *precision* and *accuracy* when describing measured quantities.

- Learn the rules for determining significant figures in reported measurements.
- Know how to represent numbers using scientific notation.
- Apply the rules of significant figures to reporting calculated values.
- Be able to recognize exact numbers.
- Know when and how to apply the rules for rounding.
- Use significant figures in calculations. Example 1.2

1.6 SI Units

- Become familiar with the SI (metric) system of units, including the SI prefixes.
- Convert from one temperature scale to another. Example 1.3

1.7 Derived Units

- Define and provide examples of derived units.
- Calculate the density of a substance. Example 1.4
- Use density to relate mass and volume. Example 1.5

1.8 Units and Dimensional Analysis (Factor-Label Method)

- Apply dimensional analysis to solving numerical problems.
- Convert from one metric unit to another metric unit. Example 1.6
- Convert from one metric volume to another metric volume. Example 1.7
- Convert from any unit to another unit. Example 1.8

Self-Assessment and Review Questions

Key: These questions test your understanding of the ideas you worked with in the chapter. Each section ends with four multiple-choice questions that you can use to help assess whether you have understood the main concepts; these are answered in the Answers to Self-Assessment Questions in the back of the book. There are also six additional multiple-choice questions available at the student website for further practice.

1.1 Discuss some ways in which chemistry has changed technology. Give one or more examples of how chemistry has affected another science.

1.2 Define the terms *experiment* and *theory*. How are theory and experiment related? What is a hypothesis?

1.3 Illustrate the steps in the scientific method using Rosenberg's discovery of the anticancer activity of cisplatin.

1.4 Define the terms *matter* and *mass*. What is the difference between mass and weight?

1.5 State the law of conservation of mass. Describe how you might demonstrate this law.

1.6 A chemical reaction is often accompanied by definite changes in appearance. For example, heat and light may be emitted, and there may be a change of color of the substances. Figure 1.9 shows the reactions of the metal mercury with oxygen in air. Describe the changes that occur.

1.7 Characterize gases, liquids, and solids in terms of compressibility and fluidity.

1.8 Choose a substance and give several of its physical properties and several of its chemical properties.

1.9 Give examples of an element, a compound, a heterogeneous mixture, and a homogeneous mixture.

1.10 What phases or states of matter are present in a glass of bubbling carbonated beverage that contains ice cubes?

1.11 What distinguishes an element from a compound? Can a compound also be an element?

1.12 What is meant by the precision of a measurement? How is it indicated?

1.13 Two rules are used to decide how to round the result of a calculation to the correct number of significant figures. Use a calculation to illustrate each rule. Explain how you obtained the number of significant figures in the answers.

1.14 Distinguish between a measured number and an exact number. Give examples of each.

1.15 How does the International System (SI) obtain units of different size from a given unit? How does the International System obtain units for all possible physical quantities from only seven base units?

1.16 What is an absolute temperature scale? How are degrees Celsius related to kelvins?

1.17 Define *density*. Describe some uses of density.

1.18 Why should units be carried along with numbers in a calculation?

1.19 When the quantity 12.9 g is added to 2×10^{-02} g, how many significant figures should be reported in the answer?
   a. one   **b.** two   **c.** three   **d.** four   **e.** five

1.20 You perform an experiment in the lab and determine that there are 36.3 inches in a meter. Using this experimental value, how many millimeters are there in 1.34 feet?
   a. 4.43×10^2 mm
   b. 4.05×10^2 mm
   c. 44.3 mm
   d. 4.43×10^5 mm
   e. 4.05×10^8 mm

1.21 A 75.0-g sample of a pure liquid, liquid A, with a density of 3.00 g/mL is mixed with a 50.0-mL sample of a pure liquid, liquid B, with a density of 2.00 g/mL. What is the total volume of the mixture? (Assume there is no reaction upon the mixing of A and B.)
   a. 275 mL
   b. 175 mL
   c. 125 mL
   d. 100. mL
   e. 75 mL

1.22 Which of the following represents the *smallest* mass?
   a. 23 cg
   b. 2.3×10^3 μg
   c. 0.23 mg
   d. 0.23 g
   e. 2.3×10^{-2} kg

Concept Explorations

Key: Concept explorations are comprehensive problems that provide a framework that will enable you to explore and learn many of the critical concepts and ideas in each chapter. If you master the concepts associated with these explorations, you will have a better understanding of many important chemistry ideas and will be more successful in solving all types of chemistry problems. These problems are well suited for group work and for use as in-class activities.

1.23 Physical and Chemical Changes

Say you are presented with two beakers, beaker A and beaker B, each containing a white, powdery compound.

a. From your initial observations, you suspect that the two beakers contain the same compound. Describe, in general terms, some experiments in a laboratory that you could do to help prove or disprove that the beakers contain the same compound.

b. Would it be easier to prove that the compounds are the same or to prove that they different? Explain your reasoning.

c. Which of the experiments that you listed above are the most convincing in determining whether the compounds are the same? Justify your answer.

d. A friend states that the best experiment for determining whether the compounds are the same is to see if they both dissolve in water. He proceeds to take 10.0 g of each compound and places them in separate beakers, each containing 100 mL of water. Both compounds completely dissolve. He then states, "Since the same amount of both substances dissolved in the same volume of water, they must both have the same chemical composition." Is he justified in making this claim? Why or why not?

1.24 Significant Figures
Part 1

a. Consider three masses that you wish to add together: 3 g, 1.4 g, and 3.3 g. These numbers represent measured values. Add the numbers together and report your answer to the correct number of significant figures.

b. Now perform the addition in a stepwise fashion in the following manner. Add 3 g and 1.4 g, reporting this sum to the correct number of significant figures. Next, take the number from the first step and add it to 3.3 g, reporting this sum to the correct number of significant figures.

c. Compare your answers from performing the addition in the two distinct ways presented in parts a and b. Does one of the answers represent a "better" way of reporting the results of the addition? If your answer is yes, explain why your choice is better.

d. A student performs the calculation $(5.0 \times 5.143 \text{ g}) + 2.80 \text{ g}$ and, being mindful of significant figures, reports an answer of 29 g. Is this the correct answer? If not, what might this student have done incorrectly?

e. Another student performs the calculation $(5 \times 5.143 \text{ g}) + 2.80$ and reports an answer of 29 g. Is this the correct answer? If not, what might this student have done incorrectly?

f. Yet another student performs the calculation $(5.00 \times 5.143 \text{ g}) + 2.80$ and reports an answer of 28.5 g. Is this the correct answer? If not, what did this student probably do incorrectly?

g. Referring to the calculations above, outline a procedure or rule(s) that will always enable you to report answers using the correct number of significant figures.

Part 2

a. A student wants to determine the volume of 27.2 g of a substance. He looks up the density of the material in a reference book, where it is reported to be 2.4451 g/cm³. He performs the calculation in the following manner:

$$27.2 \text{ g} \times 1.0 \text{ cm}^3/2.4 \text{ g} = 11.3 \text{ cm}^3$$

Is the calculated answer correct? If not, explain why it is not correct.

b. Another student performs the calculation in the following manner:

$$27.2 \text{ g} \times 1.00 \text{ cm}^3/2.45 \text{ g} = 11.1 \text{ cm}^3$$

Is this a "better" answer than that of the first student? Is this the "best" answer, or could it be "improved"? Explain.

c. Say that you have ten ball bearings, each having a mass of 1.234 g and a density of 3.1569 g/cm³. Calculate the volume of these ten ball bearings. In performing the calculation, present your work as unit conversions, and report your answer to the correct number of significant figures.

d. Explain how the answer that you calculated in part c is the "best" answer to the problem?

Conceptual Problems

Key: These problems are designed to check your understanding of the concepts associated with some of the main topics presented in the chapter. A strong conceptual understanding of chemistry is the foundation for both applying chemical knowledge and solving chemical problems. These problems vary in level of difficulty and often can be used as a basis for group discussion.

1.25

a. Sodium metal is partially melted. What are the two phases present?

b. A sample of sand is composed of granules of quartz (silicon dioxide) and seashells (calcium carbonate). The sand is mixed with water. What phases are present?

1.26 A material is believed to be a compound. Suppose you have several samples of this material obtained from various places around the world. Comment on what you would expect to find upon observing the melting point and color for each sample. What would you expect to find upon determining the elemental composition for each sample?

1.27 You need a thermometer that is accurate to $\pm 5°C$ to conduct some experiments in the temperature range of 0°C to 100°C. You find one in your lab drawer that has lost its markings.
  a. What experiments could you do to make sure your thermometer is suitable for your experiments?
  b. Assuming that the thermometer works, what procedure could you follow to put a scale on your thermometer that has the desired accuracy?

1.28 Imagine that you get the chance to shoot five arrows at each of the targets depicted below. On each of the targets, indicate the pattern that the five arrows make when
  a. You have poor accuracy and good precision.
  b. You have poor accuracy and poor precision.
  c. You have good accuracy and good precision.

1.29 Say you live in a climate where the temperature ranges from $-100°F$ to 20°F and you want to define a new temperature scale, YS (YS is the "Your Scale" temperature scale), which defines this range as 0.0°YS to 100.0°YS.
  a. Come up with an equation that would allow you to convert between °F and °YS.
  b. Using your equation, what would be the temperature in °F if it were 66°YS?

1.30 You are presented with a piece of metal in a jar. It is your job to determine what the metal is. What are some physical properties that you could measure in order to determine the type of metal? You suspect that the metal might be sodium; what are some chemical properties that you could investigate? (See Section 1.4 for some ideas.)

1.31 You have two identical boxes with interior dimensions of 8.0 cm × 8.0 cm × 8.0 cm. You completely fill one of the boxes with wooden spheres that are 1.6 cm in diameter. The other box gets filled with wooden cubes that are 1.6 cm on each edge. After putting the lid on the filled boxes, you then measure the density of each. Which one is more dense?

1.32 Consider the following compounds and their densities.

Substance	Density (g/mL)	Substance	Density (g/mL)
Isopropyl alcohol	0.785	Toluene	0.866
n-Butyl alcohol	0.810	Ethylene glycol	1.114

You create a column of the liquids in a glass cylinder with the most dense material on the bottom layer and the least dense on the top. You do not allow the liquids to mix.
  a. First you drop a plastic bead that has a density of 0.24 g/cm³ into the column. What do you expect to observe?
  b. Next you drop a different plastic bead that has a volume of 0.043 mL and a mass of 3.92×10^{-2} g into the column. What would you expect to observe in this case?
  c. You drop another bead into the column and observe that it makes it all the way to the bottom of the column. What can you conclude about the density of this bead?

1.33
  a. Which of the following items have a mass of about 1 g?
    a grain of sand
    a paper clip
    a nickel
    a 5.0-gallon bucket of water
    a brick
    a car
  b. What is the approximate mass (using SI mass units) of each of the items in part a?

1.34 What is the length of the nail reported to the correct number of significant figures?

Centimeters

1.35 For these questions, be sure to apply the rules for significant figures.
  a. You are conducting an experiment where you need the volume of a box; you take the length, height, and width measurements and then multiply the values together to find the volume. You report the volume of the box as 0.310 m³. If two of your measurements were 0.7120 m and 0.52145 m, what was the other measurement?
  b. If you were to add the two measurements from the first part of the problem to a third length measurement with the reported result of 1.509 m, what was the value of the third measurement?

1.36 You are teaching a class of second graders some chemistry, and they are confused about an object's mass versus its density. Keeping in mind that most second graders don't understand fractions, how would you explain these two ideas and illustrate how they differ? What examples would you use as a part of your explanation?

Practice Problems

Key: These problems are for practice in applying problem-solving skills. They are divided by topic, and some are keyed to exercises (see the ends of the exercises). The problems are arranged in matched pairs; the odd-numbered problem of each pair is listed first and its answer is given in the back of the book.

Conservation of Mass

1.37   A 15.9-g sample of sodium carbonate is added to a solution of acetic acid weighing 20.0 g. The two substances react, releasing carbon dioxide gas to the atmosphere. After reaction, the contents of the reaction vessel weighs 29.3 g. What is the mass of carbon dioxide given off during the reaction?

1.38   Some iron wire weighing 5.6 g is placed in a beaker and covered with 15.0 g of dilute hydrochloric acid. The acid reacts with the metal and gives off hydrogen gas, which escapes into the surrounding air. After reaction, the contents of the beaker weighs 20.4 g. What is the mass of hydrogen gas produced by the reaction?

1.39   Zinc metal reacts with yellow crystals of sulfur in a fiery reaction to produce a white powder of zinc sulfide. A chemist determines that 65.4 g of zinc reacts with 32.1 g of sulfur. How many grams of zinc sulfide could be produced from 20.0 g of zinc metal?

1.40   Aluminum metal reacts with bromine, a red-brown liquid with a noxious odor. The reaction is vigorous and produces aluminum bromide, a white crystalline substance. A sample of 27.0 g of aluminum yields 266.7 g of aluminum bromide. How many grams of bromine react with 15.0 g of aluminum?

Solids, Liquids, and Gases

1.41   Give the normal state (solid, liquid, or gas) of each of the following.
   a. sodium hydrogen carbonate (baking soda)
   b. isopropyl alcohol (rubbing alcohol)
   c. oxygen
   d. copper

1.42   Give the normal state (solid, liquid, or gas) of each of the following.
   a. potassium hydrogen tartrate (cream of tartar)
   b. lead
   c. carbon (diamond)
   d. bromine

Chemical and Physical Changes; Properties of Substances

1.43   Which of the following are physical changes and which are chemical changes?
   a. melting of sodium chloride
   b. pulverizing of rock salt
   c. burning of sulfur
   d. dissolving of salt in water

1.44   For each of the following, decide whether a physical or a chemical change is involved.
   a. dissolving of sugar in water
   b. rusting of iron
   c. burning of wood
   d. evaporation of alcohol

1.45   A sample of mercury(II) oxide was heated to produce mercury metal and oxygen gas. Then the liquid mercury was cooled to −40°C, where it solidified. A glowing wood splint was thrust into the oxygen, and the splint burst into flame. Identify each physical change and each chemical change.

1.46   Solid iodine, contaminated with salt, was heated until the iodine vaporized. The violet vapor of iodine was then cooled to yield the pure solid. Solid iodine and zinc metal powder were mixed and ignited to give a white powder. Identify each physical change and each chemical change.

1.47   The following are properties of substances. Decide whether each is a physical property or a chemical property.
   a. Chlorine gas liquefies at −35°C under normal pressure.
   b. Hydrogen burns in chlorine gas.
   c. Bromine melts at −7.2°C.
   d. Lithium is a soft, silvery-colored metal.
   e. Iron rusts in an atmosphere of moist air.

1.48   Decide whether each of the following is a physical property or a chemical property of the substance.
   a. Salt substitute, potassium chloride, dissolves in water.
   b. Seashells, calcium carbonate, fizz when immersed in vinegar.
   c. The gas hydrogen sulfide smells like rotten eggs.
   d. Fine steel wool (Fe) can be burned in air.
   e. Pure water freezes at 0°C.

1.49   Iodine is a solid having somewhat lustrous, blue-black crystals. The crystals vaporize readily to a violet-colored gas. Iodine combines with many metals. For example, aluminum combines with iodine to give aluminum iodide. Identify the physical and the chemical properties of iodine that are cited.

1.50   Mercury(II) oxide is an orange-red solid with a density of 11.1 g/cm^3. It decomposes when heated to give mercury and oxygen. The compound is insoluble in water (does not dissolve in water). Identify the physical and the chemical properties of mercury(II) oxide that are cited.

Elements, Compounds, and Mixtures

1.51   Consider the following separations of materials. State whether a physical process or a chemical reaction is involved in each separation.
   a. Sodium chloride is obtained from seawater by evaporation of the water.
   b. Mercury is obtained by heating the substance mercury(II) oxide; oxygen is also obtained.
   c. Pure water is obtained from ocean water by evaporating the water, then condensing it.
   d. Iron is produced from an iron ore that contains the substance iron(III) oxide.
   e. Gold is obtained from river sand by panning (allowing the heavy metal to settle in flowing water).

1.52   All of the following processes involve a separation of either a mixture into substances or a compound into elements. For each, decide whether a physical process or a chemical reaction is required.
   a. Sodium metal is obtained from the substance sodium chloride.
   b. Iron filings are separated from sand by using a magnet.
   c. Sugar crystals are separated from a sugar syrup by evaporation of water.
   d. Fine crystals of silver chloride are separated from a suspension of the crystals in water.
   e. Copper is produced when zinc metal is placed in a solution of copper(II) sulfate, a compound.

1.53 Label each of the following as a substance, a heterogeneous mixture, or a solution.
- **a.** seawater
- **b.** sulfur
- **c.** fluorine
- **d.** beach sand

1.54 Indicate whether each of the following materials is a substance, a heterogeneous mixture, or a solution.
- **a.** milk
- **b.** bromine
- **c.** gasoline
- **d.** aluminum

1.55 Which of the following are pure substances and which are mixtures? For each, list all of the different phases present.
- **a.** bromine liquid and its vapor
- **b.** paint, containing a liquid solution and a dispersed solid pigment
- **c.** partially molten iron
- **d.** baking powder containing sodium hydrogen carbonate and potassium hydrogen tartrate

1.56 Which of the following are pure substances and which are mixtures? For each, list all of the different phases present.
- **a.** a sugar solution with sugar crystals at the bottom
- **b.** ink containing a liquid solution with fine particles of carbon
- **c.** a sand containing quartz (silicon dioxide) and calcite (calcium carbonate)
- **d.** liquid water and steam at 100°C

Significant Figures

1.57 How many significant figures are there in each of the following measurements?
- **a.** 73.0000 g
- **b.** 0.0503 kg
- **c.** 6.300 cm
- **d.** 0.80090 m
- **e.** 5.10×10^{-7} m
- **f.** 2.010 s

1.58 How many significant figures are there in each of the following measurements?
- **a.** 301.0 kg
- **b.** 0.05930 g
- **c.** 0.224800 m
- **d.** 3.100 s
- **e.** 4.380×10^{-8} m
- **f.** 9.100×10^4 cm

1.59 The circumference of the earth at the equator is 40,000 km. This value is precise to two significant figures. Write this in scientific notation to express correctly the number of significant figures.

1.60 The astronomical unit equals the mean distance between the earth and the sun. This distance is 150,000,000 km, which is precise to three significant figures. Express this in scientific notation to the correct number of significant figures.

1.61 Do the indicated arithmetic and give the answer to the correct number of significant figures.
- **a.** $\dfrac{8.71 \times 0.0301}{0.031}$
- **b.** 0.71 + 92.2
- **c.** $934 \times 0.00435 + 107$
- **d.** $(847.89 - 847.73) \times 14673$

1.62 Do the indicated arithmetic and give the answer to the correct number of significant figures.
- **a.** $\dfrac{08.71 \times 0.57}{5.871}$
- **b.** 8.937 − 8.930

- **c.** 8.937 + 8.930
- **d.** $0.00015 \times 54.6 + 1.002$

1.63 One sphere has a radius of 5.10 cm; another has a radius of 5.00 cm. What is the difference in volume (in cubic centimeters) between the two spheres? Give the answer to the correct number of significant figures. The volume of a sphere is $(4/3)\,\pi r^3$, where $\pi = 3.1416$ and r is the radius.

1.64 A solid cylinder of iron of circular cross section with a radius of 1.500 cm has a ruler etched along its length. What is the volume of iron contained between the marks labeled 3.10 cm and 3.50 cm? The volume of a cylinder is $\pi r^2 l$, where $\pi = 3.1416$, r is the radius, and l is the length.

SI Units

1.65 Write the following measurements, without scientific notation, using the appropriate SI prefix.
- **a.** 5.89×10^{-12} s
- **b.** 0.2010 m
- **c.** 2.560×10^{-9} g
- **d.** 6.05×10^3 m

1.66 Write the following measurements, without scientific notation, using the appropriate SI prefix.
- **a.** 4.851×10^{-6} g
- **b.** 3.16×10^{-2} m
- **c.** 2.591×10^{-9} s
- **d.** 8.93×10^{-12} g

1.67 Using scientific notation, convert:
- **a.** 6.15 ps to s
- **b.** 3.781 μm to m
- **c.** 1.546 Å to m
- **d.** 9.7 mg to g

1.68 Using scientific notation, convert:
- **a.** 6.20 km to m
- **b.** 1.98 ns to s
- **c.** 2.54 cm to m
- **d.** 5.23 μg to g

Temperature Conversion

1.69 Convert:
- **a.** 68°F to degrees Celsius
- **b.** −23°F to degrees Celsius
- **c.** 26°C to degrees Fahrenheit
- **d.** −70°C to degrees Fahrenheit

1.70 Convert:
- **a.** 51°F to degrees Celsius
- **b.** −7°F to degrees Celsius
- **c.** −41°C to degrees Fahrenheit
- **d.** 22°C to degrees Fahrenheit

1.71 Salt and ice are stirred together to give a mixture to freeze ice cream. The temperature of the mixture is −21.1°C. What is this temperature in degrees Fahrenheit?

1.72 Liquid nitrogen can be used for the quick freezing of foods. The liquid boils at −196°C. What is this temperature in degrees Fahrenheit?

Density

1.73 A certain sample of the mineral galena (lead sulfide) weighs 12.4 g and has a volume of 1.64 cm^3. What is the density of galena?

1.74 A flask contains 25.0 mL of diethyl ether weighing 17.84 g. What is the density of the ether?

1.75 A liquid with a volume of 8.5 mL has a mass of 6.71 g. The liquid is either octane, ethanol, or benzene, the densities of which are 0.702 g/cm³, 0.789 g/cm³, and 0.879 g/cm³, respectively. What is the identity of the liquid?

1.76 A mineral sample has a mass of 5.95 g and a volume of 7.9 cm³. The mineral is either sphalerite (density = 4.0 g/cm³), cassiterite (density = 6.99 g/cm³), or cinnabar (density = 8.10 g/cm³). Which is it?

1.77 Platinum has a density of 21.4 g/cm³. What is the mass of 5.9 cm³ of this metal?

1.78 What is the mass of a 43.8-mL sample of gasoline, which has a density of 0.70 g/cm³?

1.79 Ethanol has a density of 0.789 g/cm³. What volume must be poured into a graduated cylinder to give 19.8 g of alcohol?

1.80 Bromine is a red-brown liquid with a density of 3.10 g/mL. A sample of bromine weighing 88.5 g occupies what volume?

Unit Conversions

1.81 Sodium hydrogen carbonate, known commercially as baking soda, reacts with acidic materials such as vinegar to release carbon dioxide gas. An experiment calls for 0.480 kg of sodium hydrogen carbonate. Express this mass in milligrams.

1.82 The acidic constituent in vinegar is acetic acid. A 10.0-mL sample of a certain vinegar contains 501 mg of acetic acid. What is this mass of acetic acid expressed in micrograms?

1.83 The different colors of light have different wavelengths. The human eye is most sensitive to light whose wavelength is 555 nm (greenish-yellow). What is this wavelength in centimeters?

1.84 Water consists of molecules (groups of atoms). A water molecule has two hydrogen atoms, each connected to an oxygen atom. The distance between any one hydrogen atom and the oxygen atom is 0.96 Å. What is this distance in meters?

1.85 The total amount of fresh water on earth is estimated to be 3.73×10^8 km³. What is this volume in cubic meters? in liters?

1.86 A submicroscopic particle suspended in a solution has a volume of 1.3 μm³. What is this volume in liters?

1.87 How many grams are there in 3.58 short tons? Note that 1 g = 0.03527 oz (ounces avoirdupois), 1 lb (pound) = 16 oz, and 1 short ton = 2000 lb. (These relations are exact.)

1.88 The calorie, the Btu (British thermal unit), and the joule are units of energy; 1 calorie = 4.184 joules (exact), and 1 Btu = 252.0 calories. Convert 3.15 Btu to joules.

1.89 The first measurement of sea depth was made in 1840 in the central South Atlantic, where a plummet was lowered 2425 fathoms. What is this depth in meters? Note that 1 fathom = 6 ft, 1 ft = 12 in., and 1 in. = 2.54×10^{-2} m. (These relations are exact.)

1.90 The estimated amount of recoverable oil from the field at Prudhoe Bay in Alaska is 1.3×10^{10} barrels. What is this amount of oil in cubic meters? One barrel = 42 gal (exact), 1 gal = 4 qt (exact), and 1 qt = 9.46×10^{-4} m³.

1.91 A fish tank is 20.0 in. long, 20.0 in. deep, and 10.0 in. high. What is the maximum volume of water, in liters, that the fish tank can hold?

1.92 The population density of worms in a particular field is 25 worms per cubic meter of soil. How many worms would there be in the top meter of soil in a field that has dimensions of 1.00 km by 2.0 km?

General Problems

Key: These problems provide more practice but are not divided by topic or keyed to exercises. Each section ends with essay questions, each of which is color-coded to refer to the *A Chemist Looks at* (gold) or *Instrumental Methods* (purple) chapter essay on which it is based. Odd-numbered problems and the even-numbered problems that follow are similar; answers to all odd-numbered problems except the essay questions are given in the back of the book.

1.93 Sodium metal reacts vigorously with water. A piece of sodium weighing 19.70 g was added to a beaker containing 126.22 g of water. During reaction, hydrogen gas was produced and bubbled from the solution. The solution, containing sodium hydroxide, weighed 145.06 g. How many grams of hydrogen gas were produced?

1.94 An antacid tablet weighing 0.853 g contained calcium carbonate as the active ingredient, in addition to an inert binder. When an acid solution weighing 56.519 g was added to the tablet, carbon dioxide gas was released, producing a fizz. The resulting solution weighed 57.152 g. How many grams of carbon dioxide were produced?

1.95 When a mixture of aluminum powder and iron(III) oxide is ignited, it produces molten iron and aluminum oxide. In an experiment, 5.40 g of aluminum was mixed with 18.50 g of iron(III) oxide. At the end of the reaction, the mixture contained 11.17 g of iron, 10.20 g of aluminum oxide, and an undetermined amount of unreacted iron(III) oxide. No aluminum was left. What is the mass of the iron(III) oxide?

1.96 When chlorine gas is bubbled into a solution of sodium bromide, the sodium bromide reacts to give bromine, a red-brown liquid, and sodium chloride (ordinary table salt). A solution was made by dissolving 20.6 g of sodium bromide in 100.0 g of water. After passing chlorine through the solution, investigators analyzed the mixture. It contained 16.0 g of bromine and 11.7 g of sodium chloride. How many grams of chlorine reacted?

1.97 A beaker weighed 53.10 g. To the beaker was added 5.348 g of iron pellets and 56.1 g of hydrochloric acid. What was the total mass of the beaker and the mixture (before reaction)? Express the answer to the correct number of significant figures.

1.98 A graduated cylinder weighed 68.1 g. To the cylinder was added 58.2 g of water and 5.279 g of sodium chloride. What was the total mass of the cylinder and the solution? Express the answer to the correct number of significant figures.

1.99 Describe each of the following as a physical or chemical property of each listed chemical substance.
  a. baking soda reacts with vinegar
  b. ice melts at 0°C
  c. graphite is a soft, black solid
  d. hydrogen burns in air

1.100 Describe each of the following as a physical or chemical property of each listed chemical substance.
  a. chlorine is a green gas
  b. zinc reacts with acids
  c. magnesium has a density of 1.74 g/cm^3
  d. iron can rust

1.101 Analyses of several samples of a material containing only iron and oxygen gave the following results. Could this material be a compound?

	Mass of Sample	Mass of Iron	Mass of Oxygen
Sample A	1.518 g	1.094 g	0.424 g
Sample B	2.056 g	1.449 g	0.607 g
Sample C	1.873 g	1.335 g	0.538 g

1.102 A red-orange solid contains only mercury and oxygen. Analyses of three different samples gave the following results. Are the data consistent with the hypothesis that the material is a compound?

	Mass of Sample	Mass of Mercury	Mass of Oxygen
Sample A	1.0410 g	0.9641 g	0.0769 g
Sample B	1.5434 g	1.4293 g	0.1141 g
Sample C	1.2183 g	1.1283 g	0.0900 g

1.103 A cubic box measures 39.3 cm on an edge. What is the volume of the box in cubic centimeters? Express the answer to the correct number of significant figures.

1.104 A cylinder with circular cross section has a radius of 2.56 cm and a height of 56.32 cm. What is the volume of the cylinder? Express the answer to the correct number of significant figures.

1.105 An aquarium has a rectangular cross section that is 47.8 in. by 12.5 in.; it is 19.5 in. high. How many U.S. gallons does the aquarium contain? One U.S. gallon equals exactly 231 in^3.

1.106 A spherical tank has a radius of 175.0 in. Calculate the volume of the tank in cubic inches; then convert this to Imperial gallons. The volume of a sphere is $(4/3) \pi r^3$, where r is the radius. One Imperial gallon equals 277.4 in^3.

1.107 Obtain the difference in volume between two spheres, one of radius 5.61 cm, the other of radius 5.85 cm. The volume V of a sphere is $(4/3) \pi r^3$, where r is the radius. Give the result to the correct number of significant figures.

1.108 What is the difference in surface area between two circles, one of radius 7.98 cm, the other of radius 8.50 cm? The surface area of a circle of radius r is πr^2. Obtain the result to the correct number of significant figures.

1.109 Perform the following arithmetic setups and express the answers to the correct number of significant figures.
  a. $\dfrac{56.1 - 51.1}{6.58}$ **b.** $\dfrac{56.1 + 51.1}{6.58}$
  c. $(9.1 + 8.6) \times 26.91$ **d.** $0.0065 \times 3.21 + 0.0911$

1.110 Perform the following arithmetic setups and report the answers to the correct number of significant figures.
  a. $\dfrac{9.345 - 9.005}{9.811}$ **b.** $\dfrac{9.345 + 9.005}{9.811}$
  c. $(7.50 + 7.53) \times 3.71$ **d.** $0.71 \times 0.36 + 17.36$

1.111 For each of the following, write the measurement in terms of an appropriate prefix and base unit.
  a. The mass of calcium per milliliter in a sample of blood serum is 0.0912 g.
  b. The radius of an oxygen atom is about 0.000000000066 m.
  c. A particular red blood cell measures 0.0000071 m.
  d. The wavelength of a certain ultraviolet radiation is 0.000000056 m.

1.112 For each of the following, write the measurement in terms of an appropriate prefix and base unit.
  a. The mass of magnesium per milliliter in a sample of blood serum is 0.0186 g.
  b. The radius of a carbon atom is about 0.000000000077 m.
  c. The hemoglobin molecule, a component of red blood cells, is 0.0000000065 m in diameter.
  d. The wavelength of a certain infrared radiation is 0.00000085 m.

1.113 Write each of the following in terms of the SI base unit (that is, express the prefix as the power of 10).
  a. 1.07 ps   **b.** 5.8 μm
  c. 319 nm   **d.** 15.3 ms

1.114 Write each of the following in terms of the SI base unit (that is, express the prefix as the power of 10).
  a. 6.6 mK   **b.** 275 pm
  c. 22.1 ms   **d.** 45 μm

1.115 Tungsten metal, which is used in lightbulb filaments, has the highest melting point of any metal (3410°C). What is this melting point in degrees Fahrenheit?

1.116 Titanium metal is used in aerospace alloys to add strength and corrosion resistance. Titanium melts at 1677°C. What is this temperature in degrees Fahrenheit?

1.117 Calcium carbonate, a white powder used in toothpastes, antacids, and other preparations, decomposes when heated to about 825°C. What is this temperature in degrees Fahrenheit?

1.118 Sodium hydrogen carbonate (baking soda) starts to decompose to sodium carbonate (soda ash) at about 50°C. What is this temperature in degrees Fahrenheit?

1.119 Gallium metal can be melted by the heat of one's hand. Its melting point is 29.8°C. What is this temperature in kelvins? in degrees Fahrenheit?

1.120 Mercury metal is liquid at normal temperatures but freezes at −38.9°C. What is this temperature in kelvins? in degrees Fahrenheit?

1.121 Zinc metal can be purified by distillation (transforming the liquid metal to vapor, then condensing the vapor back to liquid). The metal boils at normal atmospheric pressure at 1666°F. What is this temperature in degrees Celsius? in kelvins?

1.122 Iodine is a bluish-black solid. It forms a violet-colored vapor when heated. The solid melts at 236°F. What is this temperature in degrees Celsius? in kelvins?

1.123 The density of magnesium metal (used in fireworks) is 1.74 g/cm^3. Express this density in SI units (kg/m^3).

1.124 Vanadium metal is added to steel to impart strength. The density of vanadium is 5.96 g/cm^3. Express this in SI units (kg/m^3).

1.125 The density of quartz mineral was determined by adding a weighed piece to a graduated cylinder containing 51.2 mL water. After the quartz was submerged, the water level was 65.7 mL. The quartz piece weighed 38.4 g. What was the density of the quartz?

1.126 Hematite (iron ore) weighing 70.7 g was placed in a flask whose volume was 53.2 mL. The flask with hematite was then carefully filled with water and weighed. The hematite and water weighed 109.3 g. The density of the water was 0.997 g/cm^3. What was the density of the hematite?

1.127 Some bottles of colorless liquids were being labeled when the technicians accidentally mixed them up and lost track of their contents. A 15.0-mL sample withdrawn from one bottle weighed 22.3 g. The technicians knew that the liquid was either acetone, benzene, chloroform, or carbon tetrachloride (which have densities of 0.792 g/cm^3, 0.899 g/cm^3, 1.489 g/cm^3, and 1.595 g/cm^3, respectively). What was the identity of the liquid?

1.128 A solid will float on any liquid that is more dense than it is. The volume of a piece of calcite weighing 35.6 g is 12.9 cm^3. On which of the following liquids will the calcite float: carbon tetrachloride (density = 1.60 g/cm^3), methylene bromide (density = 2.50 g/cm^3), tetrabromoethane (density = 2.96 g/cm^3), methylene iodide (density = 3.33 g/cm^3)?

1.129 Platinum metal is used in jewelry; it is also used in automobile catalytic converters. What is the mass of a cube of platinum 4.40 cm on an edge? The density of platinum is 21.4 g/cm^3.

1.130 Ultrapure silicon is used to make solid-state devices, such as computer chips. What is the mass of a circular cylinder of silicon that is 12.40 cm long and has a radius of 4.00 cm? The density of silicon is 2.33 g/cm^3.

1.131 Vinegar contains acetic acid (about 5% by mass). Pure acetic acid has a strong vinegar smell but is corrosive to the skin. What volume of pure acetic acid has a mass of 35.00 g? The density of acetic acid is 1.053 g/mL.

1.132 Ethyl acetate has a characteristic fruity odor and is used as a solvent in paint lacquers and perfumes. An experiment requires 0.035 kg of ethyl acetate. What volume is this (in liters)? The density of ethyl acetate is 0.902 g/mL.

1.133 Convert:
  a. 8.45 kg to micrograms
  b. 318 μs to milliseconds
  c. 93 km to nanometers
  d. 37.1 mm to centimeters

1.134 Convert:
  a. 125 Å to micrometers
  b. 32.4 kg to milligrams
  c. 16.8 cm to millimeters
  d. 2.2 ns to microseconds

1.135 Convert:
  a. 5.91 kg of chrome yellow to milligrams
  b. 753 mg of vitamin A to micrograms
  c. 90.1 MHz (megahertz), the wavelength of an FM signal, to kilohertz
  d. 498 mJ (the joule, J, is a unit of energy) to kilojoules

1.136 Convert:
  a. 7.19 μg of cyanocobalamin (vitamin B$_{12}$) to milligrams
  b. 104 pm, the radius of a sulfur atom, to angstroms
  c. 0.010 mm, the diameter of a typical blood capillary, to centimeters
  d. 0.0605 kPa (the pascal, Pa, is a unit of pressure) to centipascals

1.137 The largest of the Great Lakes is Lake Superior, which has a volume of 12,230 km^3. What is this volume in liters?

1.138 The average flow of the Niagara River is 0.501 km^3 of water per day. What is this volume in liters?

1.139 A room measures 10.0 ft × 11.0 ft and is 9.0 ft high. What is its volume in liters?

1.140 A cylindrical settling tank is 5.0 ft deep and has a radius of 15.0 ft. What is the volume of the tank in liters?

1.141 The masses of diamonds and gems are measured in carats. A carat is defined as 200 mg. If a jeweler has 275 carats of diamonds, how many grams does she have?

1.142 One year of world production of gold was 49.6 × 10^6 troy ounces. One troy ounce equals 31.10 g. What was the world production of gold in metric tons (10^6 g) for that year?

1.143 What are some characteristics of the adhesive used for Post-it Notes?

1.144 All good experiments start with a scientific question. What was the scientific question that Art Fry was trying to answer when he embarked on finding the adhesive for the Post-it Note?

1.145 What do the various chromatographic separation techniques have in common?

1.146 Describe how gas chromatography works.

Strategy Problems

Key: As noted earlier, all of the practice and general problems are matched pairs. This section is a selection of problems that are not in matched-pair format. These challenging problems require that you employ many of the concepts and strategies that were developed in the chapter. In some cases, you will have to integrate several concepts and operational skills in order to solve the problem successfully.

1.147 When the quantity 5×10^{-2} mg is subtracted from 4.6 mg, how many significant figures should be reported in the answer?

1.148 A 33.0-g sample of an unknown liquid at 20.0°C is heated to120°C. During this heating, the density of the liquid changes from 0.854 g/cm³ to 0.797 g/cm³. What volume would this sample occupy at 120°C?

1.149 A 175-g sample of a pure liquid, liquid A, with a density of 3.00 g/mL is mixed with a 50.0-mL sample of a pure liquid, liquid B, with a density of 2.00 g/mL. What is the total volume of the mixture? (Assume there is no reaction upon the mixing of A and B.)

1.150 On a long trip you travel 832 miles in 21 hours. During this trip, you use 29 gallons of gasoline.

  a. Calculate your average speed in miles per hour.
  b. Calculate your average speed in kilometers per hour.
  c. Calculate your gas mileage in kilometers per liter.

1.151 The figures below represent a gas trapped in containers. The orange balls represent individual gas atoms. Container A on the left has a volume that is one-half the volume of container B on the right.

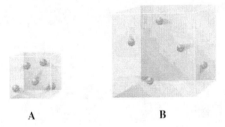

      A   B

  a. How does the mass of gas in one container compare with the mass of gas in the other?
  b. Which container has the greater density of gas?
  c. If the volume of container A were increased to the same volume as container B, how would the density of the gas in container A change?

1.152 An ice cube measures 3.50 cm on each edge and weighs 39.45 g.

  a. Calculate the density of ice.
  b. Calculate the mass of 400.4 mL of water in an ice cube.

1.153 The total length of all the DNA molecules contained in a human body is 1×10^{10} miles. The population of the United States is about 300 million. What is the total length of all the DNA of the U.S. population in lightyears? (A lightyear is the distance that light travels in a year and is 9.46×10^{15} m.)

1.154 Prospectors are considering searching for gold on a plot of land that contains 1.16 g of gold per bucket of soil. If the volume of the bucket is 4.08 L, how many grams of gold are there likely to be in 2.38×10^3 cubic feet of soil?

1.155 A solution is prepared by dissolving table salt, sodium chloride, in water at room temperature.

  a. Assuming there is no significant change in the volume of water during the preparation of the solution, how would the density of the solution compare to that of pure water?
  b. If you were to boil the solution for several minutes and then allow it to cool to room temperature, how would the density of the solution compare to the density in part a?
  c. If you took the solution prepared in part a and added more water, how would this affect the density of the solution?

1.156 Water and saline (salt) solution have in common that they are both homogeneous. How do these materials differ? Be specific and use chemical terms to describe the two systems.

Cumulative-Skills Problems

Key: These problems require two or more operational skills you learned in this chapter. In later chapters, the problems under this heading will combine skills introduced in previous chapters with those given in the current one.

1.157 When 10.0 g of marble chips (calcium carbonate) is treated with 50.0 mL of hydrochloric acid (density 1.096 g/mL), the marble dissolves, giving a solution and releasing carbon dioxide gas. The solution weighs 60.4 g. How many liters of carbon dioxide gas are released? The density of the gas is 1.798 g/L.

1.158 Zinc ore (zinc sulfide) is treated with sulfuric acid, leaving a solution with some undissolved bits of material and releasing hydrogen sulfide gas. If 10.8 g of zinc ore is treated with 50.0 mL of sulfuric acid (density 1.153 g/mL), 65.1 g of solution and undissolved material remains. In addition, hydrogen sulfide

(density 1.393 g/L) is evolved. What is the volume (in liters) of this gas?

1.159 A steel sphere has a radius of 1.58 in. If this steel has a density of 7.88 g/cm³, what is the mass of the sphere in grams?

1.160 A weather balloon filled with helium has a diameter of 3.00 ft. What is the mass in grams of the helium in the balloon at 21°C and normal pressure? The density of helium under these conditions is 0.166 g/L.

1.161 The land area of Greenland is 840,000 mi², with only 132,000 mi² free of perpetual ice. The average thickness of this ice is 5000 ft. Estimate the mass of the ice (assume two significant figures). The density of ice is 0.917 g/cm³.

1.162 Antarctica, almost completely covered in ice, has an area of 5,500,000 mi² with an average height of 7500 ft. Without the ice, the height would be only 1500 ft. Estimate the mass of this ice (two significant figures). The density of ice is 0.917 g/cm^3.

1.163   A sample of an ethanol–water solution has a volume of 54.2 cm^3 and a mass of 49.6 g. What is the percentage of ethanol (by mass) in the solution? (Assume that there is no change in volume when the pure compounds are mixed.) The density of ethanol is 0.789 g/cm^3 and that of water is 0.998 g/cm^3. Alcoholic beverages are rated in *proof*, which is a measure of the relative amount of ethanol in the beverage. Pure ethanol is exactly 200 proof; a solution that is 50% ethanol by volume is exactly 100 proof. What is the proof of the given ethanol–water solution?

1.164   You have a piece of gold jewelry weighing 9.35 g. Its volume is 0.654 cm^3. Assume that the metal is an alloy (mixture) of gold and silver, which have densities of 19.3 g/cm^3 and 10.5 g/cm^3, respectively. Also assume that there is no change in volume when the pure metals are mixed. Calculate the percentage of gold (by mass) in the alloy. The relative amount of gold in an alloy is measured in *karats*. Pure gold is 24 karats; an alloy of 50% gold is 12 karats. State the proportion of gold in the jewelry in karats.

1.165   A sample of vermilion-colored mineral was weighed in air, then weighed again while suspended in water. An object is buoyed up by the mass of the fluid displaced by the object. In air, the mineral weighed 18.49 g; in water, it weighed 16.21 g. The densities of air and water are 1.205 g/L and 0.9982 g/cm^3, respectively. What is the density of the mineral?

1.166   A sample of a bright blue mineral was weighed in air, then weighed again while suspended in water. An object is buoyed up by the mass of the fluid displaced by the object. In air, the mineral weighed 7.35 g; in water, it weighed 5.40 g. The densities of air and water are 1.205 g/L and 0.9982 g/cm^3, respectively. What is the density of the mineral?

1.167   A student gently drops an object weighing 15.8 g into an open vessel that is full of ethanol, so that a volume of ethanol spills out equal to the volume of the object. The experimenter now finds that the vessel and its contents weigh 10.5 g more than the vessel full of ethanol only. The density of ethanol is 0.789 g/cm^3. What is the density of the object?

1.168   An experimenter places a piece of a solid metal weighing 255 g into a graduated cylinder, which she then fills with liquid mercury. After weighing the cylinder and its contents, she removes the solid metal and fills the cylinder with mercury. She now finds that the cylinder and its contents weigh 101 g less than before. The density of mercury is 13.6 g/cm^3. What is the density of the solid metal?

2

Atoms, Molecules, and Ions

The probe of a scanning tunneling microscope (as sharp as a single atom!) was used to arrange iron atoms in a circle on the surface of a copper metal lattice and collect data to produce this image.

Contents and Concepts

The key concept in chemistry is that all matter is composed of very small particles called atoms. We look at atomic theory, discuss atomic structure, and finally describe the periodic table, which organizes the elements.

We explore how atoms combine in various ways to yield the millions of known substances.

odium is a soft, silvery metal. This metal cannot be handled with bare fingers, because it reacts with any moisture on the skin, causing a burn. Chlorine is a poisonous, greenish yellow gas with a choking odor. When molten sodium is placed into an atmosphere of chlorine, a dramatic reaction occurs: the sodium bursts into flame and a white, crystalline powder forms (see Figure 2.1). What is particularly interesting about this reaction is that this chemical combination of two toxic substances produces sodium chloride, the substance that we commonly call table salt.

Sodium metal and chlorine gas are particular forms of matter. In burning, they undergo a chemical change—a chemical reaction—in which these forms of matter change to a form of matter with different chemical and physical properties. How do we explain the differences in properties of different forms of matter? And how do we explain chemical reactions such as the burning of sodium metal in chlorine gas? This chapter and the next take an introductory look at these

■ See page 75 for the Media Summary.
basic questions in chemistry. In later chapters we will develop the concepts introduced here.

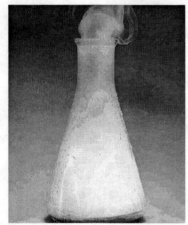

FIGURE 2.1 ▶

Reaction of sodium and chlorine
Top: Sodium metal and chlorine gas. *Bottom:* A small piece of molten sodium burning in a flask of chlorine. The product is sodium chloride, common table salt, along with lots of energy.

Atomic Theory and Atomic Structure

As noted in Chapter 1, all matter is composed of atoms. In this first part of Chapter 2, we explore the atomic theory of matter and the structure of atoms. We also examine the *periodic table*, which is an organizational chart designed to highlight similarities among the elements.

2.1 | Atomic Theory of Matter

This chapter introduces basic concepts needed in the course. Required lecture time will depend on the background of the students and the weight the instructor wants to put on certain topics, such as naming of compounds.

As we noted in Chapter 1, Lavoisier laid the experimental foundation of modern chemistry. But the British chemist John Dalton (1766–1844) provided the basic theory: all matter—whether element, compound, or mixture—is composed of small particles called atoms. The postulates, or basic statements, of Dalton's theory are presented in this section. Note that the terms *element*, *compound*, and *chemical reaction*, which were defined in Chapter 1 in terms of matter as we normally see it, are redefined here by the postulates of Dalton's theory in terms of atoms.

FIGURE 2.2 ▶

Image of iodine atoms on a platinum metal surface
This computer-screen image was obtained by a scanning tunneling microscope (discussed in Chapter 7); the color was added to the image by computer. Iodine atoms are the large peaks with pink tops. Note the "vacancy" in the array of iodine atoms. A scale shows the size of the atoms in nanometers.

Demonstration of the reaction of sodium and chlorine: Summerlin et al., *Chemical Demonstrations*, Vol. 2 (Washington, D.C.: Am. Chem. Soc., 1987), no. 30, p. 56.

Postulates of Dalton's Atomic Theory

The main points of Dalton's **atomic theory,** *an explanation of the structure of matter in terms of different combinations of very small particles,* are given by the following postulates:

1. All matter is composed of indivisible atoms. An **atom** is *an extremely small particle of matter that retains its identity during chemical reactions.* (See Figure 2.2.)

2. An **element** is *a type of matter composed of only one kind of atom,* each atom of a given kind having the same properties. Mass is one such property. Thus, the atoms of a given element have a characteristic mass. (We will need to revise this definition of element in Section 2.3 so that it is stated in modern terms.) <

> As you will see in Section 2.4, it is the average mass of an atom that is characteristic of each element on earth.

3. A **compound** is *a type of matter composed of atoms of two or more elements chemically combined in fixed proportions.* The relative numbers of any two kinds of atoms in a compound occur in simple ratios. Water, for example, a compound of the elements hydrogen and oxygen, consists of hydrogen and oxygen atoms in the ratio of 2 to 1.

4. A **chemical reaction** consists of *the rearrangement of the atoms present in the reacting substances to give new chemical combinations present in the substances formed by the reaction.* Atoms are not created, destroyed, or broken into smaller particles by any chemical reaction.

Today we know that atoms are not truly indivisible; they are themselves made up of particles. Nevertheless, Dalton's postulates are essentially correct.

Atomic Symbols and Models

It is convenient to use symbols for the atoms of the different elements. An **atomic symbol** is *a one- or two-letter notation used to represent an atom corresponding to a particular element.* < Typically, the atomic symbol consists of the first letter, capitalized, from the name of the element, sometimes with an additional letter from the name in lowercase. For example, chlorine has the symbol Cl. Other symbols are derived from a name in another language (usually Latin). Sodium is given the symbol Na from its Latin name, *natrium.* Symbols of the elements are listed in the table on the back cover.

Early in the development of his atomic theory, Dalton built spheres to represent atoms and used combinations of these spheres to represent compounds. Chemists continue to use this idea of representing atoms by three-dimensional

> The atomic names (temporary) given to newly discovered elements are derived from the atomic number (discussed in Section 2.3) using the numerical roots: nil (0), un (1), bi (2), tri (3), quad (4), pent (5), hex (6), sept (7), oct (8), and enn (9) with the ending -ium. For example, the element with atomic number 116 is ununhexium; its atomic symbol is Uuh.

models, but because we now know so much more about atoms and molecules than Dalton did, these models have become more refined. Section 2.6 describes these models in more detail.

Deductions from Dalton's Atomic Theory

Note how atomic theory explains the difference between an element and a compound. Atomic theory also explains two laws we considered earlier. One of these is the law of conservation of mass, which states that the total mass remains constant during a chemical reaction. By postulate 2, every atom has a definite mass. Because a chemical reaction only rearranges the chemical combinations of atoms (postulate 4), the mass must remain constant. The other law explained by atomic theory is the law of definite proportions (constant composition). Postulate 3 defines a compound as a type of matter containing the atoms of two or more elements in definite proportions. Because the atoms have definite mass, compounds must have the elements in definite proportions by mass.

A good theory should not only explain known facts and laws but also predict new ones. The **law of multiple proportions,** deduced by Dalton from his atomic theory, states that *when two elements form more than one compound, the masses of one element in these compounds for a fixed mass of the other element are in ratios of small whole numbers.* To illustrate this law, consider the following. If we take a fixed mass of carbon, 1.000 gram, and react it with oxygen, we end up with two compounds: one that contains 1.3321 grams of oxygen for each 1.000 gram of carbon, and one that contains 2.6642 grams of oxygen per 1.000 gram of carbon. Note that the ratio of the amounts of oxygen in the two compounds is 2 to 1 (2.6642 ÷ 1.3321), which indicates that there must be twice as much oxygen in the second compound. Applying atomic theory, if we assume that the compound that has 1.3321 grams of oxygen to 1.000 gram of carbon is CO (the combination of one carbon atom and one oxygen atom), then the compound that contains twice as much oxygen per 1.000 gram of carbon must be CO_2 (the combination of one carbon atom and two oxygen atoms). The deduction of the law of multiple proportions from atomic theory was important in convincing chemists of the validity of the theory.

Concept Check 2.1

Like Dalton, chemists continue to model atoms using spheres. Modern models are usually drawn with a computer and use different colors to represent atoms of different elements. Which of the models below represents CO_2?

2.2 | The Structure of the Atom

Although Dalton had postulated that atoms were indivisible particles, experiments conducted around the beginning of the last century showed that atoms themselves consist of particles. These experiments showed that an atom consists of two kinds of particles: a **nucleus,** *the atom's central core, which is positively charged and contains most of the atom's mass,* and one or more electrons. An **electron** is *a very light, negatively charged particle that exists in the region around the atom's positively charged nucleus.*

FIGURE 2.3 ▲

Joseph John Thomson (1856–1940)
J. J. Thomson's scientific ability was recognized early with his appointment as professor of physics in the Cavendish Laboratory at Cambridge University when he was not quite 28 years old. Soon after this appointment, Thomson began research on the discharge of electricity through gases. This work culminated in 1897 with the discovery of the electron. Thomson was awarded the Nobel Prize in physics in 1906.

FIGURE 2.4 ▲ ◼

Formation of cathode rays
Cathode rays leave the cathode, or negative electrode, and are accelerated toward the anode, or positive electrode. Some of the rays pass through the hole in the anode to form a beam, which then is bent by the electric plates in the tube.

A television tube uses the deflection of cathode rays by magnetic fields. A beam of cathode rays is directed toward a coated screen on the front of the tube, where by varying the magnetism generated by electromagnetic coils, the beam traces a luminescent image.

Discovery of the Electron

In 1897 the British physicist J. J. Thomson (Figure 2.3) conducted a series of experiments that showed that atoms were not indivisible particles. Figure 2.4 shows an experimental apparatus similar to the one used by Thomson. In this apparatus, two electrodes from a high-voltage source are sealed into a glass tube from which the air has been evacuated. The negative electrode is called the *cathode;* the positive one, the *anode*. When the high-voltage current is turned on, the glass tube emits a greenish light. Experiments showed that this greenish light is caused by the interaction of the glass with *cathode rays*, which are rays that originate from the cathode. <

After the cathode rays leave the negative electrode, they move toward the anode, where some rays pass through a hole to form a beam (Figure 2.4). This beam bends away from the negatively charged plate and toward the positively charged plate. (Cathode rays are not directly visible, but do cause certain materials such as zinc sulfide to glow so you can observe them.) Figure 2.5 shows a similar experiment, in which cathode rays are seen to bend when a magnet is brought toward them. Thomson showed that the characteristics of cathode rays are independent of the material making up the cathode. From such evidence, he concluded that a cathode ray consists of a beam of negatively charged particles (or electrons) and that electrons are constituents of all matter.

FIGURE 2.5 ▽

Bending of cathode rays by a magnet
Left: The cathode-ray beam travels from right to left. It is visible where it falls on a zinc-sulfide screen. *Center:* The beam of negative particles bends downward as the south pole of the magnet is brought toward it. *Right:* When the magnet is turned around, the beam bends in the opposite direction.

Millikan: Good to the last (oil) drop.
J. Chem. Educ. 83 (2006): 1312A.

FIGURE 2.6

Millikan's oil-drop experiment
An atomizer, or spray bottle, introduces a fine mist of oil drops into the top chamber. Several drops happen to fall through a small hole into the lower chamber, where the experimenter follows the motion of one drop with a microscope. Some of these drops have picked up one or more electrons as a result of friction in the atomizer and have become negatively charged. A negatively charged drop will be attracted upward when the experimenter turns on a current to the electric plates. The drop's upward speed (obtained by timing its rise) is related to its mass-to-charge ratio, from which you can calculate the charge on the electron.

From his experiments, Thomson could also calculate the ratio of the electron's mass, m_e, to its electric charge, e. He could not obtain either the mass or the charge separately, however. In 1909 the U.S. physicist Robert Millikan performed a series of ingenious experiments in which he obtained the charge on the electron by observing how a charged drop of oil falls in the presence and in the absence of an electric field (Figure 2.6). From this type of experiment, the charge on the electron is found to be 1.602×10^{-19} coulombs (the *coulomb*, abbreviated C, is a unit of electric charge). If you use this charge with the most recent value of the mass-to-charge ratio of the electron, you obtain an electron mass of 9.109×10^{-31} kg, which is more than 1800 times smaller than the mass of the lightest atom (hydrogen). This shows quite clearly that the electron is indeed a subatomic particle.

The Nuclear Model of the Atom

Ernest Rutherford (1871–1937), a British physicist, put forth the idea of the *nuclear model* of the atom in 1911, based on experiments done in his laboratory by Hans Geiger and Ernest Marsden. These scientists observed the effect of bombarding thin gold foil (and other metal foils) with alpha radiation from radioactive substances such as uranium (Figure 2.7). Rutherford had already shown that alpha rays consist of positively charged particles. Geiger and Marsden found that most of the alpha particles passed through a metal foil as though nothing were there, but a few (about 1 in 8000) were scattered at large angles and sometimes almost backward.

According to Rutherford's model, most of the mass of the atom (99.95% or more) is concentrated in a positively charged center, or nucleus, around which the negatively charged electrons move. Although most of the mass of an atom is in its nucleus, the nucleus occupies only a very small portion of the space of the atom. Nuclei have diameters of about 10^{-15} m (10^{-3} pm), whereas atomic diameters are about 10^{-10} m (100 pm), a hundred thousand times larger. If you were to use a golf ball to represent the nucleus, the atom would be about 3 miles in diameter!

FIGURE 2.7

Alpha-particle scattering from metal foils
Alpha radiation is produced by a radioactive source and formed into a beam by a lead plate with a hole in it. (Lead absorbs the radiation.) Scattered alpha particles are made visible by a zinc sulfide screen, which emits tiny flashes where particles strike it. A movable microscope is used for viewing the flashes.

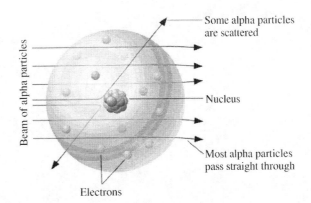

FIGURE 2.8 ▶

Representation of the scattering of alpha particles by a gold foil
Most of the alpha particles pass through the foil barely deflected. A few, however, collide with gold nuclei and are deflected at large angles. (The relative sizes of nuclei are smaller than can be drawn here.)

The nuclear model easily explains the results of bombarding gold and other metal foils with alpha particles. Alpha particles are much lighter than gold atoms. (Alpha particles are helium nuclei.) Most of the alpha particles pass through the metal atoms of the foil, undeflected by the lightweight electrons. When an alpha particle does happen to hit a metal-atom nucleus, however, it is scattered at a wide angle because it is deflected by the massive, positively charged nucleus (Figure 2.8).

Concept Check 2.2

What would be a feasible model for the atom if Geiger and Marsden had found that 7999 out of 8000 alpha particles were deflected back at the alpha-particle source?

2.3 | Nuclear Structure; Isotopes

The nucleus of an atom also has a structure; the nucleus is composed of two different kinds of particles, protons and neutrons. The type of alpha-particle scattering experiment that led to the nuclear model of the atom was also instrumental in clarifying this structure of the nucleus.

An important property of the nucleus is its electric charge. One way to determine the value of the positive charge of a nucleus is by analyzing the distribution of alpha particles scattered from a metal foil; other experiments also provide the nuclear charge. ◀ From such experiments, researchers discovered that each element has a unique nuclear charge that is an integer multiple of the magnitude of the electron charge. This integer, which is characteristic of an element, is called the *atomic number* (Z). A hydrogen atom nucleus, whose magnitude of charge equals that of the electron, has the smallest atomic number, which is 1.

In 1919, Rutherford discovered that hydrogen nuclei, or what we now call protons, form when alpha particles strike some of the lighter elements, such as nitrogen. A **proton** is *a nuclear particle having a positive charge equal to that of the electron and a mass more than 1800 times that of the electron.* When an alpha particle collides with a nitrogen atom, a proton may be knocked out of the nitrogen nucleus. The protons in a nucleus give the nucleus its positive charge.

The **atomic number** (Z) is therefore *the number of protons in the nucleus of an atom.* Because you can determine the atomic number experimentally, you can determine unambiguously whether or not a sample is a pure element or if perhaps you have discovered a new element. We can now state the definition of an element with more precision than we could in Section 2.1. An **element** is *a substance whose*

The simplest way to obtain the nuclear charge is by analyzing the x rays emitted by the element when irradiated with cathode rays. This is discussed in the essay at the end of Section 8.2.

ChemWork: Components of the Atom

ChemWork: Nuclear Particles

ChemWork: Atomic Who Am I?

TABLE 2.1	Properties of the Electron, Proton, and Neutron			
Particle	Mass (kg)	Charge (C)	Mass (amu)*	Charge (e)
Electron	9.10939×10^{-31}	-1.60218×10^{-19}	0.00055	-1
Proton	1.67262×10^{-27}	$+1.60218 \times 10^{-19}$	1.00728	$+1$
Neutron	1.67493×10^{-27}	0	1.00866	0

*The atomic mass unit (amu) equals 1.66054×10^{-27} kg; it is defined in Section 2.4.

atoms all have the same atomic number. The inside back cover of the book lists the elements and their atomic numbers (see the Table of Atomic Numbers and Atomic Masses).

The neutron was also discovered by alpha-particle scattering experiments. When beryllium metal is irradiated with alpha rays, a strongly penetrating radiation is obtained from the metal. In 1932 the British physicist James Chadwick (1891–1974) showed that this penetrating radiation consists of neutral particles, or neutrons. The **neutron** is *a nuclear particle having a mass almost identical to that of the proton but no electric charge.* When beryllium nuclei are struck by alpha particles, neutrons are knocked out. Table 2.1 compares the masses and charges of the electron and the two nuclear particles, the proton and the neutron.

Now consider the nucleus of some atom, say of the naturally occurring sodium atom. The nucleus contains 11 protons and 12 neutrons. Thus, the charge on the sodium nucleus is $+11e$, which we usually write as simply $+11$, meaning $+11$ units of electron charge e. Similarly, the nucleus of a naturally occurring aluminum atom contains 13 protons and 14 neutrons; the charge on the nucleus is $+13$.

We characterize a nucleus by its atomic number (Z) and its mass number (A). The **mass number** (A) is *the total number of protons and neutrons in a nucleus.* The nucleus of the naturally occurring sodium atom has an atomic number of 11 and a mass number of 23 (11 + 12).

A **nuclide** is *an atom characterized by a definite atomic number and mass number.* The shorthand notation for any nuclide consists of the symbol of the element with the atomic number written as a subscript on the left and the mass number as a superscript on the left. You write the *nuclide symbol* for the naturally occurring sodium nuclide as follows:

$$\text{Mass number} \longrightarrow {}^{23}_{11}\text{Na} \longleftarrow \text{Atomic number}$$

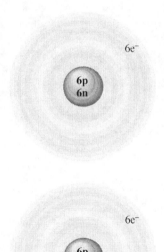

FIGURE 2.9 ▲

A representation of two isotopes of carbon
The drawing shows the basic particles making up the carbon-12 and carbon-13 isotopes. (The relative sizes of the nuclei are much exaggerated here.)

Isotopes were first suspected in about 1912 when chemically identical elements with different atomic masses were found in radioactive materials. The most convincing evidence, however, came from the mass spectrometer, discussed in Section 2.4.

An atom is normally electrically neutral, so it has as many electrons about its nucleus as the nucleus has protons; that is, the number of electrons in a neutral atom equals its atomic number. A sodium atom has a nucleus of charge $+11$, and around this nucleus are 11 electrons (with a charge of -11, giving the atom a charge of 0).

All nuclei of the atoms of a particular element have the same atomic number, but the nuclei may have different mass numbers. **Isotopes** are *atoms whose nuclei have the same atomic number but different mass numbers; that is, the nuclei have the same number of protons but different numbers of neutrons.* Sodium has only one naturally occurring isotope, which we denote by the same symbol we used for the nuclide (${}^{23}_{11}\text{Na}$); we also call the isotope sodium-23. Naturally occurring oxygen is a mixture of isotopes; it contains 99.759% oxygen-16, 0.037% oxygen-17, and 0.204% oxygen-18. <

Figure 2.9 may help you to visualize the relationship among the different subatomic particles in the isotopes of an element. The size of the nucleus as represented

ChemWork: Identifying Isotopes

ChemWork: Elementary Atomic Structure

in the figure is very much exaggerated in order to show the numbers of protons and neutrons. In fact, the space taken up by the nucleus is minuscule compared with the region occupied by electrons. Electrons, although extremely light particles, move throughout relatively large diffuse regions, or "shells," about the nucleus of an atom.

| **Example 2.1** | Writing Nuclide Symbols |

What is the nuclide symbol for a nucleus that contains 38 protons and 50 neutrons?

Problem Strategy To solve this problem, we need to keep in mind that the number of protons in the nucleus (the atomic number) is what uniquely identifies an element and that the mass number is the sum of the protons and neutrons.

Solution From the Table of Atomic Numbers and Atomic Masses on the inside back cover of this book,

you will note that the element with atomic number 38 is strontium, symbol Sr. The mass number is 38 + 50 = 88. The symbol is $^{88}_{38}$**Sr.**

Answer Check When writing elemental symbols, as you have done here, make sure that you always capitalize *only* the first letter of the symbol.

Exercise 2.1 A nucleus consists of 17 protons and 18 neutrons. What is its nuclide symbol?

An alternative example is provided in the Instructor's Resource Manual.

■ See Problems 2.47 and 2.48.

Experiments in General Chemistry, 2, "Isotopes and Mass Spectroscopy."

Some variation of isotopic composition occurs in a number of elements, and this limits the significant figures in their average atomic masses.

FIGURE 2.10 ▲

A mass spectrometer
This instrument measures the masses of atoms and molecules.

Dalton had assumed the formula for water to be HO. Using this formula and accurate data, he would have obtained 7.9367 for the relative atomic weight of oxygen.

2.4 Atomic Masses

A central feature of Dalton's atomic theory was the idea that an atom of an element has a characteristic mass. Now we know that a naturally occurring element may be a mixture of isotopes, each isotope having its own characteristic mass. However, the percentages of the different isotopes in most naturally occurring elements have remained essentially constant over time and in most cases are independent of the origin of the element. Thus, what Dalton actually calculated were *average* atomic masses (actually average *relative* masses, as we will discuss). Since you normally work with naturally occurring mixtures of elements (whether in pure form or as compounds), it is indeed these average atomic masses that you need in chemical work. <

Relative Atomic Masses

Dalton could not weigh individual atoms. What he could do was find the average mass of one atom relative to the average mass of another. We will refer to these relative atomic masses as *atomic masses*. To see how Dalton obtained his atomic masses, imagine that you burn hydrogen gas in oxygen. The product of this reaction is water, a compound of hydrogen and oxygen. By experiment, you find that 1.0000 gram of hydrogen reacts with 7.9367 g of oxygen to form water. To obtain the atomic mass of oxygen (relative to hydrogen), you need to know the relative numbers of hydrogen atoms and oxygen atoms in water. As you might imagine, Dalton had difficulty with this. Today we know that water contains two atoms of hydrogen for every atom of oxygen. So the atomic mass of oxygen is 2 × 7.9367 = 15.873 times that of the mass of the average hydrogen atom. <

Atomic Mass Units

Dalton's hydrogen-based atomic mass scale was eventually replaced by a scale based on oxygen and then, in 1961, by the present carbon-12 mass scale. This scale depends on measurements of atomic mass by an instrument called a *mass spectrometer* (Figure 2.10), which we will describe briefly later in this section. You make accurate

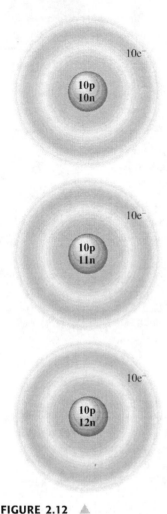

FIGURE 2.12

Representations of the three naturally occurring isotopes of Ne
Top to bottom: Ne-20, Ne-21, and Ne-22. Ne-20 is the most abundant isotope.

FIGURE 2.11

Diagram of a simple mass spectrometer, showing the separation of neon isotopes
Neon gas enters an evacuated chamber, where neon atoms form positive ions when they collide with electrons. Positively charged neon atoms, Ne^+, are accelerated from this region by the negative grid and pass between the poles of a magnet. The beam of positively charged atoms is split into three beams by the magnetic field according to the mass-to-charge ratios. The three beams then travel to a detector at the end of the tube. (The detector is shown here as a photographic plate; in modern spectrometers, the detector is electronic, and the mass positions are recorded on a computer.)

measurements of mass on this instrument by comparing the mass of an atom to the mass of a particular atom chosen as a standard. On the present atomic mass scale, the carbon-12 isotope is chosen as the standard and is arbitrarily assigned a mass of exactly 12 atomic mass units. One **atomic mass unit (amu)** is, therefore, *a mass unit equal to exactly one-twelfth the mass of a carbon-12 atom.*

On this modern scale, the **atomic mass** of an element is *the average atomic mass for the naturally occurring element, expressed in atomic mass units.* A complete table of atomic masses appears on the inside back cover of this book. (Atomic mass is sometimes referred to as atomic weight. Although the use of the term *weight* in *atomic weight* is not strictly correct, it is sanctioned by convention to mean "average atomic mass.")

Mass Spectrometry and Atomic Masses

Earlier we noted that you use a mass spectrometer to obtain accurate masses of atoms. The earliest mass spectrometers measured the mass-to-charge ratios of positively charged atoms using the same ideas that Thomson used to study electrons. Modern instruments may use other techniques, but all measure the mass-to-charge ratios of positively charged atoms (and molecules as well). Figure 2.11 shows a simplified sketch of a mass spectrometer running a neon sample (see the essay on page 98 for a discussion of modern mass spectrometry).

Mass spectrometers produce a *mass spectrum*, which shows the relative numbers of atoms for various masses. If a sample of neon, which has the three isotopes depicted in Figure 2.12, is introduced into a mass spectrometer, it produces the mass spectrum shown in Figure 2.13. This mass spectrum gives us all of the information we need to calculate the atomic mass of neon: the masses of all of the isotopes (neon-20, neon-21, and neon-22) and the relative number, or fractional abundance, of each isotope. The **fractional abundance** of an isotope is *the fraction of the total*

FIGURE 2.13

The mass spectrum of neon
Neon is separated into its isotopes Ne-20, Ne-21, and Ne-22. The height at each mass peak is proportional to the fraction of that isotope in the element.

number of atoms that is composed of a particular isotope. The fractional abundances of the neon isotopes in naturally occurring neon are neon-20, 0.9051; neon-21, 0.0027; and neon-22, 0.0922.

You calculate the atomic mass of an element by multiplying each isotopic mass by its fractional abundance and summing the values. If you do that for neon using the data given here, you will obtain 20.179 amu. The next example illustrates the calculation in full for chromium.

Example 2.2 | Determining Atomic Mass from Isotopic Masses and Fractional Abundances

Chromium, Cr, has the following isotopic masses and fractional abundances:

Mass Number	Isotopic Mass (amu)	Fractional Abundance
50	49.9461	0.0435
52	51.9405	0.8379
53	52.9407	0.0950
54	53.9389	0.0236

What is the atomic mass of chromium?

Problem Strategy The type of average used to calculate the atomic mass of an element is similar to the "average" an instructor might use to obtain a student's final grade in a class. Suppose the student has a total exam grade of 76 and a total laboratory grade of 84. The instructor decides to give a weight of 70% to the exams and 30% to the laboratory. How would the instructor calculate the final grade? He or she would multiply each type of grade by its weight factor and add the results:

$$(76 \times 0.70) + (84 \times 0.30) = 78$$

The final grade is closer to the exam grade, because the instructor chose to give the exam grade greater weight.

An alternative example is provided in the Instructor's Resource Manual. *Experiments in General Chemistry, 2,* "Isotopes and Mass Spectrometry."

Solution Multiply each isotopic mass by its fractional abundance, then sum:

$$49.9461 \text{ amu} \times 0.0435 = 2.17 \text{ amu}$$
$$51.9405 \text{ amu} \times 0.8379 = 43.52 \text{ amu}$$
$$52.9407 \text{ amu} \times 0.0950 = 5.03 \text{ amu}$$
$$53.9389 \text{ amu} \times 0.0236 = \underline{1.27 \text{ amu}}$$
$$51.99 \text{ amu}$$

The atomic mass of chromium is **51.99 amu.**

Answer Check The average mass (atomic mass) should be near the mass of the isotope with greatest abundance: in this case, 51.9405 amu with fractional abundance of 0.8379. This provides a quick check on your answer to this type of problem; any "answer" that is far from this will be incorrect.

Exercise 2.2 Chlorine consists of the following isotopes:

Isotope	Isotopic Mass (amu)	Fractional Abundance
Chlorine-35	34.96885	0.75771
Chlorine-37	36.96590	0.24229

What is the atomic mass of chlorine?

■ See Problems 2.51, 2.52, 2.53, and 2.54.

2.5 | Periodic Table of the Elements

The relationship between the periodic table and electron configurations and the periodicity of atomic properties are discussed in Chapter 8.

ChemWork: Naming Elements

ChemWork: Symbols for Elements

In 1869 the Russian chemist Dmitri Mendeleev (1834–1907) (Figure 2.14) and the German chemist J. Lothar Meyer (1830–1895), working independently, made similar discoveries. They found that when they arranged the elements in order of atomic mass, they could place them in horizontal rows, one row under the other, so that the elements in each vertical column have similar properties. *A tabular arrangement of elements in rows and columns, highlighting the regular repetition of properties of the elements*, is called a **periodic table.**

FIGURE 2.14 ▲

Dmitri Ivanovich Mendeleev (1834–1907)
Mendeleev constructed a periodic table as part of his effort to systematize chemistry. He received many international honors for his work, but his reception in czarist Russia was mixed. He had pushed for political reforms and made many enemies as a result.

FIGURE 2.15 ▼

A modern form of the periodic table
This table is also given on the inside front cover of the book.

Eventually, more accurate determinations of atomic masses revealed discrepancies in this ordering of the elements. However, in the early part of this century, it was shown that the elements are characterized by their atomic numbers, rather than atomic masses. When the elements in the periodic table are ordered by atomic number, such discrepancies vanish.

A modern version of the periodic table, with the elements arranged by atomic number, is shown in Figure 2.15 (see also inside front cover). Each entry lists the atomic number, atomic symbol, and atomic mass of an element. This is a convenient way of tabulating such information, and you should become familiar with using the periodic table for that purpose. As we develop the subject matter of chemistry throughout the text, you will see how useful the periodic table is.

Periods and Groups

The basic structure of the periodic table is its division into rows and columns, or periods and groups. A **period** consists of *the elements in any one horizontal row of the periodic table*. A **group** consists of *the elements in any one column of the periodic table*.

The first period of elements consists of only hydrogen (H) and helium (He). The second period has 8 elements, beginning with lithium (Li) and ending with neon (Ne). There is then another period of 8 elements, and this is followed by a period having 18 elements, beginning with potassium (K) and ending with krypton (Kr). The fifth period also has 18 elements. The sixth period actually consists of 32 elements, but in order for the row to fit on a page, part of it appears at the bottom of the table. Otherwise the table would have to be expanded, with the additional elements placed after barium (Ba, atomic number 56). The seventh period, though not complete, also has some of its elements placed as a row at the bottom of the table.

The groups are usually numbered. The numbering frequently seen in North America labels the groups with Roman numerals and A's and B's. In Europe a similar convention has been used, but some columns have the A's and B's interchanged. To eliminate this confusion, the International Union of Pure and Applied Chemistry (IUPAC) suggested a convention in which the columns are numbered 1 to 18. Figure 2.15 shows the traditional North American and the IUPAC conventions. When we refer to an element by its periodic group, we will use the traditional North American convention. The A groups are called *main-group* (or *representative*) *elements;* the B groups are called *transition elements.* The two rows of elements at the bottom of the table are called *inner transition elements* (the first row is referred to as the *lanthanides;* the second row, as the *actinides*).

As noted earlier, the elements in any one group have similar properties. For example, the elements in Group IA, often known as the *alkali metals,* are soft metals that react easily with water. (Hydrogen, a gas, is an exception and might better be put in a group by itself.) Sodium is an alkali metal. So is potassium. The Group VIIA elements, known as *halogens,* are also reactive elements. Chlorine is a halogen. We have already noted its vigorous reaction with sodium. Bromine, which is a red-brown liquid, is another halogen. It too reacts vigorously with sodium.

Metals, Nonmetals, and Metalloids

The elements of the periodic table in Figure 2.15 are divided by a heavy "staircase" line into metals on the left and nonmetals on the right. A **metal** is *a substance or mixture that has a characteristic luster, or shine, and is generally a good conductor of heat and electricity.* Except for mercury, the metallic elements are solids at room temperature (about 20°C). They are more or less *malleable* (can be hammered into sheets) and *ductile* (can be drawn into wire).

A **nonmetal** is *an element that does not exhibit the characteristics of a metal.* Most of the nonmetals are gases (for example, chlorine and oxygen) or solids (for example, phosphorus and sulfur). The solid nonmetals are usually hard, brittle substances. Bromine is the only liquid nonmetal.

Most of the elements bordering the staircase line in the periodic table (Figure 2.15) are metalloids, or semimetals. A **metalloid,** or **semimetal,** is *an element having both metallic and nonmetallic properties.* These elements, such as silicon (Si) and germanium (Ge), are usually good *semiconductors*—elements that, when pure, are poor conductors of electricity at room temperature but become moderately good conductors at higher temperatures. <

When these pure semiconductor elements have small amounts of certain other elements added to them (a process called doping), they become very good conductors of electricity. Semiconductors are the critical materials in solid-state electronic devices.

Exercise 2.3 By referring to the periodic table (Figure 2.15 or inside front cover), identify the group and period to which each of the following elements belongs. Then decide whether the element is a metal, nonmetal, or metalloid.

a. Se   b. Cs   c. Fe   d. Cu   e. Br

■ See Problems 2.57 and 2.58.

Concept Check 2.3

Consider the elements He, Ne, and Ar. Can you come up with a reason why they are in the same group in the periodic table?

A Chemist Looks at . . .

frontiers

Thirty Seconds on the Island of Stability

It appears that scientists have now been on the "Island of Stability"—for at least 30 seconds. In recent years, the island of stability has attracted nuclear scientists the way Mount Everest has attracted mountain climbers. Like mountain climbers, scientists have wanted to surmount their own tallest peak—discovery of the relatively stable, superheavy nuclide at the peak of stability that is surrounded by foothills comprised of less stable nuclides. Discovering the superheavy nuclide at the peak would also mean discovering a new element—a task that has had its allure since Lavoisier gave currency to the concept of elements in the late eighteenth century.

Theoretical physicists predicted the existence of the island of stability, centered at element 114 with mass number 298, in the 1960s. The term *stability* refers here to that of the atomic nucleus. An unstable nucleus tends to fall apart by radioactive decay—a piece spontaneously flies off the nucleus, leaving a different one behind. Approximately 275 nuclides are completely stable, or nonradioactive. All of these nuclides have atomic numbers (or

numbers of protons) no greater than 83 (the atomic number for the element bismuth). Beyond bismuth, all elements are radioactive and become increasingly unstable. In fact, none of the original, primeval elements past uranium (element 92)—the *transuranium* elements—exists any longer; they have long since vanished by radioactive decay. Scientists have made transuranium elements in the laboratory, however.

In February 1996, for example, scientists at Darmstadt, Germany, produced a few atoms of element 112 by bombarding a lead target with zinc atoms. Each atom of element 112 lasted only about 240 microseconds. We can represent the result by a nuclear equation, which is similar to a chemical equation (described at the end of the chapter).

$$^{70}_{30}\text{Zn} + ^{208}_{82}\text{Pb} \longrightarrow ^{277}_{112}\text{Uub} + ^{1}_{0}\text{n}$$

We introduced the nuclide symbols used here in Section 2.3. The equation is a summary of the following. A high-speed zinc-70 nucleus (as an ion, which is an electrically charged atom) smashes into a lead-208 target where, as the arrow denotes, it yields new products, a nucleus of element 112 (mass number 277) and a neutron, denoted $^{1}_{0}\text{n}$. Element 112 has the provisional name of ununbium until several other laboratories can reproduce the work, after

Chemical Substances: Formulas and Names

Atomic theory has developed steadily since Dalton's time and has become the cornerstone of chemistry. It results in an enormous simplification: all of the millions of compounds we know today are composed of the atoms of just a few elements. Now we look more closely at how we describe the composition and structure of chemical substances in terms of atoms.

2.6 | Chemical Formulas; Molecular and Ionic Substances

The **chemical formula** of a substance is *a notation that uses atomic symbols with numerical subscripts to convey the relative proportions of atoms of the different elements in the substance.* Consider the formula of aluminum oxide, Al_2O_3. This means that the compound is composed of aluminum atoms and oxygen atoms in the ratio 2 : 3. Consider the formula for sodium chloride, NaCl. When no subscript is written for a symbol, it is assumed to be 1. Therefore, the formula NaCl means which the discoverer may name it. Figure 2.16 shows the ion accelerator (UNILAC) that produced the zinc ions for this experiment.

Scientists in Dubna, north of Moscow in Russia, and their American collaborators from Lawrence Livermore Laboratory in California produced one atom of element 114 (provisional name ununquadium) in December 1998, placing scientists on the shore of the island of stability. In this experiment, scientists bombarded a plutonium-244 target with calcium-48 atoms.

$$^{48}_{20}\text{Ca} + ^{244}_{94}\text{Pu} \longrightarrow ^{289}_{114}\text{Uuq} + 3^{1}_{0}\text{n}$$

The atom of element 114 lasted about 30 seconds. While a 30-second lifetime may seem brief, it is many times longer than that seen in the previously discovered element 112. This same group of scientists has recently reported (in 2001) the discovery of element 116 (ununhexium).

As a rather bizarre footnote to this story, the "discovery" of element 118 was reported in 1999 by scientists at Lawrence Berkeley National Laboratory in California. Two years later, these scientists reported that they were unable to reproduce their results. The laboratory fired one of the scientists, who they alleged had faked the data. Fortunately, fraud is rather unusual in chemistry; when it does occur, it is discovered, as in this case, when the work cannot be reproduced. Notably, element 118 was rediscovered in 2006 by the same Russian and American team who discovered elements 114 and 116, bringing scientists one step closer to the island of stability.

FIGURE 2.16 ▲

Within the UNILAC ion accelerator
The accelerator consists of a series of electrodes arranged one after the other in a copper-plated steel container. Each electrode accelerates the ion. Eventually, the ion gains sufficient speed, and therefore energy, to cause its nucleus to fuse on collision with a target atom nucleus giving a new nucleus.

■ See Problems 2.131 and 2.132.

FIGURE 2.17 ▲

Sodium chloride model
This model of a sodium chloride crystal illustrates the 1 : 1 packing of the Na^+ and Cl^- ions.

Another way to understand the large numbers of molecules involved in relatively small quantities of matter is to consider 1 g of water (about one-fifth teaspoon). It contains 3.3×10^{22} water molecules. If you had a penny for every molecule in this quantity of water, the height of your stack of pennies would be about 300 million times the distance from the earth to the sun.

that the compound is composed of sodium atoms and chlorine atoms in the ratio 1 : 1 (Figure 2.17).

Additional information may be conveyed by different kinds of chemical formulas. To understand this, we need to look briefly at two main types of substances: molecular and ionic.

Molecular Substances

A **molecule** is *a definite group of atoms that are chemically bonded together—that is, tightly connected by attractive forces.* The nature of these strong forces is discussed in Chapters 9 and 10. A *molecular substance* is a substance that is composed of molecules, all of which are alike. The molecules in such a substance are so small that even extremely minute samples contain tremendous numbers of them. One billionth (10^{-9}) of a drop of water, for example, contains about 2 trillion (2×10^{12}) water molecules. ◄

A **molecular formula** *gives the exact number of different atoms of an element in a molecule.* The hydrogen peroxide molecule contains two hydrogen atoms and two oxygen atoms chemically bonded. Therefore, its molecular formula is H_2O_2. Other simple molecular substances are water, H_2O; ammonia, NH_3; carbon dioxide, CO_2; and ethanol (ethyl alcohol), C_2H_6O. In Chapter 3, you will see how we determine such formulas.

FIGURE 2.18 ▷

Examples of molecular and structural formulas, molecular models, and electrostatic potential maps
Three common molecules—water, ammonia, and ethanol—are shown. The electrostatic potential map representation at the bottom of the figure illustrates the distribution of electrons in the molecule using a color spectrum. Colors range from red (relatively high electron density) all the way to blue (low electron density).

	Water	Ammonia	Ethanol
Molecular formula	H_2O	NH_3	C_2H_6O

Structural formula	H—O—H	H—N—H
		    |
		    H
			H H
			| |
			H—C—C—O—H
			| |
			H H

Molecular model (ball-and-stick type)			
Molecular model (space-filling type)			
Electrostatic potential map			

FIGURE 2.19 ▲

Molecular models of some elementary substances
Top to bottom: Chlorine, Cl_2; white phosphorus, P_4; and sulfur, S_8.

The atoms in a molecule are not simply piled together randomly. Rather, the atoms are chemically bonded in a definite way. A *structural formula* is a chemical formula that shows how the atoms are bonded to one another in a molecule. For example, it is known that each of the hydrogen atoms in the water molecule is bonded to the oxygen atom. Thus, the structural formula of water is H—O—H. A line joining two atomic symbols in such a formula represents the chemical bond connecting the atoms. Figure 2.18 shows some structural formulas. Structural formulas are sometimes condensed in writing. For example, the structural formula of ethanol may be written CH_3CH_2OH or C_2H_5OH, depending on the detail you want to convey.

The atoms in a molecule are not only connected in definite ways but exhibit definite spatial arrangements as well. Chemists often construct molecular models as an aid in visualizing the shapes and sizes of molecules. Figure 2.18 shows molecular models for several compounds. While the ball-and-stick type of model shows the bonds and bond angles clearly, the space-filling type gives a more realistic feeling of the space occupied by the atoms. Chemists also use computer-generated models of molecules, which can be produced in a variety of forms.

Some elements are molecular substances and are represented by molecular formulas. Chlorine, for example, is a molecular substance and has the formula Cl_2, each molecule being composed of two chlorine atoms bonded together. Sulfur consists of molecules composed of eight atoms; its molecular formula is S_8. Helium and neon are composed of isolated atoms; their formulas are He and Ne, respectively. Other elements, such as carbon (in the form of graphite or diamond), do not have a simple molecular structure but consist of a very large, indefinite number of atoms bonded together. These elements are represented simply by their atomic symbols. (An important exception is a form of carbon called buckminsterfullerene, which was discovered in 1985 and has the molecular formula C_{60}.) Models of some elementary substances are shown in Figure 2.19.

An important class of molecular substances is the polymers. **Polymers** are *very large molecules that are made up of a number of smaller molecules repeatedly linked together.* **Monomers** are *the small molecules that are linked together to form the polymer.* A good analogy for the formation of polymers from monomers is that of making a chain of paper clips. Say you have boxes of red, blue, and yellow paper clips.

Each paper clip represents a monomer. You can make a large chain of paper clips, representing the polymer, with a variety of patterns and repeating units. One chain might involve a repeating pattern of two red, three yellow, and one blue. Another chain might consist of only blue paper clips. Just like the paper clips, the creation of a particular polymer in a laboratory involves controlling both the monomers that are being linked together and the linkage pattern.

Polymers are both natural and synthetic. Hard plastic soda bottles are made from chemically linking two different monomers in an alternating pattern. Wool and silk are natural polymers of amino acids linked by peptide bonds. Nylon® for fabrics, Kevlar® for bulletproof vests, and Nomex® for flame-retardant clothing all contain a CONH linkage. Plastics and rubbers are also polymers that are made from carbon- and hydrogen-containing monomers. Even the Teflon® coating on cookware is a polymer that is the result of linking CF_2CF_2 monomers (Figure 2.20). From these examples, it is obvious that polymers are very important molecular materials that we use every day in a wide variety of applications. For more on the chemistry of polymers, refer to Chapter 24.

Ionic Substances

Although many substances are molecular, others are composed of ions (pronounced "eye'-ons"). An **ion** is *an electrically charged particle obtained from an atom or chemically bonded group of atoms by adding or removing electrons*. Sodium chloride is a substance made up of ions.

Although isolated atoms are normally electrically neutral and therefore contain equal numbers of positive and negative charges, during the formation of certain compounds atoms can become ions. Metal atoms tend to lose electrons, whereas nonmetals tend to gain electrons. When a metal atom such as sodium and a nonmetal atom such as chlorine approach one another, an electron can transfer from the metal atom to the nonmetal atom to produce ions.

An atom that picks up an extra electron becomes *a negatively charged ion*, called an **anion** (pronounced "an'-ion"). An atom that loses an electron becomes *a positively charged ion*, called a **cation** ("cat'-ion"). A sodium atom, for example, can lose an electron to form a sodium cation (denoted Na^+). A chlorine atom can gain an electron to form a chloride anion (denoted Cl^-). A calcium atom can lose two electrons to form a calcium cation, denoted Ca^{2+}. Note that the positive-two charge on the ion is indicated by a superscript $2+$.

Some ions consist of two or more atoms chemically bonded but having an excess or deficiency of electrons so that the unit has an electric charge. An example is the sulfate ion, SO_4^{2-}. The superscript $2-$ indicates an excess of two electrons on the group of atoms.

An **ionic compound** is *a compound composed of cations and anions*. Sodium chloride consists of equal numbers of sodium ions, Na^+, and chloride ions, Cl^-. The strong attraction between positive and negative charges holds the ions together in a regular arrangement in space. For example, in sodium chloride, each Na^+ ion is surrounded by six Cl^- ions, and each Cl^- ion is surrounded by six Na^+ ions. The result is a *crystal*, which is a kind of solid having a regular three-dimensional arrangement of atoms, molecules, or (as in the case of sodium chloride) ions. Figure 2.21 shows sodium chloride crystals and two types of models used to depict the arrangement of the ions in the crystal. The number of ions in an individual sodium chloride crystal determines the size of the crystal.

The formula of an ionic compound is written by giving the smallest possible integer number of different ions in the substance, except that the charges on the ions are omitted so that the formulas merely indicate the atoms involved. For example, sodium chloride contains equal numbers of Na^+ and Cl^- ions. The formula is written NaCl (not Na^+Cl^-). Iron(III) sulfate is a compound consisting of iron(III) ions, Fe^{3+}, and sulfate ions, SO_4^{2-}, in the ratio 2 : 3. The formula is written $Fe_2(SO_4)_3$, in which parentheses enclose the formula of an ion composed of more than one atom (again, omitting ion charges); parentheses are used only when there are two or more such ions.

FIGURE 2.20 ▲

$F_2C{=}CF_2$ monomer and Teflon®

Top: Model of the monomer used to make Teflon®, CF_2CF_2. *Center:* Model showing linkage of CF_2CF_2 monomers that make Teflon®. *Bottom:* Pan with Teflon® coating.

Ionic crystals: A simple and safe lecture demonstration of the preparation of NaI from its elements. *J. Chem. Educ.* 77 (2000): 619.

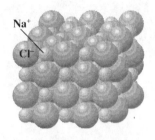

Na⁺

Cl⁻

Cl⁻   Na⁺

FIGURE 2.21

The sodium chloride crystal
Left: A photograph showing crystals of sodium chloride. *Center:* A model of a portion of a crystal detailing the regular arrangement of sodium ions and chloride ions. Each sodium ion is surrounded by six chloride ions, and each chloride ion is surrounded by six sodium ions. *Right:* A model highlighting the packing arrangement of the sodium and chloride ions in a solid sodium chloride crystal.

Although ionic substances do not contain molecules, we can speak of the smallest unit of such a substance. The **formula unit** of a substance is *the group of atoms or ions explicitly symbolized in the formula.* For example, the formula unit of water, H_2O, is the H_2O molecule. The formula unit of iron(III) sulfate, $Fe_2(SO_4)_3$, consists of two Fe^{3+} ions and three SO_4^{2-} ions. The formula unit is the smallest unit of such substances.

All substances, including ionic compounds, are electrically neutral. You can use this fact to obtain the formula of an ionic compound, given the formulas of the ions. This is illustrated in the following example.

Example 2.3 | Writing an Ionic Formula, Given the Ions

a. Chromium(III) oxide is used as a green paint pigment (Figure 2.22). It is a compound composed of Cr^{3+} and O^{2-} ions. What is the formula of chromium(III) oxide?

b. Strontium oxide is a compound composed of Sr^{2+} and O^{2-} ions. Write the formula of this compound.

Problem Strategy   Because a compound is neutral, the sum of positive and negative charges equals zero. Consider the ionic compound $CaCl_2$, which consists of one Ca^{2+} ion and two Cl^- ions. The sum of the charges is

$$\underbrace{1 \times (+2)}_{\text{Positive charge}} + \underbrace{2 \times (-1)}_{\text{Negative charge}} = 0$$

An alternative example is provided in the Instructor's Resource Manual.

FIGURE 2.22 ▲

Chromium(III) oxide
The compound is used as a green paint pigment.

(continued)

(continued)

Note that the number of calcium ions in $CaCl_2$ equals the magnitude of charge on the chloride ion (1), whereas the number of chloride ions in $CaCl_2$ equals the magnitude of charge on the calcium ion (2). In general, you use the magnitude of charge on one ion to obtain the subscript for the other ion. You may need to simplify the formula you obtain this way so that it expresses the simplest ratio of ions.

Solution   a. You can achieve electrical neutrality by taking as many cations as there are units of charge on the anion and as many anions as there are units of charge on the cation. Two Cr^{3+} ions have a total charge of 6+, and three O^{2-} ions have a total charge of 6−, giving the combination a net charge of zero. The simplest ratio of Cr^{3+} to O^{2-} is 2 : 3, and the formula is Cr_2O_3. Note that the charge (without its sign) on one ion becomes the subscript of the other ion.

$$Cr^{3+} \quad O^{2-} \qquad or \qquad Cr_2O_3$$

b. You see that equal numbers of Sr^{2+} and O^{2-} ions will give a neutral compound. Thus, the formula is SrO. If you use the units of charge to find the subscripts, you get

$$Sr^{2+} \quad O^{2-} \qquad or \qquad Sr_2O_2$$

The final formula is **SrO,** because this gives the simplest ratio of ions.

Answer Check   When writing ionic formulas, always make certain that the formula that you write reflects the smallest whole-number ratio of the ions. For example, using the technique presented in this example, Pb^{4+} and O^{2-} combine to give Pb_2O_4; however, the correct formula is PbO_2, which reflects the simplest whole-number ratio of ions.

Exercise 2.4   Potassium chromate is an important compound of chromium (Figure 2.23). It is composed of K^+ and CrO_4^{2-} ions. Write the formula of the compound.

FIGURE 2.23 ▲
Potassium chromate
Many compounds of chromium have bright colors, which is the origin of the name of the element. It comes from the Greek word *chroma,* meaning "color."

■ See Problems 2.75 and 2.76.

2.7 | Organic Compounds

An important class of *molecular substances that contain carbon combined with other elements, such as hydrogen, oxygen, and nitrogen* is **organic compounds.** Organic chemistry is the area of chemistry that is concerned with these compounds (Chapter 23 is devoted to this topic). Historically, organic compounds were restricted to those that could be produced only from living entities and were thought to contain a "vital force" based on their natural origin. The concept of the vital force was disproved in 1828 when a German chemist, Friedrick Wöhler, synthesized urea (a molecular compound in human urine, CH_4N_2O, Figure 2.24) from the molecular compounds ammonia (NH_3) and cyanic acid (HNCO). His work clearly demonstrated that a given compound is exactly the same whether it comes from a living entity or is synthesized.

Organic compounds make up the majority of all known compounds. Since 1957, more than 13 million (60%) of the recorded substances in an international materials registry have been listed as organic. You encounter organic compounds in both living and nonliving materials every day. The proteins, amino acids, enzymes, and DNA that make up your body are all either individual organic molecules or contain organic

FIGURE 2.24 ▲
Molecular model of urea (CH_4N_2O)
Urea was the first organic molecule deliberately synthesized by a chemist from non-organic compounds.

CH$_4$
Methane

C$_2$H$_6$
Ethane

C$_3$H$_8$
Propane

C$_2$H$_2$
Acetylene

C$_6$H$_6$
Benzene

CH$_3$OH
Methanol

CH$_3$CH$_2$OCH$_2$CH$_3$
Diethyl ether

molecules. Table sugar, peanut oil, antibiotic medicines, and methanol (windshield washer) are all examples of organic molecules as well. Organic chemistry and the compounds produced by the reactions of organic molecules are probably responsible for the majority of the materials that currently surround you as you read this page of text.

The simplest organic compounds are hydrocarbons. **Hydrocarbons** are *those compounds containing only hydrogen and carbon.* Common examples include methane (CH$_4$), ethane (C$_2$H$_6$), propane (C$_3$H$_8$), acetylene (C$_2$H$_2$), and benzene (C$_6$H$_6$). Hydrocarbons are used extensively as sources of energy for heating our homes, for powering internal combustion engines, and for generating electricity. They also are the starting materials for most plastics. Much of the mobility and comfort of our current civilization is built on the low cost and availability of hydrocarbons.

The chemistry of organic molecules is often determined by groups of atoms in the molecule that have characteristic chemical properties. A **functional group** is a *reactive portion of a molecule that undergoes predictable reactions.* When you use the term *alcohol* when referring to a molecular compound, you actually are indicating a molecule that contains an —OH functional group. Methyl alcohol has the chemical formula CH$_3$OH. The term *ether* indicates that an organic molecule contains an oxygen atom between two carbon atoms, as in diethyl ether (CH$_3$CH$_2$OCH$_2$CH$_3$). Table 2.2 contains a few examples of organic functional groups along with example compounds.

Chapter 23 contains a much more extensive treatment of organic chemistry. Due to its importance and its relation to living organisms, a substantial part of your future chemistry experience will likely be in the field of organic chemistry.

TABLE 2.2	Examples of Organic Functional Groups		
Functional Group	Name of Functional Group	Example Molecule	Common Use
—OH	Alcohol	Methyl alcohol (CH$_3$OH)	Windshield washer
—O—	Ether	Dimethyl ether (CH$_3$OCH$_3$)	Solvent
—COOH	Carboxylic acid	Acetic acid (CH$_3$COOH)	Acid in vinegar

2.8 | Naming Simple Compounds

ChemWork: Beginning to Name Compounds

ChemWork: Naming Compounds

Before the structural basis of chemical substances became established, compounds were named after people, places, or particular characteristics. Examples are Glauber's salt (sodium sulfate, discovered by J. R. Glauber), sal ammoniac (ammonium chloride, named after the ancient Egyptian deity Ammon from the temple near which the substance was made), and washing soda (sodium carbonate, used for softening wash water). Today several million compounds are known and thousands of new ones are discovered every year. Without a system for naming compounds, coping with this multitude of substances would be a hopeless task. **Chemical nomenclature** is *the systematic naming of chemical compounds.*

Concept Check 2.4

Identify the following compounds as being a hydrocarbon, an alcohol, an ether, or a carboxylic acid.

(a) (b) (c) (d)

If a compound is not classified as organic, as discussed in Section 2.7, it must be inorganic. **Inorganic compounds** are *composed of elements other than carbon.* A few notable exceptions to this classification scheme include carbon monoxide, carbon dioxide, carbonates, and the cyanides; all contain carbon and yet are generally considered to be inorganic.

In this section, we discuss the nomenclature of some simple inorganic compounds. We first look at the naming of ionic compounds. Then, we look at the naming of some simple molecular compounds, including binary molecular compounds (molecular compounds of two elements) and acids. Finally, we look at hydrates of ionic compounds. These substances contain water molecules in loose association with ionic compounds.

Ionic Compounds

Ionic compounds, as we saw in the previous section, are substances composed of ions. Most ionic compounds contain metal and nonmetal atoms—for example, NaCl. (The ammonium salts, such as NH_4Cl, are a prominent exception.) You name an ionic compound by giving the name of the cation followed by the name of the anion. For example,

$$\underbrace{\text{potassium}}_{\substack{\text{cation} \\ \text{name}}} \underbrace{\text{sulfate}}_{\substack{\text{anion} \\ \text{name}}}$$

Before you can name ionic compounds, you need to be able to write and name ions. The simplest ions are monatomic. A **monatomic ion** is *an ion formed from a single atom.* Table 2.3 lists common monatomic ions of the main-group elements. You

TABLE 2.3	**Common Monatomic Ions of the Main-Group Elements***						
	IA	IIA	IIIA	IVA	VA	VIA	VIIA
Period 1							H^-
Period 2	Li^+	Be^{2+}	B	C	N^{3-}	O^{2-}	F^-
Period 3	Na^+	Mg^{2+}	Al^{3+}	Si	P	S^{2-}	Cl^-
Period 4	K^+	Ca^{2+}	Ga^{3+}	Ge	As	Se^{2-}	Br^-
Period 5	Rb^+	Sr^{2+}	In^{3+}	Sn^{2+}	Sb	Te^{2-}	I^-
Period 6	Cs^+	Ba^{2+}	Tl^+, Tl^{3+}	Pb^{2+}	Bi^{3+}		

*Elements shown in color do not normally form compounds having monatomic ions.

may want to look at the table while you read first the rules for predicting the charges on such ions and then the rules for naming the monatomic ions.

Rules for Predicting the Charges on Monatomic Ions

ChemWork: Predicting Ions

ChemWork: Properties of Elements

1. Most of the main-group metallic elements have one monatomic cation with a charge equal to the group number in the periodic table (the Roman numeral). Example: aluminum, in Group IIIA, has a monatomic ion Al^{3+}.

2. Some metallic elements of high atomic number are exceptions to the previous rule; they have more than one cation. These elements have common cations with a charge equal to the group number minus 2, in addition to having a cation with a charge equal to the group number. Example: The common ion of lead is Pb^{2+}. (The group number is 4; the charge is $4 - 2$.) In addition to compounds containing Pb^{2+}, some lead compounds contain Pb^{4+}.

3. Most transition elements form more than one monatomic cation, each with a different charge. Most of these elements have one ion with a charge of +2. Example: Iron has common cations Fe^{2+} and Fe^{3+}. Copper has common cations Cu^{+} and Cu^{2+}.

4. The charge on a monatomic anion for a nonmetallic main-group element equals the group number minus 8. Example: Oxygen has the monatomic anion O^{2-}. (The group number is 6; the charge is $6 - 8$.)

Rules for Naming Monatomic Ions

1. Monatomic cations are named after the element if there is only one such ion. Example: Al^{3+} is called aluminum ion; Na^{+} is called sodium ion.

2. If there is more than one monatomic cation of an element, Rule 1 is not sufficient. The *Stock system* of nomenclature names the cations after the element, as in Rule 1, but follows this by a Roman numeral in parentheses denoting the charge on the ion. Example: Fe^{2+} is called iron(II) ion and Fe^{3+} is called iron(III) ion. <

   In an older system of nomenclature, such ions are named by adding the suffixes *-ous* and *-ic* to a stem name of the element (which may be from the Latin) to indicate the ions of lower and higher charge, respectively. Example: Fe^{2+} is called ferrous ion; Fe^{3+}, ferric ion. Cu^{+} is called cuprous ion; Cu^{2+}, cupric ion.

   Table 2.4 lists some common cations of the transition elements. Most of these elements have more than one ion, so require the Stock nomenclature system or the older suffix system. A few, such as zinc, have only a single ion that is normally encountered, and you usually name them by just the metal name. You would not be wrong, however, if, for example, you named Zn^{2+} as zinc(II) ion.

3. The names of the monatomic anions are obtained from a stem name of the element followed by the suffix *-ide*. Example: Br^{-} is called bromide ion, from the stem name *brom-* for bromine and the suffix *-ide*.

The Roman numeral actually denotes the oxidation state, or oxidation number, of the atom in the compound. For a monatomic ion, the oxidation state equals the charge. Otherwise, the oxidation state is a hypothetical charge assigned in accordance with certain rules; see Section 4.5.

TABLE 2.4	Common Cations of the Transition Elements				
Ion	Ion Name	Ion	Ion Name	Ion	Ion Name
Cr^{3+}	Chromium(III) or chromic	Co^{2+}	Cobalt(II) or cobaltous	Zn^{2+}	Zinc
Mn^{2+}	Manganese(II) or manganous	Ni^{2+}	Nickel(II) or nickel	Ag^{+}	Silver
Fe^{2+}	Iron(II) or ferrous	Cu^{+}	Copper(I) or cuprous	Cd^{2+}	Cadmium
Fe^{3+}	Iron(III) or ferric	Cu^{2+}	Copper(II) or cupric	Hg^{2+}	Mercury(II) or mercuric

TABLE 2.5	Some Common Polyatomic Ions		
Name	**Formula**	**Name**	**Formula**
Mercury(I) or mercurous	Hg_2^{2+}	Permanganate	MnO_4^-
Ammonium	NH_4^+	Nitrite	NO_2^-
Cyanide	CN^-	Nitrate	NO_3^-
Carbonate	CO_3^{2-}	Hydroxide	OH^-
Hydrogen carbonate (or bicarbonate)	HCO_3^-	Peroxide	O_2^{2-}
Acetate	$C_2H_3O_2^-$	Phosphate	PO_4^{3-}
Oxalate	$C_2O_4^{2-}$	Monohydrogen phosphate	HPO_4^{2-}
Hypochlorite	ClO^-	Dihydrogen phosphate	$H_2PO_4^-$
Chlorite	ClO_2^-	Sulfite	SO_3^{2-}
Chlorate	ClO_3^-	Sulfate	SO_4^{2-}
Perchlorate	ClO_4^-	Hydrogen sulfite (or bisulfite)	HSO_3^-
Chromate	CrO_4^{2-}	Hydrogen sulfate (or bisulfate)	HSO_4^-
Dichromate	$Cr_2O_7^{2-}$	Thiosulfate	$S_2O_3^{2-}$

SO_4^{2-}

SO_3^{2-}

FIGURE 2.25 ▲

Sulfate and sulfite oxoanions

Molecular models of the sulfate *(top)* and sulfite *(bottom)* oxoanions.

A **polyatomic ion** is *an ion consisting of two or more atoms chemically bonded together and carrying a net electric charge.* Table 2.5 lists some common polyatomic ions. The first two are cations (Hg_2^{2+} and NH_4^+); the rest are anions. There are no simple rules for writing the formulas of such ions, although you will find it helpful to note a few points.

Most of the ions in Table 2.5 are *oxoanions* (also called *oxyanions*), which consist of oxygen with another element (called the characteristic or central element). Sulfur, for example, forms the oxoanions sulfate ion, SO_4^{2-}, and sulfite ion, SO_3^{2-} (Figure 2.25). The oxoanions in the table are grouped by the characteristic element. For instance, the sulfur ions occur as a group at the end of the table.

Note that the names of the oxoanions have a stem name from the characteristic element, plus a suffix *-ate* or *-ite*. These suffixes denote the relative number of oxygen atoms in the oxoanions of a given characteristic element. The name of the oxoanion with the greater number of oxygen atoms has the suffix *-ate;* the name of the oxoanion with the lesser number of oxygen atoms has the suffix *-ite*. The sulfite ion, SO_3^{2-}, and sulfate ion, SO_4^{2-}, are examples. Another example are the two oxoanions of nitrogen listed in Table 2.5:

NO_2^- ni**tri**te ion
NO_3^- ni**tra**te ion

Unfortunately, the suffixes do not tell you the actual number of oxygen atoms in the oxoanion, only the relative number. However, if you were given the formulas of the two anions, you could name them.

The two suffixes *-ite* and *-ate* are not enough when there are more than two oxoanions of a given characteristic element. The oxoanions of chlorine are an example. Table 2.5 lists four oxoanions of chlorine: ClO^-, ClO_2^-, ClO_3^-, and ClO_4^-. In such cases, two prefixes *hypo-* and *per-* are used in addition to the two suffixes. The two oxoanions with the least number of oxygen atoms (ClO^- and ClO_2^-) are named using the suffix *-ite*, and the prefix *hypo-* is added to the one of these two ions with the fewer oxygen atoms:

ClO^- **hypo**chlo**rite** ion
ClO_2^- chlo**rite** ion

The two oxoanions with the greatest number of oxygen atoms (ClO_3^- and ClO_4^-) are named using the suffix *-ate*, and the prefix *per-* is added to the one of these two ions with the greater number of oxygen atoms:

$$ClO_3^- \quad \text{chlor\underline{ate} ion}$$
$$ClO_4^- \quad \text{per\underline{chlorate} ion}$$

Some of the polyatomic ions in Table 2.5 are oxoanions bonded to one or more hydrogen ions (H^+). They are sometimes referred to as *acid anions*, because acids are substances that provide H^+ ions. As an example, monohydrogen phosphate ion, HPO_4^{2-}, is essentially a phosphate ion (PO_4^{3-}) to which a hydrogen ion (H^+) has bonded. The prefix *mono-*, from the Greek, means "one." Similarly, *di-* is a prefix from the Greek meaning "two," so dihydrogen phosphate ion is a phosphate ion to which two hydrogen ions have bonded. In an older terminology, ions such as hydrogen carbonate and hydrogen sulfate were called bicarbonate and bisulfate, respectively.

The last anion in the table is thiosulfate ion, $S_2O_3^{2-}$. The prefix *thio-* means that an oxygen atom in the root ion name (sulfate, SO_4^{2-}) has been replaced by a sulfur atom.

There are only a few common polyatomic cations. Those listed in Table 2.5 are the mercury(I) ion (also called mercurous ion) and the ammonium ion. Mercury(I) ion is one of the few common metal ions that is not monatomic; its formula is Hg_2^{2+}. The ion charge indicated in parentheses is the charge per metal atom. The ammonium ion, NH_4^+, is one of the few common cations composed of only nonmetal atoms.

Now that we have discussed the naming of ions, let us look at the naming of ionic compounds. Example 2.4 illustrates how you name an ionic compound given its formula.

ChemWork: Beginning to Write Formulas for Compounds

Example 2.4 | Naming an Ionic Compound from Its Formula

Name the following: a. Mg_3N_2, b. $CrSO_4$.

Problem Strategy First, you need to identify the type of compound that you are dealing with. Because each of these compounds contains both metal and non-metal atoms, we expect them to be ionic, so we need to apply the rules for naming ionic compounds. When naming ionic compounds, start by writing the formulas of the cations and anions in the compound, then name the ions. Look first for any monatomic cations and anions whose charges are predictable. Use the rules given in the text to name the ions. For those metals having more than one cation, you will need to deduce the charge on the metal ion (say the ion of Cr in $CrSO_4$) from the charge on the anion. You will need to memorize or have available the formulas and names of the polyatomic anions to be able to write them from the formula of the compound.

Solution a. Magnesium, a Group IIA metal, is expected to form only a 2+ ion (Mg^{2+}, the magnesium

ion). Nitrogen (Group VA) is expected to form an anion of charge equal to the group number minus 8 (N^{3-}, the nitride ion). You can check that these ions would give the formula Mg_3N_2. The name of the compound is **magnesium nitride** (the name of the cation followed by the name of the anion).

b. Chromium is a transition element and, like most such elements, has more than one monatomic ion. You can find the charge on the Cr ion if you know the formula of the anion. From Table 2.5, you see that the SO_4 in $CrSO_4$ refers to the anion SO_4^{2-} (the sulfate ion). Therefore, the Cr cation must be Cr^{2+} to give electrical neutrality. The name of Cr^{2+} is chromium(II) ion, so the name of the compound is **chromium(II) sulfate.**

Answer Check Whenever you have to name a compound, you can check your answer to see if the name will lead you back to the correct formula.

Exercise 2.5 Write the names of the following compounds: a. CaO, b. $PbCrO_4$.

An alternative example is provided in the Instructor's Resource Manual.

■ See Problems 2.77 and 2.78.

Example 2.5	Writing the Formula from the Name of an Ionic Compound

Write formulas for the following compounds: a. iron(II) phosphate, b. titanium(IV) oxide.

Problem Strategy   As in all nomenclature problems, first determine the type of compound you are working with. The compounds presented in this problem contain both metal and nonmetal atoms, so they are ionic. Use the name of the compound, obtain the name of the ions, and then write the formulas of the ions. Finally, use the method of Example 2.3 to obtain the formula of the compound from the formulas of the ions.

Solution   a. Iron(II) phosphate contains the iron(II) ion, Fe^{2+}, and the phosphate ion, PO_4^{3-}. (You will need to have memorized the formula of the phosphate ion, or

have access to Table 2.5.) Once you know the formulas of the ions, you use the method of Example 2.3 to obtain the formula. The formula is $Fe_3(PO_4)_2$.

b. Titanium(IV) oxide is composed of titanium(IV) ions, Ti^{4+}, and oxide ions, O^{2-}. The formula of titanium(IV) oxide is TiO_2.

Answer Check   Whenever you have to write the formula of a compound from its name, make sure that the formula you have written will result in the correct name.

Exercise 2.6	A compound has the name thallium(III) nitrate. What is its formula? The symbol of thallium is Tl.

An alternative example is provided in the Instructor's Resource Manual.

■ See Problems 2.79 and 2.80.

Binary Molecular Compounds

A **binary compound** is *a compound composed of only two elements.* Binary compounds composed of a metal and a nonmetal are usually ionic and are named as ionic compounds, as we have just discussed. (For example, NaCl, $MgBr_2$, and Al_2N_3 are all binary ionic compounds.) Binary compounds composed of two nonmetals or metalloids are usually molecular and are named using a prefix system. Examples of binary molecular compounds are H_2O, NH_3, and CCl_4. Using this prefix system, you name the two elements using the order given by the formula of the compound.

Order of Elements in the Formula   The order of elements in the formula of a binary molecular compound is established by convention. By this convention, the nonmetal or metalloid occurring first in the following sequence is written first in the formula of the compound.

Element   B Si C Sb As P N H Te Se S I Br Cl O F
Group   IIIA IVA   VA   VIA   VIIA

You can reproduce this order easily if you have a periodic table available. You arrange the nonmetals and metalloids in the order of the groups of the periodic table, listing the elements from the bottom of the group upward. Then you place H between Groups VA and VIA, and move O so that it is just before F.

This order places the nonmetals and metalloids approximately in order of increasing nonmetallic character. Thus, in the formula, the first element is the more metallic and the second element is the more nonmetallic, similar to the situation with binary ionic compounds. For example, the compound whose molecule contains three fluorine atoms and one nitrogen atom is written NF_3, not F_3N.

Rules for Naming Binary Molecular Compounds   Now let us look at the rules for naming binary molecular compounds by the *prefix system.*

1. The name of the compound usually has the elements in the order given in the formula.

TABLE 2.6

Greek Prefixes for Naming Compounds

Number	Prefix
1	mono-
2	di-
3	tri-
4	tetra-
5	penta-
6	hexa-
7	hepta-
8	octa-
9	nona-
10	deca-

2. You name the first element using the exact element name.

3. You name the second element by writing the stem name of the element with the suffix *-ide* (as if the element occurred as the anion).

4. You add a prefix, derived from the Greek, to each element name to denote the subscript of the element in the formula. (The Greek prefixes are listed in Table 2.6.) Generally, the prefix *mono-* is not used, unless it is needed to distinguish two compounds of the same two elements.

Consider N_2O_3. This is a binary molecular compound, as you would predict because N and O are nonmetals. According to Rule 1, you name it after the elements, N before O, following the order of elements in the formula. By Rule 2, the N is named exactly as the element (nitrogen), and by Rule 3, the O is named as the anion (oxide). The compound is a nitrogen oxide. Finally, you add prefixes to denote the subscripts in the formula (Rule 4). As Table 2.6 shows, the prefix for two is *di-*, and the prefix for three is *tri-*. The name of the compound is dinitrogen trioxide.

Here are some examples to illustrate how the prefix *mono-* is used. There is only one compound of hydrogen and chlorine: HCl. It is called hydrogen chloride, not monohydrogen monochloride, since the prefix *mono-* is not generally written. On the other hand, there are two common compounds of carbon and oxygen: CO and CO_2. They are both carbon oxides. To distinguish one from the other, we name them carbon monoxide and carbon dioxide, respectively.

Here are some other examples of prefix names for binary molecular compounds.

SF_4	sulfur tetrafluoride	SF_6	sulfur hexafluoride
ClO_2	chlorine dioxide	Cl_2O_7	dichlorine hept(a)oxide

The final vowel in a prefix is often dropped before a vowel in a stem name, for ease in pronunciation. Tetraoxide, for instance, becomes tetroxide.

A few compounds have older, well-established names. The compound H_2S would be named dihydrogen sulfide by the prefix system, but is commonly called hydrogen sulfide. NO is still called nitric oxide, although its prefix name is nitrogen monoxide. The names water and ammonia are used for H_2O and NH_3, respectively.

Example 2.6 | Naming a Binary Compound from Its Formula

Name the following compounds: a. N_2O_4, b. P_4O_6.

Problem Strategy First, you need to determine the type of compound that you are dealing with: molecular or ionic. In this case the compound contains only nonmetals, so it is molecular. Molecular compounds require that you use the Greek prefixes (Table 2.6), naming the elements in the same order as in the formulas.

Solution a. N_2O_4 contains two nitrogen atoms and four oxygen atoms. Consulting Table 2.6 reveals that the

corresponding prefixes are *di-* and *tetra-*, so the name is **di**nitrogen **tetr**oxide.

b. P_4O_6 contains four phosphorus atoms and six oxygen atoms. Consulting Table 2.6 reveals that the corresponding prefixes are *tetra-* and *hexa-*, so the name is **tetra**phosphorus **hex**oxide.

Answer Check Check to see whether the name leads back to the correct formula.

Exercise 2.7 Name the following compounds: a. Cl_2O_6, b. PCl_3, c. PCl_5.

An alternative example is provided in the Instructor's Resource Manual.

■ See Problems 2.83 and 2.84.

Example 2.7 | Writing the Formula from the Name of a Binary Compound

Give the formulas of the following compounds: a. disulfur dichloride, b. tetraphosphorus trisulfide.

Problem Strategy As always, first determine whether you are working with a molecular or ionic compound. Because these compounds contain only nonmetals, they must be molecular. Given that they are molecular, you will need to use the Greek prefixes in Table 2.6 to give you the corresponding names for each subscript.

An alternative example is provided in the Instructor's Resource Manual.

Solution You change the names of the elements to symbols and translate the prefixes to subscripts. The formulas are a. S_2Cl_2 and b. P_4S_3.

Answer Check Check to see whether the formula you have written will result in the correct name.

Exercise 2.8 Give formulas for the following compounds: a. carbon disulfide, b. sulfur trioxide.

■ See Problems 2.85 and 2.86.

Example 2.8 | Naming a Binary Chemical Compound from Its Molecular Model

Name the chemical compounds shown here.

Problem Strategy After recognizing that these are molecular compounds, start by writing down the elements using subscripts to denote how many atoms of each element occur in the compound. Next, determine which element should be written first in the chemical formula. (The more metallic element is written first.)

(a)

(b)

Solution a. The elements in the compound are O and N. There are two O atoms for each N atom, so the chemical formula could be O_2N. Applying the rule for writing the more metallic element first, the formula is rearranged to yield the correct formula, NO_2. Using Greek prefixes and naming the elements in the order in which they appear, we get the correct chemical formula: **nitrogen dioxide.**

b. Following the same procedure as part a, we get **chlorine monofluoride.**

Answer Check Make sure that the answer reflects the correct number of each of the elements given in the molecular structure.

Exercise 2.9
Using the molecular models, name the following chemical compounds:

(a)   (b)

■ See Problems 2.87 and 2.88.

FIGURE 2.26 ▲
Molecular model of nitric acid

ChemWork: Naming Acids

Acids and Corresponding Anions

Acids are an important class of compounds, and we will look closely at them in the next chapter. Here we want merely to see how we name these compounds and how they are related to the anions that we encounter in some ionic compounds. For our present purposes, an *acid* is a molecular compound that yields hydrogen ions, H^+, and an anion for each acid molecule when the acid dissolves in water. An example is nitric acid, HNO_3. The HNO_3 molecule yields one H^+ ion and one nitrate ion, NO_3^-, in aqueous (water) solution.

Nitric acid, HNO_3, is an oxoacid, or oxyacid (Figure 2.26). An **oxoacid** is *an acid containing hydrogen, oxygen, and another element (often called the central atom).* In water the oxoacid molecule yields one or more hydrogen ions, H^+, and an oxoanion. The names of the oxoacids are related to the names of the corresponding oxoanions. If you know the name of the oxoanion, you can obtain the name of the correspon-ding acid by replacing the suffix as follows:

Anion Suffix	Acid Suffix
-ate	*-ic*
-ite	*-ous*

The following diagram illustrates how to apply this information to naming oxoacids.

Acid	Contains	Name
HNO_3 ⟶	nitrate anion therefore	nitric acid
	ate to	ic
HNO_2 ⟶	nitrite anion therefore	nitrous acid
	ite to	ous

Table 2.7 lists some oxoanions and their corresponding oxoacids.

Some binary compounds of hydrogen and nonmetals yield acidic solutions when dissolved in water. These *solutions* are named like compounds by using the prefix *hydro-* and the suffix *-ic* with the stem name of the nonmetal, followed by the word *acid*. We denote the solution by the formula of the binary compound followed by (*aq*)

TABLE 2.7	Some Oxoanions and Their Corresponding Oxoacids		
Oxoanion		**Oxoacid**	
CO_3^{2-}	Carbon*ate* ion	H_2CO_3	Carbon*ic* acid
NO_2^-	Nitr*ite* ion	HNO_2	Nitr*ous* acid
NO_3^-	Nitr*ate* ion	HNO_3	Nitr*ic* acid
PO_4^{3-}	Phosph*ate* ion	H_3PO_4	Phosphor*ic* acid
SO_3^{2-}	Sulf*ite* ion	H_2SO_3	Sulfur*ous* acid
SO_4^{2-}	Sulf*ate* ion	H_2SO_4	Sulfur*ic* acid
ClO^-	*Hypo*chlor*ite* ion	$HClO$	*Hypo*chlor*ous* acid
ClO_2^-	Chlor*ite* ion	$HClO_2$	Chlor*ous* acid
ClO_3^-	Chlor*ate* ion	$HClO_3$	Chlor*ic* acid
ClO_4^-	*Per*chlor*ate* ion	$HClO_4$	*Per*chlor*ic* acid

for aqueous (water) solution. The corresponding binary compound can be distinguished from the solution by appending the state of the compound to the formula. Thus, when hydrogen chloride gas, $HCl(g)$, is dissolved in water, it forms hydrochloric acid, $HCl(aq)$.

$HCl(g)$ hydrogen chloride

$HCl(aq)$ hydrochloric acid

Here are some other examples:

Binary Compound   *Acid Solution*

$HBr(g)$, hydrogen bromide   *hydrobromic acid*, $HBr(aq)$

$HF(g)$, hydrogen fluoride   *hydrofluoric acid*, $HF(aq)$

Example 2.9 | Writing the Name and Formula of an Anion from the Acid

Selenium has an oxoacid, H_2SeO_4, called selenic acid. What is the formula and name of the corresponding anion?

Problem Strategy Knowing that H_2SeO_4 is an oxyacid, we must first determine the oxoanion name from the examples provided in Table 2.7. From the oxoanion name you determine whether a prefix (*per-* or *hypo-*) is necessary and whether the proper suffix is *-ite* or *-ate*. You then name the anion.

Solution When you remove two H^+ ions from H_2SeO_4, you obtain the SeO_4^{2-} ion. You name the ion from the acid by replacing *-ic* with *-ate*. The anion is called the **selenate ion.**

Answer Check Check to see whether the name you have written leads back to the correct formula.

Exercise 2.10 What are the name and formula of the anion corresponding to perbromic acid, $HBrO_4$?

■ See Problems 2.89 and 2.90.

An alternative example is provided in the Instructor's Resource Manual.

Hydrates

FIGURE 2.27 ▲

Copper(II) sulfate
The hydrate $CuSO_4 \cdot 5H_2O$ is blue; the anhydrous compound, $CuSO_4$, is white.

A **hydrate** is *a compound that contains water molecules weakly bound in its crystals.* These substances are often obtained by evaporating an aqueous solution of the compound. Consider copper(II) sulfate. When an aqueous solution of this substance is evaporated, blue crystals form in which each formula unit of copper(II) sulfate, $CuSO_4$, is associated with five molecules of water. The formula of the hydrate is written $CuSO_4 \cdot 5H_2O$, where a centered dot separates $CuSO_4$ and $5H_2O$. When the blue crystals of the hydrate are heated, the water is driven off, leaving behind white crystals of copper(II) sulfate without associated water, a substance called *anhydrous* copper(II) sulfate (see Figure 2.27).

Hydrates are named from the anhydrous compound, followed by the word *hydrate* with a prefix to indicate the number of water molecules per formula unit of the compound. For example, $CuSO_4 \cdot 5H_2O$ is known as copper(II) sulfate pentahydrate.

Example 2.10 | Naming a Hydrate from Its Formula

Epsom salts has the formula $MgSO_4 \cdot 7H_2O$. What is the chemical name of the substance?

Problem Strategy You need to identify the type of compound that you are dealing with, ionic or molecular. Because this compound contains both metals and nonmetals, it is ionic. However, this compound has the additional feature that it contains water molecules. Therefore, you need to apply ionic naming rules and then use Greek prefixes (Table 2.6) to indicate the number of water molecules that are part of the formula.

An alternative example is provided in the Instructor's Resource Manual.

The word *hydrate* will be used to represent water in the name.

Solution $MgSO_4$ is magnesium sulfate. $MgSO_4 \cdot 7H_2O$ is **magnesium sulfate heptahydrate.**

Answer Check Make sure that the name leads back to the formula that you started with.

Exercise 2.11   Washing soda has the formula $Na_2CO_3 \cdot 10H_2O$. What is the chemical name of this substance?

■ See Problems 2.91 and 2.92.

Example 2.11 | Writing the Formula from the Name of a Hydrate

The mineral gypsum has the chemical name calcium sulfate dihydrate. What is the chemical formula of this substance?

Problem Strategy You need to identify the type of compound that you are dealing with, ionic or molecular. Because this compound contains both metals and nonmetals, it is ionic. However, this compound has the additional feature that it contains water molecules. Therefore, we need to apply ionic naming rules and then use Greek prefixes (Table 2.6) to indicate the number of water molecules that are part of the formula. The word *hydrate* will be used to represent water in the name.

An alternative example is provided in the Instructor's Resource Manual.

Solution Calcium sulfate is composed of calcium ions (Ca^{2+}) and sulfate ions (SO_4^{2-}), so the formula of the anhydrous compound is $CaSO_4$. Since the mineral is a *di*hydrate, the formula of the compound is **$CaSO_4 \cdot 2H_2O$.**

Answer Check Make sure that the formula will result in the correct name that you started with.

Exercise 2.12   Photographers' hypo, used to fix negatives during the development process, is sodium thiosulfate pentahydrate. What is the chemical formula of this compound?

■ See Problems 2.93 and 2.94.

Concept Check 2.5

You take a job with the U.S. Environmental Protection Agency (EPA) inspecting college chemistry laboratories. On the first day of the job while inspecting Generic University you encounter a bottle with the formula Al_2Q_3 that was used as an unknown compound in an experiment. Before you send the compound off to the EPA lab for analysis, you want to narrow down the possibilities for element Q. What are the likely (real element) candidates for element Q?

Demonstration of the dehydration of copper(II) sulfate pentahydrate: Summerlin et al., *Chemical Demonstrations*, Vol. 2 (Washington, D.C.: Am. Chem. Soc., 1987), no. 38, p. 69.

Chemical Reactions: Equations

An important feature of atomic theory is its explanation of a chemical reaction as a rearrangement of the atoms of substances. The reaction of sodium metal with chlorine gas described in the chapter opening involves the rearrangement of the atoms of sodium and chlorine to give the new combination of atoms in sodium chloride. Such a rearrangement of atoms is conveniently represented by a chemical equation, which uses chemical formulas.

2.9 | Writing Chemical Equations

A **chemical equation** is *the symbolic representation of a chemical reaction in terms of chemical formulas.* For example, the burning of sodium in chlorine to produce sodium chloride is written

$$2Na + Cl_2 \longrightarrow 2NaCl$$

The formulas on the left side of an equation (before the arrow) represent the reactants; a **reactant** is *a starting substance in a chemical reaction.* The arrow means "react to form" or "yield." The formulas on the right side represent the products; a **product** is *a substance that results from a reaction.* Note the *coefficient* of 2 in front of the formula NaCl. Coefficients in front of the formula give the relative number of molecules or formula units involved in the reaction. When no coefficient is written, it is understood to be 1.

In many cases, it is useful to indicate the states or phases of the substances in an equation. You do this by placing appropriate labels indicating the phases within parentheses following the formulas of the substances. You use the following phase labels:

(g) = gas, (l) = liquid, (s) = solid, (aq) = aqueous (water) solution

When you use these labels, the previous equation becomes

$$2Na(s) + Cl_2(g) \longrightarrow 2NaCl(s)$$

You can also indicate in an equation the conditions under which a reaction takes place. If the reactants are heated to make the reaction go, you can indicate this by putting the symbol Δ (capital Greek delta) over the arrow. For example, the equation

$$2NaNO_3(s) \xrightarrow{\Delta} 2NaNO_2(s) + O_2(g)$$

indicates that solid sodium nitrate, $NaNO_3$, decomposes when heated to give solid sodium nitrite, $NaNO_2$, and oxygen gas, O_2.

When an aqueous solution of hydrogen peroxide, H_2O_2, comes in contact with platinum metal, Pt, the hydrogen peroxide decomposes into water and oxygen gas. The platinum acts as a *catalyst*, a substance that speeds up a reaction without undergoing any net change itself. You write the equation for this reaction as follows. The catalyst, Pt, is written over the arrow. <

$$2H_2O_2(aq) \xrightarrow{Pt} 2H_2O(l) + O_2(g)$$

You also can combine the symbol Δ with the formula of a catalyst, placing one above the arrow and the other below the arrow.

Platinum is a silvery-white metal used for jewelry. It is also valuable as a catalyst for many reactions, including those that occur in the catalytic converters of automobiles.

2.10 | Balancing Chemical Equations

When the coefficients in a chemical equation are correctly given, the numbers of atoms of each element are equal on both sides of the arrow. The equation is then said to be *balanced*. That a chemical equation should be balanced follows from atomic theory. A chemical reaction involves simply a recombination of the atoms; none are destroyed and none are created. Consider the burning of natural gas, which is composed mostly of methane, CH_4. Using atomic theory, you describe this as the chemical reaction of one molecule of methane, CH_4, with two molecules of oxygen, O_2, to form one molecule of carbon dioxide, CO_2, and two molecules of water, H_2O.

ChemWork: Balancing Chemical Equations

ChemWork: Characteristics of Chemical Equations

$$CH_4 \quad + \quad 2O_2 \quad \longrightarrow \quad CO_2 \quad + \quad 2H_2O$$

one molecule   +   two molecules   react to   one molecule   +   two molecules
of methane   of oxygen   form   of carbon dioxide   of water

FIGURE 2.28 ▶

Representation of the reaction of methane with oxygen
Molecular models represent the reaction of CH_4 with O_2 to give CO_2 and H_2O.

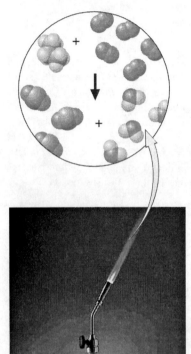

FIGURE 2.29 ▲

The burning of propane gas
Propane gas, C_3H_8, from the tank burns by reacting with oxygen, O_2, in air to give carbon dioxide, CO_2, and water, H_2O.

Figure 2.28 represents the reaction in terms of molecular models.

Before you can write a balanced chemical equation for a reaction, you must determine *by experiment* those substances that are reactants and those that are products. You must also determine the formulas of each substance. Once you know these things, you can write the balanced chemical equation.

As an example, consider the burning of propane gas (Figure 2.29). By experiment, you determine that propane reacts with oxygen in air to give carbon dioxide and water. You also determine from experiment that the formulas of propane, oxygen, carbon dioxide, and water are C_3H_8, O_2, CO_2, and H_2O, respectively. Then you can write

$$C_3H_8 + O_2 \longrightarrow CO_2 + H_2O$$

This equation is not balanced because the coefficients that give the relative number of molecules involved have not yet been determined. *To balance the equation, you select coefficients that will make the numbers of atoms of each element equal on both sides of the equation.*

Because there are three carbon atoms on the left side of the equation (C_3H_8), you must have three carbon atoms on the right. This is achieved by writing 3 for the coefficient of CO_2.

$$\underline{1}C_3H_8 + O_2 \longrightarrow \underline{3}CO_2 + H_2O$$

(We have written the coefficient for C_3H_8 to show that it is now determined; normally when the coefficient is 1, it is omitted.) Similarly, there are eight hydrogen atoms on the left (in C_3H_8), so you write 4 for the coefficient of H_2O.

$$\underline{1}C_3H_8 + O_2 \longrightarrow \underline{3}CO_2 + \underline{4}H_2O$$

The coefficients on the right are now determined, and there are ten oxygen atoms on this side of the equation: 6 from the three CO_2 molecules and 4 from the four H_2O molecules. You now write 5 for the coefficient of O_2. We drop the coefficient 1 from C_3H_8 and have the balanced equation.

$$C_3H_8 + 5O_2 \longrightarrow 3CO_2 + 4H_2O$$

It is a good idea to check your work by counting the number of atoms of each element on the left side and then on the right side of the equation.

The combustion of propane can be equally well represented by

$$2C_3H_8 + 10O_2 \longrightarrow 6CO_2 + 8H_2O$$

in which the coefficients of the previous equation have been doubled. Usually, however, it is preferable to *write the coefficients so that they are the smallest whole numbers possible*. When we refer to a balanced equation, we will assume that this is the case unless otherwise specified.

The method we have outlined—called *balancing by inspection*—is essentially a trial-and-error method. < It can be made easier, however, by observing the following rule:

Balancing equations this way is relatively quick for all but the most complicated equations. A special method for such equations is described in Chapter 19.

Balance first the atoms for elements that occur in only one substance on each side of the equation.

The usefulness of this rule is illustrated in the next example. Remember that in any formula, such as $Fe_2(SO_4)_3$, a subscript to the right of the parentheses multiplies *each* subscript within the parentheses. Thus, $Fe_2(SO_4)_3$ represents 4×3 oxygen atoms. Remember also that you cannot change a subscript in any formula; only the coefficients can be altered to balance an equation.

Example 2.12 | Balancing Simple Equations

Balance the following equations.

a. $H_3PO_3 \longrightarrow H_3PO_4 + PH_3$ b. $Ca + H_2O \longrightarrow Ca(OH)_2 + H_2$

c. $Fe_2(SO_4)_3 + NH_3 + H_2O \longrightarrow Fe(OH)_3 + (NH_4)_2SO_4$

An alternative example is provided in the Instructor's Resource Manual.

Problem Strategy Look at the chemical equation for atoms of elements that occur in only one substance on each side of the equation. Begin by balancing the equation in one of these atoms. Use the number of atoms on the left side of the arrow as the coefficient of the substance containing that element on the right side, and vice versa. After balancing one element in an equation, the rest become easier.

Solution a. Oxygen occurs in just one of the products (H_3PO_4). It is therefore easiest to balance O atoms first. To do this, note that H_3PO_3 has three O atoms; use 3 as the coefficient of H_3PO_4 on the right side. There are four O atoms in H_3PO_4 on the right side; use 4 as the coefficient of H_3PO_3 on the left side.

$$\underline{4}H_3PO_3 \longrightarrow \underline{3}H_3PO_4 + PH_3$$

This equation is now also balanced in P and H atoms. Thus, the balanced equation is

$$\mathbf{4H_3PO_3 \longrightarrow 3H_3PO_4 + PH_3}$$

b. The equation is balanced in Ca atoms as it stands.

$$\underline{1}Ca + H_2O \longrightarrow \underline{1}Ca(OH)_2 + H_2$$

O atoms occur in only one reactant and in only one product, so they are balanced next.

$$\underline{1}Ca + \underline{2}H_2O \longrightarrow \underline{1}Ca(OH)_2 + H_2$$

The equation is now also balanced in H atoms. Thus, the answer is

$$\mathbf{Ca + 2H_2O \longrightarrow Ca(OH)_2 + H_2}$$

c. To balance the equation in Fe atoms, you write

$$\underline{1}Fe_2(SO_4)_3 + NH_3 + H_2O \longrightarrow \underline{2}Fe(OH)_3 + (NH_4)_2SO_4$$

You balance the S atoms by placing the coefficient 3 for $(NH_4)_2SO_4$.

$$\underline{1}Fe_2(SO_4)_3 + \underline{6}NH_3 + H_2O \longrightarrow \underline{2}Fe(OH)_3 + \underline{3}(NH_4)_2SO_4$$

Now you balance the N atoms.

$$\underline{1}Fe_2(SO_4)_3 + \underline{6}NH_3 + H_2O \longrightarrow \underline{2}Fe(OH)_3 + \underline{3}(NH_4)_2SO_4$$

To balance the O atoms, you first count the number of O atoms on the right (18). Then you count the number of O atoms in substances on the left with known coefficients. There are 12 O's in $Fe_2(SO_4)_3$; hence, the number of remaining O's (in H_2O) must be $18 - 12 = 6$.

$$\underline{1}Fe_2(SO_4)_3 + \underline{6}NH_3 + \underline{6}H_2O \longrightarrow \underline{2}Fe(OH)_3 + \underline{3}(NH_4)_2SO_4$$

(continued)

(continued)

Finally, note that the equation is now balanced in H atoms. The answer is

$$Fe_2(SO_4)_3 + 6NH_3 + 6H_2O \longrightarrow 2Fe(OH)_3 + 3(NH_4)_2SO_4$$

Answer Check   As a final step when balancing chemical equations, always count the number of atoms of each element on both sides of the equation to make certain that they are equal.

Exercise 2.13   Find the coefficients that balance the following equations.

a. $O_2 + PCl_3 \longrightarrow POCl_3$

b. $P_4 + N_2O \longrightarrow P_4O_6 + N_2$

c. $As_2S_3 + O_2 \longrightarrow As_2O_3 + SO_2$

d. $Ca_3(PO_4)_2 + H_3PO_4 \longrightarrow Ca(H_2PO_4)_2$

■ See Problems 2.97 and 2.98.

A Checklist for Review

Important Terms

atomic theory (2.1)	atomic mass unit (amu) (2.4)	cation (2.6)
atom (2.1)	atomic mass (2.4)	ionic compound (2.6)
element (2.1, 2.3)	fractional abundance (2.4)	formula unit (2.6)
compound (2.1)	periodic table (2.5)	organic compound (2.7)
chemical reaction (2.1)	period (of periodic table) (2.5)	hydrocarbon (2.7)
atomic symbol (2.1)	group (of periodic table) (2.5)	functional group (2.7)
law of multiple	metal (2.5)	chemical nomenclature (2.8)
proportions (2.1)	nonmetal (2.5)	inorganic compound (2.8)
nucleus (2.2)	metalloid (semimetal) (2.5)	monatomic ion (2.8)
electron (2.2)	chemical formula (2.6)	polyatomic ion (2.8)
proton (2.3)	molecule (2.6)	binary compound (2.8)
atomic number (Z) (2.3)	molecular formula (2.6)	oxoacid (2.8)
neutron (2.3)	polymer (2.6)	hydrate (2.8)
mass number (A) (2.3)	monomer (2.6)	chemical equation (2.9)
nuclide (2.3)	ion (2.6)	reactant (2.9)
isotope (2.3)	anion (2.6)	product (2.9)

Summary of Facts and Concepts

Atomic theory is central to chemistry. According to this theory, all matter is composed of small particles, or *atoms*. Each *element* is composed of the same kind of atom, and a *compound* is composed of two or more elements chemically combined in fixed proportions. A *chemical reaction* consists of the rearrangement of the atoms present in the reacting substances to give new chemical combinations present in the substances formed by the reaction. Although Dalton considered atoms to be the ultimate particles of matter, we now know that atoms themselves have structure. An atom has a *nucleus* and *electrons*. These atomic particles were discovered by J. J. Thomson and Ernest Rutherford.

Thomson established that cathode rays consist of negatively charged particles, or electrons, that are constituents of all atoms.

Thomson measured the mass-to-charge ratio of the electron, and later Millikan measured its charge. From these measurements, the electron was found to be more than 1800 times lighter than the lightest atom.

Rutherford proposed the nuclear model of the atom to account for the results of experiments in which alpha particles were scattered from metal foils. According to this model, the atom consists of a central core, or nucleus, around which the electrons exist. The nucleus has most of the mass of the atom and consists of *protons* (with a positive charge) and *neutrons* (with no charge). Each chemically distinct atom has a nucleus with a specific number of protons (*atomic number*), and around the nucleus in the neutral atom are an equal number of electrons.

The number of protons plus neutrons in a nucleus equals the *mass number*. Atoms whose nuclei have the same number of protons but different number of neutrons are called *isotopes*.

The *atomic mass* can be calculated from the isotopic masses and *fractional abundances* of the isotopes in a naturally occurring element. These data can be determined by the use of a mass spectrometer, which separates ions according to their mass-to-charge ratios.

The elements can be arranged in rows and columns by atomic number to form the *periodic table*. Elements in a given *group* (column) have similar properties. (A *period* is a row in the periodic table.) Elements on the left and at the center of the table are *metals*; those on the right are *nonmetals*.

A *chemical formula* is a notation used to convey the relative proportions of the atoms of the different elements in a substance. If the substance is molecular, the formula gives the precise number of each kind of atom in the molecule. If the substance is ionic, the formula gives the relative number of different ions in the compound.

Chemical nomenclature is the systematic naming of compounds based on their formulas or structures. Rules are given for naming *ionic compounds, binary molecular compounds, acids,* and *hydrates*.

A chemical reaction occurs when the atoms in substances rearrange and combine into new substances. We represent a reaction by a *chemical equation*, writing a chemical formula for each reactant and product. The coefficients in the equation indicate the relative numbers of reactant and product molecules or formula units. Once the reactants and products and their formulas have been determined by experiment, we determine the coefficients by *balancing* the numbers of each kind of atom on both sides of the equation.

Media Summary

Visit the **student website at college.hmco.com/pic/ebbing9e** to help prepare for class, study for quizzes and exams, understand core concepts, and visualize molecular-level interactions. The following media activities are available for this chapter:

 Prepare for Class

Video Lessons *Mini lectures from chemistry experts*
Early Discoveries and the Atom
Understanding the Nucleus
Understanding Electrons
Modern Atomic Structure
Mass Spectrometry: Determining Atomic Masses
Creating the Periodic Table
Describing Chemical Formulas
Naming Chemical Compounds
An Introduction to Chemical Reactions and Equations
Balancing Chemical Equations

 Improve Your Grade

Visualizations *Molecular-level animations and lab demonstration videos*
Cathode-Ray Tube
Millikan's Oil Drop Experiment

Gold Foil Experiment
Determining Formulas for Ionic Compounds
Conservation of Mass and Balancing Equations

Tutorials *Animated examples and interactive activities*
Isotopes
Determining Formulas for Ionic Compounds
Balancing Chemical Equations

Flashcards *Key terms and definitions*
Online Flashcards

Self-Assessment Questions *Additional questions with full worked-out solutions*
6 Self-Assessment Questions

 ACE the Test

Multiple-choice quizzes
3 ACE Practice Tests

Access these resources using the passkey available free with new texts or for purchase separately.

Learning Objectives

2.1 Atomic Theory of Matter

- List the postulates of atomic theory.
- Define *element, compound,* and *chemical reaction* in the context of these postulates.
- Recognize the atomic symbols of the elements.
- Explain the significance of the law of multiple proportions.

2.2 The Structure of the Atom

- Describe Thomson's experiment in which he discovered the electron.
- Describe Rutherford's experiment that led to the nuclear model of the atom.

2.3 Nuclear Structure; Isotopes

■ Name and describe the nuclear particles making up the nucleus of the atom.
■ Define *atomic number*, *mass number*, and *nuclide*.
■ Write the nuclide symbol for a given nuclide.
■ Define and provide examples of *isotopes* of an element.
■ Write the nuclide symbol of an element. Example 2.1

2.4 Atomic Masses

■ Define *atomic mass unit* and *atomic mass*.
■ Describe how a *mass spectrometer* can be used to determine the *fractional abundance* of the isotopes of an element.
■ Determine the atomic mass of an element from the isotopic masses and fractional abundances. Example 2.2

2.5 Periodic Table of the Elements

■ Identify periods and groups on the periodic table.
■ Find the *main-group* and *transition* elements on the periodic table.
■ Locate the *alkali metal* and *halogen* groups on the periodic table.
■ Recognize the portions of the periodic table that contain the *metals*, *nonmetals*, and *metalloids* (*semimetals*).

2.6 Chemical Formulas; Molecular and Ionic Substances

■ Determine when the *chemical formula* of a compound represents a *molecule*.
■ Determine whether a chemical formula is also a *molecular formula*.
■ Define *ion*, *cation*, and *anion*.
■ Classify compounds as *ionic* or *molecular*.
■ Define and provide examples for the term *formula unit*.
■ Specify the charge on all substances, ionic and molecular.
■ Write an ionic formula, given the ions. Example 2.3

2.7 Organic Compounds

■ List the attributes of molecular substances that make them *organic compounds*.

■ Explain what makes a molecule a *hydrocarbon*.
■ Recognize some *functional groups* of organic molecules.

2.8 Naming Simple Compounds

■ Recognize *inorganic compounds*.
■ Learn the rules for predicting the charges of *monatomic ions* in ionic compounds.
■ Apply the rules for naming monatomic ions.
■ Learn the names and charges of common *polyatomic ions*.
■ Name an ionic compound from its formula. Example 2.4
■ Write the formula of an ionic compound from its name. Example 2.5
■ Determine the order of elements in a *binary (molecular) compound*.
■ Learn the rules for naming binary molecular compounds, including the Greek prefixes.
■ Name a binary compound from its formula. Example 2.6
■ Write the formula of a binary compound from its name. Example 2.7
■ Name a binary molecular compound from its molecular model. Example 2.8
■ Recognize molecular compounds that are acids.
■ Determine whether an acid is an *oxoacid*.
■ Learn the approach for naming binary acids and oxoacids.
■ Write the name and formula of an anion from the acid. Example 2.9
■ Recognize compounds that are *hydrates*.
■ Learn the rules for naming hydrates.
■ Name a hydrate from its formula. Example 2.10
■ Write the formula of a hydrate from its name. Example 2.11

2.9 Writing Chemical Equations

■ Identify the *reactants* and *products* in a chemical equation.
■ Write chemical equations using appropriate phase labels, symbols of reaction conditions, and the presence of a catalyst.

2.10 Balancing Chemical Equations

■ Determine if a chemical reaction is balanced.
■ Master the techniques for balancing chemical equations. Example 2.12

Self-Assessment and Review Questions

2.1 Describe atomic theory and discuss how it explains the great variety of different substances. How does it explain chemical reactions?

2.2 Two compounds of iron and chlorine, A and B, contain 1.270 g and 1.904 g of chlorine, respectively, for each gram of iron. Show that these amounts are in the ratio 2:3. Is this consistent with the law of multiple proportions? Explain.

2.3 Explain the operation of a cathode-ray tube. Describe the deflection of cathode rays by electrically charged plates placed within the cathode-ray tube. What does this imply about cathode rays?

2.4 Explain Millikan's oil-drop experiment.

2.5 Describe the nuclear model of the atom. How does this model explain the results of alpha-particle scattering from metal foils?

2.6 What are the different kinds of particles in the atom's nucleus? Compare their properties with each other and with those of an electron.

2.7 Describe how protons and neutrons were discovered to be constituents of nuclei.

2.8 Oxygen consists of three different _____, each having eight protons but different numbers of neutrons.

2.9 Describe how Dalton obtained relative atomic masses.

2.10 Briefly explain how a mass spectrometer works. What kinds of information does one obtain from the instrument?

2.11 Define the term *atomic mass*. Why might the values of atomic masses on a planet elsewhere in the universe be different from those on earth?

2.12 What is the name of the element in Group IVA and Period 5?

2.13 Cite some properties that are characteristic of a metal.

2.14 Ethane consists of molecules with two atoms of carbon and six atoms of hydrogen. Write the molecular formula for ethane.

2.15 What is the difference between a molecular formula and a structural formula?

2.16 What is the fundamental difference between an organic substance and an inorganic substance? Write chemical formulas of three inorganic molecules that contain carbon.

2.17 Give an example of a binary compound that is ionic. Give an example of a binary compound that is molecular.

2.18 Which of the following models represent a(n):

  a. element
  b. compound
  c. mixture
  d. ionic solid
  e. gas made up of an element and a compound
  f. mixture of elements
  g. solid element
  h. solid
  i. liquid

2.19 The compounds CuCl and $CuCl_2$ were formerly called cuprous chloride and cupric chloride, respectively. What are their names using the Stock system of nomenclature? What are the advantages of the Stock system of nomenclature over the former one?

2.20 Explain what is meant by the term *balanced chemical equation*.

2.21 How many protons, neutrons, and electrons are in $^{119}Sn^{2+}$?

  a. 50 p, 69 n, 48 e⁻
  b. 50 p, 69 n, 50 e⁻
  c. 119 p, 50 n, 69 e⁻
  d. 69 p, 50 n, 69 e
  e. 50 p, 119 n, 52 e⁻

2.22 The atomic mass of Ga is 69.72 amu. There are only two naturally occurring isotopes of gallium: ^{69}Ga, with a mass of 69.0 amu, and ^{71}Ga, with a mass of 71.0 amu. The natural abundance of the ^{69}Ga isotope is approximately:

  a. 15%
  b. 30%
  c. 50%
  d. 65%
  e. 80%

2.23 In which of the following are the name and formula correctly paired?

  a. sodium sulfite: Na_2S
  b. calcium carbonate: $Ca(CO_3)_2$
  c. magnesium hydroxide: $Mg(OH)_2$
  d. nitrite: NO_2
  e. iron (III) oxide: FeO

2.24 A chunk of an unidentified element (let's call it element "X") is reacted with sulfur to form an ionic compound with the chemical formula X_2S. Which of the following elements is the most likely identity of X?

  a. Mg
  b. Li
  c. Al
  d. C
  e. Cl

Concept Explorations

2.25 **Average Atomic Mass**

Part 1: Consider the four identical spheres below, each with a mass of 2.00 g.

Calculate the average mass of a sphere in this sample.

Part 2: Now consider a sample that consists of four spheres, each with a different mass: blue mass is 2.00 g, red mass is 1.75 g, green mass is 3.00 g, and yellow mass is 1.25 g.

  a. Calculate the average mass of a sphere in this sample.

  b. How does the average mass for a sphere in this sample compare with the average mass of the sample that consisted just of the blue spheres? How can such different samples have their averages turn out the way they did?

Part 3: Consider two jars. One jar contains 100 blue spheres, and the other jar contains 25 each of red, blue, green, and yellow colors mixed together.

  a. If you were to remove 50 blue spheres from the jar containing just the blue spheres, what would be total mass of spheres left in the jar? (Note that the masses of the spheres are given in Part 2.)

b. If you were to remove 50 spheres from the jar containing the mixture (assume you get a representative distribution of colors), what would be the total mass of spheres left in the jar?

c. In the case of the mixture of spheres, does the average mass of the spheres *necessarily* represent the mass of an individual sphere in the sample?

d. If you had 80.0 grams of spheres from the blue sample, how many spheres would you have?

e. If you had 60.0 grams of spheres from the mixed-color sample, how many spheres would you have? What assumption did you make about your sample when performing this calculation?

Part 4: Consider a sample that consists of three green spheres and one blue sphere. The green mass is 3.00 g, and the blue mass is 1.00 g.

a. Calculate the *fractional abundance* of each sphere in the sample.

b. Use the fractional abundance to calculate the average mass of the spheres in this sample.

c. How are the ideas developed in this Concept Exploration related to the atomic masses of the elements?

2.26 Model of the Atom

Consider the following depictions of two atoms, which have been greatly enlarged so you can see the subatomic particles.

a. How many protons are present in atom A?

b. What is the significance of the number of protons depicted in atom A or any atom?

c. Can you identify the real element represented by the drawing of atom A? If so, what element does it represent?

d. What is the charge on element A? Explain how you arrived at your answer.

e. Write the nuclide symbol of atom A.

f. Write the atomic symbol and the atomic number of atom B.

g. What is the mass number of atom B? How does this mass number compare with that of atom A?

h. What is the charge on atom B?

i. Write the nuclide symbol of element B.

j. Draw pictures like those above of $^6_3Li^+$ and $^6_3Li^-$ atoms. What are the mass number and atomic number of each of these atoms?

k. Consider the two atoms depicted in this problem and the two that you just drew. What is the total number of lithium isotopes depicted? How did you make your decision?

l. Is the mass number of an isotope of an atom equal to the mass of the isotope of the atom? Be sure to explain your answer.

Conceptual Problems

2.27 One of the early models of the atom proposed that atoms were wispy balls of positive charge with the electrons evenly distributed throughout. What would you expect to observe if you conducted Rutherford's experiment and the atom had this structure?

2.28 A friend is trying to balance the following equation:

$$N_2 + H_2 \longrightarrow NH_3$$

He presents you with his version of the "balanced" equation:

$$N + H_3 \longrightarrow NH_3$$

You immediately recognize that he has committed a serious error; however, he argues that there is nothing wrong, since the equation is balanced. What reason can you give to convince him that his "method" of balancing the equation is flawed?

2.29 Given that the periodic table is an organizational scheme for the elements, what might be some other logical ways in which to group the elements that would provide meaningful chemical information in a periodic table of your own devising?

2.30 You discover a new set of polyatomic anions that has the newly discovered element "X" combined with oxygen. Since you made the discovery, you get to choose the names for these new polyatomic ions. In developing the names, you want to pay attention to convention. A colleague in your lab has come up with a name that she really likes for one of the ions. How would you name the following in a way consistent with her name?

Formula	Name
$XO_4{}^{2-}$	
$XO_3{}^{2-}$	
$XO_2{}^{2-}$	excite
XO^{2-}	

2.31 You have the mythical metal element "X" that can exist as X^+, X^{2+}, and X^{5+} ions.

a. What would be the chemical formula for compounds formed from the combination of each of the X ions and $SO_4{}^{2-}$?

b. If the name of the element X is exy, what would be the names of each of the compounds from part a of this problem?

2.32 Match the molecular model with the correct chemical formula: CH_3OH, NH_3, KCl, H_2O.

(a)   (b)   (c)   (d)

2.33 Consider a hypothetical case in which the charge on a proton is twice that of an electron. Using this hypothetical case, and the fact that atoms maintain a charge of 0, how many protons, neutrons, and electrons would a potassium-39 atom contain?

2.34 Currently, the atomic mass unit (amu) is based on being exactly one-twelfth the mass of a carbon-12 atom and is equal to 1.66×10^{-27} kg.

   a. If the amu were based on sodium-23 with a mass equal to exactly 1/23 of the mass of a sodium-23 atom, would the mass of the amu be different?

   b. If the new mass of the amu based on sodium-23 is 1.67×10^{-27} kg, how would the mass of a hydrogen atom, in amu, compare with the current mass of a hydrogen atom in amu?

2.35 For each of the following chemical reactions, write the correct element and/or compound symbols, formulas, and coefficients needed to produce complete, balanced equations. In all cases, the reactants are elements and the products are binary compounds.

   a. _____ + _____ ⟶ LiCl
   b. _____ + _____ ⟶ Na_2S
   c. __Al__ + __Br_2__ ⟶
   d. __Mg__ + __N_2__ ⟶
   e. _____ + _____ ⟶ Ca_3P_2

2.36 You perform a chemical reaction using the hypothetical elements A and B. These elements are represented by their molecular models shown below:

A B_2

The product of the reaction represented by molecular models is

   a. Using the molecular models and the boxes, present a balanced chemical equation for the reaction of elements A and B.

   b. Using the symbols A and B_2 for the chemical reaction, write a balanced chemical equation.

   c. What are some real-element possibilities for element B?

Practice Problems

2.37 What is the name of the element represented by each of the following atomic symbols?
   a. Ar   **b.** Zn   **c.** Ag   **d.** Mg

2.38 For each atomic symbol, give the name of the element.
   a. Ca   **b.** Cu   **c.** Hg   **d.** Sn

2.39 Give the atomic symbol for each of the following elements.
   a. potassium   **b.** sulfur   **c.** iron   **d.** manganese

2.40 Give the atomic symbol for each of the following elements.
   a. carbon   **b.** sodium   **c.** nickel   **d.** lead

Electrons, Protons, and Neutrons

2.41 A student has determined the mass-to-charge ratio for an electron to be 5.64×10^{-12} kg/C. In another experiment, using Millikan's oil-drop apparatus, he found the charge on the electron to be 1.605×10^{-19} C. What would be the mass of the electron, according to these data?

2.42 The mass-to-charge ratio for the positive ion F^+ is 1.97×10^{-7} kg/C. Using the value of 1.602×10^{-19} C for the charge on the ion, calculate the mass of the fluorine atom. (The mass of the electron is negligible compared with that of the ion, so the ion mass is essentially the atomic mass.)

2.43 The following table gives the number of protons and neutrons in the nuclei of various atoms. Which atom is the isotope of atom A? Which atom has the same mass number as atom A?

	Protons	*Neutrons*
Atom A	18	19
Atom B	16	19
Atom C	18	18
Atom D	17	20

2.44 The following table gives the number of protons and neutrons in the nuclei of various atoms. Which atom is the isotope of atom A? Which atom has the same mass number as atom A?

	Protons	*Neutrons*
Atom A	32	39
Atom B	32	38
Atom C	38	50
Atom D	33	38

2.45 Naturally occurring chlorine is a mixture of the isotopes Cl-35 and Cl-37. How many protons and how many neutrons are there in each isotope? How many electrons are there in the neutral atoms?

2.46 Naturally occurring lithium is a mixture of ${}_3^6Li$ and ${}_3^7Li$. Give the number of protons, neutrons, and electrons in the neutral atom of each isotope.

2.47 What is the nuclide symbol for the nucleus that contains 14 protons and 14 neutrons?

2.48 An atom contains 11 protons and 11 neutrons. What is the nuclide symbol for the nucleus?

Atomic Masses

2.49 Ammonia is a gas with a characteristic pungent odor. It is sold as a water solution for use in household cleaning. The gas is a compound of nitrogen and hydrogen in the atomic ratio 1 : 3. A sample of ammonia contains 7.933 g N and 1.712 g H. What is the atomic mass of N relative to H?

2.50 Hydrogen sulfide is a gas with the odor of rotten eggs. The gas can sometimes be detected in automobile exhaust. It is a compound of hydrogen and sulfur in the atomic ratio 2 : 1. A sample of hydrogen sulfide contains 0.587 g H and 9.330 g S. What is the atomic mass of S relative to H?

2.51 Calculate the atomic mass of an element with two naturally occurring isotopes, from the following data:

Isotope	Isotopic Mass (amu)	Fractional Abundance
X-63	62.930	0.6909
X-65	64.928	0.3091

What is the identity of element X?

2.52 An element has two naturally occurring isotopes with the following masses and abundances:

Isotopic Mass (amu)	Fractional Abundance
49.9472	2.500×10^{-3}
50.9440	0.9975

What is the atomic mass of this element? What is the identity of the element?

2.53 An element has three naturally occurring isotopes with the following masses and abundances:

Isotopic Mass (amu)	Fractional Abundance
38.964	0.9326
39.964	1.000×10^{-4}
40.962	0.0673

Calculate the atomic mass of this element. What is the identity of the element?

2.54 An element has three naturally occurring isotopes with the following masses and abundances:

Isotopic Mass (amu)	Fractional Abundance
27.977	0.9221
28.976	0.0470
29.974	0.0309

Calculate the atomic mass of this element. What is the identity of the element?

2.55 While traveling to a distant universe, you discover the hypothetical element "X." You obtain a representative sample of the element and discover that it is made up of two isotopes, X-23 and X-25. To help your science team calculate the atomic mass of the substance, you send the following drawing of your sample with your report.

In the report, you also inform the science team that the gold atoms are X-23, which have an isotopic mass of 23.02 amu, and the green atoms are X-25, which have an isotopic mass of 25.147 amu. What is the atomic mass of element X?

2.56 While roaming a parallel universe, you discover the hypothetical element "Z." You obtain a representative sample of the element and discover that it is made up of two isotopes, Z-47 and Z-51. To help your science team calculate the atomic mass of the substance, you send the following drawing of your sample with your report.

In the report, you also inform the science team that the blue atoms are Z-47, which have an isotopic mass of 47.510 amu, and the orange atoms are Z-51, which have an isotopic mass of 51.126 amu. What is the atomic mass of element Z?

Periodic Table

2.57 Identify the group and period for each of the following. Refer to the periodic table (Figure 2.15 or inside front cover). Label each as a metal, nonmetal, or metalloid.
    a. C   **b.** Po   **c.** Cr   **d.** Mg   **e.** B

2.58 Refer to the periodic table (Figure 2.15 or inside front cover) and obtain the group and period for each of the following elements. Also determine whether the element is a metal, nonmetal, or metalloid.
    a. S   **b.** Fe   **c.** Ba   **d.** Cu   **e.** Ne

2.59 Refer to the periodic table (Figure 2.15 or inside front cover) and answer the following questions.
    a. What Group VIA element is a metalloid?
    b. What is the Group IIIA element in Period 3?

2.60 Refer to the periodic table (Figure 2.15 or inside front cover) and answer the following questions.
    a. What Group VA element is a metal?
    b. What is the Group IIA element in Period 3?

2.61 Give one example (atomic symbol and name) for each of the following.
    a. a main-group (representative) element in the second period
    b. an alkali metal
    c. a transition element in the fourth period
    d. a lanthanide element

2.62 Give one example (atomic symbol and name) for each of the following.
    a. a transition element in the fifth period
    b. a halogen
    c. a main-group (representative) element in the second period
    d. an actinide element

Molecular and Ionic Substances

2.63 The normal form of the element sulfur is a brittle, yellow solid. This is a molecular substance, S_8. If this solid is vaporized, it first forms S_8 molecules; but at high temperature, S_2 molecules are formed. How do the molecules of the solid sulfur and of the hot vapor differ? How are the molecules alike?

2.64 White phosphorus is available in sticks, which have a waxy appearance. This is a molecular substance, P_4. When this solid is vaporized, it first forms P_4 molecules; but at high temperature, P_2 molecules are formed. How do the molecules of white phosphorus and those of the hot vapor differ? How are the molecules alike?

2.65 A 1.50-g sample of nitrous oxide (an anesthetic, sometimes called laughing gas) contains 2.05×10^{22} N_2O molecules. How many nitrogen atoms are in this sample? How many nitrogen atoms are in 1.00 g of nitrous oxide?

2.66 Nitric acid is composed of HNO_3 molecules. A sample weighing 4.50 g contains 4.30×10^{22} HNO_3 molecules. How many nitrogen atoms are in this sample? How many oxygen atoms are in 2.81 g of nitric acid?

2.67 A sample of ammonia, NH_3, contains 3.3×10^{21} hydrogen atoms. How many NH_3 molecules are in this sample?

2.68 A sample of ethanol (ethyl alcohol), C_2H_5OH, contains 4.2×10^{23} hydrogen atoms. How many C_2H_5OH molecules are in this sample?

2.69 Give the molecular formula for each of the following structural formulas.

a. hydrazine

b. H—O—O—H
hydrogen peroxide

c. isopropyl alcohol

d. phosphorus trichloride

2.70 What molecular formula corresponds to each of the following structural formulas?

a. glycerol

b. disilane

c. hydroxylamine

d. sulfur tetrafluoride

2.71 Write the molecular formula for each of the following compounds represented by molecular models.

(a)   (b)   (c)

2.72 Write the molecular formula for each of the following compounds represented by molecular models.

(a)   (b)   (c)

2.73 Iron(II) nitrate has the formula $Fe(NO_3)_2$. What is the ratio of iron atoms to oxygen atoms in this compound?

2.74 Ammonium phosphate, $(NH_4)_3PO_4$, has how many hydrogen atoms for each oxygen atom?

2.75 Write the formula for the compound of each of the following pairs of ions.
  a. Fe^{3+} and CN^-
  b. K^+ and SO_4^{2-}
  c. Li^+ and N^{3-}
  d. Ca^{2+} and P^{3-}

2.76 For each of the following pairs of ions, write the formula of the corresponding compound.
  a. Co^{2+} and N^{3-}
  b. NH_4^+ and PO_4^{3-}
  c. Na^+ and Co_3^{2-}
  d. Fe^{3+} and OH^-

Chemical Nomenclature

2.77 Name the following compounds.
  a. Na_2SO_4 b. CaS c. $CuCl$ d. Cr_2O_3

2.78 Name the following compounds.
  a. Na_2O
  b. Mn_2O_3
  c. NH_4HCO_3
  d. $Cu(NO_3)_2$

2.79 Write the formulas of:
  a. lead(II) permanganate
  b. barium hydrogen carbonate
  c. cesium sulfide
  d. iron(II) acetate

2.80 Write the formulas of:
a. sodium thiosulfate
b. copper(I) hydroxide
c. calcium hydrogen carbonate
d. nickel(II) phosphide

2.81 For each of the following binary compounds, decide whether the compound is expected to be ionic or molecular.
a. SeF_4 b. LiBr   c. SiF_4 d. Cs_2O

2.82 For each of the following binary compounds, decide whether the compound is expected to be ionic or molecular.
a. AlN   b. As_4O_6 c. ClF_3 d. Fe_2O_3

2.83 Give systematic names to the following binary compounds.
a. N_2O b. P_4O_{10} c. $AsCl_3$ d. Cl_2O_7

2.84 Give systematic names to the following binary compounds.
a. N_2F_2 b. CCl_4 c. N_2O_5 d. As_4O_6

2.85 Write the formulas of the following compounds.
a. nitrogen tribromide
b. xenon tetroxide
c. oxygen difluoride
d. dichlorine pentoxide

2.86 Write the formulas of the following compounds.
a. chlorine trifluoride
b. nitrogen dioxide
c. dinitrogen tetrafluoride
d. phosphorus pentafluoride

2.87 Write the systematic name for each of the following compounds represented by a molecular model.

(a)   (b)   (c)

2.88 Write the systematic name for each of the following molecules represented by a molecular model.

(a)   (b)   (c)

2.89 Give the name and formula of the acid corresponding to each of the following oxoanions.
a. bromate ion, BrO_3^-
b. hyponitrite ion, $N_2O_2^{2-}$
c. disulfite ion, $S_2O_5^{2-}$
d. arsenate ion, AsO_4^{3-}

2.90 Give the name and formula of the acid corresponding to each of the following oxoanions.
a. selenite ion, SeO_3^{2-}
b. sulfite ion, SO_3^{2-}

c. hypoiodite ion, IO^-
d. nitrite ion, NO_2^-

2.91 Glauber's salt has the formula $Na_2SO_4 \cdot 10H_2O$. What is the chemical name of this substance?

2.92 Emerald-green crystals of the substance $NiSO_4 \cdot 6H_2O$ are used in nickel plating. What is the chemical name of this compound?

2.93 Iron(II) sulfate heptahydrate is a blue-green, crystalline compound used to prepare other iron compounds. What is the formula of iron(II) sulfate heptahydrate?

2.94 Cobalt(II) chloride hexahydrate has a pink color. It loses water on heating and changes to a blue-colored compound. What is the formula of cobalt(II) chloride hexahydrate?

Chemical Equations

2.95 For the balanced chemical equation $Pb(NO_3)_2 + K_2CO_3 \longrightarrow PbCO_3 + 2KNO_3$, how many oxygen atoms are on the left side?

2.96 In the equation $2PbS + O_2 \longrightarrow 2PbO + 2SO_2$, how many oxygen atoms are there on the right side? Is the equation balanced as written?

2.97 Balance the following equations.
a. $Sn + NaOH \longrightarrow Na_2SnO_2 + H_2$
b. $Al + Fe_3O_4 \longrightarrow Al_2O_3 + Fe$
c. $CH_3OH + O_2 \longrightarrow CO_2 + H_2O$
d. $P_4O_{10} + H_2O \longrightarrow H_3PO_4$
e. $PCl_5 + H_2O \longrightarrow H_3PO_4 + HCl$

2.98 Balance the following equations.
a. $Cl_2O_7 + H_2O \longrightarrow HClO_4$
b. $MnO_2 + HCl \longrightarrow MnCl_2 + Cl_2 + H_2O$
c. $Na_2S_2O_3 + I_2 \longrightarrow NaI + Na_2S_4O_6$
d. $Al_4C_3 + H_2O \longrightarrow Al(OH)_3 + CH_4$
e. $NO_2 + H_2O \longrightarrow HNO_3 + NO$

2.99 Solid calcium phosphate and aqueous sulfuric acid solution react to give calcium sulfate, which comes out of the solution as a solid. The other product is phosphoric acid, which remains in solution. Write a balanced equation for the reaction using complete formulas for the compounds with phase labels.

2.100 Solid sodium metal reacts with water, giving a solution of sodium hydroxide and releasing hydrogen gas. Write a balanced equation for the reaction using complete formulas for the compounds with phase labels.

2.101 An aqueous solution of ammonium chloride and barium hydroxide is heated, and the compounds react to give off ammonia gas. Barium chloride solution and water are also products. Write a balanced equation for the reaction using complete formulas for the compounds with phase labels; indicate that the reactants are heated.

2.102 Lead metal is produced by heating solid lead(II) sulfide with solid lead(II) sulfate, resulting in liquid lead and sulfur dioxide gas. Write a balanced equation for the reaction using complete formulas for the compounds with phase labels; indicate that the reactants are heated.

General Problems

2.103 Two samples of different compounds of nitrogen and oxygen have the following compositions. Show that the compounds follow the law of multiple proportions. What is the ratio of oxygen in the two compounds for a fixed amount of nitrogen?

	Amount N	Amount O
Compound A	1.206 g	2.755 g
Compound B	1.651 g	4.714 g

2.104 Two samples of different compounds of sulfur and oxygen have the following compositions. Show that the compounds follow the law of multiple proportions. What is the ratio of oxygen in the two compounds for a fixed amount of sulfur?

	Amount S	Amount O
Compound A	1.210 g	1.811 g
Compound B	1.783 g	1.779 g

2.105 In a series of oil-drop experiments, the charges measured on the oil drops were -3.20×10^{-19} C, -6.40×10^{-19} C, -9.60×10^{-19} C, and -1.12×10^{-18} C. What is the smallest difference in charge between any two drops? If this is assumed to be the charge on the electron, how many excess electrons are there on each drop?

2.106 In a hypothetical universe, an oil-drop experiment gave the following measurements of charges on oil drops: -5.55×10^{-19} C, -9.25×10^{-19} C, -1.11×10^{-18} C, and -1.48×10^{-18} C. Assume that the smallest difference in charge equals the unit of negative charge in this universe. What is the value of this unit of charge? How many units of excess negative charge are there on each oil drop?

2.107 Compounds of europium, Eu, are used to make color television screens. The europium nucleus has a charge of $+63$. How many electrons are there in the neutral atom? in the Eu^{3+} ion?

2.108 Cesium, Cs, is used in photoelectric cells ("electric eyes"). The cesium nucleus has a charge of $+55$. What is the number of electrons in the neutral atom? in the Cs^+ ion?

2.109 A nucleus of mass number 81 contains 46 neutrons. An atomic ion of this element has 36 electrons in it. Write the symbol for this atomic ion (give the symbol for the nucleus and give the ionic charge as a right superscript).

2.110 One isotope of a metallic element has mass number 80 and has 55 neutrons in the nucleus. An atomic ion has 23 electrons. Write the symbol for this ion (give the symbol for the nucleus and give the ionic charge as a right superscript).

2.111 Obtain the fractional abundances for the two naturally occurring isotopes of copper. The masses of the isotopes are $^{63}_{29}$Cu, 62.9298 amu; $^{65}_{29}$Cu, 64.9278 amu. The atomic mass is 63.546 amu.

2.112 Silver has two naturally occurring isotopes, one of mass 106.91 amu and the other of mass 108.90 amu. Find the fractional abundances for these two isotopes. The atomic mass is 107.87 amu.

2.113 Identify the following elements, giving their name and atomic symbol.
  a. a nonmetal that is normally a liquid
  b. a normally gaseous element in Group IA
  c. a transition element in Group VB, Period 5
  d. the halogen in Period 2

2.114 Identify the following elements, giving their name and atomic symbol.
  a. a normally liquid element in Group VIIA
  b. a metal that is normally a liquid
  c. a main-group element in Group IIIA, Period 4
  d. the alkali metal in Period 5

2.115 Give the names of the following ions.
  a. Cr^{3+} **b.** Pb^{4+} **c.** Cu^+ **d.** Cu^{2+}

2.116 Give the names of the following ions.
  a. Mn^{2+} **b.** Ni^{2+} **c.** Co^{2+} **d.** Co^{3+}

2.117 Write formulas for all the ionic compounds that can be formed by combinations of these ions: Na^+, Ni^{2+}, SO_4^{2-}, and Cl^-.

2.118 Write formulas for all the ionic compounds that can be formed by combinations of these ions: Ca^{2+}, Cr^{3+}, O^{2-}, and NO_3^-.

2.119 Name the following compounds.
  a. $Sn_3(PO_4)_2$
  b. NH_4NO_2
  c. $Mg(OH)_2$
  d. $CrSO_4$

2.120 Name the following compounds.
  a. $Cu(NO_2)_2$ **b.** $(NH_4)_3P$
  c. Na_2SO_4 **d.** $HgCl_2$

2.121 Give the formulas for the following compounds.
  a. mercury(I) sulfide
  b. cobalt(III) sulfite
  c. ammonium dichromate
  d. aluminum nitride

2.122 Give the formulas for the following compounds.
  a. hydrogen peroxide
  b. aluminum phosphate
  c. lead(IV) phosphide
  d. boron trifluoride

2.123 Name the following molecular compounds.
  a. $AsBr_3$ **b.** H_2Se **c.** P_2O_5 **d.** SiO_2

2.124 Name the following molecular compounds.
  a. ClF_4 **b.** CS_2 **c.** NF_3 **d.** SF_6

2.125 Balance the following equations.
  a. $C_2H_6 + O_2 \longrightarrow CO_2 + H_2O$
  b. $P_4O_6 + H_2O \longrightarrow H_3PO_3$
  c. $KClO_3 \longrightarrow KCl + KClO_4$
  d. $(NH_4)_2SO_4 + NaOH \longrightarrow NH_3 + H_2O + Na_2SO_4$
  e. $NBr_3 + NaOH \longrightarrow N_2 + NaBr + HOBr$

2.126 Balance the following equations.
  a. $NaOH + H_3PO_4 \longrightarrow Na_3PO_4 + H_2O$
  b. $SiCl_4 + H_2O \longrightarrow SiO_2 + HCl$
  c. $Ca_3(PO_4)_2 + C \longrightarrow Ca_3P_2 + CO$
  d. $H_2S + O_2 \longrightarrow SO_2 + H_2O$
  e. $N_2O_5 \longrightarrow NO_2 + O_2$

2.127 A monatomic ion has a charge of $+2$. The nucleus of the ion has a mass number of 62. The number of neutrons in the nucleus is 1.21 times that of the number of protons. How many electrons are in the ion? What is the name of the element?

2.128 A monatomic ion has a charge of $+1$. The nucleus of the ion has a mass number of 85. The number of neutrons in the nucleus is 1.30 times that of the number of protons. How many electrons are in the ion? What is the name of the element?

2.129 Natural carbon, which has an atomic mass of 12.011 amu, consists of carbon-12 and carbon-13 isotopes. Given that the mass of carbon-13 is 13.00335 amu, what would be the average atomic mass (in amu) of a carbon sample prepared by mixing equal numbers of carbon atoms from a sample of natural carbon and a sample of pure carbon-13?

2.130 Natural chlorine, which has an atomic mass of 35.4527 amu, consists of chlorine-35 and chlorine-37 isotopes. Given that the mass of chlorine-35 is 34.96885 amu, what is the average atomic mass (in amu) of a chlorine sample prepared by mixing equal numbers of chlorine atoms from a sample of natural chlorine and a sample of pure chlorine-35?

2.131 Describe the island of stability. What nuclide is predicted to be most stable?

2.132 Write the equation for the nuclear reaction in which element 112 was first produced.

Strategy Problems

2.133 Correct any mistakes in the naming of the following compounds or ions.
  SO_3: sulfite
  NO_2: nitrite
  $PO_4{}^{3-}$: phosphite ion
  N_2: nitride
  $Mg(OH)_2$: maganese dihydroxide

2.134 An unknown metal (let's call it "M") is reacted with sulfur to produce a compound with the chemical formula M_2S_3. What is the charge on the metal in the compound M_2S_3? Name a metal that could be metal M.

2.135 Aluminum is reacted with sulfur to form a binary compound. Write the balanced chemical reaction and write the name of the compound formed by the reaction.

2.136 Ammonia gas reacts with molecular oxygen gas to form nitrogen monoxide gas and liquid water. Write the complete balanced reaction with all proper state symbols.

2.137 A hypothetical element X is found to have an atomic mass of 37.45 amu. Element X has only two isotopes, X-37 and X-38. The X-37 isotope has a fractional abundance of 0.7721 and an isotopic mass of 37.24. What is the isotopic mass of the other isotope?

2.138 A monotomic ion has a charge of $+3$. The nucleus of the ion has a mass number of 27. The number of neutrons in the nucleus is equal to the number of electrons in a S^{2+} ion. Identify the element and indicate the number of protons, neutrons, and electrons.

2.139 A small crystal of $CaCl_2$ that weighs 0.12 g contains 6.5×10^{20} formula units of $CaCl_2$. What is the total number of ions (cations and anions) that make up this crystal?

2.140 Write the formulas and names for all the ionic compounds that can form by combinations of the following ions: Mg^{2+}, Pb^{4+}, the carbonate anion, and the phosphide anion.

2.141 Name the following compounds:
  SO_3
  HNO_2
  Mg_3N_3
  HBr
  $Cu_3(PO_4)_2$
  $CuSO_4 \cdot 5H_2O$

2.142 The $IO_3{}^-$ anion is called iodate. There are three related ions: IO^-, $IO_2{}^-$, and $IO_4{}^-$. Using what you have learned about similar groups of anions, write the name for each of the following compounds:
  $Pb(IO_3)_2$
  KIO_4
  $Zn(IO)_2$
  $Al(IO_2)_3$

Cumulative-Skills Problems

2.143 There are 2.619×10^{22} atoms in 1.000 g of sodium. Assume that sodium atoms are spheres of radius 1.86 Å and that they are lined up side by side. How many miles in length is the line of sodium atoms?

2.144 There are 1.699×10^{22} atoms in 1.000 g of chlorine. Assume that chlorine atoms are spheres of radius 0.99 Å and that they are lined up side by side. How many miles in length is the line of chlorine atoms?

2.145 A sample of green crystals of nickel(II) sulfate heptahydrate was heated carefully to produce the bluish green nickel(II) sulfate hexahydrate. What are the formulas of the hydrates? If 8.753 g of the heptahydrate produces 8.192 g of the hexahydrate, how many grams of anhydrous nickel(II) sulfate could be obtained?

2.146 Cobalt(II) sulfate heptahydrate has pink-colored crystals. When heated carefully, it produces cobalt(II) sulfate monohydrate, which has red crystals. What are the formulas of these hydrates? If 3.548 g of the heptahydrate yields 2.184 g of the monohydrate, how many grams of the anhydrous cobalt(II) sulfate could be obtained?

2.147 A sample of metallic element X, weighing 3.177 g, combines with 0.6015 L of O_2 gas (at normal pressure and 20.0°C) to form the metal oxide with the formula XO. If the density of O_2 gas under these conditions is 1.330 g/L, what is the mass of this oxygen? The atomic mass of oxygen is 15.9994 amu. What is the atomic mass of X? What is the identity of X?

2.148 A sample of metallic element X, weighing 4.315 g, combines with 0.4810 L of Cl_2 gas (at normal pressure and 20.0°C) to form the metal chloride with the formula XCl. If the density of Cl_2 gas under these conditions is 2.948 g/L, what is the mass of the chlorine? The atomic mass of chlorine is 35.453 amu. What is the atomic mass of X? What is the identity of X?

3

Calculations with Chemical Formulas and Equations

Zinc and iodine react to produce zinc iodide, a solution used to find flaws in composite airplane wings. Zinc iodide solution sprayed on a wing will fill a crack, if present, which shows up on an x ray as an opaque area (from the absorption of x rays by iodine atoms).

Contents and Concepts

Here we will establish a critical relationship between the mass of a chemical substance and the quantity of that substance (in moles).

Explore how the percentage composition and mass percentage of the elements in a chemical substance can be used to determine the chemical formula.

Develop a molar interpretation of chemical equations, which then allows for calculation of the quantities of reactants and products.

cetic acid (ah-see'-tik acid) is a colorless liquid with a sharp, vinegary
odor. In fact, vinegar contains acetic acid, which accounts for
vinegar's odor and sour taste. The name *vinegar* derives from the
French word *vinaigre*, meaning "sour wine." Vinegar results from the
fermentation of wine or cider by certain bacteria. These bacteria require
oxygen, and the overall chemical change is the reaction of ethanol (alcohol)
in wine with oxygen to give acetic acid (Figure 3.1).

    Laboratory preparation of acetic acid may also start from ethanol,
which reacts with oxygen in two steps. First, ethanol reacts with oxygen to
yield a compound called acetaldehyde, in addition to water. In the second
step, the acetaldehyde reacts with more oxygen to produce acetic acid. (The
human body also produces acetaldehyde and then acetic acid from alcohol,
as it attempts to eliminate alcohol from the system.)

FIGURE 3.1 ▲

Electrostatic potential map of acetic acid molecule (CH₃COOH)

Acetic acid is the compound responsible for the sour taste and smell of vinegar.

    This chapter focuses on two basic questions, which we can illustrate
using these compounds: How do you determine the chemical formula of a
substance such as acetic acid (or acetaldehyde)? How much acetic acid can
you prepare from a given quantity of ethanol (or a given quantity of acetaldehyde)? These
types of questions are very important in chemistry. You must know the formulas of all the
substances involved in a reaction before you can write the chemical equation, and you need
the balanced chemical equation to determine the quantitative relationships among the different substances in the reaction. We begin by discussing how you
relate number of atoms or molecules to grams of substance, because
this is the key to answering both questions.

▇ See page 113 for the Media Summary.

This chapter develops the mole concept and related calculations.

Mass and Moles of Substance

You buy a quantity of groceries in several ways. You often purchase items such as
oranges and lemons by counting out a particular number. Some things, such as eggs and
soda, can be purchased in a "package" that represents a known quantity—for example,
a dozen or a case. Bulk foods, such as peanuts or hard candy, are usually purchased by
mass, because it is too tedious to count them out, and because we know that a given
mass yields a certain quantity of the item. All three of these methods are used by
chemists to determine the quantity of matter: counting, using a package that represents
a quantity, and measuring the mass. For a chemist, it is a relatively easy matter to weigh
a substance to obtain the mass. However, the number of atoms or molecules in even a
seemingly minute amount is much too large to count. (You may recall from Section 2.6
that a billionth of a drop of water contains 2×10^{12} H_2O molecules.) Nevertheless,
chemists are interested in knowing such numbers. How many atoms of carbon are there
in one molecule of acetic acid? How many molecules of acetic acid can be obtained
from one molecule of ethanol? Before we look at how chemists solve this problem of
measuring numbers of atoms, molecules, and ions, we must look at the concept of
molecular mass (or molecular weight) and formula mass (or formula weight) and introduce the package chemists call the mole.

3.1 | Molecular Mass and Formula Mass

In Chapter 2 (Section 2.4), we discussed the concept of atomic mass. We can easily
extend this idea to include molecular mass. The **molecular mass** (MM) of a substance
is *the sum of the atomic masses of all the atoms in a molecule of the substance.* It is,

therefore, the average mass of a molecule of that substance, expressed in atomic mass units. For example, the molecular mass of water, H_2O, is 18.0 amu (2 × 1.0 amu from two H atoms plus 16.0 amu from one O atom). If the molecular formula for the substance is not known, you can determine the molecular mass experimentally by means of a mass spectrometer. In later chapters we will discuss simple, inexpensive methods for determining molecular mass.

The **formula mass** (FM) of a substance is *the sum of the atomic masses of all atoms in a formula unit of the compound,* whether molecular or not. Sodium chloride, with the formula unit NaCl, has a formula mass of 58.44 amu (22.99 amu from Na plus 35.45 amu from Cl). NaCl is ionic, so strictly speaking the expression "molecular mass of NaCl" has no meaning. On the other hand, the molecular mass and the formula mass calculated from the molecular formula of a substance are identical. <

Some chemists use the term molecular mass in a less strict sense for ionic as well as molecular compounds.

Example 3.1 | Calculating the Formula Mass from a Formula

Calculate the formula mass of each of the following to three significant figures, using a table of atomic masses (AM): a. chloroform, $CHCl_3$; b. iron(III) sulfate, $Fe_2(SO_4)_3$.

Problem Strategy Identify the number and type of atoms in the chemical formula. Use the periodic table to obtain the atomic mass of each of the elements present in the compounds. Taking into account the number of each atom present in the formula, sum the masses. If atoms in the formula are enclosed within parentheses as in part b, the number of each element within the parentheses should be multiplied by the subscript that follows the final, or closing, parenthesis.

Solution   a. The calculation is

1 × AM of C =	12.0 amu
1 × AM of H =	1.0 amu
3 × AM of Cl = 3 × 35.45 amu =	106.4 amu
FM of $CHCl_3$ =	119.4 amu

The answer rounded to three significant figures is **119 amu.**

b. The calculation is

2 × AM of Fe =	2 × 55.8 amu =	111.6 amu
3 × AM of S =	3 × 32.1 amu =	96.3 amu
3 × 4 × AM of O =	12 × 16.00 amu =	192.0 amu
FM of $Fe_2(SO_4)_3$ =		399.9 amu

The answer rounded to three significant figures is **4.00 × 10² amu.**

Answer Check The most common error when calculating formula masses is not correctly accounting for those atoms that are enclosed in parentheses.

Exercise 3.1   Calculate the formula masses of the following compounds, using a table of atomic masses. Give the answers to three significant figures. a. nitrogen dioxide, NO_2; b. glucose, $C_6H_{12}O_6$; c. sodium hydroxide, NaOH; d. magnesium hydroxide, $Mg(OH)_2$.

An alternative example is provided in the Instructor's Resource Manual.

■ See Problems 3.27 and 3.28.

Example 3.2 | Calculating the Formula Mass from Molecular Models

For the following two compounds, write the molecular formula and calculate the formula mass to four significant figures:

(a)   (b)

(continued)

(continued)

Problem Strategy   In order to calculate the formula mass, you need to have the total number of each type of atom present in the structure, so look at the structure and keep a tally of all the atoms present.

Solution   a. This molecular model is of a molecule that is composed of two O and two H atoms. For inorganic compounds, the elements in a chemical formula are written in order such that the most metallic element is listed first. (Even though H is not metallic, it is positioned in the periodic table in such a way that it is considered to be a metal when writing formulas.) Hence, the chemical formula is H_2O_2. Using the same approach as Example 3.1, calculating the formula mass yields **34.02 amu.**

b. This molecular model represents a molecule made up of one N atom, three O atoms, and one H atom. The chemical formula is then HNO_3. The formula mass is **63.01 amu.**

Answer Check   Always make sure that your answer is reasonable. If you obtain a molecular mass of more than 200 amu for a simple molecular compound (this is possible but not typical), it is advisable to check your work closely.

(a)   (b)

Exercise 3.2   For the following compounds, write the molecular formula and calculate the formula mass to three significant figures.

■ See Problems 3.29 and 3.30.

3.2 | The Mole Concept

Measuring Avogadro's number on the overhead projector (OP). *J. Chem. Educ.* 70 (1993): 252.

ChemWork: Comparing Number of Hydrogen Atoms

ChemWork: Comparing Atoms of Different Elements

Demonstration of mole concept: show a mole of various substances.

When we prepare a compound industrially or even study a reaction in the laboratory, we deal with tremendous numbers of molecules or ions. Suppose you wish to prepare acetic acid, starting from 10.0 g of ethanol. This small sample (less than 3 teaspoonsful) contains 1.31×10^{23} molecules, a truly staggering number. Imagine a device that counts molecules at the rate of one million per second. It would take more than four billion years—nearly the age of the earth—for this device to count that many molecules! Chemists have adopted the *mole concept* as a convenient way to deal with the enormous numbers of molecules or ions in the samples they work with.

Definition of Mole and Molar Mass

A **mole** (symbol **mol**) is defined as *the quantity of a given substance that contains as many molecules or formula units as the number of atoms in exactly 12 g of carbon-12.* One mole of ethanol, for example, contains the same number of ethanol molecules as there are carbon atoms in 12 g of carbon-12.

The number of atoms in a 12-g sample of carbon-12 is called **Avogadro's number** (to which we give the symbol N_A). Recent measurements of this number give the value 6.0221367×10^{23}, which to three significant figures is 6.02×10^{23}.

A mole of a substance contains Avogadro's number (6.02×10^{23}) of molecules (or formula units). The term *mole*, like a dozen or a gross, thus refers to a particular number of things. A dozen eggs equals 12 eggs, a gross of pencils equals 144 pencils, and a mole of ethanol equals 6.02×10^{23} ethanol molecules.

In using the term *mole* for ionic substances, we mean the number of formula units of the substance. For example, a mole of sodium carbonate, Na_2CO_3, is a quantity containing 6.02×10^{23} Na_2CO_3 units. But each formula unit of Na_2CO_3 contains two Na^+ ions and one CO_3^{2-} ion. Therefore, a mole of Na_2CO_3 also contains $2 \times 6.02 \times 10^{23}$ Na^+ ions and $1 \times 6.02 \times 10^{23}$ CO_3^{2-} ions. ◄

Sodium carbonate, Na_2CO_3, is a white, crystalline solid known commercially as soda ash. Large amounts of soda ash are used in the manufacture of glass. The hydrated compound, $Na_2CO_3 \cdot 10H_2O$, is known as washing soda.

FIGURE 3.2 ▶

One mole each of various substances
Clockwise from top left: 1-octanol
($C_8H_{17}OH$); mercury(II) iodide (HgI_2);
methanol (CH_3OH); sulfur (S_8).

ChemWork: Molar Mass

Ethanol
C_2H_5OH

When using the term *mole*, it is important to specify the formula of the unit to avoid any misunderstanding. For example, a mole of oxygen atoms (with the formula O) contains 6.02×10^{23} O atoms. A mole of oxygen molecules (formula O_2) contains 6.02×10^{23} O_2 molecules—that is, $2 \times 6.02 \times 10^{23}$ O atoms.

The **molar mass** of a substance is *the mass of one mole of the substance.* Carbon-12 has a molar mass of exactly 12 g/mol, by definition.

> For all substances, the molar mass in grams per mole is numerically equal to the formula mass in atomic mass units.

Ethanol, whose molecular formula is C_2H_6O (frequently written as the condensed structural formula C_2H_5OH), has a molecular mass of 46.1 amu and a molar mass of 46.1 g/mol. Figure 3.2 shows molar amounts of different substances.

Example 3.3 | Calculating the Mass of an Atom or Molecule

a. What is the mass in grams of a chlorine atom, Cl?

b. What is the mass in grams of a hydrogen chloride molecule, HCl?

Problem Strategy In order to solve this type of problem, we need to consider using molar mass and the relationship between the number of atoms or molecules and the molar mass.

Solution a. The atomic mass of Cl is 35.5 amu, so the molar mass of Cl is 35.5 g/mol. Dividing 35.5 g (per mole) by 6.02×10^{23} (Avogadro's number) gives the mass of one atom.

$$\text{Mass of a Cl atom} = \frac{35.5 \text{ g}}{6.02 \times 10^{23}} = \mathbf{5.90 \times 10^{-23} \text{ g}}$$

b. The molecular mass of HCl equals the AM of H plus the AM of Cl, or 1.01 amu + 35.5 amu = 36.5 amu. Therefore, 1 mol HCl contains 36.5 g HCl and

$$\text{Mass of an HCl molecule} = \frac{36.5 \text{ g}}{6.02 \times 10^{23}} = \mathbf{6.06 \times 10^{-23} \text{ g}}$$

Answer Check As you know, individual atoms and molecules are incredibly small. Therefore, whenever you are asked to calculate the mass of a few atoms or molecules, you should expect a very small mass.

Exercise 3.3 a. What is the mass in grams of a calcium atom, Ca? b. What is the mass in grams of an ethanol molecule, C_2H_5OH?

An alternative example is provided in the Instructor's Resource Manual.

■ See Problems 3.33, 3.34, 3.35, and 3.36.

Mole Calculations

ChemWork: Determining Moles of a Compound

ChemWork: Moles of a Compound

> *Alternatively, because the molar mass is the mass per mole, you can relate mass and moles by means of the formula*
>
> *Molar mass = mass/moles*

ChemWork: Stoichiometry Conversions

ChemWork: Molecular Stoichiometry

Now that you know how to find the mass of one mole of substance, there are two important questions to ask. First, how much does a given number of moles of a substance weigh? Second, how many moles of a given formula unit does a given mass of substance contain? Both questions are easily answered using dimensional analysis, or the conversion-factor method. <

To illustrate, consider the conversion of grams of ethanol, C_2H_5OH, to moles of ethanol. The molar mass of ethanol is 46.1 g/mol, so we write

$$1 \text{ mol } C_2H_5OH = 46.1 \text{ g } C_2H_5OH$$

Thus, the factor converting grams of ethanol to moles of ethanol is 1 mol C_2H_5OH/46.1 g C_2H_5OH. To convert moles of ethanol to grams of ethanol, we simply invert the conversion factor (46.1 g C_2H_5OH/1 mol C_2H_5OH). Note that the unit you are converting *from* is on the bottom of the conversion factor; the unit you are converting *to* is on the top.

Again, suppose you are going to prepare acetic acid from 10.0 g of ethanol, C_2H_5OH. How many moles of C_2H_5OH is this? You convert 10.0 g C_2H_5OH to moles C_2H_5OH by multiplying by the appropriate conversion factor.

$$10.0 \text{ g } C_2H_5OH \times \frac{1 \text{ mol } C_2H_5OH}{46.1 \text{ g } C_2H_5OH} = 0.217 \text{ mol } C_2H_5OH$$

The following examples further illustrate this conversion-factor technique.

Example 3.4 | Converting Moles of Substance to Grams

Zinc iodide, ZnI_2, can be prepared by the direct combination of elements (Figure 3.3). A chemist determines from the amounts of elements that 0.0654 mol ZnI_2 can form. How many grams of zinc iodide is this?

Problem Strategy Use the formula mass to write the factor that converts from mol ZnI_2 to g ZnI_2. Note that the unit you are converting from (mol ZnI_2) is on the bottom of the conversion factor, and the unit you are converting to (g ZnI_2) is on the top.

Solution The molar mass of ZnI_2 is 319 g/mol. (The formula mass is 319 amu, which is obtained by summing the atomic masses in the formula.) Therefore,

$$0.0654 \text{ mol } ZnI_2 \times \frac{319 \text{ g } ZnI_2}{1 \text{ mol } ZnI_2} = \textbf{20.9 g } ZnI_2$$

Answer Check Whenever you solve a problem of this type, be sure to write all units, making certain that they will cancel. This "built-in" feature of dimensional analysis ensures that you are correctly using the conversion factors.

FIGURE 3.3 ▲

Reaction of zinc and iodine
Heat from the reaction of the elements causes some iodine to vaporize (violet vapor).

Exercise 3.4 Hydrogen peroxide, H_2O_2, is a colorless liquid. A concentrated solution of it is used as a source of oxygen for rocket propellant fuels. Dilute aqueous solutions are used as a bleach. Analysis of a solution shows that it contains 0.909 mol H_2O_2 in 1.00 L of solution. What is the mass of hydrogen peroxide in this volume of solution?

An alternative example is provided in the Instructor's Resource Manual. ■ See Problems 3.37, 3.38, 3.39, and 3.40.

Example 3.5 | Converting Grams of Substance to Moles

Lead(II) chromate, $PbCrO_4$, is a yellow paint pigment (called chrome yellow) prepared by a precipitation reaction (Figure 3.4). In a preparation, 45.6 g of lead(II) chromate is obtained as a precipitate. How many moles of $PbCrO_4$ is this?

Problem Strategy Since we are starting with a mass of $PbCrO_4$, we need the conversion factor for grams of $PbCrO_4$ to moles of $PbCrO_4$. The molar mass of $PbCrO_4$ will provide this information.

Solution The molar mass of $PbCrO_4$ is 323 g/mol. That is,

$$1 \text{ mol } PbCrO_4 = 323 \text{ g } PbCrO_4$$

Therefore,

$$45.6 \text{ g } PbCrO_4 \times \frac{1 \text{ mol } PbCrO_4}{323 \text{ g } PbCrO_4} = \textbf{0.141 mol } PbCrO_4$$

FIGURE 3.4 ▲
Preparation of lead(II) chromate
When lead(II) nitrate solution (colorless) is added to potassium chromate solution (clear yellow), bright yellow solid lead(II) chromate forms (giving a cloudlike formation of fine crystals).

Answer Check Note that the given amount of material in this problem (45.6 g $PbCrO_4$) is much less than its molar mass (323 g/mol). Therefore, we would expect the number of moles of $PbCrO_4$ to be much less than 1, which is the case here. Quick, alert comparisons such as this can be very valuable in checking for calculation errors.

Exercise 3.5   Nitric acid, HNO_3, is a colorless, corrosive liquid used in the manufacture of nitrogen fertilizers and explosives. In an experiment to develop new explosives for mining operations, a sample containing 28.5 g of nitric acid was poured into a beaker. How many moles of HNO_3 are there in this sample of nitric acid?

Two alternative examples are provided in the Instructor's Resource Manual.

■ See Problems 3.41 and 3.42.

Example 3.6 | Calculating the Number of Molecules in a Given Mass

How many molecules are there in a 3.46-g sample of hydrogen chloride, HCl?

An alternative example is provided in the Instructor's Resource Manual.

Problem Strategy The number of molecules in a sample is related to moles of compound (1 mol HCl = 6.02×10^{23} HCl molecules). Therefore, if you first convert grams HCl to moles, then you can convert moles to number of molecules.

Solution Here is the calculation:

$$3.46 \text{ g HCl} \times \frac{1 \text{ mol HCl}}{36.5 \text{ g HCl}} \times \frac{6.02 \times 10^{23} \text{ HCl molecules}}{1 \text{ mol HCl}}$$

$$= \textbf{5.71} \times \textbf{10}^{22} \textbf{ HCl molecules}$$

Note how the units in the numerator of a factor are canceled by the units in the denominator of the following factor.

Answer Check A very common mistake made when solving this type of problem is to use an incorrect conversion factor, such as 1 mol HCl = 6.02×10^{23} g HCl. If this statement

(continued)

(*continued*)

were true, the mass of HCl contained in a mole would be far more than the mass of all the matter in the Milky Way galaxy! Therefore, if you end up with a gigantic mass for an answer, or get stuck on how to use the quantity 6.02×10^{23} as a conversion factor, improper unit assignment is a likely culprit.

Exercise 3.6   Hydrogen cyanide, HCN, is a volatile, colorless liquid with the odor of certain fruit pits (such as peach and cherry pits). The compound is highly poisonous. How many molecules are there in 56 mg HCN, the average toxic dose?

■ See Problems 3.45, 3.46, 3.47, and 3.48.

Concept Check 3.1
You have 1.5 moles of tricycles.

a. How many moles of seats do you have?

b. How many moles of tires do you have?

c. How could you use parts a and b as an analogy to teach a friend about the number of moles of OH^- ions in 1.5 moles of $Mg(OH)_2$?

Determining Chemical Formulas

When a chemist has discovered a new compound, the first question to answer is, What is the formula? To answer, you begin by analyzing the compound to determine amounts of the elements for a given amount of compound. This is conveniently expressed as **percentage composition**—that is, as *the mass percentages of each element in the compound*. You then determine the formula from this percentage composition. If the compound is a molecular substance, you must also find the molecular mass of the compound in order to determine the molecular formula.

The next section describes the calculation of mass percentages. Then, in two following sections, we describe how to determine a chemical formula.

3.3 | Mass Percentages from the Formula

ChemWork: Percent Composition

ChemWork: Calculating Percent Composition

ChemWork: Percent Composition for Polyatomic Salts

Suppose that A is a part of something—that is, part of a whole. It could be an element in a compound or one substance in a mixture. We define the **mass percentage** of A as the parts of A *per hundred parts of the total, by mass*. That is,

$$\text{Mass \% } A = \frac{\text{mass of } A \text{ in the whole}}{\text{mass of the whole}} \times 100\%$$

You can look at the mass percentage of A as the number of grams of A in 100 g of the whole.

The next example will provide practice with the concept of mass percentage. In this example we will start with a compound (formaldehyde, CH_2O) whose formula is given and obtain the percentage composition.

Example 3.7 | Calculating the Percentage Composition from the Formula

Formaldehyde, CH_2O, is a toxic gas with a pungent odor. Large quantities are consumed in the manufacture of plastics (Figure 3.5), and a water solution of the compound is used to preserve biological specimens. Calculate the mass percentages of the elements in formaldehyde (give answers to three significant figures).

Problem Strategy To calculate mass percentage, you need the mass of an element in a given mass of compound. You can get this information by interpreting the formula in molar terms and then converting moles to masses, using a table of atomic masses. Thus, 1 mol CH_2O has a mass of 30.0 g and contains 1 mol C (12.0 g), 2 mol H (2 × 1.01 g), and 1 mol O (16.0 g). You divide each mass of element by the molar mass, then multiply by 100, to obtain the mass percentage.

Solution Here are the calculations:

$$\% \ C = \frac{12.0 \ g}{30.0 \ g} \times 100\% = \mathbf{40.0\%}$$

$$\% \ H = \frac{2 \times 1.01 \ g}{30.0 \ g} \times 100\% = \mathbf{6.73\%}$$

You can calculate the percentage of O in the same way, but it can also be found by subtracting the percentages of C and H from 100%:

$$\% \ O = 100\% - (40.0\% + 6.73\%) = \mathbf{53.3\%}$$

Answer Check A typical mistake when working a mass percentage problem is to forget to account for the number of moles of each element given in the chemical formula. An example would be to answer this question as though the formula were CHO instead of CH_2O.

Exercise 3.7 Ammonium nitrate, NH_4NO_3, which is prepared from nitric acid, is used as a nitrogen fertilizer. Calculate the mass percentages of the elements in ammonium nitrate (to three significant figures).

FIGURE 3.5 ▲
Preparing resorcinol-formaldehyde plastic
Top: The clear solution contains formaldehyde, CH_2O, and resorcinol, $C_6H_4(OH)_2$. The formation of the plastic is started by adding several drops of potassium hydroxide. *Bottom:* The red plastic has formed in the beaker.

An alternative example is provided in the Instructor's Resource Manual.   ■ See Problems 3.57, 3.58, 3.59, and 3.60.

Example 3.8 | Calculating the Mass of an Element in a Given Mass of Compound

How many grams of carbon are there in 83.5 g of formaldehyde, CH_2O? Use the percentage composition obtained in the previous example (40.0% C, 6.73% H, 53.3% O).

An alternative example is provided in the Instructor's Resource Manual.

Problem Strategy Solving this type of problem requires that you first calculate the mass percentage of the element of interest, carbon in this case (as noted in the problem, this was done in Example 3.7). Multiplication of this percentage, expressed as a decimal, times the mass of formaldehyde in the sample, will yield the mass of carbon present.

Solution CH_2O is 40.0% C, so the mass of carbon in 83.5 g CH_2O is

$$83.5 \ g \times 0.400 = \mathbf{33.4 \ g}$$

Formaldehyde
CH_2O

(*continued*)

(*continued*)

Answer Check Make sure that you have converted the percent to a decimal prior to multiplication. An answer that is more than the starting mass of material is an indication that you probably made this mistake.

Exercise 3.8   How many grams of nitrogen, N, are there in a fertilizer containing 48.5 g of ammonium nitrate and no other nitrogen-containing compound? See Exercise 3.7 for the percentage composition of NH_4NO_3.

■ See Problems 3.61 and 3.62.

3.4 | Elemental Analysis: Percentages of Carbon, Hydrogen, and Oxygen

You might want to begin Section 3.4 with this simpler example. An iron oxide was heated in a stream of hydrogen gas. If 1.534 g of the oxide yields 1.110 g of iron, what is the percentage composition? (The formula is Fe_3O_4.)

Sodium hydroxide reacts with carbon dioxide according to the following equations:

$NaOH + CO_2 \longrightarrow NaHCO_3$
$2NaOH + CO_2 \longrightarrow Na_2CO_3 + H_2O$

FIGURE 3.6 ▼

Combustion method for determining the percentages of carbon and hydrogen in a compound
The compound is placed in the sample dish and is heated by the furnace. Vapor of the compound burns in O_2 in the presence of CuO pellets, giving CO_2 and H_2O. The water vapor is collected by a drying agent, and CO_2 combines with the sodium hydroxide. Amounts of CO_2 and H_2O are obtained by weighing the U-tubes before and after combustion.

Suppose you have a newly discovered compound whose formula you wish to determine. The first step is to obtain its percentage composition. As an example, consider the determination of the percentages of carbon, hydrogen, and oxygen in compounds containing only these three elements. The basic idea is this: You burn a sample of the compound of known mass and get CO_2 and H_2O. Next you relate the masses of CO_2 and H_2O to the masses of carbon and hydrogen. Then you calculate the mass percentages of C and H. You find the mass percentage of O by subtracting the mass percentages of C and H from 100.

Figure 3.6 shows an apparatus used to find the amount of carbon and hydrogen in a compound. The compound is burned in a stream of oxygen gas. The vapor of the compound and its combustion products pass over copper pellets coated with copper(II) oxide, CuO, which supplies additional oxygen and ensures that the compound is completely burned. As a result of the combustion, every mole of carbon (C) in the compound ends up as a mole of carbon dioxide (CO_2), and every mole of hydrogen (H) ends up as one-half mole of water (H_2O). The water is collected by a drying agent, a substance that has a strong affinity for water. The carbon dioxide is collected by chemical reaction with sodium hydroxide, NaOH. < By weighing the U-tubes containing the drying agent and the sodium hydroxide before and after combustion, it is possible to determine the masses of water and carbon dioxide produced. From these data, you can calculate the percentage composition of the compound.

The chapter opened with a discussion of acetic acid. The next example shows how to determine the percentage composition of this substance from combustion data. We will use this percentage composition later in Example 3.12 to determine the formula of acetic acid.

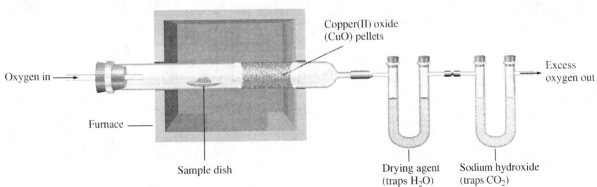

Copper(II) oxide
(CuO) pellets

Oxygen in →

Excess
oxygen out

Furnace ——

Sample dish

Drying agent
(traps H_2O)

Sodium hydroxide
(traps CO_2)

Example 3.9	Calculating the Percentages of C and H by Combustion

Acetic acid contains only C, H, and O. A 4.24-mg sample of acetic acid is completely burned. It gives 6.21 mg of carbon dioxide and 2.54 mg of water. What is the mass percentage of each element in acetic acid?

An alternative example is provided in the Instructor's Resource Manual.

Problem Strategy   Note that in the products of the combustion, all of the carbon from the sample ends up in the CO_2, all of the hydrogen ends up in the H_2O, and the oxygen is in both compounds. Because of this, you should concentrate first on the carbon and hydrogen and worry about the oxygen last. If we can determine the mass of carbon and hydrogen in the original sample, we should then be able to determine the percentage of each of these elements present in the compound. Once we know the mass percentages of carbon and hydrogen in the original compound, the remaining mass percentage (100% total) must be due to oxygen. Let's start by determining the mass of carbon that was originally contained in the compound. You first convert the mass of CO_2 to moles of CO_2. Then you convert this to moles of C, noting that 1 mol C produces 1 mol CO_2. Finally, you convert to mass of C. Similarly, for hydrogen, you convert the mass of H_2O to mol H_2O, then to mol H, and finally to mass of H. (Remember that 1 mol H_2O produces 2 mol H.) Once you have the masses of C and H, you can calculate the mass percentages. Subtract from 100% to get % O.

Solution   Following is the calculation of grams C:

$$6.21 \times 10^{-3} \text{ g CO}_2 \times \frac{1 \text{ mol CO}_2}{44.0 \text{ g CO}_2} \times \frac{1 \text{ mol C}}{1 \text{ mol CO}_2} \times \frac{12.0 \text{ g C}}{1 \text{ mol C}}$$
$$= 1.69 \times 10^{-3} \text{ g C (or 1.69 mg C}$$

For hydrogen, you note that 1 mol H_2O yields 2 mol H, so you write

$$2.54 \times 10^{-3} \text{ g H}_2O \times \frac{1 \text{ mol H}_2O}{18.0 \text{ g H}_2O} \times \frac{2 \text{ mol H}}{1 \text{ mol H}_2O} \times \frac{1.01 \text{ g H}}{1 \text{ mol H}}$$
$$= 2.85 \times 10^{-4} \text{ g H (or 0.285 mg H)}$$

You can now calculate the mass percentages of C and H in acetic acid.

$$\text{Mass \% C} = \frac{1.69 \text{ mg}}{4.24 \text{ mg}} \times 100\% = 39.9\%$$

$$\text{Mass \% H} = \frac{0.285 \text{ mg}}{4.24 \text{ mg}} \times 100\% = 6.72\%$$

You find the mass percentage of oxygen by subtracting the sum of these percentages from 100%:

$$\text{Mass \% O} = 100\% - (39.9\% + 6.72\%) = 53.4\%$$

Thus, the percentage composition of acetic acid is **39.9% C, 6.7% H, and 53.4% O.**

Answer Check   The most common error for this type of problem is not taking into account the fact that each mole of water contains two moles of hydrogen.

Exercise 3.9   A 3.87-mg sample of ascorbic acid (vitamin C) gives 5.80 mg CO_2 and 1.58 mg H_2O on combustion. What is the percentage composition of this compound (the mass percentage of each element)? Ascorbic acid contains only C, H, and O.

■ See Problems 3.63 and 3.64.

Concept Check 3.2

You perform combustion analysis on a compound that contains only C and H.

a. Considering the fact that the combustion products CO_2 and H_2O are colorless, how can you tell if some of the product got trapped in the CuO pellets (see Figure 3.6)?

b. Would your calculated results of mass percentage of C and H be affected if some of the combustion products got trapped in the CuO pellets? If your answer is yes, how might your results differ from the expected values for the compound?

3.5 | Determining Formulas

The percentage composition of a compound leads directly to its empirical formula. An **empirical formula** (or **simplest formula**) for a compound is *the formula of a substance written with the smallest integer (whole number) subscripts.* For most ionic substances, the empirical formula is the formula of the compound. < This is often not the case for molecular substances. For example, hydrogen peroxide has the molecular formula H_2O_2. The molecular formula, you may recall, tells you the precise number of atoms of different elements in a molecule of the substance. The empirical formula, however, merely tells you the ratio of numbers of atoms in the compound. The empirical formula of hydrogen peroxide (H_2O_2) is HO (Figure 3.7).

Compounds with different molecular formulas can have the same empirical formula, and such substances will have the same percentage composition. An example is acetylene, C_2H_2, and benzene, C_6H_6. Acetylene is a gas used as a fuel and also in welding. Benzene, in contrast, is a liquid that is used in the manufacture of plastics and is a component of gasoline. Table 3.1 illustrates how these two compounds, with the same empirical formula, but different molecular formulas, also have different chemical structures. Because the empirical formulas of acetylene and benzene are the same, they have the same percentage composition: 92.3% C and 7.7% H, by mass.

To obtain the molecular formula of a substance, you need two pieces of information: (1) as in the previous section, the percentage composition, from which the empirical formula can be determined; and (2) the molecular mass. The molecular mass allows you to choose the correct multiple of the empirical formula for the molecular formula. We will illustrate these steps in the next three examples.

The formula of sodium peroxide, an ionic compound of Na^+ and O_2^{2-}, is Na_2O_2. Its empirical formula is NaO.

H_2O_2

FIGURE 3.7 ▲

Molecular model of hydrogen peroxide (H_2O_2)
Hydrogen peroxide has the empirical formula HO and the molecular formula H_2O_2. In order to arrive at the correct structure of molecular compounds like H_2O_2 shown here, chemists must have the molecular formula.

ChemWork: Empirical and Molecular Formulas

ChemWork: Burning Glucose

TABLE 3.1	Molecular Models of Two Compounds That Have the Empirical Formula CH
	Although benzene and acetylene have the same empirical formula, they do not have the same molecular formula or structure.

Compound	Empirical Formula	Molecular Formula	Molecular Model
Acetylene	CH	C_2H_2	
Benzene	CH	C_6H_6	

Instrumental Methods

Mass Spectrometry and Molecular Formula

Some very sophisticated instruments have become indispensable in modern chemical research. One such instrument is the mass spectrometer, which measures the masses of positive ions produced from a very small sample and displays the data as a *mass spectrum* (see Figure 3.8). This mass spectrum can be used to identify a substance or to obtain the molecular formula of a newly prepared compound.

Positive ions of molecules, like those of atoms, can be generated by bombarding the gas, or vapor of the substance, with electrons. The mass spectra of molecules, however, are usually much more complicated than those of atoms. One reason is that the molecular ions produced often break into fragments, giving several different kinds of positive ions. Consider the CH_2Cl_2 molecule (methylene chloride). When this molecule is struck by a high-energy electron, a positive ion $CH_2Cl_2^+$ may form.

$$CH_2Cl_2 + e^- \longrightarrow CH_2Cl_2^+ + 2e^-$$

The $CH_2Cl_2^+$ ion gains a great deal of energy from the collision of CH_2Cl_2 with the electron, and the ion frequently loses this energy by breaking into smaller pieces. One way is

$$CH_2Cl_2^+ \longrightarrow CH_2Cl^+ + Cl$$

Thus, the original molecule, even one as simple as CH_2Cl_2, can give rise to a number of ions.

The second reason for the complexity of the mass spectrum of a molecular substance is that many of the atoms in any ion can occur with different isotopic mass, so each ion often has many peaks. The mass spectrum of methylene chloride, CH_2Cl_2, is shown in Figure 3.8. Fourteen peaks are clearly visible. A larger molecule can give an even more complicated spectrum.

Because of the complexity of the mass spectrum, it can be used as a "fingerprint" in identifying a compound. Only methylene chloride has exactly the spectrum shown in Figure 3.8. Thus, by comparing the mass spectrum of an unknown substance with those in a catalog of mass spectra of known compounds, you can determine its identity. The more information you have about the compound, the shorter the search through the catalog of spectra.

The mass spectrum itself contains a wealth of information about molecular structure. Some experience is needed to analyze the spectrum of a compound, but you can get an idea of how it is done by looking at Figure 3.8. Suppose you do not know the identity of the compound.

Empirical Formula from the Composition

The empirical formula of a compound shows the ratios of numbers of atoms in the compound. You can find this formula from the composition of the compound by converting masses of the elements to moles. The next two examples show these calculations in detail.

Example 3.10	Determining the Empirical Formula from Masses of Elements (Binary Compound)

A compound of nitrogen and oxygen is analyzed, and a sample weighing 1.587 g is found to contain 0.483 g N and 1.104 g O. What is the empirical formula of the compound?

Problem Strategy This compound has the formula N_xO_y, where x and y are whole numbers that we need to determine. Masses of N and O are given in the problem. If we convert the masses of each of these elements to moles, they will be proportional to the subscripts in the empirical formula. The formula must be the smallest integer ratio of the elements. To obtain the smallest integers from the moles, we divide each by the smallest one. If the results are all whole numbers, they will be the subscripts in the formula. (Otherwise, you will need to multiply by some factor, as illustrated in Example 3.11.)

(continued)

FIGURE 3.8 ▶

Mass spectrum of methylene chloride, CH_2Cl_2
The lines at higher mass correspond to ions of the original molecule. Several lines occur because of the presence of different isotopes in the ion.

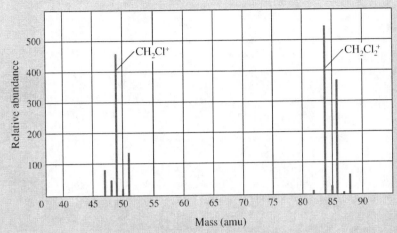

The most intense peaks at the greatest mass often correspond to the ion from the original molecule and give you the molecular mass. Thus, you would expect the peaks at mass 84 and mass 86 to be from the original molecular ion, so the molecular mass is approximately 84 to 86.

An elemental analysis is also possible. The two most intense peaks in Figure 3.8 are at 84 amu and 49 amu. They differ by 35 amu. Perhaps the original molecule that gives the peak at 84 amu contains a chlorine-35 atom, which is lost to give the peak at 49 amu. If this is true, you should expect a weaker peak at mass 86, corresponding to the original molecular ion with chlorine-37 in place of a chlorine-35 atom. This is indeed what you see.

The relative heights of the peaks, which depend on the natural abundances of atoms, are also important, because they give you additional information about the elements present. The relative heights can also tell you how many atoms of a given element are in the original molecule. Naturally occurring chlorine is 75.8% chlorine-35 and 24.2% chlorine-37. If the original molecule contained only one Cl atom, the peaks at 84 amu and 86 amu would be in the ratio 0.758 : 0.242. That is, the peak at 86 amu would be about one-third the height of the one at 84 amu. In fact, the relative height is twice this value. This means that the molecular ion contains two chlorine atoms, because the chance that any such ion contains one chlorine-37 atom is then twice as great. Thus, simply by comparing relative peak heights, you can both confirm the presence of particular elements and obtain the molecular formula.

■ See Problems 3.109 and 3.110.

(continued)

Solution   You convert the masses to moles:

$$0.483 \text{ g N} \times \frac{1 \text{ mol N}}{14.0 \text{ g N}} = 0.0345 \text{ mol N}$$

$$1.104 \text{ g O} \times \frac{1 \text{ mol O}}{16.00 \text{ g O}} = 0.06900 \text{ mol O}$$

In order to obtain the smallest integers, you divide each mole number by the smaller one (0.0345 mol). For N, you get 1.00; for O, you get 2.00. Thus, the ratio of number of N atoms to the number of O atoms is 1 to 2. Hence, the empirical formula is NO_2.

Answer Check   Keep in mind that the empirical formula determined by this type of calculation is not necessarily the molecular formula of the compound. The only information that it provides is the smallest whole-number ratio of the elements.

Exercise 3.10   A sample of compound weighing 83.5 g contains 33.4 g of sulfur. The rest is oxygen. What is the empirical formula?

An alternative example is provided in the Instructor's Resource Manual.

■ See Problems 3.65 and 3.66.

Example 3.11 | Determining the Empirical Formula from Percentage Composition (General)

Chromium forms compounds of various colors. (The word *chromium* comes from the Greek *khroma*, meaning "color"; see Figure 3.9.) Sodium dichromate is the most important commercial chromium compound, from which many other chromium compounds are manufactured. It is a bright orange, crystalline substance. An analysis of sodium dichromate gives the following mass percentages: 17.5% Na, 39.7% Cr, and 42.8% O. What is the empirical formula of this compound? (Sodium dichromate is ionic, so it has no molecular formula.)

Problem Strategy Here we need to determine the whole-number values for x, y, and z in the compound $Na_xCr_yO_z$. The first task is to use the percent composition data to determine the moles of Na, Cr, and O in the compound. Then we can use mole ratios of these elements to determine the empirical formula. Assume for the purposes of this calculation that you have 100.0 g of substance. Then the mass of each element in the sample equals the numerical value of the percentage. For example, the quantity of sodium in sodium dichromate is 17.5 g, since the substance is 17.5% Na. Now convert the masses to moles and divide each mole number by the smallest. In this example, you do not obtain a series of integers, or whole numbers, from this division. You will need to find a whole-number factor to multiply these results by to obtain integers. Normally this factor will be 2 or 3, though it might be larger.

FIGURE 3.9 ▲

Chromium compounds of different colors
Clockwise from top: Potassium chromate, K_2CrO_4; chromium(VI) oxide, CrO_3; chromium(III) sulfate, $Cr_2(SO_4)_3$; chromium metal; potassium dichromate, $K_2Cr_2O_7$; chromium(III) oxide, Cr_2O_3.

An alternative example is provided in the Instructor's Resource Manual.

Solution Of the 100.0 g of sodium dichromate, 17.5 g is Na, 39.7 g is Cr, and 42.8 g is O. You convert these amounts to moles.

$$17.5 \text{ g Na} \times \frac{1 \text{ mol Na}}{23.0 \text{ g Na}} = 0.761 \text{ mol Na}$$

$$39.7 \text{ g Cr} \times \frac{1 \text{ mol Cr}}{52.0 \text{ g Cr}} = 0.763 \text{ mol Cr}$$

$$42.8 \text{ g O} \times \frac{1 \text{ mol O}}{16.0 \text{ g O}} = 2.68 \text{ mol O}$$

Now you divide all the mole numbers by the smallest one.

$$\text{For Na: } \frac{0.761 \text{ mol}}{0.761 \text{ mol}} = 1.00$$

$$\text{For Cr: } \frac{0.763 \text{ mol}}{0.761 \text{ mol}} = 1.00$$

$$\text{For O: } \frac{2.68 \text{ mol}}{0.761 \text{ mol}} = 3.52$$

You must decide whether these numbers are integers (whole numbers), within experimental error. If you round off the last digit, which is subject to experimental error, you get $Na_{1.0}Cr_{1.0}O_{3.5}$. In this case, the subscripts are not all integers. However, they can be made into integers by multiplying each one by 2; you get $Na_{2.0}Cr_{2.0}O_{7.0}$. Thus, the empirical formula is **$Na_2Cr_2O_7$.**

Answer Check If you are working this type of problem and are not arriving at an answer that is readily converted to integers, it might be that you did not carry forward enough significant figures throughout the calculation and/or that you rounded intermediate calculations.

Exercise 3.11 Benzoic acid is a white, crystalline powder used as a food preservative. The compound contains 68.8% C, 5.0% H, and 26.2% O, by mass. What is its empirical formula?

■ See Problems 3.67, 3.68, 3.69, and 3.70.

Molecular Formula from Empirical Formula

The molecular formula of a compound is a multiple of its empirical formula. For example, the molecular formula of acetylene, C_2H_2, is equivalent to $(CH)_2$, and the molecular formula of benzene, C_6H_6, is equivalent to $(CH)_6$. Therefore, the molecular mass is some multiple of the empirical formula mass, which is obtained by summing the atomic masses of the atoms in the empirical formula. For any molecular compound, you can write

$$\text{Molecular mass} = n \times \text{empirical formula mass}$$

where n is the number of empirical formula units in the molecule. You get the molecular formula by multiplying the subscripts of the empirical formula by n, which you calculate from the equation

$$n = \frac{\text{molecular mass}}{\text{empirical formula mass}}$$

Once you determine the empirical formula for a compound, you can calculate its empirical formula mass. If you have an experimental determination of its molecular mass, you can calculate n and then the molecular formula. The next example illustrates how you use percentage composition and molecular mass to determine the molecular formula of acetic acid.

Example 3.12 | Determining the Molecular Formula from Percentage Composition and Molecular Mass

In Example 3.9, we found the percentage composition of acetic acid to be 39.9% C, 6.7% H, and 53.4% O. Determine the empirical formula. The molecular mass of acetic acid was determined by experiment to be 60.0 amu. What is its molecular formula?

Two alternative examples are provided in the Instructor's Resource Manual.

Problem Strategy This problem employs the same general strategy as Example 3.11, with a few additional steps. In this case the compound is composed of C, H, and O. After determining the empirical formula of the compound, you calculate the empirical formula mass. You then determine how many times more massive the molecular compound is than the empirical compound by dividing the molecular mass by the empirical formula mass. You now have a factor by which the subscripts of the empirical formula need to be multiplied to arrive at the molecular formula.

Solution A sample of 100.0 g of acetic acid contains 39.9 g C, 6.7 g H, and 53.4 g O. Converting these masses to moles gives 3.33 mol C, 6.6 mol H, and 3.34 mol O. Dividing the mole numbers by the smallest one gives 1.00 for C, 2.0 for H, and 1.00 for O. **The empirical formula of acetic acid is CH_2O.** (You may have noted that the percentage composition of acetic acid is, within experimental error, the same as that of formaldehyde—see Example 3.7—so they must have the same empirical formula.) The empirical formula mass is 30.0 amu. Dividing the empirical formula mass into the moecular mass gives the number by which the subscripts in CH_2O must be multiplied.

$$n = \frac{\text{molecular mass}}{\text{empirical formula mass}} = \frac{60.0 \text{ amu}}{30.0 \text{ amu}} = 2.00$$

FIGURE 3.10 ▲

Molecular model of acetic acid

The molecular formula of acetic acid is $(CH_2O)_2$, or $C_2H_4O_2$. (A molecular model of acetic acid is shown in Figure 3.10.)

(*continued*)

(continued)

Answer Check   Calculate the molecular mass of your answer. It should agree with the molecular mass of the compound given in the problem.

Exercise 3.12   The percentage composition of acetaldehyde is 54.5% C, 9.2% H, and 36.3% O, and its molecular mass is 44 amu. Obtain the molecular formula of acetaldehyde.

■ See Problems 3.73, 3.74, 3.75, and 3.76.

The condensed structural formula for acetaldehyde is CH_3CHO. Its structural formula is

$$
\begin{array}{c}
\quad\; H \quad\; O \\
\quad\; | \quad\quad \| \\
H - C - C - H \\
\quad\; | \\
\quad\; H
\end{array}
$$

Determining this structural formula requires additional information.

The formula of acetic acid is often written $HC_2H_3O_2$ to indicate that one of the hydrogen atoms is acidic (lost easily), while the other three are not (Figure 3.10). Now that you know the formulas of acetic acid and acetaldehyde (determined from the data in Exercise 3.12 to be C_2H_4O), you can write the equations for the preparation of acetic acid described in the chapter opener. < The first step consists of reacting ethanol with oxygen to obtain acetaldehyde and water. If you write the chemical equation and balance it, you obtain

$$2C_2H_5OH + O_2 \longrightarrow 2C_2H_4O + 2H_2O$$
$$\text{ethanol} \qquad\qquad\qquad\quad \text{acetaldehyde}$$

In practice, the reaction is carried out with the reactants as gases (gas phase) at about 400°C using silver as a catalyst.

The second step consists of reacting acetaldehyde with oxygen to obtain acetic acid. Acetaldehyde liquid is mixed with a catalyst—manganese(II) acetate—and air is bubbled through it. The balanced equation is

$$2C_2H_4O + O_2 \longrightarrow 2HC_2H_3O_2$$
$$\text{acetaldehyde} \qquad\qquad\quad \text{acetic acid}$$

Once you have this balanced equation, you are in a position to answer quantitative questions such as, How much acetic acid can you obtain from a 10.0-g sample of acetaldehyde? You will see how to answer such questions in the next sections.

Concept Check 3.3

A friend has some questions about empirical formulas and molecular formulas. You can assume that he is good at performing the calculations.

a. For a problem that asked him to determine the empirical formula, he came up with the answer $C_2H_8O_2$. Is this a possible answer to the problem? If not, what guidance would you offer your friend?

b. For another problem he came up with the answer $C_{1.5}H_4$ as the empirical formula. Is this answer correct? Once again, if it isn't correct, what could you do to help your friend?

c. Since you have been a big help, your friend asks one more question. He completed a problem of the same type as Example 3.12. His answers indicate that the compound had an empirical formula of C_3H_8O and the molecular formula C_3H_8O. Is this result possible?

Stoichiometry: Quantitative Relations in Chemical Reactions

In Chapter 2, we described a chemical equation as a representation of what occurs when molecules react. We will now study chemical equations more closely to answer questions about the stoichiometry of reactions. **Stoichiometry** (pronounced "stoy-key-om'-e-tree") is *the calculation of the quantities of reactants and products involved in a chemical reaction.* It is based on the chemical equation and on the relationship between mass and moles. Such calculations are fundamental to most quantitative work in chemistry. In the next sections, we will use the industrial Haber process for the production of ammonia to illustrate stoichiometric calculations.

3.6 | Molar Interpretation of a Chemical Equation

In the Haber process for producing ammonia, NH_3, nitrogen (from the atmosphere) reacts with hydrogen at high temperature and pressure.

$$N_2(g) + 3H_2(g) \longrightarrow 2NH_3(g)$$

Hydrogen is usually obtained from natural gas or petroleum and so is relatively expensive. For this reason, the price of hydrogen partly determines the price of ammonia. Thus, an important question to answer is, How much hydrogen is required to give a particular quantity of ammonia? For example, how much hydrogen would be needed to produce one ton (907 kg) of ammonia? Similar kinds of questions arise throughout chemical research and industry.

To answer such quantitative questions, you must first look at the balanced chemical equation: one N_2 molecule and three H_2 molecules react to produce two NH_3 molecules (see models above). A similar statement involving multiples of these numbers of molecules is also correct. For example, 6.02×10^{23} N_2 molecules react with $3 \times 6.02 \times 10^{23}$ H_2 molecules, giving $2 \times 6.02 \times 10^{23}$ NH_3 molecules. This last statement can be put in molar terminology: one mole of N_2 reacts with three moles of H_2 to give two moles of NH_3.

> You may interpret a chemical equation either in terms of numbers of molecules (or ions or formula units) or in terms of numbers of moles, depending on your needs.

Because moles can be converted to mass, you can also give a mass interpretation of a chemical equation. The molar masses of N_2, H_2, and NH_3 are 28.0, 2.02, and 17.0 g/mol, respectively. Therefore, 28.0 g of N_2 reacts with 3×2.02 g of H_2 to yield 2×17.0 g of NH_3.

We summarize these three interpretations as follows:

N_2	+	$3H_2$	$\longrightarrow$	$2NH_3$	
1 molecule N_2	+	3 molecules H_2	$\longrightarrow$	2 molecules NH_3	(molecular interpretation)
1 mol N_2	+	3 mol H_2	$\longrightarrow$	2 mol NH_3	(molar interpretation)
28.0 g N_2	+	3×2.02 g H_2	$\longrightarrow$	2×17.0 g NH_3	(mass interpretation)

Suppose you ask how many grams of atmospheric nitrogen will react with 6.06 g (3×2.02 g) of hydrogen. You see from the last equation that the answer is 28.0 g N_2. We formulated this question for one mole of atmospheric nitrogen. Recalling the question posed earlier, you may ask how much hydrogen (in kg) is needed to yield 907 kg of ammonia in the Haber process. The solution to this problem depends on the fact that *the number of moles involved in a reaction is proportional to the coefficients in the balanced chemical equation.* In the next section, we will describe a procedure for solving such problems.

Exercise 3.13 In an industrial process, hydrogen chloride, HCl, is prepared by burning hydrogen gas, H_2, in an atmosphere of chlorine, Cl_2. Write the chemical equation for the reaction. Below the equation, give the molecular, molar, and mass interpretations.

■ See Problems 3.77 and 3.78.

3.7

ChemWork: Finding the Amount of Compound in an Impure Sample

ChemWork: Thermite Stoichiometry

ChemWork: Finding the Mass of Lithium Carbonate

ChemWork: Burning Pentane

Amounts of Substances in a Chemical Reaction

You see from the preceding discussion that a balanced chemical equation relates the amounts of substances in a reaction. The coefficients in the equation can be given a molar interpretation, and using this interpretation you can, for example, calculate the moles of product obtained from any given moles of reactant. Also, you can extend this type of calculation to answer questions about masses of reactants and products.

Again consider the Haber process for producing ammonia gas. Suppose you have a mixture of H_2 and N_2, and 4.8 mol H_2 in this mixture reacts with N_2 to produce NH_3. How many moles of NH_3 can you produce from this quantity of H_2? In asking questions like this, you assume that the mixture contains a sufficient quantity of the other reactant (N_2, in this case).

The balanced chemical equation for the Haber process tells you that 3 mol H_2 produce 2 mol NH_3. You can express this as a conversion factor: <

This conversion factor simply expresses the fact that the mole ratio of NH_3 to H_2 in the reaction is 2 to 3.

$$\underbrace{\frac{2 \text{ mol } NH_3}{3 \text{ mol } H_2}}_{\substack{\text{Converts from} \\ \text{mol } H_2 \text{ to mol } NH_3}}$$

Multiplying any quantity of H_2 by this conversion factor mathematically converts that quantity of H_2 to the quantity of NH_3 as specified by the balanced chemical equation. Note that you write the conversion factor with the quantity you are converting *from* on the bottom (3 mol H_2), and the quantity you are converting *to* on the top (2 mol NH_3).

To calculate the quantity of NH_3 produced from 4.8 mol H_2, you write 4.8 mol H_2 and multiply this by the preceding conversion factor:

$$4.8 \text{ mol } H_2 \times \frac{2 \text{ mol } NH_3}{3 \text{ mol } H_2} = 3.2 \text{ mol } NH_3$$

Note how the unit mol H_2 cancels to give the answer in mol NH_3.

In this calculation, you converted moles of reactant to moles of product.

$$\text{Moles reactant} \longrightarrow \text{moles product}$$

It is just as easy to calculate the moles of reactant needed to obtain the specified moles of product. You mathematically convert moles of product to moles of reactant.

$$\text{Moles product} \longrightarrow \text{moles reactant}$$

To set up the conversion factor, you refer to the balanced chemical equation and place the quantity you are converting from on the bottom and the quantity you are converting to on the top.

$$\underbrace{\frac{3 \text{ mol } H_2}{2 \text{ mol } NH_3}}_{\substack{\text{Converts from} \\ \text{mol } NH_3 \text{ to mol } H_2}}$$

Now consider the problem asked in the previous section: How much hydrogen (in kg) is needed to yield 907 kg of ammonia by the Haber process? The balanced chemical equation directly relates moles of substances, not masses. Therefore, you must first convert the mass of ammonia to moles of ammonia, then convert moles of ammonia to moles of hydrogen. Finally, you convert moles of hydrogen to mass of hydrogen.

$$\text{Mass } NH_3 \longrightarrow \text{mol } NH_3 \longrightarrow \text{mol } H_2 \longrightarrow \text{mass } H_2$$

You learned how to convert mass to moles, and vice versa, in Section 3.2.

FIGURE 3.11

Steps in a stoichiometric calculation
You convert the mass of substance A in a reaction to moles of substance A, then to moles of another substance B, and finally to mass of substance B.

The calculation to convert 907 kg NH_3, or 9.07×10^5 g NH_3, to mol NH_3 is as follows:

$$9.07 \times 10^5 \text{ g NH}_3 \times \underbrace{\frac{1 \text{ mol NH}_3}{17.0 \text{ g NH}_3}}_{\substack{\text{Converts from} \\ \text{g NH}_3 \text{ to mol NH}_3}} = 5.34 \times 10^4 \text{ mol NH}_3$$

Now you convert from moles NH_3 to moles H_2.

$$5.34 \times 10^4 \text{ mol NH}_3 \times \underbrace{\frac{3 \text{ mol H}_2}{2 \text{ mol NH}_3}}_{\substack{\text{Converts from} \\ \text{mol NH}_3 \text{ to mol H}_2}} = 8.01 \times 10^4 \text{ mol H}_2$$

Finally, you convert moles H_2 to grams H_2.

$$8.01 \times 10^4 \text{ mol H}_2 \times \underbrace{\frac{2.02 \text{ g H}_2}{1 \text{ mol H}_2}}_{\substack{\text{Converts from} \\ \text{mol H}_2 \text{ to g H}_2}} = 1.62 \times 10^5 \text{ g H}_2$$

The result says that to produce 907 kg NH_3, you need 1.62×10^5 g H_2, or 162 kg H_2.

Once you feel comfortable with the individual conversions, you can do this type of calculation in a single step by multiplying successively by conversion factors, as follows:

$$9.07 \times 10^5 \text{ g NH}_3 \times \frac{1 \text{ mol NH}_3}{17.0 \text{ g NH}_3} \times \frac{3 \text{ mol H}_2}{2 \text{ mol NH}_3} \times \frac{2.02 \text{ g H}_2}{1 \text{ mol H}_2} =$$
$$1.62 \times 10^5 \text{ g H}_2 \text{ (or 162 kg H}_2)$$

Note that the unit in the denominator of each conversion factor cancels the unit in the numerator of the preceding factor. Figure 3.11 illustrates this calculation diagrammatically.

The following two examples illustrate additional variations of this type of calculation.

Example 3.13 | Relating the Quantity of Reactant to Quantity of Product

Hematite, Fe_2O_3, is an important ore of iron; see Figure 3.12. (An ore is a natural substance from which the metal can be profitably obtained.) The free metal is obtained by reacting hematite with carbon monoxide, CO, in a blast furnace. Carbon monoxide is formed in the furnace by partial combustion of carbon. The reaction is

$$Fe_2O_3(s) + 3CO(g) \longrightarrow 2Fe(s) + 3CO_2(g)$$

How many grams of iron can be produced from 1.00 kg Fe_2O_3?

Problem Strategy This calculation involves the conversion of a quantity of Fe_2O_3 to a quantity of Fe. In performing this calculation, we assume that there is enough CO for the complete reaction of the Fe_2O_3. An essential feature of this type of calculation is that you must use the information from the balanced

FIGURE 3.12

Hematite
The name of this iron mineral stems from the Greek word for blood, which alludes to the color of certain forms of the mineral.

(continued)

(continued)

chemical equation to convert from the moles of a given substance to the moles of another substance. Therefore, you first convert the mass of Fe_2O_3 (1.00 kg Fe_2O_3 = 1.0×10^3 g Fe_2O_3) to moles of Fe_2O_3. Then, using the relationship from the balanced chemical equation, you convert moles of Fe_2O_3 to moles of Fe. Finally, you convert the moles of Fe to grams of Fe.

Solution   The calculation is as follows:

$$1.00 \times 10^3 \text{ g Fe}_2\text{O}_3 \times \frac{1 \text{ mol Fe}_2\text{O}_3}{160 \text{ g Fe}_2\text{O}_3} \times \frac{2 \text{ mol Fe}}{1 \text{ mol Fe}_2\text{O}_3} \times \frac{55.8 \text{ g Fe}}{1 \text{ mol Fe}} = \textbf{698 g Fe}$$

Answer Check   When calculating the mass of product produced in a chemical reaction such as this, keep in mind that the total mass of reactants must equal the total mass of products. Because of this, you should be suspicious of any calculation where you find a few grams of reactant produces a large mass of product.

Exercise 3.14   Sodium is a soft, reactive metal that instantly reacts with water to give hydrogen gas and a solution of sodium hydroxide, NaOH. How many grams of sodium metal are needed to give 7.81 g of hydrogen by this reaction? (Remember to write the balanced equation first.)

An alternative example is provided in the Instructor's Resource Manual.   ■ See Problems 3.83, 3.84, 3.85, and 3.86.

Example 3.14 | Relating the Quantities of Two Reactants (or Two Products)

Today chlorine is prepared from sodium chloride by electrochemical decomposition. Formerly chlorine was produced by heating hydrochloric acid with pyrolusite (manganese dioxide, MnO_2), a common manganese ore. Small amounts of chlorine may be prepared in the laboratory by the same reaction (see Figure 3.13):

$$4HCl(aq) + MnO_2(s) \longrightarrow 2H_2O(l) + MnCl_2(aq) + Cl_2(g)$$

How many grams of HCl react with 5.00 g of manganese dioxide, according to this equation?

Problem Strategy   When starting a problem like this, determine and note which quantities in the balanced chemical equation are being related. Here you are looking at the two reactants, and the relationship is that 4 mol HCl reacts with 1 mol MnO_2. Answer this problem following the same strategy as outlined in Example 3.13, only this time use the relationship between the HCl and MnO_2.

Solution   You write what is given (5.00 g MnO_2) and convert this to moles, then to moles of what is desired (mol HCl). Finally you convert this to mass (g HCl). The calculation is:

$$5.00 \text{ g MnO}_2 \times \frac{1 \text{ mol MnO}_2}{86.9 \text{ g MnO}_2} \times \frac{4 \text{ mol HCl}}{1 \text{ mol MnO}_2} \times \frac{36.5 \text{ g HCl}}{1 \text{ mol HCl}} = \textbf{8.40 g HCl}$$

Answer Check   To avoid incorrect answers, before starting any stoichiometry problem, make sure that the chemical equation is complete and balanced and that the chemical formulas are correct.

FIGURE 3.13
Preparation of chlorine
Concentrated hydrochloric acid was added to manganese dioxide in the beaker. Note the formation of yellowish green gas (chlorine), which is depicted by molecular models.

(continued)

(continued)

Exercise 3.15   Sphalerite is a zinc sulfide (ZnS) mineral and an important commercial source of zinc metal. The first step in the processing of the ore consists of heating the sulfide with oxygen to give zinc oxide, ZnO, and sulfur dioxide, SO_2. How many kilograms of oxygen gas combine with 5.00×10^3 g of zinc sulfide in this reaction? (You must first write the balanced chemical equation.)

An alternative example is provided in the Instructor's Resource Manual.

■ See Problems 3.87 and 3.88.

Exercise 3.16   The British chemist Joseph Priestley prepared oxygen in 1774 by heating mercury(II) oxide, HgO. Mercury metal is the other product. If 6.47 g of oxygen is collected, how many grams of mercury metal are also produced?

■ See Problems 3.89 and 3.90.

Concept Check 3.4

The main reaction of a charcoal grill is $C(s) + O_2(g) \longrightarrow CO_2(g)$. Which of the statements below are incorrect? Why?

a. 1 atom of carbon reacts with 1 molecule of oxygen to produce 1 molecule of CO_2.

b. 1 g of C reacts with 1 g of O_2 to produce 2 grams of CO_2.

c. 1 g of C reacts with 0.5 g of O_2 to produce 1 g of CO_2.

d. 12 g of C reacts with 32 g of O_2 to produce 44 g of CO_2.

e. 1 mol of C reacts with 1 mol of O_2 to produce 1 mol of CO_2.

f. 1 mol of C reacts with 0.5 mol of O_2 to produce 1 mol of CO_2.

ChemWork: Nylon Stoichiometry

ChemWork: Making Acrylonitrile

3.8 | Limiting Reactant; Theoretical and Percentage Yields

Interactive demonstrations for mole ratios and limiting reagents. *J. Chem. Educ.* 83 (2006): 741.

Often reactants are added to a reaction vessel in amounts different from the molar proportions given by the chemical equation. In such cases, only one of the reactants may be completely consumed at the end of the reaction, whereas some amounts of other reactants will remain unreacted. The **limiting reactant** (or **limiting reagent**) is *the reactant that is entirely consumed when a reaction goes to completion*. A reactant that

Experiments in General Chemistry, 3A, "The Empirical Formula of an Oxide."

ChemWork: Finding Maximum Moles of Product

ChemWork: Formation of Sodium Amide

ChemWork: Formation of Sodium Sulfite

is not completely consumed is often referred to as an *excess reactant.* Once one of the reactants is used up, the reaction stops. This means that:

The moles of product are always determined by the starting moles of limiting reactant.

A couple of analogies may help you understand the limiting reactant problem. Suppose you want to make some cheese sandwiches. Each is made from two slices of bread and a slice of cheese. Let's write that in the form of a chemical equation:

2 slices bread + 1 slice cheese ⟶ 1 sandwich

You look in the kitchen and see that you have six slices of bread and two slices of cheese. The six slices of bread would be enough to make three sandwiches if you had enough cheese. The two slices of cheese would be enough to make two sandwiches if you had enough bread. How many sandwiches can you make? What you will find is that once you have made two sandwiches, you will be out of cheese (Figure 3.14). Cheese is the "limiting reactant" in the language of chemistry. If you look at each "reactant," and ask how much "product" you can make from it, the reactant that limits your amount of product is called the limiting reactant.

Here is another analogy. Suppose you are supervising the assembly of automobiles. Your plant has in stock 300 steering wheels and 900 tires, plus an excess of every other needed component. How many autos can you assemble from this stock? Here is the "balanced equation" for the auto assembly:

1 steering wheel + 4 tires + other components ⟶ 1 auto

One way to solve this problem is to calculate the number of autos that you could assemble from each component. In this case, you only need to concentrate on the effects of the steering wheels and tires since production will not be limited by the other, excess components. Looking at the equation, you can determine that from 300 steering wheels, you could assemble 300 autos; from 900 tires you could assemble $900 \div 4 = 225$ autos.

How many autos can you produce, 225 or 300? Note that by the time you have assembled 225 autos, you will have exhausted your stock of tires, so no more autos can be assembled. Tires are the "limiting reactant," since they limit the number of automobiles that you can actually assemble (225).

You can set up these calculations in the same way for a chemical reaction. First, you calculate the numbers of autos you could assemble from the number of steering

FIGURE 3.14 ▷

Limiting reactant analogy using cheese sandwiches
Start with six slices of bread, two slices of cheese, and the sandwich-making equation. Even though you have extra bread, you are limited to making two sandwiches by the amount of cheese you have on hand. Cheese is the limiting reactant.

wheels and from the number of tires available, and then you compare the results. From the balanced equation, you can see that one steering wheel is equivalent to one auto, and four tires are equivalent to one auto. Therefore:

$$300 \text{ steering wheels} \times \frac{1 \text{ auto}}{1 \text{ steering wheel}} = 300 \text{ autos}$$

$$900 \text{ tires} \times \frac{1 \text{ auto}}{4 \text{ tires}} = 225 \text{ autos}$$

Comparing the numbers of autos produced (225 autos versus 300 autos), you conclude that tires are the limiting component. (The component producing the fewer autos is the limiting component.) Note that apart from the units (or factor labels), the calculation is identical with what was done previously.

Now consider a chemical reaction, the burning of hydrogen in oxygen.

$$2H_2(g) + O_2(g) \longrightarrow 2H_2O(g)$$

Suppose you put 1 mol H_2 and 1 mol O_2 into a reaction vessel. How many moles of H_2O will be produced? First, you note that 2 mol H_2 produces 2 mol H_2O and that 1 mol O_2 produces 2 mol H_2O. Now you calculate the moles of H_2O that you could produce from each quantity of reactant, assuming that there is sufficient other reactant.

$$1 \text{ mol } H_2 \times \frac{2 \text{ mol } H_2O}{2 \text{ mol } H_2} = 1 \text{ mol } H_2O$$

$$1 \text{ mol } O_2 \times \frac{2 \text{ mol } H_2O}{1 \text{ mol } O_2} = 2 \text{ mol } H_2O$$

Comparing these results, you see that hydrogen, H_2, yields the least amount of product, so it must be the limiting reactant. By the time 1 mol H_2O is produced, all of the hydrogen is used up; the reaction stops. Oxygen, O_2, is the excess reactant. Figure 3.15 depicts this reaction from a molecular viewpoint.

We can summarize the limiting-reactant problem as follows. Suppose you are given the amounts of reactants added to a vessel, and you wish to calculate the amount of product obtained when the reaction is complete. Unless you know that the reactants have been added in the molar proportions given by the chemical equation, the problem is twofold: (1) you must first identify the limiting reactant; (2) you then calculate the amount of product from the amount of limiting reactant. The next examples illustrate the steps.

FIGURE 3.15

Molecular view of 2H₂ + O₂ ⟶ 2H₂O reaction with H₂ as the limiting reactant
When an equal number of moles of H_2 and O_2 are reacted according to the equation $2H_2 + O_2 \longrightarrow 2H_2O$, all of the H_2 completely reacts, whereas only half of the O_2 is consumed. In this case, the H_2 is the limiting reactant and the O_2 is the excess reactant.

H_2 reactant O_2 reactant H_2O produced and O_2 unreacted (excess)

Example 3.15	Calculating with a Limiting Reactant (Involving Moles)

Zinc metal reacts with hydrochloric acid by the following reaction:

$$Zn(s) + 2HCl(aq) \longrightarrow ZnCl_2(aq) + H_2(g)$$

If 0.30 mol Zn is added to hydrochloric acid containing 0.52 mol HCl, how many moles of H_2 are produced?

Problem Strategy

Step 1: Which is the limiting reactant? To answer this, using the relationship from the balanced chemical equation, you take each reactant in turn and ask how much product (H_2) would be obtained if each were totally consumed. The reactant that gives the smaller amount of product is the limiting reactant. (Remember how you obtained the limiting component in the auto-assembly analogy.)

Step 2: You obtain the amount of product actually obtained from the amount of limiting reactant.

Solution

Step 1:

$$0.30 \text{ mol Zn} \times \frac{1 \text{ mol } H_2}{1 \text{ mol Zn}} = 0.30 \text{ mol } H_2$$

$$0.52 \text{ mol HCl} \times \frac{1 \text{ mol } H_2}{2 \text{ mol HCl}} = 0.26 \text{ mol } H_2$$

You see that hydrochloric acid must be the limiting reactant and that some zinc must be left unconsumed. (Zinc is the excess reactant.)

Step 2: Since HCl is the limiting reactant, the amount of H_2 produced must be **0.26 mol.**

Answer Check A common assumption that often leads to errors in solving a problem of this type is to assume that whichever reactant is present in the least quantity (in mass or moles of material) is automatically the limiting reactant. Note how that assumption would have led to an incorrect answer in this problem. Always be sure to account for the stoichiometry of the balanced chemical equation.

Exercise 3.17   Aluminum chloride, $AlCl_3$, is used as a catalyst in various industrial reactions. It is prepared from hydrogen chloride gas and aluminum metal shavings.

$$2Al(s) + 6HCl(g) \longrightarrow 2AlCl_3(s) + 3H_2(g)$$

Suppose a reaction vessel contains 0.15 mol Al and 0.35 mol HCl. How many moles of $AlCl_3$ can be prepared from this mixture?

An alternative example is provided in the Instructor's Resource Manual.

■ See Problems 3.91 and 3.92.

Example 3.16	Calculating with a Limiting Reactant (Involving Masses)

In a process for producing acetic acid, oxygen gas is bubbled into acetaldehyde, CH_3CHO, containing manganese(II) acetate (catalyst) under pressure at 60°C.

$$2CH_3CHO(l) + O_2(g) \longrightarrow 2HC_2H_3O_2(l)$$

An alternative example is provided in the Instructor's Resource Manual.

In a laboratory test of this reaction, 20.0 g CH_3CHO and 10.0 g O_2 were put into a reaction vessel. a. How many grams of acetic acid can be produced by this reaction from these amounts of reactants? b. How many grams of the excess reactant remain after the reaction is complete?

Problem Strategy

a. This part is similar to the preceding example, but now you must convert grams of each reactant (acetaldehyde and oxygen) to moles of product (acetic acid). From these results, you decide which is the limiting reactant and the moles of product obtained, which you convert to grams of product.

b. In order to calculate the amount of excess reactant remaining after the reaction is complete, you need to know the identity of the excess reactant and how much of this excess reactant was needed for the reaction. The result from Step 1 provides the identity of the limiting reactant,

(continued)

(continued)

so you will know which reactant was in excess. From the moles of product produced by the limiting reactant, you calculate the grams of the excess reactant needed in the reaction. You now know how much of this excess reactant was consumed, so subtracting the amount consumed from the starting amount will yield the amount of excess reactant that remains.

Solution

a. How much acetic acid is produced?

Step 1: To determine which reactant is limiting, you convert grams of each reactant (20.0 g CH_3CHO and 10.0 g O_2) to moles of product, $HC_2H_3O_2$. Acetaldehyde has a molar mass of 44.1 g/mol, and oxygen has a molar mass of 32.0 g/mol.

$$20.0 \text{ g } CH_3CHO \times \frac{1 \text{ mol } CH_3CHO}{44.1 \text{ g } CH_3CHO} \times \frac{2 \text{ mol } HC_2H_3O_2}{2 \text{ mol } CH_3CHO} = 0.454 \text{ mol } HC_2H_3O_2$$

$$10.0 \text{ g } O_2 \times \frac{1 \text{ mol } O_2}{32.0 \text{ g } O_2} \times \frac{2 \text{ mol } HC_2H_3O_2}{1 \text{ mol } O_2} = 0.625 \text{ mol } HC_2H_3O_2$$

Thus, acetaldehyde, CH_3CHO, is the limiting reactant, so 0.454 mol $HC_2H_3O_2$ was produced.

Step 2: You convert 0.454 mol $HC_2H_3O_2$ to grams of $HC_2H_3O_2$.

$$0.454 \text{ mol } HC_2H_3O_2 \times \frac{60.1 \text{ g } HC_2H_3O_2}{1 \text{ mol } HC_2H_3O_2} = \textbf{27.3 g } HC_2H_3O_2$$

b. How much of the excess reactant (oxygen) was left over? You convert the moles of acetic acid to grams of oxygen (the quantity of oxygen needed to produce this amount of acetic acid).

$$0.454 \text{ mol } HC_2H_3O_2 \times \frac{1 \text{ mol } O_2}{2 \text{ mol } HC_2H_3O_2} \times \frac{32.0 \text{ g } O_2}{1 \text{ mol } O_2} = 7.26 \text{ g } O_2$$

You started with 10.0 g O_2, so the quantity remaining is

$$(10.0 - 7.26) \text{ g } O_2 = \textbf{2.7 g } O_2 \quad \text{(mass remaining)}$$

Answer Check Whenever you are confronted with a stoichiometry problem you should always determine if you are going to have to solve a limiting reactant problem like this one, or a problem like Example 3.13 that involves a single reactant and one reactant in excess. A good rule of thumb is that when two or more reactant quantities are specified, you should approach the problem as was done here.

FIGURE 3.16 ▲

Reaction of zinc and sulfur
When a hot nail is stuck into a pile of zinc and sulfur, a fiery reaction occurs and zinc sulfide forms.

Exercise 3.18 In an experiment, 7.36 g of zinc was heated with 6.45 g of sulfur (Figure 3.16). Assume that these substances react according to the equation

$$8Zn + S_8 \longrightarrow 8ZnS$$

What amount of zinc sulfide was produced?

■ See Problems 3.93 and 3.94.

The **theoretical yield** of product is *the maximum amount of product that can be obtained by a reaction from given amounts of reactants.* It is the amount that you calculate from the stoichiometry based on the limiting reactant. In Example 3.16, the theoretical yield of acetic acid is 27.3 g. In practice, the *actual yield* of a product may be much less for several possible reasons. First, some product may be lost during the

Such reactions reach chemical equilibrium. We will discuss equilibrium quantitatively in Chapter 14.

Experiments in General Chemistry, 3B, "Hydrates and Their Thermal Decompositions."

process of separating it from the final reaction mixture. Second, there may be other, competing reactions that occur simultaneously with the reactant on which the theoretical yield is based. Finally, many reactions appear to stop before they reach completion; they give mixtures of reactants and products. <

It is important to know the actual yield from a reaction in order to make economic decisions about a preparation method. The reactants for a given method may not be too costly per kilogram, but if the actual yield is very low, the final cost can be very high. The **percentage yield** of product is *the actual yield (experimentally determined) expressed as a percentage of the theoretical yield (calculated).*

$$\text{Percentage yield} = \frac{\text{actual yield}}{\text{theoretical yield}} \times 100\%$$

To illustrate the calculation of percentage yield, recall that the theoretical yield of acetic acid calculated in Example 3.16 was 27.3 g. If the actual yield of acetic acid obtained in an experiment, using the amounts of reactants given in Example 3.16, is 23.8 g, then

$$\text{Percentage yield of } HC_2H_3O_2 = \frac{23.8 \text{ g}}{27.3 \text{ g}} \times 100\% = 87.2\%$$

Exercise 3.19 New industrial plants for acetic acid react liquid methanol with carbon monoxide in the presence of a catalyst.

$$CH_3OH(l) + CO(g) \longrightarrow HC_2H_3O_2(l)$$

In an experiment, 15.0 g of methanol and 10.0 g of carbon monoxide were placed in a reaction vessel. What is the theoretical yield of acetic acid? If the actual yield is 19.1 g, what is the percentage yield?

Two alternative exercises are provided in the Instructor's Resource Manual. ■ See Problems 3.97 and 3.98.

Concept Check 3.5

You perform the hypothetical reaction of an element, $X_2(g)$, with another element, $Y(g)$, to produce $XY(g)$.

a. Write the balanced chemical equation for the reaction.

b. If X_2 and Y were mixed in the quantities shown in the container on the left below and allowed to react, which of the three options is the correct representation of the contents of the container after the reaction has occurred?

c. Using the information presented in part b, identify the limiting reactant.

A Checklist for Review

Important Terms

molecular mass (3.1)
formula mass (3.1)
mole (mol) (3.2)
Avogadro's number (N_A) (3.2)

molar mass (3.2)
percentage composition (3.3)
mass percentage (3.3)
empirical (simplest) formula (3.5)

stoichiometry (3.6)
limiting reactant (reagent) (3.8)
theoretical yield (3.8)
percentage yield (3.8)

Key Equations

$$\text{Mass \% } A = \frac{\text{mass of } A \text{ in the whole}}{\text{mass of the whole}} \times 100\% \qquad \text{Percentage yield} = \frac{\text{actual yield}}{\text{theoretical yield}} \times 100\%$$

$$n = \frac{\text{molecular mass}}{\text{empirical formula mass}}$$

Summary of Facts and Concepts

A *formula mass* equals the sum of the atomic masses of the atoms in the formula of a compound. If the formula corresponds to that of a molecule, this sum of atomic masses equals the *molecular mass* of the compound. The mass of *Avogadro's number* (6.02×10^{23}) of formula units—that is, the mass of one *mole* of substance—equals the mass in grams that corresponds to the numerical value of the formula mass in amu. This mass is called the *molar mass*.

The *empirical formula (simplest formula)* of a compound is obtained from the *percentage composition* of the substance, which is expressed as *mass percentages* of the elements. To calculate the empirical formula, you convert mass percentages to ratios of moles, which, when expressed in smallest whole numbers, give the subscripts in the formula. A molecular formula is a multiple of the empirical formula; this multiple is determined from the experimental value of the molecular mass.

A chemical equation may be interpreted in terms of moles of reactants and products, as well as in terms of molecules. Using this *molar interpretation*, you can convert from the mass of one substance in a chemical equation to the mass of another. The maximum amount of product from a reaction is determined by the *limiting reactant*, the reactant that is completely used up; the other reactants are in excess.

Media Summary

Visit the **student website at college.hmco.com/pic/ebbing9e** to help prepare for class, study for quizzes and exams, understand core concepts, and visualize molecular-level interactions. The following media activities are available for this chapter:

 Prepare for Class

■ **Video Lessons** *Mini lectures from chemistry experts*
The Mole and Avogadro's Number
Introducing Conversion of Masses, Moles, and Number of Particles
Finding Empirical and Molecular Formulas
Stoichiometry and Chemical Equations
Finding Limiting Reagents
CIA Demonstration: Self-Inflating Hydrogen Balloons
Theoretical Yield and Percent Yield
A Problem Involving the Combined Concepts of Stoichiometry

 Improve Your Grade

■ **Visualizations** *Molecular-level animations and lab demonstration videos*
Oxidation of Zinc with Iodine

Limiting Reactant
Oxygen, Hydrogen, Soap Bubbles, and Balloons

■ **Tutorials** *Animated examples and interactive activities*
Formula Mass
Limiting Reactants: Part One
Limiting Reactants: Part Two

■ **Flashcards** *Key terms and definitions*
Online Flashcards

■ **Self-Assessment Questions** *Additional questions with full worked-out solutions*
6 Self-Assessment Questions

 ACE the Test

Multiple-choice quizzes
3 ACE Practice Tests

Access these resources using the passkey available free with new texts or for purchase separately.

Learning Objectives

3.1 Molecular Mass and Formula Mass

■ Define the terms *molecular mass* and *formula mass* of a substance.
■ Calculate the formula mass from a formula. Example 3.1
■ Calculate the formula mass from molecular models. Example 3.2

3.2 The Mole Concept

■ Define the quantity called the *mole*.
■ Learn *Avogadro's number*.
■ Understand how the *molar mass* is related to the formula mass of a substance.
■ Calculate the mass of atoms and molecules. Example 3.3
■ Perform calculations using the mole.
■ Convert from moles of substance to grams of substance. Example 3.4
■ Convert from grams of substance to moles of substance. Example 3.5
■ Calculate the number of molecules in a given mass of substance. Example 3.6

3.3 Mass Percentages from the Formula

■ Define *mass percentage*.
■ Calculate the percentage composition of the elements in a compound. Example 3.7
■ Calculate the mass of an element in a given mass of compound. Example 3.8

3.4 Elemental Analysis: Percentage of Carbon, Hydrogen, and Oxygen

■ Describe how C, H, and O combustion analysis is performed.
■ Calculate the percentage of C, H, and O from combustion data. Example 3.9

3.5 Determining Formulas

■ Define *empirical formula*.
■ Determine the empirical formula of a binary compound from the masses of its elements. Example 3.10
■ Determine the empirical formula from the percentage composition. Example 3.11
■ Understand the relationship between the molecular mass of a substance and its *empirical formula mass*.
■ Determine the molecular formula from the percentage composition and molecular mass. Example 3.12

3.6 Molar Interpretation of a Chemical Equation

■ Relate the coefficients in a balanced chemical equation to the number of molecules or moles (*molar interpretation*).

3.7 Amounts of Substances in a Chemical Reaction

■ Use the coefficients in a chemical reaction to perform calculations.
■ Relate the quantities of reactant to the quantity of product. Example 3.13
■ Relate the quantities of two reactants or two products. Example 3.14

3.8 Limiting Reactant; Theoretical and Percentage Yields

■ Understand how a *limiting reactant* or *limiting reagent* determines the moles of product formed during a chemical reaction and how much *excess reactant* remains.
■ Calculate with a limiting reactant involving moles. Example 3.15
■ Calculate with a limiting reactant involving masses. Example 3.16
■ Define and calculate the *theoretical yield* of chemical reactions.
■ Determine the *percentage yield* of a chemical reaction.

Self-Assessment and Review Questions

3.1 What is the difference between a formula mass and a molecular mass? Could a given substance have both a formula mass and a molecular mass?

3.2 Describe in words how to obtain the formula mass of a compound from the formula.

3.3 One mole of N_2 contains how many N_2 molecules? How many N atoms are there in one mole of N_2? One mole of iron(III) sulfate, $Fe_2(SO_4)_3$, contains how many moles of SO_4^{2-} ions? How many moles of O atoms?

3.4 Explain what is involved in determining the composition of a compound of C, H, and O by combustion.

3.5 Explain what is involved in obtaining the empirical formula from the percentage composition.

3.6 A substance has the molecular formula $C_6H_{12}O_2$. What is its empirical formula?

3.7 Hydrogen peroxide has the empirical formula HO and an empirical formula weight of 17.0 amu. If the molecular mass is 34.0 amu, what is the molecular formula?

3.8 Describe in words the meaning of the equation

$$CH_4 + 2O_2 \longrightarrow CO_2 + 2H_2O$$

using a molecular, a molar, and then a mass interpretation.

3.9 Explain how a chemical equation can be used to relate the masses of different substances involved in a reaction.

3.10 What is a limiting reactant in a reaction mixture? Explain how it determines the amount of product.

3.11 Come up with some examples of limiting reactants that use the concept but don't involve chemical reactions.

3.12 Explain why it is impossible to have a theoretical yield of more than 100%.

3.13 How many grams of NH_3 will have the same number of molecules as 15.0 g of C_6H_6?

  a. 3.27
  b. 1.92
  c. 15.0
  d. 17.0
  e. 14.2

3.14 Which of the following has the largest number of molecules?

  a. 1 g of benzene, C_6H_6
  b. 1 g of formaldehyde, CH_2O
  c. 1 g of TNT, $C_7H_5N_3O_6$
  d. 1 g of naphthalene, $C_{10}H_8$
  e. 1 g of glucose, $C_6H_{12}O_6$

3.15 How many atoms are present in 123 g of magnesium cyanide?

  a. 9.7×10^{23}
  b. 2.91×10^{24}
  c. 2.83×10^{28}
  d. 4.85×10^{24}
  e. 5.65×10^{27}

3.16 When 2.56 g of a compound containing only carbon, hydrogen, and oxygen is burned completely, 3.84 g of CO_2 and 1.05 g of H_2O are produced. What is the empirical formula of the compound?

  a. $C_3H_4O_3$
  b. $C_5H_6O_4$
  c. $C_5H_6O_5$
  d. $C_4H_4O_3$
  e. $C_4H_6O_3$

Concept Explorations

3.17 Moles and Molar Mass

Part 1: The mole provides a convenient package where we can make a connection between the mass of a substance and the number (count) of that substance. This is a familiar concept if you have ever bought nails at a hardware store, where you purchase nails by mass rather than count. Typically, there is a scale provided for weighing the nails. For example, a notice placed above the nail bin might read, "For the nails in the bin below, there are 500 nails per kg." Using this conversion factor, perform the following calculations.

  a. How many nails would you have if you had 0.2 kg?
  b. If you had 10 dozen nails, what would be their mass?
  c. What is the mass of one nail?
  d. What is the mass of 2.0 moles of nails?

Part 2: The periodic table provides information about each element that serves somewhat the same purpose as the label on the nail bin described in Part 1, only in this case, the mass (molar mass) of each element is the number of grams of the element that contain 6.02×10^{23} atoms or molecules of the element. As you are aware, the quantity 6.02×10^{23} is called the mole.

  a. If you had 0.2 kg of helium, how many helium atoms would you have?
  b. If you had 10 dozen helium atoms, what would be their mass?
  c. What is the mass of one helium atom?
  d. What is the mass of 2.0 moles of helium atoms?

Part 3: Say there is a newly defined "package" called the binkle. One binkle is defined as being exactly 3×10^{12}.

  a. If you had 1.0 kg of nails and 1.0 kg of helium atoms, would you expect them to have the same number of binkles? Using complete sentences, explain your answer.
  b. If you had 3.5 binkles of nails and 3.5 binkles of helium atoms, which quantity would have more (count) and which would have more mass? Using complete sentences, explain your answers.
  c. Which would contain more atoms, 3.5 g of helium or 3.5 g of lithium? Using complete sentences, explain your answer.

3.18 Moles Within Moles and Molar Mass

Part 1

  a. How many hydrogen and oxygen atoms are present in 1 molecule of H_2O?
  b. How many moles of hydrogen and oxygen atoms are present in 1 mol H_2O?
  c. What are the masses of hydrogen and oxygen in 1.0 mol H_2O?
  d. What is the mass of 1.0 mol H_2O?

Part 2: Two hypothetical ionic compounds are discovered with the chemical formulas XCl_2 and YCl_2, where X and Y represent symbols of the imaginary elements. Chemical analysis of the two compounds reveals that 0.25 mol XCl_2 has a mass of 100.0 g and 0.50 mol YCl_2 has a mass of 125.0 g.

  a. What are the molar masses of XCl_2 and YCl_2?
  b. If you had 1.0-mol samples of XCl_2 and YCl_2, how would the number of chloride ions compare?
  c. If you had 1.0-mol samples of XCl_2 and YCl_2, how would the masses of elements X and Y compare?

d. What is the mass of chloride ions present in 1.0 mol XCl_2 and 1.0 mol YCl_2?

e. What are the molar masses of elements X and Y?

f. How many moles of X ions and chloride ions would be present in a 200.0-g sample of XCl_2?

g. How many grams of Y ions would be present in a 250.0-g sample of YCl_2?

h. What would be the molar mass of the compound YBr_3?

Part 3: A minute sample of $AlCl_3$ is analyzed for chlorine. The analysis reveals that there are 12 chloride ions present in the sample. How many aluminum ions must be present in the sample?

a. What is the total mass of $AlCl_3$ in this sample?

b. How many moles of $AlCl_3$ are in this sample?

Conceptual Problems

3.19 You react nitrogen and hydrogen in a container to produce ammonia, $NH_3(g)$. The following figure depicts the contents of the container after the reaction is complete.

a. Write a balanced chemical equation for the reaction.
b. What is the limiting reactant?
c. How many molecules of the limiting reactant would you need to add to the container in order to have a complete reaction (convert all reactants to products)?

3.20 Propane, C_3H_8, is the fuel of choice in a gas barbecue. When burning, the balanced equation is

$$C_3H_8 + 5O_2 \longrightarrow 3CO_2 + 4H_2O$$

a. What is the limiting reactant in cooking with a gas grill?
b. If the grill will not light and you know that you have an ample flow of propane to the burner, what is the limiting reactant?
c. When using a gas grill you can sometimes turn the gas up to the point at which the flame becomes yellow and smokey. In terms of the chemical reaction, what is happening?

3.21 A critical point to master in becoming proficient at solving problems is evaluating whether or not your answer is reasonable. A friend asks you to look over her homework to see if she has done the calculations correctly. Shown below are descriptions of some of her answers. Without using your calculator or doing calculations on paper, see if you can judge the answers below as being reasonable or ones that will require her to go back and work the problems again.

a. 0.33 mol of an element has a mass of 1.0×10^{-3} g.
b. The mass of one molecule of water is 1.80×10^{-10} g.
c. There are 3.01×10^{23} atoms of Na in 0.500 mol of Na.
d. The molar mass of CO_2 is 44.0 kg/mol.

3.22 An exciting, and often loud, chemical demonstration involves the simple reaction of hydrogen gas and oxygen gas to produce water vapor:

$$2H_2(g) + O_2(g) \longrightarrow 2H_2O(g)$$

The reaction is carried out in soap bubbles or balloons that are filled with the reactant gases. We get the reaction to proceed by igniting the bubbles or balloons. The more H_2O that is formed during the reaction, the bigger the bang. Explain the following observations.

a. A bubble containing just H_2 makes a quiet "fffft" sound when ignited.
b. When a bubble containing equal amounts of H_2 and O_2 is ignited, a sizable bang results.
c. When a bubble containing a ratio of 2 to 1 in the amounts of H_2 and O_2 is ignited, the loudest bang results.
d. When a bubble containing just O_2 is ignited, virtually no sound is made.

3.23 High cost and limited availability of a reactant often dictate which reactant is limiting in a particular process. Identify the limiting reactant when the reactions below are run, and come up with a reason to support your decision.

a. Burning charcoal on a grill:

$$C(s) + O_2(g) \longrightarrow CO_2(g)$$

b. Burning a chunk of Mg in water:

$$Mg(s) + 2H_2O(l) \longrightarrow Mg(OH)_2(aq) + H_2(g)$$

c. The Haber process of ammonia production:

$$3H_2(g) + N_2(g) \longrightarrow 2NH_3(g)$$

3.24 A few hydrogen and oxygen molecules are introduced into a container in the quantities depicted in the following drawing. The gases are then ignited by a spark, causing them to react and form H_2O.

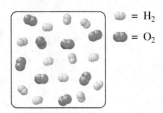

a. What is the maximum number of water molecules that can be formed in the chemical reaction?
b. Draw a molecular level representation of the container's contents after the chemical reaction.

3.25 A friend asks if you would be willing to check several homework problems to see if she is on the right track. Following are the problems and her proposed solutions. When you identify the problem with her work, make the appropriate correction.

a. Calculate the number of moles of calcium in 27.0 g of Ca.

$$27.0 \text{ g Ca} \times \frac{1 \text{ mol Ca}}{6.022 \times 10^{23} \text{ g Ca}} = ?$$

b. Calculate the number of potassium ions in 2.5 mol of K_2SO_4.

$$2.5 \text{ mol } K_2SO_4 \times \frac{1 \text{ mol } K^+ \text{ ions}}{1 \text{ mol } K_2SO_4}$$

$$\times \frac{6.022 \times 10^{23} \text{ K}^+ \text{ ions}}{1 \text{ mol } K^+ \text{ ions}} = ?$$

c. Sodium reacts with water according to the following chemical equation.

$$2Na + 2H_2O \longrightarrow H_2 + 2NaOH$$

Assuming complete reaction, calculate the number of moles of water required to react with 0.50 mol of Na.

$$0.50 \text{ mol Na} \times \frac{1 \text{ mol } H_2O}{2 \text{ mol Na}} = ?$$

Practice Problems

Formula Masses and Mole Calculations

3.27 Find the formula masses of the following substances to three significant figures.
  a. methanol, CH_3OH
  b. nitrogen trioxide, NO_3
  c. potassium carbonate, K_2CO_3
  d. nickel phosphate, $Ni_3(PO_4)_2$

3.28 Find the formula masses of the following substances to three significant figures.
  a. sulfuric acid, K_2SO_4
  b. phosphorus pentachloride, PCl_5
  c. potassium sulfite, K_2SO_3
  d. calcium hydroxide, $Ca(OH)_2$

3.29 Calculate the formula mass of the following molecules to three significant figures.

(a)   (b)

3.30 Calculate the formula mass of the following molecules to three significant figures.

(a)   (b)

3.26 A friend is doing his chemistry homework and is working with the following chemical reaction.

$$2C_2H_2(g) + 5O_2(g) \longrightarrow 4CO_2(g) + 2H_2O(g)$$

He tells you that if he reacts 2 moles of C_2H_2 with 4 moles of O_2, then the C_2H_2 is the limiting reactant since there are fewer moles of C_2H_2 than O_2.
  a. How would you explain to him where he went wrong with his reasoning (what concept is he missing)?
  b. After providing your friend with the explanation from part a, he still doesn't believe you because he *had* a homework problem where 2 moles of calcium were reacted with 4 moles of sulfur and he needed to determine the limiting reactant. The reaction is

$$Ca(s) + S(s) \longrightarrow CaS(s)$$

He obtained the correct answer, Ca, by reasoning that since there were fewer moles of calcium reacting, calcium *had* to be the limiting reactant. How would you explain his reasoning flaw and why he got "lucky" in choosing the answer that he did?

3.31 Ammonium nitrate, NH_4NO_3, is used as a nitrogen fertilizer and in explosives. What is the molar mass of NH_4NO_3?

3.32 Phosphoric acid, H_3PO_4, is used to make phosphate fertilizers and detergents and is also used in carbonated beverages. What is the molar mass of H_3PO_4?

3.33 Calculate the mass (in grams) of each of the following species.
  a. Na atom   **b.** N atom
  c. CH_3Cl molecule   **d.** $Hg(NO_3)_2$ formula unit

3.34 Calculate the mass (in grams) of each of the following species.
  a. Ar atom   **b.** Te atom
  c. PBr_3 molecule   **d.** $Fe(OH)_3$ formula unit

3.35 Diethyl ether, $(C_2H_5)_2O$, commonly known as ether, is used as an anesthetic. What is the mass in grams of a molecule of diethyl ether?

3.36 Glycerol, $C_3H_8O_3$, is used as a moistening agent for candy and is the starting material for nitroglycerin. Calculate the mass of a glycerol molecule in grams.

3.37 Calculate the mass in grams of the following.
  a. 0.15 mol Na   **b.** 0.594 mol S
  c. 2.78 mol CH_2Cl_2 **d.** 38 mol $(NH_4)_2S$

3.38 Calculate the mass in grams of the following.
  a. 0.205 mol Fe   **b.** 0.79 mol F
  c. 5.8 mol CO_2 **d.** 48.1 mol K_2CrO_4

3.39 Boric acid, H_3BO_3, is a mild antiseptic and is often used as an eyewash. A sample contains 0.543 mol H_3BO_3. What is the mass of boric acid in the sample?

3.40 Carbon disulfide, CS_2, is a colorless, highly flammable liquid used in the manufacture of rayon and cellophane. A sample contains 0.0205 mol CS_2. Calculate the mass of carbon disulfide in the sample.

3.41 Obtain the moles of substance in the following.
  a. 2.86 g C   **b.** 7.05 g Cl_2
  c. 76 g C_4H_{10} **d.** 26.2 g $Al_2(CO_3)_3$

3.42 Obtain the moles of substance in the following.
  a. 2.57 g As
  b. 7.83 g S_8
  c. 36.5 g N_2H_4
  d. 227 g $Al_2(SO_4)_3$

3.43 Calcium sulfate, $CaSO_4$, is a white, crystalline powder. Gypsum is a mineral, or natural substance, that is a hydrate of calcium sulfate. A 1.000-g sample of gypsum contains 0.791 g $CaSO_4$. How many moles of $CaSO_4$ are there in this sample? Assuming that the rest of the sample is water, how many moles of H_2O are there in the sample? Show that the result is consistent with the formula $CaSO_4 \cdot 2H_2O$.

3.44 A 1.547-g sample of blue copper(II) sulfate pentahydrate, $CuSO_4 \cdot 5H_2O$, is heated carefully to drive off the water. The white crystals of $CuSO_4$ that are left behind have a mass of 0.989 g. How many moles of H_2O were in the original sample? Show that the relative molar amounts of $CuSO_4$ and H_2O agree with the formula of the hydrate.

3.45 Calculate the following.
  a. number of atoms in 8.21 g Li
  b. number of atoms in 32.0 g Br_2
  c. number of molecules in 45 g NH_3
  d. number of formula units in 201 g $PbCrO_4$
  e. number of SO_4^{2-} ions in 14.3 g $Cr_2(SO_4)_3$

3.46 Calculate the following.
  a. number of atoms in 25.7 g Al
  b. number of atoms in 8.71 g I_2
  c. number of molecules in 14.9 g N_2O_5
  d. number of formula units in 3.31 g $NaClO_4$
  e. number of Ca^{2+} ions in 4.71 g $Ca_3(PO_4)_2$

3.47 Carbon tetrachloride is a colorless liquid used in the manufacture of fluorocarbons and as an industrial solvent. How many molecules are there in 7.58 mg of carbon tetrachloride?

3.48 Chlorine trifluoride is a colorless, reactive gas used in nuclear fuel reprocessing. How many molecules are there in a 5.88-mg sample of chlorine trifluoride?

Mass Percentage

3.49 A 1.836-g sample of coal contains 1.584 g C. Calculate the mass percentage of C in the coal.

3.50 A 6.01-g aqueous solution of isopropyl alcohol contains 4.01 g of isopropyl alcohol. What is the mass percentage of isopropyl alcohol in the solution?

3.51 Phosphorus oxychloride is the starting compound for preparing substances used as flame retardants for plastics. An 8.53-mg sample of phosphorus oxychloride contains 1.72 mg of phosphorus. What is the mass percentage of phosphorus in the compound?

3.52 Ethyl mercaptan is an odorous substance added to natural gas to make leaks easily detectable. A sample of ethyl mercaptan weighing 3.17 mg contains 1.64 mg of sulfur. What is the mass percentage of sulfur in the substance?

3.53 A fertilizer is advertised as containing 14.0% nitrogen (by mass). How much nitrogen is there in 4.15 kg of fertilizer?

3.54 Seawater contains 0.0065% (by mass) of bromine. How many grams of bromine are there in 2.50 L of seawater? The density of seawater is 1.025 g/cm^3.

3.55 A sample of an alloy of aluminum contains 0.0898 mol Al and 0.0381 mol Mg. What are the mass percentages of Al and Mg in the alloy?

3.56 A sample of gas mixture from a neon sign contains 0.0856 mol Ne and 0.0254 mol Kr. What are the mass percentages of Ne and Kr in the gas mixture?

Chemical Formulas

3.57 Calculate the percentage composition for each of the following compounds (three significant figures).
  a. CO   **b.** CO_2
  c. NaH_2PO_4 **d.** $Co(NO_3)_2$

3.58 Calculate the percentage composition for each of the following compounds (three significant figures).
  a. NO_2
  b. H_2O_2
  c. $KClO_4$
  d. $Mg(NO_2)_2$

3.59 Calculate the mass percentage of each element in toluene, represented by the following molecular model.

3.60 Calculate the mass percentage of each element in 2-propanol, represented by the following molecular model.

3.61 Which contains more carbon, 6.01 g of glucose, $C_6H_{12}O_6$, or 5.85 g of ethanol, C_2H_6O?

3.62 Which contains more sulfur, 40.8 g of calcium sulfate, $CaSO_4$, or 35.2 g of sodium sulfite, Na_2SO_3?

3.63 Ethylene glycol is used as an automobile antifreeze and in the manufacture of polyester fibers. The name glycol stems from the sweet taste of this poisonous compound. Combustion of 6.38 mg of ethylene glycol gives 9.06 mg CO_2 and 5.58 mg H_2O. The compound contains only C, H, and O. What are the mass percentages of the elements in ethylene glycol?

3.64 Phenol, commonly known as carbolic acid, was used by Joseph Lister as an antiseptic for surgery in 1865. Its principal use today is in the manufacture of phenolic resins and plastics. Combustion of 5.23 mg of phenol yields 14.67 mg CO_2 and 3.01 mg H_2O. Phenol contains only C, H, and O. What is the percentage of each element in this substance?

3.65 An oxide of osmium (symbol Os) is a pale yellow solid. If 2.89 g of the compound contains 2.16 g of osmium, what is its empirical formula?

3.66 An oxide of tungsten (symbol W) is a bright yellow solid. If 5.34 g of the compound contains 4.23 g of tungsten, what is its empirical formula?

3.67 Potassium manganate is a dark green, crystalline substance whose composition is 39.6% K, 27.9% Mn, and 32.5% O, by mass. What is its empirical formula?

3.68 Hydroquinone, used as a photographic developer, is 65.4% C, 5.5% H, and 29.1% O, by mass. What is the empirical formula of hydroquinone?

3.69 Acrylic acid, used in the manufacture of acrylic plastics, has the composition 50.0% C, 5.6% H, and 44.4% O. What is its empirical formula?

3.70 Malonic acid is used in the manufacture of barbiturates (sleeping pills). The composition of the acid is 34.6% C, 3.9% H, and 61.5% O. What is malonic acid's empirical formula?

3.71 Two compounds have the same composition: 92.25% C and 7.75% H.
  a. Obtain the empirical formula corresponding to this composition.
  b. One of the compounds has a molecular mass of 52.03 amu; the other, of 78.05 amu. Obtain the molecular formulas of both compounds.

3.72 Two compounds have the same composition: 85.62% C and 14.38% H.
  a. Obtain the empirical formula corresponding to this composition.
  b. One of the compounds has a molecular mass of 28.03 amu; the other, of 56.06 amu. Obtain the molecular formulas of both compounds.

3.73 Putrescine, a substance produced by decaying animals, has the empirical formula C_2H_6N. Several determinations of molecular mass give values in the range of 87 to 90 amu. Find the molecular formula of putrescine.

3.74 Compounds of boron with hydrogen are called boranes. One of these boranes has the empirical formula BH_3 and a molecular mass of 28 amu. What is its molecular formula?

3.75 Oxalic acid is a toxic substance used by laundries to remove rust stains. Its composition is 26.7% C, 2.2% H, and 71.1% O (by mass), and its molecular mass is 90 amu. What is its molecular formula?

3.76 Adipic acid is used in the manufacture of nylon. The composition of the acid is 49.3% C, 6.9% H, and 43.8% O (by mass), and the molecular mass is 146 amu. What is the molecular formula?

Stoichiometry: Quantitative Relations in Reactions

3.77 Ethylene, C_2H_4, burns in oxygen to give carbon dioxide, CO_2, and water. Write the equation for the reaction, giving molecular, molar, and mass interpretations below the equation.

3.78 Hydrogen sulfide gas, H_2S, burns in oxygen to give sulfur dioxide, SO_2, and water. Write the equation for the reaction, giving molecular, molar, and mass interpretations below the equation.

3.79 Butane, C_4H_{10}, burns with the oxygen in air to give carbon dioxide and water.

$$2C_4H_{10}(g) + 13O_2(g) \longrightarrow 8CO_2(g) + 10H_2O(g)$$

What is the amount (in moles) of carbon dioxide produced from 0.30 mol C_4H_{10}?

3.80 Ethanol, C_2H_5OH, burns with the oxygen in air to give carbon dioxide and water.

$$C_2H_5OH(l) + 3O_2(g) \longrightarrow 2CO_2(g) + 3H_2O(l)$$

What is the amount (in moles) of water produced from 0.69 mol C_2H_5OH?

3.81 Iron in the form of fine wire burns in oxygen to form iron(III) oxide.

$$4Fe(s) + 3O_2(g) \longrightarrow 2Fe_2O_3(s)$$

How many moles of O_2 are needed to produce 3.91 mol Fe_2O_3?

3.82 Nickel(II) chloride reacts with sodium phosphate to precipitate nickel(II) phosphate.

$$3NiCl_2(aq) + 2Na_3PO_4(aq) \longrightarrow Ni_3(PO_4)_2(s) + 6NaCl(aq)$$

How many moles of nickel(II) chloride are needed to produce 0.517 mol nickel(II) phosphate?

3.83 Nitric acid, HNO_3, is manufactured by the Ostwald process, in which nitrogen dioxide, NO_2, reacts with water.

$$3NO_2(g) + H_2O(l) \longrightarrow 2HNO_3(aq) + NO(g)$$

How many grams of nitrogen dioxide are required in this reaction to produce 7.50 g HNO_3?

3.84 White phosphorus, P_4, is prepared by fusing calcium phosphate, $Ca_3(PO_4)_2$, with carbon, C, and sand, SiO_2, in an electric furnace.

$$2Ca_3(PO_4)_2(s) + 6SiO_2(s) + 10C(s) \longrightarrow$$
$$P_4(g) + 6CaSiO_3(l) + 10CO(g)$$

How many grams of calcium phosphate are required to give 15.0 g of phosphorus?

3.85 Tungsten metal, W, is used to make incandescent bulb filaments. The metal is produced from the yellow tungsten(VI) oxide, WO_3, by reaction with hydrogen.

$$WO_3(s) + 3H_2(g) \longrightarrow W(s) + 3H_2O(g)$$

How many grams of tungsten can be obtained from 4.81 kg of hydrogen with excess tungsten(VI) oxide?

3.86 Acrylonitrile, C_3H_3N, is the starting material for the production of a kind of synthetic fiber (acrylics). It can be made from propylene, C_3H_6, by reaction with nitric oxide, NO.

$$4C_3H_6(g) + 6NO(g) \longrightarrow 4C_3H_3N(g) + 6H_2O(g) + N_2(g)$$

How many grams of acrylonitrile are obtained from 452 kg of propylene and excess NO?

3.87 The following reaction, depicted using molecular models, is used to make carbon tetrachloride, CCl_4, a solvent and starting material for the manufacture of fluorocarbon refrigerants and aerosol propellants.

Calculate the number of grams of carbon disulfide, CS_2, needed for a laboratory-scale reaction with 62.7 g of chlorine, Cl_2.

3.88 Using the following reaction (depicted using molecular models), large quantities of ammonia are burned in the presence of a platinum catalyst to give nitric oxide, as the first step in the preparation of nitric acid.

Suppose a vessel contains 6.1 g of NH_3, how many grams of O_2 are needed for a complete reaction?

3.89 When dinitrogen pentoxide, N_2O_5, a white solid, is heated, it decomposes to nitrogen dioxide and oxygen.

$$2N_2O_5(s) \xrightarrow{\Delta} 4NO_2(g) + O_2(g)$$

If a sample of N_2O_5 produces 1.315 g O_2, how many grams of NO_2 are formed?

3.90 Copper metal reacts with nitric acid. Assume that the reaction is

$$3Cu(s) + 8HNO_3(aq) \longrightarrow$$
$$3Cu(NO_3)_2(aq) + 2NO(g) + 4H_2O(l)$$

If 6.01 g $Cu(NO_3)_2$ is eventually obtained, how many grams of nitrogen monoxide, NO, would have formed?

Limiting Reactant; Theoretical and Percentage Yields

3.91 Potassium superoxide, KO_2, is used in rebreathing gas masks to generate oxygen.

$$4KO_2(s) + 2H_2O(l) \longrightarrow 4KOH(s) + 3O_2(g)$$

If a reaction vessel contains 0.25 mol KO_2 and 0.15 mol H_2O, what is the limiting reactant? How many moles of oxygen can be produced?

3.92 Solutions of sodium hypochlorite, NaClO, are sold as a bleach (such as Clorox). They are prepared by the reaction of chlorine with sodium hydroxide.

$$2NaOH(aq) + Cl_2(g) \longrightarrow NaCl(aq) + NaClO(aq) + H_2O(l)$$

If you have 1.23 mol of NaOH in solution and 1.47 mol of Cl_2 gas available to react, which is the limiting reactant? How many moles of NaClO(aq) could be obtained?

3.93 Methanol, CH_3OH, is prepared industrially from the gas-phase catalytic balanced reaction that has been depicted here using molecular models.

In a laboratory test, a reaction vessel was filled with 35.4 g CO and 10.2 g H_2. How many grams of methanol would be produced in a complete reaction? Which reactant remains unconsumed at the end of the reaction? How many grams of it remain?

3.94 Carbon disulfide, CS_2, burns in oxygen. Complete combustion gives the balanced reaction that has been depicted here using molecular models.

Calculate the grams of sulfur dioxide, SO_2, produced when a mixture of 35.0 g of carbon disulfide and 30.0 g of oxygen reacts. Which reactant remains unconsumed at the end of the combustion? How many grams remain?

3.95 Titanium, which is used to make airplane engines and frames, can be obtained from titanium(IV) tetrachloride, which in turn is obtained from titanium(IV) dioxide by the following process:

$$3TiO_2(s) + 4C(s) + 6Cl_2(g) \longrightarrow$$
$$3TiCl_4(g) + 2CO_2(g) + 2CO(g)$$

A vessel contains 4.15 g TiO_2, 5.67 g C, and 6.78 g Cl_2. Suppose the reaction goes to completion as written. How many grams of titanium(IV) tetrachloride can be produced?

3.96 Hydrogen cyanide, HCN, is prepared from ammonia, air, and natural gas (CH_4) by the following process:

$$2NH_3(g) + 3O_2(g) + 2CH_4(g) \xrightarrow{\text{Pt}} 2HCN(g) + 6H_2O(g)$$

Hydrogen cyanide is used to prepare sodium cyanide, which is used in part to obtain gold from gold-containing rock. If a reaction vessel contains 11.5 g NH_3, 12.0 g O_2, and 10.5 g CH_4, what is the maximum mass in grams of hydrogen cyanide that could be made, assuming the reaction goes to completion as written?

3.97 Aspirin (acetylsalicylic acid) is prepared by heating salicylic acid, $C_7H_6O_3$, with acetic anhydride, $C_4H_6O_3$. The other product is acetic acid, $C_2H_4O_2$.

$$C_7H_6O_3 + C_4H_6O_3 \longrightarrow C_9H_8O_4 + C_2H_4O_2$$

General Problems

3.99 Caffeine, the stimulant in coffee and tea, has the molecular formula $C_8H_{10}N_4O_2$. Calculate the mass percentage of each element in the substance. Give the answers to three significant figures.

3.100 Morphine, a narcotic substance obtained from opium, has the molecular formula $C_{17}H_{19}NO_3$. What is the mass percentage of each element in morphine (to three significant figures)?

3.101 A moth repellent, *para*-dichlorobenzene, has the composition 49.1% C, 2.7% H, and 48.2% Cl. Its molecular mass is 147 amu. What is its molecular formula?

3.102 Sorbic acid is added to food as a mold inhibitor. Its composition is 64.3% C, 7.2% H, and 28.5% O, and its molecular mass is 112 amu. What is its molecular formula?

3.103 Thiophene is a liquid compound of the elements C, H, and S. A sample of thiophene weighing 7.96 mg was burned in oxygen, giving 16.65 mg CO_2. Another sample was subjected to a series of reactions that transformed all of the sulfur in the compound to barium sulfate. If 4.31 mg of thiophene gave 11.96 mg of barium sulfate, what is the empirical formula of thiophene? Its molecular mass is 84 amu. What is its molecular formula?

3.104 Aniline, a starting compound for urethane plastic foams, consists of C, H, and N. Combustion of such compounds yields CO_2, H_2O, and N_2 as products. If the combustion of 9.71 mg of aniline yields 6.63 mg H_2O and 1.46 mg N_2, what is its empirical formula? The molecular mass of aniline is 93 amu. What is its molecular formula?

3.105 A sample of limestone (containing calcium carbonate, $CaCO_3$) weighing 438 mg is treated with oxalic acid, $H_2C_2O_4$, to give calcium oxalate, CaC_2O_4.

$$CaCO_3(s) + H_2C_2O_4(aq) \longrightarrow$$
$$CaC_2O_4(s) + H_2O(l) + CO_2(g)$$

The mass of the calcium oxalate produced is 472 mg. What is the mass percentage of calcium carbonate in this limestone?

What is the theoretical yield (in grams) of aspirin, $C_9H_8O_4$, when 2.00 g of salicylic acid is heated with 4.00 g of acetic anhydride? If the actual yield of aspirin is 1.86 g, what is the percentage yield?

3.98 Methyl salicylate (oil of wintergreen) is prepared by heating salicylic acid, $C_7H_6O_3$, with methanol, CH_3OH.

$$C_7H_6O_3 + CH_3OH \longrightarrow C_8H_8O_3 + H_2O$$

In an experiment, 1.50 g of salicylic acid is reacted with 11.20 g of methanol. The yield of methyl salicylate, $C_8H_8O_3$, is 1.27 g. What is the percentage yield?

3.106 A titanium ore contains rutile (TiO_2) plus some iron oxide and silica. When it is heated with carbon in the presence of chlorine, titanium tetrachloride, $TiCl_4$, is formed.

$$TiO_2(s) + C(s) + 2Cl_2(g) \longrightarrow TiCl_4(g) + CO_2(g)$$

Titanium tetrachloride, a liquid, can be distilled from the mixture. If 35.4 g of titanium tetrachloride is recovered from 17.4 g of crude ore, what is the mass percentage of TiO_2 in the ore (assuming all TiO_2 reacts)?

3.107 Ethylene oxide, C_2H_4O, is made by the oxidation of ethylene, C_2H_4.

$$2C_2H_4(g) + O_2(g) \longrightarrow 2C_2H_4O(g)$$

Ethylene oxide is used to make ethylene glycol for automobile antifreeze. In a pilot study, 10.6 g of ethylene gave 9.91 g of ethylene oxide. What is the percentage yield of ethylene oxide?

3.108 Nitrobenzene, $C_6H_5NO_2$, an important raw material for the dye industry, is prepared from benzene, C_6H_6, and nitric acid, HNO_3.

$$C_6H_6(l) + HNO_3(l) \longrightarrow C_6H_5NO_2(l) + H_2O(l)$$

When 22.4 g of benzene and an excess of HNO_3 are used, what is the theoretical yield of nitrobenzene? If 31.6 g of nitrobenzene is recovered, what is the percentage yield?

3.109 Zinc metal can be obtained from zinc oxide, ZnO, by reaction at high temperature with carbon monoxide, CO.

$$ZnO(s) + CO(g) \longrightarrow Zn(s) + CO_2(g)$$

The carbon monoxide is obtained from carbon.

$$2C(s) + O_2(g) \longrightarrow 2CO(g)$$

What is the maximum amount of zinc that can be obtained from 75.0 g of zinc oxide and 50.0 g of carbon?

3.110 Hydrogen cyanide, HCN, can be made by a two-step process. First, ammonia is reacted with O_2 to give nitric oxide, NO.

$$4NH_3(g) + 5O_2(g) \longrightarrow 4NO(g) + 6H_2O(g)$$

Then nitric oxide is reacted with methane, CH_4.

$$2NO(g) + 2CH_4(g) \longrightarrow 2HCN(g) + 2H_2O(g) + H_2(g)$$

When 24.2 g of ammonia and 25.1 g of methane are used, how many grams of hydrogen cyanide can be produced?

3.111   Calcium carbide, CaC_2, used to produce acetylene, C_2H_2, is prepared by heating calcium oxide, CaO, and carbon, C, to high temperature.

$$CaO(s) + 3C(s) \longrightarrow CaC_2(s) + CO(g)$$

If a mixture contains 2.60 kg of each reactant, how many grams of calcium carbide can be prepared?

3.112   A mixture consisting of 11.9 g of calcium fluoride, CaF_2, and 10.3 g of sulfuric acid, H_2SO_4, is heated to drive off hydrogen fluoride, HF.

$$CaF_2(s) + H_2SO_4(l) \longrightarrow 2HF(g) + CaSO_4(s)$$

What is the maximum number of grams of hydrogen fluoride that can be obtained?

3.113   Alloys, or metallic mixtures, of mercury with another metal are called amalgams. Sodium in sodium amalgam reacts with water. (Mercury does not.)

$$2Na(s) + 2H_2O(l) \longrightarrow 2NaOH(aq) + H_2(g)$$

If a 15.23-g sample of sodium amalgam evolves 0.108 g of hydrogen, what is the percentage of sodium in the amalgam?

3.114   A sample of sandstone consists of silica, SiO_2, and calcite, $CaCO_3$. When the sandstone is heated, calcium carbonate, $CaCO_3$, decomposes into calcium oxide, CaO, and carbon dioxide.

$$CaCO_3(s) \longrightarrow CaO(s) + CO_2(g)$$

What is the percentage of silica in the sandstone if 18.7 mg of the rock yields 3.95 mg of carbon dioxide?

3.115   What type of information can you obtain from a compound using a mass spectrometer?

3.116   Why is the mass spectrum of a molecule much more complicated than that of an atom?

Strategy Problems

3.117   Exactly 4.0 g of hydrogen gas combines with 32 g of oxygen gas according to the following reaction.

$$2H_2 + O_2 \longrightarrow 2H_2O$$

  a. How many hydrogen molecules are required to completely react with 48 oxygen molecules?
  b. If you ran the reaction and it produced 5.0 mol H_2O, how many moles of both O_2 and H_2 did you start with?
  c. If you started with 37.5 g O_2, how many grams of H_2 did you start with to have a complete reaction?
  d. How many grams of O_2 and H_2 were reacted to produce 30.0 g H_2O?

3.118   Aluminum metal reacts with iron(III) oxide to produce aluminum oxide and iron metal.

  a. How many moles of Fe_2O_3 are required to completely react with 41 g Al?
  b. How many moles of Fe are produced by the reaction of 3.14 mol Fe_2O_3 and 99.1 g Al?
  c. How many atoms of Al are required to produce 7.0 g Fe?

3.119   Consider the equation

$$2KOH + H_2SO_4 \longrightarrow K_2SO_4 + 2H_2O$$

  a. If 25 g H_2SO_4 is reacted with 7.7 g KOH, how many grams of K_2SO_4 are produced?
  b. For part a of this problem, identify the limiting reactant and calculate the mass of excess reactant that remains after the reaction is completed.
  c. Calculate the theoretical yield of the reaction. How many grams of material would you expect to obtain if the reaction has a 47.2% yield?

3.120   You perform combustion analysis on 255 mg of a molecule that contains only C, H, and O, and you find that 561 mg CO_2 is produced, along with 306 mg H_2O.

  a. If the molecule contains only C, H, and O, what is the empirical formula?

  b. If the molar mass of the compound is 180 g/mol, what is the molecular formula of the compound?

3.121   When ammonia and oxygen are reacted, they produce nitric oxide and water. When 8.5 g of ammonia is allowed to react with an excess of O_2, the reaction produces 12.0 g of nitrogen monoxide. What is the percentage yield of the reaction?

3.122   A 3.0-L sample of paint that has a density of 4.65 g/mL is found to contain 27.5 g $Pb_3N_2(s)$. How many grams of lead were in the paint sample?

3.123   A 12.1-g sample of Na_2SO_3 is mixed with a 15.5-g sample of $MgSO_4$. What is the total mass of oxygen present in the mixture?

3.124   Potassium superoxide, KO_2, is employed in a self-contained breathing apparatus used by emergency personnel as a source of oxygen. The reaction is

$$4KO_2(s) + 2H_2O(l) \longrightarrow 4KOH(s) + 3O_2(g)$$

Say a self-contained breathing apparatus is charged with 750 g KO_2 and then is used to produce 195 g of oxygen. Was all of the KO_2 consumed in this reaction? If the KO_2 wasn't all consumed, how much is left over and what mass of additional O_2 could be produced?

3.125   Calcium carbonate is a common ingredient in stomach antacids. If an antacid tablet has 68.4 mg of calcium carbonate, how many moles of calcium carbonate are there in 175 tablets?

3.126   While cleaning out your closet, you find a jar labeled "2.21 moles lead nitrite." Since Stock convention was not used, you do not know the oxidation number of the lead. You weigh the contents, and find a mass of 6.61×10^5 mg. What is the percentage composition of nitrite?

3.127 A 0.500-g mixture of Cu_2O and CuO contains 0.425 g Cu. What is the mass of CuO in the mixture?

3.128 A mixture of Fe_2O_3 and FeO was found to contain 72.00% Fe by mass. What is the mass of Fe_2O_3 in 0.500 g of this mixture?

3.129 Hemoglobin is the oxygen-carrying molecule of red blood cells, consisting of a protein and a nonprotein substance. The nonprotein substance is called heme. A sample of heme weighing 35.2 mg contains 3.19 mg of iron. If a heme molecule contains one atom of iron, what is the molecular mass of heme?

3.130 Penicillin V was treated chemically to convert sulfur to barium sulfate, $BaSO_4$. An 8.19-mg sample of penicillin V gave 5.46 mg $BaSO_4$. What is the percentage of sulfur in penicillin V? If there is one sulfur atom in the molecule, what is the molecular mass?

3.131 A 3.41-g sample of a metallic element, M, reacts completely with 0.0158 mol of a gas, X_2, to form 4.52 g MX. What are the identities of M and X?

3.132 1.92 g M^+ ion reacts with 0.158 mol X^- ion to produce a compound, MX_2, which is 86.8% X by mass. What are the identities of M^+ and X^-?

3.133 An alloy of iron (54.7%), nickel (45.0%), and manganese (0.3%) has a density of 8.17 g/cm^3. How many iron atoms are there in a block of alloy measuring 10.0 cm × 20.0 cm × 15.0 cm?

3.134 An alloy of iron (71.0%), cobalt (12.0%), and molybdenum (17.0%) has a density of 8.20 g/cm^3. How many cobalt atoms are there in a cylinder with a radius of 2.50 cm and a length of 10.0 cm?

4

Chemical Reactions

Adding lead(II) nitrate to potassium iodide gives a yellow precipitate of lead(II) iodide. Precipitation reactions are important in biological organisms—for example, in the production of bone (calcium phosphate) and seashell (calcium carbonate).

Contents and Concepts

hemical reactions are the heart of chemistry. Some reactions, such as those accompanying a forest fire or the explosion of dynamite, are quite dramatic. Others are much less obvious, although all chemical reactions must involve detectable change. A chemical reaction involves a change from reactant substances to product substances, and the product substances will have physical and chemical properties different from those of the reactants.

Figure 4.1 shows an experimenter adding a colorless solution of potassium iodide, KI, to a colorless solution of lead(II) nitrate, $Pb(NO_3)_2$. What you see is the formation of a cloud of bright yellow crystals where the two solutions have come into contact, clear evidence of a chemical reaction. The bright yellow crystals are lead(II) iodide, PbI_2, one of the reaction products. We call a solid that forms during a chemical reaction in solution a *precipitate*; the reaction is a precipitation reaction.

In this chapter, we will discuss the major types of chemical reactions, including precipitation reactions. Some of the most important reactions we will describe involve ions in aqueous (water) solution. Therefore, we will first look at these ions and see how we represent by chemical equations the reactions involving ions in aqueous solution.

Some questions we will answer are: What is the evidence for ions in solution? How do we write chemical equations for reactions involving ions? How can we classify and describe the many reactions we observe so that we can begin to understand them? What is the quantitative description of solutions and reactions in solution?

FIGURE 4.1

Reaction of potassium iodide solution and lead(II) nitrate solution
The reactant solutions are colorless, but one of the products, lead(II) iodide, forms as a yellow precipitate.

■ See pages 163–164 for the Media Summary.

Ions in Aqueous Solution

You probably have heard that you should not operate electrical equipment while standing in water. And you may have read a murder mystery in which the victim was electrocuted when an electrical appliance "accidentally" fell into his or her bath water. Actually, if the water were truly pure, the person would be safe from electrocution, because pure water is a nonconductor of electricity. Bath water, or water as it flows from the faucet, however, is a *solution* of water with small amounts of dissolved substances in it, and these dissolved substances make the solution an electrical conductor. This allows an electric current to flow from an electrical appliance to the human body. Let us look at the nature of such solutions.

4.1 | Ionic Theory of Solutions and Solubility Rules

Arrhenius submitted his ionic theory as part of his doctoral dissertation to the faculty at Uppsala, Sweden, in 1884. It was not well received and he barely passed. In 1903, however, he was awarded the Nobel Prize in chemistry for this theory.

Chemists began studying the electrical behavior of substances in the early nineteenth century, and they knew that you could make pure water electrically conducting by dissolving certain substances in it. In 1884, the young Swedish chemist Svante Arrhenius proposed the *ionic theory of solutions* to account for this conductivity. He said that certain substances produce freely moving ions when they dissolve in water, and these ions conduct an electric current in an aqueous solution. <

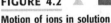

● Cl⁻
● Na⁺

FIGURE 4.2 ▲ 📽

Motion of ions in solution

Ions are in fixed positions in a crystal. During the solution process, however, ions leave the crystal and become freely moving. Note that Na⁺ ions (small gray spheres) are attracted to the negative wire, whereas Cl⁻ ions (large green spheres) are attracted to the positive wire.

Demonstration of conductivity of liquid versus frozen solution: Summerlin et al., *Chemical Demonstrations,* Vol. 2 (Washington, D.C.: Am. Chem. Soc., 1987), no. 71, p. 132.

Suppose you dissolve sodium chloride, NaCl, in water. From our discussion in Section 2.6, you may remember that sodium chloride is an ionic solid consisting of sodium ions, Na⁺, and chloride ions, Cl⁻, held in a regular, fixed array. When you dissolve solid sodium chloride in water, the Na⁺ and Cl⁻ ions go into solution as freely moving ions. Now suppose you dip electric wires that are connected to the poles of a battery into a solution of sodium chloride. The wire that connects to the positive pole of the battery attracts the negatively charged chloride ions in solution, because of their opposite charges. Similarly, the wire connected to the negative pole of the battery attracts the positively charged sodium ions in solution (Figure 4.2). Thus, the ions in the solution begin to move, and these moving charges form the electric current in the solution. (In a wire, it is moving electrons that constitute the electric current.)

Now consider pure water. Water consists of molecules, each of which is electrically neutral. Since each molecule carries no net electric charge, it carries no overall electric charge when it moves. Thus, pure water is a nonconductor of electricity.

In summary, although water is itself nonconducting, it has the ability to dissolve various substances, some of which go into solution as freely moving ions. An aqueous solution of ions is electrically conducting.

Electrolytes and Nonelectrolytes

We can divide the substances that dissolve in water into two broad classes, electrolytes and nonelectrolytes. An **electrolyte** is *a substance that dissolves in water to give an electrically conducting solution.* Sodium chloride, table salt, is an example of an electrolyte. When most ionic substances dissolve in water, ions that were in fixed sites in the crystalline solid go into the surrounding aqueous solution, where they are free to move about. The resulting solution is conducting because the moving ions form an electric current. Thus, in general, *ionic solids that dissolve in water are electrolytes.*

Not all electrolytes are ionic substances. Certain molecular substances dissolve in water to form ions. The resulting solution is electrically conducting, and so we say that the molecular substance is an electrolyte. An example is hydrogen chloride gas, HCl(*g*), which is a molecular substance. Hydrogen chloride gas dissolves in water, giving HCl(*aq*), which in turn produces hydrogen ions, H⁺, and chloride ions, Cl⁻, in aqueous solution. (The solution of H⁺ and Cl⁻ ions is called hydrochloric acid.)

$$HCl(aq) \xrightarrow{\text{H}_2\text{O}} H^+(aq) + Cl^-(aq)$$

We will look more closely at molecular electrolytes, such as HCl, at the end of this section.

A **nonelectrolyte** is *a substance that dissolves in water to give a nonconducting or very poorly conducting solution.* A common example is sucrose, $C_{12}H_{22}O_{11}$, which is ordinary table sugar. Another example is methanol, CH_3OH, a compound used in car window washer solution. Both of these are molecular substances. The solution process occurs because molecules of the substance mix with molecules of water. Molecules are electrically neutral and cannot carry an electric current, so the solution is electrically nonconducting.

Observing the Electrical Conductivity of a Solution

Figure 4.3 shows a simple apparatus that allows you to observe the ability of a solution to conduct an electric current. The apparatus has two electrodes; here they are flat metal plates, dipping into the solution in a beaker. One electrode connects directly to a battery through a wire. The other electrode connects by a wire to a light bulb

FIGURE 4.3

Testing the electrical conductivity of a solution

Left: Pure water does not conduct; therefore, the bulb does not light. *Right:* A solution of sodium chloride allows the current to pass through it, and the bulb lights.

that connects with another wire to the other side of the battery. For an electric current to flow from the battery, there must be a complete circuit, which allows the current to flow from the positive pole of the battery through the circuit to the negative pole of the battery. To have a complete circuit, the solution in the beaker must conduct electricity, as the wires do. If the solution is conducting, the circuit is complete and the bulb lights. If the solution is nonconducting, the circuit is incomplete and the bulb does not light.

The beaker shown on the left side of Figure 4.3 contains pure water. Because the bulb is not lit, we conclude that pure water is a nonconductor (or very poor conductor) of electricity, which is what we expect from our earlier discussion. The beaker shown on the right side of Figure 4.3 contains a solution of sodium chloride in water. In this case, the bulb burns brightly, showing that the solution is a very good conductor of electricity, due to the movement of ions in the solution.

How brightly the bulb lights tells you whether the solution is a very good conductor (contains a "strong" electrolyte) or only a moderately good conductor (contains a "weak" electrolyte). The solution of sodium chloride burns brightly, so we conclude that sodium chloride is a strong electrolyte. Let us look more closely at such strong and weak electrolytes.

Strong and Weak Electrolytes

When electrolytes dissolve in water they produce ions, but to varying extents. A **strong electrolyte** is *an electrolyte that exists in solution almost entirely as ions*. Most ionic solids that dissolve in water do so by going into the solution almost completely as ions, so they are strong electrolytes. An example is sodium chloride. We can represent the dissolution of sodium chloride in water by the following equation:

$$NaCl(s) \xrightarrow{H_2O} Na^+(aq) + Cl^-(aq)$$

A **weak electrolyte** is *an electrolyte that dissolves in water to give a relatively small percentage of ions*. These are generally molecular substances. Ammonia, NH_3, is an example. Pure ammonia is a gas that readily dissolves in water and goes into solution as ammonia molecules, $NH_3(aq)$. When you buy "ammonia" in the grocery store, you are buying an aqueous solution of ammonia. Ammonia molecules react with water to form ammonium ions, NH_4^+, and hydroxide ions, OH^-.

$$NH_3(aq) + H_2O(l) \longrightarrow NH_4^+(aq) + OH^-(aq)$$

However, these ions, $NH_4^+ + OH^-$, react with each other to give back ammonia molecules and water molecules.

$$NH_4^+(aq) + OH^-(aq) \longrightarrow NH_3(aq) + H_2O(l)$$

FIGURE 4.4 ▷

Comparing strong and weak electrolytes
The apparatus is similar to that in Figure 4.3, but this time strong and weak electrolytes are compared. The solution on the left is of HCl (a strong electrolyte) and that on the right is of NH₃ (a weak electrolyte). Note how much more brightly the bulb on the left burns compared with that on the right.

Both reactions, the original one and its reverse, occur constantly and simultaneously. We denote this situation by writing a single equation with a double arrow:

$$NH_3(aq) + H_2O(l) \rightleftharpoons NH_4^+(aq) + OH^-(aq)$$

As a result of this forward and reverse reaction, just a small percentage of the NH₃ molecules (about 3%) have reacted at any given moment to form ions. Thus, ammonia is a weak electrolyte. The electrical conductivities of a strong and a weak electrolyte are contrasted in Figure 4.4.

Most soluble molecular substances are either nonelectrolytes or weak electrolytes. An exception is hydrogen chloride gas, HCl(g), which dissolves in water to produce hydrogen ions and chloride ions. We represent its reaction with water by an equation with a single arrow:

$$HCl(aq) \longrightarrow H^+(aq) + Cl^-(aq)$$

Since hydrogen chloride dissolves to give almost entirely ions, hydrogen chloride (or hydrochloric acid) is a strong electrolyte.

Solubility Rules

It is clear from the preceding discussion that substances vary widely in their *solubility,* or ability to dissolve, in water. Some compounds, such as sodium chloride and ethyl alcohol (CH₃CH₂OH), dissolve readily and are said to be *soluble.* Others, such as calcium carbonate (which occurs naturally as limestone and marble) and benzene (C₆H₆), have quite limited solubilities and are thus said to be *insoluble.*

Soluble ionic compounds form solutions that contain many ions and therefore are strong electrolytes. To predict the solubility of ionic compounds, chemists have developed solubility rules. Table 4.1 lists eight solubility rules for ionic compounds. These rules apply to most of the common ionic compounds that we will discuss in this course. Example 4.1 illustrates how to use the rules.

| **Example 4.1** | Using the Solubility Rules |

Determine whether the following compounds are soluble or insoluble in water.

a. Hg₂Cl₂   b. KI   c. lead(II) nitrate

Problem Strategy   You should refer to Table 4.1 for the solubility rules of ionic compounds to see which compounds are soluble in water. The soluble ionic

(continued)

(*continued*)

compounds are those that readily dissolve in water. The insoluble compounds hardly dissolve at all.

Solution   a. According to Rule 3 in Table 4.1, most compounds that contain chloride, Cl^-, are soluble. However, Hg_2Cl_2 is listed as one of the exceptions to this rule, so it does not dissolve in water. Therefore, **Hg_2Cl_2 is not soluble in water.**

b. According to both Rule 1, Group IA compounds are soluble, and Rule 3, most iodides are soluble, KI is expected to be soluble. Therefore, **KI is soluble in water.**

c. According to Rule 2, compounds containing nitrates, NO_3^-, are soluble. Since there are no exceptions to this rule, **lead(II) nitrate, $Pb(NO_3)_2$, is soluble in water.**

Answer Check   Most incorrect determinations of solubility occur when the exceptions are overlooked, so always be sure to check the exceptions column of Table 4.1.

Exercise 4.1   Determine whether the following compounds are soluble or insoluble in water.

a. NaBr   b. $Ba(OH)_2$ c. calcium carbonate

■ See Problems 4.29 and 4.30.

Let us summarize the main points in this section. Compounds that dissolve in water are soluble; those that dissolve little, or not at all, are insoluble. Soluble substances are either electrolytes or nonelectrolytes. Nonelectrolytes form non-conducting aqueous solutions because they dissolve completely as molecules. Electrolytes form electrically conducting solutions in water because they dissolve to give ions in solution. Electrolytes can be strong or weak. Almost all soluble ionic substances are strong electrolytes. Soluble molecular substances usually are nonelectrolytes or weak electrolytes; the latter solution consists primarily of molecules, but has a small percentage of ions. Ammonia, NH_3, is an example of a molecular substance that is a weak electrolyte. A few molecular substances (such as HCl) dissolve almost entirely as ions in the solution and are therefore strong electrolytes. The solubility rules can be used to predict the solubility of ionic compounds in water.

TABLE 4.1	Solubility Rules for Ionic Compounds		
Rule	Applies to	Statement	Exceptions
1	Li^+, Na^+, K^+, NH_4^+	Group IA and ammonium compounds are soluble.	—
2	$C_2H_3O_2^-$, NO_3^-	Acetates and nitrates are soluble.	—
3	Cl^-, Br^-, I^-	Most chlorides, bromides, and iodides are soluble.	$AgCl$, Hg_2Cl_2, $PbCl_2$, $AgBr$, $HgBr_2$, Hg_2Br_2, $PbBr_2$, AgI, HgI_2, Hg_2I_2, PbI_2
4	SO_4^{2-}	Most sulfates are soluble.	$CaSO_4$, $SrSO_4$, $BaSO_4$, Ag_2SO_4, Hg_2SO_4, $PbSO_4$
5	CO_3^{2-}	Most carbonates are insoluble.	Group IA carbonates, $(NH_4)_2CO_3$
6	PO_4^{3-}	Most phosphates are insoluble.	Group IA phosphates, $(NH_4)_3PO_4$
7	S^{2-}	Most sulfides are insoluble.	Group IA sulfides, $(NH_4)_2S$
8	OH^-	Most hydroxides are insoluble.	Group IA hydroxides, $Ca(OH)_2$, $Sr(OH)_2$, $Ba(OH)_2$

Concept Check 4.1

LiI(s) and CH_3OH(l) are introduced into separate beakers containing water. Using the drawings shown here, label each beaker with the appropriate compound and indicate whether you would expect each substance to be a strong electrolyte, a weak electrolyte, or a nonelectrolyte.

4.2 | Molecular and Ionic Equations

We use chemical equations to help us describe chemical reactions. For a reaction involving ions, we have a choice of chemical equations, depending on the kind of information we want to convey. We can represent such a reaction by a *molecular equation,* a *complete ionic equation,* or a *net ionic equation.*

To illustrate these different kinds of equations, consider the preparation of precipitated calcium carbonate, $CaCO_3$. This white, fine, powdery compound is used as a paper filler to brighten and retain ink, as an antacid (as in the trade-named Tums), and as a mild abrasive in toothpastes. One way to prepare this compound is to react calcium hydroxide, $Ca(OH)_2$, with sodium carbonate, Na_2CO_3. Let us look at the different ways to write the equation for this reaction.

Molecular Equations

You could write the equation for this reaction as follows:

$$Ca(OH)_2(aq) + Na_2CO_3(aq) \longrightarrow CaCO_3(s) + 2NaOH(aq)$$

We call this a **molecular equation,** which is *a chemical equation in which the reactants and products are written as if they were molecular substances, even though they may actually exist in solution as ions.* The molecular equation is useful because it is explicit about what the reactant solutions are and what products you obtain. The equation says that you add aqueous solutions of calcium hydroxide and sodium carbonate to the reaction vessel. As a result of the reaction, the insoluble, white calcium carbonate solid forms in the solution; that is, calcium carbonate precipitates. After you remove the precipitate, you are left with a solution of sodium hydroxide. The molecular equation closely describes what you actually do in the laboratory or in an industrial process.

Complete Ionic Equations

Although a molecular equation is useful in describing the actual reactant and product substances, it does not tell you what is happening at the level of ions. That is, it does not give you an ionic-theory interpretation of the reaction. Because this kind of information is useful, you often need to rewrite the molecular equation as an ionic equation.

Again, consider the reaction of calcium hydroxide, $Ca(OH)_2$, and sodium carbonate, Na_2CO_3. Both are soluble ionic substances and therefore strong electrolytes; when they dissolve in water, they go into solution as ions. Each formula unit of $Ca(OH)_2$ forms one Ca^{2+} ion and two OH^- ions in solution. If you want to emphasize that the solution contains freely moving ions, it would be better to write $Ca^{2+}(aq) + 2OH^-(aq)$ in place of $Ca(OH)_2(aq)$. Similarly, each formula unit of Na_2CO_3 forms two Na^+ ions and one CO_3^{2-} ion in solution, and you would emphasize this by writing $2Na^+(aq) + CO_3^{2-}(aq)$ in place of $Na_2CO_3(aq)$. The reactant side of the equation becomes

$$Ca^{2+}(aq) + 2OH^-(aq) + 2Na^+(aq) + CO_3^{2-}(aq) \longrightarrow$$

Thus, the reaction mixture begins as a solution of four different kinds of ions.

Now let us look at the product side of the equation. One product is the precipitate $CaCO_3(s)$. According to the solubility rules, this is an insoluble ionic compound, so it will exist in water as a solid. We leave the formula as $CaCO_3(s)$ to convey this information in the equation. On the other hand, NaOH is a soluble ionic substance and therefore a strong electrolyte; it dissolves in aqueous solution to give the freely moving ions, which we denote by writing $Na^+(aq) + OH^-(aq)$. The complete equation is

$$Ca^{2+}(aq) + 2OH^-(aq) + 2Na^+(aq) + CO_3^{2-}(aq) \longrightarrow$$
$$CaCO_3(s) + 2Na^+(aq) + 2OH^-(aq)$$

The purpose of such a *complete ionic equation* is to represent each substance by its predominant form in the reaction mixture. For example, if the substance is a soluble ionic compound, it probably dissolves as individual ions (so it is a strong electrolyte). In a complete ionic equation, you represent the compound as separate ions. If the substance is a weak electrolyte, it is present in solution primarily as molecules, so you represent it by its molecular formula. If the substance is an insoluble ionic compound, you represent it by the formula of the compound, not by the formulas of the separate ions in solution.

Thus, a **complete ionic equation** is *a chemical equation in which strong electrolytes (such as soluble ionic compounds) are written as separate ions in the solution.* You represent other reactants and products by the formulas of the compounds, indicating any soluble substance by (*aq*) after its formula and any insoluble solid substance by (*s*) after its formula.

Net Ionic Equations

In the complete ionic equation representing the reaction of calcium hydroxide and sodium carbonate, some ions (OH^- and Na^+) appear on both sides of the equation. This means that nothing happens to these ions as the reaction occurs. They are called spectator ions. A **spectator ion** is *an ion in an ionic equation that does not take part in the reaction.* You can cancel such ions from both sides to express the essential reaction that occurs.

$$Ca^{2+}(aq) + 2\cancel{OH^-(aq)} + 2\cancel{Na^+(aq)} + CO_3^{2-}(aq) \longrightarrow$$
$$CaCO_3(s) + 2\cancel{Na^+(aq)} + 2\cancel{OH^-(aq)}$$

The resulting equation is

$$Ca^{2+}(aq) + CO_3^{2-}(aq) \longrightarrow CaCO_3(s)$$

This is the **net ionic equation,** *an ionic equation from which spectator ions have been canceled.* It shows that the reaction that actually occurs at the ionic level is between calcium ions and carbonate ions to form solid calcium carbonate.

From the net ionic equation, you can see that mixing any solution of calcium ion with any solution of carbonate ion will give you this same reaction. For example, the strong electrolyte calcium nitrate, $Ca(NO_3)$, dissolves readily in water to provide a source of calcium ions. (According to the solubility rules, calcium nitrate is soluble, so it goes into solution as Ca^{2+} and NO_3^- ions.) Similarly, the strong electrolyte potassium carbonate, K_2CO_3, dissolves readily in water to provide a source of carbonate ions. (According to the solubility rules, potassium carbonate is soluble, so it goes into solution as K^+ and CO_3^{2-} ions.) When you mix solutions of these two compounds, you obtain a solution of calcium ions and carbonate ions, which react to form the insoluble calcium carbonate. The other product is potassium nitrate, a soluble ionic compound, and therefore a strong electrolyte. The molecular equation representing the reaction is

$$Ca(NO_3)_2(aq) + K_2CO_3(aq) \longrightarrow CaCO_3(s) + 2KNO_3(aq)$$

You obtain the complete ionic equation from this molecular equation by rewriting each of the soluble ionic compounds as ions, but retaining the formula for the precipitate $CaCO_3(s)$:

$$Ca^{2+}(aq) + 2\cancel{NO_3^-(aq)} + 2\cancel{K^+(aq)} + CO_3^{2-}(aq) \longrightarrow$$
$$CaCO_3(s) + 2\cancel{K^+(aq)} + 2\cancel{NO_3^-(aq)}$$

The net ionic equation is

$$Ca^{2+}(aq) + CO_3^{2-}(aq) \longrightarrow CaCO_3(s)$$

Note that the net ionic equation is identical to the one obtained from the reaction of $Ca(OH)_2$ and Na_2CO_3. The essential reaction is the same whether you mix solutions of calcium hydroxide and sodium carbonate or solutions of calcium nitrate and potassium carbonate.

The value of the net ionic equation is its generality. For example, seawater contains Ca^{2+} and CO_3^{2-} ions from various sources. Whatever the sources of these ions, you expect them to react to form a precipitate of calcium carbonate. In seawater, this precipitate results in sediments of calcium carbonate, which eventually form limestone (Figure 4.5).

FIGURE 4.5
Limestone formations
It is believed that most limestone formed as a precipitate of calcium carbonate (and other carbonates) from seawater. The photograph shows limestone formations at Bryce Point, Bryce Canyon National Park, Utah. More than 60 million years ago, this area was covered by seawater.

Example 4.2 | Writing Net Ionic Equations

Write a net ionic equation for each of the following molecular equations.

a. $2HClO_4(aq) + Ca(OH)_2(aq) \longrightarrow Ca(ClO_4)_2(aq) + 2H_2O(l)$
Perchloric acid, $HClO_4$, is a strong electrolyte, forming H^+ and ClO_4^- ions in solution. $Ca(ClO_4)_2$ is a soluble ionic compound.

b. $HC_2H_3O_2(aq) + NaOH(aq) \longrightarrow NaC_2H_3O_2(aq) + H_2O(l)$
Acetic acid, $HC_2H_3O_2$, is a molecular substance and a weak electrolyte.

An alternative example is provided in the Instructor's Resource Manual.

Problem Strategy You will need to convert the molecular equation to the complete ionic equation, then cancel spectator ions to obtain the net ionic equation. For each ionic compound in the reaction, use the solubility rules to determine if the compound will be soluble (in the solution as ions) or insoluble (present as an undissolved solid). For the complete ionic equation, represent all of the strong electrolytes by their separate ions in solution, adding (aq) after the formula of each. Retain the formulas of the other compounds. An ionic compound should have (aq) after its formula if it is soluble or (s) if it is insoluble.

Solution a. According to the solubility rules presented in Table 4.1 and the problem statement, $Ca(OH)_2$ and $Ca(ClO_4)_2$ are soluble ionic compounds, so they are strong

(continued)

(*continued*)

electrolytes. The problem statement notes that $HClO_4$ is also a strong electrolyte. You write each strong electrolyte in the form of separate ions. Water, H_2O, is a nonelectrolyte (or very weak electrolyte), so you retain its molecular formula. The complete ionic equation is

$$2H^+(aq) + 2ClO_4^-(aq) + Ca^{2+}(aq) + 2OH^-(aq) \longrightarrow Ca^{2+}(aq) + 2ClO_4^-(aq) + 2H_2O(l)$$

After canceling spectator ions and dividing by 2, you get the following net ionic equation:

$$H^+(aq) + OH^-(aq) \longrightarrow H_2O(l)$$

b. According to the solubility rules, NaOH and $NaC_2H_3O_2$ are soluble ionic compounds, so they are strong electrolytes. The problem statement notes that $HC_2H_3O_2$ is a weak electrolyte, which you write by its molecular formula. Water, H_2O, is a nonelectrolyte, so you retain its molecular formula also. The complete ionic equation is

$$HC_2H_3O_2(aq) + Na^+(aq) + OH^-(aq) \longrightarrow Na^+(aq) + C_2H_3O_2^-(aq) + H_2O(l)$$

and the net ionic equation is

$$HC_2H_3O_2(aq) + OH^-(aq) \longrightarrow C_2H_3O_2^-(aq) + H_2O(l)$$

Answer Check If both of the reactants are strong electrolytes and a reaction occurs, your correct net ionic equation should not have any ions as products of the reaction. In this case, because the reaction is with a weak electrolyte, ions in the net ionic equation are possible.

Exercise 4.2   Write complete ionic and net ionic equations for each of the following molecular equations.

a. $2HNO_3(aq) + Mg(OH)_2(s) \longrightarrow 2H_2O(l) + Mg(NO_3)_2(aq)$
 Nitric acid, HNO_3, is a strong electrolyte.

b. $Pb(NO_3)_2(aq) + Na_2SO_4(aq) \longrightarrow PbSO_4(s) + 2NaNO_3(aq)$

■ See Problems 4.33 and 4.34.

Types of Chemical Reactions

Demonstration of precipitation: Summerlin and Ealy, *Chemical Demonstrations*, Vol. 1 (Washington, D.C.: Am. Chem. Soc., 1985), no. 12–14, pp. 23–25; Summerlin et al., *Chemical Demonstrations*, Vol. 2 (Washington, D.C.: Am. Chem. Soc., 1987), no. 65–66, pp. 121–125.

Among the several million known substances, many millions of chemical reactions are possible. Beginning students are often bewildered by the possibilities. How can I know whether two substances will react whether they are mixed? How can I predict the products? Although it is not possible to give completely general answers to these questions, it is possible to make sense of chemical reactions. Most of the reactions we will study belong to one of three types:

1. Precipitation reactions. In these reactions, you mix solutions of two ionic substances, and a solid ionic substance (a precipitate) forms.

2. Acid–base reactions. An acid substance reacts with a substance called a base. Such reactions involve the transfer of a proton between reactants.

3. Oxidation–reduction reactions. These involve the transfer of electrons between reactants.

ChemWork: Predicting Precipitates

ChemWork: What Is the Precipitate?

Demonstration of metathesis reaction between solid Pb(NO$_3$)$_2$ and solid KI: Summerlin and Ealy, *Chemical Demonstrations*, Vol. 1 (Washington, D.C.: Am. Chem. Soc., 1985), no. 75, p. 121.

Demonstration of variation of conductivity during a metathesis reaction (decrease of ions): Summerlin et al., *Chemical Demonstrations*, . Vol. 2 (Washington, D.C.: Am. Chem. Soc., 1987), no. 70, pp. 130–131.

.

FIGURE 4.6 ▲

Reaction of magnesium chloride and silver nitrate
Magnesium chloride solution is added to a beaker of silver nitrate solution. A white precipitate of silver chloride forms.

| *The reactants MgCl$_2$ and AgNO$_3$ must be added in correct amounts; otherwise, the excess reactant will remain along with the product Mg(NO$_3$)$_2$.*

We will look at each of these types of reactions. By the time you finish this chapter, you should feel much more comfortable with the descriptions of chemical reactions that you will encounter in this course.

4.3 | Precipitation Reactions

In the previous section, we used a precipitation reaction to illustrate how to convert a molecular equation to an ionic equation. A precipitation reaction occurs in aqueous solution because one product is insoluble. A **precipitate** is *an insoluble solid compound formed during a chemical reaction in solution.* To predict whether a precipitate will form when you mix two solutions of ionic compounds, you need to know whether any of the potential products that might form are insoluble. This is another application of the solubility rules (Section 4.1).

Predicting Precipitation Reactions

Now let us see how you would go about predicting whether a precipitation reaction will occur. Suppose you mix together solutions of magnesium chloride, MgCl$_2$, and silver nitrate, AgNO$_3$. You can write the potential reactants as follows:

$$MgCl_2 + AgNO_3 \longrightarrow$$

How can you tell if a reaction will occur, and if it does, what products to expect?

When you write a precipitation reaction as a molecular equation, the reaction has the form of an exchange reaction. An **exchange** (or **metathesis**) **reaction** is *a reaction between compounds that, when written as a molecular equation, appears to involve the exchange of parts between the two reactants.* In a precipitation reaction, the anions exchange between the two cations (or vice versa).

Let us momentarily assume that a reaction does occur between magnesium chloride and silver nitrate. If you exchange the anions, you get silver chloride and magnesium nitrate. Once you figure out the formulas of these potential products, you can write the molecular equation. The formulas are AgCl and Mg(NO$_3$)$_2$. (If you do not recall how to write the formula of an ionic compound, given the ions, turn back to Example 2.3.) The balanced equation, assuming there *is* a reaction, is

$$MgCl_2 + 2AgNO_3 \longrightarrow 2AgCl + Mg(NO_3)_2$$

Let us verify that MgCl$_2$ and AgNO$_3$ are soluble and then check the solubilities of the products. Rule 3 in Table 4.1 says that chlorides are soluble, with certain exceptions, which do not include magnesium chloride. Thus, we predict that magnesium chloride is soluble. Rule 2 indicates that nitrates are soluble, so AgNO$_3$ is soluble as well. The potential products are silver chloride and magnesium nitrate. According to Rule 3, silver chloride is one of the exceptions to the general solubility of chlorides. Therefore, we predict that the silver chloride is insoluble. Magnesium nitrate is soluble according to Rule 2.

Now we can append the appropriate phase labels to the compounds in the preceding equation.

$$MgCl_2(aq) + 2AgNO_3(aq) \longrightarrow 2AgCl(s) + Mg(NO_3)_2(aq)$$

We predict that reaction occurs because silver chloride is insoluble, and precipitates from the reaction mixture. Figure 4.6 shows the formation of the white silver chloride from this reaction. If you separate the precipitate from the solution by pouring it through filter paper, the solution that passes through (the filtrate) contains magnesium nitrate, which you could obtain by evaporating the water. The molecular equation is a summary of the actual reactants and products in the reaction. <

To see the reaction that occurs on an ionic level, you need to rewrite the molecular equation as a net ionic equation. You first write the strong electrolytes (here soluble ionic compounds) in the form of ions, leaving the formula of the precipitate unchanged.

$$Mg^{2+}(aq) + 2Cl^-(aq) + 2Ag^+(aq) + 2NO_3^-(aq) \longrightarrow$$
$$2AgCl(s) + Mg^{2+}(aq) + 2NO_3^-(aq)$$

After canceling spectator ions and reducing the coefficients to the smallest whole numbers, you obtain the net ionic equation:

$$Ag^+(aq) + Cl^-(aq) \longrightarrow AgCl(s)$$

This equation represents the essential reaction that occurs: Ag^+ ions and Cl^- ions in aqueous solution react to form solid silver chloride.

If silver chloride were soluble, a reaction would not have occurred. When you first mix solutions of $MgCl_2(aq)$ and $AgNO_3(aq)$, you obtain a solution of four ions: $Mg^{2+}(aq)$, $Cl^-(aq)$, $Ag^+(aq)$, and $NO_3^-(aq)$. If no precipitate formed, you would end up simply with a solution of these four ions. However, because Ag^+ and Cl^- react to give the precipitate AgCl, the effect is to remove these ions from the reaction mixture as an insoluble compound and leave behind a solution of $Mg(NO_3)_2(aq)$.

| **Example 4.3** | Deciding Whether Precipitation Occurs |

For each of the following, decide whether a precipitation reaction occurs. If it does, write the balanced molecular equation and then the net ionic equation. If no reaction occurs, write the compounds followed by an arrow and then *NR* (no reaction).

Two alternative examples are provided in the Instructor's Resource Manual.

a. Aqueous solutions of sodium chloride and iron(II) nitrate are mixed.

b. Aqueous solutions of aluminum sulfate and sodium hydroxide are mixed.

Problem Strategy When aqueous solutions containing soluble salts are mixed, a precipitation reaction occurs if an insoluble compound (precipitate) forms. Start by writing the formulas of the compounds that are mixed. (If you have trouble with this, see Examples 2.3 and 2.4.) Then, assuming momentarily that the compounds do react, write the exchange reaction. Make sure that you write the correct formulas of the products. Using the solubility rules, append phase labels to each formula in the equation consulting the solubility rules. If one of the products forms an insoluble compound (precipitate), reaction occurs; otherwise, no reaction occurs.

Solution   a. The formulas of the compounds are NaCl and $Fe(NO_3)_2$. Exchanging anions, you get sodium nitrate, $NaNO_3$, and iron(II) chloride, $FeCl_2$. The equation for the exchange reaction is

$$NaCl + Fe(NO_3)_2 \longrightarrow NaNO_3 + FeCl_2 \quad \text{(not balanced)}$$

Referring to Table 4.1, note that NaCl and $NaNO_3$ are soluble (Rule 1). Also, iron(II) nitrate is soluble (Rule 2), and iron(II) chloride is soluble. (Rule 3 says that chlorides are soluble with some exceptions, none of which include $FeCl_2$.) Since there is no precipitate, no reaction occurs. You obtain simply an aqueous solution of the four different ions (Na^+, Cl^-, Fe^{2+}, and NO_3^-). For the answer, we write

$$\textbf{NaCl}(aq) + \textbf{Fe(NO}_3)_2(aq) \longrightarrow \textbf{NR}$$

b. The formulas of the compounds are $Al_2(SO_4)_3$ and NaOH. Exchanging anions, you get aluminum hydroxide, $Al(OH)_3$, and sodium sulfate, Na_2SO_4. The equation for the exchange reaction is

$$Al_2(SO_4)_3 + NaOH \longrightarrow Al(OH)_3 + Na_2SO_4 \quad \text{(not balanced)}$$

(continued)

(continued)

From Table 4.1, you see that $Al_2(SO_4)_3$ is soluble (Rule 4), NaOH and Na_2SO_4 are soluble (Rule 1), and $Al(OH)_3$ is insoluble (Rule 8). Thus, aluminum hydroxide precipitates. The balanced molecular equation with phase labels is

$$Al_2(SO_4)_3(aq) + 6NaOH(aq) \longrightarrow 2Al(OH)_3(s) + 3Na_2SO_4(aq)$$

To get the net ionic equation, you write the strong electrolytes (here, soluble ionic compounds) as ions in aqueous solution and cancel spectator ions.

$$2Al^{3+}(aq) + 3\cancel{SO_4^{2-}(aq)} + \cancel{6Na^+(aq)} + 6OH^-(aq) \longrightarrow$$
$$2Al(OH)_3(s) + \cancel{6Na^+(aq)} + 3\cancel{SO_4^{2-}(aq)}$$

The net ionic equation is

$$Al^{3+}(aq) + 3OH^-(aq) \longrightarrow Al(OH)_3(s)$$

Thus, aluminum ion reacts with hydroxide ion to precipitate aluminum hydroxide.

Answer Check   One of the most critical aspects of getting this type of problem right is making certain that you are using the correct chemical formulas for the reactants and products.

Exercise 4.3   You mix aqueous solutions of sodium iodide and lead(II) acetate. If a reaction occurs, write the balanced molecular equation and the net ionic equation. If no reaction occurs, indicate this by writing the formulas of the compounds and an arrow followed by *NR*.

■ See Problems 4.37, 4.38, 4.39, and 4.40.

Concept Check 4.2

Your lab partner tells you that she mixed two solutions that contain ions. You analyze the solution and find that it contains the ions and precipitate shown in the beaker.

a. Write the molecular equation for the reaction.

b. Write the complete ionic equation for the reaction.

c. Write the net ionic equation for the reaction.

$Na^+(aq)$

$C_2H_3O_2^-(aq)$

$SrSO_4(s)$

4.4 | Acid–Base Reactions

Demonstration of acid–base indicators: Bassam Z. Shakhashiri, *Chemical Demonstrations*, Vol. 3 (Madison: University of Wisconsin Press, 1989), no. 8.1–8.3, pp. 33–49; Summerlin and Ealy, *Chemical Demonstrations*, Vol. 1 (Washington, D.C.: Am. Chem. Soc., 1985), no. 22–25, pp. 37–40.

Acids and bases are some of the most important electrolytes. You can recognize acids and bases by some simple properties. Acids have a sour taste. Solutions of bases, on the other hand, have a bitter taste and a soapy feel. (Of course, you should *never* taste laboratory chemicals.) Some examples of acids are acetic acid, present in vinegar; citric acid, a constituent of lemon juice; and hydrochloric acid, found in the digestive fluid of the stomach. An example of a base is aqueous ammonia, often used as a household cleaner. Table 4.2 lists further examples; see also Figure 4.7.

Another simple property of acids and bases is their ability to cause color changes in certain dyes. An **acid–base indicator** is *a dye used to distinguish between acidic and basic solutions by means of the color changes it undergoes in these solutions.* Such dyes are common in natural materials. The amber color of tea, for example, is lightened by the addition of lemon juice (citric acid). Red cabbage juice changes to

TABLE 4.2	Common Acids and Bases	
Name	Formula	Remarks
Acids		
Acetic acid	$HC_2H_3O_2$	Found in vinegar
Acetylsalicylic acid	$HC_9H_7O_4$	Aspirin
Ascorbic acid	$H_2C_6H_6O_6$	Vitamin C
Citric acid	$H_3C_6H_5O_7$	Found in lemon juice
Hydrochloric acid	HCl	Found in gastric juice (digestive fluid in stomach)
Sulfuric acid	H_2SO_4	Battery acid
Bases		
Ammonia	NH_3	Aqueous solution used as a household cleaner
Calcium hydroxide	$Ca(OH)_2$	Slaked lime (used in mortar for building construction)
Magnesium hydroxide	$Mg(OH)_2$	Milk of magnesia (antacid and laxative)
Sodium hydroxide	NaOH	Drain cleaners, oven cleaners

Sodium hydroxide   Magnesium hydroxide
NaOH $Mg(OH)_2$

Acetic acid   Ascorbic acid
$HC_2H_3O_2$ Acetylsalicylic acid $H_2C_6H_6O_6$
$HC_9H_7O_4$

FIGURE 4.7

Household acids and bases
Shown are a variety of household products that are either acids or bases.

FIGURE 4.8 ▶

Red cabbage juice as an acid–base indicator
Left: Preparation of red cabbage juice. The beaker (green solution) contains red cabbage juice and sodium bicarbonate (baking soda). *Right:* Red cabbage juice has been added from a pipet to solutions in the beakers. These solutions vary in acidity from highly acidic on the left to highly basic on the right.

Demonstration of properties of acids and bases: Bassam Z. Shakhashiri, *Chemical Demonstrations*, Vol. 3 (Madison: University of Wisconsin Press, 1989), no. 8.5, p. 58.

green and then yellow when a base is added (Figure 4.8). The green and yellow colors change back to red when an acid is added. Litmus is a common laboratory acid–base indicator. This dye, produced from certain species of lichens, turns red in acidic solution and blue in basic solution. Phenolphthalein (fee′ nol thay′ leen), another laboratory acid–base indicator, is colorless in acidic solution and pink in basic solution.

An important chemical characteristic of acids and bases is the way they react with one another. To understand these acid–base reactions, we need to have precise definitions of the terms *acid* and *base*.

Definitions of Acid and Base

When Arrhenius developed his ionic theory of solutions, he also gave the classic definitions of acids and bases. According to Arrhenius, an **acid** is *a substance that produces hydrogen ions, H⁺, when it dissolves in water.* An example is nitric acid, HNO_3, a molecular substance that dissolves in water to give H^+ and NO_3^-.

$$HNO_3(aq) \xrightarrow{H_2O} H^+(aq) + NO_3^-(aq)$$

Demonstration of indicators from plants: Bassam Z. Shakhashiri, *Chemical Demonstrations,* Vol. 3 (Madison: University of Wisconsin Press, 1989), no. 8.4, pp. 50–57.

Solutions of ammonia are sometimes called ammonium hydroxide and given the formula NH₄OH(aq), based on analogy with NaOH. No NH₄OH molecule or compound has ever been found, however.

Acid–base chemistry according to Robert Boyle: Chemical reactions in words as well as symbols. *J. Chem. Educ.* 83 (2006): 1001.

The Brønsted–Lowry concept is treated in detail in Chapter 15.

Demonstration of the conductivity of strong and weak acids: Bassam Z. Shakhashiri, *Chemical Demonstrations,* Vol. 3 (Madison: University of Wisconsin Press, 1989), no. 8.21, pp. 140–145.

The H⁺(aq) ion has variable structure in solution. In solids, there is evidence for [H(H₂O)ₙ]⁺, where n is 1, 2, 3, 4, or 6.

An Arrhenius **base** is *a substance that produces hydroxide ions, OH⁻, when it dissolves in water.* For example, sodium hydroxide is a base.

$$NaOH(s) \xrightarrow{H_2O} Na^+(aq) + OH^-(aq)$$

The molecular substance ammonia, NH_3, is also a base because it yields hydroxide ions when it reacts with water. <

$$NH_3(aq) + H_2O(l) \rightleftharpoons NH_4^+(aq) + OH^-(aq)$$

Although the Arrhenius concept of acids and bases is useful, it is somewhat limited. For example, it tends to single out the OH⁻ ion as the source of base character, when other ions or molecules can play a similar role. In 1923, Johannes N. Brønsted and Thomas M. Lowry independently noted that many reactions involve nothing more than the transfer of a proton (H⁺) between reactants, and they realized that they could use this idea to expand the definitions of acids and bases to describe a large class of chemical reactions. In this view, acid–base reactions are *proton-transfer reactions.*

Consider the preceding reaction. It involves the transfer of a proton from the water molecule, H_2O, to the ammonia molecule, NH_3.

$$NH_3(aq) + H_2O(l) \rightleftharpoons NH_4^+(aq) + OH^-(aq)$$

Once the proton, H⁺, has left the H_2O molecule, it leaves behind an OH⁻ ion. When the H⁺ adds to NH_3, an NH_4^+ ion results. H_2O is said to *donate* a proton to NH_3, and NH_3 is said to *accept* a proton from H_2O.

Brønsted and Lowry defined an **acid** as *the species (molecule or ion) that donates a proton to another species in a proton-transfer reaction.* They defined a **base** as *the species (molecule or ion) that accepts a proton in a proton-transfer reaction.* In the reaction of ammonia with water, the H_2O molecule is the acid, because it donates a proton. The NH_3 molecule is a base, because it accepts a proton.

$$\underset{base}{NH_3(aq)} + \underset{acid}{H_2O(l)} \rightleftharpoons NH_4^+(aq) + OH^-(aq)$$

The dissolution of nitric acid, HNO_3, in water is actually a proton-transfer reaction, although the following equation, which we used as an illustration of an Arrhenius acid, does not spell that out.

$$HNO_3(aq) \xrightarrow{H_2O} H^+(aq) + NO_3^-(aq)$$

To see that this is a proton-transfer reaction, we need to clarify the structure of the hydrogen ion, $H^+(aq)$. This ion consists of a proton (H^+) in association with water molecules, which is what (aq) means. This is not a weak association, however, because the proton (or hydrogen nucleus) would be expected to attract electrons strongly to itself. In fact, the $H^+(aq)$ ion might be better thought of as a proton chemically bonded to a water molecule to give the H_3O^+ ion, with other water molecules less strongly associated with this ion, which we represent by the phase-labeled formula $H_3O^+(aq)$. Written in this form, we usually call this the *hydronium ion.* It is important to understand that the hydrogen ion, $H^+(aq)$, and the hydronium ion, $H_3O^+(aq)$, represent precisely the same physical ion. For simplicity, we often write the formula for this ion as $H^+(aq)$, but when we want to be explicit about the proton-transfer aspect of a reaction, we write the formula as $H_3O^+(aq)$. <

Now let us rewrite the preceding equation by replacing $H^+(aq)$ by $H_3O^+(aq)$. To maintain a balanced equation, we will also need to add $H_2O(l)$ to the left side.

$$HNO_3(aq) + H_2O(l) \longrightarrow NO_3^-(aq) + H_3O^+(aq)$$

Note that the reaction involves simply a transfer of a proton (H^+) from HNO_3 to H_2O:

$$\underset{\text{acid}}{HNO_3(aq)} + \underset{\text{base}}{H_2O(l)} \longrightarrow NO_3^-(aq) + H_3O^+(aq)$$

The HNO_3 molecule is an acid (proton donor) and H_2O is a base (proton acceptor). Note that H_2O may function as an acid or a base, depending on the other reactant.

The Arrhenius definitions and those of Brønsted and Lowry are essentially equivalent for aqueous solutions, although their points of view are different. For instance, sodium hydroxide and ammonia are bases in the Arrhenius view because they increase the percentage of OH^- ion in the aqueous solution. They are bases in the Brønsted–Lowry view because they provide species (OH^- from the strong electrolyte sodium hydroxide and NH_3 from ammonia) that can accept protons. <

Strong and Weak Acids and Bases

Acids and bases are classified as strong or weak, depending on whether they are strong or weak electrolytes. A **strong acid** is *an acid that ionizes completely in water; it is a strong electrolyte.* Hydrochloric acid, $HCl(aq)$, and nitric acid, $HNO_3(aq)$, are examples of strong acids. Using the hydronium ion notation, we write the respective equations as follows:

$$HCl(aq) + H_2O(l) \longrightarrow H_3O^+(aq) + Cl^-(aq)$$

$$HNO_3(aq) + H_2O(l) \longrightarrow H_3O^+(aq) + NO_3^-(aq)$$

Table 4.3 lists six common strong acids. Most of the other acids we will discuss are weak acids.

A **weak acid** is *an acid that only partly ionizes in water; it is a weak electrolyte.* Examples of weak acids are hydrocyanic acid, $HCN(aq)$, and hydrofluoric acid, $HF(aq)$. These molecules react with water to produce a small percentage of ions in solution.

$$HCN(aq) + H_2O(l) \rightleftharpoons H_3O^+(aq) + CN^-(aq)$$

$$HF(aq) + H_2O(l) \rightleftharpoons H_3O^+(aq) + F^-(aq)$$

Figure 4.9 presents molecular views of the strong acid $HCl(aq)$ and the weak acid $HF(aq)$. Note how both the strong and weak acid undergo the same reaction with water (proton donors); however, in the case of the weak acid such as HF, only a small portion of the acid molecules actually undergoes reaction leaving the majority of the acid molecules unreacted. On the other hand, strong acids like HCl and HNO_3 undergo complete reaction with water. The result is that weak acids can produce little H_3O^+ in aqueous solution, whereas strong acids can produce large amounts. Hence, when chemists refer to a weak acid, they are often thinking about a substance that produces a limited amount of $H_3O^+(aq)$, whereas when chemists refer to a strong acid, they are thinking about a substance that can produce large amounts of $H_3O^+(aq)$.

TABLE 4.3

Common Strong Acids and Bases

Strong Acids	Strong Bases
$HClO_4$	$LiOH$
H_2SO_4	$NaOH$
HI	KOH
HBr	$Ca(OH)_2$
HCl	$Sr(OH)_2$
HNO_3	$Ba(OH)_2$

We will discuss the Brønsted–Lowry concept of acids and bases more thoroughly in Chapter 15.

⬤ = H_3O^+
⬤ = Cl^-
⬤ = F^-
⬤ = HF

A

B

FIGURE 4.9 △

Molecular views comparing the strong acid HCl and the weak acid HF in water (H_2O molecules are omitted for clarity)
Top: Due to its complete reaction with water, the strong acid HCl exists as the hydronium ion, $H_3O^+(aq)$, and $Cl^-(aq)$ in aqueous solution. Because of this complete reaction, there are essentially no $HCl(aq)$ molecules in the solution. *Bottom:* Due to the reaction with only very few of the water molecules, the weak acid $HF(aq)$ exists in aqueous solution largely as $HF(aq)$ molecules, with very little $H_3O^+(aq)$ and $F^-(aq)$ being produced.

A **strong base** is *a base that is present in aqueous solution entirely as ions, one of which is OH⁻; it is a strong electrolyte.* The ionic compound sodium hydroxide, NaOH, is an example of a strong base. It dissolves in water as Na^+ and OH^-.

$$NaOH(s) \xrightarrow{\text{H}_2\text{O}} Na^+(aq) + OH^-(aq)$$

The hydroxides of Groups IA and IIA elements, except for beryllium hydroxide, are strong bases (see Table 4.3).

A **weak base** is *a base that is only partly ionized in water; it is a weak electrolyte.* Ammonia, NH_3, is an example.

$$NH_3(aq) + H_2O(l) \rightleftharpoons NH_4^+(aq) + OH^-(aq)$$

You will find it important to be able to identify an acid or base as strong or weak. When you write an ionic equation, you represent strong acids and bases by the ions they form and weak acids and bases by the formulas of the compounds. < The next example will give you some practice identifying acids and bases as strong or weak.

In many cases, when chemists are thinking about strong versus weak bases in aqueous solution, they consider a weak base to be a substance that can produce only limited amounts of OH^- (aq) and a strong base to be a substance that can produce large amounts of OH^- (aq).

Example 4.4	Classifying Acids and Bases as Strong or Weak

Identify each of the following compounds as a strong or weak acid or base:

a. LiOH   b. $HC_2H_3O_2$ c. HBr   d. HNO_2

Problem Strategy   Refer to Table 4.3 for the common strong acids and bases. You can assume that other acids and bases are weak.

Solution

a. As noted in Table 4.3, **LiOH is a strong base.**

b. Acetic acid, $HC_2H_3O_2$, is not one of the strong acids listed in Table 4.3; therefore, we assume **$HC_2H_3O_2$ is a weak acid.**

c. As noted in Table 4.3, **HBr is a strong acid.**

d. Nitrous acid, HNO_2, is not one of the strong acids listed in Table 4.3; therefore, we assume **HNO_2 is a weak acid.**

Answer Check   Do not fall into the trap of assuming that if a compound has OH in the formula, it must be a base. For example, methyl alcohol, CH_3OH, has OH in the formula, but it is not a strong base. Likewise, do not assume that a compound is an acid just because it has H.

Exercise 4.4   Label each of the following as a strong or weak acid or base:

a. H_3PO_4 b. HClO   c. $HClO_4$ d. $Sr(OH)_2$

An alternative example is provided in the Instructor's Resource Manual.   ■ See Problems 4.41 and 4.42.

Neutralization Reactions

Demonstration of neutralization of acid by milk of magnesia: Summerlin et al., Chemical Demonstrations, Vol. 2 (Washington, D.C.: Am. Chem. Soc., 1987), no. 90, p. 171.

One of the chemical properties of acids and bases is that they neutralize one another. A **neutralization reaction** is *a reaction of an acid and a base that results in an ionic compound and possibly water.* When a base is added to an acid solution, the acid is said to be neutralized. *The ionic compound that is a product of a neutralization reaction is called a **salt**.* Most ionic compounds other than hydroxides and oxides are salts. Salts can be obtained from neutralization reactions such as

$$\underset{\text{acid}}{2HCl(aq)} + \underset{\text{base}}{Ca(OH)_2(aq)} \longrightarrow \underset{\text{salt}}{CaCl_2(aq)} + 2H_2O(l)$$

$$\underset{\text{acid}}{HCN(aq)} + \underset{\text{base}}{KOH(aq)} \longrightarrow \underset{\text{salt}}{KCN(aq)} + H_2O(l)$$

The salt formed in a neutralization reaction consists of cations obtained from the base and anions obtained from the acid. In the first example, the base is $Ca(OH)_2$, which supplies Ca^{2+} cations; the acid is HCl, which supplies Cl^- anions. The salt contains Ca^{2+} and Cl^- ions ($CaCl_2$).

We wrote these reactions as molecular equations. Written in this form, the equations make explicit the reactant compounds and the salts produced. However, to discuss the essential reactions that occur, you need to write the net ionic equations. You will see that the net ionic equation for each acid–base reaction involves the transfer of a proton.

The first reaction involves a strong acid, $HCl(aq)$, and a strong base, $Ca(OH)_2(aq)$. Both $Ca(OH)_2$ and the product $CaCl_2$, being soluble ionic compounds, are strong electrolytes. Writing these strong electrolytes in the form of ions gives the following complete ionic equation:

$$2H^+(aq) + 2Cl^-(aq) + Ca^{2+}(aq) + 2OH^-(aq) \longrightarrow Ca^{2+}(aq) + 2Cl^-(aq) + 2H_2O(l)$$

Canceling spectator ions and dividing by 2 give the net ionic equation:

$$H^+(aq) + OH^-(aq) \longrightarrow H_2O(l)$$

Note the transfer of a proton from the hydrogen ion (or hydronium ion, H_3O^+) to the hydroxide ion.

The second reaction involves $HCN(aq)$, a weak acid, and $KOH(aq)$, a strong base; the product is KCN, a strong electrolyte. The net ionic equation is

$$HCN(aq) + OH^-(aq) \longrightarrow CN^-(aq) + H_2O(l)$$

Note the proton transfer, characteristic of an acid–base reaction.

In each of these examples, hydroxide ions latch strongly onto protons to form water. Because water is a very stable substance, it effectively provides the driving force of the reaction.

Although water is one of the products in most neutralization reactions, the reaction of an acid with the base ammonia provides a prominent exception. Consider the reaction of sulfuric acid with ammonia:

$$\underset{\text{acid}}{H_2SO_4(aq)} + \underset{\text{base}}{2NH_3(aq)} \longrightarrow \underset{\text{salt}}{(NH_4)_2SO_4(aq)}$$

The net ionic equation is

$$H^+(aq) + NH_3(aq) \longrightarrow NH_4^+(aq)$$

Note the proton transfer, a hallmark of an acid–base reaction. In this case, NH_3 molecules latch onto protons and form relatively stable NH_4^+ ions.

Example 4.5 | Writing an Equation for a Neutralization

Write the molecular equation and then the net ionic equation for the neutralization of nitrous acid, HNO_2, by sodium hydroxide, NaOH, both in aqueous solution. Use an arrow with H^+ over it to show the proton transfer.

An alternative example is provided in the Instructor's Resource Manual.

Problem Strategy Because this is a neutralization reaction, you know that the reactants are an acid and a base and that there will be a salt and possibly water as a product. Therefore, start by writing the acid and base reactants and the salt product. Recall that the salt consists of cations from the base and anions from the acid. Note also that water is frequently a product; if it is, you will not be able to balance the equation

(continued)

(*continued*)

without it. Once you have the balanced molecular equation, write the complete ionic equation. Do that by representing any strong electrolytes by the formulas of their ions. Finally, write the net ionic equation by canceling any spectator ions, and from it note the proton transfer.

Solution The salt consists of the cation from the base (Na^+) and the anion from the acid (NO_2^-); its formula is $NaNO_2$. You will need to add H_2O as a product to complete and balance the molecular equation:

$$HNO_2(aq) + NaOH(aq) \longrightarrow NaNO_2(aq) + H_2O(l) \quad \text{(molecular equation)}$$

Note that NaOH (a strong base) and $NaNO_2$ (a soluble ionic substance) are strong electrolytes; HNO_2 is a weak electrolyte (it is not one of the strong acids in Table 4.3). You write both NaOH and $NaNO_2$ in the form of ions. The complete ionic equation is

$$HNO_2(aq) + \cancel{Na^+(aq)} + OH^-(aq) \longrightarrow \cancel{Na^+(aq)} + NO_2^-(aq) + H_2O(l)$$

The net ionic equation is

$$HNO_2(aq) + OH^-(aq) \longrightarrow NO_2^-(aq) + H_2O(l)$$

Note that a proton is transferred from HNO_2 to the OH^- ion to yield the products:

$$\overset{\overset{\displaystyle H^+}{\frown}}{HNO_2(aq) + OH^-(aq)} \longrightarrow NO_2^-(aq) + H_2O(l) \quad \text{(net ionic equation)}$$

Answer Check Remember that correct answers include phase labels and that ions must have correct charges.

Exercise 4.5 Write the molecular equation and the net ionic equation for the neutralization of hydrocyanic acid, HCN, by lithium hydroxide, LiOH, both in aqueous solution.

■ See Problems 4.43, 4.44, 4.45, and 4.46.

Acids such as HCl and HNO_3 that have only one acidic hydrogen atom per acid molecule are called *monoprotic* acids. A **polyprotic acid** is *an acid that yields two or more acidic hydrogens per molecule*. Phosphoric acid is an example of a triprotic acid. By reacting this acid with different amounts of a base, you can obtain a series of salts:

$$H_3PO_4(aq) + NaOH(aq) \longrightarrow NaH_2PO_4(aq) + H_2O(l)$$

$$H_3PO_4(aq) + 2NaOH(aq) \longrightarrow Na_2HPO_4(aq) + 2H_2O(l)$$

$$H_3PO_4(aq) + 3NaOH(aq) \longrightarrow Na_3PO_4(aq) + 3H_2O(l)$$

Salts such as NaH_2PO_4 and Na_2HPO_4 that have acidic hydrogen atoms and can undergo neutralization with bases are called *acid salts*.

Exercise 4.6 Write molecular and net ionic equations for the successive neutralizations of each of the acidic hydrogens of sulfuric acid with potassium hydroxide. (That is, write equations for the reaction of sulfuric acid with KOH to give the acid salt and for the reaction of the acid salt with more KOH to give potassium sulfate.)

■ See Problems 4.47, 4.48, 4.49, and 4.50.

Acid–Base Reactions with Gas Formation

Certain salts, notably carbonates, sulfites, and sulfides, react with acids to form a gaseous product. Consider the reaction of sodium carbonate with hydrochloric acid. The molecular equation for the reaction is

$$\underset{\text{carbonate}}{Na_2CO_3(aq)} + \underset{\text{acid}}{2HCl(aq)} \longrightarrow \underset{\text{salt}}{2NaCl(aq)} + H_2O(l) + CO_2(g)$$

Here, a carbonate (sodium carbonate) reacts with an acid (hydrochloric acid) to produce a salt (sodium chloride), water, and carbon dioxide gas. A similar reaction is shown in Figure 4.10, in which baking soda (sodium hydrogen carbonate) reacts with the acetic acid in vinegar. Note the bubbles of carbon dioxide gas that evolve during the reaction. This reaction of a carbonate with an acid is the basis of a simple test for carbonate minerals. When you treat a carbonate mineral or rock, such as limestone, with hydrochloric acid, the material fizzes, as bubbles of odorless carbon dioxide form.

It is useful to consider the preceding reaction as an exchange, or metathesis, reaction. Recall that in an exchange reaction, you obtain the products from the reactants by exchanging the anions (or the cations) between the two reactants. In this case, we interchange the carbonate ion with the chloride ion and we obtain the following:

$$Na_2CO_3(aq) + 2HCl(aq) \longrightarrow 2NaCl(aq) + H_2CO_3(aq)$$

The last product shown in the equation is carbonic acid, H_2CO_3. (You obtain the formula of carbonic acid by noting that you need to associate two H^+ ions with the carbonate ion, CO_3^{2-}, to obtain a neutral compound.) Carbonic acid is unstable and decomposes to water and carbon dioxide gas. The overall result is the equation we wrote earlier:

$$Na_2CO_3(aq) + 2HCl(aq) \longrightarrow 2NaCl(aq) + \underset{H_2CO_3(aq)}{\underline{H_2O(l) + CO_2(g)}}$$

The net ionic equation for this reaction is

$$CO_3^{2-}(aq) + 2H^+(aq) \longrightarrow H_2O(l) + CO_2(g)$$

The carbonate ion reacts with hydrogen ion from the acid. If you write the hydrogen ion as H_3O^+ (hydronium ion), you can see also that the reaction involves a proton transfer:

$$\overset{2H^+}{\overset{\frown}{CO_3^{2-}(aq)}} + 2H_3O^+(aq) \longrightarrow H_2CO_3(aq) + 2H_2O(l) \longrightarrow 3H_2O(l) + CO_2(g)$$

From the broader perspective of the Brønsted–Lowry view, this is an acid–base reaction.

Sulfites behave similarly to carbonates. When a sulfite, such as sodium sulfite (Na_2SO_3), reacts with an acid, sulfur dioxide (SO_2) is a product. Sulfides, such as sodium sulfide (Na_2S), react with acids to produce hydrogen sulfide gas. The reaction can be viewed as a simple exchange reaction. The reactions are summarized in Table 4.4. <

Demonstration of reaction of acids with carbonates: Bassam Z. Shakhashiri, *Chemical Demonstrations,* Vol. 3 (Madison: University of Wisconsin Press, 1989), no. 8.11, pp. 96–99.

FIGURE 4.10 ▲

Reaction of a carbonate with an acid
Baking soda (sodium hydrogen carbonate) reacts with acetic acid in vinegar to evolve bubbles of carbon dioxide.

CO_3^{2-}, S^{2-}, and SO_3^{2-} are bases. Thus the net equations involve a basic anion with H^+, an acid.

TABLE 4.4	Some Ionic Compounds That Evolve Gases When Treated with Acids	
Ionic Compound	Gas	Example
Carbonate (CO_3^{2-})	CO_2	$Na_2CO_3 + 2HCl \longrightarrow 2NaCl + H_2O + CO_2$
Sulfite (SO_3^{2-})	SO_2	$Na_2SO_3 + 2HCl \longrightarrow 2NaCl + H_2O + SO_2$
Sulfide (S^{2-})	H_2S	$Na_2S + H_2SO_4 \longrightarrow Na_2SO_4 + H_2S$

Example 4.6 | Writing an Equation for a Reaction with Gas Formation

Write the molecular equation and the net ionic equation for the reaction of zinc sulfide with hydrochloric acid.

An alternative example is provided in the Instructor's Resource Manual.

Experiments in General Chemistry, 4B, "Ionic Reactions in Aqueous Solutions."

Problem Strategy Start by writing the reactants, using the solubility rules to determine the phase labels. Next think about the ways in which this reaction can occur; first try to write it as an exchange reaction. Examine the products to see whether an insoluble compound forms and/or there is gas formation; either indicates a reaction.

Solution First write the reactants, noting from Table 4.1 that most sulfides (except those of the group IA metals and $(NH_4)_2S$) are insoluble.

$$ZnS(s) + HCl(aq) \longrightarrow$$

If you look at this as an exchange reaction, the products are $ZnCl_2$ and H_2S. Since chlorides are soluble (with some exceptions, not including $ZnCl_2$), we write the following balanced equation.

$$\mathbf{ZnS}(s) + \mathbf{2HCl}(aq) \longrightarrow \mathbf{ZnCl_2}(aq) + \mathbf{H_2S}(g)$$

The complete ionic equation is

$$ZnS(s) + 2H^+(aq) + 2Cl^-(aq) \longrightarrow Zn^{2+}(aq) + 2Cl^-(aq) + H_2S(g)$$

and the net ionic equation is

$$\mathbf{ZnS}(s) + \mathbf{2H^+}(aq) \longrightarrow \mathbf{Zn^{2+}}(aq) + \mathbf{H_2S}(g)$$

Answer Check When you are trying to solve problems of this type, if starting with an exchange reaction doesn't yield the desired results, use the examples in Table 4.4 as a guide.

Exercise 4.7 Write the molecular equation and the net ionic equation for the reaction of calcium carbonate with nitric acid.

■ See Problems 4.51, 4.52, 4.53, and 4.54.

Concept Check 4.3

At times, we want to generalize the formula of certain important chemical substances; acids and bases fall into this category. Given the following reactions, try to identify the acids, bases, and some examples of what the general symbols (M and A^-) represent.

a. $MOH(s) \longrightarrow M^+(aq) + OH^-(aq)$

b. $HA(aq) + H_2O(l) \rightleftharpoons H_3O^+(aq) + A^-(aq)$

c. $H_2A(aq) + 2H_2O(l) \rightleftharpoons H_3O^+(aq) + HA^-(aq)$

d. For parts a through c, come up with real examples for M and A.

4.5 | Oxidation–Reduction Reactions

Improvement of sugar–chlorate rocket demonstration. *J. Chem. Educ.* 77 (2000): 1581.

In the two preceding sections, we described precipitation reactions (reactions producing a precipitate) and acid–base reactions (reactions involving proton transfer). Here we discuss the third major class of reactions, oxidation–reduction reactions, which are reactions involving a transfer of electrons from one species to another.

FIGURE 4.11

Reaction of iron with $Cu^{2+}(aq)$

Left: Iron nail and copper(II) sulfate solution, which has a blue color. *Center:* Fe reacts with $Cu^{2+}(aq)$ to yield $Fe^{2+}(aq)$ and $Cu(s)$. In the molecular view, water and the sulfate anion have been omitted. *Right:* The copper metal plates out on the nail.

ChemWork: Assigning Oxidation States

FIGURE 4.12

The burning of calcium metal in oxygen
The burning calcium emits a red-orange flame.

As a simple example of an oxidation–reduction reaction, let us look at what happens when you dip an iron nail into a blue solution of copper(II) sulfate (Figure 4.11). What you see is that the iron nail becomes coated with a reddish-brown tinge of metallic copper. The molecular equation for this reaction is

$$Fe(s) + CuSO_4(aq) \longrightarrow FeSO_4(aq) + Cu(s)$$

The net ionic equation is

$$Fe(s) + Cu^{2+}(aq) \longrightarrow Fe^{2+}(aq) + Cu(s)$$

The electron-transfer aspect of the reaction is apparent from this equation. Note that each iron atom in the metal loses two electrons to form an iron(II) ion, and each copper(II) ion gains two electrons to form a copper atom in the metal. The net effect is that two electrons are transferred from each iron atom in the metal to each copper(II) ion.

The concept of *oxidation numbers* was developed as a simple way of keeping track of electrons in a reaction. Using oxidation numbers, you can determine whether electrons have been transferred from one atom to another. If electrons have been transferred, an oxidation–reduction reaction has occurred.

Oxidation Numbers

We define the **oxidation number** (or **oxidation state**) of an atom in a substance as *the actual charge of the atom if it exists as a monatomic ion, or a hypothetical charge assigned to the atom in the substance by simple rules.* An oxidation–reduction reaction is one in which one or more atoms change oxidation number, implying that there has been a transfer of electrons.

Consider the combustion of calcium metal in oxygen gas (Figure 4.12).

$$2Ca(s) + O_2(g) \longrightarrow 2CaO(s)$$

This is an oxidation–reduction reaction. To see this, you assign oxidation numbers to the atoms in the equation and then note that the atoms change oxidation number during the reaction.

Since the oxidation number of an atom in an element is always zero, Ca and O in O_2 have oxidation numbers of zero. Another rule follows from the definition of oxidation number: The oxidation number of an atom that exists in a substance as a monatomic ion equals the charge on that ion. So the oxidation number of Ca in CaO

FIGURE 4.13

The burning of calcium metal in chlorine
The reaction appears similar to the burning of calcium in oxygen.

is $+2$ (the charge on Ca^{2+}), and the oxidation number of O in CaO is -2 (the charge on O^{2-}). To emphasize these oxidation numbers in an equation, we will write them above the atomic symbols in the formulas.

$$\overset{0}{2Ca}(s) + \overset{0}{O_2}(g) \longrightarrow \overset{+2 \; -2}{2CaO}(s)$$

From this, you see that the Ca and O atoms change in oxidation number during the reaction. In effect, each calcium atom in the metal loses two electrons to form Ca^{2+} ions, and each oxygen atom in O_2 gains two electrons to form O^{2-} ions. The net result is a transfer of electrons from calcium to oxygen, so this reaction is an oxidation–reduction reaction. In other words, an **oxidation–reduction reaction** (or **redox reaction**) is *a reaction in which electrons are transferred between species or in which atoms change oxidation number.*

Note that calcium has gained in oxidation number from 0 to $+2$. (Each calcium atom loses two electrons.) We say that calcium has been *oxidized*. Oxygen, on the other hand, has decreased in oxidation number from 0 to -2. (Each oxygen atom gains two electrons.) We say that oxygen has been *reduced*. An oxidation–reduction reaction always involves both oxidation (the loss of electrons) and reduction (the gain of electrons).

Formerly, the term *oxidation* meant "reaction with oxygen." The current definition greatly enlarges the meaning of this term. Consider the reaction of calcium metal with chlorine gas (Figure 4.13); the reaction looks similar to the burning of calcium in oxygen. The chemical equation is

$$\overset{0}{Ca}(s) + \overset{0}{Cl_2}(g) \longrightarrow \overset{+2 \; -1}{CaCl_2}(s)$$

In this reaction, the calcium atom is oxidized, because it increases in oxidation number (from 0 to $+2$, as in the previous equation). Chlorine is reduced; it decreases in oxidation number from 0 to -1. This is clearly an oxidation–reduction reaction that does not involve oxygen.

Oxidation-Number Rules

So far, we have used two rules for obtaining oxidation numbers: (1) the oxidation number of an atom in an element is zero, and (2) the oxidation number of an atom in a monatomic ion equals the charge on the ion. These and several other rules for assigning oxidation numbers are given in Table 4.5.

TABLE 4.5	Rules for Assigning Oxidation Numbers	
Rule	Applies to	Statement
1	Elements	The oxidation number of an atom in an element is zero.
2	Monatomic ions	The oxidation number of an atom in a monatomic ion equals the charge on the ion.
3	Oxygen	The oxidation number of oxygen is -2 in most of its compounds. (An exception is O in H_2O_2 and other peroxides, where the oxidation number is -1.)
4	Hydrogen	The oxidation number of hydrogen is $+1$ in most of its compounds. (The oxidation number of hydrogen is -1 in binary compounds with a metal, such as CaH_2.)
5	Halogens	The oxidation number of fluorine is -1 in all of its compounds. Each of the other halogens (Cl, Br, I) has an oxidation number of -1 in binary compounds, except when the other element is another halogen above it in the periodic table or the other element is oxygen.
6	Compounds and ions	The sum of the oxidation numbers of the atoms in a compound is zero. The sum of the oxidation numbers of the atoms in a polyatomic ion equals the charge on the ion.

In molecular substances, we use these rules to give the *approximate* charges on the atoms. Consider the molecule SO_2. Oxygen atoms tend to attract electrons, pulling them from other atoms (sulfur in the case of SO_2). As a result, an oxygen atom in SO_2 takes on a negative charge relative to the sulfur atom. The magnitude of the charge on an oxygen atom in a molecule is not a full -2 charge as in the O^{2-} ion. However, it is convenient to assign an oxidation number of -2 to oxygen in SO_2 (and in most other compounds of oxygen) to help us express the approximate charge distribution in the molecule. Rule 3 in Table 4.5 says that an oxygen atom has an oxidation number of -2 in most of its compounds.

Rules 4 and 5 are similar in that they tell you what to expect for the oxidation number of certain elements in their compounds. Rule 4, for instance, says that hydrogen has an oxidation number of $+1$ in most of its compounds.

Rule 6 states that the sum of the oxidation numbers of the atoms in a compound is zero. This rule follows from the interpretation of oxidation numbers as (hypothetical) charges on the atoms. Because any compound is electrically neutral, the sum of the charges on its atoms must be zero. This rule is easily extended to ions: the sum of the oxidation numbers (hypothetical charges) of the atoms in a polyatomic ion equals the charge on the ion.

You can use Rule 6 to obtain the oxidation number of one atom in a compound or ion, if you know the oxidation numbers of the other atoms in the compound or ion. Consider the SO_2 molecule. According to Rule 6,

$$\text{(Oxidation number of S)} + 2 \times \text{(oxidation number of O)} = 0$$

or

$$\text{(Oxidation number of S)} + 2 \times (-2) = 0.$$

Therefore,

$$\text{Oxidation number of S (in } SO_2) = -2 \times (-2) = +4$$

The next example illustrates how to use the rules in Table 4.5 to assign oxidation numbers.

Example 4.7 | Assigning Oxidation Numbers

Use the rules from Table 4.5 to obtain the oxidation number of the chlorine atom in each of the following: (a) $HClO_4$ (perchloric acid), (b) ClO_3^- (chlorate ion).

Two alternative examples are provided in the Instructor's Resource Manual.

Problem Strategy We need to apply the rules in Table 4.5. Rule 6 is the best place to start. Therefore, in each case, write the expression for the sum of the oxidation numbers, equating this to zero for a compound or to the charge for an ion. Now, use Rules 2 to 5 to substitute oxidation numbers for particular atoms, such as -2 for oxygen and $+1$ for hydrogen, and solve for the unknown oxidation number (Cl in this example).

Solution a. For perchloric acid, Rule 6 gives the equation

$$\text{(Oxidation number of H)} + \text{(oxidation number of Cl)} + 4 \times \text{(oxidation number of O)} = 0$$

Using Rules 3 and 4, you obtain

$$(+1) + \text{(oxidation number of Cl)} + 4 \times (-2) = 0$$

(continued)

(continued)

Therefore,

$$\text{Oxidation number of Cl (in } HClO_4) = -(+1) - 4 \times (-2) = +7$$

b. For the chlorate ion, Rule 6 gives the equation

$$(\text{Oxidation number of Cl}) + 3 \times (\text{oxidation number of O}) = -1$$

Using Rule 3, you obtain

$$(\text{Oxidation number of Cl}) + 3 \times (-2) = -1$$

Therefore,

$$\text{Oxidation number of Cl (in } ClO_3^-) = -1 - 3 \times (-2) = +5$$

Answer Check   Because most compounds do not have elements with very large positive or very large negative oxidation numbers, you should always be on the alert for a *possible* assignment mistake when you find oxidation states greater than +6 or less than −4. (From this example you see that a +7 oxidation state is possible; however, it occurs in only a limited number of cases.)

Exercise 4.8   Obtain the oxidation numbers of the atoms in each of the following: (a) potassium dichromate, $K_2Cr_2O_7$, (b) permanganate ion, MnO_4^-.

■ See Problems 4.55, 4.56, 4.57, and 4.58.

Describing Oxidation–Reduction Reactions

We use special terminology to describe oxidation–reduction reactions. To illustrate this, we will look again at the reaction of iron with copper(II) sulfate. The net ionic equation is

$$\overset{0}{Fe}(s) + \overset{+2}{Cu^{2+}}(aq) \longrightarrow \overset{+2}{Fe^{2+}}(aq) + \overset{0}{Cu}(s)$$

We can write this reaction in terms of two half-reactions. A **half-reaction** is *one of two parts of an oxidation–reduction reaction, one part of which involves a loss of electrons (or increase of oxidation number) and the other a gain of electrons (or decrease of oxidation number)*. The half-reactions for the preceding equation are

$$\overset{0}{Fe}(s) \longrightarrow \overset{+2}{Fe^{2+}}(aq) + 2e^- \qquad \text{(electrons lost by Fe)}$$

$$\overset{+2}{Cu^{2+}}(aq) + 2e^- \longrightarrow \overset{0}{Cu}(s) \qquad \text{(electrons gained by } Cu^{2+})$$

Oxidation is *the half-reaction in which there is a loss of electrons by a species (or an increase of oxidation number of an atom)*. **Reduction** is *the half-reaction in which there is a gain of electrons by a species (or a decrease in the oxidation number of an atom)*. Thus, the equation $Fe(s) \longrightarrow Fe^{2+}(aq) + 2e^-$ represents the oxidation half-reaction, and the equation $Cu^{2+}(aq) + 2e^- \longrightarrow Cu(s)$ represents the reduction half-reaction.

Recall that a species that is *oxidized* loses electrons (or contains an atom that increases in oxidation number) and a species that is *reduced* gains electrons (or contains an atom that decreases in oxidation number). An **oxidizing agent** is *a species that oxidizes another species; it is itself reduced*. Similarly, a **reducing agent** is *a species that reduces another species; it is itself oxidized.* In our example reaction, the copper(II) ion is the oxidizing agent, whereas iron metal is the reducing agent.

The relationships among these terms are shown in the following diagram for the reaction of iron with copper(II) ion.

Some Common Oxidation–Reduction Reactions

Many oxidation–reduction reactions can be described as one of the following:

1. Combination reaction

2. Decomposition reaction

3. Displacement reaction

4. Combustion reaction

We will describe examples of each of these in this section.

Combination Reactions   A **combination reaction** is *a reaction in which two substances combine to form a third substance.* Note that not all combination reactions are oxidation–reduction reactions. However, the simplest cases are those in which two elements react to form a compound; these are clearly oxidation–reduction reactions. In Chapter 2, we discussed the reaction of sodium metal and chlorine gas, which is a redox reaction (Figure 4.14).

$$2Na(s) + Cl_2(g) \longrightarrow 2NaCl(s)$$

FIGURE 4.14 ▼

Combination reaction
Left: Sodium metal and chlorine gas.
Right: The spectacular combination reaction of sodium and chlorine.

FIGURE 4.15

Decomposition reaction
The decomposition reaction of mercury(II) oxide into its elements, mercury and oxygen.

Demonstration of metal/metal salt displacement reactions: Summerlin and Ealy, *Chemical Demonstrations*, Vol. 1 (Washington, D.C.: Am. Chem. Soc., 1985), no. 96, p. 151.

Antimony and chlorine also combine in a fiery reaction.

$$2Sb + 3Cl_2 \longrightarrow 2SbCl_3$$

Some combination reactions involve compounds as reactants and are not oxidation–reduction reactions. For example,

$$CaO(s) + SO_2(g) \longrightarrow CaSO_3(s)$$

(If you check the oxidation numbers, you will see that this is not an oxidation–reduction reaction.)

Decomposition Reactions   A **decomposition reaction** is *a reaction in which a single compound reacts to give two or more substances.* Often these reactions occur when the temperature is raised. In Chapter 1, we described the decomposition of mercury(II) oxide into its elements when the compound is heated (Figure 4.15). This is an oxidation–reduction reaction.

$$2HgO(s) \xrightarrow{\Delta} 2Hg(l) + O_2(g)$$

Another example is the preparation of oxygen by heating potassium chlorate with manganese(IV) oxide as a catalyst.

$$2KClO_3(s) \xrightarrow[MnO_2]{\Delta} 2KCl(s) + 3O_2(g)$$

In this reaction, a compound decomposes into another compound and an element; it also is an oxidation–reduction reaction.

Not all decomposition reactions are of the oxidation–reduction type. For example, calcium carbonate at high temperatures decomposes into calcium oxide and carbon dioxide.

$$CaCO_3(s) \xrightarrow{\Delta} CaO(s) + CO_2(g)$$

Is there a change in oxidation numbers? If not, this confirms that this is not an oxidation–reduction reaction.

Displacement Reactions   A **displacement reaction** (also called a **single-replacement reaction**) is *a reaction in which an element reacts with a compound, displacing another element from it.* Since these reactions involve an element and one of its compounds, these must be oxidation–reduction reactions. An example is the reaction that occurs when you dip a copper metal strip into a solution of silver nitrate.

$$Cu(s) + 2AgNO_3(aq) \longrightarrow Cu(NO_3)_2(aq) + 2Ag(s)$$

From the molecular equation, it appears that copper displaces silver in silver nitrate, producing crystals of silver metal and a greenish-blue solution of copper(II) nitrate. The net ionic equation, however, shows that the reaction involves the transfer of electrons from copper metal to silver ion:

$$Cu(s) + 2Ag^+(aq) \longrightarrow Cu^{2+}(aq) + 2Ag(s)$$

When you dip a zinc metal strip into an acid solution, bubbles of hydrogen form on the metal and escape from the solution (Figure 4.16).

$$Zn(s) + 2HCl(aq) \longrightarrow ZnCl_2(aq) + H_2(g)$$

Zinc displaces hydrogen in the acid, producing zinc chloride solution and hydrogen gas. The net ionic equation is

$$Zn(s) + 2H^+(aq) \longrightarrow Zn^{2+}(aq) + H_2(g)$$

Whether a reaction occurs between a given element and a monatomic ion depends on the relative ease with which the two species gain or lose electrons. Table 4.6 shows the activity series of the elements, a listing of the elements in decreasing order of their ease of losing electrons during reactions in aqueous solution. The metals listed at the top are the strongest reducing agents (they lose-electrons easily); those at the bottom, the weakest. A free element reacts with the monatomic ion of another element if the free element is above the other element in the activity series. The highlighted elements react slowly with liquid water, but readily with steam, to give H_2.

Consider this reaction:

$$2K(s) + 2H^+(aq) \longrightarrow 2K^+(aq) + H_2(g)$$

You would expect this reaction to proceed as written, because potassium metal (K) is well above hydrogen in the activity series. In fact, potassium metal reacts violently with water, which contains only a very small percentage of H^+ ions. Imagine the reaction of potassium metal with a strong acid like HCl!

TABLE 4.6	Activity Series of the Elements
React vigorously with acidic solutions and water to give H_2	Li K Ba Ca Na
React with acids to give H_2	Mg Al Zn Cr Fe Cd Co Ni Sn Pb
	H$_2$
Do not react with acids to give H_2*	Cu Hg Ag Au

*Cu, Hg, and Ag react with HNO_3 but do not produce H_2. In these reactions, the metal is oxidized to the metal ion, and NO_3^- ion is reduced to NO_2 or other nitrogen species.

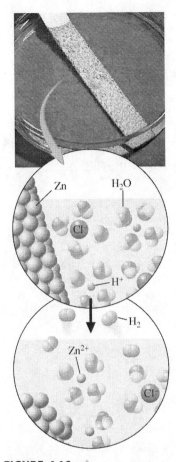

FIGURE 4.16 ▲

Displacement reaction
Displacement reaction of zinc metal and hydrochloric acid. Hydrogen gas formed in the reaction bubbles from the metal surface that dips into the acid.

Demonstration of a displacement reaction: Summerlin et al., *Chemical Demonstrations*, Vol. 2 (Washington, D.C.: Am. Chem. Soc., 1987), no. 105, p. 107.

Combustion Reactions A **combustion reaction** is *a reaction in which a substance reacts with oxygen, usually with the rapid release of heat to produce a flame.* The products include one or more oxides. Oxygen changes oxidation number from 0 to −2, so combustions are oxidation–reduction reactions.

Organic compounds usually burn in oxygen or air to yield carbon dioxide. If the compound contains hydrogen (as most do), water is also a product. For instance, butane (C_4H_{10}) burns in air as follows:

$$2C_4H_{10}(g) + 13O_2(g) \longrightarrow 8CO_2(g) + 10H_2O(g)$$

Many metals burn in air as well. Although chunks of iron do not burn readily in air, iron wool, which consists of fine strands of iron, does (Figure 4.17 on page 152). The increased surface area of the metal in iron wool allows oxygen from air to react quickly with it.

$$4Fe(s) + 3O_2(g) \longrightarrow 2Fe_2O_3(s)$$

4.6 | Balancing Simple Oxidation–Reduction Equations

Balancing equations was discussed in Section 2.10.

Oxidation–reduction reactions can often be quite difficult to balance. < Some are so complex in fact that chemists have written computer programs to accomplish the task. In this section, we will develop a method for balancing simple oxidation–reduction reactions that can later be generalized for far more complex reactions. One of the advantages of using this technique for even simple reactions is that you focus on what makes oxidation–reduction reactions different from other reaction types. See Chapter 19 for a comprehensive treatment of this topic.

At first glance, the equation representing the reaction of zinc metal with silver(I) ions in solution might appear to be balanced.

$$Zn(s) + Ag^+(aq) \longrightarrow Zn^{2+}(aq) + Ag(s)$$

However, because a balanced chemical equation must have a charge balance as well as a mass balance, this equation is not balanced: it has a total charge of +1 for the reactants and +2 for the products. Let us apply the half-reaction method for balancing this equation.

Half-Reaction Method Applied to Simple Oxidation–Reduction Equations

The *half-reaction method* consists of first separating the equation into two half-reactions, one for oxidation, the other for reduction. You balance each half-reaction, then combine them to obtain a balanced oxidation–reduction reaction. Here is an illustration of the process. First we identify the species being oxidized and reduced and assign the appropriate oxidation states.

$$\overset{0}{Zn}(s) + \overset{+1}{Ag^+}(aq) \longrightarrow \overset{+2}{Zn^{2+}}(aq) + \overset{0}{Ag}(s)$$

Next, write the half-reactions in an unbalanced form.

$$Zn \longrightarrow Zn^{2+} \qquad \text{(oxidation)}$$
$$Ag^+ \longrightarrow Ag \qquad \text{(reduction)}$$

Next, balance the charge in each equation by adding electrons to the more positive side to create balanced half-reactions. Following this procedure, the balanced half-reactions are:

$$Zn \longrightarrow Zn^{2+} + 2e^- \qquad \text{(oxidation half-reaction)}$$
$$Ag^+ + e^- \longrightarrow Ag \qquad \text{(reduction half-reaction)}$$

Note that the number of electrons that Zn loses during the oxidation process (two) exceeds the number of electrons gained by Ag^+ during the reduction (one). Since, according to the reduction half-reaction, each Ag^+ is capable of gaining only one electron, we need to double the amount of Ag^+ in order for it to accept all of the electrons produced by Zn during oxidation. To meet this goal and obtain the balanced oxidation–reduction reaction, we multiply each half-reaction by a factor (integer) so that when we add them together, the electrons cancel. We multiply the first equation by 1 (the number of electrons in the second half-reaction) and multiply the second equation by 2 (the number of electrons in the first half-reaction).

$$1 \times (Zn \longrightarrow Zn^{2+} + 2e^-)$$
$$\underline{2 \times (Ag^+ + e^- \longrightarrow Ag)}$$
$$Zn + 2Ag^+ + \cancel{2e^-} \longrightarrow Zn^{2+} + 2Ag + \cancel{2e^-}$$

The electrons cancel, which finally yields the balanced oxidation–reduction equation:

$$Zn(s) + 2Ag^+(aq) \longrightarrow Zn^{2+}(aq) + 2Ag(s)$$

Example 4.8 further illustrates this technique.

FIGURE 4.17 ▲

The combustion of iron wool
Iron reacts with oxygen in the air to produce iron(III) oxide, Fe_2O_3. The reaction is similar to the rusting of iron but is much faster.

Example 4.8	Balancing Simple Oxidation–Reduction Reactions by the Half-Reaction Method

Consider a more difficult problem, the combination (oxidation–reduction) reaction of magnesium metal and nitrogen gas:

$$Mg(s) + N_2(g) \longrightarrow Mg_3N_2(s)$$

Apply the half-reaction method to balance this equation.

Problem Strategy   Start by identifying the species undergoing oxidation and reduction and assigning oxidation numbers. Then write the two balanced half-reactions, keeping in mind that you add the electrons to the more positive side of the reaction. Next, multiply each of the half-reactions by a whole number that will cancel the electrons on each side of the equation. Finally, add the half-reactions together to yield the balanced equation.

Solution   Identify the oxidation states of the elements:

$$\overset{0}{Mg}(s) + \overset{0}{N_2}(g) \longrightarrow \overset{+2\ -3}{Mg_3N_2}(s)$$

In this problem, a molecular compound, nitrogen (N_2), is undergoing reduction. When a species undergoing reduction or oxidation is a molecule, write the formula of the molecule (do not split it up) in the half-reaction. Also, make sure that both the mass and the charge are balanced. (Note the $6e^-$ required to balance the charge due to the $2N^{3-}$.)

$$Mg \longrightarrow Mg^{2+} + 2e^- \qquad \text{(balanced oxidation half-reaction)}$$
$$N_2 + 6e^- \longrightarrow 2N^{3-} \qquad \text{(balanced reduction half-reaction)}$$

We now need to multiply each half-reaction by a factor that will cancel the electrons.

$$3 \times (Mg \longrightarrow Mg^{2+} + 2e^-)$$
$$\underline{1 \times (N_2 + 6e^- \longrightarrow 2N^{3-})}$$
$$3Mg + N_2 + \cancel{6e^-} \longrightarrow 3Mg^{2+} + 2N^{3-} + \cancel{6e^-}$$

Therefore, the balanced combination (oxidation–reduction) reaction is

$$\mathbf{3Mg + N_2 \longrightarrow 3Mg^{2+} + 2N^{3-}}$$

From inspecting the coefficients in this reaction, looking at the original equation, and knowing that Mg^{2+} and N^{3-} will combine to form an ionic compound (Mg_3N_2), we can rewrite the equation in the following form:

$$3Mg(s) + N_2(g) \longrightarrow Mg_3N_2(s)$$

Answer Check   Do a final check for balance by counting the number of atoms of each element on both sides of the equation.

Exercise 4.9   Use the half-reaction method to balance the equation $Ca(s) + Cl_2(g) \longrightarrow CaCl_2(s)$.

■ See Problems 4.65 and 4.66.

Working with Solutions

The majority of the chemical reactions discussed in this chapter take place in solution. This is because the reaction between two solid reactants often proceeds very slowly or not at all. In a solid, the molecules or ions in a crystal tend to occupy approximately fixed positions, so the chance of two molecules or ions coming together to react is small. In liquid solutions, reactant molecules are free to move throughout the liquid; therefore, reaction is much faster. When you run reactions in liquid solutions, it is convenient to dispense the amounts of reactants by measuring out volumes of reactant solutions. In the next two sections, we will discuss calculations involved in making up solutions, and in Section 4.10 we will describe stoichiometric calculations involving such solutions.

4.7   Molar Concentration

ChemWork: Concentration of Ions

ChemWork: Concentration of Chloride Ions

ChemWork: Molarity of Solutions

When we dissolve a substance in a liquid, we call the substance the *solute* and the liquid the *solvent*. Consider ammonia solutions. Ammonia gas dissolves readily in water, and aqueous ammonia solutions are often used in the laboratory. In such solutions, ammonia gas is the solute and water is the solvent.

The general term *concentration* refers to the quantity of solute in a standard quantity of solution. Qualitatively, we say that a solution is *dilute* when the solute concentration is low and *concentrated* when the solute concentration is high. Usually these terms are used in a comparative sense and do not refer to a specific concentration. We say that one solution is more dilute, or less concentrated, than another. However, for commercially available solutions, the term *concentrated* refers to the maximum, or near maximum, concentration available. For example, concentrated aqueous ammonia contains about 28% NH_3 by mass.

In this example, we expressed the concentration quantitatively by giving the mass percentage of solute—that is, the mass of solute in 100 g of solution. However, we need a unit of concentration that is convenient for dispensing reactants in solution, such as one that specifies moles of solute per solution volume.

Molar concentration, or **molarity (*M*),** is defined as *the moles of solute dissolved in one liter (cubic decimeter) of solution.*

$$\text{Molarity } (M) = \frac{\text{moles of solute}}{\text{liters of solution}}$$

An aqueous solution that is 0.15 *M* NH_3 (read this as "0.15 molar NH_3") contains 0.15 mol NH_3 per liter of solution. If you want to prepare a solution that is, for example, 0.200 *M* $CuSO_4$, you place 0.200 mol $CuSO_4$ in a 1.000-L volumetric flask, or a proportional amount in a flask of a different size (Figure 4.18). You add a small quantity of water to dissolve the $CuSO_4$. Then you fill the flask with additional water to the mark on the neck and mix the solution. The following example shows how to calculate the molarity of a solution given the mass of solute and the volume of solution.

Example 4.9 | Calculating Molarity from Mass and Volume

A sample of $NaNO_3$ weighing 0.38 g is placed in a 50.0 mL volumetric flask. The flask is then filled with water to the mark on the neck, dissolving the solid. What is the molarity of the resulting solution?

Problem Strategy To calculate the molarity, you need the moles of solute. Therefore, you first convert grams $NaNO_3$ to moles. The molarity equals the moles of solute divided by the liters of solution.

(continued)

FIGURE 4.18 ▲

Preparing a 0.200 *M* CuSO₄ solution

Left: 0.0500 mol CuSO₄·5H₂O (12.48 g) is weighed on a platform balance. *Center:* The copper(II) sulfate pentahydrate is transferred carefully to the volumetric flask. *Right:* Water is added to bring the solution level to the mark on the neck of the 250-mL volumetric flask. The molarity is 0.0500 mol/0.250 L = 0.200 *M*.

(continued)

Solution You find that 0.38 g NaNO₃ is $4.\underline{4}7 \times 10^{-3}$ mol NaNO₃; the last significant figure is underlined. The volume of solution is 50.0 mL, or 50.0×10^{-3} L, so the molarity is

$$\text{Molarity} = \frac{4.\underline{4}7 \times 10^{-3} \text{ mol NaNO}_3}{50.0 \times 10^{-3} \text{ L soln}} = \textbf{0.089 } \textit{M} \textbf{ NaNO}_3$$

Answer Check Although very dilute solutions are possible, there is a limit as to how concentrated solutions can be. Therefore, any answer that leads to solution concentrations that are in excess of 20 *M* should be suspect.

Exercise 4.10 A sample of sodium chloride, NaCl, weighing 0.0678 g is placed in a 25.0-mL volumetric flask. Enough water is added to dissolve the NaCl, and then the flask is filled to the mark with water and carefully shaken to mix the contents. What is the molarity of the resulting solution?

An alternative example is provided in the Instructor's Resource Manual.

■ See Problems 4.67, 4.68, 4.69, and 4.70.

The advantage of molarity as a concentration unit is that the amount of solute is related to the volume of solution. Rather than having to weigh out a specified mass of substance, you can instead measure out a definite volume of solution of the substance, which is usually easier. As the following example illustrates, molarity can be used as a factor for converting from moles of solute to liters of solution, and vice versa.

Example 4.10 | Using Molarity as a Conversion Factor

An experiment calls for the addition to a reaction vessel of 0.184 g of sodium hydroxide, NaOH, in aqueous solution. How many milliliters of 0.150 *M* NaOH should be added?

An alternative example is provided in the Instructor's Resource Manual.

Problem Strategy Because molarity relates moles of solute to volume of solution, you first need to convert grams of NaOH to moles of NaOH. Then, you can convert moles NaOH

(continued)

(continued)

to liters of solution, using the molarity as a conversion factor. Here, 0.150 M means that 1 L of solution contains 0.150 moles of solute, so the conversion factor is

$$\underbrace{\frac{1 \text{ L soln}}{0.150 \text{ mol NaOH}}}_{\substack{\text{Converts} \\ \text{mol NaOH to L soln}}}$$

Solution   Here is the calculation. (The molar mass of NaOH is 40.0 g/mol.)

$$0.184 \text{ g NaOH} \times \frac{1 \text{ mol NaOH}}{40.0 \text{ g NaOH}} \times \frac{1 \text{ L soln}}{0.150 \text{ mol NaOH}} = 3.07 \times 10^{-2} \text{ L soln (or 30.7 mL)}$$

You need to add **30.7 mL** of 0.150 M NaOH solution to the reaction vessel.

Answer Check   Note that the mass of NaOH required for the experiment is relatively small. Because of this, you should not expect that a large volume of the 0.150 M NaOH solution will be required.

Exercise 4.11   How many milliliters of 0.163 M NaCl are required to give 0.0958 g of sodium chloride?

■ See Problems 4.71, 4.72, 4.73, and 4.74.

Exercise 4.12   How many moles of sodium chloride should be put in a 50.0-mL volumetric flask to give a 0.15 M NaCl solution when the flask is filled to the mark with water? How many grams of NaCl is this?

■ See Problems 4.75, 4.76, 4.77, and 4.78.

4.8 | Diluting Solutions

Experiments in General Chemistry, 4A, "Conductivity of Aqueous Solutions."

ChemWork: Making Solutions

ChemWork: Dilution of Solutions

ChemWork: Diluting a Solution

ChemWork: Dilution Volume

Commercially available aqueous ammonia (28.0% NH_3) is 14.8 M NH_3. Suppose, however, that you want a solution that is 1.00 M NH_3. You need to dilute the concentrated solution with a definite quantity of water. For this purpose, you must know the relationship between the molarity of the solution before dilution (the *initial molarity*) and that after dilution (the *final molarity*).

To obtain this relationship, first recall the equation defining molarity:

$$\text{Molarity} = \frac{\text{moles of solute}}{\text{liters of solution}}$$

You can rearrange this to give

$$\text{Moles of solute} = \text{molarity} \times \text{liters of solution}$$

The product of molarity and the volume (in liters) gives the moles of solute in the solution. Writing M_i for the initial molar concentration and V_i for the initial volume of solution, you get

$$\text{Moles of solute} = M_i \times V_i$$

When the solution is diluted by adding more water, the concentration and volume change to M_f (the final molar concentration) and V_f (the final volume), and the moles of solute equals

$$\text{Moles of solute} = M_f \times V_f$$

FIGURE 4.19 ▶

Molecular view of the dilution process
Top: A molecular view of a solution of Cl_2 dissolved in water. *Bottom:* The solution after performing a dilution by adding water. Note how the number of moles of Cl_2 in the container does not change when performing the dilution; only the concentration changes. In this particular case, the concentration of Cl_2 drops to half of the starting concentration because the volume was doubled.

Add water (solvent)

FIGURE 4.20 ▲

Preparing a solution by diluting a concentrated one
A volume of concentrated ammonia, similar to the one in the beaker, has been added to the volumetric flask. Here water is being added from the plastic squeeze bottle to bring the volume up to the mark on the flask.

Because the moles of solute has not changed during the dilution (Figure 4.19),

$$M_i \times V_i = M_f \times V_f$$

(Note: You can use any volume units, but both V_i and V_f must be in the same units.)
The next example illustrates how you can use this formula to find the volume of a concentrated solution needed to prepare a given volume of dilute solution.

| **Example 4.11** | Diluting a Solution |

You are given a solution of 14.8 *M* NH_3. How many milliliters of this solution do you require to give 100.0 mL of 1.00 *M* NH_3 when diluted (Figure 4.20)?

Problem Strategy Because this problem is a dilution, you can use the dilution formula. In this case you want to know the initial volume (V_i) of the solution that you are going to dilute; all of the other quantities needed for the formula are given in the problem.

Solution You know the final volume (100.0 mL), final concentration (1.00 *M*), and initial concentration (14.8 *M*). You write the dilution formula and rearrange it to give the initial volume.

$$M_i V_i = M_f V_f$$

$$V_i = \frac{M_f V_f}{M_i}$$

Now you substitute the known values into the right side of the equation.

$$V_i = \frac{1.00\,M \times 100.0\ \text{mL}}{14.8\,M} = \textbf{6.76 mL}$$

Answer Check When you perform a dilution, the volume of the more concentrated solution should always be less than the volume of the final solution, as it is in the photo. Related to this concept is the fact that the initial concentration of a solution is always greater than the final concentration after dilution. These two concepts will enable you to check the reasonableness of your calculated quantities whenever you use the dilution equation.

Exercise 4.13 You have a solution that is 1.5 *M* H_2SO_4 (sulfuric acid). How many milliliters of this acid do you need to prepare 100.0 mL of 0.18 *M* H_2SO_4?

An alternative example is provided in the Instructor's Resource Manual.

■ See Problems 4.79 and 4.80.

Concept Check 4.4

Consider the following beakers. Each contains a solution of the hypothetical atom X.

      A   B   C   D

a. Arrange the beakers in order of increasing concentration of X.

b. Without adding or removing X, what specific things could you do to make the concentrations of X equal in each beaker? (*Hint:* Think about dilutions.)

Quantitative Analysis

Analytical chemistry deals with the determination of composition of materials—that is, the analysis of materials. The materials that one might analyze include air, water, food, hair, body fluids, pharmaceutical preparations, and so forth. The analysis of materials is divided into qualitative and quantitative analysis. *Qualitative analysis* involves the identification of substances or species present in a material. For instance, you might determine that a sample of water contains lead(II) ion. **Quantitative analysis,** which we will discuss in the last sections of this chapter, involves *the determination of the amount of a substance or species present in a material.* In a quantitative analysis, you might determine that the amount of lead(II) ion in a sample of water is 0.067 mg/L.

4.9 | Gravimetric Analysis

ChemWork: Finding the Mass of a Product

ChemWork: Determining Mass Percent

ChemWork: Solution Stoichiometry

Gravimetric analysis is *a type of quantitative analysis in which the amount of a species in a material is determined by converting the species to a product that can be isolated completely and weighed.* Precipitation reactions are frequently used in gravimetric analyses. In these reactions, you determine the amount of an ionic species by precipitating it from solution. The precipitate, or solid formed in the reaction, is then filtered from the solution, dried, and weighed. The advantages of a gravimetric analysis are its simplicity (at least in theory) and its accuracy. The chief disadvantage is that it requires meticulous, time-consuming work. Because of this, whenever possible, chemists use modern instrumental methods.

As an example of a gravimetric analysis, consider the problem of determining the amount of lead in a sample of drinking water. Lead, if it occurs in the water, probably exists as the lead(II) ion, Pb^{2+}. Lead(II) sulfate is a very insoluble compound of lead(II) ion. When sodium sulfate, Na_2SO_4, is added to a solution containing Pb^{2+}, lead(II) sulfate precipitates (that is, $PbSO_4$ comes out of the solution as a fine, crystalline solid). If you assume that the lead is present in solution as lead(II) nitrate, you can write the following equation for the reaction:

$$Na_2SO_4(aq) + Pb(NO_3)_2(aq) \longrightarrow 2NaNO_3(aq) + PbSO_4(s)$$

You can separate the white precipitate of lead(II) sulfate from the solution by filtration. Then you dry and weigh the precipitate. Figure 4.21 shows the laboratory setup used in a similar analysis.

FIGURE 4.21

Gravimetric analysis for barium ion

Left: A solution of potassium chromate (yellow) is poured down a stirring rod into a solution containing an unknown amount of barium ion, Ba^{2+}. The yellow precipitate that forms is barium chromate, $BaCrO_4$. *Right:* The solution is filtered by pouring it into a crucible containing a porous glass partition. Afterward, the crucible is heated to dry the barium chromate. By weighing the crucible before and afterward, you can determine the mass of precipitate.

Example 4.12 — Determining the Amount of a Species by Gravimetric Analysis

A 1.000-L sample of polluted water was analyzed for lead(II) ion, Pb^{2+}, by adding an excess of sodium sulfate to it. The mass of lead(II) sulfate that precipitated was 229.8 mg. What is the mass of lead in a liter of the water? Give the answer as milligrams of lead per liter of solution.

An alternative example is provided in the Instructor's Resource Manual.

Problem Strategy Because an excess of sodium sulfate was added to the solution, you can expect that all of the lead is precipitated as lead(II) sulfate, $PbSO_4$. If you determine the percentage of lead in the $PbSO_4$ precipitate, you can calculate the quantity of lead in the water sample.

Solution Following Example 3.7, you obtain the mass percentage of Pb in $PbSO_4$ by dividing the molar mass of Pb by the molar mass of $PbSO_4$, then multiplying by 100%:

$$\% \text{ Pb} = \frac{207.2 \text{ g/mol}}{303.3 \text{ g/mol}} \times 100\% = 68.32\%$$

Therefore, the 1.000-L sample of water contains

$$\text{Amount Pb in sample} = 229.8 \text{ mg } PbSO_4 \times 0.6832 = 157.0 \text{ mg Pb}$$

The water sample contains **157.0 mg Pb per liter.**

Answer Check Check to make sure that the mass of the element of interest, 157.0 mg Pb in this case, is less than the total mass of the precipitate, 229.8 mg in this case. If you do not find this to be true, you have made an error.

Exercise 4.14 You are given a sample of limestone, which is mostly $CaCO_3$, to determine the mass percentage of Ca in the rock. You dissolve the limestone in hydrochloric acid, which gives a solution of calcium chloride. Then you precipitate the calcium ion in solution by adding sodium oxalate, $Na_2C_2O_4$. The precipitate is calcium oxalate, CaC_2O_4. You find that a sample of limestone weighing 128.3 mg gives 140.2 mg of CaC_2O_4. What is the mass percentage of calcium in the limestone?

■ See Problems 4.83 and 4.84.

4.10 | **Volumetric Analysis**

ChemWork: Finding the Molar Mass of an Acid

ChemWork: The Percent of Sulfur in Coal

As you saw earlier, you can use molarity as a conversion factor, and in this way you can calculate the volume of solution that is equivalent to a given mass of solute (see Example 4.10). This means that you can replace mass measurements in solution reactions by volume measurements. In the next example, we look at the volumes of solutions involved in a given reaction.

| **Example 4.13** | Calculating the Volume of Reactant Solution Needed |

Consider the reaction of sulfuric acid, H_2SO_4, with sodium hydroxide, NaOH.

$$H_2SO_4(aq) + 2NaOH(aq) \longrightarrow 2H_2O(l) + Na_2SO_4(aq)$$

Suppose a beaker contains 35.0 mL of 0.175 M H_2SO_4. How many milliliters of 0.250 M NaOH must be added to react completely with the sulfuric acid?

ChemWork: Concentration of Base

ChemWork: Neutralization Reaction

An alternative example is provided in the Instructor's Resource Manual.

Problem Strategy This is a stoichiometry problem that involves the reaction of sulfuric acid and sodium hydroxide. You have a known volume and concentration of H_2SO_4 in the beaker, and you want to determine what volume of a known concentration of NaOH is required for complete reaction. If you can determine the number of moles of H_2SO_4 that are contained in the beaker, you can then use the balanced chemical reaction to determine the number of moles of NaOH required to react completely with the H_2SO_4. Finally, you can use the concentration of the NaOH to determine the required volume of NaOH. Following this strategy, you convert from 35.0 mL (or 35.0×10^{-3} L) H_2SO_4 solution to moles H_2SO_4 (using the molarity of H_2SO_4), then to moles NaOH (from the chemical equation). Finally, you convert this to volume of NaOH solution (using the molarity of NaOH).

Solution The calculation is as follows:

$$35.0 \times 10^{-3} \text{ L } H_2SO_4 \text{ soln} \times \frac{0.175 \text{ mol } H_2SO_4}{1 \text{ L } H_2SO_4 \text{ soln}} \times \frac{2 \text{ mol NaOH}}{1 \text{ mol } H_2SO_4} \times$$

$$\frac{1 \text{ L NaOH soln}}{0.250 \text{ mol NaOH}} = 4.90 \times 10^{-2} \text{ L NaOH soln (or 49.0 mL NaOH soln)}$$

Thus, 35.0 mL of 0.175 M sulfuric acid solution reacts with exactly **49.0 mL** of 0.250 M sodium hydroxide solution.

Answer Check Whenever you perform a titration calculation, be sure that you have taken into account the stoichiometry of the reaction between the acid and base (use the balanced chemical equation). In this case, two moles of NaOH are required to neutralize each mole of acid. Furthermore, when performing titration calculations, do not be tempted to apply the dilution equation to solve the problem. If you were to take such an approach here, you would arrive at an incorrect result since the dilution equation fails to take into account the stoichiometry of the reaction.

Exercise 4.15 Nickel sulfate, $NiSO_4$, reacts with sodium phosphate, Na_3PO_4, to give a pale yellow-green precipitate of nickel phosphate, $Ni_3(PO_4)_2$, and a solution of sodium sulfate, Na_2SO_4.

$$3NiSO_4(aq) + 2Na_3PO_4(aq) \longrightarrow Ni_3(PO_4)_2(s) + 3Na_2SO_4(aq)$$

How many milliliters of 0.375 M $NiSO_4$ will react with 45.7 mL of 0.265 M Na_3PO_4?

■ See Problems 4.89 and 4.90.

FIGURE 4.22

Titration of an unknown amount of HCl with NaOH

Left: The flask contains HCl and a few drops of phenolphthalein indicator; the buret contains 0.207 *M* NaOH (the buret reading is 44.97 mL). *Center:* NaOH was added to the solution in the flask until a persistent faint pink color was reached, marking the endpoint of the titration (the buret reading is 49.44 mL). The amount of HCl can be determined from the volume of NaOH used (4.47 mL); see Example 4.14. *Right:* The addition of several drops of NaOH solution beyond the endpoint gives a deep pink color.

ChemWork: Precipitation of Silver Chloride

ChemWork: Concentration of Ions After Precipitation of Silver Chloride

ChemWork: Precipitation of Barium Phosphate

An indicator is a substance that undergoes a color change when a reaction approaches completion. See Section 4.4.

An important method for determining the amount of a particular substance is based on measuring the volume of reactant solution. Suppose substance *A* reacts in solution with substance *B*. If you know the volume and concentration of a solution of *B* that just reacts with substance *A* in a sample, you can determine the amount of *A*. **Titration** is *a procedure for determining the amount of substance* A *by adding a carefully measured volume of a solution with known concentration of* B *until the reaction of* A *and* B *is just complete.* **Volumetric analysis** is *a method of analysis based on titration.*

Figure 4.22 shows a flask containing hydrochloric acid with an unknown amount of HCl being titrated with sodium hydroxide solution, NaOH, of known molarity. The reaction is

$$NaOH(aq) + HCl(aq) \longrightarrow NaCl(aq) + H_2O(l)$$

To the HCl solution are added a few drops of phenolphthalein indicator. ◁ Phenolphthalein is colorless in the hydrochloric acid but turns pink at the completion of the reaction of NaOH with HCl. Sodium hydroxide with a concentration of 0.207 *M* is contained in a *buret*, a glass tube graduated to measure the volume of liquid delivered from the stopcock. The solution in the buret is added to the HCl in the flask until the phenolphthalein just changes from colorless to pink. At this point, the reaction is complete and the volume of NaOH that reacts with the HCl is read from the buret. This volume is then used to obtain the mass of HCl in the original solution.

Example 4.14	Calculating the Quantity of Substance in a Titrated Solution

A flask contains a solution with an unknown amount of HCl. This solution is titrated with 0.207 *M* NaOH. It takes 4.47 mL NaOH to complete the reaction. What is the mass of the HCl?

An alternative example is provided in the Instructor's Resource Manual.

Problem Strategy First, in order to determine the stoichiometry of the reaction, you start by writing the balanced chemical equation.

$$NaOH(aq) + HCl(aq) \longrightarrow NaCl(aq) + H_2O(l)$$

If you use the numerical information from the problem to determine the moles of NaOH added to the solution, you then can use the stoichiometry of the reaction to determine the

(continued)

(continued)

moles of HCl that reacted. Once you know the moles of HCl, you can use the molar mass of HCl to calculate the mass of HCl. Employing this strategy, you convert the volume of NaOH (4.47×10^{-3} L NaOH solution) to moles NaOH (from the molarity of NaOH). Then you convert moles NaOH to moles HCl (from the chemical equation). Finally, you convert moles HCl to grams HCl.

Solution The calculation is as follows:

$$4.47 \times 10^{-3} \text{ L NaOH soln} \times \frac{0.207 \text{ mol NaOH}}{1 \text{ L NaOH soln}} \times \frac{1 \text{ mol HCl}}{1 \text{ mol NaOH}} \times \frac{36.5 \text{ g HCl}}{1 \text{ mol HCl}}$$

$$= \textbf{0.0338 g HCl}$$

> Experiments in General Chemistry, 4C, "How Much Acetic Acid Is in Vinegar?"

Answer Check Before you perform the titration calculations, always write down the balanced chemical equation.

Exercise 4.16 A 5.00-g sample of vinegar is titrated with 0.108 M NaOH. If the vinegar requires 39.1 mL of the NaOH solution for complete reaction, what is the mass percentage of acetic acid, $HC_2H_3O_2$, in the vinegar? The reaction is

$$HC_2H_3O_2(aq) + NaOH(aq) \longrightarrow NaC_2H_3O_2(aq) + H_2O(l)$$

■ See Problems 4.91 and 4.92.

Concept Check 4.5

Consider three flasks, each containing 0.10 mol of acid. You need to learn something about the acids in each of the flasks, so you perform titration using an NaOH solution. Here are the results of the experiment:

Flask A   10 mL of NaOH required for neutralization
Flask B   20 mL of NaOH required for neutralization
Flask C   30 mL of NaOH required for neutralization

a. What have you learned about each of these acids from performing the experiment?

b. Could you use the results of this experiment to determine the concentration of the NaOH? If not, what assumption about the molecular formulas of the acids would allow you to make the concentration determination?

A Checklist for Review

Important Terms

electrolyte (4.1)
nonelectrolyte (4.1)
strong electrolyte (4.1)
weak electrolyte (4.1)
molecular equation (4.2)
complete ionic equation (4.2)
spectator ion (4.2)
net ionic equation (4.2)
precipitate (4.3)
exchange (metathesis) reaction (4.3)
acid–base indicator (4.4)

acid (Arrhenius) (4.4)
base (Arrhenius) (4.4)
acid (Brønsted–Lowry) (4.4)
base (Brønsted–Lowry) (4.4)
strong acid (4.4)
weak acid (4.4)
strong base (4.4)
weak base (4.4)
neutralization reaction (4.4)
salt (4.4)
polyprotic acid (4.4)

oxidation number
  (oxidation state) (4.5)
oxidation–reduction reaction
  (redox reaction) (4.5)
half-reaction (4.5)
oxidation (4.5)
reduction (4.5)
oxidizing agent (4.5)
reducing agent (4.5)
combination reaction (4.5)
decomposition reaction (4.5)

displacement reaction (single-replacement reaction) (4.5)
combustion reaction (4.5)

molar concentration (molarity) (M) (4.7)
quantitative analysis (4.9)

gravimetric analysis (4.9)
titration (4.10)
volumetric analysis (4.10)

Key Equations

$$\text{Molarity } (M) = \frac{\text{moles of solute}}{\text{liters of solution}}$$

$$M_i \times V_i = M_f \times V_f$$

Summary of Facts and Concepts

Reactions often involve ions in aqueous solution. Many of the compounds in such reactions are *electrolytes*, which are substances that dissolve in water to give ions. Electrolytes that exist in solution almost entirely as ions are called *strong electrolytes*. Electrolytes that dissolve in water to give a relatively small percentage of ions are called *weak electrolytes*. The *solubility rules* can be used to predict the extent to which an ionic compound will dissolve in water. Most soluble ionic compounds are strong electrolytes.

We can represent a reaction involving ions in one of three different ways, depending on what information we want to convey. A *molecular equation* is one in which substances are written as if they were molecular, even though they are ionic. This equation closely describes what you actually do in the laboratory. However, this equation does not describe what is happening at the level of ions and molecules. For that purpose, we rewrite the molecular equation as a *complete ionic equation* by replacing the formulas for strong electrolytes by their ion formulas. If you cancel *spectator ions* from the complete ionic equation, you obtain the *net ionic equation*.

Most of the important reactions we consider in this course can be divided into three major classes: (1) precipitation reactions, (2) acid–base reactions, and (3) oxidation–reduction reactions. A *precipitation reaction* occurs in aqueous solution because one product is insoluble. You can decide whether two ionic compounds will result in a precipitation reaction, if you know from solubility rules that one of the potential products is insoluble.

Acids are substances that yield hydrogen ions in aqueous solution or donate protons. *Bases* are substances that yield hydroxide ions in aqueous solution or accept protons. These *acid–base reactions* are proton-transfer reactions. In this chapter, we covered neutralization reactions (reactions of acids and bases to yield salts) and reactions of certain salts with acids to yield a gas.

Oxidation–reduction reactions are reactions involving a transfer of electrons from one species to another or a change in the oxidation number of atoms. The concept of *oxidation numbers* helps us describe this type of reaction. The atom that increases in oxidation number is said to undergo *oxidation;* the atom that decreases in oxidation number is said to undergo *reduction.* Oxidation and reduction must occur together in a reaction. Many oxidation–reduction reactions fall into the following categories: combination reactions, decomposition reactions, displacement reactions, and combustion reactions. Oxidation–reduction reactions can be balanced by the *half-reaction method.*

Molar concentration, or *molarity,* is the moles of solute in a liter of solution. Knowing the molarity allows you to calculate the amount of solute in any volume of solution. Because the moles of solute are constant during the *dilution of a solution,* you can determine to what volume to dilute a concentrated solution to give one of desired molarity.

Quantitative analysis involves the determination of the amount of a species in a material. In *gravimetric analysis,* you determine the amount of a species by converting it to a product you can weigh. In *volumetric analysis,* you determine the amount of a species by titration. *Titration* is a method of chemical analysis in which you measure the volume of solution of known molarity that reacts with a compound of unknown amount. You determine the amount of the compound from this volume of solution.

Media Summary

Visit the **student website at college.hmco.com/pic/ebbing9e** to help prepare for class, study for quizzes and exams, understand core concepts, and visualize molecular-level interactions. The following media activities are available for this chapter:

 Prepare for Class

Video Lessons *Mini lectures from chemistry experts*
Properties of Solutions
CIA Demonstration: The Electrified Pickle
CIA Demonstration: Conductivity Apparatus—Ionic Versus Covalent Bonds
Precipitation Reactions
Acid–Base Reactions
CIA Demonstration: The Ammonia Fountain
CIA Demonstration: Natural Acid–Base Indicators
Strong Acid–Strong Base and Weak Acid–Strong Base Reactions
Strong Acid–Weak Base and Weak Acid–Weak Base Reactions

Oxidation–Reduction Reactions
Balancing Redox Reactions and the Oxidation Number Method
Oxidation Numbers
CIA Demonstration: The Reaction Between Al and BR_2
The Activity Series of the Elements
Balancing Redox Reactions and Using the Half-Reaction Method
Concentrations of Solutions
CIA Demonstration: Dilutions
Gravimetric Analysis
Acid–Base Titrations
CIA Demonstration: Titrations
Solving Titration Problems

Improve Your Grade

■ **Visualizations** *Molecular-level animations and lab demonstration videos*
Electrified Pickle
Electrolyte Behavior
Electrolytes
Solubility Rules
Precipitation Reactions
Ammonia Fountain
Combustion Reaction: Sugar and Potassium Chlorate
Dilution
Acid–Base Titration

■ **Tutorials** *Animated examples and interactive activities*
Precipitation Reactions
Dilution

■ **Flashcards** *Key terms and definitions*
Online Flashcards

■ **Self-Assessment Questions** *Additional questions with full worked-out solutions*
6 Self-Assessment Questions

A+ ACE the Test

Multiple-choice quizzes
3 ACE Practice Tests

Access these resources using the passkey available free with new texts or for purchase separately.

Learning Objectives

4.1 Ionic Theory of Solutions and Solubility Rules

■ Describe how an ionic substance can form ions in aqueous solution.
■ Explain how an *electrolyte* makes a solution electrically conductive.
■ Give examples of substances that are electrolytes.
■ Define *nonelectrolyte*, and provide an example of a molecular substance that is a nonelectrolyte.
■ Compare the properties of solutions that contain *strong electrolytes* and *weak electrolytes*.
■ Learn the *solubility rules* for ionic compounds.
■ Use the solubility rules. Example 4.1

4.2 Molecular and Ionic Equations

■ Write the *molecular equation* of a chemical reaction.
■ From the molecular equation of both strong electrolytes and weak electrolytes, determine the *complete ionic equation*.
■ From the complete ionic equation, write the *net ionic equation*.
■ Write net ionic equations. Example 4.2

4.3 Precipitation Reactions

■ Recognize *precipitation* (*exchange*) reactions.
■ Write molecular, complete ionic, and net ionic equations for precipitation reactions.
■ Decide whether a precipitation reaction will occur. Example 4.3
■ Determine the product of a precipitation reaction.

4.4 Acid–Base Reactions

■ Understand how an *acid–base* indicator is used to determine whether a solution is acidic or basic.
■ Define *Arrhenius acid* and *Arrhenius base*.
■ Write the chemical equation of an Arrhenius base in aqueous solution.
■ Define *Brønsted–Lowry acid* and *Brønsted–Lowry base*.

■ Write the chemical equation of a Brønsted–Lowry base in aqueous solution.
■ Write the chemical equation of an acid in aqueous solution using a *hydronium ion*.
■ Learn the common *strong acids* and *strong bases*.
■ Distinguish between a strong acid and a *weak acid* and the solutions they form.
■ Distinguish between a strong base and a *weak base* and the solutions they form.
■ Classify acids and bases as strong or weak. Example 4.4
■ Recognize *neutralization reactions*.
■ Write an equation for a neutralization reaction. Example 4.5
■ Write the reactions for a *polyprotic acid* in aqueous solution.
■ Recognize acid–base reactions that lead to gas formation.
■ Write an equation for a reaction with gas formation. Example 4.6

4.5 Oxidation–Reduction Reactions

■ Define *oxidation–reduction* reaction.
■ Learn the oxidation-number rules.
■ Assign oxidation numbers. Example 4.7
■ Write the *half-reactions* of an oxidation–reduction reaction.
■ Determine the species undergoing *oxidation* and *reduction*.
■ Recognize *combination reactions, decomposition reactions, displacement reactions*, and *combustion reactions*.
■ Use the activity series to predict when displacement reactions will occur.

4.6 Balancing Simple Oxidation–Reduction Equations

■ Balance simple oxidation–reduction reactions by the half-reaction method. Example 4.8

4.7 Molar Concentration

■ Define *molarity* or *molar concentration* of a solution.
■ Calculate the molarity from mass and volume. Example 4.9
■ Use molarity as a conversion factor. Example 4.10

4.8 Diluting Solutions

■ Describe what happens to the concentration of a solution when it is diluted.
■ Perform calculations associated with dilution.
■ Diluting a solution. Example 4.11

4.9 Gravimetric Analysis

■ Determine the amount of a species by *gravimetric analysis.* Example 4.12

4.10 Volumetric Analysis

■ Calculate the volume of reactant solution needed to perform a reaction. Example 4.13
■ Understand how to perform a *titration.*
■ Calculate the quantity of substance in a titrated solution. Example 4.14

Self-Assessment and Review Questions

4.1 Explain why some electrolyte solutions are strongly conducting, whereas others are weakly conducting.

4.2 Define the terms *strong electrolyte* and *weak electrolyte.* Give an example of each.

4.3 Explain the terms *soluble* and *insoluble.* Use the solubility rules to write the formula of an insoluble ionic compound.

4.4 What are the advantages and disadvantages of using a molecular equation to represent an ionic reaction?

4.5 What is a *spectator ion*? Illustrate with a complete ionic reaction.

4.6 What is a net ionic equation? What is the value in using a net ionic equation? Give an example.

4.7 What are the major types of chemical reactions? Give a brief description and an example of each.

4.8 Describe in words how you would prepare pure crystalline $AgCl$ and $NaNO_3$ from solid $AgNO_3$ and solid $NaCl$.

4.9 Give an example of a neutralization reaction. Label the acid, base, and salt.

4.10 Give an example of a polyprotic acid and write equations for the successive neutralizations of the acidic hydrogen atoms of the acid molecule to produce a series of salts.

4.11 Why must oxidation and reduction occur together in a reaction?

4.12 Give an example of a displacement reaction. What is the oxidizing agent? What is the reducing agent?

4.13 Why is the product of molar concentration and volume constant for a dilution problem?

4.14 Describe how the amount of sodium hydroxide in a mixture can be determined by titration with hydrochloric acid of known molarity.

4.15 What is the net ionic equation for the following molecular equation?

$$HF(aq) + KOH(aq) \longrightarrow KF(aq) + H_2O(l)$$

Hydrofluoric acid, HF, is a molecular substance and a weak electrolyte.

  a. $H^+(aq) + OH^-(aq) \longrightarrow H_2O(l)$
  b. $H^+(aq) + KOH(aq) \longrightarrow K^+(aq) + H_2O(l)$
  c. $HF(aq) + KOH(aq) \longrightarrow K^+(aq) + F^-(aq)$
  d. $HF(aq) + K^+(aq) + OH^-(aq) \longrightarrow KF(aq) + H_2O(l)$
  e. $HF(aq) + OH^-(aq) \longrightarrow F^-(aq) + H_2O(l)$

4.16 An aqueous sodium hydroxide solution mixed with an aqueous magnesium nitrate solution yields which of the following products?

  a. magnesium hydroxide(*aq*)
  b. magnesium dihydroxide(*s*)
  c. magnesium hydroxide(*s*)
  d. dimagnesium hydroxide(*s*)
  e. sodium nitrate(*l*)

4.17 Which of the following compounds would produce the highest concentration of Cl^- ions when 0.10 mol of each is placed in separate beakers containing equal volumes of water?

  a. $NaCl$
  b. $PbCl_2$
  c. $HClO_4$
  d. $MgCl_2$
  e. HCl

4.18 In an aqueous 0.10 *M* HNO_2 solution (HNO_2 is a weak electrolyte), which of the following would you expect to see in the highest concentration?

  a. H_3O^+
  b. NO_2^-
  c. H^+
  d. HNO_2
  e. OH^-

Concept Explorations

4.19 **The Behavior of Substances in Water**
Part 1

  a. Ammonia, NH_3, is a weak electrolyte. It forms ions in solution by *reacting* with water molecules to form the ammonium ion and hydroxide ion. Write the balanced chemical reaction for this process, including state symbols.

  b. From everyday experience you are probably aware that table sugar (sucrose), $C_{12}H_{22}O_{11}$, is soluble in water. When sucrose dissolves in water, it doesn't form ions through any reaction with water. It just *dissolves* without forming ions, so it is a nonelectrolyte. Write the chemical equation for the dissolving of sucrose in water.

c. Both NH_3 and $C_{12}H_{22}O_{11}$ are soluble molecular compounds, yet they behave differently in aqueous solution. Briefly explain why one is a weak electrolyte and the other is a nonelectrolyte.

d. Hydrochloric acid, HCl, is a molecular compound that is a strong electrolyte. Write the chemical reaction of HCl with water.

e. Compare the ammonia reaction with that of hydrochloric acid. Why are both of these substances considered electrolytes?

f. Explain why HCl is a strong electrolyte and ammonia is a weak electrolyte.

g. Classify each of the following substances as either ionic or molecular.

   KCl NH_3 CO_2 $MgBr_2$ HCl $Ca(OH)_2$ PbS $HC_2H_3O_2$

h. For those compounds above that you classified as ionic, use the solubility rules to determine which are soluble.

i. The majority of ionic substances are solids at room temperature. Describe what you would observe if you placed a soluble ionic compound and an insoluble ionic compound in separate beakers of water.

j. Write the chemical equation(s), including state symbols, for what happens when each soluble ionic compound that you identified above is placed in water. Are these substances reacting with water when they are added to water?

k. How would you classify the soluble ionic compounds: strong electrolyte, weak electrolyte, or nonelectrolyte? Explain your answer.

l. Sodium chloride, NaCl, is a strong electrolyte, as is hydroiodic acid, HI. Write the chemical equations for what happens when these substances are added to water.

m. Are NaCl and HI strong electrolytes because they have similar behavior in aqueous solution? If not, describe, using words and equations, the different chemical process that takes place in each case.

Part 2: You have two hypothetical molecular compounds, AX and AY. AX is a strong electrolyte and AY is a weak electrolyte. The compounds undergo the following chemical reactions when added to water.

$$AX(aq) + H_2O(l) \longrightarrow AH_2O^+(aq) + X^-(aq)$$
$$AY(aq) + H_2O(l) \longrightarrow AH_2O^+(aq) + Y^-(aq)$$

a. Explain how the relative amounts of AX(aq) and AY(aq) would compare if you had a beaker of water with AX and a beaker of water with AY.

b. How would the relative amounts of $X^-(aq)$ and $Y^-(aq)$ in the two beakers compare? Be sure to explain your answer.

4.20 Working with Concentration (Molarity Concepts)

Note: You should be able to answer all of the following questions without using a calculator.

Part 1

a. Both NaCl and $MgCl_2$ are soluble ionic compounds. Write the balanced chemical equations for these two substances dissolving in water.

b. Consider the pictures below. These pictures represent 1.0-L solutions of 1.0 M NaCl(aq) and 1.0 M $MgCl_2$(aq). The representations of the ions in solution are the correct relative amounts. Water molecules have been omitted for clarity. Correctly label each of the beakers, provide a key to help identify the ions, and give a brief explanation of how you made your assignments.

Keeping in mind that the pictures represent the relative amounts of ions in the solution and that the numerical information about these solutions is presented above, answer the following questions c through f.

c. How many moles of NaCl and $MgCl_2$ are in each beaker?

d. How many moles of chloride ions are in each beaker? How did you arrive at this answer?

e. What is the concentration of chloride ions in each beaker? Without using mathematical equations, briefly explain how you obtained your answer.

f. Explain how it is that the concentrations of chloride ions in these beakers are different even though the concentrations of each substance (compound) are the same.

Part 2: Say you were to dump out half of the $MgCl_2$ solution from the beaker above.

a. What would be the concentration of the $MgCl_2$(aq) ion and of the chloride ions in the remaining solution?

b. How many moles of the $MgCl_2$ and of the chloride ions would remain in the beaker?

c. Explain why the concentration of $MgCl_2$(aq) *would not* change, whereas the number of moles of $MgCl_2$ *would* change when solution was removed from the beaker. As part of your answer, you are encouraged to use pictures.

Part 3: Consider the beaker containing 1.0 L of the 1.0 M NaCl(aq) solution. You now add 1.0 L of water to this beaker.

a. What is the concentration of this NaCl(aq) solution?

b. How many moles of NaCl are present in the 2.0 L of NaCl(aq) solution?

c. Explain why the concentration of NaCl(aq) *does* change with the addition of water, whereas the number of moles *does not* change. Here again, you are encouraged to use pictures to help answer the question.

4.21 You need to perform gravimetric analysis of a water sample in order to determine the amount of Ag^+ present.

   a. List three aqueous solutions that would be suitable for mixing with the sample to perform the analysis.

   b. Would adding $KNO_3(aq)$ allow you to perform the analysis?

   c. Assume you have performed the analysis and the silver solid that formed is moderately soluble. How might this affect your analysis results?

4.22 In this problem you need to draw two pictures of solutions in beakers at different points in time. Time zero ($t = 0$) will be the *hypothetical* instant at which the reactants dissolve in the solution (*if they dissolve*) *before* they react. Time after mixing ($t > 0$) will be the time required to allow sufficient interaction of the materials. For now, we assume that insoluble solids have no ions in solution and do not worry about representing the stoichiometric amounts of the dissolved ions. Here is an example: Solid NaCl and solid $AgNO_3$ are added to a beaker containing 250 mL of water.

Note that we are not showing the H_2O, and we are representing only the ions and solids in solution. Using the same conditions as the example (adding the solids to H_2O), draw pictures of the following:

   a. Solid lead(II) nitrate and solid ammonium chloride at $t = 0$ and $t > 0$

   b. FeS(s) and $NaNO_3(s)$ at $t = 0$ and $t > 0$

   c. Solid lithium iodide and solid sodium carbonate at $t = 0$ and $t > 0$

4.23 You come across a beaker that contains water, aqueous ammonium acetate, and a precipitate of calcium phosphate.

   a. Write the balanced molecular equation for a reaction between two solutions containing ions that could produce this solution.

   b. Write the complete ionic equation for the reaction in part a.

   c. Write the net ionic equation for the reaction in part a.

Solubility Rules

4.29 Using solubility rules, predict the solubility in water of the following ionic compounds.

   a. PbS   **b.** $AgNO_3$

   c. Na_2CO_3 **d.** CaI_2

4.24 Three acid samples are prepared for titration by 0.01 M NaOH:

1. Sample 1 is prepared by dissolving 0.01 mol of HCl in 50 mL of water.

2. Sample 2 is prepared by dissolving 0.01 mol of HCl in 60 mL of water.

3. Sample 3 is prepared by dissolving 0.01 mol of HCl in 70 mL of water.

   a. Without performing a formal calculation, compare the concentrations of the three acid samples (rank them from highest to lowest).

   b. When the titration is performed, which sample, if any, will require the largest volume of the 0.01 M NaOH for neutralization?

4.25 Would you expect a precipitation reaction between an ionic compound that is an electrolyte and an ionic compound that is a nonelectrolyte? Justify your answer.

4.26 Equal quantities of the hypothetical strong acid HX, weak acid HA, and weak base BZ, are added to separate beakers of water, producing the solutions depicted in the drawings. In the drawings, the relative amounts of each substance present in the solution (neglecting the water) are shown. Identify the acid or base that was used to produce each of the solutions (HX, HA, or BZ).

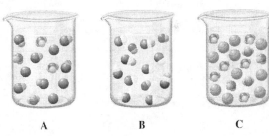

4.27 Try and answer the following questions without using a calculator.

   a. A solution is made by mixing 1.0 L of 0.5 M NaCl and 0.5 L of 1.0 M $CaCl_2$. Which ion is at the highest concentration in the solution?

   b. Another solution is made by mixing 0.50 L of 1.0 M KBr and 0.50 L of 1.0 M K_3PO_4. What is the concentration of each ion in the solution?

4.28 If one mole of the following compounds were each placed into separate beakers containing the same amount of water, rank the $Cl^-(aq)$ concentrations from highest to lowest (some may be equivalent): KCl, $AlCl_3$, $PbCl_2$, NaCl, HCl, NH_3, KOH, and HCN.

4.30 Using solubility rules, predict the solubility in water of the following ionic compounds.

   a. $Al(OH)_3$ **b.** Li_3P

   c. NH_4Cl **d.** NaOH

4.31 Using solubility rules, decide whether the following ionic solids are soluble or insoluble in water. If they are soluble, indicate what ions you would expect to be present in solution.
  a. AgBr   **b.** Li_2SO_4
  c. $Ca_3(PO_4)_2$ **d.** Na_2CO_3

4.32 Using solubility rules, decide whether the following ionic solids are soluble or insoluble in water. If they are soluble, indicate what ions you would expect to be present in solution.
  a. $(NH_4)_2SO_4$ **b.** $BaCO_3$
  c. $PbSO_4$ **d.** $Ca(NO_3)_2$

Ionic Equations

4.33 Write net ionic equations for the following molecular equations. HBr is a strong electrolyte.
  a. $HBr(aq) + KOH(aq) \longrightarrow KBr(aq) + H_2O(l)$
  b. $AgNO_3(aq) + NaBr(aq) \longrightarrow AgBr(s) + NaNO_3(aq)$
  c. $K_2S(aq) + 2HBr(aq) \longrightarrow 2KBr(aq) + H_2S(g)$
  d. $NaOH(aq) + NH_4Br(aq) \longrightarrow$
                         $NaBr(aq) + NH_3(g) + H_2O(l)$

4.34 Write net ionic equations for the following molecular equations. HBr is a strong electrolyte.
  a. $HBr(aq) + NH_3(aq) \longrightarrow NH_4Br(aq)$
  b. $2HBr(aq) + Ba(OH)_2(aq) \longrightarrow 2H_2O(l) + BaBr_2(aq)$
  c. $Pb(NO_3)_2(aq) + 2NaBr(aq) \longrightarrow PbBr_2(s) + 2NaNO_3(aq)$
  d. $MgCO_3(s) + H_2SO_4(aq) \longrightarrow$
                       $MgSO_4(aq) + H_2O(l) + CO_2(g)$

4.35 Lead(II) nitrate solution and sodium sulfate solution are mixed. Crystals of lead(II) sulfate come out of solution, leaving a solution of sodium nitrate. Write the molecular equation and the net ionic equation for the reaction.

4.36 Potassium carbonate solution reacts with aqueous hydrobromic acid to give a solution of potassium bromide, carbon dioxide gas, and water. Write the molecular equation and the net ionic equation for the reaction.

Precipitation

4.37 Write the molecular equation and the net ionic equation for each of the following aqueous reactions. If no reaction occurs, write *NR* after the arrow.
  a. $FeSO_4 + NaCl \longrightarrow$
  b. $Na_2CO_3 + MgBr_2 \longrightarrow$
  c. $MgSO_4 + NaOH \longrightarrow$
  d. $NiCl_2 + NaBr \longrightarrow$

4.38 Write the molecular equation and the net ionic equation for each of the following aqueous reactions. If no reaction occurs, write *NR* after the arrow.
  a. $AgNO_3 + NaI \longrightarrow$
  b. $Ba(NO_3)_2 + K_2SO_4 \longrightarrow$
  c. $Mg(NO_3)_2 + K_2SO_4 \longrightarrow$
  d. $CaCl_2 + Al(NO_3)_3 \longrightarrow$

4.39 For each of the following, write molecular and net ionic equations for any precipitation reaction that occurs. If no reaction occurs, indicate this.
  a. Solutions of barium nitrate and lithium sulfate are mixed.
  b. Solutions of sodium bromide and calcium nitrate are mixed.
  c. Solutions of aluminum sulfate and sodium hydroxide are mixed.

  d. Solutions of calcium bromide and sodium phosphate are mixed.

4.40 For each of the following, write molecular and net ionic equations for any precipitation reaction that occurs. If no reaction occurs, indicate this.
  a. Zinc chloride and sodium sulfide are dissolved in water.
  b. Sodium sulfide and calcium chloride are dissolved in water.
  c. Magnesium sulfate and potassium bromide are dissolved in water.
  d. Magnesium sulfate and potassium carbonate are dissolved in water.

Strong and Weak Acids and Bases

4.41 Classify each of the following as a strong or weak acid or base.
  a. HF   **b.** KOH   **c.** $HClO_4$ **d.** HIO

4.42 Classify each of the following as a strong or weak acid or base.
  a. NH_3 **b.** HCNO   **c.** $Sr(OH)_2$ **d.** HI

Neutralization Reactions

4.43 Complete and balance each of the following molecular equations (in aqueous solution); include phase labels. Then, for each, write the net ionic equation.
  a. $NaOH + HNO_3 \longrightarrow$
  b. $HCl + Ba(OH)_2 \longrightarrow$
  c. $HC_2H_3O_2 + Ca(OH)_2 \longrightarrow$
  d. $NH_3 + HNO_3 \longrightarrow$

4.44 Complete and balance each of the following molecular equations (in aqueous solution); include phase labels. Then, for each, write the net ionic equation.
  a. $Al(OH)_3 + HCl \longrightarrow$
  b. $HBr + Sr(OH)_2 \longrightarrow$
  c. $Ba(OH)_2 + HC_2H_3O_2 \longrightarrow$
  d. $HNO_3 + KOH \longrightarrow$

4.45 For each of the following, write the molecular equation, including phase labels. Then write the net ionic equation. Note that the salts formed in these reactions are soluble.
  a. the neutralization of hydrobromic acid with calcium hydroxide solution
  b. the reaction of solid aluminum hydroxide with nitric acid
  c. the reaction of aqueous hydrogen cyanide with calcium hydroxide solution
  d. the neutralization of lithium hydroxide solution by aqueous hydrogen cyanide

4.46 For each of the following, write the molecular equation, including phase labels. Then write the net ionic equation. Note that the salts formed in these reactions are soluble.
  a. the neutralization of lithium hydroxide solution by aqueous perchloric acid
  b. the reaction of barium hydroxide solution and aqueous nitrous acid
  c. the reaction of sodium hydroxide solution and aqueous nitrous acid
  d. the neutralization of aqueous hydrogen cyanide by aqueous strontium hydroxide

4.47 Complete the right side of each of the following molecular equations. Then write the net ionic equations. Assume all salts formed are soluble. Acid salts are possible.

a. $2KOH(aq) + H_3PO_4(aq) \longrightarrow$
b. $3H_2SO_4(aq) + 2Al(OH)_3(s) \longrightarrow$
c. $2HC_2H_3O_2(aq) + Ca(OH)_2(aq) \longrightarrow$
d. $H_2SO_3(aq) + NaOH(aq) \longrightarrow$

4.48 Complete the right side of each of the following molecular equations. Then write the net ionic equations. Assume all salts formed are soluble. Acid salts are possible.

a. $Ca(OH)_2(aq) + 2H_2SO_4(aq) \longrightarrow$
b. $2H_3PO_4(aq) + Ca(OH)_2(aq) \longrightarrow$
c. $NaOH(aq) + H_2SO_4(aq) \longrightarrow$
d. $Sr(OH)_2(aq) + 2H_2CO_3(aq) \longrightarrow$

4.49 Write molecular and net ionic equations for the successive neutralizations of each acidic hydrogen of sulfurous acid by aqueous calcium hydroxide. $CaSO_3$ is insoluble; the acid salt is soluble.

4.50 Write molecular and net ionic equations for the successive neutralizations of each acidic hydrogen of phosphoric acid by calcium hydroxide solution. $Ca_3(PO_4)_2$ is insoluble; assume that the acid salts are soluble.

Reactions Evolving a Gas

4.51 The following reactions occur in aqueous solution. Complete and balance the molecular equations using phase labels. Then write the net ionic equations.

a. $CaS + HBr \longrightarrow$
b. $MgCO_3 + HNO_3 \longrightarrow$
c. $K_2SO_3 + H_2SO_4 \longrightarrow$

4.52 The following reactions occur in aqueous solution. Complete and balance the molecular equations using phase labels. Then write the net ionic equations.

a. $BaCO_3 + HNO_3 \longrightarrow$
b. $K_2S + HCl \longrightarrow$
c. $CaSO_3(s) + HI \longrightarrow$

4.53 Write the molecular equation and the net ionic equation for the reaction of solid iron(II) sulfide and hydrochloric acid. Add phase labels.

4.54 Write the molecular equation and the net ionic equation for the reaction of solid barium carbonate and hydrogen bromide in aqueous solution. Add phase labels.

Oxidation Numbers

4.55 Obtain the oxidation number for the element noted in each of the following.

a. Ga in Ga_2O_3 b. Nb in NbO_2
c. Br in $KBrO_4$ d. Mn in K_2MnO_4

4.56 Obtain the oxidation number for the element noted in each of the following.

a. Cr in CrO_3 b. Hg in Hg_2Cl_2
c. Ga in $Ga(OH)_3$ d. P in Na_3PO_4

4.57 Obtain the oxidation number for the element noted in each of the following.

a. N in NH_2^- b. I in IO_3^-
c. Al in $Al(OH)_4^-$ d. Cl in $HClO_4$

4.58 Obtain the oxidation number for the element noted in each of the following.

a. N in NO_2^- b. Cr in CrO_4^{2-}
c. Zn in $Zn(OH)_4^{2-}$ d. As in $H_2AsO_3^-$

4.59 Determine the oxidation numbers of all the elements in each of the following compounds. (*Hint:* Look at the ions present.)

a. $Mn(ClO_3)_2$ b. $Fe_2(CrO_4)_3$
c. $HgCr_2O_7$ d. $Co_3(PO_4)_2$

4.60 Determine the oxidation numbers of all the elements in each of the following compounds. (*Hint:* Look at the ions present.)

a. $Hg_2(BrO_3)_2$ b. $Cr_2(SO_4)_3$
c. $CoSeO_4$ d. $Pb(OH)_2$

Describing Oxidation–Reduction Reactions

4.61 In the following reactions, label the oxidizing agent and the reducing agent.

a. $P_4(s) + 5O_2(g) \longrightarrow P_4O_{10}(s)$
b. $Co(s) + Cl_2(g) \longrightarrow CoCl_2(s)$

4.62 In the following reactions, label the oxidizing agent and the reducing agent.

a. $ZnO(s) + C(s) \longrightarrow Zn(g) + CO(g)$
b. $8Fe(s) + S_8(s) \longrightarrow 8FeS(s)$

4.63 In the following reactions, label the oxidizing agent and the reducing agent.

a. $2Al(s) + 3F_2(g) \longrightarrow 2AlF_3(s)$
b. $Hg^{2+}(aq) + NO_2^-(aq) + H_2O(l) \longrightarrow$
$Hg(s) + 2H^+(aq) + NO_3^-(aq)$

4.64 In the following reactions, label the oxidizing agent and the reducing agent.

a. $Fe_2O_3(s) + 3CO(g) \longrightarrow 2Fe(s) + 3CO_2(g)$
b. $PbS(s) + 4H_2O_2(aq) \longrightarrow PbSO_4(s) + 4H_2O(l)$

Balancing Oxidation–Reduction Reactions

4.65 Balance the following oxidation–reduction reactions by the half-reaction method.

a. $CuCl_2(aq) + Al(s) \longrightarrow AlCl_3(aq) + Cu(s)$
b. $Cr^{3+}(aq) + Zn(s) \longrightarrow Cr(s) + Zn^{2+}(aq)$

4.66 Balance the following oxidation–reduction reactions by the half-reaction method.

a. $FeI_3(aq) + Mg(s) \longrightarrow Fe(s) + MgI_2(aq)$
b. $H_2(g) + Ag^+(aq) \longrightarrow Ag(s) + H^+(aq)$

Molarity

4.67 A sample of 0.0512 mol of iron(III) chloride, $FeCl_3$, was dissolved in water to give 25.0 mL of solution. What is the molarity of the solution?

4.68 A 50.0-mL volume of $AgNO_3$ solution contains 0.0285 mol $AgNO_3$ (silver nitrate). What is the molarity of the solution?

4.69 An aqueous solution is made from 0.798 g of potassium permanganate, $KMnO_4$. If the volume of solution is 50.0 mL, what is the molarity of $KMnO_4$ in the solution?

4.70 A sample of oxalic acid, $H_2C_2O_4$, weighing 1.192 g is placed in a 100.0-mL volumetric flask, which is then filled to the mark with water. What is the molarity of the solution?

4.71 What volume of 0.120 M $CuSO_4$ is required to give 0.150 mol of copper(II) sulfate, $CuSO_4$?

4.72 How many milliliters of 0.126 M $HClO_4$ (perchloric acid) are required to give 0.102 mol $HClO_4$?

4.73 An experiment calls for 0.0353 g of potassium hydroxide, KOH. How many milliliters of 0.0176 M KOH are required?

4.74 What is the volume (in milliliters) of 0.215 M H_2SO_4 (sulfuric acid) containing 0.949 g H_2SO_4?

4.75 Heme, obtained from red blood cells, binds oxygen, O_2. How many moles of heme are there in 150 mL of 0.0019 M heme solution?

4.76 Insulin is a hormone that controls the use of glucose in the body. How many moles of insulin are required to make up 28 mL of 0.0048 M insulin solution?

4.77 How many grams of sodium dichromate, $Na_2Cr_2O_7$, should be added to a 100.0-mL volumetric flask to prepare 0.025 M $Na_2Cr_2O_7$ when the flask is filled to the mark with water?

4.78 Describe how you would prepare 2.50×10^2 mL of 0.20 M Na_2SO_4. What mass (in grams) of sodium sulfate, Na_2SO_4, is needed?

4.79 You wish to prepare 0.12 M HNO_3 from a stock solution of nitric acid that is 15.8 M. How many milliliters of the stock solution do you require to make up 1.00 L of 0.12 M HNO_3?

4.80 A chemist wants to prepare 0.50 M HCl. Commercial hydrochloric acid is 12.4 M. How many milliliters of the commercial acid does the chemist require to make up 1.50 L of the dilute acid?

4.81 A 3.50 g sample of KCl is dissolved in 10.0 mL of water. The resulting solution is then added to 60.0 mL of a 0.500 M $CaCl_2(aq)$ solution. Assuming that the volumes are additive, calculate the concentrations of each ion present in the final solution.

4.82 Calculate the concentrations of each ion present in a solution that results from mixing 50.0 mL of a 0.20 M $NaClO_3(aq)$ solution with 25.0 mL of a 0.20 M $Na_2SO_4(aq)$. Assume that the volumes are additive.

Gravimetric Analysis

4.83 A chemist added an excess of sodium sulfate to a solution of a soluble barium compound to precipitate all of the barium ion as barium sulfate, $BaSO_4$. How many grams of barium ion are in a 458-mg sample of the barium compound if a solution of the sample gave 513 mg $BaSO_4$ precipitate? What is the mass percentage of barium in the compound?

4.84 A soluble iodide was dissolved in water. Then an excess of silver nitrate, $AgNO_3$, was added to precipitate all of the iodide ion as silver iodide, AgI. If 1.545 g of the soluble iodide gave 2.185 g of silver iodide, how many grams of iodine are in the sample of soluble iodide? What is the mass percentage of iodine, I, in the compound?

4.85 Copper has compounds with copper(I) ion or copper(II) ion. A compound of copper and chlorine was treated with a solution of silver nitrate, $AgNO_3$, to convert the chloride ion in the compound to a precipitate of AgCl. A 59.40-mg sample of the copper compound gave 86.00 mg AgCl.
  a. Calculate the percentage of chlorine in the copper compound.
  b. Decide whether the formula of the compound is CuCl or $CuCl_2$.

4.86 Gold has compounds containing gold(I) ion or gold(III) ion. A compound of gold and chlorine was treated with a solution of silver nitrate, $AgNO_3$, to convert the chloride ion in the compound to a precipitate of AgCl. A 162.7-mg sample of the gold compound gave 100.3 mg AgCl.
  a. Calculate the percentage of the chlorine in the gold compound.
  b. Decide whether the formula of the compound is AuCl or $AuCl_3$.

4.87 A compound of iron and chlorine is soluble in water. An excess of silver nitrate was added to precipitate the chloride ion as silver chloride. If a 134.8-mg sample of the compound gave 304.8 mg AgCl, what is the formula of the compound?

4.88 A 1.345-g sample of a compound of barium and oxygen was dissolved in hydrochloric acid to give a solution of barium ion, which was then precipitated with an excess of potassium chromate to give 2.012 g of barium chromate, $BaCrO_4$. What is the formula of the compound?

Volumetric Analysis

4.89 What volume of 0.250 M HNO_3 (nitric acid) reacts with 44.8 mL of 0.150 M Na_2CO_3 (sodium carbonate) in the following reaction?

$$2HNO_3(aq) + Na_2CO_3(aq) \longrightarrow$$
$$2NaNO_3(aq) + H_2O(l) + CO_2(g)$$

4.90 A flask contains 49.8 mL of 0.150 M $Ca(OH)_2$ (calcium hydroxide). How many milliliters of 0.350 M Na_2CO_3 (sodium carbonate) are required to react completely with the calcium hydroxide in the following reaction?

$$Na_2CO_3(aq) + Ca(OH)_2(aq) \longrightarrow CaCO_3(s) + 2NaOH(aq)$$

4.91 How many milliliters of 0.150 M H_2SO_4 (sulfuric acid) are required to react with 8.20 g of sodium hydrogen carbonate, $NaHCO_3$, according to the following equation?

$$H_2SO_4(aq) + 2NaHCO_3(aq) \longrightarrow$$
$$Na_2SO_4(aq) + 2H_2O(l) + 2CO_2(g)$$

4.92 How many milliliters of 0.250 M $KMnO_4$ are needed to react with 3.36 g of iron(II) sulfate, $FeSO_4$? The reaction is as follows:

$$10FeSO_4(aq) + 2KMnO_4(aq) + 8H_2SO_4(aq) \longrightarrow$$
$$5Fe_2(SO_4)_3(aq) + 2MnSO_4(aq) + K_2SO_4(aq) + 8H_2O(l)$$

4.93 A solution of hydrogen peroxide, H_2O_2, is titrated with a solution of potassium permanganate, $KMnO_4$. The reaction is

$$5H_2O_2(aq) + 2KMnO_4(aq) + 3H_2SO_4(aq) \longrightarrow$$
$$5O_2(g) + 2MnSO_4(aq) + K_2SO_4(aq) + 8H_2O(l)$$

It requires 51.7 mL of 0.145 M $KMnO_4$ to titrate 20.0 g of the solution of hydrogen peroxide. What is the mass percentage of H_2O_2 in the solution?

4.94 A 3.33-g sample of iron ore is transformed to a solution of iron(II) sulfate, $FeSO_4$, and this solution is titrated with 0.150 M $K_2Cr_2O_7$ (potassium dichromate). If it requires

43.7 mL of potassium dichromate solution to titrate the iron(II) sulfate solution, what is the percentage of iron in the ore? The reaction is

$$6FeSO_4(aq) + K_2Cr_2O_7(aq) + 7H_2SO_4(aq) \longrightarrow$$
$$3Fe_2(SO_4)_3(aq) + Cr_2(SO_4)_3(aq) + 7H_2O(l) + K_2SO_4(aq)$$

General Problems

4.95 Magnesium metal reacts with hydrobromic acid to produce hydrogen gas and a solution of magnesium bromide. Write the molecular equation for this reaction. Then write the corresponding net ionic equation.

4.96 Aluminum metal reacts with perchloric acid to produce hydrogen gas and a solution of aluminum perchlorate. Write the molecular equation for this reaction. Then write the corresponding net ionic equation.

4.97 Nickel(II) sulfate solution reacts with lithium hydroxide solution to produce a precipitate of nickel(II) hydroxide and a solution of lithium sulfate. Write the molecular equation for this reaction. Then write the corresponding net ionic equation.

4.98 Potassium sulfate solution reacts with barium bromide solution to produce a precipitate of barium sulfate and a solution of potassium bromide. Write the molecular equation for this reaction. Then write the corresponding net ionic equation.

4.99 Decide whether a reaction occurs for each of the following. If it does not, write *NR* after the arrow. If it does, write the balanced molecular equation; then write the net ionic equation.
 a. $LiOH + HCN \longrightarrow$
 b. $Li_2CO_3 + HNO_3 \longrightarrow$
 c. $LiCl + AgNO_3 \longrightarrow$
 d. $LiCl + MgSO_4 \longrightarrow$

4.100 Decide whether a reaction occurs for each of the following. If it does not, write *NR* after the arrow. If it does, write the balanced molecular equation; then write the net ionic equation.
 a. $Al(OH)_3 + HNO_3 \longrightarrow$
 b. $NaBr + HClO_4 \longrightarrow$
 c. $CaCl_2 + NaNO_3 \longrightarrow$
 d. $MgSO_4 + Ba(NO_3)_2 \longrightarrow$

4.101 Complete and balance each of the following molecular equations, including phase labels, if a reaction occurs. Then write the net ionic equation. If no reaction occurs, write *NR* after the arrow.
 a. $Sr(OH)_2 + HC_2H_3O_2 \longrightarrow$
 b. $NH_4I + CsCl \longrightarrow$
 c. $NaNO_3 + CsCl \longrightarrow$
 d. $NH_4I + AgNO_3 \longrightarrow$

4.102 Complete and balance each of the following molecular equations, including phase labels, if a reaction occurs. Then

write the net ionic equation. If no reaction occurs, write *NR* after the arrow.
 a. $HClO_4 + BaCO_3 \longrightarrow$
 b. $H_2CO_3 + Sr(OH)_2 \longrightarrow$
 c. $K_3PO_4 + MgCl_2 \longrightarrow$
 d. $FeSO_4 + MgCl_2 \longrightarrow$

4.103 Describe in words how you would do each of the following preparations. Then give the molecular equation for each preparation.
 a. $CuCl_2(s)$ from $CuSO_4(s)$
 b. $Ca(C_2H_3O_2)_2(s)$ from $CaCO_3(s)$
 c. $NaNO_3(s)$ from $Na_2SO_3(s)$
 d. $MgCl_2(s)$ from $Mg(OH)_2(s)$

4.104 Describe in words how you would do each of the following preparations. Then give the molecular equation for each preparation.
 a. $MgCl_2(s)$ from $MgCO_3(s)$
 b. $NaNO_3(s)$ from $NaCl(s)$
 c. $Al(OH)_3(s)$ from $Al(NO_3)_3(s)$
 d. $HCl(aq)$ from $H_2SO_4(aq)$

4.105 Classify each of the following reactions as a combination reaction, decomposition reaction, displacement reaction, or combustion reaction.
 a. When they are heated, ammonium dichromate crystals, $(NH_4)_2Cr_2O_7$, decompose to give nitrogen, water vapor, and solid chromium(III) oxide, Cr_2O_3.
 b. When aqueous ammonium nitrite, NH_4NO_2, is heated, it gives nitrogen and water vapor.
 c. When gaseous ammonia, NH_3, reacts with hydrogen chloride gas, HCl, fine crystals of ammonium chloride, NH_4Cl, are formed.
 d. Aluminum added to an aqueous solution of sulfuric acid, H_2SO_4, forms a solution of aluminum sulfate, $Al_2(SO_4)_3$. Hydrogen gas is released.

4.106 Classify each of the following reactions as a combination reaction, decomposition reaction, displacement reaction, or combustion reaction.
 a. When solid calcium oxide, CaO, is exposed to gaseous sulfur trioxide, SO_3, solid calcium sulfate, $CaSO_4$, is formed.
 b. Calcium metal (solid) reacts with water to produce a solution of calcium hydroxide, $Ca(OH)_2$, and hydrogen gas.
 c. When solid sodium hydrogen sulfite, $NaHSO_3$, is heated, solid sodium sulfite, Na_2SO_3, sulfur dioxide gas, SO_2, and water vapor are formed.
 d. Magnesium reacts with bromine to give magnesium bromide, $MgBr_2$.

4.107 Consider the reaction of all pairs of the following compounds in water solution: $Ba(OH)_2$, $Pb(NO_3)_2$, H_2SO_4, $NaNO_3$, $MgSO_4$.
   a. Which pair (or pairs) forms one insoluble compound and one soluble compound (not water)?
   b. Which pair (or pairs) forms two insoluble compounds?
   c. Which pair (or pairs) forms one insoluble compound and water?

4.108 Consider the reaction of all pairs of the following compounds in water solution: $Sr(OH)_2$, $AgNO_3$, H_3PO_4, KNO_3, $CuSO_4$.
   a. Which pair (or pairs) forms one insoluble compound and one soluble compound (not water)?
   b. Which pair (or pairs) forms two insoluble compounds?
   c. Which pair (or pairs) forms one insoluble compound and water?

4.109 An aqueous solution contains 4.50 g of calcium chloride, $CaCl_2$, per liter. What is the molarity of $CaCl_2$? When calcium chloride dissolves in water, the calcium ions, Ca^{2+}, and chloride ions, Cl^-, in the crystal go into the solution. What is the molarity of each ion in the solution?

4.110 An aqueous solution contains 3.45 g of iron(III) sulfate, $Fe_2(SO_4)_3$, per liter. What is the molarity of $Fe_2(SO_4)_3$? When the compound dissolves in water, the Fe^{3+} ions and SO_4^{2-} ions in the crystal go into the solution. What is the molar concentration of each ion in the solution?

4.111 A stock solution of potassium dichromate, $K_2Cr_2O_7$, is made by dissolving 89.3 g of the compound in 1.00 L of solution. How many milliliters of this solution are required to prepare 1.00 L of 0.100 M $K_2Cr_2O_7$?

4.112 A 71.2-g sample of oxalic acid, $H_2C_2O_4$, was dissolved in 1.00 L of solution. How would you prepare 1.00 L of 0.150 M $H_2C_2O_4$ from this solution?

4.113 A solution contains 6.00% (by mass) NaBr (sodium bromide). The density of the solution is 1.046 g/cm³. What is the molarity of NaBr?

4.114 An aqueous solution contains 4.00% NH_3 (ammonia) by mass. The density of the aqueous ammonia is 0.979 g/mL. What is the molarity of NH_3 in the solution?

4.115 A barium mineral was dissolved in hydrochloric acid to give a solution of barium ion. An excess of potassium sulfate was added to 50.0 mL of the solution, and 1.128 g of barium sulfate precipitate formed. Assume that the original solution was barium chloride. What was the molarity of $BaCl_2$ in this solution?

4.116 Bone was dissolved in hydrochloric acid, giving 50.0 mL of solution containing calcium chloride, $CaCl_2$. To precipitate the calcium ion from the resulting solution, an excess of potassium oxalate was added. The precipitate of calcium oxalate, CaC_2O_4, weighed 1.437 g. What was the molarity of $CaCl_2$ in the solution?

4.117 You have a sample of a rat poison whose active ingredient is thallium(I) sulfate. You analyze this sample for the mass percentage of active ingredient by adding potassium iodide to precipitate yellow thallium(I) iodide. If the sample of rat poison weighed 759.0 mg and you obtained 212.2 mg of the dry precipitate, what is the mass percentage of the thallium(I) sulfate in the rat poison?

4.118 An antacid tablet has calcium carbonate as the active ingredient; other ingredients include a starch binder. You dissolve the tablet in hydrochloric acid and filter off insoluble material. You add potassium oxalate to the filtrate (containing calcium ion) to precipitate calcium oxalate. If a tablet weighing 0.680 g gave 0.629 g of calcium oxalate, what is the mass percentage of active ingredient in the tablet?

4.119 A sample of $CuSO_4 \cdot 5H_2O$ was heated to 110°C, where it lost water and gave another hydrate of copper(II) ion that contains 32.50% Cu. A 98.77-mg sample of this new hydrate gave 116.66 mg of barium sulfate precipitate when treated with a barium nitrate solution. What is the formula of the new hydrate?

4.120 A sample of $CuSO_4 \cdot 5H_2O$ was heated to 100°C, where it lost water and gave another hydrate of copper(II) ion that contained 29.76% Cu. An 85.42-mg sample of this new hydrate gave 93.33 mg of barium sulfate precipitate when treated with a barium nitrate solution. What is the formula of the new hydrate?

4.121 A water-soluble compound of gold and chlorine is treated with silver nitrate to convert the chlorine completely to silver chloride, AgCl. In an experiment, 328 mg of the compound gave 464 mg of silver chloride. Calculate the percentage of Cl in the compound. What is its empirical formula?

4.122 A solution of scandium chloride was treated with silver nitrate. The chlorine in the scandium compound was converted to silver chloride, AgCl. A 58.9-mg sample of scandium chloride gave 167.4 mg of silver chloride. What are the mass percentages of Sc and Cl in scandium chloride? What is its empirical formula?

4.123 A 0.608-g sample of fertilizer contained nitrogen as ammonium sulfate, $(NH_4)_2SO_4$. It was analyzed for nitrogen by heating with sodium hydroxide.

$$(NH_4)_2SO_4(s) + 2NaOH(aq) \longrightarrow$$
$$Na_2SO_4(aq) + 2H_2O(l) + 2NH_3(g)$$

The ammonia was collected in 46.3 mL of 0.213 M HCl (hydrochloric acid), with which it reacted.

$$NH_3(g) + HCl(aq) \longrightarrow NH_4Cl(aq)$$

This solution was titrated for excess hydrochloric acid with 44.3 mL of 0.128 M NaOH.

$$NaOH(aq) + HCl(aq) \longrightarrow NaCl(aq) + H_2O(l)$$

What is the percentage of nitrogen in the fertilizer?

4.124 An antacid tablet contains sodium hydrogen carbonate, $NaHCO_3$, and inert ingredients. A 0.500-g sample of powdered tablet was mixed with 50.0 mL of 0.190 M HCl (hydrochloric acid). The mixture was allowed to stand until it reacted.

$$NaHCO_3(s) + HCl(aq) \longrightarrow NaCl(aq) + H_2O(l) + CO_2(g)$$

The excess hydrochloric acid was titrated with 47.1 mL of 0.128 M NaOH (sodium hydroxide).

$$HCl(aq) + NaOH(aq) \longrightarrow NaCl(aq) + H_2O(l)$$

What is the percentage of sodium hydrogen carbonate in the antacid?

Strategy Problems

4.125 You order a glass of juice in a restaurant, only to discover that it is warm and too sweet. The sugar concentration of the juice is 3.47 M, but you would like it reduced to a concentration of 1.78 M. How many grams of ice should you add to 100 mL of juice, knowing that only a third of the ice will melt before you take the first sip? (The density of water is 1.00 g/mL.)

4.126 If 45.1 mL of a solution containing 8.30 g of silver nitrate is added to 30.6 mL of 0.511 M sodium carbonate solution, calculate the molarity of silver ion in the resulting solution. (Assume volumes are additive.)

4.127 If 38.2 mL of 0.248 M aluminum sulfate solution is diluted with deionized water to a total volume of 0.639 L, how many grams of aluminum ion are present in the diluted solution?

4.128 An aluminum nitrate solution is labeled 0.256 M. If 31.6 mL of this solution is diluted to a total of 63.7 mL, calculate the molarity of nitrate ion in the resulting solution.

4.129 Zinc acetate is sometimes prescribed by physicians for the treatment of Wilson's disease, which is a genetically caused condition wherein copper accumulates to toxic levels in the body. If you were to analyze a sample of zinc acetate and find that it contains 3.33×10^{23} acetate ions, how many grams of zinc acetate must be present in the sample?

4.130 Arsenic acid, H_3AsO_4, is a poisonous acid that has been used in the treatment of wood to prevent insect damage. Arsenic acid has three acidic protons. Say you take a 26.14-mL sample of arsenic acid and prepare it for titration with NaOH by adding 25.00 mL of water. The complete neutralization of this solution requires the addition of 53.07 mL of 0.6441 M NaOH solution. Write the balanced chemical reaction for the titration, and calculate the molarity of the arsenic acid sample.

4.131 When the following equation is balanced by the half-reaction method using the smallest set of whole-number stoichiometric coefficients possible, how many electrons are canceled when the two half-reactions are added together?

$$K(s) + N_2(g) \Rightarrow K_3N(s)$$

4.132 Identify each of the following reactions as being a neutralization, precipitation, or oxidation–reduction reaction.

a. $Fe_2O_3(s) + 3CO(g) \longrightarrow 2Fe(s) + 3CO_2(g)$

b. $Na_2SO_4(aq) + Hg(NO_3)_2(aq) \longrightarrow$
$$HgSO_4(s) + 2NaNO_3(aq)$$

c. $CsOH(aq) + HClO_4(aq) \longrightarrow$
$$Cs^+(aq) + 2H_2O(l) + ClO_4^-(aq)$$

d. $Mg(NO_3)_2(g) + Na_2S(aq) \longrightarrow MgS(s) + 2NaNO_3(aq)$

4.133 A 414-mL sample of 0.196 M $MgBr_2$ solution is prepared in a large flask. A 43.0-mL portion of the solution is then placed into an empty 100.0-mL beaker. What is the concentration of the solution in the beaker?

4.134 Three 1.0-g samples of $PbCl_2$, KCl, and $CaCl_2$ are placed in separate 500-mL beakers. In each case, enough 25°C water is added to bring the total volume of the mixture to 250 mL. Each of the mixtures is then stirred for five minutes. Which of the mixtures will have the highest concentration of chloride (Cl^-) ion?

Cumulative-Skills Problems

4.135 Lead(II) nitrate reacts with cesium sulfate in an aqueous precipitation reaction. What are the formulas of lead(II) nitrate and cesium sulfate? Write the molecular equation and net ionic equation for the reaction. What are the names of the products? Give the molecular equation for another reaction that produces the same precipitate.

4.136 Silver nitrate reacts with strontium chloride in an aqueous precipitation reaction. What are the formulas of silver nitrate and strontium chloride? Write the molecular equation and net ionic equation for the reaction. What are the names of the products? Give the molecular equation for another reaction that produces the same precipitate.

4.137 Elemental bromine is the source of bromine compounds. The element is produced from certain brine solutions that occur naturally. These brines are essentially solutions of calcium bromide that, when treated with chlorine gas, yield bromine in a displacement reaction. What are the molecular equation and net ionic equation for the reaction? A solution containing 40.0 g of calcium bromide requires 14.2 g of chlorine to react completely with it, and 22.2 g of calcium chloride is produced in addition to whatever bromine is obtained. How many grams of calcium bromide are required to produce 10.0 pounds of bromine?

4.138 Barium carbonate is the source of barium compounds. It is produced in an aqueous precipitation reaction from barium sulfide and sodium carbonate. (Barium sulfide is a soluble compound obtained by heating the mineral barite, which is barium sulfate, with carbon.) What are the molecular equation and net ionic equation for the precipitation reaction? A solution containing 33.9 g of barium sulfide requires 21.2 g of sodium carbonate to react completely with it, and 15.6 g of sodium sulfide is produced in addition to whatever barium carbonate is obtained. How many grams of barium sulfide are required to produce 5.00 tons of barium carbonate? (One ton equals 2000 pounds.)

4.139 Mercury(II) nitrate is treated with hydrogen sulfide, H_2S, forming a precipitate and a solution. Write the molecular equation and the net ionic equation for the reaction. An acid is formed; is it strong or weak? Name each of the products. If 81.15 g of mercury(II) nitrate and 8.52 g of hydrogen sulfide are mixed in 550.0 g of water to form 58.16 g of precipitate, what is the mass of the solution after the reaction?

4.140 Mercury(II) nitrate is treated with hydrogen sulfide, H_2S, forming a precipitate and a solution. Write the molecular equation and the net ionic equation for the reaction. An acid is formed; is it strong or weak? Name each of the products. If 65.65 g of mercury(II) nitrate and 4.26 g of hydrogen sulfide are mixed in 395.0 g of water to form 54.16 g of precipitate, what is the mass of the solution after the reaction?

4.141 Iron forms a sulfide with the approximate formula Fe_7S_8. Assume that the oxidation state of sulfur is -2 and that iron atoms exist in both $+2$ and $+3$ oxidation states. What is the ratio of Fe(II) atoms to Fe(III) atoms in this compound?

4.142 A transition metal X forms an oxide of formula X_2O_3. It is found that only 50% of X atoms in this compound are in the $+3$ oxidation state. The only other stable oxidation states of X are $+2$ and $+5$. What percentage of X atoms are in the $+2$ oxidation state in this compound?

4.143 What volume of a solution of ethanol, C_2H_6O, that is 94.0% ethanol by mass contains 0.200 mol C_2H_6O? The density of the solution is 0.807 g/mL.

4.144 What volume of a solution of ethylene glycol, $C_2H_6O_2$, that is 56.0% ethylene glycol by mass contains 0.350 mol $C_2H_6O_2$? The density of the solution is 1.072 g/mL.

4.145 A 10.0-mL sample of potassium iodide solution was analyzed by adding an excess of silver nitrate solution to produce silver iodide crystals, which were filtered from the solution.

$$KI(aq) + AgNO_3(aq) \longrightarrow KNO_3(aq) + AgI(s)$$

If 2.183 g of silver iodide was obtained, what was the molarity of the original KI solution?

4.146 A 25.0-mL sample of sodium sulfate solution was analyzed by adding an excess of barium chloride solution to produce barium sulfate crystals, which were filtered from the solution.

$$Na_2SO_4(aq) + BaCl_2(aq) \longrightarrow 2NaCl(aq) + BaSO_4(s)$$

If 5.719 g of barium sulfate was obtained, what was the molarity of the original Na_2SO_4 solution?

4.147 A metal, M, was converted to the sulfate, $M_2(SO_4)_3$. Then a solution of the sulfate was treated with barium chloride to give barium sulfate crystals, which were filtered off.

$$M_2(SO_4)_3(aq) + 3BaCl_2(aq) \longrightarrow 2MCl_3(aq) + 3BaSO_4(s)$$

If 1.200 g of the metal gave 6.026 g of barium sulfate, what is the atomic weight of the metal? What is the metal?

4.148 A metal, M, was converted to the chloride, MCl_2. Then a solution of the chloride was treated with silver nitrate to give silver chloride crystals, which were filtered from the solution.

$$MCl_2(aq) + 2AgNO_3(aq) \longrightarrow M(NO_3)_2(aq) + 2AgCl(s)$$

If 2.434 g of the metal gave 7.964 g of silver chloride, what is the atomic weight of the metal? What is the metal?

4.149 Phosphoric acid is prepared by dissolving phosphorus(V) oxide, P_4O_{10}, in water. What is the balanced equation for this reaction? How many grams of P_4O_{10} are required to make 1.50 L of aqueous solution containing 5.00% phosphoric acid by mass? The density of the solution is 1.025 g/mL.

4.150 Iron(III) chloride can be prepared by reacting iron metal with chlorine. What is the balanced equation for this reaction? How many grams of iron are required to make 3.00 L of aqueous solution containing 9.00% iron(III) chloride by mass? The density of the solution is 1.067 g/mL.

4.151 An alloy of aluminum and magnesium was treated with sodium hydroxide solution, in which only aluminum reacts.

$$2Al(s) + 2NaOH(aq) + 6H_2O(l) \longrightarrow$$
$$2NaAl(OH)_4(aq) + 3H_2(g)$$

If a sample of alloy weighing 1.118 g gave 0.1068 g of hydrogen, what is the percentage of aluminum in the alloy?

4.152 An alloy of iron and carbon was treated with sulfuric acid, in which only iron reacts.

$$2Fe(s) + 3H_2SO_4(aq) \longrightarrow Fe_2(SO_4)_3(aq) + 3H_2(g)$$

If a sample of alloy weighing 2.358 g gave 0.1152 g of hydrogen, what is the percentage of iron in the alloy?

4.153 Determine the volume of sulfuric acid solution needed to prepare 37.4 g of aluminum sulfate, $Al_2(SO_4)_3$, by the reaction

$$2Al(s) + 3H_2SO_4(aq) \longrightarrow Al_2(SO_4)_3(aq) + 3H_2(g)$$

The sulfuric acid solution, whose density is 1.104 g/mL, contains 15.0% H_2SO_4 by mass.

4.154 Determine the volume of sodium hydroxide solution needed to prepare 26.2 g sodium phosphate, Na_3PO_4, by the reaction

$$3NaOH(aq) + H_3PO_4(aq) \longrightarrow Na_3PO_4(aq) + 3H_2O(l)$$

The sodium hydroxide solution, whose density is 1.133 g/mL, contains 12.0% NaOH by mass.

4.155 The active ingredients of an antacid tablet contained only magnesium hydroxide and aluminum hydroxide. Complete neutralization of a sample of the active ingredients required 48.5 mL of 0.187 M hydrochloric acid. The chloride salts from this neutralization were obtained by evaporation of the filtrate from the titration; they weighed 0.4200 g. What was the percentage by mass of magnesium hydroxide in the active ingredients of the antacid tablet?

4.156 The active ingredients in an antacid tablet contained only calcium carbonate and magnesium carbonate. Complete reaction of a sample of the active ingredients required 41.33 mL of 0.08750 M hydrochloric acid. The chloride salts from the reaction were obtained by evaporation of the filtrate from this titration; they weighed 0.1900 g. What was the percentage by mass of the calcium carbonate in the active ingredients of the antacid tablet?

7

Quantum Theory of the Atom

Colored flames from several metal compounds; the visible light is emitted from the metal atoms. The yellow emission from sodium atoms is used in sodium street lamps.

Contents and Concepts

To understand the formation of chemical bonds, you need to know something about the electronic structure of atoms. Because light gives us information about this structure, we begin by discussing the nature of light. Then we look at the Bohr theory of the simplest atom, hydrogen.

The Bohr theory firmly establishes the concept of energy levels but fails to account for the details of atomic structure. Here we discuss some basic notions of quantum mechanics, which is the theory currently applied to extremely small particles, such as electrons in atoms.

Accdording to Rutherford's model (Section 2.2), an atom consists of a nucleus many times smaller than the atom itself, with electrons occupying the remaining space. How are the electrons distributed in this space? Or, we might ask, what are the electrons doing in the atom?

The answer was to come from an unexpected area: the study of colored flames. When metal compounds burn in a flame, they emit bright colors (Figure 7.1). The spectacular colors of fireworks are due to the burning of metal compounds. Lithium and strontium compounds give a deep red color; barium compounds, a green color; and copper compounds, a bluish green color.

FIGURE 7.1

Flame tests of Groups IA and IIA elements

A wire loop containing a sample of a metal compound is placed in a flame. *Left to right:* flames of lithium (red), sodium (yellow), strontium (red), and calcium (orange).

Although the red flames of lithium and strontium appear similar, the light from each can be resolved (separated) by means of a prism into distinctly different colors. This resolution easily distinguishes the two elements. A prism disperses the colors of white light just as small raindrops spread the colors of sunlight into a rainbow or spectrum. But the light from a flame, when passed through a prism, reveals something other than a rainbow. Instead of the continuous range of color from red to yellow to violet, the spectrum from a strontium flame, for example, shows a cluster of red lines and blue lines against a black background. The spectrum of lithium is different, showing a red line, a yellow line, and two blue lines against a black background. (See Figure 7.2.)

Each element, in fact, has a characteristic line spectrum because of the emission of light from atoms in the hot gas. The spectra can be used to identify elements. How is it that each atom emits particular colors of light? What does a line spectrum tell us about the structure of an atom? If you know something about the structures of atoms, can you explain the formation of ions and molecules? We will answer these questions in this and the next few chapters.

■ **See pages 286–287 for the Media Summary.**

This chapter can immediately follow Chapter 2, if you wish.

An improved flame test for qualitative analysis using a multi-channel UV-visible spectrophotometer, *J. Chem. Educ.* 83 (2006): 277.

Flame tests that are portable, storable, and easy to use, *J. Chem. Educ.* 75 (1998): 55.

Light Waves, Photons, and the Bohr Theory

In Chapter 2 we looked at the *basic structure* of atoms and we introduced the concept of a chemical bond. To understand the formation of a chemical bond between atoms, however, you need to know something about the *electronic structure* of atoms. The present theory of the electronic structure of atoms started with an explanation of the colored light produced in hot gases and flames. Before we can discuss this, we need to describe the nature of light.

FIGURE 7.2

Emission (line) spectra of some elements
The lines correspond to visible light emitted by atoms. (Wavelengths of lines are given in nanometers.)

7.1 The Wave Nature of Light

Demonstration of line spectra: Have students observe atomic line spectra from flames, gas discharge tubes, and incandescent bulbs using diffraction gratings made of acetate film in slide mounts (available from Edmund Scientific Company).

If you drop a stone into one end of a quiet pond, the impact of the stone with the water starts an up-and-down motion of the water surface. This up-and-down motion travels outward from where the stone hit; it is a familiar example of a wave. A *wave* is a continuously repeating change or oscillation in matter or in a physical field. Light is also a wave. It consists of oscillations in electric and magnetic fields that can travel through space. Visible light, x rays, and radio waves are all forms of *electromagnetic radiation*.

You characterize a wave by its wavelength and frequency. The **wavelength,** denoted by the Greek letter λ (lambda), is *the distance between any two adjacent identical points of a wave.* Thus, the wavelength is the distance between two adjacent peaks or troughs of a wave. Figure 7.3 shows a cross section of a water wave at a given moment, with the wavelength (λ) identified. Radio waves have wavelengths from approximately 100 mm to several hundred meters. Visible light has much shorter wavelengths, about 10^{-6} m. Wavelengths of visible light are often given in nanometers (1 nm = 10^{-9} m). For example, light of wavelength 5.55×10^{-7} m, the greenish yellow light to which the human eye is most sensitive, equals 555 nm.

The **frequency** of a wave is *the number of wavelengths of that wave that pass a fixed point in one unit of time* (usually one second). For example, imagine you are anchored in a small boat on a pond when a stone is dropped into the water. Waves travel outward from this point and move past your boat. The number of wavelengths

FIGURE 7.3

Water wave (ripple)
The wavelength (λ) is the distance between any two adjacent identical points of a wave, such as two adjacent peaks or two adjacent troughs.

FIGURE 7.4

Relation between wavelength and frequency

Both waves are traveling at the same speed. The top wave has a wavelength twice that of the bottom wave. The bottom wave, however, has twice the frequency of the top wave.

> To understand how fast the speed of light is, it might help to realize that it takes only 2.5 s for radar waves (which travel at the speed of light) to leave Earth, bounce off the moon, and return—a total distance of 478,000 miles.

that pass you in one second is the frequency of that wave. Frequency is denoted by the Greek letter ν (nu, pronounced "new"). The unit of frequency is /s, or s^{-1}, also called the *hertz* (Hz).

The wavelength and frequency of a wave are related to each other. Figure 7.4 shows two waves, each traveling from left to right at the same speed; that is, each wave moves the same total length in 1s. The top wave, however, has a wavelength twice that of the bottom wave. In 1s, two complete wavelengths of the top wave move left to right from the origin. It has a frequency of 2/s, or 2 Hz. In the same time, four complete wavelengths of the bottom wave move left to right from the origin. It has a frequency of 4/s, or 4 Hz. Note that for two waves traveling with a given speed, wavelength and frequency are inversely related: the greater the wavelength, the lower the frequency, and vice versa. In general, with a wave of frequency ν and wavelength λ, there are ν wavelengths, each of length λ, that pass a fixed point every second. The product $\nu\lambda$ is the total length of the wave that has passed the point in 1s. This length of wave per second is the speed of the wave. For light of speed c,

$$c = \nu\lambda$$

The speed of light waves in a vacuum is a constant and is independent of wavelength or frequency. This speed is 3.00×10^8 m/s, which is the value for c that we use in the following examples. <

Example 7.1 | **Obtaining the Wavelength of Light from Its Frequency**

What is the wavelength of the yellow sodium emission, which has a frequency of 5.09×10^{14}/s?

An alternative example is provided in the Instructor's Resource Manual.

Problem Strategy   Note that frequency and wavelength are related (their product equals the speed of light). Write this as an equation, and then rearrange it to give the wavelength on the left and the frequency and speed of light on the right.

Solution   The frequency and wavelength are related by the formula $c = \nu\lambda$. You rearrange this formula to give

$$\lambda = \frac{c}{\nu}$$

in which c is the speed of light (3.00×10^8 m/s). Substituting yields

$$\lambda = \frac{3.00 \times 10^8 \text{ m/s}}{5.09 \times 10^{14}\text{/s}} = 5.89 \times 10^{-7} \text{ m, or } \textbf{589 nm}$$

Answer Check   Make sure you use the same units for c and ν (we used SI units in the solution). Check that the units cancel on the right to give the units of wavelength. As a check on your arithmetic, note that the wavelength for the answer should be in the visible range (400 nm to 800 nm).

Exercise 7.1   The frequency of the strong red line in the spectrum of potassium is 3.91×10^{14}/s. What is the wavelength of this light in nanometers?

■ See Problems 7.35 and 7.36.

Example 7.2 | Obtaining the Frequency of Light from Its Wavelength

What is the frequency of violet light with a wavelength of 408 nm?

Problem Strategy Rearrange the equation relating frequency and wavelength so that the frequency is on the left and the wavelength and speed of light are on the right.

An alternative example is provided in the Instructor's Resource Manual.

Solution You rearrange the equation relating frequency and wavelength to give

$$\nu = \frac{c}{\lambda}$$

Substituting for λ (408 nm = 408×10^{-9} m) gives

$$\nu = \frac{3.00 \times 10^8 \text{ m/s}}{408 \times 10^{-9} \text{ m}} = \mathbf{7.35 \times 10^{14}/s}$$

Answer Check Use the same units for wavelength and speed of light; then check that the units cancel after substituting to give the units of frequency. We have used SI units here.

In 1854, Kirchhoff found that each element has a unique spectrum. Later, Bunsen and Kirchhoff developed the prism spectroscope and used it to confirm their discovery of two new elements, cesium (in 1860) and rubidium (in 1861).

Exercise 7.2 The element cesium was discovered in 1860 by Robert Bunsen and Gustav Kirchhoff, who found two bright blue lines in the spectrum of a substance isolated from a mineral water. One of the spectral lines of cesium has a wavelength of 456 nm. What is its frequency? >

■ See Problems 7.37 and 7.38.

The range of frequencies or wavelengths of electromagnetic radiation is called the **electromagnetic spectrum,** shown in Figure 7.5. Visible light extends from the violet end of the spectrum, which has a wavelength of about 400 nm, to the red end, with a wavelength of less than 800 nm. Beyond these extremes, electromagnetic radiation is not visible to the human eye. Infrared radiation has wavelengths greater than 800 nm (greater than the wavelength of red light), and ultraviolet radiation has wavelengths less than 400 nm (less than the wavelength of violet light).

FIGURE 7.5 ▼

The electromagnetic spectrum
Divisions between regions are not defined precisely.

Visible spectrum

Concept Check 7.1
Laser light of a specific frequency falls on a crystal that converts this light into one with double the original frequency. How is the wavelength of this frequency-doubled light related to the wavelength of the original laser light? Suppose the original laser light was red. In which region of the spectrum would the frequency-doubled light be? (If this is in the visible region, what color is the light?)

7.2 | Quantum Effects and Photons

Isaac Newton, who studied the properties of light in the seventeenth century, believed that light consisted of a beam of particles. In 1801, however, British physicist Thomas Young showed that light, like waves, could be diffracted. *Diffraction* is a property of waves in which the waves spread out when they encounter an obstruction or small hole about the size of the wavelength. You can observe diffraction by viewing a light source through a hole—for example, a streetlight through a mesh curtain. The image of the streetlight is blurred by diffraction.

By the early part of the twentieth century, the wave theory of light appeared to be well entrenched. But in 1905 the German physicist Albert Einstein (1879–1955; emigrated to the United States in 1933) discovered that he could explain a phenomenon known as the *photoelectric effect* by postulating that light had both wave and particle properties. Einstein based this idea on the work of the German physicist Max Planck (1858–1947).

Planck's Quantization of Energy

In 1900 Max Planck found a theoretical formula that exactly describes the intensity of light of various frequencies emitted by a hot solid at different temperatures. < Earlier, others had shown experimentally that the light of maximum intensity from a hot solid varies in a definite way with temperature. A solid glows red at 750°C, then white as the temperature increases to 1200°C. At the lower temperature, chiefly red light is emitted. As the temperature increases, more yellow and blue light become mixed with the red, giving white light. <

According to Planck, the atoms of the solid oscillate, or vibrate, with a definite frequency v, depending on the solid. But in order to reproduce the results of experiments on glowing solids, he found it necessary to accept a strange idea. An atom could have only certain energies of vibration, E, those allowed by the formula

$$E = nhv, \quad n = 1, 2, 3, \ldots$$

where h is a constant, now called **Planck's constant,** *a physical constant relating energy and frequency, having the value* 6.63×10^{-34} *J·s*. The value of n must be 1 or 2 or some other whole number. Thus, the only energies a vibrating atom can have are hv, $2hv$, $3hv$, and so forth.

The numbers symbolized by n are called *quantum numbers*. The vibrational energies of the atoms are said to be *quantized*; that is, the possible energies are limited to certain values.

The quantization of energy seems contradicted by everyday experience. Consider the potential energy of an object, such as a tennis ball. Its potential energy depends on its height above the surface of the earth: the greater the upward height, the greater the potential energy. (Recall the discussion of potential energy in Section 6.1.) We have no problem in placing the tennis ball at any height, so it can have any energy. Imagine, however, that you could only place the tennis ball on the steps of a stairway. In that case, you could only put the tennis ball on one of the steps, so the potential energy of the tennis ball could have only certain values; its energy would be quantized. Of course, this restriction of the tennis ball is artificial;

ChemWork: Wavelengths from the Heavens

ChemWork: Removing Electrons from a Metal

Max Planck was professor of physics at the University of Berlin when he did this research. He received the Nobel Prize in physics for it in 1918.

Radiation emitted from the human body and warm objects is mostly infrared, which is detected by burglar alarms, military night-vision scopes, and similar equipment.

in fact, a tennis ball can have a range of energies, not just particular values. As we will see, quantum effects depend on the mass of the object: the smaller the mass, the more likely you will see quantum effects. Atoms, and particularly electrons, have small enough masses to exhibit quantization of energy; tennis balls do not.

Photoelectric Effect

Albert Einstein obtained his Ph.D. in 1905. In the same year he published five ground breaking research papers: one on the photoelectric effect (for which he received the Nobel Prize in physics in 1921); two on special relativity; a paper on the determination of molecular size; and one on Brownian motion (which led to experiments that tested kinetic-molecular theory and ended remaining doubts about the existence of atoms and molecules).

Planck himself was uneasy with the quantization assumption and tried unsuccessfully to eliminate it from his theory. Albert Einstein, on the other hand, boldly extended Planck's work to include the structure of light itself. Einstein reasoned that if a vibrating atom changed energy, say from $3h\nu$ to $2h\nu$, it would decrease in energy by $h\nu$, and this energy would be emitted as a bit (or quantum) of light energy. He therefore postulated that light consists of quanta (now called **photons**), or *particles of electromagnetic energy, with energy E proportional to the observed frequency of the light:* <

$$E = h\nu$$

In 1905 Einstein used this photon concept to explain the photoelectric effect.

The **photoelectric effect** is *the ejection of electrons from the surface of a metal or from another material when light shines on it* (see Figure 7.6). Electrons are ejected, however, only when the frequency of light exceeds a certain *threshold value* characteristic of the particular metal. For example, although violet light will cause potassium metal to eject electrons, no amount of red light (which has a lower frequency) has any effect.

To explain this dependence of the photoelectric effect on the frequency, Einstein assumed that an electron is ejected from a metal when it is struck by a single photon. Therefore, this photon must have at least enough energy to remove the electron from the attractive forces of the metal. No matter how many photons strike the metal, if no single one has sufficient energy, an electron cannot be ejected. A photon of red light has insufficient energy to remove an electron from potassium. But a photon corresponding to the threshold frequency has just enough energy, and at higher frequencies it has more than enough energy. When the photon hits the metal, its energy $h\nu$ is taken up by the electron. The photon ceases to exist as a particle; it is said to be *absorbed*.

The wave and particle pictures of light should be regarded as complementary views of the same physical entity. This is called the *wave–particle duality* of light. The equation $E = h\nu$ displays this duality; E is the energy of a light particle or photon, and ν is the frequency of the associated wave. Neither the wave nor the particle view alone is a complete description of light.

FIGURE 7.6

The photoelectric effect

Light shines on a metal surface, knocking out electrons. The metal surface is contained in an evacuated tube, which allows the ejected electrons to be accelerated to a positively charged plate. As long as light of sufficient frequency shines on the metal, free electrons are produced and a current flows through the tube. (The current is measured by an ammeter.) When the light is turned off, the current stops flowing.

Example 7.3	Calculating the Energy of a Photon

The red spectral line of lithium occurs at 671 nm (6.71×10^{-7} m). Calculate the energy of one photon of this light.

An alternative example is provided in the Instructor's Resource Manual.

Problem Strategy   Note that the energy of a photon is related to its corresponding frequency. Therefore, you will first need to obtain this frequency from the wavelength of the spectral line.

Solution   The frequency of this light is

$$\nu = \frac{c}{\lambda} = \frac{3.00 \times 10^8 \text{ m/s}}{6.71 \times 10^{-7} \text{ m}} = 4.47 \times 10^{14}/s$$

(continued)

A Chemist Looks at . . .

daily life

Zapping Hamburger with Gamma Rays

In 1993 in Seattle, Washington, four children died and hundreds of people became sick from food poisoning when they ate undercooked hamburgers containing a dangerous strain of a normally harmless bacterium, *Escherichia coli*. A similar bout of food poisoning from hamburgers containing the dangerous strain of E. *coli* occurred in the summer of 1997; 17 people became ill. This time the tainted hamburger was traced to a meat processor in Nebraska, which immediately recalled 25 million pounds of ground beef. Within months, the U.S. Food and Drug Administration approved the irradiation of red meat by gamma rays to kill harmful bacteria. Gamma rays are a form of electromagnetic radiation similar to x rays, but the photons of gamma rays have higher energy.

The idea of using high-energy radiation to disinfect foods is not new (Figure 7.7). It has been known for about 50 years that high-energy radiation kills bacteria and molds in foods, prolonging their shelf life. Gamma rays kill organisms by breaking up the DNA molecules within their cells. This DNA holds the information for producing vital cell proteins.

Currently, the gamma rays used in food irradiation come from the radioactive decay of cobalt-60. It is perhaps this association with radioactivity that has slowed the acceptance of irradiation as a food disinfectant. However, food is not made radioactive by irradiating it with gamma rays. The two major concerns about food irradiation—whether a food's nutritional value might be significantly diminished and whether decomposition products might cause cancer—appear to be without foundation. Irradiation of foods with gamma rays may soon join pasteurization as a way to protect our food supply from harmful bacteria.

FIGURE 7.7 ▲
Gamma irradiation of foods
Here, fresh produce has been irradiated to reduce spoilage and to ensure that the produce does not contain harmful bacteria. Now, meat can also be irradiated.

■ See Problems 7.91 and 7.92.

(continued)

Hence, the energy of one photon is

$$E = h\nu = 6.63 \times 10^{-34} \text{ J·s} \times 4.47 \times 10^{14}/\text{s} = \textbf{2.96} \times \textbf{10}^{-19} \textbf{ J}$$

Answer Check Be sure to use the same systems of units for the wavelength, the speed of light, and Planck's constant. Check that units cancel to give the proper units for energy in the final answer.

Exercise 7.3 The following are representative wavelengths in the infrared, ultraviolet, and x-ray regions of the electromagnetic spectrum, respectively: 1.0×10^{-6} m, 1.0×10^{-8} m, and 1.0×10^{-10} m. What is the energy of a photon of each radiation? Which has the greatest amount of energy per photon? Which has the least?

■ See Problems 7.43, 7.44, 7.45, and 7.46.

7.3 | The Bohr Theory of the Hydrogen Atom

According to Rutherford's nuclear model, the atom consists of a nucleus with most of the mass of the atom and a positive charge, around which move enough electrons to make the atom electrically neutral. But this model, offered in 1911, posed a dilemma. Using the then-current theory, one could show that an electrically charged particle (such as an electron) that revolves around a center would continuously lose energy as electromagnetic radiation. As an electron in an atom lost energy, it would spiral into the nucleus (in about 10^{-10} s, according to available theory). The stability of the atom could not be explained.

A solution to this theoretical dilemma was found in 1913 by Niels Bohr (1885–1962), a Danish physicist, who at the time was working with Rutherford (see Figure 7.8). Using the work of Planck and Einstein, Bohr applied a new theory to the simplest atom, hydrogen. Before we look at Bohr's theory, we need to consider the line spectra of atoms, which we looked at briefly in the chapter opening.

Atomic Line Spectra

As described in the previous section, a heated solid emits light. A heated tungsten filament in an ordinary lightbulb is a typical example. With a prism we can spread out the light from a bulb to give a **continuous spectrum**—that is, *a spectrum containing light of all wavelengths*, like that of a rainbow (see Figure 7.9). The light emitted by a heated gas, however, yields different results. Rather than a continuous spectrum, with all colors of the rainbow, we obtain a **line spectrum**—*a spectrum showing only certain colors or specific wavelengths of light*. When the light from a hydrogen gas discharge tube (in which an electrical discharge heats hydrogen gas) is separated into its components by a prism, it gives a spectrum of lines, each line corresponding to light of a given wavelength. The light produced in the discharge tube is emitted by hydrogen atoms. Figure 7.2 shows the line spectrum of the hydrogen atom, as well as line spectra of other atoms.

The line spectrum of the hydrogen atom is especially simple. In the visible region, it consists of only four lines (a red, a blue-green, a blue, and a violet), although others appear in the infrared and ultraviolet regions. In 1885 J. J. Balmer showed that the wavelengths λ in the visible spectrum of hydrogen could be reproduced by a simple formula:

$$\frac{1}{\lambda} = 1.097 \times 10^7 /\text{m} \left(\frac{1}{2^2} - \frac{1}{n^2} \right)$$

FIGURE 7.8 ▲

Niels Bohr (1885–1962)
After Bohr developed his quantum theory of the hydrogen atom, he used his ideas to explain the periodic behavior of the elements. Later, when the new quantum mechanics was discovered by Schrödinger and Heisenberg, Bohr spent much of his time developing its philosophical basis. He received the Nobel Prize in physics in 1922.

ChemWork: Hydrogen Wavelengths

ChemWork: How Many Lines for H?

ChemWork: Electron Transitions in H

FIGURE 7.9 ▶

Dispersion of white light by a prism
White light, entering at the left, strikes a prism, which disperses the light into a continuous spectrum of wavelengths.

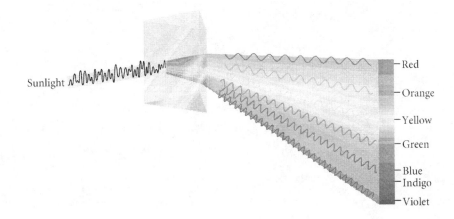

Sunlight

Red
Orange
Yellow
Green
Blue
Indigo
Violet

Here n is some whole number (integer) greater than 2. By substituting $n = 3$, for example, and calculating $1/\lambda$ and then λ, one finds $\lambda = 6.56 \times 10^{-7}$ m, or 656 nm, a wavelength corresponding to red light. The wavelengths of the other lines in the hydrogen atom visible spectrum are obtained by successively substituting $n = 4$, $n = 5$, and $n = 6$.

Bohr's Postulates

Bohr set down the following postulates to account for (1) the stability of the hydrogen atom (that the atom exists and its electron does not continuously radiate energy and spiral into the nucleus) and (2) the line spectrum of the atom.

1. Energy-level Postulate An electron can have only *specific energy values in an atom,* which are called its **energy levels.** Therefore, the atom itself can have only specific total energy values.

Bohr borrowed the idea of quantization of energy from Planck. Bohr, however, devised a rule for this quantization that could be applied to the motion of an electron in an atom. From this he derived the following formula for the energy levels of the electron in the hydrogen atom:

$$E = -\frac{R_H}{n^2} \qquad n = 1, 2, 3, \ldots \infty \qquad \text{(for H atom)}$$

where R_H is a constant (expressed in energy units) with the value 2.179×10^{-18} J. Different values of the possible energies of the electron are obtained by putting in different values of n, which can have only the integral values 1, 2, 3, and so forth (up to infinity, ∞). Here n is called the *principal quantum number*. The diagram in Figure 7.10 shows the energy levels of the electron in the H atom. <

> The energies have negative values because the energy of the separated nucleus and electron is taken to be zero. As the nucleus and electron come together to form a stable state of the atom, energy is released and the energy becomes less than zero, or negative.

2. Transitions Between Energy Levels An electron in an atom can change energy only by going from one energy level to another energy level. By so doing, the electron undergoes a *transition.*

By using only these two postulates, Bohr was able to explain Balmer's formula for the wavelengths in the spectrum of the hydrogen atom. According to Bohr, the emission of light from an atom occurs as follows. An electron in a higher energy level (initial energy level, E_i) undergoes a transition to a lower energy level (final energy level, E_f) (see Figure 7.10). In this process, the electron loses energy, which is emitted as a photon. Balmer's formula follows by this reasoning: The energy lost by the hydrogen atom is $\Delta E = E_f - E_i$. If we write n_i for the principal quantum number of the initial energy level, and n_f for the principal quantum number of the final energy level, then from Postulate 1,

$$E_i = -\frac{R_H}{n_i^2} \qquad \text{and} \qquad E_f = -\frac{R_H}{n_f^2}$$

so

$$\Delta E = \left(-\frac{R_H}{n_f^2}\right) - \left(-\frac{R_H}{n_i^2}\right) = -R_H\left(\frac{1}{n_f^2} - \frac{1}{n_i^2}\right)$$

For example, if the electron undergoes a transition from $n_i = 4$ to $n_f = 2$,

$$\Delta E = -2.179 \times 10^{-18} \text{ J}\left(\frac{1}{2^2} - \frac{1}{4^2}\right) = -4.086 \times 10^{-19} \text{ J}$$

The sign of the energy change is negative. This means that energy equal to 4.086×10^{-19} J is lost by the atom in the form of a photon.

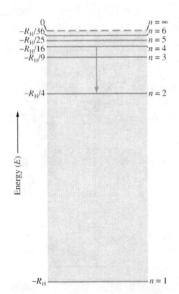

FIGURE 7.10 ▲

Energy-level diagram for the electron in the hydrogen atom

Energy is plotted on the vertical axis (in fractional multiples of R_H). The arrow represents an electron transition (discussed in Postulate 2) from level $n = 4$ to level $n = 2$. Light of wavelength 486 nm (blue-green) is emitted. (See Example 7.4 for the calculation of this wavelength.)

FIGURE 7.11

Transitions of the electron in the hydrogen atom
The diagram shows the Lyman, Balmer, and Paschen series of transitions that occur for $n_f = 1$, 2, and 3, respectively.

In general, the energy of the emitted photon, $h\nu$, equals the positive energy lost by the atom $(-\Delta E)$:

$$\text{Energy of emitted photon} = h\nu = -\Delta E = -(E_f - E_i)$$

That is,

$$h\nu = R_H\left(\frac{1}{n_f^2} - \frac{1}{n_i^2}\right)$$

Recalling that $\nu = c/\lambda$, you can rewrite this as

$$\frac{1}{\lambda} = \frac{R_H}{hc}\left(\frac{1}{n_f^2} - \frac{1}{n_i^2}\right)$$

By substituting $R_H = 2.179 \times 10^{-18}$ J, $h = 6.626 \times 10^{-34}$ J·s, and $c = 2.998 \times 10^8$ m/s, you find that $R_H/hc = 1.097 \times 10^7$/m, which is the constant given in the Balmer formula. In Balmer's formula, the quantum number n_f is 2. This means that Balmer's formula gives wavelengths that occur when electrons in H atoms undergo transitions from energy levels $n_i > 2$ to level $n_f = 2$. If you change n_f to other integers, you obtain different series of lines (or wavelengths) for the spectrum of the H atom (see Figure 7.11).

Example 7.4	Determining the Wavelength or Frequency of a Hydrogen Atom Transition

What is the wavelength of light emitted when the electron in a hydrogen atom undergoes a transition from energy level $n = 4$ to level $n = 2$?

An alternative example is provided in the Instructor's Resource Manual.

Problem Strategy Remember that the wavelength or frequency of a transition depends on the difference in energies of the levels involved. For an H atom, the energy levels are $E = -R_H/n^2$. You calculate the difference in energy for the two levels *to obtain the energy of the photon*. Then, calculate the frequency and wavelength of the emitted light. (Although you could do this problem by "plugging into" the previously derived equation for $1/\lambda$, the method followed here requires you to remember only key formulas, shown in color in the text.)

Solution From the formula for the energy levels, you know that

$$E_i = \frac{-R_H}{4^2} = \frac{-R_H}{16} \qquad \text{and} \qquad E_f = \frac{-R_H}{2^2} = \frac{-R_H}{4}$$

You subtract the lower value from the higher value, to get a positive result. (The energy of the photon is positive. If your result is negative, it means you calculated $E_f - E_i$, rather than $E_i - E_f$. Simply reverse the subtraction to obtain a positive result.) Because this result equals the energy of the photon, you equate it to $h\nu$:

$$\left(\frac{-R_H}{16}\right) - \left(\frac{-R_H}{4}\right) = \frac{-4R_H + 16R_H}{64} = \frac{-R_H + 4R_H}{16} = \frac{3R_H}{16} = h\nu$$

The frequency of the light emitted is

$$\nu = \frac{3R_H}{16h} = \frac{3}{16} \times \frac{2.179 \times 10^{-18}\,\cancel{J}}{6.626 \times 10^{-34}\,\cancel{J}\cdot\text{s}} = 6.17 \times 10^{14}/\text{s}$$

(continued)

A Chemist Looks at . . .

materials

Lasers and Compact Disc Players

Lasers are sources of intense, highly directed beams of *monochromatic* light—light of very narrow wavelength range. The word *laser* is an acronym meaning light amplification by stimulated emission of radiation. Many different kinds of lasers now exist, but the general principle of a laser can be understood by looking at the ruby laser, the first type constructed (in 1960).

Ruby is aluminum oxide containing a small concentration of chromium(III) ions, Cr^{3+}, in place of some aluminum ions. The electron transitions in a ruby laser are those of Cr^{3+} ions. Figure 7.12 shows an energy-level diagram of this ion in ruby. When you shine light of wavelength 545 nm on a ruby crystal, the light is absorbed and Cr^{3+} undergoes a transition from level 1 to level 3. Most of the ions in level 3 then undergo *radiationless transitions* to level 2. (In these transitions, the ions lose energy as heat to the crystal, rather than by emitting photons.) When an intense green light at 545 nm is flashed on a ruby crystal, Cr^{3+} ions of the ruby end up in level 2. Like all excited states, level 2 spontaneously emits photons, going to the ground state. But whereas most excited states quickly (within 10^{-8} s) emit photons, level 2 has a much longer lifetime (a fraction of a millisecond), resulting in a buildup of excited Cr^{3+} ions in this level. If these accumulated excited ions can be triggered to emit all at once, or nearly so, an intense emission of monochromatic light at 694 nm will occur.

The process of *stimulated emission* is ideal for this triggering. When a photon corresponding to 694 nm encounters a Cr^{3+} ion in level 2, it stimulates the ion to undergo the transition from level 2 to level 1. The ion emits a photon corresponding to exactly the same wavelength as the original photon. In place of just one photon, there are now two photons, the original one and the one obtained by stimulated emission. The net effect is to increase the intensity of the light at this wavelength. Thus, a weak light

FIGURE 7.12 ▲

Energy levels of the chromium(III) ion in ruby
The energy levels have been numbered by increasing energy from 1 to 3. (Level 3 is broadened in the solid state.) When chromium(III) ions absorb the 545-nm portion of the light from a flash lamp, electrons in the ions first undergo transitions to level 3 and then radiationless transitions to level 2. (The energy is lost as heat.) Electrons accumulate in level 2 until more exist in level 2 than in level 1. Then a photon from a spontaneous emission from level 2 to level 1 can stimulate the emission from other atoms in level 2. These photons move back and forth between reflective surfaces, stimulating additional emissions and forming a laser pulse at 694 nm.

at 694 nm can be amplified by stimulated emission of the excited ruby.

Figure 7.13 shows a sketch of a ruby laser. A flash lamp emits green light (at 545 nm) that is absorbed by the ruby, building up a concentration of Cr^{3+} in level 2. A few of these excited ions spontaneously emit photons corresponding to 694 nm (red light), and these photons then stimulate other ions to emit, which in turn stimulate more ions to emit, and so forth, resulting in a pulse of laser light at 694 nm.

Laser light is *coherent*. This means that the waves forming the beam are all in phase; that is, the waves have their maxima and minima at the same points in space and time. The property of coherence of a laser beam is used in compact disc (CD) audio players (Figure 7.14). Music is encoded on the disc in the form of pits, or indentations, on a spiral track. When the disc is played, a small laser beam scans the track and is reflected back to a detector. Light reflected from an indentation is out of phase with light from the laser and interferes with it. Because of this interference, the reflected beam is diminished in intensity and gives a diminished detector signal. Fluctuations in the signal are then converted to sound.

FIGURE 7.13 ▲ ◧

A ruby laser

A flash lamp encircles a ruby rod. Light of 545 nm (green) from the flash "pumps" electrons from level 1 to level 3, then level 2, from which stimulated emission forms a laser pulse at 694 nm (red). The stimulated emission bounces back and forth between reflective surfaces at the ends of the ruby rod, building up a coherent laser beam. One end has a partially reflective surface to allow the laser beam to exit from the ruby.

FIGURE 7.14 ▶ ◧

How a compact disc player works

Music or other information is encoded in the form of pits on a compact disc. Lenses direct laser light to the disc, which reflects it back. Light reflected from a pit is out of phase with light from the laser, and these two waves interfere, reducing the intensity of the wave. As the disc moves around, light is reflected from either the main surface at full intensity (on) or from a pit at reduced intensity (off). A light-sensitive detector converts this reflected light to a digital signal (a series of on and off pulses). A converter changes this signal to one that speakers can accept.

See Problems 7.93 and 7.94.

(continued)

Since $\lambda = c/\nu$,

$$\lambda = \frac{3.00 \times 10^8 \text{ m/s}}{6.17 \times 10^{14}/\text{s}} = 4.86 \times 10^{-7} \text{ m, or } \mathbf{486 \text{ nm}}$$

The color is blue-green (see Figure 7.10).

Answer Check   Balmer lines (lines ending with $n = 2$) are in the visible region of the spectrum. Wavelengths of visible light are in the range of 400 nm to about 800 nm. Note that the answer lies in this range.

Exercise 7.4   Calculate the wavelength of light emitted from the hydrogen atom when the electron undergoes a transition from level $n = 3$ to level $n = 1$.

■ See Problems 7.49, 7.50, 7.51, and 7.52.

Experiments in General Chemistry, 7, "The Absorption Spectrum of Cobalt(II) Chloride."

Experiments in General Chemistry, I-10.

According to Bohr's theory, the *emission* of light from an atom occurs when an electron undergoes a transition from an upper energy level to a lower one. To complete the explanation, we need to describe how the electron gets into the upper level prior to emission. Normally, the electron in a hydrogen atom exists in its lowest, or $n = 1$, level. To get into a higher energy level, the electron must gain energy, or be *excited*. One way this can happen is through the collision of two hydrogen atoms. During this collision, some of the kinetic energy of one atom can be gained by the electron of another atom, thereby boosting, or exciting, the electron from the $n = 1$ level to a higher energy level. The excitation of atoms and the subsequent emission of light are most likely to occur in a hot gas, where atoms have large kinetic energies.

Bohr's theory explains not only the emission but also the *absorption* of light. When an electron in the hydrogen atom undergoes a transition from $n = 3$ to $n = 2$, a photon of red light (wavelength 656 nm) is emitted. When red light of wavelength 656 nm shines on a hydrogen atom in the $n = 2$ level, a photon can be absorbed. If the photon is absorbed, the energy is gained by the electron, which undergoes a transition to the $n = 3$ level. (This is the reverse of the emission process we just discussed.) Materials that have a color, such as dyed textiles and painted walls, appear colored because of the absorption of light. For example, when white light falls on a substance that absorbs red light, the color components that are not absorbed, the yellow and blue light, are reflected. The substance appears blue-green.

Postulates 1 and 2 hold for atoms other than hydrogen, except that the energy levels cannot be obtained by a simple formula. However, if you know the wavelength of the emitted light, you can relate it to ν and then to the difference in energy levels of the atom. The energy levels of atoms have been experimentally determined in this way.

Exercise 7.5   What is the difference in energy levels of the sodium atom if emitted light has a wavelength of 589 nm?

■ See Problems 7.55 and 7.56.

Concept Check 7.2

An atom has a line spectrum consisting of a red line and a blue line. Assume that each line corresponds to a transition between two adjacent energy levels. Sketch an energy-level diagram with three energy levels that might explain this line spectrum, indicating the transitions on this diagram. Consider the transition from the highest energy level on this diagram to the lowest energy level. How would you describe the color or region of the spectrum corresponding to this transition?

Quantum Mechanics and Quantum Numbers

Bohr's theory firmly established the concept of atomic energy levels. It was unsuccessful, however, in accounting for the details of atomic structure and in predicting energy levels for atoms other than hydrogen. Further understanding of atomic structure required other theoretical developments.

7.4 Quantum Mechanics

Current ideas about atomic structure depend on the principles of *quantum mechanics*, a theory that applies to submicroscopic (that is, extremely small) particles of matter, such as electrons. The development of this theory was stimulated by the discovery of the de Broglie relation.

ChemWork: de Broglie Wavelengths

A photon has a rest mass of zero but a relativistic mass m as a result of its motion. Einstein's equation $E = mc^2$ relates this relativistic mass to the energy of the photon, which also equals $h\nu$. Therefore, $mc^2 = h\nu$, or $mc = h\nu/c = h/\lambda$.

FIGURE 7.15 ▲

Scanning electron microscope
This microscope can resolve details down to 3 nm in a sample. The operator places the sample inside the chamber at the left and views the image on the video screens.

FIGURE 7.16 ▲

Scanning electron microscope image
This image is of a wasp's head. Color has been added by computer for contrast in discerning different parts of the image.

de Broglie Relation

According to Einstein, light has not only wave properties, which we characterize by frequency and wavelength, but also particle properties. For example, a particle of light, the photon, has a definite energy $E = h\nu$. One can also show that the photon has momentum. (The momentum of a particle is the product of its mass and speed.) This momentum, mc, is related to the wavelength of the light: $mc = h/\lambda$ or $\lambda = h/mc$. <

In 1923 the French physicist Louis de Broglie reasoned that if light (considered as a wave) exhibits particle aspects, then perhaps particles of matter show characteristics of waves under the proper circumstances. He therefore postulated that a particle of matter of mass m and speed v has an associated wavelength, by analogy with light:

$$\lambda = \frac{h}{mv}$$

The equation $\lambda = h/mv$ is called the **de Broglie relation.**

If matter has wave properties, why are they not commonly observed? Calculation using the de Broglie relation shows that a baseball (0.145 kg) moving at about 60 mi/hr (27 m/s) has a wavelength of about 10^{-34} m, a value so incredibly small that such waves cannot be detected. On the other hand, electrons moving at only moderate speeds have wavelengths of a few hundred picometers (1 pm = 10^{-12} m). Under the proper circumstances, the wave character of electrons should be observable.

The wave property of electrons was first demonstrated in 1927 by C. Davisson and L. H. Germer in the United States and by George Paget Thomson (son of J. J. Thomson) in Britain. They showed that a beam of electrons, just like x rays, can be diffracted by a crystal. The German physicist Ernst Ruska used this wave property to construct the first *electron microscope* in 1933; he shared the 1986 Nobel Prize in physics for this work. A modern instrument is shown in Figure 7.15. The *resolving power*, or ability to distinguish detail, of a microscope that uses waves depends on their wavelength. To resolve detail the size of several hundred picometers, we need a wavelength on that order. X rays have wavelengths in this range, but so far no practical means have been found for focusing them. Electrons, on the other hand, are readily focused with electric and magnetic fields. Figure 7.16 shows a photograph taken with an electron microscope, displaying the detail that is possible with this instrument.

Example 7.5   Calculate the Wavelength of a Moving Particle

a. Calculate the wavelength (in meters) of the wave associated with a 1.00-kg mass moving at 1.00 km/hr. b. What is the wavelength (in picometers) associated with an electron, whose mass is 9.11×10^{-31} kg, traveling at a speed of 4.19×10^6 m/s? (This speed can be attained by an electron accelerated between two charged plates differing by 50.0 volts; voltages in the kilovolt range are used in electron microscopes.)

An alternative example is provided in the Instructor's Resource Manual.

Problem Strategy   The questions ask for the wavelength associated with a moving mass, which is given by de Broglie's relation, $\lambda = h/mv$. Be careful to use consistent units in substituting into this equation. If you use SI units, then in part a you will need to convert km/hr to m/s. In part b, you will need to convert the answer in meters to picometers.

Solution   a. A speed v of 1.00 km/hr equals

$$1.00 \; \frac{km}{hr} \times \frac{1 \; hr}{3600 \; s} \times \frac{10^3 \; m}{1 \; km} = 0.278 \; m/s$$

Substituting quantities (all expressed in SI units for consistency), you get

$$\lambda = \frac{h}{mv} = \frac{6.63 \times 10^{-34} \; J \cdot s}{1.00 \; kg \times 0.278 \; m/s} = \mathbf{2.38 \times 10^{-33} \; m}$$

b. $\lambda = \dfrac{h}{mv} = \dfrac{6.63 \times 10^{-34} \; J \cdot s}{9.11 \times 10^{-31} \; kg \times 4.19 \times 10^6 \; m/s} = 1.74 \times 10^{-10} \; m = \mathbf{174 \; pm}$

Answer Check   Make sure that you are using the correct equation for the de Broglie relation; units should cancel to give units of length (for wavelength). Check that the final units are those asked for in the problem statement.

Exercise 7.6   Calculate the wavelength (in picometers) associated with an electron traveling at a speed of 2.19×10^6 m/s.

■ See Problems 7.57 and 7.58.

Concept Check 7.3

A proton is approximately 2000 times heavier than an electron. How would the speeds of these particles compare if their corresponding wavelengths were about equal?

Wave Functions

De Broglie's relation applies quantitatively only to particles in a force-free environment. It cannot be applied directly to an electron in an atom, where the electron is subject to the attractive force of the nucleus. But in 1926 Erwin Schrödinger, guided by de Broglie's work, devised a theory that could be used to find the wave properties of electrons in atoms and molecules. *The branch of physics that mathematically describes the wave properties of submicroscopic particles* is called **quantum mechanics** or **wave mechanics.** <

Schrödinger received the Nobel Prize in physics in 1933 for his wave formulation of quantum mechanics. Werner Heisenberg won the Nobel Prize the previous year for his matrix-algebra formulation of quantum mechanics. The two formulations yield identical results.

Without going into the mathematics of quantum mechanics here, we will discuss some of the most important conclusions of the theory. In particular, quantum mechanics alters the way we think about the motion of particles. Our usual concept of motion comes from what we see in the everyday world. We might, for instance, visually follow a ball that has been thrown. The path of the ball is given by its position and velocity (or momentum) at various times. We are therefore conditioned to think in terms of a continuous path for moving objects. In Bohr's theory, the electron was thought of as moving about, or orbiting, the nucleus in the way the earth orbits the sun. Quantum mechanics vastly changes this view of motion. We can no longer think of an electron as having a precise orbit in an atom. To describe such an orbit, we would have to know the exact position of the electron at various times and exactly how long it would take it to travel to a nearby position in the orbit. That is, at any moment we would have to know not only the precise position but also the precise momentum (mass times speed) of the electron.

In 1927 Werner Heisenberg showed from quantum mechanics that it is impossible to know simultaneously, with absolute precision, both the position and the momentum of a particle such as an electron. Heisenberg's **uncertainty principle** is *a relation that states that the product of the uncertainty in position and the uncertainty in momentum of a particle can be no smaller than Planck's constant divided by 4π.* Thus, letting Δx be the uncertainty in the x coordinate of the particle and letting Δp_x be the uncertainty in the momentum in the x direction, we have

$$(\Delta x)(\Delta p_x) \geq \frac{h}{4\pi}$$

There are similar relations in the y and z directions. The uncertainty principle says that the more precisely you know the position (the smaller Δx, Δy, and Δz), the less well you know the momentum of the particle (the larger Δp_x, Δp_y, and Δp_z). In other words, if you know very well where a particle is, you cannot know where it is going!

The uncertainty principle is significant only for particles of very small mass such as electrons. You can see this by noting that the momentum equals mass times velocity, so $p_x = mv_x$. The preceding relation becomes

$$(\Delta x)(\Delta v_x) \geq \frac{h}{4\pi m}$$

For dust particles and baseballs, where m is relatively large, the term on the right becomes nearly zero, and the uncertainties of position and velocity are quite small. The path of a baseball has meaning. For electrons, however, the uncertainties in position and momentum are normally quite large. We cannot describe the electron in an atom as moving in a definite orbit.

Although quantum mechanics does not allow us to describe the electron in the hydrogen atom as moving in an orbit, it does allow us to make *statistical* statements about where we would find the electron if we were to look for it. For example, we can obtain the *probability* of finding an electron at a certain point in a hydrogen atom. Although we cannot say that an electron will definitely be at a particular position at a given time, we can say that the electron is likely (or not likely) to be at this position.

Information about a particle in a given energy level (such as an electron in an atom) is contained in a mathematical expression called a *wave function*, denoted by the Greek letter psi, ψ. The wave function is obtained by solving an equation of quantum mechanics (Schrödinger's equation). Its square, ψ^2, gives the probability of finding the particle within a region of space.

The wave function and its square, ψ^2, have values for all locations about a nucleus. Figure 7.17 shows values of ψ^2 for the electron in the lowest energy level of the hydrogen atom along a line starting from the nucleus. Note that ψ^2 is large near the nucleus ($r = 0$), indicating that the electron is most likely to be found in this region. The value of ψ^2 decreases rapidly as the distance from the nucleus increases, but ψ^2 never goes to exactly zero, although the probability does become extremely small at large distances from the nucleus. This means that an atom does not have a definite boundary, unlike in the Bohr model of the atom.

Figure 7.18 shows another view of this electron probability. The graph plots the probability of finding the electron in different spherical shells at particular distances

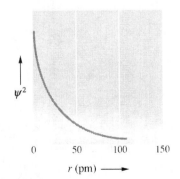

ψ^2

0   50   100   150

r (pm) ⟶

FIGURE 7.17 ▲

Plot of ψ^2 for the lowest energy level of the hydrogen atom

The square of the wave function is plotted versus the distance, r, from the nucleus.

Scanning Tunneling Microscopy

The 1986 Nobel Prize in physics went to three physicists for their work in developing microscopes for viewing extremely small objects. Half of the prize went to Ernst Ruska for the development of the electron microscope, described earlier. The other half was awarded to Gerd Binnig and Heinrich Rohrer, at IBM's research laboratory in Zurich, Switzerland, for their invention of the *scanning tunneling microscope* in 1981. This instrument makes possible the viewing of atoms and molecules on a solid surface (Figure 7.19).

The scanning tunneling microscope is based on the concept of quantum mechanical *tunneling*, which in turn depends on the probability interpretation of quantum mechanics. Consider a hydrogen atom, which consists of an electron about a proton (call it A), and imagine another proton (called B) some distance from the first. In classical terms, if we were to move the electron from the region of proton A to the region of proton B, energy would have to be supplied to remove the electron from the attractive field of proton A. Quantum mechanics, however, gives us a different picture. The probability of the electron in the hydrogen atom being at a location far from proton A, say near proton B, is very small but not zero. In effect, this means that the electron, which nominally belongs to proton A, may find itself near proton B without extra energy having been supplied. The electron is said to have *tunneled* from one atom to another.

FIGURE 7.19 ▲

Scanning tunneling microscope image of benzene molecules on a metal surface
Benzene molecules, C_6H_6, are arranged in a regular array on a rhodium metal surface.

The scanning tunneling microscope consists of a tungsten metal needle with an extremely fine point (the probe) placed close to the sample to be viewed (Figure 7.20). If the probe is close enough to the sample, electrons can tunnel from the probe to the sample. The probability for this can be increased by having a small voltage applied between the probe and sample. Electrons tunneling from the probe to the sample give rise to a measurable electric current. The magnitude of the current depends on the distance between the probe and the sample (as well as on the wave function of the atom in the sample). By adjusting this distance, the current can be maintained at a fixed value. As the probe scans the sample, it moves toward or away from

FIGURE 7.18 ▷

Probability of finding an electron in a spherical shell about the nucleus
(A) The diagram shows the probability density for an electron in a hydrogen atom. The region is marked off in shells about the nucleus. *(B)* The graph shows the probability of finding the electron within shells at various distances from the nucleus (radial probability). The curve exhibits a maximum, which means that the radial probability is greatest for a given distance from the nucleus.

A

B

FIGURE 7.20

The scanning tunneling microscope

A tunneling current flows between the probe and the sample when there is a small voltage between them. A feedback circuit, which provides this voltage, senses the current and varies the voltage on a piezoelectric rod (z-drive) in order to keep the distance constant between the probe and sample. A computer has been programmed to provide voltages to the x-drive and the y-drive to move the probe over the surface of the sample.

the sample to maintain a fixed current; in effect, the probe follows the contours of the sample. (The probe is attached to the end of a *piezoelectric* rod, which undergoes very small changes in length when small voltages are applied to it.)

Researchers routinely use the scanning tunneling microscope to study the arrangement of atoms and molecules

on surfaces. Lately, scientists have also used the microscope probe to move atoms about a surface in an effort to construct miniature devices. Figure 7.21 shows 48 iron atoms that were arranged in a circle on a copper surface. Each of the iron atoms looks like a sharp mountain peak rising from a plain. Inside this "quantum corral" (as it has come to be called), you can see the wavelike distribution of electrons trapped within. Here is graphic proof of the wavelike nature of electrons!

FIGURE 7.21

Quantum corral

IBM scientists used a scanning tunneling microscope probe to arrange 48 iron atoms in a circle on a copper metal surface. The iron atoms appear as the tall peaks in the diagram. Note the wavelike ripple of electrons trapped within the circle of atoms (called *a quantum corral*). [IBM Research Division, Almaden Research Center; research done by Donald M. Eigler and coworkers.]

■ See Problems 7.95 and 7.96.

from the nucleus, rather than the probability at a point. Even though the probability of finding the electron at a point near the nucleus is high, the volume of any shell there is small. Therefore, the probability of finding the electron *within a shell* is greatest at some distance from the nucleus. This distance just happens to equal the radius that Bohr calculated for an electron orbit in his model.

7.5 | Quantum Numbers and Atomic Orbitals

Three different quantum numbers are needed because there are three dimensions to space.

According to quantum mechanics, each electron in an atom is described by four different quantum numbers, three of which (n, l, and m_l) specify the wave function that gives the probability of finding the electron at various points in space. < *A wave function for an electron in an atom* is called an **atomic orbital.** An atomic orbital is pictured

281

qualitatively by describing the region of space where there is high probability of finding the electrons. The atomic orbital so pictured has a definite shape. A fourth quantum number (m_s) refers to a magnetic property of electrons called *spin*. We first look at quantum numbers, then at atomic orbitals.

Quantum Numbers

The allowed values and general meaning of each of the four quantum numbers of an electron in an atom are as follows:

1. Principal Quantum Number (n)   *This quantum number is the one on which the energy of an electron in an atom principally depends; it can have any positive value: 1, 2, 3, and so on.* The energy of an electron in an atom depends *principally* on n. The smaller n is, the lower the energy. In the case of the hydrogen atom or single-electron atomic ions, such as Li^{2+} and He^+, n is the only quantum number determining the energy (which is given by Bohr's formula, discussed in Section 7.3). For other atoms, the energy also depends to a slight extent on the l quantum number.

The *size* of an orbital also depends on n. The larger the value of n is, the larger the orbital. Orbitals of the same quantum state n are said to belong to the same *shell*. Shells are sometimes designated by the following letters:

Letter	K	L	M	N . . .
n	1	2	3	4 . . .

2. Angular Momentum Quantum Number (l)   (Also Called *Azimuthal Quantum Number*)   *This quantum number distinguishes orbitals of given n having different shapes; it can have any integer value from 0 to n − 1.* Within each shell of quantum number n, there are n different kinds of orbitals, each with a distinctive shape denoted by an l quantum number. For example, if an electron has a principal quantum number of 3, the possible values for l are 0, 1, and 2. Thus, within the M shell ($n = 3$), there are three kinds of orbitals, each having a different shape for the region where the electron is most likely to be found. These orbital shapes will be discussed later in this section.

Although the energy of an orbital is principally determined by the n quantum number, the energy also depends somewhat on the l quantum number (except for the H atom). For a given n, the energy of an orbital increases with l.

Orbitals of the same n but different l are said to belong to different *subshells* of a given shell. The different subshells are usually denoted by letters as follows:

Letter	s	p	d	f	g . . .
l	0	1	2	3	4 . . .

To denote a subshell within a particular shell, we write the value of the n quantum number for the shell, followed by the letter designation for the subshell. For example, $2p$ denotes a subshell with quantum numbers $n = 2$ and $l = 1$. <

The rather odd choice of letter symbols for l quantum numbers survives from old spectroscopic terminology (describing the lines in a spectrum as sharp, principal, diffuse, and fundamental).

3. Magnetic Quantum Number (m$_l$)   *This quantum number distinguishes orbitals of given n and l—that is, of given energy and shape but having a different orientation in space; the allowed values are the integers from −l to +l.* For $l = 0$ (s subshell), the allowed m_l quantum number is 0 only; there is only one orbital in the s subshell. For $l = 1$ (p subshell), $m_l = -1$, 0, and $+1$; there are three different orbitals in the p subshell. The orbitals have the same shape but different orientations in space. In

| TABLE 7.1 | | **Permissible Values of Quantum Numbers for Atomic Orbitals** | | |

n	l	m_l*	Subshell Notation	Number of Orbitals in the Subshell
1	0	0	$1s$	1
2	0	0	$2s$	1
2	1	$-1, 0, +1$	$2p$	3
3	0	0	$3s$	1
3	1	$-1, 0, +1$	$3p$	3
3	2	$-2, -1, 0, +1, +2$	$3d$	5
4	0	0	$4s$	1
4	1	$-1, 0, +1$	$4p$	3
4	2	$-2, -1, 0, +1, +2$	$4d$	5
4	3	$-3, -2, -1, 0, +1, +2, +3$	$4f$	7

*Any one of the m_l quantum numbers may be associated with the n and l quantum numbers on the same line.

FIGURE 7.22 ▼

Orbital energies of the hydrogen atom
The lines for each subshell indicate the number of different orbitals of that subshell. (Note break in the energy scale.)

Electron spin will be discussed further in Section 8.1.

addition, all orbitals of a given subshell have the same energy. Note that there are $2l + 1$ orbitals in each subshell of quantum number l.

4. Spin Quantum Number (m_s) *This quantum number refers to the two possible orientations of the spin axis of an electron; possible values are $+\frac{1}{2}$ and $-\frac{1}{2}$.* An electron acts as though it were spinning on its axis like the earth. Such an electron spin would give rise to a circulating electric charge that would generate a magnetic field. In this way, an electron behaves like a small bar magnet, with a north and a south pole. <

Table 7.1 lists the permissible quantum numbers for all orbitals through the $n = 4$ shell. These values follow from the rules just given. Energies for the orbitals are shown in Figure 7.22 for the hydrogen atom. Note that all orbitals with the same principal quantum number n have the same energy. For atoms with more than one electron, however, only orbitals in the same subshell (denoted by a given n and l) have the same energy. We will have more to say about orbital energies in Chapter 8.

| **Example 7.6** | Applying the Rules for Quantum Numbers |

State whether each of the following sets of quantum numbers is permissible for an electron in an atom. If a set is not permissible, explain why.

a. $n = 1, l = 1, m_l = 0, m_s = +\frac{1}{2}$

b. $n = 3, l = 1, m_l = -2, m_s = -\frac{1}{2}$

c. $n = 2, l = 1, m_l = 0, m_s = +\frac{1}{2}$

d. $n = 2, l = 0, m_l = 0, m_s = 1$

Problem Strategy Apply the rules for quantum numbers in order, first to n, then to l and m_l, and finally

(continued)

(continued)

to m_s. A set of quantum numbers is impermissible if it disobeys any rule.

Solution   a. **Not permissible.** The l quantum number is equal to n; it must be less than n.

b. **Not permissible.** The magnitude of the m_l quantum number (that is, the m_l value, ignoring its sign) must not be greater than l.

c. **Permissible.**

d. **Not permissible.** The m_s quantum number can be only $+\frac{1}{2}$ or $-\frac{1}{2}$.

Answer Check   Check that n is a positive integer (it cannot be zero). Also, check that l is a positive integer

An alternative example is provided in the Instructor's Resource Manual.

(but zero is allowed) and that m_l is an integer whose magnitude (its value except for sign) is equal to or less than l. The m_s quantum number can be only $+\frac{1}{2}$ or $-\frac{1}{2}$.

Exercise 7.7   Explain why each of the following sets of quantum numbers is not permissible for an orbital.

a. $n = 0,\ l = 1,\ m_l = 0,\ m_s = +\frac{1}{2}$

b. $n = 2,\ l = 3,\ m_l = 0,\ m_s = -\frac{1}{2}$

c. $n = 3,\ l = 2,\ m_l = +3,\ m_s = +\frac{1}{2}$

d. $n = 3,\ l = 2,\ m_l = +2,\ m_s = 0$

■ See Problems 7.69 and 7.70.

1s orbital

2s orbital

FIGURE 7.23

Cross-sectional representations of the probability distributions of s orbitals
In a 1s orbital, the probability distribution is largest near the nucleus. In a 2s orbital, it is greatest in a spherical shell about the nucleus. Note the relative "size" of the orbitals, indicated by the 99% contours.

Atomic Orbital Shapes

An s orbital has a spherical shape, though specific details of the probability distribution depend on the value of n. Figure 7.23 shows cross-sectional representations of the probability distributions of a $1s$ and a $2s$ orbital. The color shading is darker where the electron is more likely to be found. In the case of a $1s$ orbital, the electron is most likely to be found near the nucleus. The shading becomes lighter as the distance from the nucleus increases, indicating that the electron is less likely to be found there.

The orbital does not abruptly end at some particular distance from the nucleus. An atom, therefore, has an indefinite extension, or "size." We can gauge the "size" of the orbital by means of the *99% contour*. The electron has a 99% probability of being found within the space of the 99% contour (the sphere indicated by the dashed line in the diagram).

A $2s$ orbital differs in detail from a $1s$ orbital. The electron in a $2s$ orbital is likely to be found in two regions, one near the nucleus and the other in a spherical shell about the nucleus. (The electron is most likely to be here.) The 99% contour shows that the $2s$ orbital is larger than the $1s$ orbital.

A cross-sectional diagram cannot portray the three-dimensional aspect of the $1s$ and $2s$ atomic orbitals. Figure 7.24 shows cutaway diagrams, which better illustrate this three-dimensionality.

There are three p orbitals in each p subshell. All p orbitals have the same basic shape (two lobes arranged along a straight line with the nucleus between the lobes) but differ in their orientations in space. Because the three orbitals are set at right angles to each other, we can show each one as oriented along a different coordinate axis (Figure 7.25). We denote these orbitals as $2p_x$, $2p_y$, and $2p_z$. A $2p_x$ orbital has its greatest electron probability along the x-axis, a $2p_y$ orbital along the y-axis, and a $2p_z$ orbital along the z-axis. Other p orbitals, such as $3p$, have this same general shape, with differences in detail depending on n. We will discuss s and p orbital shapes again in Chapter 10 in reference to chemical bonding.

There are five d orbitals, which have more complicated shapes than do s and p orbitals. These are represented in Figure 7.26.

99% contour

99% contour

1s orbital

2s orbital

FIGURE 7.24 ▲

Cutaway diagrams showing the spherical shape of s orbitals

In both diagrams, a segment of each orbital is cut away to reveal the electron distribution of the orbital.

We will discuss d orbitals in Chapter 22, when we look at the bonding in compounds of the transition elements.

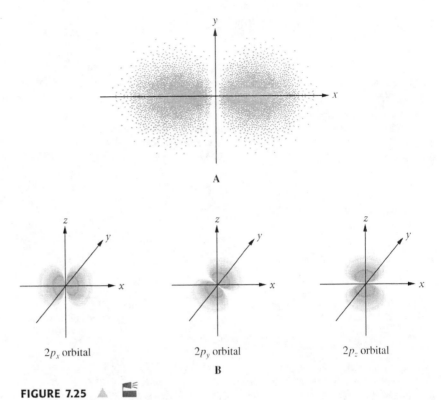

A

$2p_x$ orbital $2p_y$ orbital $2p_z$ orbital

B

FIGURE 7.25 ▲

The 2p orbitals

(A) Electron distribution in the $2p_x$ orbital. Note that it consists of two lobes oriented along the x-axis. (B) Orientations of the three 2p orbitals. The drawings depict the general shape and orientation of the orbitals, but not the detailed electron distribution as in (A).

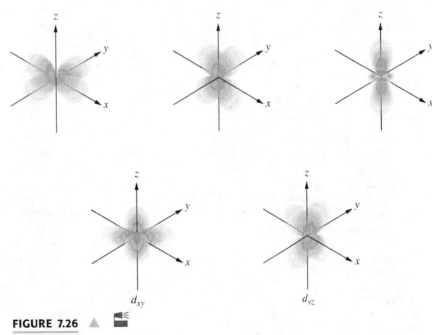

d_{xy} d_{yz}

FIGURE 7.26 ▲

The five 3d orbitals

These are labeled by subscripts, as in d_{xy}, that describe their mathematical characteristics.

A Checklist for Review

Important Terms

wavelength (λ) (7.1)
frequency (v) (7.1)
electromagnetic spectrum (7.1)
Planck's constant (7.2)
photons (7.2)
photoelectric effect (7.2)

continuous spectrum (7.3)
line spectrum (7.3)
energy levels (7.3)
de Broglie relation (7.4)
quantum (wave) mechanics (7.4)
uncertainty principle (7.4)

atomic orbital (7.5)
principal quantum number (n) (7.5)
**angular momentum quantum
number (l)** (7.5)
magnetic quantum number (m_l) (7.5)
spin quantum number (m_s) (7.5)

Key Equations

$c = v\lambda$

$E = hv$

$E = -\dfrac{R_H}{n^2}$ $n = 1, 2, 3, \ldots \infty$ (for H atom)

Energy of emitted photon $= hv = -(E_f - E_i)$

$\lambda = \dfrac{h}{mv}$

Summary of Facts and Concepts

One way to study the electronic structure of the atom is to analyze the electromagnetic radiation that is emitted from an atom. Electromagnetic radiation is characterized by its *wavelength* λ and frequency v, and these quantities are related to the speed of light c ($c = v\lambda$).

Einstein showed that light consists of particles (*photons*), each of energy $E = hv$, where h is Planck's constant. According to Bohr, electrons in an atom have *energy levels,* and when an electron in a higher energy level drops (or undergoes a transition) to a lower energy level, a photon is emitted. The energy of the photon equals the difference in energy between the two levels.

Electrons and other particles of matter have both particle and wave properties. For a particle of mass m and speed v, the

wavelength is related to momentum mv by the *de Broglie relation:* $\lambda = h/mv$. The wave properties of a particle are described by a *wave function,* from which we can get the probability of finding the particle in different regions of space.

Each electron in an atom is characterized by four different quantum numbers. The distribution of an electron in space—its *atomic orbital*—is characterized by three of these quantum numbers: the principal quantum number, the angular momentum quantum number, and the magnetic quantum number. The fourth quantum number (spin quantum number) describes the magnetism of the electron.

Media Summary

Visit the **student website at college.hmco.com/pic/ebbing9e** to help prepare for class, study for quizzes and exams, understand core concepts, and visualize molecular-level interactions. The following media activities are available for this chapter:

 Prepare for Class

■ **Video Lessons** *Mini lectures from chemistry experts*
CIA Demonstration: Flame Colors
The Wave Nature of Light
Absorption and Emission
The Ultraviolet Catastrophe
The Photoelectric Effect
The Bohr Model
The Wave Nature of Matter
The Heisenberg Uncertainty Principle
Atomic Orbital Size
Atomic Orbital Shapes and Quantum Numbers

 Improve Your Grade

■ **Visualizations** *Molecular-level animations and lab
demonstration videos*
Flame Tests
The Line Spectrum of Hydrogen
Electromagnetic Waves
Refraction of White Light
Photoelectric Effect
1s Orbital
2p_x Orbital
2p_y Orbital

$2p_z$ Orbital
$3d_{x^2-y^2}$ Orbital
$3d_{xy}$ Orbital
$3d_{xz}$ Orbital
$3d_{yz}$ Orbital
$3d_{z^2}$ Orbital

■ **Flashcards** *Key terms and definitions*
   Online Flashcards

Access these resources using the passkey available free with new texts or for purchase separately.

■ **Self-Assessment Questions** *Additional questions with full worked-out solutions*
   6 Self-Assessment Questions

 ACE the Test

Multiple-choice quizzes
3 ACE Practice Tests

Learning Objectives

7.1 The Wave Nature of Light

■ Define the *wavelength* and *frequency* of a wave.
■ Relate the wavelength, frequency, and speed of light. Examples 7.1 and 7.2
■ Describe the different regions of the electromagnetic spectrum.

7.2 Quantum Effects and Photons

■ State Planck's quantization of vibrational energy.
■ Define *Planck's constant* and *photon*.
■ Describe the photoelectric effect.
■ Calculate the energy of a photon from its frequency or wavelength. Example 7.3

7.3 The Bohr Theory of the Hydrogen Atom

■ State the postulates of Bohr's theory of the hydrogen atom.
■ Relate the energy of a photon to the associated energy levels of an atom.

■ Determine the wavelength or frequency of a hydrogen atom transition. Example 7.4
■ Describe the difference between *emission* and *absorption* of light by an atom.

7.4 Quantum Mechanics

■ State the de Broglie relation.
■ Calculate the wavelength of a moving particle. Example 7.5
■ Define *quantum mechanics*.
■ State Heisenberg's uncertainty principle.
■ Relate the wave function for an electron to the probability of finding it at a location in space.

7.5 Quantum Numbers and Atomic Orbitals

■ Define *atomic orbital*.
■ Define each of the quantum numbers for an atomic orbital.
■ State the rules for the allowed values for each quantum number.
■ Apply the rules for quantum numbers. Example 7.6
■ Describe the shapes of *s*, *p*, and *d* orbitals.

Self-Assessment and Review Questions

7.1 Give a brief wave description of light. What are two characteristics of light waves?

7.2 What is the mathematical relationship among the different characteristics of light waves? State the meaning of each of the terms in the equation.

7.3 Briefly describe the portions of the electromagnetic spectrum, starting with shortest wavelengths and going to longer wavelengths.

7.4 Planck originated the idea that energies can be quantized. What does the term *quantized* mean? What was Planck trying to explain when he was led to the concept of quantization of energy? Give the formula he arrived at and explain each of the terms in the formula.

7.5 In your own words, explain the photoelectric effect. How does the photon concept explain this effect?

7.6 Describe the wave–particle picture of light.

7.7 Give the equation that relates particle properties of light. Explain the meaning of each symbol in the equation.

7.8 Physical theory at the time Rutherford proposed his nuclear model of the atom was not able to explain how this model could give a stable atom. Explain the nature of this difficulty.

7.9 Explain the main features of Bohr's theory. Do these features solve the difficulty alluded to in Question 7.8?

7.10 Explain the process of emission of light by an atom.

7.11 Explain the process of absorption of light by an atom.

7.12 What is the evidence for electron waves? Give a practical application.

7.13 What kind of information does a wave function give about an electron in an atom?

7.14 The atom is sometimes said to be similar to a miniature planetary system, with electrons orbiting the nucleus. What does the uncertainty principle have to say about this view of the atom?

7.15 Bohr described the hydrogen atom as an electron orbiting a hydrogen nucleus. Although certain aspects of his theory are still valid, his theory agreed quantitatively with experiment only in the case of the hydrogen atom. In what way does quantum mechanics change Bohr's original picture of the hydrogen atom?

7.16 Give the possible values of (a) the principal quantum number, (b) the angular momentum quantum number, (c) the magnetic quantum number, and (d) the spin quantum number.

7.17 What is the notation for the subshell in which $n = 4$ and $l = 3$? How many orbitals are in this subshell?

7.18 What is the general shape of an s orbital? of a p orbital?

7.19 Which of the following statements about a hydrogen atom is *false*?

  a. An electron in the $n = 1$ level of the hydrogen atom is in its ground state.

  b. On average, an electron in the $n = 3$ level is farther from the nucleus than an electron in the $n = 2$ state.

  c. The wavelength of light emitted when the electron goes from the $n = 3$ level to the $n = 1$ level is the same as the wavelength of light absorbed when the electron goes from the $n = 1$ level to $n = 3$ level.

  d. An electron in the $n = 1$ level is higher in energy than an electron in the $n = 4$ level.

  e. Light of greater frequency is required for a transition from the $n = 1$ level to $n = 3$ level than is required for a transition from the $n = 2$ level to $n = 3$ level.

7.20 Which of the following statements is (are) true?

  I. The product of wavelength and frequency of light is a constant.

  II. As the energy of electromagnetic radiation increases, its frequency decreases.

  III. As the wavelength of light increases, its frequency increases.

  a. I only

  b. II only

  c. III only

  d. I and III only

  e. II and III only

7.21 Of the following possible transitions of an electron in a hydrogen atom, which emits light of the highest energy?

  a. Transition from the $n = 1$ to the $n = 3$ level

  b. Transition from the $n = 1$ to the $n = 2$ level

  c. Transition from the $n = 3$ to the $n = 1$ level

  d. Transition from the $n = 2$ to the $n = 1$ level

  e. Transition from the $n = 5$ to the $n = 4$ level

7.22 What wavelength of electromagnetic radiation corresponds to a frequency of 3.46×10^{13} s^{-1}?

  a. 8.66×10^{-6} m

  b. 1.15×10^{5} m

  c. 7.65×10^{-29} m

  d. 9.10×10^{-6} m

  e. 8.99×10^{-6} m

Concept Explorations

7.23 Light, Energy, and the Hydrogen Atom

  a. Which has the greater wavelength, blue light or red light?

  b. How do the frequencies of blue light and red light compare?

  c. How does the energy of blue light compare with that of red light?

  d. Does blue light have a greater speed than red light?

  e. How does the energy of three photons from a blue light source compare with the energy of one photon of blue light from the same source? How does the energy of two photons corresponding to a wavelength of 451 nm (blue light) compare with the energy of three photons corresponding to a wavelength of 704 nm (red light)?

  f. A hydrogen atom with an electron in its ground state interacts with a photon of light with a wavelength of 1.22×10^{-6} m. Could the electron make a transition from the ground state to a higher energy level? If it does make a transition, indicate which one. If no transition can occur, explain.

  g. If you have one mole of hydrogen atoms with their electrons in the $n = 1$ level, what is the minimum number of photons you would need to interact with these atoms in order to have all of their electrons promoted to the $n = 3$ level? What wavelength of light would you need to perform this experiment?

7.24 Investigating Energy Levels

Consider the hypothetical atom X that has one electron like the H atom but has different energy levels. The energies of an electron in an X atom are described by the equation

$$E = -\frac{R_H}{n^3}$$

where R_H is the same as for hydrogen (2.179×10^{-18} J). Answer the following questions, *without calculating energy values*.

  a. How would the ground-state energy levels of X and H compare?

  b. Would the energy of an electron in the $n = 2$ level of H be higher or lower than that of an electron in the $n = 2$ level of X? Explain your answer.

  c. How do the spacings of the energy levels of X and H compare?

  d. Which would involve the emission of a higher frequency of light, the transition of an electron in an H atom from the $n = 5$ to the $n = 3$ level or a similar transition in an X atom?

  e. Which atom, X or H, would require more energy to completely remove its electron?

  f. A photon corresponding to a particular frequency of blue light produces a transition from the $n = 2$ to the $n = 5$ level of a hydrogen atom. Could this photon produce the same transition ($n = 2$ to $n = 5$) in an atom of X? Explain.

Conceptual Problems

7.25 Consider two beams of the same yellow light. Imagine that one beam has its wavelength doubled; the other has its frequency doubled. Which of these two beams is then in the ultraviolet region?

7.26 Some infrared radiation has a wavelength that is 1000 times larger than that of a certain visible light. This visible light has a frequency that is 1000 times smaller than that of some X radiation. How many times more energy is there in a photon of this X radiation than there is in a photon of the infrared radiation?

7.27 One photon of green light has less than twice the energy of two photons of red light. Consider two hypothetical experiments. In one experiment, potassium metal is exposed to one photon of green light; in another experiment, potassium metal is exposed to two photons of red light. In one of these experiments, no electrons are ejected by the photoelectric effect (no matter how many times this experiment is repeated). In the other experiment, at least one electron was observed to be ejected. What is the maximum number of electrons that could be ejected during this other experiment, one or two?

7.28 An atom in its ground state absorbs a photon (photon 1), then quickly emits another photon (photon 2). One of these photons corresponds to ultraviolet radiation, whereas the other one corresponds to red light. Explain what is happening. Which electromagnetic radiation, ultraviolet or red light, is associated with the emitted photon (photon 2)?

7.29 Three emission lines involving three energy levels in an atom occur at wavelengths x, $1.5x$, and $3.0x$ nanometers. Which wavelength corresponds to the transition from the highest to the lowest of the three energy levels?

7.30 An atom emits yellow light when an electron makes the transition from the $n = 5$ to the $n = 1$ level. In separate experiments, suppose you bombarded the $n = 1$ level of this atom with red light, yellow light (obtained from the previous emission), and blue light. In which experiment or experiments would the electron be promoted to the $n = 5$ level?

7.31 Which of the following particles has the longest wavelength?

a. an electron traveling at x meters per second

b. a proton traveling at x meters per second

c. a proton traveling at $2x$ meters per second

7.32 Imagine a world in which the rule for the l quantum number is that values start with 1 and go up to n. The rules for the n and m_l quantum numbers are unchanged from those of our world. Write the quantum numbers for the first two shells (i.e., $n = 1$ and $n = 2$).

7.33 Given the following energy level diagram for an atom that contains an electron in the $n = 3$ level, answer the following questions.

a. Which transition of the electron will emit light of the lowest frequency?

b. Using only those levels depicted in the diagram, which transition of the electron would require the highest-frequency light?

c. If the transition from the $n = 3$ level to the $n = 1$ level emits green light, what color light is absorbed when an electron makes the transition from the $n = 1$ to $n = 3$ level?

7.34 The following shapes each represent an orbital of an atom in a hypothetical universe. The small circle is the location of the nucleus in each orbital.

a. If you placed an electron in each orbital, which one would be higher in energy?

b. When an electron makes a transition from the orbital represented on the right to the orbital on the left, would you expect energy to be absorbed or released?

c. Draw a sketch of an orbital of the same type that would be higher in energy than either of the two pictured orbitals.

Practice Problems

Electromagnetic Waves

7.35 Radio waves in the AM region have frequencies in the range 530 to 1700 kilocycles per second (530 to 1700 kHz). Calculate the wavelength corresponding to a radio wave of frequency 1.365×10^6/s (that is, 1365 kHz).

7.36 Microwaves have frequencies in the range 10^9 to 10^{12}/s (cycles per second), equivalent to between 1 gigahertz and 1 terahertz. What is the wavelength of microwave radiation whose frequency is 1.258×10^{10}/s?

7.37 Light with a wavelength of 478 nm lies in the blue region of the visible spectrum. Calculate the frequency of this light.

7.38 Calculate the frequency associated with light of wavelength 656 nm. (This corresponds to one of the wavelengths of light emitted by the hydrogen atom.)

7.39 At its closest approach, Mars is 56 million km from Earth. How long would it take to send a radio message from a space probe of Mars to Earth when the planets are at this closest distance?

7.40 The space probe *Pioneer 11* was launched April 5, 1973, and reached Jupiter in December 1974, traveling a distance of 998 million km. How long did it take an electromagnetic signal to travel to Earth from *Pioneer 11* when it was near Jupiter?

7.41 The meter was defined in 1963 as the length equal to 1,650,763.73 wavelengths of the orange-red radiation emitted by the krypton-86 atom (the meter has since been redefined). What is the wavelength of this transition? What is the frequency?

7.42 The second is defined as the time it takes for 9,192,631,770 wavelengths of a certain transition of the cesium-133 atom to pass a fixed point. What is the frequency of this electromagnetic radiation? What is the wavelength?

Photons

7.43 What is the energy of a photon corresponding to radio waves of frequency 1.365×10^6/s?

7.44 What is the energy of a photon corresponding to microwave radiation of frequency 1.258×10^{10}/s?

7.45 The green line in the atomic spectrum of thallium has a wavelength of 535 nm. Calculate the energy of a photon of this light.

7.46 Indium compounds give a blue-violet flame test. The atomic emission responsible for this blue-violet color has a wavelength of 451 nm. Obtain the energy of a single photon of this wavelength.

7.47 A particular transition of the rubidium atom emits light whose frequency is 3.84×10^{14} Hz. (Hz is the abbreviation for *hertz*, which is equivalent to the unit /s, or s^{-1}.) Is this light in the visible spectrum? If so, what is the color of the light? (See Figure 7.5.)

7.48 Barium atoms have a particular transition that emits light of frequency 5.41×10^{14} Hz. (Hz is the abbreviation for *hertz*, which is equivalent to the unit /s, or s^{-1}.) Is this light in the visible spectrum? If so, what is the color of the light? (See Figure 7.5.)

Bohr Theory

7.49 An electron in a hydrogen atom in the level $n = 5$ undergoes a transition to level $n = 3$. What is the frequency of the emitted radiation?

7.50 Calculate the frequency of electromagnetic radiation emitted by the hydrogen atom in the electron transition from $n = 4$ to $n = 3$.

7.51 The first line of the Lyman series of the hydrogen atom emission results from a transition from the $n = 2$ level to the $n = 1$ level. What is the wavelength of the emitted photon? Using Figure 7.5, describe the region of the electromagnetic spectrum in which this emission lies.

7.52 What is the wavelength of the electromagnetic radiation emitted from a hydrogen atom when the electron undergoes the transition $n = 5$ to $n = 4$? In what region of the spectrum does this line occur? (See Figure 7.5.)

7.53 Calculate the shortest wavelength of the electromagnetic radiation emitted by the hydrogen atom in undergoing a transition from the $n = 6$ level.

7.54 Calculate the longest wavelength of the electromagnetic radiation emitted by the hydrogen atom in undergoing a transition from the $n = 7$ level.

7.55 What is the difference in energy between the two levels responsible for the violet emission line of the calcium atom at 422.7 nm?

7.56 What is the difference in energy between the two levels responsible for the ultraviolet emission line of the magnesium atom at 285.2 nm?

de Broglie Waves

Note: Masses of the electron, proton, and neutron are listed on the inside back cover of this book.

7.57 What is the wavelength of a neutron traveling at a speed of 4.15 km/s? (Neutrons of these speeds are obtained from a nuclear pile.)

7.58 What is the wavelength of a proton traveling at a speed of 6.58 km/s? What would be the region of the spectrum for electromagnetic radiation of this wavelength?

7.59 At what speed must an electron travel to have a wavelength of 10.0 pm?

7.60 At what speed must a neutron travel to have a wavelength of 12.0 pm?

7.61 What is the de Broglie wavelength of a 145-g baseball traveling at 30.0 m/s (67.1 mph)? Is the wavelength much smaller or much larger than the diameter of an atom (on the order of 100 pm)?

7.62 What is the de Broglie wavelength of an oxygen molecule, O_2, traveling at 521 m/s? Is the wavelength much smaller or much larger than the diameter of an atom (on the order of 100 pm)?

Atomic Orbitals

7.63 If the n quantum number of an atomic orbital is 4, what are the possible values of l? If the l quantum number is 3, what are the possible values of m_l?

7.64 The n quantum number of an atomic orbital is 6. What are the possible values of l? What are the possible values of m_l if the l quantum number is 5?

7.65 How many subshells are there in the M shell? How many orbitals are there in the f subshell?

7.66 How many subshells are there in the N shell? How many orbitals are there in the g subshell?

7.67 Give the notation (using letter designations for l) for the subshells denoted by the following quantum numbers.
   a. $n = 6, l = 2$ **c.** $n = 4, l = 3$
   b. $n = 5, l = 4$ **d.** $n = 6, l = 1$

7.68 Give the notation (using letter designations for l) for the subshells denoted by the following quantum numbers.
   a. $n = 3, l = 2$
   b. $n = 4, l = 0$
   c. $n = 4, l = 1$
   d. $n = 5, l = 3$

7.69 Explain why each of the following sets of quantum numbers would not be permissible for an electron, according to the rules for quantum numbers.

   a. $n = 1, l = 0, m_l = 0, m_s = +1$
   b. $n = 1, l = 3, m_l = +3, m_s = +\frac{1}{2}$
   c. $n = 3, l = 2, m_l = +3, m_s = -\frac{1}{2}$
   d. $n = 0, l = 1, m_l = 0, m_s = +\frac{1}{2}$
   e. $n = 2, l = 1, m_l = -1, m_s = +\frac{3}{2}$

General Problems

7.71 The blue line of the strontium atom emission has a wavelength of 461 nm. What is the frequency of this light? What is the energy of a photon of this light?

7.72 The barium atom has an emission with wavelength 554 nm (green). Calculate the frequency of this light and the energy of a photon of this light.

7.73 The energy of a photon is 4.10×10^{-19} J. What is the wavelength of the corresponding light? What is the color of this light?

7.74 The energy of a photon is 3.34×10^{-19} J. What is the wavelength of the corresponding light? What is the color of this light?

7.75 The photoelectric work function of a metal is the minimum energy needed to eject an electron by irradiating the metal with light. For calcium, this work function equals 4.34×10^{-19} J. What is the minimum frequency of light for the photoelectric effect in calcium?

7.76 The photoelectric work function for magnesium is 5.90×10^{-19} J. (The work function is the minimum energy needed to eject an electron from the metal by irradiating it with light.) Calculate the minimum frequency of light required to eject electrons from magnesium.

7.77 Light of wavelength 345 nm shines on a piece of calcium metal. What is the speed of the ejected electron? (Light energy greater than that of the work function of calcium ends up as kinetic energy of the ejected electron. See Problem 7.75 for the definition of work function and its value for calcium.)

7.78 Light of wavelength 276 nm shines on a piece of magnesium metal. What is the speed of the ejected electron? (Light energy greater than that of the work function of magnesium ends up as kinetic energy of the ejected electron. See Problem 7.76 for the definition of work function and its value for magnesium.)

7.79 Calculate the wavelength of the Balmer line of the hydrogen spectrum in which the initial n quantum number is 5 and the final n quantum number is 2.

7.80 Calculate the wavelength of the Balmer line of the hydrogen spectrum in which the initial n quantum number is 6 and the final n quantum number is 2.

7.81 One of the lines in the Balmer series of the hydrogen atom emission spectrum is at 397 nm. It results from a transition from an upper energy level to $n = 2$. What is the principal quantum number of the upper level?

7.82 A line of the Lyman series of the hydrogen atom spectrum has the wavelength 9.50×10^{-8} m. It results from a transition from an upper energy level to $n = 1$. What is the principal quantum number of the upper level?

7.70 State which of the following sets of quantum numbers would be possible and which impossible for an electron in an atom.

   a. $n = 2, l = 0, m_l = 0, m_s = +\frac{1}{2}$
   b. $n = 1, l = 1, m_l = 0, m_s = +\frac{1}{2}$
   c. $n = 0, l = 0, m_l = 0, m_s = -\frac{1}{2}$
   d. $n = 2, l = 1, m_l = -1, m_s = +\frac{1}{2}$
   e. $n = 2, l = 1, m_l = -2, m_s = +\frac{1}{2}$

7.83 A hydrogen-like ion has a nucleus of charge $+Ze$ and a single electron outside this nucleus. The energy levels of these ions are $-Z^2 R_H/n^2$ (where Z = atomic number). Calculate the wavelength of the transition from $n = 3$ to $n = 2$ for He^+, a hydrogen-like ion. In what region of the spectrum does this emission occur?

7.84 What is the wavelength of the transition from $n = 5$ to $n = 3$ for Li^{2+}? In what region of the spectrum does this emission occur? Li^{2+} is a hydrogen-like ion. Such an ion has a nucleus of charge $+Ze$ and a single electron outside this nucleus. The energy levels of the ion are $-Z^2 R_H/n^2$, where Z is the atomic number.

7.85 An electron microscope employs a beam of electrons to obtain an image of an object. What energy must be imparted to each electron of the beam to obtain a wavelength of 10.0 pm? Obtain the energy in electron volts (eV) (1 eV = 1.602×10^{-19} J).

7.86 Neutrons are used to obtain images of the hydrogen atoms in molecules. What energy must be imparted to each neutron in a neutron beam to obtain a wavelength of 10.0 pm? Obtain the energy in electron volts (eV) (1 eV = 1.602×10^{-19} J).

7.87 What is the number of different orbitals in each of the following subshells?

   a. 3d   **b.** 4f   **c.** 4p   **d.** 5s

7.88 What is the number of different orbitals in each of the following subshells?

   a. 6g   **b.** 4f   **c.** 6s   **d.** 5p

7.89 List the possible subshells for the $n = 6$ shell.

7.90 List the possible subshells for the $n = 7$ shell.

7.91 What are gamma rays? How does the gamma radiation of foods improve their shelf life?

7.92 How can gamma rays that are used in food irradiation be produced? Does such irradiated food show any radioactivity?

7.93 The word *laser* is an acronym meaning *l*ight *a*mplification by *s*timulated *e*mission of *r*adiation. What is the stimulated emission of radiation?

7.94 Explain how lasers are used to "read" a compact disc.

7.95 Explain the concept of quantum mechanical tunneling.

7.96 Explain how the probe in a scanning tunneling microscope scans a sample on the surface of a metal.

Strategy Problems

7.97 What wavelength of electromagnetic radiation corresponds to a frequency of 7.76×10^9 s^{-1}? Note that Planck's constant is 6.63×10^{-34} J·s, and the speed of light is 3.00×10^8 m/s.

7.98 AM radio stations broadcast at frequencies between 530 kHz and 1700 kHz. (1 kHz = 10^3 s^{-1}.) For a station broadcasting at 1.69×10^3 kHz, what is the energy of this radio wave? Note that Planck's constant is 6.63×10^{-34} J·s, and the speed of light is 3.00×10^8 m/s.

7.99 The photoelectric *work function* of a metal is the minimum energy required to eject an electron by shining light on the metal. The work function of calcium is 4.60×10^{-19} J. What is the longest wavelength of light (in nanometers) that can cause an electron to be ejected from calcium metal.

7.100 Calculate the shortest wavelength of *visible* light (in nanometers) seen in the spectrum of the hydrogen atom. What are the principal quantum numbers for the levels in this transition? Does Figure 7.11 include all visible lines?

7.101 Light of wavelength 1.03×10^{-7} m is emitted when an electron in an excited level of a hydrogen atom undergoes a transition to the $n = 1$ level. What is the region of the spectrum of this light? What is the principal quantum number of the excited level?

7.102 It requires 799 kJ of energy to break one mole of carbon–oxygen double bonds in carbon dioxide. What wavelength of light does this correspond to per bond? Is there any transition in the hydrogen atom that has at least this quantity of energy in one photon?

7.103 The root-mean-square speed of an oxygen molecule, O_2, at 21°C is 479 m/s. Calculate the de Broglie wavelength for an O_2 molecule traveling at this speed. How does this wavelength compare with the approximate length of this molecule, which is about 242 pm? (For this comparison, state the wavelength as a percentage of the molecular length).

7.104 A particular microwave oven delivers 800 watts. (A watt is a unit of power, which is the joules of energy delivered, or used, per second.) If the oven uses microwave radiation of wavelength 12.2 cm, how many photons of this radiation are required to heat 1.00 g of water 1.00°C, assuming that all of the photons are absorbed?

7.105 For each of the following combinations of quantum numbers, make changes that produce an allowed combination. Count 3 for each change of n, 2 for each change of l, and 1 for each change of m_l. What is the lowest possible count that you can obtain?

    a. $n = 3, l = 0, m_l = -2$ **c.** $n = 3, l = 3, m_l = -3$
    b. $n = 5, l = 5, m_l = 4$ **d.** $n = 5, l = 6, m_l = 3$

7.106 The term *degeneracy* means the number of different quantum states of an atom or molecule having the same energy. For example, the degeneracy of the $n = 2$ level of the hydrogen atom is 4 (a $2s$ quantum state, and three different $2p$ states). What is the degeneracy of the $n = 5$ level?

Cumulative-Skills Problems

7.107 The energy required to dissociate the Cl_2 molecule to Cl atoms is 239 kJ/mol Cl_2. If the dissociation of a Cl_2 molecule were accomplished by the absorption of a single photon whose energy was exactly the quantity required, what would be its wavelength (in meters)?

7.108 The energy required to dissociate the H_2 molecule to H atoms is 432 kJ/mol H_2. If the dissociation of an H_2 molecule were accomplished by the absorption of a single photon whose energy was exactly the quantity required, what would be its wavelength (in meters)?

7.109 A microwave oven heats by radiating food with microwave radiation, which is absorbed by the food and converted to heat. Suppose an oven's radiation wavelength is 12.5 cm. A container with 0.250 L of water was placed in the oven, and the temperature of the water rose from 20.0°C to 100.0°C. How many photons of this microwave radiation were required? Assume that all the energy from the radiation was used to raise the temperature of the water.

7.110 Warm objects emit electromagnetic radiation in the infrared region. Heat lamps employ this principle to generate infrared radiation. Water absorbs infrared radiation with wavelengths near 2.80 μm. Suppose this radiation is absorbed by the water and converted to heat. A 1.00-L sample of water absorbs infrared radiation, and its temperature increases from 20.0°C to 30.0°C. How many photons of this radiation are used to heat the water?

7.111 Light with a wavelength of 425 nm fell on a potassium surface, and electrons were ejected at a speed of 4.88×10^5 m/s. What energy was expended in removing an electron from the metal? Express the answer in joules (per electron) and in kilojoules per mole (of electrons).

7.112 Light with a wavelength of 405 nm fell on a strontium surface, and electrons were ejected. If the speed of an ejected electron is 3.36×10^5 m/s, what energy was expended in removing the electron from the metal? Express the answer in joules (per electron) and in kilojoules per mole (of electrons).

7.113 When an electron is accelerated by a voltage difference, the kinetic energy acquired by the electron equals the voltage times the charge on the electron. Thus, one volt imparts a kinetic energy of 1.602×10^{-19} volt-coulombs, which equals 1.602×10^{-19} J. What is the wavelength associated with electrons accelerated by 4.00×10^3 volts?

7.114 When an electron is accelerated by a voltage difference, the kinetic energy acquired by the electron equals the voltage times the charge on the electron. Thus, one volt imparts a kinetic energy of 1.602×10^{-19} volt-coulombs, or 1.602×10^{-19} J. What is the wavelength for electrons accelerated by 1.00×10^4 volts?

8

Electron Configurations and Periodicity

Sodium metal reacts vigorously with water to produce hydrogen gas (which catches fire); other Group IA metals similarly react with water. The other product is sodium hydroxide, which is used in products such as oven cleaner and soap.

Contents and Concepts

In the previous chapter, you learned that we characterize an atomic orbital by four quantum numbers: n, l, m_l, and m_s. In the first section, we look further at electron spin; then we discuss how electrons are distributed among the possible orbitals of an atom.

You learned how the periodic table can be explained by the periodicity of the ground-state configurations of the elements. Now we will look at various aspects of the periodicity of the elements.

Marie Curie, a Polish-born French chemist, and her husband, Pierre, announced the discovery of radium in 1898 (Figure 8.1). They had separated a very radioactive mixture from pitchblende, an ore of uranium. This mixture was primarily a compound of barium. When the mixture was heated in a flame, however, it gave a new atomic line spectrum, in addition to the spectrum for barium. The Curies based their discovery of a new element on this finding. It took them four more years to obtain a pure compound of radium. Radium, like uranium, is a radioactive element. But in most of its chemical and physical properties, radium is similar to the non-radioactive element barium. It was this similarity that made the final separation of the new element so difficult.

Chemists had long known that groups of elements have similar properties. In 1869 Dmitri Mendeleev found that when the elements were arranged in a particular way, they fell into columns, with elements in the same column displaying similar properties. Thus, Mendeleev placed beryllium, calcium, strontium, and barium in one column. Now, with the Curies' discovery, radium was added to this column.

Mendeleev's arrangement of the elements, the *periodic table*, was originally based on the observed chemical and physical properties of the elements and their compounds. We now explain this arrangement in terms of the electronic structure of atoms. In this chapter we will look at this electronic structure and its relationship to the periodic table of elements.

■ See pages 321–322 for the Media Summary.

In the preceding chapter, we introduced atomic orbitals and quantum numbers. Here we look at the electron configurations of atoms and the periodic behavior of the elements.

FIGURE 8.1 ▲

Marie Sklodowska Curie (1867–1934), with Pierre Curie
Marie Sklodowska Curie, born in Warsaw, Poland, began her doctoral work with Henri Becquerel soon after he discovered the spontaneous radiation emitted by uranium salts. She found this radiation to be an atomic property and coined the word *radioactivity* for it. In 1903 the Curies and Becquerel were awarded the Nobel Prize in physics for their discovery of radioactivity. Three years later, Pierre Curie was killed in a carriage accident. Marie Curie continued their work on radium and in 1911 was awarded the Nobel Prize in chemistry for the discovery of polonium and radium and the isolation of pure radium metal. This was the first time a scientist had received two Nobel awards. (Since then two others have been so honored.)

Electronic Structure of Atoms

In Chapter 7 we found that an electron in an atom has four quantum numbers—n, l, m_l, and m_s—associated with it. The first three quantum numbers characterize the orbital that describes the region of space where an electron is most likely to be found; we say that the electron "occupies" this orbital. The spin quantum number, m_s, describes the spin orientation of an electron. In the first section, we will look further at electron spin; then we will discuss how electrons are distributed among the possible orbitals of an atom.

8.1 | Electron Spin and the Pauli Exclusion Principle

ChemWork: Electron Designations

ChemWork: Quantum Numbers

ChemWork: Quantum Numbers 2

Otto Stern and Walther Gerlach first observed electron spin magnetism in 1921. They directed a beam of silver atoms into the field of a specially designed magnet. The same experiment can be done with hydrogen atoms. The beam of hydrogen atoms is split into two by the magnetic field; half of the atoms are bent in one direction and

FIGURE 8.2 ▶

The Stern–Gerlach experiment
The diagram shows the experiment using hydrogen atoms (simpler to interpret theoretically), although the original experiment employed silver atoms. A beam of hydrogen atoms (shown in blue) is split into two by a nonuniform magnetic field. One beam consists of atoms each with an electron having $m_s = +\frac{1}{2}$; the other beam consists of atoms each having an electron with $m_s = -\frac{1}{2}$.

half in the other (see Figure 8.2). The fact that the atoms are affected by the laboratory magnet shows that they themselves act as magnets.

The beam of hydrogen atoms is split into two because the electron in each atom behaves as a tiny magnet with only two possible orientations. In effect, the electron acts as though it were a ball of spinning charge (Figure 8.3), and, like a circulating electric charge, the electron would create a magnetic field. Electron spin, however, is subject to a quantum restriction on the possible directions of the spin axis. The resulting directions of spin magnetism correspond to spin quantum numbers $m_s = +\frac{1}{2}$ and $m_s = -\frac{1}{2}$. ◀

Protons and many nuclei also have spin. See the Instrumental Methods essay at the end of this section.

Electron Configurations and Orbital Diagrams

An **electron configuration** of an atom is *a particular distribution of electrons among available subshells.* The notation for a configuration lists the subshell symbols, one after the other, with a superscript giving the number of electrons in that subshell. For example, a configuration of the lithium atom (atomic number 3) with two electrons in the 1s subshell and one electron in the 2s subshell is written $1s^2 2s^1$.

The notation for a configuration gives the number of electrons in each subshell, but we use *a diagram to show how the orbitals of a subshell are occupied by electrons.* It is called an **orbital diagram.** An orbital is represented by a circle. Each group of orbitals in a subshell is labeled by its subshell notation. An electron in an orbital is shown by an arrow; the arrow points up when $m_s = +\frac{1}{2}$ and down when $m_s = -\frac{1}{2}$. The orbital diagram

shows the electronic structure of an atom in which there are two electrons in the 1s subshell, or orbital (one electron with $m_s = +\frac{1}{2}$, the other with $m_s = -\frac{1}{2}$); two electrons in the 2s subshell ($m_s = +\frac{1}{2}$, $m_s = -\frac{1}{2}$); and one electron in the 2p subshell ($m_s = +\frac{1}{2}$). The electron configuration is $1s^2 2s^2 2p^1$.

Pauli Exclusion Principle

Not all of the conceivable arrangements of electrons among the orbitals of an atom are physically possible. The **Pauli exclusion principle,** which summarizes experimental observations, states that *no two electrons in an atom can have the same four quantum numbers.* If one electron in an atom has the quantum numbers $n = 1$, $l = 0$, $m_l = 0$, and $m_s = +\frac{1}{2}$, no other electron can have these same quantum numbers. In other words, you cannot place two electrons with the same value of m_s in a 1s orbital. The orbital diagram

1s

is not a possible arrangement of electrons.

FIGURE 8.3 ▲

A representation of electron spin
The two possible spin orientations are indicated by the models. By convention, the spin direction is given as shown by the large arrow on the spin axis. Electrons behave as tiny bar magnets, as shown in the figure.

Instrumental Methods

Nuclear Magnetic Resonance (NMR)

You have just seen that electrons have a spin and as a result behave like tiny magnets. Protons and neutrons similarly have spins. Therefore, depending on the arrangement of protons and neutrons, a nucleus could have spin. A nucleus with spin will act like a bar magnet, similar to the electron although many times smaller in magnitude. Examples of nuclei with spin are hydrogen-1 (proton), carbon-13 (but carbon-12, the most abundant nuclide of carbon, has no spin), and fluorine-19.

Although nuclear magnetism is much smaller than that of electrons, with the correct equipment it is easily seen and in fact forms the basis of *nuclear magnetic resonance* (NMR) spectroscopy, one of the most important methods for determining molecular structure. Nuclear magnetism also forms the basis of the medical diagnostic tool *magnetic resonance imaging,* or MRI (Figure 8.4).

The essential features of NMR can be seen if you consider the proton. Like the electron, the proton has two spin states. In the absence of a magnetic field, these spin states have the same energy, but in the field of a strong magnet (external field), they have different energies. The state in which the proton magnetism is aligned with the external field, so the south pole of the proton magnet faces the north pole of the external magnet, will have lower energy. The state in which the proton magnet is turned 180°, with its south pole facing the south pole of the external magnet, will have higher energy. Now if a proton in the lower spin state is irradiated with electromagnetic waves of the proper frequency (in which the photon has energy equal to the difference in energy of the spin states), the proton will change to the higher spin state. The frequency absorbed by the proton depends on the magnitude of the magnetic field. For the magnets used in these instruments, the radiation lies in the radio-frequency range. Frequencies commonly used are 300 MHz and 900 MHz.

Figure 8.5 shows a diagram of an NMR spectrometer. It consists of a sample in the field of a variable electromagnet and near two coils, one a radio wave transmitter and the other a receiver coil perpendicular to the transmitter coil (so that the receiver will not pick up the signal from the transmitter). Suppose the transmitter radiates waves of 300 MHz. If the sample absorbs these radio waves, protons will undergo transitions from the lower to the higher spin state. Once protons are in the higher energy state, they tend to lose energy, going back to the lower spin state and radiating 300-MHz radio waves. Thus, the sample acts like a transmitter, but one with coils in various directions, so the signal can be detected by the receiver coil.

In general, the sample will not absorb at the chosen frequency. But you can change the energy difference between spin states, and therefore the frequency that is absorbed by the sample, by increasing or decreasing the magnitude of the external magnetic field using small coils on the magnet pole faces. In so doing you can, in effect, "tune" the sample, or bring it into "resonance" with the transmitter frequency. (Alternatively, many modern instruments vary the transmitter frequency to obtain resonance.)

Because each proton in a substance is surrounded by electrons that have their own magnetic fields, the magnetic

FIGURE 8.4 ▶

Magnetic resonance imaging

A patient's head is placed in a large magnet and subjected to a radio pulse. Proton spin transitions give rise to a radio wave emission that can be analyzed electronically and converted by computer to a two-dimensional image of a plane portion of the brain. Paul C. Lauterbur, a chemist at the University of Illinois (Urbana), and Sir Peter Mansfield, University of Nottingham (UK), won the Nobel Prize in Physiology or Medicine in 2003 for their work in the early 1970s in developing MRI.

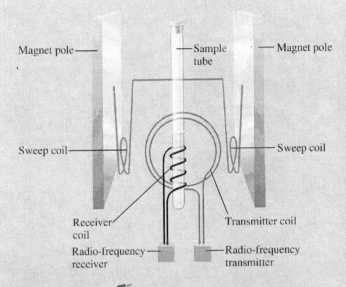

Magnet pole ——

—— Sample tube

—— Magnet pole

Sweep coil ——

—— Sweep coil

Receiver coil

Transmitter coil

Radio-frequency receiver

Radio-frequency transmitter

FIGURE 8.5 ▲

Nuclear magnetic resonance spectrometer
A sample in the tube is in a magnetic field, which can be varied by changing the electric current in the *sweep* coils (shown in green). A radio-frequency transmitter radiates radio waves from a coil (shown in red) to the sample. The sample absorbs these waves if the radio frequency corresponds to the difference in energy of the sample's nuclear spin states. When the nuclear spins go back to the ground state, the sample emits radio waves, which are detected by the receiver coil (in black).

environment of a proton depends to some extent on the bonding, or chemical, environment in which the proton is involved. So, the external magnetic field needed to bring a proton into resonance with the 300-MHz radiation, say, varies with the chemical (bonding) environment. A spectrum is produced by recording the magnetic field (or frequency) at which the protons in a molecule produce a resonance signal. Figure 8.6 shows a high-resolution NMR spectrum of ethanol.

Ethanol, whose molecular structure is

$$H-O-\underset{\underset{H}{|}}{\overset{\overset{H}{|}}{C}}-\underset{\underset{H}{|}}{\overset{\overset{H}{|}}{C}}-H$$

has protons in three different chemical environments: a proton bonded to an oxygen atom (H—O—), the protons in a —CH$_2$— group, and the protons in a —CH$_3$ group. Each of these three types of protons shows up as a

peak or, as we will see, a group of peaks in the NMR spectrum. The position of the center of a group of peaks for a given proton relative to some standard is referred to as the *chemical shift* for that proton, because it depends on the chemical environment of the proton. By measuring the area under the peaks for a given type of proton (usually done electronically by the spectrometer), a researcher can discover the number of protons of that type, effectively giving the chemist structural information about the molecule.

As we noted earlier, a given proton may give rise to several peaks in a high-resolution spectrum. (At low resolution, these separate peaks may appear as only one for each proton.) For example, the protons for the —CH$_2$— group of ethanol give four closely spaced peaks. These peaks arise because of the interaction of the proton spins on this group with those protons on the adjacent —CH$_3$ group. The number of peaks (four) for the —CH$_2$— group is one more than the number of protons on the adjacent group (three).

NMR spectroscopy is one of the most important tools a chemist has in determining the identity of a substance and its molecular structure. The method is quick and can yield such information as the chemical bonding environment of the protons and the number of protons having a given environment. It can also give information about other nuclei, such as carbon-13.

FIGURE 8.6 ▲

High-resolution NMR spectrum of ethanol, CH$_3$CH$_2$OH
The protons of a given type occur as a peak or closely spaced group of peaks. The position of the center of such a group of peaks relative to some standard is referred to as the *chemical shift*. The peaks within a group arise from the interaction of the spins between protons of one type with those of another type.

■ See Problems 8.85 and 8.86.

Because there are only two possible values of m_s, an orbital can hold no more than two electrons—and then only if the two electrons have different spin quantum numbers. In an orbital diagram, an orbital with two electrons must be written with arrows pointing in opposite directions. The two electrons are said to have opposite spins. We can restate the Pauli exclusion principle:

Pauli exclusion principle: An orbital can hold at most two electrons, and then only if the electrons have opposite spins.

Each subshell holds a maximum of twice as many electrons as the number of orbitals in the subshell. Thus, a $2p$ subshell, which has three orbitals (with $m_l = -1$, 0, and $+1$), can hold a maximum of six electrons. The maximum number of electrons in various subshells is given in the following table.

Subshell	Number of Orbitals	Maximum Number of Electrons
$s\ (l = 0)$	1	2
$p\ (l = 1)$	3	6
$d\ (l = 2)$	5	10
$f\ (l = 3)$	7	14

Example 8.1 | Applying the Pauli Exclusion Principle

Which of the following orbital diagrams or electron configurations are possible and which are impossible, according to the Pauli exclusion principle? Explain.

An alternative example is provided in the Instructor's Resource Manual.

a. ⊕ ⊕ ⊕○○
   $1s$ $2s$ $2p$

b. ⊕ ⊕ ○○○
   $1s$ $2s$ $2p$

c. ⊕ ⊕ ⊕○○
   $1s$ $2s$ $2p$

d. $1s^3 2s^1$

e. $1s^2 2s^1 2p^7$

f. $1s^2 2s^2 2p^6 3s^2 3p^6 3d^8 4s^2$

Problem Strategy In any orbital diagram, make sure that each orbital contains no more than two electrons, which have opposite spins. In any electron configuration, make sure that an orbital of given l contains no more than $2(2l + 1)$ electrons (there are $2l + 1$ different orbitals of given l, and each of these orbitals can hold two electrons).

Solution a. **Possible** orbital diagram. b. **Impossible** orbital diagram; there are three electrons in the $2s$ orbital. c. **Impossible** orbital diagram; there are two electrons in a $2p$ orbital with the same spin. d. **Impossible** electron configuration; there are three electrons in the $1s$ subshell (one orbital). e. **Impossible** electron configuration; there are seven electrons in the $2p$ subshell (which can hold only six electrons). f. **Possible.** Note that the $3d$ subshell can hold as many as ten electrons.

Answer Check The overarching idea here is that each orbital in an atom can hold a maximum of only two electrons, and then only if the two electrons have opposite spins. For example, a p subshell has three orbitals and therefore holds a maximum of six electrons.

(continued)

(*continued*)

Exercise 8.1   Look at the following orbital diagrams and electron configurations. Which are possible and which are not, according to the Pauli exclusion principle? Explain.

a. ⊙ ⊙ ○○○
    1s 2s 2p

b. ⊙ ⊙ ⊛⊛⊛
    1s 2s 2p

c. ⊛ ⊛ ⊛⊛⊛
    1s 2s 2p

d. $1s^2 2s^2 2p^4$

e. $1s^2 2s^4 2p^2$

f. $1s^2 2s^2 2p^6 3s^2 3p^{10} 3d^{10}$

■ See Problems 8.41, 8.42, 8.43, and 8.44.

8.2 | Building-Up Principle and the Periodic Table

The transition of the sodium atom from the excited state $1s^2 2s^2 2p^6 3p^1$ to the ground state $1s^2 2s^2 2p^6 3s^1$ is accompanied by the emission of yellow light at 589 nm. Excited states of an atom are needed to describe its spectrum.

Every atom has an infinite number of possible electron configurations. The configuration associated with the lowest energy level of the atom corresponds to a quantum-mechanical state called the *ground state*. Other configurations correspond to *excited states*, associated with energy levels other than the lowest. For example, the ground state of the sodium atom is known from experiment to have the electron configuration $1s^2 2s^2 2p^6 3s^1$. The electron configuration $1s^2 2s^2 2p^6 3p^1$ represents an excited state of the sodium atom. <

The chemical properties of an atom are related primarily to the electron configuration of its ground state. Table 8.1 lists the experimentally determined ground-state

TABLE 8.1 | Ground-State Electron Configurations of Atoms Z = 1 to 36*

Z	Element	Configuration	Z	Element	Configuration
1	H	$1s^1$	19	K	$1s^2 2s^2 2p^6 3s^2 3p^6 4s^1$
2	He	$1s^2$	20	Ca	$1s^2 2s^2 2p^6 3s^2 3p^6 4s^2$
3	Li	$1s^2 2s^1$	21	Sc	$1s^2 2s^2 2p^6 3s^2 3p^6 3d^1 4s^2$
4	Be	$1s^2 2s^2$	22	Ti	$1s^2 2s^2 2p^6 3s^2 3p^6 3d^2 4s^2$
5	B	$1s^2 2s^2 2p^1$	23	V	$1s^2 2s^2 2p^6 3s^2 3p^6 3d^3 4s^2$
6	C	$1s^2 2s^2 2p^2$	24	Cr	$1s^2 2s^2 2p^6 3s^2 3p^6 3d^5 4s^1$
7	N	$1s^2 2s^2 2p^3$	25	Mn	$1s^2 2s^2 2p^6 3s^2 3p^6 3d^5 4s^2$
8	O	$1s^2 2s^2 2p^4$	26	Fe	$1s^2 2s^2 2p^6 3s^2 3p^6 3d^6 4s^2$
9	F	$1s^2 2s^2 2p^5$	27	Co	$1s^2 2s^2 2p^6 3s^2 3p^6 3d^7 4s^2$
10	Ne	$1s^2 2s^2 2p^6$	28	Ni	$1s^2 2s^2 2p^6 3s^2 3p^6 3d^8 4s^2$
11	Na	$1s^2 2s^2 2p^6 3s^1$	29	Cu	$1s^2 2s^2 2p^6 3s^2 3p^6 3d^{10} 4s^1$
12	Mg	$1s^2 2s^2 2p^6 3s^2$	30	Zn	$1s^2 2s^2 2p^6 3s^2 3p^6 3d^{10} 4s^2$
13	Al	$1s^2 2s^2 2p^6 3s^2 3p^1$	31	Ga	$1s^2 2s^2 2p^6 3s^2 3p^6 3d^{10} 4s^2 4p^1$
14	Si	$1s^2 2s^2 2p^6 3s^2 3p^2$	32	Ge	$1s^2 2s^2 2p^6 3s^2 3p^6 3d^{10} 4s^2 4p^2$
15	P	$1s^2 2s^2 2p^6 3s^2 3p^3$	33	As	$1s^2 2s^2 2p^6 3s^2 3p^6 3d^{10} 4s^2 4p^3$
16	S	$1s^2 2s^2 2p^6 3s^2 3p^4$	34	Se	$1s^2 2s^2 2p^6 3s^2 3p^6 3d^{10} 4s^2 4p^4$
17	Cl	$1s^2 2s^2 2p^6 3s^2 3p^5$	35	Br	$1s^2 2s^2 2p^6 3s^2 3p^6 3d^{10} 4s^2 4p^5$
18	Ar	$1s^2 2s^2 2p^6 3s^2 3p^6$	36	Kr	$1s^2 2s^2 2p^6 3s^2 3p^6 3d^{10} 4s^2 4p^6$

*A complete table appears in Appendix D.

FIGURE 8.7 ▲

A mnemonic diagram for the building-up order (diagonal rule)

You obtain this diagram by writing the subshell(s) in rows, each row having sub-shell(s) of given n. Within each row, you arrange the subshell(s) by increasing l. (You can stop after writing the nf subshell(s), since no known elements contain g or higher subshell(s).) Now, starting with the $1s$ subshell(s), draw a series of diagonals, as shown. The building-up order is the order in which these diagonals strike the subshell(s).

| *The quantum numbers and characteristics of orbitals were discussed in Section 7.5.*

electron configurations of atoms $Z = 1$ to $Z = 36$. (A complete table appears in Appendix D.)

Building-Up Principle (Aufbau Principle)

Most of the configurations in Table 8.1 can be explained in terms of the **building-up principle** (or **Aufbau principle**), *a scheme used to reproduce the electron configurations of the ground states of atoms by successively filling subshells with electrons in a specific order (the building-up order).* Following this principle, you obtain the electron configuration of an atom by successively filling subshells in the following order: $1s, 2s, 2p, 3s, 3p, 4s, 3d, 4p, 5s, 4d, 5p, 6s, 4f, 5d, 6p, 7s, 5f$. This order reproduces the experimentally determined electron configurations (with some exceptions, which we will discuss later). You need not memorize this order. As you will see, you can very easily obtain it from the periodic table. (You can also reproduce this order from the mnemonic diagram shown in Figure 8.7.)

The building-up order corresponds for the most part to increasing energy of the subshells. You might expect this. By filling orbitals of lowest energy first, you usually get the lowest total energy (ground state) of the atom. Recall that the energy of an orbital depends only on the quantum numbers n and l. < (The energy of the H atom, however, depends only on n.) Orbitals with the same n and l but different m_l—that is, different orbitals of the same subshell—have the same energy. The energy depends primarily on n, increasing with its value. For example, a $3s$ orbital has greater energy than a $2s$ orbital. Except for the H atom, the energies of orbitals with the same n increase with the l quantum number. A $3p$ orbital has slightly greater energy than a $3s$ orbital. The orbital of lowest energy is $1s$; next higher are $2s$ and $2p$, then $3s$ and $3p$. The order of these subshells by energy, from $1s$ to $3p$, follows the building-up order as listed earlier.

When subshells have nearly the same energy, however, the building-up order is not strictly determined by the order of their energies. The ground-state configurations, which we are trying to predict by the building-up order, are determined by the *total* energies of the atoms. The total energy of an atom depends not only on the energies of the subshells but also on the energies of interaction among the different subshells. It so happens that for all elements with $Z = 21$ or greater, the energy of the $3d$ subshell is lower than the energy of the $4s$ subshell (Figure 8.8), which is opposite to the

FIGURE 8.8 ▷

Orbital energies for the scandium atom ($Z = 21$)

Note that in the scandium atom, unlike the hydrogen atom, the subshells for each n are spread apart in energy. Thus, the $2p$ energy is above the $2s$. Similarly, the $n = 3$ subshells are spread to give the order $3s < 3p < 3d$. The $3d$ subshell energy is now just below the $4s$. (Values for this figure were calculated from theory by Charlotte F. Fischer, Vanderbilt University.)

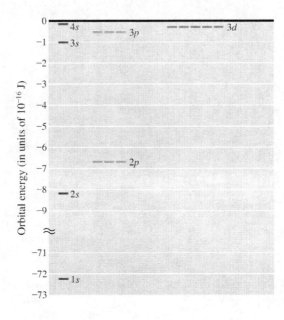

building-up order. You need the building-up order to predict the electron configurations of the ground states of atoms.

Now you can see how to reproduce the electron configurations of Table 8.1 using the building-up principle. Remember that the number of electrons in a neutral atom equals the atomic number Z. (The nuclear charge is +Z.) In the case of the simplest atom, hydrogen (Z = 1), you obtain the ground state by placing the single electron into the $1s$ orbital, giving the configuration $1s^1$ (this is read as "one-ess-one"). Now you go to helium (Z = 2). The first electron goes into the $1s$ orbital, as in hydrogen, followed by the second electron, because any orbital can hold two electrons. The configuration is $1s^2$. Filling the $n = 1$ shell creates a very stable configuration, and as a result, helium is chemically unreactive.

You continue this way through the elements, each time increasing Z by 1 and adding another electron. You obtain the configuration of an atom from that of the preceding element by adding an electron into the next available orbital, following the building-up order. In lithium (Z = 3), the first two electrons give the configuration $1s^2$, like helium, but the third electron goes into the next higher orbital in the building-up order, because the $1s$ orbital is now filled. This gives the configuration $1s^2 2s^1$. In beryllium (Z = 4), the fourth electron fills the $2s$ orbital, giving the configuration $1s^2 2s^2$.

Using the abbreviation [He] for $1s^2$, the configurations are

| Z = 3 | lithium | $1s^2 2s^1$ or [He]$2s^1$ |
| Z = 4 | beryllium | $1s^2 2s^2$ or [He]$2s^2$ |

With boron (Z = 5), the electrons begin filling the $2p$ subshell. You get

Z = 5	boron	$1s^2 2s^2 2p^1$ or [He]$2s^2 2p^1$
Z = 6	carbon	$1s^2 2s^2 2p^2$ or [He]$2s^2 2p^2$
⋮		
Z = 10	neon	$1s^2 2s^2 2p^6$ or [He]$2s^2 2p^6$

Having filled the $2p$ subshell, you again find a particularly stable configuration. Neon is chemically unreactive as a result.

With sodium (Z = 11), the $3s$ orbital begins to fill. Using the abbreviation [Ne] for $1s^2 2s^2 2p^6$, you have

| Z = 11 | sodium | $1s^2 2s^2 2p^6 3s^1$ or [Ne]$3s^1$ |
| Z = 12 | magnesium | $1s^2 2s^2 2p^6 3s^2$ or [Ne]$3s^2$ |

Then the $3p$ subshell begins to fill.

Z = 13	aluminum	$1s^2 2s^2 2p^6 3s^2 3p^1$ or [Ne]$3s^2 3p^1$
⋮		
Z = 18	argon	$1s^2 2s^2 2p^6 3s^2 3p^6$ or [Ne]$3s^2 3p^6$

Although the building-up order reproduces the ground-state electron configurations, it has no other significance. The order by n (and then by l within a given n), however, generally places the most easily ionized orbitals at the far right. For example, the electron configuration of Fe (in order by shells) is $1s^2 2s^2 2p^6 3s^2 3p^6 3d^6 4s^2$. The 4s electrons ionize first.

With the $3p$ subshell filled, a stable configuration has been attained; argon is an unreactive element.

Now the $4s$ orbital begins to fill. You get [Ar]$4s^1$ for potassium (Z = 19) and [Ar]$4s^2$ for calcium (Z = 20) ([Ar] = $1s^2 2s^2 2p^6 3s^2 3p^6$). At this point the $3d$ subshell begins to fill. You get [Ar]$3d^1 4s^2$ for scandium (Z = 21), [Ar]$3d^2 4s^2$ for titanium (Z = 22), and [Ar]$3d^3 4s^2$ for vanadium (Z = 23). *Note that we have written the configurations with subshells arranged in order by shells.* This generally places the subshells in order by energy and puts the subshells involved in chemical reactions at the far right. <

Let us skip to zinc (Z = 30). The $3d$ subshell has filled; the configuration is [Ar]$3d^{10} 4s^2$. Now the $4p$ subshell begins to fill, starting with gallium (Z = 31), configuration $[Ar]3d^{10}4s^24p^1$, and ending with krypton ($Z = 36$), configuration $[Ar]3d^{10}4s^24p^6$.

Electron Configurations and the Periodic Table

ChemWork: Writing Electron Configurations

ChemWork: Identifying Elements by Configurations

ChemWork: Modern Atomic Theory and Electron Configurations

By this time you can see a pattern develop among the ground-state electron configurations of the atoms. This pattern explains the periodic table, which was briefly described in Section 2.5. Consider helium, neon, argon, and krypton, elements in Group VIIIA of the periodic table. Neon, argon, and krypton have configurations in which a p subshell has just filled. (Helium has a filled $1s$ subshell; no $1p$ subshell is possible.)

helium	$1s^2$
neon	$1s^22s^22p^6$
argon	$1s^22s^22p^63s^23p^6$
krypton	$1s^22s^22p^63s^23p^63d^{10}4s^24p^6$

These elements are the first members of the group called *noble gases* because of their relative unreactivity.

Look now at the configurations of beryllium, magnesium, and calcium, members of the group of *alkaline earth metals* (Group IIA), which are similar, moderately reactive elements.

beryllium	$1s^22s^2$	or	$[He]2s^2$
magnesium	$1s^22s^22p^63s^2$	or	$[Ne]3s^2$
calcium	$1s^22s^22p^63s^23p^64s^2$	or	$[Ar]4s^2$

Each of these configurations consists of a **noble-gas core,** that is, *an inner-shell configuration corresponding to one of the noble gases,* plus two outer electrons with an ns^2 configuration.

The elements boron, aluminum, and gallium (Group IIIA) also have similarities. Their configurations are

boron	$1s^22s^22p^1$	or	$[He]2s^22p^1$
aluminum	$1s^22s^22p^63s^23p^1$	or	$[Ne]3s^23p^1$
gallium	$1s^22s^22p^63s^23p^63d^{10}4s^24p^1$	or	$[Ar]3d^{10}4s^24p^1$

Boron and aluminum have noble-gas cores plus three electrons with the configuration ns^2np^1. Gallium has an additional filled $3d$ subshell. *The noble-gas core together with $(n-1)d^{10}$ electrons is often referred to as a* **pseudo-noble-gas core,** because these electrons usually are not involved in chemical reactions.

An electron in an atom outside the noble-gas or pseudo-noble-gas core is called a **valence electron.** Such electrons are primarily involved in chemical reactions, and similarities among the configurations of valence electrons (the *valence-shell configurations*) account for similarities of the chemical properties among groups of elements.

Figure 8.9 shows a periodic table with the valence-shell configurations included. Note the similarity in electron configuration within any group (column) of elements. This similarity explains what chemists since Mendeleev have known—the properties of elements in any group are similar.

The *main-group* (or *representative*) *elements* all have valence-shell configurations ns^anp^b, with some choice of a and b. (b could be equal to 0.) In other words, the outer s or p subshell is being filled. Similarly, in the *d-block transition elements* (often called simply *transition elements* or *transition metals*), a d subshell is being filled. In the *f-block transition elements* (or *inner transition elements*), an

Main-Group Elements
s subshell fills

Transition Metals
d subshell fills

Main-Group Elements
p subshell fills

	Atomic number
1 H $1s^1$	Symbol
	Valence-shell configuration

Inner Transition Metals
f subshell fills

Lanthanides

Actinides

Main-group elements   Transition metals   Inner transition metals

FIGURE 8.9 ▲

A periodic table
This table shows the valence-shell configurations of the elements.

f subshell is being filled. (See Figure 8.9 or Appendix D for the configurations of these elements.)

Exceptions to the Building-Up Principle

There does not appear to be a simple explanation that is generally agreed on for why these configurations do not follow the building-up principle.

As we have said, the building-up principle reproduces most of the ground-state configurations correctly. There are some exceptions, however, and chromium ($Z = 24$) is the first we encounter. The building-up principle predicts the configuration $[Ar]3d^44s^2$, though the correct one is found experimentally to be $[Ar]3d^54s^1$. These two configurations are actually very close in total energy because of the closeness in energies of the $3d$ and $4s$ orbitals (Figure 8.8). For that reason, small effects can influence which of the two configurations is actually lower in energy. Copper ($Z = 29$) is another exception to the building-up principle, which predicts the configuration $[Ar]3d^94s^2$, although experiment shows the ground-state configuration to be $[Ar]3d^{10}4s^1$.

More exceptions occur among the heavier transition elements, where the outer subshells are very close together. We must concede that simplicity was not the uppermost concern in the construction of the universe!

We need not dwell on these exceptions beyond noting that they occur. The point to remember is that the configuration predicted by the building-up principle is very close in energy to the ground-state configuration (if it is not the ground state). Most of the qualitative conclusions regarding the chemistry of an element are not materially affected by arguing from the configuration given by the building-up principle. ◁

Instrumental Methods

X Rays, Atomic Numbers, and Orbital Structure (Photoelectron Spectroscopy)

In 1913 Henry G. J. Moseley, a student of Rutherford, used the technique of *x-ray spectroscopy* (just discovered by Max von Laue) to determine the atomic numbers of the elements. X rays are produced in a cathode-ray tube when the electron beam (cathode ray) falls on a metal target. The explanation for the production of x rays is as follows: When an electron in the cathode ray hits a metal atom in the target, it can (if it has sufficient energy) knock an electron from an inner shell of the atom. This produces a metal ion with an electron missing from an inner orbital. The electron configuration is unstable, and an electron from an orbital of higher energy drops into the half-filled orbital and a photon is emitted. The photon corresponds to electromagnetic radiation in the x-ray region.

The energies of the inner orbitals of an atom and the energy changes between them depend on the nuclear charge, +Z. Therefore, the photon energies $h\nu$ and the frequencies ν of emitted x rays depend on the atomic number Z of the metal atom in the target. Figure 8.10 shows the x-ray spectra Moseley obtained with various metal targets. The direct dependence of the x-ray spectrum on atomic number provides an unequivocal way of deciding whether a substance is a pure element or not.

A related technique, *x-ray photoelectron spectroscopy*, experimentally confirms our theoretical view of the orbital structure of the atom. Instead of irradiating a sample with an electron beam and analyzing the frequencies of emitted x rays, you irradiate a sample with x rays and analyze the kinetic energies of ejected electrons. In other words, you observe the *photoelectric effect* on the sample (see Section 7.2).

As an example of photoelectron spectroscopy, consider a sample of neon gas (Ne atoms). Suppose the sample

FIGURE 8.10 ▶

X-ray spectra of the elements calcium to zinc, obtained by Moseley

Each line results from an emission of given wavelength. Because of the volatility of zinc, Moseley used brass (a copper–zinc alloy) to observe the spectrum of zinc. Note the copper lines in brass. Also note how the lines progress to the right (indicating increasing wavelength or decreasing energy difference) with decreasing atomic number. (From J. J. Lagowski, *The Structure of Atoms* (Boston: Houghton Mifflin, 1964), Figure 26, p. 80. Used by permission.)

Wavelength ⟶

Concept Check 8.1

Imagine a world in which the Pauli principle is "No more than one electron can occupy an atomic orbital, irrespective of its spin." How many elements would there be in the second row of the periodic table, assuming that nothing else is different about this world?

8.3 | Writing Electron Configurations Using the Periodic Table

See Judith Strong, "The Periodic Table and Electron Configurations," *J. Chem. Educ.* 1986, 63, 834.

To discuss bonding and the chemistry of the elements coherently, you must be able to reproduce the atomic configurations with ease, following the building-up principle. All you need is some facility in recall of the building-up order of subshells.

is irradiated with x rays of a specific frequency great enough to remove a 1s electron from the neon atom. Part of the energy of the x-ray photon, $h\nu$, is used to remove the electron from the atom. (This is the *ionization energy, I.E.*, for that electron.) The remaining energy appears as kinetic energy, E_k, of the ejected electron. From the law of conservation of energy, you can write

$$E_k = h\nu - I.E.$$

Because $h\nu$ is fixed, E_k will depend linearly on *I.E.*, the ionization energy.

If you look at the electrons ejected from neon, you find that they have kinetic energies related to the ionization energies from all possible orbitals (1s, 2s, and 2p) in the atom. When you scan the various kinetic energies of ejected electrons, you see a spectrum with peaks corresponding to the different occupied orbitals (see Figure 8.11A). These ionization energies are approximately equal to the positive values of the orbital energies (Figure 8.11B), so this spectrum provides direct experimental verification of the discrete energy levels associated with the electrons of the atom.

FIGURE 8.11 ▲

X-ray photoelectron spectrum of neon

(A) Each peak shows the energy of the ejected electrons. The energy of each x-ray photon is 200.9×10^{-18} J. *(B)* The energy-level diagram for neon. The transitions that occur in the photoelectron spectrum are to $n = \infty$, where the energy $= 0$.

■ See Problems 8.87 and 8.88.

One approach is to recall the structure of the periodic table. Because that structure is basic, it offers a sound way to remember the building-up order. There is a definite pattern to the order of filling of the subshells as you go through the elements in the periodic table, and from this you can write the building-up order. Figure 8.12 shows a periodic table stressing this pattern. For example, in the violet-colored area, an *ns* subshell is being filled. In the blue-colored area, an *np* subshell is being filled. The value of *n* is obtained from the period (row) number. In the red area, an $(n - 1)d$ subshell is being filled.

You read the building-up order by starting with the first period, in which the 1s subshell is being filled. In the second period, you have 2s (violet area); then, staying in the same period but jumping across, you have 2p (blue area). In the third period, you have 3s and 3p; in the fourth period, 4s (violet area), 3d (red area), and 4p (blue area). This

FIGURE 8.12
A periodic table illustrating the building-up order
The colored areas of elements show the different subshells that are filling with those elements.

pattern should become clear enough to visualize with a periodic table that is not labeled with the subshells, such as the one on the inside front cover of this book. The detailed method is illustrated in the next example. (An alternative way to reconstruct the building-up order of subshells is to write the diagram in Figure 8.7.)

> *Note on writing electron configurations of atoms:* If you write the configuration of an atom with its subshells arranged by shells, the orbitals will usually be in order by energy, with the subshells used to describe chemical reactions at the far right. For example, the configuration of Br would be written $[Ar]3d^{10}4s^24p^5$. However, you will also see the orbitals in a configuration written in the building-up order, which is an empirical order that has been found to reproduce most of the atomic configurations. The configuration of Br would be written $[Ar]4s^23d^{10}4p^5$. Ask your instructor whether he or she has a preference.

ChemWork: Electron Configurations

Example 8.2 | Determining the Configuration of an Atom Using the Building-Up Principle

Use the building-up principle to obtain the configuration for the ground state of the gallium atom (Z = 31). Give the configuration in complete form (do not abbreviate for the core). What is the valence-shell configuration?

Problem Strategy Write the subshells in their building-up order. You can use any periodic table to do this. All you have to remember is the pattern in which subshells are filled as you progress through the table (Figure 8.12). Go through the periods, starting with hydrogen, writing the subshells that are being filled, and stopping with the element whose configuration you want (gallium in this example). Then you distribute the electrons (equal to the atomic number of the element) to the subshells. The valence-shell configuration includes only the subshells outside the noble-gas or pseudo-noble-gas core.

Solution From a periodic table, you get the following building-up order:

	1s	2s 2p	3s 3p	4s 3d 4p
Period:	first	second	third	fourth

Now you fill the subshells with electrons, remembering that you have a total of 31 electrons to distribute. You get

$$1s^22s^22p^63s^23p^64s^23d^{10}4p^1$$

Or, if you rearrange the subshells by shells, you write

$$\mathbf{1s^22s^22p^63s^23p^63d^{10}4s^24p^1}$$

The valence-shell configuration is $\mathbf{4s^24p^1}$.

(continued)

(continued)

Answer Check The principal quantum number of the valence shell must equal the period of the element. If your answer is not consistent with this, examine your work for error. Here, gallium is in period 4, and the principal quantum number of the valence shell is 4.

An alternative example is provided in the Instructor's Resource Manual.

Exercise 8.2 Use the building-up principle to obtain the electron configuration for the ground state of the manganese atom (Z = 25).

■ See Problems 8.47, 8.48, 8.49, and 8.50.

In many cases, you need only the configuration of the outer electrons. You can determine this from the position of the element in the periodic table. Recall that the valence-shell configuration of a main-group element is $ns^a np^b$, where n, the principal quantum number of the outer shell, also equals the period number for the element. The total number of valence electrons, which equals $a + b$, can be obtained from the group number. For example, gallium is in Period 4, so $n = 4$. It is in Group IIIA, so the number of valence electrons is 3. This gives the valence-shell configuration $4s^2 4p^1$. The configuration of outer shells of a transition element is obtained in a similar fashion. The next example gives the details.

Example 8.3 Determining the Configuration of an Atom Using the Period and Group Numbers

What are the configurations for the outer electrons of a. tellurium, Z = 52, and b. nickel, Z = 28?

Problem Strategy Find the period and the group number (the Roman numeral) of the element for the atom. Note whether it is a main-group or a transition element.

If the atom is that of a main-group element, the valence configuration is $ns^a np^b$, where n equals the period of the element and $a + b$ equals the group number (which equals the number of valence electrons). Distribute these electrons to the ns orbital; then distribute any remaining electrons to the np orbitals.

If the atom is that of a transition element, the outer-shell configuration is $(n - 1)d^{a-2} ns^2$, where n equals the period and a is the group number—except for Group VIIIB, which has three columns. For Group VIIIB, count 8, 9, then 10 for successive columns, which then equals a.

Solution a. You locate tellurium in a periodic table and find it to be in Period 5, Group VIA. Thus, it is a main-group element, and the outer subshells are $5s$ and $5p$. These subshells contain six electrons, because the group is VIA. The valence-shell configuration is $5s^2 5p^4$.
b. Nickel is a Period 4 transition element, in which

the general form of the outer-shell configuration is $3d^{a-2} 4s^2$. To determine a, you note that it equals the Roman numeral group number up to iron (8). After that you count Co as 9 and Ni as 10. Hence, the outer-shell configuration is $3d^8 4s^2$.

Answer Check Note whether the configuration does follow the general form, either for a main-group element or a transition element. Check that the principal quantum number, n, equals the period of the element. For a main-group element, the total number of valence electrons should equal the group number. For a transition element, the number of electrons in the outer shell equals a.

Exercise 8.3 Using the periodic table on the inside front cover, write the valence-shell configuration of arsenic (As).

■ See Problems 8.51, 8.52, 8.53, and 8.54.

Exercise 8.4 The lead atom has the ground-state configuration $[Xe]4f^{14}5d^{10}6s^2 6p^2$. Find the period and group for this element. From its position in the periodic table, would you classify lead as a main-group element, a transition element, or an inner transition element?

■ See Problems 8.55 and 8.56.

An alternative example is provided in the Instructor's Resource Manual.

Concept Check 8.2

Two elements in Period 3 are adjacent to one another in the periodic table. The ground-state atom of one element has only *s* electrons in its valence shell; the other one has at least one *p* electron in its valence shell. Identify the elements.

8.4 | Orbital Diagrams of Atoms; Hund's Rule

In discussing the ground states of atoms, we have not yet described how the electrons are arranged within each subshell. There may be several different ways of arranging electrons in a particular configuration. Consider the carbon atom ($Z = 6$) with the ground-state configuration $1s^2 2s^2 2p^2$. Three possible arrangements are given in the following orbital diagrams.

These orbital diagrams show different states of the carbon atom. Each state has a different energy and, as you will see, different magnetic characteristics.

Hund's Rule

In about 1927, Friedrich Hund discovered an empirical rule determining the lowest-energy arrangement of electrons in a subshell. **Hund's rule** states that *the lowest-energy arrangement of electrons in a subshell is obtained by putting electrons into separate orbitals of the subshell with the same spin before pairing electrons.* Let us see how this would apply to the carbon atom, whose ground-state configuration is $1s^2 2s^2 2p^2$. The first four electrons go into the $1s$ and $2s$ orbitals.

The next two electrons go into separate $2p$ orbitals, with both electrons having the same spin, following Hund's rule.

We see that the orbital diagram corresponding to the lowest energy is the one we previously labeled Diagram 1.

To apply Hund's rule to the oxygen atom, whose ground-state configuration is $1s^2 2s^2 2p^4$, we place the first seven electrons as follows:

The last electron is paired with one of the $2p$ electrons to give a doubly occupied orbital. The orbital diagram for the ground state of the oxygen atom is

In the following example, Hund's rule is used to determine the orbital diagram for the ground state of a more complicated atom. Table 8.2 gives orbital diagrams for the ground states of the first ten elements.

Example 8.4	Applying Hund's Rule

Write an orbital diagram for the ground state of the iron atom.

Problem Strategy First obtain the electron configuration, as described in Example 8.2. Then draw circles for the orbitals of each subshell. A filled subshell should have doubly occupied orbitals (two electrons with opposite spins). For a partially filled subshell, apply Hund's rule, putting electrons into separate orbitals with the same spin (either all up or all down) before pairing electrons.

Solution The electron configuration of the iron atom is $1s^2 2s^2 2p^6 3s^2 3p^6 3d^6 4s^2$. All the subshells except the $3d$ are filled. In placing the six electrons in the $3d$ subshell, you note that the first five go into separate $3d$ orbitals with their spin arrows in the same direction. The sixth

electron must doubly occupy a $3d$ orbital. The orbital diagram is

You can write this diagram in abbreviated form using [Ar] for the argon-like core of the iron atom:

Answer Check Check that you have started with the correct configuration for the atom. Then note that you have followed Hund's rule for a partially filled subshell.

Exercise 8.5   Write an orbital diagram for the ground state of the phosphorus atom ($Z = 15$). Write all orbitals.

An alternative example is provided in the Instructor's Resource Manual.

■ See Problems 8.57 and 8.58.

TABLE 8.2	Orbital Diagrams for the Ground States of Atoms from $Z = 1$ to $Z = 10$				
				Orbital Diagram	
Atom	Z	Configuration	$1s$	$2s$	$2p$
Hydrogen	1	$1s^1$	⊙	○	○○○
Helium	2	$1s^2$	⊙	○	○○○
Lithium	3	$1s^2 2s^1$	⊙	⊙	○○○
Beryllium	4	$1s^2 2s^2$	⊙	⊙	○○○
Boron	5	$1s^2 2s^2 2p^1$	⊙	⊙	⊙○○
Carbon	6	$1s^2 2s^2 2p^2$	⊙	⊙	⊙⊙○
Nitrogen	7	$1s^2 2s^2 2p^3$	⊙	⊙	⊙⊙⊙
Oxygen	8	$1s^2 2s^2 2p^4$	⊙	⊙	⊙⊙⊙
Fluorine	9	$1s^2 2s^2 2p^5$	⊙	⊙	⊙⊙⊙
Neon	10	$1s^2 2s^2 2p^6$	⊙	⊙	⊙⊙⊙

ChemWork: Unpaired Electrons

Demonstrations on paramagnetism with an electronic balance, *J. Chem. Educ.* 75 (1998): 61.

Observation of magnetic repulsion acting on nitrogen bubble on water surface—A simple experiment of studying diamagnetic property of nitrogen, *J. Chem. Educ.* 74 (1997): 943.

Magnetic Properties of Atoms

The magnetic properties of a substance can reveal certain information about the arrangement of electrons in an atom (or molecule). Although an electron in an atom behaves like a small magnet, the magnetic attractions from two electrons that are opposite in spin cancel each other. As a result, an atom that has only doubly occupied orbitals has no net spin magnetism. However, an atom with *unpaired* electrons—that is, with an excess of one kind of spin—does exhibit a net magnetism.

A Chemist Looks at . . .

frontiers

Levitating Frogs and People

Have you ever seen a magic act in which a person rises above the stage in apparent defiance of gravity? Magicians have often included such acts of "levitation" as part of their performances. Of course, magical levitation uses tricks to deceive you. But levitation can be done, without tricks, using the known laws of electromagnetism.

Recently, researchers wanted to demonstrate that you can levitate almost anything if you have the proper magnetic field. They placed a frog within the magnetic field of a powerful electromagnet (which consists of an electric current flowing through a coil of wire). The frog floated in midair above the coil, at the point where the upward repulsion of the frog from the magnetic field just balanced the downward force of gravity (Figure 8.13).

We don't usually think of things such as frogs as being magnetic. In fact, most materials, including most substances in a biological organism, are diamagnetic. They contain pairs of electrons, in which the magnetism of each electron in a pair offsets the equal and opposite magnetism of the other electron. You might expect diamagnetic materials to be nonmagnetic because of this balance of opposite electron spins. But when you place a diamagnetic material in an external magnetic field, its electrons move so as to induce, or generate, a smaller magnetic field that is opposite in direction to the external field. This results in a repulsive force between the diamagnetic material and the external field. The repulsive force, though generally small, can be easily observed if the external magnet is large enough. Although, with a sufficiently large magnet, it would be possible to levitate a person as well as a frog, the researchers don't plan to do that.

FIGURE 8.13 ▲

Levitation of a frog

A frog placed in a powerful magnetic field, generated by a current flowing through a water-cooled coil of wire, appears to float in midair in defiance of gravity. The frog contains materials that are diamagnetic (composed of electron pairs), which are repelled by the magnetic field.

■ See Problems 8.89 and 8.90.

The strong, permanent magnetism seen in iron objects is called ferromagnetism *and is due to the cooperative alignment of electron spins in many iron atoms. Paramagnetism is a much weaker effect. Nevertheless, paramagnetic substances can be attracted to a strong magnet. Liquid oxygen is composed of paramagnetic O_2 molecules. When poured over a magnet, the liquid clings to the poles. (See Figure 10.29.)*

The magnetic properties of an atom can be observed. The most direct way is to determine whether the atomic substance is attracted to the field of a strong magnet. A **paramagnetic substance** is *a substance that is weakly attracted by a magnetic field, and this attraction is generally the result of unpaired electrons.* < For example, sodium vapor has been found experimentally to be paramagnetic. The explanation is that the vapor consists primarily of sodium atoms, each containing an unpaired electron. (The configuration is $[Ne]3s^1$.) A **diamagnetic substance** is *a substance that is not attracted by a magnetic field or is very slightly repelled by such a field. This property generally means that the substance has only paired electrons.* Mercury vapor is found experimentally to be diamagnetic. The explanation is that mercury vapor consists of mercury atoms, with the electron configuration $[Xe]4f^{14}5d^{10}6s^2$, which has only paired electrons.

We expect the different orbital diagrams presented at the beginning of this section for the $1s^22s^22p^2$ configuration of the carbon atom to have different magnetic properties. Diagram 1, predicted by Hund's rule to be the ground state, would give a magnetic atom, whereas the other diagrams would not. If we could prepare a vapor of carbon atoms, it should be attracted to a magnet. (It should be paramagnetic.) It is difficult to prepare a vapor of free carbon atoms in sufficient concentration to observe a result. However, the visible–ultraviolet spectrum of carbon atoms can be obtained easily from dilute vapor. From an analysis of this spectrum, it is possible to show that the ground-state atom is magnetic, which is consistent with the prediction of Hund's rule.

Periodicity of the Elements

You have seen that the periodic table that Mendeleev discovered in 1869 can be explained by the periodicity of the ground-state electron configurations of the atoms. Now we will look at various aspects of the periodicity of the elements.

8.5 | Mendeleev's Predictions from the Periodic Table

One of Mendeleev's periodic tables is reproduced in Figure 8.14. Though somewhat different from modern tables, it shows essentially the same arrangement. In this early form of the periodic table, within each column some elements were placed toward the left side and some toward the right. With some exceptions, the elements on a given side have similar properties. Mendeleev left spaces in his periodic table for what he felt were undiscovered elements. There are blank spaces in his row 5—for example, one directly under aluminum and another under silicon (looking at just the elements on the right side of the column). By writing the known elements in this row with their atomic weights, he could determine approximate values (between the known ones) for the missing elements (values in parentheses).

Cu	Zn	—	—	As	Se	Br
63 amu	65 amu	(68 amu)	(72 amu)	75 amu	78 amu	80 amu

The Group III element directly under aluminum Mendeleev called eka-aluminum, with the symbol Ea. (*Eka* is the Sanskrit word meaning "first"; thus eka-aluminum is the first element under aluminum.) The known Group III elements have oxides of the form R_2O_3, so Mendeleev predicted that eka-aluminum would have an oxide with the formula Ea_2O_3.

The physical properties of this undiscovered element could be predicted by comparing values for the neighboring known elements. For eka-aluminum Mendeleev

FIGURE 8.14 ▶

Mendeleev's periodic table

This one was published in 1872.

Reihen	Gruppe I. — R^2O	Gruppe II. — RO	Gruppe III. — R^2O^3	Gruppe IV. RH⁴ RO^2	Gruppe V. RH³ R^2O^5	Gruppe VI. RH² RO^3	Gruppe VII. RH R^2O^7	Gruppe VIII. — RO^4
1	H=1							
2	Li=7	Be=9,4	B=11	C=12	N=14	O=16	F=19	
3	Na=23	Mg=24	Al=27,3	Si=28	P=31	S=32	Cl=35,5	
4	K=39	Ca=40	—=44	Ti=48	V=51	Cr=52	Mn=55	Fe=56, Co=59, Ni=59, Cu=63.
5	(Cu=63)	Zn=65	—=68	—=72	As=75	Se=78	Br=80	
6	Rb=85	Sr=87	?Yt=88	Zr=90	Nb=94	Mo=96	—=100	Ru=104, Rh=104, Pd=106, Ag=108.
7	(Ag=108)	Cd=112	In=113	Sn=118	Sb=122	Te=125	J=127	
8	Cs=133	Ba=137	?Di=138	?Ce=140	—	—	—	— — —
9	(—)							
10	—		?Er=178	?La=180	Ta=182	W=184	—	Os=195, Ir=197, Pt=198, Au=199.
11	(Au=199)	Hg=200	Tl=204	Pb=207	Bi=208			
12	—	—	—	Th=231		U=240	—	— — —

Tabelle II.

predicted a density of 5.9 g/cm³, a low *melting point* (the temperature at which a substance melts), and a high *boiling point* (the temperature at which a substance boils).

In 1874 the French chemist Paul-Émile Lecoq de Boisbaudran found two previously unidentified lines in the atomic spectrum of a sample of sphalerite (a zinc sulfide, ZnS, mineral). Realizing he was on the verge of a discovery, Lecoq de Boisbaudran quickly prepared a large batch of the zinc mineral, from which he isolated a gram of a new element. He called this new element gallium. The properties of gallium were remarkably close to those Mendeleev predicted for eka-aluminum.

Property	Predicted for Eka-Aluminum	Found for Gallium
Atomic weight	68 amu	69.7 amu
Formula of oxide	Ea_2O_3	Ga_2O_3
Density of the element	5.9 g/cm³	5.91 g/cm³
Melting point of the element	Low	30.1°C
Boiling point of the element	High	1983°C

The predictive power of Mendeleev's periodic table was demonstrated again when scandium (eka-boron) was discovered in 1879 and germanium (eka-silicon) in 1886. Both elements had properties remarkably like those predicted by Mendeleev. These early successes won acceptance for the organizational and predictive power of the periodic table.

8.6 | Some Periodic Properties

ChemWork: Periodic Trends in Atomic Radii

ChemWork: Comparing Atomic Radii

ChemWork: Atomic Size

The electron configurations of the atoms display a periodic variation with increasing atomic number (nuclear charge). As a result, the elements show periodic variations of physical and chemical behavior. The **periodic law** states that *when the elements are arranged by atomic number, their physical and chemical properties vary periodically.* In this section, we will look at three physical properties of an atom: atomic radius, ionization energy, and electron affinity. These three quantities, especially ionization energy and electron affinity, are important in discussions of chemical bonding (the subject of Chapter 9).

Atomic Radius

An atom does not have a definite size, because the statistical distribution of electrons does not abruptly end but merely decreases to very small values as the distance from the nucleus increases. This can be seen in the plot of the electron distribution for the argon atom, shown in Figure 8.15. Consequently, atomic size must be defined in a somewhat arbitrary manner, so various measures of atomic size exist. The atomic radii plotted in Figure 8.16 and also represented in Figure 8.17 are *covalent radii*, which are obtained from measurements of distances between the nuclei of atoms in the chemical bonds of molecular substances. (The determination and use of covalent radii are discussed in Chapter 9.)

Figures 8.16 and 8.17 show the following general trends in size of atomic radii:

1. Within each period (horizontal row), the atomic radius tends to decrease with increasing atomic number (nuclear charge). The largest atom in a period is a Group IA atom and the smallest is a noble-gas atom.

2. Within each group (vertical column), the atomic radius tends to increase with the period number.

FIGURE 8.15 ▲

Electron distribution for the argon atom
This is a radial distribution, showing the probability of finding an electron at a given distance from the nucleus. The distribution shows three maxima, for the $n = 1$, $n = 2$, and $n = 3$ shells. The outermost maximum occurs at 66 pm; then the distribution falls steadily, becoming negligibly small after several hundred picometers.

FIGURE 8.16

Atomic radius (covalent radius) versus atomic number
Note that the curve is periodic (tends to repeat). Each period of elements begins with the Group IA atom, and the atomic radius tends to decrease until the Group VIIIA atom. (Values for He, Ne, and Ar are estimated because there are no known compounds.)

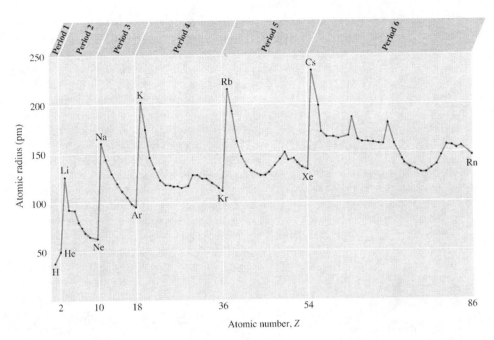

The atomic radius increases greatly going from any noble-gas atom to the following Group IA atom, giving the curve in Figure 8.16 a saw-tooth appearance. A similar diagram is obtained for other measures of atomic size.

These general trends in atomic radius can be explained if you look at the two factors that primarily determine the size of the outermost orbital. One factor is the principal quantum number n of the orbital; the larger n is, the larger the size of the orbital. The other factor is the effective nuclear charge acting on an electron in the orbital;

FIGURE 8.17

Representation of atomic radii (covalent radii) of the main-group elements
Note the trends within each period and each group.

increasing the effective nuclear charge reduces the size of the orbital by pulling the electrons inward. The **effective nuclear charge** is *the positive charge that an electron experiences from the nucleus, equal to the nuclear charge but reduced by any shielding or screening from any intervening electron distribution.* Consider the effective nuclear charge on the $2s$ electron in the lithium atom (configuration $1s^2 2s^1$). The nuclear charge is $3e$, but the effect of this charge on the $2s$ electron is reduced by the distribution of the two $1s$ electrons lying between the nucleus and the $2s$ electron (roughly, each core electron reduces the nuclear charge by $1e$).

Consider a given period of elements. The principal quantum number of the outer orbitals remains constant. However, the effective nuclear charge increases, because the nuclear charge increases and the number of core electrons remains constant. Consequently, the size of the outermost orbital and, therefore, the radius of the atom decrease with increasing Z in any period.

Now consider a given column of elements. The effective nuclear charge remains nearly constant (approximately equal to e times the number of valence electrons), but n gets larger. You observe that the atomic radius increases.

ChemWork: Identifying Elements by Atomic Properties

ChemWork: Atomic Properties

ChemWork: Comparing Atomic Properties

Example 8.5	Determining Relative Atomic Sizes from Periodic Trends

Refer to a periodic table and use the trends noted for size of atomic radii to arrange the following in order of increasing atomic radius: Al, C, Si.

Problem Strategy The general trends in atomic radius are that it decreases left to right in a period and that it increases from top to bottom of a group. Compare any two elements in the same period, or in the same group, to decide which of the two is smaller. From this, decide the order of the elements.

Solution Note that C is above Si in Group IVA. Therefore, the radius of C is smaller than that of Si (the

atomic radius increases going down a group of elements). Note that Al and Si are in the same period. Therefore, the radius of Si is smaller than that of Al (radius decreases with Z in a period). Hence the order of elements by increasing radius is **C, Si, Al.**

Answer Check After you have decided on the order of the atoms, check that the atomic radius does indeed increase, left to right, as asked for in the problem.

Exercise 8.6 Using a periodic table, arrange the following in order of increasing atomic radius: Na, Be, Mg.

An alternative example is provided in the Instructor's Resource Manual.

■ See Problems 8.61 and 8.62.

ChemWork: Periodic Trends for First Ionization Energies

ChemWork: Comparing Ionization Energies

ChemWork: Ionization Energies of Atoms

Ionization Energy

The **first ionization energy** (or **first ionization potential**) of an atom is *the minimum energy needed to remove the highest-energy (that is, the outermost) electron from the neutral atom in the gaseous state.* (When the unqualified term *ionization energy* is used, it generally means first ionization energy.) For the lithium atom, the first ionization energy is the energy needed for the following process (electron configurations are in parentheses):

$$\text{Li}(1s^2 2s^1) \longrightarrow \text{Li}^+(1s^2) + e^-$$

Values of this energy are usually quoted for one mole of atoms (6.02×10^{23} atoms). The ionization energy of the lithium atom is 520 kJ/mol. <

Ionization energies display a periodic variation when plotted against atomic number, as Figure 8.18 shows. Within any period, values tend to increase with atomic number. Thus, the lowest values in a period are found for the Group IA elements *(alkali metals).* It is characteristic of reactive metals such as these to lose electrons easily. The

Ionization energies are often measured in electron volts (eV). This is the amount of energy imparted to an electron when it is accelerated through an electrical potential of one volt. One electron volt is equivalent to 96.5 kJ/mol. (This is an easy conversion to remember; it is approximately one hundred kilojoules per mole.)

FIGURE 8.18 ▶

Ionization energy versus atomic number

Top: Note that the values tend to increase within each period, except for small drops in ionization energy at the Group IIIA and VIA elements. Large drops occur when a new period begins. *Bottom:* Note the trends within each period. The size of the sphere for each atom indicates the relative magnitude of ionization energy.

largest ionization energies in any period occur for the noble-gas elements. In other words, a noble-gas atom loses electrons with difficulty, which is partly responsible for the stability of the noble-gas configurations and the unreactivity of the noble gases.

This general trend—increasing ionization energy with atomic number in a given period—can be explained as follows: The energy needed to remove an electron from the outer shell is proportional to the effective nuclear charge divided by the average distance between electron and nucleus. (This distance is inversely proportional to the effective nuclear charge.) Hence, the ionization energy is proportional to the square of the effective nuclear charge and increases going across a period.

Small deviations from this general trend occur. A IIIA element (ns^2np^1) has smaller ionization energy than the preceding IIA element (ns^2). Apparently, the np electron of the IIIA element is more easily removed than one of the ns electrons of the preceding IIA element. Also note that a VIA element (ns^2np^4) has smaller ionization energy than the preceding VA element. As a result of electron repulsion, it is easier to remove an electron from the doubly occupied np orbital of the VIA element than from a singly occupied orbital of the preceding VA element.

Ionization energies tend to decrease going down any column of main-group elements. This is because atomic size increases going down the column.

Example 8.6 | Determining Relative Ionization Energies from Periodic Trends

Using a periodic table only, arrange the following elements in order of increasing ionization energy: Ar, Se, S.

Problem Strategy The general trends in (first) ionization energy are that it increases from left to right in a period and that it decreases from top to bottom of a group. Compare any two elements in the same period, or in the same group, to decide which of the two is smaller. From this, decide the order of the elements.

Solution Note that Se is below S in Group VIA. Therefore, the ionization energy of Se should be less than that of S. Also, S and Ar are in the same period,

with Z increasing from S to Ar. Therefore, the ionization energy of S should be less than that of Ar. Hence the order is **Se, S, Ar.**

Answer Check After you have decided on the order of the atoms, check that the ionization energy does indeed increase, left to right, as asked for in the problem.

Exercise 8.7   The first ionization energy of the chlorine atom is 1251 kJ/mol. Without looking at Figure 8.18, state which of the following values would be the more likely ionization energy for the iodine atom. Explain. a. 1000 kJ/mol. b. 1400 kJ/mol.

An alternative example is provided in the Instructor's Resource Manual.

■ See Problems 8.63 and 8.64.

The electrons of an atom can be removed successively. The energies required at each step are known as the *first* ionization energy, the *second* ionization energy, and so forth. Table 8.3 lists the successive ionization energies of the first ten elements. Note that the ionization energies for a given element increase as more electrons are removed. The first and second ionization energies of beryllium (electron configuration $1s^22s^2$) are 899 kJ/mol and 1757 kJ/mol, respectively. The first ionization energy

TABLE 8.3	Successive Ionization Energies of the First Ten Elements (kJ/mol)*						
Element	First	Second	Third	Fourth	Fifth	Sixth	Seventh
H	1312						
He	2372	5250					
Li	520	7298	11,815				
Be	899	1757	14,848	21,006			
B	801	2427	3660	25,025	32,826		
C	1086	2353	4620	6222	37,829	47,276	
N	1402	2857	4578	7475	9445	53,265	64,358
O	1314	3388	5300	7469	10,989	13,326	71,333
F	1681	3374	6020	8407	11,022	15,164	17,867
Ne	2081	3952	6122	9370	12,177	15,238	19,998

*Ionization energies to the right of a vertical line correspond to removal of electrons from the core of the atom.

is the energy needed to remove a $2s$ electron from the Be atom. The second ionization energy is the energy needed to remove a $2s$ electron from the positive ion Be^{+}. Its value is greater than that of the first ionization energy because the electron is being removed from a positive ion, which strongly attracts the electron.

Note that there is a large jump in value from the second ionization energy of Be (1757 kJ/mol) to the third ionization energy (14,848 kJ/mol). The second ionization energy corresponds to removing a valence electron (from the $2s$ orbital), which is relatively easy. The third ionization energy corresponds to removing an electron from the core of the atom (from the $1s$ orbital)—that is, from a noble-gas configuration ($1s^2$). A vertical line in Table 8.3 separates the energies needed to remove valence electrons from those needed to remove core electrons. For each element, a large increase in ionization energy occurs when this line is crossed. The large increase results from the fact that once the valence electrons are removed, a stable noble-gas configuration is obtained. Further ionizations become much more difficult. We will see in Chapter 9 that metal atoms often form compounds by losing valence electrons; core electrons are not significantly involved in the formation of compounds.

Electron Affinity

When a neutral atom in the gaseous state picks up an electron to form a stable negative ion, energy is released. For example, a chlorine atom can pick up an electron to give a chloride ion, Cl^{-}, and 349 kJ/mol of energy is released. You write the process as follows, with electron configurations noted in parentheses:

$$Cl([Ne]3s^2 3p^5) + e^- \longrightarrow Cl^-([Ne]3s^2 3p^6)$$

The **electron affinity** is *the energy change for the process of adding an electron to a neutral atom in the gaseous state to form a negative ion.* If the negative ion is stable (does not spontaneously disintegrate into the neutral atom and free electron), the energy change for its formation is a negative number. Thus, the electron affinity of Cl is -349 kJ/mol. Large negative numbers such as this indicate that a very stable negative ion is formed. Small negative numbers indicate that a less stable ion is formed. Table 8.4 gives the electron affinities of the main-group elements. <

Electron affinities are also defined with positive values for the formation of stable ions.

TABLE 8.4	Electron Affinities of the Main-Group Elements (kJ/mol)*					
Period	IA	IIIA	IVA	VA	VIA	VIIA
1	H −73					
2	Li −60	B −27	C −122	N 0	O −141	F −328
3	Na −53	, Al −44	Si −134	P −72	S −200	Cl −349
4	K −48	Ga −30	Ge −120	As −77	Se −195	Br −325
5	Rb −47	In −30	Sn −121	Sb −101	Te −190	I −295
6	Cs −45	Tl −30	Pb −110	Bi −110	Po −180	At −270

*Atoms of the alkaline earth metals (Group IIA) and the noble gases (Group VIIIA) do not form stable negative ions.

Electron affinities, *E.A.*, have a periodic variation, just as atomic radii and ionization energies do, though somewhat more complicated. To see this variation, consider each of the main groups of elements beginning with Group IA. All of the Group IA elements have small negative electron affinities. When you add an electron to a lithium atom, for example, it goes into the $2s$ orbital to form a moderately stable negative ion, releasing energy.

$$\text{Li}(1s^22s^1) + e^- \longrightarrow \text{Li}^-(1s^22s^2); \; E.A. = -60 \text{ kJ/mol}$$

None of the Group IIA elements form stable negative ions; that is, the electron affinities of these elements are positive. Each of the atoms has a filled ns subshell, so that if you were to add an electron, it would have to go into the next higher energy subshell (np). Instead of releasing energy, the atom would absorb energy. For example,

$$\text{Be}(1s^22s^2) + e^- \longrightarrow \text{Be}^-(1s^22s^22p^1); \; E.A. > 0$$

(For a similar reason, the Group VIIIA elements also do not form stable negative ions.)

From Group IIIA to Group VIIA, the added electron goes into the np subshell of the valence shell. With the exception of the Group VA elements, the electron affinities tend toward more negative values as you progress to the right through these elements in any period (more energy is released and stabler negative ions are formed). The electron affinity of a Group VA element is generally less negative than the preceding Group IVA element. Note the trend in electron affinities in the following:

$$\text{B}(1s^22s^22p^1) + e^- \longrightarrow \text{B}^-(1s^22s^22p^2); \; E.A. = -27 \text{ kJ/mol}$$
$$\text{C}(1s^22s^22p^2) + e^- \longrightarrow \text{C}^-(1s^22s^22p^3); \; E.A. = -122 \text{ kJ/mol}$$
$$\text{N}(1s^22s^22p^3) + e^- \longrightarrow \text{N}^-(1s^22s^22p^4); \; E.A. = 0 \text{ kJ/mol}$$
$$\text{O}(1s^22s^22p^4) + e^- \longrightarrow \text{O}^-(1s^22s^22p^5); \; E.A. = -141 \text{ kJ/mol}$$
$$\text{F}(1s^22s^22p^5) + e^- \longrightarrow \text{F}^-(1s^22s^22p^6); \; E.A. = -328 \text{ kJ/mol}$$

Broadly speaking, the general trend is toward more negative electron affinities from left to right in any period. Note especially that the Group VIA and Group VIIA elements have the largest negative electron affinities of any of the main-group elements. Therefore, these elements have compounds containing monatomic anions (such as F^- and O^{2-}).

Exercise 8.8   Without looking at Table 8.4 but using the general comments in this section, decide which has the larger negative electron affinity, C or F.

■ See Problems 8.65 and 8.66.

Concept Check 8.3

Given the following information for element E, identify the element's group in the periodic table: The electron affinity of E is positive (that is, it does not form a stable negative ion). The first ionization energy of E is less than the second ionization energy, which in turn is very much less than its third ionization energy.

8.7 | Periodicity in the Main-Group Elements

Experiments in General Chemistry, 8, "Solubilities within a Family."

The chemical and physical properties of the main-group elements clearly display periodic character. For instance, as pointed out in Section 2.5, the metallic elements lie to the left of the "staircase" line in the periodic table (see inside front cover), nonmetals lie to the right, and the metalloids (with intermediate characteristics) lie along this line. So, as you move left to right in any row of the periodic table, the metallic character of the elements decreases. As you progress down a column, however, the elements tend to increase in metallic character.

These variations of metallic–nonmetallic character can be attributed in part to variations in the ionization energies of the corresponding atoms. Elements with low ionization energy tend to be metallic, whereas those with high ionization energy tend to be nonmetallic. As you saw in the previous section, ionization energy is a periodic property, so it is not surprising that the metallic–nonmetallic character of an element is similarly periodic.

The basic–acidic behavior of the oxides of the elements is a good indicator of the metallic–nonmetallic character of the elements. Oxides are classified as basic or acidic depending on their reactions with acids and bases. A **basic oxide** is *an oxide that reacts with acids.* Most metal oxides are basic. An **acidic oxide** is *an oxide that reacts with bases.* Most nonmetal oxides are acidic oxides. An **amphoteric oxide** is *an oxide that has both basic and acidic properties.*

In the following brief descriptions of the main-group elements, we will note the metallic–nonmetallic behavior of the elements, as well as the basic–acidic character of the oxides. Although elements in a given group are expected to be similar, the degree of similarity does vary among the groups. The alkali metals (Group IA) show marked similarities, as do the halogens (Group VIIA). On the other hand, the Group IVA elements range from a nonmetal (carbon) at the top of the column to a metal (lead) at the bottom. In either case, however, the changes from one element in a column to the next lower one are systematic, and the periodic table helps us to correlate these systematic changes.

Demonstration of reactivity of metals with water: see the Instructor's Resource Manual, under lecture demonstrations for Chapter 8.

Hydrogen ($1s^1$)

Although the electron configuration of hydrogen would seem to place the element in Group IA, its properties are quite different, and it seems best to consider this element as belonging in a group by itself. The element is a colorless gas composed of H_2 molecules. <

At very high pressures, however, hydrogen is believed to have metallic properties.

Group IA Elements, the Alkali Metals (ns^1)

The *alkali metals* are soft and reactive, with the reactivities increasing as you move down the column of elements. All of the metals react with water to produce hydrogen.

$$2Li(s) + 2H_2O(l) \longrightarrow 2LiOH(aq) + H_2(g)$$

The vigor of the reaction increases from lithium (moderate) to rubidium (violent). All of the alkali metals form basic oxides with the general formula R_2O.

Group IIA Elements, the Alkaline Earth Metals (ns^2)

The *alkaline earth metals* are also chemically reactive but much less so than the alkali metals. Reactivities increase going down the group. The alkaline earth metals form basic oxides with the general formula RO.

Group IIIA Elements (ns^2np^1)

Groups IA and IIA exhibit only slight increases in metallic character down a column, but with Group IIIA we see a significant increase. The first Group IIIA element, boron, is a metalloid. Other elements in this group—aluminum, gallium, indium, and thallium—are metals. (Gallium is a curious metal; it melts readily in the palm of the hand—see Figure 8.19.)

FIGURE 8.19 ▲

Gallium

This metal melts from the heat of a hand.

The oxides in this group have the general formula R_2O_3. Boron oxide, B_2O_3, is an acidic oxide; aluminum oxide, Al_2O_3, and gallium oxide, Ga_2O_3, are amphoteric oxides. The change in the oxides from acidic to amphoteric to basic is indicative of an increase in metallic character of the elements.

Group IVA Elements (ns^2np^2)

This group shows the most distinct change in metallic character. It begins with the nonmetal carbon, C, followed by the metalloids silicon, Si, and germanium, Ge, and then the metals tin, Sn, and lead, Pb. Both tin and lead were known to the ancients. <

All the elements in this group form oxides with the general formula RO_2, which progress from acidic to amphoteric. Carbon dioxide, CO_2, an acidic oxide, is a gas. (Carbon also forms the monoxide, CO.) Silicon dioxide, SiO_2, an acidic oxide, exists as quartz and white sand (particles of quartz). Germanium dioxide, GeO_2, is acidic, though less so than silicon dioxide. Tin dioxide, SnO_2, an amphoteric oxide, is found as the mineral cassiterite, the principal ore of tin. Lead dioxide, PbO_2, is amphoteric. Lead has a more stable monoxide, PbO. Figure 8.20 shows oxides of some Group IVA elements.

Group VA Elements (ns^2np^3)

The Group VA elements also show the distinct transition from nonmetal (nitrogen, N, and phosphorus, P) to metalloid (arsenic, As, and antimony, Sb) to metal (bismuth, Bi). Nitrogen occurs as a colorless, odorless, relatively unreactive gas with N_2 molecules; white phosphorus is a white, waxy solid with P_4 molecules. Gray arsenic is a brittle solid with metallic luster; antimony is a brittle solid with a silvery, metallic luster. Bismuth is a hard, lustrous metal with a pinkish tinge.

The Group VA elements form oxides with empirical formulas R_2O_3 and R_2O_5. In some cases, the molecular formulas are twice these formulas—that is, R_4O_6 and R_4O_{10}. Nitrogen has the acidic oxides N_2O_3 and N_2O_5, although it also has other, better known oxides, such as NO. Phosphorus has the acidic oxides P_4O_6 and P_4O_{10}. Arsenic has the acidic oxides As_2O_3 and As_2O_5; antimony has the amphoteric oxides Sb_2O_3 and Sb_2O_5; and bismuth has the basic oxide Bi_2O_3.

Group VIA Elements, the Chalcogens (ns^2np^4)

These elements, the *chalcogens* (pronounced kal'-ke-jens), show the transition from nonmetal (oxygen, O, sulfur, S, and selenium, Se) to metalloid (tellurium, Te) to metal (polonium, Po). Oxygen occurs as a colorless, odorless gas with O_2 molecules. It also has an allotrope, ozone, with molecular formula O_3. Sulfur is a brittle, yellow solid with molecular formula S_8. Tellurium is a shiny gray, brittle solid; polonium is a silvery metal.

Sulfur, selenium, and tellurium form oxides with the formulas RO_2 and RO_3. (Sulfur burns in air to form sulfur dioxide; see Figure 8.21.) These oxides, except for TeO_2, are acidic; TeO_2 is amphoteric. Polonium has an oxide PoO_2, which is amphoteric, though more basic in character than TeO_2.

Group VIIA Elements, the Halogens (ns^2np^5)

The *halogens* are reactive nonmetals with the general molecular formula X_2, where X symbolizes a halogen. Fluorine, F_2, is a pale yellow gas; chlorine, Cl_2, a pale greenish yellow gas; bromine, Br_2, a reddish brown liquid; and iodine, I_2, a bluish black

Bronze, one of the first alloys (metallic mixtures) used by humans, contains about 90% copper and 10% tin. Bronze melts at a lower temperature than copper but is much harder.

FIGURE 8.20 ▲

Oxides of some Group IVA elements
Powdered lead monoxide (yellow), lead dioxide (dark brown), tin dioxide (white), and crystalline silicon dioxide (clear quartz).

FIGURE 8.21 ▲

Burning sulfur
The combustion of sulfur in air gives a blue flame. The product is primarily sulfur dioxide, detectable by its acrid odor.

FIGURE 8.22 ▲ 📧

The halogens
From left to right, the flasks contain chlorine, bromine, and iodine. (Bromine and iodine were warmed to produce the vapors; bromine is normally a reddish brown liquid and iodine a bluish black solid.)

solid that has a violet vapor (see Figure 8.22). Little is known about the chemistry of astatine, At, because all isotopes are radioactive with very short half-lives. (The half-life of a radioactive isotope is the time it takes for half of the isotope to decay, or break down, to another element.) It might be expected to be a metalloid.

Each halogen forms several compounds with oxygen; these are generally unstable, acidic oxides.

Group VIIIA Elements, the Noble Gases (ns^2np^6)

The Group VIIIA elements exist as gases consisting of uncombined atoms. For a long time these elements were thought to be chemically inert, because no compounds were known. Then, in the early 1960s, several compounds of xenon were prepared. Now compounds are also known for argon, krypton, and radon. These elements are known as the *noble gases* because of their relative unreactivity.

Concept Check 8.4

A certain element is a metalloid that forms an acidic oxide with the formula R_2O_5. Identify the element.

A Checklist for Review

Important Terms

electron configuration (8.1)
orbital diagram (8.1)
Pauli exclusion principle (8.1)
building-up (Aufbau) principle (8.2)
noble-gas core (8.2)
pseudo-noble-gas core (8.2)

valence electron (8.2)
Hund's rule (8.4)
paramagnetic substance (8.4)
diamagnetic substance (8.4)
periodic law (8.6)
effective nuclear charge (8.6)

first ionization energy (first
    ionization potential) (8.6)
electron affinity (8.6)
basic oxide (8.7)
acidic oxide (8.7)
amphoteric oxide (8.7)

Summary of Facts and Concepts

To understand the similarities that exist among the members of a group of elements, it is necessary to know the *electron configurations* for the ground states of atoms. Only those arrangements of electrons allowed by the *Pauli exclusion principle* are possible. The ground-state configuration of an atom represents the electron arrangement that has the lowest total energy. This arrangement can be reproduced by the *building-up principle* (Aufbau principle), where electrons fill the subshells in particular order (the building-up order) consistent with the Pauli exclusion principle. The arrangement of electrons in partially filled subshells is governed by *Hund's rule.*

Elements in the same group of the periodic table have similar valence-shell configurations. As a result, chemical and physical properties of the elements show periodic behavior. *Atomic radii,* for example, tend to decrease across any period (left to right) and increase down any group (top to bottom). *First ionization energies* tend to increase across a period and decrease down a group. *Electron affinities* of the Group VIA and Group VIIA elements have large negative values.

Media Summary

Visit the **student website at college.hmco.com/pic/ebbing9e** to help prepare for class, study for quizzes and exams, understand core concepts, and visualize molecular-level interactions. The following media activities are available for this chapter:

 Prepare for Class

■ **Video Lessons** *Mini lectures from chemistry experts*
Understanding Electron Spin
Electron Shielding

Electron Configurations Through Neon
Electron Configurations Beyond Neon
Periodic Relationships
Periodic and Atomic Sizes
Ionization Energy

Electron Affinity
Transition Metals and Nonmetals
Hydrogen, Alkali Metals, and Alkaline Earth Metals

 Improve Your Grade

■ **Visualizations** *Molecular-level animations and lab demonstration videos*
Orbital Energies
Periodic Table Trends
Determining the Atomic Radius of a Nonmetal (Carbon)
Determining the Atomic Radius of a Nonmetal (Chlorine)
Determining the Atomic Radius of a Metal (Molybdenum)

■ **Tutorials** *Animated examples and interactive activities*
Aufbau Principle

■ **Flashcards** *Key terms and definitions*
Online Flashcards

■ **Self-Assessment Questions** *Additional questions with full worked-out solutions*
6 Self-Assessment Questions

 ACE the Test

Multiple-choice quizzes
3 ACE Practice Tests

Access these resources using the passkey available free with new texts or for purchase separately.

Learning Objectives

8.1 Electron Spin and the Pauli Exclusion Principle

■ Define *electron configuration* and *orbital diagram.*
■ State the Pauli exclusion principle.
■ Apply the Pauli exclusion principle. Example 8.1

8.2 Building-Up Principle and the Periodic Table

■ Define *building-up principle.*
■ Define *noble-gas core, pseudo-noble-gas core,* and *valence electron.*
■ Define *main-group element* and (*d-block* and *f-block*) *transition element.*

8.3 Writing Electron Configurations Using the Periodic Table

■ Determine the configuration of an atom using the building-up principle. Example 8.2
■ Determine the configuration of an atom using the period and group numbers. Example 8.3

8.4 Orbital Diagrams of Atoms; Hund's Rule

■ State Hund's rule.
■ Apply Hund's rule. Example 8.4
■ Define *paramagnetic substance* and *diamagnetic substance.*

8.5 Mendeleev's Predictions from the Periodic Table

■ Describe how Mendeleev predicted the properties of undiscovered elements.

8.6 Some Periodic Properties

■ State the periodic law.
■ State the general periodic trends in size of atomic radii.
■ Define *effective nuclear charge.*
■ Determine relative atomic sizes from periodic trends. Example 8.5
■ State the general periodic trends in ionization energy.
■ Define *first ionization energy.*
■ Determine relative ionization energies from periodic trends. Example 8.6
■ Define *electron affinity.*
■ State the broad general trend in electron affinity across any period.

8.7 Periodicity in the Main-Group Elements

■ Define *basic oxide, acidic oxide,* and *amphoteric oxide.*
■ State the main group corresponding to an *alkali metal,* an *alkaline earth metal,* a *chalcogen,* a *halogen,* and a *noble gas.*
■ Describe the change in metallic/nonmetallic character (or reactivities) in going through any main group of elements.

Self-Assessment and Review Questions

8.1 Describe the experiment of Stern and Gerlach. How are the results for the hydrogen atom explained?
8.2 Describe the model of electron spin given in the text. What are the restrictions on electron spin?

8.3 How does the Pauli exclusion principle limit the possible electron configurations of an atom?
8.4 What is the maximum number of electrons that can occupy a g subshell ($l = 4$)?

8.5 List the orbitals in order of increasing orbital energy up to and including $3p$ orbitals.

8.6 Define each of the following: noble-gas core, pseudo-noble-gas core, valence electron.

8.7 Give two different possible orbital diagrams for the $1s^2 2s^2 2p^4$ configuration of the oxygen atom, one of which should correspond to the ground state. Label the diagram for the ground state.

8.8 Define the terms *diamagnetic substance* and *paramagnetic substance*. Does the ground-state oxygen atom give a diamagnetic or a paramagnetic substance? Explain.

8.9 What kind of subshell is being filled in Groups IA and IIA? in Groups IIIA to VIIIA? in the transition elements? in the lanthanides and actinides?

8.10 How was Mendeleev able to predict the properties of gallium before it was discovered?

8.11 Describe the major trends that emerge when atomic radii are plotted against atomic number. Describe the trends observed when first ionization energies are plotted against atomic number.

8.12 What atom has the smallest radius among the alkaline earth elements?

8.13 What main group in the periodic table has elements with the most negative electron affinities for each period? What electron configurations of neutral atoms have only unstable negative ions?

8.14 The ions Na^+ and Mg^{2+} occur in chemical compounds, but the ions Na^{2+} and Mg^{3+} do not. Explain.

8.15 Describe the major trends in metallic character observed in the periodic table of the elements.

8.16 Distinguish between an acidic and a basic oxide. Give examples of each.

8.17 What is the name of the alkali metal atom with valence-shell configuration $5s^1$?

8.18 What would you predict for the atomic number of the halogen under astatine in the periodic table?

8.19 List the elements in Groups IIIA to VIA in the same order as in the periodic table. Label each element as a metal, a metalloid, or a nonmetal. Does each column of elements display the expected trend of increasing metallic characteristics?

8.20 For the list of elements you made for Question 8.19, note whether the oxides of each element are acidic, basic, or amphoteric.

8.21 Write an equation for the reaction of potassium metal with water.

8.22 From what is said in Section 8.7 about Group IIA elements, list some properties of barium.

8.23 Give the names and formulas of two oxides of carbon.

8.24 Match each description in the left column with the appropriate element in the right column.

a. A waxy, white solid, normally stored under water   Sulfur
                              Sodium
b. A yellow solid that burns in air   White phosphorus
c. A reddish brown liquid   Bromine
d. A soft, light metal that reacts vigorously with water

8.25 Phosphorus has _____ unpaired electrons.
  a. 1   **b.** 2   **c.** 3   **d.** 4   **e.** 5

8.26 Which of the following atoms, designated by their electron configurations, has the *highest* ionization energy?
  a. $[Ne]3s^2 3p^2$
  b. $[Ne]3s^2 3p^3$
  c. $[Ar]3d^{10} 4s^2 4p^3$
  d. $[Kr]4d^{10} 5s^2 5p^3$
  e. $[Xe]4f^{14} 5d^{10} 6s^2 6p^3$

8.27 When trying to remove electrons from Be, which of the following sets of ionization energy makes the most sense going from first to third ionization energy?
  a. First IE 900 KJ/mol, second IE 1750 kJ/mol, third IE 15,000 kJ/mol
  b. First IE 1750 KJ/mol, second IE 900 kJ/mol, third IE 15,000 kJ/mol
  c. First IE 15,000 KJ/mol, second IE 1750 kJ/mol, third IE 900 kJ/mol
  d. First IE 900 KJ/mol, second IE 15,000 kJ/mol, third IE 22,000 kJ/mol
  e. First IE 900 KJ/mol, second IE 1750 kJ/mol, third IE 1850 kJ/mol

8.28 Consider the following orderings.
  I. $Al < Si < P < S$
  II. $Be < Mg < Ca < Sr$
  III. $I < Br < Cl < F$
Which of these give(s) a correct trend in atomic size?
  a. I only
  b. II only
  c. III only
  d. I and II only
  e. II and III only

Concept Explorations

8.29 Periodic Properties I

A hypothetical element, X, has the following ionization energy values:

    First ionization energy: 900 kJ/mol
    Second ionization energy: 1750 kJ/mol
    Third ionization energy: 14,900 kJ/mol
    Fourth ionization energy: 21,000 kJ/mol

Another element, Y, has the following ionization energy values:

    First ionization energy: 1200 kJ/mol
    Second ionization energy: 2500 kJ/mol
    Third ionization energy: 19,900 kJ/mol
    Fourth ionization energy: 26,000 kJ/mol

a. To what family of the periodic table would element X be most likely to belong? Explain?

b. What charge would you expect element X to have when it forms an ion?

c. If you were to place elements X and Y into the periodic table, would element Y be in the same period as element X? If not in the same period, where might they be relative to each other in the periodic table?

d. Would an atom of Y be smaller or larger than an atom of X? Explain your reasoning.

8.30 Periodic Properties II
Consider two hypothetical elements, W and Z. Element W has an electron affinity of −300 kJ/mol, and element Z has an electron affinity of −75 kJ/mol.

a. If you have a W ion and a Z ion, from which ion would it require more energy to remove an electron? Explain your answer.

b. If elements W and Z are in the same period of the periodic table, which atom would you expect to have the greater atomic radius? Why?

c. Assuming that the elements are in the same period, which element would you expect to have the smaller first ionization energy?

d. Do the valence electrons in element Z feel a greater effective nuclear charge than those in element W? Explain how you arrived at your answer.

Conceptual Problems

8.31 Suppose that the Pauli exclusion principle were "No more than two electrons can have the same four quantum numbers." What would be the electron configurations of the ground states for the first six elements of the periodic table, assuming that, except for the Pauli principle, the usual building-up principle held?

8.32 Imagine a world in which all quantum numbers, except the l quantum number, are as they are in the real world. In this imaginary world, l begins with 1 and goes up to n (the value of the principal quantum number). Assume that the orbitals fill in the order by n, then l; that is, the first orbital to fill is for $n = 1$, $l = 1$; the next orbital to fill is for $n = 2$, $l = 1$, and so forth. How many elements would there be in the first period of the periodic table?

8.33 Two elements in Period 5 are adjacent to one another in the periodic table. The ground-state atom of one element has only s electrons in its valence shell; the other has at least one d electron in an unfilled shell. Identify the elements.

8.34 Two elements are in the same column of the periodic table, one above the other. The ground-state atom of one element has two s electrons in its outer shell, and no d electrons anywhere in its configuration. The other element has d electrons in its configuration. Identify the elements.

8.35 You travel to an alternate universe where the atomic orbitals are different from those on earth, but all other aspects of the atoms are the same. In this universe, you find that the first (lowest energy) orbital is filled with three electrons and the second orbital can hold a maximum of nine electrons. You discover an element Z that has five electrons in its atom. Would you expect Z to be more likely to form a cation or an anion? Indicate a possible charge on this ion.

8.36 Would you expect to find an element having both a very large (positive) first ionization energy and an electron affinity that is much less than zero (large but negative)? Explain.

8.37 Two elements are in the same group, one following the other. One is a metalloid; the other is a metal. Both form oxides of the formula RO_2. The first is acidic; the next is amphoteric. Identify the two elements.

8.38 A metalloid has an acidic oxide of the formula R_2O_3. The element has no oxide of the formula R_2O_5. What is the name of the element?

8.39 Given the following information, identify the group from the periodic table that contains elements that behave like main-group element "E."

(i) The electron affinity of E is greater than zero.

(ii) The ionization energy (IE) trend for element E is: first ionization energy < second ionization energy <<< third ionization energy.

(iii) Samples of E are lustrous and are good electrical conductors.

8.40 A hypothetical element A has the following properties:

First ionization energy: 850 kJ/mol

Second ionization energy: 1700 kJ/mol

Third ionization energy: 13,999 kJ/mol

a. If you were to react element A with oxygen, what would be the chemical formula of the resulting compound?

b. Write the balanced chemical reaction of A reacting with oxygen to give the product from part a.

c. Would you expect the product of the chemical reaction of A with oxygen to be a basic, an acidic, or an amphoteric oxide?

Practice Problems

Pauli Exclusion Principle

8.41 Which of the following orbital diagrams are allowed by the Pauli exclusion principle? Explain how you arrived at this decision. Give the electron configuration for the allowed ones.

a. ⇅   ⇅   ⇅↑↑
   1s   2s   2p

b. ⇅   ⇅   ⇅↑↑
   1s   2s   2p

c. ↑↑   ⇅   ⇅↑↓
   1s   2s   2p

d. ⇅   ↑↑↑   ⇅↑◯
   1s   2s   2p

8.42 Which of the following orbital diagrams are allowed and which are not allowed by the Pauli exclusion principle? Explain. For those that are allowed, write the electron configuration.

a. ⑴ ⑴ ⑴⑴◯   b. ⑴ ⑴ ⑴⑴⑴
   1s 2s   2p   1s 2s   2p

c. ⑴ ⑴ ⑴◯◯   d. ⑴ ⑴ ⑴⑴⑴
   1s 2s   2p   1s 2s   2p

8.43 Which of the following electron configurations are possible? Explain why the others are not.
a. $1s^1 2s^2 2p^7$ b. $1s^2 2s^2 2p^6 3s^3 3d^7$
c. $1s^2 2s^2 2p^5$ d. $1s^2 2s^2 2p^6 3s^3 3d^8$

8.44 Choose the electron configurations that are possible from among the following. Explain why the others are impossible.
a. $1s^2 2s^1 2p^6$ b. $1s^2 2s^2 2p^8$
c. $1s^2 2s^3 2p^6 3s^3 3p^6 3d^7$ d. $1s^2 2s^2 2p^6 3s^1 3d^9$

8.45 Write all of the possible orbital diagrams for the electron configuration $1s^2 2p^1$. (There are six different diagrams.)

8.46 Give the different orbital diagrams for the configuration $1s^1 2p^1$. (There are twelve different diagrams.)

Building-Up Principle and Hund's Rule

8.47 Give the electron configuration of the ground state of iodine, using the building-up principle.

8.48 Use the building-up principle to obtain the ground-state configuration of phosphorus.

8.49 Use the building-up principle to obtain the electron configuration of the ground state of manganese.

8.50 Give the electron configuration of the ground state of cobalt, using the building-up principle.

8.51 Bromine is a Group VIIA element in Period 4. Deduce the valence-shell configuration of bromine.

8.52 Antimony is a Group VA element in Period 5. Write the valence-shell configuration of antimony.

8.53 Zirconium is a Group IVB element in Period 5. What would you expect for the valence-shell configuration of zirconium?

8.54 Titanium is a Group IVB element in Period 4. What would you expect for the configuration of outer electrons of manganese?

8.55 Thallium has the ground-state configuration $[Xe]4f^{14}5d^{10}6s^2 6p^1$. Give the group and period for this element. Classify it as a main-group, a d-transition, or an f-transition element.

8.56 The configuration for the ground state of iridium is $[Xe]4f^{14}5d^7 6s^2$. What are the group and period for this element? Is it a main-group, a d-transition, or an f-transition element?

8.57 Write the orbital diagram for the ground state of cobalt. The electron configuration is $[Ar]3d^7 4s^2$.

8.58 Write the orbital diagram for the ground state of terbium. The electron configuration is $[Xe]4f^9 6s^2$.

8.59 Write an orbital diagram for the ground state of the potassium atom. Is the atomic substance diamagnetic or paramagnetic?

8.60 Write an orbital diagram for the ground state of the calcium atom. Is the atomic substance diamagnetic or paramagnetic?

Periodic Trends

8.61 Order the following elements by increasing atomic radius according to what you expect from periodic trends: Se, S, As.

8.62 Using periodic trends, arrange the following elements in order of increasing atomic radius: O, P, S.

8.63 Using periodic trends, arrange the following elements by increasing ionization energy: Ar, Na, Cl, Al.

8.64 Arrange the following elements in order of increasing ionization energy: Mg, Ca, S. Do not look at Figure 8.18.

8.65 From what you know in a general way about electron affinities, state which member of each of the following pairs has the greater negative value: (a) As, Br (b) F, Li.

8.66 From what you know in a general way about electron affinities, state which member of each of the following pairs has the greater negative value: (a) Cl, S (b) Se, K.

8.67 If potassium chlorate has the formula $KClO_3$, what formula would you expect for lithium bromate?

8.68 Write the simplest formulas expected for two oxides of selenium.

General Problems

8.69 Write the complete ground-state electron configuration of the strontium atom, Sr, using the building-up principle.

8.70 Write the complete ground-state electron configuration of the tin atom, Sn, using the building-up principle.

8.71 Obtain the valence-shell configuration of the polonium atom, Po, using the position of this atom in the periodic table.

8.72 Obtain the valence-shell configuration of the thallium atom, Tl, using the position of this atom in the periodic table.

8.73 Write the orbital diagram for the ground state of the arsenic atom. Give all orbitals.

8.74 Write the orbital diagram for the ground state of the germanium atom. Give all orbitals.

8.75 For eka-lead, predict the electron configuration, whether the element is a metal or nonmetal, and the formula of an oxide.

8.76 For eka-bismuth, predict the electron configuration, whether the element is a metal or nonmetal, and the formula of an oxide.

8.77 From Figure 8.18, predict the first ionization energy of francium ($Z = 87$).

8.78 From Figure 8.18, predict the first ionization energy of astatine ($Z = 85$).

8.79 Write the orbital diagram corresponding to the ground state of Nb, whose configuration is $[Kr]4d^45s^1$.

8.80 Write the orbital diagram for the ground state of ruthenium. The configuration is $[Kr]4d^75s^1$.

8.81 Match each set of characteristics on the left with an element in the column at the right.

a. A reactive nonmetal; the atom has a large negative electron affinity

b. A soft metal; the atom has low ionization energy

c. A metalloid that forms an oxide of formula R_2O_3

d. A chemically unreactive gas

Sodium (Na)
Antimony (Sb)
Argon (Ar)
Chlorine (Cl_2)

8.82 Match each element on the right with a set of characteristics on the left.

a. A reactive, pale yellow gas; the atom has a large negative electron affinity

b. A soft metal that reacts with water to produce hydrogen

c. A metal that forms an oxide of formula R_2O_3

d. A colorless gas; the atom has a moderately large negative electron affinity

Oxygen (O_2)
Gallium (Ga)
Barium (Ba)
Fluorine (F_2)

8.83 Find the electron configuration of the element with $Z = 23$. From this, give its group and period in the periodic table. Classify the element as a main-group, a d-block transition, or an f-block transition element.

8.84 Find the electron configuration of the element with $Z = 33$. From this, give its group and period in the periodic table. Is this a main-group, a d-block transition, or an f-block transition element?

8.85 What property of an atom does nuclear magnetic resonance depend on? What frequency range of the electromagnetic spectrum does NMR use?

8.86 Explain the origin of the "chemical shift" seen for a proton in a molecule.

8.87 Explain how x rays are produced when an electron beam falls on a metal target.

8.88 Describe how x-ray photoelectron spectroscopy is done. What kind of information is obtained from photoelectron spectroscopy?

8.89 How is it possible for a diamagnetic material to be levitated by a magnetic field?

8.90 Researchers have shown that it is possible to levitate diamagnetic materials. What animal did they use in their experiments to show this?

Strategy Problems

8.91 A metallic element, M, reacts vigorously with water to form a solution of MOH. If M is in Period 5, what is the ground-state electron configuration of the atom?

8.92 A nonmetallic element, R, burns brightly in air to give the oxide R_4O_{10}. If R is in Period 3, what is the ground-state valence-shell configuration of the atom?

8.93 The ground-state electron configuration of an atom is $1s^22s^22p^63s^23p^4$. What is the valence-shell configuration of the atom in the same group, but in Period 5?

8.94 An atom of an element has the following ground-state configuration: $[Xe]4f^{14}5d^96s^1$. Using this configuration, give the symbol of the element. Explain your reasoning.

8.95 An atom of an element has the following ground-state configuration: $[Kr]4d^{10}5s^25p^b$. If the element is in Group VIA, what is the symbol of the element? What is b?

8.96 A main-group atom in Period 5 has the following orbital diagram for its valence shell (ground state): ⇅ ↑↑↑.

What is the symbol for the element? Write the formula of the oxide containing the most oxygen.

8.97 Write the orbital diagram for the ground-state valence electrons of the main-group atom in Period 5 that has the smallest radius. Explain how you got this answer.

8.98 Using the periodic table, decide which of the following atoms you expect to have the largest radius: H, Sc, As, Br, V, K. Why?

8.99 An atom easily loses two electrons to form the ion R^{+2}. The element, which is in Period 6, forms the oxides RO and RO_2. Give the orbital diagram for the ground-state valence shell of the element that immediately follows R in the periodic table.

8.100 List three elements in order of increasing ionization energy. Two of the elements should be halogens (but not F), and the other should be Se.

Cumulative-Skills Problems

8.101 A 2.50-g sample of barium reacted completely with water. What is the equation for the reaction? How many milliliters of dry H_2 evolved at 21°C and 748 mmHg?

8.102 A sample of cesium metal reacted completely with water, evolving 48.1 mL of dry H_2 at 19°C and 768 mmHg. What is the equation for the reaction? What was the mass of cesium in the sample?

8.103 What is the formula of radium oxide? What is the percentage of radium in this oxide?

8.104 What is the formula of hydrogen telluride? What is the percentage of tellurium in this compound?

8.105 How much energy would be required to ionize 5.00 mg of $Na(g)$ atoms to $Na^+(g)$ ions? The first ionization energy of Na atoms is 496 kJ/mol.

8.106 How much energy is evolved when 2.65 mg of $Cl(g)$ atoms adds electrons to give $Cl^-(g)$ ions?

8.107 Using the Bohr formula for the energy levels, calculate the energy required to raise the electron in a hydrogen atom from $n = 1$ to $n = \infty$. Express the result for 1 mol H atoms. Because the $n = \infty$ level corresponds to removal of the electron from the atom, this energy equals the ionization energy of the H atom.

8.108 Calculate the ionization energy of the He^+ ion in kJ/mol (this would be the second ionization energy of He). See Problem 8.107. The Bohr formula for the energy levels of an ion consisting of a nucleus of charge Z and a single electron is $-R_H Z^2/n^2$.

8.109 The lattice energy of an ionic solid such as NaCl is the enthalpy change $\Delta H°$ for the process in which the solid changes to ions. For example,

$$NaCl(s) \longrightarrow Na^+(g) + Cl^-(g) \qquad \Delta H = 786 \text{ kJ/mol}$$

Assume that the ionization energy and electron affinity are ΔH values for the processes defined by those terms. The ionization energy of Na is 496 kJ/mol. Use this, the electron affinity from Table 8.4, and the lattice energy of NaCl to calculate ΔH for the following process:

$$Na(g) + Cl(g) \longrightarrow NaCl(s)$$

8.110 Calculate ΔH for the following process:

$$K(g) + Br(g) \longrightarrow KBr(s)$$

The lattice energy of KBr is 689 kJ/mol, and the ionization energy of K is 419 kJ/mol. The electron affinity of Br is given in Table 8.4. See Problem 8.109.

9

Ionic and Covalent Bonding

The shape of snowflakes results from bonding (and intermolecular) forces in H_2O.

Contents and Concepts

Molten salts and aqueous solutions of salts are electrically conducting. This conductivity results from the motion of ions in the liquids. This suggests the possibility that ions exist in certain solids, held together by the attraction of ions of opposite charge.

Not all bonds can be ionic. Hydrogen, H_2, is a clear example, in which there is a strong bond between two like atoms. The bonding in the hydrogen molecule is covalent. A covalent bond forms between atoms by the sharing of a pair of electrons.

The properties of a substance, such as sodium chloride (Figure 9.1), are determined in part by the chemical bonds that hold the atoms together. A *chemical bond* is a strong attractive force that exists between certain atoms in a substance. In Chapter 2 we described how sodium (a silvery metal) reacts with chlorine (a pale greenish yellow gas) to produce sodium chloride (table salt, a white solid). The substances in this reaction are quite different, as are their chemical bonds. Sodium chloride, NaCl, consists of Na^+ and Cl^- ions held in a regular arrangement, or crystal, by *ionic bonds*. Ionic bonding results from the attractive force of oppositely charged ions.

A second kind of chemical bond is a *covalent bond*. In a covalent bond, two atoms share valence electrons (outer-shell electrons), which are attracted to the positively charged cores of both atoms, thus linking them. For example, chlorine gas consists of Cl_2 molecules. You would not expect the two Cl atoms in each Cl_2 molecule to acquire the opposite charges required for ionic bonding. Rather, a covalent bond holds the two atoms together. This is consistent with the equal sharing of electrons that you would expect between identical atoms. In most molecules, the atoms are linked by covalent bonds.

Metallic bonding, seen in sodium and other metals, represents another important type of bonding. A crystal of sodium metal consists of a regular arrangement of sodium atoms. The valence electrons of these atoms move throughout the crystal, attracted to the positive cores of all Na^+ ions. This attraction holds the crystal together.

What determines the type of bonding in each substance? How do you describe the bonding in various substances? In this chapter we will look at some simple, useful concepts of bonding that can help us answer these questions. We will be concerned with ionic and covalent bonds in particular.

■ See pages 364–365 for the Media Summary.

FIGURE 9.1 ▲

Sodium chloride crystals
Natural crystals of sodium chloride mineral (halite).

Ionic Bonds

This chapter builds on Chapters 7 and 8; thus, the discussions of ionization energy and electron affinity at the end of Chapter 8 flow smoothly into the discussion of ionic bonding at the beginning of this chapter.

The first explanation of chemical bonding was suggested by the properties of *salts*, substances now known to be ionic. Salts are generally crystalline solids that melt at high temperatures. Sodium chloride, for example, melts at 801°C. A molten salt (the liquid after melting) conducts an electric current. A salt dissolved in water gives a solution that also conducts an electric current. The electrical conductivity of the molten salt and the salt solution results from the motion of ions in the liquids. This suggests the possibility that ions exist in certain solids, held together by the attraction of opposite charges.

9.1 | **Describing Ionic Bonds**

Experiments in General Chemistry, 9A, "The Identity of an Insoluble Precipitate."

An **ionic bond** is *a chemical bond formed by the electrostatic attraction between positive and negative ions.* The bond forms between two atoms when one or more electrons are transferred from the valence shell of one atom to the valence shell of the other. The atom that loses electrons becomes a *cation* (positive ion), and the atom that gains electrons becomes an *anion* (negative ion). Any given ion tends to attract as many neighboring ions of opposite charge as possible. When large numbers of ions gather together, they form an ionic solid. The solid normally has a regular, crystalline structure that allows for the maximum attraction of ions, given their particular sizes.

To understand why ionic bonding occurs, consider the transfer of a valence electron from a sodium atom (electron configuration $[\text{Ne}]3s^1$) to the valence shell of a chlorine atom ($[\text{Ne}]3s^2 3p^5$). You can represent the electron transfer by the following equation:

$$\text{Na}([\text{Ne}]3s^1) + \text{Cl}([\text{Ne}]3s^2 3p^5) \longrightarrow \text{Na}^+([\text{Ne}]) + \text{Cl}^-([\text{Ne}]3s^2 3p^6)$$

As a result of the electron transfer, ions are formed, each of which has a noble-gas configuration. The sodium atom has lost its $3s$ electron and has taken on the neon configuration, $[\text{Ne}]$. The chlorine atom has accepted the electron into its $3p$ subshell and has taken on the argon configuration, $[\text{Ne}]3s^2 3p^6$. Such noble-gas configurations and the corresponding ions are particularly stable. This stability of the ions accounts in part for the formation of the ionic solid NaCl. Once a cation or anion forms, it attracts ions of opposite charge. Within the sodium chloride crystal, NaCl, every Na^+ ion is surrounded by six Cl^- ions, and every Cl^- ion by six Na^+ ions. (Figure 2.19 shows the arrangement of ions in the NaCl crystal.)

Lewis Electron-Dot Symbols

You can simplify the preceding equation for the electron transfer between Na and Cl by writing Lewis electron-dot symbols for the atoms and monatomic ions. A **Lewis electron-dot symbol** is *a symbol in which the electrons in the valence shell of an atom or ion are represented by dots placed around the letter symbol of the element.* Table 9.1 lists Lewis symbols and corresponding valence-shell electron configurations for the atoms of the second and third periods. Note that dots are placed one to each side of a letter symbol until all four sides are occupied. Then the dots are written two to a side until all valence electrons are accounted for. The exact placement of the single dots is immaterial. For example, the single dot in the Lewis symbol for chlorine can be written on any one of the four sides. [This pairing of dots does not always correspond to the pairing of electrons in the ground state. Thus, you write $\cdot\dot{\text{B}}\cdot$ for boron, rather than $:\text{B}\cdot$, which more closely corresponds to the ground-state configuration $[\text{He}]2s^2 2p^1$. The first symbol better reflects boron's chemistry, in which each single electron (single dot) tends to be involved in bond formation.]

The equation representing the transfer of an electron from the sodium atom to the chlorine atom is

$$\text{Na}\cdot\ +\ \cdot\ddot{\underset{\cdot\cdot}{\text{Cl}}}: \longrightarrow \text{Na}^+\ +\ [:\ddot{\underset{\cdot\cdot}{\text{Cl}}}:]^-$$

The noble-gas configurations of the ions are apparent from the symbols. No dots are shown for the cation. (All valence electrons have been removed, leaving the noble-gas core.) Eight dots are shown in brackets for the anion (noble-gas configuration $ns^2 np^6$).

TABLE 9.1		Lewis Electron-Dot Symbols for Atoms of the Second and Third Periods						
Period	IA ns^1	IIA ns^2	IIIA $ns^2 np^1$	IVA $ns^2 np^2$	VA $ns^2 np^3$	VIA $ns^2 np^4$	VIIA $ns^2 np^5$	VIIIA $ns^2 np^6$
Second	Li·	·Be·	·Ḃ·	·Ċ·	:Ṅ·	:Ö·	:Ḟ·	:Ṅe:
Third	Na·	·Mg·	·Äl·	·Ṡi·	:Ṗ·	:Ṡ·	:Ċl·	:Är:

Example 9.1	Using Lewis Symbols to Represent Ionic Bond Formation

Use Lewis electron-dot symbols to represent the transfer of electrons from magnesium to fluorine atoms to form ions with noble-gas configurations.

Problem Strategy Write down the Lewis symbols for the two atoms. Note how many electrons the metal atom should lose to assume a noble-gas configuration (all of the dots, representing valence electrons) and how many electrons the nonmetal atom should gain to assume such a configuration (enough to give eight dots about the atomic symbol). Represent the transfer of electrons between ions diagrammatically in the form of an equation.

Solution The Lewis symbols for the atoms are $:\ddot{F}\cdot$ and $\cdot Mg\cdot$ (see Table 9.1). The magnesium atom loses

two electrons to assume a noble-gas configuration. But because a fluorine atom can accept only one electron to fill its valence shell, two fluorine atoms must take part in the electron transfer. We can represent this electron transfer as follows:

$$:\ddot{F}\cdot \ + \ \cdot Mg\cdot \ + \ \cdot\ddot{F}: \ \longrightarrow \ [:\ddot{F}:]^- \ + \ Mg^{2+} \ + \ [:\ddot{F}:]^-$$

Answer Check Check that you have the correct symbols for the atoms and that the symbols for the ions do have noble-gas configurations.

Exercise 9.1 Represent the transfer of electrons from magnesium to oxygen atoms to assume noble-gas configurations. Use Lewis electron-dot symbols.

An alternative example is provided in the Instructor's Resource Manual.

■ See Problems 9.37 and 9.38.

Note that the Lewis symbols for Be, B, and C show the maximum number of unpaired electrons to reflect the usual bonding situation and differ from what you might write given the ground-state electron configurations.

ChemWork: Calculating Heat of Formation

Ionization energies and electron affinities of atoms were discussed in Section 8.6.

Energy Involved in Ionic Bonding

You have seen in a qualitative way why a sodium atom and a chlorine atom might be expected to form an ionic bond. It is instructive, however, to look at the energy changes involved in ionic bond formation. From this analysis, you can gain further understanding of why certain atoms bond ionically and others do not.

If atoms come together and bond, there should be a net decrease in energy, because the bonded state should be more stable and therefore at a lower energy level. Consider again the formation of an ionic bond between a sodium atom and a chlorine atom. You can think of this as occurring in two steps: (1) An electron is transferred between the two separate atoms to give ions. (2) The ions then attract one another to form an ionic bond. In reality, the transfer of the electron and the formation of an ionic bond occur simultaneously, rather than in discrete steps, as the atoms approach one another. But the *net* quantity of energy involved is the same whether the steps occur one after the other or at the same time.

The first step requires removal of the $3s$ electron from the sodium atom and the addition of this electron to the valence shell of the chlorine atom. Removing the electron from the sodium atom requires energy (the first ionization energy of the sodium atom, which equals 496 kJ/mol). Adding the electron to the chlorine atom releases energy (the electron affinity of the chlorine atom, which equals −349 kJ/mol). < It requires more energy to remove an electron from the sodium atom than is gained when the electron is added to the chlorine atom. That is, the formation of ions from the atoms is not in itself energetically favorable. It requires additional energy equal to at least (496 − 349) kJ/mol, or 147 kJ/mol, to form ions (Figure 9.2, Step 1).

When positive and negative ions bond, however, more than enough energy is released to supply this additional requirement. What principally determines the energy released when ions bond is the attraction of oppositely charged ions. You can estimate this energy from *Coulomb's law* if you make the simplifying assumption that the ions are spheres, just touching, with a distance between nuclei equal to that in the NaCl crystal. From experiment, this distance is 282 pm, or 2.82×10^{-10} m.

FIGURE 9.2 ▶ ◀

Energetics of ionic bonding
The transfer of an electron from an Na atom to a Cl atom is not in itself energetically favorable; it requires 147 kJ/mol of energy (Step 1). However, 493 kJ of energy is released when these oppositely charged ions come together to form ion pairs (Step 2a). Moreover, additional energy (293 kJ) is released when these ion pairs form the solid NaCl crystal (Step 2b). The lattice energy released when one mole each of Na^+ and Cl^- ions react to produce NaCl(s) is 786 kJ/mol, and the overall process of NaCl formation is energetically favorable, releasing 639 kJ/mol if one starts with gaseous Na and Cl atoms.

The energy value −493 kJ/mol is approximate, because of the simplifying assumption we made.

According to Coulomb's law, the energy E obtained in bringing two ions with electric charges Q_1 and Q_2 from infinite separation to a distance r apart is

$$E = \frac{kQ_1Q_2}{r}$$

Here k is a physical constant, equal to 8.99×10^9 J·m/C² (C is the symbol for coulomb); the charge on Na^+ is $+e$ and that on Cl^- is $-e$, where e equals 1.602×10^{-19} C. Therefore,

$$E = \frac{-(8.99 \times 10^9 \text{ J·m/C}^2) \times (1.602 \times 10^{-19} \text{ C})^2}{2.82 \times 10^{-10} \text{ m}} = -8.18 \times 10^{-19} \text{ J}$$

The minus sign means energy is released. This energy is for the formation of one ion pair. To express this for one mole of NaCl, we multiply by Avogadro's number, 6.02×10^{23}. We obtain −493 kJ/mol for the energy obtained when one mole of Na^+ and one mole of Cl^- come together to form NaCl ion pairs (Figure 9.2, Step 2a). ◀

The attraction of oppositely charged ions does not stop with the bonding of pairs of ions. The maximum attraction of ions of opposite charge with the minimum repulsion of ions of the same charge is obtained with the formation of the crystalline solid. Then additional energy is released (Figure 9.2, Step 2b).

The energy released when a crystalline solid forms from ions is related to the lattice energy of the solid. The **lattice energy** is *the change in energy that occurs when an ionic solid is separated into isolated ions in the gas phase.* For sodium chloride, the process is

$$\text{NaCl}(s) \longrightarrow \text{Na}^+(g) + \text{Cl}^-(g)$$

The distances between ions in the crystal are continuously enlarged until the ions are very far apart. The energy required for this process is the lattice energy of NaCl. You can calculate this energy from Coulomb's law or obtain an experimental value from thermodynamic data. The value, +786 kJ/mol, is for just the opposite process of the one we were considering earlier, in which ions come together to bond, forming the solid. When ions come together to bond, this energy is −786 kJ/mol (Figure 9.2, Step 2). Consequently, the net energy obtained when gaseous Na and Cl atoms form solid NaCl is (−786 + 147) kJ/mol = −639 kJ/mol. The negative sign shows that there has been a net decrease in energy, which you expect when stable bonding has occurred.

From this energy analysis, you can see that two elements bond ionically if the ionization energy of one is sufficiently small and the electron affinity of the other is sufficiently large and negative. This situation exists between a reactive metal (which has low ionization energy) and a reactive nonmetal (which has large negative electron affinity). In general, bonding between a metal and a nonmetal is ionic. This energy analysis also explains why ionic bonding normally results in a solid rather than in ion-pair molecules.

Lattice Energies from the Born–Haber Cycle

If you have not covered Hess's law, you may want to omit this subsection.

Ionic crystals: A simple and safe lecture demonstration of the preparation of NaI from its elements, *J. Chem. Educ.* 77 (2000): 619. (This demonstration can be done in conjunction with a discussion of the Haber cycle for NaI.)

The preceding energy analysis requires us to know the lattice energy of solid sodium chloride. Direct experimental determination of the lattice energy of an ionic solid is difficult. However, this quantity can be indirectly determined from experiment by means of a thermochemical "cycle" originated by Max Born and Fritz Haber in 1919 and now called the *Born–Haber cycle*. The reasoning is based on Hess's law.

To obtain the lattice energy of NaCl, you think of solid sodium chloride being formed from the elements by two different routes, as shown in Figure 9.3. In one route, NaCl(s) is formed directly from the elements, Na(s) and $\frac{1}{2}Cl_2(g)$. The enthalpy change for this is ΔH_f°, which is given in Table 6.2 as −411 kJ per mole of NaCl. The second route consists of five steps:

1. *Sublimation of sodium.* Metallic sodium is vaporized to a gas of sodium atoms. (*Sublimation* is the transformation of a solid to a gas.) The enthalpy change for this process, measured experimentally, is 108 kJ per mole of sodium.

2. *Dissociation of chlorine.* Chlorine molecules are dissociated to atoms. The enthalpy change for this equals the Cl—Cl bond dissociation energy, which is 240 kJ per mole of bonds, or 120 kJ per mole of Cl atoms.

3. *Ionization of sodium.* Sodium atoms are ionized to Na^+ ions. The enthalpy change is essentially the ionization energy of atomic sodium, which equals 496 kJ per mole of Na.

4. *Formation of chloride ion.* The electrons from the ionization of sodium atoms are transferred to chlorine atoms. The enthalpy change for this is the electron affinity of atomic chlorine, which equals −349 kJ per mole of Cl atoms.

5. *Formation of NaCl(s) from ions.* The ions Na^+ and Cl^- formed in Steps 3 and 4 combine to give solid sodium chloride. Because this process is just the reverse of the one corresponding to the lattice energy (breaking the solid into ions), the enthalpy change is the negative of the lattice energy. If we let U be the lattice energy, the enthalpy change for Step 5 is $-U$.

FIGURE 9.3 ▶

Born–Haber cycle for NaCl
The formation of NaCl(s) from the elements is accomplished by two different routes. The direct route is the formation reaction (shown in boldface), and the enthalpy change is ΔH_f°. The indirect route occurs in five steps.

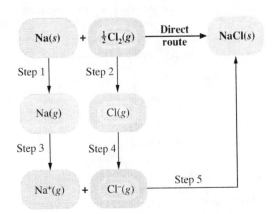

Let us write these five steps and add them. We also add the corresponding enthalpy changes, following Hess's law.

$$
\begin{array}{lll}
\text{Na}(s) & \longrightarrow \text{Na}(g) & \Delta H_1 = 108 \text{ kJ} \\
\tfrac{1}{2}\text{Cl}_2(g) & \longrightarrow \text{Cl}(g) & \Delta H_2 = 120 \text{ kJ} \\
\text{Na}(g) & \longrightarrow \text{Na}^+(g) + e^-(g) & \Delta H_3 = 496 \text{ kJ} \\
\text{Cl}(g) + e^-(g) & \longrightarrow \text{Cl}^-(g) & \Delta H_4 = -349 \text{ kJ} \\
\text{Na}^+(g) + \text{Cl}^-(g) & \longrightarrow \text{NaCl}(s) & \Delta H_5 = -U \\
\hline
\text{Na}(s) + \tfrac{1}{2}\text{Cl}_2(g) & \longrightarrow \text{NaCl}(s) & \Delta H_f^\circ = 375 \text{ kJ} - U
\end{array}
$$

In summing the equations, we have canceled terms that appear on both the left and right sides of the arrows. The final equation is simply the formation reaction for NaCl(s). Adding the enthalpy changes, we find that the enthalpy change for this formation reaction is 375 kJ $- U$. But the enthalpy of formation has been determined calorimetrically and equals -411 kJ. Equating these two values, we get

$$375 \text{ kJ} - U = -411 \text{ kJ}$$

Solving for U yields the lattice energy of NaCl:

$$U = (375 + 411) \text{ kJ} = 786 \text{ kJ}$$

Properties of Ionic Substances

Typically, ionic substances are high-melting solids. Sodium chloride, NaCl, ordinary salt, melts at 801°C, and magnesium oxide, MgO, a ceramic, melts at 2800°C. The explanation for the high melting points of these substances is simple.

Small, spherical cations and anions interact by strong bonds that essentially depend on the electrical force of attraction described by Coulomb's law. Large groups of such cations and anions attract one another with strong ionic bonds linking all of the ions together, forming a crystalline solid. When you heat any solid, the atoms or ions of that solid begin to vibrate; and, as you raise the temperature, these atoms or ions vibrate through larger and larger distances. At a high enough temperature, the atoms or ions of the solid may move sufficiently far apart that the solid melts to a liquid (or the solid may simply decompose to different substances). The temperature at which melting occurs depends on the strength of the interaction between the atoms or ions. Typical ionic solids require high temperatures for this process to occur because of the strong interactions between the ions.

Coulomb's law also explains why magnesium oxide, which is composed of ions having double charges (Mg^{2+} and O^{2-}), has such a high melting point compared with sodium chloride (Na^+ and Cl^-). Coulomb interactions depend on the product of the ion charges. For NaCl, this is 1×1, whereas for MgO, this is 2×2, or 4 times greater. (Coulomb's law also depends on the distance between charges, or ions, which is about the same in NaCl and MgO.) The much larger Coulomb interaction in MgO requires a much greater temperature to initiate melting.

The liquid melt from an ionic solid consists of ions, and so the liquid conducts an electric current. If the ionic solid dissolves in a molecular liquid, such as water, the resulting solution consists of ions dispersed among molecules; the solution also conducts an electric current.

Recently, as the accompanying essay on ionic liquids describes, chemists have prepared ionic substances that behave atypically. Their unusual properties are the result of large, nonspherical cations that lead to especially weak ionic bonding. The melting points of these ionic substances are unusually low; often they are liquids at room temperature (that is, their melting points are below room temperature).

A Chemist Looks at . . .

Ionic Liquids and Green Chemistry

frontiers

New substances with peculiar or strange behavior have always intrigued chemists. The German chemist Hennig Brand in 1669 discovered a white, waxy solid that he called "cold fire," because it glowed in the dark—a strange property then and still captivating today. He tried to keep the recipe (lengthy boiling of putrid urine) secret, but people's fascination with the waxy solid, which was white phosphorus, proved irresistible.

Modern chemists continue to expand the boundaries of known materials. They have discovered plastics that conduct electricity like metals and materials that look solid but are so porous they are almost as light as air. Now chemists have produced room-temperature ionic liquids (Figure 9.4). Most of these are clear, well-behaved substances that look and pour much like water, and like water their strength is as solvents (liquids that dissolve other substances). In fact, they promise to be "super solvents."

FIGURE 9.5 ▲

The ions composing an ionic liquid
Shown here are space-filling models of the ions composing *N*-butylpyridinium nitrate. Note the bulky cation and small nitrate anion.

Given a material—an organic substance, a plastic, or even a rock—researchers believe you will be able to find an ionic liquid that is capable of dissolving it!

Compare room-temperature ionic liquids with their more prosaic cousins. Sodium chloride, a typical example, is solid at room temperature and doesn't melt until exposed to temperatures over 800°C. The molten liquid, though clear, is very corrosive (chemically reactive). The high melting point of sodium chloride is easily explained. It consists of small, spherical ions that pack closely together. Thus, the ions interact strongly, giving a solid with a high melting point. Room-temperature ionic liquids, by contrast, consist of large, nonspherical cations with various anions (Figure 9.5). It is the large, bulky cations that keep the ions from packing closely; the large distances between ions result in weak interactions, yielding a substance whose melting point is often well below room temperature.

The demand for *green chemistry*, the commercial production of chemicals using environmentally sound methods, has spurred much of the research into ionic liquids. Many chemical processes use volatile organic solvents. These solvents are liquids that evaporate easily into the surrounding air, where they can contribute to air pollution. Organic solvents are often flammable, too. Ionic liquids are neither volatile nor flammable. In addition to these environmental rewards, however, ionic liquids appear to offer another bonus: The proper choice of ionic liquid may improve the yield and lower the costs of a chemical process.

Copyright 2000 American Chemical Society

FIGURE 9.4 ▲

Room-temperature ionic liquid
Hélène Olivier of the French Petroleum Institute displays a tube containing an ionic liquid (including a blue nickel compound) with a hydrocarbon liquid above it. Typical liquids, such as a hydrocarbon, are molecular substances, whereas ionic liquids are composed of ions.

■ See Problems 9.111 and 9.112.

9.2 | Electron Configurations of Ions

In the previous section, we described the formation of ions from atoms. Often you can understand what monatomic ions form by looking at the electron configurations of the atoms and deciding what configurations you would expect for the ions.

Ions of the Main-Group Elements

ChemWork: Electron Configurations of Ions

ChemWork: Electron Configurations for Ions

ChemWork: Noble Gas Configurations and Ions

In Chapter 2, we listed the common monatomic ions of the main-group elements (Table 2.3). Most of the cations are obtained by removing all the valence electrons from the atoms of metallic elements. Once these atoms have lost their valence electrons, they have stable noble-gas or pseudo-noble-gas configurations. The stability of these configurations can be seen by looking at the successive ionization energies of some atoms. Table 9.2 lists the first through the fourth ionization energies of Na, Mg, and Al. The energy needed to remove the first electron from the Na atom is only 496 kJ/mol (first ionization energy). But the energy required to remove another electron (the second ionization energy) is nearly ten times greater (4562 kJ/mol). The electron in this case must be taken from Na^+, which has a neon configuration. Magnesium and aluminum atoms are similar. Their valence electrons are easily removed, but the energy needed to take an electron from either of the ions that result (Mg^{2+} and Al^{3+}) is extremely high. That is why no compounds are found with ions having charges greater than the group number.

The loss of successive electrons from an atom requires increasingly more energy. Consequently, Group IIIA elements show less tendency to form ionic compounds than do Group IA and IIA elements, which primarily form ionic compounds. Boron, in fact, forms no compounds with B^{3+} ions. The bonding is normally covalent, a topic discussed later in this chapter. However, the tendency to form ions becomes greater going down any column of the periodic table because of decreasing ionization energy. The remaining elements of Group IIIA do form compounds containing 3+ ions.

There is also a tendency for Group IIIA to VA elements of higher periods, particularly Period 6, to form compounds with ions having a positive charge of two less than the group number. Thallium in IIIA, Period 6, has compounds with 1+ ions and compounds with 3+ ions. Ions with charge equal to the group number minus two are obtained when the np electrons of an atom are lost but the ns^2 electrons are retained. For example,

$$Tl([Xe]4f^{14}5d^{10}6s^26p^1) \longrightarrow Tl^+([Xe]4f^{14}5d^{10}6s^2) + e^-$$

Few compounds of 4+ ions are known because the energy required to form ions is so great. The first three elements of Group IVA—C, Si, and Ge—are nonmetals (or metalloids) and usually form covalent rather than ionic bonds. Tin and lead, however, the fourth and fifth elements of Group IVA, commonly form compounds with 2+ ions

TABLE 9.2	Ionization Energies of Na, Mg, and Al (in kJ/mol)*			
		Successive Ionization Energies		
Element	First	Second	Third	Fourth
Na	496	4,562	6,912	9,543
Mg	738	1,451	7,733	10,540
Al	578	1,817	2,745	11,577

*Energies for the ionization of valence electrons lie to the left of the colored line.

Interestingly, lithium metal reacts with nitrogen at room temperature to form a layer of lithium nitride, Li_3N, on the metal surface (see photo above).

(ionic charge equal to the group number minus two). For example, tin forms tin(II) chloride, $SnCl_2$, which is an ionic compound. It also forms tin(IV) chloride, $SnCl_4$, but this is a covalent, not an ionic, compound. Bismuth, in Group VA, is a metallic element that forms compounds of Bi^{3+} (ionic charge equal to the group number minus two), where only the $6p$ electrons have been lost.

Group VIA and Group VIIA elements, whose atoms have the largest negative electron affinities, would be expected to form monatomic ions by gaining electrons to give noble-gas or pseudo-noble-gas configurations. An atom of a Group VIIA element (valence-shell configuration ns^2np^5) picks up one electron to give a $1-$ anion (ns^2np^6); examples are F^- and Cl^-. (Hydrogen also forms compounds of the $1-$ ion, H^-. The hydride ion, H^-, has a $1s^2$ configuration, like the noble-gas atom helium.) An atom of a Group VIA element (valence-shell configuration ns^2np^4) picks up two electrons to give a $2-$ anion (ns^2np^6); examples are O^{2-} and S^{2-}. Although the electron affinity of nitrogen ($2s^22p^3$) is zero, the N^{3-} ion ($2s^22p^6$) is stable in the presence of certain positive ions, including Li^+ and those of the alkaline earth elements. <

To summarize, the common monatomic ions found in compounds of the main-group elements fall into three categories (see Table 2.3):

1. Cations of Groups IA to IIIA having noble-gas or pseudo-noble-gas configurations. The ion charges equal the group numbers.

2. Cations of Groups IIIA to VA having ns^2 electron configurations. The ion charges equal the group numbers minus two. Examples are Tl^+, Sn^{2+}, Pb^{2+}, and Bi^{3+}.

3. Anions of Groups VA to VIIA having noble-gas or pseudo-noble-gas configurations. The ion charges equal the group numbers minus eight.

Example 9.2 | Writing the Electron Configuration and Lewis Symbol for a Main-Group Ion

Write the electron configuration and the Lewis symbol for N^{3-}.

Problem Strategy Recall the three categories of main-group monatomic ions: (1) cations of Groups IA to IIIA usually have ion charges equal to group numbers; (2) cations of Groups IIIA to VA may have ion charges equal to group numbers minus two—an example is Tl^+; and (3) anions of Groups VA to VIIIA have charges equal to the group numbers minus eight. Write the electron configuration of the atom, and then subtract or add electrons to give the ion. Similarly, write the Lewis symbol of the atom, and subtracting or adding dots to give the ion.

Solution The electron configuration of the N atom is $[He]2s^22p^3$. By gaining three electrons, the atom

assumes a $3-$ charge and the neon configuration $[He]2s^22p^6$. The Lewis symbol is

$$[:\ddot{N}:]^{3-}$$

Answer Check Check that the ion has a noble-gas or pseudo-noble-gas configuration and that the Lewis symbol has eight dots, or none, around the atomic symbol.

Exercise 9.2 Write the electron configuration and the Lewis symbol for Ca^{2+} and for S^{2-}.

■ See Problems 9.39 and 9.40.

Exercise 9.3 Write the electron configurations of Pb and Pb^{2+}.

■ See Problems 9.41 and 9.42.

An alternative example is provided in the Instructor's Resource Manual.

Polyatomic Ions

Many ions, particularly anions, are polyatomic. Some common polyatomic ions are listed in Table 2.5. The atoms in these ions are held together by covalent bonds, which we will discuss in Section 9.4.

FIGURE 9.6

Common transition-metal cations in aqueous solution
Left to right: Cr^{3+} (red-violet), Mn^{2+} (pale pink), Fe^{2+} (pale green), Fe^{3+} (pale yellow), Co^{2+} (pink), Ni^{2+} (green), Cu^{2+} (blue), Zn^{2+} (colorless).

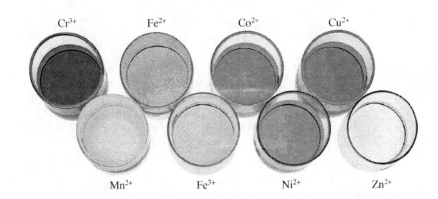

Demonstration of the color of transition-metal ions. Place dishes of aqueous solutions on overhead and project.

Transition-Metal Ions

Most transition elements form several cations of different charges. For example, iron has the cations Fe^{2+} and Fe^{3+}. Neither has a noble-gas configuration; that would require the energetically impossible loss of eight electrons from the neutral atom.

In forming ions in compounds, the atoms of transition elements generally lose the ns electrons first; then they may lose one or more $(n-1)d$ electrons. The 2+ ions are common for the transition elements and are obtained by the loss of the highest-energy s electrons from the atom. Many transition elements also form 3+ ions by losing one $(n-1)d$ electron in addition to the two ns electrons. Table 2.4 lists some common transition-metal ions. Many compounds of transition-metal ions are colored because of transitions involving d electrons, whereas the compounds of the main-group elements are usually colorless (Figure 9.6).

Example 9.3 | Writing Electron Configurations of Transition-Metal Ions

Write the electron configurations of Fe^{2+} and Fe^{3+}.

Problem Strategy After obtaining the electron configuration of the atom (using the building-up principle as in Example 8.2 or Example 8.3), remove ns electrons, then $(n-1)d$ electrons, until you have the correct positive charge on the ion.

Solution The electron configuration of the Fe atom $(Z = 26)$ is $[Ar]3d^6 4s^2$. To obtain the configuration of Fe^{2+}, remove the $4s^2$ electrons. To obtain the configuration of Fe^{3+}, also remove a $3d$ electron. **The configuration of Fe^{2+} is $[Ar]3d^6$, and that of Fe^{3+} is $[Ar]3d^5$.**

An alternative example is provided in the Instructor's Resource Manual.

Answer Check Check that the number of outer electrons in an ion is correct. The number of outer electrons equals the group number (but count the columns of Group VIIIB as 8, 9, and 10) minus the ion charge. For example, the configuration of Fe^{2+} is given as $[Ar]3d^6$. Iron is in the first column of Group VIIIB (count 8); the ion has two fewer electrons $(8 - 2 = 6)$. This checks with the configuration as written.

Exercise 9.4 Write the electron configuration of Mn^{2+}.

■ See Problems 9.43 and 9.44.

Concept Check 9.1

The following are electron configurations for some ions. Which ones would you expect to see in chemical compounds? State the concept or rule you used to decide for or against any ion.

a. Fe^{2+} $[Ar]3d^4 4s^2$ b. N^{2-} $[He]2s^2 2p^5$ c. Zn^{2+} $[Ar]3d^{10}$

d. Na^{2+} $[He]2s^2 2p^5$ e. Ca^{2+} $[Ne]3s^2 3p^6$

FIGURE 9.7

Determining the iodide ion radius in the lithium iodide (LiI) crystal
(A) A three-dimensional view of the crystal. *(B)* Cross section through a layer of ions. Iodide ions are assumed to be spheres in contact with one another. The distance between iodine nuclei (426 pm) is determined experimentally. One-half of this distance (213 pm) equals the iodide ion radius.

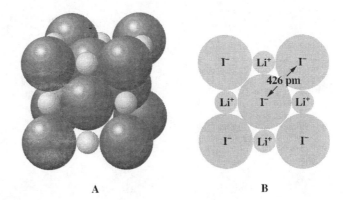

A   B

The study of crystal structure by x-ray diffraction is discussed in Chapter 11.

9.3 | Ionic Radii

A monatomic ion, like an atom, is a nucleus surrounded by a distribution of electrons. The **ionic radius** is *a measure of the size of the spherical region around the nucleus of an ion within which the electrons are most likely to be found.* As for an atomic radius, defining an ionic radius is somewhat arbitrary, because an electron distribution never abruptly ends. However, if we imagine ions to be spheres of definite size, we can obtain their radii from known distances between nuclei in crystals. (These distances can be determined accurately by observing how crystals diffract x rays.) ◁

To understand how you compute ionic radii, consider the determination of the radius of an I^- ion in a lithium iodide (LiI) crystal. Figure 9.7 depicts a layer of ions in LiI. The distance between adjacent iodine nuclei equals twice the I^- radius. From x-ray diffraction experiments, the iodine–iodine distance is found to be 426 pm (1 pm = 1×10^{-12} m). Therefore, the I^- radius in LiI is $\frac{1}{2} \times$ 426 pm = 213 pm. Other crystals give approximately the same radius for the I^- ion. Table 9.3, which lists average values of ionic radii obtained from many compounds of the main-group elements, gives 216 pm for the I^- radius.

That you can find values of ionic radii that agree with the known structures of many crystals is strong evidence for the existence of ions in the solid state. Moreover, these values of ionic radii compare with atomic radii in ways that you might expect. For example, you expect a cation to be smaller and an anion to be larger than the corresponding atom (see Figure 9.8).

Na
[He] $2s^2 2p^6 3s^1$ Na$^+$
                        [He] $2s^2 2p^6$

Cl
[Ne] $3s^2 3p^5$ Cl$^-$
                    [Ne] $3s^2 3p^6$

FIGURE 9.8 ▲

Comparison of atomic and ionic radii
Note that the sodium atom loses its outer shell in forming the Na$^+$ ion. Thus, the cation is smaller than the atom. The Cl$^-$ ion is larger than the Cl atom, because the same nuclear charge holds a greater number of electrons less strongly.

TABLE 9.3	**Ionic Radii (in pm) of Some Main-Group Elements**				
Period	IA	IIA	IIIA	VIA	VIIA
2	Li$^+$	Be^{2+}		O^{2-}	F$^-$
	60	31		140	136
3	Na$^+$	Mg^{2+}	Al^{3+}	S^{2-}	Cl$^-$
	95	65	50	184	181
4	K$^+$	Ca^{2+}	Ga^{3+}	Se^{2-}	Br$^-$
	133	99	62	198	195
5	Rb$^+$	Sr^{2+}	In^{3+}	Te^{2-}	I$^-$
	148	113	81	221	216
6	Cs$^+$	Ba^{2+}	Tl^{3+}		
	169	135	95		

A cation formed when an atom loses all its valence electrons is smaller than the atom because it has one less shell of electrons. But even when only some of the valence electrons are lost from an atom, the ion is smaller. With fewer electrons in the valence orbitals, the electron–electron repulsion is initially less, so these orbitals can shrink to increase the attraction of the electrons for the nucleus. Similarly, because an anion has more electrons than the atom, the electron–electron repulsion is greater, so the valence orbitals expand. Thus, the anion radius is larger than the atomic radius.

Exercise 9.5   Which has the larger radius, S or S^{2-}? Explain.

See Problems 9.45 and 9.46.

The ionic radii of the main-group elements shown in Table 9.3 follow a regular pattern, just as atomic radii do. *Ionic radii increase down any column because of the addition of electron shells.*

Exercise 9.6   Without looking at Table 9.3, arrange the following ions in order of increasing ionic radius: Sr^{2+}, Mg^{2+}, Ca^{2+}. (You may use a periodic table.)

See Problems 9.47 and 9.48.

The pattern across a period becomes clear if you look first at the cations and then at the anions. For example, in the third period we have

Cation	Na^+	Mg^{2+}	Al^{3+}
Radius (pm)	95	65	50

All of these ions have the neon configuration $1s^2 2s^2 2p^6$ but different nuclear charges; that is, they are isoelectronic. **Isoelectronic** *refers to different species having the same number and configuration of electrons.* To understand the decrease in radius from Na^+ to Al^{3+}, imagine the nuclear charge (atomic number) of Na^+ to increase. With each increase of charge, the orbitals contract due to the greater attractive force of the nucleus. Thus, in any isoelectronic sequence of atomic ions, the ionic radius decreases with increasing atomic number (just as it does for the atoms).

If you look at the anions in the third-period elements, you notice that they are much larger than the cations in the same period. This abrupt increase in ionic radius is due to the fact that the anions S^{2-} and Cl^- have configurations with one more shell of electrons than the cations. And because these anions also constitute an isoelectronic sequence (with argon configuration), the ionic radius decreases with atomic number (as with the atoms):

Anion	S^{2-}	Cl^-
Radius (pm)	184	181

Thus, *in general, across a period the cations decrease in radius. When you reach the anions, there is an abrupt increase in radius, and then the radius again decreases.*

Example 9.4	Using Periodic Trends to Obtain Relative Ionic Radii

Without looking at Table 9.3, arrange the following ions in order of decreasing ionic radius: F^-, Mg^{2+}, O^{2-}. (You may use a periodic table.)

Problem Strategy Note that in a series of isoelectronic ions, the ion radius decreases with an increase in nuclear charge (or atomic number).

Solution Note that F^-, Mg^{2+}, and O^{2-} are isoelectronic. If you arrange them by increasing nuclear charge,

they will be in order of decreasing ionic radius. **The order is O^{2-}, F^-, Mg^{2+}.**

Answer Check Check that the ions are isoelectronic by writing their electron configurations.

Exercise 9.7 Without looking at Table 9.3, arrange the following ions in order of increasing ionic radius: Cl^-, Ca^{2+}, P^{3-}. (You may use a periodic table.)

An alternative example is provided in the Instructor's Resource Manual.

■ See Problems 9.49 and 9.50.

Covalent Bonds

Experiments in General Chemistry, 9B, "From Oil of Wintergreen to Salicylic Acid."

G. N. Lewis (1875–1946) was professor of chemistry at the University of California at Berkeley. Well known for work on chemical bonding, he was also noted for his research in molecular spectroscopy and thermodynamics (the study of heat involved in chemical and physical processes).

In the preceding sections we looked at ionic substances, which are typically high-melting solids. Many substances, however, are molecular—gases, liquids, or low-melting solids consisting of molecules (Figure 9.9). A molecule is a group of atoms, frequently nonmetal atoms, strongly linked by chemical bonds. Often the forces that hold atoms together in a molecular substance cannot be understood on the basis of the attraction of oppositely charged ions (the ionic model). An obvious example is the molecule H_2, in which the two H atoms are held together tightly and no ions are present. In 1916 Gilbert Newton Lewis proposed that the strong attractive force between two atoms in a molecule results from a **covalent bond,** *a chemical bond formed by the sharing of a pair of electrons between atoms.* < In 1926 Walter Heitler and Fritz London showed that the covalent bond in H_2 could be quantitatively explained by the newly discovered theory of quantum mechanics. We will discuss the descriptive aspects of covalent bonding in the following sections.

FIGURE 9.9 ▶

Two molecular substances
Left: Iodoform, CHI_3, is a low-melting, yellow solid (m.p. 120°C). *Right:* Carbon tetrachloride, CCl_4, is a colorless liquid.

9.4 | ## Describing Covalent Bonds

Consider the formation of a covalent bond between two H atoms to give the H_2 molecule. As the atoms approach one another, their $1s$ orbitals begin to overlap. Each electron can then occupy the space around both atoms. In other words, the two electrons can be shared by the atoms (Figure 9.10). The electrons are attracted simultaneously by the positive charges of the two hydrogen nuclei. This attraction that bonds the electrons to both nuclei is the force holding the atoms together. Although ions do not exist in H_2, the force that holds the atoms together can still be regarded as arising from the attraction of oppositely charged particles: nuclei and electrons.

It is interesting to see how the potential energy of the atoms changes as they approach and then bond. Figure 9.11 shows the potential energy of the atoms for various distances between nuclei. The potential energy of the atoms when they are some distance apart is indicated by a position on the potential-energy curve at the far right. As the atoms approach (moving from right to left on the potential-energy curve), the potential energy gets lower and lower. The decrease in energy is a reflection of the bonding of the atoms. Eventually, as the atoms get close enough, the repulsion of the positive charges on the nuclei becomes larger than the attraction of electrons for nuclei. In other words, the potential energy reaches a minimum value and then increases. The distance between nuclei at this minimum energy is called the *bond length* of H_2. It is the normal distance between nuclei in the molecule.

Now imagine the reverse process. You start with the H_2 molecule, the atoms at their normal bond length apart (at the minimum of the potential-energy curve). To separate the atoms in the molecule, energy must be added (you move along the curve to the flat portion at the right). The energy that must be added is called the *bond dissociation energy*. The larger the bond dissociation energy, the stronger the bond.

Lewis Formulas

You can represent the formation of the covalent bond in H_2 from atoms as follows:

$$H \cdot + \cdot H \longrightarrow H : H$$

This uses the Lewis electron-dot symbol for the hydrogen atoms and represents the covalent bond by a pair of dots. Recall that the two electrons from the covalent bond

H(*g*)   H(*g*) H_2(*g*)

FIGURE 9.10 ▲

The electron probability distribution for the H_2 molecule

The electron density (shown in red) occupies the space around both atoms.

FIGURE 9.11 ▶

Potential-energy curve for H_2

The stable molecule occurs at the bond distance corresponding to the minimum in the potential-energy curve.

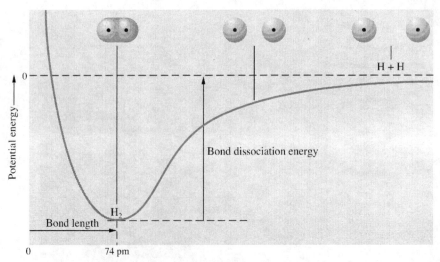

spend part of the time in the region of each atom. In this sense, each atom in H_2 has a helium configuration. We can draw a circle about each atom to emphasize this.

$$(H \! : \! H)$$

The formation of a bond between H and Cl to give an HCl molecule can be represented in a similar way.

$$H \cdot \; + \; \cdot \ddot{\underset{..}{Cl}} : \; \longrightarrow \; \left(H \! : \! \ddot{\underset{..}{Cl}} : \right)$$

As the two atoms approach each other, unpaired electrons on each atom pair up to form a covalent bond. The pair of electrons is shared by the two atoms. Each atom then acquires a noble-gas configuration of electrons, the H atom having two electrons about it (as in He), and the Cl atom having eight valence electrons about it (as in Ar).

A formula using dots to represent valence electrons is called a **Lewis electron-dot formula.** An electron pair represented by a pair of dots in such a formula is either a **bonding pair** *(an electron pair shared between two atoms)* or a **lone,** or **nonbonding, pair** *(an electron pair that remains on one atom and is not shared).* For example,

$$H : \ddot{\underset{..}{Cl}} : \; \longleftarrow \text{lone pairs}$$
$$\underset{\text{bonding pair}}{\nwarrow}$$

Bonding pairs are often represented by dashes rather than by pairs of dots.

Frequently, the number of covalent bonds formed by an atom equals the number of unpaired electrons shown in its Lewis symbol. Consider the formation of NH_3.

$$3H \cdot \; + \; \cdot \overset{.}{\underset{.}{N}} : \; \longrightarrow \; H : \overset{\overset{\displaystyle H}{..}}{\underset{\underset{\displaystyle H}{..}}{N}} :$$

Each bond is formed between an unpaired electron on one atom and an unpaired electron on another atom. In many instances, the number of bonds formed by an atom in Groups IVA to VIIA equals the number of unpaired electrons, which is eight minus the group number. For example, a nitrogen atom (Group VA) forms $8 - 5 = 3$ covalent bonds. <

Coordinate Covalent Bonds

When bonds form between atoms that both donate an electron, you have

$$A \cdot + \cdot B \longrightarrow A : B$$

However, it is possible for both electrons to come from the same atom. A **coordinate covalent bond** is *a bond formed when both electrons of the bond are donated by one atom:*

$$A + : B \longrightarrow A : B$$

A coordinate covalent bond is not essentially different from other covalent bonds; it involves the sharing of a pair of electrons between two atoms. An example is the formation of the ammonium ion, in which an electron pair on the N atom of NH_3 forms a bond with H^+.

$$H^+ \; + : NH_3 \; \longrightarrow \; \left[H : \overset{\overset{\displaystyle H}{..}}{\underset{\underset{\displaystyle H}{..}}{N}} : H \right]^+$$

The new N—H bond is clearly identical to the other N—H bonds.

Octet Rule

In each of the molecules we have described so far, the atoms have obtained noble-gas configurations through the sharing of electrons. Atoms other than hydrogen have

A systematic scheme for writing Lewis formulas is described in Section 9.6; here we simply introduce Lewis formulas.

The numbers of unpaired electrons in the Lewis symbols for the atoms of elements in Groups IA and IIIA equal the group numbers. But except for the first elements of these groups, the atoms usually form ionic bonds.

A Chemist Looks at . . .

Chemical Bonds in Nitroglycerin

Nitroglycerin gained a nasty reputation soon after its discovery in 1846. Unless kept cold, the pale yellow, oily liquid detonates from even the mildest vibration. In the French film *The Wages of Fear*, four men agree to drive two trucks loaded with nitroglycerin over mountainous roads from a remote village in South America. They are to drive the nitroglycerin to an out-of-control oil-well fire, where the explosive will be used to close off the well. On the way, they find the road obstructed by a huge boulder that has rolled across it, and they decide to blast the boulder out of their way using some of their explosive cargo. You see one of the men gingerly pouring nitroglycerin from a thermos bottle down a stick and into a hole in the rock. Beads of sweat form on his contorted face, while he tries desperately to suspend his breathing and any extra movement that might set off the nitroglycerin.

Here is the structure of nitroglycerin (also see the molecular model in Figure 9.12):

With just a little jostling, nitroglycerin, $C_3H_5(ONO_2)_3$, can rearrange its atoms to give stable products:

$$4C_3H_5(ONO_2)_3(l) \longrightarrow$$
$$6N_2(g) + 12CO_2(g) + 10H_2O(g) + O_2(g)$$

The stability of the products results from their strong bonds, which are much stronger than those in nitroglycerin. Nitrogen, for example, has a strong nitrogen–nitrogen triple bond, and carbon dioxide has two strong carbon–oxygen double bonds. The explosive force of the reaction results from both the rapid reaction and from the large volume increase on forming gaseous products.

In 1867, the Swedish chemist Alfred Nobel discovered that nitroglycerin behaved better when absorbed on diatomaceous earth, a crumbly rock, giving an explosive mixture that Nobel called *dynamite*. Part of the wealth he made from his explosive factories was left in trust to establish the Nobel Prizes. Although explosives are often associated in people's minds with war, they do have many peacetime uses, including road building, mining, and demolition (Figure 9.13).

FIGURE 9.13 ▲
Demolition of a building
Explosives are placed at predetermined positions so that when they are detonated, the building collapses on itself.

FIGURE 9.12 ▲
Molecular model of nitroglycerin
In this ball-and-stick model, carbon atoms are gray, hydrogen atoms are light blue, oxygen atoms are red, and nitrogen atoms are dark blue.

■ See Problems 9.113 and 9.114.

obtained eight electrons in their valence shells; hydrogen atoms have obtained two. *The tendency of atoms in molecules to have eight electrons in their valence shells (two for hydrogen atoms)* is known as the **octet rule.** Many of the molecules we will discuss follow the octet rule. Some do not.

Multiple Bonds

In the molecules we have described so far, each of the bonds has been a **single bond**— that is, *a covalent bond in which a single pair of electrons is shared by two atoms.* But it is possible for atoms to share two or more electron pairs. A **double bond** is *a covalent bond in which two pairs of electrons are shared by two atoms.* A **triple bond** is *a covalent bond in which three pairs of electrons are shared by two atoms.* As examples, consider ethylene, C_2H_4, and acetylene, C_2H_2. Their Lewis formulas are

Ethylene

Acetylene

Note the octet of electrons on each C atom. Double bonds form primarily with C, N, O, and S atoms. Triple bonds form mostly to C and N atoms.

9.5 Polar Covalent Bonds; Electronegativity

A covalent bond involves the sharing of at least one pair of electrons between two atoms. When the atoms are alike, as in the case of the H—H bond of H_2, the bonding electrons are shared equally. That is, the electrons spend the same amount of time in the vicinity of each atom. But when the two atoms are of different elements, the bonding electrons need not be shared equally. A **polar covalent bond** (or simply *polar bond*) is *a covalent bond in which the bonding electrons spend more time near one atom than the other.* For example, in the case of the HCl molecule (Figure 9.14), the bonding electrons spend more time near the chlorine atom than the hydrogen atom.

You can consider the polar covalent bond as intermediate between a *nonpolar* covalent bond, as in H_2, and an ionic bond, as in NaCl. From this point of view, an ionic bond is simply an extreme example of a polar covalent bond. To illustrate, we can represent the bonding in H_2, HCl, and NaCl with electron-dot formulas as follows:

The bonding pairs of electrons are equally shared in H_2, unequally shared in HCl, and essentially not shared in NaCl. Thus, it is possible to arrange different bonds to form a gradual transition from nonpolar covalent to ionic.

Electronegativity is *a measure of the ability of an atom in a molecule to draw bonding electrons to itself.* Several electronegativity scales have been proposed. In 1934 Robert S. Mulliken suggested on theoretical grounds that the electronegativity (X) of an atom be given as half its ionization energy (*I.E.*) minus electron affinity (*E.A.*). <

$$X = \frac{I.E. - E.A.}{2}$$

Ethylene

Acetylene

FIGURE 9.14 ▲
The HCl molecule
A molecular model.

ChemWork: Bond Types Between Atoms

ChemWork: Predicting Bonds Between Atoms

ChemWork: Bond Types in Compounds

ChemWork: Classifying Bonds in Molecules

ChemWork: Comparing Bonds

ChemWork: Comparing Electronegativities

ChemWork: Comparing Bond Polarity

Robert S. Mulliken received the Nobel Prize in chemistry in 1966 for his work on molecular orbital theory (discussed in Chapter 10).

— Increasing electronegativity —

Decreasing electronegativity

FIGURE 9.15 ▲

Electronegativities of the elements
The values given are those of Pauling (those in gray are not known).

An atom such as fluorine that tends to pick up electrons easily (large negative *E.A.*) and hold on to them strongly (large *I.E.*) has a large electronegativity. On the other hand, an atom such as lithium or cesium that loses electrons readily (small *I.E.*) and has little tendency to gain electrons (small negative or positive *E.A.*) has a small electronegativity. Until recently, only a few electron affinities had been measured. For this reason, Mulliken's scale has had limited utility. A more widely used scale was derived earlier by Linus Pauling from bond energies, which are discussed later in this chapter. Pauling's electronegativity values are given in Figure 9.15. Because electronegativities depend somewhat on the bonds formed, these values are actually average ones. <

Fluorine, the most electronegative element, was assigned a value of 4.0 on Pauling's scale. Lithium, at the left end of the same period, has a value of 1.0. Cesium, in the same column but below lithium, has a value of 0.7. *In general, electronegativity increases from left to right and decreases from top to bottom in the periodic table.* Metals are the least electronegative elements (they are *electropositive*) and nonmetals the most electronegative.

> Linus Pauling received the Nobel Prize in chemistry in 1954 for his work on the nature of the chemical bond. In 1962 he received the Nobel Peace Prize.

The absolute value of the difference in electronegativity of two bonded atoms gives a rough measure of the polarity to be expected in a bond. When this difference is small, the bond is nonpolar. When it is large, the bond is polar (or, if the difference is very large, perhaps ionic). The electronegativity differences for the bonds H—H, H—Cl, and Na—Cl are 0.0, 0.9, and 2.1, respectively, following the expected order. Differences in electronegativity explain why ionic bonds usually form between a metal atom and a nonmetal atom; the electronegativity difference would be largest between these elements. On the other hand, covalent bonds form primarily between two nonmetals because the electronegativity differences are small. <

> The electronegativity difference in metal–metal bonding would also be small. This bonding frequently involves delocalized metallic bonding, briefly described in Section 9.7.

Example 9.5 | Using Electronegativities to Obtain Relative Bond Polarities

Use electronegativity values (Figure 9.15) to arrange the following bonds in order of increasing polarity: P—H, H—O, C—Cl.

Problem Strategy Order the bonds by the increasing positive value of the difference of electronegativities of the atoms forming the bond. The

(continued)

(*continued*)

bonds should then be roughly in order of increasing polarity.

Solution   The absolute values of the electronegativity differences are P—H, 0.0; H—O, 1.4; C—Cl, 0.5. Hence, the order is **P—H, C—Cl, H—O.**

An alternative example is provided in the Instructor's Resource Manual.

Answer Check   Make sure you have the correct electronegativities and differences.

Exercise 9.8   Using electronegativities, decide which of the following bonds is most polar: C—O, C—S, H—Br.

■ See Problems 9.57 and 9.58.

Lewis formulas do not directly convey information about molecular shape. For example, the Lewis formula of methane, CH₄, is written as the flat (two-dimensional) formula

$$
\begin{array}{c}
\text{H} \\
\text{..} \\
\text{H:C:H} \\
\text{..} \\
\text{H}
\end{array}
$$

The actual methane molecule, however, is not flat; it has a three-dimensional structure, as explained in Chapter 10.

You can use an electronegativity scale to predict the direction in which the electrons shift during bond formation; the electrons are pulled toward the more electronegative atom. For example, consider the H—Cl bond. Because the Cl atom ($X = 3.0$) is more electronegative than the H atom ($X = 2.1$), the bonding electrons in H—Cl are pulled toward Cl. Because the bonding electrons spend most of their time around the Cl atom, that end of the bond acquires a partial negative charge (indicated $\delta-$). The H-atom end of the bond has a partial positive charge ($\delta+$). You can show this as follows:

$$
\overset{\delta+ \quad \delta-}{\text{H—Cl}}
$$

The HCl molecule is said to be a *polar molecule*. We will say more about polar molecules when we look at molecular structures in Chapter 10.

9.6 Writing Lewis Electron-Dot Formulas

This section describes the rules for writing Lewis formulas; these are then elaborated on in Sections 9.7 to 9.9.

The Lewis electron-dot formula of a molecule is similar to the structural formula in that it shows how atoms are bonded. Bonding electron pairs are indicated either by two dots or by a dash. In addition to the bonding electrons, however, an electron-dot formula shows the positions of lone pairs of electrons, whereas the structural formula does not. Thus, the electron-dot formula is a simple two-dimensional representation of the positions of electrons in a molecule. In the next chapter we will see how to predict the three-dimensional shape of a molecule from the two-dimensional electron-dot formula. In this section we will discuss the steps for writing the electron-dot formula for a molecule made from atoms of the main-group elements. <

Before you can write the Lewis formula of a molecule (or a polyatomic ion), you must know the *skeleton structure* of the molecule. The skeleton structure tells you which atoms are bonded to one another (without regard to whether the bonds are single or not).

Normally the skeleton structure must be found by experiment. For simple molecules, you can often predict the skeleton structure. For instance, many small molecules or polyatomic ions consist of a central atom around which are bonded atoms of greater electronegativity, such as F, Cl, and O. Note the structural formula (and molecular model) of phosphorus oxychloride, POCl₃ (Figure 9.16). The phosphorus atom is surrounded by more electronegative atoms. (In some cases, H atoms surround a more electronegative atom as in H₂O and NH₃, but H cannot be a central atom because it normally forms only one bond.) Similarly, *oxoacids* are substances in which O atoms (and possibly other electronegative atoms) are bonded to a central atom, with one or more H atoms usually bonded to O atoms. An example is chlorosulfonic acid, HSO₃Cl (Figure 9.17).

Another useful idea for predicting skeleton structures is that molecules or polyatomic ions with symmetrical formulas often have symmetrical structures. For

$$
\begin{array}{c}
\text{Cl} \\
| \\
\text{Cl—P—O} \\
| \\
\text{Cl}
\end{array}
$$

Phosphorus oxychloride
POCl₃

FIGURE 9.16 ▲

Lewis formula and molecular model of phosphorus oxychloride molecule
The central atom, P, is surrounded by O and Cl atoms.

$$O$$
$$\overset{\displaystyle O}{\underset{\displaystyle Cl}{O-S-O-H}}$$

Chlorosulfonic acid
HSO_3Cl

FIGURE 9.17

Lewis formula and molecular model of chlorosulfonic acid molecule

This oxoacid has the central atom, S, surrounded by O atoms and a Cl atom.

example, disulfur dichloride, S_2Cl_2, is symmetrical, with the more electronegative Cl atoms around the S atoms: Cl—S—S—Cl.

Once you know the skeleton structure of a molecule, you can find the Lewis formula by applying the following four steps. These steps allow you to write electron-dot formulas even when the central atom does not follow the octet rule.

Step 1: *Calculate the total number of valence electrons* for the molecule by summing the number of valence electrons (= group number) for each atom. If you are writing the Lewis formula of a polyatomic anion, you *add* the number of negative charges to this total. (For CO_3^{2-} you add 2 because the -2 charge indicates that there are two more electrons than are provided by the neutral atoms.) For a polyatomic cation, you *subtract* the number of positive charges from the total. (For NH_4^+ you subtract 1.)

Step 2: *Write the skeleton structure of the molecule or ion*, connecting every bonded pair of atoms by a pair of dots (or a dash).

Step 3: *Distribute electrons to the atoms surrounding the central atom (or atoms)* to satisfy the octet rule for these surrounding atoms.

Step 4: *Distribute the remaining electrons as pairs to the central atom (or atoms)*, after subtracting the number of electrons already distributed from the total found in Step 1. If there are fewer than eight electrons on the central atom, this suggests that a multiple bond is present. (Two electrons fewer than an octet suggests a double bond; four fewer suggests a triple bond or two double bonds.) To obtain a multiple bond, move one or two electron pairs (depending on whether the bond is to be double or triple) from a surrounding atom to the bond connecting the central atom. Atoms that often form multiple bonds are C, N, O, and S.

The next several examples illustrate how to write the Lewis electron-dot formula for a small molecule, given the molecular formula.

Example 9.6	Writing Lewis Formulas (Single Bonds Only)

Sulfur dichloride, SCl_2, is a red, fuming liquid used in the manufacture of insecticides. Write the Lewis formula for the molecule.

An alternative example is provided in the Instructor's Resource Manual.

Problem Strategy   You follow the four steps: (1) Calculate the total number of valence electrons. (2) Write the skeleton structure with two electrons to each bond between atoms. (3) Distribute electrons to the outer atoms to satisfy the octet rule. (4) Distribute the remaining electrons to the central atom.

Solution   The number of valence electrons from an atom equals the group number: 6 for S, 7 for each Cl, for a total of 20 electrons. You expect the skeleton structure to have S as the central atom, with the more electronegative Cl atoms bonded to it. After connecting atoms by electron pairs and distributing electrons to the outer atoms, you have

$$:\overset{..}{Cl}:S:\overset{..}{Cl}: \quad \text{or} \quad :\overset{..}{Cl}-S-\overset{..}{Cl}:$$

This accounts for 8 electron pairs, or 16 electrons. Subtracting this from the total number of electrons (20) gives 4 electrons, or 2 electron pairs. You place these on the central atom (S). The final Lewis formula is

$$:\overset{..}{\underset{..}{Cl}}:\overset{..}{\underset{..}{S}}:\overset{..}{\underset{..}{Cl}}: \quad \text{or} \quad :\overset{..}{\underset{..}{Cl}}-\overset{..}{\underset{..}{S}}-\overset{..}{\underset{..}{Cl}}:$$

SCl_2

(continued)

(continued)

Answer Check   In general, atoms surrounding the central atom have four electron pairs (an octet) about them. Note that our answer follows this "octet" rule. Even the central atom often follows this octet rule, as it does here. (We will see some exceptions to this octet rule for the central atom, however.)

Exercise 9.9   Dichlorodifluoromethane, CCl_2F_2, is a gas used as a refrigerant and aerosol propellant. Write the Lewis formula for CCl_2F_2.

■ See Problems 9.61 and 9.62.

Example 9.7	Writing Lewis Formulas (Including Multiple Bonds)

Carbonyl chloride, or phosgene, $COCl_2$, is a highly toxic gas used as a starting material for the preparation of polyurethane plastics. What is the electron-dot formula of $COCl_2$?

An alternative example is provided in the Instructor's Resource Manual.

Problem Strategy   You follow the four steps as in the previous example, but after distributing the remaining electrons to the central atom, you find that it does not have an octet. To rectify this, you transfer an electron pair from an outer atom to form a double bond (part of Step 4). Do you move the electron pair from the Cl or the O atom? It helps to remember that C, N, O, and S atoms often form double bonds. In this case, you move the electron pair from the O atom.

Solution   The total number of valence electrons is $4 + 6 + (2 \times 7) = 24$. You expect the more electropositive atom, C, to be central, with the O and Cl atoms bonded to it. After distributing electron pairs to these surrounding atoms, you have

$$:\!\ddot{C}l\!:\!C\!:\!\ddot{O}\!: \quad \text{or} \quad :\!\ddot{C}l\!-\!C\!-\!\ddot{O}\!:$$
$$:\!\ddot{C}l\!: \qquad\qquad\qquad :\!\ddot{C}l\!:$$

This accounts for all 24 valence electrons, leaving only 6 electrons on C. This is two fewer than an octet, so you move a pair of electrons on the O atom to give a carbon–oxygen double bond. The electron-dot formula of $COCl_2$ is

$$:\!\ddot{C}l\!:\!C\!:\!:\!\ddot{O} \quad \text{or} \quad :\!\ddot{C}l\!-\!C\!=\!\ddot{O}$$
$$:\!\ddot{C}l\!: \qquad\qquad\qquad :\!\ddot{C}l\!:$$

Answer Check   Note that the atoms surrounding the central atom have four electron pairs about them; that is, they follow the octet rule. The central atom also follows the octet rule, although exceptions occur.

$COCl_2$

Exercise 9.10   Write the electron-dot formula of carbon dioxide, CO_2.

■ See Problems 9.63 and 9.64.

Example 9.8	Writing Lewis Formulas (Ionic Species)

Obtain the electron-dot formula (Lewis formula) of the BF_4^- ion.

An alternative example is provided in the Instructor's Resource Manual.

Problem Strategy   After calculating the total number of valence electrons for the neutral atoms, you add or subtract electrons to account for the ion charge. If the ion is negative,

(continued)

(continued)

add electrons to give the negative charge. If the ion is positive, subtract electrons to give the positive charge. Once you have the total number of valence electrons in the ion, proceed with the rest of the steps to write the electron-dot formula.

Solution   The total valence electrons provided by the boron and four fluorine atoms is $3 + (4 \times 7) = 31$. Because the anion has a charge of -1, it has one more electron than is provided by the neutral atoms. Thus, the total number of valence electrons is 32 (or 16 electron pairs). You assume that the skeleton structure has boron as the central atom, with the more electronegative F atoms bonded to it. After connecting the B and F atoms by bonds and placing electron pairs around the F atoms to satisfy the octet rule, you obtain

$$
\begin{array}{c}
:\!\ddot{F}\!: \\
:\!\ddot{F}\!:\!\ddot{B}\!:\!\ddot{F}\!: \\
:\!\ddot{F}\!:
\end{array}
\quad \text{or} \quad
\begin{array}{c}
:\!\ddot{F}\!: \\
| \\
:\!\ddot{F}\!-\!B\!-\!\ddot{F}\!: \\
| \\
:\!\ddot{F}\!:
\end{array}
$$

This uses up all 32 electrons. The charge on the entire ion is indicated by the minus sign written as a superscript to square brackets enclosing the electron-dot formula.

$$
\left[\begin{array}{c}
:\!\ddot{F}\!: \\
:\!\ddot{F}\!:\!\ddot{B}\!:\!\ddot{F}\!: \\
:\!\ddot{F}\!:
\end{array}\right]^{-}
\quad \text{or} \quad
\left[\begin{array}{c}
:\!\ddot{F}\!: \\
| \\
:\!\ddot{F}\!-\!B\!-\!\ddot{F}\!: \\
| \\
:\!\ddot{F}\!:
\end{array}\right]^{-}
$$

BF_4^-

Answer Check   Note that the atoms surrounding the central atom have four electron pairs about them; that is, they follow the octet rule. The central atom also follows the octet rule, although exceptions occur.

Exercise 9.11   Write the electron-dot formula of a. the hydronium ion, H_3O^+; b. the chlorite ion, ClO_2^-.

■ See Problems 9.65 and 9.66.

Concept Check 9.2

Each of the following may seem, at first glance, to be plausible electron-dot formulas for the molecule N_2F_2. Most, however, are incorrect for some reason. What concepts or rules apply to each, either to cast it aside or to keep it as the correct formula?

a. $:\!\ddot{F}\!:\!\ddot{N}\!:\!\ddot{N}\!:\!\ddot{F}\!:$ b. $:\!\ddot{F}\!:\!N\!:\!:\!N\!:\!\ddot{F}\!:$ c. $:\!\ddot{F}\!:\!:\!N\!:\!N\!:\!\ddot{F}\!:$

d. $:\!\ddot{F}\!:\!\ddot{N}\!:\!\ddot{N}\!:\!\ddot{F}\!:$ e. $:\!\ddot{F}\!:\!N\!:\!:\!\ddot{F}\!:\!N\!:$ f. $:\!\ddot{F}\!:\!N\ N\!:\!\ddot{F}\!:$

9.7 | Delocalized Bonding: Resonance

We have assumed up to now that the bonding electrons are localized in the region between two atoms. In some cases, however, this assumption does not fit the experimental data. Suppose, for example, that you try to write an electron-dot formula for ozone, O_3. You find that you can write two formulas:

In formula A, the oxygen–oxygen bond on the left is a double bond and the oxygen–oxygen bond on the right is a single bond. In formula B, the situation is just the opposite. Experiment shows, however, that both bonds in O_3 are identical. Therefore, neither formula can be correct. <

According to theory, one of the bonding pairs in ozone is spread over the region of all three atoms rather than associated with a particular oxygen–oxygen bond. This is called **delocalized bonding**, *a type of bonding in which a bonding pair of electrons is spread over a number of atoms rather than localized between two.* We might symbolically describe the delocalized bonding in ozone as follows:

(For clarity, only the bonding pairs are given.) The broken line indicates a bonding pair of electrons that spans three nuclei rather than only two. In effect, the oxygen–oxygen bond is neither a single bond nor a double bond but an intermediate type.

A single electron-dot formula cannot properly describe delocalized bonding. Instead, a resonance description is often used. According to the **resonance description,** *you describe the electron structure of a molecule having delocalized bonding by writing all possible electron-dot formulas.* These are called the *resonance formulas* of the molecule. The actual electron distribution of the molecule is a composite of these resonance formulas.

The electron structure of ozone can be described in terms of the two resonance formulas presented at the start of this section. By convention, we usually write all of the resonance formulas and connect them by double-headed arrows. For ozone we would write

Unfortunately, this notation can be misinterpreted. It does not mean that the ozone molecule flips back and forth between two forms. There is only one ozone molecule. The double-headed arrow means that you should form a mental picture of the molecule by fusing the various resonance formulas. The left oxygen–oxygen bond is double in formula A and the right one is double in formula B, so you must picture an electron pair that actually encompasses both bonds.

Attempting to write electron-dot formulas leads you to recognize that delocalized bonding exists in many molecules. Whenever you can write several plausible electron-dot formulas—which often differ merely in the allocation of single and double bonds to the same kinds of atoms (as in ozone)—you can expect delocalized bonding

The lengths of the two oxygen–oxygen bonds (that is, the distances between the atomic nuclei) are both 128 pm.

Example 9.9 Writing Resonance Formulas

Describe the electron structure of the carbonate ion, CO_3^{2-}, in terms of electron-dot formulas.

Problem Strategy Write at least one electron-dot formula for a molecule or ion. If the formula has both single and multiple bonds, note whether it is possible to write other electron-dot formulas differing only in the placement of single and double bonds.

An alternative example is provided in the Instructor's Resource Manual.

(continued)

(continued)

Solution One possible electron-dot formula for the carbonate ion is

$$\left[\begin{matrix} :\ddot{O}: \\ \| \\ C \\ :\ddot{O} \quad \ddot{O}: \end{matrix}\right]^{2-}$$

Because you expect all carbon–oxygen bonds to be equivalent, you must describe the electron structure in resonance terms.

$$\left[\begin{matrix} :\ddot{O}: \\ | \\ C \\ :\ddot{O} \quad \ddot{O}: \end{matrix}\right]^{2-} \longleftrightarrow \left[\begin{matrix} :\ddot{O}: \\ | \\ C \\ :\ddot{O} \quad \ddot{O}: \end{matrix}\right]^{2-} \longleftrightarrow \left[\begin{matrix} :\ddot{O}: \\ | \\ C \\ :\ddot{O} \quad \ddot{O}: \end{matrix}\right]^{2-}$$

You expect one electron pair to be delocalized over the region of all three carbon–oxygen bonds.

CO_3^{2-}

Answer Check Note that the skeleton structure is the same for all resonance formulas. This must be so, because they represent the same molecule. Also, note that the atoms about the central atom follow the octet rule. (The central atom in this case also follows the octet rule.)

Exercise 9.12 Describe the bonding in NO_3^- using resonance formulas.

■ See Problems 9.67, 9.68, 9.69, and 9.70.

Sodium ions

Valence electrons move throughout metal

FIGURE 9.18 ▲

Delocalized bonding in sodium metal
The metal consists of positive sodium ions in a "sea" of valence electrons. Valence (bonding) electrons are free to move throughout the metal crystal (beige area).

ChemWork: Lewis Structures

Metals are extreme examples of delocalized bonding. A sodium metal crystal, for example, can be regarded as an array of Na^+ ions surrounded by a "sea" of electrons (Figure 9.18). The valence, or bonding, electrons are delocalized over the entire metal crystal. The freedom of these electrons to move throughout the crystal is responsible for the electrical conductivity of a metal.

9.8 | Exceptions to the Octet Rule

Many molecules composed of atoms of the main-group elements have electronic structures that satisfy the octet rule, but a number of them do not. A few molecules, such as NO, have an odd number of electrons and so cannot satisfy the octet rule. Other exceptions to the octet rule fall into two groups—one a group of molecules with an atom having fewer than eight valence electrons around it and the other a group of molecules with an atom having more than eight valence electrons around it.

The exceptions in which the central atom has more than eight valence electrons around it are fairly numerous. Phosphorus pentafluoride is a simple example. This is a colorless gas of PF_5 molecules. Each molecule consists of a phosphorus atom surrounded by the more electronegative fluorine atoms (Figure 9.19). Following the steps outlined in Section 9.6, you arrive at the following electron-dot formula, in which the phosphorus atom has ten valence electrons around it:

$$\begin{matrix} :\ddot{F}: & \ddot{F}: \\ & | & / \\ :\ddot{F}-P & \\ & | & \backslash \\ :\ddot{F}: & \ddot{F}: \end{matrix}$$

FIGURE 9.19 ▲

Phosphorus pentafluoride, PF$_5$
A ball-and-stick molecular model.

The octet rule stems from the fact that the main-group elements in most cases employ only an ns and three np valence-shell orbitals in bonding, and these orbitals hold eight electrons. Elements of the second period are restricted to these orbitals, but from the third period on, the elements also have unfilled nd orbitals, which may be used in bonding. For example, the valence-shell configuration of phosphorus is $3s^23p^3$. Using just these $3s$ and $3p$ orbitals, the phosphorus atom can accept only three additional electrons, forming three covalent bonds (as in PF_3). However, more bonds can be formed if the empty $3d$ orbitals of the atom are used. If each of the five electrons of the phosphorus atom is paired with unpaired electrons of fluorine atoms, PF_5 can be formed. In this way, phosphorus forms both the trifluoride and the pentafluoride. By contrast, nitrogen (which has no available d orbitals in its valence shell) forms only the trifluoride, NF_3.

Example 9.10   Writing Lewis Formulas (Exceptions to the Octet Rule)

Xenon, a noble gas, forms a number of compounds. One of these is xenon tetrafluoride, XeF_4, a white, crystalline solid first prepared in 1962. What is the electron-dot formula of the XeF_4 molecule?

Problem Strategy   You follow the four steps outlined in Section 9.6. In Step 4, when you distribute the remaining electrons to the central atom, you find that it has more than an octet.

Solution   There are 8 valence electrons from the Xe atom and 7 from each F atom, for a total of 36 valence electrons. For the skeleton structure, you draw the Xe atom surrounded by the electronegative F atoms. After placing electron pairs on the F atoms to satisfy the octet rule for them, you have

This accounts for 16 pairs, or 32 electrons. A total of 36 electrons is available, so you put an additional $36 - 32 = 4$ electrons (2 pairs) on the Xe atom. The Lewis formula is

Answer Check   Note that the atoms surrounding the central atom follow the octet rule, although the central atom itself does not. The central atom is from a period greater than 2, so it has a valence shell that can accommodate more than eight electrons.

Exercise 9.13   Sulfur tetrafluoride, SF_4, is a colorless gas. Write the electron-dot formula of the SF_4 molecule.

An alternative example is provided in the Instructor's Resource Manual.

■ See Problems 9.71 and 9.72.

The other group of exceptions to the octet rule consists mostly of molecules containing Group IIA or IIIA atoms. Consider boron trifluoride, BF_3. The molecule consists of boron surrounded by the much more electronegative fluorine atoms. The total number of valence electrons is $3 + (3 \times 7) = 24$. If you connect boron and fluorine atoms by electron pairs and fill out the fluorine atoms with octets of electrons, you obtain

$$
\begin{array}{c}
:\ddot{F}: \\
| \\
:\ddot{F}\!-\!B \\
| \\
:\ddot{F}:
\end{array}
$$

If you now follow with Step 4 of the procedure outlined in Section 9.6, you note that the boron atom has only six electrons on it. You write the following resonance formulas, each having a double bond:

$$:\ddot{F}: \qquad :\ddot{F}: \qquad :\ddot{F}:$$
$$:\ddot{F}-\overset{\parallel}{B} \longleftrightarrow \ddot{F}=\overset{|}{B} \longleftrightarrow :\ddot{F}-\overset{|}{B}$$
$$:\ddot{F}: \qquad :\ddot{F}: \qquad :\ddot{F}:$$

In fact, there is evidence to suggest that the first formula written—the one with all single bonds and in which boron has only six electrons around it—describes the chemistry of boron trifluoride very well. For example, boron trifluoride reacts with molecules having a lone pair, such as with ammonia, NH_3, to give the compound BF_3NH_3. The reaction is easy to describe in terms of the formula in which boron has only six electrons around it.

$$:\ddot{F}: \quad H \qquad\qquad :\ddot{F}: \quad H$$
$$:\ddot{F}-\overset{|}{B} \quad + \quad :\overset{|}{N}-H \longrightarrow :\ddot{F}-\overset{|}{B}:\overset{|}{N}-H$$
$$:\ddot{F}: \quad H \qquad\qquad :\ddot{F}: \quad H$$

coordinate covalent bond

In this reaction, a coordinate covalent bond forms between the boron and nitrogen atoms, and the boron achieves an octet of electrons.

The chemistry of BF_3 thus appears to support an electron structure with boron having only six electrons around it. No doubt, resonance involving all four of the Lewis formulas that we have drawn best describes the actual electron structure of boron trifluoride, but the relative importance of the different resonance formulas is not settled. <

Other examples of molecules with Group IIIA atoms (such as Al) or Group IIA atoms (such as Be) display electron structures similar to that of boron trifluoride. For example, the BeF_2 molecule (found in the vapor over the heated solid BeF_2) has the Lewis formula

$$:\ddot{F}:Be:\ddot{F}:$$

Aluminum chloride, $AlCl_3$, offers an interesting study in bonding. At room temperature, the substance is a white, crystalline solid and an ionic compound, as might be expected for a binary compound of a metal and a nonmetal. However, the substance has a relatively low melting point (192°C) for an ionic compound. Apparently this is due to the fact that instead of melting to a liquid of ions, as happens with most ionic solids, the compound forms Al_2Cl_6 molecules (Figure 9.20), with Lewis formula

$$\overset{\displaystyle :\ddot{C}l: \quad :\ddot{C}l: \quad :\ddot{C}l:}{\underset{:\ddot{C}l: \quad :\ddot{C}l: \quad :\ddot{C}l:}{Al \qquad Al}}$$

Each atom has an octet of electrons around it. Note that two of the Cl atoms are in *bridge* positions, with each Cl atom having two covalent bonds. When this liquid is heated, it vaporizes as Al_2Cl_6 molecules. As the vapor is further heated, these molecules break up into $AlCl_3$ molecules. These molecules have an electron structure similar to that of BF_3.

The B–F bond length (130 pm) is shorter than expected for a single bond (152 pm), which indicates partial double-bond character. See the discussion in Section 9.10 on bond length and bond order.

FIGURE 9.20 ▲

The Al₂Cl₆ molecule

A ball-and-stick molecular model.

Exercise 9.14   Beryllium chloride, $BeCl_2$, is a solid substance consisting of long (essentially infinite) chains of atoms with Cl atoms in bridge positions.

However, if the solid is heated, it forms a vapor of $BeCl_2$ molecules. Write the electron-dot formula of the $BeCl_2$ molecule.

■ See Problems 9.73 and 9.74.

9.9 | Formal Charge and Lewis Formulas

Earlier we looked at writing the Lewis formula for carbonyl chloride, $COCl_2$ (Example 9.7). In the solution to that example, we wrote the answer as follows:

You may recall that we had to decide whether to draw the double bond between C and O or between C and Cl. We decided in favor of a carbon-oxygen double bond by applying the simple idea that multiple bonds most likely involve C, N, O, and S atoms. In this section, we will describe how you can use the concept of formal charge to determine the best Lewis formula. Formal charge is also a help in writing the skeleton structure of a molecule.

The **formal charge** of an atom in a Lewis formula is *the hypothetical charge you obtain by assuming that bonding electrons are equally shared between bonded atoms and that the electrons of each lone pair belong completely to one atom.* ◁ When you use the Lewis formula that most clearly describes the bonding, the formal charges give you an approximate distribution of electrons in the molecule. Let us see how you would obtain the formal charges, given several possible Lewis formulas of a molecule, and how you would use these formal charges to determine the best Lewis formula.

You begin by writing the possible Lewis formulas. For $COCl_2$, you can write

For each formula, you apply the following *rules for formal charge* to assign the valence electrons to individual atoms:

1. Half of the electrons of a bond are assigned to each atom in the bond (counting each dash as two electrons).

2. Both electrons of a lone pair are assigned to the atom to which the lone pair belongs.

You calculate the formal charge on an atom by taking the number of valence electrons on the free atom (equal to the group number) and subtracting the number of electrons you assigned the atom by the rules of formal charge; that is,

Formal charge = valence electrons on free atom $- \frac{1}{2}$(number of electrons in a bond)
                                                       $-$ (number of lone-pair electrons)

As a check on your work, you should note that the sum of the formal charges equals the charge on the molecular species (zero for a neutral molecule).

The rules for computing oxidation number are similar, except that both bonding electrons are assigned to the more electronegative atom.

Consider a Cl atom in the first Lewis formula we wrote for $COCl_2$. You begin by counting the electrons assigned to the Cl atom by the rules of formal charge. You have 1 electron from the single bond and 6 from the lone-pair electrons, for a total of 7. The formal charge of Cl equals the number of valence electrons (7) less the number of assigned electrons (7). This gives a formal charge of 0 for the Cl atom. Similar calculations of formal charge give 0 for each of the other atoms in the Lewis formula.

Now look at the second Lewis formula we wrote for $COCl_2$ and assign the electrons by the rules for formal charge. For the Cl atom having the double bond, you count 2 electrons from the double bond and 4 from the lone pairs, for a total of 6. The formal charge of the Cl atom is $7 - 6 = +1$. For the O atom, you count 1 electron from the single bond and 6 from the lone-pair electrons, for a total of 7. The number of valence electrons on the free O atom is 6, so the formal charge of the O atom is $6 - 7 = -1$. The formal charge of each of the other atoms is 0.

We indicate the formal charges in a Lewis formula by inserting circled numbers near the atoms (writing + for +1 and − for −1). For the formulas given earlier for $COCl_2$, the formal charges are shown as follows:

$$:\ddot{C}l-C=\ddot{O} \qquad \oplus \ddot{C}l=C-\ddot{O}:\ominus \qquad :\ddot{C}l-C-\ddot{O}:\ominus$$
$$\quad | \qquad\qquad\qquad | \qquad\qquad\qquad\quad \|$$
$$:\ddot{C}l: \qquad\qquad\quad :\ddot{C}l: \qquad\qquad\quad :\ddot{C}l:$$
$$\qquad\qquad\qquad\qquad\qquad\qquad\qquad\qquad\qquad\quad \oplus$$

Now we can discuss three rules that are useful in writing Lewis formulas.

> **RULE A** Whenever you can write several Lewis formulas for a molecule, choose the one having the lowest magnitudes of formal charges.
>
> **RULE B** When two proposed Lewis formulas for a molecule have the same magnitudes of formal charges, choose the one having the negative formal charge on the more electronegative atom.
>
> **RULE C** When possible, choose Lewis formulas that do not have like charges on adjacent atoms.

The second and third formulas for $COCl_2$ have formal charges on the Cl and O atoms. The first formula, however, has zero formal charges for all atoms. So by Rule A, this formula most closely approximates the actual electron distribution. You would write it as the best description by a single Lewis formula. (To be more precise, you could consider a resonance description involving all three Lewis formulas. However, the Lewis formulas would not participate equally in the resonance description; the first one would predominate.)

You can also use formal charges to help you choose the most likely skeleton structure from several possibilities. Consider thionyl chloride, $SOCl_2$. Which of the following Lewis formulas is most plausible? Note that these Lewis formulas have quite different atomic arrangements, so they should not be considered as simply different resonance formulas of the same molecule.

$$:\ddot{C}l: \qquad\qquad :\ddot{C}l: \qquad\qquad :\ddot{S}:\ominus$$
$$\quad | \qquad\qquad\qquad | \qquad\qquad\qquad |$$
$$:\ddot{C}l-\ddot{S}-\ddot{O}: \quad :\ddot{C}l-\ddot{O}-\ddot{S}: \quad :\ddot{C}l-\ddot{C}l-\ddot{O}:$$
$$\qquad\oplus\quad\ominus \qquad\qquad\oplus\quad\ominus \qquad\qquad\text{+2}\quad\ominus$$

You can verify these formal charges using the method we have outlined here. The last formula has a +2 formal charge on the Cl atom, which is larger in magnitude than the formal charges on any atoms in the other two formulas. Therefore, using Rule A, you would not consider the last formula a plausible structure. To choose between the first and second structures, you apply Rule B. According to this rule, you would choose the first structure over the second, because the first one associates a negative formal charge with the more electronegative atom (O), whereas the second structure associates a positive charge with the more electronegative atom. Note that this application of formal charge gives the same result that you would obtain by assuming that the least electronegative atom is the central atom.

Now that you have one Lewis formula with the appropriate skeleton structure for $SOCl_2$, you should explore the possibility of other Lewis formulas with this skeleton structure. You can write a Lewis formula that has a sulfur–oxygen double bond.

This formula has formal charges of zero for each atom; so according to Rule A, it should be closer to the actual electron distribution than the previous formula. (You could write a resonance description involving both formulas.) Note that the sulfur atom has 10 electrons around it. As long as the atom has available *d* orbitals for bonding (as any element in the third and higher periods will have), the atom need not obey the octet rule. The next example further illustrates the application of formal charges in choosing the appropriate Lewis formula.

$SOCl_2$

Example 9.11 | Using Formal Charges to Determine the Best Lewis Formula

Write the Lewis formula that best describes the charge distribution in the sulfuric acid molecule, H_2SO_4, according to the rules of formal charge.

An alternative example is provided in the Instructor's Resource Manual.

Problem Strategy Draw the skeleton structure of the molecule or ion, and then follow the steps for writing electron-dot formulas. Note that you can move electron pairs into bonding regions to obtain additional formulas (having multiple bonds). The formal charge of an atom in a formula equals the group number of the atom minus the number of electrons assigned to the atom by the rules of formal charge (half of the electrons of connecting bonds plus all of the lone-pair electrons on the atom). Apply Rules A, B, and C given before this example to decide which Lewis formula is best.

Solution Assume a skeleton structure in which the S atom is surrounded by the more electronegative O atoms; the H atoms are then attached to two of the O atoms. The following is a possible Lewis formula having single bonds:

$$H-\overset{..}{\underset{..}{O}}-\overset{\overset{\displaystyle ..}{\underset{\displaystyle ..}{O}}}{\underset{\overset{\displaystyle ..}{\underset{\displaystyle ..}{O}}}{S}}-\overset{..}{\underset{..}{O}}-H$$

H_2SO_4

You calculate the formal charge of each O atom bonded to an H atom as follows: You assign the O atom 2 electrons from the two single bonds and 4 electrons from the two lone pairs, for a total of 6 electrons. Because the number of valence electrons on the O atom is 6, the formal charge is $6 - 6 = 0$. For each of the other two O atoms, you assign 1 electron from the one single bond and 6 electrons from the three lone pairs, for a total of 7. The formal charge is $6 - 7 = -1$. For the S atom, you assign 4 electrons from the four single bonds, for a total of 4. Because the number of valence electrons is 6, the formal charge is $6 - 4 = +2$. The formal charge of each of the H atoms is $1 - 1 = 0$. The Lewis formula with formal charges is

$$H-\overset{..}{\underset{..}{O}}-\overset{\overset{\displaystyle ..}{\underset{\displaystyle ..}{O}}{}^{\ominus}}{\underset{\overset{\displaystyle ..}{\underset{\displaystyle ..}{O}}{}^{\ominus}}{\overset{(+2)}{S}}}-\overset{..}{\underset{..}{O}}-H$$

(continued)

(continued)

You can also write a Lewis formula that has zero formal charges for atoms, if you form sulfur–oxygen double bonds:

$$\begin{array}{c} : \ddot{O} : \\ \parallel \\ H - \ddot{O} - S - \ddot{O} - H \\ \parallel \\ : \ddot{O} : \end{array}$$

To the top O atom, you assign 2 electrons from the double bond and 4 electrons from the two lone pairs, for a total of 6 electrons. The formal charge is $6 - 6 = 0$. To the S atom, you assign a total of 6 electrons from bonds. The formal charge is $6 - 6 = 0$. The formal charges of the other atoms are also 0. Thus, this Lewis formula should be a better representation of the electron distribution in the H_2SO_4 molecule.

Answer Check The sum of the formal charges on any formula should equal the charge on the species, which is zero for a neutral molecule.

Exercise 9.15   Write the Lewis formula that best describes the phosphoric acid molecule, H_3PO_4.

■ See Problems 9.77 and 9.78.

Concept Check 9.3

Which of the models shown below most accurately represents the hydrogen cyanide molecule, HCN? Write the electron-dot formula that most closely agrees with this model. State any concept or rule you used in arriving at your answer.

(a)   (b)   (c)   (d)

9.10 | Bond Length and Bond Order

ChemWork: Relative Bond Lengths

Bond length (or **bond distance**) is *the distance between the nuclei in a bond*. Bond lengths are determined experimentally using x-ray diffraction or the analysis of molecular spectra. Knowing the bond length in a particular molecule can sometimes provide a clue to the type of bonding present.

In many cases, bond lengths for covalent single bonds in compounds can be predicted from covalent radii. **Covalent radii** are *values assigned to atoms in such a way that the sum of covalent radii of atoms A and B predicts an approximate A—B bond length*. Thus, the radius of the Cl atom might be taken to be half the Cl—Cl bond length (198 pm). The covalent radius of Cl would be $\frac{1}{2} \times 198$ pm $= 99$ pm. Table 9.4 lists single-bond covalent radii for

Although a double bond is stronger than a single bond, it is not necessarily less reactive. Ethylene, $CH_2{=}CH_2$, for example, is more reactive than ethane, $CH_3{-}CH_3$, where carbon atoms are linked through a single bond. The reactivity of ethylene results from the simultaneous formation of a number of strong single bonds. See Section 9.11.

nonmetallic elements. To predict the bond length of C—Cl, you add the covalent radii of the two atoms, C and Cl. You get $(77 + 99)$ pm $= 176$ pm, which compares favorably with the experimental value of 178 pm found in most compounds.

TABLE 9.4

Single-Bond Covalent Radii for Nonmetallic Elements (in pm)

				H
				37
B	C	N	O	F
88	77	70	66	64
	Si	P	S	Cl
	117	110	104	99
		As	Se	Br
		121	117	114
			Te	I
			137	133

Exercise 9.16   Estimate the O—H bond length in H_2O from the covalent radii listed in Table 9.4.

■ See Problems 9.79, 9.80, 9.81, and 9.82.

See the margin note at the bottom of the preceding page.

The **bond order,** defined in terms of the Lewis formula, is *the number of pairs of electrons in a bond.* For example, in C : C the bond order is 1 (single bond); in C : : C the bond order is 2 (double bond). Bond length depends on bond order. As the bond order increases, the bond strength increases and the nuclei are pulled inward, decreasing the bond length. Look at carbon–carbon bonds. The average C—C bond length is 154 pm, whereas C=C is 134 pm long and C≡C is 120 pm long. <

Example 9.12 | Relating Bond Order and Bond Length

Consider the molecules N_2H_4, N_2, and N_2F_2. Which molecule has the shortest nitrogen–nitrogen bond? Which has the longest nitrogen–nitrogen bond?

Problem Strategy First, write the electron-dot formulas for the molecules. Then note that the length of a bond between atoms decreases with bond order.

Solution First write the Lewis formulas:

$$H—\overset{\displaystyle |}{\underset{\displaystyle |}{N}}—\overset{\displaystyle |}{\underset{\displaystyle |}{N}}—H \qquad :N\equiv N: \qquad :\overset{..}{F}—N=N—\overset{..}{F}:$$

$$N_2H_4 \qquad\qquad N_2 \qquad\qquad N_2F_2$$

The nitrogen–nitrogen bond should be shortest in N_2, where it is a triple bond, and longest in N_2H_4, where it is a single bond. (Experimental values for the

nitrogen–nitrogen bond lengths are 109 pm for N_2, 122 pm for N_2F_2, and 147 pm for N_2H_4.)

Answer Check Check that you have written the electron-dot formulas correctly.

Exercise 9.17   Formic acid, isolated in 1670, is the irritant in ant bites. The structure of formic acid is

$$H—C=O$$
$$\underset{\displaystyle H}{\overset{\displaystyle |}{O}}$$

One of the carbon–oxygen bonds has a length of 136 pm; the other is 123 pm long. What is the length of the C=O bond in formic acid?

An alternative example is provided in the Instructor's Resource Manual.

■ See Problems 9.83 and 9.84.

9.11 | Bond Energy

ChemWork: Estimating ΔH

ChemWork: Estimating ΔH for Ionization Reactions

In Section 9.4, when we described the formation of a covalent bond, we introduced the concept of bond dissociation energy, the energy required to break a particular bond in a molecule (see Figure 9.11). The bond dissociation energy is a measure of the strength of a particular bond and is essentially the *enthalpy change* for a gas-phase reaction in which a bond breaks. The enthalpy change, ΔH, is the heat absorbed in a reaction carried out at constant pressure (heat of reaction).

Consider the experimentally determined enthalpy changes for the breaking, or dissociation, of a C—H bond in methane, CH_4, and in ethane, C_2H_6, in the gas phase:

$$H—\overset{\displaystyle H}{\underset{\displaystyle H}{\overset{\displaystyle |}{\underset{\displaystyle |}{C}}}}—H(g) \longrightarrow H—\overset{\displaystyle H}{\underset{\displaystyle H}{\overset{\displaystyle |}{\underset{\displaystyle |}{C}}}}(g) + H(g) \qquad \Delta H = 435 \text{ kJ}$$

$$H—\overset{\displaystyle H}{\underset{\displaystyle H}{\overset{\displaystyle |}{\underset{\displaystyle |}{C}}}}—\overset{\displaystyle H}{\underset{\displaystyle H}{\overset{\displaystyle |}{\underset{\displaystyle |}{C}}}}—H(g) \longrightarrow H—\overset{\displaystyle H}{\underset{\displaystyle H}{\overset{\displaystyle |}{\underset{\displaystyle |}{C}}}}—\overset{\displaystyle H}{\underset{\displaystyle H}{\overset{\displaystyle |}{\underset{\displaystyle |}{C}}}}(g) + H(g) \qquad \Delta H = 410 \text{ kJ}$$

Note that the ΔH values are approximately the same in the two cases. This suggests that the enthalpy change for the dissociation of a C—H bond may be about the same in other molecules. Comparisons of this sort lead to the conclusion that we can obtain approximate values of energies of various bonds.

We define the A—B **bond energy** (denoted *BE*) as *the average enthalpy change for the breaking of an A—B bond in a molecule in the gas phase*. For example, to calculate a value for the C—H bond energy, or *BE*(C—H), you might look at the experimentally determined enthalpy change for the breaking of all the C—H bonds in methane:

$$CH_4(g) \longrightarrow C(g) + 4H(g); \Delta H = 1662 \text{ kJ}$$

Because four C—H bonds are broken, you obtain an average value for breaking one C—H bond by dividing the enthalpy change for the reaction by 4:

$$BE(C\text{—}H) = \tfrac{1}{4} \times 1662 \text{ kJ} = 416 \text{ kJ}$$

Similar calculations with other molecules, such as ethane, would yield approximately the same values for the C—H bond energy.

Table 9.5 lists values of some bond energies. Because it takes energy to break a bond, bond energies are always positive numbers. When a bond is formed, the energy is equal to the negative of the bond energy (energy is released).

Bond energy is a measure of the strength of a bond: the larger the bond energy, the stronger the chemical bond. Note from Table 9.5 that the bonds C—C, C=C, and C≡C have energies of 346, 602, and 835 kJ/mol, respectively. These numbers indicate that the triple bond is stronger than the double bond, which in turn is stronger than the single bond.

You can use this table of bond energies to estimate heats of reaction, or enthalpy changes, ΔH, for gaseous reactions. To illustrate this, find ΔH for the following reaction (Figure 9.21):

$$CH_4(g) + Cl_2(g) \longrightarrow CH_3Cl(g) + HCl(g)$$

TABLE 9.5	Bond Energies (in kJ/mol)*							
				Single Bonds				
	H	C	N	O	S	F	Cl	Br	I
H	432								
C	411	346							
N	386	305	167						
O	459	358	201	142					
S	363	272	—	—	226				
F	565	485	283	190	284	155			
Cl	428	327	313	218	255	249	240		
Br	362	285	—	201	217	249	216	190	
I	295	213	—	201	—	278	208	175	149

Multiple Bonds					
C=C	602	C=N	615	C=O	745 (799 in CO₂)
C≡C	835	C≡N	887	C≡O	1072
N=N	418	N=O	607	S=O (in SO₂)	532
N≡N	942	O=O	494	S=O (in SO₃)	469

*Data are taken from J. E. Huheey, Keiter, and Keiter, *Inorganic Chemistry*, 4th ed. (New York: HarperCollins, 1993), pp. A21–A34.

FIGURE 9.21 ▷

Reaction of methane with chlorine
Molecular models illustrate the reaction $CH_4 + Cl_2 \longrightarrow CH_3Cl + HCl$.

You can *imagine* that the reaction takes place in steps involving the breaking and forming of bonds. Starting with the reactants, you suppose that one C—H bond and the Cl—Cl bond break.

$$\begin{array}{c} H \\ | \\ H-C-H + Cl-Cl \\ | \\ H \end{array} \longrightarrow \begin{array}{c} H \\ | \\ H-C + H + Cl + Cl \\ | \\ H \end{array}$$

The enthalpy change is $BE(C\text{—}H) + BE(Cl\text{—}Cl)$. Now you reassemble the fragments to give the products.

$$\begin{array}{c} H \\ | \\ H-C + H + Cl + Cl \\ | \\ H \end{array} \longrightarrow \begin{array}{c} H \\ | \\ H-C-Cl + H-Cl \\ | \\ H \end{array}$$

In this case, C—Cl and H—Cl bonds are formed, and the enthalpy change equals the negative of the bond energies $-BE(C\text{—}Cl) - BE(H\text{—}Cl)$. Substituting bond-energy values from Table 9.5, you get the enthalpy of reaction.

$$\Delta H \simeq BE(C\text{—}H) + BE(Cl\text{—}Cl) - BE(C\text{—}Cl) - BE(H\text{—}Cl)$$
$$= (411 + 240 - 327 - 428)\,\text{kJ}$$
$$= -104\,\text{kJ}$$

The negative sign means that heat is released by the reaction. Because the bond-energy concept is only approximate, this value is only approximate (the experimental value is −101 kJ).

> In general, the enthalpy of reaction is (approximately) equal to the sum of the bond energies for bonds broken minus the sum of the bond energies for bonds formed.

Rather than calculating a heat of reaction from bond energies, you usually obtain the heat of reaction from thermochemical data, because these are generally known more accurately. If the thermochemical data are not known, however, bond energies can give you a reasonable estimate of the heat of reaction.

Bond energies are perhaps of greatest value when you try to explain heats of reaction or to understand the relative stabilities of compounds. In general, a reaction is exothermic (gives off heat) if weak bonds are replaced by strong bonds (see Figure 9.22). In the reaction we just discussed, two bonds were broken and replaced by two new, stronger bonds. In the following example, a strong bond (C═C) is replaced by two weaker ones (two C—C bonds). Although the single bond is weaker than the double bond, as you would expect, two C—C bonds *together* create an energetically more stable situation than one C═C bond.

FIGURE 9.22 ▽

Explosion of nitrogen triiodide–ammonia complex
The red-brown complex of nitrogen triiodide and ammonia is so sensitive to explosion that it can be detonated with a feather. Nitrogen–iodine single bonds are replaced by very stable nitrogen–nitrogen triple bonds (N_2) and iodine–iodine single bonds (I_2).

Instrumental Methods

Infrared Spectroscopy and Vibrations of Chemical Bonds

A chemical bond acts like a stiff spring connecting nuclei. As a result, the nuclei in a molecule vibrate, rather than maintaining fixed positions relative to each other. Nuclear vibration is depicted in Figure 9.23, which shows a spring model of HCl.

This vibration of molecules is revealed in their absorption of infrared radiation. (An instrument for observing the absorption of infrared radiation is shown in Figure 9.24.) The frequency of radiation absorbed equals the frequencies of nuclear vibrations. For example, the H—Cl bond vibrates at a frequency of 8.652×10^{13} vibrations per second. If radiation of this frequency falls on the molecule, it absorbs the radiation, which is in the infrared region, and begins vibrating more strongly.

The infrared absorption spectrum of a molecule of even moderate size can have a rather complicated

FIGURE 9.24 ▲

A Fourier transform infrared (FTIR) spectrometer
A Nicolet 560 E.S.P. FT-IR spectrometer.

appearance. Figure 9.25 shows the infrared (IR) spectrum of ethyl butyrate, a compound present in pineapple flavor. The complicated appearance of the IR spectrum is actually an advantage. Two different compounds are unlikely to have exactly the same IR spectrum. Therefore, the IR spectrum can act as a compound's "fingerprint."

The IR spectrum of a compound can also yield structural information. Suppose you would like to obtain the structural formula of ethyl butyrate. The molecular formula, determined from combustion analysis, is $C_6H_{12}O_2$. Important information about this structure can be obtained from Figure 9.25.

You first need to be able to read such a spectrum. Instead of plotting an IR spectrum in frequency units (since

FIGURE 9.23 ▲

Vibration of the HCl molecule
The vibrating molecule is represented here by a spring model. The atoms in the molecule vibrate; that is, they move constantly back and forth.

Example 9.13	Estimating ΔH from Bond Energies

Polyethylene is formed by linking many ethylene molecules into long chains. Estimate the enthalpy change per mole of ethylene for this reaction (shown below), using bond energies.

An alternative example is provided in the Instructor's Resource Manual.

(continued)

362

FIGURE 9.25 ▲

Infrared spectrum of ethyl butyrate

Note the peaks corresponding to vibrations of C=O and C—O bonds. The molecular structure is shown at the bottom left. [From NIST Mass Spec Data Center, S.E.Stein, director, "IR and Mass Spectra" *in NIST Chemistry WebBook, NIST Standard Reference Database Number 69,* Eds. W.G. Mallard and P.J. Linstrom, February 2000, National Institute of Standards and Technology, Gaithersburg, MD, 20899 (http//webbook.nist.gov). © 1991, 1994, 1996, 1997, 1998, 1999, 2000 copyright by the U.S. Secretary of Commerce on behalf of the United States of America. All rights reserved.]

the frequencies are very large), you usually would give the frequencies in *wavenumbers*, which are proportional to frequency. To get the wavenumber, you divide the frequency by the speed of light expressed in centimeters per second. For example, HCl absorbs at $(8.652 \times 10^{13}$ s$^{-1})/(2.998 \times 10^{10}$ cm/s$) = 2886$ cm^{-1} (wavenumbers). Wavenumber, or sometimes wavelength, is plotted along the horizontal axis.

Percent transmittance—that is, the percent of radiation that passes through a sample—is plotted on the vertical axis. When a molecule absorbs radiation of a given frequency or wavenumber, this is seen in the spectrum as an inverted spike (peak) at that wavenumber. Certain structural features of molecules appear as absorption peaks in definite regions of the infrared spectrum. For example, the absorption peak at 1730 cm^{-1} is characteristic of the C=O bond. With some knowledge of where various bonds absorb, one can identify other peaks, including that of C—O at 1180 cm^{-1}. (Generally, the IR peak for an A—B bond occurs at lower wavenumber than for an A=B bond.) The IR spectrum does not reveal the complete structure, but it provides important clues. Data from other instruments, such as the mass spectrometer (page 98), give additional clues.

■ See Problems 9.115 and 9.116.

(continued)

Problem Strategy Break bonds in the reactants, and then form new bonds to give the products. The approximate enthalpy change equals the sum of the bond energies for the bonds broken minus the sum of the bond energies for the bonds formed.

Solution Imagine the reaction to involve the breaking of the carbon–carbon double bonds and the formation of carbon–carbon single bonds. For a very long chain, the net result is that for every C=C bond broken, two C—C bonds are formed.

$$\Delta H \simeq [602 - (2 \times 346)] \text{ kJ} = \mathbf{-90 \text{ kJ}}$$

Answer Check Note whether the sign of ΔH agrees with what you would expect. Perhaps weak bonds have been replaced by strong bonds, in which case ΔH should be negative. Here, every double bond is replaced by two single bonds, so ΔH should be negative, as it is.

(continued)

(continued)

Exercise 9.18   Use bond energies to estimate the enthalpy change for the combustion of ethylene, C_2H_4, according to the equation

$$C_2H_4(g) + 3O_2(g) \longrightarrow 2CO_2(g) + 2H_2O(g)$$

■ See Problems 9.85 and 9.86.

A Checklist for Review

Important Terms

ionic bond (9.1)
Lewis electron-dot symbol (9.1)
lattice energy (9.1)
ionic radius (9.3)
isoelectronic (9.3)
covalent bond (9.4)
Lewis electron-dot formula (9.4)
bonding pair (9.4)

lone (nonbonding) pair (9.4)
coordinate covalent bond (9.4)
octet rule (9.4)
single bond (9.4)
double bond (9.4)
triple bond (9.4)
polar covalent bond (9.5)
electronegativity (9.5)

delocalized bonding (9.7)
resonance description (9.7)
formal charge (9.9)
bond length (bond distance) (9.10)
covalent radii (9.10)
bond order (9.10)
bond energy (9.11)

Summary of Facts and Concepts

An *ionic bond* is a strong attractive force holding ions together. An ionic bond can form between two atoms by the transfer of electrons from the valence shell of one atom to the valence shell of the other. Many similar ions attract one another to form a crystalline solid, in which positive ions are surrounded by negative ions and negative ions are surrounded by positive ions. As a result, ionic solids are typically high-melting solids. Monatomic cations of the main-group elements have charges equal to the group number (or in some cases, the group number minus two). Monatomic anions of the main-group elements have charges equal to the group number minus eight.

A *covalent bond* is a strong attractive force that holds two atoms together by their sharing of electrons. These bonding electrons are attracted simultaneously to both atomic nuclei, and they spend part of the time near one atom and part of the time near the other. If an electron pair is not equally shared, the bond is *polar*. This polarity results from the difference in *electronegativities* of the atoms—that is, from the unequal abilities of the atoms to draw bonding electrons to themselves.

Lewis electron-dot formulas are simple representations of the valence-shell electrons of atoms in molecules and ions. You can apply simple rules to draw these formulas. In molecules with *delocalized bonding*, it is not possible to describe accurately the electron distribution with a single Lewis formula. For these molecules, you must use *resonance*. Although the atoms in Lewis formulas often satisfy the octet rule, *exceptions to the octet rule* are not uncommon. You can obtain the Lewis formulas for these exceptions by following the rules for writing Lewis formulas. The concept of *formal charge* will often help you decide which of several Lewis formulas gives the best description of a molecule or ion.

Bond lengths can be estimated from the *covalent radii* of atoms. Bond length depends on *bond order*; as the bond order increases, the bond length decreases. The A—B *bond energy* is the average enthalpy change when an A—B bond is broken. You can use bond energies to estimate ΔH for gas-phase reactions.

Media Summary

Visit the **student website at college.hmco.com/pic/ebbing9e** to help prepare for class, study for quizzes and exams, understand core concepts, and visualize molecular-level interactions. The following media activities are available for this chapter:

 Prepare for Class

■ **Video Lessons** *Mini lectures from chemistry experts*
Valence Electrons and Chemical Bonding
Ionic Bonds

Lewis Dot Structure for Covalent Bonds
Predicting Lewis Dot Structures
An Introduction to Electronegativity
Resonance Structures
Formal Charge

Electronegativity, Formal Charge, and Resonance
Bond Properties
Using Bond Dissociation Energies

 Improve Your Grade

Visualizations *Molecular-level animations and lab demonstration videos*
Born–Haber Cycle for NaCl(s)
Ionic Radii
Bonding in H_2
Covalent Bonding
Electron Sea Model

Tutorials *Animated examples and interactive activities*
Lewis structures

Flashcards *Key terms and definitions*
Online Flashcards

Self-Assessment Questions *Additional questions with full worked-out solutions*
6 Self-Assessment Questions

 ACE the Test

Multiple-choice quizzes
3 ACE Practice Tests

Access these resources using the passkey available free with new texts or for purchase separately.

Learning Objectives

9.1 Describing Ionic Bonds

■ Define *ionic bond*.
■ Explain the *Lewis electron-dot symbol* of an atom.
■ Use Lewis symbols to represent ionic bond formation. Example 9.1
■ Describe the energetics of ionic bonding.
■ Define *lattice energy*.
■ Describe the Born–Haber cycle to obtain a lattice energy from thermodynamic data.
■ Describe some general properties of ionic substances.

9.2 Electron Configurations of Ions

■ State the three categories of monatomic ions of the main-group elements.
■ Write the electron configuration and Lewis symbol for a main-group ion. Example 9.2
■ Note the polyatomic ions given earlier in Table 2.5.
■ Note the formation of 2+ and 3+ transition-metal ions.
■ Write electron configurations of transition-metal ions. Example 9.3

9.3 Ionic Radii

■ Define *ionic radius*.
■ Define *isoelectronic ions*.
■ Use periodic trends to obtain relative ionic radii. Example 9.4

9.4 Describing Covalent Bonds

■ Describe the formation of a covalent bond between two atoms.
■ Define *Lewis electron-dot formula*.
■ Define *bonding pair* and *lone (nonbonding) pair* of electrons.
■ Define *coordinate covalent bond*.
■ State the octet rule.
■ Define *single bond*, *double bond*, and *triple bond*.

9.5 Polar Covalent Bonds; Electronegativity

■ Define *polar covalent bond*.
■ Define *electronegativity*.

■ State the general periodic trends in the electronegativity.
■ Use electronegativity to obtain relative bond polarity. Example 9.5

9.6 Writing Lewis Electron-Dot Formulas

■ Write Lewis formulas with single bonds only. Example 9.6
■ Write Lewis formulas having multiple bonds. Example 9.7
■ Write Lewis formulas for ionic species. Example 9.8

9.7 Delocalized Bonding; Resonance

■ Define *delocalized bonding*.
■ Define *resonance description*.
■ Write resonance formulas. Example 9.9

9.8 Exceptions to the Octet Rule

■ Write Lewis formulas (exceptions to the octet rule). Example 9.10
■ Note exceptions to the octet rule in Group IIA and Group IIIA elements.

9.9 Formal Charge and Lewis Formulas

■ Define *formal charge*.
■ State the rules for obtaining formal charge.
■ State two rules useful in writing Lewis formulas.
■ Use formal charges to determine the best Lewis formula. Example 9.11

9.10 Bond Length and Bond Order

■ Define *bond length (bond distance)*.
■ Define *covalent radii*.
■ Define *bond order*.
■ Explain how bond order and bond length are related. Example 9.12

9.11 Bond Energy

■ Define *bond energy*.
■ Estimate ΔH from bond energies. Example 9.13

Self-Assessment and Review Questions

9.1 Describe the formation of a sodium chloride crystal from atoms.

9.2 Why does sodium chloride normally exist as a crystal rather than as a molecule composed of one cation and one anion?

9.3 Explain what energy terms are involved in the formation of an ionic solid from atoms. In what way should these terms change (become larger or smaller) to give the lowest energy possible for the solid?

9.4 Define lattice energy for potassium bromide.

9.5 Why do most monatomic cations of the main-group elements have a charge equal to the group number? Why do most monatomic anions of these elements have a charge equal to the group number minus eight?

9.6 The 2+ ions of transition elements are common. Explain why this might be expected.

9.7 Explain how ionic radii are obtained from known distances between nuclei in crystals.

9.8 Describe the trends shown by the radii of the monatomic ions for the main-group elements both across a period and down a column.

9.9 Describe the formation of a covalent bond in H_2 from atoms. What does it mean to say that the bonding electrons are shared by the two atoms?

9.10 Draw a potential-energy diagram for a molecule such as Cl_2. Indicate the bond length (194 pm) and the bond dissociation energy (240 kJ/mol).

9.11 Give an example of a molecule that has a coordinate covalent bond.

9.12 The octet rule correctly predicts the Lewis formula of many molecules involving main-group elements. Explain why this is so.

9.13 Describe the general trends in electronegativities of the elements in the periodic table both across a period and down a column.

9.14 What is the qualitative relationship between bond polarity and electronegativity difference?

9.15 What is a resonance description of a molecule? Why is this concept required if we wish to retain Lewis formulas as a description of the electron structure of molecules?

9.16 Describe the kinds of exceptions to the octet rule that we encounter in compounds of the main-group elements. Give examples.

9.17 What is the relationship between bond order and bond length? Use an example to illustrate it.

9.18 Define bond energy. Explain how one can use bond energies to estimate the heat of reaction.

9.19 Which of the following contains *both* ionic and covalent bonds in the same compound?
  a. $BaCO_3$ **b.** $MgCl_2$
  c. BaO **d.** H_2S
  e. $SO_4{}^{2-}$

9.20 The radii of the species S, S^+, and S^- *decrease* in the following order:
  a. $S^+ > S > S^-$
  b. $S^+ > S > S$
  c. $S > S^- > S^+$
  d. $S > S^+ > S^-$
  e. $S^- > S > S^+$

9.21 Which of the following is the ground-state electron configuration of a C^{3-} ion?
  a. $1s^2 2s^2 2p^4$
  b. $[He]2s^2 2p^6$
  c. $[He]2s^1$
  d. $1s^2 2s^2 2p^5$
  e. $1s^2 2s^2 2p^6 3s^1$

9.22 The element X below could be

$$\cdot \overset{\displaystyle ..}{\underset{\displaystyle ..}{X}} \cdot$$

  a. sulfur
  b. iodine
  c. aluminum
  d. phosphorus
  e. silicon

Concept Explorations

9.23 **Forming Ionic Compounds**

a. Consider a metal atom, which we will give the symbol M. Metal M can readily form the M^+ cation. If the sphere on the left below represents the metal atom M, which of the other three spheres would probably represent the M^+ cation? Explain your choice.

b. Consider a nonmetal atom, which we will give the symbol X. The element X is a gas at room temperature and can easily form the X^- anion. If atom X is represented by the sphere on the left below, which of the other three spheres would probably represent the X^- anion. Explain your choice.

c. On the basis of the information given previously, write a balanced chemical equation for the reaction that occurs when metal M reacts with nonmetal X. Include state symbols for the reactants and products.

d. Is the product of the reaction of M and X a molecule or an ionic compound? Provide justification for your answer.

e. Which of the representations below is the most appropriate to describe the compound of M and X, according to your answer for part d? Explain how you arrived at your choice.

9.24 Bond Energy

When atoms of the hypothetical element X are placed together, they rapidly undergo reaction to form the X_2 molecule:

$$X(g) + X(g) \longrightarrow X_2(g)$$

a. Would you predict that this reaction is exothermic or endothermic? Explain.

b. Is the bond energy of X_2 a positive or a negative quantity? Why?

c. Suppose ΔH for the reaction is -500 kJ/mol. Estimate the bond energy of the X_2 molecule.

d. Another hypothetical molecular compound, $Y_2(g)$, has a bond energy of 750 kJ/mol, and the molecular compound $XY(g)$ has a bond energy of 1500 kJ/mol. Using bond-energy information, calculate ΔH for the following reaction.

$$X_2(g) + Y_2(g) \longrightarrow 2XY(g)$$

e. Given the following information, as well as the information previously presented, predict whether or not the hypothetical ionic compound AX is likely to form. In this compound, A forms the A^+ cation, and X forms the X^- anion. Be sure to justify your answer.

Reaction: $A(g) + \frac{1}{2}X_2(g) \longrightarrow AX(s)$

The first ionization energy of $A(g)$ is 400 kJ/mol.

The electron affinity of $X(g)$ is -525 kJ/mol.

The lattice energy of $AX(s)$ is 100 kJ/mol.

f. If you predicted that no ionic compound would form from the reaction in part e, what minimum amount of $AX(s)$ lattice energy might lead to compound formation?

9.25 You land on a distant planet in another universe and find that the $n = 1$ level can hold a maximum of 4 electrons, the $n = 2$ level can hold a maximum of 5 electrons, and the $n = 3$ level can hold a maximum of 3 electrons. Like our universe, protons have a charge of $+1$, electrons have a charge of -1, and opposite charges attract. Also, a filled shell results in greater stability of an atom, so the atom tends to gain or lose electrons to give a filled shell. Predict the formula of a compound that results from the reaction of a neutral metal atom X, which has 7 electrons, and a neutral nonmetal atom Y, which has 3 electrons.

9.26 Which of the following represent configurations of thallium ions in compounds? Explain your decision in each case.

a. Tl^{2+} $[Xe]4f^{14}5d^{10}6p^1$ **b.** Tl^{3+} $[Xe]4f^{14}5d^{10}$
c. Tl^{4+} $[Xe]4f^{14}5d^9$ **d.** Tl^+ $[Xe]4f^{14}5d^{10}6s^2$

9.27 Below on the left side are models of two atoms, one from a metal, the other from a nonmetal. On the right side are corresponding monatomic ions of those atoms. Decide which of these ions is the cation and which is the anion. Label atoms as "metal" or "nonmetal," as appropriate.

9.28 Predict a possible monatomic ion for Element 117, Uus. Given the spherical models below, which should be labeled "atom" and which should be labeled "ion"?

9.29 Examine each of the following electron-dot formulas and decide whether the formula is correct, or whether you could write a formula that better approximates the electron structure of the molecule. State which concepts or rules you use in each case to arrive at your conclusion.

a. $:\overset{..}{N}:\overset{..}{N}:$ **b.** $:\overset{..}{Cl}:C:::N:$

c. $H:C::\overset{..}{F}$ **d.** $:\overset{..}{O}:$
       $:\overset{..}{O}:$ $H:\overset{..}{O}::C::\overset{..}{O}:H$

9.30 For each of the following molecular models, write an appropriate Lewis formula.

(a)   (b)   (c)   (d)

9.31 For each of the following molecular formulas, draw the most reasonable skeleton structure.
  a. CH_2Cl_2 **b.** HNO_2 **c.** NOF   **d.** N_2O_4
What rule or concept did you use to obtain each structure?

9.32 Below are three resonance formulas for N_2O (nitrous oxide). Rank these in terms of how closely you think each one represents the true electron structure of the molecule. State the rules and concepts you use to do this ranking.

  a. $:\ddot{N}{-}N{\equiv}O:$ **b.** $:N{\equiv}N{-}\ddot{O}:$ **c.** $:\ddot{N}{=}N{=}\ddot{O}$

9.33 Sodium, Na, reacts with element X to form an ionic compound with the formula Na_3X.
  a. What is the formula of the compound you expect to form when calcium, Ca, reacts with element X?
  b. Would you expect this compound to be ionic or molecular?

9.34 The enthalpy change for each of the following reactions was calculated using bond energies. The bond energies of X—O, Y—O, and Z—O are all equal.

$$X{-}X + O{=}O \longrightarrow X{-}O{-}O{-}X; \ \Delta H = -275 \text{ kJ}$$
$$Y{-}Y + O{=}O \longrightarrow Y{-}O{-}O{-}Y; \ \Delta H = +275 \text{ kJ}$$
$$Z{-}Z + O{=}O \longrightarrow Z{-}O{-}O{-}Z; \ \Delta H = -100 \text{ kJ}$$

  a. Rank the bonds X—X, Y—Y, and Z—Z from strongest to weakest.
  b. Compare the energies required to completely dissociate each of the products to atoms.
  c. If O_2 molecules were O—O instead of O=O, how would this change ΔH for each reaction?

Practice Problems

Ionic Bonding

9.35 Write Lewis symbols for the following:
  a. P   **b.** P^{3-} **c.** Ga   **d.** Ga^{3+}

9.36 Write Lewis symbols for the following:
  a. Br   **b.** Br^- **c.** Sr   **d.** Sr^{2+}

9.37 Use Lewis symbols to represent the transfer of electrons between the following atoms to form ions with noble-gas configurations:
  a. Ca and Br   **b.** K and I

9.38 Use Lewis symbols to represent the electron transfer between the following atoms to give ions with noble-gas configurations:
  a. Mg and S   **b.** Ba and I

9.39 For each of the following, write the electron configuration and Lewis symbol:
  a. As   **b.** As^{3+} **c.** Se   **d.** Se^{2-}

9.40 For each of the following, write the electron configuration and Lewis symbol:
  a. In   **b.** In^- **c.** K^+ **d.** I^-

9.41 Write the electron configurations of Bi and Bi^{3+}.

9.42 Write the electron configurations of Sn and Sn^{2+}.

9.43 Give the electron configurations of Ni^{2+} and Ni^{3+}.

9.44 Give the electron configurations of Cu^+ and Cu^{2+}.

Ionic Radii

9.45 Arrange the members of each of the following pairs in order of increasing radius and explain the order:
  a. Sr, Sr^{2+} **b.** Br, Br^-

9.46 Arrange the members of each of the following pairs in order of increasing radius and explain the order:
  a. Te, Te^{2-} **b.** Al, Al^{3+}

9.47 Without looking at Table 9.3, arrange the following in order of increasing ionic radius: Se^{2-}, Te^{2-}, S^{2-}. Explain how you arrived at this order. (You may use a periodic table.)

9.48 Which has the larger radius, N^{3-} or P^{3-}? Explain. (You may use a periodic table.)

9.49 Arrange the following in order of increasing ionic radius: F^-, Na^+, and N^{3-}. Explain this order. (You may use a periodic table.)

9.50 Arrange the following in order of increasing ionic radius: Cl^-, Na^+, and S^{2-}. Explain this order. (You may use a periodic table.)

Covalent Bonding

9.51 Use Lewis symbols to show the reaction of atoms to form hydrogen selenide, H_2Se. Indicate bonding pairs and lone pairs in the electron-dot formula of this compound.

9.52 Use Lewis symbols to show the reaction of atoms to form arsine, AsH_3. Indicate which electron pairs in the Lewis formula of AsH_3 are bonding and which are lone pairs.

9.53 Assuming that the atoms form the normal number of covalent bonds, give the molecular formula of the simplest compound of arsenic and bromine atoms.

9.54 Assuming that the atoms form the normal number of covalent bonds, give the molecular formula of the simplest compound of silicon and chlorine atoms.

Polar Covalent Bonds; Electronegativity

9.55 Using a periodic table (not Figure 9.15), arrange the following in order of increasing electronegativity:
  a. P, O, N   **b.** Na, Al, Mg   **c.** C, Al, Si

9.56 With the aid of a periodic table (not Figure 9.15), arrange the following in order of increasing electronegativity:
  a. Sr, Ca, Rb   **b.** Ca, Ge, Ga   **c.** Se, As, Sb

9.57 Arrange the following bonds in order of increasing polarity using electronegativities of atoms: P—O, C—Cl, As—Br.

9.58 Decide which of the following bonds is least polar on the basis of electronegativities of atoms: H—N, Si—Br, N—Cl.

9.59 Indicate the partial charges for the bonds given in Problem 9.57, using the symbols δ^+ and δ^-.

9.60 Indicate the partial charges for the bonds given in Problem 9.58, using the symbols δ^+ and δ^-.

Writing Lewis Formulas

9.61 Write Lewis formulas for the following molecules:
   a. Br_2 **b.** H_2S **c.** NF_3

9.62 Write Lewis formulas for the following molecules:
   a. NOCl   **b.** PBr_3 **c.** IF

9.63 Write Lewis formulas for the following molecules:
   a. P_2 **b.** $COBr_2$ **c.** HNO_2

9.64 Write Lewis formulas for the following molecules:
   a. CO   **b.** BrCN   **c.** N_2F_2

9.65 Write Lewis formulas for the following ions:
   a. ClO^- **b.** $SnCl_3^-$ **c.** S_2^{2-}

9.66 Write Lewis formulas for the following ions:
   a. IBr_2^+ **b.** ClF_2^+ **c.** CN^-

Resonance

9.67 Write resonance descriptions for the following:
   a. HNO_3 **b.** SO_3

9.68 Write resonance descriptions for the following:
   a. NO_2^- **b.** FNO_2

9.69 Use resonance to describe the electron structure of nitromethane, CH_3NO_2. The skeleton structure is

9.70 Give the resonance description of the formate ion. The skeleton structure is

$$\left[\begin{array}{c} O \\ \| \\ H-C-O \end{array} \right]^-$$

Exceptions to the Octet Rule

9.71 Write Lewis formulas for the following:
   a. XeF_2 **b.** SeF_4 **c.** TeF_6 **d.** XeF_5^+

9.72 Write Lewis formulas for the following:
   a. I_3^- **b.** ClF_3 **c.** IF_4^- **d.** BrF_5

9.73 Write Lewis formulas for the following:
   a. BCl_3 **b.** $TlCl_2^+$ **c.** $BeBr_2$

9.74 Write Lewis formulas for the following:
   a. AlI_3 **b.** $BeCl_2$ **c.** BeF_3^-

Formal Charge and Lewis Formulas

9.75 Write a Lewis formula for each of the following, assuming that the octet rule holds for the atoms. Then obtain the formal charges of the atoms.
   a. O_3 **b.** CO   **c.** HNO_3

9.76 Write a Lewis formula for each of the following, assuming that the octet rule holds for the atoms. Then obtain the formal charges of the atoms.
   a. ClNO   **b.** $POCl_3$ **c.** N_2O (NNO)

9.77 For each of the following, use formal charges to choose the Lewis formula that gives the best description of the electron distribution:
   a. SOF_2
   b. H_2SO_3
   c. $HClO_2$

9.78 For each of the following, use formal charges to choose the Lewis formula that gives the best description of the electron distribution:
   a. ClO_2F
   b. SO_3
   c. BrO_3^-

Bond Length, Bond Order, and Bond Energy

9.79 Use covalent radii (Table 9.4) to estimate the length of the P—F bond in phosphorus trifluoride, PF_3.

9.80 What do you expect for the B—F bond length in boron trifluoride, BF_3, on the basis of covalent radii (Table 9.4)?

9.81 Calculate the bond length for each of the following single bonds, using covalent radii (Table 9.4):
   a. C—H
   b. S—Cl
   c. Br—Cl
   d. Si—O

9.82 Calculate the C—H and C—Cl bond lengths in chloroform, $CHCl_3$, using values for the covalent radii from Table 9.4. How do these values compare with the experimental values: C—H, 107 pm; C—Cl, 177 pm?

9.83 One of the following compounds has a carbon–nitrogen bond length of 116 pm; the other has a carbon–nitrogen bond length of 147 pm. Match a bond length with each compound.

Methylamine   Acetonitrile

9.84 Which of the following two compounds has the shorter carbon–oxygen bond?

Methanol   Formaldehyde

9.85 Use bond energies (Table 9.5) to estimate ΔH for the following gas-phase reaction.

$$\underset{\substack{H \quad H \\ | \quad | \\ H \quad H}}{C=C} + H-Br \longrightarrow \underset{\substack{H \quad H \\ | \quad | \\ H \quad H}}{H-C-C}-Br$$

This is called an "addition" reaction, because a compound (HBr) is added across the double bond.

9.86 A commercial process for preparing ethanol (ethyl alcohol), C_2H_5OH, consists of passing ethylene gas, C_2H_4, and steam over an acid catalyst (to speed up the reaction). The gas-phase reaction is

$$\underset{\substack{H \quad H \\ | \quad | \\ H \quad H}}{C=C} + H-O-H \longrightarrow \underset{\substack{H \quad H \\ | \quad | \\ H \quad H}}{H-C-C}-O-H$$

Estimate ΔH for this reaction, using bond energies (Table 9.5).

General Problems

9.87 For each of the following pairs of elements, state whether the binary compound formed is likely to be ionic or covalent. Give the formula and name of the compound.
a. Sr, O **b.** C, Br **c.** Ga, F **d.** N, Br

9.88 For each of the following pairs of elements, state whether the binary compound formed is likely to be ionic or covalent. Give the formula and name of the compound.
a. Na, S **b.** Al, F **c.** Ca, Cl **d.** Si, Br

9.89 Give the Lewis formula for the arsenate ion, AsO_4^{3-}. Write the formula of lead(II) arsenate.

9.90 Give the Lewis formula for the selenite ion, SeO_3^{2-}. Write the formula of aluminum selenite.

9.91 Iodic acid, HIO_3, is a colorless, crystalline compound. What is the electron-dot formula of iodic acid?

9.92 Selenic acid, H_2SeO_4, is a crystalline substance and a strong acid. Write the electron-dot formula of selenic acid.

9.93 Sodium amide, known commercially as sodamide, is used in preparing indigo, the dye used to color blue jeans. It is an ionic compound with the formula $NaNH_2$. What is the electron-dot formula of the amide anion, NH_2^-?

9.94 Lithium aluminum hydride, $LiAlH_4$, is an important reducing agent (an element or compound that generally has a strong tendency to give up electrons in its chemical reactions). Write the electron-dot formula of the AlH_4^- ion.

9.95 Nitronium perchlorate, NO_2ClO_4, is a reactive salt of the nitronium ion NO_2^+. Write the electron-dot formula of NO_2^+.

9.96 Solid phosphorus pentabromide, PBr_5, has been shown to have the ionic structure $[PBr_4^+][Br^-]$. Write the electron-dot formula of the PBr_4^+ cation.

9.97 Write electron-dot formulas for the following:
a. $SeOCl_2$ **b.** CSe_2 **c.** $GaCl_4^-$ **d.** C_2^{2-}

9.98 Write electron-dot formulas for the following:
a. $POBr_3$ **b.** Si_2H_6 **c.** IF_2^+ **d.** NO^+

9.99 Write Lewis formulas for the following:
a. $SbCl_3$ **b.** ICN **c.** ICl_3 **d.** IF_5

9.100 Write Lewis formulas for the following:
a. $AlCl_4^-$ **b.** AlF_6^{3-} **c.** BrF_3 **d.** IF_6^+

9.101 Give resonance descriptions for the following:
a. SeO_2 **b.** N_2O_4

9.102 Give resonance descriptions for the following:
a. CH_3NO_2 **b.** $C_2O_4^{2-}$

9.103 The compound S_2N_2 has a cyclic structure with alternating sulfur and nitrogen atoms. Draw all resonance formulas in which the atoms obey the octet rule. Of these, select those in which the formal charges of all atoms are closest to zero.

9.104 Acetic acid has the structure $CH_3CO(OH)$, in which the OH group is bonded to a C atom. The two carbon–oxygen bonds have different lengths. When an acetic acid molecule loses the H from the OH group to form the acetate ion, the two carbon–oxygen bonds become equal in length. Explain.

9.105 The atoms in N_2O_5 are connected as follows:

$$\underset{O}{\overset{O}{\diagup}}N-O-N\underset{O}{\overset{O}{\diagdown}}$$

No attempt has been made here to indicate whether a bond is single or double or whether there is resonance. Obtain the Lewis formula (or formulas). The N—O bond lengths are 118 pm and 136 pm. Indicate the lengths of the bonds in the compound.

9.106 Methyl nitrite has the structure

$$\underset{\substack{| \\ H}}{\overset{\substack{H \\ |}}{H-C}}-O-N-O$$

No attempt has been made here to indicate whether a bond is single or double or whether there is resonance. Obtain the Lewis formula (or formulas). The N—O bond lengths are 122 pm and 137 pm. Indicate the lengths of the N—O bonds in the compound.

9.107 Use bond energies to estimate ΔH for the reaction

$$H_2(g) + O_2(g) \longrightarrow H_2O_2(g)$$

9.108 Use bond energies to estimate ΔH for the reaction

$$2H_2(g) + N_2(g) \longrightarrow N_2H_4(g)$$

9.109 Use bond energies to estimate ΔH for the reaction

$$N_2F_2(g) + F_2(g) \longrightarrow N_2F_4(g)$$

9.110 Use bond energies to estimate ΔH for the reaction

$$HCN(g) + 2H_2(g) \longrightarrow CH_3NH_2(g)$$

9.111 Compare the properties of an ionic material such as sodium chloride with a room-temperature ionic liquid. Explain this difference.

9.112 What advantages does using an ionic liquid as a solvent have over using an organic solvent?

Strategy Problems

9.117 Which of the following Lewis structures is (or are) *not* correct?

a. $[\ \ddot{Al}\cdot\ ]^{3+}$ **b.** $[:\ddot{F}:]^-$ **c.** $[:\ddot{O}:]^{2-}$ **d.** $\cdot Mg$ **e.** $\cdot \ddot{Si}\cdot$

9.118 Which of the following are isoelectronic with the potassium ion, K^+? What are the electron configurations of these species?

a. Ar   **b.** Cl^+ **c.** Kr   **d.** Cl^- **e.** Ca^+

9.119 An ion M^{2+} has the configuration $[Ar]3d^2$, and an atom has the configuration $[Ar]4s^2$. Identify the ion and the atom.

9.120 Give the symbol of an atomic ion for each of the following electron configurations:

a. $1s^2 2s^2 2p^6 3s^2 3p^6$
b. $1s^2 2s^2 2p^6 3s^2 3p^6 4s^1$
c. $1s^2 2s^2 2p^6 3s^2 3p^6 3d^8$
d. $1s^2 2s^2 2p^6 3s^2 3p^6 3d^{10} 4s^2$
e. $1s^2 2s^2 2p^6 3s^2 3p^6 3d^{10} 4s^2 4p^6$

9.121 Which of the following molecules possesses a double bond? If none do, so state. Which species has an atom with a nonzero formal charge?

a. I_2 **b.** SF_4 **c.** $COCl_2$ **d.** C_2H_4 **e.** CN^-

9.113 Explain the decomposition of nitroglycerin in terms of relative bond energies.

9.114 How did the Swedish chemist Alfred Nobel manage to tame the decomposition of nitroglycerin?

9.115 What property of a chemical bond gives rise to the infrared spectrum of a compound?

9.116 What kind of information can be obtained about a compound from its infrared spectrum?

9.122 Which of the following molecules contains *only* double bonds? If none do, so state.

a. NCCN   **b.** CO_2 **c.** C_2H_4 **d.** O_3 **e.** N_2

9.123 Draw resonance structures for the azide ion, N_3^-, and for the nitronium ion, NO_2^+. Decide which resonance structure is the best description of each ion.

9.124 Two fourth-period atoms, one of a transition metal, M, and the other of a main-group nonmetal, X, form a compound with the formula M_2X_3. What is the electron configuration of atom X if M is Fe? What is the configuration of X if M is Co?

9.125 Consider hypothetical elements X and Y. Suppose the enthalpy of formation of the compound XY is -336 kJ/mol, the bond energy for X_2 is 414 kJ/mol, and the bond energy for Y_2 is 159 kJ/mol. Estimate the XY bond energy in units of kJ/mol.

9.126 Nitrous oxide, N_2O, has a linear structure NNO. Write resonance formulas for this molecule and from them estimate the NN bond length in the molecule. Use the data in Example 9.12.

Cumulative-Skills Problems

9.127 Phosphorous acid, H_3PO_3, has the structure $(HO)_2PHO$, in which one H atom is bonded to the P atom, and two H atoms are bonded to O atoms. For each bond to an H atom, decide whether it is polar or nonpolar. Assume that only polar-bonded H atoms are acidic. Write the balanced equation for the complete neutralization of phosphorous acid with sodium hydroxide. A 200.0-mL sample of H_3PO_3 requires 22.50 mL of 0.1250 M NaOH for complete neutralization. What is the molarity of the H_3PO_3 solution?

9.128 Hypophosphorous acid, H_3PO_2, has the structure $(HO)PH_2O$, in which two H atoms are bonded to the P atom, and one H atom is bonded to an O atom. For each bond to an H atom,

decide whether it is polar or nonpolar. Assume that only polar-bonded H atoms are acidic. Write the balanced equation for the complete neutralization of hypophosphorous acid with sodium hydroxide. A 200.0-mL sample of H_3PO_2 requires 22.50 mL of 0.1250 M NaOH for complete neutralization. What is the molarity of the H_3PO_2 solution?

9.129 An ionic compound has the following composition (by mass): Mg, 10.9%; Cl, 31.8%; O, 57.3%. What are the formula and name of the compound? Write the Lewis formulas for the ions.

9.130 An ionic compound has the following composition (by mass): Ca, 30.3%; N, 21.2%; O, 48.5%. What are the formula and name of the compound? Write the Lewis formulas for the ions.

9.131 A gaseous compound has the following composition by mass: C, 25.0%; H, 2.1%; F, 39.6%; O, 33.3%. Its molecular mass is 48.0 amu. Write the Lewis formula for the molecule.

9.132 A liquid compound used in dry cleaning contains 14.5% C and 85.5% Cl by mass and has a molecular mass of 166 amu. Write the Lewis formula for the molecule.

9.133 A compound of tin and chlorine is a colorless liquid. The vapor has a density of 7.49 g/L at 151°C and 1.00 atm. What is the molecular mass of the compound? Why do you think the compound is molecular and not ionic? Write the Lewis formula for the molecule.

9.134 A compound of arsenic and fluorine is a gas. A sample weighing 0.100 g occupies 14.2 mL at 23°C and 765 mmHg. What is the molecular mass of the compound? Write the Lewis formula for the molecule.

9.135 Calculate the enthalpy of reaction for

$$HCN(g) \longrightarrow H(g) + C(g) + N(g)$$

from enthalpies of formation (see Appendix C). Given that the C—H bond energy is 411 kJ/mol, obtain a value for the C≡N bond energy. Compare your result with the value given in Table 9.5.

9.136 Assume the values of the C—H and C—C bond energies given in Table 9.5. Then, using data given in Appendix C, calculate the C=O bond energy in acetaldehyde,

$$
\begin{array}{c}
\text{H} \quad \text{O} \\
| \quad\quad || \\
\text{H—C—C—H} \\
| \\
\text{H}
\end{array}
$$

Compare your result with the value given in Table 9.5.

9.137 According to Pauling, the A—B bond energy is equal to the average of the A—A and B—B bond energies plus an energy contribution from the polar character of the bond:

$$BE(A\text{—}B) = \tfrac{1}{2}\,[BE(A\text{—}A) + BE(B\text{—}B)] + k(X_A - X_B)^2]$$

Here X_A and X_B are the electronegativities of atoms A and B, and k is a constant equal to 98.6 kJ. Assume that the electronegativity of H is 2.1. Use the formula to calculate the electronegativity of oxygen.

9.138 Because known compounds with N—I bonds tend to be unstable, there are no thermodynamic data available with which to calculate the N—I bond energy. However, we can estimate a value from Pauling's formula relating electronegativities and bond energies (see Problem 9.137). Using Pauling's electronegativities and the bond energies given in Table 9.5, calculate the N—I bond energy.

9.139 Using Mulliken's formula, calculate a value for the electronegativity of chlorine. Use values of the ionization energy from Figure 8.18 and values of the electron affinity from Table 8.4. Divide this result (in kJ/mol) by 230 to get a value comparable to Pauling's scale.

9.140 Using Mulliken's formula, calculate a value for the electronegativity of oxygen. Convert the result to a value on Pauling's scale. See Problem 9.139.

10

Molecular Geometry and Chemical Bonding Theory

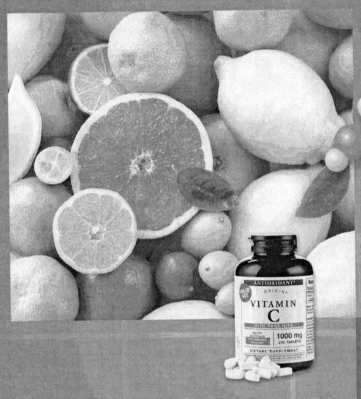

Humans are one of the few animals unable to produce vitamin C (ascorbic acid) naturally and must obtain it through the diet (such as citrus fruits) or from supplements. The space-filling model shows the three-dimensional shape of the ascorbic acid molecule.

Contents and Concepts

We can predict the molecular geometry of a molecule, its general shape as determined by the relative positions of atomic nuclei, with a simple model: the valence-shell electron-pair repulsion model. After exploring molecular geometry, we explain chemical bonding by means of valence bond theory, which gives us insight into why bonds form and why they have definite directions in space, giving particular molecular geometries.

Although valence bond theory satisfactorily describes most molecules, it has trouble explaining the bonding in a molecule such as oxygen, O_2, which has even numbers of electrons but is paramagnetic. Molecular orbital theory is an alternative theory that views the electronic structure of molecules much the way we think of atoms: in terms of orbitals that are successively occupied by electrons.

373

e know from various experiments that molecules have definite structures; that is, the atoms of a molecule have definite positions relative to one another in three-dimensional space. Consider two molecules: boron trifluoride, BF_3, and phosphorus trifluoride, PF_3. Both have the same general formula, AX_3, but their molecular structures are very different (Figure 10.1). Boron trifluoride is a planar, or flat, molecule. The angle between any two B—F bonds is 120°. The geometry or general shape of the BF_3 molecule is said to be *trigonal planar* (trigonal because the figure described by imaginary lines connecting the F atoms has three sides). Phosphorus trifluoride is nonplanar, and the angle between any two P—F bonds is 96°. If you imagine lines connecting the fluorine atoms, these lines and those of the P—F bonds describe a pyramid with the phosphorus atom at its apex. The geometry of the PF_3 molecule is said to be *trigonal pyramidal*. How do you explain such different molecular geometries?

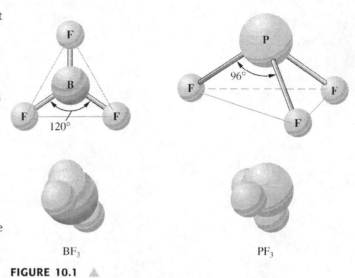

FIGURE 10.1 ▲

Molecular models of BF_3 and PF_3

Although both molecules have the general formula AX_3, boron trifluoride is planar (flat), whereas phosphorus trifluoride is pyramidal (pyramid shaped).

Subtle differences in structure are also possible. Consider the following molecular structures, which differ only in the arrangement of the atoms about the C=C bond; such molecules are referred to as *isomers*.

This chapter includes more advanced bonding concepts than those presented in the previous chapter. It follows that chapter naturally, but you can postpone or abbreviate the material as you wish.

```
   H         H             H         Cl
     \      /                \       /
      C = C                    C = C
     /      \                /       \
   Cl        Cl            Cl          H
```

cis-1,2-Dichloroethene   *trans*-1,2-Dichloroethene

In the *cis* compound, both H atoms are on the same side of the C=C bond; in the *trans* compound, they are on opposite sides. These structural formulas represent entirely different compounds, as their boiling points clearly demonstrate. Cis-1,2-dichloroethene boils at 60°C; trans-1,2-dichloroethene boils at 48°C. The differences between such *cis* and *trans* compounds can be quite important. The central molecular event in the detection of light by the human eye involves the transformation of a *cis* compound to its corresponding *trans* compound after the absorption of a photon of light. How do you explain the existence of *cis* and *trans* compounds?

In this chapter we discuss how to explain the geometries of molecules in terms of their electronic structures. We also explore two theories of chemical bonding: valence bond theory and molecular orbital theory.

■ See page 410 for the Media Summary.

Molecular Geometry and Directional Bonding

Experiments in General Chemistry, 10B, "Molecular Architecture of Tetrahedral Molecules."

Molecular geometry is *the general shape of a molecule, as determined by the relative positions of the atomic nuclei.* There is a simple model that allows you to predict molecular geometries, or shapes, from Lewis formulas. This valence-shell electron-pair model usually predicts the correct general shape of a molecule. It does not explain chemical bonding, however. For this you must look at a theory, such as valence bond theory, that is based on quantum mechanics. Valence bond theory provides further insight into why bonds form and, at the same time, reveals that bonds have definite directions in space, resulting in particular molecular geometries.

10.1 The Valence-Shell Electron-Pair Repulsion (VSEPR) Model

The **valence-shell electron-pair repulsion (VSEPR) model** *predicts the shapes of molecules and ions by assuming that the valence-shell electron pairs are arranged about each atom so that electron pairs are kept as far away from one another as possible, thus minimizing electron-pair repulsions.* < The possible arrangements assumed by different numbers of electron pairs about an atom are shown in Figure 10.2. (If you tie various numbers of similar balloons together, they assume these same arrangements; see Figure 10.3.)

The acronym VSEPR is pronounced "vesper."

ChemWork: Shapes of Molecules 1

For example, if there are only two electron pairs in the valence shell of an atom, these pairs tend to be at opposite sides of the nucleus, so that repulsion is minimized. This gives a *linear* arrangement of electron pairs; that is, the electron pairs mainly occupy regions of space at an angle of 180° to one another (Figure 10.2).

If three electron pairs are in the valence shell of an atom, they tend to be arranged in a plane directed toward the corners of a triangle of equal sides (equilateral triangle). This arrangement is *trigonal planar,* in which the regions of space occupied by electron pairs are directed at 120° angles to one another (Figure 10.2).

FIGURE 10.2

Arrangement of electron pairs about an atom

Black lines give the directions of electron pairs about atom A. The blue lines merely help depict the geometric arrangement of electron pairs.

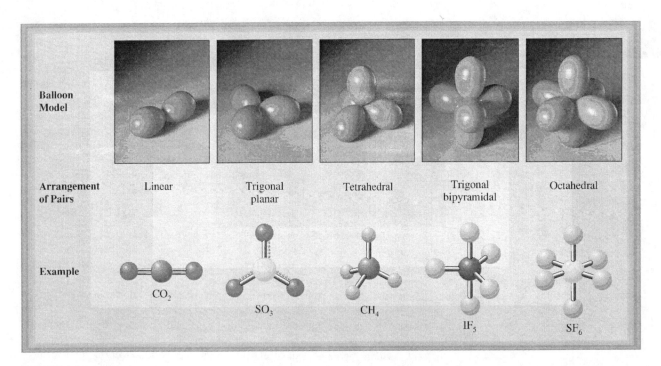

FIGURE 10.3 ▲

Balloon models of electron-pair arrangements

When you tie similar balloons together, they assume the arrangements shown. These arrangements are the same as those assumed by valence electron pairs about an atom, as in the examples.

Four electron pairs in the valence shell of an atom tend to have a *tetrahedral* arrangement. That is, if you imagine the atom at the center of a regular tetrahedron, each region of space in which an electron pair mainly lies extends toward a corner, or vertex (Figure 10.2). (A regular tetrahedron is a geometrical shape with four faces, each an equilateral triangle. Thus, it has the form of a triangular pyramid.) The regions of space mainly occupied by electron pairs are directed at approximately 109.5° angles to one another.

When you determine the geometry of a molecule experimentally, you locate the positions of the atoms, not the electron pairs. To predict the relative positions of atoms around a given atom using the VSEPR model, you first note the arrangement of valence-shell electron pairs around that central atom. Some of these electron pairs are bonding pairs and some are lone pairs. *The direction in space of the bonding pairs gives you the molecular geometry.* To consider examples of the method, we will first look at molecules AX_n in which the central atom A is surrounded by two, three, or four valence-shell electron pairs. Later we will look at molecules in which A is surrounded by five or six valence-shell electron pairs.

Central Atom with Two, Three, or Four Valence-Shell Electron Pairs

Show large molecular models of different geometries.

Examples of geometries in which two, three, or four valence-shell electron pairs surround a central atom are shown in Figure 10.4.

Beryllium fluoride, BeF_2, is normally a solid. The BeF_2 molecule exists in the vapor phase at high temperature.

Two Electron Pairs (Linear Arrangement)   To find the geometry of the molecule AX_n, you first determine the number of valence-shell electron pairs around atom A. You can get this information from the electron-dot formula. For example, following the rules given in Section 9.6, you can find the electron-dot formula for the BeF_2 molecule. <

$$: \overset{\cdot\cdot}{\underset{\cdot\cdot}{F}} : Be : \overset{\cdot\cdot}{\underset{\cdot\cdot}{F}} :$$

There are two electron pairs in the valence shell for beryllium, and the VSEPR model predicts that they will have a linear arrangement (see Figure 10.2). Fluorine atoms are bonded in the same direction as the electron pairs. Hence, the geometry of the BeF_2 molecule is *linear*—that is, the atoms are arranged in a straight line (see Figure 10.4).

BeF_2

Electron Pairs			Arrangement of Pairs	Molecular Geometry		Example	
Total	Bonding	Lone					
2	2	0	Linear	Linear AX$_2$		BeF$_2$	F—Be—F
3	3	0	Trigonal planar	Trigonal planar AX$_3$		BF$_3$	
	2	1		Bent (or angular) AX$_2$	—Lone pair	SO$_2$	
4	4	0	Tetrahedral	Tetrahedral AX$_4$		CH$_4$	
	3	1		Trigonal pyramidal AX$_3$		NH$_3$	
	2	2		Bent (or angular) AX$_2$		H$_2$O	

FIGURE 10.4

Molecular geometries

Central atom with two, three, or four valence-shell electron pairs. The notation in the column at the right provides a convenient way to represent the shape of a molecule drawn on a flat surface. A straight line represents a bond or electron pair in the plane of the page. A dashed line represents a bond or electron pair extending behind the page. A wedge represents a bond or electron pair extending above (in front of) the page.

BF$_3$

The VSEPR model can also be applied to molecules with multiple bonds. In this case, each multiple bond is treated as though it were a single electron pair. (All pairs of a multiple bond are required to be in approximately the same region.) To predict the geometry of carbon dioxide, for example, you first write the electron-dot formula.

$$:\overset{..}{O}::C::\overset{..}{O}:$$

You have two double bonds, or two electron groups, about the carbon atom, and these are treated as though there were two pairs on carbon. Thus, according to the VSEPR model, the bonds are arranged linearly and the geometry of carbon dioxide is linear.

Three Electron Pairs (Trigonal Planar Arrangement)   Let us now predict the geometry of the boron trifluoride molecule, BF$_3$, introduced in the chapter opening. The electron-dot formula is

$$\begin{array}{c} :\overset{..}{F}: \\ :\overset{..}{F}:B:\overset{..}{F}: \end{array}$$

The three electron pairs on boron have a trigonal planar arrangement, and the molecular geometry, which is determined by the directions of the bonding pairs, is also *trigonal planar* (Figures 10.1 and 10.4).

CH$_4$

NH$_3$

H$_2$O

Sulfur dioxide, SO$_2$, provides an example of a molecule with three electron groups about the S atom; one group is a lone pair. This molecule requires a resonance description, so it gives us a chance to see how the VSEPR model can be applied in such cases. The resonance description can be written

$$\ddot{O}=\overset{\ddot{}}{S}-\ddot{\underset{..}{O}}: \longleftrightarrow :\ddot{\underset{..}{O}}-\overset{\ddot{}}{S}=\ddot{O} \longleftrightarrow :\ddot{\underset{..}{O}}\overset{\ddot{}}{S}\ddot{\underset{..}{O}}:$$

Whichever formula you consider, sulfur has three groups of electrons about it. These groups have a trigonal planar arrangement, so sulfur dioxide is a *bent*, or *angular*, molecule (Figure 10.4). In general, whenever you consider a resonance description, you can use any of the resonance formulas to predict the molecular geometry with the VSEPR model.

Note the difference between the *arrangement of electron pairs* and the *molecular geometry*, or the arrangement of nuclei. What you usually "see" by means of x-ray diffraction and similar methods are the nuclear positions—that is, the molecular geometry. Unseen, but nevertheless important, are the lone pairs, which occupy definite positions about an atom according to the VSEPR model.

Four Electron Pairs (Tetrahedral Arrangement)   The common and most important case of four electron pairs about the central atom (the octet rule) leads to three different molecular geometries, depending on the number of bonds formed. Note the following examples.

$$\begin{array}{ccc}
\text{H} & \text{H} & \text{H} \\
\overset{..}{\text{H} : \text{C} : \text{H}} & \overset{..}{: \text{N} : \text{H}} & \overset{..}{: \text{O} : \text{H}} \\
\text{H} & \text{H} &
\end{array}$$

CH$_4$	NH$_3$	H$_2$O
Molecular geometry: tetrahedral	trigonal pyramidal	bent

In each of these examples, the electron pairs are arranged tetrahedrally, and two or more atoms are bonded in these tetrahedral directions to give the different geometries (Figure 10.4).

When all electron pairs are bonding, as in methane, CH$_4$, the molecular geometry is *tetrahedral* (Figure 10.5). When three of the pairs are bonding and one pair is nonbonding, as in ammonia, NH$_3$, the molecular geometry is *trigonal pyramidal*. Note that the nitrogen atom is at the apex of the pyramid, and the three hydrogen atoms extend downward to form the triangular base of the pyramid.

Now you can answer the question raised in the chapter opening: Why is the BF$_3$ molecule trigonal planar and the PF$_3$ molecule trigonal pyramidal? The difference occurs because in BF$_3$ there are three pairs of electrons around boron, and in PF$_3$ there are four pairs of electrons around phosphorus. As in NH$_3$, there are three bonding pairs and one lone pair in PF$_3$, which give rise to the trigonal pyramidal geometry.

Steps in the Prediction of Geometry by the VSEPR Model   Let us summarize the steps to follow in order to predict the geometry of an AX$_n$ molecule or ion by the VSEPR method. (All X atoms of AX$_n$ need not be identical.)

Step 1: Write the electron-dot formula from the molecular formula.

Step 2: Determine from the electron-dot formula the number of electron pairs around the central atom, including bonding and nonbonding pairs. (Count a multiple bond as one pair. If resonance occurs, use one resonance formula to determine this number.)

Step 3: Determine the arrangement of these electron pairs about the central atom (see Figure 10.2).

Step 4: Obtain the molecular geometry from the directions of the bonding pairs for this arrangement (see Figure 10.4).

FIGURE 10.5 ▲

The methane molecule
A ball-and-stick model shows the tetrahedral arrangement of bonds. This model is within an electrostatic-potential map, showing the electron density about the molecule by gradations of color. Thus, the red color means high density, which occurs in the C—H bonding regions.

Concept Check 10.1

An atom in a molecule is surrounded by four pairs of electrons: one lone pair and three bonding pairs. Describe how the four electron pairs are arranged about the atom. How are any three of these pairs arranged in space? What is the geometry about this central atom, taking into account just the bonded atoms?

| Example 10.1 | Predicting Molecular Geometries (Two, Three, or Four Electron Pairs) |

Predict the geometry of the following molecules or ions, using the VSEPR method: a. $BeCl_2$; b. NO_2^-; c. $SiCl_4$.

An alternative example is provided in the Instructor's Resource Manual.

Problem Strategy After drawing the Lewis formula for a molecule, determine the number of electron groups about the central atom. This number determines the arrangement of the electron groups (Figure 10.2). The geometry is determined by the arrangement of bonds to the central atom (Figure 10.4).

Solution a. Following the steps outlined in Sections 9.6 and 9.8 for writing Lewis formulas, you distribute the valence electrons to the skeleton structure of $BeCl_2$ as follows:

$$:Cl:Be:Cl:$$

The two pairs on Be have a linear arrangement, indicating a **linear** molecular geometry for $BeCl_2$. (See Figure 10.4; 2 electron pairs, 0 lone pairs.)

$BeCl_2$

b. The nitrite ion, NO_2^-, has the following resonance description:

$$\left[:\ddot{O}\!-\!\ddot{N}\!=\!\ddot{O}: \right] \longleftrightarrow \left[:\ddot{O}\!=\!\ddot{N}\!-\!\ddot{O}: \right]$$

The N atom has three electron groups (one single bond, one double bond, and one lone pair) about it. Therefore the molecular geometry of the NO_2^- ion is **bent.** (See Figure 10.4; 2 bonding pairs, 1 lone pair.)

NO_2^-

c. The electron-dot formula of $SiCl_4$ is

$$:Cl: \atop :Cl:Si:Cl: \atop :Cl:$$

The molecular geometry is **tetrahedral.** (See Figure 10.4; 4 bonding pairs, 0 lone pairs.)

$SiCl_4$

Answer Check Be careful not to confuse the name for the arrangement of valence electron pairs with the name for the molecular geometry. The geometry refers only to the arrangement of bonds. In this example, the nitrite ion, NO_2^-, has a trigonal planar arrangement of valence electron pairs and a bent geometry (arrangement of the bonds).

Exercise 10.1 Use the VSEPR method to predict the geometry of the following ion and molecules: a. ClO_3^-; b. OF_2; c. SiF_4.

■ See Problems 10.33, 10.34, 10.35, and 10.36.

Bond Angles and the Effect of Lone Pairs

The VSEPR model allows you to predict the approximate angles between bonds in molecules. For example, it tells you that CH_4 should have a tetrahedral geometry and that the H—C—H bond angles should be 109.5° (see Figure 10.2). Because all of the valence-shell electron pairs about the carbon atom are bonding and all of the bonds

FIGURE 10.6 ▷

H—A—H bond angles in some molecules
Experimentally determined bond angles are shown for CH_4, CH_3Cl, NH_3, and H_2O, represented here by models.

CH$_4$ 109.5°   CH$_3$Cl 110°   NH$_3$ 107°   H$_2$O 105°

are alike, you expect the CH_4 molecule to have an exact tetrahedral geometry. However, if one or more of the electron pairs is nonbonding or if there are dissimilar bonds, all four valence-shell electron pairs will not be alike. Then you expect the bond angles to deviate from the 109.5° predicted by an exact tetrahedral geometry. This is indeed what you see. Experimentally determined H—A—H bond angles (A is the central atom) in CH_4, CH_3Cl, NH_3, and H_2O are shown in Figure 10.6.

The increase or decrease of bond angles from the ideal values is often predictable. *A lone pair tends to require more space than a corresponding bonding pair.* You can explain this as follows: A lone pair of electrons is attracted to only one atomic core, whereas a bonding pair is attracted to two. As a result, the lone pair is spatially more diffuse, while the bonding pair is drawn more tightly to the nuclei. Consider the trigonal pyramidal molecule NH_3. The lone pair on the nitrogen atom requires more space than the bonding pairs. Therefore, the N—H bonds are effectively pushed away from the lone pair, and the H—N—H bond angles become smaller than the tetrahedral value of 109.5°. How much smaller, the VSEPR model cannot tell you. The experimental value of an H—N—H bond angle is a few degrees smaller (107°). But the trigonal pyramidal molecule PF_3, mentioned in the chapter opening, has an F—P—F bond angle of 96°, which is significantly smaller than the exact tetrahedral value.

Multiple bonds require more space than single bonds because of the greater number of electrons. You therefore expect the C=O bond in the formaldehyde molecule, CH_2O, to require more space than the C—H bonds. You predict that the H—C—H bond angle will be smaller than the 120° seen in an exact trigonal planar geometry, such as the F—B—F angle in BF_3. Similarly, you expect the H—C—H bond angles in the ethylene molecule, CH_2CH_2, to be smaller than the trigonal planar value. Experimental values are shown in Figure 10.7.

You may decide not to treat five and six electron pairs, particularly if you are short of time.

116° CH$_2$O   117° CH$_2$CH$_2$

FIGURE 10.7 ▲

H—C—H bond angles in molecules with carbon double bond
Bond angles are shown for formaldehyde, CH_2O, and ethylene, CH_2CH_2, represented here by models.

Central Atom with Five or Six Valence-Shell Electron Pairs

Five electron pairs tend to have a *trigonal bipyramidal arrangement.* The electron pairs tend to be directed to the corners of a trigonal bipyramid, a figure formed by placing the face of one tetrahedron onto the face of another tetrahedron (see Figure 10.2).

Six electron pairs tend to have an *octahedral arrangement.* The electron pairs tend to be directed to the corners of a regular octahedron, a figure that has eight triangular faces and six vertexes, or corners (see Figure 10.2).

FIGURE 10.8 ▼

Molecular geometries
Central atom with five or six valence-shell
electron pairs.

Five Electron Pairs (Trigonal Bipyramidal Arrangement) Large atoms like phosphorus can accommodate more than eight valence electrons. The phosphorus atom in phosphorus pentachloride, PCl_5, has five electron pairs in its valence shell. With five electron pairs around phosphorus, all bonding, PCl_5 should have a *trigonal bipyramidal geometry* (Figure 10.8). Note, however, that the vertexes of the trigonal bipyramid are not all equivalent (that is, the angles between the electron pairs are not

Electron Pairs			Arrangement of Pairs	Molecular Geometry	Example
Total	Bonding	Lone			
5	5	0	Trigonal bipyramidal	Trigonal bipyramidal AX$_5$	PCl$_5$
	4	1		Seesaw (or distorted tetrahedron) AX$_4$	SF$_4$
	3	2		T-shaped AX$_3$	ClF$_3$
	2	3		Linear AX$_2$	XeF$_2$
6	6	0	Octahedral	Octahedral AX$_6$	SF$_6$
	5	1		Square pyramidal AX$_5$	IF$_5$
	4	2		Square planar AX$_4$	XeF$_4$

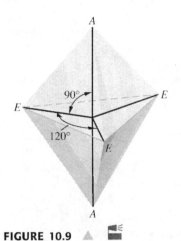

FIGURE 10.9 ▲

Trigonal bipyramidal arrangement of electron pairs
Electron pairs are directed along the black lines to the vertices of a trigonal bipyramid. Equatorial directions are labeled *E*, and axial directions are labeled *A*.

FIGURE 10.10 ▲

The sulfur tetrafluoride molecule
Molecular model.

FIGURE 10.11 ▲

The chlorine trifluoride molecule
Molecular model.

FIGURE 10.12 ▲

The xenon difluoride molecule
Molecular model.

all the same). Thus, the directions to which the electron pairs point are not equivalent. Two of the directions, called *axial directions*, form an axis through the central atom (see Figure 10.9). They are 180° apart. The other three directions are called *equatorial directions*. These point toward the corners of the equilateral triangle that lies on a plane through the central atom, perpendicular (at 90°) to the axial directions. The equatorial directions are 120° from each other.

Molecular geometries other than trigonal bipyramidal are possible when one or more of the five electron pairs are lone pairs. Consider the sulfur tetrafluoride molecule, SF_4. The Lewis electron-dot formula is

The five electron pairs about sulfur should have a trigonal bipyramidal arrangement. Because the axial and equatorial positions of the electron pairs are not equivalent, you must decide in which of these positions the lone pair appears.

The lone pair acts as though it is somewhat "larger" than a bonding pair. Therefore, the total repulsion between all pairs should be lower if the lone pair is in a position that puts it directly adjacent to the smallest number of other pairs.

An electron pair in an equatorial position is directly adjacent to only *two* other pairs—the two axial pairs at 90°. The other two equatorial pairs are farther away at 120°. An electron pair in an axial position is directly adjacent to *three* other pairs—the three equatorial pairs at 90°. The other axial pair is much farther away at 180°.

Thus you expect lone pairs to occupy equatorial positions in the trigonal bipyramidal arrangement. For sulfur tetrafluoride, this gives a *seesaw* (or *distorted tetrahedral*) *geometry* (Figure 10.10).

Chlorine trifluoride, ClF_3, has the electron-dot formula

$$:\ddot{F}:$$
$$:\ddot{F}—\ddot{Cl}:$$
$$:\ddot{F}:$$

The lone pairs on chlorine occupy two of the equatorial positions of the trigonal bipyramidal arrangement, giving a *T-shaped geometry* (Figure 10.11). The four atoms of the molecule all lie in one plane, with the chlorine nucleus at the intersection of the "T."

Xenon difluoride, XeF_2, has the electron-dot formula

$$:\ddot{F}:$$
$$:\ddot{Xe}:$$
$$:\ddot{F}:$$

The three lone pairs on xenon occupy the equatorial positions of the trigonal bipyramidal arrangement, giving a *linear geometry* (Figure 10.12).

Six Electron Pairs (Octahedral Arrangement) There are six electron pairs (all bonding pairs) about sulfur in sulfur hexafluoride, SF_6. Thus, it has an *octahedral geometry*, with sulfur at the center of the octahedron and fluorine atoms at the vertexes (Figure 10.8).

Iodine pentafluoride, IF_5, has the electron-dot formula

FIGURE 10.13 ▲

The iodine pentafluoride molecule
Molecular model.

The lone pair on iodine occupies one of the six equivalent positions in the octahedral arrangement, giving a *square pyramidal geometry* (Figure 10.13). The name derives from the shape formed by drawing lines between atoms.

Xenon tetrafluoride, XeF_4, has the electron-dot formula

FIGURE 10.14 ▲

The xenon tetrafluoride molecule
Molecular model.

The two lone pairs on xenon occupy opposing positions in the octahedral arrangement to minimize their repulsion. The result is a *square planar geometry* (Figure 10.14).

Example 10.2	Predicting Molecular Geometries (Five or Six Electron Pairs)

What do you expect for the geometry of tellurium tetrachloride, $TeCl_4$?

Problem Strategy   After drawing the Lewis formula for a molecule, determine the number of electron groups about the central atom. This number determines the arrangement of the electron groups (Figure 10.2). The geometry is determined by the arrangement of bonds to the central atom (Figure 10.8).

Solution   First you distribute the valence electrons to the Cl atoms to satisfy the octet rule. Then you allocate the remaining valence electrons to the central atom, Te (following the steps outlined in Section 9.6). The electron-dot formula is

There are five electron pairs in the valence shell of Te in $TeCl_4$. Of these, four are bonding pairs and one is a lone pair. The arrangement of electron pairs is trigonal bipyramidal. You expect the lone pair to occupy an equatorial position, so $TeCl_4$ has a **seesaw** molecular geometry. (See Figure 10.8; 4 bonding pairs, 1 lone pair.)

Answer Check   Again, be careful to distinguish the name for the arrangement of valence electron pairs from the name for the molecular geometry.

Exercise 10.2   According to the VSEPR model, what molecular geometry would you predict for iodine trichloride, ICl_3?

An alternative example is provided in the Instructor's Resource Manual.

■ See Problems 10.39, 10.40, 10.41, and 10.42.

10.2 | **Dipole Moment and Molecular Geometry**

The VSEPR model provides a simple procedure for predicting the geometry of a molecule. However, predictions must be verified by experiment. Information about the geometry of a molecule can sometimes be obtained from an experimental quantity

A Chemist Looks at . . .

Left-Handed and Right-Handed Molecules

daily life

This morning, half asleep, I (D. E.) tried to put my left glove on my right hand. Silly mistake, of course. A person's two hands are similar but not identical. If I look at my hands, say, with both palms toward me, the thumbs point in opposite directions. But, if I now hold the palm of my right hand toward a mirror and compare that image with my actual left hand, I see that the thumbs point in the same direction. A person's left hand looks like the mirror image of his or her right hand, and vice versa. You can mentally superimpose one hand onto the mirror image of the other hand. Yet the two hands are themselves nonsuperimposable. Some molecules have this "handedness" property too, and this possibility gives rise to a subtle kind of isomerism.

The presence of handedness in molecules depends on the fact that the atoms in the molecules occupy specific places in three-dimensional space. In most organic molecules, this property depends on the tetrahedral bonding of the carbon atom. Consider a carbon atom bonded to four different kinds of groups, say, —H, —OH, —CH₃, and —COOH. (The resulting molecule is called lactic acid.) Two isomers are possible in which one isomer

is the mirror image of the other, but the two isomers are themselves not identical (they are nonsuperimposable) (see Figure 10.15). However, all four groups bonded to this carbon atom must be different to have this isomerism. If you replace the —OH group of lactic acid by, say, an H atom, the molecule and its mirror image become identical. There are no isomers; there is just one kind of molecule.

The two lactic acid isomers shown in Figure 10.15 are labeled D-lactic acid and L-lactic acid (D is for *dextro*, meaning right; L is for *levo*, meaning left). They might be expected to have quite similar properties, and they do. They have identical melting points, boiling points, and solubilities, for instance. And if we try to prepare lactic acid in the laboratory, we almost always get an equal molar mixture of the D and L isomers. But the biological origins of the molecules are different. Only D-lactic acid occurs in sour milk, whereas only L-lactic acid forms in muscle tissue after exercising. (If you overexercise, lactic acid accumulates in muscle tissue, causing soreness.)

Biological molecules frequently have the handedness character. The chemical substance responsible for the flavor of spearmint is L-carvone. The substance responsible for the flavor of caraway seeds, which you see in some rye bread, is D-carvone (see Figure 10.16). Here are two substances whose molecules differ only in being mirror images of one another. Yet, they have strikingly different flavors: one is minty; the other is pungent aromatic.

called the dipole moment, which is related to the polarity of the bonds in a molecule. The **dipole moment** is *a quantitative measure of the degree of charge separation in a molecule*. The polarity of a bond, such as that in HCl, is characterized by a separation of electric charge. We can represent this in HCl by indicating partial charges, δ^+ and δ^-, on the atoms.

$$\overset{\delta^+}{H}—\overset{\delta^-}{Cl}$$

Any molecule that has a net separation of charge, as in HCl, has a dipole moment. A molecule in which the distribution of electric charge is equivalent to charges $+\delta$ and $-\delta$ separated by a distance d has a dipole moment equal to δd. Dipole moments are

FIGURE 10.15 ▶

Isomers of lactic acid

Note that the two molecules labeled D-lactic acid and L-lactic acid are mirror images and cannot be superimposed on one another. See Figure 10.4 for an explanation of the notation used to represent the tetrahedral geometry.

D-lactic acid

L-lactic acid

—COOH means

D-Carvone

L-Carvone

FIGURE 10.16 ▲

Spearmint and caraway

Spearmint leaves contain L-carvone; caraway seeds contain D-carvone.

 See Problems 10.83 and 10.84.

usually measured in units of *debyes* (D). In SI units, dipole moments are measured in coulomb-meters (C·m), and $1 \text{ D} = 3.34 \times 10^{-30}$ C·m.

Measurements of dipole moments are based on the fact that polar molecules (molecules having a dipole moment) can be oriented by an electric field. Figure 10.17 shows an electric field generated by charged plates. Note that the polar molecules tend to align themselves so that the negative ends of the molecules point toward the positive plate, and the positive ends point toward the negative plate. This orientation of the molecules affects the *capacitance* of the charged plates (the capacity of the plates to hold a charge). Consequently, measurements of the capacitance of plates separated by different substances can be used to obtain the dipole moments of those substances. Figure 10.18 shows a simple demonstration that distinguishes between a polar liquid

FIGURE 10.17

Alignment of polar molecules by an electric field

(A) A polar substance is placed between metal plates. *(B)* When the plates are connected to an electric voltage (whose direction is shown by the + and − signs), the polar molecules align so that their negative ends point toward the positive plate.

Metal plates

A   B

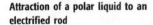

FIGURE 10.18

Attraction of a polar liquid to an electrified rod

Left: Water is a polar liquid; it is attracted to the electrically charged rod. The capacitance of the polar liquid (due to the alignment of polar molecules) stabilizes a charge separation induced in the column of liquid by the charged rod. Charges of signs opposite to those on the rod form on the liquid surface near the rod, resulting in a net attraction. *Right:* Carbon tetrachloride, CCl_4, is a nonpolar liquid; it is not attracted to the glass rod.

(one whose molecules have a dipole moment) and a nonpolar liquid. The polar liquid, but not the nonpolar one, is attracted to a charged rod.

You can sometimes relate the presence or absence of a dipole moment in a molecule to its molecular geometry. For example, consider the carbon dioxide molecule. Each carbon–oxygen bond has a polarity in which the more electronegative oxygen atom has a partial negative charge.

$$\overset{\delta^-}{O}=\overset{2\delta^+}{C}=\overset{\delta^-}{O}$$

We will denote the dipole-moment contribution from each bond (the bond dipole) by an arrow with a positive sign at one end ($\leftrightarrow$). The dipole-moment arrow points from the positive partial charge toward the negative partial charge. Thus, you can rewrite the formula for carbon dioxide as

$$\overset{\leftarrow}{O}=\vec{C}=O$$

Each bond dipole, like a force, is a *vector* quantity; that is, it has both magnitude and direction. Like forces, two bond dipoles of equal magnitude but opposite direction cancel each other. (Think of two groups of people in a tug of war. As long as each group pulls on the rope with the same force but in the opposite direction, there is no movement—the net force is zero.) Because the two carbon–oxygen bonds in CO_2 are equal but point in opposite directions, they give a net dipole moment of zero for the molecule.

For comparison, consider the water molecule. The bond dipoles point from the hydrogen atoms toward the more electronegative oxygen.

$$\overset{\nearrow \overset{O}{} \nwarrow}{\underset{H}{} \quad \underset{H}{}}$$

Here, the two bond dipoles do not point directly toward or away from each other. As a result, they add together to give a nonzero dipole moment for the molecule.

$$\overset{\uparrow}{\underset{H}{} \overset{O}{} \underset{H}{}}$$

The dipole moment of H_2O has been observed to be 1.94 D.

The fact that the water molecule has a dipole moment is excellent experimental evidence for a bent geometry. If the H_2O molecule were linear, the dipole moment would be zero.

The analysis we have just made for two different geometries of AX_2 molecules can be extended to other AX_n molecules (in which all X atoms are identical). Table 10.1 summarizes the relationship between molecular geometry and dipole moment. Those geometries in which A—X bonds are directed symmetrically about the central atom

TABLE 10.1	Relationship Between Molecular Geometry and Dipole Moment	
Formula	Molecular Geometry	Dipole Moment*
AX	Linear	Can be nonzero
AX_2	Linear	Zero
	Bent	Can be nonzero
AX_3	Trigonal planar	Zero
	Trigonal pyramidal	Can be nonzero
	T-shaped	Can be nonzero
AX_4	Tetrahedral	Zero
	Square planar	Zero
	Seesaw	Can be nonzero
AX_5	Trigonal bipyramidal	Zero
	Square pyramidal	Can be nonzero
AX_6	Octahedral	Zero

*All X atoms are assumed to be identical.

(for example, linear, trigonal planar, and tetrahedral) give molecules of zero dipole moment; that is, the molecules are *nonpolar*. Those geometries in which the X atoms tend to be on one side of the molecule (for example, bent and trigonal pyramidal) can have nonzero dipole moments; that is, they can give *polar* molecules.

Example 10.3 | Relating Dipole Moment and Molecular Geometry

Each of the following molecules has a nonzero dipole moment. Select the molecular geometry that is consistent with this information. Explain your reasoning.

a. SO_2 linear, bent

b. PH_3 trigonal planar, trigonal pyramidal

Problem Strategy Because the dipole moment is a *vector* quantity, it can happen that nonzero bond dipoles cancel one another to give a molecule with zero dipole moment. Look for bonds that are symmetrically arranged to oppose one another (think of a tug of war between bonds). Table 10.1 summarizes the relationship between geometry and dipole moment.

Solution a. In the linear geometry, the S—O bond contributions to the dipole moment would cancel, giving a zero dipole moment. That would not happen in the **bent** geometry; hence, this must be the geometry for the SO_2 molecule. b. In the trigonal planar geometry, the bond contributions to the dipole moment would cancel,

giving a zero dipole moment. That would not occur in the **trigonal pyramidal** geometry; hence, this is a possible molecular geometry for PH_3.

Answer Check Make sure that you have the correct geometry for the molecule, and note how the bonds either oppose one another, to give zero dipole moment, or else do not oppose and so give a dipole moment.

Exercise 10.3   Bromine trifluoride, BrF_3, has a nonzero dipole moment. Indicate which of the following geometries are consistent with this information: a. trigonal planar; b. trigonal pyramidal; c. T-shaped.

■ See Problems 10.43 and 10.44.

Exercise 10.4   Which of the following would be expected to have a dipole moment of zero on the basis of symmetry? Explain. a. $SOCl_2$; b. SiF_4; c. OF_2.

■ See Problems 10.45 and 10.46.

An alternative example is provided in the Instructor's Resource Manual.

FIGURE 10.19 ▲

Explanation of the small dipole moment of NF₃

The lone-pair and bond contributions to the dipole moment of NF₃ tend to offset one another.

| *Can you explain why NH₃ has such a large dipole moment compared with NF₃?*

In Example 10.3, the fact that certain molecular geometries necessarily imply a zero dipole moment allowed us to eliminate these geometries when considering a molecule with a nonzero dipole moment. The reverse argument does not follow, however. For example, suppose a molecule of the type AX_3 is found to have no measurable dipole moment. It may be that the geometry is trigonal planar. Another possibility, however, is that the geometry is trigonal pyramidal or T-shaped, but the lone pairs on the central atom offset the polarity of the bonds.

You can see this effect of lone pairs on the dipole moment of nitrogen trifluoride, NF_3. Judging by the electronegativity difference, you would expect each N—F bond to be quite polar. Yet the dipole moment of nitrogen trifluoride is only 0.2 D. (By contrast, ammonia has a dipole moment of 1.47 D.) The explanation for the small dipole moment in NF_3 appears in Figure 10.19. The lone pair on nitrogen has a dipole-moment contribution that is directed outward from the nucleus, because the electrons are offset from the nuclear center. This dipole-moment contribution thus opposes the N—F bond moments. <

Effect of Polarity on Molecular Properties

Whether a molecule has a dipole moment (that is, whether it is polar or nonpolar) can affect its properties. We will explore this issue in detail in the next chapter (Section 11.5). Briefly, though, we can see why *cis-* and *trans-*1,2-dichloroethene, mentioned in the chapter opening, have different boiling points. The C—Cl bonds are quite polar, because of the relatively large electronegativity difference between C and Cl atoms (0.9); the H—C bonds have moderate polarity (electronegativity difference of 0.4). The bond dipoles (light arrows) add together in *cis-*1,2-dichloroethene to give a polar molecule (the total dipole moment is indicated by the heavy arrow). (Note that the electronegative Cl atoms are on the same side in the *cis* molecule.) In the *trans* molecule, the bond dipoles subtract to give a nonpolar molecule.

*cis-*1,2-Dichloroethene   *trans-*1,2-Dichloroethene

In a liquid, polar molecules tend to orient so that positive ends of molecules are attracted to negative ends. This results in an attractive force between molecules (an *intermolecular* force), which increases the energy required for the liquid to boil, and therefore increases the boiling point. Recall that the *trans* compound boils at 48°C, whereas the *cis* compound boils at a higher temperature, 60°C.

Concept Check 10.2

Two molecules, each with the general formula AX_3, have different dipole moments. Molecule Y has a dipole moment of zero, whereas molecule Z has a nonzero dipole moment. From this information, what can you say about the geometries of Y and Z?

Valence Bond Theory

The VSEPR model is usually a satisfactory method for predicting molecular geometries. To understand bonding and electronic structure, however, you must look to quantum mechanics. We will consider two theories stemming from quantum mechanics: valence bond theory and molecular orbital theory. Both use the methods of quantum mechanics but make different simplifying assumptions. In this section, we will look in a qualitative way at the basic ideas involved in **valence bond theory,** *an approximate theory to explain the electron pair or covalent bond by quantum mechanics.*

Basic Theory

According to valence bond theory, a bond forms between two atoms when the following conditions are met:

1. An orbital on one atom comes to occupy a portion of the same region of space as an orbital on the other atom. The two orbitals are said to *overlap.*

2. The total number of electrons in both orbitals is no more than two.

As the orbital of one atom overlaps the orbital of another, the electrons in the orbitals begin to move about both atoms. Because the electrons are attracted to both nuclei at once, they pull the atoms together. Strength of bonding depends on the amount of overlap; the greater the overlap, the greater the bond strength. The two orbitals cannot contain more than two electrons because a given region of space can hold only two electrons with opposite spin.

For example, consider the formation of the H_2 molecule from atoms. Each atom has the electron configuration $1s^1$. As the H atoms approach each other, their $1s$ orbitals begin to overlap and a covalent bond forms (Figure 10.20). Valence bond theory also explains why two He atoms (each with electron configuration $1s^2$) do not bond. Suppose two He atoms approach one another and their $1s$ orbitals begin to overlap. Each orbital is doubly occupied, so the sharing of electrons between atoms would place the four valence electrons from the two atoms in the same region. This, of course, could not happen. As the orbitals begin to overlap, each electron pair strongly repels the other. The atoms come together, then fly apart.

Because the strength of bonding depends on orbital overlap, orbitals other than *s* orbitals bond only in given directions. *Orbitals bond in the directions in which they protrude or point, to obtain maximum overlap.* Consider the bonding between a hydrogen atom and a chlorine atom to give the HCl molecule. A chlorine atom has the electron configuration $[Ne]3s^23p^5$. Of the orbitals in the valence shell of the chlorine atom, three are doubly occupied by electrons and one (a $3p$ orbital) is singly occupied. The bonding of the hydrogen atom has to occur with the singly occupied $3p$ orbital of chlorine. For the strongest bonding to occur, the maximum overlap of orbitals is required. The $1s$ orbital of hydrogen must overlap along the axis of the singly occupied $3p$ orbital of chlorine (see Figure 10.21).

$$1s \qquad 1s \qquad\qquad 1s\ \ 1s$$
$$\text{H} \qquad\quad \text{H} \qquad\qquad\qquad \text{H}_2$$

FIGURE 10.20

Formation of H₂
The H—H bond forms when the 1s orbitals, one from each atom, overlap.

$$1s \qquad\qquad 3p$$

FIGURE 10.21

Bonding in HCl
The bond forms by the overlap of a hydrogen 1s orbital (blue) along the axis of a chlorine 3p orbital (green).

Hybrid Orbitals

From what has been said, you might expect the number of bonds formed by a given atom to equal the number of unpaired electrons in its valence shell. Chlorine, whose orbital diagram is

$$1s \qquad 2s \qquad\quad 2p \qquad\quad 3s \qquad\quad 3p$$

has one unpaired electron and forms one bond. Oxygen, whose orbital diagram is

$$1s \qquad 2s \qquad\quad 2p$$

has two unpaired electrons and forms two bonds, as in H_2O.

However, consider the carbon atom, whose orbital diagram is

$1s$ $2s$ $2p$

You might expect this atom to bond to two hydrogen atoms to form the CH_2 molecule. Although this molecule is known to be present momentarily during some reactions, it is very reactive and cannot be isolated. But methane, CH_4, in which the carbon atom bonds to four hydrogen atoms, is well known. In fact, a carbon atom usually forms four bonds.

You might explain this as follows: Four unpaired electrons are formed when an electron from the $2s$ orbital of the carbon atom is *promoted* (excited) to the vacant $2p$ orbital.

It would require energy to promote the carbon atom this way, but more than enough energy would be obtained from the formation of two additional covalent bonds. One bond would form from the overlap of the carbon $2s$ orbital with a hydrogen $1s$ orbital. Each of the other three bonds would form from a carbon $2p$ orbital and a hydrogen $1s$ orbital.

Experiment shows, however, that the four C—H bonds in methane are identical. ◄ This implies that the carbon orbitals involved in bonding are also equivalent. For this reason, valence bond theory assumes that the four valence orbitals of the carbon atom combine during the bonding process to form four new, but equivalent, hybrid orbitals. **Hybrid orbitals** are *orbitals used to describe bonding that are obtained by taking combinations of atomic orbitals of the isolated atoms.* In this case, a set of hybrid orbitals is constructed from one s orbital and three p orbitals, so they are called sp^3 hybrid orbitals. Calculations from theory show that each sp^3 hybrid orbital has a large lobe pointing in one direction and a small lobe pointing in the opposite direction. The four sp^3 hybrid orbitals point in tetrahedral directions. Figure 10.22A shows the shape of

Nuclear magnetic resonance (page 296) and infrared spectroscopy (page 362) both show that CH_4 has four equivalent C—H bonds.

FIGURE 10.22

Spatial arrangement of sp^3 hybrid orbitals

(A) The shape of a single sp^3 hybrid orbital. Each orbital consists of two lobes. One lobe is small, but dense, and concentrated near the nucleus. The other lobe is large, but diffuse. Bonding occurs with the large lobe, since it extends farther from the nucleus. *(B)* The four hybrid orbitals are arranged tetrahedrally in space. (Small lobes are omitted here for clarity, and large lobes are stylized and greatly narrowed for ease in depicting the directional bonding.) *(C)* Bonding in CH_4. Each C—H bond is formed by the overlap of a $1s$ orbital from a hydrogen atom and an sp^3 hybrid orbital of the carbon atom.

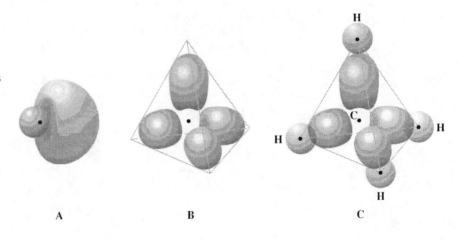

a single sp^3 orbital; Figure 10.22B shows a stylized set of four orbitals pointing in tetrahedral directions.

The C—H bonds in methane, CH_4, are described by valence bond theory as the overlapping of each sp^3 hybrid orbital of the carbon atom with $1s$ orbitals of hydrogen atoms (see Figure 10.22C). Thus, the bonds are arranged tetrahedrally, which is predicted by the VSEPR model. You can represent the hybridization of carbon and the bonding of hydrogen to the carbon atom in methane as follows:

Here the blue arrows represent electrons originally belonging to hydrogen atoms.

Hybrid orbitals can be formed from various numbers of atomic orbitals. *The number of hybrid orbitals formed always equals the number of atomic orbitals used.* For example, if you combine an s orbital and two p orbitals to get a set of equivalent orbitals, you get three hybrid orbitals (called sp^2 hybrid orbitals). A set of hybrid orbitals always has definite directional characteristics. Here, all three sp^2 hybrid orbitals lie in a plane and are directed at $120°$ angles to one another; that is, they have a trigonal planar arrangement. Some possible hybrid orbitals and their geometric arrangements are listed in Table 10.2 and shown in Figure 10.23. Note that the geometric arrangements of hybrid orbitals are the same as those for electron pairs in the VSEPR model.

Only two of the three p orbitals are used to form sp^2 hybrid orbitals. The unhybridized p orbital is perpendicular to the plane of the sp^2 hybrid orbitals. Similarly, only one of the three p orbitals is used to form sp hybrid orbitals. The two unhybridized p orbitals are perpendicular to the axis of the sp hybrid orbitals and perpendicular to each other. We will use these facts when we discuss multiple bonding in the next section.

Now that you know something about hybrid orbitals, let us develop a general scheme for describing the bonding about any atom (we will call this the central atom). First, notice from Table 10.2 that there is a relationship between type of hybrid orbitals on an atom and the geometric arrangement of those orbitals. If you know one, you can infer the other. Thus, if you know the geometric arrangement, you know what hybrid orbitals to use in the bond description of the central atom. Your first task in describing

TABLE 10.2	Kinds of Hybrid Orbitals		
Hybrid Orbitals	Geometric Arrangement	Number of Orbitals	Example
sp	Linear	2	Be in BeF_2
sp^2	Trigonal planar	3	B in BF_3
sp^3	Tetrahedral	4	C in CH_4
sp^3d	Trigonal bipyramidal	5	P in PCl_5
sp^3d^2	Octahedral	6	S in SF_6

FIGURE 10.23

Diagrams of hybrid orbitals showing their spatial arrangements
Each lobe shown is one hybrid orbital (small lobes are omitted for clarity).

Linear arrangement: sp hybrid orbitals

Trigonal planar arrangement: sp^2 hybrid orbitals

Tetrahedral arrangement: sp^3 hybrid orbitals

180°

120°

109.5°

Trigonal bipyramidal arrangement: sp^3d hybrid orbitals

Octahedral arrangement: sp^3d^2 hybrid orbitals

the bonding, then, is to obtain the geometric arrangement about the central atom. In lieu of experimental information about the geometry, you can use the VSEPR model, since it proves to be a fairly good predictor of molecular geometry. To obtain the bonding description about any atom in a molecule, you proceed as follows:

Step 1: Write the Lewis electron-dot formula of the molecule.

Step 2: From the Lewis formula, use the VSEPR model to obtain the arrangement of electron pairs about this atom.

Step 3: From the geometric arrangement of the electron pairs, deduce the type of hybrid orbitals on this atom required for the bonding description (see Table 10.2).

Step 4: Assign valence electrons to the hybrid orbitals of this atom one at a time, pairing them only when necessary.

Step 5: Form bonds to this atom by overlapping singly occupied orbitals of other atoms with the singly occupied hybrid orbitals of this atom.

As an application of this scheme, let us look at the BF_3 molecule and obtain the bond description of the boron atom. Following Step 1, you write the Lewis formula of BF_3.

$$:\ddot{F}: \\ | \\ B\!-\!\ddot{F}: \\ | \\ :\ddot{F}:$$

Now you apply the VSEPR model to the boron atom (Step 2). There are three electron pairs about the boron atom, so they are expected to have a planar trigonal arrangement. Looking at Table 10.2 (Step 3), you note that the three sp^2 hybrid orbitals have a trigonal planar arrangement. In Step 4, you assign the valence electrons of the boron atom to the hybrid orbitals. Finally, in Step 5, you imagine three fluorine atoms approaching the boron atom. The singly occupied $2p$ orbital on a fluorine atom overlaps one of the sp^2 hybrid orbitals on boron, forming a covalent bond. Three such B—F bonds form. Note that one of the $2p$ orbitals of boron remains unhybridized and is unoccupied by electrons. It is oriented perpendicular to the molecular plane. You can summarize these steps using orbital diagrams as follows:

B atom (ground state)

B atom (hybridized)

B atom (in BF_3)

B—F bonds

The next example further illustrates how to describe the bonding about an atom in a molecule. To solve problems of this type, you need to know the geometric arrangements of the hybrid orbitals listed in Table 10.2.

Example 10.4 | Applying Valence Bond Theory (Two, Three, or Four Electron Pairs)

Describe the bonding in H_2O according to valence bond theory. Assume that the molecular geometry is the same as given by the VSEPR model.

An alternative example is provided in the Instructor's Resource Manual.

Problem Strategy   From the Lewis formula for a molecule, determine its geometry about the central atom using the VSEPR model. From this geometry, determine the hybrid orbitals on this atom, assigning its valence electrons to these orbitals one at a time. Finally, form bonds by overlapping these hybrid orbitals with orbitals of the other atoms.

Solution   The Lewis formula for H_2O is

$$H-\overset{\displaystyle ..}{\underset{\displaystyle |}{O}}:$$
$$H$$

Note that there are four pairs of electrons about the oxygen atom. According to the VSEPR model, these are directed tetrahedrally, and from Table 10.2 you see that you should use sp^3 hybrid orbitals. Each O—H bond is formed by the overlap of a $1s$ orbital of a hydrogen atom with one of the singly occupied sp^3 hybrid orbitals of the oxygen atom. You can represent the bonding to the oxygen atom in H_2O as follows (see also Figure 10.24):

O atom (ground state)

O atom (hybridized)

O atom (in H_2O)

O—H bonds

lone pairs

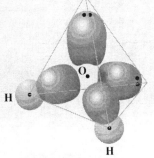

FIGURE 10.24

Bonding in H_2O

Orbitals on oxygen are sp^3 hybridized; bonding is tetrahedral.

(continued)

(continued)

Answer Check   Check that you have the correct Lewis formula for the molecule and that you have the correct geometry about the central atom and the correct hybrid orbitals (Table 10.2).

Exercise 10.5   Using hybrid orbitals, describe the bonding in NH_3 according to valence bond theory.

■ See Problems 10.47, 10.48, 10.49, and 10.50.

The actual angle between O—H bonds in H_2O has been experimentally determined to be 104.5°. Because this is close to the tetrahedral angle (109.5°), the description of bonding given in Example 10.4 is essentially correct. To be more precise, you should note that the hybrid orbitals for bonds and lone pairs are not exactly equivalent. The lone pairs are somewhat larger than bonding pairs. Because they take up more space, the lone pairs push the bonding pairs closer together than they are in the exact tetrahedral case.

As the next example illustrates, hybrid orbitals are also useful for describing bonding when the central atom of a molecule is surrounded by more than eight valence electrons.

Example 10.5 | Applying Valence Bond Theory (Five or Six Electron Pairs)

Describe the bonding in XeF_4 using hybrid orbitals.

An alternative example is provided in the Instructor's Resource Manual.

Problem Strategy   From the Lewis formula for a molecule, determine its geometry about the central atom using the VSEPR model. From this geometry, determine the hybrid orbitals on this atom, assigning its valence electrons to these orbitals one at a time. Finally, form bonds by overlapping these hybrid orbitals with orbitals of the other atoms.

Solution   The Lewis formula of XeF_4 is

The xenon atom has four single bonds and two lone pairs. It will require six orbitals to describe the bonding. This suggests that you use sp^3d^2 hybrid orbitals on xenon (according to Table 10.2). Each fluorine atom (valence-shell configuration $2s^2 2p^5$) has one singly occupied orbital, so you assume that this orbital is used in bonding. Each Xe—F bond is formed by the overlap of a xenon sp^3d^2 hybrid orbital with a singly occupied fluorine $2p$ orbital. You can summarize this as follows:

(continued)

(continued)

Answer Check Check that you have the correct Lewis formula for the molecule and that you have the correct geometry about the central atom and the correct hybrid orbitals (Table 10.2).

Exercise 10.6   Describe the bonding in PCl_5 using hybrid orbitals.

■ See Problems 10.53, 10.54, 10.55, and 10.56.

10.4 | Description of Multiple Bonding

ChemWork: Colorful Molecules

ChemWork: Molecular Structures

ChemWork: Bonding in an Organic Molecule

ChemWork: Hybridization in an Organic Molecule

ChemWork: Hybridization

In the previous section, we described bonding as the overlap of *one* orbital from each of the bonding atoms. Now we consider the possibility that *more than one* orbital from each bonding atom might overlap, resulting in a multiple bond.

As an example, consider the ethylene molecule.

$$H_2C = CH_2$$

One hybrid orbital is needed for each bond (whether a single or a multiple bond) and for each lone pair. Because each carbon atom is bonded to three other atoms and there are no lone pairs, three hybrid orbitals are needed. This suggests the use of sp^2 hybrid orbitals on each carbon atom (there are three sp^2 hybrid orbitals; see Table 10.2). Thus, during bonding, the $2s$ orbital and two of the $2p$ orbitals of each carbon atom form three hybrid orbitals having trigonal planar orientation. A third $2p$ orbital on each carbon atom remains unhybridized and is perpendicular to the plane of the three sp^2 hybrid orbitals.

C atom (ground state)   C atom (hybridized)

To describe the multiple bonding in ethylene, we must distinguish between two kinds of bonds. A **σ (sigma) bond** *has a cylindrical shape about the bond axis.* It is formed either when two *s* orbitals overlap, as in H_2 (Figure 10.25A), or when an orbital with directional character, such as a *p* orbital or a hybrid orbital, overlaps another orbital *along their axis* (Figure 10.25B). The bonds we discussed in the previous section are σ bonds.

A **π (pi) bond** *has an electron distribution above and below the bond axis.* It is formed by the *sideways* overlap of two parallel *p* orbitals (see Figure 10.25C). A sideways overlap will not give so strong a bond as an along-the-axis overlap of two *p* orbitals. A π bond occurs when two parallel orbitals are still available after strong σ bonds have formed.

FIGURE 10.25 ▶

Sigma and pi bonds
(A) The formation of a σ bond by the overlap of two s orbitals. *(B)* A σ bond can also be formed by the overlap of two p orbitals along their axes. *(C)* When two p orbitals overlap sideways, a π bond is formed.

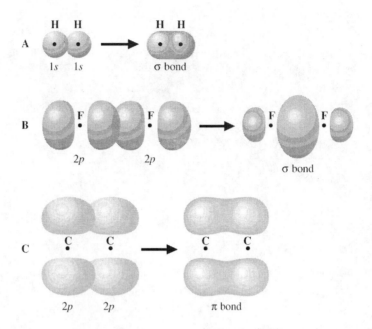

Now imagine that the separate atoms of ethylene move into their normal molecular positions. Each sp^2 hybrid carbon orbital overlaps a 1s orbital of a hydrogen atom or an sp^2 hybrid orbital of another carbon atom to form a σ bond (Figure 10.26A). Together, the σ bonds give the molecular framework of ethylene.

As you see from the orbital diagram for the hybridized C atom, a single 2p orbital still remains on each carbon atom. These orbitals are perpendicular to the plane of the hybrid orbitals; that is, they are perpendicular to the —CH₂ plane. Note that the two —CH₂ planes can rotate about the carbon–carbon axis without affecting the overlap of the hybrid orbitals. As these planes rotate, the 2p orbitals also rotate. When the —CH₂ planes rotate so that the 2p orbitals become parallel, the orbitals overlap to give a π bond (Figure 10.26B).

You therefore describe the carbon–carbon double bond as one σ bond and one π bond. Note that when the two 2p orbitals are parallel, the two —CH₂ ends of the molecule lie in the same plane. Thus, the formation of a π bond "locks" the two ends into a flat, rigid molecule.

FIGURE 10.26 ▼

Bonding in ethylene
(A) The σ-bond framework in ethylene, formed by the overlap of sp^2 hybrid orbitals on C atoms and 1s orbitals on H atoms. *(B)* The formation of the π bonds in ethylene. When the 2p orbitals are perpendicular to one another, there is no overlap and no bond formation. When the two —CH₂ groups rotate so that the 2p orbitals are parallel, a π bond forms.

FIGURE 10.27

Bonding in acetylene
(A) The σ-bond framework. *(B)* Two 2p orbitals on each carbon atom begin to overlap (symbolized by lines) to form two π bonds.

σ bonds

A

Two π bonds

B

You can describe the triple bonding in acetylene, H—C≡C—H, in similar fashion. Because each carbon atom is bonded to two other atoms and there are no lone pairs, two hybrid orbitals are needed. This suggests *sp* hybridization (see Table 10.2).

These *sp* hybrid orbitals have a linear arrangement, so the H—C—C—H geometry is linear. Bonds formed by the overlap of these hybrid orbitals are σ bonds. The two 2p orbitals not used to construct hybrid orbitals are perpendicular to the bond axis and to each other. They are used to form two π bonds. Thus, the carbon–carbon triple bond consists of one σ bond and two π bonds (see Figure 10.27).

Example 10.6 | Applying Valence Bond Theory (Multiple Bonding)

Describe the bonding on a given N atom in dinitrogen difluoride, N_2F_2, using valence bond theory.

An alternative example is provided in the Instructor's Resource Manual.

Problem Strategy From the Lewis formula, determine the hybrid orbitals on the double-bonded atoms. Do this by counting the number of electron groups about each atom, and from this determine the kind of hybrid orbitals used. Form a σ bond between the double-bonded atoms by overlapping a hybrid orbital of one atom with a hybrid orbital of the other atom. Also, form σ bonds from these atoms to other atoms. Use any unhybridized *p* orbitals on the central atoms to form π bonds between them.

Solution The electron-dot formula of N_2F_2 is

(continued)

(continued)

Note that a double bond is described as a π bond plus a σ bond. Hybrid orbitals are needed to describe each σ bond and each lone pair (a total of three hybrid orbitals for each N atom). This suggests sp^2 hybridization (see Table 10.2). According to this description, one of the sp^2 hybrid orbitals is used to form the N—F bond, another to form the σ bond of N=N, and the third to hold the lone pair on the N atom. The $2p$ orbitals on each N atom overlap to form the π bond of N=N. Hybridization and bonding of the N atoms are shown as follows:

N atom (ground state) → N atom (hybridized) → N atom (in N_2F_2)

Answer Check Check that the number of hybrid orbitals on an atom of a multiple bond equals the number of sigma bonds plus lone pairs on that atom.

Exercise 10.7 Describe the bonding on the carbon atom in carbon dioxide, CO_2, using valence bond theory.

■ See Problems 10.57 and 10.58.

Experiments in General Chemistry, 10A, "Geometric Isomers. "

The π-bond description of the double bond agrees well with experiment. The *geometric*, or *cis–trans*, *isomers* of the compound 1,2-dichloroethene (described in the chapter opening) illustrate this. *Isomers* are compounds of the same molecular formula but with different arrangements of the atoms. (The numbers in the name 1,2-dichloroethene refer to the positions of the chlorine atoms; one chlorine atom is attached to carbon atom 1 and the other to carbon atom 2.) The structures of these isomers of 1,2-dichloroethene are

cis-1,2-Dichloroethene   *trans*-1,2-Dichloroethene

To transform one isomer into the other, one end of the molecule must be rotated as the other remains fixed. For this to happen, the π bond must be broken. Breaking the π bond requires considerable energy, so the *cis* and *trans* compounds are not easily interconverted. Contrast this with 1,2-dichloroethane (Figure 10.28), in which the two ends of the molecule can rotate without breaking any bonds. Here isomers corresponding to different spatial orientations of the two chlorine atoms cannot be prepared, because the two ends rotate freely with respect to one another. There is only one compound.

As we noted in the chapter opening, *cis* and *trans* isomers have different properties. The *cis* isomer of 1,2-dichloroethene boils at 60°C, the *trans* compound at 48°C.

FIGURE 10.28

Lack of geometric isomers in 1,2-dichloroethane

Because of rotation about the carbon–carbon bond in 1,2-dichloroethane, geometric isomers are not possible. Note that the molecule pictured in (A) can be twisted easily to give the molecule pictured in (B).

A B

These isomers can also be differentiated on the basis of dipole moment. The *trans* compound has no dipole moment because it is symmetrical (the polar C—Cl bonds point in opposite directions and so cancel). However, the *cis* compound has a dipole moment of 1.85 D.

It is possible to convert one isomer to another if sufficient energy is supplied—say by chemical reaction. The role of the conversion of a *cis* isomer to its *trans* isomer in human vision is discussed in the essay at the end of Section 10.7.

Exercise 10.8   Dinitrogen difluoride (see Example 10.6) exists as *cis* and *trans* isomers. Write structural formulas for these isomers and explain (in terms of the valence bond theory of the double bond) why they exist.

■ See Problems 10.59 and 10.60.

Concept Check 10.3

An atom in a molecule has one single bond and one triple bond to other atoms. What hybrid orbitals do you expect for this atom? Describe how you arrive at your answer.

Molecular Orbital Theory

In the preceding sections, we looked at a simple version of valence bond theory. Although simple valence bond theory satisfactorily describes most of the molecules we encounter, it does not apply to all molecules. For example, according to this theory any molecule with an even number of electrons should be diamagnetic (not attracted to a magnet), because we assume the electrons to be paired and to have opposite spins. In fact, a few molecules with an even number of electrons are paramagnetic (attracted to a magnet), indicating that some of the electrons are not paired. The best-known example of such a paramagnetic molecule is O_2. Because of the paramagnetism of O_2, liquid oxygen sticks to a magnet when poured over it

(Figure 10.29). Although valence bond theory can be extended to explain the electronic structure of O_2, molecular orbital theory (an alternative bonding theory) provides a straightforward explanation of the paramagnetism of O_2.

Molecular orbital theory is *a theory of the electronic structure of molecules in terms of molecular orbitals, which may spread over several atoms or the entire molecule.* This theory views the electronic structure of molecules to be much like the electronic structure of atoms. Each molecular orbital has a definite energy. To obtain the ground state of a molecule, electrons are put into orbitals of lowest energy, consistent with the Pauli exclusion principle, just as in atoms.

| 10.5 | ## Principles of Molecular Orbital Theory |

You can think of a molecular orbital as being formed from a combination of atomic orbitals. As atoms approach each other and their atomic orbitals overlap, molecular orbitals are formed.

Bonding and Antibonding Orbitals

Consider the H_2 molecule. As the atoms approach to form the molecule, their $1s$ orbitals overlap. One molecular orbital is obtained by adding the two $1s$ orbitals (see Figure 10.30). Note that where the atomic orbitals overlap, their values sum to give a larger result. This means that in this molecular orbital, electrons are often found in the region between the two nuclei where the electrons can hold the nuclei together. *Molecular orbitals that are concentrated in regions between nuclei* are called **bonding orbitals.** The bonding orbital in H_2, which we have just described, is denoted σ_{1s}. The σ (sigma) means that the molecular orbital has a cylindrical shape about the bond axis. The subscript $1s$ tells us that the molecular orbital was obtained from $1s$ atomic orbitals.

Another molecular orbital is obtained by subtracting the $1s$ orbital on one atom from the $1s$ orbital on the other (Figure 10.30). When the orbitals are subtracted, the resulting values in the region of the overlap are close to zero. This means that in this molecular orbital, the electrons spend little time between the nuclei. *Molecular orbitals having zero values in the region between two nuclei and therefore concentrated in other regions* are called **antibonding orbitals.** The antibonding orbital in H_2, which we have just described, is denoted σ_{1s}^*. The asterisk, which you read as "star," tells us that the molecular orbital is antibonding.

Figure 10.31 shows the energies of the molecular orbitals σ_{1s} and σ_{1s}^* relative to the atomic orbitals. Energies of the separate atomic orbitals are represented by heavy

FIGURE 10.29

Paramagnetism of oxygen, O_2
Liquid oxygen is poured between the poles of a strong magnet. Oxygen adheres to the poles, showing that it is paramagnetic.

FIGURE 10.30 ▶ ◼

Formation of bonding and antibonding orbitals from $1s$ orbitals of hydrogen atoms
When the two $1s$ orbitals overlap, they can either add to give a bonding molecular orbital or subtract to give an antibonding molecular orbital.

Addition of orbitals builds up
electron density in overlap region

$1s$ $1s$ Bonding orbital

Subtraction of orbitals results in low
electron density in the overlap region

$1s$ $1s$ Antibonding orbital

FIGURE 10.31

Relative energies of the 1s orbital of the H atom and the σ_{1s} and σ^*_{1s} molecular orbitals of H_2

Arrows denote occupation of the σ_{1s} orbital by electrons in the ground state of H_2.

black lines at the far left and right. The energies of the molecular orbitals are shown by heavy black lines in the center. (These are connected by dashed lines to show which atomic orbitals were used to obtain the molecular orbitals.) Note that the energy of a bonding orbital is less than that of the separate atomic orbitals, whereas the energy of an antibonding orbital is higher.

You obtain the electron configuration for the ground state of H_2 by placing the two electrons (one from each atom) into the lower-energy orbital (see Figure 10.31). The orbital diagram is

$\sigma_{1s} \quad \sigma^*_{1s}$

and the electron configuration is $(\sigma_{1s})^2$. Because the energy of the two electrons is lower than their energies in the isolated atoms, the H_2 molecule is stable.

Configurations involving the σ^*_{1s} orbital describe excited states of the molecule. As an example of an excited state, you can write the orbital diagram

$\sigma_{1s} \quad \sigma^*_{1s}$

The corresponding electron configuration is $(\sigma_{1s})^1(\sigma^*_{1s})^1$.

You obtain a similar set of orbitals when you consider the approach of two helium atoms. To obtain the ground state of He_2, you note that there are four electrons, two from each atom, that would fill the molecular orbitals. Two electrons go into the σ_{1s} orbital and two go into the σ^*_{1s} orbital. The orbital diagram is

$\sigma_{1s} \quad \sigma^*_{1s}$

and the configuration is $(\sigma_{1s})^2(\sigma^*_{1s})^2$. The energy decrease from the bonding electrons is offset by the energy increase from the antibonding electrons. Hence, He_2 is not a stable molecule. Molecular orbital theory therefore explains why the element helium exists as a monatomic gas, whereas hydrogen is diatomic.

Bond Order

The term *bond order* refers to the number of bonds that exist between two atoms. In molecular orbital theory, the bond order of a diatomic molecule is defined as one-half the difference between the number of electrons in bonding orbitals, n_b, and the number of electrons in antibonding orbitals, n_a.

$$\text{Bond order} = \tfrac{1}{2}(n_b - n_a)$$

For H_2, which has two bonding electrons,

$$\text{Bond order} = \tfrac{1}{2}(2 - 0) = 1$$

That is, H_2 has a single bond. For He_2, which has two bonding and two antibonding electrons,

$$\text{Bond order} = \tfrac{1}{2}(2 - 2) = 0$$

> For a Lewis formula, the bond order equals the number of electron pairs shared between two atoms (see Section 9.10).

Bond orders need not be whole numbers; half-integral bond orders of $\tfrac{1}{2}$, $\tfrac{3}{2}$, and so forth are also possible. For example, the H_2^+ molecular ion, which is formed in mass spectrometers, has the configuration $(\sigma_{1s})^1$ and a bond order of $\tfrac{1}{2}(1 - 0) = \tfrac{1}{2}$.

Factors That Determine Orbital Interaction

The H_2 and He_2 molecules are relatively simple. A 1s orbital on one atom interacts with the 1s orbital on the other atom. But now let us consider the Li_2 molecule. Each Li atom has 1s and 2s orbitals. Which orbitals interact to form molecular orbitals? To find out, you need to understand the factors that determine orbital interaction.

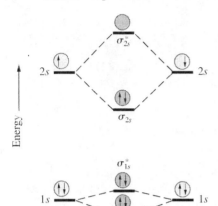

FIGURE 10.32 ▲

The energies of the molecular orbitals of Li₂

Arrows indicate the occupation of these orbitals by electrons in the ground state.

However, small shifts in the energy of the core electrons due to bonding can be measured by x-ray photoelectron spectroscopy (page 304).

The strength of the interaction between two atomic orbitals to form molecular orbitals is determined by two factors: (1) the energy difference between the interacting orbitals and (2) the magnitude of their overlap. *For the interaction to be strong, the energies of the two orbitals must be approximately equal and the overlap must be large.*

From this last statement, you see that when two Li atoms approach one another to form Li₂, only like orbitals on the two atoms interact appreciably. The $2s$ orbital of one lithium atom interacts with the $2s$ orbital of the other atom, but the $2s$ orbital from one atom does not interact with the $1s$ orbital of the other atom, because their energies are quite different. Also, because the $2s$ orbitals are outer orbitals, they are able to overlap and interact strongly when the atoms approach. As in H₂, these atomic orbitals interact to give a bonding orbital (denoted σ_{2s}) and an antibonding orbital (denoted σ_{2s}^*). However, even though the $1s$ orbitals of the two atoms have the same energy, they do not overlap appreciably and so interact weakly. (The difference in energy between σ_{1s} and σ_{1s}^* is very small.) Figure 10.32 gives the relative energies of the orbitals.

You obtain the ground-state configuration of Li₂ by putting six electrons (three from each atom) into the molecular orbitals of lowest energy. The configuration of the diatomic molecule Li₂ is

$$\text{Li}_2 \qquad (\sigma_{1s})^2(\sigma_{1s}^*)^2(\sigma_{2s})^2$$

The $(\sigma_{1s})^2(\sigma_{1s}^*)^2$ part of the configuration is often abbreviated KK (which denotes the K shells, or inner shells, of the two atoms). These electrons do not have a significant effect on bonding. <

$$\text{Li}_2 \qquad \text{KK}(\sigma_{2s})^2$$

In calculating bond order, we can ignore KK (it includes two bonding and two antibonding electrons). Thus, the bond order is 1, as in H₂.

In Be₂, the energy diagram is similar to that in Figure 10.32. You have eight electrons to distribute (four from each Be atom). The ground-state configuration of Be₂ is

$$\text{Be}_2 \qquad \text{KK}(\sigma_{2s})^2(\sigma_{2s}^*)^2$$

Note that the configuration has two bonding and two antibonding electrons outside the K shells. Thus, the bond order is $\frac{1}{2}(2 - 2) = 0$. No bond is formed, so the Be₂ molecule, like the He₂ molecule, is unstable.

10.6 | Electron Configurations of Diatomic Molecules of the Second-Period Elements

ChemWork: Molecular Orbital Predictions

ChemWork: Molecular Orbitals in Homonuclear Ions

ChemWork: Molecular Orbitals in Heteronuclear Ions

The previous section looked at the electron configurations of some simple molecules: H₂, He₂, Li₂, and Be₂. These are **homonuclear diatomic molecules**—that is, *molecules composed of two like nuclei.* (**Heteronuclear diatomic molecules** are *molecules composed of two different nuclei*—for example, CO and NO.) To find the electron configurations of other homonuclear diatomic molecules, we need to have additional molecular orbitals.

We have already looked at the formation of molecular orbitals from s atomic orbitals. Now we need to consider the formation of molecular orbitals from p atomic orbitals. There are two different ways in which $2p$ atomic orbitals can interact. One set of $2p$ orbitals can overlap along their axes to give one bonding and one antibonding σ orbital (σ_{2p} and σ_{2p}^*). The other two sets of $2p$ orbitals then overlap sideways to give two bonding and two antibonding π orbitals (π_{2p} and π_{2p}^*). (See Figure 10.33.)

Figure 10.34 shows the relative energies of the molecular orbitals obtained from $2s$ and $2p$ atomic orbitals. This order of molecular orbitals reproduces the known electron configurations of homonuclear diatomic molecules composed of elements in the second row of the periodic table. < The order of filling is

This order gives the correct number of electrons in subshells, even though in O₂ and F₂ the energy of σ_{2p} is below π_{2p}.

$$\sigma_{2s} \quad \sigma_{2s}^* \quad \pi_{2p} \quad \sigma_{2p} \quad \pi_{2p}^* \quad \sigma_{2p}^*$$

FIGURE 10.33

The different ways in which 2p orbitals can interact

When the 2p orbitals overlap along their axes, they form σ_{2p} and σ_{2p}^* molecular orbitals. When they overlap sideways, they form π_{2p} and π_{2p}^* molecular orbitals.

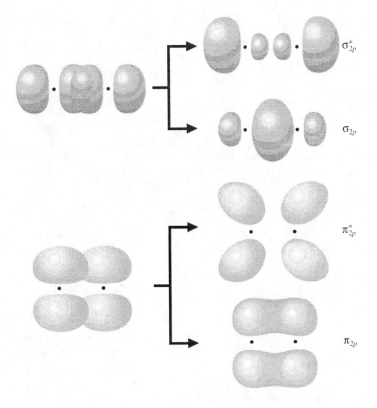

Note that there are two orbitals in the π subshell and two orbitals in the π^* subshell. Because each orbital can hold two electrons, a π or π^* subshell can hold four electrons. The next example shows how you can use the order of filling to obtain the orbital diagram, magnetic character, electron configuration, and bond order of a homonuclear diatomic molecule.

FIGURE 10.34

Relative energies of molecular orbitals of homonuclear diatomic molecules (excluding K shells)

The arrows show the occupation of molecular orbitals by the valence electrons of N_2.

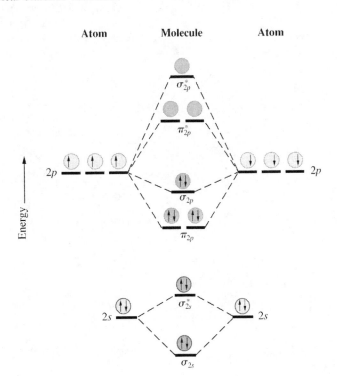

Example 10.7 | Describing Molecular Orbital Configurations (Homonuclear Diatomic Molecules)

Give the orbital diagram of the O_2 molecule. Is the molecular substance diamagnetic or paramagnetic? What is the electron configuration? What is the bond order of O_2?

Problem Strategy Note the order of filling of molecular orbitals for the second-row homonuclear diatomic molecules (given just before this example). Now assign the valence electrons to these orbitals in this order. Pay attention to both the Pauli exclusion principle (no more than two electrons to an orbital, and then only with opposed spins) and Hund's rule (fill all orbitals of a subshell with one electron each—and with the same spins—before pairing electrons in any orbital). Decide whether the substance is diamagnetic (all electrons paired) or paramagnetic (unpaired electrons). Then calculate the bond order equal to $\frac{1}{2}$(number of bonding electrons − number of antibonding electrons).

Solution There are 12 valence electrons in O_2 (six from each atom), which occupy the molecular orbitals as shown in the following orbital diagram:

KK ⦿⦿ ⦿⦿ ⦿⦿⦿⦿ ⦿⦿ ⦿○○
σ_{2s} σ_{2s}^* π_{2p} σ_{2p} π_{2p}^* σ_{2p}^*

Note that the two electrons in the π_{2p}^* subshell must go into different orbitals with their spins in the same direction (Hund's rule). Because there are two unpaired electrons, the molecular substance is **paramagnetic.** The electron configuration is

$$KK(\sigma_{2s})^2(\sigma_{2s}^*)^2(\pi_{2p})^4(\sigma_{2p})^2(\pi_{2p}^*)^2$$

There are eight bonding electrons and four antibonding electrons. Therefore,

$$\text{Bond order} = \frac{1}{2}(8 - 4) = \mathbf{2}$$

Answer Check Check that the number of electrons assigned to orbitals equals the number of valence electrons of the two atoms. Make sure that the Pauli exclusion principle and Hund's rule have been properly applied.

Exercise 10.9 The C_2 molecule exists in the vapor phase over carbon at high temperature. Describe the molecular orbital structure of this molecule; that is, give the orbital diagram and electron configuration. Would you expect the molecular substance to be diamagnetic or paramagnetic? What is the bond order for C_2?

An alternative example is provided in the Instructor's Resource Manual.

■ See Problems 10.61 and 10.62.

Table 10.3 compares experimentally determined bond lengths, bond dissociation energies, and magnetic character of the second-period homonuclear diatomic molecules with the bond order calculated from molecular orbital theory, as in the preceding example. Note that as the bond order increases, bond length tends to decrease and bond dissociation energy tends to increase. You should be able to verify that the

TABLE 10.3 | **Theoretical Bond Orders and Experimental Data for the Second-Period Homonuclear Diatomic Molecules**

Molecule	Bond Order	Bond Length (pm)	Bond Dissociation Energy (kJ/mol)	Magnetic Character
Li_2	1	267	110	Diamagnetic
Be_2	0	*	*	*
B_2	1	159	290	Paramagnetic
C_2	2	124	602	Diamagnetic
N_2	3	110	942	Diamagnetic
O_2	2	121	494	Paramagnetic
F_2	1	142	155	Diamagnetic
Ne_2	0	*	*	*

The symbol * means that no stable molecule has been observed.

experimentally determined magnetic character of the molecule, given in the last column of the table, is correctly predicted by molecular orbital theory.

When the atoms in a heteronuclear diatomic molecule are close to one another in a row of the periodic table, the molecular orbitals have the same relative order of energies as those for homonuclear diatomic molecules. In this case you can obtain the electron configurations in the same way, as the next example illustrates.

Example 10.8 | Describing Molecular Orbital Configurations (Heteronuclear Diatomic Molecules)

Write the orbital diagram for nitrogen monoxide (nitric oxide), NO. What is the bond order of NO?

Problem Strategy If the two different atoms of the molecule are close to one another in the periodic table, then you can assume that the order of filling is the same as that for homonuclear diatomic molecules. After that, the procedure is similar to that for a homonuclear molecule (see Example 10.7).

Solution You assume that the order of filling of orbitals is the same as for homonuclear diatomic molecules. There are 11 valence electrons in NO. Thus, the orbital diagram is

$$\mathrm{KK}\ \underset{\sigma_{2s}}{\boxed{\uparrow\downarrow}}\ \underset{\sigma_{2s}^*}{\boxed{\uparrow\downarrow}}\ \underset{\pi_{2p}}{\boxed{\uparrow\downarrow}\ \boxed{\uparrow\downarrow}}\ \underset{\sigma_{2p}}{\boxed{\uparrow\downarrow}}\ \underset{\pi_{2p}^*}{\boxed{\uparrow}\ \bigcirc}\ \underset{\sigma_{2p}^*}{\bigcirc}$$

Because there are eight bonding and three antibonding electrons,

$$\text{Bond order} = \tfrac{1}{2}(8 - 3) = \tfrac{5}{2}$$

Answer Check Check that the number of electrons assigned to orbitals equals the number of valence electrons of the two atoms. Make sure that the Pauli exclusion principle and Hund's rule have been properly applied.

Exercise 10.10   Give the orbital diagram and electron configuration for the carbon monoxide molecule, CO. What is the bond order of CO? Is the molecule diamagnetic or paramagnetic?

■ See Problems 10.63 and 10.64.

An alternative example is provided in the Instructor's Resource Manual.

When the two atoms in a heteronuclear diatomic molecule differ appreciably, you can no longer use the scheme appropriate for homonuclear diatomic molecules. The HF molecule is an example. Figure 10.35 (on page 406) shows the relative energies of the molecular orbitals that form. Sigma bonding and antibonding orbitals are formed by combining the 1s orbital on the H atom with the 2p orbital on the F atom that lies along the bond axis. The 2s orbital and the other 2p orbitals on fluorine remain as *nonbonding* orbitals (neither bonding nor antibonding). Note that the energy of the 2p subshell in fluorine is lower than the energy of the 1s orbital in hydrogen, because the fluorine electrons are more tightly held. As a result, the bonding orbital is made up of a greater percentage of the 2p fluorine orbital than of the 1s hydrogen orbital. This means that electrons in the bonding molecular orbital spend more time in the vicinity of the fluorine atom; that is, the H—F bond is polar, with the F atom having a small negative charge.

10.7   Molecular Orbitals and Delocalized Bonding

One of the advantages of using molecular orbital theory is the simple way in which it describes molecules with delocalized bonding. Whereas valence bond theory requires two or more resonance formulas, molecular orbital theory describes the bonding in terms of a single electron configuration.

Consider the ozone molecule as an example. In the previous chapter, we described this molecule in terms of resonance as follows:

O_3

$$\ddot{\text{:}}\overset{\displaystyle \ddot{O}}{\underset{\text{:}\ddot{O}\text{:} \quad \text{:}\ddot{O}\text{:}}{}} \longleftrightarrow \overset{\displaystyle \ddot{O}}{\underset{\text{:}\ddot{O}\text{:} \quad \text{:}\ddot{O}\text{:}}{}}$$

H atom   HF molecule   F atom

FIGURE 10.35

Relative energies of molecular orbitals in the valence shell of HF

Arrows show the occupation of orbitals by electrons.

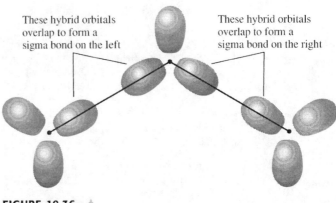

These hybrid orbitals overlap to form a sigma bond on the left

These hybrid orbitals overlap to form a sigma bond on the right

FIGURE 10.36

Hybrid orbitals on oxygen atoms of ozone, O_3

Each oxygen atom has sp^2 hybrid orbitals. One hybrid orbital on the center atom and one hybrid orbital on the left atom overlap to form a single bond at the left. Similar orbitals at the right form another single bond. Each atom has a π orbital perpendicular to the plane of these hybrid orbitals.

Some of these electrons are localized either on one atom or between an oxygen–oxygen bond (these are printed in black). The other electrons are delocalized (these are printed in blue). They are the electron pairs that change position in going from one resonance formula to the other.

Each O atom has three localized electron pairs about it, which suggests that each atom uses sp^2 hybrid orbitals (see Table 10.2). The overlap of one hybrid orbital on the center O atom with a hybrid orbital on the end O atom at the left forms the left O—O bond (Figure 10.36). The overlap of another hybrid orbital on the center O atom with a hybrid orbital on the end O atom at the right forms the other O—O bond. This leaves one hybrid orbital on the center O atom and two on each of the end O atoms for lone pairs.

After the hybrid orbitals are formed, one unhybridized p orbital remains on each O atom. These three p orbitals are perpendicular to the plane of the molecule and parallel to one another. They can overlap sideways to give three π molecular orbitals. (Three interacting atomic orbitals produce three molecular orbitals.) All three will span the entire molecule (Figure 10.37). One of these orbitals turns out to be antibonding; one is nonbonding (that is, it has an energy equal to that of the isolated atoms); and the third is bonding.

The bonding and nonbonding π orbitals are both doubly occupied. This agrees with the resonance description, in which one delocalized pair is bonding and the other is a lone (nonbonding) pair on the end oxygen atoms.

Antibonding π orbital   Nonbonding π orbital   Bonding π orbital

FIGURE 10.37

The electron distributions of the π molecular orbitals of O_3

Note that one molecular orbital is nonbonding. It describes a lone pair of electrons that can be on either end-oxygen atom.

A Chemist Looks at . . .

Human Vision

life science

Human vision, as well as the detection of light by other organisms, is known to involve a compound called 11-cis-retinal. The structural formula is shown on the left side of Figure 10.38. This compound, which is derived from vitamin A, is contained in two kinds of cells—rod cells and cone cells—located in the retina of the eye. Rod cells are responsible for vision in dim light. They give the sensation of light or dark but no sensation of color. Cone cells are responsible for color vision, but they require bright light. Color vision is possible because three types of cone cells exist: one type absorbs light in the red region of the spectrum, another absorbs in the green region, and a third absorbs in the blue region. In each of these different cells, 11-cis-retinal is attached to a different protein molecule, which affects the region of light that is absorbed by retinal.

When a photon of light is absorbed by 11-cis-retinal, it is transformed to 11-trans-retinal (see Figure 10.38). This small change at one carbon–carbon double bond results in a large movement of one end of the molecule with respect to the other. In other words, the absorption of a single photon results in a significant change in molecular geometry. This change in shape of retinal also affects the shape of the protein molecule to which it is attached, and this change results in a sequence of events, not completely understood, in which an electrical signal is generated.

To understand the cis–trans conversion when a photon is absorbed, consider the similar, but simpler, molecule cis-1,2-dichloroethene (see structural formula on page 374). The double bond consists of a σ bond and a π bond. The π bond results from two electrons in a π-type molecular orbital. A corresponding antibonding orbital, π*, has higher energy than the π orbital and is unoccupied in the ground state. When a photon of light in the ultraviolet region (near 180 nm) is absorbed by cis-1,2-dichloroethene, an electron in the π orbital undergoes a transition to the π* orbital. Whereas there were previously two electrons in the bonding π orbital (contributing one bond), there is now one electron in the bonding orbital and one in the antibonding orbital (with zero net bonding). As a result of the absorption of a photon, the double bond becomes a single bond and rotation about the bond is now possible. The cis isomer tends to rotate to the trans isomer, which is more stable. Then energy is lost as heat, and the electron in the π* orbital undergoes a transition back to the π orbital; the single bond becomes a double bond again. The net result is the conversion of the cis isomer to the trans isomer.

Retinal differs from dichloroethene in having six double bonds alternating with single bonds instead of only one double bond. The alternating double and single bonds give a rigid structure, and when the middle double bond undergoes the cis-to-trans change, a large movement of atoms occurs. Another result of a long chain of alternating double and single bonds is a change in the wavelength of light absorbed in the π-to-π* transition. Dichloroethene absorbs in the ultraviolet region, but retinal attached to its protein absorbs in the visible region. (The attached protein also alters the wavelength of absorbed light.) Many biological compounds that are colored consist of long chains of alternating double and single bonds. β-Carotene, a yellow pigment in carrots, has this structure. It is broken down in the body to give vitamin A, from which retinal is derived.

FIGURE 10.38 ▶

The cis–trans conversion of retinal on absorption of light
Note the large movement of atoms caused by the rotation about the double bond between carbon atoms 11 and 12.

Rotation about this bond

11-cis-Retinal

light

11-trans-Retinal

■ See Problems 10.85 and 10.86.

407

A Chemist Looks at . . .

environment

Stratospheric Ozone (An Absorber of Ultraviolet Rays)

Ozone (also known as trioxygen, O_3) is a reactive form of oxygen having a bent molecular geometry, as you would predict from its resonance formulas:

Ozone forms in the atmosphere whenever O_2 is irradiated by ultraviolet light or subjected to electrical discharges. On bright sunny days, you might notice the fresh-air smell of dilute ozone (trioxygen, O_3). Around electrical equipment, however, ozone often occurs in higher concentrations and has a disagreeable odor.

Although ozone occurs at ground level and is an ingredient of *photochemical smog*, it is an essential component of the *stratosphere*, which occurs at about 10 to 15 km above ground level. Ozone in the stratosphere absorbs ultraviolet radiation between 200 and 300 nm, which is vitally important to life on earth. Radiation from the sun contains ultraviolet rays that are harmful to the DNA of biological organisms. Oxygen, O_2, absorbs the most energetic of these ultraviolet rays in the earth's upper atmosphere, but only ozone in the stratosphere absorbs the remaining ultraviolet radiation that is destructive to life on earth (Figure 10.39).

FIGURE 10.39 ▶

The solar spectrum
Radiation below 200 nm is absorbed in the upper atmosphere by O_2. Ultraviolet radiation between 200 and 300 nm is absorbed by O_3 in the stratosphere.

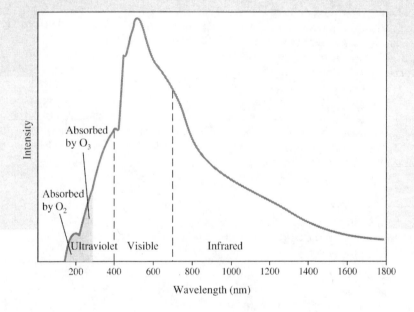

A Checklist for Review

Important Terms

molecular geometry (10.1)
valence-shell electron-pair repulsion (VSEPR) model (10.1)
dipole moment (10.2)
valence bond theory (10.3)

hybrid orbitals (10.3)
σ (sigma) bond (10.4)
π (pi) bond (10.4)
molecular orbital theory (10.5)
bonding orbitals (10.5)
antibonding orbitals (10.5)

homonuclear diatomic molecules (10.6)
heteronuclear diatomic molecules (10.6)

In 1974, Mario J. Molina and F. Sherwood Rowland expressed concern that chlorofluorocarbons (CFCs), such as $CClF_3$ and CCl_2F_2, would be a source of chlorine atoms that could catalyze the decomposition of ozone in the stratosphere, so that the ozone would be destroyed faster than it could be produced. The chlorofluorocarbons are relatively inert compounds used as refrigerants, spray-can propellants, and blowing agents (substances used to produce plastic foams). As a result of their inertness, however, CFCs concentrate in the atmosphere, where they steadily rise into the stratosphere. Once they are in the stratosphere, ultraviolet light decomposes them to form chlorine atoms, which react with ozone to form ClO and O_2. The ClO molecules react with oxygen atoms in the stratosphere to regenerate Cl atoms.

$$Cl(g) + O_3(g) \longrightarrow ClO(g) + O_2(g)$$
$$ClO(g) + O(g) \longrightarrow Cl(g) + O_2(g)$$
$$\overline{O_3(g) + O(g) \longrightarrow 2O_2(g)}$$

The net result is the decomposition of ozone to dioxygen. Chlorine atoms are consumed in the first step but regenerated in the second. Thus, chlorine atoms are not used up, so they function as a catalyst.

In 1985, British researchers reported that the ozone over the Antarctic had been declining precipitously each spring for several years, although it returned the following winter. Then in August 1987, an expedition was assembled to begin flights through the "ozone hole" with instruments (Figure 10.40). Researchers found that wherever ozone is depleted in the stratosphere, chlorine monoxide (ClO) appears, as expected if chlorine atoms are catalyzing the depletion (see the previous reactions). The chlorofluorocarbons are the suspected source of these chlorine atoms, and by international treaty they are being phased out of production. Refrigerators and air conditioners, for example, now use hydrofluorocarbons (HFCs), such as R410A, which is a mixture of CH_2F_2 and CF_3CHF_2.

In October 1995, Sherwood Rowland (University of California, Irvine), Mario Molina (Massachusetts Institute of Technology), and Paul Crutzen (Max Planck Institute, Mainz, Germany) were awarded the Nobel Prize in chemistry for their work on stratospheric ozone depletion. Crutzen studied the effect of nitrogen oxides in catalyzing the decomposition of ozone.

FIGURE 10.40 ▲

Total stratospheric ozone over the Southern Hemisphere
This computer image shows the total quantity of ozone over the Southern Hemisphere in Dobson units (equivalent to the thickness, in units of 10^{-2} mm, of total ozone, assuming it to be compressed to 1 atm at 0°C). The ozone depletion is shown near the South Pole (pink color; black color indicates no data). The data are from the SBUV/2 instrument on board the National Oceanic and Atmospheric Administration's polar orbiting satellite.

■ See Problems 10.87 and 10.88.

Summary of Facts and Concepts

Molecular geometry refers to the spatial arrangement of atoms in a molecule. The *valence-shell electron-pair repulsion (VSEPR) model* is a simple model for predicting molecular geometries. It is based on the idea that the valence-shell electron pairs are arranged symmetrically about an atom to minimize electron-pair repulsion. The geometry about an atom is then determined by the directions of the bonding pairs. Information about the geometry of a molecule can sometimes be obtained from the experimentally determined presence or absence of a *dipole moment*.

The bonding and geometry in a molecule can be described in terms of *valence bond theory*. In this theory, a bond is formed by the overlap of orbitals from two atoms. *Hybrid orbitals*, a set of equivalent orbitals formed by combining atomic orbitals, are often needed to describe this bond. Multiple bonds occur via the overlap of atomic orbitals to give σ bonds and π bonds. *Cis–trans* isomers result from the molecular rigidity imposed by a π bond.

Molecular orbital theory can also be used to explain bonding in molecules. According to this theory, electrons in a molecule occupy orbitals that may spread over the entire molecule.

You can think of these molecular orbitals as constructed from atomic orbitals. Thus, when two atoms approach to form a diatomic molecule, the atomic orbitals interact to form *bonding* and *antibonding* molecular orbitals. The electron configuration of a diatomic molecule such as O_2 can be predicted from the order of filling of the molecular orbitals. From this configuration, you can predict the bond order and whether the molecular substance is diamagnetic or paramagnetic.

Media Summary

Visit the **student website at college.hmco.com/pic/ebbing9e** to help prepare for class, study for quizzes and exams, understand core concepts, and visualize molecular-level interactions. The following media activities are available for this chapter:

 Prepare for Class

■ **Video Lessons** *Mini lectures from chemistry experts*
Valence-Shell Electron-Pair Repulsion Theory
Molecular Shapes for Steric Numbers 2–4
Predicting Molecular Characteristics Using VSEPR Theory
Molecular Shapes for Steric Numbers 5 and 6
Valence Bond Theory
An Introduction to Hybrid Orbitals
Pi Bonds
CIA Demonstration: The Paramagnetism of Oxygen
Molecular Orbital Theory
Applications of the Molecular Orbital Theory
Beyond Homonuclear Diatomics

 Improve Your Grade

■ **Visualizations** *Molecular-level animations and lab demonstration videos*
VSEPR
VSEPR: Two Electron Pair
VSEPR: Four Electron Pair
VSEPR: Three Electron Pair
VSEPR: Iodine Pentafluoride

Polar Molecules
Hybridization: sp
Hybridization: sp^2
Hybridization: sp^3
Formation of C—C Double Bond in Ethylene
The Magnetic Properties of Liquid Nitrogen and Oxygen
Sigma Bonding and Antibonding Orbitals
Pi Bonding and Antibonding Orbitals
Molecular Orbital Diagram (N_2)
Delocalized Pi Bonding in the Nitrate Ion

■ **Tutorials** *Animated examples and interactive activities*
VSEPR Theory
Hybridization

■ **Flashcards** *Key terms and definitions*
Online Flashcards

■ **Self-Assessment Questions** *Additional questions with full worked-out solutions*
6 Self-Assessment Questions

 ACE the Test

Multiple-choice quizzes
3 ACE Practice Tests

Access these resources using the passkey available free with new texts or for purchase separately.

Learning Objectives

10.1 The Valence-Shell Electron-Pair Repulsion (VSEPR) Model

■ Define *molecular geometry.*
■ Define *valence-shell electron-pair repulsion model.*
■ Note the difference between the arrangement of electron pairs about a central atom and molecular geometry.
■ Note the four steps in the prediction of geometry by the VSEPR model.
■ Predict the molecular geometry (two, three, or four electron pairs). Example 10.1
■ Note that a lone pair tends to require more space than a corresponding bonding pair and that a multiple bond requires more space than a single bond.
■ Predict the molecular geometry (five or six electron pairs). Example 10.2

10.2 Dipole Moment and Molecular Geometry

■ Define *dipole moment.*
■ Explain the relationship between dipole moment and molecular geometry. Example 10.3
■ Note that the polarity of a molecule can affect certain properties, such as a boiling point.

10.3 Valence Bond Theory

■ Define *valence bond theory.*
■ State the two conditions needed for bond formation, according to valence bond theory.
■ Define *hybrid orbitals.*
■ State the five steps in describing bonding, following the valence bond theory.

- Apply valence bond theory (two, three, or four electron pairs). Example 10.4
- Apply valence bond theory (five or six electron pairs). Example 10.5

10.4 Description of Multiple Bonding

- Define σ (*sigma*) *bond*.
- Define π (*pi*) *bond*.
- Apply valence bond theory (multiple bonding). Example 10.6
- Explain geometric, or *cis–trans*, isomers in terms of the π-bond description of a double bond.

10.5 Principles of Molecular Orbital Theory

- Define *molecular orbital theory*.
- Define *bonding orbitals* and *antibonding orbitals*.
- Define *bond order*.

- State the two factors that determine the strength of interaction between two atomic orbitals.
- Describe the electron configurations of H_2, He_2, Li_2, and Be_2.

10.6 Electron Configurations of Diatomic Molecules of the Second-Period Elements

- Define *homonuclear diatomic molecules* and *heteronuclear diatomic molecules*.
- Describe molecular orbital configurations (homonuclear diatomic molecules). Example 10.7
- Describe molecular orbital configurations (heteronuclear diatomic molecules). Example 10.8

10.7 Molecular Orbitals and Delocalized Bonding

- Describe the delocalized bonding in molecules such as O_3.

Self-Assessment and Review Questions

10.1 Describe the main features of the VSEPR model.

10.2 According to the VSEPR model, what are the arrangements of two, three, four, five, and six valence-shell electron pairs about an atom?

10.3 Why is a lone pair expected to occupy an equatorial position instead of an axial position in the trigonal bipyramidal arrangement?

10.4 Why is it possible for a molecule to have polar bonds, yet have a dipole moment of zero?

10.5 Explain why nitrogen trifluoride has a small dipole moment even though it has polar bonds in a trigonal pyramidal arrangement.

10.6 Explain in terms of valence bond theory why the orbitals used on an atom give rise to a particular geometry about that atom.

10.7 What is the angle between two sp^3 hybrid orbitals?

10.8 What is the difference between a sigma bond and a pi bond?

10.9 Describe the bonding in ethylene, C_2H_4, in terms of valence bond theory.

10.10 How does the valence bond description of a carbon–carbon double bond account for *cis–trans* isomers?

10.11 What are the differences between a bonding and an antibonding molecular orbital of a diatomic molecule?

10.12 What factors determine the strength of interaction between two atomic orbitals to form a molecular orbital?

10.13 Describe the formation of bonding and antibonding molecular orbitals resulting from the interaction of two $2s$ orbitals.

10.14 Describe the formation of molecular orbitals resulting from the interaction of two $2p$ orbitals.

10.15 How does molecular orbital theory describe the bonding in the HF molecule?

10.16 Describe the bonding in O_3, using molecular orbital theory. Compare this with the resonance description.

10.17 According to the VSEPR model, the H—P—H bond angle in PH_3 is
  a. 120°   **b.** 109.5°   **c.** 90°
  d. a little less than 120°   **e.** a little less than 109.5°

10.18 Which of the following molecular geometries does the XeF_5^+ cation exhibit?
  a. tetradral
  b. T-shaped
  c. octahedral
  d. square pyramidal
  e. trigonal bipyramidal

10.19 Which of the following would be a polar molecule?
  a. CO_2 **b.** H_2S **c.** CH_4 **d.** SF_6 **e.** BeF_2

10.20 What is the bond order of NO?
  a. $\frac{1}{2}$ **b.** 1   **c.** $\frac{3}{2}$ **d.** 3   **e.** $\frac{5}{2}$

Concept Explorations

10.21 Best Lewis Formula and Molecular Geometry

A student writes the Lewis electron-dot formula for the carbonate anion, CO_3^{2-}, as

a. Does this Lewis formula obey the octet rule? Explain. What are the formal charges on the atoms? Try describing the bonding for this formula in valence bond terms. Do you have any difficulty doing this?

b. Does this Lewis formula give a reasonable description of the electron structure, or is there a better one? If there is a better Lewis formula, write it down and explain why it is better.

c. The same student writes the following resonance description for CO_2:

Is there something wrong with this description? (What would you predict as the geometries of these formulas?)

d. Is one or the other formula a better description? Could a value for the dipole moment help you decide?

e. Can you write a Lewis formula that gives an even better description of CO_2? Explain your answer.

10.22 Molecular Geometry and Bonding

a. Shown here are several potential Lewis electron-dot formulas for the SeO_2 molecule.

Are there any electron-dot formulas that you expect to give the best description? How would you describe the bonding in terms of electron-dot formulas?

b. Describe the bonding in SeO_2 in valence bond terms. If there is delocalized bonding, note this in your description and explain how molecular orbital theory can be useful here.

c. Determine the arrangement of electron pairs about Se in the SeO_2 molecule. What would you expect for the molecular geometry of the SeO_2 molecule?

d. Would you expect the O—Se—O angle in the SeO_2 molecule to be greater than, equal to, or less than 120°. Explain your answer.

e. Draw an electron-dot formula for the H_2Se molecule and determine its molecular geometry.

f. Compare the H—Se—H bond angle to the O—Se—O bond angle. Is it larger or smaller? Explain.

g. Determine whether the H_2Se and SeO_2 molecules have dipole moments. Describe how you arrived at your answer.

Conceptual Problems

10.23 Match the following molecular substances with one of the molecular models (i) to (iv) that correctly depicts the geometry of the corresponding molecule.

a. SeO_2 **b.** $BeCl_2$ **c.** PBr_3 **d.** BCl_3

(i)   (ii)

(iii)   (iv)

10.24 Which of the following molecular models correctly depicts the geometry of ClCN?

(a)   (b)

10.25 Suppose that an ethane molecule, CH_3CH_3, is broken into two CH_3 molecules in such a way that one :CH_3 molecule retains the electron pair that was originally the one making up the C—C bond. The other CH_3 molecule has two fewer

electrons. Imagine that momentarily this CH_3 molecule has the geometry it had in the ethane molecule. Describe the electron repulsions present in this molecule, and indicate how they would be expected to rearrange its geometry.

10.26 Suppose that a BF_3 molecule approaches the lone pair on the N atom of an :NH_3 molecule, and that a bond forms between the B atom and the N atom. Consider the arrangement of electron pairs about the B atom at the moment of this bond formation, and describe the repulsions among the electron pairs and how they might be expected to change the geometry about the B atom.

10.27 Indicate what hybrid orbital depicted below is expected for the central atom of each of the following:

a. BeF_2 **b.** SiF_4 **c.** SeF_4 **d.** RnF_4

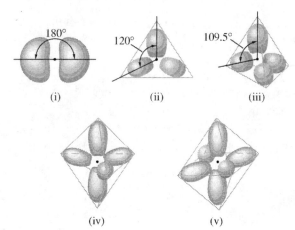

10.28 An atom in a molecule has two bonds to other atoms and one lone pair. What kind of hybrid orbitals do you expect for this atom? Describe how you arrived at your answer.

10.29 Two compounds have the same molecular formula, $C_2H_2Br_2$. One has a dipole moment; the other does not. Both compounds react with bromine, Br_2, to produce the same compound. This reaction is a generally accepted test for double bonds, and each bromine atom of Br_2 adds to a different atom of the double bond. What is the identity of the original compounds? Describe the argument you use.

10.30 A neutral molecule is identified as a tetrafluoride, XF_4, where X is an unknown atom. If the molecule has a dipole moment of 0.63 D, can you give some possibilities for the identity of X?

10.31 Acetic acid, the sour constituent of vinegar, has the following structure:

$$O$$
$$\|$$
$$CH_3C—OH$$
$$\quad a \quad b \quad c$$

Indicate what geometry given below is expected to be found about each of the atoms labeled a, b, and c.

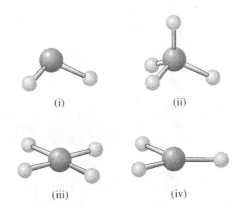

(i) (ii)

(iii) (iv)

10.32 What are the bond angles predicted by the VSEPR model about the carbon atom in the formate ion, HCO_2^-? Considering that the bonds to this atom are not identical, would you expect the experimental values to agree precisely with the VSEPR values? How might they differ?

Practice Problems

The VSEPR Model

10.33 Predict the shape or geometry of the following molecules, using the VSEPR model.
a. SiF_4 **b.** SF_2 **c.** COF_2 **d.** PCl_3

10.34 Use the electron-pair repulsion model to predict the geometry of the following molecules:
a. $GeCl_2$ **b.** NF_3 **c.** SCl_2 **d.** XeO_4

10.35 Predict the geometry of the following ions, using the electron-pair repulsion model.
a. ClO_3^- **b.** PO_4^{3-} **c.** SCN^- **d.** H_3O^+

10.36 Use the VSEPR model to predict the geometry of the following ions:
a. N_3^- **b.** BH_4^- **c.** SO_3^{2-} **d.** NO_2^-

10.37 For each of the following molecules, state the bond angle (or bond angles, as appropriate) that you would expect to see on the central atom based on the simple VSEPR model. Would you expect the actual bond angles to be greater or less than this?
a. CCl_4 **b.** SCl_2 **c.** $COCl_2$ **d.** AsH_3

10.38 For each of the following molecules, state the bond angle (or bond angles, as appropriate) that you would expect to see on the central atom based on the simple VSEPR model. Would you expect the actual bond angles to be greater or less than this?
a. NCl_3 **b.** CF_2CF_2 **c.** GeF_4 **d.** OF_2

10.39 What geometry is expected for the following molecules, according to the VSEPR model?
a. PF_5 **b.** BrF_3 **c.** BrF_5 **d.** SCl_4

10.40 From the electron-pair repulsion model, predict the geometry of the following molecules:
a. ClF_5 **b.** SbF_5 **c.** SeF_4 **d.** TeF_6

10.41 Predict the geometries of the following ions, using the VSEPR model.
a. $SnCl_5^-$ **b.** PF_6^- **c.** ClF_2^- **d.** IF_4^-

10.42 Name the geometries expected for the following ions, according to the electron-pair repulsion model.
a. ICl_2^- **b.** BrF_4^- **c.** ClF_6^+ **d.** ClF_4^+

Dipole Moment and Molecular Geometry

10.43 (a) The molecule AsF_3 has a dipole moment of 2.59 D. Which of the following geometries are possible: trigonal planar, trigonal pyramidal, or T-shaped? (b) The molecule H_2S has a dipole moment of 0.97 D. Is the geometry linear or bent?

10.44 (a) The molecule BrF_3 has a dipole moment of 1.19 D. Which of the following geometries are possible: trigonal planar, trigonal pyramidal, or T-shaped? (b) The molecule $TeCl_4$ has a dipole moment of 2.54 D. Is the geometry tetrahedral, seesaw, or square planar?

10.45 Which of the following molecules would be expected to have zero dipole moment on the basis of their geometry?
a. CS_2 **b.** TeF_2 **c.** $SeCl_4$ **d.** XeF_4

10.46 Which of the following molecules would be expected to have a dipole moment of zero because of symmetry?
a. SeF_2
b. BeI_2
c. TeF_6
d. TeF_4

Valence Bond Theory

10.47   What hybrid orbitals would be expected for the central atom in each of the following molecules or ions?

(a)   (b)

10.48   What hybrid orbitals would be expected for the central atom in each of the following molecules or ions?

(a)   (b)

10.49   What hybrid orbitals would be expected for the central atom in each of the following molecules or ions?
   a. $SeCl_2$ **b.** NO_2^- **c.** CO_2 **d.** COF_2

10.50   What hybrid orbitals would be expected for the central atom in each of the following molecules or ions?
   a. $GeCl_4$ **b.** PBr_3 **c.** BeF_2 **d.** SO_2

10.51   (a) Mercury(II) chloride dissolves in water to give poorly conducting solutions, indicating that the compound is largely nonionized in solution—it dissolves as $HgCl_2$ molecules. Describe the bonding of the $HgCl_2$ molecule, using valence bond theory. (b) Phosphorus trichloride, PCl_3, is a colorless liquid with a highly irritating vapor. Describe the bonding in the PCl_3 molecule, using valence bond theory. Use hybrid orbitals.

10.52   (a) Nitrogen trifluoride, NF_3, is a relatively unreactive, colorless gas. How would you describe the bonding in the NF_3 molecule in terms of valence bond theory? Use hybrid orbitals. (b) Silicon tetrafluoride, SiF_4, is a colorless gas formed when hydrofluoric acid attacks silica (SiO_2) or glass. Describe the bonding in the SiF_4 molecule, using valence bond theory.

10.53   What hybrid orbitals would be expected for the central atom in each of the following?
   a. XeF_2
   b. BrF_5
   c. PCl_5
   d. ClF_4^+

10.54   What hybrid orbitals would be expected for the central atom in each of the following?
   a. BrF_3 **b.** TeF_4 **c.** XeF_4 **d.** IF_4^-

10.55   Phosphorus pentachloride is normally a white solid. It exists in this state as the ionic compound $[PCl_4^+][PCl_6^-]$.

Describe the electron structure of the PCl_6^- ion in terms of valence bond theory.

10.56   Iodine, I_2, dissolves in an aqueous solution of iodide ion, I^-, to give the triiodide ion, I_3^-. This ion consists of one iodine atom bonded to two others. Describe the bonding of I_3^- in terms of valence bond theory.

10.57   (a) Formaldehyde, H_2CO, is a colorless, pungent gas used to make plastics. Give the valence bond description of the formaldehyde molecule. (Both hydrogen atoms are attached to the carbon atom.) (b) Nitrogen, N_2, makes up about 80% of the earth's atmosphere. Give the valence bond description of this molecule.

10.58   (a) The molecule HN=NH exists as a transient species in certain reactions. Give the valence bond description of this species. (b) Hydrogen cyanide, HCN, is a very poisonous gas or liquid with the odor of bitter almonds. Give the valence bond description of HCN. (Carbon is the central atom.)

10.59   The hyponitrite ion, ^-O—N=N—O^-, exists in solid compounds as the *trans* isomer. Using valence bond theory, explain why *cis–trans* isomers might be expected for this ion. Draw structural formulas of the *cis–trans* isomers.

10.60   Fumaric acid, $C_4H_4O_4$, occurs in the metabolism of glucose in the cells of plants and animals. It is used commercially in beverages. The structural formula of fumaric acid is

$$
\begin{array}{ccc}
\text{H} & & \text{COOH} \\
 & \diagdown \;\; \text{C} & \\
 & \| & \\
 & \text{C} \;\; \diagup & \\
\text{HOOC} & & \text{H}
\end{array}
$$

(—COOH is an abbreviation

$$
\text{for} \;\; -\!\!\overset{\text{O}}{\underset{\|}{\text{C}}}\!-\!\text{O}\!-\!\text{H})
$$

Maleic acid is the *cis* isomer of fumaric acid. Using valence bond theory, explain why these isomers are possible.

Molecular Orbital Theory

10.61   Describe the electronic structure of each of the following, using molecular orbital theory. Calculate the bond order of each and decide whether it should be stable. For each, state whether the substance is diamagnetic or paramagnetic.
   a. B_2 **b.** B_2^+ **c.** O_2^-

10.62   Use molecular orbital theory to describe the bonding in the following. For each one, find the bond order and decide whether it is stable. Is the substance diamagnetic or paramagnetic?
   a. Be_2^+
   b. Ne_2
   c. B_2^-

10.63   Assume that the cyanide ion, CN^-, has molecular orbitals similar to those of a homonuclear diatomic molecule. Write the configuration and bond order of CN^-. Is a substance of the ion diamagnetic or paramagnetic?

10.64   Write the molecular orbital configuration of the diatomic molecule BN. What is the bond order of BN? Is the substance diamagnetic or paramagnetic? Use the order of energies that was given for homonuclear diatomic molecules.

General Problems

10.65 Predict the molecular geometry of the following:
a. $SnCl_2$ **b.** $COBr_2$ **c.** ICl_2^- **d.** PCl_6^-

10.66 Predict the molecular geometry of the following:
a. HOF   **b.** NH_4^+ **c.** PF_5 **d.** ClF_4^+

10.67 Which of the following molecules or ions are linear?
a. SeF_2 **b.** $CHCl_3$ **c.** SeF_4 **d.** SnF_6^{2-}

10.68 Which of the following molecules or ions are trigonal planar?
a. BBr_3 **b.** AsH_3 **c.** ClF_4^- **d.** TeF_5^-

10.69 Describe the hybrid orbitals used by each carbon atom in the following molecules:

a. **b.** $N \equiv C - C \equiv N$

10.70 Describe the hybrid orbitals used by each nitrogen atom in the following molecules:

a. $H - N - N - H$ **b.** $N \equiv C - C \equiv N$

10.71 Explain how the dipole moment could be used to distinguish between the *cis* and *trans* isomers of 1,2-dibromoethene:

cis   *trans*

10.72 Two compounds have the formula $Pt(NH_3)_2Cl_2$. (Compound B is *cisplatin*, mentioned in the opening to Chapter 1.) They have square planar structures. One is expected to have a dipole moment; the other is not. Which one would have a dipole moment?

(a)   (b)

10.73 Explain in terms of bonding theory why all four hydrogen atoms of allene, $H_2C = C = CH_2$, cannot lie in the same plane.

10.74 Explain in terms of bonding theory why all atoms of $H_2C = C = C = CH_2$ must lie in the same plane.

10.75 What is the molecular orbital configuration of HeH^+? Do you expect the ion to be stable?

10.76 What is the molecular orbital configuration of He_2^+? Do you expect the ion to be stable?

10.77 Calcium carbide, CaC_2, consists of Ca^{2+} and C_2^{2-} (acetylide) ions. Write the molecular orbital configuration and bond order of the acetylide ion, C_2^{2-}.

10.78 Sodium peroxide, Na_2O_2, consists of Na^+ and O_2^{2-} (peroxide) ions. Write the molecular orbital configuration and bond order of the peroxide ion, O_2^{2-}.

10.79 The oxygen–oxygen bond in O_2^+ is 112 pm and in O_2 is 121 pm. Explain why the bond length in O_2^+ is shorter than in O_2. Would you expect the bond length in O_2^- to be longer or shorter than that in O_2? Why?

10.80 The nitrogen–nitrogen bond distance in N_2 is 109 pm. On the basis of bond orders, would you expect the bond distance in N_2^+ to be less than or greater than 109 pm? Answer the same question for N_2^-.

10.81 Using molecular orbital theory, determine the electronic structure of the first excited electronic state of N_2. What differences are expected in the properties of the excited state of N_2 compared with the same properties of the ground state?

10.82 The ionization energy of O_2 is smaller than the ionization energy of atomic O; the opposite is true for the ionization energies of N_2 and atomic N. Explain this behavior in terms of the molecular orbital energy diagrams of O_2 and N_2.

10.83 Describe the property of "handedness." What is it about the bonding of atoms in molecules that can give rise to handedness in molecules?

10.84 Biological molecules frequently display handedness. Describe the difference between the molecule responsible for the flavor of spearmint and the molecule responsible for the flavor of caraway seeds. In which way are the molecules similar and in which way do they differ?

10.85 Color vision results from the absorption of light by the cone cells of the retina. Briefly describe how different types of cone cells give rise to color vision. What is the chemical substance primarily responsible for human vision? How can its color absorption be changed?

10.86 Describe the *cis–trans* conversion that occurs in the ultraviolet absorption of *cis*-1,2-dichloroethene.

10.87 What is the biological importance of stratospheric ozone? Explain.

10.88 In 1995, Sherwood Rowland and Mario Molina received the Nobel Prize in chemistry. Explain in some detail the work they did for which they were awarded this prize.

Strategy Problems

10.89 Calcium carbide, CaC_2, has an ionic structure with ions Ca^{2+} and C_2^{2-}. Give the valence bond description of the bonding in the C_2^{2-} ion. Now write the MO configuration of this ion. What is the bond order according to this configuration? Compare the valence bond and molecular orbital descriptions.

10.90 Write Lewis formulas for the BF molecule (two with a single B—F bond, two with a double B—F bond, and one with a triple B—F bond) in which the octet rule is satisfied for at least one of the atoms. Obtain the formal charges of the atoms. Based on the information you have, is there one formula that you think best describes the molecule? Explain. For this best Lewis formula, give the valence bond description of the bonding.

10.91 Boron trifluoride, BF_3, reacts with ammonia, NH_3, to form an addition compound, BF_3NH_3. Describe the geometries about the B and the F atoms in this compound. Describe the hybridization on these two atoms. Now describe the bonding between the B and F atoms, using valence bond theory. Compare the geometries and hybridization of these atoms in this addition compound with that in the reactant molecules BF_3 and NH_3.

10.92 Acetylsalicylic acid (aspirin) has the structure shown by the following molecular model:

Describe the geometry and bonding about the carbon atom shown at the top of the model, in which the carbon atom (in black) is bonded to two oxygen atoms (red) and to another carbon atom. One of the oxygen atoms is bonded to a hydrogen atom (blue).

10.93 A molecule XF_6 (having no lone pairs) has a dipole moment of zero. (X denotes an unidentified element.) When two atoms of fluorine have been taken away, you get the molecule XF_4, which has dipole moment of 0.632 D.

$$XF_6 \longrightarrow XF_4 + 2F$$

Describe the molecular geometry and bonding for each molecule. What are some possibilities for X?

10.94 Three different compounds have the same molecular formula, $C_2H_2F_2$; call them A, B, and C. Compound A has a dipole moment of 2.42 D, compound B has a dipole moment of 1.38 D, and compound C has a dipole moment of 0 D. All three compounds react with hydrogen, H_2:

$$C_2H_2F_2 + H_2 \longrightarrow C_2H_4F_2$$

Compound A gives product D (molecular formula $C_2H_4F_2$), compound B gives product E (same molecular formula, $C_2H_4F_2$, but different from product D), and compound C gives product D. Identify the structural formulas of compounds A, B, and C.

10.95 Obtain a Lewis formula of H_2N_2. This molecule exhibits isomerism (it has two isomers). Sketch the electron-dot formulas of these isomers. Describe the bonding in terms of valence bond theory, and explain this isomerism in terms of this bonding description.

10.96 Dioxygen, O_2, has sometimes been represented by the electron-dot formula

$$\ddot{O}=\ddot{O}$$

Note, however, that this formula implies that all electrons are paired. Give the molecular orbital description of the state of the O_2 molecule of lowest energy *in which all electrons are paired in this way*. Compare this configuration with that of the ground state of O_2. In what way are they similar, and in what way are they different?

10.97 Solid sulfur normally consists of crystals of S_8 molecules, but when heated strongly, the solid vaporizes to give S_2 molecules (among other molecular species). Describe the bonding in S_2 in molecular orbital terms, assuming the orbitals are analogous to those of the preceding period. What would you expect to happen to the sulfur–sulfur bond length if two electrons were added to give the S_2^{2-} ion? What would you expect to happen to the bond length if, instead, two electrons were taken away to give S_2^{2+}?

10.98 Formaldehyde has the formula H_2CO. Describe the bonding between the C and O atoms in VB terms. Formaldehyde absorbs UV light at about 270 nm. The absorption is described as a π to π^* transition. Explain in molecular orbital terms what is involved.

Cumulative-Skills Problems

10.99 A molecular compound is composed of 60.4% Xe, 22.1% O, and 17.5% F, by mass. If the molecular weight is 217.3 amu, what is the molecular formula? What is the Lewis formula? Predict the molecular geometry using the VSEPR model. Describe the bonding, using valence bond theory.

10.100 A molecular compound is composed of 58.8% Xe, 7.2% O, and 34.0% F, by mass. If the molecular weight is 223 amu, what is the molecular formula? What is the Lewis formula? Predict the molecular geometry using the VSEPR model. Describe the bonding, using valence bond theory.

10.101 A compound of chlorine and fluorine, ClF_n, reacts at about 75°C with uranium metal to produce uranium hexafluoride, UF_6, and chlorine monofluoride, $ClF(g)$. A quantity of uranium produced 3.53 g UF_6 and 343 mL ClF at 75°C and 2.50 atm. What is the formula (n) of the compound? Describe the bonding in the molecule, using valence bond theory.

10.102 Excess fluorine, $F_2(g)$, reacts at 150°C with bromine, $Br_2(g)$, to give a compound BrF_n. If 423 mL $Br_2(g)$ at 150°C and 748 mmHg produced 4.20 g BrF_n, what is n? Describe the bonding in the molecule, using valence bond theory.

10.103 Each of the following compounds has a nitrogen–nitrogen bond: N_2, N_2H_4, N_2F_2. Match each compound with one of the following bond lengths: 110 pm, 122 pm, 145 pm. Describe the geometry about one of the N atoms in each compound. What hybrid orbitals are needed to describe the bonding in valence bond theory?

10.104 The bond length in C_2 is 131 pm. Compare this with the bond lengths in C_2H_2 (120 pm), C_2H_4 (134 pm), and C_2H_6 (153 pm). What bond order would you predict for C_2 from its bond length? Does this agree with the molecular orbital configuration you would predict for C_2?

10.105 Draw resonance formulas of the nitric acid molecule, HNO_3. What is the geometry about the N atom? What is the hybridization on N? Use bond energies and one Lewis formula for HNO_3 to estimate ΔH_f° for $HNO_3(g)$. The actual value of ΔH_f° for $HNO_3(g)$ is -135 kJ/mol, which is lower than the estimated value because of stabilization of HNO_3 by resonance. The

resonance energy is defined as ΔH_f° (estimated) $- \Delta H_f^\circ$ (actual). What is the resonance energy of HNO_3?

10.106 One resonance formula of benzene, C_6H_6, is

What is the other resonance formula? What is the geometry about a carbon atom? What hybridization would be used in valence bond theory to describe the bonding? The ΔH_f° for $C_6H_6(g)$ is -83 kJ/mol; ΔH_f° for $C(g)$ is 715 kJ/mol. Obtain the resonance energy of benzene. (See Problem 10.105.)

CHAPTER 5

The Gaseous State

■ SOLUTIONS TO EXERCISES

Note on significant figures: If the final answer to a solution needs to be rounded off, it is given first with one nonsignificant figure, and the last significant figure is underlined. The final answer is then rounded to the correct number of significant figures. In multistep problems, intermediate answers are given with at least one nonsignificant figure; however, only the final answer has been rounded off.

5.1. First, convert to atm ($57 \text{ kPa} = 57 \times 10^3 \text{ Pa}$).

$$57 \times 10^3 \text{ Pa} \times \frac{1 \text{ atm}}{1.01325 \times 10^5 \text{ Pa}} = 0.5\underline{6}2 = 0.56 \text{ atm}$$

Next, convert to mmHg.

$$57 \times 10^3 \text{ Pa} \times \frac{760 \text{ mmHg}}{1.01325 \times 10^5 \text{ Pa}} = 42\underline{7}.5 = 4.3 \times 10^2 \text{ mmHg}$$

5.2. Application of Boyle's law gives

$$V_f = V_i \times \frac{P_i}{P_f} = 20.0 \text{ L} \times \frac{1.00 \text{ atm}}{0.830 \text{ atm}} = 24.\underline{0}96 = 24.1 \text{ L}$$

5.3. First, convert the temperatures to the Kelvin scale.

$T_i = (19 + 273) = 292 \text{ K}$

$T_f = (25 + 273) = 298 \text{ K}$

Following is the data table.

$V_i = 4.38 \text{ dm}^3$	$P_i = 101 \text{ kPa}$	$T_i = 292 \text{ K}$
$V_f = ?$	$P_f = 101 \text{ kPa}$	$T_f = 298 \text{ K}$

Apply Charles's law to obtain

$$V_f = V_i \times \frac{T_f}{T_i} = 4.38 \text{ dm}^3 \times \frac{298 \text{ K}}{292 \text{ K}} = 4.4\underline{7}0 = 4.47 \text{ dm}^3$$

Copyright © Cengage Learning. All rights reserved.

5.4. First, convert the temperatures to kelvins.

$$T_i = (24 + 273) = 297 \text{ K}$$

$$T_f = (35 + 273) = 308 \text{ K}$$

Following is the data table.

$V_i = 5.41 \text{ dm}^3$	$P_i = 101.5 \text{ kPa}$	$T_i = 297 \text{ K}$
$V_f = ?$	$P_f = 102.8 \text{ kPa}$	$T_f = 308 \text{ K}$

Apply both Boyle's law and Charles's law combined to get

$$V_f = V_i \times \frac{P_i}{P_f} \times \frac{T_f}{T_i} = 5.41 \text{ dm}^3 \times \frac{101.5 \text{ kPa}}{102.8 \text{ kPa}} \times \frac{308 \text{ K}}{297 \text{ K}} = 5.5\underline{3}9 = 5.54 \text{ dm}^3$$

5.5. Use the ideal gas law, $PV = nRT$, and solve for n:

$$n = \frac{PV}{RT} = \left(\frac{V}{RT}\right)P$$

Note that everything in parentheses is constant. Therefore, you can write

$$n = \text{constant} \times P$$

Or, expressing this as a proportion,

$$n \propto P$$

5.6. First, convert the mass of O_2 to moles of O_2 (molar mass 32.00 g/mol) and convert temperature to kelvins.

$$T = 23 + 273 = 296 \text{ K}$$

$$3.03 \text{ kg O}_2 \times \frac{1000 \text{ g}}{1 \text{ kg}} \times \frac{1 \text{ mol O}_2}{32.00 \text{ g O}_2} = 94.\underline{6}88 \text{ mol O}_2$$

Summarize the data in a table.

Variable	Value
P	?
V	50.0 L
T	296 K
n	94.\underline{6}88 mol

Solve the ideal gas equation for P, and substitute the data to get

$$P = \frac{nRT}{V} = \frac{(94.\underline{6}88)(0.08206 \text{ L} \cdot \text{atm/K} \cdot \text{mol})(296 \text{ K})}{50.0 \text{ L}} = 46.\underline{0}0 = 46.0 \text{ atm}$$

Copyright © Cengage Learning. All rights reserved.

5.7.   The data given are

Variable	Value
P	752 mmHg x $\dfrac{1\ atm}{760\ mmHg}$ = 0.98947 atm
V	1 L (exact number)
T	(21 + 273) = 294 K
n	?

Using the ideal gas law, solve for n, the moles of helium.

$$n = \frac{PV}{RT} = \frac{(0.98947\ atm)(1\ L)}{(0.08206\ L \cdot atm/K \cdot mol)(294\ K)} = 0.04101\ mol$$

Now convert mol He to grams.

$$0.04101\ mol\ He\ \times\ \frac{4.00\ g\ He}{1\ mol\ He} = 0.16404\ g\ He$$

Therefore, the density of He at 21°C and 752 mmHg is 0.164 g/L.

The difference in mass between one liter of air and one liter of helium is

Mass air − mass He = 1.188 g − 0.16404 g = 1.02396 = 1.024 g difference

5.8.   Tabulate the values of the variables.

Variable	Value
P	0.862 atm
V	1 L (exact number)
T	(25 + 273) = 298 K
n	?

From the ideal gas law, $PV = nRT$, you obtain

$$n = \frac{PV}{RT} = \frac{(0.862\ atm)(1\ L)}{(0.08206\ L \cdot atm/K \cdot mol)(298\ K)} = 0.03525\ mol$$

Dividing the mass of the vapor by moles gives you the mass per mole (the molar mass).

$$Molar\ mass = \frac{grams\ vapor}{moles\ vapor} = \frac{2.26\ g}{0.03525\ mol} = 64.114\ g/mol$$

Therefore, the molecular mass is 64.1 amu.

Copyright © Cengage Learning. All rights reserved.

5.9. First, determine the number of moles of Cl_2 from the mass of HCl (molar mass 36.46 g/mol) and from the stoichiometry of the chemical equation:

$$9.41 \text{ g HCl } \times \frac{1 \text{ mol HCl}}{36.46 \text{ g HCl}} \times \frac{5 \text{ mol Cl}_2}{16 \text{ mol HCl}} = 0.080653 \text{ mol Cl}_2$$

Tabulate the values of the variables:

Variable	Value
P	$787 \text{ mmHg } \times \dfrac{1 \text{ atm}}{760 \text{ mmHg}} = 1.0355 \text{ atm}$
T	$(40 + 273) \text{ K} = 313 \text{ K}$
n	0.080653 mol
V	?

Rearrange the ideal gas law to obtain V:

$$V = \frac{nRT}{P} = \frac{(0.080653 \text{ mol})(0.08206 \text{ L}\cdot\text{atm/K}\cdot\text{mol})(313 \text{ K})}{1.0355 \text{ atm}} = 2.001 = 2.00 \text{ L}$$

5.10. Each gas obeys the ideal gas law. In each case, convert grams to moles and substitute into the ideal gas law to determine the partial pressure of each.

$$1.031 \text{ g O}_2 \times \frac{1 \text{ mol O}_2}{32.00 \text{ g O}_2} = 0.0322188 \text{ mol O}_2$$

$$P = \frac{nRT}{V} = \frac{(0.0322188)(0.08206 \text{ L}\cdot\text{atm/K}\cdot\text{mol})(291 \text{ K})}{10.0 \text{ L}} = 0.076936 \text{ atm}$$

$$0.572 \text{ g CO}_2 \times \frac{1 \text{ mol CO}_2}{44.01 \text{ g CO}_2} = 0.012997 \text{ mol CO}_2$$

$$P = \frac{nRT}{V} = \frac{(0.012997)(0.08206 \text{ L}\cdot\text{atm/K}\cdot\text{mol})(291 \text{ K})}{10.0 \text{ L}} = 0.031036 \text{ atm}$$

The total pressure is equal to the sum of the partial pressures:

$$P = P_{O_2} + P_{CO_2} = 0.076936 + 0.031036 = 0.10797 = 0.1080 \text{ atm}$$

The mole fraction of oxygen in the mixture is

$$\text{Mole fraction O}_2 = \frac{P_{O_2}}{P} = \frac{0.07694 \text{ atm}}{0.10802 \text{ atm}} = 0.7122 = 0.712$$

Copyright © Cengage Learning. All rights reserved.

5.11. Determine the number of moles of O_2 from the mass of $KClO_3$ and from the stoichiometry of the chemical reaction.

$$1.300 \text{ g } KClO_3 \text{ x } \frac{1 \text{ mol } KClO_3}{122.5 \text{ g } KClO_3} \text{ x } \frac{3 \text{ mol } O_2}{2 \text{ mol } KClO_3} = 0.0159184 \text{ mol } O_2$$

The vapor pressure of water at 23°C is 21.1 mmHg (Table 5.6). Find the partial pressure of O_2 using Dalton's law:

$$P = P_{O_2} + P_{H_2O}$$

$$P_{O_2} = P - P_{H_2O} = (745 - 21.1) \text{ mmHg} = 723.9 \text{ mmHg}$$

Solve for the volume using the ideal gas law.

Variable	Value
P	$723.9 \text{ mmHg x } \dfrac{1 \text{ atm}}{760 \text{ mmHg}} = 0.9525 \text{ atm}$
V	?
T	$(23 + 273) = 296 \text{ K}$
n	0.0159184

From the ideal gas law, $PV = nRT$, you have

$$V = \frac{nRT}{P} = \frac{(0.0159184 \text{ mol})(0.08206 \text{ L} \cdot \text{atm/K} \cdot \text{mol})(296 \text{ K})}{0.9525 \text{ atm}} = 0.4059 = 0.406 \text{ L}$$

5.12. The absolute temperature is $(22 + 273) = 295$ K. In SI units, the molar mass of carbon tetrachloride, CCl_4, is 153.8×10^{-3} kg/mol. Therefore,

$$u = \left(\frac{3RT}{M}\right)^{1/2} = \left(\frac{3 \times 8.31 \text{ kg} \cdot \text{m}^2/(\text{s}^2 \cdot \text{K} \cdot \text{mol}) \times 295 \text{ K}}{153.8 \times 10^{-3} \text{ kg/mol}}\right)^{1/2} = 218.7 = 219 \text{ m/s}$$

5.13. Determine the rms molecular speed for N_2 at 455°C (728 K):

$$u = \left(\frac{3RT}{M}\right)^{1/2} = \left(\frac{3 \times 8.31 \text{ kg} \cdot \text{m}^2/(\text{s}^2 \cdot \text{K} \cdot \text{mol}) \times 728 \text{ K}}{28.02 \times 10^{-3} \text{ kg/mol}}\right)^{1/2} = 804.81 \text{ m/s}$$

After writing this equation with the same speed for H_2, square both sides and solve for T. The molar mass of H_2 in SI units is 2.016×10^{-3} kg/mol. Therefore,

$$T = \frac{u^2 M}{3R} = \frac{(804.81)^2 (2.016 \times 10^{-3} \text{ kg/mol})}{(3)(8.31 \text{ kg} \cdot \text{m}^2/\text{s}^2 \cdot \text{K} \cdot \text{mol})} = 52.379 = 52.4 \text{ K}$$

Because the average kinetic energy of a molecule is proportional to only T, the temperature at which an H_2 molecule has the same average kinetic energy as an N_2 molecule at 455°C is exactly the same temperature, 455°C.

Copyright © Cengage Learning. All rights reserved.

5.14. The two rates of effusion are inversely proportional to the square roots of their molar masses, so you can write

$$\frac{\text{Rate of effusion of } O_2}{\text{Rate of effusion of He}} = \sqrt{\frac{M_m(\text{He})}{M_m(O_2)}}$$

where $M_m(\text{He})$ is the molar mass of He (4.00 g/mol) and $M_m(O_2)$ is the molar mass of O_2 (32.00 g/mol). Substituting these values into the formula gives

$$\frac{\text{Rate of effusion of } O_2}{\text{Rate of effusion of He}} = \sqrt{\frac{4.00 \text{ g/mol}}{32.00 \text{ g/mol}}} = 0.35\underline{3}55$$

Rearranging gives

Rate of effusion of O_2 = 0.35$\underline{3}$55 x rate of effusion of He.

Now, the problem states that the rate of effusion can be given in terms of volume of gas effused per second, so

$$\frac{\text{Volume of } O_2}{\text{Time for } O_2} = 0.35\underline{3}55 \text{ x } \frac{\text{Volume of He}}{\text{Time for He}}$$

Substituting in the values gives

$$\frac{10.0 \text{ mL}}{\text{Time for } O_2} = 0.35\underline{3}55 \text{ x } \frac{10.0 \text{ mL}}{3.52 \text{ s}}$$

Rearranging gives

$$\text{Time for } O_2 = \frac{3.52 \text{ s}}{0.35\underline{3}55} = 9.9\underline{5}6 = 9.96 \text{ s}$$

5.15. The problem states that the rate of effusion is inversely proportional to the time it takes for a gas to effuse, so you can write

$$\frac{\text{Rate of effusion of } H_2}{\text{Rate of effusion of gas}} = \frac{\text{time for gas}}{\text{time for } H_2} = \sqrt{\frac{M_m(\text{gas})}{M_m(H_2)}} = 4.67$$

Rearranging and solving for $M_m(H_2)$ gives

$$M_m(\text{gas}) = (4.67)^2 \text{ x } M_m(H_2) = (4.67)^2 \text{ x } 2.016 \text{ g/mol} = 43.\underline{9}6 = 44.0 \text{ g/mol}$$

Thus, the molecular mass of the gas is 44.0 amu.

Copyright © Cengage Learning. All rights reserved.

5.16. From Table 5.7, $a = 5.570$ $L^2 \cdot atm/mol^2$ and $b = 0.06499$ L/mol. Substitute these values into the van der Waals equation, along with $R = 0.08206$ L·atm/K·mol, $T = 273.2$ K, $n = 1.000$ mol, and $V = 22.41$ L.

$$P = \frac{nRT}{(V - nb)} - \frac{n^2a}{V^2}$$

$$P = \frac{(1.00 \text{ mol})(0.08206 \text{ L} \cdot atm/K \cdot mol)(273.2 \text{ K})}{22.41 \text{ L} - (1.00 \text{ mol})(0.06499 \text{ L/mol})} - \frac{(1.00 \text{ mol})^2 (5.570 \text{ L}^2 \cdot atm/mol^2)}{(22.41 \text{ L})^2}$$

$$= 1.00\underline{33} - 0.0110\underline{91} = 0.99\underline{221} = 0.992 \text{ atm}$$

Using the ideal gas law, $P = 1.00\underline{04}$ atm (larger).

■ ANSWERS TO SELF-ASSESSMENT AND REVIEW QUESTIONS

5.1. Pressure is the force exerted per unit area of surface. Force is further defined as mass multiplied by acceleration. The SI unit of mass is kg, of acceleration is m/s^2, and of area is m^2. Therefore, the SI unit of pressure (Pascal) is given by

$$\text{Pressure} = \frac{\text{force}}{\text{area}} = \frac{\text{mass x acceleration}}{\text{area}} = \frac{\text{kg x } m/s^2}{m^2} = \frac{\text{kg}}{m \cdot s^2} = \text{Pa}$$

5.2. A manometer is a device that measures the pressure of a gas in a vessel. The gas pressure in the flask is proportional to the difference in height between the liquid levels in the manometer (Figure 5.4).

5.3. The general relationship between the pressure (P) and the height (h) of the liquid in a manometer is $P = gdh$. Therefore, the variables that determine the height of the liquid in a manometer are the density (d) of the liquid and the pressure of the gas being measured. The acceleration of gravity (g) is a constant, 9.81 m/s^2.

5.4. From Boyle's law, $PV = $ constant. Because this is true for conditions P_i and V_i as well as conditions P_f and V_f, we can write

$$P_f V_f = P_i V_i = \text{constant}$$

Dividing both sides of this equation by P_f gives

$$V_f = V_i \text{ x } \frac{P_i}{P_f}$$

5.5. A linear relationship between variables such as x and y is given by the mathematical relation

$$y = a + bx$$

The variable y is directly proportional to x only if $a = 0$.

Copyright © Cengage Learning. All rights reserved.

5.6.   First, find the equivalent of absolute zero on the Fahrenheit scale. Converting $-273.15°C$ to degrees Fahrenheit, you obtain $-459.67°F$. Since the volume of a gas varies linearly with the temperature, you get the following linear relationship:

$$V = a + bt_F$$

where t_F is the temperature on the Fahrenheit scale. Since the volume of a gas is zero at absolute zero, you get

$$0 = a + b(-459.67), \text{ or } a = 459.67b$$

The equation can now be rewritten as

$$V = 459.67b + bt_F = b(459.67 + t_F) = bT_F$$

where T_F is the temperature in the new absolute scale based on the Fahrenheit scale. The relationship is

$$T_F = t_F + 459.67$$

5.7.   From Charles's law, $V = $ constant x T. Because this is true for conditions T_i and V_i as well as conditions T_f and V_f, we can write

$$\frac{V_f}{T_f} = \frac{V_i}{T_i} = \text{constant}$$

Multiplying both sides of the equation by T_f gives

$$V_f = V_i \text{ x } \frac{T_f}{T_i}$$

5.8.   Avogadro's law states that equal volumes of any two gases at the same temperature and pressure contain the same number of molecules. The law of combining volumes states that the volumes of reactant gases at a given pressure and temperature are in ratios of small whole numbers. The combining-volume law may be explained from Avogadro's law using the reaction $N_2 + 3H_2 \rightarrow 2NH_3$ as follows. In this equation, the molecules are in a ratio of small whole numbers, 1 to 3 to 2. In Avogadro's law, these numbers represent volumes. But since equal volumes contain the same number of molecules, the ratios for volumes are the same as the ratios for molecules.

5.9.   The standard conditions are $0°C$ and 1 atm pressure (STP).

5.10. The molar gas volume, V_m, is the volume of one mole of gas at any given temperature and pressure. At standard conditions (STP), the molar gas volume equals 22.4 L.

5.11. Boyle's law ($V \propto 1/P$) and Charles's law ($V \propto T$) can be combined and expressed in a single statement: the volume occupied by a given amount of gas is proportional to the absolute temperature divided by the pressure. In equation form, this is

$$V = \text{constant x } \frac{T}{P}$$

Copyright © Cengage Learning. All rights reserved.

The constant is independent of temperature and pressure but does depend on the amount of gas. For one mole, the constant will have a specific value, denoted as R. The molar volume, V_m, is

$$V_m = R \times \frac{T}{P}$$

Because V_m has the same value for all gases, we can write this equation for n moles of gas if we multiply both sides by n. This yields the equation

$$nV_m = \frac{nRT}{P}$$

Because V_m is the volume per mole, nV_m is the total volume V. Substituting gives

$$V = \frac{nRT}{P} \quad \text{or} \quad PV = nRT$$

5.12. The variables in the ideal gas law are P, V, n, and T. The SI units of these variables are pascals (P), cubic meters (V), moles (n), and kelvins (T).

5.13. Use the value of R from Table 5.5 and the conversion factor 1 atm = 760 mmHg. This gives

$$0.082058 \frac{\text{L} \cdot \text{atm}}{\text{K} \cdot \text{mol}} \times \frac{760 \text{ mmHg}}{1 \text{ atm}} = 62.3640 = 62.364 \frac{\text{L} \cdot \text{mmHg}}{\text{K} \cdot \text{mol}}$$

5.14. Six empirical gas laws can be obtained. They can be stated as follows:

$P \times V$ = constant   (T and n constant)

$\dfrac{P}{T}$ = constant   (V and n constant)

$\dfrac{P}{n}$ = constant   (T and V constant)

$\dfrac{V}{T}$ = constant   (P and n constant)

$\dfrac{V}{n}$ = constant   (P and T constant)

$n \times T$ = constant   (P and V constant)

5.15. The postulates and supporting evidence are the following:

(1) Gases are composed of molecules whose sizes are negligible compared with the distance between them.

(2) Molecules move randomly in straight lines in all directions and at various speeds.

(3) The forces of attraction or repulsion between two molecules (intermolecular forces) in a gas are very weak or negligible, except when they collide.

Copyright © Cengage Learning. All rights reserved.

(4)   When molecules collide with one another, the collisions are elastic.

(5)   The average kinetic energy of a molecule is proportional to the absolute temperature.

One example of evidence that supports the kinetic theory of gases is Boyle's law. Constant temperature means that the average molecular force from collision remains constant. If you increase the volume, you decrease the number of collisions per unit wall area, thus lowering the pressure in accordance with Boyle's law. Another example is Charles's law. If you raise the temperature, you increase the average molecular force from a collision with the wall, thus increasing the pressure. For the pressure to remain constant, it is necessary for the volume to increase so that the frequency of collisions with the wall decreases. Thus, when you raise the temperature of a gas while keeping the pressure constant, the volume increases in accordance with Charles's law.

5.16. Boyle's law requires the temperature to be constant. Postulate 5 of the kinetic theory holds that the average kinetic energy of a molecule is constant at constant temperature. Therefore, the average molecular force from collisions is constant. If we increase the volume of a gas, this decreases the number of molecules per unit volume and so decreases the frequency of collisions per unit wall area, causing the pressure to decrease in accordance with Boyle's law.

5.17. According to kinetic theory, the pressure of a gas results from the bombardment of container walls by molecules.

5.18. The rms speed of a molecule equals $(3RT/M_m)^{1/2}$. Therefore, it varies directly with the square root of the absolute temperature. The rms speed does not depend on the molar volume.

5.19. A gas appears to diffuse more slowly because it never travels very far in one direction before it collides with another molecule and moves in another direction. Thus, it must travel a very long, crooked path as the result of collisions.

5.20. Effusion is the process in which a gas flows through a small hole in a container. It results from the gas molecules encountering the hole by chance, rather than by colliding with the walls of the container. The faster the molecules move, the more likely they are to encounter the hole. Thus, the rate of effusion depends on the average molecular speed, which depends inversely on molecular mass.

5.21. The behavior of a gas begins to deviate significantly from that predicted by the ideal gas law at high pressures and at relatively low temperatures.

5.22. The constant a is the proportionality constant in the van der Waals equation related to intermolecular forces The term nb represents the volume occupied by n moles of molecules.

5.23. The answer is a; "the greater the volume occupied by a given amount of gas, the higher the intermolecular force" is not part of the kinetic-molecular theory.

5.24. The answer is c, the container volume didn't change.

Copyright © Cengage Learning. All rights reserved.

5.25. The answer is b, to occupy the entire 22.4 L volume of the box.

5.26. The answer is d; it is *not* true that the Ar atoms hit the walls of the flask with the greatest force of the three gases.

■ SOLUTIONS TO PRACTICE PROBLEMS

Note on significant figures: If the final answer to a solution needs to be rounded off, it is given first with one nonsignificant figure, and the last significant figure is underlined. The final answer is then rounded to the correct number of significant figures. In multistep problems, intermediate answers are given with at least one nonsignificant figure; however, only the final answer has been rounded off.

5.37. Use the conversion factor 1 atm = 760 mmHg.

$$0.047 \text{ atm} \times \frac{760 \text{ mmHg}}{1 \text{ atm}} = 35.7 = 36 \text{ mmHg}$$

5.39. Using Boyle's law, solve for V_f of the neon gas at 1.292 atm pressure.

$$V_f = V_i \times \frac{P_i}{P_f} = 3.15 \text{ L} \times \frac{0.951 \text{ atm}}{1.292 \text{ atm}} = 2.318 = 2.32 \text{ L}$$

5.41. Using Boyle's law, let V_f = volume at 0.974 atm (P_f), V_i = 50.0 L, and P_i = 19.8 atm.

$$V_f = V_i \times \frac{P_i}{P_f} = 50.0 \text{ L} \times \frac{19.8 \text{ atm}}{0.974 \text{ atm}} = 1016.4 = 1.02 \times 10^3 \text{ L}$$

5.43. Using Boyle's law, let P_i = pressure of 315 cm³ of gas, and solve for it.

$$P_i = P_f \times \frac{V_f}{V_i} = 2.51 \text{ kPa} \times \frac{0.0457 \text{ cm}^3}{315 \text{ cm}^3} = 3.641 \times 10^{-4} = 3.64 \times 10^{-4} \text{ kPa}$$

5.45. Use Charles's law: T_i = 18°C + 273 = 291 K, and T_f = 0°C + 273 = 273 K.

$$V_f = V_i \times \frac{T_f}{T_i} = 3.92 \text{ mL} \times \frac{273 \text{ K}}{291 \text{ K}} = 3.677 = 3.68 \text{ mL}$$

5.47. Use Charles's law: T_i = 22°C + 273 = 295 K, and T_f = −197°C + 273 = 76 K.

$$V_f = V_i \times \frac{T_f}{T_i} = 2.54 \text{ L} \times \frac{76 \text{ K}}{295 \text{ K}} = 0.654 = 0.65 \text{ L}$$

Copyright © Cengage Learning. All rights reserved.

5.49. Use Charles's law: $T_i = 25°C + 273 = 298$ K, and V_f is the difference between the vessel's volume of 39.5 cm^3 and the 7.7 cm^3 of ethanol that is forced into the vessel.

$$T_f = T_i \times \frac{V_f}{V_i} = 298 \text{ K} \times \frac{(39.5 \text{ - } 7.7) \text{ cm}^3}{39.5 \text{ cm}^3} = 239.9 \text{ K } (-33.2 \text{ or } -33°C)$$

5.51. Use the combined law: $T_i = 31°C + 273 = 304$ K, and $T_f = 0°C + 273 = 273$ K.

$$V_f = V_i \times \frac{P_i}{P_f} \times \frac{T_f}{T_i} - 35.5 \text{ mL} \times \frac{753 \text{ mmHg}}{760 \text{ mmHg}} \times \frac{273 \text{ K}}{304 \text{ K}} = 31.58 - 31.6 \text{ mL}$$

5.53. The balanced equation is

$$4NH_3 + 5O_2 \rightarrow 4NO + 6H_2O$$

The ratio of moles of NH_3 to moles of NO is 4 to 4, or 1 to 1, so one volume of NH_3 will produce one volume of NO at the same temperature and pressure.

5.55. Solve the ideal gas law for V:

$$V = \frac{nRT}{P} = nRT\left(\frac{1}{P}\right)$$

If the temperature and number of moles are held constant, then the product nRT is constant, and volume is inversely proportional to pressure:

$$V = \text{constant} \times \frac{1}{P}$$

5.57. Calculate the moles of oxygen, and then solve the ideal gas law for P:

$$n = 91.3 \text{ g} \times \frac{1 \text{ mol O}_2}{32.00 \text{ g O}_2} = 2.853 \text{ mol O}_2$$

$$P = \frac{nRT}{V} = \frac{(2.853 \text{ mol}) (0.08206 \text{ L} \cdot \text{atm}/\text{K} \cdot \text{ mol}) (294 \text{ K})}{8.58 \text{ L}} = 8.022 = 8.02 \text{ atm}$$

5.59. Using the moles of chlorine, solve the ideal gas law for V:

$$V = \frac{nRT}{P} = \frac{(3.50 \text{ mol})(0.08206 \text{ L} \cdot \text{atm}/\text{K} \cdot \text{mol})(307 \text{ K})}{4.00 \text{ atm}} = 22.04 = 22.0 \text{ L}$$

5.61. Solve the ideal gas law for temperature in K, and convert to °C:

$$T = \frac{PV}{nR} = \frac{(3.50 \text{ atm}) (4.00 \text{ L})}{(0.410 \text{ mol})(0.08206 \text{ L} \cdot \text{atm}/\text{K} \cdot \text{mol})} = 416.1 = 416 \text{ K}$$

$$°C = 416 - 273 = 143°C$$

Copyright © Cengage Learning. All rights reserved.

5.63. Because density equals mass per unit volume, calculating the mass of 1 L (exact number) of gas will give the density of the gas. Start from the ideal gas law, and calculate n; then convert the moles of gas to grams using the molar mass.

$$n = \frac{PV}{RT} = \frac{(751/760 \text{ atm})(1 \text{ L})}{(0.08206 \text{ L} \cdot \text{atm/K} \cdot \text{mol})(304 \text{ K})} = 0.03961 \text{ mol}$$

$$0.03961 \text{ mol} \times \frac{17.03 \text{ g}}{1 \text{ mol}} = 0.67458 = 0.675 \text{ g}$$

Therefore, the density of NH_3 at 31°C is 0.675 g/L.

5.65. Calculate the mass of 1 L (exact number) using the ideal gas law; convert to mass.

$$n = \frac{PV}{RT} = \frac{(0.897 \text{ atm})(1 \text{ L})}{(0.08206 \text{ L} \cdot \text{atm/K} \cdot \text{mol})(297 \text{ K})} = 0.036804 \text{ mol}$$

$$0.036804 \text{ mol} \times \frac{58.12 \text{ g}}{1 \text{ mol}} = 2.139 = 2.14 \text{ g}$$

Therefore, the density of C_4H_{10} is 2.14 g/L.

5.67. The ideal gas law gives n moles, which then are divided into the mass of 1.585 g for molar mass.

$$n = \frac{PV}{RT} = \frac{(753/760 \text{ atm})(1 \text{ L})}{(0.08206 \text{ L} \cdot \text{atm/K} \cdot \text{mol})(363 \text{ K})} = 0.033262 \text{ mol}$$

$$\text{Molar mass} = \frac{1.585 \text{ g}}{0.033262 \text{ mol}} = 47.651 \text{ g/mol}$$

The molecular weight is 47.7 amu.

5.69. The moles in 250 mL (0.250 L) of the compound are obtained from the ideal gas law. The 2.56-g mass of the gas then is divided by the moles to obtain the molar mass and molecular mass.

$$n = \frac{PV}{RT} = \frac{(786/760 \text{ atm})(0.250 \text{ L})}{(0.08206 \text{ L} \cdot \text{atm/K} \cdot \text{mol})(394 \text{ K})} = 0.007996 \text{ mol}$$

$$\text{Molar mass} = \frac{2.56 \text{ g}}{0.007996 \text{ mol}} = 3.201 \times 10^2 = 3.20 \times 10^2 \text{ g/mol}$$

The molecular mass is 3.20×10^2 amu.

5.71. For a gas at a given temperature and pressure, the density depends on molecular mass (or, for a mixture, on average molecular mass). Thus, at the same temperature and pressure, the density of NH_4Cl gas would be greater than that of a mixture of NH_3 and HCl, because the average molecular mass of NH_3 and HCl would be lower than that of NH_4Cl.

Copyright © Cengage Learning. All rights reserved.

5.73. The 0.050 mol CaC_2 will form 0.050 mol C_2H_2. The volume is found from the ideal gas law:

$$V = \frac{(0.050 \text{ mol})(0.08206 \text{ L} \cdot \text{atm/K} \cdot \text{mol})(299 \text{ K})}{684/760 \text{ atm}} = 1.\underline{3}6 = 1.4 \text{ L}$$

5.75. Use the equation to obtain the moles of CO_2 and then the ideal gas law to obtain the volume.

$$2\text{LiOH}(s) + CO_2(g) \rightarrow \text{Li}_2CO_3(aq) + H_2O(l)$$

$$327 \text{ g LiOH } \times \frac{1 \text{ mol LiOH}}{23.95 \text{ g LiOH}} \times \frac{1 \text{ mol } CO_2}{2 \text{ mol LiOH}} = 6.8\underline{2}67 \text{ mol } CO_2$$

$$V = \frac{(6.8\underline{2}67 \text{ mol})(0.08206 \text{ L} \cdot \text{atm/K} \cdot \text{mol})(294 \text{ K})}{781/760 \text{ atm}} = 16\underline{0}.2 = 160. \text{ L}$$

5.77. Use the equation to obtain the moles of ammonia and then the ideal gas law to obtain the volume.

$$2NH_3(g) + CO_2(g) \rightarrow NH_2CONH_2(aq) + H_2O(l)$$

$$908 \text{ g urea } \times \frac{1 \text{ mol urea}}{60.06 \text{ g urea}} \times \frac{2 \text{ mol } NH_3}{1 \text{ mol urea}} = 30.\underline{2}3 \text{ mol } NH_3$$

$$V = \frac{(30.\underline{2}3 \text{ mol})(0.08206 \text{ L} \cdot \text{atm/K} \cdot \text{mol})(298 \text{ K})}{3.00 \text{ atm}} = 24\underline{6}.4 = 246 \text{ L}$$

5.79. Use the equation to obtain the moles of ammonia and then the ideal gas law to obtain the volume.

$$2NH_3(g) + H_2SO_4(aq) \rightarrow (NH_4)_2SO_4(aq)$$

$$150.0 \text{ g } (NH_4)_2SO_4 \times \frac{1 \text{ mol } (NH_4)_2SO_4}{132.1 \text{ g } (NH_4)_2SO_4} \times \frac{2 \text{ mol } NH_3}{1 \text{ mol } (NH_4)_2SO_4}$$

$$= 2.2\underline{7}10 \text{ mol } NH_3$$

$$V = \frac{nRT}{P} = \frac{(2.2710 \text{ mol})(0.08206 \text{ L} \cdot \text{atm/K} \cdot \text{mol})(288 \text{ K})}{1.15 \text{ atm}} = 46.\underline{6}7 = 46.7 \text{ L}$$

5.81. Calculate the partial pressure of each gas; then add the pressures since the total pressure is equal to the sum of the partial pressures:

$$P(\text{He}) = \frac{(0.0200 \text{ mol})(0.08206 \text{ L} \cdot \text{atm/K} \cdot \text{mol})(283 \text{ K})}{2.50 \text{ L}} = 0.18\underline{5}78 \text{ atm}$$

$$P(H_2) = \frac{(0.0100 \text{ mol})(0.08206 \text{ L} \cdot \text{atm/K} \cdot \text{mol})(283 \text{ K})}{2.50 \text{ L}} = 0.092\underline{8}9 \text{ atm}$$

Total pressure $= 0.18587 = 0.09289 = 0.27\underline{8}67 = 0.279$

Copyright © Cengage Learning. All rights reserved.

5.83. Convert mass of O_2 and mass of He to moles. Use the ideal gas law to calculate the partial pressures, and then add to obtain the total pressures.

$$0.00103 \text{ g O}_2 \text{ x } \frac{1 \text{ mol O}_2}{32.00 \text{ g O}_2} = 3.2\underline{1}9 \times 10^{-5} \text{ mol O}_2$$

$$0.00056 \text{ g He } \text{ x } \frac{1 \text{ mol He}}{4.00 \text{ g He}} = 1.\underline{4}0 \times 10^{-4} \text{ mol}$$

$$P = \frac{nRT}{V} = \frac{(3.219 \times 10^{-5} \text{ mol})(0.08206 \text{ L} \cdot \text{atm/K} \cdot \text{mol})(288 \text{ K})}{0.2000 \text{ L}}$$

$$= 0.00380\underline{4} \text{ atm O}_2$$

$$P = \frac{nRT}{V} = \frac{(1.40 \times 10^{-4} \text{ mol})(0.08206 \text{ L} \cdot \text{atm/K} \cdot \text{mol})(288 \text{ K})}{0.2000 \text{ L}}$$

$$= 0.016\underline{5}4 \text{ atm He}$$

$$P = P_{O_2} + P_{He} = 0.003804 \text{ atm} + 0.01654 \text{ atm} = 0.02\underline{0}3 = 0.020 \text{ atm}$$

5.85. For each gas, $P(\text{gas}) = P$ x (mole fraction of gas).

$P(H_2)$	= 760 mmHg x 0.250 = 19\underline{0}.0	= 190 mmHg
$P(CO_2)$	= 760 mmHg x 0.650 = 49\underline{4}.0	= 494 mmHg
$P(HCl)$	= 760 mmHg x 0.054 = 4\underline{1}.04	= 41 mmHg
$P(HF)$	= 760 mmHg x 0.028 = 2\underline{1}.28	= 21 mmHg
$P(SO_2)$	= 760 mmHg x 0.017 = 1\underline{2}.92	= 13 mmHg
$P(H_2S)$	= 760 mmHg x 0.001 = 0.\underline{7}6	= 0.8 mmHg

5.87. The total pressure is the sum of the partial pressures of CO and H_2O, so

$$P_{CO} = P - P_{water} = 689 \text{ mmHg} - 23.8 \text{ mmHg} = 66\underline{5}.2 \text{ mmHg}$$

$$n_{CO} = \frac{P_{CO}V}{RT} = \frac{(665/760 \text{ atm})(3.85 \text{ L})}{(0.08206 \text{ L} \cdot \text{atm/K} \cdot \text{mol})(298 \text{ K})} = 0.137\underline{8} \text{ mol CO}$$

$$0.137\underline{8} \text{ mol CO } \text{ x } \frac{1 \text{ mol HCOOH}}{1 \text{ mol CO}} \text{ x } \frac{46.03 \text{ g HCOOH}}{1 \text{ mol HCOOH}} = 6.3\underline{4}2 = 6.34 \text{ g HCOOH}$$

Copyright © Cengage Learning. All rights reserved.

5.89. Substitute 298 K (25°C) and 398 K (125°C) into Maxwell's distribution:

$$u_{25} = \left(\frac{3RT}{M}\right)^{1/2} = \left(\frac{3 \times 8.31 \text{ kg} \cdot \text{m}^2/(\text{s}^2 \cdot \text{K} \cdot \text{mol}) \times 298 \text{ K}}{28.02 \times 10^{-3} \text{ kg/mol}}\right)^{1/2}$$

$$= 5.1\underline{4}9 \times 10^2 = 5.15 \times 10^2 \text{ m/s}$$

$$u_{125} = \left(\frac{3RT}{M}\right)^{1/2} = \left(\frac{3 \times 8.31 \text{ kg} \cdot \text{m}^2/(\text{s}^2 \cdot \text{K} \cdot \text{mol}) \times 398 \text{ K}}{28.02 \times 10^{-3} \text{ kg/mol}}\right)^{1/2}$$

$$= 5.9\underline{5}07 \times 10^2 = 5.95 \times 10^2 \text{ m/s}$$

Graph as in Figure 5.25.

5.91. Substitute 330 K (57°C) into Maxwell's distribution:

$$u_{330 \text{ K}} = \left(\frac{3RT}{M}\right)^{1/2} = \left(\frac{3 \times 8.31 \text{ kg} \cdot \text{m}^2/(\text{s}^2 \cdot \text{K} \cdot \text{mol}) \times 330 \text{ K}}{352 \times 10^{-3} \text{ kg/mol}}\right)^{1/2}$$

$$= 1.5\underline{2}8 \times 10^2 = 1.53 \times 10^2 \text{ m/s}$$

5.93. Because $u(CO_2) = u(H_2)$, we can equate the two right-hand sides of the Maxwell distributions:

$$\left(\frac{3RT(CO_2)}{M_m(CO_2)}\right)^{1/2} = \left(\frac{3RT(H_2)}{M_m(H_2)}\right)^{1/2}$$

Squaring both sides, rearranging to solve for $T(CO_2)$, and substituting numerical values, we have

$$T(CO_2) = T(H_2) \times \frac{M_m(CO_2)}{M_m(H_2)} = 298 \text{ K} \times \frac{44.01 \text{ g/mol}}{2.016 \text{ g/mol}} = 65\underline{0}5.4 \text{ K}$$

Thus the temperature is

$$T = 65\underline{0}5.4 - 273 = 62\underline{3}2 = 6.23 \times 10^3 \text{ °C}$$

5.95. The rates of effusion are directly related to the rms speed. Assume the temperature is the same for both, and write a ratio of two Maxwell distributions.

$$\frac{u_{N_2}}{u_{O_2}} = \frac{\left(\frac{3RT}{M_m(N_2)}\right)^{1/2}}{\left(\frac{3RT}{M_m(O_2)}\right)^{1/2}} = \left(\frac{M_m(O_2)}{M_m(N_2)}\right)^{1/2} = \left(\frac{32.00 \text{ g/mol}}{28.02 \text{ g/mol}}\right)^{1/2}$$

$$= 1.06\underline{8}6 = 1.069$$

Thus the ratio of the rates of effusion of N_2 and O_2 is 1.069 to 1.

Copyright © Cengage Learning. All rights reserved.

5.97. The rates of effusion are directly related to the rms speed. Assume the temperature is the same for both, and write a ratio of two Maxwell distributions.

$$\frac{u_{H_2}}{u_{I_2}} = \left(\frac{M_m(I_2)}{M_m(H_2)}\right)^{1/2} = \left(\frac{253.8 \text{ g/mol}}{2.016 \text{ g/mol}}\right)^{1/2} = 11.2\underline{2}0 = 11.22$$

Because hydrogen diffuses 11.22 times as fast as iodine, the time it would take would be 1/11.22 of the time required for iodine:

$$t(H_2) = 39 \text{ s} \times (1/11.22) = 3.\underline{4}7 = 3.5 \text{ s}$$

5.99. Since the volume of gas produced is directly related to the rate of effusion, the ratio of the volumes of gas can be written in terms of the ratio of the rms speeds. This in turn can be written in terms of the masses of the particles.

$$\frac{4.83 \text{ mL gas}}{9.23 \text{ mL Ar}} = \frac{u_{gas}}{u_{Ar}} = \left(\frac{M_m(Ar)}{M_m(gas)}\right)^{1/2} = \left(\frac{39.95 \text{ g/mol}}{M_m(gas)}\right)^{1/2}$$

Squaring both sides gives

$$0.273\underline{8}3 = \frac{39.95 \text{ g/mol}}{M_m(gas)}$$

Solving for the molar mass gives

$$M_m(gas) = \frac{39.95 \text{ g/mol}}{0.27383} = 14\underline{5}.8 \text{ g/mol}; \text{ molecular mass} = 146 \text{ amu}$$

5.101. Solving the van der Waals equation for $n = 1$ and $T = 355.2$ K for P gives

$$P = \frac{RT}{(V - b)} - \frac{a}{V^2} = \frac{(0.08206 \text{ L} \cdot \text{atm/K} \cdot \text{mol})(355.2 \text{ K})}{(30.00 \text{ L} - 0.08710 \text{ L})} - \frac{12.56 \text{ L}^2 \cdot \text{atm}}{(30.00 \text{ L})^2}$$

$$P = 0.974\underline{4}19 - 0.0139\underline{5}55 = 0.960\underline{4}6 = 0.9605 \text{ atm}$$

$$P(\text{ideal gas law}) = 0.971\underline{5}9 \text{ atm}$$

5.103. To calculate a/V^2 in the van der Waals equation, we obtain V from the ideal gas law at 1.00 atm:

$$V = \frac{RT}{P} = \frac{(0.08206 \text{ L} \cdot \text{atm/K} \cdot \text{mol})(273 \text{ K})}{1.00 \text{ atm}} = 22.40 \text{ L}$$

$$\frac{a}{V^2} = \frac{5.570}{(22.4 \text{ L})^2} = 1.1\underline{1}0 \times 10^{-2}$$

Copyright © Cengage Learning. All rights reserved.

At 1.00 atm, $V = 22.4$ L, and $a/V^2 = 1.110 \times 10^{-2}$. Substituting into the van der Waals equation:

$$V = \dfrac{RT}{P + \dfrac{a}{V^2}} + b = \dfrac{(0.08206 \ \text{L} \bullet \text{atm/ K} \bullet \text{mol})(273 \ \text{K})}{(1.00 + 1.110 \times 10^{-2})\,\text{atm}} + 0.06499 = 22.\underline{2}2 = 22.2 \ \text{L}$$

At 10.0 atm, the van der Waals equation gives 2.08 L. The ideal gas law gives 22.4 L for 1.00 atm and 2.24 L for 10.0 atm.

■ SOLUTIONS TO GENERAL PROBLEMS

5.105. Calculate the mass of 1 cm^2 of the 20.5 m of water above the air in the glass. The volume is the product of the area of 1 cm^2 and the height of 20.5×10^2 cm (20.5 m) of water. The density of 1.00 g/cm^3 must be used to convert volume to mass:

$$m = d \times V$$

$$m = 1.00 \ \text{g/cm}^3 \times (1.00 \ \text{cm}^2 \times 20.5 \times 10^2 \ \text{cm}) = 2.05 \times 10^3 \ \text{g, or 2.05 kg}$$

The pressure exerted on an object at the bottom of the column of water is

$$P = \dfrac{\text{force}}{\text{area}} = \dfrac{(m)(g)}{\text{area}} = \dfrac{(2.05 \ \text{kg})(9.807 \ \text{m/s}^2)}{(1.00 \ \text{cm}^2)\left(\dfrac{10^{-2} \ \text{m}}{1 \ \text{cm}}\right)^2} = 2.01 \times 10^5 \ \text{kg/ms}^2$$

$$= 2.01 \times 10^5 \ \text{Pa}$$

The total pressure on the air in the tumbler equals the sum of the barometric pressure and the water pressure:

$$P = 1.00 \times 10^2 \ \text{kPa} + 2.01 \times 10^2 \ \text{kPa} = 3.01 \times 10^2 \ \text{kPa}$$

Multiply the initial volume by a factor accounting for the change in pressure to find V_f:

$$V_f = V_i \times \dfrac{P_i}{P_f} = 243 \ \text{cm}^3 \times \left(\dfrac{1.00 \times 10^2 \ \text{kPa}}{3.01 \times 10^2 \ \text{kPa}}\right) = 80.\underline{7}3 = 80.7 \ \text{cm}^3$$

5.107. Use the combined gas law and solve for V_f:

$$V_f = V_i \times \dfrac{P_i}{P_f} \times \dfrac{T_f}{T_i} = 201 \ \text{mL} \times \dfrac{738 \ \text{mmHg}}{760 \ \text{mmHg}} \times \dfrac{273 \ \text{K}}{294 \ \text{K}} = 18\underline{1}.24 = 181 \ \text{mL}$$

5.109. Use the combined gas law and solve for V_f:

$$V_f = V_i \times \dfrac{P_i}{P_f} \times \dfrac{T_f}{T_i} = 5.0 \ \text{dm}^3 \times \dfrac{100.0 \ \text{kPa}}{79.0 \ \text{kPa}} \times \dfrac{293 \ \text{K}}{287 \ \text{K}} = 6.\underline{4}6 = 6.5 \ \text{dm}^3$$

Copyright © Cengage Learning. All rights reserved.

5.111. Use the ideal gas law to calculate the moles of helium, and combine this with Avogadro's number to obtain the number of helium atoms:

$$n = \frac{PV}{RT} = \frac{(765/760 \text{ atm})(0.01205 \text{ L})}{(0.08206 \text{ L} \cdot \text{atm/K} \cdot \text{mol})(296 \text{ K})} = 4.9\underline{9}3 \times 10^{-4} \text{ mol}$$

$$4.993 \times 10^{-4} \text{ mol He} \times \frac{6.022 \times 10^{23} \text{ He}^{2+} \text{ ions}}{1 \text{ mol He}} \times \frac{1 \text{ atom}}{1 \text{ He}^{2+} \text{ ion}} = 3.0\underline{0}67 \times 10^{20}$$

$$= 3.01 \times 10^{20} \text{ atoms}$$

5.113. Calculate the molar mass, M_m, by dividing the mass of 1 liter of air by the moles of the gas from the ideal gas equation:

$$M_m = \frac{\text{mass}}{n} = 1.2929 \text{ g air} \times \frac{(0.082058 \text{ L} \cdot \text{atm/K} \cdot \text{ mol}) (273.15 \text{ K})}{(1 \text{ atm})(1 \text{ L})}$$

$$= 28.97\underline{9}2 \text{ g/mol} = 28.979 \text{ g/ mol (amu)}$$

5.115. Use the ideal gas law to calculate the moles of CO_2. Then convert to mass of LiOH.

$$n = \frac{PV}{RT} = \frac{(1.00 \text{ atm})(5.8 \times 10^2 \text{ L})}{(0.08206 \text{ L} \cdot \text{atm/K} \cdot \text{mol})(273 \text{ K})} = 25.\underline{8}9 \text{ mol CO}_2$$

$$25.\underline{8}9 \text{ mol CO}_2 \times \frac{2 \text{ mol LiOH}}{1 \text{ mol CO}_2} \times \frac{23.95 \text{ g LiOH}}{1 \text{ mol LiOH}} = 1\underline{2}40 = 1.2 \times 10^3 \text{ g LiOH}$$

5.117.   Convert mass to moles of $KClO_3$, and then use the equation below to convert to moles of O_2. Use the ideal gas law to convert moles of O_2 to pressure at 25°C (298 K).

$$2KClO_3(s) \rightarrow 2KCl(s) + 3O_2(g)$$

$$170.0 \text{ g KClO}_3 \times \frac{1 \text{ mol KClO}_3}{122.55 \text{ g KClO}_3} \times \frac{3 \text{ mol O}_2}{2 \text{ mol KClO}_3} = 2.0\underline{8}0 \text{ mol O}_2$$

$$P = \frac{nRT}{V} = \frac{(2.0\underline{8}0 \text{ mol}) (0.08206 \text{ L} \cdot \text{atm/ K} \cdot \text{mol}) (298 \text{ K})}{2.50 \text{ L}} = 20.\underline{3}53 = 20.4 \text{ atm O}_2$$

5.119. Find the number of moles of CO_2 first. Then convert this to moles of HCl and molarity of HCl.

$$n = \frac{(727 / 760 \text{ atm}) \times 0.141 \text{ L}}{0.08206 \text{ L} \cdot \text{atm/K} \cdot \text{mol} \times 300 \text{ K}} = 0.00547\underline{8}8 \text{ mol}$$

$$\text{mol HCl} = 0.0054788 \text{ mol CO}_2 \times (2 \text{ mol HCl} /1 \text{ mol CO}_2) = 0.0109\underline{5}7 \text{ mol}$$

$$M \text{ HCl} = 0.0109\underline{5}7 \text{ mol HCl} \div 0.0249 \text{ L HCl} = 0.44\underline{0}0 = 0.440 \text{ mol/L HCl}$$

Copyright © Cengage Learning. All rights reserved.

5.121. The number of moles of carbon dioxide is

$$n = \frac{646\ /760\ \text{atm}\ \times\ 0.1500\ \text{L}}{0.08206\ \text{L} \cdot \text{atm/ K} \cdot \text{mol}\ \times\ 300\ \text{K}} = 0.005179\ \text{mol}$$

The number of moles of molecular acid used is

0.1250 mol/L × 0.04141 L = 0.005176 mol acid

Thus, the acid is H_2SO_4 since 1 mole of H_2SO_4 reacts to form 1 mole of CO_2

5.123. Use Maxwell's distribution to calculate the temperature in kelvins; then convert to °C.

$$T = \frac{u^2 M_m}{3R} = \frac{(0.605 \times 10^3\ \text{m/s})^2\ (17.03 \times 10^{-3}\ \text{kg/mol})}{3\ (8.31\ \text{kg} \cdot \text{m}^2/\text{s}^2 \cdot \text{K} \cdot \text{mol})} = 250.0 = 250.\ \text{K}\ (-23°\text{C})$$

5.125. Calculate the ratio of the root-mean-square (rms) molecular speeds, which is the same as the ratio of the rates of effusion:

$$\frac{u\ [U(235)F_6]}{u\ [U(238)F_6]} = \left(\frac{M_m[U(238)F_6]}{M_m[U(235)F_6]} \right)^{1/2} = \left(\frac{352.04\ \text{g/ mol}}{349.03\ \text{g/ mol}} \right)^{1/2} = 1.004302 = 1.0043$$

5.127. First, calculate the apparent molar masses at each pressure using the ideal gas law. Only the calculation of the apparent molar mass for 0.2500 atm will be shown; the other values will be summarized in a table.

$$n = \frac{PV}{RT} = \frac{(0.2500\ \text{atm})\,(3.1908\ \text{L})}{(0.082057\ \text{L} \cdot \text{atm/K} \cdot \text{mol})\,(273.15\ \text{K})} = 3.55896 \times 10^{-2}\ \text{mol}$$

Apparent molar mass $= \dfrac{1.000\ \text{g}}{3.55896 \times 10^{-2}\ \text{mol}} = 28.098 = 28.10\ \text{g/mol}$

The following table summarizes the apparent molar masses calculated as above for all P's; these data are plotted in the graph below the table.

P (atm)	App. Molar Mass (g/mol)
0.2500	28.10
0.5000	28.14
0.7500	28.19
1.0000	28.26

Copyright © Cengage Learning. All rights reserved.

Extrapolation back to $P = 0$ gives 28.07 g/mol for the molar mass of the unknown gas (CO).

5.129. Use $CO + 1/2 O_2 \rightarrow CO_2$, instead of 2CO. First, find the moles of CO and O_2 by using the ideal gas law.

$$n_{CO} = \frac{PV}{RT} = \frac{(0.500 \text{ atm})(2.00 \text{ L})}{(0.08206 \text{ L} \cdot \text{atm/K} \cdot \text{mol})(300 \text{ K})} = 0.0406\underline{2} \text{ mol}$$

$$n_{O_2} = \frac{PV}{RT} = \frac{(1.00 \text{ atm})(1.00 \text{ L})}{(0.08206 \text{ L} \cdot \text{atm/K} \cdot \text{mol})(300 \text{ K})} = 0.0406\underline{2} \text{ mol}$$

There are equal amounts of CO and O_2, but (from the equation) only half as many moles of O_2 as CO are required for the reaction. Therefore, when 0.04062 mol CO has been consumed, only 0.04062/2 mol O_2 will have been used up. Then 0.04062/2 mol O_2 will remain, and 0.04062 mol CO_2 will have been produced. At the end,

$$n_{CO} = 0 \text{ mol}; \quad n_{O_2} = 0.0202 \text{ mol}; \quad \text{and } n_{CO_2} = 0.04062 \text{ mol}$$

However, the total volume with the valve open is 3.00 L, so the partial pressures of O_2 and CO_2 must be calculated from the ideal gas law for each:

$$\frac{nRT}{V} = \frac{(0.0203 \text{ mol O}_2)(0.08206 \text{ L} \cdot \text{atm/K} \cdot \text{mol})(300 \text{ K})}{3.00 \text{ L}} = 0.166\underline{5}8 = 0.167 \text{ atm O}_2$$

$$\frac{nRT}{V} = \frac{(0.04062 \text{ mol CO}_2)(0.08206 \text{ L} \cdot \text{atm/K} \cdot \text{mol})(300 \text{ K})}{3.00 \text{ L}}$$

$$= 0.333\underline{3}2 = 0.333 \text{ atm CO}_2$$

Copyright © Cengage Learning. All rights reserved.

■ SOLUTIONS TO CUMULATIVE-SKILLS PROBLEMS

5.145.   Assume a 100.0-g sample, giving 85.2 g CH_4 and 14.8 g C_2H_6. Convert each to moles:

$$85.2 \text{ g } CH_4 \times \frac{1 \text{ mol } CH_4}{16.04 \text{ g } CH_4} = 5.3\underline{1}1 \text{ mol } CH_4$$

$$14.8 \text{ g } C_2H_6 \times \frac{1 \text{ mol } CH_4}{16.04 \text{ g } CH_4} = 0.49\underline{2}1 \text{ mol } C_2H_6$$

$$V_{CH_4} = \frac{(5.311 \text{ mol})(0.08206 \text{ L} \cdot \text{atm/K} \cdot \text{mol})(291 \text{ K})}{(771/760) \text{ atm}} = 12\underline{5}.03 \text{ L}$$

$$V_{C_2H_6} = \frac{(0.4921 \text{ mol})(0.08206 \text{ L} \cdot \text{atm/K} \cdot \text{mol})(291 \text{ K})}{(771/760) \text{ atm}} = 11.\underline{5}8 \text{ L}$$

The density is calculated as follows:

$$d = \frac{85.2 \text{ g } CH_4 + 14.8 \text{ g } C_2H_6}{(125.03 + 11.58) \text{ L}} = 0.73\underline{1}9 = 0.732 \text{ g/L}$$

5.147.   First, subtract the height of mercury equivalent to the 25.00 cm (250 mm) of water inside the tube from 771 mmHg to get P_{gas}. Then subtract the vapor pressure of water, 18.7 mmHg, from P_{gas} to get P_{O_2}

$$h_{Hg} = \frac{(h_W)(d_W)}{d_{Hg}} = \frac{250 \text{ mm} \times 0.99987 \text{ g/cm}^3}{13.596 \text{ g/cm}^3} = 18.\underline{3}8 \text{ mmHg}$$

$$P_{gas} = P - P_{25 \text{ cm water}} = 771 \text{ mmHg} - 18.38 \text{ mmHg} = 75\underline{2}.62 \text{ mmHg}$$

$$P_{O_2} = 752.62 \text{ mmHg} - 18.7 \text{ mmHg} = 73\underline{3}.92 \text{ mmHg}$$

$$n = \frac{PV}{RT} = \frac{(733.92/760 \text{ atm})(0.0310 \text{ L})}{(0.08206 \text{ L} \cdot \text{atm/K} \cdot \text{mol})(294 \text{ K})} = 0.00124\underline{0}8 \text{ mol } O_2$$

$$\text{Mass} = (2 \times 0.0012408) \text{ mol } Na_2O_2 \times \frac{77.98 \text{ g } Na_2O_2}{1 \text{ mol } Na_2O_2} = 0.19\underline{3}5 = 0.194 \text{ g } Na_2O_2$$

Copyright © Cengage Learning. All rights reserved.

5.149. First find the moles of CO_2:

$$n = \frac{PV}{RT} = \frac{(785/760 \text{ atm})(1.94 \text{ L})}{(0.08206 \text{ L} \cdot \text{atm/K} \cdot \text{mol})(298 \text{ K})} = 0.08194 \text{ mol CO}$$

Set up one equation in one unknown: x = mol $CaCO_3$; $(0.08194 - x)$ = mol $MgCO_3$.

$$7.85 \text{ g} = (100.1 \text{ g/mol})x + (84.32 \text{ g/mol})(0.08194 - x)$$

$$x = \frac{(7.85 - 6.9092)}{(100.1 - 84.32)} = 0.05962 \text{ mol CaCO}_3$$

$$(0.08194 - x) = 0.02232 \text{ mol MgCO}_3$$

$$CaCO_3 = \frac{0.05962 \text{ mol CaCO}_3 \times 100.1 \text{ g/mol}}{7.85 \text{ g}} \times 100\% = 76.02 = 76\%$$

$$\text{Percent MgCO}_3 = 100.00\% - 76.02\% = 23.98 = 24\%$$

5.151. Write a mass-balance equation to solve for the moles of each gas, using 28.01 g/mol for the molar mass of N_2 and 20.18 g/mol for the molar mass of Ne. Let y equal moles of each gas:

$$28.01 y + 20.18 y = 10.0 \text{ g}$$

$$y = (10.0 \div 48.19) = 0.20751 \text{ mol}$$

Total moles $(n) = 0.41502$ mol (use below)

Use the ideal gas law to calculate the volume, which can then be used to calculate density.

$$\frac{(0.41502 \text{ mol})(0.08206 \text{ L} \cdot \text{atm/K} \cdot \text{mol})(500 \text{ K})}{15.00 \text{ atm}} = 1.1352 \text{ L}$$

$$d = 10.0 \text{ g} \div 1.1352 \text{ L} = 8.808 = 8.81 \text{ g/L}$$

5.153. Rearrange the equation $PM_m = dRT$ to find the quantity RT/M_m. Then plug into the equation for the root-mean-square speed.

$$\frac{RT}{M_m} = \frac{P}{d}$$

$$u = \left(\frac{3RT}{M_m}\right)^{1/2} = \left(\frac{3P}{d}\right)^{1/2} = \left(\frac{3\left(\frac{675}{760}\right) \text{ atm} \times (8.31 \text{ kg} \cdot \text{m}^2/\text{s}^2 \cdot \text{K} \cdot \text{mol})}{(3.00 \times 10^{-3} \text{ kg/L})(0.08206 \text{ L} \cdot \text{atm}/\text{K} \cdot \text{mol})}\right)^{1/2}$$

$$= 2.9990 \times 10^2 = 3.00 \times 10^2 \text{ m/s}$$

Copyright © Cengage Learning. All rights reserved.

CHAPTER 6

Thermochemistry

■ **SOLUTIONS TO EXERCISES**

Note on significant figures: If the final answer to a solution needs to be rounded off, it is given first with one nonsignificant figure, and the last significant figure is underlined. The final answer is then rounded to the correct number of significant figures. In multistep problems, intermediate answers are given with at least one nonsignificant figure; however, only the final answer has been rounded off.

6.1. Substitute into the formula $E_k = 1/2\, mv^2$ using SI units:

$$E_k = 1/2 \times 9.11 \times 10^{-31} \text{ kg} \times (5.0 \times 10^6 \text{ m/s})^2 = 1.\underline{1}3 \times 10^{-17} = 1.1 \times 10^{-17} \text{ J}$$

$$1.13 \times 10^{-17} \text{ J} \times \frac{1 \text{ cal}}{4.184 \text{ J}} = 2.\underline{7}2 \times 10^{-18} = 2.7 \times 10^{-18} \text{ cal}$$

6.2. Heat is evolved; therefore, the reaction is exothermic. The value of q is -1170 kJ.

6.3. The thermochemical equation is

$$2N_2H_4(l) + N_2O_4(l) \rightarrow 3N_2(g) + 4H_2O(g); \ \Delta H = -1049 \text{ kJ}$$

ΔH equals -1049 kJ for 1 mol N_2H_4 and for 2 mol N_2H_4.

6.4.

a. $N_2H_4(l) + 1/2N_2O_4(l) \rightarrow 3/2N_2(g) + 2H_2O(g); \ \Delta H = -524.5 \text{ kJ}$

b. $4H_2O(g) + 3N_2(g) \rightarrow 2N_2H_4(l) + N_2O_4(l); \ \Delta H = 1049 \text{ kJ}$

6.5. The reaction is

$$2N_2H_4(l) + N_2O_4(l) \rightarrow 3N_2(g) + 4H_2O(g); \ \Delta H = -1049 \text{ kJ}$$

$$10.0 \text{ g } N_2H_4 \times \frac{1 \text{ mol } N_2H_4}{32.02 \text{ g}} \times \frac{1 \text{ mol } N_2O_4}{2 \text{ mol } N_2H_4} \times \frac{-1049 \text{ kJ}}{1 \text{ mol } N_2O_4} = -16\underline{3}.80 = -164 \text{ kJ}$$

Copyright © Cengage Learning. All rights reserved.

6.6. Substitute into the equation $q = s \times m \times \Delta t$ to obtain the heat transferred. The temperature change is

$$\Delta t = t_f - t_i = 100.0°C - 20.0°C = 80.0°C$$

Therefore,

$$q = s \times m \; \Delta t = 0.449 J/(g \cdot °C) \times 5.00 \text{ g} \times 80.0°C = 1.796 \times 10^2 = 1.80 \times 10^2 \text{ J}$$

6.7. The total mass of the solution is obtained by adding the volumes together and by using the density of water (1.000 g/mL). This gives $33 + 42 = 75$ mL, or 75 g. The heat absorbed by the solution is

$$q = s \times m \times \Delta t = 4.184 \text{ J/(g} \cdot °C) \times 75 \text{ g} \times (31.8°C - 25.0°C) = 2133.8 \text{ J}$$

The heat released by the reaction, q_{rxn}, is equal to the negative of this value, or -2133.8 J. To obtain the enthalpy change for the reaction, you need to calculate the moles of HCl that reacted. This is

$$\text{Mol HCl} = 1.20 \text{ mol/L} \times 0.033 \text{ L} = 0.0396 \text{ mol}$$

The enthalpy change for the reaction can now be calculated.

$$\Delta H = \frac{-2133.8 \text{ J}}{0.0396 \text{ mol}} = -53884 \text{ J/mol} = -54 \text{ kJ/mol}$$

Expressing this result as a thermochemical equation, you have

$$HCl(aq) + NaOH(aq) \rightarrow NaCl(aq) + H_2O(l); \quad \Delta H = -54 \text{ kJ}$$

6.8. Use Hess's law to find ΔH for $4Al(s) + 3MnO_2(s) \rightarrow 2Al_2O_3(s) + 3Mn(s)$ from the following data for equations 1 and 2:

$$2Al(s) + 3/2 O_2(g) \rightarrow Al_2O_3(s); \quad \Delta H = -1676 \text{ kJ} \quad (1)$$

$$Mn(s) + O_2(g) \rightarrow MnO_2(s); \quad \Delta H = -520 \text{ kJ} \quad (2)$$

If you take equation 1 and multiply it by 2, you obtain

$$4Al(s) + 3O_2(g) \rightarrow 2Al_2O_3(s); \quad \Delta H = 2 \times (-1676 \text{ kJ}) = -3352 \text{ kJ}$$

Since the desired reaction has three MnO_2 on the left side, reverse equation 2 and multiply it by 3. The result is

$$3MnO_2(s) \rightarrow 3Mn(s) + 3O_2(g) \quad \Delta H = -3 \times (-520 \text{ kJ}) = 1560 \text{ kJ}$$

If you add the two equations and corresponding enthalpy changes, you obtain the enthalpy change of the desired equation.

$4Al(s) + 3O_2(g)$	$\rightarrow$	$2Al_2O_3(s)$	$\Delta H = -3352 \text{ kJ}$
$3MnO_2(s)$	$\rightarrow$	$3Mn(s) + 3O_2(g)$	$\Delta H = 1560 \text{ kJ}$
$4Al(s) + 3MnO_2(s)$	$\rightarrow$	$2Al_2O_3(s) + 3Mn(s)$	$\Delta H = -1792 \text{ kJ}$

Copyright © Cengage Learning. All rights reserved.

6.9. The vaporization process, with the $\Delta H°_f$ values given below the substances, is

$$H_2O(l) \rightarrow H_2O(g)$$

-285.8   -241.8   (kJ)

The calculation is

$$\Delta H°_{vap} = \Sigma n\,\Delta H°_f\,(products) - \Sigma m\,\Delta H°_f\,(reactants) = \Delta H°_f\,[H_2O(g)] - \Delta H°_f\,[H_2O(l)]$$

$$= (-241.8\ kJ) - (-285.8\ kJ) = 44.0\ kJ$$

6.10. The reaction, with the $\Delta H°_f$ values given below the substances, is

$$3NO_2(g) \quad + \quad H_2O(l) \quad \rightarrow \quad 2HNO_3(aq) \quad + \quad NO(g)$$

33.10   -285.8   -207.4   90.29   (kJ)

The calculation is

$$\Delta H°_{rxn} = \Sigma n\,\Delta H°_f\,(products) - \Sigma m\,\Delta H°_f\,(reactants)$$

$$= [2\ \Delta H°_f\ (HNO_3) + \Delta H°_f\ (NO)] - [3\ \Delta H°_f\ (NO_2) + \Delta H°_f\ (H_2O)]$$

$$= [2(-207.4) + (90.29)]\ kJ - [3(33.10) + (-285.8)]\ kJ = -138.\underline{0}1 = -138.0\ kJ$$

6.11. The net chemical reaction, with the $\Delta H°_f$ values given below the substances, is

$$2\,NH_4{}^+(aq) \quad + \quad 2OH^-(aq) \quad \rightarrow \quad 2NH_3(g) \quad + \quad 2H_2O(l)$$

2(-132.5)   2(-230.0)   2(-45.90)   2(-285.8)   (kJ)

The calculation is

$$\Delta H°_{rxn} = [2\ \Delta H°_f\ (NH_3) + 2\ \Delta H°_f\ (H_2O)] - [2\ \Delta H°_f\ (NH_4{}^+) + 2\ \Delta H°_f\ (OH^-)]$$

$$= [2(-45.90) + 2(-285.8)] - [2(-132.5) + 2(-230.0)] = 61.\underline{6}0 = 61.6\ kJ$$

■ ANSWERS TO SELF-ASSESSMENT AND REVIEW QUESTIONS

6.1. Energy is the potential or capacity to move matter. Kinetic energy is the energy associated with an object by virtue of its motion. Potential energy is the energy an object has by virtue of its position in a field of force. Internal energy is the sum of the kinetic and potential energies of the particles making up a substance.

6.2. In terms of SI base units, a joule is $kg{\cdot}m^2/s^2$.

6.3. Originally, a calorie was defined as the amount of energy required to raise the temperature of one gram of water by one degree Celsius. At present, the calorie is defined as 4.184 J.

Copyright © Cengage Learning. All rights reserved.

6.4. At either of the two highest points above the earth in a pendulum's cycle, the energy of the pendulum is all potential energy and is equal to the product mgh (m = mass of pendulum, g = constant acceleration of gravity, and h = height of pendulum). As the pendulum moves downward, its potential energy decreases from mgh to near zero, depending on how close it comes to the earth's surface. During the downward motion, its potential energy is converted to kinetic energy. When it reaches the lowest point (middle) of its cycle, the pendulum has its maximum kinetic energy and minimum potential energy. As it rises above the lowest point, its kinetic energy begins to be converted to potential energy. When it reaches the other high point in its cycle, the energy of the pendulum is again all potential energy. By the law of conservation of energy, this energy cannot be lost, only converted to other forms. At rest, the energy of the pendulum has been transferred to the surroundings in the form of heat.

6.5. As the heat flows into the gas, the gas molecules gain energy and move at a greater average speed. The internal energy of the gas increases.

6.6. An exothermic reaction is a chemical reaction or a physical change in which heat is evolved (q is negative). For example, burning one mole of methane, $CH_4(g)$, yields carbon dioxide, water, and 890 kJ of heat. An endothermic reaction is a chemical reaction or physical change in which heat is absorbed (q is positive). For example, the reaction of one mole of barium hydroxide with ammonium nitrate absorbs 170.8 kJ of heat in order to form ammonia, water, and barium nitrate.

6.7. Changes in internal energy depend only on the initial and final states of the system, which are determined by variables such as temperature and pressure. Such changes do not depend on any previous history of the system.

6.8. The enthalpy change equals the heat of reaction at constant pressure.

6.9. At constant pressure, the enthalpy change is positive (the enthalpy increases) for an endothermic reaction.

6.10. It is important to give the states when writing an equation for ΔH because ΔH depends on the states of all reactants and products. If any state changes, ΔH changes.

6.11. When the equation for the reaction is doubled, the enthalpy is also doubled. When the equation is reversed, the sign of ΔH is also reversed.

6.12. First, convert the 10.0 g of water to moles of water, using its molar mass (18.02 g/mol). Next, using the equation, multiply the moles of water by the appropriate mole ratio (1 mol CH_4 / 2 mol H_2O). Finally, multiply the moles of CH_4 by the heat of the reaction (-890.3 kJ/mol CH_4).

Copyright © Cengage Learning. All rights reserved.

6.13. The heat capacity (C) of a substance is the quantity of heat needed to raise the temperature of the sample of substance one degree Celsius (or one kelvin). The specific heat of a substance is the quantity of heat required to raise the temperature of one gram of a substance by one degree Celsius (or one kelvin) at constant pressure.

6.14. A simple calorimeter consists of an insulated container (for example, a pair of styrene coffee cups as in Figure 6.12) with a thermometer. The heat of the reaction is obtained by conducting the reaction in the calorimeter. The temperature of the mixture is measured before and after the reaction, and since this is a constant-pressure process, the heat is directly related to the enthalpy change, ΔH.

6.15. Hess's law states that for a chemical equation that can be written as the sum of two or more steps, the enthalpy change for the overall equation is the sum of the enthalpy changes for the individual steps. In other words, no matter how you go from reactants to products, the enthalpy change for the overall chemical change is the same. This is because enthalpy is a state function.

6.16. No, you can still obtain the enthalpy for the desired reaction. You will need to come up with a system of reactions that can be combined to give the desired reaction and will need to know the enthalpy changes for each of the steps. Then, using Hess's law, you can obtain the enthalpy change for the reaction under study.

6.17. The thermodynamic standard state consists of the standard thermodynamic conditions chosen for substances when listing or comparing thermodynamic data: one atm pressure and the specified temperature (usually 25°C).

6.18. The reference form of an element is the most stable form (physical state and allotrope) of the element under standard thermodynamic conditions. The standard enthalpy of formation of an element in its reference form is zero.

6.19. The standard enthalpy of formation of a substance, ΔH°_f, is the enthalpy change for the formation of one mole of the substance in its standard state from its elements in their reference form and in their standard states.

6.20. The equation for the formation of $H_2S(g)$ is

$$H_2(g) + 1/8 S_8(\text{rhombic}) \rightarrow H_2S(g)$$

6.21. The reaction of $C(g) + 4H(g) \rightarrow CH_4(g)$ is not an appropriate equation for calculating the ΔH°_f of methane because the most stable form of each element is not used. Both $H_2(g)$ and $C(\text{graphite})$ should be used instead of $H(g)$ and $C(g)$, respectively.

Copyright © Cengage Learning. All rights reserved.

6.22. A fuel is any substance that is burned or similarly reacted to provide heat and other forms of energy. The fossil fuels are petroleum (oil), gas, and coal. They were formed millions of years ago when aquatic plants and animals were buried and compressed by layers of sediment at the bottoms of swamps and seas. Over time, this organic matter was converted by bacterial decay and pressure to fossil fuels.

6.23. One of the ways of converting coal to methane involves the water-gas reaction.

$$C(s) + H_2O(g) \rightarrow CO(g) + H_2(g)$$

In this reaction, steam is passed over hot coal. This mixture is then reacted over a catalyst to give methane.

$$CO(g) + 3H_2(g) \rightarrow CH_4(g) + H_2O(g)$$

6.24. Some possible rocket fuel/oxidizer combinations are H_2/O_2 and hydrazine/dinitrogen tetroxide. The chemical equations for their reactions are

$$H_2(g) + 1/2O_2(g) \rightarrow H_2O(g); \quad \Delta H^\circ = -242 \text{ kJ}$$
$$2N_2H_4(l) + N_2O_4(l) \rightarrow 3N_2(g) + 4H_2O(g); \quad \Delta H^\circ = -1049 \text{ kJ}$$

6.25. The answer is d, burning enough butane to produce one mole of water.

6.26. The answer is b, 40.°C.

6.27. The answer is c, endothermic, and the temperature of the resulting solution falls.

6.28. The answer is c, the water with the mercury will be the hottest.

■ SOLUTIONS TO PRACTICE PROBLEMS

Note on significant figures: If the final answer to a solution needs to be rounded off, it is given first with one nonsignificant figure, and the last significant figure is underlined. The final answer is then rounded to the correct number of significant figures. In multistep problems, intermediate answers are given with at least one nonsignificant figure; however, only the final answer has been rounded off.

6.41. The heat released, in kilocalories, is

$$-445.1 \text{ kJ} \times \frac{1000 \text{ J}}{1 \text{ kJ}} \times \frac{1 \text{ cal}}{4.184 \text{ J}} \times \frac{1 \text{ kcal}}{1000 \text{ cal}} = -106.\underline{3}8 = -106.4 \text{ kcal}$$

Copyright © Cengage Learning. All rights reserved.

6.43. The kinetic energy, in joules, is

$$E_k = 1/2 \times 4.85 \times 10^3 \text{ lb} \times \frac{0.4536 \text{ kg}}{1 \text{ lb}} \times \left[\frac{57 \text{ mi}}{1 \text{ h}}\right]^2 \times \left[\frac{1609 \text{ m}}{1 \text{ mi}}\right]^2 \times \left[\frac{1 \text{ h}}{3600 \text{ s}}\right]^2$$

$$= 7.\underline{1}3 \times 10^5 = 7.1 \times 10^5 \text{ J}$$

The kinetic energy, in calories, is

$$E_k = 7.\underline{1}3 \times 10^5 \text{ J} \times \frac{1 \text{ cal}}{4.184 \text{ J}} = 1.\underline{7}0 \times 10^5 = 1.7 \times 10^5 \text{ cal}$$

6.45. To insert the mass of one molecule of ClO_2 in the formula, multiply the molar mass by the reciprocal of Avogadro's number. The kinetic energy in joules is

$$E_k = 1/2 \times \frac{67.45 \text{ g}}{1 \text{ mol}} \times \frac{1 \text{ mol}}{6.022 \times 10^{23} \text{ molec.}} \times \frac{1 \text{ kg}}{1000 \text{ g}} \times \left[\frac{306 \text{ m}}{1 \text{ s}}\right]^2$$

$$= 5.2\underline{4}3 \times 10^{-21} = 5.24 \times 10^{-21} \text{ J/molec.}$$

6.47. Endothermic reactions absorb heat, so the sign of q will be positive because energy must be gained by the system from the surroundings. The flask will feel cold to the touch.

6.49. The gain of 66.2 kJ of heat per 2 mol NO_2 means the reaction is endothermic. Because energy is gained by the system from the surroundings, q is positive and is +66.2 kJ for 2 mol NO_2 reacting.

6.51. The reaction of Fe(s) with HCl must yield H_2 and $FeCl_2$. To balance the hydrogen, 2HCl must be written as a reactant:

$$Fe(s) + 2HCl(aq) \rightarrow FeCl_2(aq) + H_2(g)$$

To write a thermochemical equation, the sign of ΔH must be negative because heat is evolved:

$$Fe(s) + 2HCl(aq) \rightarrow FeCl_2(aq) + H_2(g); \quad \Delta H = -89.1 \text{ kJ}$$

6.53. The first equation is

$$P_4(s) + 5O_2(g) \rightarrow P_4O_{10}(s); \quad \Delta H = -3010 \text{ kJ}$$

The second equation is

$$P_4O_{10}(s) \rightarrow P_4(s) + 5O_2(g); \quad \Delta H = ?$$

The second equation has been obtained by reversing the first equation. Therefore, to obtain ΔH for the second equation, ΔH for the first equation must be reversed in sign: $-(-3010) = +3010$ kJ.

Copyright © Cengage Learning. All rights reserved.

6.55. The first equation is

$$1/4P_4O_{10}(s) + 3/2H_2O(l) \rightarrow H_3PO_4(aq); \quad \Delta H = -96.2 \text{ kJ}$$

The second equation is

$$P_4O_{10}(s) + 6H_2O(l) \rightarrow 4H_3PO_4(aq); \quad \Delta H = ?$$

The second equation has been obtained from the first by multiplying each coefficient by 4. Therefore, to obtain the ΔH for the second equation, the ΔH for the first equation must be multiplied by 4; that is, $-96.2 \times 4 = -38\underline{4}.8 = 385 \text{ kJ}$

6.57. Because nitric oxide is written as NO in the equation, the molar mass of NO equals 30.01 g per mol NO. From the equation, 2 mol NO evolve 114 kJ heat. Divide the 114 kJ by the 2 mol NO and by the 30.01 g/mol NO to obtain the amount of heat evolved per gram of NO:

$$\frac{-114 \text{ kJ}}{2 \text{ mol NO}} \times \frac{1 \text{ mol NO}}{30.01 \text{ g NO}} = 1.8\underline{9}9 = \frac{-1.90 \text{ kJ}}{\text{g NO}}$$

6.59. The molar mass of ammonia is 17.03 g/mol. From the equation, 4 mol NH_3 evolve 1267 kJ of heat. Divide 35.8 g NH_3 by its molar mass and the 4 mol NH_3 in the equation to obtain the amount of heat evolved:

$$35.8 \text{ g NH}_3 \times \frac{1 \text{ mol NH}_3}{17.03 \text{ g NH}_3} \times \frac{-1267 \text{ kJ}}{4 \text{ mol NH}_3} = -6.6\underline{5}8 \times 10^2 = -6.66 \times 10^2 \text{ kJ}$$

6.61. The molar mass of C_3H_8 is 44.06 g/mol. From the equation, 1 mol C_3H_8 evolves 2043 kJ heat. This gives

$$-369 \text{ kJ} \times \frac{1 \text{ mol C}_3\text{H}_8}{-2043 \text{ kJ}} \times \frac{44.06 \text{ g C}_3\text{H}_8}{1 \text{ mol C}_3\text{H}_8} = 7.9\underline{5}7 = 7.96 \text{ g C}_3\text{H}_8$$

6.63. Multiply the 180 g (0.180 kg) of water by the specific heat of 4.18 J/(g•°C) and by Δt to obtain heat in joules:

$$180 \text{ g} \times (96°C - 19°C) \times \frac{4.18 \text{ J}}{1 \text{ g} \bullet °C} = 5\underline{7}934 = 5.8 \times 10^4 \text{ J}$$

6.65. Use the 2.26×10^3 J/g (2.26 kJ/g) heat of vaporization to calculate the heat of condensation. Then use it to calculate Δt, the temperature change.

$$\text{Heat of condensation} = \frac{2.26 \times 10^3 \text{ J}}{1 \text{ g}} \times 168 \text{ g} = 3.7\underline{9}68 \times 10^5 \text{ J}$$

$$\text{Temperature change} = \Delta t = \frac{3.7968 \times 10^5 \text{ J}}{6.44 \times 10^4 \text{ g}} \times \frac{1 \text{ g} \bullet °C}{1.015 \text{ J}} = 5.8\underline{0}85 = 5.81°C$$

Copyright © Cengage Learning. All rights reserved.

6.67. The enthalpy change for the reaction is equal in magnitude and opposite in sign to the heat-energy
change occurring from the cooling of the solution and calorimeter.

$$q_{calorimeter} = (1071 \text{ J/°C})(21.56°C - 25.00°C) = -3684.2 \text{ J}$$

Thus, 15.3 g $NaNO_3$ is equivalent to -3684.2 J heat energy. The amount of heat absorbed by
1.000 mol $NaNO_3$ is calculated from $+3684.2$ J (opposite sign):

$$1.000 \text{ mol } NaNO_3 \text{ x } \frac{85.00 \text{ g } NaNO_3}{1 \text{ mol } NaNO_3} \text{ x } \frac{3684.2 \text{ J}}{15.3 \text{ g } NaNO_3} = 2.0468 \text{ x } 10^4 \text{ J}$$

Thus, the enthalpy change, ΔH, for the reaction is 2.05 x 10^4 J, or 20.5 kJ, per mol $NaNO_3$.

6.69. The energy change for the reaction is equal in magnitude and opposite in sign to the heat energy
produced from the warming of the solution and the calorimeter.

$$q_{calorimeter} = (9.63 \text{ kJ/°C})(33.73 - 25.00°C) = +84.069 \text{ kJ}$$

Thus, 2.84 g C_2H_5OH is equivalent to 84.069 kJ heat energy. The amount of heat released by
1.000 mol C_2H_5OH is calculated from -84.069 kJ (opposite sign):

$$1.00 \text{ mol } C_2H_5OH \text{ x } \frac{46.07 \text{ g } C_2H_5OH}{1 \text{ mol } C_2H_5OH} \text{ x } \frac{-84.069 \text{ kJ}}{2.84 \text{ g } C_2H_5OH} = -1363.75 \text{ kJ}$$

Thus, the enthalpy change, ΔH, for the reaction is -1.36 x 10^3 kJ/mol ethanol.

6.71. Using the equations in the data, reverse the direction of the first reaction, and reverse the sign of
its ΔH. Then multiply the second equation by 2, multiply its ΔH by 2, and add. Setup:

$N_2(g)$	+	$2H_2O(l)$	→	$N_2H_4(l)$ + $O_2(g)$;	ΔH =	(-622.2 kJ) x (-1)
$2H_2(g)$	+	$O_2(g)$	→	$2H_2O(l)$;	ΔH =	(-285.8 kJ) x (2)
$N_2(g)$	+	$2H_2(g)$	→	$N_2H_4(l)$;	ΔH =	50.6 kJ

6.73. Using the equations in the data, multiply the second equation by 2, and reverse its direction; do
the same to its ΔH. Then multiply the first equation by 2 and its ΔH by 2. Finally, multiply the
third equation by 3 and its ΔH by 3. Then add. Setup:

$4NH_3(g)$	→ $2N_2(g)$ + $6H_2(g)$;	ΔH =	(-91.8 kJ) x (-2)
$2N_2(g) + 2O_2(g)$	→ $4NO(g)$;	ΔH =	(180.6 kJ) x (2)
$6H_2(g) + 3O_2(g)$	→ $6H_2O(g)$;	ΔH =	(-483.7 kJ) x (3)
$4NH_3(g)$ + $5O_2(g)$	→ $4NO(g)$ + $6H_2O(g)$;	ΔH =	-906.3 kJ

6.75. After reversing the second equation in the data, add all the equations. Setup:

$C_2H_4(g) + 3O_2(g)$	→	$2CO_2(g) + 2H_2O(l)$;	$\Delta H = (-1411 \text{ kJ})$
$2CO_2(g) + 3H_2O(l)$	→	$C_2H_6(g) + 7/2O_2(g)$;	$\Delta H = (-1560)$ x (-1)
$H_2(g) + 1/2O_2(g)$	→	$H_2O(l)$;	$\Delta H = (-286 \text{ kJ})$
$C_2H_4(g) + H_2(g)$	→	$C_2H_6(g)$;	$\Delta H = -137$ kJ

Copyright © Cengage Learning. All rights reserved.

6.77. Write the $\Delta H°$ values (Appendix C) underneath each compound in the balanced equation:

$$C_2H_5OH(l) \;\rightarrow\; C_2H_5OH(g)$$
$$-277.7 \qquad\qquad -235.4 \qquad \text{(kJ)}$$

$\Delta H°_{vap} = [\,\Delta H°_f(C_2H_5OH(g))\,] - [\,\Delta H°_f(C_2H_5OH(l))\,] = [-235.4] - [-277.7] = +42.3 \text{ kJ}$

6.79. Write the $\Delta H°$ values (Table 6.2) underneath each compound in the balanced equation:

$$2H_2S(g) \;+\; 3O_2(g) \;\rightarrow\; 2H_2O(l) \;+\; 2SO_2(g)$$
$$2(-20.50) \qquad 3(0) \qquad\qquad 2(-285.8) \qquad 2(-296.8) \;\;\text{(kJ)}$$

$\Delta H° = \Sigma n\Delta H°_f(\text{products}) - \Sigma m\Delta H°_f(\text{reactants})$
$\quad = [2(-285.8) + 2(-296.8)] - [2(-20.50) + 3(0)] \text{ kJ} = -1124.\underline{2}0 = -1124.2 \text{ kJ}$

6.81. Write the $\Delta H°$ values (Appendix C) underneath each compound in the balanced equation:

$$Fe_2O_3(s) \;+\; 3CO(g) \;\rightarrow\; 2Fe(s) \;+\; 3CO_2(g)$$
$$-825.5 \qquad 3(-110.5) \qquad\quad 2(0) \qquad 3(-393.5) \;\;\text{(kJ)}$$

$\Delta H° = \Sigma n\Delta H°_f(\text{products}) - \Sigma m\Delta H°_f(\text{reactants})$
$\quad = [2(0) + 3(-393.5)] - [(-825.5) + 3(-110.5)] = -23.5 \text{ kJ}$

6.83. Write the $\Delta H°$ values (Table 6.2) underneath each compound in the balanced equation:

$$HCl(g) \;\rightarrow\; H^+(aq) \qquad Cl^-(aq)$$
$$-92.31 \qquad\quad 0 \qquad\qquad -167.2 \;\text{(kJ)}$$

$\Delta H° = \Sigma n\Delta H°_f(\text{products}) - \Sigma m\Delta H°_f(\text{reactants})$
$\quad = [(0) + (-167.2)] - [-92.31] = -74.\underline{8}9 = -74.9 \text{ kJ}$

6.85. Calculate the molar heat of formation from the equation with the $\Delta H°$ values below each substance; then convert to the heat for 10.0 g of $MgCO_3$ using the molar mass of 84.3.

$$MgCO_3(s) \;\rightarrow\; MgO(s) \;+\; CO_2(g)$$
$$-1111.7 \qquad\quad -601.2 \qquad\quad -393.5 \;\;\text{(kJ)}$$

$\Delta H° = \Sigma n\Delta H°_f(\text{products}) - \Sigma m\Delta H°_f(\text{reactants})$
$\Delta H° = -601.2 \text{ kJ} + (-393.5 \text{ kJ}) - (-1111.7 \text{ kJ}) = 11\underline{7}.0 \text{ kJ}$

$$\text{Heat} = 10.0 \text{ g} \times \frac{1 \text{ mol}}{84.3 \text{ g}} \times \frac{117.0 \text{ kJ}}{\text{mol}} = 13.\underline{8}7 = 13.9 \text{ kJ}$$

Copyright © Cengage Learning. All rights reserved.

■ SOLUTIONS TO GENERAL PROBLEMS

6.87. The SI units of force must be kg•m/s^2 (= newton, N) to be consistent with the joule, the SI unit of energy:

$$\frac{kg \bullet m}{s^2} \ x \ m \ = \ \frac{kg \bullet m^2}{s^2} \ = \ joule, \ J$$

6.89. Using Table 1.5 and 4.184 J/cal, convert the 686 Btu/lb to J/g:

$$\frac{686 \ Btu}{1 \ lb} \ x \ \frac{252 \ cal}{1 \ Btu} \ x \ \frac{4.184 \ J}{1 \ cal} \ x \ \frac{1 \ lb}{0.4536 \ kg} \ x \ \frac{1 \ kg}{10^3 \ g}$$

$$= \ 1.5\underline{9}4 \ x \ 10^3 \ = \ 1.59 \ x \ 10^3 \ J/g$$

6.91. Substitute into the equation $E_p = mgh$, and convert to SI units.

$$E_p \ = \ 1.00 \ lb \ x \ \frac{9.807 \ m}{s^2} \ x \ 167 \ ft \ x \ \frac{0.4536 \ kg}{1 \ lb} \ x \ \frac{0.9144 \ m}{3 \ ft}$$

$$= \ \frac{22\underline{6}.433 \ kg \bullet m^2}{s^2} \ = \ 226 \ J$$

At the bottom, all the potential energy is converted to kinetic energy, so $E_k = 226.433$ kg•m^2/s^2. Because $E_k = 1/2mv^2$, solve for v, the speed (velocity):

$$v \ = \ \sqrt{\frac{E_k}{1/2 \ x \ m}} \ = \ \sqrt{\frac{226.433 \ kg \bullet m^2/s^2}{1/2 \ x \ 1.00 \ lb \ x \ 0.4536 \ kg/lb}} \ = \ 31.\underline{6}0 \ = \ 31.6 \ m/s$$

6.93. The equation is

$$CaCO_3(s) \ \rightarrow \ CaO(s) \ + \ CO_2(g); \ \ \Delta H \ = \ 177.9 \ kJ$$

Use the molar mass of 100.08 g/mol to convert the heat per mole to heat per 27.3 g.

$$21.3 \ g \ CaCO_3 \ x \ \frac{1 \ mol \ CaCO_3}{100.08 \ g \ CaCO_3} \ x \ \frac{177.9 \ kJ}{1 \ mol \ CaCO_3} \ = \ 37.\underline{8}6 \ = \ 37.9 \ kJ$$

6.95. The equation is

$$2HCHO_2(l) \ + \ O_2(g) \ \rightarrow \ 2CO_2(g) \ + \ 2H_2O(l)$$

Use the molar mass of 46.03 g/mol to convert −30.3 kJ/5.48 g to ΔH per mole of acid.

$$\frac{-30.3 \ kJ}{5.48 \ g \ HCHO_2} \ x \ \frac{46.03 \ g \ HCHO_2}{1 \ mol \ HCHO_2} \ = \ -25\underline{4}.508 \ = \ -255 \ kJ/mol$$

Copyright © Cengage Learning. All rights reserved.

6.97. The heat gained by the water at the lower temperature equals the heat lost by the water at the higher temperature. Each heat term is $s \times m \times \Delta t$. This gives

$$(4.184 \text{ J/g} \cdot °C)(54.9 \text{ g})(t_f - 31.5°C) = (4.184 \text{ J/g} \cdot °C)(21.0 \text{ g})(52.7°C - t_f)$$

The specific heat and the units can be canceled from both sides to give

$$(54.9)(t_f - 31.5°C) = (21.0)(52.7°C - t_f)$$

After rearranging, you get $75.9 \, t_f = 2836.05$. This gives $t_f = 37.\underline{3}6 = 37.4°C$.

6.99. Divide the 235 J heat by the mass of lead and the Δt to obtain the specific heat.

$$\text{Specific heat} = \frac{235 \text{ J}}{121.6 \text{ g } (35.5°C - 20.4°C)} = 0.127\underline{9}8 = \frac{0.128 \text{ J}}{\text{g} \cdot °C}$$

6.101. The energy used to heat the Zn comes from cooling the water. Calculate q for water:

$$q_{wat} = \text{specific heat} \times \text{mass} \times \Delta t$$

$$q_{wat} = \frac{4.18 \text{ J}}{\text{g} \cdot °C} \times 50.0 \text{ g} \times (96.68°C - 100.00°C) = -69\underline{3}.88 \text{ J}$$

The sign of q for the Zn is the reverse of the sign of q for water because the Zn is absorbing heat:

$$q_{met} = -(q_{wat}) = -(-693.88) = 69\underline{3}.88 \text{ J}$$

$$\text{Specific heat} = \frac{693.88 \text{ J}}{25.3 \text{ g } (96.68°C - 25.00°C)} = 0.38\underline{2}6 = \frac{0.383 \text{ J}}{\text{g} \cdot °C}$$

6.103. First, multiply the molarities by the volumes, in liters, to get the moles of NaOH and the moles of HCl, and thus determine the limiting reactant.

$$\text{Mol NaOH} = M \times V = 0.996 \, M \times 0.0141 \text{ L} = 0.0140\underline{4} \text{ mol}$$

$$\text{Mol HCl} = M \times V = 0.905 \, M \times 0.0323 \text{ L} = 0.0292\underline{3} \text{ mol}$$

Therefore, NaOH is the limiting reactant. The total volume of the system is 14.1 mL + 32.3 mL = 46.4 mL. Since the density of water is 1.00 g/mL, the total mass of the system is 46.4 g. Next, set the heat released by the reaction (mol × enthalpy of reaction) equal to the heat absorbed by the water ($s \times m \times \Delta t$). This gives

$$(0.01404 \text{ mol})(55.8 \times 10^3 \text{ J/mol}) = (4.184 \text{ J/g} \cdot °C)(46.4 \text{ g})(t_f - 21.6°C)$$

After dividing, this gives $t_f - 21.6°C = 4.035°C$, or $t_f = 25.\underline{6}3 = 25.6°C$.

6.105. Use Δt and the heat capacity of 547 J/°C to calculate q:

$$q = C\Delta t = (547 \text{ J/°C})(36.66 - 25.00)°C = 6.3\underline{7}8 \times 10^3 \text{ J } (6.3\underline{7}8 \text{ kJ})$$

Energy is released in the solution process in raising the temperature, so ΔH is negative:

$$\Delta H = \frac{-6.378 \text{ kJ}}{6.48 \text{ g LiOH}} \times \frac{23.95 \text{ g LiOH}}{1 \text{ mol LiOH}} = -23.\underline{5}7 = -23.6 \text{ kJ/mol}$$

Copyright © Cengage Learning. All rights reserved.

6.107. Use Δt and the heat capacity of 13.43 kJ/°C to calculate q:

$$q = C\Delta t = (13.43 \text{ kJ/°C})(35.84 - 25.00)\text{°C} = 145.\underline{5}81 \text{ kJ}$$

As in the previous two problems, the sign of ΔH must be reversed, making the heat negative:

$$\Delta H = \frac{-145.581 \text{ kJ}}{10.00 \text{ g HC}_2\text{H}_3\text{O}_2} \times \frac{60.05 \text{ g HC}_2\text{H}_3\text{O}_2}{1 \text{ mol HC}_2\text{H}_3\text{O}_2} = -874.\underline{2}1 = -874.2 \text{ kJ/mol}$$

6.109. Using the equations in the data, reverse the direction of the first reaction, and reverse the sign of its ΔH. Then add the second and third equations and their ΔH's.

$H_2O(g) + SO_2(g)$	$\rightarrow$	$H_2S(g) + 3/2 O_2(g)$;	$\Delta H = (-518 \text{ kJ}) \times (-1)$
$H_2(g) + 1/2 O_2(g)$	$\rightarrow$	$H_2O(g)$;	$\Delta H = (-242 \text{ kJ})$
$1/8 S_8(\text{rh.}) + O_2(g)$	$\rightarrow$	$SO_2(g)$;	$\Delta H = (-297 \text{ kJ})$
$H_2(g) + 1/8 S_8(\text{rh.})$	$\rightarrow$	$H_2S(g)$;	$\Delta H = -21 \text{ kJ}$

6.111. Write the $\Delta H°$ values (Table 6.2) underneath each compound in the balanced equation.

$$CH_4(g) + H_2O(g) \rightarrow CO(g) + 3H_2(g)$$

$$-74.9 \qquad -241.8 \qquad -110.5 \qquad 3(0) \text{ (kJ)}$$

$$\Delta H° = [-110.5 + 3(0)] - [(-74.87) + (-241.8)] = 206.\underline{1}7 = 206.2 \text{ kJ}$$

6.113. Write the $\Delta H°$ values (Table 6.2) underneath each compound in the balanced equation. The $\Delta H_f°$ of -635 kJ/mol CaO is given in the problem.

$$CaCO_3(s) \rightarrow CaO(s) + CO_2(g)$$

$$-1206.9 \qquad -635 \qquad -393.5 \text{ (kJ)}$$

$$\Delta H° = [(-635) + (-393.5)] - [-1206.9] = 17\underline{8}.4 = 178 \text{ kJ}$$

6.115. Calculate the molar heat of reaction from the equation with the $\Delta H°$ values below each substance; then convert to the heat for the reaction at 25°C.

$$2H_2(g) + O_2(g) \rightarrow 2H_2O(l)$$

$$0.0 \text{ kJ} \qquad 0.0 \text{ kJ} \qquad -285.8 \text{ kJ}$$

$$\Delta H° = 2 \times (-285.8 \text{ kJ}) - 0 - 0 = -571.6 \text{ kJ}$$

The moles of oxygen in 2.000 L with a density of 1.11 g/L is

$$2.000 \text{ L O}_2 \times \frac{1.11 \text{ g O}_2}{1 \text{ L O}_2} \times \frac{1 \text{ mol O}_2}{32.0 \text{ g O}_2} = 0.069\underline{3}7 \text{ mol O}_2$$

The heat of reaction from 0.06937 mol O_2 is

Copyright © Cengage Learning. All rights reserved.

$$0.69\underline{3}7 \text{ mol } O_2 \text{ x } \frac{-571.6 \text{ kJ}}{\text{mol } O_2} = -39.\underline{6}54 = -39.7 \text{ kJ}$$

6.117. Let ΔH_f° = the unknown standard enthalpy of formation for sucrose. Then write this symbol and the other ΔH_f° values underneath each compound in the balanced equation, and solve for ΔH_f° using the ΔH° of -5641 kJ for the reaction.

$$C_{12}H_{22}O_{11}(s) \quad + \quad 12O_2(g) \quad \rightarrow \quad 12CO_2(g) \quad + \quad 11H_2O(l)$$

$$\Delta H_f{}^{\circ} \qquad\qquad 12(0) \qquad\qquad 12(\text{-}393.5) \qquad 11(\text{-}285.8) \qquad (kJ)$$

$$\Delta H^{\circ} = -5641 = [12(-393.5) + 11(-285.8)] - [\Delta H_f^{\circ} + 12(0)]$$

$$\Delta H_f^{\circ} = -2225 \text{ kJ/mol sucrose}$$

6.119. First, calculate the heat evolved from the molar amounts represented by the balanced equation. From Appendix C, obtain the individual heats of formation, and write those below the reactants and products in the balanced equation. Then multiply the molar heats of formation by the number of moles in the balanced equation, and write those products below the molar heats of formation.

$$2Al(s) \quad + \quad 3NH_4NO_3(s) \quad \rightarrow \quad 3N_2(g) \quad + \quad 6H_2O(g) \quad + \quad Al_2O_3(s)$$

0.0 kJ	-365.6 kJ	0.0 kJ	-241.8	-1675.7 kJ (kJ/mol)
0.0 kJ	-1096.8 kJ	0.0 kJ	-1450.8	-1675.7 kJ (kJ/eqn.)

The total heat of reaction of 2 mol Al and 3 mol NH_4NO_3 is

$$\Delta H = -1450.8 - 1675.7 - (-1096.8 \text{ kJ}) = -2029.7 \text{ kJ}$$

Now, 245 kJ represents the following fraction of the total heat of reaction:

$$\frac{245 \text{ kJ}}{2029.7 \text{ kJ}} = 0.120\underline{7}$$

Thus, 245 kJ requires the fraction 0.1207 of the moles of each reactant: 0.1207 x 2, or 0.24$\underline{1}$4, mol of Al and 0.1207 x 3, or 0.36$\underline{2}$1, mol of NH_4NO_3. The mass of each reactant and the mass of the mixture are as follows:

0.2414 mol Al x 26.98 g/mol Al $= 6.5\underline{1}3$ g of Al

0.3621 mol NH_4NO_3 x 80.04 g/mol $NH_4NO_3 = 28.\underline{9}8$ g NH_4NO_3

6.513 g Al $+ 28.98$ g $NH_4NO_3 = 35.\underline{4}9 = 35.5$ g of the mixture

Copyright © Cengage Learning. All rights reserved.

■ SOLUTIONS TO CUMULATIVE-SKILLS PROBLEMS

6.133. The heat lost, q, by the water(s) with a temperature higher than the final temperature must be equal to the heat gained, q, by the water(s) with a temperature lower than the final temperature.

q(lost by water at higher temp) $= q$(gained by water at lower temp)

$\Sigma (s \times m \times \Delta t) = \Sigma (s \times m \times \Delta t)$

Divide both sides of the equation by the specific heat, s, to eliminate this term, and substitute the other values. Since the mass of the water at 50.0°C is greater than the sum of the masses of the other two waters, assume the final temperature will be greater than 37°C and greater than 15°C. Use this to set up the three Δt expressions, and write one equation in one unknown, letting t equal the final temperature. Simplify by omitting the "grams" from 45.0 g, 25.0 g, and 15.0 g.

$\Sigma (m \times \Delta t) = \Sigma (m \times \Delta t)$

$45.0 \times (50.0°C - t) = 25.0 \times (t - 15.0°C) + 15.0 \times (t - 37°C)$

$2250°C - 45.0\,t = 25.0\,t - 375°C + 15.0\,t - 555.0°C$

$-85.0\,t = -3180°C$

$t = 37.\underline{4}1 = 37.4°C$ (the final temperature)

6.135. First, calculate the mole fraction of each gas in the product, assuming 100 g product:

Mol CO $= 33$ g CO $\times$ 1 mol CO/28.01 g CO $= 1.\underline{1}78$ mol CO

Mol $CO_2 = 67$ g $CO_2 \times$ 1 mol CO_2/44.01 g $CO_2 = 1.\underline{5}22$ mol CO_2

$$\text{Mol frac. CO} = \frac{1.178 \text{ mol CO}}{(1.178 + 1.522) \text{ mol}} = 0.4\underline{3}63$$

$$\text{Mol frac. } CO_2 = \frac{1.522 \text{ mol } CO_2}{(1.178 + 1.522) \text{ mol}} = 0.5\underline{6}37$$

Now, calculate the starting moles of C, which equal the total moles of CO and CO_2:

Starting mol C(s) $= 1.00$ g C $\times$ 1 mol C/12.01 g C

$= 0.083\underline{2}6$ mol C $=$ mol CO $+ CO_2$

Use the mole fractions to convert mol CO $+ CO_2$ to mol CO and mol CO_2:

$$\text{Mol CO} = \frac{0.4363 \text{ mol CO}}{1 \text{ mol total}} \times 0.08326 \text{ mol total} = 0.036\underline{3}3 \text{ mol CO}$$

$$\text{Mol } CO_2 = \frac{0.5637 \text{ mol } CO_2}{1 \text{ mol total}} \times 0.08326 \text{ mol total} = 0.046\underline{9}3 \text{ mol } CO_2$$

Copyright © Cengage Learning. All rights reserved.

Now, use enthalpies of formation (Table 6.2) to calculate the heat of combustion for both:

$C(s)$	+	$1/2 O_2(g)$	$\rightarrow$	$CO(g)$
0.03633		excess		0.03633 (mol)
0		0		-110.5 (kJ/mol)
0		0		-110.5 (kJ/mol)

$C(s)$	+	$O_2(g)$	$\rightarrow$	$CO_2(g)$
0.04693		excess		0.04693 (mol)
0		0		-393.5 (kJ/mol)
0		0		-18.47 (kJ/0.04693 mol)

Total ΔH = -4.014 + (-18.47) = -2$\underline{2}$.48 = -22 kJ

Heat released = 22 kJ

6.137. The $\Delta H°$ for the reactions to produce CO and CO_2 in each case is equal to the $\Delta H_f°$ of the respective gases. Thus $\Delta H°$ to produce CO is -110.5 kJ/mol, and $\Delta H°$ to produce CO_2 is -393.5 kJ/mol. Since 1 mol graphite is needed to produce 1 mol either CO or CO_2, one equation in one unknown can be written for the heat produced, using m for the moles of CO and $(2.00 - m)$ for moles of CO_2.

$$-481 \text{ kJ} = m \text{ x } (-110.5 \text{ kJ}) + (2.00 - m) \text{ x } (-393.5 \text{ kJ})$$

$$-481 = -110.5\,m - 787 + 393.5\,m$$

mol CO = m = 1.0$\underline{8}$1;   mass CO = 1.081 x 28.0 g/mol = 30.$\underline{2}$6 = 30.3 g

mol CO_2 = $(2.00 - m)$ = 0.9$\underline{1}$9;   mass CO_2 = 0.9$\underline{1}$9 mol x 44.0 g/mol = 4$\underline{0}$.4 = 40. g

6.139. The equation is

$$4NH_3(g) + 5O_2(g) \rightarrow 4NO(g) + 6H_2O(g); \quad \Delta H° = -906 \text{ kJ}$$

First, determine the limiting reactant by calculating the moles of NH_3 and of O_2; then, assuming one of the reactants is totally consumed, calculate the moles of the other reactant needed for the reaction.

$$10.0 \text{ g } NH_3 \text{ x } \frac{1 \text{ mol } NH_3}{17.03 \text{ g } NH_3} = 0.58\underline{7}2 \text{ mol } NH_3$$

$$20.0 \text{ g } O_2 \text{ x } \frac{1 \text{ mol } O_2}{32.00 \text{ g } O_2} = 0.62\underline{5}0 \text{ mol } O_2$$

$$0.62\underline{5}0 \text{ mol } O_2 \text{ x } \frac{4 \text{ mol } NH_3}{5 \text{ mol } O_2} = 0.500 \text{ mol } NH_3 \text{ needed}$$

Because NH_3 is present in excess of what is needed, O_2 must be the limiting reactant. Now calculate the heat released on the basis of the complete reaction of 0.622250 mol O_2:

Copyright © Cengage Learning. All rights reserved.

$$\Delta H = \frac{-906 \text{ kJ}}{5 \text{ mol O}_2} \times 0.6250 \text{ mol O}_2 = -11\underline{3}.25 = -113 \text{ kJ}$$

The heat released by the complete reaction of the 20.0 g (0.6250 mol) of $O_2(g)$ is 113 kJ.

6.141. The equation is

$$N_2(g) + 3H_2(g) \rightarrow 2NH_3(g); \;\; \Delta H^\circ = -91.8 \text{ kJ}$$

a. To find the heat evolved from the production of 1.00 L of NH_3, convert the 1.00 L to mol NH_3 using the density and molar mass (17.03 g/mol). Then convert the moles to heat (ΔH) using ΔH°.

$$\text{Mol NH}_3 = \frac{d \times V}{M_M} = \frac{0.696 \text{ g/L} \times 1 \text{ L}}{17.03 \text{ g/mol}} = 0.040\underline{8}7 \text{ mol NH}_3$$

$$\Delta H = \frac{-91.8 \text{ kJ}}{2 \text{ mol NH}_3} \times 0.040\underline{8}7 \text{ mol NH}_3 = -1.8\underline{7}6 \text{ (1.88 kJ heat evolved)}$$

b. First, find the moles of N_2 using the density and molar mass (28.02 g/mol). Then convert to the heat needed to raise the N_2 from 25°C to 400°C.

$$\text{Mol N}_2 = \frac{d \times V}{M_M} = \frac{1.145 \text{ g/L} \times 0.500 \text{ L}}{28.02 \text{ g/mol}} = 0.020\underline{4}3 \text{ mol N}_2$$

$$0.020\underline{4}3 \text{ mol N}_2 \times \frac{29.12 \text{ J}}{\text{mol} \cdot °C} \times (400 - 25)°C = 22\underline{3}.2 \text{ J (0.223}\underline{2} \text{ kJ)}$$

$$\text{Percent heat for N}_2 = \frac{0.2232 \text{ kJ}}{1.876 \text{ kJ}} \times 100\% = 11.\underline{8}9 = 11.9\%$$

6.143. The glucose equation is

$$C_6H_{12}O_6 + 6O_2 \rightarrow 6CO_2 + 6H_2O; \;\; \Delta H^\circ = -280\underline{2}.8 \text{ kJ}$$

Convert the 2.50×10^3 kcal to mol of glucose using the ΔH° of -2802.8 kJ for the reaction and the conversion factor of 4.184 kJ/kcal:

$$2.50 \times 10^3 \text{ kcal} \times \frac{4.184 \text{ kJ}}{1.000 \text{ kcal}} \times \frac{1 \text{ mol glucose}}{2802.8 \text{ kJ}} = 3.7\underline{3}19 \text{ mol glucose}$$

Next, convert mol glucose to mol LiOH using the above equation for glucose and the equation for LiOH:

$$2\text{LiOH}(s) + CO_2(g) \rightarrow \text{Li}_2CO_3(s) + H_2O(l)$$

$$3.7\underline{3}19 \text{ mol glucose} \times \frac{6 \text{ mol CO}_2}{1 \text{ mol glucose}} \times \frac{2 \text{ mol LiOH}}{1 \text{ mol CO}_2} = 44.\underline{7}83 \text{ mol LiOH}$$

Finally, use the molar mass of LiOH to convert moles to mass:

$$44.783 \text{ mol LiOH} \times \frac{23.95 \text{ g LiOH}}{1 \text{ mol LiOH}} = 1.0\underline{7}25 \times 10^3 \text{ g (1.07 kg) LiOH}$$

Copyright © Cengage Learning. All rights reserved.

CHAPTER 11

States of Matter; Liquids and Solids

■ SOLUTIONS TO EXERCISES

Note on significant figures: If the final answer to a solution needs to be rounded off, it is given first with one nonsignificant figure, and the last significant figure is underlined. The final answer is then rounded to the correct number of significant figures. In multistep problems, intermediate answers are given with at least one nonsignificant figure; however, only the final answer has been rounded off.

11.1. First, calculate the heat required to vaporize 1.00 kg of ammonia:

$$1.00 \text{ kg NH}_3 \text{ x } \frac{1000 \text{ g}}{1 \text{ kg}} \text{ x } \frac{1 \text{ mol NH}_3}{17.03 \text{ g NH}_3} \text{ x } \frac{23.4 \text{ kJ}}{1 \text{ mol}} = 13\underline{7}4.04 \text{ kJ}$$

The amount of water at 0°C that can be frozen to ice at 0°C with this heat is

$$13\underline{7}4.04 \text{ kJ } \text{ x } \frac{1 \text{ mol H}_2\text{O}}{6.01 \text{ kJ}} \text{ x } \frac{18.01 \text{ g H}_2\text{O}}{1 \text{ mol H}_2\text{O}} = 41\underline{1}7.54\text{g} = 4.12 \text{ kg H}_2\text{O}$$

11.2. Use the two-point form of the Clausius-Clapeyron equation to calculate P_2:

$$\ln \frac{P_2}{760 \text{ mmHg}} = \frac{26.8 \text{ x } 10^3 \text{ J/mol}}{8.31 \text{ J/(K} \cdot \text{mol})} \left[\frac{1}{319 \text{ K}} - \frac{1}{308 \text{ K}} \right]$$

$$= 3225 \text{ K} \left[\frac{-1.12 \text{ x } 10^{-4}}{\text{K}} \right] = -0.36\underline{1}06$$

Converting to antilogs gives

$$\frac{P_2}{760 \text{ mmHg}} = \text{antilog}(-0.36106) = e^{-0.36106} = 0.69\underline{6}93$$

$$P_2 = 0.69693 \text{ x } 760 \text{ mmHg} = 529.6 = 5.30 \text{ x } 10^2 \text{ mmHg}$$

11.3. Use the two-point form of the Clausius-Clapeyron equation to solve for ΔH_{vap}:

$$\ln \frac{757 \text{ mmHg}}{522 \text{ mmHg}} = \frac{\Delta H_{vap}}{8.31 \text{ J/(K} \cdot \text{mol})} \left[\frac{1}{368 \text{ K}} - \frac{1}{378 \text{ K}} \right]$$

$$0.37\underline{1}69 = \frac{\Delta H_{vap}}{8.31 \text{ J/(K} \cdot \text{mol})} \left[\frac{7.188 \text{ x } 10^{-5}}{\text{K}} \right]$$

$$\Delta H_{vap} = 4.2\underline{9}6 \text{ x } 10^4 \text{ J/mol} \quad (43.0 \text{ kJ/mol})$$

Copyright © Cengage Learning. All rights reserved.

11.4.

    a.   Liquefy methyl chloride by a sufficient increase in pressure below 144°C.

    b.   Liquefy oxygen by compressing to 50 atm below −119°C.

11.5.

    a.   Propanol has a hydrogen atom bonded to an oxygen atom. Therefore, hydrogen bonding is expected. Because propanol is polar (from the O–H bond), we also expect dipole-dipole forces. Weak London forces exist, too, because such forces exist between all molecules.

    b.   Linear carbon dioxide is not polar, so only London forces exist among CO_2 molecules.

    c.   Bent sulfur dioxide is polar, so we expect dipole-dipole forces; we also expect the usual London forces.

11.6. The order of increasing vapor pressure is butane (C_4H_{10}), propane (C_3H_8), and ethane (C_2H_6). Because London forces tend to increase with increasing molecular mass, we would expect the molecule with the highest molecular mass to have the lowest vapor pressure.

11.7. Because ethanol has an H atom bonded to an O atom, strong hydrogen bonding exists in ethanol but not in methyl chloride. Hydrogen bonding explains the lower vapor pressure of ethanol compared to methyl chloride.

11.8.

    a.   Zinc, a metal, is a metallic solid.

    b.   Sodium iodide, an ionic substance, exists as an ionic solid.

    c.   Silicon carbide, a compound in which carbon and silicon might be expected to form covalent bonds to other carbon and silicon atoms, exists as a covalent network solid.

    d.   Methane, at room temperature a gaseous molecular compound with covalent bonds, freezes as a molecular solid.

11.9. Only $MgSO_4$ is an ionic solid; C_2H_5OH, CH_4, and CH_3Cl form molecular solids; thus $MgSO_4$ should have the highest melting point. Of the molecular solids, CH_4 has the lowest molecular mass (16.0 amu) and would be expected to have the lowest melting point. Both C_2H_5OH and CH_3Cl have approximately the same molecular masses (46.0 amu vs. 50.5 amu), but C_2H_5OH exhibits strong hydrogen bonding and, therefore, would be expected to have the higher melting point. The order of increasing melting points is CH_4, CH_3Cl, C_2H_5OH, and $MgSO_4$.

11.10.   Each of the four corners of the cell contains one atom, which is shared by a total of four unit cells. Therefore, the corners contribute one whole atom.

$$\frac{\text{Atoms}}{\text{Unit cell}} = 4 \text{ corners} \times \frac{1/4 \text{ atom}}{1 \text{ corner}} = 1 \text{ atom}$$

Copyright © Cengage Learning. All rights reserved.

11.11. Use the edge length to calculate the volume of the unit cell. Then, use the density to determine the mass of one atom. Divide the molar mass by the mass of one atom.

$$V = (3.509 \times 10^{-10} \text{ m})^3 = 4.3\underline{2}1 \times 10^{-29} \text{ m}^3$$

$$d = \frac{0.534 \text{ g}}{1 \text{ cm}^3} \times \left[\frac{100 \text{ cm}}{1 \text{ m}}\right]^3 = 5.34 \times 10^5 \text{ g/m}^3$$

Mass of 1 unit $= d \times V$

$$= (5.34 \times 10^5 \text{ g/m}^3) \times (4.321 \times 10^{-29} \text{ m}^3) = 2.3\underline{0}74 \times 10^{-23} \text{ g}$$

There are two atoms in a body-centered cubic unit cell; thus, the mass of one lithium atom is

$$1/2 \times 2.3074 \times 10^{-23} \text{ g} = 1.1\underline{5}37 \times 10^{-23} \text{ g}$$

The known atomic mass of lithium is 6.941 amu, so Avogadro's number is

$$N_A = \frac{6.941 \text{ g/mol}}{1.1537 \times 10^{-23} \text{ g/atom}} = 6.0\underline{1}6 \times 10^{23} = 6.02 \times 10^{23} \text{ atoms/mol}$$

11.12. Use Avogadro's number to convert the molar mass of potassium to the mass per one atom.

$$\frac{39.0983 \text{ g K}}{1 \text{ mol K}} \times \frac{1 \text{ mol K}}{6.022 \times 10^{23} \text{ atoms}} = \frac{6.4925 \times 10^{-23} \text{ g K}}{1 \text{ atom}}$$

There are two K atoms per unit cell; therefore, the mass per unit cell is

$$\frac{6.4925 \times 10^{-23} \text{ g K}}{1 \text{ atom}} \times \frac{2 \text{ atoms}}{1 \text{ unit cell}} = \frac{1.2985 \times 10^{-22} \text{ g}}{1 \text{ unit cell}}$$

The density of 0.856 g/cm^3 is equal to the mass of one unit cell divided by its unknown volume, V. After solving for V, determine the edge length from the cube root of the volume.

$$0.856 \text{ g/cm}^3 = \frac{1.29\underline{8}5 \times 10^{-22} \text{ g}}{V}$$

$$V = \frac{1.29\underline{8}5 \times 10^{-22} \text{ g}}{0.856 \text{ g/cm}^3} = 1.5\underline{1}7 \times 10^{-22} \text{ cm}^3 \ (1.517 \times 10^{-28} \text{ m}^3)$$

Edge length $= \sqrt[3]{1.5\underline{1}7 \times 10^{-28} \text{ m}^3} = 5.3\underline{3}3 \times 10^{-10} = 5.33 \times 10^{-10} \text{ m} \ (533 \text{ pm})$

■ ANSWERS TO SELF-ASSESSMENT AND REVIEW QUESTIONS

11.1. The six different phase transitions, with examples in parentheses, are melting (snow melting), sublimation (dry ice subliming directly to carbon dioxide gas), freezing (water freezing), vaporization (water evaporating), condensation (dew forming on the ground), and gas-solid condensation or deposition (frost forming on the ground).

11.2. Iodine can be purified by heating it in a beaker covered with a dish containing ice or ice water. Only pure iodine should sublime, crystallizing on the cold bottom surface of the dish above the iodine. The common impurities in iodine do not sublime nor do they vaporize significantly.

Copyright © Cengage Learning. All rights reserved.

11.3. The vapor pressure of a liquid is the partial pressure of the vapor over the liquid, measured at equilibrium. In molecular terms, vapor pressure involves molecules of a liquid vaporizing from the liquid phase, colliding with any surface above the liquid, and exerting pressure on it. The equilibrium is a dynamic one because molecules of the liquid are continually leaving the liquid phase and returning to it from the vapor phase.

11.4. Steam at 100°C will melt more ice than the same weight of water at 100°C because it contains much more energy in the form of its heat of vaporization. It will transfer this energy to the ice and condense in doing so. The condensed steam and the water will both transfer heat to the ice as the temperature then drops.

11.5. The heat of fusion is smaller than the heat of vaporization because melting requires only enough energy for molecules to escape from their sites in the crystal lattice, leaving other molecular attractions intact. In vaporization, sufficient energy must be added to break almost all molecular attractions and also to do the work of pushing back the atmosphere.

11.6. Evaporation leads to cooling of a liquid because the gaseous molecules require heat to evaporate; as they leave the other liquid molecules, they remove the heat energy required to vaporize them. This leaves less energy in the liquid, the temperature of which then drops.

11.7. As the temperature increases for a liquid and its vapor in the closed vessel, the two, which are separated by a meniscus, gradually become identical. The meniscus first becomes fuzzy and then disappears altogether as the temperature reaches the critical temperature. Above this temperature, only the vapor exists.

11.8. A permanent gas can be liquefied only by lowering the temperature below its critical temperature while compressing the gas.

11.9. The pressure in the cylinder of nitrogen at room temperature (above its critical temperature of −147°C) decreases continuously as gas is released because the number of molecules in the vapor phase, which governs the pressure, decreases continuously. The pressure in the cylinder of propane at room temperature (below its critical temperature) is constant because liquid propane and gaseous propane exist at equilibrium in the cylinder. The pressure will remain constant at the vapor pressure of propane until only gaseous propane remains. At that point, the pressure will decrease until all of the propane is gone.

11.10. The vapor pressure of a liquid depends on the intermolecular forces in the liquid phase since the ease with which a molecule leaves the liquid phase depends on how strongly it is attracted to the other molecules. If such molecules attract each other strongly, the vapor pressure will be relatively low; if they attract each other weakly, the vapor pressure will be relatively high.

11.11. Surface tension makes a liquid act as though it had a skin, because for an object to break through the surface, the surface area must increase. This requires energy, so there is some resistance to the object breaking through the surface.

Copyright © Cengage Learning. All rights reserved.

11.12. London forces, also known as dispersion forces, originate between any two molecules that are weakly attracted to each other by means of small instantaneous dipoles that occur as a result of the varying positions of the electrons during their movement about their nuclei.

11.13. Hydrogen bonding is a weak to moderate attractive force that exists between a hydrogen atom covalently bonded to a very electronegative atom, X (N, O, or F), and a lone pair of electrons on another small, electronegative atom, Y. (X and Y may be the same or different elements.) Hydrogen bonding in water involves a hydrogen atom of one water molecule bonding to a lone pair of electrons on the oxygen atom of another water molecule.

11.14. Molecular substances have relatively low melting points because the forces broken by melting are weak intermolecular attractions in the solid state, not strong bonding attractions.

11.15. A crystalline solid has a well-defined, orderly structure; an amorphous solid has a random arrangement of structural units.

11.16. In a face-centered cubic cell, there are atoms at the center of each face of the unit cell in addition to those at the corners.

11.17. The structure of thallium(I) iodide is a simple cubic lattice for both the metal ions and the anions. Thus, the structure consists of two interpenetrating cubic lattices of cation and anion.

11.18. The coordination number of Cs^+ in CsCl is 8; the coordination number of Na^+ in NaCl is 6; and the coordination number of Zn^{2+} in ZnS is 4.

11.19. Starting with the edge length of a cubic crystal, we can calculate the volume of a unit cell by cubing the edge length. Next, knowing the density of the crystalline solid, we can calculate the mass of the atoms in the unit cell. Then, the mass of the atoms in the unit cell is divided by the number of atoms in the unit cell, to give the mass of one atom. Dividing the mass of one mole of the crystal by the mass of one atom yields a value for Avogadro's number.

11.20. X rays can strike a crystal and be reflected at various angles; at most angles, the reflected waves will be out of phase and will interfere destructively. At certain angles, however, the reflected waves will be in phase and will interfere constructively, giving rise to a diffraction pattern.

11.21. The answer is e, cooling the H_2O sample from 105°C to 84°C.

11.22. The answer is d, sublime.

11.23. The answer is c, London (dispersion) forces.

11.24. The answer is b, 6.40×10^7 pm^3.

Copyright © Cengage Learning. All rights reserved.

■ SOLUTIONS TO PRACTICE PROBLEMS

Note on significant figures: If the final answer to a solution needs to be rounded off, it is given first with one nonsignificant figure, and the last significant figure is underlined. The final answer is then rounded to the correct number of significant figures. In multistep problems, intermediate answers are given with at least one nonsignificant figure; however, only the final answer has been rounded off.

11.37.

    a.   Vaporization

    b.   Freezing of eggs and sublimation of ice

    c.   Condensation

    d.   Gas-solid condensation, deposition

    e.   Freezing

11.39.   Dropping a line from the intersection of a 350-mmHg line with the diethyl ether curve in Figure 11.7 intersects the temperature axis at about 10°C.

11.41.   The total amount of energy provided by the heater in 4.54 min is

$$4.54 \text{ min} \times \frac{60 \text{ s}}{1 \text{ min}} \times \frac{3.48 \text{ J}}{\text{s}} = 94\underline{7}.95 \text{ J} \ (0.94\underline{7}95 \text{ kJ})$$

The heat of fusion per mole of I_2 is

$$\frac{0.9479 \text{ kJ}}{15.5 \text{ g } I_2} \times \frac{2 \times 126.9 \text{ g } I_2}{\text{mol } I_2} = 15.\underline{5}2 = \frac{15.5 \text{ kJ}}{\text{mol } I_2}$$

11.43.   The heat absorbed per 2.25 g of isopropyl alcohol, C_3H_8O, is

$$2.25 \text{ g } C_3H_8O \times \frac{1 \text{ mol } C_3H_8O}{60.09 \text{ g } C_3H_8O} \times \frac{42.1 \text{ kJ}}{1 \text{ mol } C_3H_8O} = 1.5\underline{7}6 = 1.58 \text{ kJ}$$

11.45.   Because all the heat released by freezing the water is used to evaporate the remaining water, you must first calculate the amount of heat released in the freezing:

$$9.31 \text{ g } H_2O \times \frac{\text{mol } H_2O}{18.02 \text{ g } H_2O} \times \frac{6.01 \text{ kJ}}{\text{mol } H_2O} = 3.10\underline{5}05 \text{ kJ}$$

Finally, calculate the mass of H_2O that was vaporized by the 3.10505 kJ of heat:

$$3.10505 \text{ kJ} \times \frac{18.02 \text{ g } H_2O}{1 \text{ mol } H_2O} \times \frac{1 \text{ mol } H_2O}{44.9 \text{ kJ}} = 1.2\underline{4}6 = 1.25 \text{ g } H_2O$$

Copyright © Cengage Learning. All rights reserved.

11.47.   Calculate how much heat is released by cooling 64.3 g of H_2O from 55°C to 15°C.

$$\text{Heat released} = (64.3\text{ g})(15°C - 55°C)\left(\frac{4.18\text{ J}}{1\text{ g}\bullet°C}\right) = -1.0\underline{7}509 \times 10^4\text{ J} = -1\underline{0}.7509\text{ kJ}$$

The heat released is used first to melt the ice and then to warm the liquid from 0°C to 15°C. Let the mass of ice equal y grams. Then, for fusion, and for warming, we have

$$\text{Fusion: } (y\text{ g }H_2O) \times \frac{1\text{ mol }H_2O}{18.02\text{ g }H_2O} \times \frac{6.01\text{ kJ}}{1\text{ mol }H_2O} = 0.33\underline{3}5\ y\text{ kJ}$$

$$\text{Warming: } (y\text{ g }H_2O)(15°C - 0°C)\left(\frac{4.18\text{ J}}{1\text{ g}\bullet°C}\right) = 6\underline{2}.70\ y\text{ J }\ (0.06\underline{2}70\ y\text{ kJ})$$

Because the total heat required for melting and warming must equal the heat released by cooling, equate the two, and solve for y.

$$10.7509\text{ kJ} = 0.3335y\text{ kJ} + 0.0627y\text{ kJ} = y(0.3335 + 0.0627)\text{ kJ}$$

$$y = 1\underline{0}.7509\text{ kJ} \div 0.39\underline{6}2\text{ kJ} = 2\underline{7}.13\text{ (grams)}$$

Thus, 27 g of ice was added.

11.49.   At the normal boiling point, the vapor pressure of a liquid is 760.0 mmHg. Use the Clausius-Clapeyron equation to find P_2 when $P_1 = 760.0$ mmHg, $T_1 = 334.85$ K (61.7°C), and $T_2 = 309.35$ K (36.2°C). Also use $\Delta H_{vap} = 31.4 \times 10^3$ J/mol.

$$\ln\frac{P_2}{P_1} = \frac{\Delta H_{vap}}{R}\left(\frac{1}{T_1} - \frac{1}{T_2}\right)$$

$$\ln\frac{P_2}{760\text{ mmHg}} = \frac{31.4 \times 10^3\text{ J/mol}}{8.31\text{ J/K}\bullet\text{mol}}\left(\frac{1}{334.85\text{ K}} - \frac{1}{309.35\text{ K}}\right) = -0.930\underline{1}8$$

Taking antilogs of both sides gives

$$\frac{P_2}{760\text{ mmHg}} = e^{-0.93018} = 0.39\underline{4}4$$

$$P_2 = 0.3944 \times 760\text{ mmHg} = 29\underline{9}.8 = 3.00 \times 10^2\text{ mmHg (300. mmHg)}$$

11.51.   From the Clausius-Clapeyron equation,

$$\Delta H_{vap} = R\left(\frac{T_2\ T_1}{T_2 - T_1}\right)\left[\ln\frac{P_2}{P_1}\right] = [8.31\text{ J/(K}\bullet\text{mol)}]\left[\frac{(553.2\text{ K})(524.2\text{ K})}{(553.2 - 524.2)\text{ K}}\right]\left[\ln\frac{760.0\text{ mmHg}}{400.0\text{ mmHg}}\right]$$

$$= 5.3\underline{3}36 \times 10^4\text{ J/ mol} = 53.3\text{ kJ/ mol}$$

11.53.

    a.   At point A, the substance will be a gas.

    b.   The substance will be a gas.

Copyright © Cengage Learning. All rights reserved.

c.   The substance will be a liquid.

d.   No

11.55.   The phase diagram for oxygen is shown below. It is plotted from these points: triple point = −219°C, boiling point = −183°C, and critical point = −118°C. The graph is not drawn to scale.

11.57.   Liquefied at 25°C: SO_2 and C_2H_2. To liquefy CH_4, lower its temperature below −82°C, and then compress it. To liquefy CO, lower its temperature below −140°C, and then compress it.

11.59. Br_2 phase diagram:

a.   Circle "solid." The pressure of 40 mmHg is lower than the pressure at the triple point, so the liquid phase cannot exist.

b.   Circle "liquid." The pressure of 400 mmHg is above the triple point, so the gas will condense to a liquid.

Copyright © Cengage Learning. All rights reserved.

11.61.   Yes, the heats of vaporization of 0.9, 5.6, and 20.4 kJ/mol (for H_2, N_2, and Cl_2, respectively) increase in the order of the respective molecular masses of 2.016, 28.02, and 71.0. (London forces increase in order of increasing molecular mass.)

11.63.

    a.   London forces

    b.   London and dipole-dipole forces, hydrogen bonding

    c.   London and dipole-dipole forces

    d.   London forces

11.65.   The order is $CCl_4 < SiCl_4 < GeCl_4$ (in order of increasing molecular mass).

11.67. CCl_4 has the lowest vapor pressure because it has the largest molecular mass and the greatest London forces even though $HCCl_3$ and H_3CCl have dipole-dipole interactions.

11.69.   The order of increasing vapor pressure is $HOCH_2CH_2OH$, FCH_2CH_2OH, FCH_2CH_2F. There is no hydrogen bonding in the third molecule; the second molecule can hydrogen-bond at only one end; and the first molecule can hydrogen-bond at both ends for the strongest interaction.

11.71.   The order is $CH_4 < C_2H_6 < CH_3OH < CH_2OHCH_2OH$. The weakest forces are the London forces in CH_4 and C_2H_6, which increase with molecular mass. The next-strongest interaction is in CH_3OH, which can hydrogen-bond at only one end of the molecule. The strongest interaction is in the last molecule, which can hydrogen-bond at both ends.

11.73.

    a.   Metallic

    b.   Metallic

    c.   Covalent network

    d.   Molecular

    e.   Ionic

11.75.

    a.   Metallic

    b.   Covalent network (like diamond)

    c.   Molecular

    d.   Molecular

Copyright © Cengage Learning. All rights reserved.

11.77. The order is $(C_2H_5)_2O < C_4H_9OH < KCl < CaO$. Melting points increase in the order of attraction between molecules or ions in the solid state. Hydrogen bonding in C_4H_9OH causes it to melt at a higher temperature than $(C_2H_5)_2O$. Both KCl and CaO are ionic solids with much stronger attraction than the organic molecules. In CaO, the higher charges cause the lattice energy to be higher than in KCl.

11.79.

    a.   Low-melting and brittle

    b.   High-melting, hard, and brittle

    c.   Malleable and electrically conducting

    d.   Hard and high-melting

11.81.

    a.   LiCl

    b.   SiC

    c. CHI_3

    d.   Co

11.83. In a simple cubic lattice with one atom at each lattice point, there are atoms only at the corners of unit cells. Each corner is shared by eight unit cells, and there are eight corners per unit cell. Therefore, there is one atom per unit cell.

11.85. Calculate the volume of the unit cell, change density to g/m^3, and then convert volume to mass, using density:

$$\text{Volume} = (2.866 \times 10^{-10} \text{ m})^3 = 2.354 \times 20^{-29} \text{ m}^3$$

$$\frac{7.87 \text{ g}}{1 \text{ cm}^3} \times \left(\frac{100 \text{ cm}}{1 \text{ m}}\right)^3 = 7.87 \times 10^6 \text{ g/m}^3$$

$$\text{Mass of one cell} = (7.87 \times 10^6 \text{ g/m}^3) \times (2.354 \times 10^{-29} \text{ m}^3) = 1.8\underline{5}26 \times 10^{-22} \text{ g}$$

Because Fe is a body-centered cubic cell, there are two Fe atoms in the cell, and

$$\text{Mass of one Fe atom} = (1.8526 \times 10^{-22} \text{ g}) \div 2 = 9.2\underline{6}3 \times 10^{-23} \text{ g}$$

Using the molar mass to calculate the mass of one Fe atom, you find the agreement is good:

$$\frac{55.85 \text{ g Fe}}{1 \text{ mol Fe}} \times \frac{1 \text{ mol Fe}}{6.022 \times 10^{23} \text{ Fe atoms}} = 9.27\underline{4}3 \times 10^{-23} \text{ g/Fe atom}$$

Copyright © Cengage Learning. All rights reserved.

11.87.   There are four Cu atoms in the face-centered cubic structure, so the mass of one cell is

$$4 \text{ Cu atoms } \times \frac{1 \text{ mol Cu}}{6.022 \times 10^{23} \text{ Cu atoms}} \times \frac{63.5 \text{ g Cu}}{1 \text{ mol Cu}} = 4.2\underline{1}8 \times 10^{-22} \text{ g}$$

$$\text{Cell volume } = \frac{4.218 \times 10^{-22} \text{ g}}{8.93 \text{ g/cm}^3} = 4.7\underline{2}3 \times 10^{-23} \text{ cm}^3$$

All edges are the same length in a cubic cell, so the edge length, l, is

$$l = \sqrt[3]{V} = \sqrt[3]{4.723 \times 10^{-23} \text{ cm}^3} = 3.6\underline{1}4 \times 10^{-8}$$
$$= 3.61 \times 10^{-8} \text{ cm } (361 \text{ pm})$$

11.89.   Calculate the volume from the edge length of 407.9 pm (4.079×10^{-8} cm), and then use it to calculate the mass of the unit cell:

$$\text{Cell volume } = (4.079 \times 10^{-8} \text{ cm}^3 = 6.7869 \times 10^{-23} \text{ cm}^3$$
$$\text{Cell mass } = (19.3 \text{ g/cm}^3)(6.7869 \times 20^{-23} \text{ cm}^3) = 1.3\underline{0}98 \times 10^{-21} \text{ g}$$

Calculate the mass of one gold atom:

$$1 \text{ Au atom } \times \frac{1 \text{ mol Au}}{6.022 \times 10^{23} \text{ Au atoms}} \times \frac{196.97 \text{ g Au}}{1 \text{ mol Au}} = 3.27\underline{0}8 \times 10^{-22} \text{ g}$$

$$\frac{1.3098 \times 10^{-21} \text{ g}}{1 \text{ unit cell}} \times \frac{1 \text{ Au atom}}{3.2708 \times 10^{-22} \text{ g Au}} = \frac{4.0\underline{0}4 \text{ Au atoms}}{\text{unit cell}}$$

Since there are four atoms per unit cell, it is a face-centered cubic.

11.91.   Calculate the volume from the edge (316.5 pm = 3.165×10^{-8} cm). Use it to calculate the mass:

$$\text{Cell volume } = (3.165 \times 10^{-8} \text{ cm})^3 = 3.17\underline{0}5 \times 10^{-23} \text{ cm}^3$$

For a body-centered cubic lattice, there are two atoms per cell, so their mass is

$$2 \text{ W atoms } \times \frac{1 \text{ mol W}}{6.022 \times 10^{23} \text{ W atoms}} \times \frac{183.8 \text{ g W}}{1 \text{ mol W}} = 6.10\underline{4}3 \times 10^{-22} \text{ g W}$$

$$\text{Density } = \frac{6.1043 \times 10^{-22} \text{ g W}}{3.1705 \times 10^{-23} \text{ cm}^3} = 19.2\underline{5}3 = 19.25 \text{ g/cm}^3$$

Copyright © Cengage Learning. All rights reserved.

11.93.   Use Avogadro's number to calculate the number of atoms in 1.74 g ($= d$ x 1.000 cm^3):

$$1.74 \text{ g Mg } \times \frac{1 \text{ mol Mg}}{24.305 \text{ g Mg}} \times \frac{6.022 \times 10^{23} \text{ Mg atoms}}{1 \text{ mol Mg}}$$

$$= 4.311 \times 10^{22} \text{ Mg atoms}$$

Because the space occupied by the Mg atoms = 0.741 cm^3, each atom's volume is

$$\text{Volume 1 Mg atom } = \frac{0.741 \text{ cm}^3}{4.311 \times 10^{22} \text{ Mg atoms}} = 1.7\underline{1}9 \times 10^{-23} \text{ cm}^3$$

$$\text{Volume } = \frac{4\pi r^3}{3}$$

so

$$r = \sqrt[3]{\frac{3V}{4\pi}} = \sqrt[3]{\frac{3}{4\pi}(1.719 \times 10^{-23} \text{ cm}^3)} = 1.6\underline{0}1 \times 10^{-8} = 1.60 \times 10^{-8} \text{ cm}$$

$$= 1.60 \times 10^2 \text{ pm}$$

■ SOLUTIONS TO GENERAL PROBLEMS

11.95.   Water vapor deposits directly to solid water (frost) without forming liquid water. After heating, most of the frost melted to liquid water, which then vaporized to water vapor. Some of the frost may have sublimed directly to water vapor.

11.97.   From Table 5.6, the vapor pressures are 18.7 mmHg at 21°C and 12.8 mmHg at 15°C. If the moisture did not begin to condense until the air had been cooled to 15°C, then the partial pressure of water in the air at 21°C must have been 12.8 mmHg. The relative humidity is

$$\text{Percent relative humidity } = \frac{12.8 \text{ mmHg}}{18.7 \text{ mmHg}} \times 100\% = 68.\underline{4}4 = 68.4 \text{ percent}$$

11.99.   After labeling the problem data as shown below, use the Clausius-Clapeyron equation to obtain ΔH_{vap}, which can then be used to calculate the boiling point.

At $T_1 = 299.3$ K, $P_1 = 100.0$ mmHg; at $T_2 = 333.8$ K, $P_2 = 400.0$ mmHg

$$\ln \frac{400.0 \text{ mmHg}}{100.0 \text{ mmHg}} = \frac{\Delta H_{vap}}{8.31 \text{ J/(K} \bullet \text{mol)}} \left[\frac{333.8 \text{ K} - 299.3 \text{ K}}{333.8 \text{ K} \times 299.3 \text{ K}} \right]$$

$$1.38\underline{6}2 = \Delta H_{vap} (4.15\underline{3}5 \times 10^{-5} \text{ mol/J})$$

$$\Delta H_{vap} = 33.37 \times 10^3 \text{ J/mol} (33.4 \text{ kJ/mol})$$

Copyright © Cengage Learning. All rights reserved.

Now, use this value of ΔH_{vap} and the following data to calculate the boiling point:

At T_1 = 299.3 K, P_1 = 100.0 mmHg; at T_2 (boiling pt.), P_2 = 760 mmHg

$$\ln \frac{760.0 \text{ mmHg}}{100.0 \text{ mmHg}} = \frac{33.4 \times 10^3 \text{ J/mol}}{8.314 \text{ J}/(\text{K} \cdot \text{mol})} \left[\frac{1}{299.3 \text{ K}} - \frac{1}{T_2} \right]$$

$$2.0281 = 4.0144 \times 10^3 \text{ K} \left[\frac{1}{299.3 \text{ K}} - \frac{1}{T_2} \right]$$

$$\frac{1}{T_2} = \frac{1}{299.3 \text{ K}} - \frac{2.0281}{4.0144 \times 10^3 \text{ K}} = 2.8359 \times 10^{-3}/\text{K}$$

$$T_2 = 352.6 = 353 \text{ K} (80°\text{C})$$

11.101.

a. As this gas is compressed at 20°C, it will condense into a liquid because 20°C is above the triple point but below the critical point.

b. As this gas is compressed at −70°C, it will condense directly to the solid phase because the temperature of −70°C is below the triple point.

c. As this gas is compressed at 40°C, it will not condense because 40°C is above the critical point.

11.103. In propanol, hydrogen bonding exists between the hydrogen of the OH group and the lone pair of electrons of oxygen of the OH group of an adjacent propanol molecule. For two adjacent propanol molecules, the hydrogen bond may be represented as follows:

C_3H_7–O–H•••O(H)C_3H_7

11.105. Ethylene glycol molecules are capable of hydrogen bonding to each other, whereas pentane molecules are not. The greater intermolecular forces in ethylene glycol are reflected in greater resistance to flow (viscosity) and high boiling point.

11.107. Aluminum (Group IIIA) forms a metallic solid. Silicon (Group IVA) forms a covalent network solid. Phosphorus (Group VA) forms a molecular solid. Sulfur (Group VIA) forms a molecular (amorphous) solid.

11.109.

a. Lower: KCl. The lattice energy should be lower for ions with a lower charge. A lower lattice energy implies a lower melting point.

b. Lower: CCl_4. Both are molecular solids, so the compound with the lower molecular mass should have weaker London forces and, therefore, the lower melting point.

c. Lower: Zn. Melting points for Group IIB metals are lower than for metals near the middle of the transition-metal series.

Copyright © Cengage Learning. All rights reserved.

d.   Lower: C_2H_5Cl. Ethyl chloride cannot hydrogen-bond, but acetic acid can. The compound with the weaker intermolecular forces has the lower melting point.

11.111. The face-centered cubic structure means one atom is at each lattice point. All edges are the same length in such a structure, so the volume is

$$\text{Volume} = l^3 = (3.839 \times 10^{-8} \text{ cm})^3 = 5.6579 \times 10^{-23} \text{ cm}^3$$

$$\text{Mass of unit cell} = dV = (22.42 \text{ g/cm}^3)(5.6579 \times 10^{-23} \text{ cm}^3) = 1.2685 \times 10^{-21} \text{ g}$$

There are four atoms in a face-centered cubic cell, so

$$\text{Mass of one Ir atom} = \text{mass of unit cell} \div 4 = (1.2685 \times 10^{-21} \text{ g}) \div 4$$

$$= 3.1712 \times 10^{-22} \text{ g}$$

$$\text{Molar mass of Ir} = (3.1712 \times 10^{-22} \text{ g/Ir atom}) \times (6.022 \times 10^{23} \text{ Ir atoms/mol})$$

$$= 190.96 = 191.0 \text{ g/mol} \quad (\text{The atomic mass} = 191.0 \text{ amu.})$$

11.113. From Problem 11.87, the cell edge length (l) is 361.4 pm. There are four copper atom radii along the diagonal of a unit-cell face. Because the diagonal square $= l^2 + l^2$ (Pythagorean theorem),

$$4r = \sqrt{2\,l^2} = \sqrt{2}\,l, \text{ or } r = \frac{\sqrt{2}}{4}(361.4 \text{ pm}) = 127.7 = 128 \text{ pm}$$

11.115. The body diagonal (diagonal passing through the center of the cell) is four times the radius, r, of a sphere. Also, from the geometry of a cube and the Pythagorean theorem, the body diagonal equals $\sqrt{3}\,l$, where l is the edge length of the unit cell. Thus

$$4r = \sqrt{3}\,l$$

or

$$l = \frac{4r}{\sqrt{3}}$$

Because the unit cell contains two spheres, the volume occupied by the spheres is

$$V_{\text{spheres}} = 2 \times \frac{4}{3}\pi r^3$$

and

$$V_{\text{cell}} = l^3 = \left[\frac{4r}{\sqrt{3}}\right]^3 = \frac{64r^3}{3\sqrt{3}}$$

Finally, to obtain the percent volume of the cell occupied, divide V_{spheres} by V_{cell}:

$$\text{Percent } V = \frac{V_{\text{spheres}}}{V_{\text{cell}}} \times 100\% = \frac{2\left[\frac{4\pi r^3}{3}\right]}{\frac{64r^3}{3\sqrt{3}}} \times 100\% = \frac{\pi\sqrt{3}}{8} \times 100\%$$

$$= 68.01 = 68.0\%$$

Copyright © Cengage Learning. All rights reserved.

11.117.

a. The boiling point increases as the size (number of electrons in the atom or molecule) increases. The London forces or dispersion forces increase.

b. Hydrogen bonding occurs between the H–F molecules and is much stronger than the London forces.

c. In addition to the dispersion forces, the hydrogen halides are polar (have dipole moments), so there are dipole-dipole interactions.

11.119.

a. Diamond and silicon carbide are covalent network solids with strong covalent bonds between all the atoms. Graphite is a layered structure, and the forces holding the layers together are weak dispersion forces.

b. Silicon dioxide is a giant molecule with an infinite array of O–S–O bonds. Each silicon is bonded to four oxygen atoms in a covalent network solid. Carbon dioxide is a discrete, nonpolar molecule.

11.121.

a. CO_2 consists of discrete nonpolar molecules that are held together in the solid by weak dispersion forces. SiO_2 is a covalent network solid with all the atoms held together by strong covalent bonds.

b. HF(l) has extensive hydrogen bonding among the molecules. HCl(l) boils much lower because it doesn't have hydrogen bonding.

c. SiF_4 is a larger molecule (it has more electrons than CF_4), so it has stronger dispersion forces and a higher boiling point than CF_4. Both molecules are tetrahadrally symmetrical and, therefore, nonpolar.

■ SOLUTIONS TO CUMULATIVE-SKILLS PROBLEMS

11.143. Use the ideal gas law to calculate n, the number of moles of N_2:

$$N_2: n = \frac{PV}{RT} = \frac{(745/760 \text{ atm})(5.40 \text{ L})}{(0.082057 \text{ L} \cdot \text{atm/K} \cdot \text{mol})(293 \text{ K})} = 0.220\underline{1} \text{ mol}$$

$$C_3H_8O: n = 0.6149 \text{ g C}_3\text{H}_8\text{O} \times \frac{1 \text{ mol C}_3\text{H}_8\text{O}}{60.094 \text{ g C}_3\text{H}_8\text{O}} = 0.01023\underline{2} \text{ mol}$$

$$X_{C_3H_8O} = \frac{0.010232 \text{ mol C}_3\text{H}_8\text{O}}{(0.010232 \text{ mol} + 0.2201 \text{ mol})} = 0.0444\underline{2} \text{ mole fraction}$$

Partial P = 0.04442 x 745 mmHg = 33.$\underline{0}$93 mmHg = 33.1 mmHg

Vapor pressure of C_3H_8O = 33.1 mmHg

Copyright © Cengage Learning. All rights reserved.

11.145. Calculate the moles of HCN in 10.0 mL of the solution (density = 0.687 g HCN/mL HCN):

$$10.0 \text{ mL HCN } \times \frac{0.687 \text{ g HCN}}{1 \text{ mL HCN}} \times \frac{1 \text{ mol HCN}}{27.03 \text{ g HCN}} = 0.25\underline{4}1 \text{ mol HCN}$$

$$0.2541 \text{ mol HCN}(l) \quad \rightarrow \quad 0.2541 \text{ mol HCN}(g)$$

$$(\Delta H_f^{\circ} = 108.9 \text{ kJ/mol}) \qquad (\Delta H_f^{\circ} = 135 \text{ kJ/mol})$$

$$\Delta H^{\circ} = 0.2541 \text{ mol } \times [135 \text{ kJ/mol} - 108.9 \text{ kJ/mol}] = 6.\underline{6}33 = 6.6 \text{ kJ}$$

11.147. First, convert the mass to moles; then multiply by the standard heat of formation to obtain the heat absorbed in vaporizing this mass:

$$12.5 \text{ g P}_4 \times \frac{1 \text{ mol P}_4}{123.88 \text{ g P}_4} = 0.10\underline{0}9 \text{ mol P}_4$$

$$0.1009 \text{ mol P}_4 \times \frac{95.4 \text{ J}}{^{\circ}\text{C} \cdot \text{mol P}_4} \times (44.1^{\circ}\text{C} - 25.0^{\circ}\text{C}) = 18\underline{3}.86 \text{ J} = 0.18\underline{3}86 \text{ kJ}$$

$$2.63 \text{ kJ/mol P}_4 \times 0.1009 \text{ mol P}_4 = 0.26\underline{5}37 \text{ kJ}$$

Total heat = $0.26537 \text{ kJ} + 0.18386 \text{ kJ} = 0.44\underline{9}23 = 0.449 \text{ kJ} = 449 \text{ J}$

11.149. Use the ideal gas law to calculate the total number of moles of monomer and dimer:

$$n = \frac{PV}{RT} = \frac{(436/760)\text{atm } \times 1.000 \text{ L}}{[0.082057 \text{ L} \cdot \text{atm}/(\text{K} \cdot \text{mol})] \times 373.75 \text{ K}}$$

$$= 0.018\underline{7}057 \text{ mol monomer } + \text{ dimer}$$

$$(0.018\underline{7}057 \text{ mol monomer } + \text{ dimer}) \times \frac{0.630 \text{ mol dimer}}{1 \text{ mol dimer } + \text{ monomer}} = 0.011\underline{7}8 \text{ mol dimer}$$

$$0.0187057 \text{ mol both } - 0.01178 \text{ mol dimer } = 0.006\underline{9}2 \text{ mol monomer}$$

$$\text{Mass dimer} = 0.011\underline{7}8 \text{ mol dimer } \times \frac{120.1 \text{ g dimer}}{1 \text{ mol dimer}} = 1.4\underline{1}4 \text{ g dimer}$$

$$\text{Mass monomer} = 0.00692 \text{ mol monomer } \times \frac{60.05 \text{ g monomer}}{1 \text{ mol monomer}} = 0.4\underline{1}55 \text{ g monomer}$$

$$\text{Density} = \frac{1.414 \text{ g} + 0.4155 \text{ g}}{1.000 \text{ L}} = 1.8\underline{2}9 = 1.83 \text{ g/L vapor}$$

Copyright © Cengage Learning. All rights reserved.

CHAPTER 12

Solutions

■ SOLUTIONS TO EXERCISES

Note on significant figures: If the final answer to a solution needs to be rounded off, it is given first with one nonsignificant figure, and the last significant figure is underlined. The final answer is then rounded to the correct number of significant figures. In multistep problems, intermediate answers are given with at least one nonsignificant figure; however, only the final answer has been rounded off.

12.1. An example of a solid solution prepared from a liquid and a solid is a dental filling made of liquid mercury and solid silver.

12.2. The C_4H_9OH molecules will be more soluble in water because their –OH ends can form hydrogen bonds with water.

12.3. The Na^+ ion has a larger energy of hydration because its ionic radius is smaller, giving Na^+ a more concentrated electric field than K^+.

12.4. Write Henry's law $(S = k_H P)$ for 159 mmHg (P_2), and divide it by Henry's law for 1 atm, or 760 mmHg (P_1). Then substitute the experimental values of P_1, P_2, and S_1 to solve for S_2.

$$\frac{S_2}{S_1} = \frac{k_H P_2}{k_H P_1} = \frac{P_2}{P_1}$$

Solving for S_2 gives

$$S_2 = \frac{P_2 S_1}{P_1} = \frac{(159 \text{ mmHg})(0.0404 \text{ g } O_2/L)}{760 \text{ mmHg}} = 8.4\underline{5}2 \times 10^{-3} = 8.45 \times 10^{-3} \text{ g } O_2/L$$

12.5. The mass of HCl in 20.2% HCl (0.202 = fraction of HCl) is

$$0.202 \times 35.0 \text{ g} = 7.0\underline{7}0 = 7.07 \text{ g HCl}$$

The mass of H_2O in 20.2% HCl is

$$35.0 \text{ g solution} - 7.07 \text{ g HCl} = 27.9\underline{3} = 27.9 \text{ g } H_2O$$

Copyright © Cengage Learning. All rights reserved.

12.6. Calculate the moles of toluene using its molar mass of 92.14 g/mol:

$$35.6 \text{ g toluene} \times \frac{1 \text{ mol toluene}}{92.14 \text{ g toluene}} = 0.386\underline{3} \text{ mol toluene}$$

To calculate molality, divide the moles of toluene by the mass in kg of the solvent (C_6H_6):

$$\text{Molality} \times \frac{0.3863 \text{ mol toluene}}{0.125 \text{ kg solvent}} = 3.09\underline{0}4 = 3.09 \text{ } m \text{ toluene}$$

12.7. The number of moles of toluene = 0.3863 (previous exercise); the number of moles of benzene is

$$125 \text{ g benzene} \times \frac{1 \text{ mol benzene}}{78.11 \text{ g benzene}} = 1.6\underline{0}03 \text{ mol benzene}$$

The total number of moles is 1.6003 + 0.3863 = 1.9\underline{8}66, and the mole fractions are

$$\text{Mole fraction benzene} \times \frac{1.6003 \text{ mol benzene}}{1.9866 \text{ mol}} = 0.805\underline{5}4 = 0.806$$

$$\text{Mole fraction toluene} \times \frac{0.3863 \text{ mol toluene}}{1.9866 \text{ mol}} = 0.194\underline{4} = 0.194$$

The sum of the mole fractions = 1.000.

12.8. This solution contains 0.120 moles of methanol dissolved in 1.00 kg of ethanol. The number of moles in 1.00 kg of ethanol is

$$1.00 \times 10^3 \text{ g } C_2H_5OH \times \frac{1 \text{ mol } C_2H_5OH}{46.07 \text{ g } C_2H_5OH} = 21.\underline{7}06 \text{ mol } C_2H_5OH$$

The total number of moles is 21.706 + 0.120 = 21.\underline{8}26, and the mole fractions are

$$\text{Mole fraction } C_2H_5OH = \frac{21.706 \text{ mol } C_2H_5OH}{21.826 \text{ mol}} = 0.994\underline{5}01 = 0.995$$

$$\text{Mole fraction } CH_3OH = \frac{0.120 \text{ mol } CH_3OH}{21.826 \text{ mol}} = 0.0054\underline{9}8 = 0.00550$$

The sum of the mole fractions is 1.000.

12.9. One mole of solution contains 0.250 mol methanol and 0.750 mol ethanol. The mass of this amount of ethanol, the solvent, is

$$0.750 \text{ mol } C_2H_5OH \times \frac{46.07 \text{ g } C_2H_5OH}{1 \text{ mol } C_2H_5OH} = 34.\underline{5}5 \text{ g } C_2H_5OH \text{ (0.03455 kg)}$$

The molality of methanol in the ethanol solvent is

$$\frac{0.250 \text{ mol } CH_3OH}{0.03455 \text{ kg } C_2H_5OH} = 7.2\underline{3}58 = 7.24 \text{ m } CH_3OH$$

Copyright © Cengage Learning. All rights reserved.

12.10.   Assume an amount of solution contains 1 kg of water. The mass of urea in this mass is

$$3.42 \text{ mol urea } \times \frac{60.05 \text{ g urea}}{1 \text{ mol urea}} = 20\underline{5}.4 \text{ g urea}$$

The total mass of solution is $205.4 + 1000.0 \text{ g} = 120\underline{5}.4 \text{ g}$. The volume and molarity are

$$\text{Volume of solution} = 120\underline{5}.4 \text{ g} \times \frac{1 \text{ mL}}{1.045 \text{ g}} = 115\underline{3}.49 \text{ mL} = 1.15349 \text{ L}$$

$$\text{Molarity} = \frac{3.42 \text{ mol urea}}{1.15349 \text{ L solution}} = 2.9\underline{6}49 \text{ mol/L} = 2.96 \, M$$

12.11.   Assume a volume equal to 1.000 L of solution. Then

$$\text{Mass of solution} = 1.029 \text{ g/mL} \times (1.000 \times 10^3 \text{ mL}) = 1029 \text{ g}$$

$$\text{Mass of urea} = 2.00 \text{ mol urea} \times \frac{60.05 \text{ g urea}}{1 \text{ mol urea}} = 120.1 \text{ g urea}$$

$$\text{Mass of water} = (1029 - 120.1) \text{ g} = 90\underline{8}.9 \text{ g water } (0.90\underline{8}9 \text{ kg})$$

$$\text{Molality} = \frac{2.00 \text{ mol urea}}{0.9089 \text{ kg solvent}} = 2.2\underline{0}04 = 2.20 \, m \text{ urea}$$

12.12.   Calculate the moles of naphthalene and the moles of chloroform:

$$0.515 \text{ g C}_{10}\text{H}_8 \times \frac{1 \text{ mol C}_{10}\text{H}_8}{128.17 \text{ g C}_{10}\text{H}_8} = 0.00401\underline{8} \text{ mol C}_{10}\text{H}_8$$

$$60.8 \text{ g CHCl}_3 \times \frac{1 \text{ mol CHCl}_3}{119.38 \text{ g CHCl}_3} = 0.50\underline{9}29 \text{ mol CHCl}_3$$

The total number of moles is $0.004018 + 0.50929 = 0.51\underline{3}3 \text{ mol}$, and the mole fraction of chloroform is

$$\text{Mole fraction CHCl}_3 = \frac{0.50929 \text{ mol CHCl}_3}{0.5133 \text{ mol}} = 0.99\underline{2}1$$

$$\text{Mole fraction C}_{10}\text{H}_8 = \frac{0.004018 \text{ mol C}_{10}\text{H}_8}{0.5133 \text{ mol}} = 0.0078\underline{2}8$$

The vapor-pressure lowering is

$$\Delta P = P^\circ X_{\text{C}_{10}\text{H}_8} = (156 \text{ mmHg})(0.007828) = 1.2\underline{2}1 = 1.22 \text{ mmHg}$$

Use Raoult's law to calculate the vapor pressure of chloroform:

$$P = P^\circ X_{\text{CHCl}_3} = (156 \text{ mmHg})(0.9921) = 15\underline{4}.7 = 155 \text{ mmHg}$$

Copyright © Cengage Learning. All rights reserved.

12.13. Solve for c_m in the freezing-point-depression equation ($\Delta T = K_f c_m$; K_f in Table 12.3):

$$c_m = \frac{\Delta T}{K_f} = \frac{0.150°C}{1.858°C/m} = 0.80\underline{7}3 \ m$$

Use the molal concentration to solve for the mass of ethylene glycol:

$$\frac{0.08073 \ \text{mol glycol}}{1 \ \text{kg solvent}} \ \text{x} \ 0.0378 \ \text{kg solvent} = 0.00305\underline{1} \ \text{mol glycol}$$

$$0.003051 \ \text{mol glycol} \ \text{x} \ \frac{62.1 \ \text{g glycol}}{1 \ \text{mol glycol}} = 1.8\underline{9}4 \ \text{x} \ 10^{-1} = 1.89 \ \text{x} \ 10^{-1} \ \text{g glycol}$$

12.14. Calculate the moles of ascorbic acid (vitamin C) from the molality, and then divide the mass of 0.930 g by the number of moles to obtain the molar mass:

$$\frac{0.0555 \ \text{mol vit. C}}{1 \ \text{kg H}_2\text{O}} \ \text{x} \ 0.0950 \ \text{kg H}_2\text{O} = 0.00527\underline{2} \ \text{mol vit C}$$

$$\frac{0.930 \ \text{g vit. C}}{0.005272 \ \text{mol vit. C}} = 17\underline{6}.4 = 176 \ \text{g/mol}$$

The molecular mass of ascorbic acid, or vitamin C, is 176 amu.

12.15. The molal concentration of white phosphorus is

$$c_m = \frac{\Delta T}{K_b} = \frac{0.159°C}{2.40°C/m} = 0.066\underline{2}5 \ m$$

The number of moles of white phosphorus (P_x) present in this solution is

$$\frac{0.06625 \ \text{mol P}_x}{1 \ \text{kg CS}_2} \ \text{x} \ 0.0250 \ \text{kg CS}_2 = 0.00165\underline{6} \ \text{mol P}_x$$

The molar mass of white phosphorus equals the mass divided by moles:

$$0.205 \ \text{g} \div 0.001656 \ \text{mol} = 12\underline{3}.77 = 124 \ \text{g/mol}$$

Thus, the molecular mass of P_x is 124 amu. The number of P atoms in the molecule of white phosphorus is obtained by dividing the molecular mass by the atomic mass of P:

$$\frac{123.77 \ \text{amu P}_x}{30.97 \ \text{amu P}} = 3.9\underline{9}65 = 4.00$$

Hence, the molecular formula is P_4 ($x = 4$).

Copyright © Cengage Learning. All rights reserved.

12.16.   The number of moles of sucrose is

$$5.0 \text{ g sucrose } \times \frac{1 \text{ mol sucrose}}{342.3 \text{ g sucrose}} = 0.01\underline{4}6 \text{ mol sucrose}$$

The molarity of the solution is

$$\frac{0.0146 \text{ mol sucrose}}{0.100 \text{ L}} = 0.1\underline{4}6 \ M \text{ sucrose}$$

The osmotic pressure, π, is equal to MRT and is calculated as follows:

$$\frac{0.146 \text{ mol sucrose}}{1 \text{ L}} \times \frac{0.0821 \text{ L} \bullet \text{atm}}{\text{K} \bullet \text{mol}} \times 293 \text{ K} = 3.\underline{5}1 = 3.5 \text{ atm}$$

12.17.   The number of ions from each formula unit is i. Here,

$$i = 1 + 2 = 3$$

The boiling-point elevation is

$$\Delta T_b = K_b c_m = 3 \times \frac{0.512°\text{C}}{m} \times 0.050 \ m = 0.07\underline{6}81 = 0.077°\text{C}$$

The boiling point of aqueous $MgCl_2$ is 100.077°C.

12.18. $AlCl_3$ would be most effective in coagulating colloidal sulfur because of the greater magnitude of charge on the Al ion (3+).

■ ANSWERS TO SELF-ASSESSMENT AND REVIEW QUESTIONS

12.1. An example of a gaseous solution is air, in which nitrogen (78%) acts as a solvent for a gas such as oxygen (21%). Recall that the solvent is the component that is present in greater amount. An example of a liquid solution containing a gas is any carbonated beverage in which water acts as the solvent for carbon dioxide gas. Ethanol in water is an example of a liquid-liquid solution. An example of a solid solution is any gold-silver alloy.

12.2. The two factors that explain differences in solubilities are (1) the natural tendency of substances to mix together, or the natural tendency of substances to become disordered, and (2) the relative forces of attraction between solute species (or solvent species) compared to that between the solute and solvent species. The strongest interactions are always achieved.

12.3. This is not a case of "like dissolves like." There are strong hydrogen-bonding forces between the water molecules. For the octane to mix with water, hydrogen bonds must be broken and replaced by the much weaker London forces between water and octane. Thus, octane does not dissolve in water, because the maximum forces of attraction among molecules are obtained if it does not dissolve.

Copyright © Cengage Learning. All rights reserved.

12.4. In most cases, the wide differences in solubility can be explained in terms of the different energies of attraction between ions in the crystal and between ions and water. Hydration energy is used to measure the attraction of ions for water molecules, and lattice energy is used to measure the attraction of positive ions for negative ions in the crystal lattice. An ionic substance is soluble when the hydration energy is much larger than the lattice energy. An ionic substance is insoluble when the lattice energy is much larger than the hydration energy.

12.5. A sodium chloride crystal dissolves in water because of two factors. The positive Na^+ ion is strongly attracted to the oxygen (negative end of the water dipole) and dissolves as $Na^+(aq)$. The negative Cl^- ion is strongly attracted to the hydrogens (positive end of the water dipole) and dissolves as $Cl^-(aq)$.

12.6. When the temperature (energy of a solution) is increased, the solubility of an ionic compound usually increases. A number of salts are exceptions to this rule, particularly a number of calcium salts such as calcium acetate, calcium sulfate, and calcium hydroxide (although the solubilities of calcium bromide, calcium chloride, calcium fluoride, and calcium iodide all increase with temperature).

12.7. Calcium chloride is an example of a salt that releases heat when it dissolves (exothermic heat of solution). Ammonium nitrate is an example of a salt that absorbs heat when it dissolves (endothermic heat of solution).

12.8. As the temperature of the solution was increased by heating, the concentration of the dissolved gas would decrease.

12.9. A carbonated beverage must be stored in a closed container because carbonated beverages must contain more carbon dioxide than is soluble in water at atmospheric pressure. It is possible to add carbon dioxide under pressure to a closed container before it is sealed and increase the solubility of carbon dioxide. This is an illustration of Le Châtelier's principle, which states that the equilibrium between gaseous and dissolved carbon dioxide is shifted in favor of the dissolved carbon dioxide by an increase in pressure.

12.10. According to Le Châtelier's principle, a gas is more soluble in a liquid at higher pressures because, when the gas dissolves in the liquid, the system decreases in volume, tending to decrease the applied pressure. However, when a solid dissolves in a liquid, there is very little volume change. Thus, pressure has very little effect on the solubility of a solid in a liquid.

12.11. The four ways to express the concentration of a solute in a solution are (1) molarity, which is moles per liter; (2) mass percentage of solute, which is the percentage by mass of solute contained in a given mass of solution; (3) molality, which is the moles of solute per kilogram of solvent; and (4) mole fraction, which is the moles of the component substance divided by the total moles of solution.

Copyright © Cengage Learning. All rights reserved.

12.12.   The vapor pressure of the solvent of the dilute solution is larger than the vapor pressure of the solvent of the more concentrated solution (Raoult's law). Thus, the more dilute solution loses solvent and becomes more concentrated while the solvent molecules in the vapor state condense into the concentrated solution, making it more dilute. After sufficient time has passed, the vapor pressure of the solvent in the closed container will reach a steady value (equilibrium), at which time the concentration of solute will be the same in the two solutions.

12.13.   In fractional distillation, the vapor that first appears over a solution will have a greater mole fraction of the more volatile component. If a portion of this is vaporized and condensed, the liquid will be still richer in the more volatile component. After successive distillation stages, eventually the more volatile component will be obtained in pure form (Figure 12.20).

12.14.   The boiling point of the solution is higher because the nonvolatile solute lowers the vapor pressure of the solvent. Thus, the temperature must be increased to a value greater than the boiling point of the pure solvent to achieve a vapor pressure equal to atmospheric pressure.

12.15.   One application is the use of ethylene glycol in automobile radiators as antifreeze; the glycol-water mixture usually has a freezing point well below the average low temperature during the winter. A second application is spreading sodium chloride on icy roads in the winter to melt the ice. The ice usually melts, because at equilibrium, a concentrated solution of NaCl usually freezes at a temperature below that of the roads.

12.16.   If a pressure greater than the osmotic pressure of the ocean water is applied, the natural osmotic flow can be reversed. Then, the water solvent flows from the ocean water through a membrane to a more dilute solution or to pure water, leaving behind the salt and other ionic compounds from the ocean in a more concentrated solution.

12.17.   Part of the light from the sun is scattered in the direction of an observer by fine particles in the clouds (Tyndall effect) rather than being completely absorbed by the clouds. The scattered light becomes visible against the darker background of dense clouds.

12.18.   Fog is an aerosol, whipped cream is a foam, mayonnaise is an emulsion, solid silver chloride dispersed in water is a sol, and fruit jelly is a gel.

12.19.   The polar –OH group on glycerol allows it to interact (hydrogen-bond) with the polar water molecules, which means it is like water and, therefore, will dissolve in water. Benzene is a nonpolar molecule, which indicates that it is not "like" water and, therefore, will not dissolve in water.

12.20.   Soap removes oil from a fabric by absorbing the oil into the hydrophobic centers of the soap micelles and off the surface of the fabric. Rinsing removes the micelles from contact with the fabric and leaves only water on the fabric, which can then be dried.

12.21.   The answer is a, 6.50×10^{-2} mol.

Copyright © Cengage Learning. All rights reserved.

12.22.   The answer is c, 8.66 *m*.

12.23.   The answer is e, 25.3 g/mol.

12.24.   The answer is a, the solution would freeze at a lower temperature than pure water.

■ SOLUTIONS TO PRACTICE PROBLEMS

Note on significant figures: If the final answer to a solution needs to be rounded off, it is given first with one nonsignificant figure, and the last significant figure is underlined. The final answer is then rounded to the correct number of significant figures. In multistep problems, intermediate answers are given with at least one nonsignificant figure; however, only the final answer has been rounded off. Atomic masses are rounded to two decimal places, except for that of hydrogen.

12.37.   An example of a liquid solution prepared by dissolving a gas in a liquid is household ammonia, which consists of ammonia (NH_3) gas dissolved in water.

12.39.   Boric acid would be more soluble in ethanol because this acid is polar and is more soluble in a more polar solvent. It can also hydrogen-bond to ethanol but not to benzene.

12.41.   The order of increasing solubility is $H_2O < CH_2OHCH_2OH < C_{10}H_{22}$. The solubility in nonpolar hexane increases with the decreasing polarity of the solute.

12.43.   The Al^{3+} ion has both a greater charge and a smaller ionic radius than Mg^{2+}, so Al^{3+} should have a greater energy of hydration.

12.45.   The order is $Ba(IO_3)_2 < Sr(IO_3)_2 < Ca(IO_3)_2 < Mg(IO_3)_2$. The iodate ion is fairly large, so the lattice energy for all these iodates should change to a smaller degree than the hydration energy of the cations. Therefore, solubility should increase with decreasing cation radius.

12.47.   Using Henry's law, let S_1 = the solubility at 1.00 atm (P_1), and S_2 = the solubility at 5.50 atm (P_2).

$$S_2 = \frac{P_2 S_1}{P_1} = \frac{(5.50 \text{ atm})(0.161 \text{ g}/100 \text{ mL})}{1.00 \text{ atm}} = 0.88\underline{5}5 = 0.886 \text{ g}/100 \text{ mL}$$

12.49.   First, calculate the mass of KI in the solution; then calculate the mass of water needed.

$$\text{Mass KI} = 72.5 \text{ g} \times \frac{5.00 \text{ g KI}}{100 \text{ g solution}} = 3.6\underline{2}50 = 3.63 \text{ g KI}$$

$$\text{Mass H}_2\text{O} = 72.5 \text{ g soln} - 3.6250 \text{ g KI} = 68.\underline{8}75 = 68.9 \text{ g H}_2\text{O}$$

Dissolve 3.63 g KI in 68.9 g of water.

Copyright © Cengage Learning. All rights reserved.

12.51. Multiply the mass of KI by 100 g of solution per 5.00 g KI (reciprocal of percentage).

$$0.258 \text{ g KI } \times \frac{100 \text{ g solution}}{5.00 \text{ g KI}} = 5.1\underline{6}0 = 5.16 \text{ g solution}$$

12.53. Convert mass of vanillin ($C_8H_8O_3$, molar mass 152.14 g/mol) to moles, convert mg of ether to kg, and divide for molality.

$$0.0391 \text{ g vanillin } \times \frac{1 \text{ mol vanillin}}{152.14 \text{ g vanillin}} = 2.5\underline{7}0 \times 10^{-4} \text{ mol vanillin}$$

$$168.5 \text{ mg ether} \times 1 \text{ kg}/10^6 \text{ mg} = 168.5 \times 10^{-6} \text{ kg ether}$$

$$\text{Molality} = \frac{2.570 \times 10^{-4} \text{ mol vanillin}}{168.5 \times 10^{-6} \text{ kg ether}} = 1.5\underline{2}52 = 1.53 \; m \text{ vanillin}$$

12.55. Convert mass of fructose ($C_6H_{12}O_6$, molar mass 180.16 g/mol) to moles, and then multiply by one kg H_2O per 0.125 mol fructose (the reciprocal of molality).

$$1.75 \text{ g fructose } \times \frac{1 \text{ mol fructose}}{180.16 \text{ g fructose}} \times \frac{1 \text{ kg H}_2\text{O}}{0.125 \text{ mol fructose}} = 0.077\underline{7}0 \text{ kg } (77.7 \text{ g H}_2\text{O})$$

12.57. Convert masses to moles, and then calculate the mole fractions.

$$65.0 \text{ g alc. } \times \frac{1 \text{ mol alc.}}{60.09 \text{ g alc.}} = 1.0\underline{8}17 \text{ mol alc.}$$

$$35.0 \text{ g H}_2\text{O } \times \frac{1 \text{ mol H}_2\text{O}}{18.02 \text{ g H}_2\text{O}} = 1.9\underline{4}22 = 1.94 \text{ mol H}_2\text{O}$$

$$\text{Mole fraction alc.} = \frac{\text{mol alc.}}{\text{total mol}} = \frac{1.0817 \text{ mol}}{3.0239 \text{ mol}} = 0.35\underline{7}7 = 0.358$$

$$\text{Mole fraction H}_2\text{O} = \frac{\text{mol H}_2\text{O}}{\text{total mol}} = \frac{1.9422 \text{ mol}}{3.0239 \text{ mol}} = 0.64\underline{2}2 = 0.642$$

12.59. In the solution, for every 0.650 mol of NaClO there is 1.00 kg, or 1.00×10^3 g, of H_2O, so

$$1.00 \times 10^3 \text{ g H}_2\text{O } \times \frac{1 \text{ mol H}_2\text{O}}{18.02 \text{ g H}_2\text{O}} = 55.\underline{4}9 \text{ mol H}_2\text{O}$$

$$\text{Total mol} = 55.\underline{4}9 \text{ mol H}_2\text{O} + 0.650 \text{ mol NaClO} = 56.\underline{1}4 \text{ mol}$$

$$\text{Mole fraction NaClO} = \frac{\text{mol NaClO}}{\text{total mol}} = \frac{0.650 \text{ mol}}{56.\underline{1}\,4 \text{ mol}} = 0.011\underline{5}7 = 0.0116$$

Copyright © Cengage Learning. All rights reserved.

12.61. The total moles of solution $= 3.31$ mol $H_2O + 1.00$ mol HCl $= 4.31$ mol

Mole fraction HCl $= \dfrac{1 \text{ mol HCl}}{4.31 \text{ mol}} = 0.23\underline{2}01 = 0.232$

$3.31 \text{ mol } H_2O \times \dfrac{18.02 \text{ g } H_2O}{1 \text{ mol } H_2O} \times \dfrac{1 \text{ kg } H_2O}{10^3 \text{ g } H_2O} = 5.9\underline{6}5 \times 10^{-2} \text{ kg } H_2O$

Molality $= \dfrac{1.00 \text{ mol HCl}}{5.965 \times 10^{-2} \text{ kg } H_2O} = 16.\underline{7}6 = 16.8\ m$

12.63. The mass of 1.000 L of solution is 1.022 kg. In the solution, there is 0.580 mol $H_2C_2O_4$ (OA) for every 1.0000 kg of water. Convert this number of moles to mass.

$0.580 \text{ mol OA} \times \dfrac{90.04 \text{ g OA}}{1 \text{ mol OA}} \times \dfrac{1 \text{ kg OA}}{10^3 \text{ g OA}} = 0.052\underline{2}2 \text{ kg OA}$

The total mass of the solution containing 1.000 kg H_2O and 0.580 mol OA is calculated as follows:

Mass $= 1.0000 \text{ kg } H_2O + 0.05222 \text{ kg OA} = 1.052\underline{2}2 \text{ kg}$

Use this to relate the mass of 1.000 L (1.022 kg) of solution to the amount of solute:

$1.022 \text{ kg solution} \times \dfrac{0.580 \text{ mol OA}}{1.05222 \text{ kg solution}} = 0.56\underline{3}3 \text{ mol OA}$

Molarity $= \dfrac{0.5633 \text{ mol OA}}{1.00 \text{ L solution}} = 0.56\underline{3}3 = 0.563\ M$

12.65. In 1.000 L of vinegar, there is 0.763 mol of acetic acid. The total mass of the 1.000-L solution is 1.004 kg. Start by calculating the mass of acetic acid (AA) in the solution.

$0.763 \text{ mol AA} \times \dfrac{60.05 \text{ g AA}}{1 \text{ mol AA}} = 45.\underline{8}2 \text{ g AA} \ (0.045\underline{8}2 \text{ kg AA})$

The mass of water may be found by difference:

Mass $H_2O = 1.004 \text{ kg soln} - 0.04582 \text{ kg AA} = 0.95\underline{8}2 \text{ kg } H_2O$

Molality $= \dfrac{0.763 \text{ mol AA}}{0.9582 \text{ kg } H_2O} = 0.79\underline{6}2 = 0.796\ m$

Copyright © Cengage Learning. All rights reserved.

12.67.   To find the mole fraction of sucrose, first find the amounts of both sucrose (suc.) and water:

$$20.2 \text{ g sucrose } \times \frac{1 \text{ mol sucrose}}{342.30 \text{ g sucrose}} = 0.05901 \text{ mol sucrose}$$

$$70.1 \text{ g H}_2\text{O } \times \frac{1 \text{ mol H}_2\text{O}}{18.02 \text{ g H}_2\text{O}} = 3.890 \text{ mol H}_2\text{O}$$

$$X_{\text{sucrose}} = \frac{0.05901 \text{ mol sucrose}}{(3.890 + 0.05901) \text{ mol}} = 0.01494$$

From Raoult's law, the vapor pressure (P) and lowering (ΔP) are

$$P = P^\circ_{\text{H}_2\text{O}} \, X_{\text{H}_2\text{O}} = P^\circ_{\text{H}_2\text{O}} \, (1 - X_{\text{suc.}}) = (42.2 \text{ mmHg})(1 - 0.01494)$$

$$= 41.569 = 41.6 \text{ mmHg}$$

$$\Delta P = P^\circ_{\text{H}_2\text{O}} \, X_{\text{suc.}} = (42.2 \text{ mmHg})(0.01494) = 0.6306 = 0.631 \text{ mmHg}$$

12.69.   Find the molality of glycerol (gly.) in the solution first:

$$0.150 \text{ g gly. } \times \frac{1 \text{ mol gly.}}{92.095 \text{ g gly.}} = 0.001628 \text{ mol gly.}$$

$$\text{Molality} = \frac{0.001628 \text{ mol gly.}}{0.0200 \text{ kg solvent}} = 0.081437 \, m$$

Substitute $K_b = 0.512°C/m$ and $K_f = 1.858 °C/m$ (Table 12.3) into equations for ΔT_b and ΔT_f:

$$\Delta T_b = K_b m = 0.512°C/m \times 0.081437 \, m = 0.04169°C$$

$$T_b = 100.000 + 0.04169 = 100.04169 = 100.042°C$$

$$\Delta T_f = K_f m = 1.858°C/m \times 0.081437 \, m = 0.15131°C$$

$$T_f = 0.000 - 0.15131 = -0.15131 = -0.151°C$$

12.71.   Calculate ΔT_f, the freezing-point depression, and, using $K_f = 1.858°C/m$ (Table 12.3), the molality, c_m.

$$\Delta T_f = 0.000°C - (-0.086°C) = 0.086°C$$

$$c_m = \frac{\Delta T_f}{K_f} = \frac{0.086°C}{1.858°C/m} = 4.628 \times 10^{-2} = 4.6 \times 10^{-2} \, m$$

12.73.   Find the moles of unknown solute from the definition of molality:

$$\text{Mol}_{\text{solute}} = m \times \text{kg solvent} = \frac{0.0698 \text{ mol}}{1 \text{ kg solvent}} \times 0.002135 \text{ kg solvent} = 1.490 \times 10^{-4} \text{ mol}$$

$$\text{Molar mass} = \frac{0.0182 \text{ g}}{1.490 \times 10^{-4} \text{ mol}} = 122.1 = 122 \text{ g/mol}$$

Copyright © Cengage Learning. All rights reserved.

The molecular mass is 122 amu.

Copyright © Cengage Learning. All rights reserved.

12.75.   Calculate ΔT_f, the freezing-point depression, and, using $K_f = 1.858°C/m$ (Table 12.3), the molality, c_m.

$$\Delta T_f = 26.84°C - 25.70°C = 1.14°C$$

$$c_m = \frac{\Delta T_f}{K_f} = \frac{1.14°C}{8.00°C/m} = 0.14\underline{2}5\ m$$

Find the moles of solute by rearranging the definition of molality:

$$\text{Mol} = m \times \text{kg solvent} = \frac{0.1425\ \text{mol}}{1\ \text{kg solvent}} \times 103 \times 10^{-6}\ \text{kg solvent} = 1.4\underline{6}7 \times 10^{-5}\ \text{mol}$$

$$\text{Molar mass} = \frac{2.39 \times 10^{-3}\ \text{g}}{1.467 \times 10^{-5}\ \text{mol}} = 16\underline{2}.9 = 163\ \text{g/mol}$$

The molecular mass is 163 amu.

12.77.   Use the equation for osmotic pressure (π) to solve for the molarity of the solution.

$$M = \frac{\pi}{RT} = \frac{1.47\ \text{mmHg} \times \left(\dfrac{1\ \text{atm}}{760\ \text{mmHg}}\right)}{(0.0821\ \text{L} \cdot \text{atm/K} \cdot \text{mol})(21 + 273)\text{K}} = 8.0\underline{1}3 \times 10^{-5}\ \text{mol/L}$$

Now, find the number of moles in 106 mL (0.106 L) using the molarity.

$$0.106\ \text{L} \times \frac{8.013 \times 10^{-5}\ \text{mol}}{1\ \text{L}} = 8.4\underline{9}4 \times 10^{-6}\ \text{mol}$$

$$\text{Molar mass} = \frac{0.582\ \text{g}}{8.494 \times 10^{-6}\ \text{mol}} = 6.8\underline{5}1 \times 10^4 = 6.85 \times 10^4\ \text{g/mol}$$

The molecular mass is 6.85×10^4 amu.

12.79.   Begin by noting that $i = 3$. Then calculate ΔT_f from the product of $iK_f c_m$:

$$3 \times \frac{1.858°C}{m} \times 0.0075\ m = 0.041\underline{8}°C$$

The freezing point $= 0.000°C - 0.0418°C = -0.041\underline{8} = -0.042°C$.

12.81.   Begin by calculating the molarity of $Cr(NH_3)_5Cl_3$.

$$1.40 \times 10^{-2}\ \text{g}\ Cr(NH_3)_5Cl_3 \times \frac{1\ \text{mol}\ Cr(NH_3)_5Cl_3}{243.5\ \text{g}\ Cr(NH_3)_5Cl_3} = 5.7\underline{4}9 \times 10^{-5}\ \text{mol}\ Cr(NH_3)_5Cl_3$$

$$\text{Molarity} = \frac{5.749 \times 10^{-5}\ \text{mol}\ Cr(NH_3)_5Cl_3}{0.0250\ \text{L}} = 0.0022\underline{9}9\ M$$

Copyright © Cengage Learning. All rights reserved.

Now find the hypothetical osmotic pressure, assuming $Cr(NH_3)_5Cl_3$ does not ionize:

$$\pi = MRT = (2.30 \times 10^{-3} \, M) \times \frac{0.0821 \, \text{L} \cdot \text{atm}}{\text{K} \cdot \text{mol}} \times 298 \, \text{K} \times \frac{760 \, \text{mmHg}}{1 \, \text{atm}} = 42.\underline{7}7 \, \text{mmHg}$$

The measured osmotic pressure is greater than the hypothetical osmotic pressure. The number of ions formed per formula unit equals the ratio of the measured pressure to the hypothetical pressure:

$$i = \frac{119 \, \text{mmHg}}{42.77 \, \text{mmHg}} = 2.7\underline{8}2 \cong 3 \, \text{ions/formula unit}$$

12.83.

    a.   Aerosol (liquid water in air)

    b.   Sol [solid $Mg(OH)_2$ in liquid water]

    c.   Foam (air in liquid soap solution)

    d.   Sol (solid silt in liquid water)

12.85.   Because the As_2S_3 particles are negatively charged, the effective coagulation requires a highly charged cation, so $Al_2(SO_4)_3$ is the best choice.

■ SOLUTIONS TO GENERAL PROBLEMS

12.87.   Using Henry's law [$S_2 = S_1 \times (P_2/P_1)$, where $P_1 = 1.00$ atm], find the solubility of each gas at P_2, its partial pressure. For N_2, $P_2 = 0.800 \times 1.00$ atm $= 0.800$ atm; for O_2, $P_2 = 0.200$ atm.

$$N_2: S_1 \times \frac{P_2}{P_1} = (0.0175 \, \text{g/L H}_2\text{O}) \times \frac{0.800 \, \text{atm}}{1.00 \, \text{atm}} = 0.0140\underline{0} \, \text{g/L H}_2\text{O}$$

$$O_2: S_2 \times \frac{P_2}{P_1} = (0.0393 \, \text{g/L H}_2\text{O}) \times \frac{0.200 \, \text{atm}}{1.00 \, \text{atm}} = 0.00786\underline{0} \, \text{g/L H}_2\text{O}$$

In 1.00 L of the water, there are 0.0140 g of N_2 and 0.00786 g of O_2. If the water is heated to drive off both dissolved gases, the gas mixture that is expelled will contain 0.0140 g of N_2 and 0.00786 g of O_2.

Convert both masses to moles using the molar masses:

$$0.0140 \, \text{g N}_2 \times \frac{1 \, \text{mol N}_2}{28.01 \, \text{g N}_2} = 4.9\underline{9}8 \times 10^{-4} \, \text{mol}$$

$$0.00786 \, \text{g O}_2 \times \frac{1 \, \text{mol O}_2}{32.00 \, \text{g O}_2} = 2.4\underline{5}6 \times 10^{-4} \, \text{mol}$$

Copyright © Cengage Learning. All rights reserved.

Now calculate the mole fraction of each gas:

$$X_{N_2} = \frac{\text{mol } N_2}{\text{total mol}} = \frac{4.998 \times 10^{-4} \text{ mol}}{(4.998 + 2.456) \times 10^{-4} \text{ mol}} = 0.67\underline{0}51 = 0.671$$

$$X_{O_2} = 1 - X_{N_2} = 1 - 0.67\underline{0}51 = 0.32\underline{9}49 = 0.329$$

12.89. Assume a volume of 1.000 L whose mass is then 1.024 kg. Use the percent composition given to find the mass of each of the components of the solution.

$$1.024 \text{ kg soln} \times \frac{8.50 \text{ kg NH}_4\text{Cl}}{100.00 \text{ kg soln}} = 0.087\underline{0}4 \text{ kg NH}_4\text{Cl}$$

Mass of H_2O = 1.024 kg soln − 0.08704 kg NH_4Cl = 0.9370 kg H_2O

Convert mass of NH_4Cl and water to moles:

$$87.04 \text{ g NH}_4\text{Cl} \times \frac{1 \text{ mol NH}_4\text{Cl}}{53.49 \text{ g NH}_4\text{Cl}} = 1.6\underline{2}7 \text{ mol NH}_4\text{Cl}$$

$$937.0 \text{ g H}_2O \times \frac{1 \text{ mol H}_2O}{18.015 \text{ g H}_2O} = 52.\underline{0}1 \text{ mol H}_2O$$

$$\text{Molarity} = \frac{\text{mol NH}_4\text{Cl}}{\text{L solution}} = \frac{1.627 \text{ mol}}{1.00 \text{ L}} = 1.6\underline{2}7 = 1.63 \, M$$

$$\text{Molality} = \frac{\text{mol NH}_4\text{Cl}}{\text{kg H}_2O} = \frac{1.627 \text{ mol}}{0.9370 \text{ kg H}_2O} = 1.7\underline{3}6 = 1.74 \, m$$

$$X_{NH_4Cl} = \frac{\text{mol NH}_4\text{Cl}}{\text{total moles}} = \frac{1.627 \text{ mol}}{(52.01 + 1.627) \text{ mol}} = 0.030\underline{3}3 = 0.0303$$

12.91. In 1.00 mol of gas mixture, there are 0.51 mol of propane (pro.) and 0.49 mol of butane (but.). First, calculate the masses of these components.

$$0.51 \text{ mol pro.} \times \frac{44.10 \text{ g pro.}}{1 \text{ mol pro.}} = 22.491 \text{ g pro.}$$

$$0.49 \text{ mol but.} \times \frac{58.12 \text{ g but.}}{1 \text{ mol but.}} = 28.478 \text{ g but.}$$

The mass of 1.00 mol of gas mixture is the sum of the masses of the two components:

22.491 g pro. + 28.478 g but. = 50.969 g mixture

Therefore, in 50.969 g of the mixture, there are 22.491 g of propane and 28.478 g of butane.

Copyright © Cengage Learning. All rights reserved.

For a sample with a mass of 55 g,

$$55 \text{ g mixture } \times \frac{22.491 \text{ g pro.}}{50.969 \text{ g mixture}} = 24.26 = 24 \text{ g pro.}$$

$$55 \text{ g mixture } \times \frac{28.478 \text{ g but.}}{50.969 \text{ g mixture}} = 30.73 = 31 \text{ g but.}$$

12.93. $P_{ED} = P°_{ED}(X_{ED}) = 173 \text{ mmHg } (0.25) = 43.25 \text{ mmHg}$

$P_{PD} = P°_{PD}(X_{PD}) = 127 \text{ mmHg } (0.75) = 95.25 \text{ mmHg}$

$P = P_{ED} + P_{PD} = 43.25 + 95.25 = 138.50 = 139 \text{ mmHg}$

12.95.   Calculate the moles of $KAl(SO_4)_2 \cdot 12H_2O$ using its molar mass of 474.4 g/mol, and use this to calculate the three concentrations.

a.   The moles of $KAl(SO_4)_2 \cdot 12H_2O$ are calculated below, using the abbreviation "Hyd" for the formula of $KAl(SO_4)_2 \cdot 12H_2O$.

$$\text{moles Hyd} = 0.1186 \text{ g Hyd } \times \frac{1 \text{ mol Hyd}}{474.4 \text{ g Hyd}} = 0.00025000 = 0.0002500 \text{ mol}$$

Note that 1 mol of $KAl(SO_4)_2 \cdot 12H_2O$ contains 1 mole of $KAl(SO_4)_2$, so the molarity of $KAl(SO_4)_2$ can be calculated using the moles of $KAl(SO_4)_2 \cdot 12H_2O$.

$$\frac{\text{mol}}{L} = \frac{0.0002500 \text{ mol Hyd}}{1.000 \text{ L soln}} \times \frac{1 \text{ mol KAl(SO}_4)_2}{1 \text{ mol Hyd}} = 0.0002500 \ M \text{ KAl(SO}_4)_2$$

b.   The molarity of the SO_4^{2-} ion will be twice that of the $KAl(SO_4)_2$.

$$\frac{\text{mol SO}_4^{2-}}{L} = 0.0002500 \ M \text{ KAl(SO}_4)_2 \times \frac{2 \text{ mol SO}_4^{2-}}{1 \text{ mol KAl(SO}_4)_2} = 0.0005000 \ M$$

c.   Since the density of the solution is 1.00 g/mL, the mass of 1.000 L of solution is 1000 g, or 1.000 kg. Since molality is moles per 1.000 kg of solvent, the molality of $KAl(SO_4)_2$ equals 0.0002500 mol divided by 1.000 kg or 0.0002500 m (the same as the molarity).

12.97.   In 1.00 kg of a saturated solution of urea, there are 0.41 kg of urea (a molecular solute) and 0.59 kg of water. First, convert the mass of urea to moles.

$$0.41 \times 10^3 \text{ g urea } \times \frac{1 \text{ mol urea}}{60.06 \text{ g urea}} = 6.826 \text{ mol urea}$$

Then find the molality of the urea in the solution:

$$\text{Molality} = \frac{\text{mol urea}}{\text{kg H}_2\text{O}} \times \frac{6.826 \text{ mol urea}}{0.59 \text{ kg}} = 11.57 \ m$$

$\Delta T_f = K_f c_m = (1.858°C/m)(11.57 \ m) = 21.4°C$

$T_f = 0.0°C - 21.4°C = -21.4 = -21°C$

Copyright © Cengage Learning. All rights reserved.

12.99. $M = \dfrac{\pi}{RT} = \dfrac{7.7 \text{ atm}}{(0.0821 \text{ L}\bullet \text{atm/K}\bullet \text{mol})(37 \ + \ 273)\text{K}} = 0.3\underline{0}2 = 0.30 \text{ mol/L}$

12.101. Consider the equation $\Delta T_f = iK_f c_m$. For $CaCl_2$, $i = 3$; for glucose, $i = 1$. Because $c_m = 0.10$ for both solutions, the product of i and c_m will be larger for $CaCl_2$, as will ΔT_f. The solution of $CaCl_2$ will thus have the lower freezing point.

12.103. Assume there is 1.000 L of the solution, which will contain 18 mol H_2SO_4, molar mass 98.09 g/mol. The mass of the solution is

$$\text{Mass solution} = \dfrac{18 \text{ mol} \times 98.09 \text{ g/mol}}{0.98} = 1\underline{8}02 \text{ g}$$

Thus, the density of the solution is

$$d = \dfrac{1802 \text{ g}}{1000 \text{ mL}} = 1.8\underline{0}2 = 1.8 \text{ g/mL}$$

The mass of water in the solution is

$$\text{Mass } H_2O = 1802 \text{ g} \times 0.02 = \underline{3}6.0 \text{ g} = 0.0\underline{3}60 \text{ kg}$$

Thus, the molality of the solution is

$$m = \dfrac{18 \text{ mol } H_2SO_4}{0.0360 \text{ Kg}} = \underline{5}00 = 5 \times 10^2 \ m$$

12.105. Use the freezing-point-depression equation to find the molality of the solution. The freezing point of pure cyclohexane is 6.55°C, and $K_f = 20.0°C/m$. Thus

$$m = \dfrac{\Delta T_f}{K_f} = \dfrac{(6.55 \text{ - } 5.28)°C}{20.0°C/m} = 0.063\underline{5}0 \ m$$

The moles of the compound are

$$\text{Moles of compound} = \dfrac{0.06350 \text{ mol}}{1 \text{ kg solvent}} \times 0.00538 \text{ kg} = 3.4\underline{1}6 \times 10^{-4} \text{ mol}$$

The molar mass of the compound is

$$\text{Molar mass} = \dfrac{0.125 \text{ g}}{3.416 \times 10^{-4} \text{ mol}} = 36\underline{5}.8 \text{ g/mol}$$

Copyright © Cengage Learning. All rights reserved.

The moles of the elements in 100 g of the compound are

$$\text{Moles of Mn} = 28.17 \text{ g Mn} \times \frac{1 \text{ mol}}{54.94 \text{ g Mn}} = 0.51274 \text{ mol}$$

$$\text{Moles of C} = 30.80 \text{ g C} \times \frac{1 \text{ mol}}{12.01 \text{ g C}} = 2.5645 \text{ mol}$$

$$\text{Moles of O} = 41.03 \text{ g O} \times \frac{1 \text{ mol}}{16.00 \text{ g O}} = 2.5644 \text{ mol}$$

This gives mole ratios of 1 mol Mn to 5 mol C to 5 mol O. Therefore, the empirical formula of the compound is MnC_5O_5. The mass of this formula unit is approximately 195 amu. Since the molar mass of the compound is 366. g/mol, the value of n is

$$n = \frac{366 \text{ g/mol}}{195 \text{ g/unit}} = 1.88, \text{ or } 2$$

Therefore, the formula of the compound is $Mn_2C_{10}O_{10}$.

12.107.

a. Use the freezing-point-depression equation to find the molality of the solution. The freezing point of pure water is 0°C and $K_f = 1.858°C/m$. Thus

$$m = \frac{\Delta T_f}{K_f} = \frac{[0 - (-2.2)]°C}{1.858°C/m} = 1.184 \ m$$

The moles of the compound are

$$\text{Moles of compound} = \frac{1.184 \text{ mol}}{1 \text{ kg solvent}} \times 0.100 \text{ kg} = 0.1184 \text{ mol}$$

The molar mass of the compound is

$$\text{Molar mass} = \frac{18.0 \text{ g}}{0.1184 \text{ mol}} = 152.0 \text{ g/mol}$$

The moles of the elements in 100 g of the compound are

$$\text{Moles of C} = 48.64 \text{ g C} \times \frac{1 \text{ mol}}{12.01 \text{ g C}} = 4.0500 \text{ mol}$$

$$\text{Moles of H} = 8.16 \text{ g H} \times \frac{1 \text{ mol}}{1.008 \text{ g H}} = 8.095 \text{ mol}$$

$$\text{Moles of O} = 43.20 \text{ g O} \times \frac{1 \text{ mol}}{16.00 \text{ g O}} = 2.7000 \text{ mol}$$

Copyright © Cengage Learning. All rights reserved.

This gives mole ratios of 1.5 mol C to 3 mol H to 1 mol O. Multiplying by 2 gives ratios of 3 mol C to 6 mol H to 2 mol O. Therefore, the empirical formula of the compound is $C_3H_6O_2$. The mass of this formula unit is approximately 74 amu. Since the molar mass of the compound is 152.0. g/mol, the value of n is

$$n = \frac{152.0 \text{ g/mol}}{74 \text{ g/unit}} = 2.05, \text{ or } 2$$

Therefore, the formula of the compound is $C_6H_{12}O_4$.

b.   The molar mass of the compound is (to the nearest tenth of a gram)

$$6(12.01) + 12(1.008) + 4(16.00) = 148.\underline{1}56 = 148.2 \text{ g/mol}$$

12.109. Use the freezing-point-depression equation to find the molality of the solution. The freezing point of pure water is 0°C, and $K_f = 1.86°C/m$. Thus

$$m = \frac{\Delta T_f}{K_f} = \frac{[0 - (-2.3)]°C}{1.86°C/m} = 1.\underline{2}4 \text{ } m$$

Since this is a relatively dilute solution, we can assume the molarity and molality of the fish blood are approximately equal. The calculated molarity is for the total number of particles, assuming they behave ideally.

$$\pi = MRT = 1.\underline{2}4 \text{ mol/L} \times 0.08206 \text{ L}\bullet\text{atm/K}\bullet\text{mol} \times 298.2 \text{ K} = 3\underline{0}.3 = 30. \text{ atm}$$

■ SOLUTIONS TO CUMULATIVE-SKILLS PROBLEMS

12.125. First, determine the initial moles of each ion present in the solution before any reaction has occurred. There are five ions present: Na^+, 2 x 0.375 = 0.750 mol; CO_3^{2-}, 0.375 mol; Ca^{2+}, 0.125 mol; Ag^+, 0.200 mol; and NO_3^-, 0.200 + 2 x 0.125 = 0.450 mol. Two precipitates form: $CaCO_3$ and Ag_2CO_3. The balanced net ionic equations for their formation are

$$Ca^{2+}(aq) + CO_3^{2-}(aq) \rightarrow CaCO_3(s)$$

$$2Ag^+(aq) + CO_3^{2-}(aq) \rightarrow Ag_2CO_3(s)$$

There is sufficient CO_3^{2-} to precipitate all of the Ca^{2+} and all of the Ag^+ ions. The moles of excess CO_3^{2-} are calculated as follows: 0.375 − 0.125 − 1/2 x 0.200 = 0.150 mol remaining. Since the volume is 2.000 L, the molarities of the various ions are

$$M \text{ of } CO_3^{2-} \text{ left} = 0.150 \text{ mol} \div 2.000 \text{ L} = 0.0750 \text{ } M$$

$$M \text{ of } NO_3^- \text{ left} = 0.450 \text{ mol} \div 2.000 \text{ L} = 0.225 \text{ } M$$

$$M \text{ of } Na^+ \text{ left} = 0.750 \text{ mol} \div 2.000 \text{ L} = 0.375 \text{ } M$$

Copyright © Cengage Learning. All rights reserved.

12.127.

$Na^+(g) + Cl^-(g)$	$\rightarrow$	$NaCl(s)$	$\Delta H = 787$ kJ/mol
$NaCl(s)$	$\rightarrow$	$Na^+(aq) + Cl^-(aq)$	$\Delta H = +4$ kJ/mol

$$Na^+(g) + Cl^-(g) \rightarrow Na^+(aq) + Cl^-(aq) \qquad \Delta H = 783 \text{ kJ/mol}$$

The heat of hydration of Na^+ is

$Na^+(g) + Cl^-(g)$	$\rightarrow$	$Na^+(aq) + Cl^-(aq)$	$\Delta H = 783$ kJ/mol
$Cl^-(aq)$	$\rightarrow$	$Cl^-(g)$	$\Delta H = +338$ kJ/mol

$$Na^+(g) \rightarrow Na^+(aq) \qquad \Delta H = 445 \text{ kJ/mol}$$

12.129. $15.0 \text{ g MgSO}_4 \bullet 7H_2O \times \dfrac{1 \text{ mol}}{246.5 \text{ g}} = 0.060\underline{8}54 \text{ mol MgSO}_4 \bullet 7H_2O$

$0.060854 \text{ mol MgSO}_4 \bullet 7H_2O \times \dfrac{7 \text{ mol H}_2O}{1 \text{ mol hydrate}} \times \dfrac{18.0 \text{ g H}_2O}{1 \text{ mol H}_2O} = 7.6\underline{6}7 \text{ g H}_2O$

$\text{kg H}_2O = (100.0 \text{ g H}_2O + 7.667 \text{ g H}_2O) \times \dfrac{1 \text{ kg H}_2O}{1000 \text{ g H}_2O} = 0.107\underline{6}6 \text{ kg H}_2O$

$m = \dfrac{0.060854 \text{ mol MgSO}_4}{0.10766 \text{ kg H}_2O} = 0.56\underline{5}2 \text{ mol/kg} = 0.565 \, m$

12.131. $15.0 \text{ g CuSO}_4 \bullet 5H_2O \times \dfrac{1 \text{ mol}}{249.7 \text{ g}} = 0.060\underline{0}7 \text{ mol CuSO}_4 \bullet 5H_2O, \text{ or CuSO}_4$

$100 \text{ g soln} \times \dfrac{1 \text{ mL soln}}{1.167 \text{ g soln}} \times \dfrac{1 \text{ L}}{1000 \text{ mL}} = 0.08568\underline{9} \text{ L}$

$M = \dfrac{0.06007 \text{ mol CuSO}_4}{0.085689 \text{ L}} = 0.70\underline{1}02 = 0.701 \text{ mol/L}$

12.133. $0.159°C \times \dfrac{m}{1.858°C} = 0.0855\underline{7} \, m = \dfrac{0.08557 \text{ mol AA} + H^+}{1000 \text{ g (or 1000 mL) H}_2O}$

Note that $0.0830 \text{ mol AA} + \text{mol } H^+ = 0.08557 \text{ mol/L (AA} + H^+)$.

Moles of $H^+ = 0.08557 - 0.0830 = 0.002\underline{5}7 \text{ mol}$

$\text{Percent dissoc.} = \dfrac{\text{mol } H^+}{\text{mol AA}} \times 100\% = \dfrac{0.00257 \text{ mol}}{0.0830 \text{ mol}} \times 100\% = 3.\underline{0}9 = 3.1\%$

Copyright © Cengage Learning. All rights reserved.

12.135. Calculate the empirical formula first, using the masses of C, O, and H in 1.000 g:

$$1.434 \text{ g CO}_2 \ \times \ \frac{12.01 \text{ g C}}{44.01 \text{ g CO}_2} \ = \ 0.39132 \text{ g C}$$

$$0.783 \text{ g H}_2\text{O} \ \times \ \frac{2.016 \text{ g H}}{18.016 \text{ g H}_2\text{O}} \ = \ 0.08761 \text{ g H}$$

g O $=$ 1.000 g $-$ 0.39132 g $-$ 0.08761 g $=$ 0.5211 g O

Mol C $=$ 0.39132 g C $\times$ 1 mol/12.01 g $=$ 0.03258 mol C (lowest integer $= 1$)

Mol H $=$ 0.08761 g H $\times$ 1 mol/1.008 g $=$ 0.08691 mol H (lowest integer $= 8/3$)

Mol O $=$ 0.5211 g O $\times$ 1 mol/16.00 g $=$ 0.03257 mol O (lowest integer $= 1$)

Therefore, the empirical formula is $C_3H_8O_3$. The formula mass from the freezing point is calculated by first finding the molality:

0.0894°C $\times$ $(m/1.858°C)$ $=$ 0.04811 $=$ (0.04811 mol/1000 g H_2O)

(0.04811 mol/1000 g H_2O) $\times$ 25.0 g H_2O $=$ 0.001203 mol (in 25.0 g H_2O)

Molar mass $=$ M_m $=$ 0.1107 g/0.001203 mol $=$ 92.02 g/mol

Because this is also the formula mass, the molecular formula is also $C_3H_8O_3$.

Copyright © Cengage Learning. All rights reserved.

CHAPTER 13

Rates of Reaction

■ SOLUTIONS TO EXERCISES

Note on significant figures: If the final answer to a solution needs to be rounded off, it is given first with one nonsignificant figure, and the last significant figure is underlined. The final answer is then rounded to the correct number of significant figures. In multistep problems, intermediate answers are given with at least one nonsignificant figure; however, only the final answer has been rounded off.

13.1. Rate of formation of $NO_2F = \Delta[NO_2F]/\Delta t$. Rate of reaction of $NO_2 = -\Delta[NO_2]/\Delta t$. Divide each rate by the coefficient of the corresponding substance in the equation:

$$1/2 \frac{\Delta[NO_2F]}{\Delta t} = -1/2 \frac{\Delta[NO_2]}{\Delta t}; \quad \text{or} \quad \frac{\Delta[NO_2F]}{\Delta t} = -\frac{\Delta[NO_2]}{\Delta t}$$

13.2. $\text{Rate} = -\frac{\Delta[I^-]}{\Delta t} = -\frac{\Delta[0.00101 \text{ M} - 0.00169 \text{ M}]}{8.00 \text{ s} - 2.00 \text{ s}} = 1.\underline{1}3 \times 10^{-4} = 1.1 \times 10^{-4} M/s$

13.3. The order with respect to CO is zero and with respect to NO_2 is 2. The overall order is 2, the sum of the exponents in the rate law.

13.4. By comparing Experiments 1 and 2, you see the rate is quadrupled when the $[NO_2]$ is doubled. Thus, the reaction is second order in NO_2, and the rate law is

$$\text{Rate} = k[NO_2]^2$$

The rate constant may be found by substituting experimental values into the rate-law expression. Based on values from Experiment 1,

$$k = \frac{\text{rate}}{[NO_2]^2} = \frac{7.1 \times 10 \text{ mol/(L} \cdot \text{s})}{(0.010 \text{ mol/L})^2} = 0.7\underline{1}0 = 0.71 \text{ L/(mol} \cdot \text{s})$$

Copyright © Cengage Learning. All rights reserved.

13.5.

a. For $[N_2O_5]$ after 6.00×10^2 s, use the first-order rate law, and solve for the concentration at time t:

$$\ln\frac{[N_2O_5]_t}{[1.65 \times 10^{-2}\ M]} = -(4.80 \times 10^{-4}\ /s)(6.00 \times 10^2\ s) = -0.2880$$

Take the antilog of both sides to get

$$\frac{[N_2O_5]_t}{[1.65 \times 10^{-2}\ M]} = e^{-0.2880} = 0.74976$$

Hence,

$$[N_2O_5]_t = 1.65 \times 10^{-2}\ M \times 0.74976 = 0.01237 = 0.0124\ mol/L$$

b. Substitute the values into the rate equation to get

$$\ln\frac{10.0\%}{100.0\%} = -(4.80 \times 10^{-4}/s) \times t$$

Taking the log on the left side gives $\ln(0.100) = -2.30258$. Hence,

$$-2.30258 = -(4.80 \times 10^{-4}\ /s) \times t$$

Or,

$$t = \frac{2.30258}{4.80 \times 10^{-4}/s} = 4797 = 4.80 \times 10^3\ s\ (80.0\ min)$$

13.6. Substitute $k = 9.2/s$ into the equation relating k and $t_{1/2}$.

$$t_{1/2} = \frac{0.693}{k} = \frac{0.693}{9.2/s} = 0.0753 = 0.075\ s$$

By definition, the half-life is the amount of time it takes to decrease the amount of substance present by one-half. Thus, it takes 0.0753 s for concentration to decrease by 50% and another 0.0753 s for the concentration to decrease by 50% of the remaining 50% (to 25% left), for a total of 0.1506, or 0.151 s.

13.7. Solve for E_a by substituting the given values into the two-temperature Arrhenius equation:

$$\ln\frac{2.14 \times 10^{-2}}{1.05 \times 10^{-3}} = \frac{E_a}{8.31\ J/(mol \cdot K)}\left(\frac{1}{759\ K} - \frac{1}{836\ K}\right)$$

$$3.0146 = \frac{E_a}{8.31\ J/(mol \cdot K)}\ (1.2135 \times 10^{-4}\ /K)$$

$$E_a = \frac{3.0146 \times 8.31\ J/mol}{1.2135 \times 10^{-4}} = 2.064 \times 10^5 = 2.06 \times 10^5\ J/mol$$

Copyright © Cengage Learning. All rights reserved.

Solve for the rate constant, k_2, at 865 K by using the same equation and using $E_a = 2.064 \times 10^5$ J/mol:

$$\ln \frac{k_2}{2.14 \times 10^{-2}/(M^{1/2} \cdot s)} = \frac{2.064 \times 10^5 \text{ J/mol}}{8.31 \text{ J/(mol} \cdot \text{K)}} \left(\frac{1}{836 \text{ K}} - \frac{1}{865 \text{ K}} \right) = 0.99623$$

Taking antilogarithms,

$$\frac{k_2}{2.14 \times 10^{-2}/(M^{1/2} \cdot s)} = e^{0.99623} = 2.7080$$

$$k_2 = 2.7080 \times (2.14 \times 10^{-2})/(M^{1/2} \cdot s) = 5.7952 \times 10^{-2} = 5.80 \times 10^{-2} \ (M^{1/2} \cdot s)$$

13.8. The net chemical equation is the overall sum of the two elementary reactions:

$$
\begin{array}{rcl}
H_2O_2 + I^- & \rightarrow & H_2O + IO^- \\
\underline{H_2O_2 + IO^-} & \underline{\rightarrow} & \underline{H_2O + O_2 + I^-} \\
2H_2O_2 & \rightarrow & 2H_2O + O_2
\end{array}
$$

The IO^- is an intermediate; I^- is a catalyst. Neither appears in the net equation.

13.9. The reaction is bimolecular because it is an elementary reaction that involves two molecules.

13.10. For $NO_2 + NO_2 \rightarrow N_2O_4$, the rate law is

Rate $= k[NO_2]^2$

(The rate must be proportional to the concentration of both reactant molecules.)

13.11. The first step is the slow, rate-determining step. Therefore, the rate law predicted by the mechanism given is

Rate $= k_1 [H_2O_2][I^-]$

13.12. According to the rate-determining (slow) step, the rate law is

Rate $= k_2[NO_3][NO]$

Eliminate NO_3 from the rate law by looking at the first step, which is fast and reaches equilibrium. At equilibrium, the forward rate and the reverse rate are equal.

$k_1[NO][O_2] = k_{-1}[NO_3]$

Therefore, $[NO_3] = (k_1/k_{-1})[NO][O_2]$, so

$$\text{Rate} = \frac{k_2 k_1}{k_{-1}} [NO]^2[O_2] = k[NO]^2[O_2]$$

where $k_2(k_1/k_{-1})$ has been replaced by k, which represents the experimentally observed rate constant.

Copyright © Cengage Learning. All rights reserved.

■ ANSWERS TO SELF-ASSESSMENT AND REVIEW QUESTIONS

13.1. The four variables that can affect rate are (1) the concentrations of the reactants, although in some cases a particular reactant's concentration does not affect the rate; (2) the presence and concentration of a catalyst; (3) the temperature of the reaction; and (4) the surface area of any solid reactant or solid catalyst.

13.2. The rate of reaction of HBr can be defined as the decrease in HBr concentration (or the increase in Br_2 product formed) over the time interval, Δt:

$$\text{Rate} = -1/4\,\frac{\Delta[\text{HBr}]}{\Delta t} = 1/2\,\frac{\Delta[\text{Br}_2]}{\Delta t} \quad \text{or} \quad -\frac{\Delta[\text{HBr}]}{\Delta t} = 2\,\frac{\Delta[\text{Br}_2]}{\Delta t}$$

13.3. Two physical properties used to determine the rate are color, or absorption of electromagnetic radiation, and pressure. If a reactant or product is colored, or absorbs a different type of electromagnetic radiation than the other species, then measurement of the change in color (change in absorption of electromagnetic radiation) may be used to determine the rate. If a gas reaction involves a change in the number of gaseous molecules, measurement of the pressure change may be used to determine the rate.

13.4. Use the general example of a rate law in Section 13.3, where A and B react to give D and E with C as a catalyst:

$\text{Rate} = k\,[\text{A}]^m\,[\text{B}]^n\,[\text{C}]^p$

Note that the exponents m, n, and p are the orders of the individual reactants and catalyst. Assuming that m and n are positive numbers, the rate law predicts that increasing the concentrations of A and/or B will increase the rate. In addition, the rate will be increased by increasing the surface of the solid catalyst (making it as finely divided as possible, etc.). Finally, increasing the temperature will increase the rate constant, k, and increase the rate.

13.5. An example that illustrates that exponents have no relationship to coefficients is the reaction of nitrogen monoxide and hydrogen from Example 13.12 in the text.

$2NO + 2H_2 \rightarrow N_2 + 2H_2O$.

The experimental rate law given there is

$\text{Rate} = k[\text{NO}]^2[\text{H}_2]$

Thus, the exponent for hydrogen is 1, not 2 like the coefficient, and the overall order is 3, not 4 like the sum of the coefficients.

13.6. The rate law for this reaction of iodide ion, arsenic acid, and hydrogen ion is

$\text{Rate} = k[\text{I}^-][\text{H}_3\text{AsO}_4]\,[\text{H}^+]$

The overall order is $1 + 1 + 1 = 3$ (third order).

Copyright © Cengage Learning. All rights reserved.

13.7. Use m to symbolize the reaction order as is done in the text. Then, from the table for m and the change in rate in the text, m is 2 when the rate is quadrupled (increased fourfold). Using the equation in the text gives the same result:

2^m = new rate/old rate = 4/1; thus, $m = 2$

13.8. Use m to symbolize the reaction order as is done in the text. The table for m and the change in rate in the text cannot be used in this case. When $m = 0.5$, the new rate should be found using the equation in the text:

$2^{0.50} = \sqrt{2} = 1.41$ = new rate/old rate

Thus, the new rate is 1.41 times the old rate.

13.9. Use the half-life concept to answer the question without an equation. If the half-life for the reaction of A(g) is 25 s, then the time for A(g) to decrease to 1/4 the initial value is two half-lives, or 2 x 25 = 50 s. The time for A(g) to decrease to 1/8 the initial value is three half-lives, or 3 x 25 = 75 s.

13.10.   The half-life equation for a first-order reaction is $t_{1/2} = 0.693/k$. The half-life for the reaction is constant, independent of the reactant concentration. For a second-order reaction, the half-life equation is $t_{1/2} = 1/(k[A]_o)$, and it depends on the initial reactant concentration.

13.11.   According to transition-state theory, the two factors that determine whether a collision results in reaction or not are (1) the molecules must collide with the proper orientation to form the activated complex, and (2) the activated complex formed must have a kinetic energy greater than the activation energy.

13.12.   The potential-energy diagram for the exothermic reaction of A and B to give activated complex $AB^{\ddagger}$ and products C and D is given below.

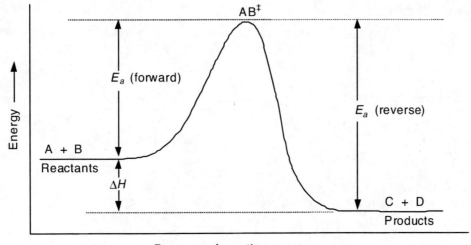

Copyright © Cengage Learning. All rights reserved.

13.13. The activated complex for the reaction of NO_2^- with NO_3 to give NO, NO_2, and O_2 has the structure below (dashed lines represent bonds about to form or break):

O–N–O–O–N($-$O)$_2$

13.14. The Arrhenius equation expressed with the base e is

$k = A\,e^{-E_a/RT}$

The A term is the frequency factor and is equal to the product of p and Z from collision theory. The term p is the fraction of collisions with properly oriented reactant molecules, and Z is the frequency of collisions. Thus, A is the number of collisions with the molecules properly oriented. The E_a term is the activation energy, the minimum energy of collision required for two molecules to react. The R term is the gas constant, and T is the absolute temperature.

13.15. In the reaction of $NO_2(g)$ with $CO(g)$, an example of an intermediate is the temporary formation of NO_3 from the reaction of two NO_2 molecules in the first step:

$NO_2 + NO_2 \rightarrow NO_3 + NO$

$NO_3 + CO \rightarrow NO_2 + CO_2$

13.16. It is generally impossible to predict the rate law from the equation alone, because most reactions consist of several elementary steps whose combined result is summarized in the rate law. If these elementary steps are unknown, the rate law cannot be predicted.

13.17. The mechanism cannot be $2NO_2Cl \rightarrow 2NO_2 + Cl_2$ because the reaction is first order in NO_2Cl. The order in NO_2Cl would have to reflect the total number of molecules (two) for the proposed mechanism, but it does not.

13.18. The characteristic of the rate-determining step in a mechanism is that it is, relatively speaking, the slowest step of all the elementary steps (even though it may occur in seconds). Thus, the rate of disappearance of reactant(s) is limited by the rate of this step.

13.19. For the rate of decomposition of N_2O_4,

Rate $= k_1[N_2O_4]$

For the rate of formation of N_2O_4,

Rate $= k_{-1}[NO_2]^2$

At equilibrium the rates are equal, so

$k_1[N_2O_4] = k_{-1}[NO_2]^2$

$[N_2O_4] = (k_{-1}/k_1)\,[NO_2]^2$

13.20. A catalyst operates by providing a pathway (mechanism) that occurs faster than the uncatalyzed pathway (mechanism) of the reaction. The catalyst is not consumed because after reacting in an early step, it is regenerated in a later step.

Copyright © Cengage Learning. All rights reserved.

13.21.   In physical adsorption, molecules adhere to a surface through *weak* intermediate forces, whereas in chemisorption, the molecules adhere to the surface by *stronger* chemical bonding.

13.22.   In the first step of catalytic hydrogenation of ethylene, the ethylene and hydrogen molecules diffuse to the catalyst surface and undergo chemisorption. Then the *pi* electrons of ethylene form temporary bonds to the metal catalyst, and the hydrogen molecule breaks into two hydrogen atoms. The hydrogen atoms next migrate to an ethylene held in position on the metal catalyst surface, forming ethane. Finally, because it cannot bond to the catalyst, the ethane diffuses away from the surface.

13.23.   The answer is c, $[A] = 0.0250\ M$, $[B] = 0.0400\ M$.

13.24.   The answer is e, I and III only.

13.25.   The answer is e; if the rate law for the reaction is Rate $= k[E]^2[F]$, then doubling the concentration of E will cause the rate to increase by a factor of 4 (4 times faster).

13.26.   The answer is c, doubling the $[C]_o$ while keeping the $[A]_o$ and $[B]_o$ constant.

■ SOLUTIONS TO PRACTICE PROBLEMS

Note on significant figures: If the final answer to a solution needs to be rounded off, it is given first with one nonsignificant figure, and the last significant figure is underlined. The final answer is then rounded to the correct number of significant figures. In multistep problems, intermediate answers are given with at least one nonsignificant figure; however, only the final answer has been rounded off.

13.39.   For the reaction $2NO_2 \rightarrow 2NO + O_2$, the rate of decomposition of NO_2 and the rate of formation of O_2 are, respectively,

Rate $= - \Delta[NO_2]/\Delta t$

Rate $= \Delta[O_2]/\Delta t$

To relate the two rates, divide each rate by the coefficient of the corresponding substance in the chemical equation and equate them.

$$-1/2 \frac{\Delta[NO_2]}{\Delta t} = \frac{\Delta[O_2]}{\Delta t}$$

Copyright © Cengage Learning. All rights reserved.

13.41.   For the reaction $5Br^- + BrO_3^- + 6H^+ \rightarrow 3Br_2 + 3H_2O$, the rate of decomposition of Br^- and the rate of decomposition of BrO_3^- are, respectively,

$$Rate = -\Delta[Br^-]/\Delta t$$

$$Rate = -\Delta[BrO_3^-]/\Delta t$$

To relate the two rates, divide each rate by the coefficient of the corresponding substance in the chemical equation and equate them.

$$1/5\frac{\Delta[Br^-]}{\Delta t} = \frac{\Delta[BrO_3^-]}{\Delta t}$$

13.43. $Rate = -\dfrac{\Delta[NH_4NO_2]}{\Delta t} = -\dfrac{[0.0432\ M\ -\ 0.500\ M]}{[3.00\ hr\ -\ 0.00\ hr]} = 2.\underline{2}7 \times 10^{-2} = 2.3 \times 10^{-2}\ M/hr$

13.45. $Rate = -\dfrac{\Delta[Azo.]}{\Delta t} = -\dfrac{[0.0101\ M\ -\ 0.0150\ M]}{7.00\ min\ -\ 0.00\ min} \times \dfrac{1\ min}{60\ sec} = 1.\underline{1}6 \times 10^{-5} = 1.2 \times 10^{-5}\ M/s$

13.47.   If the rate law is $Rate = k[H_2S][Cl_2]$, the order with respect to H_2S is 1 (first order), and the order with respect to Cl_2 is also 1 (first-order). The overall order is $1 + 1 = 2$, second-order.

13.49.   If the rate law is $Rate = k[MnO_4^-][H_2C_2O_4]$, the order with respect to MnO_4^- is 1 (first order), the order with respect to $H_2C_2O_4$ is 1 (first order), and the order with respect to H^+ is zero. The overall order is 2, second order.

13.51.   The reaction rate doubles when the concentration of CH_3NNCH_3 is doubled, so the reaction is first order in azomethane. The rate equation should have the form

$$Rate = k[CH_3NNCH_3]$$

Substituting values for the rate and concentration yields a value for k:

$$k = \frac{rate}{[Azo.]} = \frac{2.8 \times 10^{-6}\ M/s}{1.13 \times 10^{-2}\ M} = 2.\underline{4}7 \times 10^{-4} = 2.5 \times 10^{-4}/s$$

13.53.   Doubling [NO] quadruples the rate, so the reaction is second order in NO. Doubling $[H_2]$ doubles the rate, so the reaction is first order in H_2. The rate law should have the form

$$Rate = k[NO]^2[H_2]$$

Substituting values for the rate and concentrations yields a value for k:

$$k = \frac{rate}{[NO]^2[H_2]} = \frac{2.6 \times 10^{-5}\ M/s}{[6.4 \times 10^{-3}\ M]^2[2.2 \times 10^{-3}\ M]} = 2.\underline{8}8 \times 10^2 = 2.9 \times 10^2/M^2s$$

Copyright © Cengage Learning. All rights reserved.

13.55. By comparing Experiments 1 and 2, you see that tripling $[ClO_2]$ increases the rate ninefold; that is, $3^m = 9$, so $m = 2$ (and the reaction is second order in ClO_2). From Experiments 2 and 3, you see that tripling $[OH^-]$ triples the rate, so the reaction is first order in OH^-. The rate law is

$$\text{Rate} = k[ClO_2]^2[OH^-]$$

Substituting values for the rate and concentrations yields a value for k:

$$k = \frac{\text{rate}}{[ClO_2]^2[OH^-]} = \frac{0.0248 \ M/s}{[0.060 \ M]^2[0.030 \ M]} = 2.\underline{2}9 \times 10^2 = 2.3 \times 10^2/M^2s$$

13.57. Let $[SO_2Cl_2]_o = 0.0248 \ M$ and $[SO_2Cl_2]_t =$ the concentration after 2.0 hr. Substituting these and $k = 2.2 \times 10^{-5}/s$ into the first-order rate equation gives

$$\ln\frac{[SO_2Cl_2]_t}{[0.0248 \ M]} = -(2.2 \times 10^{-5}/s)\left(2.0 \ hr \ \times \ \frac{3600 \ s}{1 \ hr}\right) = -0.1\underline{5}84$$

Taking the antilog of both sides gives

$$\frac{[SO_2Cl_2]_t}{[0.0248 \ M]} = e^{-0.1584} = 0.8\underline{5}35$$

Solving for $[SO_2Cl_2]_t$ gives

$$[SO_2Cl_2]_t = 0.8\underline{5}25 \times [0.0248 \ M] = 0.02\underline{1}16 = 0.021 = 2.1 \times 10^{-2} \ M$$

13.59. The second-order integrated rate law is

$$\frac{1}{[A]_t} = kt + \frac{1}{[A]_o}$$

Using a rate constant value of 0.225 L/(mol·s) and an initial concentration of 0.293 mol/L, after 35.4 s the concentration of A is

$$\frac{1}{[A]_t} = 0.225 \ \text{L/(mol·s)} \times 35.4 \ s + \frac{1}{0.293 \ \text{mol/L}}$$

$$\frac{1}{[A]_t} = 7.9\underline{6}5 \ \text{L/mol} + 3.4\underline{1}2 \ \text{L/mol} = 11.3\underline{7}7 \ \text{L/mol}$$

$$[A]_t = \frac{1}{11.377 \ \text{L/mol}} = 0.0878\underline{8}9 = 0.08789 \ M$$

Copyright © Cengage Learning. All rights reserved.

13.61. First, find the rate constant, k, by substituting experimental values into the first-order rate equation. Let $[\text{Et. Cl.}]_o = 0.00100\ M$, $[\text{Et. Cl.}]_t = 0.00067\ M$, and $t = 155$ s. Solving for k yields

$$k = -\frac{\ln\dfrac{[0.00067\ M]_t}{[0.00100\ M]_o}}{155\ \text{s}} = 2.\underline{5}83 \times 10^{-3}/\text{s}$$

Now let $[\text{Et. Cl.}]_t =$ the concentration after 256 s, $[\text{Et. Cl.}]_o$ again $= 0.00100\ M$, and use the value of k of $1.5\underline{6}4 \times 10^{-3}/\text{s}$ to calculate $[\text{Et. Cl.}]_t$.

$$\ln\frac{[\text{Et. Cl.}]_t}{[0.00100\ M]} = -(2.584 \times 10^{-3}/\text{s})(256\ \text{s}) = -0.6\underline{6}14$$

Converting both sides to antilogs gives

$$\frac{[\text{Et. Cl.}]_t}{[0.00100\ M]} = 0.5\underline{1}61$$

$$[\text{Et. Cl.}]_t = 0.5161 \times [0.00100\ M] = 5.\underline{1}6 \times 10^{-4} = 5.2 \times 10^{-4}\ M$$

13.63. For a first-order reaction, divide 0.693 by the rate constant to find the half-life:

$$t_{1/2} = 0.693/(6.3 \times 10^{-4}/\text{s}) = 1.\underline{1}0 \times 10^3 = 1.1 \times 10^3\ \text{s}\ (1\underline{8}.3\ \text{min})$$

Now, use the half-life to determine the concentrations. When the concentration decreases to 50.0% of its initial value, this is equal to the half-life.

$$t_{50.0\%\ \text{left}} = t_{1/2} = 1.10 \times 10^3\ \text{s}$$

When the concentration decreases to 25.0% of its initial value, this is equal to two half-lives.

$$t_{25.0\%\ \text{left}} = t_{1/4\ \text{left}} = 2 \times t_{1/2} = 2 \times (1.10 \times 10^3\ \text{s}) = 2.\underline{2}0 \times 10^3\ \text{s}\ (37\ \text{min})$$

13.65. For a first-order reaction, divide 0.693 by the rate constant to find the half-life:

$$t_{1/2} = 0.693/(2.0 \times 10^{-6}/\text{s}) = 3.\underline{4}65 \times 10^5\ \text{s}\ (9\underline{6}.25\ \text{or}\ 96\ \text{hr})$$

$$t_{25\%\ \text{left}} = t_{1/4\ \text{left}} = 2 \times t_{1/2} = 2 \times 96.25\ \text{hr} = 1\underline{9}2.5 = 1.9 \times 10^2\ \text{hr}$$

$$t_{12.5\%\ \text{left}} = t_{1/8\ \text{left}} = 3 \times t_{1/2} = 3 \times 96.25\ \text{hr} = 2\underline{8}8.75 = 2.9 \times 10^2\ \text{hr}$$

$$t_{6.25\%\ \text{left}} = t_{1/16\ \text{left}} = 4 \times t_{1/2} = 4 \times 96.25\ \text{hr} = 3\underline{8}5.0 = 3.9 \times 10^2\ \text{hr}$$

$$t_{3.125\%\ \text{left}} = t_{1/32\ \text{left}} = 5 \times t_{1/2} = 5 \times 96.25\ \text{hr} = 4\underline{8}1.25 = 4.8 \times 10^2\ \text{hr}$$

13.67. The half-life for a second-order reaction is

$$t_{1/2} = \frac{1}{k[A]_o}$$

Using a rate constant of 0.413 L/(mol·s) and an initial A concentration of 5.25×10^{-3} mol/L, the half-life is

$$t_{1/2} = \frac{1}{(0.413\ \text{L/(mol·s)})(5.25 \times 10^{-3}\ \text{mol/L})} = 46\underline{1}.2 = 461\ \text{s}$$

Copyright © Cengage Learning. All rights reserved.

13.69. Use the first-order rate equation, and solve for time, t. Let $[Cr^{3+}]_o = 100.0\%$; then the concentration at time t, $[Cr^{3+}]_t$, $= (100.0\% - 85.0\%$, or $15.0\%)$. Use $k = 2.0 \times 10^{-6}/s$.

$$\ln \frac{[15.0]}{[100.0]} = -(2.0 \times 10^{-6}/s)\, t$$

$$t = -\frac{\ln(0.150)}{2.0 \times 10^{-6}/s} = 9.\underline{4}8 \times 10^5 \text{ s, or } 2.6 \times 10^2 \text{ hr}$$

13.71. The rate law for a zero-order reaction is

$$[A] = -kt + [A]_o.$$

Using a rate constant of 8.1×10^{-2} mol/(L•s) and an initial concentration of $0.10\ M$, the time it would take for the concentration to change to $1.0 \times 10^{-2}\ M$ is

$$1.0 \times 10^{-2}\ M = -8.1 \times 10^{-2} \text{ mol/(L•s)} \times t + 0.10\ M$$

$$t = \frac{0.10\ M\ -\ 1.0 \times 10^{-2}\ M}{8.1 \times 10^{-2}\ M/s} = 1.\underline{1}1 = 1.1 \text{ s}$$

13.73. For the first-order plot, follow Figure 13.9, and plot $\ln [ClO_2]$ versus the time in seconds. The data used for plotting are

t, sec	$[ClO_2]$, M	$\ln [ClO_2]$
0.00	4.77×10^{-4}	-7.647
1.00	4.31×10^{-4}	-7.749
2.00	3.91×10^{-4}	-7.846
3.00	3.53×10^{-4}	-7.949
5.00	2.89×10^{-4}	-8.149
10.00	1.76×10^{-4}	-8.645
30.00	2.4×10^{-5}	-10.63
50.00	3.2×10^{-5}	-12.65

The plot yields an approximate straight line, demonstrating the reaction is first order in $[ClO_2]$. The slope of the line may be calculated from the difference between the last point and the first point:

$$\text{Slope} = \frac{[(-12.65)\ -\ (-7.647)]}{[50.00\ -\ 0.00]s} = -0.10\underline{0}1/s$$

Just as the slope, m, was obtained for the plot in Figure 13.9, you can also equate m to $-k$, and calculate k as follows:

$$k = -\text{slope} = 0.10\underline{0}1 = 0.100/s$$

Copyright © Cengage Learning. All rights reserved.

13.75. The potential-energy diagram, not drawn to scale, is below. Because the activation energy for the forward reaction is +10 kJ, and $\Delta H° = -200$ kJ, the activation energy for the reverse reaction is +210 kJ.

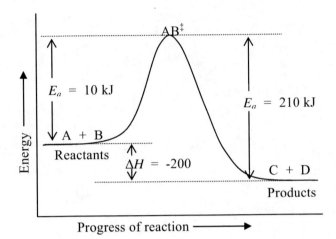

13.77. Solve the two-temperature Arrhenius equation for E_a by substituting $T_1 = 308$ K (from 35°C), $k_1 = 1.4 \times 10^{-4}$/s, $T_2 = 318$ K (from 45°C), and $k_2 = 5.0 \times 10^{-4}$/s:

$$\ln \frac{5.0 \times 10^{-4}}{1.4 \times 10^{-4}} = \frac{E_a}{8.31 \text{ J/(mol} \cdot \text{K)}} \left(\frac{1}{308 \text{ K}} - \frac{1}{318 \text{ K}} \right)$$

Rearranging E_a to the left side and calculating [1/308 − 1/318] give

$$E_a = \frac{8.31 \text{ J/K} \times \ln(3.5714)}{1.0209 \times 10^{-4}/\text{K}} = 1.\underline{0}37 \times 10^5 = 1.0 \times 10^5 \text{ J/mol}$$

To find the rate at 55°C (328 K), use the first equation. Let k_2 in the numerator be the unknown and solve:

$$\ln \frac{k_2}{1.4 \times 10^{-4}} = \frac{1.037 \times 10^5 \text{ J/mol}}{8.31 \text{ J/(mol} \cdot \text{K)}} \left(\frac{1}{308 \text{ K}} - \frac{1}{328 \text{ K}} \right) = 2.\underline{4}68$$

$$\frac{k_2}{1.4 \times 10^{-4}} = 1\underline{1}.80$$

$$k_2 = 11.80 \times (1.4 \times 10^{-4}/\text{s}) = 1.\underline{6}52 \times 10^{-3} = 1.7 \times 10^{-3}/\text{s}$$

Copyright © Cengage Learning. All rights reserved.

13.79. Because the rate constant is proportional to the rate of a reaction, tripling the rate at 25°C means that the rate constant at 25°C is also tripled. Thus, $k_{35} = 3k_{25}$, and the latter can be substituted for k_{25} in the Arrhenius equation:

$$\ln \frac{3\,k_{25}}{k_{25}} = \frac{E_a}{8.31\ \text{J/(mol} \cdot \text{K)}} \left(\frac{1}{298\ \text{K}} - \frac{1}{308\ \text{K}} \right)$$

$$1.0986 = (1.3\underline{1}1 \times 10^{-5}\ \text{mol/J})\ E_a$$

$$E_a = \frac{1.0986}{1.311 \times 10^{-5}\ \text{mol/J}} = 8.3\underline{7}9 \times 10^4\ \text{J/mol} = 83.8\ \text{kJ/mol}$$

13.81. For plotting $\ln k$ versus $1/T$, the data below are used:

k	$\ln k$	$1/T$ (1/K)
0.527	−0.64055	1.686×10^{-3}
0.776	−0.25360	1.658×10^{-3}
1.121	0.11422	1.631×10^{-3}
1.607	0.47436	1.605×10^{-3}

The plot yields an approximately straight line. The slope of the line is calculated from the difference between the last and the first points:

$$\text{Slope} = \frac{(0.47436) - (-0.64055)}{[1.605 \times 10^{-3} - 1.686 \times 10^{-3}]/\text{K}} = -13\underline{7}64\ \text{K}$$

Because the slope $= -E_a/R$, you can solve for E_a using $R = 8.31$ J/K:

$$\frac{-E_a}{8.31\ \text{J/ (K} \cdot \text{mol)}} = -13764\ \text{K}$$

$$E_a = 13764\ \text{K} \times 8.31\ \text{J/K} = 1.\underline{1}43 \times 10^5\ \text{J/mol, or }1.1 \times 10^2\ \text{kJ/mol}$$

13.83. The $NOCl_2$ is a reaction intermediate that is produced in the first reaction and consumed in the second. The overall reaction is the sum of the two elementary reactions:

$$NO + Cl_2 \rightarrow NOCl_2$$
$$\underline{NOCl_2 + NO \rightarrow 2NOCl}$$
$$2NO + Cl_2 \rightarrow 2NOCl$$

13.85.

    a.   Bimolecular

    b.   Bimolecular

    c.   Unimolecular

    d.   Termolecular

Copyright © Cengage Learning. All rights reserved.

13.87.

a. Only O_3 occurs on the left side of the equation, so the rate law is

Rate = $k[O_3]$

b. Both $NOCl_2$ and NO occur on the left side of the equation, so the rate law is

Rate = $k[NOCl_2][NO]$

13.89. Step 1 of the isomerization of cyclopropane, C_3H_6, is slow, so the rate law for the overall reaction will be the rate law for this step, with $k_1 = k$, the overall rate constant:

Rate = $k[C_3H_6]^2$

13.91. Step 2 of this reaction is slow, so the rate law for the overall reaction would appear to be the rate law for this step:

Rate = $k_2[I]^2[H_2]$

However, the rate law includes an intermediate, the I atom, and cannot be used unless the intermediate is eliminated. This can be done only using an equation for Step 1. At equilibrium, you can write the following equality for Step 1:

$k_1[I_2] = k_{-1} [I]^2$

Rearranging and then substituting for the $[I]^2$ term yield

$[I]^2 = [I_2] \dfrac{k_1}{k_{-1}}$

Rate = $k_2(k_1/k_{-1})[I_2][H_2] = k[I_2][H_2]$ (k = the overall rate constant)

13.93. The Br^- ion is the catalyst. It is consumed in the first step and regenerated in the second step. It speeds up the reaction by providing a pathway with a lower activation energy than that of a reaction pathway involving no Br^-. The overall reaction is obtained by adding the two steps together:

$2H_2O_2 \rightarrow 2H_2O + O_2$

Bromide ion is added to the mixture to give the catalytic activity, and BrO^- is an intermediate.

Copyright © Cengage Learning. All rights reserved.

■ SOLUTIONS TO GENERAL PROBLEMS

13.95. All rates of reaction are calculated by dividing the decrease in concentration by the difference in times; hence, only the setup for the first rate (after 10 minutes) is given below. This setup is

$$\text{Rate (10 min)} = -\frac{(1.29 - 1.50) \times 10^{-2}\ M}{(10 - 0)\ \text{min}} \times \frac{1\ \text{min}}{60\ \text{s}} = 3.5 \times 10^{-6}\ M/s$$

A summary of the times and rates is given in the table.

Time, min	Rate
10	$3.\underline{5}0 \times 10^{-6} = 3.5 \times 10^{-6}\ M/s$
20	$3.\underline{1}7 \times 10^{-6} = 3.2 \times 10^{-6}\ M/s$
30	$2.\underline{5}0 \times 10^{-6} = 2.5 \times 10^{-6}\ M/s$

13.97. The calculation of the average concentration and the division of the rate by the average concentration are the same for all three time intervals. Thus, only the setup for the first interval is given:

$$k_{10\ \text{min}} = \frac{\text{rate}}{\text{avg. conc.}} = \frac{3.50 \times 10^{-6}\ M/s}{\left[\dfrac{(1.50 + 1.29) \times 10^{-2}\ M}{2} \right]} = 2.5\underline{0}8 \times 10^{-4}/s$$

A summary of the times, rate constants, and average rate constant is given in the table.

Time	Rate	k
10 min	$3.50 \times 10^{-6}\ M/s$	$2.\underline{5}08 \times 10^{-4}/s$
20 min	$3.17 \times 10^{-6}\ M/s$	$2.\underline{6}52 \times 10^{-4}/s$
30 min	$2.50 \times 10^{-6}\ M/s$	$2.\underline{4}39 \times 10^{-4}/s$
-----	---- average k	$2.\underline{5}33 \times 10^{-4} = 2.5 \times 10^{-4}/s$

13.99. Use the first-order rate equation $k = 1.26 \times 10^{-4}/s$, the initial methyl acetate $[MA]_o = 100\%$, and $[MA]_t = (100\% - 65\%, \text{ or } 35\%)$.

$$t = -\frac{\ln\dfrac{35\%}{100\%}}{1.26 \times 10^{-4}/s} = 8.3\underline{3}19 \times 10^3 = 8.33 \times 10^3\ s$$

13.101. Use $k = 1.26 \times 10^{-4}/s$, and substitute into the $t_{1/2}$ equation:

$$t_{1/2} = \frac{0.693}{k} = \frac{0.693}{1.26 \times 10^{-4}/s} = 5.5\underline{0}0 \times 10^3 = 5.50 \times 10^3\ s\ (1.53\ \text{hr})$$

Copyright © Cengage Learning. All rights reserved.

13.103. First, find the rate constant from the first-order rate equation, substituting the initial concentration of [comp.]$_o$ = 0.0350 M, and the [comp.]$_t$ = 0.0250 M.

$$\ln\frac{0.0250\ M}{0.0350\ M} = -k\ (65\ s)$$

Rearranging and solving for k give

$$k = \frac{\left(\ln\dfrac{0.0250\ M}{0.0350\ M}\right)}{65\ s} = 5.\underline{1}7 \times 10^{-3}/s$$

Now, arrange the first-order rate equation to solve for [comp.]$_t$; substitute the above value of k, again using [comp.]$_o$ = 0.0350 M.

$$\ln\frac{[comp.]_t}{0.0350\ M} = -(5.18 \times 10^{-3}/s)(88\ s) = -0.4\underline{5}58$$

Taking the antilog of both sides gives

$$\frac{[comp.]_t}{0.0350\ M} = e^{-0.4558} = 0.6\underline{3}39$$

$$[comp]_t = 0.6\underline{3}39 \times [0.0350\ M]_o = 0.02\underline{2}1 = 0.022\ M$$

13.105.

a.   The rate constant for a second-order reaction is related to the half-life by

$$k = \frac{1}{t_{1/2}[A]_o}$$

Using a half-life of 5.92 × 10^{-2} s and an initial A concentration of 0.50 mol/L, the rate constant is

$$k = \frac{1}{(5.92 \times 10^{-2}\ s)(0.50\ mol/L)} = 3\underline{3}.78 = 34\ L/(mol\cdot s)$$

b.   The second-order integrated rate law is

$$\frac{1}{[A]_t} = kt + \frac{1}{[A]_o}$$

Using an initial concentration of C$_4$H$_8$ (A) of 0.010 M, after 3.6 × 10^2 s, the concentration will be

$$\frac{1}{[A]_t} = 33.78\ L/(mol\cdot s)(3.6 \times 10^2\ s) + \frac{1}{0.010\ mol/L}$$

$$\frac{1}{[A]_t} = 1\underline{2},162\ L/mol + 1\underline{0}0.0\ L/mol = 1\underline{2},262\ L/mol$$

$$[A]_t = \frac{1}{12,262\ L/mol} = 8.\underline{1}55 \times 10^{-5} = 8.2 \times 10^{-5}\ M$$

Copyright © Cengage Learning. All rights reserved.

13.107. The second-order integrated rate law is

$$\frac{1}{[A]_t} = kt + \frac{1}{[A]_o}$$

The starting concentration of NO_2 (A) is 0.050 M. Using a rate constant of 0.775 L/(mol•s), after 2.5×10^2 s the concentration of NO_2 will be

$$\frac{1}{[A]_t} = 0.775 \text{ L/(mol•s)}(2.5 \times 10^2 \text{ s}) + \frac{1}{0.050 \text{ mol/L}}$$

$$\frac{1}{[A]_t} = 1\underline{9}3 \text{ L/mol} + 2\underline{0}.0 \text{ L/mol} = 2\underline{1}3. \text{ L/mol}$$

$$[A]_t = \frac{1}{213 \text{ L/mol}} = 4.\underline{6}7 \times 10^{-3} = 4.7 \times 10^{-3} \ M$$

The half-life is

$$t_{1/2} = \frac{1}{k[A]_o}$$

Using a rate constant of 0.775 L/(mol•s) and an initial A concentration of 0.10 mol/L, the half-life is

$$t_{1/2} = \frac{1}{(0.775 \text{ L/(mol•s)})(0.050 \text{ mol/L})} = 2\underline{5}.80 = 26 \text{ s}$$

13.109. The $\ln[CH_3NNCH_3]$ and time data for the plot are tabulated below.

t min	$\ln[CH_3NNCH_3]$
0	−4.1997
10	−4.3505
20	−4.5098
30	−4.6564

Copyright © Cengage Learning. All rights reserved.

The slope, m, is calculated from the graph:

$$m = \frac{(-4.6564) - (-4.1997)}{(30 - 0)\ \text{min}}$$

$$= -0.01\underline{5}22\ /\text{min}$$

Because the slope also $= -k$, this gives

$$k = -(-0.01522/\text{min})(1\ \text{min}/60\ \text{s}) = 2.\underline{5}3 \times 10^{-4} = 2.5 \times 10^{-4}/\text{s}$$

13.111. The rate law for a zero-order reaction is

$$[A] = -kt + [A]_o.$$

Using a rate constant of 3.7×10^{-6} mol/(L•s) and an initial concentration of 5.0×10^{-4} M, the time it would take for the concentration to drop to 5.0×10^{-5} M is

$$5.0 \times 10^{-5}\ M = -8.1 \times 10^{-2}\ \text{mol/(L•s)} \times t + 5.0 \times 10^{-4}\ M$$

$$t = \frac{(5.0 \times 10^{-4}\ M) - (5.0 \times 10^{-5}\ M)}{3.7 \times 10^{-6}\ M/s} = 1\underline{2}1.6 = 1.2 \times 10^2\ \text{s}$$

The half-life for a zero-order reaction is

$$t_{1/2} = \frac{[A]_o}{2k} = \frac{5.0 \times 10^{-4}\ M}{2(3.7 \times 10^{-6}\ M/s)} = 6\underline{7}.57 = 68\ \text{s}$$

13.113. Rearrange the two-temperature Arrhenius equation to solve for E_a in joules, using $k_1 = 0.498$ M/s at $T_1 = 592$ K (319°C) and $k_2 = 1.81$ M/s at 627 K (354°C). Assume $(1/T_1 - 1/T_2)$ has three significant figures.

$$E_a = \frac{(8.31\ \text{J/mol•K})\ \ln\left(\dfrac{1.81}{0.498}\right)}{\left(\dfrac{1}{592\ \text{K}} - \dfrac{1}{627\ \text{K}}\right)} = 1.1\underline{3}7 \times 10^5\ \text{J/mol} = 114\ \text{kJ/mol}$$

To obtain A, rearrange the ln form of the one-temperature Arrhenius equation; substitute the value of E_a obtained above, and use $k_1 = 0.498$ M/s at $T_1 = 592$ K.

$$\ln A = \ln 0.498 + \frac{1.137 \times 10^5\ \text{J/mol}}{8.31\ \text{J/(mol•K)} \times 592\ \text{K}} = 22.\underline{4}20$$

$$A = \underline{5}.46 \times 10^9 = 5 \times 10^9$$

To obtain k at 420°C (693 K), also use the ln form of the one-temperature Arrhenius equation:

$$\ln k = 22.420 - \frac{1.137 \times 10^5\ \text{J/mol}}{8.31\ \text{J/(mol•K)} \times 693\,\text{K}} = 2.\underline{6}71$$

$$k = e^{2.671} = 1\underline{4}.45 = 14\ M/s$$

Copyright © Cengage Learning. All rights reserved.

13.115. If the reaction occurs in one step, the coefficients of NO_2 and CO in this elementary reaction are each one, so the rate law should be

Rate = $k[NO_2][CO]$

13.117. The slow step determines the observed rate, so the overall rate constant, k, should be equal to the rate constant for the first step, and the rate law should be

Rate = $k[NO_2Br]$

13.119. The slow step determines the observed rate; assuming k_2 is the rate constant for the second step, the rate law would appear to be

Rate = $k_2[NH_3][HOCN]$

However, this rate law includes two intermediate substances that are neither reactants nor products. The rate law cannot be used unless both are eliminated. This can be done only using an equation from Step 1. At equilibrium in Step 1, you can write the following equality, assuming k_1 and k_{-1} are the rate constants for the forward and back reactions, respectively:

$k_1[NH_4^+][OCN^-] = k_{-1}[NH_3][HOCN]$

Rearranging and then substituting for the $[NH_3][HOCN]$ product give

$[NH_3][HOCN] = (k_1/k_{-1})[NH_4^+][OCN^-]$

Rate = $k_2(k_1/k_{-1})[NH_4^+][OCN^-] = k[NH_4^+][OCN^-]$ (k = overall rate constant)

13.121.

a. The reaction is first order in O_2 because the rate doubled with a doubling of the oxygen concentration. The reaction is second order in NO because the rate increased by a factor of 8 when both the NO and O_2 concentrations were doubled.

Rate = $k[NO]^2[O_2]$

b. The initial rate of the reaction for Experiment 4 can be determined by first calculating the value of the rate constant using Experiment 1 for the data.

0.80×10^{-2} $M/s = k[4.5 \times 10^{-2}\ M]^2[2.2 \times 10^{-2}\ M]$

Solving for the rate constant gives

$k = 1.\underline{7}96 \times 10^2\ M^{-2}s^{-1}$

Now, use the data in Experiment 4 and the rate constant to determine the initial rate of the reaction.

Rate = $1.796 \times 10^2\ M^{-2}s^{-1}\ [3.8 \times 10^{-1}\ M]^2[4.6 \times 10^{-3}\ M]$

Rate = $0.1\underline{1}9 = 0.12$ mol/L•s

Copyright © Cengage Learning. All rights reserved.

13.123.

    a.

        i)   Rate will decrease because OH^- will react with H_3O^+ and lower its concentration.

        ii)   Rate will decrease because the dilution with water will decrease both the H_3O^+ and the CH_3CSNH_2 concentration.

    b.

        i)   The catalyst will provide another pathway, and k will increase because E_a will be smaller.

        ii)   The rate constant changes with temperature, and it will decrease with a decrease in temperature, because fewer molecules will have enough energy to react.

13.125.

    a.   The diagram:

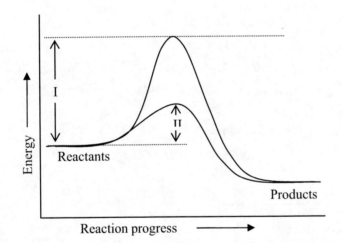

    b.   In the diagram, I represents the activation energy for the uncatalyzed reaction, and II represents the activation energy for the catalyzed reaction. A catalyst provides another pathway for a chemical reaction, and with a lower activation energy, more molecules have enough energy to react, so the reaction will be faster.

13.127.

    a.   The rate of a chemical reaction is the change in the concentration of a reactant or product with time. For a reactant,

        $-\Delta c/\Delta t$ or $-d[c]/dt$

    b.   The rate changes because the concentration of the reactant has changed.

        Rate $= k[A]^m$

Copyright © Cengage Learning. All rights reserved.

c.   Rate = $k[A]^m[B]^n$

The rate will equal k when the reactants all have 1.00 M concentrations, or if the reaction is zeroth order.

■ SOLUTIONS TO CUMULATIVE-SKILLS PROBLEMS

13.141. The balanced equation is

$$2N_2O_5 \quad \rightarrow \quad 4NO_2 + O_2.$$

Note that the number of moles of O_2 formed will be one-half the number of moles of N_2O_5 decomposed. Now use the integrated form of the first-order rate law to calculate the fraction of the 1.00 mol N_2O_5 decomposing in 20.0 hr, or 1200 min.

$$\ln \frac{[N_2O_5]_t}{[N_2O_5]_o} = -kt = -(6.2 \times 10^{-4}/\text{min})(1200 \text{ min}) = -0.7\underline{4}4$$

$$\frac{[N_2O_5]_t}{[N_2O_5]_o} = e^{-0.744} = 0.4\underline{7}52$$

Fraction of N_2O_5 decomposed = $1.000 - 0.4\underline{7}52 = 0.5\underline{2}48$

Since there is 1.00 mol of N_2O_5 present at the start, the moles of N_2O_5 decomposed is 0.5$\underline{2}$48 mol. Thus,

Moles of O_2 formed = (1 O_2/2 N_2O_5) x 0.5248 mol N_2O_5 = 0.2$\underline{6}$237 mol O_2

Now, use the ideal gas law to calculate the volume of this number of moles of O_2 gas at 45°C and 780 mmHg.

$$V = \frac{nRT}{P} = \frac{(0.26237 \text{ mol})(0.08206 \text{ L} \cdot \text{atm}/ (\text{K} \cdot \text{mol}))(318 \text{ K})}{(770/ 760) \text{ atm}} = 6.\underline{7}58 = 6.8 \text{ L}$$

13.143. Using the first-order rate law, the initial rate of decomposition is given by

Rate = $k[H_2O_2] = (7.40 \times 10^{-4}/\text{s})$ x $(1.50 \text{ } M \text{ } H_2O_2) = 1.110 \times 10^{-3} \text{ } M \text{ } H_2O_2/\text{s}$

The heat liberated per second per mol H_2O_2 can be found by first calculating the standard enthalpy of the decomposition of 1 mol H_2O_2:

$$H_2O_2(aq) \quad \rightarrow \quad H_2O(l) \quad + \quad 1/2 \text{ } O_2(g)$$

ΔH_f° = -191.2 kJ/mol   -285.8 kJ/mol   0 kJ/mol

For the reaction, the standard enthalpy change is

$\Delta H^\circ = -285.8$ kJ/mol $- (-191.2$ kJ/mol$) = -94.\underline{6}0$ kJ/mol H_2O_2

The heat liberated per second is

$$\frac{94.60 \text{ kJ}}{\text{mol } H_2O_2} \text{ x } \frac{1.110 \times 10^{-3} \text{ mol } H_2O_2}{\text{L} \cdot \text{s}} \text{ x } 2.00 \text{ L} = 0.21\underline{0}01 = 0.210 \text{ kJ/s}$$

Copyright © Cengage Learning. All rights reserved.

13.145. Use the ideal gas law ($P/RT = n/V$) to calculate the mol/L of each gas:

$$[O_2] = \frac{(345/760)\,\text{atm}}{0.082057\ \text{L}\bullet\text{atm}/(\text{K}\bullet\text{mol}) \times 612\ \text{K}} = 0.009039\ \text{mol O}_2/\text{L}$$

$$[NO] = \frac{(155/760)\,\text{atm}}{0.082057\ \text{L}\bullet\text{atm}/(\text{K}\bullet\text{mol}) \times 612\ \text{K}} = 0.004061\ \text{mol NO/L}$$

The rate of decrease of NO is

$$\frac{1.16 \times 10^{-5}\ \text{L}^2}{\text{mol}^2\bullet\text{s}} \times \left(\frac{4.061 \times 10^{-3}\ \text{mol}}{1\ \text{L}}\right)^2 \times \frac{9.039 \times 10^{-3}\ \text{mol}}{1\ \text{L}} = 1.729 \times 10^{-12}\ \text{mol}/(\text{L}\bullet\text{s})$$

The rate of decrease in atm/s is found by multiplying by RT:

$$\frac{1.729 \times 10^{-12}\ \text{mol}}{\text{L}\bullet\text{s}} \times \frac{0.082057\ \text{L}\bullet\text{atm}}{\text{K}\bullet\text{mol}} \times 612\ \text{K} = 8.682 \times 10^{-11}\ \text{atm/s}$$

The rate of decrease in mmHg/s is

$$8.682 \times 10^{-11}\ \text{atm/s} \times (760\ \text{mmHg/atm}) = 6.598 \times 10^{-8} = 6.60 \times 10^{-8}\ \text{mmHg/s}$$

Copyright © Cengage Learning. All rights reserved.

CHAPTER 14

Chemical Equilibrium

■ SOLUTIONS TO EXERCISES

Note on significant figures: If the final answer to a solution needs to be rounded off, it is given first with one nonsignificant figure, and the last significant figure is underlined. The final answer is then rounded to the correct number of significant figures. In multistep problems, intermediate answers are given with at least one nonsignificant figure; however, only the final answer has been rounded off.

14.1. Use the table approach, and give the starting numbers, the change, and the equilibrium number of moles of each.

Amt. (mol)	$CO(g)$	+	$H_2O(g)$	$\rightleftharpoons$	$CO_2(g)$	+	$H_2(g)$
Starting	1.00		1.00		0		0
Change	$-x$		$-x$		$+x$		$+x$
Equilibrium	$(1.00 - x)$		$(1.00 - x)$		x		$x = 0.43$

Because we are given that $x = 0.43$ in the statement of the problem, we can use that to calculate the equilibrium amounts of the reactants and products:

Equilibrium amount CO $= 1.00 - 0.43 = 0.57$ mol

Equilibrium amount $H_2O = 1.00 - 0.43 = 0.57$ mol

Equilibrium amount $CO_2 = x = 0.43$ mol

Equilibrium amount $H_2 = x = 0.43$ mol

14.2. For the equation $2NO_2 + 7H_2 \rightarrow 2NH_3 + 4H_2O$, the expression for the equilibrium constant, K_c, is

$$K_c = \frac{[NH_3]^2 [H_2O]^4}{[NO_2]^2 [H_2]^7}$$

Notice that each concentration term is raised to a power equal to its coefficient in the chemical equation.

For the equation $NO_2 + 7/2H_2 \rightarrow NH_3 + 2H_2O$, the expression for the equilibrium constant, K_c, is

$$K_c = \frac{[NH_3][H_2O]^2}{[NO_2][H_2]^{7/2}}$$

Note the correspondence between the power and coefficient for each molecule.

Copyright © Cengage Learning. All rights reserved.

14.3. The chemical equation for the reaction is

$$CO(g) + H_2O(g) \rightleftharpoons H_2(g) + CO_2(g)$$

The expression for the equilibrium constant for this reaction is

$$K_c = \frac{[CO_2][H_2]}{[CO][H_2O]}$$

We obtain the concentration of each substance by dividing the moles of substance by its volume. The equilibrium concentrations are as follows: $[CO] = 0.057$ M, $[H_2O] = 0.057$ M, $[CO_2] = 0.043$ M, and $[H_2] = 0.043$ M. Substituting these values into the equation for the equilibrium constant gives

$$K_c = \frac{(0.043)(0.043)}{(0.057)(0.057)} = 0.5\underline{6}9 = 0.57$$

14.4. Use the table approach, and give the starting concentrations, the change, and the equilibrium concentration of each by dividing moles by volume in liters.

Conc. (M)	$2H_2S(g)$ $\rightleftharpoons$	$2H_2(g)$	+	$S_2(g)$
Starting	0.0100	0		0
Change	$-2x$	$+2x$ (= 0.00285)		$+x$
Equilibrium	$0.0100 - 2x$	$2x$		x

Because the problem states that 0.00285 M H_2 was formed, we can use the 0.00285 M to calculate the other concentrations. The S_2 molarity should be one-half that, or $0.0014\underline{2}5$ M, and the H_2S molarity should be $0.0100 - 0.00285$, or $0.007\underline{1}5$ M. Substituting into the equilibrium expression gives

$$K_c = \frac{[H_2]^2[S_2]}{[H_2S]^2} = \frac{(0.00285)^2(0.001425)}{(0.00715)^2} = 2.\underline{2}6 \times 10^{-4} = 2.3 \times 10^{-4}$$

14.5. Use the expression that relates K_c to K_p:

$$K_p = K_c(RT)^{\Delta n}$$

The Δn term is the sum of the coefficients of the gaseous products minus the sum of the coefficients of the gaseous reactants. In this case, $\Delta n = (2 - 1) = 1$, and K_p is

$$K_p = (3.26 \times 10^{-2})(0.0821 \times 464)^1 = 1.2\underline{4}1 = 1.24$$

14.6. For a heterogeneous equilibrium, the concentration terms for liquids and solids are omitted because such concentrations are constant at a given temperature and are incorporated into the measured value of K_c. For this case, K_c is defined as

$$K_c = \frac{[Ni(CO)_4]}{[CO]^4}$$

Copyright © Cengage Learning. All rights reserved.

14.7. Because the equilibrium constant is very large ($> 10^4$), the equilibrium mixture will contain mostly products. Rearrange the K_c expression to solve for $[NO_2]$.

$$[NO_2] = \sqrt{K_c[O_2][NO]^2} = \sqrt{(4.0 \times 10^{13})(2.0 \times 10^{-6})(2.0 \times 10^{-6})^2} = 1.\underline{7}8 \times 10^{-2}$$
$$= 1.8 \times 10^{-2} = 0.018 \ M$$

14.8. First, divide moles by volume in liters to convert to molar concentrations, giving $0.00015 \ M \ CO_2$ and $0.010 \ M \ CO$. Substitute these values into the reaction quotient and calculate Q.

$$Q = \frac{[CO]^2}{[CO_2]} = \frac{(0.010)^2}{(0.00015)} = 0.6\underline{6}6 = 0.67$$

Because $Q = 0.67$ and is less than K_c, the reaction will go to the right, forming more CO.

14.9. Rearrange the K_c expression, and substitute for K_c ($= 0.0415$) and the given moles per 1.00 L to solve for moles per 1.00 L of PCl_5.

$$[PCl_5] = \frac{[PCl_3][Cl_2]}{K_c} = \frac{(0.020)(0.020)}{0.0415} = 9.\underline{6}3 \times 10^{-3} = 9.6 \times 10^{-3} \ M$$

Because the volume is 1.00 L, the moles of $PCl_5 = 0.0096$ mol.

14.10. Use the table approach, and give the starting number, the change, and the equilibrium number of moles of each.

Amt. (mol)	$H_2(g)$	+	$I_2(g)$	$\rightleftharpoons$	$2HI(g)$
Starting	0.500		0.500		0
Change	$-x$		$-x$		$+2x$
Equilibrium	$0.500 - x$		$0.500 - x$		$2x$

Substitute the equilibrium concentrations into the expression for K_c ($= 49.7$).

$$K_c = \frac{[HI]^2}{[H_2][I_2]} ; 49.7 = \frac{(2x)^2}{(0.500 - x)(0.500 - x)} = \frac{(2x)^2}{(0.500 - x)^2}$$

Taking the square root of both sides of the right-hand equation and solving for x gives

$$\pm 7.05 = \frac{2x}{(0.500 - x)}, \text{ or } \pm 7.05(0.500 - x) = 2x$$

Using the positive root, $x = 0.3\underline{9}0$.

Using the negative root, $x = 0.6\underline{9}8$ (this must be rejected because 0.698 is greater than the 0.500 starting number of moles).

Substituting $x = 0.390$ mol into the last line of the table to solve for equilibrium concentrations gives these amounts: 0.11 mol H_2, 0.11 mol I_2, and 0.78 mol HI.

Copyright © Cengage Learning. All rights reserved.

14.11. Use the table approach for starting, change, and equilibrium concentrations of each species.

Conc. (M)	$PCl_5(g)$	$\rightleftharpoons$	$PCl_3(g)$	+	$Cl_2(g)$
Starting	1.00		0		0
Change	$-x$		$+x$		$+x$
Equilibrium	$1.00 - x$		x		x

Substitute the equilibrium-concentration expressions from the table into the equilibrium equation, and solve for x using the quadratic formula.

$$[PCl_3][Cl_2] = K_c \times [PCl_5] = 0.0211(1.00 - x) = x^2$$

$$x^2 + 0.0211x - 0.0211 = 0$$

$$x = \frac{-0.0211 \pm \sqrt{(0.0211)^2 - 4(-0.0211)}}{2} = \frac{-0.0211 \pm 0.2913}{2}$$

$x = -0.1562$ (impossible; reject), or $x = 0.135\underline{0}9 = 0.135\ M$ (logical)

Solve for the equilibrium concentrations using $x = 0.135\ M$: $[PCl_5] = 0.86\ M$, $[Cl_2] = 0.135\ M$, and $[PCl_3] = 0.135\ M$.

14.12.

a. Increasing the pressure will cause a net reaction to occur from right to left, and more $CaCO_3$ will form.

b. Increasing the concentration of hydrogen will cause a net reaction to occur from right to left, forming more Fe and H_2O.

14.13.

a. Because there are equal numbers of moles of gas on both sides of the equation, increasing the pressure will not increase the amount of product.

b. Because the reaction increases the number of moles of gas, increasing the pressure will decrease the amount of product.

c. Because the reaction decreases the number of moles of gas, increasing the pressure will increase the amount of product.

14.14. Because this is an endothermic reaction and absorbs heat, high temperatures will be more favorable to the production of carbon monoxide.

14.15. Because this is an endothermic reaction and absorbs heat, high temperatures will give the best yield of carbon monoxide. Because the reaction increases the number of moles of gas, decreasing the pressure will also increase the yield.

Copyright © Cengage Learning. All rights reserved.

■ ANSWERS TO SELF-ASSESSMENT AND REVIEW QUESTIONS

14.1. A reasonable graph showing the decrease in concentration of $N_2O_4(g)$ and the increase in concentration of $NO_2(g)$ is shown below.

At first, the concentration of N_2O_4 is large, and the rate of the forward reaction is large, but then as the concentration of N_2O_4 decreases, the rate of the forward reaction decreases. In contrast, the concentration of NO_2 builds up from zero to a low concentration. Thus, the initial rate of the reverse reaction is zero, but it steadily increases as the concentration of NO_2 increases. Eventually, the two rates become equal when the reaction reaches equilibrium. This is a dynamic equilibrium because both the forward and reverse reactions are occurring at all times, even though there is no net change in concentration at equilibrium.

14.2. The 1.0 mol of $H_2(g)$ and 1.0 mol of $I_2(g)$ in the first mixture reach equilibrium when the amounts of reactants decrease to 0.50 mol each and when the amount of product increases to 1.0 mol. The total number of moles of the reactants at the start is 2.0 mol, which is the same number of moles as in the second mixture, the 2.0 mol of HI that is to be allowed to come to equilibrium. The second mixture should produce the same number of moles of H_2, I_2, and HI at equilibrium, because if the total number of moles is constant, it should not matter from which direction an equilibrium is approached.

14.3. The equilibrium constant for a gaseous reaction can be written using partial pressures instead of concentrations because all the reactants and products are in the same vessel. Therefore, at constant temperature, the pressure, P, is proportional to the concentration, n/V. (The ideal gas law says that $P = [n/V]RT$.)

Copyright © Cengage Learning. All rights reserved.

14.4. The addition of reactions 1 and 2 yields reaction 3:

(Reaction 1)	HCN +	OH^-	$\rightleftharpoons$	CN^- +	H_2O
(Reaction 2)		H_2O	$\rightleftharpoons$	H^+ +	OH^-
(Reaction 3)		HCN	$\rightleftharpoons$	H^+ +	CN^-

The rule states that if a given equation can be obtained from the sum of other equations, the equilibrium constant for the given equation equals the product of the other equilibrium constants. Thus, K for reaction 3 is

$$K = K_1 \times K_2 = (4.9 \times 10^4) \times (1.0 \times 10^{-14}) = 4.9 \times 10^{-10}$$

14.5.

a. Homogeneous equilibrium. All substances are gases and thus exist in one phase, a mixture of gases.

b. Heterogeneous equilibrium. The two copper compounds are solids, but the other substances are gases. This fulfills the definition of a heterogeneous equilibrium.

c. Homogeneous equilibrium. All substances are gases and thus exist in one phase, a mixture of gases.

d. Heterogeneous equilibrium. The two copper-containing substances are solids, but the other substances are gases. This fulfills the definition of a heterogeneous equilibrium.

14.6. Pure liquids and solids can be ignored in an equilibrium-constant expression because their concentrations do not change. (If a solid is present, it has not dissolved in any gas or solution present.) In effect, concentrations of liquids and solids are incorporated into the value of K_c, as discussed in the chapter.

14.7. A qualitative interpretation of the equilibrium constant involves using the magnitude of the equilibrium constant to predict the relative amounts of reactants and products at equilibrium. If K_c is around 1, the equilibrium mixture contains appreciable amounts (same order of magnitude) of reactants and products. If K_c is large, the equilibrium mixture is mostly products. If K_c is small, the equilibrium mixture is mostly reactants. The type of reaction governs what "large" and "small" values are; but for some types of reactions, "large" might be no less than 10^2 to 10^4, whereas "small" might be no more than 10^{-4} to 10^{-2}.

14.8. The reaction quotient, Q_c, is an expression that has the same form as the equilibrium-constant expression but whose concentrations are not necessarily equilibrium concentrations. It is useful in determining whether a reaction mixture is at equilibrium or, if not, what direction the reaction will go as it approaches equilibrium.

14.9. The ways in which the equilibrium composition of a mixture can be altered are (1) changing concentrations by removing some of the products and/or some of the reactants, (2) changing the partial pressure of a gaseous reactant and/or a gaseous product, and (3) changing the temperature of the reaction mixture. (Adding a catalyst cannot alter the equilibrium concentration; it can affect only the rate of reaction.)

Copyright © Cengage Learning. All rights reserved.

14.10.   The role of the platinum is that of a catalyst; it provides conditions (a surface) suitable for speeding up the attainment of equilibrium. The platinum has no effect on the equilibrium composition of the mixture even though it greatly increases the rate of reaction.

14.11.   In some cases, a catalyst can affect the product in a reaction because it affects only the rate of one reaction out of several reactions that are possible. If two reactions are possible, and the uncatalyzed rate of one is much slower but that is the only reaction that is catalyzed, then the products with and without a catalyst will be different. The Ostwald process is a good example. In the absence of a catalyst, NH_3 burns in O_2 to form only N_2 and H_2O, even though it is possible for NH_3 to react to form NO and H_2O. Ostwald found that adding a platinum catalyst favors the formation of the NO and H_2O almost to the exclusion of the N_2 and H_2O.

14.12.   Four ways in which the yield of ammonia can be improved are (1) removing the gaseous NH_3 from the equilibrium by liquefying it, (2) increasing the nitrogen or hydrogen concentration, (3) increasing the total pressure on the mixture (the moles of gas decrease), and (4) lowering the temperature ($\Delta H°$ is negative, so heat is evolved). Each causes a shift to the right in accordance with Le Châtelier's principle.

14.13.   The answer is d, 2.10 moles.

14.14.   The answer is a, 1.24.

14.15.   The answer is c, 0.157.

14.16.   The answer is b, $Q_c = 6.33 \times 10^{-4}$; the concentration of NOBr increases.

Copyright © Cengage Learning. All rights reserved.

■ SOLUTIONS TO PRACTICE PROBLEMS

Note on significant figures: If the final answer to a solution needs to be rounded off, it is given first with one nonsignificant figure, and the last significant figure is underlined. The final answer is then rounded to the correct number of significant figures. In multistep problems, intermediate answers are given with at least one nonsignificant figure; however, only the final answer has been rounded off.

14.29. Use the table approach, and give the starting, change, and equilibrium number of moles of each.

Amt. (mol)	$PCl_5(g)$	$\rightleftharpoons$	$PCl_3(g)$	+	$Cl_2(g)$
Starting	2.500		0		0
Change	$-x$		$+x$		$+x$
Equilibrium	$2.500 - x$		$x = 0.338$		x

Since the equilibrium amount of PCl_3 is given in the problem, this tells you $x = 0.338$. The equilibrium amounts for the other substances can now be determined.

Equilibrium amount $Cl_2 = x = 0.338$ mol

Equilibrium amount $PCl_5 = 2.500 - x = 2.500 - 0.338 = 2.162$ mol

Therefore, the amounts of the substances in the equilibrium mixture are 2.162 mol PCl_5, 0.338 mol PCl_3, and 0.338 mol Cl_2.

14.31. Use the table approach, and give the starting, change, and equilibrium number of moles of each.

Amt. (mol)	$N_2(g)$	+	$3H_2(g)$	$\rightleftharpoons$	$2NH_3(g)$
Starting	0.600		1.800		0
Change	$-x$		$-3x$		$+2x$
Equilibrium	$0.600 - x$		$1.800 - 3x$		$2x = 0.048$

Since the equilibrium amount of NH_3 is given in the problem, this tells you $x = 0.024$. The equilibrium amounts for the other substances can now be determined.

Equilibrium amount $N_2 = 0.600 - 0.024 = 0.576$ mol

Equilibrium amount $H_2 = 1.800 - 3 \times (0.024) = 1.728$ mol

Therefore, the amounts of the substances in the equilibrium mixture are 0.576 mol N_2, 1.728 mol H_2, and 0.048 mol NH_3.

14.33. Use the table approach, and give the starting, change, and equilibrium number of moles of each.

Amt. (mol)	$2SO_2(g)$	+	$O_2(g)$	$\rightleftharpoons$	$2SO_3(g)$
Starting	0.0400		0.0200		0
Change	$-2x$		$-x$		$+2x$
Equilibrium	$0.0400 - 2x$		$0.0200 - x$		$2x \, (= 0.0296)$

Therefore, $x = 0.0148$, and the amounts of substances at equilibrium are 0.0104 mol SO_2, 0.0052 mol O_2, and 0.0296 mol SO_3.

Copyright © Cengage Learning. All rights reserved.

14.35.

a. $K_c = \dfrac{[NO_2][NO]}{[N_2O_3]}$

b. $K_c = \dfrac{[H_2]^2[S_2]}{[H_2S]^2}$

c. $K_c = \dfrac{[NO_2]^2}{[NO]^2[O_2]}$

d. $K_c = \dfrac{[P(NH_2)_3][HCl]^3}{[PCl_3][NH_3]^3}$

14.37. The reaction is $2H_2S(g) + 3O_2(g) \rightleftharpoons 2H_2O(g) + 2SO_2(g)$.

14.39. When the reaction is halved, the equilibrium-constant expression is

$$K_c = \dfrac{[NO_2]^2[O_2]^{1/2}}{[N_2O_5]}$$

When the reaction is then reversed, the equilibrium-constant expression becomes

$$K_c = \dfrac{[N_2O_5]}{[NO_2]^2[O_2]^{1/2}}$$

14.41. Because $K_c = 1.84$ for 2HI $\rightleftharpoons$ $H_2 + I_2$, the value of K_c for $H_2 + I_2 \rightleftharpoons$ 2HI must be the reciprocal of K_c for the first reaction. Mathematically, this can be shown as follows:

Forward: $K_c = \dfrac{[H_2][I_2]}{[HI]^2} = 1.84$

Reverse: $K_c = \dfrac{[HI]^2}{[H_2][I_2]} = \dfrac{1}{\dfrac{[H_2][I_2]}{[HI]^2}} = \dfrac{1}{K_c(f)}$

Thus, for the reverse reaction, K_c is calculated as follows:

$K_c = 1 \div 1.84 = 5.434 \times 10^{-1} = 0.543$

14.43. First, calculate the molar concentration of each of the compounds in the equations:

$[H_2] = 0.488$ mol $H_2 \div 6.00$ L $= 0.08133\ M$

$[I_2] = 0.206$ mol $I_2 \div 6.00$ L $= 0.03433\ M$

$[HI] = 2.250$ mol HI $\div 6.00$ L $= 0.3750\ M$

Now, substitute these into the K_c expression:

$$K_c = \dfrac{(0.3750)^2}{(0.08133)(0.03433)} = 50.36 = 50.4$$

Copyright © Cengage Learning. All rights reserved.

14.45. Substitute the following concentrations into the K_c expression:

$$[SO_3] = 0.0296 \text{ mol} \div 2.000 \text{ L} = 0.01480 \ M$$

$$[SO_2] = 0.0104 \text{ mol} \div 2.000 \text{ L} = 0.005200 \ M$$

$$[O_2] = 0.0052 \text{ mol} \div 2.000 \text{ L} = 0.00260 \ M$$

$$K_c = \frac{(0.01480)^2}{(0.005200)^2(0.00260)} = 3.11 \times 10^3 = 3.1 \times 10^3$$

14.47. For each mole of NOBr that reacts, $(1.000 - 0.094 = 0.906)$ mol remains. Starting with 2.00 mol NOBr, this means that 2 x 0.906 mol NOBr, or 1.812 mol NOBr, remains. Because the volume is 1.00 L, the concentration of NOBr at equilibrium is 1.812 M. Assemble a table of starting, change, and equilibrium concentrations:

Conc. (M)	2NOBr(g)	$\rightleftharpoons$	2NO(g)	+	Br$_2$(g)
Starting	2.00		0		0
Change	$-2x$		$+2x$		$+x$
Equilibrium	$2.00 - 2x \ (= 1.812)$		$2x$		x

Because $2.00 - 2x = 1.812$, $x = 0.094 \ M$. Therefore, the equilibrium concentrations are [NOBr] = 1.812 M, [NO] = 0.188 M, and [Br$_2$] = 0.094 M.

$$K_c = \frac{[NO]^2[Br_2]}{[NOBr]^2} = \frac{(0.188)^2(0.094)}{(1.812)^2} = 1.01 \times 10^{-3} = 1.0 \times 10^{-3}$$

14.49.

a. $K_p = \dfrac{P_{HBr}^2}{P_{H_2} P_{Br_2}}$

b. $K_p = \dfrac{P_{CH_4} P_{H_2S}^2}{P_{CS_2} P_{H_2}^4}$

c. $K_p = \dfrac{P_{H_2O}^2 P_{Cl_2}^2}{P_{HCl}^4 P_{O_2}}$

d. $K_p = \dfrac{P_{CH_3OH}}{P_{CO} P_{H_2}^2}$

14.51. There are 3 mol of gaseous product for every 8 mol of gaseous reactant, so $\Delta n = 3 - 5 = -2$. Using this, calculate K_p from K_c:

$$K_p = K_c(RT)^{\Delta n} = 0.28 (0.0821 \times 1173)^{-2} = 3.019 \times 10^{-5} = 3.0 \times 10^{-5}$$

Copyright © Cengage Learning. All rights reserved.

14.53. For each 1 mol of gaseous product, there are 1.5 mol of gaseous reactants; thus, $\Delta n = 1 - 1.5 = -0.5$. Using this, calculate K_c from K_p:

$$K_c = \frac{K_p}{(RT)^{\Delta n}} = \frac{6.55}{(0.0821 \times 900)^{-0.5}} = 6.55 \times (0.0821 \times 900)^{0.5} = 56.\underline{3}03 = 56.3$$

14.55.

    a. $K_c = \dfrac{[CO]^2}{[CO_2]}$

    b. $K_c = \dfrac{[CO_2]}{[CO]}$

    c. $K_c = \dfrac{[CO_2]}{[SO_2][O_2]^{1/2}}$

    d. $K_c = [Pb^{2+}][I^-]^2$

14.57.

    a.   Not complete; K_c is very small (10^{-31}), indicating very little reaction.

    b.   Nearly complete; K_c is very large (10^{21}), indicating nearly complete reaction.

14.59. K_c is extremely small, indicating very little reaction at room temperature. Because the decomposition of HF yields equal amounts of H_2 and F_2, at equilibrium $[H_2] = [F_2]$. So, for the decomposition of HF,

$$K_c = \frac{[H_2][F_2]}{[HF]^2} = \frac{[H_2]^2}{[HF]^2}$$

$$[H_2] = K_c^{1/2}[HF] = (1.0 \times 10^{-95})^{1/2}(1.0\ M) = 3.\underline{1}6 \times 10^{-48} = 3.2 \times 10^{-48}\ mol/L$$

This result does agree with what is expected from the very small magnitude of K_c.

14.61. Calculate Q, the reaction quotient, and compare it to the equilibrium constant ($K_c = 3.07 \times 10^{-4}$). If Q is larger, the reaction will go to the left; if Q is smaller, the reaction will go to the right; if they are equal, the reaction is at equilibrium. In all cases, Q is found by combining these terms:

$$Q = \frac{[NO]^2[Br_2]}{[NOBr]^2}$$

    a. $Q = \dfrac{(0.0162)^2(0.0123)}{(0.0720)^2} = 6.2\underline{2}6 \times 10^{-4} = 6.23 \times 10^{-4}$

        $Q > K_c$. The reaction should go to the left.

Copyright © Cengage Learning. All rights reserved.

b. $Q = \dfrac{(0.0159)^2(0.0139)}{(0.121)^2} = 2.400 \times 10^{-4} = 2.40 \times 10^{-4}$

$Q < K_c$. The reaction should go to the right.

c. $Q = \dfrac{(0.0134)^2(0.0181)}{(0.103)^2} = 3.063 \times 10^{-4} = 3.06 \times 10^{-4}$

$Q = K_c$. The reaction should be at equilibrium.

d. $Q = \dfrac{(0.0121)^2(0.0105)}{(0.0472)^2} = 6.900 \times 10^{-4} = 6.90 \times 10^{-4}$

$Q > K_c$. The reaction should go to the left.

14.63. Calculate Q, the reaction quotient, and compare it to the equilibrium constant. If Q is larger, the reaction will go to the left, and vice versa. Q is found by combining these terms:

$$Q = \frac{[CH_3OH]}{[CO][H_2]^2} = \frac{(0.020)}{(0.010)(0.010)^2} = 20.0 \ (>10.5)$$

The reaction goes to the left.

14.65. Substitute into the expression for K_c and solve for $[COCl_2]$:

$$K_c = 1.23 \times 10^3 = \frac{[COCl_2]}{[CO][Cl_2]} = \frac{[COCl_2]}{(0.012)(0.025)}$$

$$[COCl_2] = (1.23 \times 10^3)(0.012)(0.025) = 0.369 = 0.37\ M$$

14.67. Divide moles of substance by the volume 5.0 L to obtain concentration. The starting concentrations are $3.0 \times 10^{-4}\ M$ for both $[I_2]$ and $[Br_2]$. Assemble a table of starting, change, and equilibrium concentrations.

Conc. (M)	$I_2(g)$	+	$Br_2(g)$	⇌	2 IBr(g)
Starting	3.0×10^{-4}		3.0×10^{-4}		0
Change	$-x$		$-x$		$+2x$
Equilibrium	$(3.0 \times 10^{-4}) - x$		$(3.0 \times 10^{-4}) - x$		$2x$

Substituting into the equilibrium-constant expression gives

$$K_c = 1.2 \times 10^2 = \frac{[IBr]^2}{[I_2][Br_2]} = \frac{(2x)^2}{(3.0 \times 10^{-4} - x)(3.0 \times 10^{-4} - x)}$$

Taking the square root of both sides yields

$$10.95 = \frac{(2x)}{(3.0 \times 10^{-4} - x)}$$

Copyright © Cengage Learning. All rights reserved.

Rearranging and simplifying the right side give

$$(3.0 \times 10^{-4} - x) = \frac{(2x)}{10.95} = (0.1\underline{8}2\ x)$$

$$x = 2.\underline{5}3 \times 10^{-4}\ M$$

Thus, $[I_2] = [Br_2] = 4.\underline{7}0 \times 10^{-5} = 4.7 \times 10^{-5}\ M$, and $[IBr] = 5.\underline{0}6 \times 10^{-4} = 5.1 \times 10^{-4}\ M$.

14.69. Divide moles of substance by the volume 1.25 L to obtain concentration. The starting concentration is 1.00 M for $[CO_2]$, but the concentration of carbon, a solid, is omitted. Assemble a table of starting, change, and equilibrium concentrations.

Conc. (M)	$CO_2(g)$	+	$C(s)$	$\rightleftharpoons$	$2CO(g)$
Starting	1.00				0
Change	$-x$				$+2x$
Equilibrium	$1.00 - x$				$2x$

Substituting into the equilibrium expression for K_c gives

$$K_c = 14.0 = \frac{[CO]^2}{[CO_2]} = \frac{(2x)^2}{(1.00 - x)}$$

Rearranging and solving for x yield

$$14.0 - 14.0x = 4x^2$$

$$4x^2 + 14.0x - 14.0 = 0 \quad (\text{quadratic equation})$$

Using the solution to the quadratic equation gives

$$x = \frac{-14.0 \pm \sqrt{(14.0)^2 - 4(4)(-14.0)}}{2(4)}$$

$x = -4.31$ (impossible; reject), or $x = 0.81\underline{1}7 = 0.812\ M$ (logical)

Thus, $[CO_2] = 0.19\ M$, and $[CO] = 1.62\ M$.

14.71. Divide moles of substance by the volume 10.00 L to obtain concentration. The starting concentrations are 0.1000 M for $[CO]$ and 0.3000 M for $[H_2]$. Assemble a table of starting, change, and equilibrium concentrations.

Conc. (M)	$CO(g)$	+	$3H_2(g)$	$\rightleftharpoons$	$CH_4(g)$	+	$H_2O(g)$
Starting	0.1000		0.3000		0		0
Change	$-x$		$-3x$		$+x$		$+x$
Equilibrium	$0.1000 - x$		$0.3000 - 3x$		x		x

Substituting into the equilibrium expression for K_c gives

$$K_c = 3.92 = \frac{[CH_4][H_2O]}{[CO][H_2]^3} = \frac{x^2}{(0.1000 - x)[3(0.1000 - x)]^3} = \frac{x^2}{27(0.1000 - x)^4}$$

Copyright © Cengage Learning. All rights reserved.

Multiplying both sides by 27 and taking the square root of both sides give

$$10.29 = \frac{x}{(0.1000 - x)^2}$$

Or,

$$10.29x^2 - 3.058x + 0.1029 = 0$$

Using the solution to the quadratic equation yields

$$x = \frac{3.058 \pm \sqrt{(-3.058)^2 - 4(10.29)(0.1029)}}{2(10.29)}$$

$x = 0.2585$ (can't be > 0.1000, so reject), or $x = 0.03868 = 0.0387\ M$ (use)

Thus, $[CO] = 0.0613\ M$, $[H_2] = 0.1839\ M$, $[CH_4] = 0.0387\ M$, and $[H_2O] = 0.0387\ M$.

14.73. Forward direction

14.75.

    a.   A pressure increase has no effect because the number of moles of reactants equals that of products.

    b.   A pressure increase has no effect because the number of moles of reactants equals that of products.

    c.   A pressure increase causes the reaction to go to the left because the number of moles of reactants is less than that of products.

14.77. The fraction would not increase because an increase in temperature decreases the amounts of products of an exothermic reaction.

14.79. The value of $\Delta H°$ is calculated from the $\Delta H_f°$ values below each substance in the reaction:

$$2NO_2(g) \ + \ 7H_2(g) \ \rightleftharpoons \ 2NH_3(g) \ + \ 4H_2O(g)$$
$$2(33.10) \quad\quad 7(0) \quad\quad\quad\quad 2(-45.9) \quad\quad 4(-241.8)$$

$\Delta H° = -967.2 + (-91.8) - 66.20 = -1125.2$ kJ/2 mol NO_2

The equilibrium constant will decrease with temperature because raising the temperature of an exothermic reaction causes the reaction to go farther to the left.

14.81. Because the reaction is exothermic, the formation of products will be favored by low temperatures. Because there are more molecules of gaseous products than of gaseous reactants, the formation of products will be favored by low pressures.

Copyright © Cengage Learning. All rights reserved.

■ SOLUTIONS TO GENERAL PROBLEMS

14.83. Substitute the concentrations into the equilibrium expression to calculate K_c.

$$K_c = \frac{[CH_3OH]}{[CO][H_2]^2} = \frac{(0.015)}{(0.096)(0.191)^2} = 4.\underline{2}8 = 4.3$$

14.85. Assume 100.00 g of gas: 90.55 g CO, and 9.45 g CO_2. The moles of each are

$$90.55 \text{ g CO} \times \frac{1 \text{ mol CO}}{28.01 \text{ g CO}} = 3.23\underline{2}8 \text{ mol COI}$$

$$9.45 \text{ g CO}_2 \times \frac{1 \text{ mol CO}_2}{44.01 \text{ g CO}_2} = 0.21\underline{4}7 \text{ mol CO}_2$$

Total moles of gas = (3.2328 + 0.2147) mol = 3.44$\underline{7}$5 mol. Use the ideal gas law to convert to the volume of gaseous solution:

$$V = \frac{nRT}{P} = \frac{(3.4475 \text{ mol})(0.082057 \text{ L} \cdot \text{atm/K} \cdot \text{mol})(850 + 273)\text{K}}{1.000 \text{ atm}} = 317.\underline{6}9 \text{ L}$$

The concentrations are

$$[CO] = \frac{3.2328 \text{ mol CO}}{317.69 \text{ L}} = 0.01017\underline{6} \ M$$

$$[CO_2] = \frac{0.2147 \text{ mol CO}_2}{317.69 \text{ L}} = 6.7\underline{5}8 \times 10^{-4} \ M$$

Find K_c by substituting into the equilibrium expression:

$$K_c = \frac{[CO]^2}{[CO_2]} = \frac{(0.010176)^2}{(6.758 \times 10^{-4})} = 0.15\underline{3}2 = 0.153$$

14.87. After calculating the concentrations after mixing, calculate Q, the reaction quotient, and compare it with K_c.

$$[N_2] = [H_2] = 1.00 \text{ mol} \div 2.00 \text{ L} = 0.500 \ M$$

$$[NH_3] = 2.00 \text{ mol} \div 2.00 \text{ L} = 1.00 \ M$$

$$Q = \frac{[NH_3]^2}{[N_2][H_2]^3} = \frac{(1.00)^2}{(0.500)(0.500)^3} = 16.\underline{0}0 = 16.0$$

Because Q is greater than K_c, the reaction will go in the reverse direction (to the left) to reach equilibrium.

Copyright © Cengage Learning. All rights reserved.

14.89. To calculate the concentrations after mixing, assume the volume to be 1.00 L, symbolized as V. Because the volumes in the numerator and denominator cancel each other, they do not matter. Assume a 1.00-L volume and calculate Q, the reaction quotient, and compare it with K_c.

$$[CO] = [H_2O] = [CO_2] = [H_2] = 1.00 \text{ mol}/1.00 \text{ L}$$

$$Q = \frac{[CO_2][H_2]}{[CO][H_2O]} = \frac{(1.00 \text{ mol}/1.00 \text{ L})(1.00 \text{ mol}/1.00 \text{ L})}{(1.000 \text{ mol}/1.00 \text{ L})(1.00 \text{ mol}/1.00 \text{ L})} = 1.\underline{0}0$$

Because Q is greater than K_c, the reaction will go in the reverse direction (left) to reach equilibrium.

14.91. Assemble a table of starting, change, and equilibrium concentrations, letting $2x$ = the change in [HBr].

Conc. (M)	2HBr(g)	$\rightleftharpoons$	H$_2$(g)	+	Br$_2$(g)
Starting	0.010		0		0
Change	$-2x$		$+x$		$+x$
Equilibrium	$0.010 - 2x$		X		x

$$K_c = 0.016 = \frac{[H_2][Br_2]}{[HBr]^2} = \frac{(x)(x)}{(0.010 - 2x)^2}$$

$$0.1\underline{2}6 = \frac{(x)}{(0.010 - 2x)}$$

$$1.26 \times 10^{-3} - (2.52 \times 10^{-1})x = x$$

$$x = (1.26 \times 10^{-3}) \div 1.252 = 1.\underline{0}06 \times 10^{-3} = 1.0 \times 10^{-3} \, M$$

Therefore, [HBr] = 0.008 M, or 0.008 mol; [H$_2$] = 0.0010 M, or 0.0010 mol; and [Br$_2$] = 0.0010 M, or 0.0010 mol.

14.93. The starting concentration of COCl$_2$ = 1.00 mol $\div$ 25.00 L = 0.0400 M. Assemble a table of starting, change, and equilibrium concentrations.

Conc. (M)	COCl$_2$(g)	$\rightleftharpoons$	Cl$_2$(g)	+	CO(g)
Starting	0.0400		0		0
Change	$-x$		$+x$		$+x$
Equilibrium	$0.0400 - x$		x		x

Substituting into the equilibrium expression for K_c gives

$$K_c = 8.05 \times 10^{-4} = \frac{[CO][Cl_2]}{[COCl_2]} = \frac{(x)(x)}{(0.0400 - x)}$$

Copyright © Cengage Learning. All rights reserved.

Rearranging and solving for x yield

$$3.22 \times 10^{-5} - (8.05 \times 10^{-4})x - x^2 = 0$$

$$x^2 + (8.05 \times 10^{-4})x - 3.22 \times 10^{-5} = 0 \text{ (quadratic equation)}$$

Using the solution to the quadratic equation gives

$$x = \frac{-(8.05 \times 10^{-4}) \pm \sqrt{(8.05 \times 10^{-4})^2 - 4(1)(-3.22 \times 10^{-5})}}{2(1)}$$

$x = -6.09 \times 10^{-3}$ (impossible; reject), or $x = 5.2\underline{8}6 \times 10^{-3}$ (logical; use)

Percent dissoc. = (change ÷ starting) x 100% = (0.005286 ÷ 0.0400) x 100%

$$= 13.\underline{2}1 = 13.2\%$$

14.95. Using 1.00 mol/10.00 L, or 0.100 M, and 4.00 mol/10.00 L, or 0.400 M, for the respective starting concentrations for CO and H_2, assemble a table of starting, change, and equilibrium concentrations.

Conc. (M)	CO(g)	+	3H$_2$(g)	⇌	CH$_2$(g)	+	H$_2$O(g)
Starting	0.100		0.400		0		0
Change	$-x$		$-3x$		$+x$		$+x$
Equilibrium	$0.100 - x$		$0.400 - 3x$		X		x

Substituting into the equilibrium expression for K_c gives

$$K_c = 3.92 = \frac{[CH_4][H_2O]}{[CO][H_2]^3} = \frac{x^2}{(0.100 - x)(0.400 - 3x)^3}$$

$$f(x) = \frac{x^2}{(0.100 - x)(0.400 - 3x)^3}$$

Because K_c is > 1 (> 50% reaction), choose $x = 0.05$ (about half of CO reacting), and use that for the first entry in the table of x, f(x), and interpretations.

x	f(x)	Interpretation
0.05	3.20	$x > 0.05$
0.06	8.45	$x < 0.06$
0.055	5.18	$x < 0.055$
0.0525	4.07	$x < 0.0525$ (but close)
0.052	3.87	f(x) of 3.87 ≅ 3.92

At equilibrium, concentrations and moles are CO: 0.048 M and 0.48 mol; H_2: 0.244 M and 2.44 mol; CH_4: 0.052 M and 0.52 mol; and H_2O: 0.052 M and 0.52 mol.

14.97. The dissociation is endothermic.

Copyright © Cengage Learning. All rights reserved.

14.99. For $N_2 + 3H_2 \rightleftharpoons 2NH_3$, K_p is defined in terms of pressures as

$$K_p = \frac{P_{NH_3}{}^2}{P_{N_2} P_{H_2}{}^3}$$

But by the ideal gas law, where $[\,i\,] = $ mol/L,

$$P_i = (n_i RT)/V, \text{ or } P_i = [\,i\,]RT$$

Substituting the right-hand equality into the K_p expression gives

$$K_p = \frac{[NH_3]^2 (RT)^2}{[N_2](RT)\,[H_2]^3 (RT)^3} = \frac{[NH_3]^2}{[N_2][H_2]^3}(RT)^{-2}$$

$$K_p = K_c(RT)^{-2}, \text{ or } K_c = K_p (RT)^2$$

14.101.

a. The change in the number of moles of gas for the reaction is $\Delta n = 2 - 1 = 1$. Using this, calculate K_p from K_c:

$$K_p = K_c(RT)^{\Delta n} = 0.153\,(0.08206 \times 1123)^1 = 14.\underline{0}99 = 14.1$$

b. Use the table approach, and give the starting, change, and equilibrium pressures in atm.

Press. (atm)	C(s) +	$CO_2(g)$ $\rightleftharpoons$	$2CO(g)$
Starting		1.50	0
Change		$-x$	$+2x$
Equilibrium		$1.50 - x$	$2x$

Substituting into the equilibrium-constant expression gives

$$K_p = 14.10 = \frac{P_{CO}^2}{P_{CO_2}} = \frac{(2x)^2}{(1.50 - x)}$$

Rearranging and solving for x give a quadratic equation.

$$4x^2 + 14.10x - 21.15 = 0$$

Using the quadratic formula gives

$$x = \frac{-14.10 \pm \sqrt{(14.10)^2 - (4)(4)(-21.15)}}{2(4)}$$

$$x = 1.1\underline{3}5 \text{ (positive root)}$$

Thus, at equilibrium, the pressures of CO and CO_2 are

$$P_{CO_2} = 1.50 - 1.1\underline{3}5 = 0.3\underline{6}5 = 0.37 \text{ atm}$$

$$P_{CO} = 2x = 2(1.1\underline{3}5) = 2.2\underline{7}0 = 2.27 \text{ atm}$$

c. Because the reaction is endothermic, the equilibrium will shift to the left, and the pressure of CO will decrease.

Copyright © Cengage Learning. All rights reserved.

14.103.

a. The molar mass of PCl_5 is 208.22 g/mol. Thus, the initial concentration of PCl_5 is

$$\frac{35.8 \text{ g PCl}_5 \ \times \ \dfrac{1 \text{ mol PCl}_5}{208.22 \text{ g PCl}_5}}{5.0 \text{ L}} = 0.03\underline{4}4 \ M$$

Use the table approach, and give the starting, change, and equilibrium concentrations.

Conc. (M)	$PCl_3(g)$	+	$Cl_2(g)$	$\rightleftharpoons$	$PCl_5(g)$
Starting	0		0		0.03$\underline{4}$4
Change	x		x		$-x$
Equilibrium	x		x		0.03$\underline{4}$4 $- x$

Substituting into the equilibrium-constant expression gives

$$K_c = 4.1 = \frac{[PCl_5]}{[PCl_3][Cl_2]} = \frac{0.0344 - x}{x^2}$$

Rearranging and solving for x gives a quadratic equation.

$$4.1x^2 + x - 0.0344 = 0$$

Using the quadratic formula gives

$$x = \frac{-1 \pm \sqrt{(1)^2 - (4)(4.1)(-0.0344)}}{2(4.1)}$$

$$x = 0.03\underline{0}6 \ (\text{positive root})$$

Thus, at equilibrium, $[PCl_3] = [Cl_2] = x = 0.031 \ M$. The concentration of PCl_5 is

$$[PCl_5] = .03\underline{4}4 - x = 0.0344 - 0.0306 = 0.00\underline{3}8 = 0.004 \ M.$$

b. The fraction of PCl_5 decomposed is

$$\text{Fraction decomposed} = \frac{0.0306 \text{ M}}{0.03\underline{4}4 \text{ M}} = 0.8\underline{8}9 = 0.89$$

c. There would be a greater pressure, so, in order to minimize the increase in pressure, less PCl_5 would decompose.

14.105. The initial moles of $SbCl_5$ (molar mass 299.01 g/mol) are

$$65.4 \text{ g SbCl}_5 \ \times \ \frac{1 \text{ mol SbCl}_5}{299.01 \text{ g SbCl}_5} = 0.21\underline{8}7 \text{ mol}$$

The initial pressure of $SbCl_5$ is

$$P = \frac{nRT}{V} = \frac{(0.2187 \text{ mol})(0.08206 \text{ L} \cdot \text{atm} / \text{K} \cdot \text{mol})(468 \text{ K})}{5.00 \text{ L}} = 1.6\underline{8}0 \text{ atm}$$

Copyright © Cengage Learning. All rights reserved.

Use the table approach, and give the starting, change, and equilibrium pressures in atm.

Press. (atm)	$SbCl_5(g)$	$\rightleftharpoons$	$SbCl_3(g)$	+	$Cl_2(g)$
Starting	1.680		0		0
Change	$-x$		x		x
Equilibrium	(1.680)(0.642)		(1.680)(0.358)		(1.680)(0.358)

At equilibrium, 35.8% of the $SbCl_5$ is decomposed, so $x = (1.680)(0.358)$ in this table. The equilibrium-constant expression is

$$K_p = \frac{P_{SbCl_3} \cdot P_{Cl_2}}{P_{SbCl_5}} = \frac{(1.680 \times 0.358)^2}{1.680 \times 0.642} = 0.33\underline{5}4 = 0.335$$

14.107.

a. The initial concentration of SO_2Cl_2 (molar mass 134.97 g/mol) is

$$\frac{8.25 \text{ g } SO_2Cl_2 \times \dfrac{1 \text{ mol } SO_2Cl_2}{134.97 \text{ g } SO_2Cl_2}}{1.00 \text{ L}} = 0.061\underline{1}2 \ M$$

Use the table approach, and give the starting, change, and equilibrium concentrations.

Conc. (M)	$SO_2Cl_2(g)$	$\rightleftharpoons$	$SO_2(g)$	+	$Cl_2(g)$
Starting	0.06112		0		0
Change	$-x$		x		x
Equilibrium	$0.06112 - x$		x		x

Substituting into the equilibrium-constant expression gives

$$K_c = \frac{[SO_2][Cl_2]}{[SO_2Cl_2]} = \frac{x^2}{(0.06112 - x)} = 0.045$$

Rearranging and solving for x give a quadratic equation.

$$x^2 + 0.045x - 0.0027506 = 0$$

Using the quadratic formula gives

$$x = \frac{-(0.045) \pm \sqrt{(0.045)^2 - (4)(1)(-0.0027506)}}{2(1)}$$

$$x = 0.034\underline{5}6 \text{ (positive root)}$$

The concentrations at equilibrium are $[SO_2] = [Cl_2] = x = 0.034 \ M$. For SO_2Cl_2,

$$[SO_2Cl_2] = 0.06112 - x = 0.06112 - 0.03\underline{4}56 = 0.02\underline{6}55 = 0.027 \text{ M}.$$

b. The fraction of SO_2Cl_2 decomposed is

$$\text{Fraction decomposed} = \frac{0.03456 \ M}{0.06112 \ M} = 0.5\underline{6}5 = 0.57$$

c. This would shift the equilibrium to the left and decrease the fraction of SO_2Cl_2 that has decomposed.

Copyright © Cengage Learning. All rights reserved.

14.109.

a.   First, determine the initial concentration of the dimer assuming complete reaction. The reaction can be described as $2A \rightarrow D$. Therefore, the initial concentration of dimer is one-half of the concentration of monomer, or 2.0×10^{-4} M. Next, allow the dimer to dissociate into the monomer in equilibrium. Use the table approach, and give the starting, change, and equilibrium concentrations.

Conc. (M)	$D(g)$	$\rightleftharpoons$	$2A(g)$
Starting	2.0×10^{-4}		0
Change	$-x$		$2x$
Equilibrium	$2.0 \times 10^{-4} - x$		$2x$

Substituting into the equilibrium-constant expression gives

$$K_c = \frac{[A]^2}{[D]} = \frac{(2x)^2}{(2.0 \times 10^{-4} - x)} = \frac{1}{3.2 \times 10^4} = 3.125 \times 10^{-5}$$

Rearranging and solving for x give a quadratic equation.

$$4x^2 + (3.125 \times 10^{-5})x - (6.250 \times 10^{-9}) = 0$$

Using the quadratic formula gives

$$x = \frac{-(3.125 \times 10^{-5}) \pm \sqrt{(3.125 \times 10^{-5})^2 - (4)(4)(-6.250 \times 10^{-9})}}{2(4)}$$

$x = 3.\underline{5}8 \times 10^{-5}$ (positive root)

Thus, the concentrations at equilibrium are

$$[CH_3COOH] = 2x = 2(3.\underline{5}8 \times 10^{-5}) = 7.\underline{1}6 \times 10^{-5} = 7.2 \times 10^{-5} \ M$$

$$[Dimer] = 2.0 \times 10^{-4} - 3.\underline{5}8 \times 10^{-5} = 1.\underline{6}4 \times 10^{-4} = 1.6 \times 10^{-4} \ M$$

b.   Some hydrogen bonding can occur that results in a more stable system. The proposed structure of the dimer is

c.   An increase in the temperature would facilitate bond breaking and would decrease the amount of dimer. We could also use a Le Châtelier-type argument.

Copyright © Cengage Learning. All rights reserved.

14.111. The molar mass of Br_2 is 159.82 g/mol. Thus, the initial concentration of Br_2 is

$$\frac{18.22 \text{ g Br}_2 \times \dfrac{1 \text{ mol Br}_2}{159.82 \text{ g Br}_2}}{1.00 \text{ L}} = 0.11\underline{4}0 \ M$$

Use the table approach, and give the starting, change, and equilibrium concentrations.

Conc. (M)	$2NO(g)$	+	$Br_2(g)$	$\rightleftharpoons$	$2NOBr(g)$
Starting	0.112		0.11$\underline{4}$0		0
Change	$-2x$		$-x$		$2x$
Equilibrium	$0.112 - 2x = 0.02\underline{9}60$		$= 0.1140 - x$ $0.07\underline{2}80$		$2x \ (= 0.0824 \ M)$ $= 0.0824$

Substituting into the equilibrium-constant expression gives

$$K_c = \frac{[NOBr]^2}{[NO]^2[Br_2]} = \frac{(0.0824)^2}{(0.02960)^2(0.07280)} = 1\underline{0}6.4 = 1.1 \times 10^2$$

■ SOLUTIONS TO CUMULATIVE-SKILLS PROBLEMS

14.125. For $Sb_2S_3(s) + 3H_2(g) \rightleftharpoons 2Sb(s) + 3H_2S(g)$ $[+3Pb^{2+} \rightarrow 3PbS(s) + 6H^+]$:

Starting M of $H_2(g) = 0.0100$ mol $\div$ 2.50 L $= 0.00400 \ M \ H_2$

1.029 g PbS $\div$ 239.26 g PbS/mol $H_2S = 4.30\underline{0}7 \times 10^{-3}$ mol H_2S

4.3007 $\times 10^{-3}$ mol H_2S $\div$ 2.50 L $= [1.7203 \times 10^{-3}] = M$ of H_2S

Conc. (M)	$3H_2(g)$	+	$Sb_2S_3(s)$	$\rightleftharpoons$	$3H_2S(g)$	+	$2Sb(s)$
Starting	0.00400				0		
Change	-0.0017203				$+0.0017203$		
Equilibrium	0.0022797				0.0017203		

Substituting into the equilibrium expression for K_c gives

$$K_c = \frac{[H_2S]^3}{[H_2]^3} = \frac{(0.0017203)^3}{(0.0022797)^3} = 0.42\underline{9}7 = 0.430$$

Copyright © Cengage Learning. All rights reserved.

14.127. for $PCl_5(g) \rightleftharpoons PCl_3(g) + Cl_2(g)$:

Starting M of $PCl_5 = 0.0100$ mol $\div 2.00$ L $= 0.00500$ M

Conc. (M)	$PCl_5(g)$ $\rightleftharpoons$	$PCl_3(g)$ +	$Cl_2(g)$
Starting	0.00500	0	0
Change	$-x$	$+x$	$+x$
Equilibrium	$0.00500 - x$	x	x

Substituting into the equilibrium expression for K_c gives

$$K_c = 4.15 \times 10^{-2} = \frac{[PCl_3][Cl_2]}{[PCl_5]} = \frac{(x)(x)}{(0.00500 - x)}$$

$$x^2 + (4.15 \times 10^{-2})x - 2.075 \times 10^{-4} = 0 \text{ (quadratic)}$$

Solving the quadratic equation gives $x = -4.60 \times 10^{-2}$ (impossible) and $x = 4.51 \times 10^{-3}$ M (use).

Total M of gas $= 0.00451 + 0.00451 + 0.00049 = 0.009510$ M

$P = (n/V)RT = (0.009510\ M)[0.082057\ \text{L·atm/(K·mol)}](523\ K) = 0.4081 = 0.408$ atm

Copyright © Cengage Learning. All rights reserved.

CHAPTER 15

Acids and Bases

■ **SOLUTIONS TO EXERCISES**

Note on significant figures: If the final answer to a solution needs to be rounded off, it is given first with one nonsignificant figure, and the last significant figure is underlined. The final answer is then rounded to the correct number of significant figures. In multistep problems, intermediate answers are given with at least one nonsignificant figure; however, only the final answer has been rounded off.

15.1. See labels below reaction:

$$H_2CO_3(aq) \;+\; CN^-(aq) \;\rightleftharpoons\; HCN(aq) \;+\; HCO_3^-(aq)$$

     acid   base   acid   base

H_2CO_3 is the proton donor (Brønsted-Lowry acid) on the left, and HCN is the proton donor (Brønsted-Lowry acid) on the right. The CN^- and HCO_3^- ions are proton acceptors (Brønsted-Lowry bases). HCN is the conjugate acid of CN^-.

15.2. Part a involves molecules with all single bonds; part b does not, so bonds are drawn in.

a.

Lewis acid   Lewis base

b.

Lewis acid   Lewis base

Copyright © Cengage Learning. All rights reserved.

15.3. The $HC_2H_3O_2$ is a stronger acid than H_2S, and HS^- is a stronger base than the $C_2H_3O_2^-$ ion. The equilibrium favors the weaker acid and weaker base; therefore, the reactants are favored.

15.4.

    a. PH_3

    b.   HI

    c. H_2SO_3

    d. H_3AsO_4

    e. HSO_4^-

15.5. A 0.125 M solution of $Ba(OH)_2$, a strong base, ionizes completely to yield 0.125 M Ba^{2+} ion and 2 x 0.125 M, or 0.250 M, OH^- ion. Use the K_w equation to calculate the $[H_3O^+]$.

$$[H_3O^+] = \frac{K_w}{[OH^-]} = \frac{1.0 \times 10^{-14}}{(0.250)} = 4.0\underline{0} \times 10^{-14} = 4.0 \times 10^{-14} \, M$$

15.6. Use the K_w equation to calculate the $[H_3O^+]$.

$$[H_3O^+] = \frac{K_w}{[OH^-]} = \frac{1.0 \times 10^{-14}}{1.0 \times 10^{-5}} = 1.0\underline{0} \times 10^{-9} = 1.0 \times 10^{-9} \, M$$

Since the $[H_3O^+]$ concentration is less than 1.0×10^{-7}, the solution is basic.

15.7. Calculate the negative log of the $[H_3O^+]$:

$$pH = -\log [H_3O^+] = -\log (0.045) = 1.3\underline{4}6 = 1.35$$

15.8. Calculate the pOH of 0.025 M OH^-, and then subtract from 14.00 to find pH:

$$pOH = -\log [OH^-] = -\log (0.025) = 1.6\underline{0}2$$

$$pH = 14.00 - 1.602 \doteq 12.3\underline{9}7 = 12.40$$

15.9. Because pH = 3.16, by definition $\log [H_3O^+] = -3.16$. Enter this on the calculator and convert to the antilog (number) of -3.16.

$$[H_3O^+] = \text{antilog} (-3.16) = 10^{-3.16} = 6.9\underline{1} \times 10^{-4} = 6.9 \times 10^{-4} \, M$$

15.10. Find the pOH by subtracting the pOH from 14.00. Then enter -3.40 on the calculator to convert to the antilog (number) corresponding to -3.40.

$$pOH = 14.00 - 10.6 = 3.\underline{4}0$$

$$[H_3O^+] = \text{antilog} (-3.40) = 10^{-3.40} = \underline{3}.98 \times 10^{-4} = 4 \times 10^{-4} \, M$$

Copyright © Cengage Learning. All rights reserved.

■ ANSWERS TO SELF-ASSESSMENT AND REVIEW QUESTIONS

15.1. You can classify these acids using the information in Section 15.1. Also recall that all diatomic acids of Group VIIA halides are strong except for HF.

    a.   Weak

    b.   Weak

    c.   Strong

    d.   Strong

    e.   Weak

    f.   Weak

15.2. In Section 15.1, we are told that all neutralizations involving strong acids and bases evolve 55.90 kJ of heat per mole of H_3O^+. Thus, the thermochemical evidence for the Arrhenius concept is based on the fact that when 1 mol of any strong acid (1 mol H_3O^+) is neutralized by 1 mole of any strong base (1 mol OH^-), the heat of neutralization is always the same ($\Delta H° = -55.90$ kJ/mol).

15.3. A Brønsted-Lowry acid is a molecule or ion that donates an H^+ ion (proton donor) to a base in a proton-transfer reaction. A Brønsted-Lowry base is a molecule or ion that accepts an H^+ ion (proton acceptor) from an acid in a proton-transfer reaction. An example of an acid-base equation:

$$HF(aq) \quad + \quad NH_3(aq) \quad \rightarrow \quad NH_4^+(aq) \quad + \quad F^-(aq)$$

    acid   base   acid   base

15.4. The conjugate acid of a base is a species that differs from the base by only one H^+. Consider the base, HSO_3^-. Its conjugate acid would be H_2SO_3 but not H_2SO_4. H_2SO_4 differs from HSO_3^- by one H and one O.

15.5. You can write the equations by considering that $H_2PO_3^-$ is both a Brønsted-Lowry acid and a Brønsted-Lowry base. The $H_2PO_3^-$ acts as a Brønsted-Lowry acid when it reacts with a base such as OH^-:

$$H_2PO_3^-(aq) + OH^-(aq) \rightarrow HPO_3^{2-}(aq) + H_2O(l)$$

The $H_2PO_3^-$ acts as a Brønsted-Lowry base when it reacts with an acid such as HCl:

$$H_2PO_3^-(aq) + HCl(aq) \rightarrow H_3PO_3(aq) + Cl^-(aq)$$

15.6. The Brønsted-Lowry concept enlarges on the Arrhenius concept in the following ways: (1) It expands the concept of a base to include any species that accepts protons, not just the OH^- ion or compounds containing the OH^- ion. (2) It enlarges the concepts of acids and bases to include ions as well as molecules. (3) It enables us to write acid-base reactions in nonaqueous solutions as well as in aqueous solutions, whereas the Arrhenius concept applies only to aqueous solutions. (4) It allows some species to be considered as acids or bases, depending on the other reactant with which they are mixed.

Copyright © Cengage Learning. All rights reserved.

15.7. According to the Lewis concept, an acid is an electron-pair acceptor and a base is an electron-pair donor. An example is

$$Ag^+(aq) \ + \ 2(:NH_3) \quad \rightarrow \quad Ag(NH_3)_2{}^+(aq)$$

$$\text{acid} \qquad\quad \text{base}$$

15.8. Recall that the weaker the acid, the stronger it holds on to its proton(s). Thus, if a reaction mixture consists of a stronger acid and base and a weaker acid and base, the weaker-acid side will always be favored because the proton(s) will bond more strongly to the weaker acid.

15.9. The two factors that determine the strength of an acid are (1) the polarity of the bond to which the H atom is attached, and (2) the strength of the bond, or how tightly the proton is held by the atom to which it is bonded. An increase in the polarity of the bond makes it easier to remove the proton, increasing the strength of the acid. An increase in the strength of the bond makes it more difficult to remove the proton, decreasing the strength of the acid. The strength of the bond depends in turn on the size of the atom, so larger atoms have weaker bonds, whereas smaller atoms have stronger bonds.

15.10. The self-ionization of water is the reaction of two water molecules in which a proton is transferred from one molecule to the other to form H_3O^+ and OH^- ions. At 25°C, the K_w expression is $K_w = [H_3O^+][OH^-] = 1.0 \times 10^{-14}$.

15.11. The $pH = -\log[H_3O^+]$ of an aqueous solution. Measure pH by using electrodes and a pH meter or by interpolating the pH from the color changes of a series of acid-base indicators.

15.12. A solution of pH 4 has a $[H_3O^+] = 1 \times 10^{-4}\ M$ and is more acidic than a solution of pH 5, which has a $[H_3O^+] = 1 \times 10^{-5}\ M$.

15.13. For a neutral solution, $[H_3O^+] = [OH^-]$; thus, the $[H_3O^+]$ of a neutral solution at 37°C is the square root of K_w at 37°C:

$$[H_3O^+] \ = \ \sqrt{2.5 \times 10^{-14}} \ = \ 1.\underline{5}8 \times 10^{-7}\ M$$

$$pH \ = \ -\log(1.58 \times 10^{-7}) \ = \ 6.8\underline{01} \ = \ 6.80$$

15.14. Because $pH + pOH = pK_w$ at any temperature,

$$pH \ + \ pOH \ = \ -\log(2.5 \times 10^{-14}) \ = \ 13.60$$

15.15. The answer is a, F^-.

15.16. The answer is d, Fe^{3+}.

Copyright © Cengage Learning. All rights reserved.

15.17. The answer is d, 3.8×10^{-13} M.

15.18. The answer is b, 3.5×10^{-5} M.

■ SOLUTIONS TO PRACTICE PROBLEMS

Note on significant figures: If the final answer to a solution needs to be rounded off, it is given first with one nonsignificant figure, and the last significant figure is underlined. The final answer is then rounded to the correct number of significant figures. In multistep problems, intermediate answers are given with at least one nonsignificant figure; however, only the final answer has been rounded off.

15.29. The reaction with labels of "acid" and "base" written below is as follows:

$$OH^-(aq) \; + \; HF(aq) \; \rightleftharpoons \; F^-(aq) \; + \; H_2O(l)$$
base   acid   base   acid

15.31.

    a. $PO_4{}^{3-}$

    b. HS^-

    c. $NO_2{}^-$

    d. $HAsO_4{}^{2-}$

15.33.

    a. $HClO$

    b. $AsH_4{}^+$

    c. H_3PO_4

    d. $HTeO_3{}^-$

15.35. Each equation is given below with the labels for acid and base:

$$HSO_4{}^-(aq) \; + \; NH_3(aq) \; \rightleftharpoons \; SO_4{}^{2-}(aq) \; + \; NH_4{}^+(aq)$$
a.   acid   base   acid   base

The conjugate acid-base pairs are $HSO_4{}^-$, $SO_4{}^{2-}$, and $NH_4{}^+$, NH_3.

$$HPO_4{}^{2-}(aq) \; + \; NH_4{}^+(aq) \; \rightleftharpoons \; H_2PO_4{}^-(aq) \; + \; NH_3(aq)$$
b.   base   acid   base   acid

The conjugate acid-base pairs are $H_2PO_4{}^-$, $HPO_4{}^{2-}$, and $NH_4{}^+$, NH_3.

Copyright © Cengage Learning. All rights reserved.

$$Al(H_2O)_6{}^{3+}(aq) \ + \ H_2O(l) \ \rightleftharpoons \ Al(H_2O)_5(OH)^{2+}(aq) \ + \ H_3O^+(aq)$$

acid   base   acid   base

c.

The conjugate acid-base pairs are $Al(H_2O)_6{}^{3+}$, $Al(H_2O)_5(OH)^{2+}$, and H_3O^+, H_2O.

$$SO_3{}^{2-}(aq) \ + \ NH_4{}^+(aq) \ \rightleftharpoons \ HSO_3{}^-(aq) \ + \ NH_3(aq)$$

base   acid   base   acid

d.

The conjugate acid-base pairs are $HSO_3{}^-$, $SO_3{}^{2-}$, and $NH_4{}^+$, NH_3.

15.37. The reaction is

Lewis   Lewis
base   acid

15.39.

a.   The completed equation is

$$AlCl_3 \ + \ Cl^- \ \rightleftharpoons \ AlCl_4{}^-$$

The Lewis formula representation is

$AlCl_3$ is the electron-pair acceptor and is the acid. Cl^- is the electron-pair donor and is the base.

b.   The completed equation is

$$I^- \ + \ I_2 \ \rightleftharpoons \ I_3{}^-$$

The Lewis formula representation is

I_2 is the electron-pair acceptor and is the acid. The I^- ion is the electron-pair donor and is the base.

Copyright © Cengage Learning. All rights reserved.

15.41.

    a.   Each water molecule donates a pair of electrons to copper(II), making the water molecule a Lewis base and the Cu^{2+} ion a Lewis acid.

    b.   The AsH_3 donates a pair of electrons to the boron atom in BBr_3, making AsH_3 a Lewis base and the BBr_3 molecule a Lewis acid.

15.43.   The equation is $H_2S + HOCH_2CH_2NH_2 \rightarrow HOCH_2CH_2NH_3^+ + HS^-$. The H_2S is a Lewis acid, and $HOCH_2CH_2NH_2$ is a Lewis base. The hydrogen ion from H_2S accepts a pair of electrons from the N atom in $HOCH_2CH_2NH_2$.

15.45.   The reaction is $HSO_4^- + ClO^- \rightarrow HClO + SO_4^{2-}$. According to Table 15.2, HClO is a weaker acid than HSO_4^-. Because the equilibrium for this type of reaction favors formation of the weaker acid (or weaker base), the reaction occurs to a significant extent.

15.47.

    a. NH_4^+ is a weaker acid than H_3PO_4, so the left-hand species are favored at equilibrium.

    b.   HCN is a weaker acid than H_2S, so the left-hand species are favored at equilibrium.

    c. H_2O is a weaker acid than HCO_3^-, so the right-hand species are favored at equilibrium.

    d. H_2O is a weaker acid than $Al(H_2O)_6^{3+}$, so the right-hand species are favored at equilibrium.

15.49.   Trichloroacetic acid is the stronger acid because, in general, the equilibrium favors the formation of the weaker acid, which is formic acid in this case.

15.51.

    a. H_2S is stronger because acid strength decreases with increasing anion charge for polyprotic acid species.

    b. H_2SO_3 is stronger because, for a series of oxoacids, acid strength increases with increasing electronegativity.

    c.   HBr is stronger because Br is more electronegative than Se. Within a period, acid strength increases as electronegativity increases.

    d. HIO_4 is stronger because acid strength increases with the number of oxygen atoms bonded to the central atom.

    e. H_2S is stronger because, within a group, acid strength increases with the increasing size of the central atom in binary acids.

15.53.

    a. $[H_3O^+] = 1.2\ M$

$$[OH^-] = \frac{K_w}{[H_3O^+]} = \frac{1.0 \times 10^{-14}}{1.2} = 8.\underline{3}3 \times 10^{-15} = 8.3 \times 10^{-15}\ M$$

Copyright © Cengage Learning. All rights reserved.

272 **Chapter 15: Acids and Bases**

b. $[OH^-] = 0.32\ M$

$$[H_3O^+] = \frac{K_w}{[OH^-]} = \frac{1.0 \times 10^{-14}}{0.32} = 3.\underline{1}2 \times 10^{-14} = 3.1 \times 10^{-14}\ M$$

c. $[OH^-] = 2 \times (0.085\ M) = 0.170\ M$

$$[H_3O^+] = \frac{K_w}{[OH^-]} = \frac{1.0 \times 10^{-14}}{0.170} = 5.\underline{8}8 \times 10^{-14} = 5.9 \times 10^{-14}\ M$$

d. $[H_3O^+] = 0.38\ M$

$$[OH^-] = \frac{K_w}{[H_3O^+]} = \frac{1.0 \times 10^{-14}}{0.38} = 2.\underline{6}3 \times 10^{-14} = 2.6 \times 10^{-14}\ M$$

15.55. The $[H_3O^+] = 0.050\ M$ (HCl is a strong acid); using K_w, the $[OH^-] = 2.0 \times 10^{-13}\ M$.

15.57. Because the $Ba(OH)_2$ forms two OH^- per formula unit, the $[OH^-] = 2 \times 0.0085 = 0.017\ M$.

$$[H_3O^+] = \frac{K_w}{[OH^-]} = \frac{1.0 \times 10^{-14}}{0.017} = 5.\underline{8}8 \times 10^{-13} = 5.9 \times 10^{-13}\ M$$

15.59

a. $5 \times 10^{-6}\ M\ H_3O^+ > 1.0 \times 10^{-7}$, so the solution is acidic.

b.   Use K_w to determine $[H_3O^+]$.

$$[H_3O^+] = \frac{K_w}{[OH^-]} = \frac{1.00 \times 10^{-14}}{5 \times 10^{-9}} = 2.0 \times 10^{-6} = 2 \times 10^{-6}\ M$$

Since $2 \times 10^{-6}\ M > 1.0 \times 10^{-7}$, the solution is acidic.

c.   When $[OH^-] = 1.0 \times 10^{-7}\ M$, $[H_3O^+] = 1.0 \times 10^{-7}\ M$, and the solution is neutral.

d. $2 \times 10^{-9}\ M\ H_3O^+ < 1.0 \times 10^{-7}$, so the solution is basic.

15.61. The $[H_3O^+]$ calculated below is $> 1.0 \times 10^{-7}\ M$, so the solution is acidic.

$$[H_3O^+] = \frac{K_w}{[OH^-]} = \frac{1.00 \times 10^{-14}}{1.5 \times 10^{-9}} = 6.\underline{6}6 \times 10^{-6} = 6.7 \times 10^{-6}\ M$$

15.63.

a.   pH 4.6, acidic solution

b.   pH 7.0, neutral solution

c.   pH 1.6, acidic solution

d.   pH 10.5, basic solution

Copyright © Cengage Learning. All rights reserved.

15.65.

    a.   Acidic ($3.5 < 7.0$)

    b.   Neutral ($7.0 = 7.0$)

    c.   Basic ($9.0 > 7.0$)

    d.   Acidic ($5.5 < 7.0$)

15.67.   Record the same number of places after the decimal point in the pH as the number of significant figures in the $[H_3O^+]$.

    a. $-\log (1.0 \times 10^{-8}) = 8.0\underline{00} = 8.00$

    b. $-\log (5.0 \times 10^{-12}) = 11.3\underline{01} = 11.30$

    c. $-\log (7.5 \times 10^{-3}) = 2.1\underline{24} = 2.12$

    d. $-\log (6.35 \times 10^{-9}) = 8.19\underline{72} = 8.197$

15.69.   Record the same number of places after the decimal point in the pH as the number of significant figures in the $[H_3O^+]$.

    $-\log (7.5 \times 10^{-3}) = 2.1\underline{249} = 2.12$

15.71.

    a. $pOH = -\log (5.25 \times 10^{-9}) = 8.27\underline{98}$; $pH = 14.00 - 8.2798 = 5.7\underline{202} = 5.72$

    b. $pOH = -\log (8.3 \times 10^{-3}) = 2.0\underline{809}$; $pH = 14.00 - 2.0809 = 11.9\underline{1908} = 11.92$

    c. $pOH = -\log (3.6 \times 10^{-12}) = 11.44\underline{36}$; $pH = 14.00 - 11.4436 = 2.5\underline{563} = 2.56$

    d. $pOH = -\log (2.1 \times 10^{-8}) = 7.67\underline{77}$; $pH = 14.00 - 7.6777 = 6.3\underline{22} = 6.32$

15.73.   First, convert the $[OH^-]$ to $[H_3O^+]$ using the K_w equation. Then find the pH, recording the same number of places after the decimal point in the pH as the number of significant figures in the $[H_3O^+]$.

    $[H_3O^+] = K_w \div [OH^-] = (1.0 \times 10^{-14}) \div (0.0040) = 2.\underline{50} \times 10^{-12} \, M$

    $pH = -\log (2.50 \times 10^{-12}) = 11.6\underline{02} = 11.60$

15.75.   From the definition, $pH = -\log [H_3O^+]$ and $-pH = \log [H_3O^+]$, so enter the negative value of the pH on the calculator, and use the inverse and log keys (or 10^x) key to find the antilog of $-pH$.

    $\log [H_3O^+] = -pH = -5.12$

    $[H_3O^+] = \text{antilog} (-5.12) = 10^{-5.12} = 7.\underline{58} \times 10^{-6} = 7.6 \times 10^{-6} \, M$

Copyright © Cengage Learning. All rights reserved.

15.77. From the definition, pH = $-\log[H_3O^+]$ and $-$pH = $\log[H_3O^+]$, so enter the negative value of the pH on the calculator, and use the inverse and log keys (or 10^x) key to find the antilog of $-$pH. Then use the K_w equation to calculate $[OH^-]$ from $[H_3O^+]$.

$$\log[H_3O^+] = -pH = -11.63$$

$$[H_3O^+] = \text{antilog}(-11.63) = 10^{-11.63} = 2.\underline{3}4 \times 10^{-12}\ M$$

$$[OH^-] = K_w \div [H_3O^+] = (1.0 \times 10^{-14}) \div (2.34 \times 10^{-12}) = 4.\underline{2}7 \times 10^{-3} = 4.3 \times 10^{-3}\ M$$

15.79. First, calculate the molarity of the OH^- ion from the mass of NaOH. Next, convert the $[OH^-]$ to $[H_3O^+]$ using the K_w equation. Then find the pH, recording the same number of places after the decimal point in the pH as the number of significant figures in the $[H_3O^+]$.

$$\frac{5.80\ g\ NaOH}{1.00\ L} \times \frac{1\ mol\ NaOH}{40.01\ g\ NaOH} = \frac{0.1450\ mol\ NaOH}{1.00\ L} = 0.14\underline{5}0\ M\ OH^-$$

$$[H_3O^+] = K_w \div [OH^-] = (1.0 \times 10^{-14}) \div (0.1450) = 6.\underline{8}96 \times 10^{-14}\ M$$

$$pH = -\log[H_3O^+] = -\log(6.896 \times 10^{-14}) = 13.1\underline{6}14 = 13.16$$

15.81. Figure 15.10 shows that the methyl-red indicator is yellow at pH values above about 5.5 (slightly past the midpoint of the range for methyl red). Bromthymol blue is yellow at pH values up to about 6.5 (slightly below the midpoint of the range for bromthymol blue). Therefore, the pH of the solution is between 5.5 and 6.5, and the solution is acidic.

■ SOLUTIONS TO GENERAL PROBLEMS

15.83.

a. BaO is a base; $BaO + H_2O \rightarrow Ba^{2+} + 2OH^-$

b. H_2S is an acid; $H_2S + H_2O \rightarrow H_3O^+ + HS^-$

c. CH_3NH_2 is a base; $CH_3NH_2 + H_2O \rightarrow CH_3NH_3^+ + OH^-$

d. SO_2 is an acid; $SO_2 + 2H_2O \rightarrow H_3O^+ + HSO_3^-$

15.85.

a. $H_2O_2(aq) + S^{2-}(aq) \rightarrow HO_2^-(aq) + HS^-(aq)$

b. $HCO_3^-(aq) + OH^-(aq) \rightarrow CO_3^{2-}(aq) + H_2O(l)$

c. $NH_4^+(aq) + CN^-(aq) \rightarrow NH_3(aq) + HCN(aq)$

d. $H_2PO_4^-(aq) + OH^-(aq) \rightarrow HPO_4^{2-}(aq) + H_2O(l)$

Copyright © Cengage Learning. All rights reserved.

15.87.

    a.   The ClO^- ion is a Brønsted base, and water is a Brønsted acid. The complete chemical equation is $ClO^-(aq) + H_2O(l) \rightleftharpoons HClO(aq) + OH^-(aq)$. The equilibrium does not favor the products because ClO^- is a weaker base than OH^-. In Lewis language, a proton from H_2O acts as a Lewis acid by accepting a pair of electrons on the oxygen of ClO^-.

$$H^+ \ + \ \left[:\!\overset{\cdot\cdot}{\underset{\cdot\cdot}{Cl}}\!:\!\overset{\cdot\cdot}{\underset{\cdot\cdot}{O}}\!: \right]^- \ \longrightarrow \ :\!\overset{\cdot\cdot}{\underset{\cdot\cdot}{Cl}}\!:\!\overset{\cdot\cdot}{\underset{\cdot\cdot}{O}}\!:H$$

    b.   The NH_2^- ion is a Brønsted base, and NH_4^+ is a Brønsted acid. The complete chemical equation is $NH_4^+ + NH_2^- \rightleftharpoons 2NH_3$. The equilibrium favors the products because the reactants form the solvent, a weakly ionized molecule. In Lewis language, the proton from NH_4^+ acts as a Lewis acid by accepting a pair of electrons on the nitrogen of NH_2^-.

$$\left[\begin{matrix} H \\ \overset{\cdot\cdot}{H:N:H} \\ \underset{\cdot\cdot}{} \\ H \end{matrix} \right]^+ \ + \ \left[\begin{matrix} \overset{\cdot\cdot}{} \\ :N:H \\ \underset{\cdot\cdot}{} \\ H \end{matrix} \right]^- \ \longrightarrow \ 2 \begin{matrix} \overset{\cdot\cdot}{} \\ H:N:H \\ \underset{\cdot\cdot}{} \\ H \end{matrix}$$

15.89.   Table 15.2 shows that HNO_2 is a stronger acid than HF. Because an acid-base reaction normally goes in the direction of the weaker acid, the reaction is more likely to go in the direction written

$$HNO_2 + F^- \rightleftharpoons HF + NO_2^-$$

15.91.   The order is $H_2S < H_2Se < HBr$. H_2Se is stronger than H_2S because, within a group, acid strength increases with increasing size of the central atom in binary acids. HBr is a strong acid, whereas the others are weak acids.

15.93.   The KOH is a strong base and is fully ionized in solution, so you can use its formula and molar concentration to determine the $[OH^-]$ of the solution. Therefore, the 0.25 M KOH contains 0.25 M OH^-. The $[H_3O^+]$ is obtained from the K_w expression:

$$K_w = 1.0 \times 10^{-14} = [H_3O^+] \times 0.25\ M\ OH^-$$

$$[H_3O^+] = \frac{1.0 \times 10^{-14}}{0.25} = 4.\underline{00} \times 10^{-14} = 4.0 \times 10^{-14}\ M$$

15.95.   Enter the H_3O^+ concentration of 1.5×10^{-3} into the calculator, press the log key, and press the sign key to change the negative log to a positive log. This follows the negative-log definition of pH. The number of decimal places of the pH should equal the significant figures in the H_3O^+.

$$pH = -\log[H_3O^+] = -\log(1.5 \times 10^{-3}) = 2.8\underline{2}3 = 2.82$$

Copyright © Cengage Learning. All rights reserved.

15.97. Find the pOH from the pH using $pH + pOH = 14.00$. Then calculate the $[OH^-]$ from the pOH by entering the pOH into the calculator, pressing the sign key to change the positive log to a negative log, and finding the antilog. On some calculators, the antilog is found by using the inverse of the log; on other calculators, the antilog is found using the 10^x key. The number of significant figures in the $[OH^-]$ should equal the number of decimal places in the pOH.

$$pOH = 14.00 - 3.15 = 10.85$$

$$[OH^-] = \text{antilog}(-10.85) = 10^{-10.85} = 1.\underline{4}12 \times 10^{-11} = 1.4 \times 10^{-11} \, M$$

15.99.

a. $H_2SO_4(aq) + 2NaHCO_3(aq) \rightarrow Na_2SO_4(aq) + 2CO_2(g) + 2H_2O(l)$ (molecular)

   $H_3O^+(aq) + HCO_3^-(aq) \rightarrow CO_2(g) + 2H_2O(l)$ (net ionic)

b. The total moles of H_3O^+ from the H_2SO_4 is

$$\text{Moles of } H_3O^+ = \frac{0.437 \text{ mol } H_2SO_4}{1 \text{ L}} \times 0.02500 \text{ L} \times \frac{2 \text{ mol } H_3O^+}{1 \text{ mol } H_2SO_4}$$

$$= 0.021\underline{8}5 \text{ mol } H_3O^+$$

The moles of H_3O^+ that reacted with the NaOH is given by

$$\text{Moles of } H_3O^+ = \frac{0.108 \text{ mol NaOH}}{1 \text{ L}} \times 0.0354 \text{ L} = 0.00382\underline{3} \text{ mol}$$

The moles of $NaHCO_3$ present in the original sample is equal to the moles of H_3O^+ that reacted with the HCO_3^-, which is given by

$$\text{Total moles } H_3O^+ - \text{moles } H_3O^+ \text{ reacted with the NaOH} = \text{moles } HCO_3^-$$

$$0.021\underline{8}5 \text{ mol} - 0.003823 \text{ mol} = 0.018\underline{0}3 = 0.0180 \text{ mol NaHCO}_3$$

c. The mass of $NaHCO_3$ (molar mass 84.01 g/mol) present in the original sample is

$$0.01803 \text{ mol NaHCO}_3 \times \frac{84.01 \text{ g NaHCO}_3}{1 \text{ mol NaHCO}_3} = 1.5\underline{1}4 \text{ g}$$

Thus, the percent $NaHCO_3$ in the original sample is given by

$$\text{Percent NaHCO}_3 = \frac{1.514 \text{ g}}{2.500 \text{ g}} \times 100\% = 60.\underline{5}6 = 60.6\%$$

The percent KCl in the original sample is

$$\text{Percent KCl} = 100 - 60.56 = 39.\underline{4}4 = 39.4\%$$

15.101. $HCO_3^-(aq) + H_2O(l) \rightleftharpoons H_3O^+(aq) + CO_3^{2-}(aq)$

   $HCO_3^-(aq) + H_2O(l) \rightleftharpoons H_2CO_3(aq) + OH^-(aq)$

   $HCO_3^-(aq) + Na^+(aq) + OH^-(aq) \rightleftharpoons Na^+(aq) + CO_3^{2-}(aq) + H_2O(l)$

   $HCO_3^-(aq) + H^+(aq) + Cl^-(aq) \rightleftharpoons H_2O(l) + CO_2(g) + Cl^-(aq)$

Copyright © Cengage Learning. All rights reserved.

15.103. $CaH_2(s) + 2H_2O(l) \rightarrow Ca(OH)_2(s) + 2H_2(g)$

The hydride ion is a stronger base because it took an H^+ from water, leaving the OH^- ion. Every time a strong base is added to water, it will react with the water, leaving the OH^- as the product, so a strong base cannot exist in water.

15.105.

a. $2HF(l) \rightleftharpoons H_2F^+ + F^-$

b. NaF will be a base because F^- is a conjugate base of HF.

c. $HClO_4 + HF \rightarrow H_2F^+ + ClO_4^-$

The conjugate acid is H_2F^+.

15.107. The reaction of ammonia with water is given by

$$NH_3(aq) + H_2O(l) \rightleftharpoons NH_4^+(aq) + OH^-(aq)$$

The initial concentration of NH_3 (molar mass 17.03 g/mol) is

$$Molarity = \frac{4.25 \text{ g NH}_3 \times \frac{1 \text{ mol NH}_3}{17.03 \text{ g NH}_3}}{0.2500 \text{ L}} = 0.99\underline{8}2 \ M$$

Since the NH_3 is 0.42% reacted, the concentration of OH^- is

$[OH^-] = 0.9982 \ M \times 0.0042 = 0.004\underline{1}9 \ M$

$pOH = -\log[OH^-] = -\log(0.00419) = 2.3\underline{7}8$

$pH = 14 - pOH = 14 - 2.3\underline{7}8 = 11.6\underline{2}2 = 11.62$

■ SOLUTIONS TO CUMULATIVE-SKILLS PROBLEMS

15.123. For $(HO)_mYO_n$ acids, acid strength increases with n regardless of the number of OH's. The structure of H_3PO_4 is $(HO)_3PO$; because H_3PO_3 and H_3PO_4 have about the same acidity, H_3PO_3 must also have $n = 1$; thus, $m = 2$. This leaves one H, which must bond to phosphorus, giving a structure of $(HO)_2(O)PH$. Assuming that only two H's react with NaOH, the mass of NaOH that reacts with 1.00 g of H_3PO_3 (PA) is calculated as follows:

$$1.00 \text{ g PA} \times \frac{1 \text{ mol PA}}{81.994 \text{ g PA}} \times \frac{2 \text{ mol NaOH}}{1 \text{ mol PA}} \times \frac{40.00 \text{ g NaOH}}{1 \text{ mol NaOH}}$$

$$= 0.975\underline{6} = 0.976 \text{ g NaOH}$$

Copyright © Cengage Learning. All rights reserved.

15.125. BF_3 acts as a Lewis acid, accepting an electron pair from NH_3:

$$BF_3 + :NH_3 \rightarrow F_3B:NH_3$$

The NH_3 acts as a Lewis base in donating an electron pair to BF_3. When 10.0 g of each are mixed, the BF_3 is the limiting reagent because it has the higher formula mass. The mass of $BF_3:NH_3$ formed is

$$10.0 \text{ g } BF_3 \times \frac{1 \text{ mol } BF_3}{67.81 \text{ g } BF_3} \times \frac{1 \text{ mol } BF_3:NH_3}{1 \text{ mol } BF_3} \times \frac{84.84 \text{ g } BF_3:NH_3}{1 \text{ mol } BF_3:NH_3}$$

$$= 12.\underline{5}1 = 12.5 \text{ g } BF_3:NH_3$$

Copyright © Cengage Learning. All rights reserved.

CHAPTER 16

Acid-Base Equilibria

■ SOLUTIONS TO EXERCISES

Note on significant figures: If the final answer to a solution needs to be rounded off, it is given first with one nonsignificant figure, and the last significant figure is underlined. The final answer is then rounded to the correct number of significant figures. In multistep problems, intermediate answers are given with at least one nonsignificant figure; however, only the final answer has been rounded off.

16.1. Abbreviate the formula of lactic acid as HL. To solve, assemble a table of starting, change, and equilibrium concentrations.

Conc. (M)	HL + H$_2$O $\rightleftharpoons$	H$_3$O$^+$ +	L$^-$
Starting	0.025	0	0
Change	$-x$	$+x$	$+x$
Equilibrium	0.025 $-$ x	x	x

Substituting into the equilibrium-constant equation gives

$$K_a = \frac{[H_3O^+][L^-]}{[HL]} = \frac{(x)^2}{(0.025 - x)}$$

The value of x equals the value of the molarity of the H$_3$O$^+$ ion, which can be obtained from the pH:

$$[H_3O^+] = \text{antilog}(-pH) = \text{antilog}(-2.75) = 0.001\underline{7}8 \ M$$

Substitute this value for x into the equation to get

$$K_a = \frac{(x)^2}{(0.025 - x)} = \frac{(0.00178)^2}{(0.025 - 0.00178)} = 1.\underline{3}6 \times 10^{-4} = 1.4 \times 10^{-4}$$

The degree of ionization is

$$\text{Degree of ionization} = \frac{0.00178}{0.025} = 0.071$$

16.2. To solve, assemble a table of starting, change, and equilibrium concentrations. Use HAc as the symbol for acetic acid.

Conc. (M)	HAc + H$_2$O $\rightleftharpoons$	H$_3$O$^+$ +	Ac$^-$
Starting	0.10	0	0
Change	$-x$	$+x$	$+x$
Equilibrium	0.10 $-$ x	x	x

Copyright © Cengage Learning. All rights reserved.

Now, substitute these concentrations and the value of K_a into the equilibrium-constant equation for acid ionization:

$$K_a = \frac{[H_3O^+][Ac^-]}{[HAc]} = \frac{(x)^2}{(0.10 - x)} = 1.7 \times 10^{-5}$$

Solve the equation for x, assuming x is much smaller than 0.10, so $(0.10 - x) \cong 0.10$.

$$\frac{(x)^2}{(0.10)} \cong 1.7 \times 10^{-5}$$

$$x^2 = 1.7 \times 10^{-5} \times 0.10 = 1.7 \times 10^{-6}$$

$$x = 0.00130 \ M$$

Check to make sure the assumption that $(0.10 - x) \cong 0.10$ is valid:

$$0.10 - 0.00130 = 0.0987, = 0.10 \quad \text{(to two significant figures)}$$

The concentrations of hydronium ion and acetate ion are

$$[H_3O^+] = [Ac^-] = x = 0.0013 = 1.3 \times 10^{-3} \ M$$

The pH of the solution is

$$pH = -\log[H_3O^+] = -\log(0.00130) = 2.884 = 2.88$$

The degree of ionization is

$$\text{Degree of ionization} = \frac{0.00130}{0.10} = 0.0130 = 0.013$$

16.3. Abbreviate the formula for pyruvic acid as HPy. To solve, assemble a table of starting, change, and equilibrium concentrations:

Conc. (M)	HPy + H_2O	$\rightleftharpoons$	H_3O^+ +	Py^-
Starting	0.0030		0	0
Change	$-x$		$+x$	$+x$
Equilibrium	$0.0030 - x$		x	x

Substitute the equilibrium concentrations and the value of K_a into the equilibrium-constant expression to get

$$K_a = \frac{[H_3O^+][Py^-]}{[HPy]} = \frac{(x)^2}{(0.0030 - x)} = 1.4 \times 10^{-4}$$

Note that the concentration of acid divided by K_a is $0.0030/1.4 \times 10^{-4} = 21$, which is considerably smaller than 100. Thus, you can expect that x cannot be ignored compared with 0.0030. The quadratic formula must be used. Rearrange the preceding equation to put it into the form $ax^2 + bx + c = 0$.

$$x^2 + 1.4 \times 10^{-4} x - 4.20 \times 10^{-7} = 0$$

Substitute into the quadratic formula to get

$$x = \frac{-1.4 \times 10^{-4} \pm \sqrt{(1.4 \times 10^{-4})^2 + 4(4.20 \times 10^{-7})}}{2} = \frac{-1.4 \times 10^{-4} \pm 1.303 \times 10^{-3}}{2}$$

Copyright © Cengage Learning. All rights reserved.

Using the positive root, $x = [H_3O^+] = 5.\underline{8}1 \times 10^{-4} M$. Now you can calculate the pH.

$$pH = -\log [H_3O^+] = -\log (5.81 \times 10^{-4}) = 3.2\underline{3}50 = 3.24$$

16.4. To solve, note that $K_{a_1} = 1.3 \times 10^{-2} > K_{a_2} = 6.3 \times 10^{-8}$, and hence the second ionization and K_{a_2} can be ignored. Assemble a table of starting, change, and equilibrium concentrations.

Conc. (M)	$H_2SO_3 + H_2O \rightleftharpoons$	H_3O^+	$+$	HSO_3^-
Starting	0.25	0		0
Change	$-x$	$+x$		$+x$
Equilibrium	$0.25 - x$	x		x

Substitute into the equilibrium-constant expression for the first ionization.

$$K_{a_1} = \frac{[H_3O^+][HSO_3^-]}{[H_2SO_3]} = \frac{(x)^2}{(0.25 - x)} = 1.3 \times 10^{-2} = 0.013$$

This gives $x^2 + 0.013x - 0.00325 = 0$.

Note that the concentration of acid divided by K_a is $0.25/0.013 = 19$, which is considerably smaller than 100. Thus, you can expect that x cannot be ignored compared with 0.25. Reorganize the above equilibrium-constant expression into the form $ax^2 + bx + c = 0$, and substitute for a, b, and c in the quadratic formula.

$$x = \frac{-0.013 \pm \sqrt{(0.013)^2 + 4(0.00325)}}{2} = \frac{-0.013 \pm 0.1147}{2}$$

Using the positive root, $x = [H_3O^+] = 0.05\underline{0}87 M$.

$$pH = -\log (0.05\underline{0}87) = 1.2\underline{9}3$$

To calculate $[SO_3^{2-}]$, which will be represented by y, use the second ionization. Assume the starting concentrations of H_3O^+ and HSO_3^- are those from the first equilibrium.

Conc. (M)	$HSO_3^- + H_2O \rightleftharpoons$	H_3O^+	$+$	SO_3^{2-}
Starting	0.05\underline{0}8	0.05\underline{0}8		0
Change	$-y$	$+y$		$+y$
Equilibrium	$0.05\underline{0}8 - y$	$0.05\underline{0}8 - y$		y

Now, substitute into the K_{a_2} expression for the second ionization.

$$K_{a_2} = \frac{[H_3O^+][SO_3^{2-}]}{[HSO_3^-]} = \frac{(0.0508 + y)(y)}{(0.0508 - y)} = 6.3 \times 10^{-8}$$

Assuming y is much smaller than 0.0508, note that the $(0.0508 + y)$ cancels the $(0.0508 - y)$ term, leaving $y \cong K_{a_2}$, or

$$y = [SO_3^{2-}] \cong 6.3 \times 10^{-8} M$$

16.5. Convert the pH first to pOH and then to $[OH^-]$:

$$pOH = 14.00 - pH = 14.00 - 9.84 = 4.16$$

$$[OH^-] = \text{antilog} (-4.16) = 6.\underline{9}2 \times 10^{-5} M$$

Copyright © Cengage Learning. All rights reserved.

Using the symbol Qu for quinine, assemble a table of starting, change, and equilibrium concentrations.

Conc. (M)	Qu + H_2O $\rightleftharpoons$	HQu^+ +	OH^-
Starting	0.0015	0	0
Change	$-x$	$+x$	$+x$
Equilibrium	$0.0015 - x$	x	x

Note that $x = 6.\underline{9}2 \times 10^{-5}$. Substitute into the equilibrium-constant expression to get

$$K_b = \frac{[HQ^+][OH^-]}{[Qu]} = \frac{(x)^2}{(0.0015 - x)} = \frac{(6.92 \times 10^{-5})^2}{(0.0015 - 6.92 \times 10^{-5})} = 3.\underline{3}46 \times 10^{-6}$$

$$= 3.3 \times 10^{-6}$$

16.6. Assemble a table of starting, change, and equilibrium concentrations.

Conc. (M)	NH_3 + H_2O $\rightleftharpoons$	NH_4^+ +	OH^-
Starting	0.20	0	0
Change	$-x$	$+x$	$+x$
Equilibrium	$0.20 - x$	x	x

Assume x is small enough to ignore compared with 0.20. Substitute into the equilibrium-constant expression to get

$$K_b = \frac{[NH_4^+][OH^-]}{[NH_3]} = \frac{(x)^2}{(0.20 - x)} \cong \frac{(x)^2}{(0.20)} = 1.8 \times 10^{-5}$$

Solving for x gives

$$x^2 = (0.20) \times 1.8 \times 10^{-5} = 3.6 \times 10^{-6}$$

$$x = [OH^-] \cong 1.\underline{8}9 \times 10^{-3}\ M\ \text{(Note that } x \text{ is negligible compared to 0.20.)}$$

Now calculate the hydronium-ion concentration.

$$[H_3O^+] = \frac{K_w}{[OH^-]} = \frac{1.0 \times 10^{-14}}{1.89 \times 10^{-3}} = 5.\underline{2}9 \times 10^{-12} = 5.3 \times 10^{-12}\ M$$

16.7.

a.   Acidic. NH_4NO_3 is the salt of a weak base (NH_4OH) and a strong acid (HNO_3), so a solution of NH_4NO_3 is acidic because of the hydrolysis of NH_4^+.

b.   Neutral. KNO_3 is the salt of a strong base (KOH) and a strong acid (HNO_3), so a solution of NH_4NO_3 is neutral because none of the ions hydrolyze.

c.   Acidic. $Al(NO_3)_3$ is the salt of a weak base [$Al(OH)_3$] and a strong acid (HNO_3), so a solution of $Al(NO_3)_3$ is acidic because of the hydrolysis of Al^{3+}.

Copyright © Cengage Learning. All rights reserved.

16.8.

    a.   Calculate K_b of the F^- ion from the K_a of its conjugate acid, HF:

$$K_b = \frac{K_w}{K_a} = \frac{1.0 \times 10^{-14}}{6.8 \times 10^{-4}} = 1.\underline{4}7 \times 10^{-11} = 1.5 \times 10^{-11}$$

    b.   Calculate K_a of $C_6H_5NH_3^+$ from the K_b of its conjugate base, $C_6H_5NH_2$:

$$K_a = \frac{K_w}{K_b} = \frac{1.0 \times 10^{-14}}{4.2 \times 10^{-10}} = 2.\underline{3}8 \times 10^{-5} = 2.4 \times 10^{-5}$$

16.9. Assemble the usual table, writing HBen for benzoic acid and Ben⁻ for the benzoate ion. Let $0.015 - x$ equal the equilibrium concentration of the benzoate anion.

Conc. (M)	Ben⁻ + H₂O ⇌	HBen +	OH⁻
Starting	0.015	0	0
Change	−x	+x	+x
Equilibrium	0.0015 − x	x	x

Calculate K_b for the benzoate ion from K_a for HBen

$$K_b = \frac{K_w}{K_a} = \frac{1.0 \times 10^{-14}}{6.3 \times 10^{-5}} = 1.\underline{5}8 \times 10^{-10}$$

Substitute into the equilibrium-constant expression. Assume x is much smaller than 0.015.

$$K_b = \frac{[HBen][OH^-]}{[Ben^-]} = \frac{(x)^2}{(0.015 - x)} \cong \frac{(x)^2}{(0.015)} = 1.\underline{5}8 \times 10^{-10}$$

$$x = [HBen] = [OH^-] \cong 1.\underline{5}39 \times 10^{-6} \, M \quad (x \text{ is negligible compared to } 0.015.)$$

Thus, the concentration of benzoic acid in the solution is $1.5 \times 10^{-6} \, M$. The pH is

$$pOH = -\log[OH^-] = -\log(1.539 \times 10^{-6}) = 5.8\underline{1}2$$

$$pH = 14.00 - 5.812 = 8.1\underline{8}8 = 8.19$$

16.10.   Assemble the usual table, using starting $[H_3O^+] = 0.20 \, M$ from 0.20 M HCl and letting HFo symbolize $HCHO_2$.

Conc. (M)	HFo + H₂O ⇌	H₃O⁺ +	Fo⁻
Starting	0.010	0.20	0
Change	−x	+x	+x
Equilibrium	0.10 − x	0.20 + x	x

Copyright © Cengage Learning. All rights reserved.

Assume x is negligible compared to 0.10 M and 0.20 M, and substitute into the equilibrium-constant expression to get

$$K_a = \frac{[H_3O^+][Fo^-]}{[HFo]} = \frac{(0.20 + x)(x)}{(0.10 - x)} \cong \frac{(0.20)(x)}{(0.10)} = 1.7 \times 10^{-4}$$

$$x = [Fo^-] = 8.\underline{5}0 \times 10^{-5} = 8.5 \times 10^{-5} \, M$$

The degree of ionization is

$$\text{Degree of ionization} = \frac{8.50 \times 10^{-5}}{0.10} = 8.\underline{5}0 \times 10^{-4} = 8.5 \times 10^{-4}$$

16.11.   Assemble the usual table, using a starting $[CHO_2^-]$ of 0.018 M from 0.018 M NaCHO$_2$ and symbolizing HCHO$_2$ as HFo and the CHO$_2^-$ anion as Fo$^-$.

Conc. (M)	HFo + H$_2$O $\rightleftharpoons$	H$_3$O$^+$ +	Fo$^-$
Starting	0.025	0	0.018
Change	$-x$	$+x$	$+x$
Equilibrium	$0.025 - x$	x	$0.018 + x$

Substitute into the equilibrium-constant expression. Assume x is negligible compared to 0.025 M and 0.018 M.

$$K_a = \frac{[H_3O^+][Fo^-]}{[HFo]} = \frac{(0.018 + x)(x)}{(0.025 - x)} \cong \frac{(0.018)(x)}{(0.025)} = 1.7 \times 10^{-4}$$

$$x = [H_3O^+] \cong 2.\underline{3}6 \times 10^{-4} \, M$$

The pH can now be calculated.

$$\text{pH} = -\log[H_3O^+] = -\log(2.36 \times 10^{-4}) = 3.6\underline{2}7 = 3.63$$

16.12.   Let HOAc represent HC$_2$H$_3$O$_2$ and OAc$^-$ represent C$_2$H$_3$O$_2^-$. The total volume of the buffer is

$$\text{Total volume} = 30.0 \, \text{mL} + 70.0 \, \text{mL} = 100.0 \, \text{mL} = 0.1000 \, \text{L}$$

The moles of HOAc and OAc$^-$ in the buffer are

$$\text{mol HOAc} = 0.15 \, M \times 0.0300 \, \text{L} = 0.00450 \, \text{mol}$$

$$\text{mol OAc}^- = 0.20 \, M \times 0.0700 \, \text{L} = 0.0140 \, \text{mol}$$

The concentrations of HOAc and OAc$^-$ in the buffer are

$$[\text{HOAc}] = \frac{0.00450 \, \text{mol}}{0.1000 \, \text{L}} = 0.04\underline{5}0 \, M$$

$$[\text{OAc}^-] = \frac{0.0140 \, \text{mol}}{0.1000 \, \text{L}} = 0.1\underline{4}0 \, M$$

Copyright © Cengage Learning. All rights reserved.

Now, assemble these starting concentrations into a table.

Conc. (M)	HOAc + H$_2$O $\rightleftharpoons$	H$_3$O+	+	OAc$^-$
Starting	0.0450	0		0.140
Change	$-$x	+x		+x
Equilibrium	0.0450 $-$ x	x		0.140 + x

Substitute the equilibrium concentrations into the equilibrium-constant expression; then assume x is negligible compared to the starting concentrations of both HOAc and OAc$^-$.

$$K_a = \frac{[H_3O^+][OAc^-]}{[HOAc]} = \frac{(0.140 + x)(x)}{(0.0450 - x)} \cong \frac{(0.140)(x)}{(0.0450)} = 1.7 \times 10^{-5}$$

$$x = [H_3O^+] \cong 5.\underline{4}6 \times 10^{-6}\ M$$

You can now calculate the pH.

$$pH = -\log[H_3O^+] = -\log(5.46 \times 10^{-6}) = 5.2\underline{6}2 = 5.26$$

16.13. First, do the stoichiometric calculation. From Exercise 16.11, [HFo] = 0.025 M and [Fo$^-$] = 0.018 M. In 1 L of buffer, there are 0.025 mol HFo and 0.018 mol Fo$^-$. The moles of OH$^-$ (equal to moles of NaOH) added are

$$(0.10\ M) \times 0.0500\ L = 0.00500\ mol\ OH^-$$

The total volume of solution is

$$Total\ volume = 1\ L + 0.0500\ L = 1.0500\ L$$

After reaction with the OH$^-$, the moles of HFo and Fo$^-$ remaining in the solution are

$$mol\ HFo = (0.025 - 0.00500)\ mol = 0.0200\ mol$$

$$mol\ Fo^- = (0.018 + 0.00500)\ mol = 0.0230\ mol$$

The concentrations are

$$[HFo] = \frac{0.0200\ mol}{1.0500\ L} = 0.01\underline{9}0\ M$$

$$[Fo^-] = \frac{0.0230\ mol}{1.0500\ L} = 0.02\underline{1}9\ M$$

Now account for the ionization of HFo to Fo$^-$ at equilibrium by assembling the usual table.

Conc. (M)	HFo + H$_2$O $\rightleftharpoons$	H$_3$O$^+$	+	OAc$^-$
Starting	0.0190	0		0.0219
Change	$-x$	+x		+x
Equilibrium	0.0190 $-$ x	x		0.0219 + x

Copyright © Cengage Learning. All rights reserved.

Assume x is negligible compared to 0.0190 M and 0.0219 M, and substitute into the equilibrium-constant expression to get

$$K_a = \frac{[H_3O^+][Fo^-]}{[HFo]} = \frac{(0.0219 + x)(x)}{(0.0190 - x)} \cong \frac{(0.0219)(x)}{(0.0190)} = 1.7 \times 10^{-4}$$

$$x = [H_3O^+] = 1.\underline{4}7 \times 10^{-4} \ M$$

Now, calculate the pH.

$$pH = -\log[H_3O^+] = -\log(1.\underline{4}7 \times 10^{-4}) = 3.8\underline{3}1 = 3.83$$

16.14.   All the OH^- reacts with the H_3O^+ from HCl. Calculate the stoichiometric amounts of OH^- and H_3O^+.

mol H_3O^+ = (0.10 mol/L) x 0.025 L = 0.0025 mol

mol OH^- = (0.10 mol NaOH/L) x 0.015 L = 0.0015 mol

The total volume of solution is

Total volume = 0.025 L + 0.015 L = 0.040 L

Subtract the moles of OH^- from the moles of H_3O^+, and divide by the total volume to get the concentration of H_3O^+.

mol H_3O^+ left = (0.0025 − 0.0015) mol = 0.0010 mol

$$[H_3O^+] = \frac{0.0010 \ mol}{0.040 \ L} = 0.02\underline{5}0 \ M$$

Now calculate the pH.

$$pH = -\log[H_3O^+] = -\log(0.0250) = 1.6\underline{0}2 = 1.60$$

16.15.   At the equivalence point, the solution will contain NaF. The molar amount of F^- is equal to the molar amount of HF and is calculated as follows:

(0.10 mol HF/L) x 0.025 L = 0.0025 mol F^-

The volume of 0.15 M NaOH added and the total volume of solution are calculated next.

$$\text{Volume NaOH} = \frac{M_{acid}V_{acid}}{M_{base}} = \frac{(0.10 \ M)(25 \ mL)}{0.15 \ M} = 1\underline{6}.6 \ mL$$

Total volume = 25 mL + 16.6 mL = 4$\underline{1}$.6 mL = 0.04$\underline{1}$6 L

The concentration of F^- at the equivalence point can now be calculated.

$$[F^-] = \frac{0.0025 \ mol}{0.0416 \ L} = 0.06\underline{0}0 \ M$$

Next, consider the hydrolysis of F^-. Start by calculating the hydrolysis constant of F^- from the K_a of its conjugate acid, HF.

$$K_b = \frac{K_w}{K_a} = \frac{1.0 \times 10^{-14}}{6.8 \times 10^{-4}} = 1.\underline{4}7 \times 10^{-11}$$

Copyright © Cengage Learning. All rights reserved.

Now, assemble the usual table of concentrations, assume x is negligible compared to 0.0600, and calculate [OH⁻].

Conc. (M)	F⁻ + H₂O ⇌	HF +	OH⁻
Starting	0.0600	0	0.0219
Change	$-x$	$+x$	$+x$
Equilibrium	$0.0600 - x$	x	x

Substitute into the equilibrium-constant expression to get

$$K_b = \frac{[HF][OH^-]}{[F^-]} = \frac{(x)^2}{(0.0600 - x)} \cong \frac{(x)^2}{(0.0600)} = 1.\underline{4}7 \times 10^{-11}$$

$$x = [OH^-] = 9.\underline{3}9 \times 10^{-7} \, M$$

Finally, calculate the pOH and then the pH.

$$pOH = -\log[OH^-] = -\log(9.\underline{3}9 \times 10^{-7}) = 6.0\underline{2}6$$

$$pH = 14.00 - 6.0\underline{2}6 = 7.9\underline{7}4 = 7.97$$

16.16.

a. Assemble the usual table of concentrations.

Conc. (M)	NH₃ + H₂O ⇌	NH₄⁺ +	OH⁻
Starting	0.200	0	0
Change	$-x$	$+x$	$+x$
Equilibrium	$0.200 - x$	x	x

Now substitute into the equilibrium-constant expression, assume x is negligible compared to 0.200 M, and calculate [OH⁻].

$$K_b = \frac{(x)^2}{(0.200 - x)} = \frac{(x)^2}{(0.200)} = 1.8 \times 10^{-5}$$

$$x = [OH^-] = 1.8\underline{9}7 \times 10^{-3} \, M$$

Finally, calculate the pOH and then the pH.

$$pOH = -\log[OH^-] = -\log(1.8\underline{9}7 \times 10^{-3}) = 2.7\underline{2}1$$

$$pH = 14.00 - 2.721 = 11.2\underline{7}8 = 11.28$$

b. At the half-way point in the titration of a weak base with a strong acid, $pOH = pK_b$.

$$pOH = -\log(1.8 \times 10^{-5}) = 4.7\underline{4}4$$

$$pH = 14.00 - pOH = 14.00 - 4.744 = 9.2\underline{5}5 = 9.26$$

Copyright © Cengage Learning. All rights reserved.

c.   At the equivalence point, the solution will contain NH_4Cl. The molar amount of NH_4^+ is equal to the molar amount of NH_3 and is calculated as follows:

$$(0.200\ M) \times 0.0800\ L = 0.01600\ \text{mol}\ NH_4^+$$

The volume of 0.100 M HCl added and the total volume of solution are calculated next.

$$\text{Volume HCl} = \frac{M_{base}V_{base}}{M_{acid}} = \frac{(0.200\ M)(80.0\ \text{mL})}{0.100\ M} = 160.0\ \text{mL}$$

$$\text{Total volume} = 80.0\ \text{mL} + 160.0\ \text{mL} = 240.0\ \text{mL} = 0.2400\ \text{L}$$

The concentration of NH_4^+ at the equivalence point can now be calculated.

$$[NH_4^+] = \frac{0.01600\ \text{mol}}{0.2400\ \text{L}} = 0.06666\ M$$

Next, consider the hydrolysis of NH_4^+. Start by calculating the hydrolysis constant of NH_4^+ from the K_b of its conjugate base, NH_3.

$$K_a = \frac{K_w}{K_b} = \frac{1.0 \times 10^{-14}}{1.8 \times 10^{-5}} = 5.56 \times 10^{-10}$$

Now, assemble the usual table of concentrations, assume x is negligible compared to 0.06666, and calculate $[H_3O^+]$.

Conc. (M)	$NH_4^+ + H_2O$	$\rightleftharpoons$	NH_3	+	H_3O^+
Starting	0.06666		0		0
Change	$-x$		$+x$		$+x$
Equilibrium	$0.06666 - x$		x		x

Substitute into the equilibrium-constant expression to get

$$K_a = \frac{[NH_3][H_3O^+]}{[NH_4^+]} = \frac{(x)^2}{(0.06666 - x)} \cong \frac{(x)^2}{(0.06666)} = 5.56 \times 10^{-10}$$

$$x = [H_3O^+] = 6.08 \times 10^{-6}\ M$$

Finally, calculate the pH.

$$pH = -\log[H_3O^+] = -\log(6.08 \times 10^{-6}) = 5.215 = 5.22$$

d.   Calculate the moles of acid added.

$$(0.100\ M) \times 0.175\ L = 0.01750\ \text{mol}$$

The moles of base added are the same as for part c, 0.01600 mol. The excess moles of acid and the total volume are

$$\text{Moles of acid remaining} = 0.01750\ \text{mol} - 0.01600\ \text{mol} = 0.00150\ \text{mol}$$

$$V = 80.0\ \text{mL} + 175\ \text{mL} = 255.0\ \text{mL} = 0.2550\ \text{L}$$

The $[H_3O^+]$ concentration and the pH are

$$[H_3O^+] = \frac{0.00150\ \text{mol}}{0.2550\ \text{L}} = 5.882 \times 10^{-3}\ M$$

$$pH = -\log(5.882 \times 10^{-3}) = 2.230 = 2.23$$

Copyright © Cengage Learning. All rights reserved.

■ ANSWERS TO SELF-ASSESSMENT AND REVIEW QUESTIONS

16.1. The equation is

$$HCN(aq) + H_2O(l) \rightleftharpoons H_3O^+(aq) + CN^-(aq)$$

The equilibrium-constant expression is

$$K_a = \frac{[H_3O^+][CN^-]}{[HCN]}$$

16.2. HCN is the weakest acid. Its K_a of 4.9×10^{-10} is less than the K_a of 1.7×10^{-5} of $HC_2H_3O_2$; $HClO_4$ is a strong acid, of course.

16.3. Both methods involve direct measurement of the concentrations of the hydronium ion and the anion of the weak acid and calculation of the concentration of the un-ionized acid. All concentrations are substituted into the K_a expression to obtain a value for K_a. In the first method, the electrical conductivity of a solution of the weak acid is measured. The conductivity is proportional to the concentration of the hydronium ion and anion. In the second method, the pH of a known starting concentration of weak acid is measured. The pH is converted to $[H_3O^+]$, which will be equal to [anion].

16.4. The degree of ionization of a weak acid decreases as the concentration of the acid added to the solution increases. Compared to low concentrations, at high concentrations, there is less water for each weak acid molecule to react with as the weak acid ionizes:

$$HA(aq) + H_2O(l) \rightleftharpoons H_3O^+(aq) + A^-(aq)$$

16.5. You can neglect x if $C_a/K_a \geq 100$. In this case, $C_a/K_a = [(0.0010\ M \div 6.8 \times 10^{-4}) = 1.47]$, which is significantly less than 100, and x cannot be neglected in the $(0.0010 - x)$ term. This says the degree of ionization is significant.

16.6. The ionization of the first H_3O^+ is

$$H_2PHO_3(aq) + H_2O(l) \rightleftharpoons H_3O^+(aq) + HPHO_3^-(aq)$$

The equilibrium-constant expression is

$$K_{a_1} = \frac{[H_3O^+][HPHO_3^-]}{[H_2PHO_3]}$$

The ionization of the second H_3O^+ is

$$HPHO_3^-(aq) + H_2O(l) \rightleftharpoons H_3O^+(aq) + PHO_3^{2-}(aq)$$

The equilibrium-constant expression is

$$K_{a_2} = \frac{[H_3O^+][PHO_3^{2-}]}{[HPHO_3^-]}$$

Copyright © Cengage Learning. All rights reserved.

16.7. As shown in Example 16.4, the concentration of a -2 anion of a polyprotic acid in a solution of the diprotic acid alone is approximately equal to the value of K_{a_2}. For oxalic acid, begin by noting that $[H_3O^+] \cong [HC_2O_4^-]$. Then, substitute $[H_3O^+]$ for the $[HC_2O_4^-]$ term in the equilibrium-constant expression for K_{a_2}:

$$K_{a_2} = \frac{[H_3O^+][C_2O_4^{2-}]}{[HC_2O_4^-]} \cong \frac{[H_3O^+][C_2O_4^{2-}]}{[H_3O^+]} = [C_2O_4^{2-}]$$

16.8. The balanced chemical equation for the ionization of aniline is

$$C_6H_5NH_2(aq) + H_2O(l) \rightleftharpoons C_6H_5NH_3^+(aq) + OH^-(aq)$$

The equilibrium-constant equation, or expression for K_b, is defined without an $[H_2O]$ term; this term is included in the value for K_b, as discussed in Section 16.3. The expression is

$$K_b = \frac{[C_6H_5NH_3^+][OH^-]}{[C_6H_5NH_2]}$$

16.9. First, decide whether any of the three is a strong base. Because all the molecules are among the nitrogen-containing weak bases listed in Table 16.2, none is a strong base. Next, recognize that the greater the $[OH^-]$, the stronger the weak base. Because $[OH^-]$ can be calculated from the square root of the product of K_b and concentration, the larger the K_b, the greater the $[OH^-]$ and the stronger the weak base. Thus, CH_3NH_2 is the strongest of these three weak bases because its K_b is the largest.

16.10. The solution of anilinium chloride is acidic. Anilinium chloride is a salt that contains the anilinium ion, $C_6H_5NH_3^+$, and the Cl^- ion. The chloride ion does not hydrolyze because it could form only HCl, a strong acid. The anilinium ion does hydrolyze as follows:

$$C_6H_5NH_3^+ + H_2O(l) \rightleftharpoons C_6H_5NH_2 + H_3O^+$$

The equilibrium-constant expression for this reaction is

$$K_a = \frac{[C_6H_5NH_2][H_3O^+]}{[C_6H_5NH_3^+]}$$

Obtain the value for K_a by calculating the value of K_w/K_b, where K_b is the ionization constant for aniline, $C_6H_5NH_2$.

16.11. The common-ion effect is the shift in an ionic equilibrium caused by the addition of a solute that furnishes an ion that is common to, or takes part in, the equilibrium. If the equilibrium involves the ionization of a weak acid, then the common ion is usually the anion formed by the ionization of the weak acid. If the equilibrium involves the ionization of a weak base, then the common ion is usually the cation formed by the ionization of the weak base. An example is the addition of F^- ion (as NaF) to a solution of the weak acid HF, which ionizes as shown below:

$$HF(aq) + H_2O(l) \rightleftharpoons H_3O^+(aq) + F^-(aq)$$

Copyright © Cengage Learning. All rights reserved.

The effect of adding F^- to this equilibrium is that it causes a shift in the equilibrium composition to the left. The additional F^- reacts with H_3O^+, lowering its concentration and raising the concentration of HF.

16.12. The addition of CH_3NH_3Cl to 0.10 M CH_3NH_2 exerts a common-ion effect that causes the equilibrium below to exhibit a shift in composition to the left:

$$CH_3NH_2\,(aq)\ +\ H_2O(l)\ \rightleftharpoons\ CH_3NH_3^+(aq)\ +\ OH^-(aq)$$

This shift lowers the equilibrium concentration of the OH^- ion, which increases the $[H_3O^+]$. An increase in $[H_3O^+]$ lowers the pH below 11.8. The shift in composition to the left occurs according to Le Châtelier's principle, which states that a system shifts to counteract any change in composition.

16.13. A buffer is most often a solution of a mixture of two substances that is able to resist pH changes when limited amounts of acid or base are added to it. A buffer must contain a weak acid and its conjugate (weak) base. Strong acids and/or bases cannot form effective buffers because a buffer acts by converting H_3O^+ (strong acid) to the un-ionized (weak) buffer acid and by converting OH^- (strong base) to the un-ionized (weak) buffer base. An example of a buffer pair is a mixture of H_2CO_3 and HCO_3^-, the principal buffer in the blood.

16.14. The capacity of a buffer is the amount of acid or base with which the buffer can react before exhibiting a significant pH change. (A significant change in blood pH might mean 0.01–0.02 pH unit; for other systems a significant change might mean 0.5 pH unit.) A high-capacity buffer might be of the type discussed for Figure 16.11: 1 mol of buffer acid and 1 mol of buffer base. A low-capacity buffer might involve quite a bit less than these amounts: 0.01–0.05 mol of buffer acid and buffer base.

16.15. The pH of a weak base before titration is relatively high, around pH 10 for a 0.1 M solution of a typical weak base. As a strong acid titrant is added, the $[OH^-]$ decreases, and the pH decreases. At 50% neutralization, a buffer of equal amounts of acid and base is formed. The $[OH^-]$ equals the K_b, or the pOH equals the pK_b. The equivalence point is the point in a titration when a stoichiometric amount of reactant has been added. At the equivalence point, the pH is governed by the hydrolysis of the salt of the weak base formed and is usually in the pH 4–6 region. After the equivalence point, the pH decreases to a level just greater than the pH of the strong acid titrant.

16.16. If the pH is 8.0, an indicator that changes color in the basic region would be needed. Of the indicators mentioned in the text, phenolphthalein (pH 8.2–10.0) and thymol blue would work. In actual practice, cresol red (pH 7.2–8.8) would be the best choice because the pH should be closer to the middle of the range than to one end.

16.17. The answer is a, NaF.

16.18. The answer is d, slightly acidic.

16.19. The answer is a, H_2S.

Copyright © Cengage Learning. All rights reserved.

16.20. The answer is d, 5.05.

■ SOLUTIONS TO PRACTICE PROBLEMS

Note on significant figures: If the final answer to a solution needs to be rounded off, it is given first with one nonsignificant figure, and the last significant figure is underlined. The final answer is then rounded to the correct number of significant figures. In multistep problems, intermediate answers are given with at least one nonsignificant figure; however, only the final answer has been rounded off.

16.33.

a. $HBrO(aq) + H_2O(l) \rightleftharpoons H_3O^+(aq) + BrO^-(aq)$

b. $HClO_2(aq) + H_2O(l) \rightleftharpoons H_3O^+(aq) + ClO_2^-(aq)$

c. $HNO_2(aq) + H_2O(l) \rightleftharpoons H_3O^+(aq) + NO_2^-(aq)$

d. $HCN(aq) + H_2O(l) \rightleftharpoons H_3O^+(aq) + CN^-(aq)$

16.35. HAc will be used throughout as an abbreviation for acrylic acid and Ac⁻ for the acrylate ion. At the start, the H_3O^+ from the self-ionization of water is so small it is approximately zero. Once the acrylic acid solution is prepared, some of the 0.10 M HAc ionizes to H_3O^+ and Ac⁻. Then, let x equal the mol/L of HAc that ionize, forming x mol/L of H_3O^+ and x mol/L of Ac⁻ and leaving $(0.10 - x)$ M HAc in solution. We can summarize the situation in tabular form:

Conc. (M)	HAc + H₂O $\rightleftharpoons$	H₃O⁺ +	Ac⁻
Starting	0.10	0	0
Change	$-x$	$+x$	$+x$
Equilibrium	$0.10 - x$	x	x

The equilibrium-constant expression is

$$K_a = \frac{[H_3O^+][Ac^-]}{[HAc]} = \frac{x^2}{(0.10 - x)}$$

The value of x can be obtained from the pH of the solution:

$$x = [H_3O^+] = \text{antilog}(-pH) = \text{antilog}(-2.63) = 2.\underline{3}4 \times 10^{-3} = 0.002\underline{3}4\ M$$

Note that $(0.10 - x) = (0.10 - 0.00234) = 0.09766$, which is significantly different from 0.10, so x cannot be ignored in the calculation.

Thus, we substitute for x in both the numerator and the denominator to obtain the value of K_a:

$$K_a = \frac{x^2}{(0.10 - x)} = \frac{(0.00234)^2}{(0.10 - 0.00234)} = 5.\underline{6}06 \times 10^{-5} = 5.6 \times 10^{-5}$$

Copyright © Cengage Learning. All rights reserved.

16.37. To solve, assemble a table of starting, change, and equilibrium concentrations. Use HBo as the symbol for boric acid and Bo$^-$ as the symbol for $B(OH)_4^-$.

Conc. (M)	HBo + H$_2$O	H$_3$O$^+$ +	Bo$^-$
Starting	0.021	0	0
Change	$-x$	$+x$	$+x$
Equilibrium	$0.021 - x$	x	x

The value of x equals the value of the molarity of the H$_3$O$^+$ ion, which can be obtained from the equilibrium-constant expression.

Substitute into the equilibrium-constant expression, and solve for x.

$$K_a = \frac{[H_3O^+][Bo^-]}{[HBo]} = \frac{(x)^2}{(0.021 - x)} = 5.9 \times 10^{-10}$$

Solve the equation for x, assuming x is much smaller than 0.021.

$$\frac{(x)^2}{(0.021 - x)} \cong \frac{(x)^2}{(0.021)} = 5.9 \times 10^{-10}$$

$$x^2 = 5.9 \times 10^{-10} \times (0.021) = 1.239 \times 10^{-11}$$

$$x = [H_3O^+] = 3.519 \times 10^{-6} M$$

Check to make sure the assumption that $(0.021 - x) \cong 0.021$ is valid:

$$0.021 - (3.519 \times 10^{-6}) = 0.02099, or \cong 0.021 \text{ to two sig. figs.}$$

$$pH = -\log[H_3O^+] = -\log(3.519 \times 10^{-6}) = 5.453 = 5.45$$

The degree of ionization is

$$\text{Degree of ionization} = \frac{3.519 \times 10^{-6}}{(0.021)} = 0.000167 = 0.00017 = 1.7 \times 10^{-4}$$

16.39. To solve, assemble a table of starting, change, and equilibrium concentrations. Use HPaba as a symbol for p-aminobenzoic acid (PABA), and use Paba$^-$ as the symbol for the -1 anion.

Conc. (M)	HPaba + H$_2$O	H$_3$O$^+$ +	Paba$^-$
Starting	0.055	0	0
Change	$-x$	$+x$	$+x$
Equilibrium	$0.055 - x$	x	x

Write the equilibrium-constant expression in terms of chemical symbols, and then substitute the terms x and $(0.055 - x)$:

$$K_a = \frac{[H_3O^+][Paba^-]}{[HPaba]} = \frac{(x)^2}{(0.055 - x)} = 2.2 \times 10^{-5}$$

Copyright © Cengage Learning. All rights reserved.

Solve the equation for x, assuming x is smaller than 0.055.

$$x^2 = (2.2 \times 10^{-5}) \times 0.055 = 1.\underline{2}1 \times 10^{-6}$$

$$x = [H_3O^+] = [Paba^-] \cong 1.\underline{1}0 \times 10^{-3} = 0.0011 = 1.1 \times 10^{-3}\ M$$

Check to make sure the assumption that $(0.055 - x) \cong 0.055$ is valid.

$$0.055 - 0.00110 = 0.0539, \text{ or } 0.054$$

16.41.   To solve, first convert the pH to $[H_3O^+]$, which also equals $[C_2H_3O_2^-]$, here symbolized as $[Ac^-]$. Then assemble the usual table, and substitute into the equilibrium-constant expression to solve for $[HC_2H_3O_2]$, here symbolized as $[HAc]$.

$$[H_3O^+] = \text{antilog}\ (-2.68) = 2.\underline{0}89 \times 10^{-3}\ M$$

Conc. (M)	HAc + H^{2}O $\rightleftharpoons$	H^{3}O$^+$	+ Ac$^-$
Starting	x	0	0
Change	-2.089×10^{-3}	$+2.089 \times 10^{-3}$	$+2.089 \times 10^{-3}$
Equilibrium	$x - (2.089 \times 10^{-3})$	2.089×10^{-3}	2.089×10^{-3}

Write the equilibrium-constant expression in terms of chemical symbols, and then substitute the x and the $x - (2.089 \times 10^{-3})$ terms into the expression:

$$K_a = \frac{[H_3O^+][Ac^-]}{[HAc]} = \frac{(2.089 \times 10^{-3})^2}{(x - 2.089 \times 10^{-3})} = 1.7 \times 10^{-5}$$

Solve the equation for x, assuming 0.002089 is much smaller than x.

$$x = [HAc] \cong \frac{(2.089 \times 10^{-3})^2}{(1.7 \times 10^{-5})} = 0.2\underline{5}6 = 0.26\ M$$

16.43.   To solve, assemble the usual table of starting, change, and equilibrium concentrations of HF and F$^-$ ions.

Conc. (M)	HF + H$_2$O $\rightleftharpoons$	H$_3$O$^+$ +	F$^-$
Starting	0.40	0	0
Change	$-x$	$+x$	$+x$
Equilibrium	$0.40 - x$	x	x

Write the equilibrium-constant expression in terms of chemical symbols, and then substitute the terms x and $(0.040 - x)$:

$$K_a = \frac{[H_3O^+][F^-]}{[HF]} = \frac{(x)^2}{(0.040 - x)} = 6.8 \times 10^{-4}$$

Copyright © Cengage Learning. All rights reserved.

In this case, x cannot be ignored compared to 0.040 M. (If it is ignored, subtracting the calculated $[H_3O^+]$ from 0.040 yields a significant change.) The quadratic formula must be used. Reorganize the equilibrium-constant expression into the form $ax^2 + bx + c = 0$, and substitute for a, b, and c in the quadratic formula.

$$x^2 + (6.8 \times 10^{-4})x - (2.72 \times 10^{-5}) = 0$$

$$x = \frac{-6.8 \times 10^{-4} \pm \sqrt{(6.8 \times 10^{-4})^2 + 4(2.72 \times 10^{-5})}}{2}$$

$$x = \frac{-6.8 \times 10^{-4} \pm 0.01045}{2}$$

Use the positive root.

$$x = [H_3O^+] = 4.\underline{8}8 \times 10^{-3} = 0.0049 = 4.9 \times 10^{-3}\ M$$
$$pH = -\log(4.88 \times 10^{-3}) = 2.3\underline{1}1 = 2.31$$

16.45.   To solve, assemble the usual table of starting, change, and equilibrium concentrations of $(NO_2)_2C_6H_3CO_2H$, symbolized as HDin, and the $(NO_2)_2C_6H_3CO_2^-$ ion, symbolized as Din$^-$.

Conc. (M)	HDin + H$_2$O $\rightleftharpoons$	H$_3$O$^+$ +	Din$^-$
Starting	2.00	0	0
Change	$-x$	$+x$	$+x$
Equilibrium	$2.00 - x$	x	x

Write the equilibrium-constant expression in terms of chemical symbols, and then substitute the terms x and $(2.00 - x)$:

$$K_a = \frac{[H_3O^+][Din^-]}{[HDin]} = \frac{(x)^2}{(2.00 - x)} = 7.94 \times 10^{-2} = 0.0794$$

In this case, x cannot be ignored compared to 2.00 M. (If it is ignored, subtracting the calculated $[H_3O^+]$ from 2.00 yields a significant change.) The quadratic formula must be used. Reorganize the equilibrium-constant expression into the form $ax^2 + bx + c = 0$, and substitute for a, b, and c in the quadratic formula.

$$x^2 + (0.0794)x - 0.1588 = 0$$

$$x = \frac{-0.0794 \pm \sqrt{(0.0794)^2 + 4(0.1588)}}{2}$$

$$x = \frac{-0.0794 \pm 0.8009}{2}$$

Use the positive root.

$$x = [H_3O^+] = 0.36\underline{0}7 = 0.361\ M$$

Copyright © Cengage Learning. All rights reserved.

16.47.

a. To solve, note that $K_{a_1} = 1.2 \times 10^{-3} > K_{a_2} = 3.9 \times 10^{-6}$, and hence the second ionization and K_{a_2} can be neglected. Assemble a table of starting, change, and equilibrium concentrations. Let $H_2Ph = H_2C_8H_4O_4$ and $HPh^- = H\,C_8H_4O_4^-$.

Conc. (M)	$H_2Ph + H_2O$	$\rightleftharpoons$	H_3O^+	$+$	HPh^-
Starting	0.015		0		0
Change	$-x$		$+x$		$+x$
Equilibrium	$0.015 - x$		x		x

Write the equilibrium-constant expression in terms of chemical symbols, and then substitute x and $(0.015 - x)$:

$$K_{a_1} = \frac{[H_3O^+]\,[HPh^-]}{[H_2Ph]} = \frac{(x)^2}{(0.015 - x)} = 1.2 \times 10^{-3} = 0.0012$$

In this case, x cannot be ignored in the $(0.015\ M - x)$ term. (If it is ignored, the calculated $[H_3O^+]$ when subtracted from $0.0015\ M$ yields a significant change.) The quadratic formula must be used. Reorganize the equilibrium-constant expression into the form $ax^2 + bx + c = 0$, and substitute for a, b, and c in the quadratic formula.

$$x^2 + (0.0012)\,x - 1.80 \times 10^{-5} = 0$$

$$x = \frac{-0.0012 \pm \sqrt{(0.0012)^2 - 4(-1.80 \times 10^{-5})}}{2}$$

$$x = \frac{-0.0012 \pm 0.008569}{2}$$

Use the positive root.

$$x = [H_3O^+] \cong 3.\underline{6}84 \times 10^{-3} = 0.0037 = 3.7 \times 10^{-3}\ M$$

b. Because $[HPh^-] \cong [H_3O^+]$, these terms cancel in the K_{a_2} expression. This reduces to

$$[Ph^{2-}] = K_{a_2} = 3.9 \times 10^{-6}\ M.$$

16.49. The equation is

$$CH_3NH_2(aq) + H_2O(l) \rightleftharpoons CH_3NH_3^+(aq) + OH^-(aq)$$

The K_b expression is

$$K_b = \frac{[CH_3NH_3^+]\,[OH^-]}{[CH_3NH_2]}$$

Copyright © Cengage Learning. All rights reserved.

16.51. To solve, convert the pH to $[OH^-]$:

$$pOH = 14.00 - pH = 14.00 - 11.34 = 2.66$$

$$[OH^-] = \text{antilog}(-2.66) = 2.\underline{1}88 \times 10^{-3}\ M$$

Using the symbol EtN for ethanolamine, assemble a table of starting, change, and equilibrium concentrations.

Conc. (M)	EtN + H_2O	$\rightleftharpoons$	$HEtN^+$	+	OH^-
Starting	0.15		0		0
Change	$-x$		$+x$		$+x$
Equilibrium	$0.15 - (2.188 \times 10^{-3})$		2.188×10^{-3}		2.188×10^{-3}

Write the equilibrium-constant expression in terms of chemical symbols, and then substitute the terms, and solve for K_b:

$$K_b = \frac{[HEtN^+][OH^-]}{[EtN]} = \frac{(2.188 \times 10^{-3})^2}{(0.15 - 2.188 \times 10^{-3})} = 3.\underline{2}3 \times 10^{-5} = 3.2 \times 10^{-5}$$

16.53. To solve, assemble a table of starting, change, and equilibrium concentrations:

Conc. (M)	CH_3NH_2 + H_2O	$\rightleftharpoons$	$CH_3NH_3^+$	+	OH^-
Starting	0.060		0		0
Change	$-x$		$+x$		$+x$
Equilibrium	$0.060 - x$		x		x

Write the equilibrium-constant expression in terms of chemical symbols, and then substitute the terms and the value of K_b:

$$K_b = \frac{[CH_3NH_3^+][OH^-]}{[CH_3NH_2]} = \frac{(x)^2}{(0.060 - x)} = 4.4 \times 10^{-4}$$

In this case, x cannot be ignored compared to 0.060 M. (If it is ignored, subtracting the calculated $[OH^-]$ from 0.060 yields a significant change.) The quadratic formula must be used. Reorganize the equilibrium-constant expression into the form $ax^2 + bx + c = 0$, and substitute for a, b, and c in the quadratic formula.

$$x^2 + (4.4 \times 10^{-4})x - 2.64 \times 10^{-5} = 0$$

$$x = \frac{-4.4 \times 10^{-4} \pm \sqrt{(4.4 \times 10^{-4})^2 + 4(2.64 \times 10^{-5})}}{2}$$

$$x = \frac{-4.4 \times 10^{-4} \pm 0.01028}{2}$$

Use the positive root.

$$x = [OH^-] = 4.\underline{9}2 \times 10^{-3} = 0.0049 = 4.9 \times 10^{-3}\ M$$

$$pOH = -\log(4.92 \times 10^{-3}) = 2.3\underline{0}7$$

$$pH = 14.00 - 2.307 = 11.6\underline{9}2 = 11.69$$

Copyright © Cengage Learning. All rights reserved.

16.55.

 a. No hydrolysis occurs because the nitrate ion (NO_3^-) is the anion of a strong acid.

 b. Hydrolysis occurs. Equation:

$$OCl^- + H_2O \rightleftharpoons HOCl + OH^-$$

 Equilibrium-constant expression:

$$K_b = \frac{K_w}{K_a} = \frac{[HOCl][OH^-]}{[OCl^-]}$$

 c. Hydrolysis occurs. Equation:

$$NH_2NH_3^+ + H_2O \rightleftharpoons H_3O^+ + NH_2NH_2$$

 Equilibrium-constant expression:

$$K_a = \frac{K_w}{K_b} = \frac{[H_3O^+][NH_2NH_2]}{[NH_2NH_3^+]}$$

 d. No hydrolysis occurs because the bromide ion (Br^-) is the anion of a strong acid.

16.57. Acid ionization is

$$Zn(H_2O)_6^{2+}(aq) + H_2O(l) \rightleftharpoons Zn(H_2O)_5(OH)^+(aq) + H_3O^+(aq)$$

16.59.

 a. $Fe(NO_3)_3$ is a salt of a weak base, $Fe(OH)_3$, and a strong acid, HNO_3, so it would be expected to be acidic. Fe^{3+} is not in Group IA or IIA, so it would be expected to form a metal hydrate ion that would hydrolyze to form an acidic solution.

 b. Na_2CO_3 is a salt of a strong base, $NaOH$, and the anion of a weak acid, HCO_3^-, so it would be expected to be basic.

 c. $Ca(CN)_2$ is a salt of a strong base, $Ca(OH)_2$, and a weak acid, HCN, so it would be expected to be basic.

 d. NH_4ClO_4 is a salt of a weak base, NH_3, and a strong acid, $HClO_4$, so it would be expected to be acidic.

Copyright © Cengage Learning. All rights reserved.

16.61.

    a.   Both ions hydrolyze:

$$NH_4^+ + H_2O \rightleftharpoons NH_3 + H_3O^+$$

$$C_2H_3O_2^- + H_2O \rightleftharpoons HC_2H_3O_2 + OH^-$$

Calculate the K_a and K_b constants of the two to compare them:

$$NH_4^+ \text{ as an acid: } K_a = \frac{K_w}{K_b} = \frac{1.0 \times 10^{-14}}{1.8 \times 10^{-5}} = 5.\underline{5}5 \times 10^{-10}$$

$$C_2H_3O_2^- \text{ as a base: } K_b = \frac{K_w}{K_a} = \frac{1.0 \times 10^{-14}}{1.7 \times 10^{-5}} = 5.\underline{8}8 \times 10^{-10}$$

Because the K_b for the hydrolysis of $C_2H_3O_2^-$ is slightly larger than the constant, K_a, for the hydrolysis of NH_4^+, the solution will be slightly basic but close to pH 7.0.

    b.   Both ions hydrolyze:

$$C_6H_5NH_3^+ + H_2O \rightleftharpoons C_6H_5NH_2 + H_3O^+$$

$$C_2H_3O_2^- + H_2O \rightleftharpoons HC_2H_3O_2 + OH^-$$

Calculate the K_a and K_b constants of the two to compare them:

$$C_6H_5NH_3^+ \text{ as an acid: } K_a = \frac{K_w}{K_b} = \frac{1.0 \times 10^{-14}}{4.2 \times 10^{-10}} = 2.\underline{3}8 \times 10^{-5}$$

$$C_2H_3O_2^- \text{ as a base: } K_b = \frac{K_w}{K_a} = \frac{1.0 \times 10^{-14}}{1.7 \times 10^{-5}} = 5.\underline{8}8 \times 10^{-10}$$

Because the constant, K_a, for the hydrolysis of $C_6H_5NH_3^+$ is larger than the hydrolysis constant, K_b, for the hydrolysis of $C_2H_3O_2^-$, the solution will be acidic and significantly less than pH 7.0.

16.63.

    a.   The reaction is

$$NO_2^- + H_2O \rightleftharpoons HNO_2 + OH^-$$

The constant, K_b, is obtained by dividing K_w by the K_a of the conjugate acid, HNO_2:

$$K_b = \frac{K_w}{K_a} = \frac{1.0 \times 10^{-14}}{4.5 \times 10^{-4}} = 2.\underline{2}2 \times 10^{-11} = 2.2 \times 10^{-11}$$

    b.   The reaction is

$$C_5H_5NH^+ + H_2OC_5H_5N + H_3O^+$$

The constant, K_a, is obtained by dividing K_w by the K_b of the conjugate base, C_5H_5N:

$$K_a = \frac{K_w}{K_b} = \frac{1.0 \times 10^{-14}}{1.4 \times 10^{-9}} = 7.\underline{1}4 \times 10^{-6} = 7.1 \times 10^{-6}$$

Copyright © Cengage Learning. All rights reserved.

16.65. Assemble the usual table, letting $[Pr^-]$ equal the equilibrium concentration of the propionate anion (the only ion that hydrolyzes). Then calculate the K_b of the Pr^- ion from the K_a of its conjugate acid, HPr. Assume x is much smaller than the 0.025 M concentration in the denominator, and solve for x in the numerator of the equilibrium-constant expression. Finally, calculate pOH from the $[OH^-]$ and pH from the pOH.

Conc. (M)	$Pr^- + H_2O$ $\rightleftharpoons$	HPr +	OH^-
Starting	0.025	0	0
Change	$-x$	$+x$	$+x$
Equilibrium	$0.025 - x$	x	x

$$K_b = \frac{K_w}{K_a} = \frac{1.0 \times 10^{-14}}{1.3 \times 10^{-5}} = 7.\underline{6}9 \times 10^{-10}$$

Substitute into the equilibrium-constant expression.

$$K_b = \frac{[HPr][OH^-]}{[Pr^-]} = \frac{(x)^2}{(0.025 - x)} \cong \frac{(x)^2}{(0.025)} = 7.\underline{6}9 \times 10^{-10}$$

$$x = [OH^-] = [HPr] \cong 4.\underline{3}8 \times 10^{-6} = 4.4 \times 10^{-6} \, M$$

$$pOH = -\log[OH^-] = -\log(4.38 \times 10^{-6}) = 5.3\underline{5}8$$

$$pH = 14.00 - 5.358 = 8.6\underline{4}2 = 8.64$$

16.67. Assemble the usual table, letting $[PyNH^+]$ equal the equilibrium concentration of the pryridinium cation (the only ion that hydrolyzes). Then calculate the K_a of the $PyNH^+$ ion from the K_b of its conjugate base, PyN. Assume x is much smaller than the 0.15 M concentration in the denominator, and solve for x in the numerator of the equilibrium-constant expression. Finally, calculate pH from the $[H_3O^+]$.

Conc. (M)	$PyNH^+ + H_2O$ $\rightleftharpoons$	H_3O^+ +	PyN
Starting	0.15	0	0
Change	$-x$	$+x$	$+x$
Equilibrium	$0.15 - x$	x	x

$$K_a = \frac{K_w}{K_b} = \frac{1.0 \times 10^{-14}}{1.4 \times 10^{-9}} = 7.\underline{1}4 \times 10^{-6}$$

Write the equilibrium-constant expression in terms of chemical symbols and then substitute the terms and solve for K_a:

$$K_a = \frac{[PyN][H_3O^+]}{[PyNH^+]} = \frac{(x)^2}{(0.15 - x)} \cong \frac{(x)^2}{(0.15)} = 7.\underline{1}4 \times 10^{-6}$$

$$x = [H_3O^+] = [PyN] \cong 1.\underline{0}3 \times 10^{-3} = 0.0010 = 1.0 \times 10^{-3} \, M$$

$$pH = -\log[H^+] = -\log(1.03 \times 10^{-3}) = 2.9\underline{8}7 = 2.99$$

Copyright © Cengage Learning. All rights reserved.

16.69.   To solve, assemble a table of starting, change, and equilibrium concentrations for each part. For each part, assume x is much smaller than the 0.75 M starting concentration of HF. Then solve for x in the numerator of each equilibrium-constant expression by using the product of 6.8 x 10^{-4} and other terms.

a.   0.75 M Hydrofluoric acid, HF:

Conc. (M)	HF + H_2O $\rightleftharpoons$	H_3O^+ +	F^-
Starting	0.75	0	0
Change	$-x$	$+x$	$+x$
Equilibrium	$0.75 - x$	x	x

$$K_a = \frac{[H_3O^+][F^-]}{[HF]} = \frac{(x)^2}{(0.75 - x)} \cong \frac{(x)^2}{(0.75)} = 6.8 \times 10^{-4}$$

$$x^2 = 6.8 \times 10^{-4} \times (0.75)$$

$$x = [H_3O^+] = 0.02\underline{2}58 \ M$$

Check to see whether the assumption is valid.

$$0.75 - (0.02258) = 0.7\underline{2}7 = 0.73$$

This is a borderline case; the quadratic equation gives $[H_3O^+]$ = 0.02224 M, not much different. The degree of ionization is

$$\text{Degree of ionization} = \frac{0.02258}{0.75} = 0.03\underline{0}1 = 0.030$$

b.   0.75 M HF with 0.12 M HCl:

Conc. (M)	HF + H_2O $\rightleftharpoons$	H_3O^+ +	F^-
Starting	0.75	0.12	0
Change	$-x$	$+x$	$+x$
Equilibrium	$0.75 - x$	$0.12 + x$	x

Assuming x is negligible compared to 0.12 and to 0.75, substitute into the equilibrium-constant expression 0.12 for $[H_3O^+]$ from 0.12 M HCl and 0.75 from the HF:

$$K_a = \frac{[H_3O^+][F^-]}{[HF]} = \frac{(0.12 + x)(x)}{(0.75 - x)} \cong \frac{(0.12)(x)}{(0.75)} = 6.8 \times 10^{-4}$$

$$x = [F^-] = \frac{(0.75)(6.8 \times 10^{-4})}{(0.12)} \cong 4.\underline{2}50 \times 10^{-3} \ M$$

Check to see whether the assumptions are valid:

$$0.75 - (4.250 \times 10^{-3}) = 0.7\underline{4}57 = 0.75$$

$$0.12 + (4.250 \times 10^{-3}) = 0.1\underline{2}42 = 0.12$$

$$\text{Degree of ionization} = \frac{4.25 \times 10^{-3}}{0.75} = 0.005\underline{6}6 = 0.0057$$

Copyright © Cengage Learning. All rights reserved.

16.71.   Assemble the usual table, using a starting NO_2^- of 0.10 M, from 0.10 M KNO_2, and a starting HNO_2 of 0.15 M. Assume x is negligible compared to 0.10 M and 0.15 M, and solve for the x in the numerator.

Conc. (M)	HNO_2 + H_2O $\rightleftharpoons$	H_3O^+	+	NO_2^-
Starting	0.15	0		0.10
Change	$-x$	$+x$		$+x$
Equilibrium	0.15 $- x$	0.12 $+ x$		0.10 $+ x$

$$K_a = \frac{[H_3O^+][NO_2^-]}{[HNO_2]} = \frac{(0.10 + x)(x)}{(0.15 - x)} \cong \frac{(0.10)(x)}{(0.15)} = 4.5 \times 10^{-4}$$

$$x = [H_3O^+] = 6.\underline{7}5 \times 10^{-4} \ M$$

$$pH = -\log[H_3O^+] = -\log(6.75 \times 10^{-4}) = 3.1\underline{7}0 = 3.17$$

16.73.   Assemble the usual table, using a starting $CH_3NH_3^+$ of 0.15 M, from 0.15 M CH_3NH_3Cl, and a starting CH_3NH_2 of 0.10 M. Assume x is negligible compared to 0.15 M and 0.10 M, and solve for the x in the numerator.

Conc. (M)	CH_3NH_2 + H_2O $\rightleftharpoons$	OH^-	+	$CH_3NH_3^+$
Starting	0.10	0		0.15
Change	$-x$	$+x$		$+x$
Equilibrium	0.10 $- x$	x		0.15 $+ x$

$$K_b = \frac{[CH_3NH_3^+][OH^-]}{[CH_3NH_2]} = \frac{(0.15 + x)(x)}{(0.10 - x)} \cong \frac{(0.15)(x)}{(0.10)} = 4.4 \times 10^{-4}$$

$$x = [OH^-] = 2.\underline{9}3 \times 10^{-4} \ M$$

$$pOH = -\log[OH^-] = -\log(2.93 \times 10^{-4}) = 3.5\underline{3}2$$

$$pH = 14.00 - pOH = 14.00 - 3.532 = 10.4\underline{6}8 = 10.47$$

16.75.   Find the mol/L of HF and the mol/L of F^-, and assemble the usual table. Substitute the equilibrium concentrations into the equilibrium-constant expression; then, assume x is negligible compared to the starting concentrations of both HF and F^-. Solve for x in the numerator of the equilibrium-constant expression, and calculate the pH from this value.

Total volume = 0.045 L + 0.035 L = 0.080 L

(0.10 mol HF/L) x 0.035 L = 0.0035 mol HF ($\div$ 0.080 L total volume = 0.04375 M)

(0.15 mol F^-/L) x 0.045 L = 0.00675 mol F^- ($\div$ 0.080 L total volume = 0.084375 M)

Now, substitute these starting concentrations into the usual table:

Conc. (M)	HF + H_2O $\rightleftharpoons$	H_3O^+	+	F^-
Starting	0.04375	0		0.084375
Change	$-x$	$+x$		$+x$
Equilibrium	0.04375 $- x$	x		0.084375 $+ x$

Copyright © Cengage Learning. All rights reserved.

$$K_a = \frac{[H_3O^+][F^-]}{[HF]} = \frac{(x)(0.084375 + x)}{(0.04375 - x)} \cong \frac{(x)(0.084375)}{(0.04375)} = 6.8 \times 10^{-4}$$

$$x = [H_3O^+] = 3.\underline{5}2 \times 10^{-4} \ M$$

$$pH = -\log[H_3O^+] = -\log(3.52 \times 10^{-4}) = 3.4\underline{5}3 = 3.45$$

16.77. First, use the 0.10 M NH_3 and 0.10 M NH_4^+ to calculate the [OH⁻] and pH before HCl is added. Assemble a table of starting, change, and equilibrium concentrations. Assume x is negligible compared to 0.10 M, and substitute the approximate concentrations into the equilibrium-constant expression.

Conc. (M)	$NH_3 + H_2O \rightleftharpoons$	NH_4^+	+	OH⁻
Starting	0.10	0.10		0
Change	$-x$	$+x$		$+x$
Equilibrium	$0.10 - x$	$0.10 + x$		x

$$K_b = \frac{[NH_4^+][OH^-]}{[NH_3]} = \frac{(0.10 + x)(x)}{(0.10 - x)} \cong \frac{(0.10)(x)}{(0.10)} = 1.8 \times 10^{-5}$$

$$x = [OH^-] = 1 8 \times 10^{-5} \ M$$

$$pOH = -\log[OH^-] = -\log(1.8 \times 10^{-5}) = 4.7\underline{4}4$$

$$pH = 14.00 - pOH = 14.00 - 4.744 = 9.2\underline{5}52 = 9.26 \text{ (before HCl added)}$$

Now, calculate the pH after the 0.012 L (12 mL) of 0.20 M HCl is added by noting that the H_3O^+ ion reacts with the NH_3 to form additional NH_4^+. Calculate the stoichiometric amount of HCl; then subtract the moles of HCl from the moles of NH_3. Add the resulting moles of NH_4^+ to the 0.0125 starting moles of NH_4^+ in the 0.125 L of buffer.

(0.20 mol HCl/L) x 0.012 L = 0.0024 mol HCl (reacts with 0.0024 mol NH_3)

mol NH_3 left = (0.01$\underline{2}$5 − 0.0024) mol = 0.010$\underline{1}$ mol

mol NH_4^+ present = (0.0125 + 0.0024) mol = 0.0149 mol

The concentrations of NH_3 and NH_4^+ are

$$[NH_3] = \frac{0.0101 \text{ mol } NH_3}{0.137 \text{ L}} = 0.07\underline{3}7 \ M$$

$$[NH_4^+] = \frac{0.0149 \text{ mol } NH_3}{0.137 \text{ L}} = 0.1\underline{0}8 \ M$$

Now, account for the ionization of NH_3 to NH_4^+ and OH⁻ at equilibrium by assembling the usual table. Assume x is negligible compared to 0.0737 M and 0.108 M, and solve the equilibrium-constant expression for x in the numerator. Calculate the pH from x, the [OH⁻].

Conc. (M)	$NH_3 + H_2O \rightleftharpoons$	NH_4^+	+	OH⁻
Starting	0.0737	0.108		0
Change	$-x$	$+x$		$+x$
Equilibrium	$0.0737 - x$	$0.108 + x$		x

Copyright © Cengage Learning. All rights reserved.

$$K_b = \frac{[NH_4^+][OH^-]}{[NH_3]} = \frac{(0.108 + x)(x)}{(0.0737 - x)} \cong \frac{(0.108)(x)}{(0.0737)} = 1.8 \times 10^{-5}$$

$x = [OH^-] \cong 1.22 \times 10^{-5}\ M$

$pOH = -\log[OH^-] = -\log(1.22 \times 10^{-5}) = 4.913$

$pH = 14.00 - pOH = 14.00 - 4.913 = 9.086 = 9.09$ (after HCl added)

16.79.   Use the Henderson-Hasselbalch equation, where $pK_a = -\log K_a$.

$$pH = -\log K_a + \log \frac{[\text{buff. base}]}{[\text{buff. acid}]}$$

$$= -\log(1.3 \times 10^{-3}) + \log \frac{(0.10\ M)}{(0.15\ M)} = 2.710 = 2.71$$

16.81.   Calculate the K_a of the pyridinium ion from the K_b of pyridine, and then use the Henderson-Hasselbalch equation, where $pK_a = -\log K_a$.

$$K_a = \frac{K_w}{K_b} = \frac{1.0 \times 10^{-14}}{1.4 \times 10^{-9}} = 7.14 \times 10^{-6}$$

$$pH = -\log K_a + \log \frac{[\text{buff. base}]}{[\text{buff. acid}]}$$

$$= -\log(7.14 \times 10^{-6}) + \log \frac{(0.15\ M)}{(0.10\ M)} = 5.322 = 5.32$$

16.83.   Symbolize acetic acid as HOAc and sodium acetate as Na^+OAc^-. Use the Henderson-Hasselbalch equation to find the log of $[OAc^-]/[HOAc]$. Then solve for $[OAc^-]$ and for moles of NaOAc in the 2.0 L of solution.

$$pH = -\log K_a + \log \frac{[OAc^-]}{[HOAc]} = 5.00$$

$$5.00 = -\log(1.7 \times 10^{-5}) + \log \frac{[OAc^-]}{(0.10\ M)}$$

$5.00 = 4.770 + \log[OAc^-] - \log(0.10)$

$\log[OAc^-] = 5.00 - 4.770 - 1.00 = -0.770$

$[OAc^-] = 0.1698\ M$

mol NaOAc $= 0.1698$ mol/L $\times 2.0$ L $= 0.3396 = 0.34$ mol

Copyright © Cengage Learning. All rights reserved.

16.85. All the OH^- (from the NaOH) reacts with the H_3O^+ from HCl. Calculate the stoichiometric amounts of OH^- and H_3O^+, and subtract the moles of OH^- from the moles of H_3O^+. Next, divide the remaining H_3O^+ by the total volume of 0.015 L + 0.025 L, or 0.040 L, to find the $[H_3O^+]$. Then calculate the pH.

$$\text{mol } H_3O^+ = (0.10 \text{ mol HCl/L}) \times 0.025 \text{ L HCl} = 0.0025 \text{ mol } H_3O^+$$

$$\text{mol } OH^- = (0.10 \text{ mol NaOH/L}) \times 0.015 \text{ L NaOH} = 0.0015 \text{ mol } OH^-$$

$$\text{mol } H_3O^+ \text{ left} = (0.0025 - 0.0015) \text{ mol } H_3O^+ = 0.0010 \text{ mol } H_3O^+$$

$$[H_3O^+] = 0.0010 \text{ mol } H_3O^+ \div 0.040 \text{ L total volume} = 0.02\underline{5}0 \ M$$

$$pH = -\log [H_3O^+] = -\log (0.0250) = 1.6\underline{0}2 = 1.60$$

16.87. Use HBen to symbolize benzoic acid and Ben^- to symbolize the benzoate anion. At the equivalence point, equal molar amounts of HBen and NaOH react to form a solution of NaBen. Start by calculating the moles of HBen. Use this to calculate the volume of NaOH needed to neutralize all of the HBen (and use the moles of HBen as the moles of Ben^- formed at the equivalence point). Add the volume of NaOH to the original 0.050 L to find the total volume of solution.

$$\text{mol HBen} = 1.24 \text{ g HBen} \div (122.1 \text{ g HBen/mol HBen}) = 0.01016 \text{ mol HBen}$$

$$\text{Volume NaOH} = 0.01016 \text{ mol NaOH} \div (0.180 \text{ mol NaOH/L}) = 0.056\underline{4}4 \text{ L}$$

$$\text{Total volume} = 0.05644 \text{ L} + 0.050 \text{ L HBen soln} = 0.10644 \text{ L}$$

$$[Ben^-] = (0.01016 \text{ mol } Ben^- \text{ from HBen}) \div 0.10644 \text{ L} = 0.09545 \ M$$

Because the Ben^- hydrolyzes to OH^- and HBen, use this to calculate the $[OH^-]$. Start by calculating the K_b constant of Ben^- from the K_a of its conjugate acid, HBen. Then, assemble the usual table of concentrations, assume x is negligible, and calculate $[OH^-]$ and pH.

$$K_b = \frac{K_w}{K_a} = \frac{1.0 \times 10^{-14}}{6.3 \times 10^{-5}} = 1.\underline{5}9 \times 10^{-10}$$

Conc. (M)	$Ben^- + H_2O \rightleftharpoons$	$HBen +$	OH^-
Starting	0.09545	0	0
Change	$-x$	$+x$	$+x$
Equilibrium	$0.09545 - x$	x	x

$$K_b = \frac{[HBen][OH^-]}{[Ben^-]} = \frac{(x)^2}{(0.09545 - x)} \cong \frac{(x)^2}{(0.09545)} = 1.59 \times 10^{-10}$$

$$x = [OH^-] = 3.\underline{8}95 \times 10^{-6} \ M$$

$$pOH = -\log [OH^-] = -\log (3.895 \times 10^{-6}) = 5.4\underline{0}94$$

$$pH = 14.00 - 5.4094 = 8.5\underline{9}05 = 8.59$$

Copyright © Cengage Learning. All rights reserved.

16.89.   Use EtN to symbolize ethylamine and $EtNH^+$ to symbolize the ethylammonium cation. At the equivalence point, equal molar amounts of EtN and HCl react to form a solution of EtNHCl. Start by calculating the moles of EtN. Use this to calculate the volume of HCl needed to neutralize all of the EtN (and use the moles of EtN as the moles of $EtNH^+$ formed at the equivalence point). Add the volume of HCl to the original 0.032 L to find the total volume of solution.

$$(0.087 \text{ mol EtN/L}) \times 0.032 \text{ L} = 0.00278 \text{ mol EtN}$$

$$\text{Volume HCl} = 0.00278 \text{ mol HCl} \div (0.15 \text{ mol HCl/L}) = 0.0185 \text{ L}$$

$$\text{Total volume} = 0.0185 \text{ L} + 0.032 \text{ L EtN soln} = 0.0505 \text{ L}$$

$$[EtNH^+] = (0.00278 \text{ mol } EtNH^+ \text{ from EtN}) \div 0.0505 \text{ L} = 0.0550 \ M$$

Because the $EtNH^+$ hydrolyzes to H_3O^+ and EtN, use this to calculate the $[H_3O^+]$. Start by calculating the K_a constant of $EtNH^+$ from the K_b of its conjugate base, EtN. Then assemble the usual table of concentrations, assume x is negligible, and calculate $[H_3O^+]$ and pH.

$$K_a = \frac{K_w}{K_b} = \frac{1.0 \times 10^{-14}}{4.7 \times 10^{-4}} = 2.\underline{1}3 \times 10^{-11}$$

Conc. (M)	$EtNH^+ + H_2O \rightleftharpoons$	$EtN +$	H_3O^+
Starting	0.0550	0	0
Change	$-x$	$+x$	$+x$
Equilibrium	$0.0550 - x$	x	x

$$K_a = \frac{[EtN][H_3O^+]}{[EtNH^+]} = \frac{(x)^2}{(0.0550 - x)} \cong \frac{(x)^2}{(0.0550)} = 2.13 \times 10^{-11}$$

$$x = [H_3O^+] = 1.\underline{0}8 \times 10^{-6} \ M$$

$$pH = -\log [H_3O^+] = -\log (1.08 \times 10^{-6}) = 5.9\underline{6}56 = 5.97$$

16.91.

a.   Assemble the usual table of concentrations.

Conc. (M)	$CN^- + H_2O \rightleftharpoons$	$HCN +$	OH^-
Starting	0.100	0	0
Change	$-x$	$+x$	$+x$
Equilibrium	$0.100 - x$	x	x

Now substitute into the equilibrium expression, assume x is negligible compared to 0.100 M, and calculate $[OH^-]$.

$$K_b = \frac{(x)^2}{(0.100 - x)} = \frac{(x)^2}{(0.100)} = 2.0 \times 10^{-5}$$

$$x = [OH^-] = 1.\underline{4}14 \times 10^{-3} \ M$$

Finally, calculate the pOH and then the pH.

$$pOH = -\log [OH^-] = -\log (1.414 \times 10^{-3}) = 2.8\underline{9}4$$

$$pH = 14.00 - 2.894 = 11.1\underline{5}0 = 11.15$$

Copyright © Cengage Learning. All rights reserved.

b.   After 15.0 mL of 0.200 M HCl is added. The reaction is

$$CN^- + H_3O^+ \rightarrow HCN + H_2O$$

The total volume at this point is 50.0 mL + 15.0 mL = 65.0 mL.

The moles of CN^- present at the start and the moles of HCl added are

$$\text{mol } CN^- = M \times V = 0.100\ M \times 50.0 \times 10^{-3}\ L = 5.0\underline{0}0 \times 10^{-3}\ \text{mol}$$

$$\text{mol } HCl = M \times V = 0.200\ M \times 15.0 \times 10^{-3}\ L = 3.0\underline{0}0 \times 10^{-3}\ \text{mol}$$

After reaction the moles of HCN equal the moles of added HCl. The moles of CN^- present are

$$\text{mol } CN^- = 5.000 \times 10^{-3}\ \text{mol} - 3.000 \times 10^{-3} = 2.0\underline{0}0 \times 10^{-3}\ \text{mol}$$

Now calculate the concentrations.

$$[CN^-] = \frac{2.000 \times 10^{-3}\ \text{mol } CN^-}{65.0 \times 10^{-3}\ L} = 0.030\underline{7}6\ M$$

$$[HCN] = \frac{3.000 \times 10^{-3}\ \text{mol } HCN}{65.0 \times 10^{-3}\ L} = 0.046\underline{1}5\ M$$

Substitute into the K_b expression and solve for $x = [OH^-]$.

$$K_b = 2.0 \times 10^{-5} = \frac{[HCN]\,[OH^-]}{[CN^-]} = \frac{(0.04615 + x)(x)}{(0.03076 - x)} \cong \frac{(0.04615)(x)}{(0.03076)}$$

$$x = [OH^-] = \frac{(0.03076)(2.0 \times 10^{-5})}{(0.04615)} = 1.\underline{3}3 \times 10^{-5}\ M$$

Now calculate the pOH and finally the pH.

$$pOH = -\log(1.33 \times 10^{-5}) = 4.8\underline{7}5$$

$$pH = 14.00 - pOH = 14.00 - 4.875 = 9.1\underline{2}4 = 9.12$$

c.   First calculate the volume of HCl added to reach the equivalence point.

$$V_2 = \frac{M_1 V_1}{M_2} = \frac{(0.100\ M)(50.0\ \text{mL})}{(0.200\ M)} = 25.\underline{0}0\ \text{mL}$$

The total volume at this point is 50.0 mL + 25.0 mL = 75.0 mL. The equilibrium is now

$$HCN + H_2O \rightleftharpoons H_3O^+ + CN^-$$

The moles of HCN present are the same as the moles of CN^- present initially, 5.00×10^{-3} mol. The concentration is

$$[HCN] = \frac{5.000 \times 10^{-3}\ \text{mol } HCN}{75.0 \times 10^{-3}\ L} = 0.06\underline{6}6\ M$$

Copyright © Cengage Learning. All rights reserved.

Calculate the value of K_a from K_b, set up the equilibrium expression, and solve.

$$K_a = \frac{K_w}{K_b} = \frac{1.00 \times 10^{-14}}{2.0 \times 10^{-5}} = 5.\underline{0}0 \times 10^{-10}$$

$$K_a = 5.00 \times 10^{-10} = \frac{[CN^-][H_3O^+]}{[HCN]} = \frac{x^2}{(0.0666 - x)}$$

$$x = [H_3O^+] = 5.\underline{7}73 \times 10^{-6}\ M$$

$$pH = -\log (5.773 \times 10^{-6}) = 5.2\underline{3}8 = 5.24$$

d.   After the addition of 30.0 mL HCl. The volume at this point is 50.0 mL + 30.0 mL = 80.0 mL. Now calculate the molarity of the excess H_3O^+.

$$\text{mol HCl added} = M \times V = (0.200\ M)(30.0 \times 10^{-3}\ L) = 6.0\underline{0}0 \times 10^{-3}\ \text{mol}$$

$$\text{Excess mol HCl} = 6.000 \times 10^{-3}\ \text{mol} - 5.000 \times 10^{-3}\ \text{mol} = 1.0\underline{0}0 \times 10^{-3}\ \text{mol}$$

$$[H_3O^+] = \frac{1.000 \times 10^{-3}\ \text{mol HCl}}{80.0 \times 10^{-3}\ L} = 0.012\underline{5}0\ M$$

Finally, calculate the pH

$$pH = -\log (0.01250) = 1.9\underline{0}3 = 1.90$$

16.93.   Calculate the stoichiometric amounts of NH_3 and HCl, which forms NH_4^+. Then divide NH_3 and NH_4^+ by the total volume of 0.500 L + 0.200 L = 0.700 L to find the starting concentrations. Calculate the $[OH^-]$, the pOH, and the pH.

$$\text{mol } NH_3 = (0.10\ \text{mol } NH_3/L) \times 0.500\ L = 0.0500\ \text{mol } NH_3$$

$$\text{mol HCl} = (0.15\ \text{mol HCl/L}) \times 0.200\ L = 0.0300\ \text{mol HCl}\ (0.0300\ \text{mol } NH_4^+)$$

$$\text{mol } NH_3 \text{ left} = 0.0500\ \text{mol} - 0.0300\ \text{mol HCl} = 0.0200\ \text{mol } NH_3$$

$$0.02\underline{0}0\ \text{mol } NH_3 \div 0.700\ L = 0.0286\ M\ NH_3$$

$$0.03\underline{0}0\ \text{mol } NH_4^+ \div 0.700\ L = 0.0429\ M\ NH_4^+$$

Conc. (M)	$NH_3 + H_2O$	$\rightleftharpoons$	NH_4^+	+	OH^-
Starting	0.0286		0.0429		0
Change	$-x$		$+x$		$+x$
Equilibrium	$0.0286 - x$		$0.0429 + x$		x

$$K_b = \frac{[NH_4^+][OH^-]}{[NH_3]} = \frac{(0.0429 + x)(x)}{(0.0286 - x)} \cong \frac{(0.0429)(x)}{(0.0286)} = 1.8 \times 10^{-5}$$

$$x = [OH^-] = 1.\underline{2}0 \times 10^{-5}\ M$$

$$pOH = -\log [OH^-] = -\log (1.20 \times 10^{-5}) = 4.9\underline{2}0$$

$$pH = 14.00 - pOH = 14.00 - 4.920 = 9.0\underline{7}9 = 9.08$$

Copyright © Cengage Learning. All rights reserved.

■ SOLUTIONS TO GENERAL PROBLEMS

16.95. To solve, assemble a table of starting, change, and equilibrium concentrations. Use HSal to symbolize salicylic acid, and use Sal⁻ for the anion. Begin by converting pH to $[H_3O^+]$:

$$[H_3O^+] = \text{antilog}(-pH) = \text{antilog}(-2.43) = 3.72 \times 10^{-3}\ M$$

Starting M of HSal = $(2.2\ \text{g} \div 138\ \text{g/mol}) \div 1.00\ \text{L} = 0.0159\ M$

Conc. (M)	HSal + H₂O $\rightleftharpoons$	H₃O⁺ +	Sal⁻
Starting	0.0159	0	0
Change	$-x$	$+x$	$+x$
Equilibrium	$0.0159 - x$	x	x

The value of x equals the value of the molarity of the H_3O^+ ion, which is $3.72 \times 10^{-3}\ M$. Substitute into the equilibrium-constant expression to find K_a:

$$K_a = \frac{(x)^2}{(0.0159 - x)} = \frac{(3.72 \times 10^{-3})^2}{(0.0159 - 3.72 \times 10^{-3})} = 1.\underline{1}3 \times 10^{-3} = 1.1 \times 10^{-3}$$

16.97. To solve, assemble a table of starting, change, and equilibrium concentrations. Begin by converting pH to $[H_3O^+]$:

$$[H_3O^+] = \text{antilog}(-pH) = \text{antilog}(-1.73) = 1.86 \times 10^{-2}\ M$$

Starting M of HSO₄⁻ = $0.050\ M$

Conc. (M)	HSO₄⁻ + H₂O $\rightleftharpoons$	H₃O⁺ +	SO₄²⁻
Starting	0.050	0	0
Change	$-x$	$+x$	$+x$
Equilibrium	$0.050 - x$	x	x

The value of x equals the value of the molarity of the H_3O^+ ion, which is $1.86 \times 10^{-2}\ M$. Substitute into the equilibrium-constant expression to find K_{a_2}:

$$K_{a_2} = \frac{(x)^2}{(0.050 - x)} = \frac{(1.86 \times 10^{-2})^2}{(0.050 - 1.86 \times 10^{-2})} = 1.\underline{1}0 \times 10^{-2} = 1.1 \times 10^{-2}$$

16.99. For the base ionization (hydrolysis) of CN⁻ to HCN + OH⁻, the base-ionization constant is

$$K_b = \frac{K_w}{K_a} = \frac{1.0 \times 10^{-14}}{4.9 \times 10^{-10}} = 2.\underline{0}4 \times 10^{-5} = 2.0 \times 10^{-5}$$

For the base ionization (hydrolysis) of CO_3^{2-} to $HCO_3^- + OH^-$, the base-ionization constant is calculated from the ionization constant (K_{a_2}) of HCO_3^-, the conjugate acid of CO_3^{2-}.

$$K_b = \frac{K_w}{K_a} = \frac{1.0 \times 10^{-14}}{4.8 \times 10^{-11}} = 2.\underline{0}8 \times 10^{-4} = 2.1 \times 10^{-4}$$

Because the constant of CO_3^{2-} is larger, it is the stronger base.

Copyright © Cengage Learning. All rights reserved.

16.101. Assume Al^{3+} is $Al(H_2O)_6^{3+}$. Assemble the usual table to calculate the $[H_3O^+]$ and pH. Use the usual equilibrium-constant expression.

Conc. (M)	$Al(H_2O)_6^{3+} + H_2O$	$\rightleftharpoons$	H_3O^+	$+$	$Al(H_2O)_5(OH)^{2+}$
Starting	0.15		0		0
Change	$-x$		$+x$		$+x$
Equilibrium	$0.15 - x$		x		x

$$K_a = \frac{[Al(H_2O)_5(OH)^{2+}][H_3O^+]}{[Al(H_2O)_6^{3+}]} = \frac{(x)^2}{(0.15 - x)} \cong \frac{(x)^2}{(0.15)} = 1.4 \times 10^{-5}$$

$$x = [H_3O^+] = 1.\underline{4}49 \times 10^{-3}\ M$$

$$pH = -\log [H_3O^+] = -\log (1.449 \times 10^{-3}) = 2.8\underline{3}8 = 2.84$$

16.103. Calculate the concentrations of the tartaric acid (H_2Tar) and the hydrogen tartrate ion ($HTar^-$).

$$(11.0\ g\ H_2Tar \div 150.1\ g/mol) \div 1.00\ L = 0.07328\ M\ H_2Tar$$

$$(20.0\ g\ KHTar^- \div 188.2\ g/mol) \div 1.00\ L = 0.1063\ M\ [HTar^-]$$

Conc. (M)	$H_2Tar + H_2O$	$\rightleftharpoons$	H_3O^+	$+$	$HTar^-$
Starting	0.07328		0		0.1063
Change	$-x$		$+x$		$+x$
Equilibrium	$0.07328 - x$		x		$0.1063 + x$

Ignoring x compared to 0.07328 and 0.1063 and substituting into the K_{a_1} expression give

$$K_{a_1} = \frac{[H_3O^+][HTar^-]}{[H_2Tar]} = \frac{(0.1063 + x)(x)}{(0.07328 - x)} \cong \frac{(0.1063)(x)}{(0.07328)} = 1.0 \times 10^{-3}$$

$$x = [H_3O^+] = 6.\underline{8}9 \times 10^{-4}\ M$$

$$pH = -\log [H_3O^+] = -\log (6.89 \times 10^{-4}) = 3.1\underline{6}1 = 3.16$$

16.105. Use the Henderson-Hasselbalch equation, where $[H_2CO_3]$ = the buffer acid, $[HCO_3^-]$ = the buffer base, and K_{a_1} of carbonic acid is the ionization constant.

$$pH = -\log K_a + \log \frac{[HCO_3^-]}{[H_2CO_3]} = 7.40$$

$$7.40 = -\log (4.3 \times 10^{-7}) + \log \frac{[HCO_3^-]}{[H_2CO_3]}$$

$$\log \frac{[HCO_3^-]}{[H_2CO_3]} = 7.40 - 6.366 = 1.0\underline{3}4$$

$$\frac{[HCO_3^-]}{[H_2CO_3]} = \frac{10.81}{1} = \frac{11}{1}$$

Copyright © Cengage Learning. All rights reserved.

16.107. All the OH^- (from the NaOH) reacts with the H_3O^+ from HCl. Calculate the stoichiometric amounts of OH^- and H_3O^+, and subtract the moles of OH^- from the moles of H_3O^+. Next, divide the remaining H_3O^+ by the total volume of 0.456 L + 0.285 L, or 0.741 L, to find the $[H_3O^+]$. Then calculate the pH.

$$mol\ H_3O^+ = (0.10\ mol\ HCl/L)\ x\ 0.456\ L\ HCl = 0.0456\ mol\ H_3O^+$$

$$mol\ OH^- = (0.15\ mol\ NaOH/L)\ x\ 0.285\ L\ NaOH = 0.0428\ mol\ OH^-$$

$$mol\ H_3O^+\ left = (0.0456 - 0.0428)\ mol\ H_3O^+ = 0.0028\ mol\ H_3O^+$$

$$[H_3O^+] = 0.0028\ mol\ H_3O^+ \div 0.741\ L\ total\ volume = 0.0038\ M$$

$$pH = -\log[H_3O^+] = -\log(0.0038) = 2.42 = 2.4$$

16.109. Use BzN to symbolize benzylamine and $BzNH^+$ to symbolize the benzylammonium cation. At the equivalence point, equal molar amounts of BzN and HCl react to form a solution of BzNHCl. Start by calculating the moles of BzN. Use this number to calculate the volume of HCl needed to neutralize all the BzN (and use the moles of BzN as the moles of $BzNH^+$ formed at the equivalence point). Add the volume of HCl to the original 0.025 L to find the total volume of solution.

$$(0.025\ mol\ BzN/L)\ x\ 0.065\ L = 0.00162\ mol\ BzN$$

$$Volume\ HCl = 0.00162\ mol\ HCl \div (0.050\ mol\ HCl/L) = 0.0324\ L$$

$$Total\ volume = 0.025\ L + 0.0324\ L = 0.0574\ L$$

$$[BzNH^+] = (0.00162\ mol\ BzNH^+\ from\ BzN) \div 0.0574\ L = 0.0282\ M$$

Because the $BzNH^+$ hydrolyzes to H_3O^+ and BzN, use this to calculate the $[H_3O^+]$. Start by calculating the K_a constant of $BzNH^+$ from the K_b of its conjugate base, BzN. Then assemble the usual table of concentrations, assume x is negligible, and calculate $[H_3O^+]$ and pH.

$$K_a = \frac{K_w}{K_b} = \frac{1.0\ x\ 10^{-14}}{4.7\ x\ 10^{-10}} = 2.13\ x\ 10^{-5}$$

Conc. (M)	$BzNH^+ + H_2O \rightleftharpoons$	H_3O^+ +	BzN
Starting	0.0282	0	0.1056
Change	$-x$	$+x$	$+x$
Equilibrium	$0.0282 - x$	x	$0.1056 + x$

Substitute into the equilibrium-constant equation.

$$K_a = \frac{[H_3O^+][BzN]}{[BzNH^+]} = \frac{(x)^2}{(0.0282 - x)} \cong \frac{(x)^2}{(0.0282)} = 2.13\ x\ 10^{-5}$$

$$x = [H_3O^+] = 7.7502\ x\ 10^{-4}\ M$$

$$pH = -\log[H_3O^+] = -\log(7.7502\ x\ 10^{-4}) = 3.1106 = 3.11$$

Copyright © Cengage Learning. All rights reserved.

16.111.

a. $[H_3O^+] \cong 0.100 \ M$

b.   The 0.100 M H_2SO_4 ionizes to 0.100 M H_3O^+ and 0.100 M HSO_4^-. Assemble the usual table, and substitute into the K_{a_2} equilibrium-constant expression for H_2SO_4. Solve the resulting quadratic equation.

Conc. (M)	$HSO_4^- + H_2O \rightleftharpoons$		H_3O^+	$+$	SO_4^{2-}
Starting	0.100		0.100		0
Change	$-x$		$+x$		$+x$
Equilibrium	$0.100 - x$		$0.100 + x$		0

$$x^2 + 0.111 \ x - (1.10 \times 10^{-3}) = 0$$

$$x = \frac{-0.111 \pm \sqrt{(0.111)^2 + 4(1.10 \times 10^{-3})}}{2}$$

$$x = \frac{-0.111 \pm 0.1293}{2}$$

$$x = 9.\underline{1}54 \times 10^{-3} \ M$$

$$[H_3O^+] = 0.100 + x = 0.10\underline{0} + 0.009\underline{1}54 = 0.1\underline{0}9 = 0.11 \ M$$

16.113.

a.   From the pH, calculate the H_3O^+ ion concentration:

$$[H_3O^+] = 10^{-pH} = 10^{-5.82} = 1.\underline{5}1 \times 10^{-6} \ M$$

Use the table approach, giving the starting, change, and equilibrium concentrations.

Conc. (M)	$CH_3NH_3^+ + H_2O \rightleftharpoons$		CH_3NH_2	$+$	H_3O^+
Starting	0.10		0		0
Change	$-x$		$+x$		$+x$
Equilibrium	$0.10 - x$		x		0

From the hydronium-ion concentration, $x = 1.51 \times 10^{-6}$. Substituting into the equilibrium-constant expression gives

$$K_a = \frac{[CH_3NH_2][H_3O^+]}{[CH_3NH_3^+]} = \frac{(x)^2}{(0.10 - x)} \cong \frac{(1.51 \times 10^{-6})^2}{(0.10)} = 2.\underline{2}8 \times 10^{-11}$$

$$= 2.3 \times 10^{-11}$$

b.   Now, use K_w to calculate the value of K_b:

$$K_b = \frac{K_w}{K_a} = \frac{1.0 \times 10^{-14}}{2.28 \times 10^{-11}} = 4.\underline{3}8 \times 10^{-4} = 4.4 \times 10^{-4}$$

Copyright © Cengage Learning. All rights reserved.

c. The equilibrium concentration of $CH_3NH_3^+$ is approximately 0.450 mol/1.00 L = 0.450 *M*. Use $[CH_3NH_2] \cong 0.250$ *M*. For K_a, we get

$$K_a = \frac{[CH_3NH_2][H_3O^+]}{[CH_3NH_3^+]} \cong \frac{(0.250)[H_3O^+]}{(0.450)} = 2.2\underline{8} \times 10^{-11}$$

Solving for $[H_3O^+]$ gives

$$[H_3O^+] \cong \frac{(2.28 \times 10^{-11})(0.450)}{(0.250)} = 4.\underline{1}0 \times 10^{-11} \ M$$

Thus, the pH is

$$pH = -\log(4.10 \times 10^{-11}) = 10.3\underline{8}7 = 10.39$$

16.115.

a. True. Weak acids have small K_a values, so most of the solute is present as undissociated molecules.

b. True. Weak acids have small K_a values, so most of the solute is present as the molecule.

c. False. The hydroxide concentration equals the hydronium concentration only in neutral solutions.

d. False. If HA were a strong acid, the pH would be equal to 2.

e. False. The H_3O^+ would be 0.010 *M* if HA were a strong acid.

f. True. For every HA molecule that dissociates, one H_3O^+ is generated along with one A^-.

16.117.

a. At the equivalence point, moles of acid equal moles of base. Thus,

$$\text{Moles of acid} = 0.115 \text{ mol/L} \times 0.03383 \text{ L} = 3.8\underline{9}0 \times 10^{-3}$$

The molar mass is

$$\text{Molar mass} = \frac{0.288 \text{ g}}{3.890 \times 10^{-3} \text{ mol}} = 74.\underline{0}4 = 74.0 \text{ g/mol}$$

b. At the 50% titration point, pH = pK_a. Since the pH measurement wasn't made, it is necessary to obtain an $[A^-]/[HA]$ ratio. The ratio can be in terms of moles, percent, mL, or *M* because the units end up canceling out. First, use the pH to obtain the H_3O^+ ion concentration. Express the other concentrations in milliliters for convenience.

$$[H_3O^+] = 10^{-4.92} = 1.\underline{2}0 \times 10^{-5} \ M$$

$$HA_0 \cong 33.83 \text{ mL}$$

$$[HA] \cong 33.83 - 17.54 = 16.29 \text{ mL}$$

$$[A^-] \cong [OH^-] = 17.54 \text{ mL}$$

$$K_a = [H_3O^+] \times \frac{[A^-]}{[HA]} = 1.20 \times 10^{-5} \ M \times \frac{17.54 \text{ mL}}{16.29 \text{ mL}} = 1.\underline{2}9 \times 10^{-5} = 1.3 \times 10^{-5}$$

Copyright © Cengage Learning. All rights reserved.

16.119.

a.   Initial pH: Use the table approach, and give the starting, change, and equilibrium concentrations.

Conc. (M)	$NH_3 + H_2O$	$\rightleftharpoons$	NH_4^+	+	OH^-
Starting	0.10		0		0
Change	$-x$		$+x$		$+x$
Equilibrium	$0.10 - x$		x		0

Substituting into the equilibrium-constant expression gives

$$K_b = \frac{[NH_4^+][OH^-]}{[OH^-]} = \frac{(x)^2}{(0.10 - x)} \cong \frac{(x)^2}{(0.10)} = 1.8 \times 10^{-5}$$

Rearranging and solving for x give

$$x = [OH^-] = \sqrt{(0.10)(1.8 \times 10^{-5})} = 1.\underline{3}4 \times 10^{-3} \, M$$

$$pOH = -\log(1.34 \times 10^{-3}) = 2.8\underline{7}3$$

$$pH = 14 - pOH = 14 - 2.873 = 11.1\underline{2}7 = 11.13$$

30% titration point: Express the concentrations as percents for convenience.

$$[NH_3] \approx 70\% \text{ and } [NH_4^+] \approx 30\%$$

Plug into the equilibrium-constant expression.

$$K_b = \frac{[NH_4^+][OH^-]}{[NH_3]} = \frac{(30\%)(x)}{(70\%)} = 1.8 \times 10^{-5}$$

Solving for x gives

$$x = [OH^-] = 1.8 \times 10^{-5} \times \frac{70\%}{30\%} = 4.\underline{2}0 \times 10^{-5} \, M$$

$$pOH = -\log(4.20 \times 10^{-5}) = 4.3\underline{7}7$$

$$pH = 14 - pOH = 14 - 4.377 = 9.6\underline{2}3 = 9.62$$

50% titration point:

$$[NH_4^+] = [NH_3]$$

$$K_b = [OH^-] = 1.8 \times 10^{-5} \, M$$

$$pOH = -\log(1.8 \times 10^{-5}) = 4.7\underline{4}4$$

$$pH = 14 - pOH = 14 - 4.744 = 9.2\underline{5}6 = 9.26$$

100% titration point:

The NH_4Cl that is produced has undergone a twofold dilution.

$$[NH_4^+] = 0.05\underline{0}0 \, M$$

Copyright © Cengage Learning. All rights reserved.

Use the table approach, and give the starting, change, and equilibrium concentrations.

Conc. (M)	$NH_3 + H_2O$	$\rightleftharpoons$	NH_3	$+$	H_3O^+
Starting	0.0500		0		0
Change	$-x$		$+x$		$+x$
Equilibrium	$0.0500 - x$		x		x

Now, use K_w to calculate the value of K_a:

$$K_a = \frac{K_w}{K_b} = \frac{1.0 \times 10^{-14}}{1.8 \times 10^{-5}} = 5.\underline{5}5 \times 10^{-10}$$

Plug into the equilibrium-constant expression.

$$K_a = \frac{[NH_3][H_3O^+]}{[NH_4^+]} = \frac{(x)^2}{(0.0500 - x)} \cong \frac{(x)^2}{(0.0500)} = 5.55 \times 10^{-10}$$

Solving for x gives

$$x = [H_3O^+] = \sqrt{0.0500 \times \frac{1.0 \times 10^{-14}}{1.8 \times 10^{-5}}} = 5.\underline{2}7 \times 10^{-6}\ M$$

$$pH = -\log(5.27 \times 10^{-6}) = 5.2\underline{7}8 = 5.28$$

b.   The solution is acidic because the NH_4^+ ion reacts with water to produce acid. Ammonium chloride is the salt of a weak base and a strong acid.

16.121.

a.   Select the conjugate pair that has a pK_a value closest to a pH of 2.88.

$$pK_a\ (H_2C_2O_4) = 1.25$$
$$pK_a\ (H_3PO_4) = 2.16$$
$$pK_a\ (HCOOH) = 3.77$$

Therefore, the best pair is H_3PO_4 and $H_2PO_4^-$.

b.   Using the Henderson-Hasselbalch equation,

$$pH = pK_a + \log \frac{[A^-]}{[HA]}$$

$$2.88 = 2.16 + \log \frac{[A^-]}{[HA]}$$

$$\log \frac{[A^-]}{[HA]} = 0.72$$

$$\frac{[A^-]}{[HA]} = 10^{0.72} = 5.\underline{2}4$$

Copyright © Cengage Learning. All rights reserved.

Therefore, 5.24 times more conjugate base is needed than acid. Since the starting concentrations of H_3PO_4 (HA) and $H_2PO_4^-$ (A$^-$) are the same, the volume of A$^-$ needed is 5.24 times the volume of HA needed. For 50 mL of buffer, this is

$$50 \text{ mL} = \text{vol HA} + \text{vol A}^- = \text{vol HA} + 5.24 \text{ vol HA} = 6.24 \text{ vol HA}$$

Therefore, the volume of 0.10 M H_3PO_4 required is

$$\text{Volume of } H_3PO_4 = \frac{50 \text{ mL}}{6.24} = \underline{8}.01 \text{ mL} = 8 \text{ mL}$$

The volume of 0.10 M $H_2PO_4^-$ required is

$$50 \text{ mL} - 8.01 \text{ mL} = 4\underline{2}.0 \text{ mL} = 42 \text{ mL}$$

16.123.

a.   At the equivalence point, moles of base equal moles of acid. Therefore,

$$M_{NH_2OH} \times 25.0 \text{ mL} = 0.150 \ M \times 35.8 \text{ mL}$$

$$M_{NH_2OH} = \frac{0.150 \ M \times 35.8 \text{ mL}}{25.0 \text{ mL}} = 0.21\underline{4}8 = 0.215$$

b.   Concentration of NH_3OH^+ at the equivalence point is

$$[NH_3OH^+] = \frac{(25.0 \text{ mL})(0.215 \ M)}{25.0 \text{ mL} + 35.8 \text{ mL}} = 0.088\underline{4}0 \ M$$

$$K_a = \frac{K_w}{K_b} = \frac{1.0 \times 10^{-14}}{1.1 \times 10^{-8}} = 9.\underline{0}9 \times 10^{-7}$$

Use the table approach, and give the starting, change, and equilibrium concentrations.

Conc. (M)	NH_3OH^+ + H_2O	$\rightleftharpoons$	NH_2OH +	H_3O^+
Starting	0.088\underline{4}0		0	0
Change	$-x$		$+x$	$+x$
Equilibrium	0.088\underline{4}0 $- x$		x	x

Substituting into the equilibrium-constant expression gives

$$K_a = \frac{[NH_2OH][H_3O^+]}{[NH_3OH^+]} = \frac{(x)^2}{(0.08840 - x)} \cong \frac{(x)^2}{(0.08840)} = 9.\underline{0}9 \times 10^{-7}$$

Rearranging and solving for x give

$$x = [H_3O^+] = \sqrt{(0.08840)(9.\underline{0}9 \times 10^{-7})} = 2.\underline{8}3 \times 10^{-4} \ M$$

$$pH = -\log(2.\underline{8}4 \times 10^{-4}) = 3.5\underline{4}7 = 3.55$$

c.   You need an indicator to change color around a pH of 3 to 4. Therefore, the appropriate indicator is bromophenol blue. Select an indicator that changes color around the equivalence point.

Copyright © Cengage Learning. All rights reserved.

16.125.

a. $H_3O^+(aq) + NH_3(aq) \rightarrow NH_4^+(aq) + H_2O(l)$

b. $NH_4^+(aq) + OH^-(aq) \rightarrow NH_3(aq) + H_2O(l)$

c. Initial:

$$\text{mol NH}_3 = 1.0 \text{ mol/L} \times 0.100 \text{ L} = 0.1\underline{0}0 = 0.10 \text{ mol}$$

$$\text{mol NH}_4^+ = 0.50 \text{ mol/L} \times 0.100 \text{ L} \times \frac{2 \text{ mol NH}_4^+}{1 \text{ mol (NH}_4)_2\text{SO}_4} = 0.1\underline{0}0 = 0.10 \text{ mol}$$

After addition of HCl: The HCl is completely consumed by producing 0.01$\underline{0}$0 mol of NH_4^+. The amount of NH_3 is decreased by 0.01$\underline{0}$0 mol.

$$\text{mol HCl added} = 1.00 \text{ mol/L} \times 0.0100 \text{ L} = 0.01000 \text{ mol}$$

$$\text{mol NH}_3 = 0.1\underline{0}0 - 0.01000 = 0.09\underline{0}0 = 0.090 \text{ mol}$$

$$\text{mol NH}_4^+ = 0.1\underline{0}0 + 0.01000 = 0.1\underline{1}0 = 0.11 \text{ mol}$$

The reaction is

$$NH_3 + H_2O \rightleftharpoons NH_4^+ + OH^-$$

Substituting into the equilibrium-constant expression gives

$$K_b = \frac{[NH_4^+][OH^-]}{[NH_3]} = \frac{(0.110)[OH^-]}{(0.090)} = 1.8 \times 10^{-5}$$

Rearranging and solving for $[OH^-]$ give

$$[OH^-] = 1.8 \times 10^{-5} \times \frac{0.090}{0.110} = \underline{1}.47 \times 10^{-5} \, M$$

$$pOH = -\log(\underline{1}.47 \times 10^{-5}) = 4.\underline{8}3$$

$$pH = 14 - pOH = 14 - 4.\underline{8}3 = 9.\underline{1}7 = 9.2$$

d. This is a buffer system, so the ratio of NH_4^+/NH_3 has not changed very much.

16.127.

a. From the pH, $[H_3O^+] = 10^{-7.44} = 3.\underline{6}3 \times 10^{-8} \, M$. The reaction is

$$H_2PO_4^-(aq) + H_2O \rightleftharpoons H_3O^+(aq) + HPO_4^{2-}(aq) \quad K_{a_2} = 6.2 \times 10^{-8}$$

$$K_{a_2} = \frac{[HPO_4^{2-}][H_3O^+]}{[H_2PO_4^-]}$$

Rearranging gives

$$\frac{[H_2PO_4^-]}{[HPO_4^{2-}]} = \frac{[H_3O^+]}{K_{a_2}} = \frac{3.63 \times 10^{-8}}{6.2 \times 10^{-8}} = \frac{0.5\underline{8}55}{1} = 0.59 \text{ to } 1$$

Copyright © Cengage Learning. All rights reserved.

Or, using the Henderson-Hasselbalch equation,

$$pH = pK_a + \log \frac{[base]}{[acid]}$$

$$7.44 = 7.21 + \log \frac{[base]}{[acid]}$$

$$\log \frac{[base]}{[acid]} = 0.23$$

$$\frac{[base]}{[acid]} = 10^{0.23} = 1.\underline{7}1$$

You must invert each side. The result is

$$\frac{[acid]}{[base]} = \frac{1}{1.71} = \frac{0.5\underline{8}57}{1} = 0.59 \text{ to } 1$$

b. $[H_3O^+] = K_{a_2} = \dfrac{[H_2PO_4^-]}{[HPO_4^{2-}]}$

If $HPO_4^{2-} = 1.00$ mol, then when 25% of it is converted into $H_2PO_4^-$, 0.75 mol remains, and $H_2PO_4^-$ becomes $0.5\underline{8}6 + 0.25 = 0.8\underline{3}6$ mol. Therefore,

$$[H_3O^+] = 6.2 \times 10^{-8} \times \frac{0.836}{0.75} = 6.\underline{9}1 \times 10^{-8}$$

$$pH = -\log(6.\underline{9}1 \times 10^{-8}) = 7.1\underline{6}1 = 7.16$$

c.   Assume $H_2PO_4^- = 0.5\underline{8}6$ mol. Then, the numbers of moles of $H_2PO_4^-$ remaining is

$$0.5\underline{8}6 - (0.15 \times 0.5\underline{8}6) = 0.85 \times 0.5\underline{8}6 = 0.4\underline{9}8 \text{ mol left}$$

The moles of $HPO_4^{2-} = 1.00 + (0.15 \times 0.5\underline{8}6) = 1.0\underline{8}8$ mol

$$[H_3O^+] = 6.2 \times 10^{-8} \times \frac{0.498}{1.088} = 2.\underline{8}4 \times 10^{-8} \ M$$

$$pH = -\log(2.84 \times 10^{-8}) = 7.5\underline{4}7 = 7.55$$

16.129.

a. $H_2A + H_2O \rightleftharpoons H_3O^+ + HA \quad K_{a_1}$

      $HA^- + H_2O \rightleftharpoons H_3O^+ + A^{2-} \quad K_{a_2}$

      $H_2A + 2\,H_2O \rightleftharpoons 2\,H_3O^+ + A^{2-}, \quad K = K_{a_1} \times K_{a_2}$

b. $H_2A \gg H_3O^+ = HA^- \gg A^{2-}$

Copyright © Cengage Learning. All rights reserved.

c.

$$H_2A \ + \ H_2O \ \rightleftharpoons \ H_3O^+ \ + \ HA^- \qquad K_{a_1} = 1.0 \times 10^{-3}$$

$0.0250 - x \qquad\qquad\qquad x \qquad\quad x$

$$K_{a_1} = \frac{[HA^-][H_3O^+]}{[H_2A]} = \frac{(x)^2}{(0.0250 - x)} = 1.0 \times 10^{-3}$$

Rearranging into a quadratic equation and solving for x give

$$x^2 + (1.0 \times 10^{-3})x + (-2.50 \times 10^{-5}) = 0$$

$$x = \frac{-(1.0 \times 10^{-3}) \pm \sqrt{(1.0 \times 10^{-3})^2 - (4)(1)(-2.50 \times 10^{-5})}}{2}$$

$x = [H_3O^+] = [HA^-] = 4.\underline{5}2 \times 10^{-3} = 4.5 \times 10^{-3} \ M$

$pH = -\log(4.\underline{5}2 \times 10^{-3}) = 2.3\underline{4}4 = 2.34$

$[H_2A] = 0.0250 - x = 0.0250 - 4.52 \times 10^{-3} = 0.020\underline{4}8 = 0.0205 \ M$

d.

$$HA^- \ + \ H_2O \ \rightleftharpoons \ H_3O^+ \ + \ A^{2-} \qquad Ka_2 = 4.6 \times 10^{-5}$$

$4.52 \times 10^{-3} + y \qquad\qquad 4.52 \times 10^{-3} + y \quad y$

Assume y is small compared to $4.52 \times 10^{-3} \ M$. Substitute into the rearranged equilibrium-constant equation to get

$$[A^{2-}] = \frac{[HA^-]K_{a_2}}{[H_3O^+]} = \frac{(4.52 \times 10^{-3})(4.6 \times 10^{-5})}{(4.52 \times 10^{-3})} = 4.6 \times 10^{-5} \ M$$

16.131.

a. From the pH, $[H_3O^+] = 10^{-4.45} = 3.\underline{5}5 \times 10^{-5} \ M$. The $NaCH_3COO$ is generated by the acid-base reaction, resulting in the formation of a buffer solution. The reaction is

$$CH_3COOH \ + \ H_2O \ \rightleftharpoons \ H_3O^+ \ + \ CH_3COO^- \qquad K_a = 1.7 \times 10^{-5}$$

$0.15 - x \qquad\qquad\qquad x \qquad\qquad x$

$$K_a = \frac{[H_3O^+][CH_3COO^-]}{[CH_3COOH]}$$

Rearranging gives

$$\frac{[CH_3COO^-]}{[CH_3COOH]} = \frac{K_a}{[H_3O^+]}$$

$$\frac{x}{0.15 - x} = \frac{1.7 \times 10^{-5}}{3.55 \times 10^{-5}}$$

Solving for x gives $x = 0.04\underline{8}6$ mol. Therefore, the molar concentration is

$[CH_3COO^-] = 0.04\underline{8}6$ mol/0.375 L $= 0.1\underline{2}96 = 0.13 \ M$

Copyright © Cengage Learning. All rights reserved.

b.   mol OH$^-$ = mol CH$_3$COO$^-$

0.04$\underline{8}$6 mol = 0.25 M x V_{NaOH}

V_{NaOH} = 0.0486 mol/0.25 M = 0.1$\underline{9}$4 = 0.19 L (1.9 x 10^2 mL)

c.   The volume of the original acid is V = 0.375 L − 0.1$\underline{9}$4 L = 0.1$\underline{8}$1 L. Therefore, the concentration of the original acid is

[CH$_3$COOH] = 0.15 mol/0.181 L = 0.8$\underline{2}$9 = 0.83 M

■ SOLUTIONS TO CUMULATIVE-SKILLS PROBLEMS

16.145. Use the pH to calculate [H$_3$O$^+$], and then use the K_a of 1.7 x 10^{-5} and the K_a expression to calculate the molarity of acetic acid (HAc), assuming ionization is negligible. Convert molarity to mass percentage using the formula mass of 60.05 g/mol of HAc.

[H$_3$O$^+$] = antilog (−2.45) = 3.$\underline{5}$48 x 10^{-3} M

Write the equilibrium-constant expression in terms of chemical symbols, and then substitute the x and the (0.003548 M) terms into the expression:

$$K_a = \frac{[H_3O^+][Ac^-]}{[HAc]} \cong \frac{(0.003548)^2}{(x)}$$

Solve the equation for x, assuming 0.003548 is much smaller than x.

x = (0.003548)^2 ÷ (1.7 x 10^{-5}) $\cong$ [HAc] $\cong$ 0.7$\underline{4}$04 M

(0.7404 mol HAc/L) x (60.05 g/mol) x (1 L/1090 g)(100%) = 4.$\underline{0}$78 = 4.1% HAc

16.147. Find [H$_3$O$^+$] and [C$_2$H$_3$O$_2$$^-$] by solving for the approximate [H$_3$O$^+$], noting that x is much smaller than the starting 0.92 M of acetic acid. The usual table is used but is not shown; only the final setup for [H$_3$O$^+$] is shown. Use K_f = 1.858 °C/m for the constant for water.

[H$_3$O$^+$] = [C$_2$H$_3$O$_2$$^-$] = (1.7 x 10^{-5} x 0.92)$^{1/2}$ = 0.003$\underline{9}$54 M

Total molarity of acid + ions = 0.92 + 0.003954 = 0.9$\underline{2}$39

The mass of water in 1 L of solution is

1000 mL x 1.008 g/mL − 0.92 mol x 60.05 g/mol = 9$\underline{5}$2.8 g = 0.9$\underline{5}$28 kg

Molality = m = 0.9239 mol ÷ (1.000 L x 0.9528 kg H$_2$O/L) = 0.9695 m

Freezing point = −ΔT_f = −$K_f c_m$ = (−1.858 °C/m) x 0.9695 m = −1.801 = −1.8°C

Copyright © Cengage Learning. All rights reserved.

16.149. The $[H_3O^+]$ = $-$antilog (-4.35) = $4.\underline{4}6 \times 10^{-5}$ M. Note that 0.465 L of 0.0941 M NaOH will produce 0.043756 mol of acetate, Ac^-, ion. Rearranging the K_a expression for acetic acid (HAc) and Ac^- and canceling the volume in the mol/L of each, you obtain

$$\frac{[HAc]}{[Ac^-]} = \frac{[H^+]}{K_a} = \frac{4.46 \times 10^{-5}}{1.7 \times 10^{-5}} = \frac{2.63}{1.00} \cong \frac{x \text{ mol HAc}}{0.043756 \text{ mol } Ac^-}$$

x = $0.1\underline{1}49$ mol HAc

Total moles of HAc added = $0.1149 + 0.043756$ = 0.1587 mol HAc

mol/L of pure HAc = 1049 g HAc/L x (1 mol HAc/60.05 g) = $17.4\underline{6}7$ mol/L

L of pure HAc needed = 0.1587 mol HAc x (L/17.467 mol) = $0.009\underline{0}8$ L (9.1 mL)

Copyright © Cengage Learning. All rights reserved.

CHAPTER 17

Solubility and Complex-Ion Equilibria

■ **SOLUTIONS TO EXERCISES**

Note on significant figures If the final answer to a solution needs to be rounded off, it is given first with one nonsignificant figure, and the last significant figure is underlined. The final answer is then rounded to the correct number of significant figures. In multistep problems, intermediate answers are given with at least one nonsignificant figure; however, only the final answer has been rounded off.

17.1.

a. $BaSO_4(s) \rightleftharpoons Ba^{2+}(aq) + SO_4^{2-}(aq)$ $K_{sp} = [Ba^{2+}][SO_4^{2-}]$

b. $Fe(OH)_3(s) \rightleftharpoons Fe^{3+}(aq) + 3OH^-(aq)$ $K_{sp} = [Fe^{3+}][OH^-]^3$

c. $Ca_3(PO_4)_2(s) \rightleftharpoons 3Ca^{2+}(aq) + 2PO_4^{3-}(aq)$ $K_{sp} = [Ca^{2+}]^3[PO_4^{3-}]^2$

17.2. Calculate the molar solubility. Then assemble the usual concentration table, and substitute the equilibrium concentrations from it into the equilibrium-constant expression. (Because no concentrations can be given for solid AgCl, dashes are written. In later problems, similar spaces will be left blank.)

$$\frac{1.9 \times 10^{-3} \text{ g}}{1 \text{ L}} \times \frac{1 \text{ mol}}{143 \text{ g}} = 1.\underline{33} \times 10^{-5} M$$

Set up the table as usual.

Conc. (M)	AgCl(s)	$\rightleftharpoons$	Ag^+	$+$	Cl^-
Starting	—		0		0
Change	—		$+1.33 \times 10^{-5}$		$+1.33 \times 10^{-5}$
Equilibrium	—		1.33×10^{-5}		1.33×10^{-5}

$$K_{sp} = [Ag^+][Cl^-] = (1.33 \times 10^{-5})(1.33 \times 10^{-5}) = 1.\underline{7}68 \times 10^{-10} = 1.8 \times 10^{-10}$$

Copyright © Houghton Mifflin Company. All rights reserved.

17.3. Calculate the molar solubility. Then assemble the usual concentration table, and substitute from it into the equilibrium-constant expression. (Because no concentrations can be given for solid $Pb_3(AsO_4)_2$, spaces are left blank.)

$$\frac{3.0 \times 10^{-5}\ g}{1\ L} \times \frac{1\ mol}{899\ g} = 3.\underline{3}4 \times 10^{-8}\ M$$

Conc. (M)	$Pb_3(AsO_4)_2(s)$	$\rightleftharpoons$	$3Pb^{2+}$	$+$	$2AsO_4^{3-}$
Starting			0		0
Change			$+3(3.34 \times 10^{-8})$		$+2(3.34 \times 10^{-8})$
Equilibrium			$3(3.34 \times 10^{-8})$		$2(3.34 \times 10^{-8})$

$$K_{sp} = [Pb^{2+}]^3[AsO_4^{3-}]^2 = [3 \times (3.34 \times 10^{-8})]^3(2 \times 3.34 \times 10^{-8})^2 = 4.\underline{4}89 \times 10^{-36}$$
$$= 4.5 \times 10^{-36}$$

17.4. Assemble the usual concentration table. Let x equal the molar solubility of $CaSO_4$. When x mol $CaSO_4$ dissolves in 1 L of solution, x mol Ca^{2+} and x mol SO_4^{2-} form.

Conc. (M)	$CaSO_4(s)$	$\rightleftharpoons$	Ca^{2+}	$+$	SO_4^{2-}
Starting			0		0
Change			$+x$		$+x$
Equilibrium			x		x

Substitute the equilibrium concentrations into the equilibrium-constant expression, and solve for x. Then convert to g $CaSO_4$ per liter.

$$[Ca^{2+}][SO_4^{2-}] = K_{sp}$$
$$(x)(x) = x^2 = 2.4 \times 10^{-5}$$
$$x = \sqrt{(2.4 \times 10^{-5})} = 4.\underline{8}9 \times 10^{-3}\ M$$
$$\frac{4.89 \times 10^{-3}\ mol}{L} \times \frac{136\ g}{1\ mol} = 0.6\underline{6}64 = 0.67\ g/L$$

17.5.

a. Let x equal the molar solubility of BaF_2. Assemble the usual concentration table, and substitute from the table into the equilibrium-constant expression.

Conc. (M)	$BaF_2(s)$	$\rightleftharpoons$	Ba^{2+}	$+$	$2F^-$
Starting			0		0
Change			$+x$		$+2x$
Equilibrium			x		$2x$

$$[Ba^{2+}][F^-]^2 = K_{sp}$$
$$(x)(2x)^2 = 4x^3 = 1.0 \times 10^{-6}$$
$$x = \sqrt[3]{\frac{1.0 \times 10^{-6}}{4}} = 6.\underline{2}99 \times 10^{-3} = 6.3 \times 10^{-3}\ M$$

Copyright © Houghton Mifflin Company. All rights reserved.

b. At the start, before any BaF_2 dissolves, the solution contains 0.15 M F^-. At equilibrium, x mol of solid BaF_2 dissolves to yield x mol Ba^{2+} and $2x$ mol F^-. Assemble the usual concentration table, and substitute the equilibrium concentrations into the equilibrium-constant expression. As an approximation, assume x is negligible compared to 0.15 M F^-.

Conc. (M)	$BaF_2(s)$ ⇌	Ba^{2+}	+	$2F^-$
Starting		0		0.15
Change		$+x$		$+2x$
Equilibrium		x		$0.15 + 2x$

$$[Ba^{2+}][F^-]^2 = K_{sp}$$

$$(x)(0.15 + 2x)^2 \cong (x)(0.15)^2 \cong 1.0 \times 10^{-6}$$

$$x \cong \frac{1.0 \times 10^{-6}}{(0.15)^2} = 4.\underline{4}44 \times 10^{-5} = 4.4 \times 10^{-5}\ M$$

Note that adding $2x$ to 0.15 M will not change it (to two significant figures), so $2x$ is negligible compared to 0.15 M. The solubility of 4.4×10^{-5} M in 0.15 M NaF is lower than the solubility of 6.3×10^{-3} M in pure water.

17.6. Calculate the ion product, Q_c, after evaporation, assuming no precipitation has occurred. Compare it with the K_{sp}.

$$Q_c = [Ca^{2+}][SO_4^{2-}]$$

$$Q_c = (2 \times 0.0052)(2 \times 0.0041) = 8.528 \times 10^{-5}$$

Since $Q_c > K_{sp}$ (2.4×10^{-5}), precipitation occurs.

17.7. Calculate the concentrations of Pb^{2+} and SO_4^{2-}, assuming no precipitation. Use a total volume of 0.456 L + 0.255 L, or 0.711 L.

$$[Pb^{2+}] = \frac{\dfrac{0.00016\ \text{mol}}{\text{L}} \times 0.255\ \text{L}}{0.711\ \text{L}} = 5.\underline{7}4 \times 10^{-5}\ M$$

$$[SO_4^{2-}] = \frac{\dfrac{0.00023\ \text{mol}}{\text{L}} \times 0.456\ \text{L}}{0.711\ \text{L}} = 1.\underline{4}8 \times 10^{-4}\ M$$

Calculate the ion product, and compare it to K_{sp}.

$$Q_c = [Pb^{2+}][SO_4^{2-}] = (5.74 \times 10^{-5})(1.48 \times 10^{-4}) = 8.\underline{4}9 \times 10^{-9}$$

Because Q_c is less than the K_{sp} of 1.7×10^{-8}, no precipitation occurs, and the solution is unsaturated.

Copyright © Houghton Mifflin Company. All rights reserved.

17.8. The solubility of AgCN would increase as the pH decreases, because the increasing concentration of H_3O^+ would react with the CN^- to form the weakly ionized acid HCN. As CN^- is removed, more AgCN dissolves to replace the cyanide:

$$AgCN(s) \rightleftharpoons Ag^+(aq) + CN^-(aq) \quad [+ H_3O^+ \rightarrow HCN + H_2O]$$

In the case of AgCl, the chloride ion is the conjugate base of a strong acid and would, therefore, not be affected by any amount of hydrogen ion.

17.9. Because $K_f = 4.8 \times 10^{12}$ and because the starting concentration of NH_3 is much larger than that of the Cu^{2+} ion, you can make a rough assumption that most of the copper(II) is converted to $Cu(NH_3)_4^{2+}$ ion. This ion then dissociates slightly to give a small concentration of Cu^{2+} and additional NH_3. The amount of NH_3 remaining at the start after reacting with 0.015 M Cu^{2+} is

$$[0.100\ M - (4 \times 0.015\ M)] = 0.040\ M \text{ starting } NH_3$$

Assemble the usual concentration table using this starting concentration for NH_3 and assuming the starting concentration of Cu^{2+} is zero.

Conc. (M)	$Cu(NH_3)_4^{2+}$ $\rightleftharpoons$	Cu^{2+} +	$4NH_3$
Starting	0.015	0	0.040
Change	$-x$	$+x$	$+4x$
Equilibrium	$0.015 - x$	$+x$	$0.040 + 4x$

Even though this reaction is the opposite of the equation for the formation constant, the formation-constant expression can be used. Simply substitute all exact equilibrium concentrations into the formation-constant expression; then simplify the exact equation by assuming x is negligible compared to 0.015 and $4x$ is negligible compared to 0.040.

$$K_f = \frac{[Cu(NH_3)_4^{2+}]}{[Cu^{2+}][NH_3]^4} = \frac{(0.015 - x)}{(x)(0.040 + 4x)^4} \cong \frac{(0.015)}{(x)(0.040)^4} \cong 4.8 \times 10^{12}$$

Rearrange and solve for x:

$$x = [Cu^{2+}] \cong (0.015) \div [(4.8 \times 10^{12})(0.040)^4] \cong 1.22 \times 10^{-9} = 1.2 \times 10^{-9}\ M$$

17.10. Start by calculating the $[Ag^+]$ in equilibrium with the $Ag(CN)_2^-$ formed from Ag^+ and CN^-. Then use the $[Ag^+]$ to decide whether or not AgI will precipitate by calculating the ion product and comparing it with the K_{sp} of 8.3×10^{-17} for AgI. Assume all the 0.0045 M Ag^+ reacts with CN^- to form 0.0045 M $Ag(CN)_2^-$, and calculate the remaining CN^-. Use these as starting concentrations for the usual concentration table.

$$[0.20\ M\ KCN - (2 \times 0.0045\ M)] = 0.191\ M \text{ starting } CN^-$$

Conc. (M)	$Ag(CN)_2^-$ $\rightleftharpoons$	Ag^+ +	$2CN^-$
Starting	0.0045	0	0.191
Change	$-x$	$+x$	$+2x$
Equilibrium	$0.0045 - x$	x	$0.191 + 2x$

Copyright © Houghton Mifflin Company. All rights reserved.

Even though this reaction is the opposite of the equation for the formation constant, the formation-constant expression can be used. Simply substitute all exact equilibrium concentrations into the formation-constant expression; then simplify the exact equation by assuming x is negligible compared to 0.0045 and $2x$ is negligible compared to 0.191.

$$K_f = \frac{[Ag(CN)_2^-]}{[Ag^+][CN^-]^2} = \frac{(0.0045 - x)}{(x)(0.191 + 2x)^2} \cong \frac{(0.0045)}{(x)(0.191)^2} \cong 5.6 \times 10^{18}$$

Rearrange and solve for x:

$$x = [Ag^+] \cong (0.0045) \div [(5.6 \times 10^{18})(0.191)^2] \cong 2.\underline{2}02 \times 10^{-20} \ M$$

Now, calculate the ion product for AgI:

$$Q_c = [Ag^+][I^-] = (2.20 \times 10^{-20})(0.15) = 3.\underline{3}0 \times 10^{-21} = 3.3 \times 10^{-21}$$

Because Q_c is less than the K_{sp} of 8.3×10^{-17}, no precipitate will form, and the solution is unsaturated.

17.11. Obtain the overall equilibrium constant for this reaction from the product of the individual equilibrium constants of the two individual equations whose sum gives this equation:

$AgBr(s)$			$\rightleftharpoons$	$Ag^+(aq) + Br^-(aq)$		$K_{sp} = 5.0 \times 10^{-13}$
$Ag^+(aq)$	$+$	$2S_2O_3^{2-}(aq)$	$\rightleftharpoons$	$Ag(S_2O_3)_2^{3-}(aq)$		$K_f = 2.9 \times 10^{13}$
$AgBr(s)$	$+$	$2S_2O_3^{2-}(aq)$	$\rightleftharpoons$	$Ag(S_2O_3)_2^{3-}(aq) + Br^-(aq)$		$K_c = K_{sp} \times K_f = 14.5$

Assemble the usual table using $1.0 \ M$ as the starting concentration of $S_2O_3^{2-}$ and x as the unknown concentration of $Ag(S_2O_3)_2^{3-}$ formed.

Conc. (M)	$AgBr(s)$	$+$	$2S_2O_3^{2-}$	$\rightleftharpoons$	$Ag(S_2O_3)_2^{3-}$	$+ Br^-$
Starting			1.0		0	0
Change						
Change			$-2x$		$+x$	$+x$
Equilibrium			$1.0 - 2x$		x	x

The equilibrium-constant expression can now be used. Simply substitute all exact equilibrium concentrations into the equilibrium-constant expression. The solution can be obtained without using the quadratic equation.

$$K_c = \frac{[Ag(S_2O_3)_2^{3-}][Br^-]}{[S_2O_3^{2-}]^2} = \frac{(x)^2}{(1.0 - 2x)^2} = 14.5$$

Take the square root of both sides of the two right-hand terms, and solve for x:

$$\frac{x}{(1.0 - 2x)} = 3.\underline{8}08$$

$$x = 3.808 \ (1.0 - 2x)$$

$$7.62x + x = 3.808$$

$$x = 0.4\underline{4}17 = 0.44 \ M \quad \text{(molar solubility of AgBr in 1.0 } M \text{ Na}_2\text{S}_2\text{O}_3)$$

Copyright © Houghton Mifflin Company. All rights reserved.

■ ANSWERS TO SELF-ASSESSMENT AND REVIEW QUESTIONS

17.1. The solubility equation is $Ni(OH)_2(s) \rightleftharpoons Ni^{2+}(aq) + 2OH^-(aq)$. If the molar solubility of $Ni(OH)_2 = x$ molar, the concentrations of the ions in the solution must be x M Ni^{2+} and $2x$ M OH^-. Substituting into the equilibrium-constant expression gives

$$K_{sp} = [Ni^{2+}][OH^-]^2 = (x)(2x)^2 = 4x^3$$

17.2. Calcium sulfate is less soluble in a solution containing sodium sulfate because the increase in sulfate from the sodium sulfate causes the equilibrium composition in the equation below to shift to the left:

$$CaSO_4(s) \rightleftharpoons Ca^{2+}(aq) + SO_4^{2-}(aq)$$

The result is a decrease in the calcium ion concentration and a decrease in the solubility of calcium sulfate.

17.3. Substitute the 0.10 M concentration of chloride into the solubility product expression and solve for $[Ag^+]$:

$$[Ag^+] = \frac{K_{sp}}{[Cl^-]} = \frac{1.8 \times 10^{-10}}{0.10} = 1.\underline{8}0 \times 10^{-9} = 1.8 \times 10^{-9}\ M$$

17.4. In order to predict whether or not PbI_2 will precipitate when lead nitrate and potassium iodide are mixed, the concentrations of Pb^{2+} and I^- after mixing would have to be calculated first (if the concentrations are not known or are not given). Then, the value of Q_c, the ion product, would have to be calculated for PbI_2. Finally, Q_c would have to be compared with the value of K_{sp}. If $Q_c > K_{sp}$, then a precipitate will form at equilibrium. If $Q_c \leq K_{sp}$, no precipitate will form.

17.5. Barium fluoride, normally insoluble in water, dissolves in dilute hydrochloric acid because the fluoride ion, once it forms, reacts with the hydronium ion to form weakly ionized HF:

$$BaF_2(s) \rightleftharpoons Ba^{2+}(aq) + 2F^-(aq)\ [+ 2H_3O^+ \rightarrow 2HF + 2H_2O]$$

17.6. Metal ions such as Pb^{2+} and Zn^{2+} are separated by controlling the $[S^{2-}]$ in a solution of saturated H_2S by means of adjusting the pH correctly. Because the K_{sp} of 2.5×10^{-27} for PbS is smaller than the K_{sp} of 1.1×10^{-21} for ZnS, the pH can be adjusted to make the $[S^{2-}]$ just high enough to precipitate PbS without precipitating ZnS.

Copyright © Houghton Mifflin Company. All rights reserved.

17.7. When NaCl is first added to a solution of $Pb(NO_3)_2$, a precipitate of $PbCl_2$ forms. As more NaCl is added, the excess chloride reacts further with the insoluble $PbCl_2$, forming soluble complex ions of $PbCl_3^-$ and $PbCl_4^{2-}$:

$$Pb^{2+}(aq) \; + \; 2Cl^-(aq) \; \rightleftharpoons \; PbCl_2(s)$$

$$PbCl_2(s) \; + \; Cl^-(aq) \; \rightleftharpoons \; PbCl_3^-(aq)$$

$$PbCl_3^-(aq) \; + \; Cl^-(aq) \; \rightleftharpoons \; PbCl_4^{2-}(aq)$$

17.8. When a small amount of NaOH is added to a solution of $Al_2(SO_4)_3$, a precipitate of $Al(OH)_3$ forms at first. As more NaOH is added, the excess hydroxide ion reacts further with the insoluble $Al(OH)_3$, forming a soluble complex ion of $Al(OH)_4^-$.

17.9. The Ag^+, Cu^{2+}, and Ni^{2+} ions can be separated in two steps: (1) Add HCl to precipitate just the Ag^+ as AgCl, leaving the others in solution. (2) After pouring the solution away from the precipitate, add 0.3 M HCl and H_2S to precipitate only the CuS away from the Ni^{2+} ion, whose sulfide is soluble under these conditions.

17.10. By controlling the pH through the appropriate buffer, one can control the $[CO_3^{2-}]$ using the equilibrium reaction:

$$H_3O^+(aq) \; + \; CO_3^{2-}(aq) \; \rightleftharpoons \; HCO_3^-(aq) \; + \; H_2O(l)$$

Calcium carbonate is much less soluble than magnesium carbonate and thus will precipitate in weakly basic solution, whereas magnesium carbonate will not. Magnesium carbonate will precipitate only in highly basic solution. (There is the possibility that $Mg(OH)_2$ might precipitate, but the $[OH^-]$ is too low for this to occur.)

17.11. The answer is c, 9.1×10^{-40}.

17.12. The answer is e, $K_{sp} = [Ag^+]^3[PO_4^{3-}]$.

17.13. The answer is d, 1.1×10^{-8} M.

17.14. The answer is a, AX.

Copyright © Houghton Mifflin Company. All rights reserved.

■ SOLUTIONS TO PRACTICE PROBLEMS

Note on significant figures If the final answer to a solution needs to be rounded off, it is given first with one nonsignificant figure, and the last significant figure is underlined. The final answer is then rounded to the correct number of significant figures. In multistep problems, intermediate answers are given with at least one nonsignificant figure; however, only the final answer has been rounded off.

17.25.

    a.   NaBr is soluble (Group IA salts are soluble).

    b. PbI_2 is insoluble (PbI_2 is an insoluble iodide).

    c. $BaCO_3$ is insoluble (carbonates are generally insoluble).

    d. $(NH_4)_2SO_4$ is soluble (all ammonium salts are soluble).

17.27.

    a. $K_{sp} = [Mg^{2+}][OH^-]^2$

    b. $K_{sp} = [Sr^{2+}][CO_3^{2-}]$

    c. $K_{sp} = [Ca^{2+}]^3[AsO_4^{3-}]^2$

    d. $K_{sp} = [Fe^{3+}][OH^-]^3$

17.29.   Calculate molar solubility, assemble the usual table, and substitute the equilibrium concentrations from it into the equilibrium-constant expression. (Dashes are given for $AgBrO_3(s)$. In later problems, the dashes are omitted.)

$$\frac{7.2 \times 10^{-3} \text{ g}}{L} \times \frac{1 \text{ mol}}{236 \text{ g}} = 3.\underline{0}5 \times 10^{-5} \text{ M}$$

Conc. (M)	$AgBrO_3(s)$ ⇌	Ag^+	+	BrO_3^-
Starting	—	0		0
Change	—	$+3.05 \times 10^{-5}$		$+3.05 \times 10^{-5}$
Equilibrium	—	3.05×10^{-5}		3.05×10^{-5}

$$K_{sp} = [Ag^+][BrO_3^-] = (3.05 \times 10^{-5})(3.05 \times 10^{-5}) = 9.\underline{3}02 \times 10^{-10} = 9.3 \times 10^{-10}$$

Copyright © Houghton Mifflin Company. All rights reserved.

17.31. Calculate the molar solubility. Then assemble the usual concentration table, and substitute the equilibrium concentrations from it into the equilibrium-constant expression.

$$\frac{0.13\ g}{0.100\ L} \times \frac{1\ mol}{413\ g} = 3.\underline{1}47 \times 10^{-3}\ M$$

Conc. (M)	$Cu(IO_3)_2(s)$ $\rightleftharpoons$	Cu^{2+}	$+$	$2IO_3^-$
Starting		0		0
Change		$+3.147 \times 10^{-3}$		$+2 \times 3.147 \times 10^{-3}$
Equilibrium		3.147×10^{-3}		$2 \times 3.147 \times 10^{-3}$

$$K_{sp} = [Cu^{2+}][IO_3^-]^2 = (3.147 \times 10^{-3})[2(3.147 \times 10^{-3})]^2 = 1.\underline{2}47 \times 10^{-7} = 1.2 \times 10^{-7}$$

17.33. Calculate the pOH from the pH, and then convert pOH to $[OH^-]$. Then assemble the usual concentration table, and substitute the equilibrium concentrations from it into the equilibrium-constant expression.

$$pOH = 14.00 - 10.52 = 3.48$$

$$[OH^-] = antilog\ (-pOH) = antilog\ (-3.48) = 3.\underline{3}11 \times 10^{-4}\ M$$

$$[Mg^{2+}] = [OH^-] \div 2 = (3.311 \times 10^{-4}) \div 2 = 1.655 \times 10^{-4}\ M$$

Conc. (M)	$Mg(OH)_2(s)$ $\rightleftharpoons$	Mg^{2+}	$+$	$2OH^-$
Starting		0		0
Change		$+1.655 \times 10^{-4}$		$+3.311 \times 10^{-4}$
Equilibrium		1.655×10^{-4}		3.311×10^{-4}

$$K_{sp} = [Mg^{2+}][OH^-]^2 = (1.655 \times 10^{-4})(3.311 \times 10^{-4})^2 = 1.\underline{8}1 \times 10^{-11} = 1.8 \times 10^{-11}$$

17.35. Assemble the usual concentration table. Let x equal the molar solubility of $SrCO_3$. When x mol $SrCO_3$ dissolves in 1 L of solution, x mol Sr^{2+} and x mol CO_3^{2-} form.

Conc. (M)	$SrCO_3(s)$ $\rightleftharpoons$	Sr^{2+}	$+ CO_3^{2-}$
Starting		0	0
Change		$+x$	$+x$
Equilibrium		x	x

Substitute the equilibrium concentrations into the equilibrium-constant expression and solve for x. Then convert to grams $SrCO_3$ per liter.

$$[Sr^{2+}][CO_3^{2-}] = K_{sp}$$

$$(x)(x) = x^2 = 9.3 \times 10^{-10}$$

$$x = \sqrt{(9.3 \times 10^{-10})} = 3.\underline{0}4 \times 10^{-5}\ M$$

$$\frac{3.04 \times 10^{-5}\ mol}{L} \times \frac{147.63\ g}{1\ mol\ SrCO_3} = 4.\underline{5}0 \times 10^{-3} = 0.0045\ g/L$$

Copyright © Houghton Mifflin Company. All rights reserved.

17.37. Let x equal the molar solubility of PbF_2. Assemble the usual concentration table, and substitute from the table into the equilibrium-constant expression.

Conc. (M)	$PbF_2(s)$ ⇌	Pb^{2+}	+	$2F^-$
Starting		0		0
Change		$+x$		$+2x$
Equilibrium		x		$2x$

$$[Pb^{2+}][F^-]^2 = K_{sp}$$
$$(x)(2x)^2 = 4x^3 = 2.7 \times 10^{-8}$$
$$x = \sqrt[3]{\frac{2.7 \times 10^{-8}}{4}} = 1.\underline{8}8 \times 10^{-3} = 1.9 \times 10^{-3} \, M$$

17.39. At the start, before any $SrSO_4$ dissolves, the solution contains $0.23 \, M \, SO_4^{2-}$. At equilibrium, x mol of solid $SrSO_4$ dissolves to yield x mol Sr^{2+} and x mol SO_4^{2-}. Assemble the usual concentration table, and substitute the equilibrium concentrations into the equilibrium-constant expression. As an approximation, assume x is negligible compared to $0.23 \, M \, SO_4^{2-}$.

Conc. (M)	$SrSO_4(s)$ ⇌	Sr^{2+}	+	SO_4^{2-}
Starting		0		0.23
Change		$+x$		$+x$
Equilibrium		X		$0.23 + x$

$$[Sr^{2+}][SO_4^{2-}] = K_{sp}$$
$$(x)(0.23 + x) \cong (x)(0.23) \cong 2.5 \times 10^{-7}$$
$$x \cong \frac{2.5 \times 10^{-7}}{0.23} = 1.\underline{0}86 \times 10^{-6} \, M$$

$$\frac{1.086 \times 10^{-6} \, mol}{L} \times \frac{183.69 \, g}{1 \, mol \, SrSO_4} = 1.\underline{9}9 \times 10^{-4} = 2.0 \times 10^{-4} \, g/L$$

Note that adding x to 0.23 M will not change it (to two significant figures), so x is negligible compared to 0.23 M.

Copyright © Houghton Mifflin Company. All rights reserved.

17.41. Calculate the value of K_{sp} from the solubility using the concentration table. Then, using the common-ion calculation, assemble another concentration table. Use 0.020 M NaF as the starting concentration of F^- ion. Substitute the equilibrium concentrations from the table into the equilibrium-constant expression. As an approximation, assume $2x$ is negligible compared to 0.020 $M\,F^-$ ion.

$$\frac{0.016\text{ g}}{L} \times \frac{1\text{ mol MgF}_2}{62.31\text{ g}} = 2.\underline{5}67 \times 10^{-4}\,M$$

Conc. (M)	MgF$_2(s)$ $\rightleftharpoons$	Mg^{2+}	$+$	2F$^-$
Starting		0		0.13
Change		$+2.\underline{5}67 \times 10^{-4}$		$+2 \times 2.\underline{5}67 \times 10^{-4}$
Equilibrium		$2.\underline{5}67 \times 10^{-4}$		$2 \times 2.\underline{5}67 \times 10^{-4}$

$$K_{sp} = [\text{Mg}^{2+}][\text{F}^-]^2 = (2.\underline{5}67 \times 10^{-4})[2(2.\underline{5}67 \times 10^{-4})]^2 = 6.\underline{7}72 \times 10^{-11}$$

Now, use K_{sp} to calculate the molar solubility of MgF$_2$.

Conc. (M)	MgF$_2(s)$ $\rightleftharpoons$	Mg^{2+}	$+$	2F$^-$
Starting		0		0.020
Change		$+x$		$+2x$
Equilibrium		x		$0.020 + 2x$

$$[\text{Mg}^{2+}][\text{F}^-]^2 = K_{sp}$$

$$(x)(0.020 + 2x)^2 \cong (x)(0.020)^2 = 6.\underline{7}72 \times 10^{-11}$$

$$x \cong \frac{6.772 \times 10^{-11}}{(0.020)^2} = 1.\underline{6}93 \times 10^{-7}\,M$$

$$\frac{1.693 \times 10^{-7}\text{ mol}}{L} \times \frac{62.31\text{ g}}{1\text{ mol MgF}_2} = 1.\underline{0}54 \times 10^{-5} = 1.1 \times 10^{-5}\text{ g/L}$$

17.43. The concentration table follows.

Conc. (M)	MgC$_2$O$_4(s)$ $\rightleftharpoons$	Mg^{2+}	$+$	C$_2$O$_4^{2-}$
Starting		0		0.020
Change		$+x$		$+x$
Equilibrium		x		$0.020 + x$

The equilibrium-constant expression is

$$K_{sp} = [\text{Mg}^{2+}][\text{C}_2\text{O}_4^{2-}]$$

$$8.5 \times 10^{-5} = (x)(0.020 + x)$$

$$x^2 + 0.020x - (8.5 \times 10^{-5}) = 0$$

Solving the quadratic equation gives

$$x = \frac{-0.020 \pm \sqrt{(0.020)^2 + 4(8.5 \times 10^{-5})}}{2} = 0.00\underline{3}6\,M$$

Copyright © Houghton Mifflin Company. All rights reserved.

The solubility in grams per liter is

$$\frac{0.0036 \text{ mol}}{\text{L}} \times \frac{112 \text{ g}}{1 \text{ mol}} = 0.\underline{4}03 = 0.4 \text{ g/L}$$

17.45.

a.   Calculate Q_c, the ion product of the solution, using the concentrations in the problem as the concentrations present after mixing and assuming no precipitation. Then compare Q_c with K_{sp} to determine whether precipitation has occurred. Start by defining the ion product with brackets as used for the definition of K_{sp}; then use parentheses for the concentrations.

$$Q_c = [Ba^{2+}][F^-]^2$$
$$Q_c = (0.020)(0.015)^2 = 4.\underline{5}0 \times 10^{-6}$$

Since $Q_c > K_{sp}$ (1.0×10^{-6}), precipitation will occur.

b.   Calculate Q_c, the ion product of the solution, using the concentrations in the problem as the concentrations present after mixing and assuming no precipitation. Then compare Q_c with K_{sp} to determine whether precipitation has occurred. Start by defining the ion product with brackets as used for the definition of K_{sp}; then use parentheses for the concentrations.

$$Q_c = [Pb^{2+}][Cl^-]^2$$
$$Q_c = (0.035)(0.15)^2 = 7.\underline{8}7 \times 10^{-4}$$

Since $Q_c > K_{sp}$ (1.6×10^{-5}), precipitation will occur.

17.47.   Calculate the ion product, Q_c, after preparation of the solution, assuming no precipitation has occurred. Compare it with the K_{sp}.

$$Q_c = [Pb^{2+}][CrO_4^{2-}]$$
$$Q_c = (5.0 \times 10^{-4})(5.0 \times 10^{-5}) = 2.\underline{5}0 \times 10^{-8} \ M^2 \ (> K_{sp} \text{ of } 1.8 \times 10^{-14})$$

The solution is supersaturated before equilibrium is reached. At equilibrium, precipitation occurs, and the solution is saturated.

17.49.   Calculate the concentrations of Mg^{2+} and OH^-, assuming no precipitation. Use a total volume of 1.0 L + 1.0 L, or 2.0 L. (Note that the concentrations are halved when the volume is doubled.)

$$[Mg^{2+}] = \frac{\frac{0.0020 \text{ mol}}{\text{L}} \times 1.0 \text{ L}}{2.0 \text{ L}} = 1.\underline{0}0 \times 10^{-3} \ M$$

$$[OH^-] = \frac{\frac{0.00010 \text{ mol}}{\text{L}} \times 1.0 \text{ L}}{2.0 \text{ L}} = 5.\underline{0}0 \times 10^{-5} \ M$$

Calculate the ion product, and compare it to K_{sp}.

$$Q_c = [Mg^{2+}][OH^-]^2 = (1.00 \times 10^{-3})(5.00 \times 10^{-5})^2 = 2.\underline{5}0 \times 10^{-12}$$

Because Q_c is less than the K_{sp} of 1.8×10^{-11}, no precipitation occurs, and the solution is unsaturated.

Copyright © Houghton Mifflin Company. All rights reserved.

17.51. Calculate the concentrations of Ba^{2+} and F^-, assuming no precipitation. Use a total volume of 0.045 L + 0.075 L, or 0.120 L.

$$[Ba^{2+}] = \frac{\dfrac{0.0015 \text{ mol}}{L} \times 0.045 \text{ L}}{0.120 \text{ L}} = 5.\underline{6}25 \times 10^{-4} \, M$$

$$[F^-] = \frac{\dfrac{0.0025 \text{ mol}}{L} \times 0.075 \text{ L}}{0.120 \text{ L}} = 1.\underline{5}6 \times 10^{-3} \, M$$

Calculate the ion product and compare it to K_{sp}.

$$Q_c = [Ba^{2+}][F^-]^2 = (5.625 \times 10^{-4})(1.56 \times 10^{-3})^2 = 1.\underline{3}6 \times 10^{-9}$$

Because Q_c is less than the K_{sp} of 1.0×10^{-6}, no precipitation occurs, and the solution is unsaturated.

17.53. A mixture of $CaCl_2$ and K_2SO_4 can precipitate only $CaSO_4$ because KCl is soluble. Use the K_{sp} expression to calculate the $[Ca^{2+}]$ needed to just begin precipitating the $0.020 \, M \, SO_4^{2-}$ (in essentially a saturated solution). Then convert to moles.

$$[Ca^{2+}][SO_4^{2-}] = K_{sp} = 2.4 \times 10^{-5}$$

$$[Ca^{2+}] = \frac{K_{sp}}{[SO_4^{2-}]} = \frac{2.4 \times 10^{-5}}{2.0 \times 10^{-2}} = 1.\underline{2}0 \times 10^{-3} \, M$$

The number of moles in 1.5 L of this calcium-containing solution is (mol $CaCl_2$ = mol Ca^{2+}):

$$1.5 \text{ L} \times (1.20 \times 10^{-3}) \text{ mol/L} = 1.\underline{8}0 \times 10^{-3} = 0.0018 \text{ mol } CaCl_2$$

17.55. Because the $AgNO_3$ solution is relatively concentrated, ignore the dilution of the solution of Cl^- and I^- from the addition of $AgNO_3$. The $[Ag^+]$ just as the AgCl begins to precipitate can be calculated from the K_{sp} expression for AgCl using $[Cl^-] = 0.015 \, M$. Therefore, for AgCl,

$$[Ag^+][Cl^-] = K_{sp}$$

$$[Ag^+][0.015] = 1.8 \times 10^{-10}$$

$$[Ag^+] = \frac{1.8 \times 10^{-10}}{0.015} = 1.\underline{2}0 \times 10^{-8} \, M$$

The $[I^-]$ at this point can be obtained by substituting the $[Ag^+]$ into the K_{sp} expression for AgI. Therefore, for AgI,

$$[Ag^+][I^-] = K_{sp}$$

$$[1.20 \times 10^{-8}][I^-] = 8.3 \times 10^{-17}$$

$$[I^-] = \frac{8.3 \times 10^{-17}}{1.2 \times 10^{-8}} = 6.\underline{9}1 \times 10^{-9} = 6.9 \times 10^{-9} \, M$$

17.57. The net ionic equation is

$$BaF_2(s) + 2H_3O^+(aq) \rightleftharpoons Ba^{2+}(aq) + 2HF(aq) + 2H_2O(l)$$

Copyright © Houghton Mifflin Company. All rights reserved.

17.59. Calculate the value of K for the reaction of H_3O^+ with both the SO_4^{2-} and F^- anions as they form by the slight dissolving of the insoluble salts. These constants are the reciprocals of the K_a values of the conjugate acids of these anions.

$$F^-(aq) + H_3O^+(aq) \rightleftharpoons HF(aq) + H_2O(l)$$

$$K = \frac{1}{K_a} = \frac{1}{6.8 \times 10^{-4}} = 1.\underline{4}7 \times 10^3$$

$$SO_4^{2-}(aq) + H_3O^+(aq) \rightleftharpoons HSO_4^-(aq) + H_2O(l)$$

$$K = \frac{1}{K_{a_2}} = \frac{1}{1.1 \times 10^{-2}} = 9\underline{0}.9$$

Because K for the fluoride ion is relatively larger, more BaF_2 than $BaSO_4$ will dissolve in acid.

17.61. The equation is

$$Cu^+(aq) + 2 CN^-(aq) \rightleftharpoons Cu(CN)_2^-(aq)$$

The K_f expression is

$$K_f = \frac{[Cu(CN)_2^-]}{[Cu^+][CN^-]^2} = 1.0 \times 10^{16}$$

17.63. Assume the only $[Ag^+]$ is that in equilibrium with the $Ag(CN)_2^-$ formed from Ag^+ and CN^-. (In other words, assume all the 0.015 M Ag^+ reacts with CN^- to form 0.015 M $Ag(CN)_2^-$.) Subtract the CN^- that forms the 0.015 M $Ag(CN)_2^-$ from the initial 0.100 M CN^-. Use this as the starting concentration of CN^- for the usual concentration table.

$$[0.100 \ M \ NaCN - (2 \times 0.015 \ M)] = 0.070 \ M \text{ starting } CN^-$$

Conc. (M)	$Ag(CN)_2^-$	$\rightleftharpoons$	Ag^+	+	$2CN^-$
Starting	0.015		0		0.070
Change	$-x$		$+x$		$+2x$
Equilibrium	$0.015 - x$		x		$0.070 + 2x$

Even though this reaction is the opposite of the equation for the formation constant, the formation-constant expression can be used. Simply substitute all the exact equilibrium concentrations into the formation-constant expression; then simplify the exact equation by assuming x is negligible compared to 0.015 and $2x$ is negligible compared to 0.070.

$$K_f = \frac{[Ag(CN)_2^-]}{[Ag^+][CN^-]^2} = \frac{(0.015 - x)}{(x)(0.070 + 2x)^2} \cong \frac{(0.015)}{(x)(0.070)^2} \cong 5.6 \times 10^{18}$$

Rearrange and solve for $x = [Ag^+]$:

$$x \cong (0.015) \div [(5.6 \times 10^{18})(0.070)^2] \cong 5.\underline{4}6 \times 10^{-19} = 5.5 \times 10^{-19} \ M$$

Copyright © Houghton Mifflin Company. All rights reserved.

17.65. Start by calculating the $[Cd^{2+}]$ in equilibrium with the $Cd(NH_3)_4^{2+}$ formed from Cd^{2+} and NH_3. Then use the $[Cd^{2+}]$ to decide whether or not CdC_2O_4 will precipitate by calculating the ion product and comparing it with the K_{sp} of 1.5×10^{-8} for CdC_2O_4. Assume all the $0.0020\ M\ Cd^{2+}$ reacts with NH_3 to form $0.0020\ M\ Cd(NH_3)_4^{2+}$, and calculate the remaining NH_3. Use these as the starting concentrations for the usual concentration table.

$$[0.10\ M\ NH_3 - (4 \times 0.0020\ M)] = 0.0\underline{9}2\ M \text{ starting } NH_3$$

Conc. (M)	$Cd(NH_3)_4^{2+}$	$\rightleftharpoons$	Cd^{2+}	+	$4NH_3$
Starting	0.0020		0		0.092
Change	$-x$		$+x$		$+4x$
Equilibrium	$0.0020 - x$		x		$0.092 + 4x$

Even though this reaction is the opposite of the equation for the formation constant, the formation-constant expression can be used. Simply substitute all the exact equilibrium concentrations into the formation-constant expression; then simplify the exact equation by assuming x is negligible compared to 0.0020 and $4x$ is negligible compared to 0.092.

$$K_f = \frac{[Cd(NH_3)_4^{2+}]}{[Cd^{2+}][NH_3]^4} = \frac{(0.0020 - x)}{(x)(0.092 + 4x)^4} \cong \frac{(0.0020)}{(x)(0.092)^4} \cong 1.0 \times 10^7$$

Rearrange and solve for x:

$$x \cong (0.0020) \div [(1.0 \times 10^7)(0.092)^4] \cong 2.\underline{7}9 \times 10^{-6}\ M \cong [Cd^{2+}]$$

Now, calculate the ion product for CdC_2O_4:

$$Q_c = [Cd^{2+}][C_2O_4^{2-}] = (2.79 \times 10^{-6})(0.010) = 2.\underline{7}9 \times 10^{-8}$$

Because Q_c is greater than the K_{sp} of 1.5×10^{-8}, the solution is supersaturated before equilibrium. At equilibrium, a precipitate will form, and the solution will be saturated.

17.67. Using the rule from Chapter 14, obtain the overall equilibrium constant for this reaction from the product of the individual equilibrium constants of the two individual equations whose sum gives this equation.

$CdC_2O_4(s)$	$\rightleftharpoons$	$Cd^{2+}(aq) + C_2O_4^{2-}(aq)$	$K_{sp} = 1.5 \times 10^{-8}$	
$Cd^{2+}(aq) + 4NH_3(aq)$	$\rightleftharpoons$	$Cd(NH_3)_4^{2+}(aq)$	$K_f = 1.0 \times 10^7$	
$CdC_2O_4(s) + 4NH_3(aq)$	$\rightleftharpoons$	$Cd(NH_3)_4^{2+}(aq) + C_2O_4^{2-}(aq)$	$K_c = K_{sp} \times K_f = 0.15$	

Assemble the usual table using $0.10\ M$ as the starting concentration of NH_3 and x as the unknown concentration of $Cd(NH_3)_4^{2+}$ formed.

Conc. (M)	$CdC_2O_4(s)$	+	$4NH_3$	$\rightleftharpoons$	$Cd(NH_3)_4^{2+}$	+	$C_2O_4^{2-}$
Starting			0.10		0		0
Change			$-4x$		$+x$		$+x$
Equilibrium			$0.10 - 4x$		x		x

The equilibrium-constant expression can now be used. Simply substitute all the exact equilibrium concentrations into the equilibrium-constant expression.

$$K_c = \frac{[Cd(NH_3)_4^{2+}][C_2O_4^{2-}]}{[NH_3]^4} = \frac{(x)^2}{(0.10 - 4x)^4} = 0.15$$

Copyright © Houghton Mifflin Company. All rights reserved.

Take the square root of both sides of the two right-hand terms, rearrange into a quadratic equation, and solve for x:

$$\frac{x}{(0.10 - 4x)^2} = 0.3\underline{8}7$$

$$16x^2 - 3.38x + 0.010 = 0$$

$$x = \frac{3.38 \pm \sqrt{(-3.38)^2 - 4(16)(0.010)}}{2(16)} = 0.208 \text{ (too large) and } 3.\underline{0}01 \times 10^{-3}$$

Using the smaller root, $x = 3.\underline{0}01 \times 10^{-3} = 3.0 \times 10^{-3}\ M$ (molar solubility of CdC_2O_4).

17.69. The Pb^{2+}, Cd^{2+}, and Sr^{2+} ions can be separated in two steps: (1) Add HCl to precipitate only the Pb^{2+} as $PbCl_2$, leaving the others in solution. (2) After pouring the solution away from the precipitate, add 0.3 M HCl and H_2S to precipitate only the CdS away from the Sr^{2+} ion, whose sulfide is soluble under these conditions.

17.71.

a. Ag^+ is not possible because no precipitate formed with HCl.

b. Ca^{2+} is not possible if the compound contains only one cation because Mn^{2+} is indicated by the evidence. However, if the compound consists of two or more cations, Ca^{2+} is possible because no reactions were described involving Ca^{2+}.

c. Mn^{2+} is possible because a precipitate was obtained with basic sulfide ion.

d. Cd^{2+} is not possible because no precipitate was obtained with acidic sulfide solution.

■ SOLUTIONS TO GENERAL PROBLEMS

17.73. Assemble the usual concentration table. Let x equal the molar solubility of $PbSO_4$. When x mol $PbSO_4$ dissolves in 1 L of solution, x mol Pb^{2+} and x mol SO_4^{2-} form.

Conc. (M)	$PbSO_4(s)$ $\rightleftharpoons$	Pb^{2+}	+	SO_4^{2-}
Starting		0		0
Change		+x		+x
Equilibrium		x		X

Substitute the equilibrium concentrations into the equilibrium-constant expression, and solve for x.

$$[Pb^{2+}][SO_4^{2-}] = K_{sp}$$

$$(x)(x) = x^2 = 1.7 \times 10^{-8}$$

$$x = \sqrt{(1.7 \times 10^{-8})} = 1.\underline{3}03 \times 10^{-4} = 1.3 \times 10^{-4}\ M$$

Copyright © Houghton Mifflin Company. All rights reserved.

17.75. Let x equal the molar solubility of Hg_2Cl_2. Assemble the usual concentration table, and substitute from the table into the equilibrium-constant expression.

Conc. (M)	$Hg_2Cl_2(s)$ $\rightleftharpoons$	Hg_2^{2+}	+	$2Cl^-$
Starting		0		0
Change		$+x$		$+2x$
Equilibrium		x		$2x$

$$[Hg_2^{2+}][Cl^-]^2 = K_{sp}$$
$$(x)(2x)^2 = 4x^3 = 1.3 \times 10^{-18}$$
$$x = \sqrt[3]{\frac{1.3 \times 10^{-18}}{4}} = 6.\underline{8}7 \times 10^{-7} M$$

a.   Molar solubility $= 6.\underline{8}7 \times 10^{-7} = 6.9 \times 10^{-7} M$

b. $\dfrac{6.87 \times 10^{-7} \text{ mol}}{L} \times \dfrac{472.1 \text{ g } Hg_2Cl_2}{1 \text{ mol}} = 3.\underline{2}4 \times 10^{-4} = 3.2 \times 10^{-4} \text{ g/L}$

17.77. Let x equal the molar solubility of $Ce(OH)_3$. Assemble the usual concentration table, and substitute from the table into the equilibrium-constant expression.

Conc. (M)	$Ce(OH)_3(s)$ $\rightleftharpoons$	Ce^{3+}	+	$3OH^-$
Starting		0		0
Change		$+x$		$+3x$
Equilibrium		x		$3x$

$$[Ce^{3+}][OH^-]^3 = K_{sp}$$
$$(x)(3x)^3 = 27x^4 = 2.0 \times 10^{-20}$$
$$x = \sqrt[4]{\frac{2.0 \times 10^{-20}}{27}} = 5.\underline{2}16 \times 10^{-6} M$$

a.   Molar solubility $= 5.\underline{2}16 \times 10^{-6} = 5.2 \times 10^{-6} M$

b. $[OH^-] = 3x = 1.\underline{5}6 \times 10^{-5} M$

   pOH $= 4.8\underline{0}54 = 4.81$

Copyright © Houghton Mifflin Company. All rights reserved.

17.79. Calculate the pOH from the pH, and then convert pOH to $[OH^-]$. Next, assemble the usual concentration table, and substitute the equilibrium concentrations from it into the equilibrium-constant expression.

$pOH = 14.00 - 8.80 = 5.20$

$[OH^-] = $ antilog $(-pOH) = $ antilog $(-5.20) = 6.\underline{3}09 \times 10^{-6}\ M$

Conc. (M)	$Mg(OH)_2(s)$	$\rightleftharpoons$	Mg^{2+}	+	$2OH^-$
Starting			0		0
Change			+x		0
Equilibrium			x		6.309×10^{-6}

$K_{sp} = [Mg^{2+}][OH^-]^2 = (x)(6.309 \times 10^{-6})^2 = 1.8 \times 10^{-11}$

$x = \dfrac{1.8 \times 10^{-11}}{(6.309 \times 10^{-6})^2} = 0.4\underline{5}2 = 0.45\ M$

$\dfrac{0.452\ mol}{L} \times \dfrac{58.3\ g\ Mg(OH)_2}{1\ mol} = 2\underline{6}.3 = 26\ g/L$

17.81. Let x equal the change in M of Mg^{2+} and 0.10 M equal the starting OH^- concentration. Then assemble the usual concentration table, and let substitute the equilibrium concentrations from it into the equilibrium-constant expression. Assume $2x$ is negligible compared to 0.10 M, and perform an approximate calculation.

Conc. (M)	$Mg(OH)_2(s)$	$\rightleftharpoons$	Mg^{2+}	+	$2OH^-$
Starting			0		0.10
Change			+x		+2x
Equilibrium			x		$0.10 + 2x$

$K_{sp} = [Mg^{2+}][OH^-]^2 = (x)(0.10 + 2x)^2 \cong (x)(0.10)^2 \cong 1.8 \times 10^{-11}$

$x = \dfrac{1.8 \times 10^{-11}}{(0.10)^2} = 1.\underline{8}0 \times 10^{-9} = 1.8 \times 10^{-9}\ M$

17.83. To begin precipitation, you must add just slightly more sulfate ion than that required to give a saturated solution. Use the K_{sp} expression to calculate the $[SO_4^{2-}]$ needed to just begin precipitating the 0.0030 $M\ Ca^{2+}$.

$[Ca^{2+}][SO_4^{2-}] = K_{sp} = 2.4 \times 10^{-5}$

$[SO_4^{2-}] = \dfrac{K_{sp}}{[Ca^{2+}]} = \dfrac{2.4 \times 10^{-5}}{3.0 \times 10^{-3}} = 8.\underline{0}0 \times 10^{-3}\ M$

When the sulfate ion concentration slightly exceeds $8.0 \times 10^{-3}\ M$, precipitation begins.

Copyright © Houghton Mifflin Company. All rights reserved.

17.85. Calculate the concentrations of Pb^{2+} and Cl^-. Use a total volume of 3.20 L + 0.80 L, or 4.00 L.

$$[Pb^{2+}] = \frac{\dfrac{1.25 \times 10^{-3} \text{ mol}}{\text{L}} \times 3.20 \text{ L}}{4.00 \text{ L}} = 1.0\underline{0} \times 10^{-3} \, M$$

$$[Cl^-] = \frac{\dfrac{5.0 \times 10^{-1} \text{ mol}}{\text{L}} \times 0.80 \text{ L}}{4.00 \text{ L}} = 1.\underline{0}0 \times 10^{-1} \, M$$

Calculate the ion product, and compare it to K_{sp}.

$$Q_c = [Pb^{2+}][Cl^-]^2 = (1.00 \times 10^{-3})(1.00 \times 10^{-1})^2 = 1.\underline{0}0 \times 10^{-5} \, M^3$$

Because the Q_c is less than the K_{sp} of 1.6×10^{-5}, no precipitation occurs, and the solution is not saturated.

17.87. A mixture of $AgNO_3$ and $NaCl$ can precipitate only $AgCl$ because $NaNO_3$ is soluble. Use the K_{sp} expression to calculate the $[Cl^-]$ needed to prepare a saturated solution (just before precipitating the $0.0015 \, M \, Ag^+$). Then convert to moles and finally to grams.

$$[Ag^+][Cl^-] = K_{sp} = 1.8 \times 10^{-10}$$

$$[Cl^-] = \frac{K_{sp}}{[Ag^+]} = \frac{1.8 \times 10^{-10}}{1.5 \times 10^{-3}} = 1.\underline{2}0 \times 10^{-7} \, M$$

The numbers of moles and grams in 0.785 L (785 mL) of this chloride-containing solution are

$$0.785 \text{ L} \times (1.20 \times 10^{-7} \text{ mol/L}) = 9.\underline{4}2 \times 10^{-8} \text{ mol } Cl^- = 9.\underline{4}2 \times 10^{-8} \text{ mol } NaCl$$

$$(9.42 \times 10^{-8} \text{ mol } NaCl) \times (58.5 \text{ g } NaCl/1\text{mol}) = 5.\underline{5}1 \times 10^{-6} = 5.5 \times 10^{-6} \text{ g } NaCl$$

This amount of NaCl is too small to weigh on a balance.

17.89. From the magnitude of K_f, assume Fe^{3+} and SCN^- react essentially completely to form $2.00 \, M$ $Fe(SCN)^{2+}$ at equilibrium. Use $2.00 \, M$ as the starting concentration of $Fe(SCN)^{2+}$ for the usual concentration table.

Conc. (M)	Fe^{3+}	+	SCN^-	$\rightleftharpoons$	$FeSCN^{2+}$
Starting	0		0		2.00
Change	$+x$		$+x$		$-x$
Equilibrium	x		x		$2.00 - x$

Substitute all the exact equilibrium concentrations into the formation-constant expression; then simplify the exact equation by assuming x is negligible compared to $2.00 \, M$.

$$K_f = \frac{[FeSCN^{2+}]}{[Fe^{3+}][SCN^-]} = \frac{(2.00 - x)}{(x)(x)} \cong \frac{(2.00)}{x^2} \cong 9.0 \times 10^2$$

Copyright © Houghton Mifflin Company. All rights reserved.

Rearrange and solve for x:

$$x = \sqrt{\frac{2.00}{9.0 \times 10^2}} = 4.\underline{7}1 \times 10^{-2} = 4.7 \times 10^{-2} \, M$$

Fraction dissociated $= [(4.\underline{7}1 \times 10^{-2}) \div (2.00)] \times 100\% = 0.02\underline{3}5 \; (< 0.03, \text{ so acceptable})$

17.91. Obtain the overall equilibrium constant for this reaction from the product of the individual equilibrium constants of the two individual equations whose sum gives this equation:

$$\begin{array}{lll}
AgBr(s) \rightleftharpoons Ag^+(aq) + Br^-(aq) & K_{sp} = 5.0 \times 10^{-13} \\
Ag^+(aq) + 2NH_3(aq) \rightleftharpoons Ag(NH_3)_2^+(aq) & K_f = 1.7 \times 10^7 \\
\hline
AgBr(s) + 2NH_3(aq) \rightleftharpoons Ag(NH_3)_2^+(aq) + Br^-(aq) & K_c = K_{sp} \times K_f = 8.\underline{5}0 \times 10^{-6}
\end{array}$$

Assemble the usual table using 5.0 M as the starting concentration of NH_3 and x as the unknown concentration of $Ag(NH_3)_2^+$ formed.

Conc. (M)	AgBr(s) +	2NH$_3$	$\rightleftharpoons$	Ag(NH$_3$)$_2^+$ +	Br$^-$
Starting		5.0		0	0
Change		$-2x$		$+x$	$+x$
Equilibrium		$5.0 - 2x$		x	x

The equilibrium-constant expression can now be used. Simply substitute all the exact equilibrium concentrations into the equilibrium-constant expression; it will not be necessary to simplify the equation, because taking the square root of both sides removes the x^2 term.

$$K_c = \frac{[Ag(NH_3)_2^+][Br^-]}{[NH_3]^2} = \frac{x^2}{(5.0 - 2x)^2} = 8.\underline{5}0 \times 10^{-6}$$

Take the square root of both sides of the two right-hand terms and solve for x.

$$\frac{x}{(5.0 - 2x)} = 2.\underline{9}15 \times 10^{-3}$$

$$x + (5.8 \times 10^{-3})x = 1.\underline{4}575 \times 10^{-2}$$

$$x = 1.\underline{4}49 \times 10^{-2} = 1.4 \times 10^{-2} \, M \text{ (the molar solubility of AgBr in 5.0 } M \text{ NH}_3)$$

17.93. Start by recognizing that because each zinc oxalate produces one oxalate ion, the solubility of zinc oxalate equals the oxalate concentration:

$$ZnC_2O_4(s) + 4NH_3 \rightleftharpoons Zn(NH_3)_4^{2+} + C_2O_4^{2-}$$

Thus, the $[C_2O_4^{2-}] = 3.6 \times 10^{-4} \, M$. Now, calculate the $[Zn^{2+}]$ in equilibrium with the oxalate ion using the K_{sp} expression for zinc oxalate.

$$K_{sp} = [Zn^{2+}][C_2O_4^{2-}] = 1.5 \times 10^{-9}$$

$$[Zn^{2+}] = \frac{1.5 \times 10^{-9}}{3.6 \times 10^{-4}} = 4.\underline{1}6 \times 10^{-6} = 4.2 \times 10^{-6} \, M$$

Copyright © Houghton Mifflin Company. All rights reserved.

To calculate K_f, the $[Zn(NH_3)_4^{2+}]$ term must be calculated. This can be done by recognizing that the molar solubility of ZnC_2O_4 is the sum of the concentration of Zn^{2+} and $Zn(NH_3)_4^{2+}$ ions:

Molar solubility of $ZnC_2O_4 = [Zn^{2+}] + [Zn(NH_3)_4^{2+}]$

$3.6 \times 10^{-4} = (4.16 \times 10^{-6}) + [Zn(NH_3)_4^{2+}]$

$[Zn(NH_3)_4^{2+}] = (3.6 \times 10^{-4}) - (4.16 \times 10^{-6}) = 3.\underline{5}58 \times 10^{-4}\ M$

Now, the $[NH_3]$ term must be calculated by subtracting the ammonia in $[Zn(NH_3)_4^{2+}]$ from the starting NH_3 of $0.0150\ M$.

$[NH_3] = 0.0150 - 4\,[Zn(NH_3)_4^{2+}] = 0.0150 - 4(3.558 \times 10^{-4}) = 0.013\underline{5}7\ M$

Solve for K_f by substituting the known concentrations into the K_f expression:

$$K_f = \frac{[Zn(NH_3)_4^{2+}]}{[Zn^{2+}][NH_3]^4} = \frac{3.558 \times 10^{-4}}{(4.16 \times 10^{-6})(0.01357)^4} = 2.\underline{5}2 \times 10^9 = 2.5 \times 10^9$$

17.95. The OH^- formed by ionization of NH_3 (to NH_4^+ and OH^-) is a common ion that will precipitate Mg^{2+} as the slightly soluble $Mg(OH)_2$ salt. The simplest way to treat the problem is to calculate the $[OH^-]$ of $0.10\ M\ NH_3$ before the soluble Mg^{2+} salt is added. As the soluble Mg^{2+} salt is added, the $[Mg^{2+}]$ will increase until the solution is saturated with respect to $Mg(OH)_2$ (the next Mg^{2+} ions to be added will precipitate). Calculate the $[Mg^{2+}]$ at the point at which precipitation begins.

To calculate the $[OH^-]$ of $0.10\ M\ NH_3$, let x equal the moles per liter of NH_3 that ionize, forming x mol/L of NH_4^+ and x mol/L of OH^- and leaving $(0.10 - x)\ M\ NH_3$ in solution. We can summarize the situation in tabular form:

Conc. (M)	NH_3	+	H_2O	$\rightleftharpoons$	NH_4^+	+	OH^-
Starting	0.10				~0		0
Change	$-x$				$+x$		$+x$
Equilibrium	$0.10 - x$				x		x

The equilibrium-constant equation is:

$$K_c = \frac{[NH_4^+][OH^-]}{[NH_3]} = \frac{x^2}{(0.10 - x)} \cong \frac{x^2}{(0.10)}$$

The value of x can be obtained by rearranging and taking the square root:

$$[OH^-] \cong \sqrt{1.8 \times 10^{-5} \times 0.10} = 1.\underline{3}4 \times 10^{-3}\ M$$

Note that $(0.10 - x)$ is not significantly different from 0.10, so x can be ignored in the $(0.10 - x)$ term. Now, use the K_{sp} of $Mg(OH)_2$ to calculate the $[Mg^{2+}]$ of a saturated solution of $Mg(OH)_2$, which essentially will be the Mg^{2+} ion concentration when $Mg(OH)_2$ begins to precipitate.

$$[Mg^{2+}] = \frac{K_{sp}}{[OH^-]^2} = \frac{1.8 \times 10^{-11}}{(1.34 \times 10^{-3})^2} = 1.\underline{0}0 \times 10^{-5} = 1.0 \times 10^{-5}\ M$$

Copyright © Houghton Mifflin Company. All rights reserved.

17.97.

a.   Use the solubility information to calculate K_{sp}. The reaction is

$$Cu(IO_3)_2(s) \rightleftharpoons Cu^{2+}(aq) + 2IO_3^-(aq)$$

$$2.7 \times 10^{-3} \qquad 2 \times (2.7 \times 10^{-3})$$

$$K_{sp} = [Cu^{2+}][IO_3^-]^2 = [2.7 \times 10^{-3}][2 \times (2.7 \times 10^{-3})]^2 = 7.\underline{8}7 \times 10^{-8}$$

Set up an equilibrium. The reaction is

$$Cu(IO_3)_2(s) \rightleftharpoons Cu^{2+}(aq) + 2IO_3^-(aq)$$

$$y \qquad 0.35 + 2y \approx 0.35$$

$$K_{sp} = [y][0.35]^2 = 7.87 \times 10^{-8}$$

Molar solubility $= y = 6.\underline{4}2 \times 10^{-7} = 6.4 \times 10^{-7}\ M$

b.   Set up an equilibrium. The reaction is

$$Cu(IO_3)_2(s) \rightleftharpoons Cu^{2+}(aq) + 2IO_3^-(aq)$$

$$y + 0.35 \approx 0.35 \qquad 2y$$

$$K_{sp} = [0.35][2y]^2 = 7.87 \times 10^{-8}$$

Molar solubility $= y = 2.\underline{3}7 \times 10^{-4} = 2.4 \times 10^{-4}\ M$

c.   Yes, $Cu(IO_3)_2$ is a 1:2 electrolyte. It takes two IO_3^- ions to combine with one Cu^{2+} ion. The IO_3^- ion is involved as a square term in the K_{sp} expression.

17.99.

a.   Set up an equilibrium. The reaction and equilibrium-constant expression are

$$PbI_2(s) \rightleftharpoons Pb^{2+}(aq) + 2I^-(aq) \quad K_{sp} = [Pb^{2+}][I^-]^2 = 6.5 \times 10^{-9}$$

The Pb^{2+} ion concentration is 0.0150 M. Plug this in, and solve for the iodine-ion concentration.

$$[I^-] = \sqrt{\frac{6.5 \times 10^{-9}}{0.0150}} = 6.\underline{5}8 \times 10^{-4} = 6.6 \times 10^{-4}\ M$$

b.   Solve the equilibrium-constant expression for the lead-ion concentration.

$$[Pb^{2+}] = \frac{6.5 \times 10^{-9}}{(2.0 \times 10^{-3})^2} = 1.\underline{6}3 \times 10^{-3} = 1.6 \times 10^{-3}\ M$$

The percent of the lead(II) ion remaining in solution is

$$Percent\ Pb^{2+}\ remaining = \frac{1.63 \times 10^{-3}}{0.0150} \times 100\% = 1\underline{0}.9 = 11\%$$

Copyright © Houghton Mifflin Company. All rights reserved.

17.101.

a. The reaction and equilibrium-constant expression are

$$Co(OH)_2(s) \rightleftharpoons Co^{2+}(aq) + 2OH^-(aq) \quad K_{sp} = [Co^{2+}][OH^-]^2$$

From the molar solubility, $[Co^{2+}] = 5.4 \times 10^{-6}\ M$ and $[OH^-] = 2 \times (5.4 \times 10^{-6})\ M$. Therefore,

$$K_{sp} = [5.4 \times 10^{-6}][2 \times (5.4 \times 10^{-6})]^2 = 6.\underline{3}0 \times 10^{-16} = 6.3 \times 10^{-16}$$

b. From the pOH $(14 - pH)$, the $[OH^-] = 10^{-3.57} = 2.\underline{6}9 \times 10^{-4}\ M$. The molar solubility is equal to the cobalt-ion concentration at equilibrium.

$$[Co^{2+}] = \frac{K_{sp}}{[OH^-]^2} = \frac{6.3 \times 10^{-16}}{(2.69 \times 10^{-4})^2} = 8.\underline{7}1 \times 10^{-9} = 8.7 \times 10^{-9}\ M$$

c. The common-ion effect (OH$^-$) in part b decreases the solubility of Co^{2+}.

17.103.

a.

$$AgCl(s) \rightleftharpoons Ag^+(aq) + Cl^-(aq) \quad K_{sp} = 1.8 \times 10^{-10}$$
$$Ag^+(aq) + 2NH_3(aq) \rightleftharpoons Ag(NH_3)_2^+(aq) \quad K_f = 1.7 \times 10^7$$
$$\overline{AgCl(s) + 2NH_3(aq) \rightleftharpoons Ag(NH_3)_2^+(aq) + Cl^-(aq)}$$

$$K = K_{sp} \times K_f = (1.8 \times 10^{-10})(1.7 \times 10^7) = 3.\underline{0}6 \times 10^{-3} = 3.1 \times 10^{-3}$$

b. The equilibrium-constant expression is

$$\frac{[Ag(NH_3)_2^+][Cl^-]}{[NH_3]^2} = \frac{y^2}{(0.80)^2} = 3.06 \times 10^{-3}$$

$$y = [Ag(NH_3)_2^+] = 0.04\underline{4}3 = 0.044\ M$$

mol AgCl dissolved = mol Ag(NH$_3$)$_2^+$ = 0.044 mol/L $\times$ 1.00 L = 0.044 mol

$$\text{mol NH}_3 \text{ reacted} = 0.0443 \text{ mol Ag(NH}_3)_2^+ \times \frac{2\text{ mol NH}_3}{1\text{ mol Ag(NH}_3)_2^+} = 0.08\underline{8}6\text{ mol}$$

Total moles of NH$_3$ added = $0.80\ M \times 1.00\ L + 0.0886 = 0.8\underline{8}9 = 0.89$ mol

17.105.

a. The moles of NH$_4$Cl (molar mass 53.49 g/mol) are given by

$$\text{mol NH}_4\text{Cl} = 26.7\text{ g} \times \frac{1\text{ mol NH}_4\text{Cl}}{53.49\text{ g NH}_4\text{Cl}} = 0.499\underline{2}\text{ mol}$$

The reaction and equilibrium-constant expression are

$$NH_3 + H_2O \rightleftharpoons NH_4^+ + OH^- \quad K_b = \frac{[NH_4^+][OH^-]}{[NH_3]} = 1.8 \times 10^{-5}$$

Copyright © Houghton Mifflin Company. All rights reserved.

Solve the equilibrium-constant expression for [OH⁻]. The molarity of the NH_4Cl is 0.49$\underline{9}$2 mol/1.0 L = 0.4992 M.

$$[OH^-] = \frac{(1.8 \times 10^{-5})(4.2)}{(0.4992)} = 1.\underline{5}1 \times 10^{-4} = 1.5 \times 10^{-4} \, M$$

b.   The reaction and equilibrium-constant expression are

$$Mg(OH)_2 \rightleftharpoons Mg^{2+} + 2OH^- \quad K_{sp} = [Mg^{2+}][OH^-]^2 = 1.8 \times 10^{-11}$$

Solving for $[Mg^{2+}]$ gives

$$[Mg^{2+}] = \frac{(1.8 \times 10^{-11})}{(1.51 \times 10^{-4})^2} = 7.\underline{8}9 \times 10^{-4} = 7.9 \times 10^{-4} \, M$$

The percent Mg^{2+} that has been removed is given by

$$\text{Percent } Mg^{2+} \text{ removed} = \frac{0.075 - 7.89 \times 10^{-4}}{0.075} \times 100\% = 9\underline{8}.9 = 99\%$$

■ SOLUTIONS TO CUMULATIVE-SKILLS PROBLEMS

17.119. Using the K_{sp} of 1.1×10^{-21} for ZnS, calculate the $[S^{2-}]$ needed to maintain a saturated solution (without precipitation):

$$[S^{2-}] = \frac{1.1 \times 10^{-21}}{1.5 \times 10^{-4} \, M \, Zn^{2+}} = 7.\underline{3}3 \times 10^{-18} \, M$$

Next, use the overall H_2S ionization expression to calculate the $[H_3O^+]$ needed to achieve this $[S^{2-}]$ level:

$$[H_3O^+] = \sqrt{\frac{1.1 \times 10^{-20} \, (0.10 \, M)}{7.33 \times 10^{-18} \, M}} = 1.\underline{2}25 \times 10^{-2} \, M$$

Finally, calculate the buffer ratio of $[SO_4^{2-}]/[HSO_4^-]$ from the H_2SO_4 K_{a_2} expression where K_{a_2} has the value 1.1×10^{-2}:

$$\frac{[SO_4^{2-}]}{[HSO_4^-]} = \frac{K_{a_2}}{[H_3O^+]} = \frac{1.1 \times 10^{-2}}{1.225 \times 10^{-2}} = \frac{0.8979}{1.000}$$

If $[HSO_4^-] = 0.20 \, M$, then

$$[SO_4^{2-}] = 0.8979 \times 0.20 \, M = 0.1\underline{7}95 = 0.18 \, M$$

Copyright © Houghton Mifflin Company. All rights reserved.

17.121. Begin by solving for $[H_3O^+]$ in the buffer. Ignoring changes in $[HCHO_2]$ as a result of ionization in the buffer, you obtain

$$[H_3O^+] \cong 1.7 \times 10^{-4} \times \frac{0.45 \ M}{0.20 \ M} = 3.\underline{8}25 \times 10^{-4} \ M$$

You should verify that this approximation is valid (you obtain the same result from the Henderson-Hasselbalch equation). The equilibrium for the dissolution of CaF_2 in acidic solution is obtained by subtracting twice the acid ionization of HF from the solubility equilibrium of CaF_2.

$CaF_2(s)$			$\rightleftharpoons$	$Ca^{2+}(aq) + 2F^-(aq)$		K_{sp}
$2H_3O^+(aq)$	$+$	$2F^-(aq)$	$\rightleftharpoons$	$2HF(aq) + 2\ H_2O(l)$		$1/(K_a)^2$
$2H_3O^+(aq)$	$+$	$CaF_2(s)$	$\rightleftharpoons$	$Ca^{2+}(aq) + 2HF(aq) + 2\ H_2O(l)$		$K_c = K_{sp}/(K_a)^2$

Therefore, $K_c = (3.4 \times 10^{-11}) \div (6.8 \times 10^{-4})^2 = 7.\underline{3}5 \times 10^{-5}$. In order to solve the equilibrium-constant equation, you require the concentration of HF, which you obtain from the acid-ionization constant for HF.

$$K_a = \frac{[H_3O^+][F^-]}{[HF]}$$

$$6.8 \times 10^{-4} = 3.825 \times 10^{-4} \times \frac{[F^-]}{[HF]}$$

$$\frac{[F^-]}{[HF]} = 1.778, \text{ or } [F^-] = 1.\underline{7}78 \ [HF]$$

Let x be the solubility of CaF_2 in the buffer. Then $[Ca^{2+}] = x$ and $[F^-] + [HF] = 2x$. Substituting from the previous equation, you obtain

$$2x = 1.778[HF] + [HF] = 2.778[HF], \text{ or } [HF] = 2x/2.\underline{7}78$$

You can now substitute for $[H_3O^+]$ and $[HF]$ into the equation for K_c.

$$K_c = \frac{[Ca^{2+}][HF]^2}{[H_3O^+]^2} = \frac{(x)(2x/2.778)^2}{(3.825 \times 10^{-4})^2} = 7.35 \times 10^{-5}$$

$$7.35 \times 10^{-5} = (3.543 \times 10^6)x^3$$

$$x^3 = 2.075 \times 10^{-11}$$

$$x = 2.\underline{7}48 \times 10^{-4} = 2.7 \times 10^{-4} \ M$$

Copyright © Houghton Mifflin Company. All rights reserved.

17.123. The net ionic equation is

$$Ba^{2+}(aq) + 2OH^-(aq) + Mg^{2+}(aq) + SO_4^{2-}(aq) \rightleftharpoons BaSO_4(s) + Mg(OH)_2(s)$$

Start by calculating the moles per liter of each ion after mixing and before precipitation. Use a total volume of $0.0450 + 0.0670$ L $= 0.112$ L.

M of SO_4^{2-} and Mg^{2+} = (0.350 mol/L x 0.0670 L) ÷ 0.112 L = 0.20$\underline{9}$4 M

M of Ba^{2+} = (0.250 mol/L x 0.0450 L) ÷ 0.112 L = 0.10$\underline{0}$4 M

M of OH^- = (2 x 0.250 mol/L x 0.0450 L) ÷ 0.112 L = 0.20$\underline{0}$89 M

Assemble a table showing the precipitation of $BaSO_4$ and $Mg(OH)_2$.

Conc. (M)	Ba^{2+}	+ SO_4^{2-}	+ Mg^{2+} + $2OH^-$		$\rightleftharpoons$ $BaSO_4(s)$ + $Mg(OH)_2(s)$
Starting	0.1004	0.2094	0.2094	0.20089	
Change	−0.1004	−0.1004	−0.1004	−0.20089	
Equilibrium	0.0000	0.1090	0.1090	0.0000	

To calculate $[Ba^{2+}]$, use the K_{sp} expression for $BaSO_4$.

$$[Ba^{2+}] = \frac{1.1 \times 10^{-10}}{0.1090 \, M \, SO_4^{2-}} = 1.\underline{0}09 \times 10^{-9} = 1.0 \times 10^{-9} \, M$$

$$[SO_4^{2-}] = 0.10\underline{9}0 = 0.109 \, M$$

Calculate the $[OH^-]$ using the K_{sp} expression for $Mg(OH)_2$:

$$[OH^-] = \sqrt{\frac{1.8 \times 10^{-11}}{0.1090 \, M \, Mg^{2+}}} = 1.\underline{2}8 \times 10^{-5} = 1.3 \times 10^{-5} \, M$$

$$[Mg^{2+}] = 0.10\underline{9}0 = 0.109 \, M$$

Copyright © Houghton Mifflin Company. All rights reserved.

CHAPTER 18

Thermodynamics and Equilibrium

■ SOLUTIONS TO EXERCISES

Note on units and significant figures: The mole unit is omitted from all thermodynamic parameters such as $S°$, $\Delta S°$, etc. If the final answer to a solution needs to be rounded off, it is given first with one nonsignificant figure, and the last significant figure is underlined. The final answer is then rounded to the correct number of significant figures. In multistep problems, intermediate answers are given with at least one nonsignificant figure; however, only the final answer has been rounded off.

18.1. Calculate the work, w, done using $w = F \times d = (mg) \times d$. Then use w to calculate ΔE.

$$w = (mg) \times d = (2.20 \text{ kg} \times 9.80 \text{ m/s}^2) \times 0.250 \text{ m} = 5.3\underline{9}0 \text{ kg}\bullet\text{m}^2/\text{s}^2 = 5.39 \text{ J}$$

$$\Delta U = q + w = (-1.50 \text{ J}) + (5.3\underline{9}0 \text{ J}) = 3.8\underline{9}0 = 3.89 \text{ J}$$

18.2. At 1.00 atm and 25°C, the volume occupied by 1.00 mol of any of the gases in the equation is 22.41 L x (298/273) = 24.46 L. Find the change in volume:

$$CH_4(24.46 \text{ L}) + 2O_2(2 \times 24.46 \text{ L}) \rightarrow CO_2(24.46 \text{ L}) + 2H_2O(l)$$

$$\Delta V = 24.46 \text{ L} - (3 \times 24.46 \text{ L}) = -48.\underline{9}2 \text{ L}$$

Next, calculate the work, w, done on the system (its value decreases) using 1.00 atm = 1.013 x 10^5 Pa and 1.00 L = 1.00 x 10^{-3} m^3. Add this to the heat, q_p, at constant P:

$$w = -P\Delta V = -(1.013 \times 10^5 \text{ Pa}) \times (-48.92 \times 10^{-3} \text{ m}^3) = 4.9\underline{5}56 \times 10^3 \text{ J} = 4.96 \text{ kJ}$$

$$\Delta U = q_p + w = (-890.2 \text{ kJ}) + (+4.9\underline{5}56 \text{ kJ}) = -885.\underline{2}4 = -885.2 \text{ kJ}$$

18.3. When the liquid evaporates, it absorbs heat: $\Delta H_{vap} = 42.6 \text{ kJ/mol}$ (42.6 x 10^3 J/mol) at 25°C, or 298 K. The entropy change, ΔS, is

$$\Delta S = \frac{\Delta H_{vap}}{T} = \frac{42.6 \times 10^3 \text{ J/mol}}{298 \text{ K}} = 14\underline{2}.9 \text{ J/(mol}\bullet\text{K)}$$

The entropy of one mole of the vapor equals the entropy of one mole of liquid (161 J/K) plus 142.9 J/K.

$$S° = (161 + 142.9) \text{ J/(mol}\bullet\text{K)} = 30\underline{3}.9 = 304 \text{ J/(mol}\bullet\text{K)}$$

18.4.

a. $\Delta S°$ is positive because there is an increase in moles of gas ($\Delta n_{gas} = +1$) from a solid reactant forming a mole of gas. (Entropy increases.)

Copyright © Cengage Learning. All rights reserved.

b. $\Delta S°$ is positive because there is an increase in moles of gas ($\Delta n_{gas} = +1$) from a liquid reactant forming a mole of gas. (Entropy increases.)

c. $\Delta S°$ is negative because there is a decrease in moles of gas ($\Delta n_{gas} = -1$) from liquid and gaseous reactants forming two moles of solid. (Entropy decreases.)

d. $\Delta S°$ is positive because there is an increase in moles of gas ($\Delta n_{gas} = +1$) from solid and liquid reactants forming a mole of gas and four moles of an ionic compound. (Entropy increases.)

18.5. The reaction and standard entropies are given below. Multiply the $S°$ values by their stoichiometric coefficients, and subtract the entropy of the reactant from the sum of the product entropies.

$$C_6H_{12}O_6 \quad \rightarrow \quad 2C_2H_5OH(l) \quad + \quad 2CO_2(g)$$

$S°$:   212.1   2 x 160.7   2 x 213.7 J/K

$\Delta S° = \Sigma n S°(\text{products}) - \Sigma m S°(\text{reactants}) =$

        $[(2 \times 160.7 + 2 \times 213.7) - 212.1]$ J/K $= 53\underline{6}.7$ J/K

18.6. The reaction, standard enthalpy changes, and standard entropies are as follows:

$$CH_4(g) \quad + \quad 2O_2(g) \quad \rightarrow \quad CO_2(g) \quad + \quad 2H_2O(g)$$

$\Delta H_f°$:   -74.87   0   -393.5 $2 \times (-285.8)$ kJ

$S°$:   186.1   2 x 205.0   213.7 2×188.7 J/K

Calculate $\Delta H°$ and $\Delta S°$ for the reaction by taking the values for products and subtracting the values for reactants.

$\Delta H° = \Sigma n \Delta H_f°(\text{products}) - \Sigma m \Delta H_f°(\text{reactants}) =$

        $[(-393.5 + 2 \times -285.8) - (-74.87)]$ kJ $= -890.\underline{2}3$ kJ

$\Delta S° = \Sigma n S°(\text{products}) - \Sigma m S°(\text{reactants}) =$

        $[(213.7 + 2 \times 188.7) - (186.1 + 2 \times 205.0)]$ J/K $= -5.0$ J/K

Now, substitute into the equation for $\Delta G°$ in terms of $\Delta H°$ and $\Delta S°$ ($= -5.0 \times 10^{-3}$ kJ/K):

$\Delta G° = \Delta H° - T\Delta S° = -890.23$ kJ $- (298$ K$)(-5.0 \times 10^{-3}$ kJ/K$) = -888.\underline{7}4 = -888.7$ kJ

18.7. Write the values of $\Delta G_f°$ multiplied by their stoichiometric coefficients below each formula:

$$CaCO_3(s) \quad \rightarrow \quad CaO(s) \quad + \quad CO_2(g)$$

$\Delta G_f°$:   -1128.8   -603.5   -394.4 kJ

The calculation is

$\Delta G° = \Sigma n G_f°(\text{products}) - \Sigma m G_f°(\text{reactants}) =$

        $[(-603.5) + (-394.4) - (-1128.8)]$ kJ $= 130.\underline{9}$ kJ

Copyright © Cengage Learning. All rights reserved.

18.8.

$$C(graphite) \quad + \quad 2H_2(g) \quad \rightarrow \quad CH_4(g)$$

$\Delta G_f°:$ 0   0   -50.80 kJ

a. $\Delta G° = $ [(-50.80) - (0)] kJ = -50.80 kJ (spontaneous reaction)

$$2H_2(g) \quad + \quad O_2(g) \quad \rightarrow \quad 2H_2O(l)$$

$\Delta G_f°:$ 0   0   2 x (-237.1) kJ

b. $\Delta G° = $ [(2 x -237.1) - (0)] kJ = -474.2 kJ (spontaneous reaction)

$$4HCN(g) + 5O_2(g) \rightarrow 2H_2O(l) + 4CO_2(g) + 2N_2(g)$$

$\Delta G_f°:$ 4 x 124.7   0   2 x (-237.1)   4 x (-394.4)   0 kJ

$\Delta G° = $ [(2 x -237.1) + 4 x (-394.4) - (4 x 124.7)] kJ = -2550.6 kJ (spontaneous reaction)

c.

$$Ag^+(aq) \quad + \quad I^-(aq) \quad \rightarrow \quad AgI(s)$$

$\Delta G_f°:$ 77.12   -51.59   -66.19 kJ

d. $\Delta G° = $ [(-66.19) - (77.12 - 51.59)] kJ = -91.72 kJ (spontaneous reaction)

18.9.

a. $K = K_p = P_{CO_2}$

b. $K = K_{sp} = [Pb^{2+}][I^-]^2$

c. $K = \dfrac{P_{CO_2}}{[H^+][HCO_3^-]}$

18.10. First, calculate $\Delta G°$ using the $\Delta G_f°$ values from Table 18.2.

$$CaCO_3(s) \rightleftharpoons CaO(s) \quad + \quad CO_2(g)$$

$\Delta G_f°:$ -1128.8   -603.5   -394.4 kJ

Subtract $\Delta G_f°$ of reactants from that of the products:

$\Delta G_f° = \Sigma n\Delta G_f°(products) - \Sigma m\Delta G_f°(reactants) = $

    [(-603.5) + (-394.4) - (-1128.8)] kJ = 130.9 kJ

Copyright © Cengage Learning. All rights reserved.

Use the rearranged form of the equation, $\Delta G° = -RT \ln K$, to solve for $\ln K$. To get compatible units, express $\Delta G°$ in joules, and set R equal to 8.31 J/(mol•K). Substituting the numerical values into the expression gives

$$\ln K = \frac{-\Delta G°}{RT} = \frac{130.9 \times 10^3}{-8.31 \times 298} = -52.\underline{8}59$$

$$K = K_p = e^{-52.859} = \underline{1}.10 \times 10^{-23} = 1 \times 10^{-23}$$

18.11. First, calculate $\Delta G°$ using the $\Delta G_f°$ values in the exercise.

$$Mg(OH)_2(s) \rightarrow Mg^{2+}(aq) + 2OH^-(aq)$$

$\Delta G_f°$:   -833.7   -454.8   2 x (-157.3) kJ

Hence, $\Delta G°$ for the reaction is

$$\Delta G° = [2 \times (-157.3) + (-454.8) - (-833.7)] \text{ kJ} = 64.\underline{3} \text{ kJ}$$

Now, substitute numerical values into the equation relating $\ln K$ and $\Delta G°$.

$$\ln K = \frac{-\Delta G°}{RT} = \frac{64.3 \times 10^3}{-8.31 \times 298} = -25.\underline{9}65$$

$$K = K_{sp} = e^{-25.965} = \underline{5}.289 \times 10^{-12} = 5 \times 10^{-12}$$

18.12. From Appendix C, you have

$$H_2O(l) \rightleftharpoons H_2O(g)$$

$\Delta H_f°$:   -285.8   -241.8 kJ

$S°$:   69.95   188.7 J/K

Calculate $\Delta H°$ and $\Delta S°$ from these values.

$$\Delta H° = [-241.8 - (-285.8)] \text{ kJ} = 44.\underline{0} \text{ kJ}$$

$$\Delta S° = [188.7 - 69.95] \text{ J/K} = 118.\underline{7}5 \text{ J/K}$$

Substitute $\Delta H°$, $\Delta S°$ (= 0.11875 kJ/K), and T (= 318 K) into the equation for $\Delta G_T°$:

$$\Delta G_T° = \Delta H° - T\Delta S° = 44.0 \text{ kJ} - (318 \text{ K})(0.11875 \text{ kJ/K}) = 6.\underline{2}3 \text{ kJ}$$

Substitute the value of $\Delta G°$ (6.23 x 10^3 J) at 318 K into the equation relating $\ln K$ and $\Delta G°$.

$$\ln K = \frac{-\Delta G°}{RT} = \frac{6.23 \times 10^3}{-8.31 \times 318} = -2.\underline{3}60$$

$$K = K_p = e^{-2.360} = 0.0\underline{9}43 = 0.09$$

$K_p = P_{H_2O}$, so the vapor pressure of H_2O is 0.09 atm (71.7 mmHg).

The value is 71.9 mmHg in Appendix B.

Copyright © Cengage Learning. All rights reserved.

18.13. First, calculate $\Delta H°$ and $\Delta S°$ using the given $\Delta H_f°$ and $S°$ values.

$$MgCO_3(s) \rightleftharpoons MgO(s) + CO_2(g)$$

$\Delta H_f°$:	-1111.7	-601.2	-393.5 kJ
$\Delta S°$:	65.85	26.92	213.7 J/K

$\Delta H° = [-601.2 + (-393.5) - (-1111.7)]$ kJ $= 117.\underline{0}$ kJ

$\Delta S° = [(26.92 + 213.7) - 65.85]$ J/K $= 174.\underline{7}7$ J/K

Substitute these values into the expression relating T, $\Delta H°$, and $\Delta S°$ (= 0.17477 kJ/K).

$$T = \frac{\Delta H°}{\Delta S°} = \frac{117.0 \text{ kJ}}{0.17477 \text{ kJ/K}} = 66\underline{9}.45 \text{ K (lower than that for CaCO}_3)$$

■ ANSWERS TO SELF-ASSESSMENT AND REVIEW QUESTIONS

18.1. A spontaneous process is a chemical and/or a physical change that occurs by itself without the continuing intervention of an outside agency. Three examples are (1) a rock on a hilltop rolls down, (2) heat flows from a hot object to a cold one, and (3) iron rusts in moist air. Three examples of nonspontaneous processes are (1) a rock rolls uphill by itself, (2) heat flows from a cold object to a hot one, and (3) rust is converted to iron and oxygen.

18.2. Because the energy is more dispersed in liquids than in solids, liquid benzene contains more entropy than does the same quantity of frozen benzene.

18.3. The second law of thermodynamics states that for a spontaneous process, the total entropy of a system and its surroundings always increases. As stated in Section 18.2, a spontaneous process actually creates energy dispersal, or entropy.

18.4. The relationship between entropy and enthalpy can be expressed in terms of the following equation:

$$\Delta S = \frac{\Delta H - \Delta G}{T}$$

At equilibrium, ΔG equals 0, so the equation reduces to $\Delta H/T$, whereas, when not at equilibrium, $\Delta G \neq 0$, so this is not the case. In contrast to a phase change at equilibrium, the entropy change for a spontaneous chemical reaction (at constant pressure) does not equal $\Delta H/T$ because entropy is created by the spontaneous reaction. This can be an increase in the entropy of the surroundings or of the system. An example of the latter is the reaction $N_2O_4(g) \rightarrow 2NO_2(g)$, where one reactant molecule forms two product molecules, thus increasing the randomness.

18.5. The standard entropy of hydrogen gas at 25°C can be obtained by starting near 0.0 K as a reference point, where the entropy of perfect crystals of hydrogen is almost zero. Then, warm to room temperature in small increments, and calculate $\Delta S°$ for each incremental temperature change (say, 2 K) by dividing the heat absorbed by the average temperature (1 K is used as the average for 0 K to 2 K), and also take into account the entropy increases that accompany a phase change.

Copyright © Cengage Learning. All rights reserved.

18.6. To predict the sign of $\Delta S°$, look for a change, Δn_{gas}, in the number of moles of gas. If there is an increase in moles of gas in the products (Δn_{gas} is positive), then $\Delta S°$ should be positive. A decrease in moles of gas in the products suggests $\Delta S°$ should be negative.

18.7. Free energy, G, equals $H - TS$; that is, it is the difference between the enthalpy of a system and the product of temperature and entropy. The free-energy change, ΔG, equals $\Delta H - T\Delta S$.

18.8. The standard free-energy change, $\Delta G°$, equals $\Delta H° - T\Delta S°$; that is, it is the difference between the standard enthalpy change of a system and the product of temperature and the standard entropy change of a system. The standard free-energy change of formation is the free-energy change when 1 mole of a substance is formed from its elements in their stable states at 1 atm and at a standard temperature, usually 25°C.

18.9. If $\Delta G°$ for a reaction is negative, the equation for the reaction is spontaneous in the direction written; that is, the reactants form the products as written. If it is positive, then the equation as written is nonspontaneous.

18.10. In principle, if a reaction is carried out so that no entropy is produced, the useful work obtained is the maximum useful work, w_{max}, and is equal to ΔG of the reaction.

18.11. When gasoline burns in an automobile engine, the change in free energy shows up as useful work. Gasoline, a mixture of hydrocarbons such as C_8H_{18} or octane, burns to yield energy, gaseous CO_2, and gaseous H_2O.

18.12. A nonspontaneous reaction can be made to occur by coupling it with a spontaneous reaction having a sufficiently negative $\Delta G°$ to furnish the required energy. (The net $\Delta G°$ of the coupled reactions must be negative.)

Copyright © Cengage Learning. All rights reserved.

18.13. As a spontaneous reaction proceeds, the free energy decreases until equilibrium is reached at a minimum ΔG. See the diagram below.

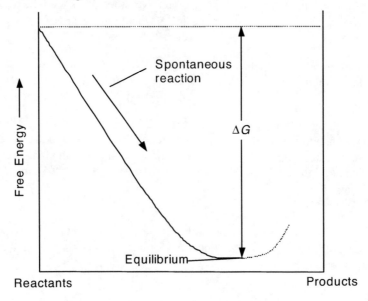

18.14. Because the equilibrium constant is related to $\Delta H°$ and $\Delta S°$ by $-RT \ln K = \Delta H° - T\Delta S°$, heat measurements alone can be used to obtain it. The standard enthalpy, $\Delta H°$, is the heat of reaction measured at constant pressure. The standard entropy change, $\Delta S°$, can be calculated from standard entropies, which are obtained from heat-capacity data.

18.15. The four combinations are as follows: (1) A negative $\Delta H°$ and a positive $\Delta S°$ always give a negative $\Delta G°$ and a spontaneous reaction. (2) A positive $\Delta H°$ and a negative $\Delta S°$ always give a positive $\Delta G°$ and a nonspontaneous reaction. (3) A negative $\Delta H°$ and a negative $\Delta S°$ may give a negative or a positive $\Delta G°$. At low temperatures, $\Delta G°$ will usually be negative and the reaction spontaneous; at high temperatures, $\Delta G°$ will usually be positive and the reaction nonspontaneous. (4) A positive $\Delta H°$ and a positive $\Delta S°$ may give a negative or a positive $\Delta G°$. At low temperatures, $\Delta G°$ will usually be positive and the reaction nonspontaneous; at high temperatures, $\Delta G°$ will usually be negative and the reaction spontaneous.

18.16. You can estimate the temperature at which a nonspontaneous reaction becomes spontaneous by substituting zero for $\Delta G°$ into the equation $\Delta G° = \Delta H° - T\Delta S°$ and then solving for T using the form $T = \Delta H°/\Delta S°$.

18.17. The answer is e, $\Delta G < 0$, $\Delta H > 0$, and $\Delta S > 0$.

18.18. The answer is c, III only.

18.19. The answer is d, 5.49 K

Copyright © Cengage Learning. All rights reserved.

18.20.   The answer is a, −956 kJ.

■ SOLUTIONS TO PRACTICE PROBLEMS

Note on significant figures: The mole unit is omitted from all thermodynamic parameters such as $S°$, $\Delta S°$, etc. If the final answer to a solution needs to be rounded off, it is given first with one nonsignificant figure, and the last significant figure is underlined. The final answer is then rounded to the correct number of significant figures. In multistep problems, intermediate answers are given with at least one nonsignificant figure; however, only the final answer has been rounded off.

18.31.   The values of q and w are −82 J and 29 J, respectively.

$$\Delta U = q + w = (-82 \text{ J}) + 29 \text{ J} = -53 \text{ J}$$

18.33.   At 100°C (373 K) and 1 atm (1.013×10^5 Pa), 1.00 mol of $H_2O(g)$ occupies

$$22.41 \text{ L} \times \frac{373 \text{ K}}{273 \text{ K}} = 30.\underline{6}19 \text{ L} \quad (30.\underline{6}19 \times 10^{-3} \text{ m}^3)$$

The work done by the chemical system in pushing back the atmosphere is

$$w = -P\Delta V = -(1.013 \times 10^5 \text{ Pa}) \times (30.619 \times 10^{-3} \text{ m}^3) = -3.10\underline{1}7 \times 10^3 \text{ J} = -3.10\underline{1}7 \text{ kJ}$$

$$\Delta U = q_p + w = (40.6\underline{6} \text{ kJ}) + (-3.1017 \text{ kJ}) = 37.5\underline{5}83 = 37.56 \text{ kJ}$$

18.35.   First, determine the enthalpy change for the reaction of 1.20 mol of $CHCl_3$.

$$\Delta H = 1.20 \text{ mol} \times \frac{29.6 \text{ kJ}}{1 \text{ mol}} = 35.\underline{5}2 \text{ kJ} = 3.5\underline{5}2 \times 10^4 \text{ J}$$

Use the equilibrium relation between ΔS and ΔH_{vap} at the boiling point (61.2°C = 334.4 K):

$$\Delta S = \frac{\Delta H}{T} = \frac{3.552 \times 10^4 \text{ J}}{334.4 \text{ K}} = 10\underline{6}.2 = 106 \text{ J/K}$$

18.37.   First, determine the enthalpy change for the condensation of 1.00 mol of $CH_3OH(l)$. $\Delta H_{cond} = -\Delta H_{vap} = -38.0$ kJ/mol.

The entropy change for this condensation at 25°C (298 K) is

$$\Delta S = \frac{\Delta H_{cond}}{T} = \frac{-3.80 \times 10^4 \text{ J}}{298 \text{ K}} = -12\underline{7}.51 \text{ J/K}$$

The entropy of one mole of liquid is calculated using the entropy of one mole of vapor, 255 J/(mol•K).

$$S_{liq} = S_{vap} + \Delta S_{cond} = 255 \text{ J/K} + (-127.51 \text{ J/K}) = 12\underline{7}.48 = 127 \text{ J/K}$$

Copyright © Cengage Learning. All rights reserved.

18.39.

a. ΔS° is negative because there is a decrease in moles of gas ($\Delta n_{gas} = -2$) from three moles of gaseous reactants forming one mole of gaseous product. (Entropy decreases.)

b. ΔS° is not predictable from the rules given. The molecules N_2, O_2 and NO are of similar size and present in equal numbers. There is no change in moles of gas ($\Delta n_{gas} = 0$), since two moles of gaseous reactants form two moles of gaseous products. Also, there is no phase change occurring.

c. ΔS° is positive because there is an increase in moles of gas ($\Delta n_{gas} = +1$) from five moles of gaseous reactants forming six moles of gaseous products. (Entropy increases.)

d. ΔS° is positive because there is an increase in moles of gas ($\Delta n_{gas} = +1$) from a solid reactant and one mole of gaseous reactant forming two moles of gaseous products. (Entropy increases.)

18.41.   The reaction and standard entropies are given below. Multiply the S° values by their stoichiometric coefficients, and subtract the entropy of the reactant from the sum of the product entropies.

$$2Na(s) \quad + \quad Cl_2(g) \quad \rightarrow \quad 2NaCl(s)$$

a. S°:   2 x 51.46   223.0   2 x 72.12 J/K

$\Delta S^\circ = \Sigma n S^\circ(\text{products}) - \Sigma m S^\circ(\text{reactants}) =$

            $[(2 \times 72.12) - (2 \times 51.46 + 223.0)]$ J/K $= -181.\underline{6}8 = -181.7$ J/K

$$Ag(s) \quad + \quad 1/2\,Cl_2(g) \quad \rightarrow \quad AgCl(s)$$

b. S°:   42.55   1/2 x 223.0   96.2 J/K

$\Delta S^\circ = \Sigma n S^\circ(\text{products}) - \Sigma m S^\circ(\text{reactants}) =$

            $[(96.2) - (42.55 + 1/2 \times 223.0)]$ J/K $= -57.\underline{8}5 = -57.9$ J/K

$$CS_2(l) \quad + \quad 3O_2(g) \quad \rightarrow \quad CO_2(g) \quad + \quad 2SO_2(g)$$

c. S°:   151.3   3 x 205.0   213.7   2 x 248.1 J/K

$\Delta S^\circ = \Sigma n S^\circ(\text{products}) - \Sigma m S^\circ(\text{reactants}) =$

            $[(213.7 + 2 \times 248.1) - (151.3 + 3 \times 205.0)]$ J/K $= -56.4$ J/K

$$2CH_3OH(l) \quad + \quad 3O_2(g) \quad \rightarrow \quad 2CO_2(g) \quad + \quad 4H_2O(g)$$

d. S°:   2 x 126.8   3 x 205.0   2 x 213.7   4 x 188.7 J/K

$\Delta S^\circ = \Sigma n S^\circ(\text{products}) - \Sigma m S^\circ(\text{reactants}) =$

            $[(2 \times 213.7 + 4 \times 188.7) - (2 \times 126.8 + 3 \times 205.0)]$ J/K $= 31\underline{3}.6 = 314$ J/K

Copyright © Cengage Learning. All rights reserved.

$$C_2H_4(g) \ + \ 3O_2(g) \quad \rightarrow \quad 2CO_2(g) \ + \ 2H_2O(l)$$

18.43. $S°$: 219.2   3 x 205.0   2 x 213.7   2 x 69.95 J/K

$\Delta S° \ = \ \Sigma n S°(\text{products}) \ - \ \Sigma m S°(\text{reactants}) \ =$

[(2 x 213.7 + 2 x 69.95) − (219.2 + 3 x 205.0)] J/K = −266.90 J/K

S decreases, as expected from the decrease in moles of gas.

18.45. The reaction, with standard enthalpies of formation and standard entropies written underneath, is

$$2CH_3OH(l) \quad + \quad 3O_2(g) \quad \rightarrow \quad 2CO_2(g) \quad + \quad 4H_2O(l)$$

$\Delta H_f°$: 2 x (-238.7)   0   2 x (-393.5)   4 x (-285.8) kJ

$S°$: 2 x 126.8   3 x 205.0   2 x 213.7   4 x 69.95 J/K

Calculate $\Delta H°$ and $\Delta S°$ for the reaction.

$\Delta H° \ = \ \Sigma n \Delta H_f°(\text{products}) \ - \ \Sigma m \Delta H_f°(\text{reactants}) \ =$

[2 x (−393.5) + 4 x (−285.8) − 2 x (−238.7)] kJ = −1452.8 kJ

$\Delta S° \ = \ \Sigma n S°(\text{products}) \ - \ \Sigma m S°(\text{reactants}) \ =$

[(2 x 213.7 + 4 x 69.95) − (2 x 126.8 + 3 x 205.0)] J/K = −161.40

= −161.4 J/K

Now, substitute into the equation for $\Delta G°$ in terms of $\Delta H°$ and $\Delta S°$ (= −0.16140 kJ/K).

$\Delta G° \ = \ \Delta H° \ - \ T\Delta S° \ = \ -1452.8$ kJ $-$ (298 K) x (−0.16140 kJ/K) = −1404.70

= −1404.7 kJ

18.47.

a. $K(s) \ + \ 1/2Br_2(l) \ \rightarrow \ KBr(s)$

b. $3/2H_2(g) \ + \ C(\text{graphite}) \ + \ 1/2Cl_2(g) \ \rightarrow \ CH_3Cl(l)$

c. $1/8S_8(\text{rhombic}) \ + \ H_2(g) \ \rightarrow \ H_2S(g)$

d. $As(s) \ + \ 3/2H_2(g) \ \rightarrow \ AsH_3(g)$

18.49. Write the values of $\Delta G_f°$ multiplied by their stoichiometric coefficients below each formula; then subtract $\Delta G_f°$ of the reactants from that of the products.

$$C_2H_4(g) \quad + \quad 3O_2(g) \quad \rightarrow \quad 2CO_2(g) \quad + \quad 2H_2O(g)$$

a. $\Delta G_f°$: 68.39   0   -394.4   2 x (-228.6) kJ

$\Delta G° \ = \ \Sigma n \Delta G_f°(\text{products}) \ - \ \Sigma m \Delta G_f°(\text{reactants}) \ =$

[2(−394.4) + 2(−228.6) − (68.39)] kJ = −1314.39 = −1314.4 kJ

Copyright © Cengage Learning. All rights reserved.

$$CaCO_3(s) \quad + \quad 2H^+(aq) \quad \rightarrow \quad Ca^{2+}(aq) \quad + \quad H_2O(l) \quad + \quad CO_2(g)$$

b. $\Delta G_f°$:   -1128.8   0   -553.5   -237.1   -394.4 kJ

$\Delta G° = \Sigma n\Delta G_f°(\text{products}) - \Sigma m\Delta G_f°(\text{reactants}) =$

$\qquad [(-553.5) + (-237.1) + (-394.4) - (-1128.8)] \text{ kJ} = -56.2 \text{ kJ}$

18.51.

a.   Spontaneous reaction

b.   Spontaneous reaction

c.   Nonspontaneous reaction

d.   Equilibrium mixture; significant amounts of both

e.   Nonspontaneous reaction

18.53.   Calculate $\Delta H°$ and $\Delta G°$ using the given $\Delta H_f°$ and $\Delta G_f°$ values.

$$Al_2O_3(s) \quad + \quad 2Fe(s) \quad \rightarrow \quad Fe_2O_3(s) \quad + \quad 2Al(s)$$

$\Delta H_f°$:   -1675.7   0   -825.5   0 kJ

$\Delta G_f°$:   -1582.3   0   -743.5   0 kJ

a.

$\Delta H° = [(-825.5) - (-1675.7)] \text{ kJ} = 850.2 \text{ kJ}$

$\Delta G° = [(-743.5) - (-1582.3)] \text{ kJ} = 838.8 \text{ kJ}$

The reaction is endothermic, absorbing 850.2 kJ of heat. The large positive value for $\Delta G°$ indicates that the equilibrium composition is mainly reactants.

$$COCl_2(g) \quad + \quad H_2O(l) \quad \rightarrow \quad CO_2(g) \quad + \quad 2HCl(g)$$

$\Delta H_f°$:   -220.1   -285.8   -393.5   2 x (-92.31) kJ

b. $\Delta G_f°$:   -205.9   -237.1   -394.4   2 x (-95.30) kJ

$\Delta H° = [-393.5 + (2)(-92.31) - (-220.1) - (-285.8)] \text{ kJ} = -72.\underline{2}2 = -72.2 \text{ kJ}$

$\Delta G° = [-394.4 + (2)(-95.30) - (-205.9) - (-237.1)] \text{ kJ} = -142.\underline{0}0 = -142.0 \text{ kJ}$

The reaction is exothermic; the $\Delta G°$ value indicates mainly products at equilibrium.

Copyright © Cengage Learning. All rights reserved.

18.55. Calculate $\Delta G°$ using the given $\Delta G_f°$ values.

$$2H_2(g) \quad + \quad O_2(g) \quad \rightarrow \quad 2H_2O(l)$$

$\Delta G_f°$:   0   0   2 x (-237.1) kJ

$\Delta G° = [2(-237.1) - 0]\,kJ = -474.2\,kJ$

Maximum work equals $\Delta G°$ equals −474.2 kJ. Because maximum work is stipulated, no entropy is produced.

18.57. Calculate $\Delta G°$ per 1 mol Zn(s) using the given $\Delta G_f°$ values.

$$Zn(s) \quad + \quad Cu^{2+}(aq) \quad \rightarrow \quad Zn^{2+}(aq) \quad + \quad Cu(s)$$

$\Delta G_f°$:   0   65.52   -147.0   0 kJ

$\Delta G° = [(-147.0) - (65.52)]\,kJ = -212.52\,kJ/mol\,Zn$

$-212.52\,kJ/mol\,Zn \times (4.85\,g \div 65.39\,g/mol\,Zn) = -15.76 = -15.8\,kJ$

Maximum work equals $\Delta G°$ equals −15.8 kJ. Because maximum work is stipulated, no entropy is produced.

18.59.

a. $K = K_p = \dfrac{P_{CO_2}P_{H_2}}{P_{CO}P_{H_2O}}$

b. $K = K_{sp} = [Mg^{2+}][OH^-]^2$

c. $K = [Li^+]^2[OH^-]^2\,P_{H_2}$

18.61. First, calculate $\Delta G°$ using the $\Delta G_f°$ values from Appendix C.

$$H_2(g) \qquad Br_2(l) \qquad \rightarrow \qquad 2HBr(g)$$

$\Delta G_f°$:   0   0   2 x (-53.50) kJ

$\Delta G° = [2(-53.50) - 0]\,kJ = -107.00\,kJ$

Use the rearranged form of the equation, $\Delta G° = -RT \ln K$, to solve for $\ln K$. To get compatible units, express $\Delta G°$ in joules, and set R equal to 8.31 J/(mol·K). Substituting the numerical values into the expression gives

$$\ln K = \frac{-\Delta G°}{RT} = \frac{-107.00 \times 10^3}{-8.31 \times 298} = 43.208$$

$$K = e^{43.208} = 5.82 \times 10^{18} = 6 \times 10^{18}$$

Copyright © Cengage Learning. All rights reserved.

360   Chapter 18: Thermodynamics and Equilibrium

18.63. First, calculate $\Delta G°$ using the $\Delta G_f°$ values from Appendix C.

$$CO(g) \;+\; 3H_2(g) \;\rightleftharpoons\; CH_4(g) \;+\; H_2O(g)$$

$\Delta G_f°$:   -137.2   0   -50.80   -228.6 kJ

Subtract $\Delta G_f°$ of the reactants from that of the products:

$$\Delta G° = [(-50.80) + (-228.6) - (-137.2)] \text{ kJ} = -142.20 \text{ kJ}$$

Use the rearranged form of the equation, $\Delta G° = -RT \ln K$, to solve for $\ln K$. To get compatible units, express $\Delta G°$ in joules, and set R equal to 8.31 J/(mol•K). Substituting the numerical values into the expression gives

$$\ln K = \frac{-\Delta G°}{RT} = \frac{-142.20 \times 10^3}{-8.31 \times 298} = 57.\underline{4}22$$

$$K = K_p = e^{57.422} = \underline{8}.67 \times 10^{24} = 9 \times 10^{24}$$

18.65. First, calculate $\Delta G°$ using the $\Delta G_f°$ values from Appendix C.

$$Fe(s) \;+\; Cu^{2+}(aq) \;\rightleftharpoons\; Fe^{2+}(aq) \;+\; Cu(s)$$

$\Delta G_f°$:   0   65.52   -78.87   0 kJ

Hence

$$\Delta G° = [(-78.87) - 65.52] \text{ kJ} = -144.39 \text{ kJ}$$

Now, substitute numerical values into the equation relating $\ln K$ and $\Delta G°$.

$$\ln K = \frac{-\Delta G°}{RT} = \frac{-144.39 \times 10^3}{-8.31 \times 298} = 58.\underline{3}06$$

Therefore,

$$K = K_c = e^{58.306} = \underline{2}.10 \times 10^{25} = 2 \times 10^{25}$$

18.67. From Appendix C, you have

$$C(graphite) \;+\; CO_2(g) \;\rightleftharpoons\; 2CO(g)$$

$\Delta H_f°$:   0   -393.5   2 x (-110.5) kJ
$S°$:   5.740   213.7   2 x (197.5) J/K

Calculate $\Delta H°$ and $\Delta S°$ from these values.

$$\Delta H° = [2(-110.5) - (-393.5)] \text{ kJ} = 172.\underline{5} \text{ kJ}$$

$$\Delta S° = [2(197.5) - (5.740 + 213.7)] \text{ J/K} = 175.\underline{5}6 \text{ J/K}$$

Substitute $\Delta H°$, $\Delta S°$ ($= 0.17556$ kJ/K), and T ($= 1273$ K) into the equation for $\Delta G_T°$.

$$\Delta G_T° = \Delta H° - T\Delta S° = 172.5 \text{ kJ} - (1273 \text{ K})(0.17556 \text{ kJ/K}) = -50.\underline{9}87 \text{ kJ}$$

Copyright © Cengage Learning. All rights reserved.

Substitute the value of $\Delta G°$ ($= -50.987 \times 10^3$ J) into the equation relating ln K and $\Delta G°$.

$$\ln K = \frac{-\Delta G°}{RT} = \frac{-50.987 \times 10^3}{-8.31 \times 1273} = 4.8\underline{1}98$$

$$K = K_p = e^{4.8198} = 12\underline{3}.9 = 1.2 \times 10^2$$

Because K_p is greater than 1, the data predict that combustion of carbon should form significant amounts of CO product at equilibrium.

18.69. First, calculate $\Delta H°$ and $\Delta S°$ using the given $\Delta H_f°$ and $S°$ values.

$$2NaHCO_3(s) \rightarrow Na_2CO_3(s) + H_2O(g) + CO_2(g)$$

$\Delta H_f°$:   2 x (-950.8)   -1130.8   -241.8   -393.5 kJ

$\Delta S°$:   2 x 101.7   138.8   188.7   213.7 J/K

$\Delta H° = [(-1130.8) + (-241.8) + (-393.5) - 2(-950.8)]$ kJ $= 135.5$ kJ

$\Delta S° = [(138.8 + 188.7 + 213.7) - 2(101.7)]$ J/K $= 337.8$ J/K $(0.3378$ kJ/K$)$

Substitute these values into $\Delta G° = \Delta H° - T\Delta S°$; let $\Delta G° = 0$, and rearrange to solve for T.

$$T = \frac{\Delta H°}{\Delta S°} = \frac{135.5 \text{ kJ}}{0.3378 \text{ kJ/K}} = 40\underline{1}.1 = 401 \text{ K}$$

■ SOLUTIONS TO GENERAL PROBLEMS

18.71. The sign of $\Delta S°$ should be positive because there is an increase in moles of gas ($\Delta n_{gas} = +5$) as the solid reactant forms five moles of gas. The reaction is endothermic, denoting a positive $\Delta H°$. The fact that the reaction is spontaneous implies that the product, $T\Delta S°$, is larger than $\Delta H°$, so $\Delta G°$ is negative, as required for a spontaneous reaction.

18.73. The ΔH value $\cong$ BE(H−H) + BE(Cl−Cl) − BE(H−Cl) $\cong [432 + 240 - 2(428)]$ kJ ~ −184 kJ, and thus the reaction is exothermic. $\Delta S°$ should be positive because there is a increase in energy dispersal with the formation of unsymmetrical molecules from symmetrical H_2 and Cl_2. The reaction should be spontaneous because the contributions of both the ΔH term and the $-T\Delta S$ term are negative.

18.75. When the liquid freezes, it releases heat: $\Delta H_{fus} = -69.0$ J/g at 16.6°C (289.8 K). The entropy change is

$$\Delta S = \frac{\Delta H_{fus}}{T} = \frac{-69.0 \text{ J/g}}{289.8 \text{ K}} \times \frac{60.05 \text{ g}}{1 \text{ mol}} = -14.\underline{3}0 = -14.3 \text{ J/(K•mol)}$$

Copyright © Cengage Learning. All rights reserved.

18.77.

a. $\Delta S°$ is negative because there is a decrease in moles of gas ($\Delta n_{gas} = -1$) from one mole of gaseous reactant forming aqueous and liquid products. (Entropy decreases.)

b. $\Delta S°$ is positive because there is an increase in moles of gas ($\Delta n_{gas} = +5$) from a solid reactant forming five moles of gas. (Entropy increases.)

c. $\Delta S°$ is positive because there is an increase in moles of gas ($\Delta n_{gas} = +3$) from two moles of gaseous reactant forming five moles of gaseous products. (Entropy increases.)

d. $\Delta S°$ is negative because there is a decrease in moles of gas ($\Delta n_{gas} = -1$) from three moles of gaseous reactants forming two moles of gaseous products. (Entropy decreases.)

18.79. $\Delta S°$ is negative because there is a decrease in the moles of gas ($\Delta n_{gas} = -2$) from three moles of gaseous reactant forming one mole of gaseous product plus liquid product.

18.81.   Calculate $\Delta S°$ from the individual $S°$ values:

$$C_2H_5OH(l) \quad + \quad O_2(g) \quad \rightarrow \quad CH_3COOH(l) \quad + \quad H_2O(l)$$

$S°:$ 160.7   205.0   159.8   69.95 J/K

$\Delta S° = \Sigma nS°(\text{products}) - \Sigma mS°(\text{reactants}) =$

$[(159.8 + 69.95) - (160.7 + 205.0)]$ J/K $= -135.\underline{9}5 = -136.0$ J/K

18.83.   Calculate $\Delta G°$ using the $\Delta G_f°$ values from Appendix C.

$$H_2(g) \quad + \quad SO_2(g) \quad \rightarrow \quad H_2S(g) \quad + \quad O_2(g)$$

$\Delta G_f°:$ 0   -300.1   -33.33   0 kJ

$\Delta G° = \Sigma n\Delta G_f°(\text{products}) - \Sigma m\Delta G_f°(\text{reactants}) =$

$[(-33.33) - (-300.1)]$ kJ $= 266.\underline{7}7 = 266.8$ kJ

Because $\Delta G°$ is positive, the reaction is nonspontaneous as written, at 25°C.

18.85.   At low (room) temperature, $\Delta G°$ or ($\Delta H° - T\Delta S°$) must be positive, but at higher temperatures, $\Delta G°$ or ($\Delta H° - T\Delta S°$) must be negative. Thus, at the higher temperatures, the $-T\Delta S°$ term must become more negative than $\Delta H°$. Thus, $\Delta S°$ must be positive and so must $\Delta H°$. If either were negative, $\Delta G°$ would not become negative at higher temperatures.

Copyright © Cengage Learning. All rights reserved.

18.87. First, calculate $\Delta G°$ using the values in Appendix C.

$$CaF_2(s) \rightleftharpoons Ca^{2+}(aq) \quad + \quad 2F^-(aq)$$

$\Delta G_f°$:   -1173.5   -553.5   2 x (-278.8) kJ

Hence, $\Delta G°$ for the reaction is

$\Delta G_f° = [-553.5 + 2(-278.8) - (-1173.5)]$ kJ $= 62.4$ kJ

Now, substitute numerical values into the equation relating ln K and $\Delta G°$.

$$\ln K = \frac{-\Delta G°}{RT} = \frac{62.4 \times 10^3}{-8.31 \times 298} = -25.\underline{1}98$$

$$K = K_{sp} = e^{-25.198} = \underline{1}.13 \times 10^{-11} = 1 \times 10^{-11}$$

18.89. From Appendix C, you have

$$COCl_2(g) \quad \rightarrow \quad CO(g) \quad + \quad Cl_2(g)$$

$\Delta H_f°$:   -220.1   -110.5   0 kJ

$S°$:   283.9   197.5   223.0 J/K

Calculate $\Delta H°$ and $\Delta S°$ from these values.

$\Delta H° = [(-110.5) - (-220.1)]$ kJ $= 109.6$ kJ

$\Delta S° = [197.5 + 223.0 - 283.9]$ J/K $= 136.6$ J/K (0.1366 kJ/K)

At 25°C: $\Delta G° = \Delta H° - T\Delta S° = 109.6$ kJ $- (298$ K$)(0.1366$ kJ/K$) = 68.\underline{8}9 = 68.9$ kJ

At 800°C: $\Delta G_T° = \Delta H° - T\Delta S° = 109.6$ kJ $- (1073$ K$)(0.1366$ kJ/K$)$

$$= -36.\underline{9}7 = -37.0 \text{ kJ}$$

Thus, $\Delta G°$ changes from a positive value and a nonspontaneous reaction at 25°C to a negative value and a spontaneous reaction at 800°C.

18.91

a.

			$\Delta H°$, kJ
$CO_2(g) + 2H_2(g)$	$\rightarrow$	$HCHO(g) + H_2O(g)$	35
$HCHO(g) + 2H_2(g)$	$\rightarrow$	$CH_4(g) + H_2O(g)$	-201
$C(s) + O_2(g)$	$\rightarrow$	$CO_2(g)$	-393
$2H_2O(g)$	$\rightarrow$	$2H_2(g) + O_2(g)$	484
$C(s) + 2H_2(g)$	$\rightarrow$	$CH_4(g)$	-75 kJ

Copyright © Cengage Learning. All rights reserved.

b.

$$C(s) \quad + \quad 2H_2(g) \quad \rightarrow \quad CH_4(g)$$

$S°$:   5.740   2 x 130.6   186.1 J/K

$\Delta S° = \Sigma nS°(\text{products}) - \Sigma mS°(\text{reactants}) =$

[186.1 − 5.740 − 2(130.6)] J/K = −80.84 J/K (−0.08084 kJ/K)

c. $\Delta G°$ for the reaction, which involves 1 mole of methane, is equal to $\Delta G_f°$ for methane and is obtained as follows:

$$\Delta G_f° = \Delta G° = \Delta H° - T\Delta S°$$
$$= -75 \text{ kJ} - (298 \text{ K})(-0.08084 \text{ kJ/K})$$
$$= -50.90 = -51 \text{ kJ/mol}$$

18.93. $\Delta H° = [-393.5 + 2(-285.8) - (-238.7)]$ kJ $= -726.4$ kJ

$$\Delta G° = \Delta H° - T\Delta S°$$
$$-702.2 \text{ kJ} = -726.4 \text{ kJ} - (298 \text{ K})(\Delta S°)$$
$$\Delta S° = -\frac{(-702.2 \text{ kJ}) - (-726.4 \text{ kJ})}{298 \text{ K}} = -0.08120 \text{ kJ/K} = -81.20 \text{ J/K}$$

$\Delta S° = -81.20$ J/K $= [2(70.0) + 213.7 - (126.8) - (3/2 \text{ mol}) \times S°(O_2)]$ J/K

$S°(O_2) = 205.40 = 205.4$ J/mol•K

18.95.

a. The first reaction is

$$SnO_2(s) \quad + \quad 2H_2(g) \quad \rightarrow \quad Sn(s) \quad + \quad 2H_2O(g)$$

$\Delta H_f°$:   -580.7   0   0   -241.8 kJ

$S°$:   52.3   130.6   51.55   188.7 J/K

$\Delta H° = [2(-241.8) - (-580.7)]$ kJ $= 97.1$ kJ $= 97.1 \times 10^3$ J

$\Delta S° = [2(188.7) + 51.55 - 2(130.6) - 52.3]$ J/K $= 115.45$ J/K

The second reaction is

$$SnO_2(s) \quad + \quad C(s) \quad \rightarrow \quad Sn(s) \quad + \quad CO_2(g)$$

$\Delta H_f°$:   -580.7   0   0   -393.5 kJ

$S°$:   52.3   5.740   51.55   213.7 J/K

$\Delta H° = [-393.5 - (-580.7)]$ kJ $= 187.2$ kJ $= 187.2 \times 10^3$ J

$\Delta S° = [213.7 + 51.55 - 5.740 - 52.3]$ J/K $= 207.21$ J/K

Copyright © Cengage Learning. All rights reserved.

b.   For H_2, at what temperature does $\Delta G = 0$?

$$0 = \Delta H^\circ - T\Delta S^\circ$$

$$T = \frac{\Delta H}{\Delta S} = \frac{97.1 \times 10^3 \text{ J}}{115.45 \text{ J/K}} = 84\underline{1}.0 = 841 \text{ K}$$

At temperatures greater than 841 K, the reaction will be spontaneous.

For C, at what temperature does $\Delta G = 0$?

$$T = \frac{\Delta H}{\Delta S} = \frac{187.2 \times 10^3 \text{ J}}{207.21 \text{ J/K}} = 90\underline{3}.4 = 903 \text{ K}$$

At temperatures greater than 904 K, the reaction will be spontaneous.

c.   From a consideration of temperature, the process with hydrogen would be preferred. But hydrogen is very expensive and carbon is cheap. On this basis, carbon would be preferred. Tin is produced commercially using carbon as the reducing agent.

18.97.

a.   Formic acid is favored because it is of lower energy than CO and H_2O.

b.   The change in entropy for the decomposition of formic acid is positive as a mole of gas is produced. Thus, the change in entropy would be the driving force for this reaction, favoring the formation of products.

18.99.

a.   If ΔG° is negative, then K must be greater than 1. Consequently, the products will predominate.

b.   The molecules must have enough energy to react when they collide with each other. Thus, it depends upon the activation energy for the reaction. Usually it is necessary to heat solids for a reaction to occur, because it is difficult to have effective collisions.

18.101.

a. $C_4H_{10}(g) + 13/2 O_2(g) \rightarrow 4CO_2(g) + 5H_2O(l)$

$$\Delta H^\circ = \frac{-49.50 \text{ kJ}}{1.000 \text{ g}} \times \frac{58.12 \text{ g}}{1 \text{ mol}} = -287\underline{6}.94 \text{ kJ/mol}$$

$$\Delta H^\circ = \Sigma n\Delta H_f^\circ(\text{products}) - \Sigma m\Delta H_f^\circ(\text{reactants})$$

$$-2876.94 \text{ kJ} = [4(-393.5) + 5(-285.8) - (1 \text{ mol}) \times \Delta H_f^\circ(C_4H_{10})] \text{ kJ}$$

$$\Delta H_f^\circ(C_4H_{10}) = -12\underline{6}.06 = -126 \text{ kJ/mol}$$

b. $\Delta G^\circ = [4(-394.4) + 5(-237.1) - (-17.2)] \text{ kJ} = -2745.\underline{9} \text{ kJ}$

Copyright © Cengage Learning. All rights reserved.

c. $\Delta G° = \Delta H° - T\Delta S°$

-2745.9 kJ $= -2876.94$ kJ $- (298$ K$) \Delta S°$

$\Delta S° = -\dfrac{(-2745.9 \text{ kJ}) - (-2876.94 \text{ kJ})}{298 \text{ K}} = -0.4397$ kJ/K $= -440.$ J/K (for one mole)

18.103.

a. $\Delta H° = [-1285 - (-1288.3)]$ kJ $= 3.3$ kJ $= 3.3 \times 10^3$ J

$\Delta S° = [89 - 158.2]$ J/K $= -69.2$ J/K

$\Delta G° = \Delta H° - T\Delta S°$

$\Delta G° = 3.3 \times 10^3$ J $- (298$ K$)(-69.2$ J/K$) = 23.921 \times 10^3$ J

Now, substitute numerical values into the equation relating ln K and $\Delta G°$.

$\ln K = \dfrac{-\Delta G°}{RT} = \dfrac{23.921 \times 10^3}{-8.31 \times 298} = -9.6599$

$K = e^{-9.6599} = 6.37 \times 10^{-5} = 6 \times 10^{-5}$

b. The change in entropy is negative, greater order, so this causes H_3PO_4 to be a weak acid. The enthalpy change reduces the acid strength of H_3PO_4, and the entropy is a very important term.

■ SOLUTIONS TO CUMULATIVE-SKILLS PROBLEMS

18.117. For the dissociation of HBr, assume ΔH and ΔS are constant over the temperature range from 25°C to 375°C, and calculate the value of each to use to calculate K at 375°C. Start by calculating $\Delta H°$ and $\Delta S°$ at 25°C, using $\Delta H_f°$ and $S°$ values.

	2HBr(g)	→	H₂(g)	+	Br₂(g)
$\Delta H_f°$:	2 x (-36.44)		0		30.91 kJ
$S°$:	2 x 198.6		130.6		245.3 J/K

Calculate $\Delta H°$ and $\Delta S°$ from these values.

$\Delta H° = [30.91 - 2(-36.44)]$ kJ $= 103.79$ kJ

$\Delta S° = [245.3 + 130.6 - 2(198.6)]$ J/K $= -21.3$ J/K

Substitute $\Delta H°$, $\Delta S°$ ($= -0.02130$ kJ/K), and T (648 K) into the equation for $\Delta G_T°$.

$\Delta G_T° = \Delta H° - T\Delta S° = 103.79$ kJ $- (648$ K$)(-0.02130$ kJ/K$) = 117.59$ kJ

$= 117.59 \times 10^3$ J

Copyright © Cengage Learning. All rights reserved.

Now, substitute numerical values into the equation relating $\ln K$ and $\Delta G°$ ($= \Delta G_T°$).

$$\ln K = \frac{-\Delta G°}{RT} = \frac{117.59 \times 10^3}{-8.31 \times 648} = -21.\underline{8}37$$

$$K = e^{-21.837} = \underline{3}.28 \times 10^{-10}$$

Assuming x equals $[H_2]$ equals $[Br_2]$, and assuming $[HBr] = (1.00 - 2x) \cong 1.00$ atm, substitute into the equilibrium expression:

$$K = \frac{[H_2][Br_2]}{[HBr]^2} = \frac{(x)(x)}{(1.00)^2} = \underline{3}.28 \times 10^{-10}$$

Solve for the approximate pressure of x:

$$x = \sqrt{(3.28 \times 10^{-10})(1.00)^2} = \underline{1}.81 \times 10^{-5} \text{ atm}$$

The percent dissociation at 1.00 atm is

$$\text{Percent dissociation} = \frac{2(1.81 \times 10^{-5} \text{ atm})}{1.00 \text{ atm}} \times 100\% = 0.00\underline{3}6\%$$

Based on Le Châtelier's principle, pressure has no effect on equilibrium. Therefore, the percent dissociation is 0.004% at 1.00 atm and at 10.0 atm.

18.119. For the dissociation of NH_3, assume ΔH and ΔS are constant over the temperature range from 25°C to 345°C, and calculate values of each to calculate K at 345°C.

$$2NH_3(g) \quad \rightarrow \quad 3H_2(g) \quad + \quad N_2(g)$$

$\Delta H_f°$:	2 x (-45.90)	0	0 kJ
$S°$:	2 x 192.7	3 x 130.6	191.6 J/K

Calculate $\Delta H°$ and $\Delta S°$ from these values.

$$\Delta H° = [0 - 2(-45.90)] \text{ kJ} = 91.80 \text{ kJ}$$

$$\Delta S° = [3(130.6) + 191.6 - 2(192.7)] \text{ J/K} = 198.0 \text{ J/K}$$

Substitute $\Delta H°$, $\Delta S°$ ($= 0.1980$ kJ/K), and T (618 K) into the equation for $\Delta G_T°$.

$$\Delta G_T° = \Delta H° - T\Delta S° = 91.8 \text{ kJ} - (618 \text{ K})(0.1980 \text{ kJ/K}) = -30.\underline{5}64 \text{ kJ}$$
$$= -30.564 \times 10^3 \text{ J}$$

Now, substitute numerical values into the equation relating $\ln K$ and $\Delta G°$ ($= \Delta G_T°$).

$$\ln K = \frac{-\Delta G°}{RT} = \frac{-30.564 \times 10^3}{-8.31 \times 618} = 5.9\underline{5}1$$

$$K = K_p = e^{5.951} = 3\underline{8}4.2$$

Now obtain K_c.

$$K_c = K_p(RT)^{-2} = (384.2)(0.0821 \times 618)^{-2} = 0.1\underline{4}92$$

Copyright © Cengage Learning. All rights reserved.

The starting concentration of NH_3 is 1.00 mol/20.0L = 0.0500 M. You obtain the following table:

	$2NH_3(g)$	$\rightarrow$	$3H_2(g)$	+	$N_2(g)$
Starting	0.0500		0		0
Change	-2x		+3x		+x
Equilibrium	0.0500 - 2x		3x		x

The equilibrium equation is

$$K_c = \frac{[H_2]^3[N_2]}{[NH_3]^2}$$

or

$$\frac{(3x)^3 x}{(0.0500 - 2x)^2} = 0.1492$$

$$\frac{x^4}{(0.0500 - 2x)^2} = \frac{0.1492}{27} = 5.528 \times 10^{-3}$$

Taking the square root of both sides of this equation gives

$$\frac{x^2}{(0.0500 - 2x)} = 0.07\underline{4}35$$

This can be rearranged into the following quadratic equation.

$$x^2 + (0.1487)x - (3.717 \times 10^{-3}) = 0$$

From the quadratic formula, you obtain

$$x = \frac{-0.1487 \pm \sqrt{(0.1487)^2 + 4(3.717 \times 10^{-3})}}{2}$$

The positive root is

$$x = 0.02\underline{1}80 \ M$$

Hence,

$$[NH_3] = 0.0500 - 2(0.02180) = 0.006\underline{4} \ M$$

$$\text{Percent } NH_3 \text{ dissociated} = \left(1 - \frac{0.0064 \ M}{0.0500 \ M}\right) \times 100\% = 8\underline{7}.2 = 87\%$$

Copyright © Cengage Learning. All rights reserved.

18.121. First, calculate $\Delta G°$ at each temperature, using $\Delta G° = -RT \ln K$:

$25.0°C$: $\Delta G° = -(0.008314 \text{ kJ/K})(298.2 \text{ K})(\ln 1.754 \text{ x } 10^{-5}) = 27.15\underline{0}1 \text{ kJ}$

$50.0°C$: $\Delta G_T° = -(0.008314 \text{ kJ/K})(323.2 \text{ K})(\ln 1.633 \text{ x } 10^{-5}) = 29.6\underline{1}84 \text{ kJ}$

Next, solve two equations in two unknowns assuming $\Delta H°$ and $\Delta S°$ are constant over the range of $25.0°C$ to $50.0°C$. Use 0.2982 K(kJ/J) and 0.3232 K(kJ/J) to convert $\Delta S°$ in J to $T\Delta S°$ in kJ.

(1) $27.1501 \text{ kJ} = \Delta H° - [0.2982 \text{ K(kJ/J) } \Delta S°]$

(2) $29.6184 \text{ kJ} = \Delta H° - [0.3232 \text{ K(kJ/J) } \Delta S°]$

Then, rearrange Equation 2, and substitute for $\Delta H°$ into Equation 2:

(3)a. $\Delta H° = 0.3232 \text{ K(kJ/J) } \Delta S° + 29.6184 \text{ kJ}$

(3)b. $27.1501 \text{ kJ} = [0.3232 \text{ K(kJ/J) } \Delta S° + 29.6184 \text{ kJ}] - [0.2982 \text{ K(kJ/J) } \Delta S°]$

Solve for $\Delta S°$:

$$\Delta S° = \frac{(29.6184 - 27.1501) \text{ kJ}}{(0.2982 - 0.3232) \text{ K/(kJ/J)}} = -98.\underline{7}3 = -98.7 \text{ J/K}$$

Substitute this value into Equation 3a and solve for $\Delta H°$:

$\Delta H° = [(0.3232) \text{ K(kJ/J) x } (-98.73 \text{ J/K})] + 29.6184 \text{ kJ} = -2.2\underline{9}1 = -2.29 \text{ kJ}$

Copyright © Cengage Learning. All rights reserved.

CHAPTER 19

Electrochemistry

■ SOLUTIONS TO EXERCISES

Note on significant figures: If the final answer to a solution needs to be rounded off, it is given first with one nonsignificant figure, and the last significant figure is underlined. The final answer is then rounded to the correct number of significant figures. In multistep problems, intermediate answers are given with at least one nonsignificant figure; however, only the final answer has been rounded off.

19.1. Assign oxidation numbers to the skeleton equation (Step 1).

$$
\begin{array}{cccc}
0 & +5 & +5 & +4 \\
I_2 + NO_3^- & \rightarrow & IO_3^- + & NO_2
\end{array}
$$

Separate into two incomplete half-reactions (Step 2). Note that iodine is oxidized (increases in oxidation number), and nitrogen is reduced (decreases in oxidation number).

$$I_2 \rightarrow IO_3^-$$

$$NO_3^- \rightarrow NO_2$$

Balance each half-reaction separately. The oxidation half-reaction is not balanced in I, so place a two in front of IO_3^- (Step 3a). Then add six H_2O's to the left side to balance O atoms (Step 3b), and add twelve H^+ ions to the right side to balance H atoms (Step 3c). Finally, add ten electrons to the right side to balance the charge (Step 3d). The balanced oxidation half-reaction is

$$I_2 + 6H_2O \rightarrow 2IO_3^- + 12H^+ + 10e^-$$

The reduction half-reaction is balanced in N (Step 3a). Add one H_2O to the right side to balance O atoms (Step 3b), and add two H^+ ion to the left side to balance H atoms. Finally, add one electron to the left side to balance the charge (Step 3d).

The balanced reduction half-reaction is

$$NO_3^- + 2H^+ + e^- \rightarrow NO_2 + H_2O$$

Multiply the reduction half-reaction by 5 so that, when added, the electrons cancel (Step 4a).

$$I_2 + 6H_2O \rightarrow 2IO_3^- + 12H^+ + 10e^-$$

$$10NO_3^- + 20H^+ + 10e^- \rightarrow 10NO_2 + 10H_2O$$

$$I_2 + 10NO_3^- + 20H^+ + 6H_2O + \cancel{10e^-} \rightarrow 2IO_3^- + 10NO_2 + 12H^+ + 10H_2O + \cancel{10e^-}$$

Copyright © Cengage Learning. All rights reserved.

Simplify the equation by canceling the twelve H^+ and six H_2O that appear on both sides. The coefficients do not need to be reduced (Step 4b). The net ionic equation is

$$I_2(s) + 10NO_3^-(aq) + 8H^+(aq) \rightarrow 2IO_3^-(aq) + 10NO_2(g) + 4H_2O(l)$$

19.2. After balancing the equation as though it were in acid solution, you obtain

$$H_2O_2 + 2ClO_2 \rightarrow 2ClO_2^- + O_2 + 2H^+$$

Add two OH^- to both sides of the equation (Step 5), and replace the two H^+ and two OH^- on the right side with two H_2O. No further cancellation is required. The balanced equation for the reaction in basic solution is

$$H_2O_2 + 2ClO_2 + 2OH^- \rightarrow 2ClO_2^- + O_2 + 2H_2O$$

19.3. Silver ion is reduced at the silver electrode (cathode). The half-reaction is

$$Ag^+(aq) + e^- \rightarrow Ag(s)$$

The nickel electrode (anode) is where oxidation occurs. The half-reaction is

$$Ni(s) \rightarrow Ni^{2+}(aq) + 2e^-$$

Electron flow in the external circuit is from the nickel electrode (anode) to the silver electrode (cathode). Positive ions will flow in the solution portion of the circuit opposite to the direction of the electrons. A sketch of the cell is given below:

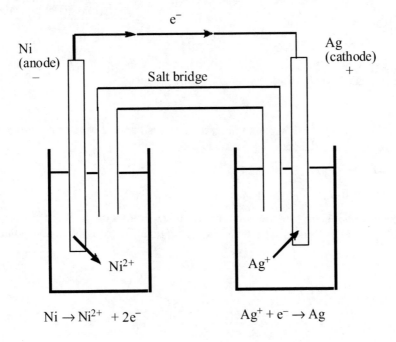

19.4. The notation for the cell is $Zn(s)|Zn^{2+}(aq)\|H^+(aq)|H_2(g)|Pt(s)$.

Copyright © Cengage Learning. All rights reserved.

19.5. The half-cell reactions are

$$Cd(s) \rightarrow Cd^{2+}(aq) + 2e^-$$
$$2H^+(aq) + 2e^- \rightarrow H_2(g)$$

Summing the half-cell reactions gives the overall cell reaction.

$$Cd(s) + 2H^+(aq) \rightarrow Cd^{2+}(aq) + H_2(g)$$

19.6. The half-reactions are

$$Zn(s) \rightarrow Zn^{2+}(aq) + 2e^-$$
$$Cu^{2+}(aq) + 2e^- \rightarrow Cu(s)$$

n equals 2, and the maximum work for the reaction as written is

$$w_{max} = -nFE_{cell} = -2 \times 9.6485 \times 10^4 \text{ C} \times 1.10 \text{ V} = -2.122 \times 10^5 \text{ V•C} = -2.12 \times 10^5 \text{ J}$$

For 6.54 g of zinc metal, the maximum work is

$$6.54 \text{ g Zn} \times \frac{1 \text{ mol Zn}}{65.39 \text{ g Zn}} \times \frac{-2.123 \times 10^5 \text{ J}}{1 \text{ mol Zn}} = -2.123 \times 10^4 = -2.12 \times 10^4 \text{ J}$$

19.7. The half-reactions and corresponding electrode potentials are

$$Ag^-(aq) + e^- \rightarrow Ag(s) \qquad\qquad 0.80 \text{ V}$$
$$NO_3^-(aq) + 4H^-(aq) + 4e^- \rightarrow NO(g) + 2H_2O(l) \quad 0.96 \text{ V}$$

The stronger oxidizing agent is the one involved in the half-reaction with the more positive standard electrode potential, so NO_3^- is the stronger oxidizing agent.

19.8. In this reaction, Cu^{2+} is the oxidizing agent on the left side; I_2 is the oxidizing reagent on the right side. The corresponding standard electrode potentials are

$$Cu^{2+}(aq) + 2e^- \rightarrow Cu(s); \; E° = 0.34 \text{ V}$$
$$I_2(s) + 2e^- \rightarrow 2I^-(aq); \quad E° = 0.54 \text{ V}$$

The stronger oxidizing agent is the one involved in the half-reaction with the more positive standard electrode potential, so I_2 is the stronger oxidizing agent. The reaction is nonspontaneous as written.

Copyright © Cengage Learning. All rights reserved.

19.9. The reduction half-reactions and standard electrode potentials are

$$Zn^{2+}(aq) + 2e^- \rightarrow Zn(s); \ E°_{Zn} = -0.76 \text{ V}$$

$$Cu^{2+}(aq) + 2e^- \rightarrow Cu(s); \ E°_{Cu} = 0.34 \text{ V}$$

Reverse the first half-reaction and its half-cell potential to obtain

$$Zn(s) \rightarrow Zn^{2+}(aq) + 2e^-; \ -E°_{Zn} = 0.76 \text{ V}$$

$$Cu^{2+}(aq) + 2e^- \rightarrow Cu(s); \ E°_{Cu} = 0.34 \text{ V}$$

Obtain the cell potential by adding the half-cell potentials.

$$E°_{cell} = E°_{Cu} - E°_{Zn} = 0.34 \text{ V} + 0.76 \text{ V} = 1.10 \text{ V}$$

19.10.   The half-cell reactions, the corresponding half-cell potentials, and their sums are displayed below:

$$Sn^{2+}(aq) \rightarrow Sn^{4+}(aq) + 2e^- \quad -E° = -0.15 \text{ V}$$

$$2Hg^{2+}(aq) + 2e^- \rightarrow Hg_2^{2+}(aq) \quad E° = 0.90 \text{ V}$$

$$Sn^{2+}(aq) + 2Hg^{2+}(aq) \rightarrow Sn^{4+}(aq) + Hg_2^{2+}(aq) \quad E°_{cell} = 0.75 \text{ V}$$

Note that each half-reaction involves two electrons; hence n equals 2. Also, $E°_{cell}$ equals 0.75 V, and the faraday constant, F, is 9.6485×10^4 C. Therefore,

$$\Delta G° = -nFE°_{cell} = -2 \times 9.6485 \times 10^4 \text{ C} \times 0.75 \text{ V} = -1.\underline{4}472 \times 10^5 \text{ J} = -1.4 \times 10^5 \text{ J}$$

Thus, the standard free-energy change is -1.4×10^2 kJ.

19.11.   Write the equation with $\Delta G_f°$'s beneath each substance.

$$Mg(s) + Cu^{2-}(aq) \rightarrow Mg^{2-}(aq) + Cu(s)$$

$\Delta G_f°: \quad \ 0 \qquad \quad 65.52 \qquad \quad -454.80 \qquad \ 0\text{KJ}$

Hence,

$$\Delta G° = \Sigma n \Delta G_f°(\text{products}) - \Sigma m \Delta G_f°(\text{reactants})$$

$$= [(-454.8) - 65.52] \text{ kJ} = -520.\underline{32} \text{ kJ} = -5.20\underline{32} \times 10^5 \text{ J}$$

Obtain n by splitting the reaction into half-reactions.

$$Mg(s) \rightarrow Mg^{2+}(aq) + 2e^-$$

$$Cu^{2+}(aq) + 2e^- \rightarrow Cu(s)$$

Each half-reaction involves two electrons, so n equals 2. Therefore,

$$\Delta G° = -nFE°_{cell}$$

$$-5.2032 \times 10^5 \text{ J} = -2 \times 9.6485 \times 10^4 \text{ C} \times E°_{cell}$$

Copyright © Cengage Learning. All rights reserved.

Rearrange and solve for $E°_{cell}$. Recall that $J = C•V$.

$$E°_{cell} = \frac{-5.2032 \times 10^5 \text{ J}}{-2 \times 9.6485 \times 10^4 \text{ C}} = 2.69\underline{6}3 = 2.696 \text{ V}$$

19.12. The half-reactions and standard electrode potentials are

$$Fe(s) \rightarrow Fe^{2+}(aq) + 2e^-; \quad -E°_{Fe} = 0.41 \text{ V}$$

$$Sn^{4+}(aq) + 2e^- \rightarrow Sn^{2+}(s); E°_{Sn^{2+}} = 0.15 \text{ V}$$

The standard cell potential for the cell is

$$E°_{cell} = E°_{Fe} - E°_{Sn^{2+}} = 0.41 \text{ V} + 0.15 \text{ V} = 0.56 \text{ V}$$

Note that n equals 2. Substitute into the equation relating $E°$ and K. Also, $K = K_c$.

$$0.56 \text{ V} = \frac{0.0592}{2} \log K_c$$

Solving for K_c, yields

$$\log K_c = 1\underline{8}.91$$

Take the antilog of both sides, you get

$$K_c = \text{antilog } (18.91) = 8.1 \times 10^{\underline{18}} = 10^{19}$$

19.13. The half-cell reactions, the corresponding half-cell potentials, and their sums are displayed below:

$$Zn(s) \rightarrow Zn^{2+}(aq) + 2e^- \qquad -E° = 0.76 \text{ V}$$

$$2Ag^+(aq) + 2e^- \rightarrow 2Ag(s) \qquad E° = 0.80 \text{ V}$$

$$Zn(s) + 2Ag^+(aq) \rightarrow Zn^{2+}(aq) + 2Ag(s) \qquad E°_{cell} = 1.56 \text{ V}$$

Note that n equals 2. The reaction quotient is

$$Q = \frac{[Zn^{2+}]}{[Ag^+]^2} = \frac{0.200}{(0.00200)^2} = 5.0\underline{0} \times 10^4$$

The standard cell potential is 1.56 V, so the Nernst equation becomes

$$E_{cell} = E°_{cell} - \frac{0.0592}{n} \log Q$$

$$= 1.56 - \frac{0.0592}{2} \log (5.00 \times 10^4)$$

$$= 1.56 - 0.13\underline{9}09 = 1.4\underline{2}09 = 1.42 \text{ V}$$

Copyright © Cengage Learning. All rights reserved.

19.14.   The half-cell reactions, the corresponding half-cell potentials, and their sums are displayed below:

$$Zn(s) \rightarrow Zn^{2+}(aq) + 2e^- \qquad -E° = 0.76 \text{ V}$$

$$Ni^{2+}(aq) + 2e^- \rightarrow Ni(s) \qquad E° = -0.23 \text{ V}$$

$$Zn(s) + Ni^{2+}(aq) \rightarrow Zn^{2+}(aq) + Ni(s) \qquad E°_{cell} = 0.53 \text{ V}$$

Note that n equals 2. The standard cell potential is 0.53 V, and the cell potential is 0.34 V, so the Nernst equation becomes

$$E_{cell} = E°_{cell} - \frac{0.0592}{n} \log Q$$

$$0.34 \text{ V} = 0.53 \text{ V} - \frac{0.0592}{2} \log Q$$

Rearrange and solve for log Q.

$$\log Q = \frac{2}{0.0592} \times (0.53 - 0.34) = 6.\underline{4}18$$

Take the antilog of both sides.

$$Q = \frac{[Zn^{2+}]}{[Ni^{2+}]} = \text{antilog} (6.418) = 2.\underline{6}23 \times 10^6$$

Substitute in $[Zn^{2+}] = 1.00 \, M$ and solve for $[Ni^{2+}]$.

$$\frac{1.00 \text{ M}}{[Ni^{2+}]} = 2.624 \times 10^6$$

$$[Ni^{2+}] = 3.\underline{8}1 \times 10^{-7} = 4 \times 10^{-7} \, M$$

19.15.

a.   The cathode reaction is $K^+(l) + e^- \rightarrow K(l)$.

The anode reaction is $2Cl^-(l) \rightarrow Cl_2(g) + 2e^-$.

b.   The cathode reaction is $K^+(l) + e^- \rightarrow K(l)$.

The anode reaction is $4OH^-(aq) \rightarrow O_2(g) + 2H_2O(g) + 4e^-$.

Copyright © Cengage Learning. All rights reserved.

19.16. The species you should consider for half-reactions are Ag^+ and H_2O. Two possible cathode reactions are

$$Ag^+(aq) + e^- \rightarrow Ag(s); \ E° = 0.80 \text{ V}$$

$$2H_2O(l) + 2e^- \rightarrow H_2(g) + 2OH^-(aq); \ E° = -0.83 \text{ V}$$

Because the silver electrode potential is larger than the reduction potential of water, Ag^+ is reduced. The only possible anode reaction is the oxidation of water. The expected half-reactions are

$$Ag^+(aq) + e^- \rightarrow Ag(s)$$

$$2H_2O(l) \rightarrow O_2(g) + 4H^+(aq) + 4e^-$$

19.17. The conversion of grams of silver to coulombs required to deposit this amount of silver is

$$0.365 \text{ g Ag} \times \frac{1 \text{ mol Ag}}{107.9 \text{ g}} \times \frac{1 \text{ mol e}^-}{1 \text{ mol Ag}} \times \frac{96,485 \text{ C}}{1 \text{ mol e}^-} = 32\underline{6}.3 \text{ C}$$

The time lapse, 216 min, equals $1.2\underline{9}6 \times 10^3$ s. Thus,

$$\text{Current} = \frac{\text{charge}}{\text{time}} = \frac{326.4 \text{ C}}{1.296 \times 10^4 \text{ s}} = 2.5\underline{1}88 \times 10^{-2} = 2.52 \times 10^{-2} \text{ A}$$

19.18. When the current flows for 1.85×10^4 s, the amount of charge is

$$0.0565 \text{ A} \times 1.85 \times 10^4 \text{ s} = 1.0\underline{4}5 \times 10^3 \text{ C}$$

Note that 4 mol of electrons are equivalent to 1 mol of O_2. Hence,

$$1.045 \times 10^3 \text{ C} \times \frac{1 \text{ mol e}^-}{96,485 \text{ C}} \times \frac{1 \text{ mol O}_2}{4 \text{ mol e}^-} \times \frac{32.00 \text{ g O}_2}{1 \text{ mol O}_2} = 0.086\underline{6}6 = 0.0867 \text{ g O}_2$$

■ ANSWERS TO SELF-ASSESSMENT AND REVIEW QUESTIONS

19.1. A voltaic cell is an electrochemical cell in which a spontaneous reaction generates an electric current (energy). An electrolytic cell is an electrochemical cell that requires electric current (energy) to drive a nonspontaneous reaction to the right.

19.2. In both the voltaic and electrolytic cells, the cathode is the electrode at which reduction occurs, and the anode is the electrode at which oxidation occurs.

19.3. The SI unit of electrical potential is the volt (V).

19.4. The faraday (F) is the magnitude of charge on 1 mol of electrons; it equals 96,485 C, or 96,485 J/V.

Copyright © Cengage Learning. All rights reserved.

19.5. It is necessary to measure the voltage of a voltaic cell when no current is flowing because the cell voltage exhibits its maximum value only when no current flows. Even if the current flows just for the time of measurement, the voltage drops enough so that what is measured is significantly less than the maximum.

19.6. Standard electrode potentials are defined relative to a standard electrode potential of zero volts (0.00, 0.000 V, etc.) for the $H^+/H_2(g)$ electrode. Because the cell potential is measured using the hydrogen electrode at standard conditions and a second electrode at standard conditions, the cell potential equals the $E°$ of the half-reaction at the second electrode.

19.7. The SI unit of energy equals joules equals coulombs times volts.

19.8. The mathematical relationships are as follows:

$$\Delta G° = -nFE°_{cell}$$

$$\Delta G° = -RT \ln K$$

Combining these two equations gives

$$\ln K = \frac{nFE°_{cell}}{RT}$$

19.9. The first step in the corrosion of iron is

$$2Fe(s) + O_2(g) + 2H_2O(l) \rightarrow 4OH^- + 2Fe^{2+}$$

The Nernst equation for this reaction is

$$E_{cell} = E°_{cell} - \frac{0.0592}{4} \log \frac{[OH^-]^4[Fe^{2+}]^2}{P_{O_2}}$$

If the pH increases, the $[OH^-]$ increases, and thus E_{cell} becomes more negative (this predicts that the reaction becomes less spontaneous). If the pH decreases, the $[OH^-]$ decreases, and thus E_{cell} becomes more positive (this predicts that the reaction becomes more spontaneous).

19.10. The zinc-carbon cell has a zinc can as the anode; the cathode is a graphite rod surrounded by a paste of manganese dioxide and carbon black. Around this is a second paste of ammonium and zinc chlorides. The electrode reactions involve oxidation of zinc metal to zinc(II) ion and reduction of $MnO_2(s)$ to $Mn_2O_3(s)$ at the cathode. The lead storage battery consists of a spongy lead anode and a lead dioxide cathode, both immersed in aqueous sulfuric acid. At the anode, the lead is oxidized to lead sulfate; at the cathode, lead dioxide is reduced to lead sulfate.

Copyright © Cengage Learning. All rights reserved.

19.11.   A fuel cell is essentially a battery that does not use up its electrodes. Instead, it operates with a continuous supply of reactants (fuel). An example is the hydrogen-oxygen fuel cell in which oxygen is reduced at one electrode to the hydroxide ion, and hydrogen is oxidized at the other electrode to water (H in the +1 oxidation state). Such a cell produces electrical energy in a spacecraft for long periods of time.

19.12.   During the rusting of iron, one end of a drop of water exposed to air acts as one electrode of a voltaic cell; at this electrode, an oxygen molecule is reduced by four electrons to four hydroxide ions. Oxidation of metallic iron to iron(II) ion at the center of the drop of water supplies the electrons, and the center serves as the other electrode of the voltaic cell. Thus, electrons flow from the center of the drop through the iron to the end of the drop.

19.13.   When iron or steel is connected to an active metal such as zinc, a voltaic cell is formed with zinc as the anode and iron as the cathode. Any type of moisture forms the electrolyte solution, and the zinc metal is then oxidized to zinc(II) ion in preference to the oxidation of iron metal. Oxygen is reduced at the cathode to hydroxide ions. If iron or steel is exposed to oxygen while connected to a less active metal such as tin, a voltaic cell is formed with iron as the anode and tin as the cathode, and iron is oxidized to iron(II) ion rather than tin being oxidized to tin(II) ion. Thus, exposed iron corrodes rapidly in a tin can. Fortunately, as long as the iron is covered by the tin, it cannot corrode.

19.14.   The addition of an ionic species such as strongly ionized sulfuric acid facilitates the passage of current through the solution.

19.15.   Sodium metal can be prepared by electrolysis of molten sodium chloride.

19.16.   The anode reaction in the electrolysis of molten potassium hydroxide is

$$4OH^- \rightarrow O_2(g) + 2H_2O(g) + 4e^-$$

19.17.   The reason why different products are obtained is that water instead of Na^+ is reduced at the cathode during the electrolysis of aqueous NaCl. This is because water has a more positive $E°$ (smaller decomposition voltage). At the anode, water instead of chloride ion is oxidized because water has a less positive $E°$ (smaller decomposition voltage).

19.18.   The Nernst equation for the electrode reaction of $2Cl^-(aq) \rightarrow Cl_2(g) + 2e^-$ is

$$E = -1.36 \text{ V} - \frac{0.0592}{2} \log \frac{1 \text{ atm}}{[Cl^-]^2} = -1.36 \text{ V} + 0.0592 \log [Cl^-]$$

This equation implies that E increases as $[Cl^-]$ increases. For a sufficiently large $[Cl^-]$, Cl^- will be more readily oxidized than the water solvent.

Copyright © Cengage Learning. All rights reserved.

19.19. The answer is c, 11.

19.20. The answer is c, $2H_2O(l) + 2e^- \rightarrow H_2(g) + 2OH^-(aq)$.

19.21. The answer is a, 123 A.

19.22. The answer is b, the copper electrode is the anode.

■ SOLUTIONS TO PRACTICE PROBLEMS

Note on significant figures: If the final answer to a solution needs to be rounded off, it is given first with one nonsignificant figure, and the last significant figure is underlined. The final answer is then rounded to the correct number of significant figures. In multistep problems, intermediate answers are given with at least one nonsignificant figure; however, only the final answer has been rounded off.

19.35. In balancing oxidation-reduction reactions in acid, the four steps in the text will be followed. For part a, each step is shown. For the other parts, only a summary is shown.

a. Assign oxidation numbers to the skeleton equation (Step 1).

$$\overset{+6}{Cr_2O_7^{2-}} + \overset{+3}{C_2O_4^{2-}} \rightarrow \overset{+3}{Cr^{3+}} + \overset{+4}{CO_2}$$

Separate into two incomplete half-reactions (Step 2). Note that carbon is oxidized (increases in oxidation number), and chromium is reduced (decreases in oxidation number).

$$C_2O_4^{2-} \rightarrow CO_2$$
$$Cr_2O_7^{2-} \rightarrow Cr^{3+}$$

Balance each half-reaction separately. The oxidation half-reaction is not balanced in C, so place a 2 in front of CO_2 (Step 3a). Finally, add two electrons to the right side to balance the charge (Step 3d). The balanced oxidation half-reaction is

$$C_2O_4^{2-} \rightarrow 2CO_2 + 2e^-$$

The reduction half-reaction is not balanced in Cr, so place a 2 in front of Cr^{3+} (Step 3a). Add seven H_2O to the right side to balance O atoms (Step 3b), and add fourteen H^+ ions to the left side to balance H atoms (step 3c). Finally, add six electrons to the left side to balance the charge (Step 3d). The balanced reduction half-reaction is

$$Cr_2O_7^{2-} + 14H^+ + 6e^- \rightarrow 2Cr^{3+} + 7H_2O$$

Copyright © Cengage Learning. All rights reserved.

Multiply the oxidation half-reaction by 3 so that, when added, the electrons cancel (Step 4a).

$$3C_2O_4^{2-} \rightarrow 6CO_2 + 6e^-$$
$$Cr_2O_7^{2-} + 14H^+ + 6e^- \rightarrow 2Cr^{3+} + 7H_2O$$

$$Cr_2O_7^{2-} + 3C_2O_4^{2-} + 14H^+ + \cancel{6e^-} \rightarrow 2Cr^{3+} + 6CO_2 + 7H_2O + \cancel{6e^-}$$

The equation does not need to be simplified any further (Step 4b). The net ionic equation is

$$Cr_2O_7^{2-} + 3C_2O_4^{2-} + 14H^+ \rightarrow 2Cr^{3+} + 6CO_2 + 7H_2O$$

b.   The two balanced half-reactions are

$$Cu \rightarrow Cu^{2+} + 2e^- \qquad \text{(oxidation)}$$
$$NO_3^- + 4H^+ + 3e^- \rightarrow NO + 2H_2O \qquad \text{(reduction)}$$

Multiply the oxidation half-reaction by 3 and the reduction half-reaction by 4, and then add together. Cancel the six electrons from each side. No further simplification is needed. The balanced equation is

$$3Cu + 2NO_3^- + 8H^+ \rightarrow 3Cu^{2+} + 2NO + 4H_2O$$

c.   The two balanced half-reactions are

$$HNO_2 + H_2O \rightarrow NO_3^- + 3H^+ + 2e^- \qquad \text{(oxidation)}$$
$$MnO_2 + 4H^+ + 2e^- \rightarrow Mn^{2+} + 2H_2O \qquad \text{(reduction)}$$

Add the two half-reactions together and cancel the two electrons from each side. Also, cancel three H^+ ions and one H_2O from each side. The balanced equation is

$$MnO_2 + HNO_2 + H^+ \rightarrow Mn^{2+} + NO_3^- + H_2O$$

d.   The two balanced half-reactions are

$$Mn^{2+} + 4H_2O \rightarrow MnO_4^- + 8H^+ + 5e^- \qquad \text{(oxidation)}$$
$$PbO_2 + SO_4^{2-} + 4H^+ + 2e^- \rightarrow PbSO_4 + 2H_2O \qquad \text{(reduction)}$$

Multiply the oxidation half-reaction by 2 and the reduction half-reaction by 5, and then add together. Cancel the ten electrons from each side. Also, cancel sixteen H^+ and eight H_2O from each side. The balanced equation is

$$5PbO_2 + 2Mn^{2+} + 5SO_4^{2-} + 4H^+ \rightarrow 5PbSO_4 + 2MnO_4^- + 2H_2O$$

e.   The two balanced half-reactions are

$$HNO_2 + H_2O \rightarrow NO_3^- + 3H^+ + 2e^- \qquad \text{(oxidation)}$$
$$Cr_2O_7^{2-} + 14H^+ + 6e^- \rightarrow 2Cr^{3+} + 7H_2O \qquad \text{(reduction)}$$

Multiply the oxidation half-reaction by 3, and then add together. Cancel the six electrons from each side. Also, cancel nine H^+ and three H_2O from each side. The balanced equation is

$$3HNO_2 + Cr_2O_7^{2-} + 5H^+ \rightarrow 2Cr^{3+} + 3NO_3^- + 4H_2O$$

Copyright © Cengage Learning. All rights reserved.

19.37. In balancing oxidation-reduction reactions in basic solution, the equation will first be balanced as if the equation were in acidic solution; then the extra two steps in the text will be followed.

a. The two balanced half-reactions are

$$Mn^{2+} + 2H_2O \rightarrow MnO_2 + 4H^+ + 2e^- \qquad \text{(oxidation)}$$
$$H_2O_2 + 2H^+ + 2e^- \rightarrow 2H_2O \qquad \text{(reduction)}$$

Add the two half-reactions together, and cancel the two electrons from each side. Also, cancel two H^+ and two H_2O from each side. The balanced equation in acidic solution is

$$Mn^{2+} + H_2O_2 \rightarrow MnO_2 + 2H^+$$

Now add two OH^- to each side (Step 5). Simplify by combining the H^+ and OH^- to give H_2O. No further simplification is required (Step 6). The balanced equation in basic solution is

$$Mn^{2+} + H_2O_2 + 2OH^- \rightarrow MnO_2 + 2H_2O$$

b. The two balanced half-reactions are

$$NO_2^- + H_2O \rightarrow NO_3^- + 2H^+ + 2e^- \qquad \text{(oxidation)}$$
$$MnO_4^- + 4H^+ + 3e^- \rightarrow MnO_2 + 2H_2O \qquad \text{(reduction)}$$

Multiply the oxidation half-reaction by 3 and the reduction half-reaction by 2, and then add together. Cancel the six electrons from each side. Also, cancel six H^+ and three H_2O from each side. The balanced equation in acidic solution is

$$2MnO_4^- + 3NO_2^- + 2H^+ \rightarrow 2MnO_2 + 3NO_3^- + H_2O$$

Now add two OH^- to each side. Simplify by combining the H^+ and OH^- to give H_2O. Then cancel one H_2O from each side. The balanced equation in basic solution is

$$2MnO_4^- + 3NO_2^- + H_2O \rightarrow 2MnO_2 + 3NO_3^- + 2OH^-$$

c. The two balanced half-reactions are

$$Mn^{2+} + 2H_2O \rightarrow MnO_2 + 4H^+ + 2e^- \qquad \text{(oxidation)}$$
$$ClO_3^- + 2H^+ + e^- \rightarrow ClO_2 + H_2O \qquad \text{(reduction)}$$

Multiply the reduction half-reaction by 2 and then add together. Cancel the two electrons from each side. Also, cancel four H^+ and two H_2O from each side. The balanced equation in acidic solution is

$$Mn^{2+} + 2ClO_3^- \rightarrow MnO_2 + 2ClO_2$$

Since there are no H^+ ions on either side, no further simplification is needed. The balanced equation in basic solution is identical to the balanced equation in acidic solution.

Copyright © Cengage Learning. All rights reserved.

d.   The two balanced half-reactions are

$$NO_2 + H_2O \rightarrow NO_3^- + 2H^+ + e^- \qquad \text{(oxidation)}$$

$$MnO_4^- + 4H^+ + 3e^- \rightarrow MnO_2 + 2H_2O \qquad \text{(reduction)}$$

Multiply the oxidation half-reaction by 3 and then add together. Cancel the three electrons from each side. Also, cancel four H^+ and two H_2O from each side. The balanced equation in acidic solution is

$$MnO_4^- + 3NO_2 + H_2O \rightarrow MnO_2 + 3NO_3^- + 2H^+$$

Now add two OH^- to each side. Simplify by combining the H^+ and OH^- to give H_2O. Then cancel one H_2O from each side. The balanced equation in basic solution is

$$MnO_4^- + 3NO_2 + 2OH^- \rightarrow MnO_2 + 3NO_3^- + H_2O$$

e.   The two balanced half-reactions are

$$Cl_2 + 6H_2O \rightarrow 2ClO_3^- + 12H^+ + 10e^- \qquad \text{(oxidation)}$$

$$Cl_2 + 2e^- \rightarrow 2Cl^- \qquad \text{(reduction)}$$

Multiply the reduction half-reaction by 5 and then add together. Cancel the ten electrons from each side. Also, divide all the coefficients by 2. The balanced equation in acidic solution is

$$3Cl_2 + 3H_2O \rightarrow 5Cl^- + ClO_3^- + 6H^+$$

Now add six OH^- to each side. Simplify by combining the H^+ and OH^- to give H_2O. Then cancel three H_2O from each side. The balanced equation in basic solution is

$$3Cl_2 + 6OH^- \rightarrow 5Cl^- + ClO_3^- + 3H_2O$$

19.39.

a.   The two balanced half-reactions are

$$8H_2S \rightarrow S_8 + 16H^+ + 16e^- \qquad \text{(oxidation)}$$

$$NO_3^- + 2H^+ + e^- \rightarrow NO_2 + H_2O \qquad \text{(reduction)}$$

Multiply the reduction half-reaction by 16, and then add together. Cancel the sixteen electrons and sixteen H^+ from each side. The balanced equation is

$$8H_2S + 16NO_3^- + 16H^+ \rightarrow S_8 + 16NO_2 + 16H_2O$$

b.   The two balanced half-reactions are

$$Cu + Cu^{2+} \rightarrow Cu^{2+} + 2e^- \qquad \text{(oxidation)}$$

$$NO_3^- + 4H^+ + 3e^- \rightarrow NO + 2H_2O \qquad \text{(reduction)}$$

Multiply the oxidation half-reaction by 3 and the reduction half-reaction by 2, and then add together. Cancel the six electrons from each side. The balanced equation is

$$2NO_3^- + 3Cu + 8H^+ \rightarrow 2NO + 3Cu^{2+} + 4H_2O$$

Copyright © Cengage Learning. All rights reserved.

c.   The two balanced half-reactions are

$$SO_2 + 2H_2O \rightarrow SO_4^{2-} + 4H^+ + 2e^- \qquad \text{(oxidation)}$$

$$MnO_4^- + 8H^+ + 5e^- \rightarrow Mn^{2+} + 4H_2O \qquad \text{(reduction)}$$

Multiply the oxidation half-reaction by 5 and the reduction half-reaction by 2, and then add together. Cancel the ten electrons from each side. Also, cancel sixteen H^+ and eight H_2O from each side. The balanced equation is

$$2MnO_4^- + 5SO_2 + 2H_2O \rightarrow 5SO_4^{2-} + 2Mn^{2+} + 4H^+$$

d.   The two balanced half-reactions are

$$Sn(OH)_3^- + 3H_2O \rightarrow Sn(OH)_6^{2-} + 3H^+ + 2e^- \qquad \text{(oxidation)}$$

$$Bi(OH)_3 + 3H^+ + 3e^- \rightarrow Bi + 3H_2O \qquad \text{(reduction)}$$

Multiply the oxidation half-reaction by 3 and the reduction half-reaction by 2, and then add together. Cancel the six electrons from each side. Also, cancel six H^+ and six H_2O from each side. The balanced equation in acidic solution is

$$2Bi(OH)_3 + 3Sn(OH)_3^- + 3H_2O \rightarrow 3Sn(OH)_6^{2-} + 2Bi + 3H^+$$

Now add three OH^- to each side. Simplify by combining the H^+ and OH^- to give H_2O. Then cancel three H_2O on each side. The balanced equation in basic solution is

$$2Bi(OH)_3 + 3Sn(OH)_3^- + 3OH^- \rightarrow 3Sn(OH)_6^{2-} + 2Bi$$

19.41.

a.   The two balanced half-reactions are

$$I^- + 3H_2O \rightarrow IO_3^- + 6H^+ + 6e^- \qquad \text{(oxidation)}$$

$$MnO_4^- + 4H^+ + 3e^- \rightarrow MnO_2 + 2H_2O \qquad \text{(reduction)}$$

Multiply the reduction half-reaction by 2, and then add together. Cancel the six electrons from each side. Also, cancel six H^+ and three H_2O from each side. The balanced equation in acidic solution is

$$2MnO_4^- + I^- + 2H^+ \rightarrow 2MnO_2 + IO_3^- + H_2O$$

Now add two OH^- to each side. Simplify by combining the H^+ and OH^- to give H_2O. Then cancel one H_2O on each side. The balanced equation in basic solution is

$$2MnO_4^- + I^- + H_2O \rightarrow 2MnO_2 + IO_3^- + 2OH^-$$

b.   The two balanced half-reactions are

$$2Cl^- \rightarrow Cl_2 + 2e^- \qquad \text{(oxidation)}$$

$$Cr_2O_4^{2-} + 14H^+ + 6e^- \rightarrow 2Cr^{3+} + 7H_2O \qquad \text{(reduction)}$$

Multiply the oxidation half-reaction by 3, and then add together. Cancel the six electrons from each side. The balanced equation is

$$Cr_2O_7^{2-} + 6Cl^- + 14H^+ \rightarrow 2Cr^{3+} + 3Cl_2 + 7H_2O$$

Copyright © Cengage Learning. All rights reserved.

384   Chapter 19: Electrochemistry

c.   The two balanced half-reactions are

$$S_8 + 16H_2O \rightarrow 8SO_2 + 32H^+ + 32e^- \quad \text{(oxidation)}$$

$$NO_3^- + 4H^+ + 3e^- \rightarrow NO + 2H_2O \quad \text{(reduction)}$$

Multiply the oxidation half-reaction by 3 and the reduction half-reaction by 32, and then add together. Cancel the ninety-six electrons from each side. Also, cancel ninety-six H^+ and forty-eight H_2O from each side. The balanced equation is

$$3S_8 + 32NO_3^- + 32H^+ \rightarrow 32NO + 24SO_2 + 16H_2O$$

d.   The two balanced half-reactions are

$$H_2O_2 \rightarrow O_2 + 2H^+ + 2e^- \quad \text{(oxidation)}$$

$$MnO_4^- + 4H^+ + 3e^- \rightarrow MnO_2 + 2H_2O \quad \text{(reduction)}$$

Multiply the oxidation half-reaction by 3 and the reduction half-reaction by 2, and then add together. Cancel the six electrons from each side. Also, cancel six H^+ from each side. The balanced equation in acidic solution is

$$3H_2O_2 + 2MnO_4^- + 2H^+ \rightarrow 3O_2 + 2MnO_2 + 4H_2O$$

Now add two OH^- to each side. Simplify by combining the H^+ and OH^- to give H_2O. Then cancel two H_2O on each side. The balanced equation in basic solution is

$$3H_2O_2 + 2MnO_4^- \rightarrow 3O_2 + 2MnO_2 + 2H_2O + 2OH^-$$

e.   The two balanced half-reactions are

$$Zn \rightarrow Zn^{2+} + 2e^- \quad \text{(oxidation)}$$

$$2NO_3^- + 12H^+ + 10e^- \rightarrow N_2 + 6H_2O \quad \text{(reduction)}$$

Multiply the oxidation half-reaction by 5, and then add together. Cancel the ten electrons from each side. The balanced equation is

$$5Zn + 2NO_3^- + 12H^+ \rightarrow N_2 + 5Zn^{2+} + 6H_2O$$

Copyright © Cengage Learning. All rights reserved.

19.43.   Sketch of the cell:

$$Mg \rightarrow Mg^{2+} + 2e^{-}$$ $$Ni^{2+} + 2e^{-} \rightarrow Ni$$

19.45.   Sketch of the cell:

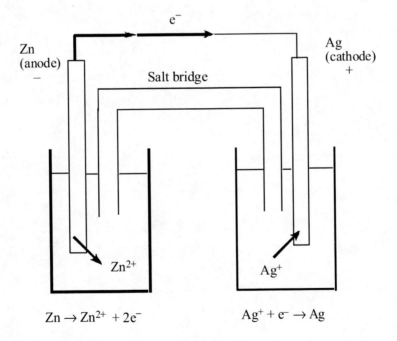

$$Zn \rightarrow Zn^{2+} + 2e^{-}$$ $$Ag^{+} + e^{-} \rightarrow Ag$$

Copyright © Cengage Learning. All rights reserved.

19.47. The electrode half-reactions and the overall cell reaction are

Anode: $Zn(s) + 2OH^-(aq) \rightarrow Zn(OH)_2(s) + 2e^-$

Cathode: $Ag_2O(s) + H_2O(l) + 2e^- \rightarrow 2Ag(s) + 2OH^-(aq)$

Overall: $Zn(s) + Ag_2O(s) + H_2O(l) \rightarrow Zn(OH)_2(s) + 2Ag(s)$

19.49. Because of its less negative $E°$, Pb^{2+} is reduced at the cathode and is written on the right; $Ni(s)$ is oxidized at the anode and is written first, at the left, in the cell notation. The notation is $Ni(s)|Ni^{2+}(aq)\|Pb^{2+}(aq)|Pb(s)$.

19.51. Because of its less negative $E°$, H^+ is reduced at the cathode and is written on the right; $Ni(s)$ is oxidized at the anode and is written first, at the left, in the cell notation. The notation is $Ni(s)|Ni^{2+}(1\ M)\|H^+(1\ M)|H_2(g)|Pt$.

19.53. The $Fe(s)$, on the left, is the reducing agent. The Ag^+, on the right, is the oxidizing agent, gaining just one electron. Multiplying its half-reaction by 2 to equalize the numbers of electrons and writing both half-reactions give the overall cell reaction:

$$Fe(s) \rightarrow Fe^{2+}(aq) + 2e^-$$

$$2Ag^+(aq) + 2e^- \rightarrow 2Ag(s)$$

$$Fe(s) + 2Ag^+(aq) \rightarrow Fe^{2+}(aq) + 2Ag(s)$$

Copyright © Cengage Learning. All rights reserved.

19.55. The half-cell reactions, the overall cell reaction, and the sketch are

$$Cd(s) \rightarrow Cd^{2+}(aq) + 2e^-$$

$$Ni^{2+}(aq) + 2e^- \rightarrow Ni(s)$$

$$Cd(s) + Ni^{2+}(aq) \rightarrow Cd^{2+}(aq) + Ni(s)$$

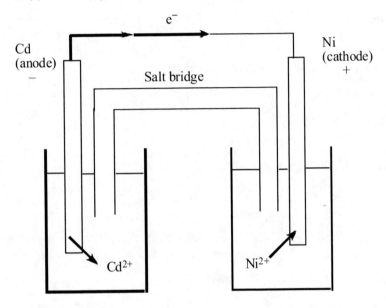

19.57. The half-cell reactions are

$$2Fe^{3+}(aq) + 2e^- \rightarrow 2Fe^{2+}(aq)$$

$$Zn(s) \rightarrow Zn^{2+}(aq) + 2e^-$$

n equals 2, and the maximum work for the reaction as written is

$$w_{max} = -nFE_{cell} = -2 \times 9.6485 \times 10^4\ C \times 0.72\ V = -1.\underline{3}89 \times 10^5\ C \bullet V = -1.\underline{3}89 \times 10^5\ J$$

Because this is the work obtained by reduction of 2 mol of Fe^{3+}, the work for 1 mol is

$$w_{max} = (-1.389 \times 10^5\ J)/2\ mol = -6.\underline{9}45 \times 10^4 = -6.9 \times 10^4\ J = -69\ kJ$$

19.59. The half-cell reactions are

$$2Ag^+(aq) + 2e^- \rightarrow 2Ag(s)$$

$$Ni(s) \rightarrow Ni^{2+}(aq) + 2e^-$$

n equals 2, and the maximum work for the reaction as written is

$$w_{max} = -nFE_{cell} = -2 \times 9.6485 \times 10^4\ C \times 0.97\ V = -1.\underline{8}7 \times 10^5\ C \bullet V = -1.\underline{8}7 \times 10^5\ J$$

For 30.0 g of nickel, the maximum work is

$$30.0\ g\ Ni \times \frac{1\ mol\ Ni}{58.69\ g\ Ni} \times \frac{-1.87 \times 10^5\ J}{1\ mol\ Ni} = -9.\underline{5}6 \times 10^4\ J = -96\ kJ$$

Copyright © Cengage Learning. All rights reserved.

19.61.   The half-reactions and corresponding electrode potentials are

$$NO_3^-(aq) + 4H^+(aq) + 3e^- \rightarrow NO(g) + 2H_2O(l) \qquad 0.96 \text{ V}$$

$$O_2(g) + 4H^+(aq) + 4e^- \rightarrow 2H_2O(l) \qquad 1.23 \text{ V}$$

$$MnO_4^-(aq) + 8H^+(aq) + 5e^- \rightarrow Mn^{2+}(aq) + 4H_2O(l) \qquad 1.49 \text{ V}$$

The order by increasing oxidizing strength is $NO_3^-(aq)$, $O_2(g)$, $MnO_4^-(aq)$.

19.63.   The half-reactions and corresponding electrode potentials are

$$Zn^{2+}(aq) + 2e^- \rightarrow Zn(s) \quad -0.76 \text{ V}$$

$$Fe^{2+}(aq) + 2e^- \rightarrow Fe(s) \quad -0.41 \text{ V}$$

$$Cu^{2+}(aq) + e^- \rightarrow Cu^+(aq) \; 0.16 \text{ V}$$

$Zn(s)$ is the strongest, and $Cu^+(aq)$ is the weakest.

19.65.

a.   In this reaction, Sn^{4+} is the oxidizing agent on the left side; Fe^{3+} is the oxidizing reagent on the right side. The corresponding standard electrode potentials are

$$Sn^{4+}(aq) + 2e^- \rightarrow Sn^{2+}(aq) \quad E° = 0.15 \text{ V}$$

$$Fe^{3+}(aq) + e^- \rightarrow Fe^{2+}(aq) \quad E° = 0.77 \text{ V}$$

The stronger oxidizing agent is the one involved in the half-reaction with the more positive standard electrode potential, so Fe^{3+} is the stronger oxidizing agent. The reaction is nonspontaneous as written.

b.   In this reaction, MnO_4^- is the oxidizing agent on the left side; O_2 is the oxidizing reagent on the right side. The corresponding standard electrode potentials are

$$O_2(g) + 4H^+(aq) + 4e^- \rightarrow 2H_2O(l) \qquad E° = 1.23 \text{ V}$$

$$MnO_4^-(aq) + 8H^+(aq) + 5e^- \rightarrow Mn^{2+}(aq) + 4H_2O(l) \qquad E° = 1.49 \text{ V}$$

The stronger oxidizing agent is the one involved in the half-reaction with the more positive standard electrode potential, so MnO_4^- is the stronger oxidizing agent. The reaction is spontaneous as written.

19.67.   The reduction half-reactions and standard electrode potentials are

$$Br_2(l) + 2e^- \rightarrow 2Br^-(aq) \quad E° = 1.07 \text{ V}$$

$$Cl_2(g) + 2e^- \rightarrow 2Cl^-(aq) \quad E° = 1.36 \text{ V}$$

$$F_2(g) + 2e^- \rightarrow 2F^-(aq) \quad E° = 2.87 \text{ V}$$

From these, you see that the order of increasing oxidizing strength is Br_2, Cl_2, F_2. Therefore, chlorine gas will oxidize Br^- but will not oxidize F^-. The balanced equation for the reaction is

$$Cl_2(g) + 2Br^-(aq) \rightarrow 2Cl^-(aq) + Br_2(l)$$

Copyright © Cengage Learning. All rights reserved.

19.69. The half-reactions and standard electrode potentials are

$$Cr(s) \rightarrow Cr^{3+}(aq) + 3e^- \quad -E°_{Cr} = 0.74 \text{ V}$$

$$Hg_2^{2+}(aq) + 2e^- \rightarrow 2Hg(l)\ E°_{Hg} = 0.80 \text{ V}$$

Obtain the cell potential by adding the half-cell potentials.

$$E°_{cell} = E°_{Hg} - E°_{Cr} = 0.80 \text{ V} + 0.74 \text{ V} = 1.54 \text{ V}$$

19.71. The half-reactions and standard electrode potentials are

$$Cr(s) \rightarrow Cr^{3+}(aq) + 3e^- \quad -E°_{Cr} = 0.74 \text{ V}$$

$$I_2(s) + 2e^- \rightarrow 2I^-(aq) \qquad E°_{I_2} = 0.54 \text{ V}$$

Obtain the cell potential by adding the half-cell potentials.

$$E°_{cell} = E°_{Cr} - E°_{I_2} = 0.54 \text{ V} + 0.74 \text{ V} = 1.28 \text{ V}$$

19.73. The half-cell reactions, the corresponding half-cell potentials, and their sums are displayed below:

$$3Cu(s) \rightarrow 3Cu^{2+}(aq) + 6e^- \qquad\qquad E° = -0.34 \text{ V}$$

$$2NO_3^-(aq) + 8H^+(aq) + 6e^- \rightarrow 2NO(g) + 4H_2O(l) \qquad E° = 0.96 \text{ V}$$

$$3Cu(s) + 2NO_3^-(aq) + 8H^+(aq) \rightarrow$$
$$3Cu^{2+}(aq) + 2NO(g) + 4H_2O(l) \qquad E° = 0.62 \text{ V}$$

Note that each half-reaction involves six electrons, hence $n = 6$. Therefore,

$$\Delta G° = -nFE°_{cell} = -6 \times 9.6485 \times 10^4 \text{ C} \times 0.62 \text{ V} = -3.\underline{5}8 \times 10^5 \text{ J} = -3.6 \times 10^5 \text{ J}$$

Thus, the standard free-energy change is -3.6×10^2 kJ.

19.75. The half-cell reactions, the corresponding half-cell potentials, and their sums are displayed below:

$$2I^-(aq) \rightarrow I_2(s) + 2e^- \qquad\qquad E° = 0.54 \text{ V}$$
$$\underline{Cl_2(g) + 2e^- \rightarrow 2Cl^-(aq)} \qquad\qquad \underline{E° = 1.36 \text{ V}}$$
$$2I^-(aq) + Cl_2(g) \rightarrow I_2(s) + 2Cl^-(aq) \qquad E°_{cell} = 0.82 \text{ V}$$

Note that each half-reaction involves two electrons, hence $n = 2$. Therefore,

$$\Delta G° = -nFE°_{cell} = -2 \times 9.6485 \times 10^4 \text{ C} \times 0.82 \text{ V} = -1.\underline{5}8 \times 10^5 \text{ J} = -1.6 \times 10^5 \text{ J}$$

Thus, the standard free-energy change is -1.6×10^2 kJ.

Copyright © Cengage Learning. All rights reserved.

19.77. Write the equation with the appropriate $\Delta G_f°$ beneath each substance.

$$Mg(s) + 2Ag^+(aq) \rightarrow Mg^{2+}(aq) + 2Ag(s)$$

$\Delta G_f°$:   0   2 x 77.12   -454.8   0KJ

Hence,

$\Delta G° = \Sigma n \Delta G_f°(\text{products}) - \Sigma m \Delta G_f°(\text{reactants})$

$= [-454.8 - 2 \times 77.12]\, kJ = -609.0\underline{0}4\, kJ = -6.09\underline{0}4 \times 10^5\, J$

Obtain n by splitting the reaction into half-reactions.

$Mg(s) \rightarrow Mg^{2+}(aq) + 2e^-$

$2Ag^+(aq) + 2e^- \rightarrow 2Ag(s)$

Each half-reaction involves two electrons, so $n = 2$. Therefore,

$\Delta G° = -nFE°_{cell}$

$-6.0904 \times 10^5\, J = -2 \times 9.6485 \times 10^4\, C \times E°_{cell}$

Rearrange and solve for $E°_{cell}$. Recall that $J = C\bullet V$.

$$E°_{cell} = \frac{-6.0904 \times 10^5\, J}{-2 \times 9.6485 \times 10^4\, C} = 3.15\underline{6}1 = 3.156\, V$$

19.79. Write the equation with the appropriate $\Delta G_f°$ beneath each substance:

$$PbO_2(s) + 2HSO_4^+(aq) + 2H^+(aq) + Pb(s) \rightarrow 2PbSO_4(s) + 2H_2O(l)$$

$\Delta G_f°$: -189.3   2(-756)   0   0   2(-813.2)   2(-237.1)KJ

Hence,

$\Delta G° = [2 \times (-813.2) + 2 \times (-237.1) - (-189.3) - 2 \times (-756)]\, kJ$

$= -399.\underline{3}0\, kJ = -3.9\underline{9}30 \times 10^5\, J$

Obtain n by splitting the reaction into half-reactions.

$Pb(s) + HSO_4^-(aq) \rightarrow PbSO_4(s) + H^+(aq) + 2e^-$

$PbO_2(s) + HSO_4^-(aq) + 3H^+(aq) + 2e^- \rightarrow PbSO_4(s) + 2H_2O(l)$

Each half-reaction involves two electrons, so $n = 2$. Therefore,

$\Delta G° = -nFE°_{cell}$

$-3.9930 \times 10^5\, J = -2 \times 9.6485 \times 10^4\, C \times E°_{cell}$

Rearrange and solve for $E°_{cell}$. Recall that $J = C\bullet V$.

$$E°_{cell} = \frac{-3.9930 \times 10^5\, J}{-2 \times 9.6485 \times 10^4\, C} = 2.0\underline{6}92 = 2.07\, V$$

Copyright © Cengage Learning. All rights reserved.

19.81. The half-reactions and standard electrode potentials are

$$Cu(s) \rightarrow Cu^{2+}(aq) + 2e^- \qquad -E^\circ_{Cu} = -0.34 \text{ V}$$

$$2Fe^{3+}(aq) + 2e^- \rightarrow 2Fe^{2+}(aq) \qquad E^\circ_{Fe^{3+}} = 0.77 \text{ V}$$

The standard cell potential for the cell is

$$E^\circ_{cell} = E^\circ_{Fe^{3+}} - E^\circ_{Cu} = 0.77 \text{ V} - 0.34 \text{ V} = 0.43 \text{ V}$$

Note that $n = 2$. Substitute into the equation relating E° and K. Note that $K = K_c$.

$$0.43 \text{ V} = \frac{0.0592}{2} \log K_c$$

Solving for K_c yields

$$\log K_c = 14.52$$

Take the antilog of both sides:

$$K_c = \text{antilog} (14.52) = 3.4 \times 10^{14} = 10^{14}$$

19.83. The half-reactions and standard electrode potentials are

$$Cu^+(aq) \rightarrow Cu^{2+}(aq) + e^- \quad -E^\circ = -0.16 \text{ V}$$

$$Cu^+(aq) + e^- \rightarrow Cu(s) \qquad E^\circ = 0.52 \text{ V}$$

The standard cell potential for the cell is

$$E^\circ_{cell} = 0.52 \text{ V} - 0.16 \text{ V} = 0.36 \text{ V}$$

Note that n equals 1. Substitute into the equation relating E° and K. Note that K equals K_c.

$$0.36 \text{ V} = \frac{0.0592}{1} \log K_c$$

Solving for K_c, you get

$$\log K_c = 6.081$$

Take the antilog of both sides:

$$K_c = \text{antilog} (6.081) = 1.2 \times 10^6 = 1 \times 10^6$$

19.85. The half-cell reactions, the corresponding half-cell potentials, and their sums are displayed below:

$$\begin{array}{ll}
2Cr(s) \rightarrow 2Cr^{3+}(aq) + 6e^- & -E^\circ = 0.74 \text{ V} \\
\underline{3Ni^{2+}(aq) + 6e^- \rightarrow 3Ni(s)} & \underline{E^\circ = -0.23 \text{ V}} \\
2Cr(s) + 3Ni^{2+}(aq) \rightarrow 2Cr^{3+}(aq) + 3Ni(s) & E^\circ_{cell} = 0.51 \text{ V}
\end{array}$$

Note that n equals 6. The reaction quotient is

$$Q = \frac{[Cr^{3+}]^2}{[Ni^{2+}]^3} = \frac{(1.0 \times 10^{-3})^2}{(1.5)^3} = 2.962 \times 10^{-7}$$

Copyright © Cengage Learning. All rights reserved.

The standard cell potential is 0.51 V, so the Nernst equation becomes

$$E_{cell} = E°_{cell} - \frac{0.0592}{n} \log Q$$

$$= 0.51 - \frac{0.0592}{6} \log (2.962 \times 10^{-7})$$

$$= 0.51 - (-0.06\underline{4}41) = 0.5\underline{7}4 = 0.57 \text{ V}$$

19.87. The half-cell reactions, the corresponding half-cell potentials, and their sums are displayed below:

$$10Br^-(aq) \rightarrow 5Br_2(l) + 10e^- \qquad -E° = -1.07 \text{ V}$$
$$\underline{2MnO_4^-(aq) + 16H^+(aq) + 10e^- \rightarrow 2Mn^{2+}(aq) + 8H_2O(l) \qquad E° = 1.49 \text{ V}}$$
$$2MnO_4^-(aq) + 10Br^-(aq) + 16H^+(aq) \rightarrow$$
$$2Mn^{2+}(aq) + 5Br_2(l) + 8H_2O(l) \qquad E°_{cell} = 0.42 \text{ V}$$

Note that n equals 10. The reaction quotient is

$$Q = \frac{[Mn^{2+}]^2}{[MnO_4^{2-}]^2[Br^-]^{10}[H^+]^{16}} = \frac{(0.15)^2}{(0.010)^2(0.010)^{10}(1.0)^{16}} = 2.\underline{2}5 \times 10^{22}$$

The standard cell potential is 0.42 V, so the Nernst equation becomes

$$E_{cell} = E°_{cell} - \frac{0.0592}{n} \log Q = 0.42 - \frac{0.0592}{10} \log (2.25 \times 10^{22})$$

$$= 0.42 - (0.1\underline{3}23) = 0.2\underline{8}76 = 0.29 \text{ V}$$

19.89. The overall reaction is

$$Cd(s) + Ni^{2+}(aq) \rightarrow Cd^{2+}(aq) + Ni(s)$$

Note that n equals 2. The reaction quotient is

$$Q = \frac{[Cd^{2+}]}{[Ni^{2+}]} = \frac{[Cd^{2+}]}{1.0} = [Cd^+]$$

The standard cell potential is 0.170 V, and the cell potential is 0.240 V, so the Nernst equation becomes

$$E_{cell} = E°_{cell} - \frac{0.0592}{n} \log Q$$

$$0.240 = 0.170 - \frac{0.0592}{2} \log Q$$

Rearrange and solve for $\log Q$.

$$\log Q = \frac{-2}{0.0592} \times (0.240 - 0.170) = -2.\underline{3}648$$

Copyright © Cengage Learning. All rights reserved.

Take the antilog of both sides.

$$Q = [Cd^{2+}] = \text{antilog} (-2.3648) = \underline{4}.31 \times 10^{-3} = 0.004 \, M$$

The Cd^{2+} concentration is 0.004 M.

19.91.

a. The cathode reaction is $Ca^{2+}(l) + 2e^- \rightarrow Ca(l)$.

The anode reaction is $S^{2-}(l) \rightarrow S(l) + 2e^-$.

b. The cathode reaction is $Cs^+(l) + e^- \rightarrow Cs(l)$.

The anode reaction is $4OH^-(l) \rightarrow O_2(g) + 2H_2O(g) + 4e^-$.

19.93.

a. The species you should consider for half-reactions are Na^+, SO_4^{2-}, and H_2O. The possible cathode reactions are

$$Na^+(aq) + e^- \rightarrow Na(s) \qquad\qquad E° = -2.71 \, V$$
$$2H_2O(l) + 2e^- \rightarrow H_2(g) + 2OH^-(aq) \qquad E° = -0.83 \, V$$

Because the electrode potential for H_2O is larger (less negative), it is easier to reduce.

The possible anode reactions are

$$2H_2O(l) \rightarrow O_2(g) + 4H^+(aq) + 4e^- \quad E° = -1.23 \, V$$
$$2SO_4^{2-}(aq) \rightarrow S_2O_4^{2-}(aq) + 2e^- \qquad E° = -2.01 \, V$$

Because the electrode potential for H_2O is less negative, it is easier to oxidize.

The expected half-reactions are

$$2H_2O(l) \rightarrow O_2(g) + 4H^+(aq) + 4e^- \qquad E° = -1.23 \, V$$
$$4H_2O(l) + 4e^- \rightarrow 2H_2(g) + 4OH^-(aq) \qquad E° = -0.83 \, V$$

The overall reaction is

$$2H_2O(l) \rightarrow 2H_2(g) + O_2(g)$$

b. The species you should consider for half-reactions are K^+, Br^-, and H_2O. The possible cathode reactions are

$$K^+(aq) + e^- \rightarrow K(s) \qquad\qquad E° = -2.92 \, V$$
$$2H_2O(l) + 2e^- \rightarrow H_2(g) + 2OH^-(aq) \qquad E° = -0.83 \, V$$

Because the electrode potential for H_2O is larger (less negative), it is easier to reduce. The possible anode reactions are

$$2H_2O(l) \rightarrow O_2(g) + 4H^+(aq) + 4e^- \qquad E° = -1.23 \, V$$
$$2Br^-(aq) \rightarrow Br_2(l) + 2e^- \qquad\qquad E° = -1.07 \, V$$

Because the electrode potential for Br^- is less negative, it is easier to oxidize.

Copyright © Cengage Learning. All rights reserved.

The expected half-reactions are

$$2Br^-(aq) \rightarrow Br_2(l) + 2e^- \qquad\qquad E° = -1.07 \text{ V}$$

$$2H_2O(l) + 2e^- \rightarrow H_2(g) + 2OH^-(aq) \qquad E° = -0.83 \text{ V}$$

The overall reaction is

$$2Br^-(aq) + 2H_2O(l) \rightarrow Br_2(l) + H_2(g) + 2OH^-$$

19.95. The conversion of grams of aluminum ($3.61 \text{ kg} = 3.61 \times 10^3 \text{ g}$) to coulombs required to give this amount of aluminum is

$$3.61 \times 10^3 \text{ g} \times \frac{1 \text{ mol Al}}{26.98 \text{ g}} \times \frac{3 \text{ mol } e^-}{1 \text{ mol Al}} \times \frac{9.6485 \times 10^4 \text{ C}}{1 \text{ mol } e^-} = 3.8\underline{7}2 \times 10^7 = 3.87 \times 10^7 \text{ C}$$

19.97. The conversion of coulombs to grams of lithium is

$$5.00 \times 10^3 \text{ C} \times \frac{1 \text{ mol } e^-}{9.6485 \times 10^4 \text{ C}} \times \frac{1 \text{ mol Li}}{1 \text{ mol } e^-} \times \frac{6.941 \text{ g Li}}{1 \text{ mol Li}} = 0.35\underline{9}6 = 0.360 \text{ g Li}$$

■ SOLUTIONS TO GENERAL PROBLEMS

19.99.

a. The half-reactions and net ionic equation are

$$3Fe(s) \rightarrow 3Fe^{2+}(aq) + 6e$$
$$\underline{2NO_3(aq) + 8H^+(aq) + 6e \rightarrow 2NO(g) + 4H_2O(l)}$$
$$3Fe(s) + 2NO_3(aq) + 8H^+(aq) \rightarrow 3Fe^{2+}(aq) + 2NO(g) + 4H_2O(l)$$

b. The half-reactions and net ionic equation are

$$3Fe^{2+}(aq) \rightarrow 3Fe^{3+}(aq) + 3e^-$$
$$\underline{NO_3^-(aq) + 4H^+(aq) + 3e^- \rightarrow NO(g) + 2H_2O(l)}$$
$$3Fe^{2+}(aq) + NO_3^-(aq) + 4H^+(aq) \rightarrow 3Fe^{3+}(aq) + NO(g) + 2H_2O(l)$$

c. Add the results from parts a and b, and divide all coefficients by a factor of 3.

$$3Fe(s) + 2NO_3^-(aq) + 8H^+(aq) \rightarrow 3Fe^{2+}(aq) + 2NO(g) + 4H_2O(l)$$
$$\underline{3Fe^{2+}(aq) + NO_3^-(aq) + 4H^+(aq) \rightarrow 3Fe^{3+}(aq) + NO(g) + 2H_2O(l)}$$
$$Fe(s) + NO_3^-(aq) + 4H^+(aq) \rightarrow Fe^{3+}(aq) + NO(g) + 2H_2O(l)$$

Copyright © Cengage Learning. All rights reserved.

19.101.

a.   The two balanced half-reactions are

$$8S^{2-} \rightarrow S_8 + 16e^- \qquad \text{(oxidation)}$$

$$MnO_4(l) + 4H^+ + 3e^- \rightarrow MnO_2 + H_2O \qquad \text{(reduction)}$$

Multiply the oxidation half-reaction by 3 and the reduction half-reaction by 16, and then add together. Cancel the forty-eight electrons from each side. The balanced equation in acidic solution is

$$16MnO_4^- + 24S^{2-} + 64H^+ \rightarrow 16MnO_2 + 3S_8 + 32H_2O$$

Now add sixty-four OH^- to each side. Simplify by combining the H^+ and OH^- to give H_2O. Then cancel thirty-two H_2O on each side. The balanced equation in basic solution is

$$16MnO_4^-(aq) + 24S^{2-}(aq) + 32H_2O(l) \rightarrow 16MnO_2(aq) + 3S_8(aq) + 64OH^-(l)$$

b.   The two balanced half-reactions are

$$HSO_3^- + H_2O \rightarrow SO_4^{2-} + 3H^+ + 2e^- \qquad \text{(oxidation)}$$

$$IO_3^- + 6H^+ + 6e^- \rightarrow I^- + 3H_2O \qquad \text{(reduction)}$$

Multiply the oxidation half-reaction by 3, and then add together. Cancel the six electrons from each side. Also, cancel six H^+ and three H_2O from each side. The balanced equation is

$$IO_3^-(aq) + 3HSO_3^-(aq) \rightarrow I^- + 3SO_4^{2-}(aq) + 3H^+(aq)$$

c.   The two balanced half-reactions are

$$Fe(OH)_2 + H_2O \rightarrow Fe(OH)_3 + H^+ + e^- \qquad \text{(oxidation)}$$

$$CrO_4^{2-} + 4H^+ + 3e^- \rightarrow Cr(OH)_4^- \qquad \text{(reduction)}$$

Multiply the oxidation half-reaction by 3, and then add together. Cancel the three electrons and cancel three H^+ from each side. The balanced equation in acidic solution is

$$CrO_4^{2-}(aq) + 3Fe(OH)_2(s) + H^+(aq) + 3H_2O(l) \rightarrow Cr(OH)_4^-(aq) + 3Fe(OH)_3(s)$$

Now add one OH^- to each side. Simplify by combining the H^+ and OH^- to give H_2O. Then, combine the H_2O's on the left side into a single term. The balanced equation in basic solution is

$$CrO_4^{2-}(aq) + 3Fe(OH)_2(aq) + 4H_2O(l) \rightarrow Cr(OH)_4^-(aq) + 3Fe(OH)_3(s) + OH^-(aq)$$

d.   The two balanced half-reactions are

$$Cl_2 + 2H_2O \rightarrow 2ClO^- + 4H^+ + 2e^- \quad \text{(oxidation)}$$

$$Cl_2 + 2e^- \rightarrow 2Cl^- \qquad \text{(reduction)}$$

Add the two half-reactions together. Cancel the two electrons from each side. Divide all the coefficients by a factor of 2. The balanced equation in acidic solution is

$$Cl_2 + H_2O \rightarrow Cl^- + ClO^- + 2H^+$$

Copyright © Cengage Learning. All rights reserved.

Now add two OH^- to each side. Simplify by combining the H^+ and OH^- to give H_2O. Then cancel one H_2O on each side. The balanced equation in basic solution is

$$Cl_2(aq) + 2OH^-(aq) \rightarrow Cl^-(aq) + ClO^-(aq) + H_2O(l)$$

19.103. This reaction takes place in basic solution. The skeleton equation is

$$Fe(OH)_2(s) + O_2(g) \rightarrow Fe(OH)_3(s)$$

The two balanced half-reactions are

$$Fe(OH)_2 + H_2O \rightarrow Fe(OH)_3 + H^+ + e^- \quad \text{(oxidation)}$$
$$O_2 + 4H^+ + 4e^- \rightarrow 2H_2O \quad \text{(reduction)}$$

Multiply the oxidation half-reaction by 4, and then add together. Cancel the four electrons from each side. Also, cancel four H^+ and two H_2O from each side. The balanced equation in acidic or in basic solution is

$$4Fe(OH)_2(s) + O_2(g) + 2H_2O(l) \rightarrow 4Fe(OH)_3(s)$$

19.105. The cell notation is $Ca(s)|Ca^{2+}(aq)||Cl_2(g)|Cl^-(aq)|Pt(s)$. The reactions are

Anode: $Ca(s) \rightarrow Ca^{2+}(aq) + 2e^-$ $\qquad\qquad\qquad -E° = 2.76$ V

Cathode: $Cl_2(g) + 2e^- \rightarrow 2Cl^-(aq)$ $\qquad\qquad\qquad E° = 1.36$ V

$E°_{cell} = 1.36$ V $+ 2.76$ V $= 4.12$ V

19.107.

a.   In this reaction, Fe^{3+} is the oxidizing agent on the left side; Ni^{2+} is the oxidizing reagent on the right side. The corresponding standard electrode potentials are

$$Ni^{2+}(aq) + 2e^- \rightarrow Ni(s) \qquad\qquad\qquad E° = -0.23 \text{ V}$$
$$Fe^{3+}(aq) + e^- \rightarrow Fe^{2+}(aq) \qquad\qquad\qquad E° = 0.77 \text{ V}$$

The stronger oxidizing agent is the one involved in the half-reaction with the more positive standard electrode potential, so Fe^{3+} is the stronger oxidizing agent. The oxidation of nickel by iron(III) is a spontaneous reaction.

b.   In this reaction, Fe^{3+} is the oxidizing agent on the left side; Sn^{4+} is the oxidizing reagent on the right side. The corresponding standard electrode potentials are

$$Sn^{4+}(aq) + 2e^- \rightarrow Sn^{2+}(aq) \qquad\qquad\qquad E° = 0.15 \text{ V}$$
$$Fe^{3+}(aq) + e^- \rightarrow Fe^{2+}(aq) \qquad\qquad\qquad E° = 0.77 \text{ V}$$

The stronger oxidizing agent is the one involved in the half-reaction with the more positive standard electrode potential, so Fe^{3+} is the stronger oxidizing agent. The oxidation of tin(II) by iron(III) is a spontaneous reaction.

Copyright © Cengage Learning. All rights reserved.

19.109. The half-cell reactions, the corresponding half-cell potentials, and their sums are displayed below:

$$Pb(s) \rightarrow Pb^{2+}(aq) + 2e^- \qquad -E° = 0.13 \text{ V}$$
$$2H^+(aq) + 2e^- \rightarrow H_2(g) \qquad E° = 0.00 \text{ V}$$
$$\overline{Pb(s) + 2H^+(aq) \rightarrow Pb^{2+}(aq) + H_2(g) \qquad E°_{cell} = 0.13 \text{ V}}$$

Note that n equals 2. Next, use K_{sp} to calculate $[Pb^{2+}]$.

$$[Pb^{2+}] = \frac{K_{sp}}{[SO_4^{2-}]} = \frac{1.7 \times 10^{-8}}{1.0} = 1.7 \times 10^{-8} \, M$$

The reaction quotient for the cell reaction is

$$Q = \frac{[Pb^{2+}] \times P_{H_2}}{[H^+]^2} = \frac{(1.7 \times 10^{-8})(1.0)}{(1.0)^2} = 1.7 \times 10^{-8}$$

The standard cell potential is 0.13 V , so the Nernst equation becomes

$$E_{cell} = E°_{cell} - \frac{0.0592}{n} \log Q$$

$$E_{cell} = 0.13 \text{ V} - \frac{0.0592}{2} \log (1.7 \times 10^{-8})$$

$$= 0.13 \text{ V} - (-0.2299 \text{ V}) = 0.3599 = 0.36 \text{ V}$$

19.111.

a. Note that $E° = 0.010$ V and n equals 2. Substitute into the equation relating $E°$ and K.

$$E° = \frac{0.0592}{n} \log K$$

$$0.010 \text{ V} = \frac{0.0592}{2} \log K$$

Solving for K, you get

$$\log K = 0.3378$$

Take the antilog of both sides:

$$K = K_c = \text{antilog} (0.3378) = 2.176 = 2.2$$

b. Substitute into the equilibrium expression using $[Sn^{2+}] = x$, and $[Pb^{2+}] = 1.0 \, M - x$.

$$K_c = \frac{[Sn^{2+}]}{[Pb^{2+}]} = \frac{x}{1.0 - x} = 2.176$$

$$x = 0.6851 \, M$$

$$[Pb^{2+}] = 1.0 \, M - x = 0.3149 = 0.3 \, M$$

Copyright © Cengage Learning. All rights reserved.

398 Chapter 19: Electrochemistry

19.113.

a. The number of faradays is

$$1.0 \text{ mol Na}^+ \times \frac{1 \text{ mol e}^-}{1 \text{ mol Na}^+} \times \frac{1\,F}{1 \text{ mol e}^-} = 1.0\,F$$

The number of coulombs is

$$1.0\,F \times \frac{96,485 \text{ C}}{1\,F} = 9.\underline{6}4 \times 10^4 = 9.6 \times 10^4 \text{ C}$$

b. The number of faradays is

$$1.0 \text{ mol Cu}^{2+} \times \frac{2 \text{ mol e}^-}{1 \text{ mol Cu}^{2+}} \times \frac{1\,F}{1 \text{ mol e}^-} = 2.0\,F$$

The number of coulombs is

$$2.0\,F \times \frac{96,485 \text{ C}}{1\,F} = 1.\underline{9}2 \times 10^5 = 1.9 \times 10^5 \text{ C}$$

c. The number of faradays is

$$1.0 \text{ g H}_2\text{O} \times \frac{1 \text{ mol H}_2\text{O}}{18.01 \text{ g H}_2\text{O}} \times \frac{2 \text{ mol e}^-}{1 \text{ mol H}_2\text{O}} \times \frac{1\,F}{1 \text{ mol e}^-} = 0.1\underline{1}10 = 0.11\,F$$

The number of coulombs is

$$0.1110\,F \times \frac{96,485 \text{ C}}{1\,F} = 1.\underline{0}7 \times 10^4 = 1.1 \times 10^4 \text{ C}$$

d. The number of faradays is

$$1.0 \text{ g Cl}^- \times \frac{1 \text{ mol Cl}^-}{35.45 \text{ g Cl}^-} \times \frac{2 \text{ mol e}^-}{2 \text{ mol Cl}^-} \times \frac{1\,F}{1 \text{ mol e}^-} = 0.02\underline{8}20 = 0.028\,F$$

The number of coulombs is

$$0.02820\,F \times \frac{96,485 \text{ C}}{1\,F} = 2.\underline{7}21 \times 10^3 = 2.7 \times 10^3 \text{ C}$$

19.115. From the electrolysis information, calculate the total moles of I_2 formed

$$65.4 \text{ s} \times (10.5 \times 10^{-3} \text{ A}) \times \frac{1 \text{ C}}{1 \text{ A} \cdot \text{s}} \times \frac{1 \text{ mol e}^-}{96,485 \text{ C}} \times \frac{1 \text{ mol I}_2}{2 \text{ mol e}^-} = 3.5\underline{5}8 \times 10^{-6} \text{ mol I}_2$$

From the balanced equation,

$$3.558 \times 10^{-6} \text{ mol I}_2 \times \frac{1 \text{ mol H}_3\text{AsO}_3}{1 \text{ mol I}_2} \times \frac{1 \text{ mol As}}{1 \text{ mol H}_3\text{AsO}_3} \times \frac{79.42 \text{ g As}}{1 \text{ mol As}}$$

$$= 2.8\underline{2}57 \times 10^{-4} = 2.83 \times 10^{-4} \text{ g As}$$

Copyright © Cengage Learning. All rights reserved.

19.117.

  a. The spontaneous chemical reaction and maximum cell potential are

$$
\begin{array}{llr}
Cd(s) & \rightarrow \quad Cd^{2+}(aq) + 2e^- & -E^\circ = 0.40 \text{ V} \\
2Ag^+(aq) + 2e^- & \rightarrow \quad 2Ag(s) & E^\circ = 0.80 \text{ V} \\
\hline
Cd(s) + 2Ag^+(aq) & \rightarrow \quad 2Ag(s) + Cd^{2+}(aq) & E^\circ_{cell} = 1.20 \text{ V}
\end{array}
$$

  b. Addition of S^{2-} would greatly decrease the $Cd^{2+}(aq)$ concentration and help shift the equilibrium to the right, thus forming more Ag. The cell potential would increase.

  c. No effect. The size of the electrode makes no difference in the potential.

19.119. Anode: $2H_2O(l) \rightarrow O_2(g) + 4H^+(aq) + 4e^-$

  Cathode: $Cu^{2+}(aq) + 2e^- \rightarrow Cu(s)$

19.121.

  a. First, find the moles of silver.

$$2.48 \text{ g Ag} \times \frac{1 \text{ mol Ag}}{107.9 \text{ g Ag}} = 0.02298 \text{ mol Ag}$$

  The number of coulombs is

$$0.02298 \text{ mol Ag} \times \frac{1 \text{ mol e}^-}{1 \text{ mol Ag}} \times \frac{9.6485 \times 10^4 \text{ C}}{1 \text{ mol e}^-} = 2218 \text{ C}$$

  Since amp x sec = coul, the number of seconds is

$$\text{Time} = \frac{2218 \text{ C}}{1.50 \text{ amp}} = 1.478 \times 10^3 = 1.48 \times 10^3 \text{ s}$$

  b. For the same amount of current, the grams of Cr would be

$$2218 \text{ C} \times \frac{1 \text{ mol e}^-}{96,485 \text{ C}} \times \frac{1 \text{ mol Cr}}{3 \text{ mol e}^-} \times \frac{52.00 \text{ g Cr}}{1 \text{ mol Cr}} = 0.3983 = 0.398 \text{ g}$$

19.123.

  a. Note that 3.50 hours = 12600 s, and the efficiency is 90.0%.

$$2.75 \text{ amp} \times 12600 \text{ s} \times \frac{1 \text{ F}}{96,485 \text{ C}} \times 0.900 = 0.3232 = 0.323 \text{ F}$$

  b. The moles of Au that were deposited is

$$\text{mol Au} = 21.221 \text{ g Au} \times \frac{1 \text{ mol Au}}{197.0 \text{ g}} = 0.107720 \text{ mol}$$

Copyright © Cengage Learning. All rights reserved.

Since $1\,F = 1$ mol e⁻, the ratio of moles of e⁻ to moles of Au is

$$\frac{\text{mol e}^-}{\text{mol Au}} = \frac{0.3232}{0.10772} = \frac{3.00}{1}$$

Thus, the ion must be Au^{3+}. The reaction is

$$Au^{3+} + 3e^- \rightarrow Au$$

19.125.

a. The half-cell reactions, the corresponding half-cell potentials, and their sums are displayed below:

$Zn(s)$	$\rightarrow$	$Zn^{2+}(aq) + 2e^-$	$-E^\circ = 0.76$ V
$Cu^{2+}(aq) + 2e^-$	$\rightarrow$	$Cu(s)$	$E^\circ = 0.34$ V
$Cu^{2+}(aq) + Zn(s)$	$\rightarrow$	$Zn^{2+}(aq) + Cu(s)$	$E^\circ = 1.10$ V

Use the Nernst equation to calculate the voltage of the cell.

$$E = E^\circ - \frac{0.0592}{n} \log Q = E^\circ - \frac{0.0592}{n} \log \frac{[Zn^{2+}]}{[Cu^{2+}]}$$

Note that n equals 2, $[Zn^{2+}] = 0.200\,M$, and $[Cu^{2+}] = 0.0100\,M$.

$$E^\circ = 1.10 \text{ V} - \frac{0.0592}{2} \log \frac{[0.200]}{[0.0100]} = 1.10 \text{ V} - 0.03851 \text{ V} = 1.0\underline{6}1 = 1.06 \text{ V}$$

b. First, calculate the moles of electrons passing through the cell.

$$1.00 \text{ amp} \times 225 \text{ s} \times \frac{1 \text{ mol e}^-}{96,485 \text{ C}} = 0.00233\underline{2} \text{ mol e}^-$$

The moles of Cu deposited are

$$0.002332 \text{ mol e}^- \times \frac{1 \text{ mol Cu}}{2 \text{ mol e}^-} = 0.00116\underline{6} \text{ mol Cu}$$

The moles of Cu remaining in the 1.00 L of solution are

$$0.0100 - 0.001166 = 0.008\underline{8}34 = 0.0088 \text{ mol}$$

Since the volume of the solution is 1.00 L, the molarity of Cu^{2+} is 0.0088 M.

19.127.

a. Write the cell reaction with the ΔG_f°'s beneath.

$$Cd(s) + Co^{2+}(aq) \rightarrow Cd^{2+}(aq) + Co(s)$$

$$\Delta G_f^\circ: \quad 0 \qquad -54.4 \qquad\qquad -77.6 \qquad 0 \text{ kJ}$$

Hence,

$$\Delta G^\circ = \Sigma n \Delta G_f^\circ(\text{products}) - \Sigma m \Delta G_f^\circ(\text{reactants})$$

$$= [-77.6 + 54.4] \text{ kJ} = -23.\underline{2} \text{ kJ} = -2.32 \times 10^4 \text{ J}$$

Copyright © Cengage Learning. All rights reserved.

b. Next, determine the standard cell potential for the cell. Note that n equals 2.

$$\Delta G^\circ = -nFE^\circ$$

$$-2.32 \times 10^4 \text{ J} = -2(9.6485 \times 10^4 \text{ C}) \times E^\circ$$

Solve for E° to get

$$E^\circ = \frac{-2.32 \times 10^4 \text{ J}}{-2(9.6485 \times 10^4 \text{ C})} = 0.120\underline{2} = 0.120 \text{ V}$$

The half-reactions and voltages are

$Cd(s)$	$\rightarrow$	$Cd^{2+}(aq) + 2e^-$	$-E^\circ_{ox} = 0.40 \text{ V}$
$Co^{2+}(aq) + 2e^-$	$\rightarrow$	$Co(s)$	$E^\circ_{red} = ?$
$Cd(s) + Co^{2+}(aq)$	$\rightarrow$	$Cd^{2+}(aq) + Co(s)$	$E^\circ = 0.1202 \text{ V}$

The cell potential is

$$E^\circ = E^\circ_{red} + (-E^\circ_{ox})$$

$$0.1202 \text{ V} = E^\circ_{red} + 0.40 \text{ V}$$

$$E^\circ_{red} = 0.1202 \text{ V} - 0.40 \text{ V} = -0.2\underline{7}97 = -0.28 \text{ V}$$

■ SOLUTIONS TO CUMULATIVE-SKILLS PROBLEMS

19.139. The half-cell reactions, the corresponding half-cell potentials, and their sums are displayed below:

$3Zn(s)$	$\rightarrow$	$3Zn^{2+}(aq) + 6e^-$	$-E^\circ = 0.76 \text{ V}$
$2Cr^{3+}(aq) + 6e^-$	$\rightarrow$	$2Cr(s)$	$E^\circ = -0.74 \text{ V}$
$2Cr^{3+}(aq) + 3Zn(s)$	$\rightarrow$	$3Zn^{2+}(aq) + 2Cr(s)$	$E^\circ = 0.02 \text{ V}$

Note that n equals 6. Therefore,

$$\Delta G^\circ = -nFE^\circ = -6(9.6485 \times 10^4 \text{ C})(0.02 \text{ V}) = -\underline{1}.158 \times 10^4 \text{ J} = -\underline{1}1.58 \text{ kJ}$$

Write the cell reaction with the ΔH_f°'s beneath.

$$2Cr^{3+}(aq) + 3Zn(s) \rightarrow 3Zn^{2+}(aq) + 2Cr(s)$$
$$\Delta H_f^\circ: \quad 2(-143.5) \qquad 0 \qquad 3(-153.9) \qquad 0 \text{ KJ}$$

Hence,

$$\Delta H^\circ = \Sigma n\Delta H_f^\circ(\text{products}) - \Sigma m\Delta H_f^\circ(\text{reactants})$$
$$= [3(-153.9) - 2(-143.5)] \text{ kJ} = -174.7 \text{ kJ}$$

Now calculate ΔS°.

$$\Delta G^\circ = \Delta H^\circ - T\Delta S^\circ$$

$$-11.58 \text{ kJ} = -174.7 \text{ kJ} - 298 \text{ K} \times \Delta S^\circ$$

Solving for ΔS° gives

$$\Delta S^\circ = \frac{-174.7 \text{ kJ} + 11.58 \text{ kJ}}{298 \text{ K}} = -0.547\underline{3} \text{ kJ/K} = -547 \text{ J/K}$$

Copyright © Cengage Learning. All rights reserved.

19.141. The half-cell reactions, the corresponding half-cell potentials, and their sums are displayed below:

$$
\begin{array}{llll}
4Br^-(aq) & \rightarrow & 2Br_2(l) + 4e^- & -E° = -1.07 \text{ V} \\
O_2(g) + 4H^+(aq) + 4e^- & \rightarrow & 2H_2O(l) & E° = 1.23 \text{ V} \\
\hline
O_2(g) + 4H^+(aq) + 4Br^-(aq) & \rightarrow & 2H_2O(l) + 2Br_2(l) & E° = 0.16 \text{ V}
\end{array}
$$

Now, convert the pH to $[H^+]$.

$$[H^+] = \text{antilog}\,(-3.60) = 2.\underline{5}1 \times 10^{-4}\,M$$

Under standard conditions, $[Br^-] = 1\,M$, and the pressure of O_2 is 1 atm. Thus, substitute into the Nernst equation, where n equals 4.

$$E = E° - \frac{0.0592}{n} \log Q = E° - \frac{0.0592}{n} \log \frac{1}{[H^+]^4[Br^-]^4 \times P_{O_2}}$$

$$= 0.16\text{ V} - \frac{0.0592}{4} \log \frac{1}{(2.51 \times 10^{-4})^4}$$

$$= 0.16\text{ V} - 0.21\underline{3}1\text{ V} = -0.0\underline{5}31 = -0.05\text{ V}$$

Thus, the reaction is nonspontaneous at this $[H^+]$.

19.143. Use the K_a to calculate [H+] for the buffer.

$$K_a = \frac{[H^+][OCN^-]}{[HOCN]} = 3.5 \times 10^{-4}$$

Rearrange, and solve for $[H^+]$, assuming [HOCN] and $[OCN^-]$ remain constant in the buffer. Thus, $[H^+] = K_a = 3.5 \times 10^{-4}\,M$.

In Problem 19.141, $E°$ for this cell reaction was found to be 0.16 V. Under standard conditions, $[Br^-] = 1\,M$, and the pressure of O_2 is 1 atm. Thus, substitute into the Nernst equation, where n equals 4.

$$E = E° - \frac{0.0592}{n} \log Q = E° - \frac{0.0592}{n} \log \frac{1}{[H^+]^4[Br^-]^4 \times P_{O_2}}$$

$$= 0.16\text{ V} - \frac{0.0592}{4} \log \frac{1}{(3.5 \times 10^{-4})^4}$$

$$= 0.16\text{ V} - 0.20\underline{4}59\text{ V} = -0.0\underline{4}455 = -0.04\text{ V}$$

Thus, the reaction is nonspontaneous at this $[H^+]$.

Copyright © Cengage Learning. All rights reserved.

19.145. The half-cell reactions, the corresponding half-cell potentials, and their sums are displayed below:

$$
\begin{array}{llll}
H_2(g) & \rightarrow & 2H^+(aq) + 2e^- & -E^\circ = -0.00\ V \\
2Ag^+(aq) + 2e^- & \rightarrow & 2Ag(s) & E^\circ = 0.80\ V \\
\hline
H_2(g) + 2Ag^+(aq) & \rightarrow & 2H^+(aq) + 2Ag(s) & E^\circ = 0.80\ V
\end{array}
$$

The standard hydrogen electrode has $[H^+] = 1.0\ M$ and the pressure of H_2 equals 1 atm. Substitute into the Nernst equation, where $E = 0.45\ V$ and n equals 2.

$$
E = E^\circ - \frac{0.0592}{n} \log Q = E^\circ - \frac{0.0592}{n} \log \frac{[H^+]^2}{[Ag^+]^2 \times P_{H_2}}
$$

$$
0.45\ V = 0.80\ V - \frac{0.0592}{2} \log \frac{1}{[Ag^+]^2}
$$

Using the properties of logs, rearrange to get

$$
0.45\ V = 0.80\ V + 0.0592 \log[Ag^+]
$$

Solve for $[Ag^+]$.

$$
\log[Ag^+] = \frac{0.45 - 0.80}{0.0592} = -5.\underline{9}12
$$

$$
[Ag^+] = 10^{-5.912} = \underline{1}.224 \times 10^{-6}\ M
$$

Finally, determine the solubility product, using $[SCN^-] = 0.10\ M$.

$$
K_{sp} = [Ag^+][SCN^-] = (1.224 \times 10^{-6})(0.10) = \underline{1}.224 \times 10^{-7} = 1 \times 10^{-7}
$$

Copyright © Cengage Learning. All rights reserved.

Appendixes

Appendix A | Mathematical Skills

Only a few basic mathematical skills are required for the study of general chemistry. But to concentrate your attention on the concepts of chemistry, you will find it necessary to have a firm grasp of these basic mathematical skills. In this appendix, we will review scientific (or exponential) notation, logarithms, simple algebraic operations, the solution of quadratic equations, and the plotting of straight-line graphs.

A.1 Scientific (Exponential) Notation

ChemWork: Scientific Notation

In chemistry, you frequently encounter very large and very small numbers. For example, the number of molecules in a liter of air at 20°C and normal barometric pressure is 25,000,000,000,000,000,000,000, and the distance between two hydrogen atoms in a hydrogen molecule is 0.000,000,000,074 meter. In these forms, such numbers are inconvenient to write and difficult to read. For this reason, you normally express them in scientific, or exponential, notation. Scientific calculators also use this notation.

In scientific notation, a number is written in the form $A \times 10^n$. A is a number greater than or equal to 1 and less than 10, and the exponent n (the nth power of 10) is a positive or negative integer. For example, 4853 is written in scientific notation as 4.853×10^3, which is 4.853 multiplied by three factors of 10:

$$4.853 \times 10^3 = 4.853 \times 10 \times 10 \times 10 = 4853$$

The number 0.0568 is written in scientific notation as 5.68×10^{-2}, which is 5.68 divided by two factors of 10:

$$5.68 \times 10^{-2} = \frac{5.68}{10 \times 10} = 0.0568$$

Any number can be conveniently transformed to scientific notation by moving the decimal point to obtain a number, A, greater than or equal to 1 and less than 10. If the decimal point is moved to the left, you multiply A by 10^n, where n equals the number of places moved. If the decimal point is moved to the right, you multiply A by 10^{-n}. Consider the number 0.00731. You must move the decimal point to the right three places. Therefore, 0.00731 equals 7.31×10^{-3}. To transform a number written in scientific notation to the usual form, the process is reversed. If the exponent is positive, the decimal point is shifted right. If the exponent is negative, the decimal point is shifted left.

Example 1 | Expressing Numbers in Scientific Notation

Express the following numbers in scientific notation:

a. 843.4   b. 0.00421   c. 1.54

Solution Shift the decimal point to get a number between 1 and 10; count the number of positions shifted.

a. $8\,4\,3\,.\,4 = \mathbf{8.434 \times 10^2}$

b. $0\,.\,0\,0\,4\,2\,1 = \mathbf{4.21 \times 10^{-3}}$

c. **leave as is or write 1.54×10^0**

Exercise 1   Express the following numbers in scientific notation:

a. 4.38   b. 4380   c. 0.000483

| **Example 2** | Converting Numbers in Scientific Notation to Usual Form |

Convert the following numbers in scientific notation to usual form:

a. 6.39×10^{-4} b. 3.275×10^{2}

Solution   a. $0.0006.39 \times 10^{-4} = \mathbf{0.000639}$

b. $3.275 \times 10^{2} = \mathbf{327.5}$

Exercise 2   Convert the following numbers in scientific notation to usual form:

a. 7.025×10^{3}

b. 8.97×10^{-4}

Addition and Subtraction

Before adding or subtracting two numbers written in scientific notation, it is necessary to express both to the same power of 10. After adding or subtracting, it may be necessary to shift the decimal point to express the result in scientific notation.

| **Example 3** | Adding and Subtracting in Scientific Notation |

Carry out the following arithmetic; give the result in scientific notation.

$$(9.42 \times 10^{-2}) + (7.6 \times 10^{-3})$$

Solution   You can shift the decimal point in either number to obtain both to the same power of 10. For example, to get both numbers to 10^{-2}, you shift the decimal point one place to the left and add 1 to the exponent in the expression 7.6×10^{-3}.

$$7.6 \times 10^{-3} = 0.76 \times 10^{-2}$$

Now you can add the two numbers.

$$(9.42 \times 10^{-2}) + (0.76 \times 10^{-2}) = (9.42 + 0.76) \times 10^{-2} = 10.18 \times 10^{-2}$$

Since 10.18 is not between 1 and 10, you shift the decimal point to express the final result in scientific notation.

$$10.18 \times 10^{-2} = \mathbf{1.018 \times 10^{-1}}$$

Exercise 3   Add the following, and express the sum in scientific notation:

$$(3.142 \times 10^{-4}) + (2.8 \times 10^{-6})$$

Multiplication and Division

To multiply two numbers in scientific notation, you first multiply the two powers of 10 by adding their exponents. Then you multiply the remaining factors. Division is handled similarly. You first move any power of 10 in the denominator to the numerator, changing the sign of the exponent. After multiplying the two powers of 10 by adding their exponents, you carry out the indicated division.

| **Example 4** | Multiplying and Dividing in Scientific Notation |

Do the following arithmetic, and express the answers in scientific notation.

a. $(6.3 \times 10^{2}) \times (2.4 \times 10^{5})$ b. $\dfrac{6.4 \times 10^{2}}{2.0 \times 10^{5}}$

(continued)

(continued)

Solution a. $(6.3 \times 10^2) \times (2.4 \times 10^5) = (6.3 \times 2.4) \times 10^7 = 15.12 \times 10^7 = $ **1.512×10^8**

b. $\dfrac{6.4 \times 10^2}{2.0 \times 10^5} = \dfrac{6.4}{2.0} \times 10^2 \times 10^{-5} = \dfrac{6.4}{2.0} \times 10^{-3} = $ **3.2×10^{-3}**

Exercise 4   Perform the following operations, expressing the answers in scientific notation:

a. $(5.4 \times 10^{-7}) \times (1.8 \times 10^8)$ b. $\dfrac{5.4 \times 10^{-7}}{6.0 \times 10^{-5}}$

Powers and Roots

A number $A \times 10^n$ raised to a power p is evaluated by raising A to the power p and multiplying the exponent in the power of 10 by p:

$$(A \times 10^n)^p = A^p \times 10^{n \times p}$$

You extract the rth root of a number $A \times 10^n$ by first moving the decimal point in A so that the exponent in the power of 10 is exactly divisible by r. Suppose this has been done, so that n in the number $A \times 10^n$ is exactly divisible by r. Then

$$\sqrt[r]{A \times 10^n} = \sqrt[r]{A} \times 10^{n/r}$$

Example 5 | Finding Powers and Roots in Scientific Notation

Evaluate the following expressions:

a. $(5.29 \times 10^2)^3$

b. $\sqrt{2.31 \times 10^7}$

Solution a. $(5.29 \times 10^2)^3 = (5.29)^3 \times 10^6 = 148 \times 10^6 = $ **1.48×10^8**

b. $\sqrt{2.31 \times 10^7} = \sqrt{23.1 \times 10^6} = \sqrt{23.1} \times 10^{6/2} = $ **4.81×10^3**

Exercise 5   Obtain the values of the following, and express them in scientific notation:

a. $(3.56 \times 10^3)^4$ b. $\sqrt{4.81 \times 10^2}$

Electronic Calculators

Scientific calculators will perform all of the arithmetic operations we have just described (as well as those discussed in the next section). On most calculators, the basic operations of addition, subtraction, multiplication, and division are similar and straightforward. However, more variation exists in raising a number to a power and extracting a root. If you have the calculator instructions, by all means read them. Otherwise, the following information may help.

Squares and square roots are usually obtained with special keys, perhaps labeled x^2 and $\sqrt{x}$. Thus, to obtain $(5.15)^2$, you enter 5.15 and press x^2. To obtain $\sqrt{5.15}$, you enter 5.15 and press $\sqrt{x}$ (or perhaps INV, for inverse, and x^2). Other powers and roots require a y^x (or a^x) key. The answer to Example 5(a), which is $(5.29 \times 10^2)^3$, would be obtained by a sequence of steps such as the following: enter 5.29×10^2, press the y^x key, enter 3, and press the $=$ key.

The same sequence can be used to extract a root. Suppose you want $\sqrt[17]{2.18 \times 10^6}$. This is equivalent to $(2.18 \times 10^6)^{1/5}$ or $(2.18 \times 10^6)^{0.2}$. If the calculator has a $1/x$ key, the sequence would be as follows: enter 2.18×10^6, press the y^x key, enter 5, press the $1/x$ key, then press the $=$ key. Some calculators have a $\sqrt[x]{y}$ key, so this can be used to extract the xth root of y, using a sequence of steps similar to that for y^x.

A.2 Logarithms

The *logarithm* to the *base a* of a number x, denoted $\log_a x$, is the exponent of the constant a needed to equal the number x. For example, suppose a is 10, and you would like the logarithm of 1000; that is, you would like the value of $\log_{10}1000$. This is the exponent, y, of 10 such that 10^y equals 1000. The value of y here is 3. Thus, $\log_{10}1000 = 3$.

Common logarithms are logarithms in which the base is 10. The common logarithm of a number x is often denoted simply as $\log x$. It is easy to see how to obtain the common logarithms of 10, 100, 1000, and so forth. But logarithms are defined for all positive numbers, not just the powers of 10. In general, the exponents, or values, of the logarithm will be decimal numbers. To understand the meaning of a decimal exponent, consider $10^{0.400}$. This is equivalent to $10^{400/1000} = 10^{2/5} = \sqrt[5]{10^2} = 2.51$. Therefore, $\log 2.51 = 0.400$. Any decimal exponent is essentially a fraction, p/r, so by evaluating the expressions $10^{p/r} = \sqrt[r]{10^p}$ one could construct a table of logarithms. In practice, power series or other methods are used.

The following are fundamental properties of all logarithms:

$$\log_a 1 = 0 \tag{1}$$

$$\log_a(A \times B) = \log_a A + \log_a B \tag{2}$$

$$\log_a \frac{A}{B} = \log_a A - \log_a B \tag{3}$$

$$\log_a A^p = p \log_a A \tag{4}$$

$$\log_a \sqrt[r]{A} = \frac{1}{r}\log_a A \tag{5}$$

These properties are very useful in working with logarithms.

Electronic calculators that evaluate logarithms are now available for about $10 or so. Their simplicity of operation makes them well worth the price. To obtain the logarithm of a number, you enter the number and press the LOG key.

Exercise 6   Find the values of (a) log 0.00582; (b) log 689.

Antilogarithm

The antilogarithm (abbreviated antilog) is the inverse of the common logarithm. Antilog x is simply 10^x. If your electronic calculator has a 10^x key, you obtain the antilogarithm of a number by entering the number and pressing the 10^x key. (It may be necessary to press an inverse key before pressing a 10^x/LOG key.) If your calculator has a y^x (or a^x) key, you enter 10, press y^x, enter x, then press the $=$ key.

Exercise 7   Evaluate (a) antilog 5.728; (b) antilog (-5.728).

Natural Logarithms and Natural Antilogarithms

The mathematical constant $e = 2.71828$, like π, occurs in many scientific and engineering problems. It is frequently seen in the natural exponential function $y = e^x$. The inverse function is called the *natural logarithm*, $x = \ln y$, where $\ln y$ is simplified notation for $\log_e y$.

Finding the natural logarithm with a calculator is analogous to finding the common logarithm, only in this case you enter the number and press the LN key. For example, you may obtain the natural logarithm of 6.2 by entering 6.2 and pressing the LN key ($\ln 6.2 = 1.82$). The natural antilogarithm of a number is the constant e raised to a power equal to the number. Therefore, the expression for natural antilogarithm of 1.34 is written as

$$\text{natural antilog } 1.34 = e^{1.34}$$

In order to evaluate the expression $e^{1.34}$ on your calculator, you can use the e^x key, or you may have to use the INV key in combination with the LN key ($e^{1.34} = 3.8$).

There are instances where you may want to relate the natural logarithm to the common logarithm; the expression is

$$\ln x = 2.303 \log x$$

Exercise 8   Evaluate (a) $\ln 9.93$; (b) $e^{1.10}$.

A.3 Algebraic Operations and Graphing

Often you are given an algebraic formula that you need to rearrange to solve for a particular quantity. As an example, suppose you would like to solve the following equation for V:

$$PV = nRT$$

You can eliminate P from the left-hand side by dividing by P. But to maintain the equality, you must perform the same operation on both sides of the equation:

$$\frac{PV}{P} = \frac{nRT}{P}$$

or

$$V = \frac{nRT}{P}$$

Quadratic Formula

A quadratic equation is one involving only powers of x in which the highest power is 2. The general form of the equation can be written

$$ax^2 + bx + c = 0$$

where a, b, and c are constants. For given values of these constants, only certain values of x are possible. (In general, there will be two values.) These values of x are said to be the solutions of the equation.

These solutions are given by the *quadratic formula:*

$$x = \frac{-b \pm \sqrt{b^2 - 4ac}}{2a}$$

In this formula, the symbol $\pm$ means that there are two possible values of x—one obtained by taking the positive sign, the other by taking the negative sign.

Example 6 | Obtaining the Solutions of a Quadratic Equation

Obtain the solutions of the following quadratic equation:

$$2.00x^2 - 1.72x - 2.86 = 0$$

Solution Using the quadratic formula, you substitute $a = 2.00$, $b = -1.72$, and $c = -2.86$. You get

$$x = \frac{1.72 \pm \sqrt{(-1.72)^2 - 4 \times 2.00 \times (-2.86)}}{2 \times 2.00} = \frac{1.72 \pm 5.08}{4.00} = \textbf{-0.840 and +1.70}$$

Mathematically there are two solutions, but in any real problem one solution may not be allowed. For example, if the solution is some physical quantity that can have only positive values, a negative solution must be rejected.

Exercise 9   Find the positive solution (or solutions) to the following equation:

$$1.80x^2 + 0.850x - 9.50 = 0$$

The Straight-Line Graph

A graph is a visual means of representing a mathematical relationship or physical data. Consider the following data table, in which values of y from some experiment are given for four values of x.

x	y
1	−1
2	1
3	3
4	5

By plotting these x, y points on a graph (Figure A.1), you see that they fall on a straight line. This suggests (but does not prove) that other points from this type of

FIGURE A.1 ▶

A straight-line plot of some data

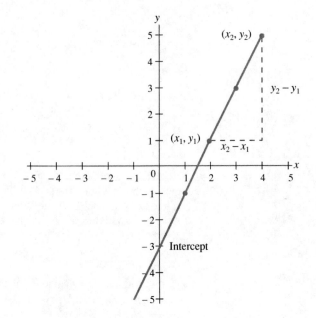

experiment might fall on the same line. It would be useful to have the mathematical equation for this line.

The general equation form of a straight line is

$$y = mx + b$$

The constant m is called the *slope* of the straight line. It is obtained by dividing the vertical distance between any two points on the line by the horizontal distance. If the two points are (x_1, y_1) and (x_2, y_2), the slope is given by the following formula:

$$\text{Slope} = \frac{y_2 - y_1}{x_2 - x_1}$$

Suppose you choose the points (2, 1) and (4, 5) from the data. Then

$$\text{Slope} = \frac{5 - 1}{4 - 2} = 2$$

For the straight line in Figure A.1, $m = 2$.

The constant b is called the *intercept*. It is the value of y at $x = 0$. From Figure A.1, you see that the intercept is -3. Therefore, $b = -3$. Hence, the equation of the straight line is

$$y = 2x - 3$$

Appendix B | Vapor Pressure of Water at Various Temperatures

Temperature (°C)	Pressure (mmHg)	Temperature (°C)	Pressure (mmHg)
0	4.6	27	26.7
5	6.5	28	28.3
10	9.2	29	30.0
11	9.8	30	31.8
12	10.5	35	42.2
13	11.2	40	55.3
14	12.0	45	71.9
15	12.8	50	92.5
16	13.6	55	118.0
17	14.5	60	149.4
18	15.5	65	187.5
19	16.5	70	233.7
20	17.5	75	289.1
21	18.7	80	355.1
22	19.8	85	433.6
23	21.1	90	525.8
24	22.4	95	633.9
25	23.8	100	760.0
26	25.2	105	906.1

Appendix C | Thermodynamic Quantities for Substances and Ions at 25°C

Substance or Ion	ΔH_f° (kJ/mol)	ΔG_f° (kJ/mol)	S° (J/mol·K)	Substance or Ion	ΔH_f° (kJ/mol)	ΔG_f° (kJ/mol)	S° (J/mol·K)
$e^-(g)$	0	0	20.87	$CaO(s)$	−635.1	−603.5	38.21
Aluminum				$Ca(OH)_2(s)$	−986.1	−898.4	83.39
$Al(s)$	0	0	28.28	$Ca_3(PO_4)_2(s)$	−4120.8	−3884.8	236.0
$Al^{3+}(aq)$	−531	−485	−321.7	$CaSO_4(s)$	−1434.1	−1321.9	106.7
$AlCl_3(s)$	−705.6	−630.0	109.3	**Carbon**			
$Al_2O_3(s)$	−1675.7	−1582.3	50.95	$C(g)$	716.7	671.3	158.0
Barium				$C(s, \text{diamond})$	1.897	2.900	2.377
$Ba(g)$	179.1	147.0	170.1	$C(s, \text{graphite})$	0	0	5.740
$Ba(s)$	0	0	62.48	$CCl_4(g)$	−95.98	−53.65	309.7
$Ba^{2+}(aq)$	−537.6	−560.7	9.6	$CCl_4(l)$	−135.4	−65.27	216.4
$BaCO_3(s)$	−1216.3	−1137.6	112.1	$CF_4(g)$	−933.2	−888.5	261.3
$BaCl_2(s)$	−858.6	−810.3	123.7	$CN^-(aq)$	151	166	118
$Ba(NO_3)_2(aq)$	−952.4	−783.4	302.5	$CO(g)$	−110.5	−137.2	197.5
$Ba(OH)_2(s)$	−946.3	−859.3	107.1	$CO_2(g)$	−393.5	−394.4	213.7
$Ba(OH)_2 \cdot$				$CO_3^{2-}(aq)$	−677.1	−527.9	−56.9
$8H_2O(s)$	−3342.2	−2793	427	$CS_2(g)$	116.9	66.85	237.9
$BaSO_4(s)$	−1473.2	−1362.3	132.2	$CS_2(l)$	89.70	65.27	151.3
Beryllium				$COCl_2(g)$	−220.1	−205.9	283.9
$Be(s)$	0	0	9.440	$HCN(aq)$	150.6	172.4	94.1
$BeO(s)$	−608.4	−579.1	13.77	$HCN(g)$	135.1	124.7	201.7
$Be(OH)_2(s)$	−905.8	−817.9	50.21	$HCN(l)$	108.9	124.9	112.8
Boron				$HCO_3^-(aq)$	−692.0	−586.8	91.2
$B(s)$	0	0	5.834	*Hydrocarbons*			
$BCl_3(l)$	−427.2	−387.4	206	$CH_4(g)$	−74.87	−50.80	186.1
$BF_3(g)$	−1135.6	−1119.0	254.2	$C_2H_2(g)$	226.7	209.2	200.9
$B_2O_3(s)$	−1271.9	−1192.8	53.95	$C_2H_4(g)$	52.47	68.39	219.2
Bromine				$C_2H_6(g)$	−84.68	−32.89	229.5
$Br(g)$	111.9	82.40	174.9	$C_3H_8(g)$	−104.7	−23.6	270.2
$Br^-(aq)$	−121.5	−104.0	82.4	$C_4H_{10}(g)$	−125.6	−17.2	310.1
$Br^-(g)$	−219.0	−238.8	163.4	$C_6H_6(g)$	82.6	129.7	269.2
$Br_2(g)$	30.91	3.159	245.3	$C_6H_6(l)$	49.0	124.4	173.4
$Br_2(l)$	0	0	152.2	*Alcohols*			
$HBr(g)$	−36.44	−53.50	198.6	$CH_3OH(g)$	−200.7	−162.0	239.7
Calcium				$CH_3OH(l)$	−238.7	−166.4	126.8
$Ca(g)$	177.8	144.1	154.8	$C_2H_5OH(g)$	−235.1	−168.6	282.6
$Ca(s)$	0	0	41.59	$C_2H_5OH(l)$	−277.7	−174.9	160.7
$Ca^+(g)$	773.8	732.1	160.5	*Aldehydes*			
$Ca^{2+}(aq)$	−542.8	−553.5	−53.1	$HCHO(g)$	−117	−113	219.0
$Ca^{2+}(g)$	1925.9	—	—	$CH_3CHO(g)$	−166.1	−133.4	246.4
$CaCO_3(s, \text{calcite})$	−1206.9	−1128.8	92.9	$CH_3CHO(l)$	−191.8	−128.3	160.4
$CaCl_2(s)$	−795.8	−748.1	104.6	*Carboxylic acids and ions*			
$CaF_2(s)$	−1225.9	−1173.5	68.57	$HCOOH(aq)$	−425.6	−351.0	92
				$HCOOH(l)$	−424.7	−361.4	129

Substance or Ion	ΔH_f° (kJ/mol)	ΔG_f° (kJ/mol)	S° (J/mol·K)	Substance or Ion	ΔH_f° (kJ/mol)	ΔG_f° (kJ/mol)	S° (J/mol·K)
$HCOO^-(aq)$	−425.6	−351.0	92	$HF(aq)$	−332.6	−278.8	−13.8
$CH_3COOH(aq)$	−486.0	−369.4	86.6	$HF(g)$	−272.5	−274.6	173.7
$CH_3COOH(l)$	−484.5	−389.9	159.8	**Hydrogen**			
$CH_3COO^-(aq)$	−486.0	−369.4	86.6	$H(g)$	218.0	203.3	114.6
Sugars				$H^+(aq)$	0	0	0
$C_6H_{12}O_6$				$H^+(g)$	1536.2	1517.0	108.8
(s, glucose)	−1273.3	−910.4	212.1	$H_2(g)$	0	0	130.6
Cesium				$H_2O(g)$	−241.8	−228.6	188.7
$Cs(g)$	76.50	49.56	175.5	$H_2O(l)$	−285.8	−237.1	69.95
$Cs(l)$	2.087	0.024	92.07	$H_2O_2(aq)$	−191.2	−134.1	143.9
$Cs(s)$	0	0	85.15	$H_2O_2(g)$	−136.1	−105.5	232.9
$CsBr(s)$	−405.7	−391.4	113.0	$H_2O_2(l)$	−187.8	−120.4	109.6
$CsCl(s)$	−442.8	−414.4	101.2	**Iodine**			
$CsF(s)$	−554.7	−525.4	88.28	$I(g)$	106.8	70.21	180.7
$CsI(s)$	−346.6	−340.6	123.1	$I^-(aq)$	−55.19	−51.59	109.6
Chlorine				$I^-(g)$	−194.6	−221.5	169.2
$Cl(g)$	121.3	105.3	165.1	$I_2(g)$	62.42	19.36	260.6
$Cl^-(aq)$	−167.2	−131.3	56.5	$I_2(s)$	0	0	116.1
$Cl^-(g)$	−234.0	−240.2	153.2	$HI(g)$	26.36	1.576	206.5
$Cl_2(g)$	0	0	223.0	**Iron**			
$HCl(aq)$	−167.2	−131.3	56.5	$Fe(g)$	415.5	369.8	180.4
$HCl(g)$	−92.31	−95.30	186.8	$Fe(l)$	12.40	10.18	34.76
Chromium				$Fe(s)$	0	0	27.32
$Cr(g)$	397.5	352.6	174.2	$Fe^{2+}(aq)$	−89.1	−78.87	−137.7
$Cr(s)$	0	0	23.62	$Fe^{3+}(aq)$	−48.5	−4.6	−315.9
$Cr^{3+}(aq)$	−143.5	——	——	$FeCl_2(s)$	−341.8	−302.3	117.9
$CrO_4^{2-}(aq)$	−881.2	−727.8	50.21	$FeCl_3(s)$	−399.4	−333.9	142.3
$Cr_2O_3(s)$	−1134.7	−1053.1	81.15	$FeO(s)$	−272.0	−251.4	60.75
$Cr_2O_7^{2-}(aq)$	−1490.3	−1301.2	262.9	$Fe_2O_3(s)$	−825.5	−743.5	87.40
Cobalt				$Fe_3O_4(s)$	−1120.9	−1017.4	145.3
$Co(g)$	426.7	382.1	179.4	$FeS_2(s)$	−171.5	−160.1	52.92
$Co(s)$	0	0	30.07	**Lead**			
$Co^{2+}(aq)$	−58.2	−54.4	113	$Pb(s)$	0	0	64.78
Copper				$Pb^{2+}(aq)$	−1.7	−24.39	10.5
$Cu(g)$	337.6	297.9	166.3	$PbBr_2(s)$	−277.4	−260.7	161.1
$Cu(s)$	0	0	33.16	$PbCO_3(s)$	−699.1	−625.5	131.0
$Cu^+(aq)$	71.67	50.00	40.6	$PbCl_2(s)$	−359.4	−314.1	136.0
$Cu^{2+}(aq)$	64.77	65.52	−99.6	$PbO(s)$	−219.4	−189.3	66.32
$CuCl_2(s)$	−205.9	−161.7	108.1	$PbO_2(s)$	−274.5	−215.4	71.80
$CuO(s)$	−156.1	−128.3	42.59	$PbS(s)$	−98.32	−96.68	91.34
$Cu_2O(s)$	−170.7	−147.9	92.36	$PbSO_4(s)$	−919.9	−813.2	148.6
Fluorine				**Lithium**			
$F(g)$	79.39	62.31	158.6	$Li(g)$	159.3	126.6	138.7
$F^-(g)$	−255.1	−262.0	145.5	$Li(s)$	0	0	29.08
$F^-(aq)$	−332.6	−278.8	−13.8				
$F_2(g)$	0	0	202.7				*(continued)*

Substance or Ion	ΔH°_f (kJ/mol)	ΔG°_f (kJ/mol)	S° (J/mol·K)	Substance or Ion	ΔH°_f (kJ/mol)	ΔG°_f (kJ/mol)	S° (J/mol·K)
$Li^+(aq)$	−278.5	−293.3	13.4	$NH_4Cl(s)$	−314.6	−203.1	94.86
$Li^+(g)$	685.7	648.5	132.9	$NH_4NO_3(s)$	−365.6	−184.0	151.1
$LiBr(s)$	−350.9	−341.6	74.06	$NO(g)$	90.29	86.60	210.6
$LiCl(s)$	−408.3	−384.0	59.30	$NO_2(g)$	33.10	51.24	239.9
$LiF(s)$	−616.9	−588.7	35.66	$NO_3^-(aq)$	−207.4	−111.3	146.4
$LiI(s)$	−270.1	−269.7	85.77	$N_2O(g)$	82.05	104.2	219.9
Magnesium				$N_2O_4(g)$	9.079	97.72	304.3
$Mg(g)$	147.1	112.6	148.5	$N_2O_4(l)$	−19.56	97.52	209.2
$Mg(s)$	0	0	32.67	$NOCl(g)$	51.71	66.08	261.6
$Mg^+(g)$	891.0	848.6	154.3	$HNO_3(aq)$	−207.4	−111.3	146.4
$Mg^{2+}(aq)$	−466.9	−454.8	−138.1	$HNO_3(g)$	−134.3	−73.99	266.3
$Mg^{2+}(g)$	2351	—	—	$HNO_3(l)$	−174.1	−80.79	155.6
$MgCO_3(s)$	−1111.7	−1028.1	65.85	**Oxygen**			
$MgCl_2(s)$	−641.6	−592.1	89.63	$O(g)$	249.2	231.8	160.9
$Mg_3N_2(s)$	−461.1	−400.9	87.86	$O_2(g)$	0	0	205.0
$MgO(s)$	−601.2	−568.9	26.92	$O_3(g)$	142.7	163.2	238.8
$Mg(OH)_2(s)$	−924.7	−833.7	63.24	$OH^-(aq)$	−230.0	−157.3	−10.75
Manganese				**Phosphorus**			
$Mn(g)$	283.3	241.0	173.6	$P(g)$	316.4	280.0	163.1
$Mn(s)$	0	0	32.01	$P(s, red)$	−17.46	−12.03	22.85
$MnO(s)$	−385.2	−362.9	59.71	$P(s, white)$	0	0	41.08
$MnO_2(s)$	−520.0	−465.2	53.05	$P_2(g)$	143.7	103.1	218.0
$MnO_4^-(aq)$	−541.4	−447.3	191.2	$P_4(g)$	58.91	24.45	279.9
Mercury				$PCl_3(g)$	−288.7	−269.6	311.6
$Hg(g)$	61.38	31.91	174.9	$PCl_5(g)$	−360.2	−290.3	364.2
$Hg(l)$	0	0	76.03	$PF_5(g)$	−1594.4	−1520.7	300.7
$Hg^{2+}(aq)$	171.1	164.4	−32.2	$PH_3(g)$	5.439	7.175	210.1
$Hg_2^{2+}(aq)$	172.3	153.6	84.5	$P_4O_{10}(s)$	−3009.9	−2723.3	228.8
$HgCl_2(s)$	−230.1	−184.0	144.5	$PO_4^{3-}(aq)$	−1277.4	−1018.8	−222
$Hg_2Cl_2(s)$	−265.2	−210.8	192.4	$POCl_3(g)$	−559.8	−514.3	325.3
$HgO(s)$	−90.79	−58.49	70.27	$POCl_3(l)$	−597.1	−520.9	222.5
Nickel				$P_4S_3(s)$	−224.6	−206.9	200.8
$Ni(g)$	430.1	384.7	182.1	$HPO_4^{2-}(aq)$	−1281	−1082	−36
$Ni(s)$	0	0	29.87	$H_2PO_4^-(aq)$	−1285	−1135	89.1
$Ni^{2+}(aq)$	−54.0	−45.6	−128.9	$H_3PO_4(aq)$	−1288.3	−1142.6	158.2
$NiCl_2(s)$	−304.9	−258.8	98.16	**Potassium**			
$NiO(s)$	−239.7	−211.7	37.99	$K(g)$	89.00	60.51	160.2
Nitrogen				$K(s)$	0	0	64.67
$N(g)$	472.7	455.6	153.2	$K^+(aq)$	−252.4	−283.3	102.5
$N_2(g)$	0	0	191.6	$K^+(g)$	514.0	481.0	154.5
$NH_3(aq)$	−80.29	−26.57	111.3	$KBr(s)$	−393.8	−380.4	95.94
$NH_3(g)$	−45.90	−16.40	192.7	$KCl(s)$	−436.7	−408.8	82.55
$NH_4^+(aq)$	−132.5	−79.37	113.4	$KF(s)$	−568.6	−538.9	66.55
$N_2H_4(g)$	95.35	159.2	238.6	$KI(s)$	−327.9	−323.0	106.4
$N_2H_4(l)$	50.63	149.4	121.4	$KClO_3(s)$	−397.7	−296.3	143.1

Substance or Ion	ΔH_f° (kJ/mol)	ΔG_f° (kJ/mol)	S° (J/mol·K)	Substance or Ion	ΔH_f° (kJ/mol)	ΔG_f° (kJ/mol)	S° (J/mol·K)
$K_2CO_3(s)$	−1150.2	−1064.5	155.5	$NaHCO_3(s)$	−950.8	−851.0	101.7
$KNO_3(s)$	−494.6	−394.9	133.1	$NaI(s)$	−287.9	−284.6	98.50
$K_2O(s)$	−363.2	−322.1	94.14	$NaNO_3(s)$	−467.9	−367.1	116.5
$KO_2(s)$	−284.5	−240.6	122.5	$NaOH(s)$	−425.9	−379.7	64.44
$K_2O_2(s)$	−495.8	−429.8	113.0	**Strontium**			
$KOH(s)$	−424.7	−378.9	78.91	$Sr(g)$	164.0	131.6	164.5
Rubidium				$Sr(s)$	0	0	55.69
$Rb(g)$	80.90	53.11	170.0	$Sr^+(g)$	719.7	679.3	170.3
$Rb(s)$	0	0	76.78	$Sr^{2+}(aq)$	−545.8	−559.4	−32.6
$RbBr(s)$	−394.6	−381.8	110.0	$Sr^{2+}(g)$	1790.6	—	—
$RbCl(s)$	−435.5	−407.8	95.90	$SrCO_3(s)$	−1220.1	−1140.1	97.1
$RbF(s)$	−549.4	—	75.3	$SrCl_2(s)$	−828.9	−781.2	114.9
$RbI(s)$	−333.8	−328.9	118.4	$SrO(s)$	−592.0	−561.4	55.52
Silicon				$SrSO_4(s)$	−1453.1	−1341.0	117
$Si(g)$	450.0	405.6	167.9	**Sulfur**			
$Si(s)$	0	0	18.82	$S(g)$	277.0	236.5	167.7
$SiC(s)$	−65.3	−62.8	16.61	$S(s, \text{monoclinic})$	0.360	0.070	33.03
$SiCl_4(l)$	−687.0	−619.9	239.7	$S(s, \text{rhombic})$	0	0	32.06
$SiF_4(g)$	−1614.9	−1572.7	282.7	$S^{2-}(aq)$	41.8	83.7	22
$SiO_2(s, \text{quartz})$	−910.9	−856.4	41.46	$S_2(g)$	128.6	79.7	228.1
Silver				$S_8(g)$	100.4	48.61	430.2
$Ag(g)$	284.6	245.7	172.9	$SO_2(g)$	−296.8	−300.1	248.1
$Ag(s)$	0	0	42.55	$SO_3(g)$	−395.8	−371.0	256.7
$Ag^+(aq)$	105.6	77.12	72.68	$SO_4^{2-}(aq)$	−909.3	−744.6	20.1
$AgBr(s)$	−100.4	−96.90	107.1	$HS^-(aq)$	−17.7	12.6	61.1
$AgCl(s)$	−127.1	−109.8	96.2	$H_2S(aq)$	−39	−27.4	122
$AgF(s)$	−204.6	—	83.7	$H_2S(g)$	−20.50	−33.33	205.6
$AgI(s)$	−61.84	−66.19	115.5	$HSO_4^-(aq)$	−887.3	−756.0	131.8
$Ag_2O(s)$	−31.05	−11.21	121.3	$H_2SO_4(l)$	−814.0	−689.9	156.9
$Ag_2S(s)$	−32.59	−40.67	144.0	**Tin**			
$AgNO_3(s)$	−124.4	−33.47	140.9	$Sn(s, \text{gray})$	−2.09	0.13	44.14
Sodium				$Sn(s, \text{white})$	0	0	51.55
$Na(g)$	107.3	76.86	153.6	$SnCl_4(l)$	−511.3	−440.2	258.6
$Na(s)$	0	0	51.46	$SnO_2(s)$	−580.7	−519.7	52.3
$Na^+(aq)$	−240.1	−261.9	59.1	**Zinc**			
$Na^+(g)$	609.3	574.4	147.8	$Zn(g)$	130.4	94.89	160.9
$NaBr(s)$	−361.4	−349.3	86.82	$Zn(s)$	0	0	41.72
$Na_2CO_3(s)$	−1130.8	−1048.0	138.8	$Zn^{2+}(aq)$	−153.9	−147.0	−112.1
$NaCl(s)$	−411.1	−384.0	72.12	$ZnCl_2(s)$	−415.1	−369.4	111.5
$NaF(s)$	−575.4	−545.1	51.21	$ZnO(s)$	−348.3	−318.3	43.64
				$ZnS(s, \text{sphalerite})$	−206.0	−201.3	−57.7

Appendix D | Electron Configurations of Atoms in the Ground State

Z	Element	Configuration	Z	Element	Configuration
1	H	$1s^1$	44	Ru	$[\text{Kr}]4d^75s^1$
2	He	$1s^2$	45	Rh	$[\text{Kr}]4d^85s^1$
3	Li	$[\text{He}]2s^1$	46	Pd	$[\text{Kr}]4d^{10}$
4	Be	$[\text{He}]2s^2$	47	Ag	$[\text{Kr}]4d^{10}5s^1$
5	B	$[\text{He}]2s^22p^1$	48	Cd	$[\text{Kr}]4d^{10}5s^2$
6	C	$[\text{He}]2s^22p^2$	49	In	$[\text{Kr}]4d^{10}5s^25p^1$
7	N	$[\text{He}]2s^22p^3$	50	Sn	$[\text{Kr}]4d^{10}5s^25p^2$
8	O	$[\text{He}]2s^22p^4$	51	Sb	$[\text{Kr}]4d^{10}5s^25p^3$
9	F	$[\text{He}]2s^22p^5$	52	Te	$[\text{Kr}]4d^{10}5s^25p^4$
10	Ne	$[\text{He}]2s^22p^6$	53	I	$[\text{Kr}]4d^{10}5s^25p^5$
11	Na	$[\text{Ne}]3s^1$	54	Xe	$[\text{Kr}]4d^{10}5s^25p^6$
12	Mg	$[\text{Ne}]3s^2$	55	Cs	$[\text{Xe}]6s^1$
13	Al	$[\text{Ne}]3s^23p^1$	56	Ba	$[\text{Xe}]6s^2$
14	Si	$[\text{Ne}]3s^23p^2$	57	La	$[\text{Xe}]5d^16s^2$
15	P	$[\text{Ne}]3s^23p^3$	58	Ce	$[\text{Xe}]4f^15d^16s^2$
16	S	$[\text{Ne}]3s^23p^4$	59	Pr	$[\text{Xe}]4f^36s^2$
17	Cl	$[\text{Ne}]3s^23p^5$	60	Nd	$[\text{Xe}]4f^46s^2$
18	Ar	$[\text{Ne}]3s^23p^6$	61	Pm	$[\text{Xe}]4f^56s^2$
19	K	$[\text{Ar}]4s^1$	62	Sm	$[\text{Xe}]4f^66s^2$
20	Ca	$[\text{Ar}]4s^2$	63	Eu	$[\text{Xe}]4f^76s^2$
21	Sc	$[\text{Ar}]3d^14s^2$	64	Gd	$[\text{Xe}]4f^75d^16s^2$
22	Ti	$[\text{Ar}]3d^24s^2$	65	Tb	$[\text{Xe}]4f^96s^2$
23	V	$[\text{Ar}]3d^34s^2$	66	Dy	$[\text{Xe}]4f^{10}6s^2$
24	Cr	$[\text{Ar}]3d^54s^1$	67	Ho	$[\text{Xe}]4f^{11}6s^2$
25	Mn	$[\text{Ar}]3d^54s^2$	68	Er	$[\text{Xe}]4f^{12}6s^2$
26	Fe	$[\text{Ar}]3d^64s^2$	69	Tm	$[\text{Xe}]4f^{13}6s^2$
27	Co	$[\text{Ar}]3d^74s^2$	70	Yb	$[\text{Xe}]4f^{14}6s^2$
28	Ni	$[\text{Ar}]3d^84s^2$	71	Lu	$[\text{Xe}]4f^{14}5d^16s^2$
29	Cu	$[\text{Ar}]3d^{10}4s^1$	72	Hf	$[\text{Xe}]4f^{14}5d^26s^2$
30	Zn	$[\text{Ar}]3d^{10}4s^2$	73	Ta	$[\text{Xe}]4f^{14}5d^36s^2$
31	Ga	$[\text{Ar}]3d^{10}4s^24p^1$	74	W	$[\text{Xe}]4f^{14}5d^46s^2$
32	Ge	$[\text{Ar}]3d^{10}4s^24p^2$	75	Re	$[\text{Xe}]4f^{14}5d^56s^2$
33	As	$[\text{Ar}]3d^{10}4s^24p^3$	76	Os	$[\text{Xe}]4f^{14}5d^66s^2$
34	Se	$[\text{Ar}]3d^{10}4s^24p^4$	77	Ir	$[\text{Xe}]4f^{14}5d^76s^2$
35	Br	$[\text{Ar}]3d^{10}4s^24p^5$	78	Pt	$[\text{Xe}]4f^{14}5d^96s^1$
36	Kr	$[\text{Ar}]3d^{10}4s^24p^6$	79	Au	$[\text{Xe}]4f^{14}5d^{10}6s^1$
37	Rb	$[\text{Kr}]5s^1$	80	Hg	$[\text{Xe}]4f^{14}5d^{10}6s^2$
38	Sr	$[\text{Kr}]5s^2$	81	Tl	$[\text{Xe}]4f^{14}5d^{10}6s^26p^1$
39	Y	$[\text{Kr}]4d^15s^2$	82	Pb	$[\text{Xe}]4f^{14}5d^{10}6s^26p^2$
40	Zr	$[\text{Kr}]4d^25s^2$	83	Bi	$[\text{Xe}]4f^{14}5d^{10}6s^26p^3$
41	Nb	$[\text{Kr}]4d^45s^1$	84	Po	$[\text{Xe}]4f^{14}5d^{10}6s^26p^4$
42	Mo	$[\text{Kr}]4d^55s^1$	85	At	$[\text{Xe}](4f^{14}5d^{10}6s^26p^5)$
43	Tc	$[\text{Kr}]4d^55s^2$	86	Rn	$[\text{Xe}]4f^{14}5d^{10}6s^26p^6$

Z	Element	Configuration	Z	Element	Configuration
87	Fr	$[\text{Rn}](7s^1)$	103	Lr	$[\text{Rn}](5f^{14}6d^17s^2)$
88	Ra	$[\text{Rn}]7s^2$	104	Rf	$[\text{Rn}](5f^{14}5d^27s^2)$
89	Ac	$[\text{Rn}]6d^16s^2$	105	Db	$[\text{Rn}](5f^{14}6d^37s^2)$
90	Th	$[\text{Rn}]6d^27s^2$	106	Sg	$[\text{Rn}](5f^{14}6d^47s^2)$
91	Pa	$[\text{Rn}](5f^26d^17s^2)$	107	Bh	$[\text{Rn}](5f^{14}6d^57s^2)$
92	U	$[\text{Rn}](5f^36d^17s^2)$	108	Hs	$[\text{Rn}](5f^{14}6d^67s^2)$
93	Np	$[\text{Rn}](5f^46d^17s^2)$	109	Mt	$[\text{Rn}](5f^{14}6d^77s^2)$
94	Pu	$[\text{Rn}]5f^67s^2$	110	Ds	$[\text{Rn}](5f^{14}6d^87s^2)$
95	Am	$[\text{Rn}]5f^77s^2$	111	Rg	$[\text{Rn}](5f^{14}6d^97s^2)$
96	Cm	$[\text{Rn}](5f^76d^17s^2)$	112	Uub	$[\text{Rn}](5f^{14}6d^{10}7s^2)$
97	Bk	$[\text{Rn}](5f^97s^2)$	113	Uut	$[\text{Rn}](5f^{14}6d^{10}7s^27p^1)$
98	Cf	$[\text{Rn}](5f^{10}7s^2)$	114	Uuq	$[\text{Rn}](5f^{14}6d^{10}7s^27p^2)$
99	Es	$[\text{Rn}](5f^{11}7s^2)$	115	Uup	$[\text{Rn}](5f^{14}6d^{10}7s^27p^3)$
100	Fm	$[\text{Rn}](5f^{12}7s^2)$	116	Uuh	$[\text{Rn}](5f^{14}6d^{10}7s^27p^4)$
101	Md	$[\text{Rn}](5f^{13}7s^2)$	118	Uuo	$[\text{Rn}](5f^{14}6d^{10}7s^27p^6)$
102	No	$[\text{Rn}](5f^{14}7s^2)$			

Configurations in this table, except those in parentheses, are taken from Charlotte E. Moore, *National Standard Reference Data Series*, National Bureau of Standards, 34 (September 1970). Those in parentheses were obtained on the basis of their assumed position in the periodic table.

Appendix E | Acid-Ionization Constants at 25°C

Substance	Formula	K_a
Acetic acid	$HC_2H_3O_2$	1.7×10^{-5}
Arsenic acid*	H_3AsO_4	6.5×10^{-3}
	$H_2AsO_4^-$	1.2×10^{-7}
	$HAsO_4^{2-}$	3.2×10^{-12}
Ascorbic acid*	$H_2C_6H_6O_6$	6.8×10^{-5}
	$HC_6H_6O_6^-$	2.8×10^{-12}
Benzoic acid	$HC_7H_5O_2$	6.3×10^{-5}
Boric acid	H_3BO_3	5.9×10^{-10}
Carbonic acid*	H_2CO_3	4.3×10^{-7}
	HCO_3^-	4.8×10^{-11}
Chromic acid*	H_2CrO_4	1.5×10^{-1}
	$HCrO_4^-$	3.2×10^{-7}
Cyanic acid	$HOCN$	3.5×10^{-4}
Formic acid	$HCHO_2$	1.7×10^{-4}
Hydrocyanic acid	HCN	4.9×10^{-10}
Hydrofluoric acid	HF	6.8×10^{-4}
Hydrogen peroxide	H_2O_2	1.8×10^{-12}
Hydrogen sulfate ion	HSO_4^-	1.1×10^{-2}
Hydrogen sulfide*	H_2S	8.9×10^{-8}
	HS^-	1.2×10^{-13}

(continued)

Substance	Formula	K_a
Hypochlorous acid	$HClO$	3.5×10^{-8}
Lactic acid	$HC_3H_5O_3$	1.3×10^{-4}
Nitrous acid	HNO_2	4.5×10^{-4}
Oxalic acid*	$H_2C_2O_4$	5.6×10^{-2}
	$HC_2O_4^-$	5.1×10^{-5}
Phenol	C_6H_5OH	1.1×10^{-10}
Phosphoric acid*	H_3PO_4	6.9×10^{-3}
	$H_2PO_4^-$	6.2×10^{-8}
	HPO_4^{2-}	4.8×10^{-13}
Phosphorous acid*	H_2PHO_3	1.6×10^{-2}
	$HPHO_3^-$	7×10^{-7}
Propionic acid	$HC_3H_5O_2$	1.3×10^{-5}
Pyruvic acid	$HC_3H_3O_3$	1.4×10^{-4}
Sulfurous acid*	H_2SO_3	1.3×10^{-2}
	HSO_3^-	6.3×10^{-8}

*The ionization constants for polyprotic acids are for successive ionizations. For example, for H_3PO_4, the equilibrium is $H_3PO_4 \!-\! H^+ + H_2PO_4^-$. For $H_2PO_4^-$, the equilibrium is $H_2PO_4^- \!-\! H^+ + HPO_4^{2-}$.

Appendix F | Base-Ionization Constants at 25°C

Substance	Formula	K_b
Ammonia	NH_3	1.8×10^{-5}
Aniline	$C_6H_5NH_2$	4.2×10^{-10}
Dimethylamine	$(CH_3)_2NH$	5.1×10^{-4}
Ethylamine	$C_2H_5NH_2$	4.7×10^{-4}
Ethylenediamine	$NH_2CH_2CH_2NH_2$	5.2×10^{-4}
Hydrazine	N_2H_4	1.7×10^{-6}
Hydroxylamine	NH_2OH	1.1×10^{-8}
Methylamine	CH_3NH_2	4.4×10^{-4}
Pyridine	C_5H_5N	1.4×10^{-9}
Trimethylamine	$(CH_3)_3N$	6.5×10^{-5}
Urea	NH_2CONH_2	1.5×10^{-14}

Appendix G | Solubility Product Constants at 25°C

Substance	Formula	K_{sp}
Aluminum hydroxide	$Al(OH)_3$	4.6×10^{-33}
Barium chromate	$BaCrO_4$	1.2×10^{-10}
Barium fluoride	BaF_2	1.0×10^{-6}
Barium sulfate	$BaSO_4$	1.1×10^{-10}
Cadmium oxalate	CdC_2O_4	1.5×10^{-8}
Cadmium sulfide	CdS	8×10^{-27}
Calcium carbonate	$CaCO_3$	3.8×10^{-9}
Calcium fluoride	CaF_2	3.4×10^{-11}
Calcium oxalate	CaC_2O_4	2.3×10^{-9}
Calcium phosphate	$Ca_3(PO_4)_2$	1×10^{-26}
Calcium sulfate	$CaSO_4$	2.4×10^{-5}
Cobalt(II) sulfide	CoS	4×10^{-21}
Copper(II) hydroxide	$Cu(OH)_2$	2.6×10^{-19}
Copper(II) sulfide	CuS	6×10^{-36}
Iron(II) hydroxide	$Fe(OH)_2$	8×10^{-16}
Iron(II) sulfide	FeS	6×10^{-18}
Iron(III) hydroxide	$Fe(OH)_3$	2.5×10^{-39}
Lead(II) arsenate	$Pb_3(AsO_4)_2$	4×10^{-36}
Lead(II) chloride	$PbCl_2$	1.6×10^{-5}
Lead(II) chromate	$PbCrO_4$	1.8×10^{-14}
Lead(II) iodide	PbI_2	6.5×10^{-9}
Lead(II) sulfate	$PbSO_4$	1.7×10^{-8}
Lead(II) sulfide	PbS	2.5×10^{-27}
Magnesium arsenate	$Mg_3(AsO_4)_2$	2×10^{-20}
Magnesium carbonate	$MgCO_3$	1.0×10^{-5}
Magnesium hydroxide	$Mg(OH)_2$	1.8×10^{-11}
Magnesium oxalate	MgC_2O_4	8.5×10^{-5}
Manganese(II) sulfide	MnS	2.5×10^{-10}
Mercury(I) chloride	Hg_2Cl_2	1.3×10^{-18}
Mercury(II) sulfide	HgS	1.6×10^{-52}
Nickel(II) hydroxide	$Ni(OH)_2$	2.0×10^{-15}
Nickel(II) sulfide	NiS	3×10^{-19}
Silver acetate	$AgC_2H_3O_2$	2.0×10^{-3}
Silver bromide	$AgBr$	5.0×10^{-13}
Silver chloride	$AgCl$	1.8×10^{-10}
Silver chromate	Ag_2CrO_4	1.1×10^{-12}
Silver iodide	AgI	8.3×10^{-17}
Silver sulfide	Ag_2S	6×10^{-50}
Strontium carbonate	$SrCO_3$	9.3×10^{-10}
Strontium chromate	$SrCrO_4$	3.5×10^{-5}
Strontium sulfate	$SrSO_4$	2.5×10^{-7}
Zinc hydroxide	$Zn(OH)_2$	2.1×10^{-16}
Zinc sulfide	ZnS	1.1×10^{-21}

Appendix H | Formation Constants of Complex Ions at 25°C

Complex Ion	K_f	Complex Ion	K_f
$Ag(CN)_2^-$	5.6×10^{18}	$Fe(CN)_6^{4-}$	1.0×10^{35}
$Ag(NH_3)_2^+$	1.7×10^7	$Fe(CN)_6^{3-}$	9.1×10^{41}
$Ag(S_2O_3)_2^{3-}$	2.9×10^{13}	$Ni(CN)_4^{2-}$	1.0×10^{31}
$Cd(NH_3)_4^{2+}$	1.0×10^7	$Ni(NH_3)_6^{2+}$	5.6×10^8
$Cu(CN)_2^-$	1.0×10^{16}	$Zn(NH_3)_4^{2+}$	2.9×10^9
$Cu(NH_3)_4^{2+}$	4.8×10^{12}	$Zn(OH)_4^{2-}$	2.8×10^{15}

Appendix I | Standard Electrode (Reduction) Potentials in Aqueous Solution at 25°C

Cathode (Reduction) Half-Reaction	Standard Potential, $E°$ (V)
$Li^+(aq) + e^- \rightleftharpoons Li(s)$	-3.04
$K^+(aq) + e^- \rightleftharpoons K(s)$	-2.92
$Ca^{2+}(aq) + 2e^- \rightleftharpoons Ca(s)$	-2.76
$Na^+(aq) + e^- \rightleftharpoons Na(s)$	-2.71
$Mg^{2+}(aq) + 2e^- \rightleftharpoons Mg(s)$	-2.38
$Al^{3+}(aq) + 3e^- \rightleftharpoons Al(s)$	-1.66
$2H_2O(l) + 2e^- \rightleftharpoons H_2(g) + 2OH^-(aq)$	-0.83
$Zn^{2+}(aq) + 2e^- \rightleftharpoons Zn(s)$	-0.76
$Cr^{3+}(aq) + 3e^- \rightleftharpoons Cr(s)$	-0.74
$Fe^{2+}(aq) + 2e^- \rightleftharpoons Fe(s)$	-0.41
$Cd^{2+}(aq) + 2e^- \rightleftharpoons Cd(s)$	-0.40
$Ni^{2+}(aq) + 2e^- \rightleftharpoons Ni(s)$	-0.23
$Sn^{2+}(aq) + 2e^- \rightleftharpoons Sn(s)$	-0.14
$Pb^{2+}(aq) + 2e^- \rightleftharpoons Pb(s)$	-0.13
$Fe^{3+}(aq) + 3e^- \rightleftharpoons Fe(s)$	-0.04
$2H^+(aq) + 2e^- \rightleftharpoons H_2(g)$	0.00
$Sn^{4+}(aq) + 2e^- \rightleftharpoons Sn^{2+}(aq)$	0.15
$Cu^{2+}(aq) + e^- \rightleftharpoons Cu^+(aq)$	0.16
$ClO_4^-(aq) + H_2O(l) + 2e^- \rightleftharpoons ClO_3^-(aq) + 2OH^-(aq)$	0.17
$AgCl(s) + e^- \rightleftharpoons Ag(s) + Cl^-(aq)$	0.22
$Cu^{2+}(aq) + 2e^- \rightleftharpoons Cu(s)$	0.34
$ClO_3^-(aq) + H_2O(l) + 2e^- \rightleftharpoons ClO_2^-(aq) + 2OH^-(aq)$	0.35
$IO^-(aq) + H_2O(l) + 2e^- \rightleftharpoons I^-(aq) + 2OH^-(aq)$	0.49
$Cu^+(aq) + e^- \rightleftharpoons Cu(s)$	0.52
$I_2(s) + 2e^- \rightleftharpoons 2I^-(aq)$	0.54
$ClO_2^-(aq) + H_2O(l) + 2e^- \rightleftharpoons ClO^-(aq) + 2OH^-(aq)$	0.59
$Fe^{3+}(aq) + e^- \rightleftharpoons Fe^{2+}(aq)$	0.77
$Hg_2^{2+}(aq) + 2e^- \rightleftharpoons 2Hg(l)$	0.80

Cathode (Reduction) Half-Reaction	Standard Potential, $E°$ (V)
$Ag^+(aq) + e^- \rightleftharpoons Ag(s)$	0.80
$Hg^{2+}(aq) + 2e^- \rightleftharpoons Hg(l)$	0.85
$ClO^-(aq) + H_2O(l) + 2e^- \rightleftharpoons Cl^-(aq) + 2OH^-(aq)$	0.90
$2Hg^{2+}(aq) + 2e^- \rightleftharpoons Hg_2^{2+}(aq)$	0.90
$NO_3^-(aq) + 4H^+(aq) + 3e^- \rightleftharpoons NO(g) + 2H_2O(l)$	0.96
$Br_2(l) + 2e^- \rightleftharpoons 2Br^-(aq)$	1.07
$O_2(g) + 4H^+(aq) + 4e^- \rightleftharpoons 2H_2O(l)$	1.23
$Cr_2O_7^{2-}(aq) + 14H^+(aq) + 6e^- \rightleftharpoons 2Cr^{3+}(aq) + 7H_2O(l)$	1.33
$Cl_2(g) + 2e^- \rightleftharpoons 2Cl^-(aq)$	1.36
$Ce^{4+}(aq) + e^- \rightleftharpoons Ce^{3+}(aq)$	1.44
$MnO_4^-(aq) + 8H^+(aq) + 5e^- \rightleftharpoons Mn^{2+}(aq) + 4H_2O(l)$	1.49
$H_2O_2(aq) + 2H^+(aq) + 2e^- \rightleftharpoons 2H_2O(l)$	1.78
$Co^{3+}(aq) + e^- \rightleftharpoons Co^{2+}(aq)$	1.82
$S_2O_8^{2-}(aq) + 2e^- \rightleftharpoons 2SO_4^{2-}(aq)$	2.01
$O_3(g) + 2H^+(aq) + 2e^- \rightleftharpoons O_2(g) + H_2O(l)$	2.07
$F_2(g) + 2e^- \rightleftharpoons 2F^-(aq)$	2.87

Note: Your answers may differ from those given here in the last significant figure.

CHAPTER 1

1.1 11.02 g   **1.2** Physical properties: soft; silver color; melts at 64°C. Chemical properties: metal, reacts with water; reacts with oxygen; reacts with chlorine.   **1.3** (a) 4.9   (b) 2.48   (c) 0.08   (d) 3   **1.4** (a) 1.84 nm   (b) 5.67 ps   (c) 7.85 mg   (d) 9.7 km   (e) 0.732 ms or 732 μs   (f) 0.154 nm or 154 pm   **1.5** (a) 39.2°C   (b) 195 K   **1.6** 7.87 g/cm^3; the object is made of iron   **1.7** 38.4 cm^3 **1.8** 1.21×10^{-7} mm   **1.9** 6.76×10^{-26} dm^3 **1.10** 3.24 m

CHAPTER 2

2.1 $^{35}_{17}$Cl   **2.2** 35.453 amu   **2.3** (a) Se: Group VIA, Period 4; nonmetal   (b) Cs: Group IA, Period 6; metal   (c) Fe: Group VIIIB, Period 4; metal   (d) Cu: Group IB, Period 4; metal   (e) Br: Group VIIA, Period 4; nonmetal   **2.4** K$_2$CrO$_4$ **2.5** (a) calcium oxide   (b) lead(II) chromate   **2.6** Tl(NO$_3$)$_3$ **2.7** (a) dichlorine hex(a)oxide   (b) phosphorus trichloride   (c) phosphorus pentachloride   **2.8** (a) CS$_2$ (b) SO$_3$ **2.9** (a) boron trifluoride   (b) hydrogen selenide   **2.10** perbromate ion, BrO$_4^-$ **2.11** sodium carbonate decahydrate   **2.12** Na$_2$S$_2$O$_3 \cdot$5H$_2$O   **2.13** (a) O$_2$ + 2PCl$_3 \longrightarrow$ 2POCl$_3$ (b) P$_4$ + 6N$_2$O $\longrightarrow$ P$_4$O$_6$ + 6N$_2$ (c) 2As$_2$S$_3$ + 9O$_2 \longrightarrow$ 2As$_2$O$_3$ + 6SO$_2$ (d) Ca$_3$(PO$_4$)$_2$ + 4H$_3$PO$_4 \longrightarrow$ 3Ca(H$_2$PO$_4$)$_2$

CHAPTER 3

3.1 (a) 46.0 amu   (b) 180 amu   (c) 40.0 amu   (d) 58.3 amu   **3.2** (a) SO$_3$, 80.1 amu   (b) H$_2$SO$_4$, 98.1 amu   **3.3** (a) 6.656×10^{-23} g   (b) 7.65×10^{-23} g   **3.4** 30.9 g H$_2$O   **3.5** 0.452 mol HNO$_3$ **3.6** 1.2×10^{21} HCN molecules   **3.7** 35.0% N, 60.0% O, 5.04% H   **3.8** 17.0 g N   **3.9** 40.9% C, 4.57% H, 54.5% O   **3.10** SO$_3$ **3.11** C$_7$H$_6$O$_2$ **3.12** C$_2$H$_4$O   **3.13**

| H$_2$ | + | Cl$_2$ | $\longrightarrow$ | 2HCl |

1 molecule H$_2$ + 1 molecule Cl$_2 \longrightarrow$ 2 molecules HCl
1 mol H$_2$ + 1 mol Cl$_2 \longrightarrow$ 2 mol HCl
2.016 g H$_2$ + 70.9 g Cl$_2 \longrightarrow$ 2 × 36.5 g HCl

3.14 178 g Na   **3.15** 2.46 kg O$_2$ **3.16** 81.1 g Hg   **3.17** 0.12 mol AlCl$_3$ **3.18** 11.0 g ZnS   **3.19** 21.4 g; 89.1%

CHAPTER 4

4.1 (a) soluble   (b) soluble   (c) insoluble   **4.2** (a) 2H$^+$(aq) + 2NO$_3^-$(aq) + Mg(OH)$_2$(s) $\longrightarrow$ 2H$_2$O(l) + Mg^{2+}(aq) + 2NO$_3^-$(aq)
2H$^+$(aq) + Mg(OH)$_2$(s) $\longrightarrow$ 2H$_2$O(l) + Mg^{2+}(aq)   (b) Pb^{2+}(aq) + 2NO$_3^-$(aq) + 2Na$^+$(aq) + SO$_4^{2-}$(aq) $\longrightarrow$ PbSO$_4$(s) + 2Na$^+$(aq) + 2NO$_3^-$(aq)
Pb^{2+}(aq) + SO$_4^{2-}$(aq) $\longrightarrow$ PbSO$_4$(s)   **4.3** 2NaI(aq) + Pb(C$_2$H$_3$O$_2$)$_2$(aq) $\longrightarrow$ PbI$_2$(s) + 2NaC$_2$H$_3$O$_2$(aq)
2I$^-$(aq) + Pb^{2+}(aq) $\longrightarrow$ PbI$_2$(s)   **4.4** (a) weak acid   (b) weak acid   (c) strong acid   (d) strong base

4.5 HCN(aq) + LiOH(aq) $\longrightarrow$ H$_2$O(l) + LiCN(aq)
HCN(aq) + OH$^-$(aq) $\longrightarrow$ H$_2$O(l) + CN$^-$(aq)   **4.6** H$_2$SO$_4$(aq) + KOH(aq) $\longrightarrow$ H$_2$O(l) + KHSO$_4$(aq)
KHSO$_4$(aq) + KOH(aq) $\longrightarrow$ H$_2$O(l) + K$_2$SO$_4$(aq)
H$^+$(aq) + OH$^-$(aq) $\longrightarrow$ H$_2$O(l)
HSO$_4^-$(aq) + OH$^-$(aq) $\longrightarrow$ H$_2$O(l) + SO$_4^{2-}$(aq)   **4.7** CaCO$_3$(s) + 2HNO$_3$(aq) $\longrightarrow$ Ca(NO$_3$)$_2$(aq) + CO$_2$(g) + H$_2$O(l)
CaCO$_3$(s) + 2H$^+$(aq) $\longrightarrow$ Ca^{2+}(aq) + CO$_2$(g) + H$_2$O(l)   **4.8** (a) K: +1, Cr: +6, O: -2 (b) Mn: +7, O: -2 **4.9** Ca + Cl$_2 \longrightarrow$ Ca^{2+} + 2Cl$^-$ **4.10** 0.0464 M NaCl   **4.11** 10.1 mL   **4.12** 0.0075 mol NaCl; 0.44 g NaCl   **4.13** 12 mL   **4.14** 34.19%   **4.15** 48.4 mL NiSO$_4$ **4.16** 5.07%

CHAPTER 5

5.1 0.56 atm, 4.3×10^2 mmHg   **5.2** 24.1 L   **5.3** 4.47 dm^3 **5.4** 5.54 dm^3 **5.5** Use $PV = nRT$. Solve for n: $n = PV/RT = P(V/RT)$. Everything within parentheses is constant; therefore, $n = $ constant $\times P$ (or $\propto P$).   **5.6** 46.0 atm   **5.7** density of He = 0.164 g/L; difference in mass between 1 L of air and 1 L of He = 1.024 g   **5.8** 64.1 amu   **5.9** 2.00 L   **5.10** $P_{O_2} = $ 0.0769 atm; $P_{CO_2} = $ 0.0310 atm; $P = $ 0.1080 atm; $X_{O_2} = $ 0.712   **5.11** 0.01591 mol O$_2$; $V = $ 0.406 L   **5.12** 219 m/s   **5.13** $T = $ 52.4 K, 728 K   **5.14** 9.96 s   **5.15** 44.0 amu   **5.16** $P_{vdW} = $ 0.992 atm; $P_{ideal} = $ 1.000 atm (larger)

CHAPTER 6

6.1 1.1×10^{-17} J, 2.7×10^{-18} cal   **6.2** exothermic; $q = -1170$ kJ   **6.3** 2N$_2$H$_4$(l) + N$_2$O$_4$(l) $\longrightarrow$ 3N$_2$(g) + 4H$_2$O(g); $\Delta H = -1049$ kJ   **6.4** (a) N$_2$H$_4$(l) + $\frac{1}{2}$N$_2$O$_4$(l) $\longrightarrow \frac{3}{2}N_2$(g) + 2H$_2$O(g); $\Delta H = -5.245 \times 10^2$ kJ   (b) 4H$_2$O(g) + 3N$_2$(g) $\longrightarrow$ N$_2$O$_4$(l) + 2N$_2$H$_4$(l); $\Delta H = 1049$ kJ   **6.5** -164 kJ   **6.6** 1.80×10^2 J   **6.7** -54 kJ; HCl(aq) + NaOH(aq) $\longrightarrow$ NaCl(aq) + H$_2$O(l); $\Delta H = -54$ kJ   **6.8** $\Delta H = -1792$ kJ   **6.9** $\Delta H°_{vap} = 44.0$ kJ   **6.10** $\Delta H° = -138.0$ kJ   **6.11** $\Delta H° = 61.6$ kJ

CHAPTER 7

7.1 767 nm   **7.2** 6.58×10^{14}/s   **7.3** 2.0×10^{-19} J, 2.0×10^{-17} J, and 2.0×10^{-15} J; greatest energy: x-ray region; least energy: infrared region   **7.4** 103 nm   **7.5** 3.38×10^{-19} J   **7.6** $\lambda = 332$ pm   **7.7** (a) The value of n must be a positive whole number greater than zero.   (b) The values of l range from 0 to $n - 1$. Here, l has a value greater than n.   (c) The values for m_l range from $-l$ to $+l$. Here, m_l has a value greater than that of l.   (d) The values for m_s are $+\frac{1}{2}$ or $-\frac{1}{2}$, not 0.

CHAPTER 8

8.1 (a) possible   (b) possible   (c) impossible. There are two electrons in a 2p orbital with the same spin.   (d) possible.   (e) impossible. Only two electrons are allowed in an s subshell.

(f) impossible. Only six electrons are allowed in a p subshell.
8.2 $1s^2 2s^2 2p^6 3s^2 3p^6 3d^{\,5} 4s^2$ **8.3** $4s^2 4p^3$ **8.4** Group IVA,
Period 6; main-group element

8.5

8.6 In order of increasing radius: Be, Mg, Na **8.7** It is more
likely that 1000 kJ/mol is the ionization energy for iodine because
ionization energies tend to decrease as atomic number increases in
a column. **8.8** F

CHAPTER 9

9.1 $\cdot Mg\cdot\; + \;:\!\ddot{O}\cdot \longrightarrow Mg^{2+} + \left[:\!\ddot{\underset{..}{O}}\!:\right]^{2-}$ **9.2** The electron

configuration for Ca^{2+} is [Ar] and its Lewis symbol is Ca^{2+}. The
electron configuration for S^{2-} is $[Ne]3s^2 3p^6$ and its Lewis symbol
is $\left[:\!\ddot{\underset{..}{S}}\!:\right]^{2-}$. **9.3** The electron configurations of Pb and Pb^{2+}
are $[Xe]4f^{\,14}5d^{10}6s^2 6p^2$ and $[Xe]4f^{\,14}5d^{10}6s^2$, respectively.
9.4 $[Ar]3d^5$ **9.5** One would expect S^{2-}, because it has two
additional electrons. **9.6** In order of increasing ionic radius:
Mg^{2+}, Ca^{2+}, Sr^{2+} **9.7** In order of increasing ionic radius:
Ca^{2+}, Cl^-, P^{3-} **9.8** C—O is the most polar bond.

9.9 **9.10** $\ddot{O}::C::\ddot{O}$ or $\ddot{O}=C=\ddot{O}$

9.11 (a) (b)

9.12

9.13 **9.14** $:\!\ddot{C}l\!-\!Be\!-\!\ddot{C}l\!:$

9.15

9.16 103 pm **9.17** 123 pm **9.18** −1304 kJ

CHAPTER 10

10.1 (a) trigonal pyramidal (b) bent (c) tetrahedral
10.2 T-shaped **10.3** (b), (c) **10.4** (b); the F atoms are
distributed in a tetrahedral arrangement to give a molecule with a
dipole moment of zero. **10.5** For the N atom:

N (ground state) = [He] and

N (hybridized) = [He]

Each N—H bond is formed by the overlap of a $1s$ orbital of a
hydrogen atom with one of the sp^3 hybrid orbitals of the nitrogen
atom. **10.6** Each P—Cl bond is formed by the overlap of a phosphorus $sp^3 d$ hybrid orbital with a singly occupied $3p$ chlorine
orbital. **10.7** The C atom is sp hybridized. A carbon–oxygen bond
is double and is composed of a σ bond and a π bond. The σ bond is
formed by the overlap of a hybrid C orbital with a $2p$ orbital of
O that lies along the axis. The π bond is formed by the sidewise
overlap of a $2p$ on C with a $2p$ on O. **10.8** The structural formulas
for the isomers are as follows:

cis   trans

These compounds exist as separate isomers. If they were inter-
changeable, one end of the molecule would have to remain fixed as
the other rotated. This would require breaking the π bond and a
considerable expenditure of energy.

10.9 KK ;
$KK(\sigma_{2s})^2(\sigma^*_{2s})^2(\pi_{2p})^4$; diamagnetic; bond order = 2

10.10 KK ;
$KK(\sigma_{2s})^2(\sigma^*_{2s})^2(\pi_{2p})^4(\sigma_{2p})^2$; bond order = 3; diamagnetic

CHAPTER 11

11.1 1.37×10^3 kJ; 4.12×10^3 g **11.2** 5.30×10^2 mmHg
11.3 43.0 kJ/mol **11.4** (a) Methyl chloride can be liquefied by
sufficiently increasing the pressure as long as the temperature is
below 144°C. (b) Oxygen can be liquefied by compression as
long as the temperature is below −119°C. **11.5** (a) hydrogen
bonding, dipole–dipole forces, and London forces (b) London
forces (c) dipole–dipole forces and London forces **11.6** In
order of increasing vapor pressure we have: butane (C_4H_{10}),
propane (C_3H_8), and ethane (C_2H_6). London forces increase with
increasing molecular mass. Therefore, one would expect the lowest
vapor pressure to correspond to the highest molecular mass.
11.7 Hydrogen bonding is negligible in methyl chloride but strong
in ethanol, which explains the lower vapor pressure of ethanol.
11.8 (a) metallic solid (b) ionic solid (c) covalent network
solid (d) molecular solid **11.9** C_2H_5OH, molecular; CH_4,
molecular; CH_3Cl, molecular; $MgSO_4$, ionic. In order of increasing
melting point: CH_4, CH_3Cl, C_2H_5OH, and $MgSO_4$. **11.10** 1 atom
11.11 6.02×10^{23}/mol **11.12** 533 pm

CHAPTER 12

12.1 A dental filling, made up of liquid mercury and solid silver, is
a solid solution. **12.2** C_4H_9OH, because of hydrogen bonding.
12.3 Na^+ **12.4** 8.45×10^{-3} g O_2/L **12.5** 7.07 g HCl;
27.9 g H_2O **12.6** 3.09 m $C_6H_5CH_3$ **12.7** mole fraction toluene =
0.194; mole fraction benzene = 0.806 **12.8** mole fraction
methanol = 0.00550; mole fraction ethanol = 0.995 **12.9** 7.24 m
CH_3OH **12.10** 2.96 M $(NH_2)_2CO$ **12.11** 2.20 m $(NH_2)_2CO$
12.12 $\Delta P = 1.22$ mmHg; P = 155 mmHg **12.13** 1.89×10^{-1} g
CH_2OHCH_2OH **12.14** 176 amu **12.15** 124 amu; P_4 **12.16** π =
3.5 atm **12.17** 100.077°C **12.18** $AlCl_3$

CHAPTER 13

13.1 $\dfrac{\Delta[NO_2F]}{\Delta t} = -\dfrac{\Delta[NO_2]}{\Delta t}$

13.2 1.1×10^{-4} M/s **13.3** zero order in [CO]; second order in [NO_2]; second order overall   **13.4** rate = $k[NO_2]^2$; $k = 0.71$ L/(mol·s)   **13.5** (a) $[N_2O_5]_t = 1.24 \times 10^{-2}$ mol/L   (b) $t = 4.80 \times 10^3$ s   **13.6** half-life = 0.075 s; decreases to 50% of initial concentration in 0.075 s, to 25% in 0.151 s   **13.7** $Ea = 2.06 \times 10^5$ J/mol, $k = 5.80 \times 10^{-2}/(M^{1/2} \cdot s)$ **13.8** $2H_2O_2 \longrightarrow 2H_2O + O_2$ **13.9** bimolecular   **13.10** rate = $k[NO_2]^2$ **13.11** rate = $k_1[H_2O_2][I^-]$ **13.12** rate = $k_2(k_1/k_{-1})[NO]^2[O_2]$

CHAPTER 14

14.1 0.57 mol CO, 0.57 mol H_2O, 0.43 mol CO_2, and 0.43 mol H_2

14.2 (a) $K_c = \dfrac{[NH_3]^2[H_2O]^4}{[NO_2]^2[H_2]^7}$ (b) $K_c = \dfrac{[NH_3][H_2O]^2}{[NO_2][H_2]^{7/2}}$

14.3 $CO(g) + H_2O(g) \rightleftharpoons H_2(g) + CO_2(g)$; 0.57   **14.4** $K_c = 2.3 \times 10^{-4}$ **14.5** $K_p = 1.24$

14.6 $K_c = \dfrac{[Ni(CO)_4]}{[CO]^4}$ **14.7** products; 0.018 M

14.8 $Q_c = 0.67$; more CO will form   **14.9** 0.0096 moles of PCl_5 **14.10** 0.11 mol H_2, 0.11 mol I_2, 0.78 mol HI   **14.11** 0.86 M PCl_5, 0.135 M PCl_3, 0.135 M Cl_2 **14.12** (a) in the reverse direction   (b) in the reverse direction   **14.13** (a) no; pressure has no effect.   (b) no   (c) yes   **14.14** high temperature   **14.15** High temperatures and low pressure would give the best yield of product.

CHAPTER 15

15.1 $H_2CO_3(aq) + CN^-(aq) \rightleftharpoons HCN(aq) + HCO_3^-(aq)$;
acid   base   acid   base
HCN is the conjugate acid of CN^-.

15.2 (a)
BF$_3$ is the Lewis acid, CH$_3$OH is the Lewis base.

(b)

O^{2-} is the Lewis base, CO_2 is the Lewis acid.
15.3 The reactants are favored.   **15.4** (a) PH$_3$ (b) HI   (c) H_2SO_3 (d) H_3AsO_4 (e) HSO_4^- **15.5** 0.250 M OH^-, 4.0×10^{-14} M H^+ **15.6** basic   **15.7** 1.35   **15.8** 12.40   **15.9** 6.9×10^{-4} M **15.10** 4×10^{-4} M

CHAPTER 16

16.1 1.4×10^{-4}; 0.071   **16.2** $[H^+] = [C_2H_3O_2^-] = 1.3 \times 10^{-3}$ M; pH = 2.89; 0.013   **16.3** 3.24   **16.4** pH = 1.29; $[SO_3^{2-}] = 6.3 \times 10^{-8}$ M **16.5** 3.3×10^{-6} **16.6** 5.3×10^{-12} M **16.7** (a) acidic   (b) neutral   (c) acidic   **16.8** (a) 1.5×10^{-11} (b) 2.4×10^{-5} **16.9** 1.5×10^{-6}; 8.19   **16.10** 8.5×10^{-5} M; 8.5×10^{-4} **16.11** 3.63   **16.12** 5.26   **16.13** 3.83   **16.14** 1.60   **16.15** 7.97   **16.16** (a) 11.28   (b) 9.26   (c) 5.22   (d) 2.23

CHAPTER 17

17.1 (a) $K_{sp} = [Ba^{2+}][SO_4^{2-}]$ (b) $K_{sp} = [Fe^{3+}][OH^-]^3$ (c) $K_{sp} = [Ca^{2+}]^3[PO_4^{3-}]^2$ **17.2** 1.8×10^{-10} **17.3** 4.5×10^{-36} **17.4** 0.67 g/L   **17.5** (a) 6.3×10^{-3} mol/L   (b) 4.4×10^{-5} mol/L   **17.6** Precipitation is expected.   **17.7** No precipitate will form.   **17.8** silver cyanide   **17.9** 1.2×10^{-9} M **17.10** No precipitate will form.   **17.11** 0.44 mol/L

CHAPTER 18

18.1 3.89 J   **18.2** -48.9 J; 4.96 kJ; -885.2 kJ   **18.3** 304 J/(mol·K)   **18.4** (a) positive   (b) positive   (c) negative   (d) positive   **18.5** 537 J/K   **18.6** -888.7 kJ   **18.7** 130.9 kJ   **18.8** All four reactions are spontaneous in the direction written.
18.9 (a) $K = P_{CO_2}$ (b) $K = [Pb^{2+}][I^-]^2$

(c) $K = \dfrac{P_{CO_2}}{[H^+][HCO_3^-]}$

18.10 1×10^{-23} **18.11** 5×10^{-12} **18.12** 9×10^{-2} atm
18.13 $T = 669.5$ K, which is lower than that for $CaCO_3$.

CHAPTER 19

19.1 $I_2(s) + 10NO_3^-(aq) + 8H^+(aq) \longrightarrow$
$\qquad\qquad\qquad 4H_2O(l) + 2IO_3^-(aq) + 10NO_2(g)$
19.2 $H_2O_2(aq) + 2ClO_2(aq) + 2OH^-(aq) \longrightarrow$
$\qquad\qquad\qquad 2ClO_2^-(aq) + O_2(g) + 2H_2O(l)$
19.3 anode: $Ni(s) \longrightarrow Ni^{2+}(aq) + 2e^-$; cathode: $Ag^+(aq) + e^- \longrightarrow Ag(s)$; electrons flow from anode to cathode; Ag^+ flows to Ag; Ni^{2+} flows away from Ni.
19.4 $Zn(s)|Zn^{2+}(aq)\|H^+(aq)|H_2(g)|Pt$
19.5 $Cd(s) + 2H^+(aq) \longrightarrow Cd^{2+}(aq) + H_2(g)$
19.6 -2.12×10^4 J   **19.7** NO_3^- **19.8** No   **19.9** 1.10 V
19.10 -1.4×10^2 kJ   **19.11** 2.696 V   **19.12** 1×10^{19} **19.13** 1.42 V   **19.14** 4×10^{-7} M Ni^{2+}
19.15 (a) $K^+(l) + e^- \longrightarrow K(l)$
$2Cl^-(l) \longrightarrow Cl_2(g) + 2e^-$
(b) $K^+(l) + e^- \longrightarrow K(l)$
$4OH^-(l) \longrightarrow O_2(g) + 2H_2O(l) + 4e^-$
19.16 $Ag^+(aq) + e^- \longrightarrow Ag(s)$ (cathode)
$2H_2O(l) \longrightarrow O_2(g) + 4H^+(aq) + 4e^-$ (anode)
19.17 2.52×10^{-2} A
19.18 8.66×10^{-2} g

CHAPTER 20

20.1 $^{40}_{19}K \longrightarrow ^{40}_{20}Ca + ^{0}_{-1}e$ **20.2** $^{235}_{92}U$ **20.3** (a) is stable; (b) and   (c) are radioactive.   **20.4** (a) positron emission   (b) beta emission   **20.5** (a) $^{40}_{20}Ca(d,p)^{41}_{20}Ca$ (b) $^{12}_{6}C + ^{2}_{1}H \longrightarrow$ $^{13}_{6}C + ^{1}_{1}H$ **20.6** $^{14}_{7}N$ **20.7** $3.2 \times 10^{-5}/s$ **20.8** 5.26 y   **20.9** $7.82 \times 10^{-10}/s$; 7.4×10^{-7} Ci   **20.10** 0.200
20.11 1.0×10^4 y   **20.12** (a) 2.58×10^9 J   (b) 6.25 MeV

CHAPTER 22

22.1 (a) pentaamminechlorocobalt(III) chloride   (b) potassium aquapentacyanocobaltate(III)   (c) pentaaquahydroxoiron(III) ion   **22.2** (a) $K_4[Fe(CN)_6]$ (b) $[Co(NH_3)_4Cl_2]Cl$ (c) $[PtCl_4]^{2-}$ **22.3** (a) no geometric isomers possible   (b) geometric isomers possible (see Fig. 22.15 for similar example)

22.4 (a) no optical isomers possible; (b) is similar to Figure 22.16

22.5

↑	↑	
↑↓	↑↓	↑↓

2 unpaired electrons   **22.6**

↑	↑	↑
	↑↓	↑↓

22.7 530 nm, 500 nm, yes; CN⁻ is a more strongly bonding ligand than H_2O.

CHAPTER 23

23.1

$$CH_3CHCH_2CH_3$$
with CH_3 on the central carbon

23.2 (a)

(b) none   **23.3** 2-bromobutane   **23.4** (a) 2,3-dimethylbutane
(b) 3-ethyl-2-methylhexane

23.5 $CH_3CH_2{-}\underset{\underset{CH_3}{|}}{\overset{\overset{CH_3}{|}}{C}}{-}CH_2CH_2CH_2CH_2CH_3$

23.6 (a) 2,4-dimethyl-2-hexene   (b) 3-propyl-1-hexene

23.7 $CH_3{-}\underset{\underset{CH_3}{|}}{C}{=}CH{-}CH_2{-}\underset{\underset{CH_3}{|}}{CH}{-}CH_2CH_3$

23.8 *cis*-3-hexene, *trans*-3-hexene

23.9 (a) propyne   (b) 3-methyl-1-pentyne

23.10 (a)

(b)

23.11 3-ethyl-3-hexanol   **23.12** (a) dimethyl ether
(b) methyl ethyl ether
23.13 (a) 2-pentanone   (b) butanal

CHAPTER 24

24.1 $-CH_2-CCl_2-CH_2-CCl_2-CH_2-CCl_2-$

Answers to Concept Checks

CHAPTER 1

1.1 (A) element   (B) compound   (C) mixture   **1.2** (a) two if you weigh under 100 lb, three if you weigh 100 lb or more (b) A 165-lb person would be reported as weighing 1.7×10^2 lb. (c) A 74.8-kg or 165-lb male would weigh 50 kg or 200 lb on the truck scale.   **1.3** (a) Meters, decimeters, or centimeters would be appropriate units.   (b) approximately 9 m   (c) 39°C would mean that you had a moderate fever.   (d) You would probably be comfortable in a 23°C room.   **1.4** You need to perform an experiment that will give you the density of the marcasite and then compare that to the density of gold.

CHAPTER 2

2.1 The molecular model on the far right that contains 3 atoms with a ratio of 1:2   **2.2** One would conclude that the atom is made up primarily of a large impenetrable mass with a positive charge. **2.3** They must have similar chemical and/or physical properties. **2.4** (a) ether   (b) alcohol   (c) carboxylic acid   (d) hydrocarbon **2.5** Q is likely to be an element in Group VIA.

CHAPTER 3

3.1 (a) 1.5 mol   (b) 4.5 mol   (c) 3.0 mol of OH^- since there are 2 mol of OH^- per mol of $Mg(OH)_2$ **3.2** (a) The total mass of C and H that you collect will be less than the total mass of material you started with.   (b) The calculated percent C and H would be less than the real value.   **3.3** (a) No, the empirical formula needs to be the smallest whole-number ratio of subscripts.   (b) No, the subscripts are not whole numbers. (c) Yes, the empirical and molecular formulas can be the same. **3.4** (a) correct   (b) incorrect   (c) incorrect   (d) correct (e) correct   (f) incorrect   (g) incorrect   (h) correct **3.5** (a) $X_2(g) + 2Y(g) \longrightarrow 2XY(g)$ (b) container 1   (c) $Y(g)$

CHAPTER 4

4.1 The left beaker contains the strong electrolyte $LiI(aq)$. The right beaker contains the nonelectrolyte $CH_3OH(aq)$. **4.2** (a) $Na_2SO_4(aq) + Sr(C_2H_3O_2)_2(aq) \longrightarrow$
$$SrSO_4(s) + 2NaC_2H_3O_2(aq)$$
(b) $2Na^+(aq) + SO_4{}^{2-}(aq) + Sr^{2+}(aq) + 2C_2H_3O_2{}^-(aq) \longrightarrow$
$$SrSO_4(s) + 2Na^+(aq) + 2C_2H_3O_2{}^-(aq)$$
(c) $Sr^{2+}(aq) + SO_4{}^{2-}(aq) \longrightarrow SrSO_4(s)$
4.3 (a) $MOH(s)$ is a base. M could be any Group I metal. (b) HA is an acid. A^- is an anion with a −1 charge.   (c) H_2A is an acid. A^{2-} is an anion with a −2 charge.   (d) $M \longrightarrow Na^+$, $A \longrightarrow C_2H_3O_2{}^-$, $A \longrightarrow SO_3{}^{2-}$.
4.4 Concentration order: A< C = D < B. Leave A alone; add water to fill beaker B; add water to double the volumes of D and C. **4.5** (a) The acid in flask C has three times as many acidic protons as the acid in flask A. The acid in flask B has two times as many acidic protons as the acid in flask A.   (b) Yes, if we assume that flask A contains a monoprotic acid.

CHAPTER 5

5.1 Since the height of the column is inversely related to the density of the liquid, the column containing the H_2O would be higher.   **5.2** (a) Step 1, pressure decrease; Step 2, pressure decrease; total change, final pressure less than starting pressure. (b) Step 1, pressure increase; Step 2, pressure increase; total change, final pressure greater than starting pressure.   **5.3** (a) All contain same amount of gas.   (b) Xe flask   (c) He flask (d) They would all still have the same number of moles. **5.4** (a) No change in H_2 pressure.   (b) They are equal.   (c) The total pressure is the sum of the pressures of the H_2 and Ar in the container   **5.5** (a) He   (b) Raise the temperature of the Ar. **5.6** (a) Pressure would be greater for ideal gas.   (b) Pressure would be less for ideal gas.   (c) Cannot make a determination because the effect of molecular volume and attractions on the pressure of a real gas is opposite.

CHAPTER 6

6.1 Sun's energy is changed to electric energy, to chemical energy (of the battery), and back to electric energy, then to kinetic energy of motor and water, and to potential energy of water.   **6.2** c and d are exothermic; d is most exothermic   **6.3** $\Delta H_{sub} = \Delta H_{fus} + \Delta H_{vap}$

CHAPTER 7

7.1 The wavelength is halved; ultraviolet.   **7.2** UV   **7.3** The proton speed would be about 2000 times smaller.

CHAPTER 8

8.1 4   **8.2** Mg and Al   **8.3** IIA   **8.4** As

CHAPTER 9

9.1 (a) excited state; not expected   (b) N^{2-} is not expected. (c) expected configuration   (d) Na^{2+} is not expected. (e) expected configuration   **9.2** (a) has 13 electron pairs; should be 12   (b) correct skeleton structure and distribution of electrons (c) Double bond between F and N atoms is less likely than single bond.   (d) no octet on left N atom   (e) incorrect skeleton structure   (f) no octets on N atoms   **9.3** (a) most accurate description (b) Electronegative N atom is not expected to be in central position. (c) not enough electron pairs to give octets on C and N atoms (would need 7 pairs)   (d) not enough electron pairs to give octets on C and N atoms (would need 6 pairs)

CHAPTER 10

10.1 The four pairs have a tetrahedral arrangement; the molecular geometry is trigonal pyramidal.   **10.2** Molecule Y is likely to be trigonal planar, but trigonal pyramidal or T-shaped geometries are possible. Molecule Z cannot have a trigonal planar geometry, but must be either trigonal pyramidal or T-shaped.   **10.3** The single and triple bonds each require a sigma bond orbital, suggesting *sp* hybrids.

CHAPTER 11

11.1 (a) (i) slightly lower   (ii) higher   (iii) more molecules
(iv) Evaporation is greater.
(v)

$t = 1$

(b) (i) slightly lower   (ii) higher   (iii) more molecules
(iv) They will be equal.
(v)

$t = 2$

11.2 Cook it longer because the H_2O temperature would be lower.   **11.3** (a) The hydrogen and oxygen would form an explosive mixture.   (b) many times greater (more positive) for the wrong reaction   (c) Apply Hess's law.   **11.4** (a) AB
(b) face-centered cubic

CHAPTER 12

12.1 (a) Mo solute, Cr solvent   (b) $MgCl_2$ solute, H_2O solvent
(c) O_2 and N_2 solutes, Ar solvent   **12.2** The A^{2+} ion must be smaller so it has a greater energy of hydration.   **12.3** At high elevations, the partial pressure of O_2 is so low that not enough dissolves in the water to sustain fish.   **12.4** A soluble, chemically similar liquid with a higher vapor pressure than water.   **12.5** To prevent water from flowing into the pickle via osmosis. The pickles would be huge and would probably burst.
12.6 Hightest to lowest: $MgCl_2 > KBr > Na_2SO_4 > NaCl$.
12.7 The iron(III) hydroxide precipitates because the electrons from the negative electrode neutralize the positive charge on the iron(III) hydroxide.

CHAPTER 13

13.1 (a) Point A has a faster instantaneous rate.   (b) No, it decreases with time.   **13.2** (a) $[Q] = 0.0\ M$ slowest (no reaction); the other two are equal in rate because they are zero order with respect to $[Q]$.   (b) Rate $= k[R]^2$ **13.3** (a) Rate of aging $=$ $(diet)^w(exercise)^x(sex)^y(occupation)^z$ (b) Gather a sample of people that have all of the factors the same except one. For example, using the equation given in part (a), you could determine the effect of diet if you had a sample of people who were the same sex, exercised the same amount, and had the same occupation. You would need to isolate each factor in this fashion to determine the exponent on each factor.   (c) 2   **13.4** Second order   **13.5** (a) the A + B reaction   (b) the E + F reaction   (c) exothermic   **13.6** (a) It will increase the rate since the activation energy, E_a, is inversely related to the rate constant, k. A decrease in E_a results in an increase in the value of k.   (b) yes   (c) No, it should be rate $= k[Y]^2$.

CHAPTER 14

14.1 $2A + B \longrightarrow 2C$ **14.2** IV with A = red, I with X = red or blue, II with C = blue   **14.3** left to right   **14.4** It is quadrupled.
14.5 I

CHAPTER 15

15.1 $HCHO_2(aq), + H_2O(l) \rightleftharpoons CHO_2^-(aq) + H_3O^+(aq)$ and $H_2O(l) + H_2O(l) \rightleftharpoons H_3O^+(aq) + OH^-(aq)$; $HCHO_2(aq)$, $H_2O(l)$, $CHO_2^-(aq)$, $OH^-(aq)$, and $H_3O^+(aq)$ **15.2** Acetate ion
15.3 B, A, C   **15.4** $NaOH$, NH_3, $HC_2H_3O_2$, HCl

CHAPTER 16

16.1 HCN, $HC_2H_3O_2$, HNO_2, HF **16.2** $B(aq) + H_2O(l) \rightleftharpoons$ $BH^+(aq) + OH^-(aq)$ weak base   **16.3** a, b   **16.4** d   **16.5** (a) Y
(b) 3   (c) beaker with 7 HA molecules

CHAPTER 17

17.1 $PbSO_4$ **17.2** $NaNO_3$ **17.3** Picture fewer Ag^+ and more Cl^- ions.   **17.4** Magnesium oxalate

CHAPTER 18

18.1 It has increased.   **18.2** The NO concentration is low at equilibrium.   **18.3** (a) $\Delta G°$ is not changed.   (b) ΔG increases.
18.4 The concentration of NO_2 increases with temperature.

CHAPTER 19

19.1 No sustainable current would flow. The wire does not contain mobile positively and negatively charged species, which are necessary to balance the accumulation of charges in each of the half-cells.   **19.2** (a) $-0.54\ V$ (b) No
(c) They both would be 1.10 V.
19.3 (a) negative   (b) Change the concentrations in a manner to increase Q, where $Q = \dfrac{[Fe^{2+}]}{[Cu^{2+}]}$.
For example: $Fe(s)|Fe^{2+}\ (1.10\ M)\|Cu^{2+}\ (0.50\ M)|Cu(s)$.
19.4 Many of the ions contained in seawater have very high reduction potentials—higher than $Fe(s)$. This means that spontaneous electrochemical reactions will occur with the $Fe(s)$, causing the iron to form ions and go into solution, while at the same time, the ions in the sea are reduced and plate out on the surface of the iron.

CHAPTER 20

20.1 (a) yes   (b) no, since the $^3_1H_2O$ molecule is more massive than $^1_1H_2O$ (c) $^3_1H_2O$ **20.2** the α particle, since it has the highest RBE   **20.3** After 50,000 years, enough half-lives have passed (about 10) that there would be almost no carbon-14 present to detect and measure.

CHAPTER 21

21.1 Given the high energy demands of animals to move and maintain body temperature, breaking the very strong triple bond of N_2 requires too much energy when compared to the lower-energy double bond of O_2.   **21.2** because the only intermolecular forces in these materials are very weak van der Waals forces

CHAPTER 22

22.1 $K_2[PtCl_6]$ **22.2** $[Co(NH_3)_4(H_2O)Br]Cl_2$
22.3 (a) Complexes A and E   (b) A and E   (c) A and E, B and C

CHAPTER 23

23.1   (a) C_7H_{16} (b) CH₃CHCHCH₂CH₃ with CH₃ groups

$$\begin{array}{c} CH_3 \\ | \\ CH_3CHCHCH_2CH_3 \\ | \\ CH_3 \end{array}$$

23.2 Blend of 90% 2,2,4-trimethylpentane and 10% heptane

23.3 (a) C_5H_{10} (b)

$$\begin{array}{ccc} H & & H \\ & C=C & \\ CH_3 & & CH_2CH_3 \end{array}$$

(c) *cis*-2-pentene

CHAPTER 24

24.1

$$\begin{array}{c} CH_3 \quad O \quad HO-\overset{\overset{\displaystyle H}{|}}{C}-CH_3 \\ H_2N-\overset{\overset{\displaystyle |}{}}{\underset{\underset{\displaystyle H}{|}}{C}}-\overset{\overset{\displaystyle \parallel}{}}{C}-N-\overset{\overset{\displaystyle |}{}}{\underset{\underset{\displaystyle H}{|}}{C}}-COOH \\ \end{array}$$

$$\begin{array}{c} HO-\overset{\overset{\displaystyle H}{|}}{C}-CH_3 \quad O \quad CH_3 \\ H_2N-\overset{}{C}-\overset{\parallel}{C}-N-\overset{}{C}-COOH \\ \quad | \quad \quad \quad | \quad | \\ \quad H \quad \quad \quad H \quad H \end{array}$$

24.2 UACGAUGCCUAAGUU

Answers to Self-Assessment Questions

CHAPTER 1
1.19 c   1.20 a   1.21 e   1.22 c

CHAPTER 2
2.21 a   2.22 d   2.23 c   2.24 b

CHAPTER 3
3.13 a   3.14 b   3.15 d   3.16 a

CHAPTER 4
4.15 e   4.16 c   4.17 d   4.18 d

CHAPTER 5
1. a   2. c   3. b   4. d

CHAPTER 6
6.25 d   6.26 b   6.27 c   6.28 c

CHAPTER 7
7.19 d   7.20 a   7.21 c   7.22 a

CHAPTER 8
8.25 c   8.26 b   8.27 a   8.28 b

CHAPTER 9
9.19 a   9.20 e   9.21 d   9.22 a

CHAPTER 10
10.17 e   10.18 d   10.19 b   10.20 e

CHAPTER 11
11.21 e   11.22 d   11.23 c   11.24 b

CHAPTER 12
12.21 a   12.22 c   12.23 e   12.24 a

CHAPTER 13
13.23 c   13.24 e   13.25 e   13.26 c

CHAPTER 14
14.13 d   14.14 a   14.15 c   14.16 b

CHAPTER 15
15.15 a   15.16 d   15.17 d   15.18 b

CHAPTER 16
16.17 a   16.18 d   16.19 a   16.20 d

CHAPTER 17
17.11 c   17.12 e   17.13 d   17.14 a

CHAPTER 18
18.17 e   18.18 c   18.19 d   18.20 a

CHAPTER 19
19.19 c   19.20 c   19.21 a   19.22 b

CHAPTER 20
20.19 b   20.20 e   20.21 d   20.22 c

CHAPTER 21
21.67 d   21.68 e   21.69 d   21.70 b

CHAPTER 22
22.27 e   22.28 a   22.29 b   22.30 a

CHAPTER 23
23.15 e   23.16 d   23.17 d   23.18 c

CHAPTER 24
24.17 d   24.18 c   24.19 d   24.20 d

CHAPTER 1

1.25 (a) solid and liquid phases (b) three phases: liquid water, solid quartz, and solid seashells

1.27 (a) Immerse the thermometer in a solution of ice and liquid water, and when the mercury stops moving, mark that point. Then immerse the thermometer in boiling water, repeat the procedure, and mark that point. (b) Take the thermometer that you marked up and make 19 evenly spaced marks between those two original points.

1.29 (a) $°F = °YS \left(\dfrac{120°F}{100°YS} \right) - 100°F$ (b) $-21°F$

1.31 The box that contains the cubes has a greater density.

1.33 (a) A paper clip has the closest mass to 1 g. (b) Your answers will vary depending on sample: grain of sand 1×10^{-5} kg, paper clip 1×10^{-3} kg, nickel 5×10^{-3} kg, 5.0-gallon bucket of water 2.0×10^1 kg, a brick 3 kg, a car 1×10^3 kg.

1.35 (a) 0.835 m (b) 0.276 m **1.37** 6.6 g **1.39** 29.8 g

1.41 (a) solid (b) liquid (c) gas (d) solid

1.43 (a) physical (b) physical (c) chemical (d) physical

1.45 heating of mercury(II) oxide = chemical change; solidification of mercury = physical change; burning of wood = chemical change **1.47** (a) physical (b) chemical (c) physical (d) physical (e) chemical **1.49** Physical properties: lustrous; blue-black crystals that vaporize readily to a violet gas. Chemical properties: combines with many metals, including aluminum.

1.51 (a) physical (b) chemical (c) physical (d) chemical (e) physical **1.53** (a) solution (b) substance (c) substance (d) heterogeneous mixture **1.55** (a) pure substance; bromine liquid, bromine gas (b) mixture; liquid solution and solid (c) pure substance; nonmolten portion (solid), liquid (d) mixture; solid sodium hydrogen carbonate and solid potassium hydrogen tartrate

1.57 (a) 6 (b) 3 (c) 4 (d) 5 (e) 3 (f) 4 **1.59** 4.0×10^4 km **1.61** (a) 8.5 (b) 92.9 (c) 111 (d) 2.3×10^3 **1.63** 32 cm^3 **1.65** (a) 5.89 ps (b) 20.10 cm (c) 2.560 ng (d) 6.05 km **1.67** (a) 6.15×10^{-12} s (b) 3.781×10^{-6} m (c) 1.546×10^{-10} m (d) 9.7×10^{-3} g **1.69** (a) 20°C (b) −31°C (c) 79°F (d) −94°F **1.71** −6.0°F **1.73** 7.56 g/cm^3 **1.75** ethanol **1.77** 1.3×10^2 g **1.79** 25.1 cm^3 **1.81** 4.80×10^5 mg **1.83** 5.55×10^{-5} cm **1.85** 3.73×10^{17} m^3; 3.73×10^{20} L **1.87** 3.25×10^6 g **1.89** 4.435×10^3 m **1.91** 65.5 L **1.93** 0.86 g **1.95** 2.53 cm^3 **1.97** 114.5 g **1.99** (a) chemical (b) physical (c) physical (d) chemical **1.101** no **1.103** 6.07×10^4 cm^3 **1.105** 50.4 gal **1.107** 9.9×10^1 cm^3 **1.109** (a) 7.6×10^{-1} (b) 1.63×10^1 (c) 4.76×10^2 (d) 1.12×10^{-1} **1.111** (a) 9.12 cg/mL (b) 66 pm (c) 7.1 μm (d) 56 nm **1.113** (a) 1.07×10^{-12} s (b) 5.8×10^{-6} m (c) 3.19×10^{-7} m (d) 1.53×10^{-2} s **1.115** 6170°F **1.117** 1.52×10^3°F **1.119** 303.0 K, 85.6°F **1.121** 907.8°C, 1180.9 K **1.123** 1.74×10^3 kg/m^3 **1.125** 2.65 g/cm^3 **1.127** chloroform **1.129** 1.82×10^3 g **1.131** 33.24 mL **1.133** (a) 8.45×10^9 μg (b) 3.18×10^{-1} ms (c) 9.3×10^{13} nm (d) 3.71 cm **1.135** (a) 5.91×10^6 mg (b) 7.53×10^5 μg (c) 9.01×10^4 kHz (d) 4.98×10^{-4} kJ **1.137** 1.2230×10^{16} L **1.139** 2.8×10^4 L **1.141** 55.0 g **1.157** 2.4 L **1.159** 2.13×10^3 g **1.161** 2.6×10^{21} L **1.163** 34%, 79 proof (2 sig. fig.) **1.165** 8.09 g/cm^3 **1.167** 2.4 g/cm^3

CHAPTER 2

2.27 Since there is no massive, positive nucleus, one would expect no or very little deflection of the alpha particles when they are shot at the gold foil. **2.29** Group them by physical properties (density, mass, color, conductivity, etc.) or by chemical properties (reaction with air, reaction with water, etc.). **2.31** (a) X_2SO_4, XSO_4, and $X_2(SO_4)_5$ (b) exy(I) sulfate, exy(II) sulfate, exy(V) sulfate **2.33** 19 protons, 20 neutrons, and 38 electrons **2.35** (a) $2Li + Cl_2 \longrightarrow 2LiCl$ (b) $2Na + S \longrightarrow Na_2S$ (c) $2Al + 3Br_2 \longrightarrow 2AlBr_3$ (d) $3Mg + N_2 \longrightarrow Mg_3N_2$ (e) $6Ca + P_4 \longrightarrow 2Ca_3P_2$ **2.37** (a) argon (b) zinc (c) silver (d) magnesium **2.39** (a) K (b) S (c) Fe (d) Mn **2.41** 9.05×10^{-31} kg **2.43** C, D **2.45** Cl-35: 17 protons, 18 neutrons, 17 electrons; Cl-37: 17 protons, 20 neutrons, 17 electrons **2.47** $^{28}_{14}$Si **2.49** 13.90 **2.51** 63.55 amu **2.53** 39.10 amu, potassium **2.55** 24.615 amu **2.57** (a) Group IVA, Period 2, nonmetal (b) Group VIA, Period 6, metal (c) Group VIB, Period 4, metal (d) Group IIA, Period 3, metal (e) Group IIIA, Period 2, metalloid **2.59** (a) Te (b) Al **2.61** (a) O, oxygen (b) Na, sodium (c) Fe, iron (d) Ce, cerium **2.63** Differences: as a solid, each molecule contains 8 sulfur atoms, whereas gas molecules contain various numbers of sulfur atoms. Alike: molecules of solid and gas contain only S—S bonds. **2.65** 4.10×10^{22} N atoms, 2.73×10^{22} N atoms **2.67** 1.1×10^{21} NH$_3$ molecules **2.69** (a) N$_2$H$_4$ (b) H$_2$O$_2$ (c) C$_3$H$_8$O (d) PCl$_3$ **2.71** (a) PCl$_5$ (b) NO$_2$ (c) C$_3$H$_6$O$_2$ **2.73** 1 Fe to 6 O **2.75** (a) Fe(CN)$_3$ (b) K$_2$SO$_4$ (c) Li$_3$N (d) Ca$_3$P$_2$ **2.77** (a) sodium sulfate (b) calcium sulfide (c) copper(I) chloride (d) chromium(III) oxide **2.79** (a) Pb(MnO$_4$)$_2$ (b) Ba(HCO$_3$)$_2$ (c) Cs$_2$S (d) Fe(C$_2$H$_3$O$_2$)$_2$ **2.81** (a) molecular (b) ionic (c) molecular (d) ionic **2.83** (a) dinitrogen monoxide (b) tetraphosphorus decoxide (c) arsenic trichloride (d) dichlorine heptoxide **2.85** (a) NBr$_3$ (b) XeO$_4$ (c) OF$_2$ (d) Cl$_2$O$_5$ **2.87** (a) selenium trioxide (b) disulfur dichloride (c) carbon monoxide **2.89** (a) bromic acid HBrO$_3$ (b) hyponitrous acid H$_2$N$_2$O$_2$ (c) disulfurous acid H$_2$S$_2$O$_5$ (d) arsenic acid H$_3$AsO$_4$ **2.91** sodium sulfate decahydrate **2.93** FeSO$_4$·7H$_2$O **2.95** 9 **2.97** (a) $Sn + 2NaOH \longrightarrow Na_2SnO_2 + H_2$ (b) $8Al + 3Fe_3O_4 \longrightarrow 4Al_2O_3 + 9Fe$ (c) $2CH_3OH + 3O_2 \longrightarrow 2CO_2 + 4H_2O$ (d) $P_4O_{10} + 6H_2O \longrightarrow 4H_3PO_4$ (e) $PCl_5 + 4H_2O \longrightarrow H_3PO_4 + 5HCl$ **2.99** $Ca_3(PO_4)_2(s) + 3H_2SO_4(aq) \longrightarrow 2H_3PO_4(aq) + 3CaSO_4(s)$

2.101 $2NH_4Cl(aq) + Ba(OH)_2(aq) \xrightarrow{\Delta} 2NH_3(g) + BaCl_2(aq) + 2H_2O(l)$

2.103 The ratio of O masses is 5 : 4 (B to A). **2.105** -1.6×10^{-19} C; 2, 4, 6, 7 **2.107** 63, 60 **2.109** $^{81}_{35}$Br$^-$ **2.111** Cu-63:0.6916, Cu-65:0.3084 **2.113** (a) bromine, Br (b) hydrogen, H (c) niobium, Nb (d) fluorine, F **2.115** (a) chromium(III) ion (b) lead(IV) ion (c) copper(I) ion (d) copper(II) ion **2.117** Na$_2$SO$_4$, NaCl, NiSO$_4$, NiCl$_2$ **2.119** (a) tin(II) phosphate (b) ammonium nitrite (c) magnesium hydroxide (d) chromium(II) sulfate **2.121** (a) Hg$_2$S (b) Co$_2$(SO$_3$)$_3$ (c) (NH$_4$)$_2$Cr$_2$O$_7$ (d) AlN **2.123** (a) arsenic tribromide (b) dihydrogen selenide (c) diphosphorus pentoxide (d) silicon dioxide **2.125** (a) $2C_2H_6 + 7O_2 \longrightarrow 4CO_2 + 6H_2O$

(b) $P_4O_6 + 6H_2O \longrightarrow 4H_3PO_3$ (c) $4KClO_3 \longrightarrow 3KClO_4 +$ KCl   (d) $(NH_4)_2SO_4 + 2NaOH \longrightarrow 2NH_3 + 2H_2O + Na_2SO_4$ (e) $2NBr_3 + 3NaOH \longrightarrow N_2 + 3NaBr + 3HOBr$ **2.127** 26, nickel **2.129** 12.507 amu   **2.143** 6.06×10^9 miles   **2.145** $NiSO_4 \cdot 7H_2O$, $NiSO_4 \cdot 6H_2O$, 4.826 g   **2.147** 0.8000 g, 63.54 amu, Cu

CHAPTER 3

3.19 (a) $3H_2(g) + N_2(g) \longrightarrow 2NH_3(g)$ (b) $H_2(g)$ (c) six molecules of H_2 **3.21** (a) unreasonable   (b) unreasonable (c) reasonable   (d) unreasonable   **3.23** (a) charcoal   (b) Mg (c) H_2 **3.25** (a) 1 mol Ca = 40.08 g Ca conversion factor correction   (b) 2 mol K^+ ions = 1 mol K_2SO_4 conversion factor correction   (c) 2 mol Na = 2 mol H_2O conversion factor correction   **3.27** (a) 32.0 amu   (b) 62.0 amu   (c) 138 amu (d) 366 amu   **3.29** (a) 64.1 amu   (b) 137 amu   **3.31** 80.05 g/mol **3.33** (a) 3.818×10^{-23} g/atom   (b) 2.326×10^{-23} g/atom (c) 8.383×10^{-23} g/molecule   (d) 5.390×10^{-22} g/unit **3.35** 1.231×10^{-22} g/molecule   **3.37** (a) 3.4 g Na   (b) 19.0 g S (c) 236 g CH_2Cl_2 (d) 2.60×10^3 g $(NH_4)_2S$ **3.39** 33.6 g **3.41** (a) 0.238 mol   (b) 9.94×10^{-2} mol   (c) 1.3 mol (d) 0.112 mol   **3.43** 5.81×10^{-3} mol $CaSO_4$; 1.16×10^{-2} mol H_2O; for every mole of $CaSO_4$ there are two moles of H_2O. **3.45** (a) 7.12×10^{23} atoms   (b) 2.41×10^{23} atoms   (c) 1.6×10^{24} molecules   (d) 3.75×10^{23} units   (e) 6.59×10^{22} SO_4^{2-} ions   **3.47** 2.97×10^{19} molecules   **3.49** 86.27%   **3.51** 20.2% **3.53** 0.581 kg   **3.55** 72.3% Al, 27.7% Mg   **3.57** (a) 42.9% C, 57.1% O   (b) 27.3% C, 72.7% O   (c) 19.2% Na, 1.68% H, 25.8% P, 53.3% O   (d) 32.2% Co, 15.3% N, 52.5% O **3.59** 91.2% C, 8.8% H   **3.61** Ethanol   **3.63** 38.7% C, 9.79% H, 51.5% O   **3.65** OsO_4 **3.67** K_2MnO_4 **3.69** $C_3H_4O_2$ **3.71** (a) CH   (b) C_4H_4, C_6H_6 **3.73** $C_4H_{12}N_2$ **3.75** $C_2H_2O_4$ **3.77** C_2H_4 + $3O_2$ $\longrightarrow$

    1 molecule C_2H_4 +   3 molecules O_2 $\longrightarrow$
    1 mole C_2H_4 +   3 molecules O_2 $\longrightarrow$
    28.054 g C_2H_4 + 3×32.00 g O_2 $\longrightarrow$

           $2CO_2$ + $2H_2O$
        2 molecules CO_2 +   2 molecules H_2O
        2 moles CO_2 +   2 moles H_2O
        2×44.01 g CO_2 + 2×18.016 g H_2O

3.79 1.2 mol CO_2 **3.81** 5.87 mol O_2 **3.83** 8.21 g NO_2 **3.85** 1.46×10^5 g W   **3.87** 22.4 g CS_2 **3.89** 7.563 g NO_2 **3.91** KO_2 is the limiting reactant; 0.19 moles of oxygen **3.93** 40.5 g CH_3OH; H_2 remains; 5.1 g H_2 **3.95** 9.07 g **3.97** 2.61 g is the theoretical yield; 71.3%   **3.99** 49.5% C, 5.19% H, 28.9% N, 16.5% O   **3.101** $C_6H_4Cl_2$ **3.103** C_4H_4S, C_4H_4S **3.105** 84.2%   **3.107** 59.5%   **3.109** 60.3 g   **3.111** 2.97×10^3 g CaC_2 **3.113** 16.2%   **3.127** 0.21 g CuO   **3.129** 616 amu **3.131** Ag and Cl   **3.133** 1.45×10^{26} Fe atoms

CHAPTER 4

4.21 (a) Any soluble salt that will form a precipitate when reacted with Ag^+ ions in solution will work; for example, $CaCl_2$, Na_2S, and $(NH_4)_2CO_3$.   (b) No precipitate would form.   (c) You would underestimate the amount of silver present in the solution. **4.23** (a) $3Ca(C_2H_3O_2)_2(aq) + 2(NH_4)_3PO_4(aq) \longrightarrow$
$\qquad\qquad\qquad Ca_3(PO_4)_2(s) + 6NH_4C_2H_3O_2(aq)$
(b) $3Ca^{2+}(aq) + 6C_2H_3O_2^-(aq) + 6NH_4^+(aq) + 2PO_4^{3-}(aq)$
$\qquad \longrightarrow Ca_3(PO_4)_2(s) + 6NH_4^+(aq) + 6C_2H_3O_2^-(aq)$

(c) $3Ca^{2+}(aq) + 2PO_4^{3-}(aq) \longrightarrow Ca_3(PO_4)_2(s)$ **4.25** Probably not, because the ionic compound that is a nonelectrolyte is not soluble.   **4.27** (a) Cl^- (b) 0.50 M Br^-, 2.0 M K^+, 0.50 M PO_4^{3-} **4.29** (a) insoluble   (b) soluble   (c) soluble (d) soluble   **4.31** (a) insoluble   (b) soluble; Li^+, SO_4^{2-} (c) insoluble   (d) soluble; Na^+, CO_3^{2-} **4.33** (a) $H^+(aq) + OH^-(aq) \longrightarrow H_2O(l)$ (b) $Ag^+(aq) + Br^-(aq) \longrightarrow AgBr(s)$ (c) $S^{2-}(aq) + 2H^+(aq) \longrightarrow H_2S(g)$ (d) $OH^-(aq) + NH_4^+(aq) \longrightarrow NH_3(g) + H_2O(l)$ **4.35** $Pb(NO_3)_2(aq) + Na_2SO_4(aq) \longrightarrow PbSO_4(s) + 2NaNO_3(aq)$; $Pb^{2+}(aq) + SO_4^{2-}(aq) \longrightarrow PbSO_4(s)$ **4.37** (a) $FeSO_4(aq) + NaCl(aq) \longrightarrow NR$ (b) $Na_2CO_3(aq) + MgBr_2(aq) \longrightarrow MgCO_3(s) + 2NaBr(aq)$; $CO_3^{2-}(aq) + Mg^{2+}(aq) \longrightarrow MgCO_3(s)$ (c) $MgSO_4(aq) + 2NaOH(aq) \longrightarrow Mg(OH)_2(s) + Na_2SO_4(aq)$; $Mg^{2+}(aq) + 2OH^-(aq) \longrightarrow Mg(OH)_2(s)$ (d) $NiCl_2(aq) + NaBr(aq) \longrightarrow NR$ **4.39** (a) $Ba(NO_3)_2(aq) + Li_2SO_4(aq) \longrightarrow$
$\qquad\qquad\qquad\qquad BaSO_4(s) + 2LiNO_3(aq)$;
$Ba^{2+}(aq) + SO_4^{2-}(aq) \longrightarrow BaSO_4(s)$
(b) $NaBr(aq) + Ca(NO_3)_2(aq) \longrightarrow NR$
(c) $Al_2(SO_4)_3(aq) + 6NaOH(aq) \longrightarrow$
$\qquad\qquad\qquad\qquad 2Al(OH)_3(s) + 3Na_2SO_4(aq)$;
$Al^{3+}(aq) + 3OH^-(aq) \longrightarrow Al(OH)_3(s)$
(d) $3CaBr_2(aq) + 2Na_3PO_4(aq) \longrightarrow Ca_3(PO_4)_2(s) + 6NaBr(aq)$;
$3Ca^{2+}(aq) + 2PO_4^{3-}(aq) \longrightarrow Ca_3(PO_4)_2(s)$
4.41 (a) weak acid   (b) strong base   (c) strong acid
(d) weak acid
4.43 (a) $NaOH(aq) + HNO_3(aq) \longrightarrow NaNO_3(aq) + H_2O(l)$;
$H^+(aq) + OH^-(aq) \longrightarrow H_2O(l)$
(b) $2HCl(aq) + Ba(OH)_2(aq) \longrightarrow 2H_2O(l) + BaCl_2(aq)$;
$H^+(aq) + OH^-(aq) \longrightarrow H_2O(l)$
(c) $2HC_2H_3O_2(aq) + Ca(OH)_2(aq) \longrightarrow$
$\qquad\qquad\qquad Ca(C_2H_3O_2)_2(aq) + 2H_2O(l)$;
$HC_2H_3O_2(aq) + OH^-(aq) \longrightarrow H_2O(l) + C_2H_3O_2^-(aq)$
(d) $NH_3(aq) + HNO_3(aq) \longrightarrow NH_4NO_3(aq)$;
$H^+(aq) + NH_3(aq) \longrightarrow NH_4^+(aq)$
4.45 (a) $2HBr(aq) + Ca(OH)_2(aq) \longrightarrow CaBr_2(aq) + 2H_2O(l)$;
$H^+(aq) + OH^-(aq) \longrightarrow H_2O(l)$
(b) $Al(OH)_3(s) + 3HNO_3(aq) \longrightarrow Al(NO_3)_3(aq) + 3H_2O(l)$;
$3H^+(aq) + Al(OH)_3(s) \longrightarrow 3H_2O(l) + Al^{3+}(aq)$
(c) $2HCN(aq) + Ca(OH)_2(aq) \longrightarrow Ca(CN)_2(aq) + 2H_2O(l)$;
$HCN(aq) + OH^-(aq) \longrightarrow H_2O(l) + CN^-(aq)$
(d) $LiOH(aq) + HCN(aq) \longrightarrow H_2O(l) + LiCN(aq)$;
$HCN(aq) + OH^-(aq) \longrightarrow H_2O(l) + CN^-(aq)$
4.47 (a) $2KOH(aq) + H_3PO_4(aq) \longrightarrow 2H_2O(l) + K_2HPO_4(aq)$;
$H_3PO_4(aq) + 2OH^-(aq) \longrightarrow 2H_2O(l) + HPO_4^{2-}(aq)$
(b) $3H_2SO_4(aq) + 2Al(OH)_3(s) \longrightarrow Al_2(SO_4)_3(aq) + 6H_2O(l)$;
$3H^+(aq) + Al(OH)_3(s) \longrightarrow Al^{3+}(aq) + 3H_2O(l)$
(c) $2HC_2H_3O_2(aq) + Ca(OH)_2(aq) \longrightarrow$
$\qquad\qquad\qquad 2H_2O(l) + Ca(C_2H_3O_2)_2(aq)$;
$HC_2H_3O_2(aq) + OH^-(aq) \longrightarrow H_2O(l) + C_2H_3O_2^-(aq)$
(d) $H_2SO_3(aq) + NaOH(aq) \longrightarrow NaHSO_3(aq) + H_2O(l)$;
$H_2SO_3(aq) + OH^-(aq) \longrightarrow HSO_3^-(aq) + H_2O(l)$
4.49 $2H_2SO_3(aq) + Ca(OH)_2(aq) \longrightarrow Ca(HSO_3)_2(aq) + 2H_2O(l)$;
$Ca(HSO_3)_2(aq) + Ca(OH)_2(aq) \longrightarrow 2CaSO_3(s) + 2H_2O(l)$;
$H_2SO_3(aq) + OH^-(aq) \longrightarrow H_2O(l) + HSO_3^-(aq)$;
$Ca^2(aq) + HSO_3^-(aq) + OH^-(aq) \longrightarrow CaSO_3(s) + H_2O(l)$

4.51 (a) $CaS(s) + 2HBr(aq) \longrightarrow CaBr_2(aq) + H_2S(g)$;
$CaS(s) + 2H^+(aq) \longrightarrow Ca^{2+}(aq) + H_2S(g)$
(b) $MgCO_3(s) + 2HNO_3(aq) \longrightarrow$
$\qquad CO_2(g) + H_2O(l) + Mg(NO_3)_2(aq)$;
$2H^+(aq) + MgCO_3(s) \longrightarrow CO_2(g) + H_2O(l) + Mg^{2+}(aq)$
(c) $K_2SO_3(aq) + H_2SO_4(aq) \longrightarrow$
$\qquad SO_2(g) + H_2O(l) + K_2SO_4(aq)$;
$2H^+(aq) + SO_3^{2-}(aq) \longrightarrow SO_2(g) + H_2O(l)$
4.53 $FeS(s) + 2HCl(aq) \longrightarrow H_2S(g) + FeCl_2(aq)$;
$FeS(s) + 2H^+(aq) \longrightarrow Fe^{2+}(aq) + H_2S(g)$　**4.55** (a) +3
(b) +4　(c) +7　(d) +6　**4.57** (a) −3　(b) +5　(c) +3
(d) +7　**4.59** (a) Mn: +2, Cl: +5, O: −2　(b) Fe: +3,
Cr: +6, O: −2　(c) Hg: +2, Cr: +6, O: −2　(d) Co: +2,
P: +5, O: −2
4.61 (a) $\quad P_4(s) \quad + \quad 5O_2(g) \longrightarrow P_4O_{10}(s)$
$\qquad\quad$reducing$\quad$ oxidizing
$\qquad\qquad$agent$\qquad\quad$agent

(b) $\quad Co(s) \quad + \quad Cl_2(g) \quad \longrightarrow CoCl_2(s)$
$\qquad$reducing$\qquad$oxidizing
$\qquad\quad$agent$\qquad\qquad$agent

4.63 (a) $\quad 2Al(s) \quad + \quad 3F_2(g) \longrightarrow 2AlF_3(s)$
$\qquad\quad$reducing$\qquad$oxidizing
$\qquad\qquad$agent$\qquad\qquad$agent

(b) $\quad Hg^{2+}(aq) + NO_2^-(aq) + H_2O(l) \longrightarrow$
$\qquad$oxidizing$\qquad$reducing
$\qquad\quad$agent$\qquad\qquad$agent

4.65 (a) $3CuCl_2(aq) + 2Al(s) \longrightarrow 2AlCl_3(aq) + 3Cu(s)$
(b) $2Cr^{3+}(aq) + 3Zn(s) \longrightarrow 2Cr(s) + 3Zn^{2+}(aq)$　**4.67** 2.05 M
4.69 0.101 M　**4.71** 1.25 L　**4.73** 35.8 mL　**4.75** 2.9×10^{-4}
mol (2 sig. fig.)　**4.77** 0.66 g　**4.79** 7.6 mL　**4.81** 0.429 M Ca^{2+};
0.671 M K^+; 1.528 M Cl^-　**4.83** 0.302 g; 65.9%
4.85 (a) 35.81%　(b) CuCl　**4.87** $FeCl_2$　**4.89** 53.8 mL nitric
acid　**4.91** 325 mL　**4.93** 3.19%
4.95 $Mg(s) + 2HBr(aq) \longrightarrow H_2(g) + MgBr_2(aq)$;
$Mg(s) + 2H^+(aq) \longrightarrow H_2(g) + Mg^{2+}(aq)$
4.97 $NiSO_4(aq) + 2LiOH(aq) \longrightarrow Ni(OH)_2(s) + Li_2SO_4(aq)$;
$Ni^{2+}(aq) + 2OH^-(aq) \longrightarrow Ni(OH)_2(s)$
4.99 (a) $LiOH(aq) + HCN(aq) \longrightarrow H_2O(l) + LiCN(aq)$;
$OH^-(aq) + HCN(aq) \longrightarrow H_2O(l) + CN^-(aq)$
(b) $Li_2CO_3(aq) + 2HNO_3(aq) \longrightarrow$
$\qquad 2LiNO_3(aq) + H_2O(l) + CO_2(g)$
$CO_3^{2-}(aq) + 2H^+(aq) \longrightarrow H_2O(l) + CO_2(g)$
(c) $LiCl(aq) + AgNO_3(aq) \longrightarrow LiNO_3(aq) + AgCl(s)$
$Cl^-(aq) + Ag^+(aq) \longrightarrow AgCl(s)$
(d) $LiCl(aq) + MgSO_4(aq) \longrightarrow NR$
4.101 (a) $Sr(OH)_2(aq) + 2HC_2H_3O_2(aq) \longrightarrow$
$\qquad Sr(C_2H_3O_2)_2(aq) + 2H_2O(l)$;
$OH^-(aq) + HC_2H_3O_2(aq) \longrightarrow H_2O(l) + C_2H_3O_2^-(aq)$
(b) $NH_4I(aq) + CsCl(aq) \longrightarrow NR$
(c) $NaNO_3(aq) + CsCl(aq) \longrightarrow NR$
(d) $NH_4I(aq) + AgNO_3(aq) \longrightarrow AgI(s) + NH_4NO_3(aq)$
$I^-(aq) + Ag^+(aq) \longrightarrow AgI(s)$
4.103 (a) $BaCl_2(aq) + CuSO_4(aq) \longrightarrow BaSO_4(s) + CuCl_2(aq)$;
$BaSO_4$ is filtered off, and the solution evaporated to give solid
$CuCl_2$
(b) $CaCO_3(s) + 2HC_2H_3O_2(aq) \longrightarrow$
$\qquad CO_2(g) + H_2O(l) + Ca(C_2H_3O_2)_2(aq)$;
evaporate H_2O to leave $Ca(C_2H_3O_2)_2(s)$
(c) $Na_2SO_3(s) + 2HNO_3(aq) \longrightarrow$
$\qquad SO_2(g) + H_2O(l) + 2NaNO_3(aq)$;
evaporate H_2O to leave $NaNO_3(s)$

(d) $Mg(OH)_2(s) + 2HCl(aq) \longrightarrow 2H_2O(l) + MgCl_2(aq)$;
evaporate H_2O to leave $MgCl_2(s)$
4.105 (a) decomposition　(b) decomposition　(c) combination
(d) displacement　**4.107** (a) $Pb(NO_3)_2 + Ba(OH)_2$, $Pb(NO_3)_2 +$
H_2SO_4, $Pb(NO_3)_2 + MgSO_4$　(b) $Ba(OH)_2 + MgSO_4$
(c) $Ba(OH)_2 + H_2SO_4$　**4.109** 0.0405 M $CaCl_2$, 0.0405 M Ca^{2+},
0.0811 M Cl^-　**4.111** 329 mL　**4.113** 0.610 M　**4.115** 0.0967 M
4.117 21.30%　**4.119** $CuSO_4 \cdot 2H_2O$　**4.121** 35.0% Cl, $AuCl_3$
4.123 9.66%　**4.135** $Pb(NO_3)_2$; Cs_2SO_4;
$Pb(NO_3)_2(aq) + Cs_2SO_4(aq) \longrightarrow PbSO_4(s) + 2CsNO_3(aq)$;
$Pb^{2+}(aq) + SO_4^{2-}(aq) \longrightarrow PbSO_4(s)$;
lead(II) sulfate; cesium nitrate;
$Pb(NO_3)_2(aq) + Na_2SO_4(aq) \longrightarrow PbSO_4(s) + 2NaNO_3(aq)$
4.137 $CaBr_2(aq) + Cl_2(g) \longrightarrow Br_2(l) + CaCl_2(aq)$;
$2Br^-(aq) + Cl_2(g) \longrightarrow Br_2(l) + 2Cl^-(aq)$; 5.67×10^3 g
4.139 $Hg(NO_3)_2(aq) + H_2S(g) \longrightarrow 2HNO_3(aq) + HgS(s)$.
$Hg^{2+}(aq) + H_2S(aq) \longrightarrow 2H^+(aq) + HgS(s)$, strong acid, nitric
acid, mercury(II) sulfide, 581.5 g　**4.141** Fe^{2+}:Fe^{3+} 5:2
4.143 0.0121 L　**4.145** 0.930 mol/L　**4.147** 69.72 g/mol, gallium
4.149 $P_4O_{10} + 6H_2O \longrightarrow 4H_3PO_4$; 55.7 g P_4O_{10}　**4.151** 85.23%
4.153 0.194 L　**4.155** 61.7%

CHAPTER 5

5.29 (a) At constant volume, the pressure of a gas is directly
proportional to temperature ($P \propto T$).　(b) At constant volume, the
pressure of a gas is directly proportional to temperature ($P \propto T$).
(c) The vapor pressure of the H_2O increases with increasing
temperature (Table 5.6).　(d) At constant temperature, the
pressure of a gas is inversely proportional to the volume ($P \propto 1/V$).
5.31 (a) increase by 2　(b) decrease by 2　(c) increase by 1.5
(d) P no change; V increase by 2　**5.33** (a) O_2　(b) H_2
(c) Both the same　(d) There will be no pressure change.
(e) 1/4　**5.35** Double the kelvin temperature or reduce the pressure by 1/2.　**5.37** 36 mmHg　**5.39** 2.32 L　**5.41** 1.02×10^3 L
5.43 3.64×10^{-4} kPa　**5.45** 3.68 mL　**5.47** 0.65 L　**5.49** 240 K
5.51 31.6 mL　**5.53** 1 volume　**5.55** $PV = nRT$; $V = nRT/P$;
if temperature and moles remain constant, $V = $ constant $\times 1/P$
5.57 8.02 atm　**5.59** 22.0 L　**5.61** 143°C　**5.63** 0.675 g/L
5.65 2.14 g/L　**5.67** 47.7 amu　**5.69** 3.20×10^2 amu　**5.71** At
the same temperature and pressure, gas density depends on molecular mass or average molecular mass of a mixture. Thus, the density
of a gas of NH_4Cl would be greater than that of a mixture of NH_3
and HCl, since NH_3 and HCl have lower molecular masses than
NH_4Cl.　**5.73** 1.4 L　**5.75** 160. L　**5.77** 247 L
5.79 $2NH_3(g) + H_2SO_4(aq) \longrightarrow (NH_4)_2SO_4(aq)$; 46.7 L
5.81 0.279 atm　**5.83** $P(O_2) = 3.80 \times 10^{-3}$ atm; P(He) = 0.017
atm; P(total) = 0.020 atm　**5.85** $P(CO_2) = 494$ mmHg; $P(H_2) =$
190. mmHg; P(HCl) = 41 mmHg; P(HF) = 21 mmHg; $P(SO_2) =$
13 mmHg; $P(H_2S) = 0.8$ mmHg　**5.87** 6.34 g　**5.89** At $T = 298$
K, $u = 5.15 \times 10^2$ m/s; at $T = 398$ K, $u = 5.95 \times 10^2$ m/s; graph
as in Figure 5.25.　**5.91** 1.53×10^2 m/s　**5.93** 6.50×10^3 K
(6.23×10^3°C)　**5.95** rate N_2/rate $O_2 = 1.069$　**5.97** 3.5 s
5.99 146 amu　**5.101** 0.9605 atm (0.9716 atm from ideal gas law)
5.103 At 1.00 atm: 22.4 L from ideal gas law, 22.2 L from van der
Waals equation; at 10.0 atm: 2.24 L from ideal gas law, 2.08 L from
van der Waals equation.　**5.105** 80.7 cm³　**5.107** 181 mL
5.109 6.5 dm³　**5.111** 3.01×10^{20} atoms　**5.113** 28.979 amu
5.115 1.2×10^3 g LiOH　**5.117** 20.4 atm　**5.119** 0.440 M

5.121 H_2SO_4 **5.123** $-23°C$ **5.125** 1.0043   **5.127** 28.07 g/mol
5.129 $P(O_2) = 0.167$ atm; $P(CO_2) = 0.333$ atm   **5.145** 0.732 g/L
5.147 0.194 g Na_2O_2 **5.149** 76% $CaCO_3$, 24% $MgCO_3$
5.151 8.81 g/L   **5.153** 3.00×10^2 m/s

CHAPTER 6

6.31 small car   **6.33** (a) negative   (b) solid   (c) higher than
final enthalpy   (d) $-20°C$ **6.35** $\Delta H = \Delta H_f - \Delta H_{vap}$
6.37 (a) A   (b) A   **6.39** Equate ΔH for the burning to ΔH_f
(products) minus ΔH_f (reactants), then solve for ΔH_f of P_4S_3. You
will need ΔH_f of P_4O_{10} and SO_2.   **6.41** -106.4 kcal
6.43 7.1×10^5 J, 1.7×10^5 cal   **6.45** 5.24×10^{-21} J/molecule
6.47 positive; cold   **6.49** endothermic; $+66.2$ kJ
6.51 $Fe(s) + 2HCl(aq) \longrightarrow FeCl_2(aq) + H_2(g)$; $\Delta H = -89.1$ kJ
6.53 $+3.010 \times 10^3$ kJ   **6.55** -385 kJ   **6.57** -1.90 kJ/g
6.59 -6.66×10^2 kJ   **6.61** 7.96 g   **6.63** 5.8×10^4 J
6.65 5.81°C   **6.67** 20.5 kJ   **6.69** -1.36×10^3 kJ   **6.71** 50.6 kJ
6.73 -906.3 kJ   **6.75** -137 kJ   **6.77** $+42.3$ kJ
6.79 -1124.2 kJ   **6.81** -23.5 kJ   **6.83** -74.9 kJ   **6.85** 13.9 kJ
6.87 kg·m²/s²   **6.89** 1.59×10^3 J/g   **6.91** 226 J, 31.6 m/s
6.93 37.9 kJ   **6.95** -255 kJ/mol   **6.97** 37.4°C   **6.99** 0.128 J/g°C
6.101 0.383 J/g°C   **6.103** 25.6°C   **6.105** -23.6 kJ/mol
6.107 -874.2 kJ/mol   **6.109** -21 kJ   **6.111** 206.2 kJ
6.113 178 kJ   **6.115** -39.7 kJ   **6.117** -2225 kJ/mol
6.119 35.5 g   **6.133** 37.4°C   **6.135** -22 kJ   **6.137** 30.3 g CO,
40.4 g CO_2 **6.139** 113 kJ   **6.141** (a) 1.88 kJ   (b) 11.9%
6.143 1.07×10^3 g LiOH

CHAPTER 7

7.25 frequency-doubled beam   **7.27** one   **7.29** x **7.31** (a)
7.33 (a) $n = 3$ to $n = 2$ (b) $n = 3$ to $n = 5$ (c) green
7.35 219.6 m   **7.37** 6.27×10^{14}/s   **7.39** 1.9×10^2 s
7.41 $6.057802106 \times 10^{-7}$ m, 4.949×10^{14}/s   **7.43** $9.044 \times$
10^{-28} J   **7.45** 3.72×10^{-19} J   **7.47** just barely; red
7.49 2.34×10^{14}/s   **7.51** 1.22×10^{-7} m, near UV   **7.53** 93.9 nm
7.55 4.699×10^{-19} J   **7.57** 95.4 pm   **7.59** 7.28×10^7 m/s
7.61 1.52×10^{-22} pm, much smaller   **7.63** $l = 0, 1, 2, 3$; $m_l =$
$-3, -2, -1, 0, 1, 2, 3$ **7.65** 3, 7   **7.67** (a) $6d$ (b) $5g$ (c) $4f$
(d) $6p$ **7.69** (a) m_s can be only $+\frac{1}{2}$ or $-\frac{1}{2}$ (b) l can be only as
large as $n - 1$ (c) m_l cannot exceed $+2$ in magnitude
(d) n cannot be 0   (e) m_s can be only $+\frac{1}{2}$ or $-\frac{1}{2}$
7.71 6.51×10^{14}/s, 4.31×10^{-19} J   **7.73** 485 nm, blue-green
7.75 6.55×10^{14}/s   **7.77** 5.59×10^5 m/s   **7.79** 4.35×10^{-7} m
7.81 7   **7.83** 1.64×10^{-7} m; near UV   **7.85** 1.50×10^4 eV
7.87 (a) five   (b) seven   (c) three   (d) one   **7.89** $6s, 6p, 6d$,
$6f, 6g, 6h$ **7.107** 5.01×10^{-7} m   **7.109** 5.26×10^{28}
7.111 3.60×10^{-19} J, 2.16×10^2 kJ/mol   **7.113** 1.94×10^{-11} m

CHAPTER 8

8.31 $1s^1$, $1s^2$, $1s^3$, $1s^4$, $1s^42s^1$, $1s^42s^2$ **8.33** Sr, Y   **8.35** Z would
form a cation of charge $2+$.   **8.37** Ge, Sn   **8.39** IIA
8.41 (a) not allowed; $2p$ electrons should have opposite spins.
(b) allowed; $1s^22s^22p^4$ (c) not allowed; $1s$ electrons should have
opposite spins.   (d) not allowed; $2s$ can hold only two electrons.
8.43 (a) impossible; $2p$ subshell can hold no more than six
electrons.   (b) impossible; $3s$ subshell can hold no more than two
electrons.   (c) possible   (d) possible

8.45 (orbital diagram)

8.47 $1s^22s^22p^63s^23p^63d^{10}4s^24p^64d^{10}5s^25p^5$ **8.49** $1s^22s^22p^63s^2$
$3p^63d^54s^2$ **8.51** $4s^24p^5$ **8.53** $4d^25s^2$ **8.55** Group IIIA,
period = 6, main-group element

8.57 [Ar] (orbital diagram) $3d$ $4s$

8.59 (orbital diagram) $1s$ $2s$ $2p$ $3s$ $3p$ $4s$
Paramagnetic
8.61 S, Se, As   **8.63** Na, Al, Cl, Ar   **8.65** (a) Br   (b) F
8.67 $LiBrO_3$ **8.69** $1s^22s^22p^63s^23p^63d^{10}4s^24p^65s^2$ **8.71** $6s^26p^4$

8.73 (orbital diagram) $1s$ $2s$ $2p$ $3s$ $3p$ $3d$
$4s$ $4p$

8.75 $[Rn]5f^{14}6d^{10}7s^27p^2$, metal, eka-PbO or eka-PbO$_2$
8.77 370 kJ/mol

8.79 [Kr] (orbital diagram) $4d$ $5s$

8.81 (a) Cl_2 (b) Na   (c) Sb   (d) Ar
8.83 $1s^22s^22p^63s^23p^63d^34s^2$, Group VB, Period 4, d-block transition element   **8.101** $Ba(s) + 2H_2O(l) \longrightarrow H_2(g) + Ba(OH)_2(aq)$;
447 mL   **8.103** RaO, 93.4% Ra   **8.105** 108 J
8.107 1.312×10^3 kJ/mol H   **8.109** -639 kJ/mol

CHAPTER 9

9.25 XY_3 **9.27** Blue ion is cation; blue atom is metal.   **9.29** b
9.31 (a) Bond Cl and H to C.   (b) Bond O atoms to N, then bond
H to one O.   (c) Bond O and F to N.   (d) Place N atoms in center
with two O atoms bonded to each N.   **9.33** (a) Ca_3X_2 (b) ionic
9.35 (a) $\cdot\ddot{P}\cdot$ (b) $[:\ddot{P}:]^{3-}$ (c) $\cdot\dot{G}a\cdot$ (d) Ga^{3+}

9.37 (a) $:\ddot{Br}\cdot + \cdot Ca \cdot + \cdot\ddot{Br}: \longrightarrow$

$[:\ddot{Br}:]^- + Ca^{2+} + [:\ddot{Br}:]^-$

(b) $K\cdot + \cdot\ddot{I}: \longrightarrow K^+ + [:\ddot{I}:]^-$

9.39 (a) $1s^22s^22p^63s^23p^63d^{10}4s^24p^3$, $:\ddot{As}\cdot$
(b) $1s^22s^22p^63s^23p^63d^{10}4s^2$, $[\cdot\ddot{As}\cdot]^{3+}$
(c) $1s^22s^22p^63s^23p^63d^{10}4s^24p^4$, $:\ddot{Se}\cdot$
(d) $1s^22s^22p^63s^23p^63d^{10}4s^24p^6$, $[:\ddot{Se}:]^{2-}$
9.41 (a) $[Xe]4f^{14}5d^{10}6s^26p^3$ (b) $[Xe]4f^{14}5d^{10}6s^2$
9.43 (a) $[Ar]3d^8$ (b) $[Ar]3d^7$ **9.45** (a) Sr^{2+}, Sr; loss of valence
electrons in Sr makes Sr^{2+} smaller.   (b) Br, Br^-; electron repulsion makes Br^- larger.   **9.47** S^{2-}, Se^{2-}, Te^{2-}. The radius increases with increasing number of filled shells.   **9.49** Na^+, F^-,
N^{3-}. The ions are isoelectronic, so the atomic radius increases with
decreasing nuclear charge.

9.51 $2H\cdot$ + $:\!Se\cdot$ ⟶ $:\!Se\!:\!H$ (with H above) Bonding pairs / Lone pairs

9.53 $AsBr_3$ **9.55** (a) P, N, O (b) Na, Mg, Al (c) Al, Si, C

9.57 C—Cl, As—Br, P—O

9.59 $\delta+$ $\delta-$ $\delta+$ $\delta-$ $\delta+$ $\delta-$
P—O,   C—Cl,   As—Br

9.61 (a) $:\!Br\!-\!Br\!:$ (b) $H\!-\!\overset{..}{\underset{..}{S}}\!-\!H$

(c) $:\!\overset{..}{F}\!:\overset{..}{N}\!:\overset{..}{F}:$ with :F: above

9.63 (a) $:\!P\!\equiv\!P\!:$ (b) $:\!O\!=\!C\!-\!Br\!:$ with :Br: above

(c) $H\!-\!\overset{..}{O}\!-\!N\!=\!\overset{..}{O}:$

9.65 (a) $\left[:\!\overset{..}{Cl}\!-\!\overset{..}{O}\!:\right]^-$ (b) $\left[:\!\overset{..}{Cl}\!-\!\overset{..}{Sn}\!-\!\overset{..}{Cl}\!:\right]^-$ with :Cl: above

(c) $\left[:\!\overset{..}{S}\!-\!\overset{..}{S}\!:\right]^{2-}$

9.67 (a) $H\!-\!\overset{..}{O}\!-\!N$ (=O above, :O: below) ⟷ $H\!-\!\overset{..}{O}\!-\!N$ (O: above, =O below)

(b) $:\!\overset{..}{O}\!-\!S\!=\!\overset{..}{O}$ ⟷ $:\!\overset{..}{O}\!-\!S\!-\!\overset{..}{O}:$ ⟷ $\overset{..}{O}\!=\!S\!-\!\overset{..}{O}:$ (each with :O: below)

9.69 $H\!-\!\overset{\overset{H}{|}}{\underset{\underset{H}{|}}{C}}\!-\!N$ (=O above, O: below) ⟷ $H\!-\!\overset{\overset{H}{|}}{\underset{\underset{H}{|}}{C}}\!-\!N$ (O: above, =O below)

9.71 (a) $:\!\overset{..}{F}\!-\!Xe\!-\!\overset{..}{F}:$ (b) $:\!\overset{..}{F}\!-\!\overset{\overset{:F:}{|}}{Se}\!-\!\overset{..}{F}:$ with :F: below

(c) $:\!\overset{..}{F}\!-\!\overset{\overset{F}{|}\underset{F}{|}}{Te}\!-\!\overset{..}{F}:$ (F top and bottom both sides) (d) $\left[\overset{\overset{F}{|}\underset{F}{|}}{Xe}\!-\!F\right]^+$ (F's around)

9.73 (a) $:\!\overset{..}{Cl}\!-\!\overset{\overset{:Cl:}{|}}{B}\!-\!\overset{..}{Cl}:$ (b) $\left[:\!\overset{..}{Cl}\!-\!Tl\!-\!\overset{..}{Cl}\!:\right]^+$

(c) $:\!\overset{..}{Br}\!-\!Be\!-\!\overset{..}{Br}:$

9.75 (a) $\overset{..}{O}\!=\!\overset{\oplus}{O}\!-\!\overset{..\ominus}{O}:$ (b) $:\!\overset{\ominus}{C}\!=\!\overset{\oplus}{O}:$

(c) $H\!-\!\overset{..}{O}\!-\!\overset{\oplus}{N}$ (⊕ N with O: above, O: ⊖ below)

9.77 (a) $\overset{\overset{:O:}{\|}}{S}$ with :F: F: below (b) $\overset{\overset{:O:}{\|}}{S}$ with O, O, H, H below

(c) $\overset{..}{O}\!=\!\overset{..}{Cl}\!-\!\overset{..}{O}\!-\!H$

9.79 174 pm   **9.81** (a) 114 pm (b) 203 pm (c) 213 pm
(d) 183 pm   **9.83** 147 pm, methylamine; 116 pm, acetonitrile
9.85 -78 kJ   **9.87** (a) ionic, SrO, strontium oxide (b) covalent, CBr_4, carbon tetrabromide (c) ionic, GaF_3, gallium(III) fluoride
(d) covalent, NBr_3, nitrogen tribromide

9.89 $\left[:\!\overset{..}{O}\!-\!\overset{\overset{:O:}{|}}{\underset{\underset{:O:}{|}}{As}}\!-\!\overset{..}{O}\!:\right]^{3-}$ or $\left[:\!\overset{..}{O}\!-\!\overset{\overset{:O:}{\|}}{\underset{\underset{:O:}{|}}{As}}\!-\!\overset{..}{O}\!:\right]^{3-}$, $Pb_3(AsO_4)_2$

9.91 $H\!-\!\overset{..}{O}\!-\!\overset{\overset{}{\underset{\underset{:O:}{|}}{I}}}{}\!-\!\overset{..}{O}:$ or $H\!-\!\overset{..}{O}\!-\!\overset{\underset{\underset{:O:}{|}}{I}}{}\!=\!\overset{..}{O}$ **9.93** $\left[H\!-\!\overset{..}{N}\!-\!H\right]^-$

9.95 $\left[:\!\overset{..}{O}\!=\!N\!=\!\overset{..}{O}:\right]^+$ **9.97** (a) $:\!\overset{..}{Cl}\!-\!\overset{\overset{:O:}{|}}{Se}\!-\!\overset{..}{Cl}:$ or

$:\!\overset{..}{Cl}\!-\!\overset{\overset{:O:}{\|}}{Se}\!-\!\overset{..}{Cl}:$ (b) $:\!\overset{..}{Se}\!=\!C\!=\!\overset{..}{Se}:$

(c) $\left[:\!\overset{..}{Cl}\!-\!\overset{\overset{:Cl:}{|}}{\underset{\underset{:Cl:}{|}}{Ga}}\!-\!\overset{..}{Cl}:\right]^-$ (d) $\left[:\!C\!\equiv\!C\!:\right]^{2-}$

9.99 (a) $:\!\overset{..}{Cl}\!-\!\overset{\overset{}{\underset{\underset{:Cl:}{|}}{Sb}}}{}\!-\!\overset{..}{Cl}:$ (b) $:\!\overset{..}{I}\!-\!C\!\equiv\!N:$

(c) $:\!\overset{..}{Cl}\!-\!\overset{\overset{}{\underset{\underset{:Cl:}{|}}{I}}}{}\!-\!\overset{..}{Cl}:$ (d) $\overset{\overset{:F:\ \ :F:}{}}{\underset{\underset{:F:\ \ :F:}{}}{I}}\!-\!\overset{..}{F}:$

9.101 (a) $\overset{..}{O}\!=\!Se\!-\!\overset{..}{O}:$ ⟷ $:\!\overset{..}{O}\!-\!Se\!=\!\overset{..}{O}$ ⟷ $\overset{..}{O}\!=\!Se\!=\!\overset{..}{O}$

(b) $\overset{\overset{:O}{}}{:O}N\!-\!N\overset{\overset{O:}{}}{:O}$ ⟷ (resonance structures) ⟷ ⟷ (four resonance forms shown)

9.103 $:\!N\overset{\overset{S}{}}{\underset{\underset{S}{}}{}}N\!:$ ⟷ $:\!N\overset{\overset{S}{}}{\underset{\underset{S}{}}{}}N\!:$ ⟷

$:\!N\overset{\overset{S}{}}{\underset{\underset{S}{}}{}}N\!:$ ⟷ $:\!N\overset{\overset{S}{}}{\underset{\underset{S}{}}{}}N\!:$

None of the resonance forms has formal charges of zero for all atoms.

9.105

The outer N—O bonds are 118 pm, and the inner N—O bonds are 136 pm. **9.107** −134 kJ **9.109** −1.60 × 10² kJ **9.127** $H_3PO_3(aq) + 2NaOH(aq) \longrightarrow Na_2HPO_3(aq) + 2H_2O(l)$, 0.007031 M **9.129** $Mg(ClO_4)_2$, magnesium perchlorate, Mg^{2+}, and

9.131

9.133 261 amu; the compound is volatile, so is molecular;

9.135 1273 kJ/mol; 862 kJ/mol compared to table value of 887 kJ/mol **9.137** 3.4 **9.139** 3.47

CHAPTER 10

10.23 (a) ii (b) i (c) iv (d) iii **10.25** Repulsion of bonding pairs is no longer balanced by C—C bond, so molecule flattens to trigonal planar geometry. **10.27** (a) i (b) iii (c) iv (d) v **10.29**

10.31 a is (ii), b is (iv), c is (i) **10.33** (a) tetrahedral (b) angular (c) trigonal planar (d) trigonal pyramidal **10.35** (a) trigonal pyramidal (b) tetrahedral (c) linear (d) trigonal pyramidal **10.37** (a) 109°; same (b) 109°; less (c) 120°; the Cl—C—Cl bond angle should be less (d) 109°; less **10.39** (a) trigonal bipyramidal (b) T-shaped (c) square pyramidal (d) distorted tetrahedral **10.41** (a) trigonal bipyramidal (b) octahedral (c) linear (d) square planar **10.43** (a) trigonal pyramidal and T-shaped (b) bent **10.45** CS_2 (linear) and XeF_4 (square planar) **10.47** (a) uses sp^3 orbitals (b) uses sp^3 orbitals **10.49** (a) sp^3 (b) sp^2 (c) sp (d) sp^2 **10.51** (a) Two single bonds and no lone pair on Hg suggests sp hybridization. An Hg—Cl bond is formed by overlapping an Hg hybrid orbital with a 3p orbital of Cl. (b) The presence of three single bonds and one lone pair on P suggests sp^3 hybridization. Each hybrid orbital overlaps a 3p orbital of a Cl atom to form a P—Cl bond. The fourth hybrid orbital contains a lone pair. **10.53** (a) sp^3d (b) sp^3d^2 (c) sp^3d (d) sp^3d

10.55 The P atom in $PCl_6{}^-$ has 6 single bonds around it and no lone pairs. This suggests sp^3d^2 hybridization. Each bond is a σ bond formed by overlap of an sp^3d^2 hybrid orbital on P with a 3p orbital on Cl. **10.57** (a) The C atom is bonded to three other atoms; therefore, we assume sp^2 hybrid orbitals. One 2p orbital remains unhybridized. Each carbon–hydrogen bond is a σ bond formed by the overlap of an sp^2 hybrid orbital on C with a 1s orbital on H. The remaining sp^2 hybrid orbital on C overlaps with a 2p orbital on O to form a σ bond. The unhybridized 2p orbital on C overlaps with a parallel 2p orbital on O to form a π bond. Together, the σ and π bonds describe the C=O bond. (b) The nitrogen atoms are sp hybridized, and a σ bond is formed by the overlap of an sp hybrid orbital from each N. The remaining sp hybrid orbitals contain lone pairs of electrons. The two unhybridized 2p orbitals on one N overlap with the unhybridized 2p orbitals on the other N to form two π bonds.

10.59

Each of the N atoms has a lone pair of electrons and is bonded to two atoms. The N atoms are sp^2 hybridized. The two possible arrangements of the oxygen atoms relative to one another are shown above. Since the π bond between the nitrogen atoms must be broken to interconvert these two forms, it is expected that the hyponitrite ion will exhibit *cis–trans* isomerization.
10.61 (a) $KK(\sigma_{2s})^2(\sigma^*_{2s})^2(\pi_{2p})^2$, bond order = 1, stable, paramagnetic (b) $KK(\sigma_{2s})^2(\sigma^*_{2s})^2(\pi_{2p})^1$, bond order = 1/2, stable, paramagnetic (c) $KK(\sigma_{2s})^2(\sigma^*_{2s})^2(\pi_{2p})^4(\sigma_{2p})^2(\pi^*_p)^3$, bond order = 3/2, stable, paramagnetic **10.63** $KK(\sigma_{2s})^2(\sigma^*_{2s})^2(\pi_{2p})^4(\sigma_{2p})^2$, bond order = 3, diamagnetic **10.65** (a) bent (b) trigonal planar (c) linear (d) octahedral **10.67** none **10.69** Left: Both carbon atoms with the double bonds are sp^2 hybridized. The carbon atom with the OH group is sp^3 hybridized. Right: Both carbon atoms are sp hybridized. **10.71** The *trans* isomer is expected to have a zero dipole moment, whereas the *cis* isomer is not. **10.73** The center carbon forms π bonds with its neighbors, which are perpendicular to each other. Each −CH₂ is perpendicular to the adjacent π bond and so must be perpendicular to each other. **10.75** $(\sigma_{1s})^2$, stable **10.77** $KK(\sigma_{2s})^2(\sigma^*_{2s})^2(\pi_{2p})^4(\sigma_{2p})^2$; 3 **10.79** $O_2{}^+$ has one less antibonding electron than O_2; $O_2{}^-$ has a longer bond because it has one more antibonding electron. **10.81** The N_2 ground state is $KK(\sigma_{2s})^2(\sigma^*_{2s})^2(\pi_{2p})^4(\sigma_{2p})^2$, the first excited state is $KK(\sigma_{2s})^2(\sigma^*_{2s})^2(\pi_{2p})^4(\sigma_{2p})^1(\pi^*_p)^1$. The transition decreases the bond order from 3 to 2, and the ground state is diamagnetic, whereas the excited state is paramagnetic.

10.99 XeO_3F_2;

trigonal bipyramidal, sp^3d hybrid
10.101 ClF_3; the Cl atom has sp^3d hybrid orbitals, giving three Cl—F bonds and two lone pairs. **10.103** (a) N_2: 110 pm, linear geometry, sp hybrids (b) N_2F_2: 122 pm, trigonal planar geometry, sp^2 hybrids (c) N_2H_4: 145 pm, tetrahedral geometry, sp^3 hybrids

10.105

trigonal planar geometry, sp^2 hybrids, $\Delta H_f^\circ = -40$ kJ/mol, resonance energy = 95 kJ

CHAPTER 11

11.27 (a) C   (b) A   (c) A   **11.29** The heat released when the liquid-to-solid phase change occurs prevents the fruit from freezing.   **11.31** (a) AB_2 (b) yes, body-centered cubic
11.33 The molecules with the higher kinetic energy evaporate, leaving behind the lower-energy molecules. Because the cup is insulated, the energy lost with the evaporated molecules is not rapidly replaced.   **11.35** (a) face-centered cubic   (b) simple cubic
11.37 (a) vaporization   (b) freezing of eggs and sublimation of ice   (c) condensation   (d) condensation (deposition)
(e) freezing   **11.39** 10°C   **11.41** 15.5 kJ/mol   **11.43** 1.58 kJ
11.45 1.25 g   **11.47** 27 g   **11.49** 3.00×10^2 mmHg
11.51 53.3 kJ/mol   **11.53** (a) gas   (b) gas   (c) liquid   (d) no
11.57 SO_2 and C_2H_2 can be liquefied at 25°C; to liquefy CH_4, reduce temperature below -82°C, then apply pressure greater than 46 atm; to liquefy CO, reduce temperature below -140°C, then apply pressure greater than 35 atm.   **11.59** (a) solid   (b) liquid
11.61 Values increase with molecular mass, as expected.
11.63 (a) London forces   (b) dipole–dipole forces, London forces, hydrogen bonding   (c) dipole–dipole forces, London forces   (d) London forces   **11.65** CCl_4, $SiCl_4$, $GeCl_4$
11.67 CCl_4; largest molecular mass and greatest London forces.
11.69 $HOCH_2CH_2OH$, FCH_2CH_2OH, FCH_2CH_2F; hydrogen bonding decreases in magnitude from left to right.   **11.71** CH_4, C_2H_6, CH_3OH, CH_2OHCH_2OH **11.73** (a) metallic   (b) metallic
(c) covalent network   (d) molecular   (e) ionic
11.75 (a) metallic   (b) covalent network   (c) molecular
(d) molecular   **11.77** $C_2H_5OC_2H_5$, C_4H_9OH, KCl, CaO
11.79 (a) low-melting, brittle   (b) high-melting, hard, and brittle
(c) malleable, electrically conducting   (d) high-melting, hard
11.81 (a) LiCl   (b) SiC   (c) CHI_3 (d) Co   **11.83** one
11.85 9.26×10^{-23} g; 9.274×10^{-23} g from AM   **11.87** 361 pm
11.89 4, fcc   **11.91** 19.25 g/cm³   **11.93** 1.72×10^{-23} cm³, 160 pm
11.95 Water vapor deposits as frost (deposition), frost melts (melting), liquid water evaporates (vaporization)   **11.97** 68.4%
11.99 80°C   **11.101** (a) condenses to liquid (and to solid at high pressure)   (b) condenses to solid   (c) remains a gas
11.103 Hydrogen bonds form between H atom of OH group on one molecule and O atom on another molecule.   **11.105** Hydrogen bonding between ethylene glycol molecules leads to higher boiling point and greater viscosity.   **11.107** Al, metallic; Si, covalent network; P, molecular; S, molecular.   **11.109** (a) KCl; smaller charges on ions   (b) CCl_4; lower molecular mass and smaller London forces   (c) Zn; Group IIB metal is lower melting
(d) C_2H_5Cl; no hydrogen bonding.   **11.111** 3.171×10^{-22} g, 191.0 amu   **11.113** 128 pm   **11.115** 68.0%   **11.117** (a) The boiling point increases with molecular size.   (b) Hydrogen bonding occurs between HF molecules.   (c) The hydrogen halides also have dipole–dipole interactions.   **11.119** (a) Diamond and silicon carbide are covalent network solids with strong covalent bonds; graphite is a layered structure with weak forces between

layers.   (b) Silicon dioxide is a covalent network solid; carbon dioxide is a small, discrete molecule.   **11.121** (a) CO_2 consists of nonpolar molecules; SiO_2 is a covalent network solid.   (b) HF has hydrogen bonding.   (c) SiF_4 is a larger molecule.   **11.143** 0.220 mol N_2, 0.01023 mol C_3H_8O, 0.0444, 33.1 mmHg, 33.1 mmHg
11.145 6.6 kJ   **11.147** 449 J   **11.149** 0.42 g monomer, 1.41 g dimer, 1.83 g/L

CHAPTER 12

12.27 There is not enough dissolved oxygen in the warm water to support trout, which need more O_2.   **12.29** The lattice energy must be less for the XZ compound.   **12.31** The charged smoke particles are neutralized by the electric current, which allows them to aggregate into large particles. These large particles are too big to be carried out the stack.   **12.33** Because the salt concentration outside the lettuce leaf is higher, water will pass out of the lettuce leaf into the dressing via osmosis.   **12.35** (a) $CaCl_2$ (b) urea
12.37 Aqueous ammonia   **12.39** Ethanol   **12.41** H_2O, CH_2OHCH_2OH, $C_{10}H_{22}$ **12.43** Al^{3+} **12.45** $Ba(IO_3)_2$, $Sr(IO_3)_2$, $Ca(IO_3)_2$, $Mg(IO_3)_2$. Because IO_3^- is large, the change in lattice energy in these iodates is small. Therefore, the hydration energy of the cation dominates the solubility trend.   **12.47** 0.886 g/100 mL
12.49 Dissolve 3.63 g KI in 68.9 g H_2O **12.51** 5.16 g
12.53 1.52 m **12.55** 77.7 g **12.57** 0.358, 0.642   **12.59** 0.0116
12.61 0.232, 16.8 m **12.63** 0.563 M **12.65** 0.796 m
12.67 41.6 mmHg, 0.631 mmHg   **12.69** $T_b = 100.042$°C, $T_f = -0.151$°C   **12.71** 4.6×10^{-2} m **12.73** 122 amu
12.75 163 amu   **12.77** 6.85×10^4 amu   **12.79** -0.042°C
12.81 $2.78 \approx 3$ **12.83** (a) aerosol   (b) sol   (c) foam   (d) sol
12.85 (c) $Al_2(SO_4)_3$ **12.87** 0.671 mol fraction N_2, 0.329 mol fraction O_2 **12.89** 1.74 m, 0.0303, 1.63 M **12.91** 24 g of propane, 31 g of butane   **12.93** 139 mmHg   **12.95** (a) 2.500×10^{-4} M (b) 5.000×10^{-4} M (c) 2.50×10^{-4} M
12.97 -21°C   **12.99** 0.30 M **12.101** 0.10 m $CaCl_2$
12.103 1.8 g/mL; 5.0×10^2 m **12.105** $Mn_2C_{10}O_{10}$
12.107 (a) $C_6H_{12}O_4$ (b) 148.2 g/mol   **12.109** 30. atm
12.125 $Ca^{2+}(aq) + CO_3^{2-}(aq) \longrightarrow CaCO_3(s)$, $2Ag^+(aq) + CO_3^{2-}(aq) \longrightarrow Ag_2CO_3(s)$, 0.0750 M CO_3^{2-}, 0.375 M Na^+, 0.225 M NO_3^- **12.127** -783 kJ/mol, -445 kJ/mol
12.129 0.565 m **12.131** 0.701 M **12.133** 3.1%
12.135 $C_3H_8O_3$

CHAPTER 13

13.29 (a) rate of depletion of A $= -\dfrac{\Delta [A]}{\Delta t}$ or rate of formation

of B $= +\dfrac{\Delta [B]}{\Delta t}$.   (b) No, the rate of depletion of A would be

faster than the rate of formation of B.   (c) $-\dfrac{\Delta [A]}{3\Delta t} = \dfrac{\Delta [B]}{2\Delta t}$

13.31 (a) rate $= k[A]^2$ (b) right   (c) right   (d) Left container rate is four times slower.   (e) right   **13.33** (a) $x = 0$ (b) $x = 1$
(c) $x = 3$ **13.35** (a) region C   (b) region A   **13.37** A number of answers will work as long as you match one of the existing concentrations of A. For example, $[A] = 2.0$ M with $[B] = 2.0$ M, or $[A] = 1.0$ M with $[B] = 2.0$ M.   **13.39** $-\frac{1}{2}\Delta[NO_2]/\Delta t = \Delta[O_2]/\Delta t$

13.41 $\frac{1}{5}\Delta[Br^-]/\Delta t = \Delta[BrO_3^-]/\Delta t$ **13.43** $2.3 \times 10^{-2}\ M/hr$
13.45 $1.2 \times 10^{-5}\ M/s$ **14.47** 1, 1, 2 **13.49** Orders with respect to MnO_4^-, $H_2C_2O_4$, and H^+ are 1, 1, 0, respectively. Overall order is 2. **13.51** rate $= k[CH_3NNCH_3]$, $k = 2.5 \times 10^{-4}/s$
13.53 rate $= k[NO]^2[H_2]$, $k = 2.9 \times 10^2/(M^2 \cdot s)$ **13.55** rate $= k[ClO_2]^2[OH^-]$, $k = 2.3 \times 10^2/(M^2 \cdot s)$ **13.57** $2.1 \times 10^{-2}\ M$
13.59 $8.79 \times 10^{-2}\ M$ **13.61** $5.2 \times 10^{-4}\ M$ **13.63** 1.1×10^3 s, 1.1×10^3 s, 2.2×10^3 s **13.65** 96 hr, 1.9×10^2 hr, 2.9×10^2 hr, 3.9×10^2 hr, 4.8×10^2 hr **13.67** 461 s **13.69** 2.6×10^2 hr
13.71 1.1 s **13.73** first-order, $k = 0.100/s$ **13.75** $E_a = 210$ kJ
13.77 1.0×10^5 J/mol, $1.7 \times 10^{-3}/s$ **13.79** 8.38×10^4 J/mol
13.81 1.1×10^2 kJ/mol **13.83** $NOCl_2$; $2NO + Cl_2 \longrightarrow 2NOCl$
13.85 (a) bimolecular (b) bimolecular (c) unimolecular
(d) termolecular **13.87** (a) rate $= k[O_3]$ (b) rate $= k[NOCl_2][NO]$ **13.89** rate $= k[C_3H_6]^2$ **13.91** rate $= (k_2k_1/k_{-1}) \times [H_2][I_2] = k[H_2][I_2]$ **13.93** $2H_2O_2 \longrightarrow 2H_2O + O_2$; Br^-; yes (BrO^-) **13.95** $3.5 \times 10^{-6}\ M/s$, $3.2 \times 10^{-6}\ M/s$, $2.5 \times 10^{-6}\ M/s$
13.97 average $k = 2.5 \times 10^{-4}/s$ **13.99** 8.33×10^3 s
13.101 5.50×10^3 s **13.103** 0.022 M **13.105** (a) 34 L/(mol·s); $8.2 \times 10^{-5}\ M$ **13.107** $4.7 \times 10^{-3}\ M$; 26 s **13.109** $2.5 \times 10^{-4}/s$
13.111 1.2×10^2 s; 68 s **13.113** 1.14×10^5 J/mol, 5×10^9, 14 M/s
13.115 rate $= k[NO_2][CO]$ **13.117** rate $= k[NO_2Br]$
13.119 rate $= (k_2k_1/k_{-1}) \times [NH_4^+][OCN^-] = k[NH_4^+][OCN^-]$
13.121 (a) rate $= k[NO]^2[O_2]$ (b) 0.12 mol/L·s
13.123 (a) i. decreases ii. decreases (b) i. increases ii. decreases
13.125 A catalyst provides another pathway with lower activation energy. **13.127** (a) Rate is the change in concentration with time. (b) It changes because the concentration of reactant changes. (c) It equals k when all reactants are 1.00 M. **13.141** 6.8 L
13.143 0.210 kJ/s **13.145** 6.60×10^{-8} mmHg/s

CHAPTER 14

14.19 $\frac{2}{3}x$ **14.21** a **14.23** (a) III (b) Both I and II shift right.
14.25 (a) shifts left (b) Concentrations of A and B increase; concentration of C decreases. **14.27** The amount of product at equilibrium is increased by increasing the pressure and decreasing the temperature. The rate of reaction is increased by increasing the temperature and using the proper catalyst. The choice of temperature is a compromise between equilibrium product concentration and rate of reaction. **14.29** 2.162 mol PCl_5, 0.338 mol PCl_3, 0.338 mol Cl_2
14.31 0.576 mol N_2, 1.728 mol H_2, 0.048 mol NH_3 **14.33** 0.0104 mol SO_2, 0.0052 mol O_2, 0.0296 mol SO_3

14.35 (a) $K_c = \dfrac{[NO_2][NO]}{[N_2O_3]}$

(b) $K_c = \dfrac{[H_2]^2[S_2]}{[H_2S]^2}$ (c) $K_c = \dfrac{[NO_2]^2}{[NO]^2[O_2]}$

(d) $K_c = \dfrac{[P(NH_2)_3][HCl]^3}{[PCl_3][NH_3]^3}$

14.37 $2H_2S(g) + 3O_2(g) \rightleftharpoons 2H_2O(g) + 2SO_2(g)$

14.39 $K_c = \dfrac{[N_2O_5]}{[NO_2]^2[O_2]^{1/2}}$

14.41 $K_c = 0.543$ **14.43** 50.4 **14.45** 3.1×10^3

14.47 1.0×10^{-3} **14.49** (a) $K_p = \dfrac{P_{HBr}^2}{P_{H_2}P_{Br_2}}$

(b) $K_p = \dfrac{P_{CH_4}P_{H_2S}^2}{P_{CS_2}P_{H_2}^4}$ (c) $K_p = \dfrac{P_{H_2O}^2P_{Cl_2}^2}{P_{HCl}^4P_{O_2}}$

(d) $K_p = \dfrac{P_{CH_3OH}}{P_{CO}P_{H_2}^2}$ **14.51** 3.0×10^{-5} **14.53** 56.3

14.55 (a) $K_c = \dfrac{[CO]^2}{[CO_2]}$ (b) $K_c = \dfrac{[CO_2]}{[CO]}$

(c) $K_c = \dfrac{[CO_2]}{[SO_2][O_2]^{1/2}}$ (d) $K_c = [Pb^{2+}][I^-]^2$

14.57 (a) not complete (b) nearly complete **14.59** no, 3.2×10^{-48} mol, yes **14.61** (a) goes to left (b) goes to right
(c) equilibrium (d) goes to left **14.63** goes to left **14.65** 0.37 M
14.67 $[I_2] = [Br_2] = 4.7 \times 10^{-5}\ M$, $[IBr] = 5.1 \times 10^{-4}\ M$
14.69 $[CO_2] = 0.19\ M$, $[CO] = 1.62\ M$ **14.71** $[CO] = 0.0613\ M$, $[H_2] = 0.1839\ M$, $[CH_4] = 0.0387\ M$, $[H_2O] = 0.0387\ M$
14.73 forward **14.75** (a) no effect (b) no effect (c) goes to left
14.77 No, the fraction of methanol would decrease.
14.79 decrease **14.81** low temperature and low pressure
14.83 4.3 **14.85** 0.153 **14.87** reverse **14.89** reverse
14.91 0.008 mol HBr, 0.0010 mol H_2, 0.0010 mol Br_2 **14.93** 13.2%
14.95 0.48 mol CO, 2.44 mol H_2, 0.52 mol CH_4, 0.52 mol H_2O
14.97 endothermic

14.99 $K_p = \dfrac{P_{NH_3}^2}{P_{N_2}P_{H_2}^3} = \dfrac{[NH_3]^2(RT)^2}{[N_2](RT)[H_2]^3(RT)^3} = K_c/(RT)^2$,

so $K_c = K_p(RT)^2$ **14.101** (a) 14.1 (b) 0.37 atm, 2.27 atm
(c) decreases **14.103** (a) $[Cl_2] = [PCl_3] = 0.031\ M$, $[PCl_5] = 0.004\ M$ (b) 0.89 (c) Less PCl_5 would decompose.
14.105 0.335 **14.107** (a) $[SO_2] = [Cl_2] = 0.0346$ mol/L, $[SO_2Cl_2] = 0.0266$ mol/L (b) 0.565 (c) decreases
14.109 (a) $7.2 \times 10^{-5}\ M$, $1.6 \times 10^{-4}\ M$ (b) hydrogen bonding occurs (c) decrease **14.111** 1.1×10^2 **14.125** 0.430
14.127 0.408 atm

CHAPTER 15

15.21 Hydroxide ion forms in the reaction $NH_3(aq) + H_2O(l) \rightleftharpoons NH_4^+(aq) + OH^-(aq)$ **15.23** The hydroxide ion acts as a base and donates a pair of electrons on the O atom, forming a bond with CO_2 to give the HCO_3^- ion. **15.25** The pH increases.
15.27 Center beaker
15.29 $OH^-(aq) + HF(aq) \rightleftharpoons H_2O(l) + F^-(aq)$
        base   acid   acid   base
15.31 (a) PO_4^{3-} (b) HS^- (c) NO_2^- (d) $HAsO_4^{2-}$
15.33 (a) HClO (b) AsH_4^+ (c) H_3PO_4 (d) $HTeO_3^-$
15.35 (a) $HSO_4^- + NH_3 \rightleftharpoons SO_4^{2-} + NH_4^-$
            acid   base   base   acid
(b) $HPO_4^{2-} + NH_4^+ \rightleftharpoons H_2PO_4^- + NH_3$
     base   acid   acid   base
(c) $Al(H_2O)_6^{3+} + H_2O \rightleftharpoons Al(H_2O)_5OH^{2+} + H_3O^+$
       acid   base   base   acid
(d) $SO_3^{2-} + NH_4^+ \rightleftharpoons HSO_3^- + NH_3$
     base   acid   acid   base
15.37 $BF_3 + :AsF_3 \longrightarrow BF_3:AsF_3$
BF_3, Lewis acid; AsF_3, Lewis base.
15.39 (a) $AlCl_3 + Cl^- \longrightarrow [AlCl_4]^-$

(b) $I^- + I_2 \longrightarrow I_3^-$

$$\left[\ddot{\underset{..}{I}}\right]^- + :\ddot{\underset{..}{I}}\ddot{\underset{..}{I}}: \longrightarrow \left[\ddot{\underset{..}{I}} - \ddot{I} - \ddot{\underset{..}{I}}:\right]^-$$

base   acid

15.41 (a) $Cu^{2+} + 6H_2O \longrightarrow Cu(H_2O)_6^{2+}$
     Lewis   Lewis
     acid   base

(b) $BBr_3 + :AsH_3 \longrightarrow Br_3B{:}AsH_3$
    Lewis   Lewis
    acid   base

15.43 $H_2S + HOCH_2CH_2NH_2 \longrightarrow HS^- + HOCH_2CH_2NH_3^+$
  Lewis   Lewis
  acid   base

The H^+ ion from H_2S accepts a pair of electrons from the N atom in $HOCH_2CH_2NH_2$. **15.45** $HSO_4^- + ClO^- \longrightarrow SO_4^{2-} + HClO$; reaction goes to the right because HClO is a weaker acid than HSO_4^-. **15.47** (a) left (b) left (c) right (d) right **15.49** trichloroacetic acid; an acid–base reaction normally goes in the direction of the weaker acid. **15.51** (a) H_2S; acid strength decreases with negative anion charge (b) H_2SO_3; acid strength increases with electronegativity (c) HBr; acid strength increases with electronegativity (d) HIO_4; acid strength increases with number of O atoms (e) H_2S; acid strength increases with central-atom size **15.53** (a) $1.2\ M\ H_3O^+$, $8.3 \times 10^{-15}\ M\ OH^-$ (b) $0.32\ M\ OH^-$, $3.1 \times 10^{-14}\ M\ H_3O^+$ (c) $0.17\ M\ OH^-$, $5.9 \times 10^{-14}\ M\ H_3O^+$ (d) $0.38\ M\ H_3O^+$, $2.6 \times 10^{-14}\ M\ OH^-$ **15.55** $[H_3O^+] = 0.050\ M$, $[OH^-] = 2.0 \times 10^{-13}\ M$ **15.57** $0.017\ M\ OH^-$, $5.9 \times 10^{-13}\ M\ H_3O^+$ **15.59** (a) acidic (b) acidic (c) neutral (d) basic **15.61** acidic **15.63** (a) acidic (b) neutral (c) acidic (d) basic **15.65** (a) acidic (b) neutral (c) basic (d) acidic **16.67** (a) 8.00 (b) 11.30 (c) 2.12 (d) 8.197 **15.69** 2.12 **15.71** (a) 5.72 (b) 11.92 (c) 2.56 (d) 6.32 **15.73** 11.60 **15.75** $7.6 \times 10^{-6}\ M$ **15.77** $4.3 \times 10^{-3}\ M$ **15.79** 13.16 **15.81** 5.5 to 6.5, acidic **15.83** (a) BaO is a base; $BaO + H_2O \longrightarrow Ba^{2+} + 2OH^-$ (b) H_2S is an acid; $H_2S + H_2O \longrightarrow H_3O^+ + HS^-$ (c) CH_3NH_2 is a base; $CH_3NH_2 + H_2O \longrightarrow CH_3NH_3^+ + OH^-$ (d) SO_2 is an acid; $SO_2 + 2H_2O \longrightarrow H_3O^+ + HSO_3^-$ **15.85** (a) $H_2O_2(aq) + S^{2-}(aq) \longrightarrow HO_2^-(aq) + HS^-(aq)$ (b) $HCO_3^-(aq) + OH^-(aq) \longrightarrow CO_3^{2-}(aq) + H_2O(l)$ (c) $NH_4^+(aq) + CN^-(aq) \longrightarrow NH_3(aq) + HCN(aq)$ (d) $H_2PO_4^-(aq) + OH^-(aq) \longrightarrow HPO_4^{2-}(aq) + H_2O(l)$ **15.87** (a) $ClO^- + H_2O \rightleftharpoons HClO + OH^-$
    base   acid   acid   base

$$\left[:\ddot{\underset{..}{Cl}} - \ddot{\underset{..}{O}}:\right]^- + H - \ddot{\underset{..}{O}} - H \longrightarrow :\ddot{\underset{..}{Cl}} - \ddot{\underset{..}{O}} - H + \left[:\ddot{\underset{..}{O}} - H\right]^-$$

(b) $NH_4^+ + NH_2^- \rightleftharpoons 2NH_3$
    acid   base

$$\left[\begin{array}{c} H \\ | \\ H-N-H \\ | \\ H \end{array}\right]^+ + \left[\begin{array}{c} H \\ | \\ :N: \\ | \\ H \end{array}\right]^- \longrightarrow 2 \begin{array}{c} H \\ | \\ :N-H \\ | \\ H \end{array}$$

15.89 $HNO_2 + F^- \rightleftharpoons NO_2^- + HF$, should go in the direction written because HF is a slightly weaker acid than HNO_2 **15.91** H_2S, H_2Se, HBr **15.93** $[H_3O^+] = 4.0 \times 10^{-14}\ M$, $[OH^-] = 0.25\ M$ **15.95** 2.82 **15.97** $1.4 \times 10^{-11}\ M$ **15.99** (a) $H_3O^+(aq) + HCO_3^-(aq) \longrightarrow CO_2(g) + 2H_2O(l)$ $H_2SO_4(aq) + 2NaHCO_3(aq) \longrightarrow$

$$Na_2SO_4(aq) + 2CO_2(g) + 2H_2O(l)$$

(b) 0.0180 mol (c) 60.6% $NaHCO_3$

15.101 $HCO_3^-(aq) + H_2O(l) \rightleftharpoons H_3O^+(aq) + CO_3^{2-}(aq)$
$HCO_3^-(aq) + H_2O(l) \rightleftharpoons H_2CO_3(aq) + OH^-(aq)$
$HCO_3^-(aq) + Na^+(aq) + OH^-(aq) \rightleftharpoons$
$$Na^+(aq) + CO_3^{2-}(aq) + H_2O(l)$$
$HCO_3^-(aq) + H^+(aq) + Cl^-(aq) \rightleftharpoons H_2O(l) + CO_2(g) + Cl^-(aq)$
15.103 $CaH_2(s) + 2H_2O(l) \longrightarrow Ca(OH)_2(s) + 2H_2(g)$; hydride ion is the stronger base **15.105** (a) $2HF(l) \rightleftharpoons H_2F^+ + F^-$
(b) base (c) $HClO_4 + HF \longrightarrow H_2F^+ + ClO_4^-$; H_2F^+
15.107 $NH_3(aq) + H_2O(l) \rightleftharpoons NH_4^+(aq) + OH^-(aq)$; 11.62

15.123 $HO - \overset{\displaystyle OH}{\underset{\displaystyle H}{\overset{|}{\underset{|}{P}}}}{=}O$; 0.976 g NaOH

15.125 $BF_3 + :NH_3 \longrightarrow F_3B:NH_3$; BF_3 is the Lewis acid, and NH_3 is the Lewis base; 12.5 g

CHAPTER 16

16.23 A **16.25** (a) $HF(aq) + H_2O(l) \rightleftharpoons H_3O^+(aq) + F^-(aq)$ (b) $F^-(aq) + H_2O(l) \rightleftharpoons HF(aq) + OH^-(aq)$ (c) $C_6H_5NH_2(aq) + H_2O(l) \rightleftharpoons C_6H_5NH_3^+(aq) + OH^-(aq)$ (d) $C_6H_5NH_3^+(aq) + H_2O(l) \rightleftharpoons C_6H_5NH_2(aq) + H_3O^+(aq)$ **16.27** Acidic, $RanH^+(aq) + H_2O(l) \rightleftharpoons Ran(aq) + H_3O^+(aq)$ **16.29** 100 mL of $0.10\ M$ NaA **16.31** (a) weak acid (b) 8.5 (c) thymol blue or phenolphthalein (need an indicator that changes color in the pH range 7 to 10) **16.33** (a) $HBrO(aq) + H_2O(l) \rightleftharpoons BrO^-(aq) + H_3O^+(aq)$ (b) $HClO_2(aq) + H_2O(l) \rightleftharpoons ClO_2^-(aq) + H_3O^+(aq)$ (c) $HNO_2(aq) + H_2O(l) \rightleftharpoons NO_2^-(aq) + H_3O^+(aq)$ (d) $HCN(aq) + H_2O(l) \rightleftharpoons CN^-(aq) + H_3O^+(aq)$ **16.35** 5.6×10^{-5} **16.37** 5.45, 1.7×10^{-4} **16.39** $[H_3O^+] = [C_6H_4NH_2COO^-] = 1.1 \times 10^{-3}\ M$ **16.41** $0.26\ M$ **16.43** $4.9 \times 10^{-3}\ M$, 2.31 **16.45** $0.361\ M$ **16.47** (a) $3.7 \times 10^{-3}\ M$ (b) $3.9 \times 10^{-6}\ M$ **16.49** $CH_3NH_2(aq) + H_2O(l) \rightleftharpoons CH_3NH_3^+(aq) + OH^-(aq)$

$$K_b = \frac{[CH_3NH_3^+][OH^-]}{[CH_3NH_2]}$$

16.51 3.2×10^{-5} **16.53** $4.9 \times 10^{-3}\ M$, 11.69 **16.55** (a) no hydrolysis (b) $OCl^-(aq) + H_2O(l) \rightleftharpoons HOCl(aq) + OH^-(aq)$

$$K_b = \frac{[HOCl][OH^-]}{[OCl^-]}$$

(c) $NH_2NH_3^+(aq) + H_2O(l) \rightleftharpoons NH_2NH_2(aq) + H_3O^+(aq)$

$$K_a = \frac{[NH_2NH_2][H_3O^+]}{[NH_2NH_3^+]} \quad \text{(d) no hydrolysis}$$

16.57 $Zn(H_2O)_6^{2+}(aq) + H_2O(l) \rightleftharpoons$
$$Zn(H_2O)_5(OH)^+(aq) + H_3O^+(aq)$$
16.59 (a) acidic (b) basic (c) basic (d) acidic **16.61** (a) nearly neutral (b) acidic **16.63** (a) 2.2×10^{-11} (b) 7.1×10^{-6} **16.65** 8.64, $4.4 \times 10^{-6}\ M$ **16.67** $1.0 \times 10^{-3}\ M$, 2.99 **16.69** (a) 0.030 (b) 0.0057 **16.71** 3.17 **16.73** 10.47 **16.75** 3.45 **16.77** 9.26, 9.09 **16.79** 2.68 **16.81** 5.32 **16.83** 0.34 mol **16.85** 1.60 **16.87** 8.59 **16.89** 5.97 **16.91** (a) 11.15 (b) 9.12 (c) 5.24 (d) 1.90 **16.93** 9.08 **16.95** 1.1×10^{-3} **16.97** 1.1×10^{-2} **16.99** $K_b(CN^-) = 2.0 \times 10^{-5}$; $K_b(CO_3^{2-}) = 2.1 \times 10^{-4}$; CO_3^{2-} **16.101** 2.84 **16.103** 3.16 **16.105** 11/1 **16.107** 2.4 **16.109** 3.11 **16.111** (a) $0.100\ M$ (b) $0.11\ M$

16.113 (a) 2.3×10^{-11} (b) 4.4×10^{-4} (c) 10.39
16.115 (a) true   (b) true   (c) false   (d) false   (e) false
(f) true   **16.117** (a) 74.0 g/mol   (b) 1.3×10^{-5}
16.119 (a) Initially: pH = 11.13; 30% titration: pH = 9.62; 50%
titration: pH = 9.26; 100% titration: pH = 5.28   (b) acidic
16.121 (a) H_3PO_4 and $H_2PO_4^-$ (b) 8 mL $H_3PO_4(aq)$ and 42 mL
$H_2PO_4^-(aq)$ **16.123** (a) 0.215 M (b) 3.55   (c) bromphenol
blue   **16.125** (a) $NH_3(aq) + H_3O^+(aq) \longrightarrow NH_4^+(aq) + H_2O(l)$
(b) $NH_4^+(aq) + OH^-(aq) \longrightarrow NH_3(aq) + H_2O(l)$ (c) moles
NH_3 before/after: 0.10/0.090; moles NH_4^+ before/after: 0.10/0.11;
pH 9.2   (d) This is a buffer system.   **16.127** (a) 0.59   (b) 7.16
(c) 7.55   **16.129** (a) $H_2A + 2H_2O \rightleftharpoons 2H_3O^+ + A^{2-}$
(b) $[H_2A] \gg [H_3O^+] = [HA^-] \gg [A^{2-}]$ (c) pH = 2.34; $[H_2A]$ =
0.0205 M (d) $4.6 \times 10^{-5} M$ **16.131** (a) 0.13 M (b) $1.9 \times$
10^2 mL   (c) 0.83 M **16.145** 4.1%   **16.147** $-1.8°C$
16.149 9.1 mL

CHAPTER 17

17.17 From the K_{sp} values, these are the more soluble: (a) silver
chloride   (b) magnesium hydroxide   **17.19** a   **17.21** middle
beaker   **17.23** Add just enough Na_2SO_4 to precipitate all Ba^{2+};
filter off $BaSO_4$; add more Na_2SO_4 to precipitate all Ca^{2+}; filter off
$CaSO_4$; Mg^{2+} remains in solution.   **17.25** (a) soluble
(b) insoluble   (c) insoluble   (d) soluble   **17.27** (a) K_{sp} =
$[Mg^{2+}][OH^-]^2$ (b) $K_{sp} = [Sr^{2+}][CO_3^{2-}]$ (c) K_{sp} =
$[Ca^{2+}]^3[AsO_4^{3-}]^2$ (d) $K_{sp} = [Fe^{3+}][OH^-]^3$ **17.29** 9.3×10^{-10}
17.31 1.2×10^{-7} **17.33** 1.8×10^{-11} **17.35** 0.0045 g/L
17.37 $1.9 \times 10^{-3} M$ **17.39** 2.0×10^{-4} g/L   **17.41** $1.1 \times$
10^{-5} g/L   **17.43** 0.4 g/L   **17.45** (a) yes   (b) yes
17.47 Lead chromate will precipitate.   **17.49** no precipitate
17.51 no precipitate   **17.53** 0.0018 mol   **17.55** $6.9 \times 10^{-9} M$
17.57 $BaF_2(s) + 2H_3O^+(aq) \longrightarrow Ba^{2+}(aq) + 2HF(aq) +$
$2H_2O(l)$ **17.59** BaF_2; F^- is the conjugate base of the weak acid
HF.   **17.61** $Cu^+(aq) + 2CN^-(aq) \longrightarrow Cu(CN)_2^-(aq)$

$$K_f = \frac{[Cu(CN)_2^-]}{[Cu^+][CN^-]^2}$$

17.63 $5.5 \times 10^{-19} M$ **17.65** will precipitate   **17.67** $3.0 \times 10^{-3} M$
17.69 Add HCl; Pb^{2+} will be precipitated as the chloride. Filter
off $PbCl_2$; add H_2S in 0.3 M H^+. Cd^{2+} will precipitate as the sulfide; filter off CdS. The filtrate contains Sr^{2+}.   **17.71** Mn^{2+}
17.73 $1.3 \times 10^{-4} M$ **17.75** (a) $6.9 \times 10^{-7} M$;   (b) $3.2 \times$
10^{-4} g/L   **17.77** (a) $5.2 \times 10^{-6} M$;   (b) pOH = 4.81
17.79 26 g/L   **17.81** $1.8 \times 10^{-9} M$ **17.83** $8.0 \times 10^{-3} M$
17.85 1.0×10^{-5}; unsaturated   **17.87** 5.5×10^{-6} g
17.89 $4.7 \times 10^{-2} M$ **17.91** $1.4 \times 10^{-2} M$ **17.93** 3.6×10^{-4}
M, $4.2 \times 10^{-6} M$, 2.5×10^9 **17.95** $1.0 \times 10^{-5} M$
17.97 (a) $6.4 \times 10^{-7} M$ (b) $2.4 \times 10^{-4} M$ (c) yes
17.99 (a) $6.6 \times 10^{-4} M$ (b) $1.6 \times 10^{-3} M$, 11%
17.101 (a) 6.3×10^{-16} (b) $8.7 \times 10^{-9} M$ (c) common-ion
effect   **17.103** (a) 3.1×10^{-3} (b) 0.044 mol; 0.044 M;
0.89 mol   **17.105** (a) $1.5 \times 10^{-4} M$ (b) 99%   **17.119** 0.18 M
17.121 $2.7 \times 10^{-4} M$ **17.123** $Ba^{2+}(aq) + 2OH^-(aq) +$
$Mg^{2+}(aq) + SO_4^{2-}(aq) \longrightarrow BaSO_4(s) + Mg(OH)_2(s)$; $[SO_4^{2-}]$ =
0.109 M; $[Ba^{2+}] = 1.0 \times 10^{-9} M$; $[Mg^{2+}]$ = 0.109 M; $[OH^-]$ =
$1.3 \times 10^{-5} M$

CHAPTER 18

18.23 (a) false   (b) false   (c) false   (d) true   (e) false
18.25 (a) 2.0 mol CO_2 (b) butane gas   (c) CO_2 at $-80°C$
(d) bromine vapor   **18.27** (a) negative   (b) negative
(c) negative   (d) zero   **18.29** (a) K_c does not change.
(b) $Q > K_c$; the reaction will go to the left.   (c) ΔG is positive;
ΔS is negative.   **18.31** -82 J, 29 J, -53 J   **18.33** 37.56 kJ
18.35 106 J/K   **18.37** -128 J/K; 127 J/K   **18.39** (a) negative
(b) not predictable   (c) positive   (d) positive
18.41 (a) -181.7 J/K   (b) -57.8 J/K   (c) -56.4 J/K
(d) 313.6 J/K   **18.43** -266.9 J/K; entropy decreases, as expected,
since moles of gas decrease.   **18.45** -1452.8 kJ, -161.4 J/K,
-1404.7 kJ   **18.47** (a) $K(s) + \frac{1}{2}Br_2(l) \longrightarrow KBr(s)$
(b) $C(graphite) + \frac{3}{2}H_2(g) + \frac{1}{2}Cl_2(g) \longrightarrow CH_3Cl(l)$
(c) $H_2(g) + \frac{1}{8}S_8$ (rhombic) $\longrightarrow H_2S(g)$
(d) $As(s) + \frac{3}{2}H_2(g) \longrightarrow AsH_3(g)$ **18.49** (a) -1331.4 kJ
(b) -56.2 kJ   **18.51** (a) spontaneous   (b) spontaneous
(c) nonspontaneous   (d) equilibrium mixture with significant
amounts of reactants and products   (e) nonspontaneous
18.53 (a) 850.2 kJ, 838.8 kJ; endothermic reaction with mainly
reactants at equilibrium   (b) -72.2 kJ, -142.0 kJ; exothermic
reaction with mainly products at equilibrium   **18.55** -474.2 kJ; 0

18.57 -15.8 kJ   **18.59** (a) $K = \dfrac{P_{CO_2}P_{H_2}}{P_{CO}P_{H_2O}}$

(b) $K = [Mg^{2+}][OH^-]^2$ (c) $K = [Li^+]^2[OH^-]^2P_{H_2}$
18.61 -107.00 kJ; 6×10^{18} **18.63** -142.2 kJ; 9×10^{24}
18.65 -144.39 kJ; 2×10^{25} **18.67** 1.2×10^2; yes   **18.69** 401.1 K
18.71 Reaction is spontaneous because $\Delta S°$ is large and positive.
18.73 -184 kJ; exothermic; positive; both ΔH and $-T\Delta S$ are
negative, so reaction is spontaneous at all T.   **18.75** -14.3 J/K
18.77 (a) negative   (b) positive   (c) positive   (d) negative
18.79 negative   **18.81** -136.0 J/K   **18.83** no, $\Delta G°$ is $+266.8$ kJ
18.85 $\Delta H°$ is positive; $\Delta S°$ is positive.   **18.87** 62.4 kJ; 1×10^{-11}
18.89 109.6 kJ; 136.6 J/K; 68.9 kJ; -37.0 kJ; nonspontaneous at
25°C, but spontaneous at 800°C   **18.91** (a) -75 kJ   (b) -80.8
J/mol·K   (c) -51 kJ/mol   **18.93** 205.4 J/mol·K
18.95 (a) 97.1 kJ; 115.5 J/K; 187.2 kJ; 207.2   (b) 841 K; 903.4 K
(c) carbon   **18.97** (a) formic acid   (b) products
18.99 (a) products   (b) need to heat to increase rate of reaction
18.101 (a) -126 kJ/mol   (b) -2745.9 kJ/mol   (c) -440 J/K
18.103 (a) 6×10^{-5} (b) Both ΔH and ΔS, but especially ΔS.
18.117 0.004%, same; $K = 3 \times 10^{-10}$ **18.119** 87%
18.121 -2.29 kJ; -98.7 J/K

CHAPTER 19

19.25 (a) no change   (b) no change   (c) The Zn strip would
dissolve, the blue color of the solution would fade, and solid copper
would precipitate out of the solution.   (d) no change   **19.27** The
Zn is a sacrificial electrode that keeps the hull from undergoing
oxidation by the dissolved ions in seawater. Zinc works because it is
more easily oxidized than Fe.   **19.29** Because more zinc is
present, the oxidation–reduction reactions in the battery will run for
a longer period of time. This assumes that the zinc is the limiting
reactant.   **19.31** Pick elements or compounds to be reduced and
one to be oxidized so that when the half-reactions are added
together, the $E°_{cell}$ is about 0.90 V. For example,

$$Cd(s) \longrightarrow Cd^{2+}(aq) + 2e^-(aq) \qquad 0.40 \text{ V}$$
$$I_2(s) + 2e^- \longrightarrow 2I^-(aq) \qquad 0.54 \text{ V}$$
$$I_2(s) + Cd^{2+}(aq) \longrightarrow 2I^-(aq) + Cd^{2+}(aq) \qquad 0.94 \text{ V}$$

19.33 (a) brighter (b) dimmer (c) dimmer (d) off
19.35 (a) $Cr_2O_7^{2-} + 14H^+ + 3C_2O_4^{2-} \longrightarrow$
$$2Cr^{3+} + 6CO_2 + 7H_2O$$
(b) $3Cu + 2NO_3^- + 8H^+ \longrightarrow 3Cu^{2+} + 2NO + 4H_2O$
(c) $MnO_2 + H^+ + HNO_2 \longrightarrow Mn^{2+} + H_2O + NO_3^-$
(d) $5PbO_2 + 2Mn^{2+} + 5SO_4^{2-} + 4H^+ \longrightarrow$
$$5PbSO_4 + 2MnO_4^- + 2H_2O$$
(e) $3HNO_2 + Cr_2O_7^{2-} + 5H^+ \longrightarrow 2Cr^{3+} + 3NO_3^- + 4H_2O$
19.37 (a) $Mn^{2+} + H_2O_2 + 2OH^- \longrightarrow MnO_2 + 2H_2O$
(b) $2MnO_4^- + 3NO_2^- + H_2O \longrightarrow 2MnO_2 + 3NO_3^- + 2OH^-$
(c) $Mn^{2+} + 2ClO_3^- \longrightarrow MnO_2 + 2ClO_2$
(d) $MnO_4^- + 3NO_2 + 2OH^- \longrightarrow MnO_2 + 3NO_3^- + H_2O$
(e) $3Cl_2 + 6OH^- \longrightarrow 5Cl^- + ClO_3^- + 3H_2O$
19.39 (a) $8H_2S + 16NO_3^- + 16H^+ \longrightarrow 16NO_2 + S_8 + 16H_2O$
(b) $2NO_3^- + 3Cu + 8H^+ \longrightarrow 2NO + 3Cu^{2+} + 4H_2O$
(c) $2MnO_4^- + 5SO_2 + 2H_2O \longrightarrow 5SO_4^{2-} + 2Mn^{2+} + 4H^+$
(d) $2Bi(OH)_3 + 3Sn(OH)_3^- + 3OH^- \longrightarrow 3Sn(OH)_6^{2-} + 2Bi$
19.41 (a) $2MnO_4^- + I^- + H_2O \longrightarrow 2MnO_2 + IO_3^- + 2OH^-$
(b) $Cr_2O_7^{2-} + 6Cl^- + 14H^+ \longrightarrow 2Cr^{3+} + 3Cl_2 + 7H_2O$
(c) $3S_8 + 32NO_3^- + 32H^+ \longrightarrow 24SO_2 + 32NO + 16H_2O$
(d) $3H_2O_2 + 2MnO_4^- \longrightarrow 3O_2 + 2MnO_2 + 2H_2O + 2OH^-$
(e) $5Zn + 2NO_3^- + 12H^+ \longrightarrow 5Zn^{2+} + N_2 + 6H_2O$
19.43 Anode: $Mg \longrightarrow Mg^{2+} + 2e^-$
Cathode: $Ni^{2+} + 2e^- \longrightarrow Ni$
Electron flow in circuit is from Mg to Ni.
19.45 $Zn(s) \longrightarrow Zn^{2+}(aq) + 2e^-$
$Ag^+(aq) + e^- \longrightarrow Ag(s)$
19.47 Anode: $Zn(s) + 2OH^-(aq) \longrightarrow Zn(OH)_2(s) + 2e^-$
Cathode: $Ag_2O(s) + H_2O(l) + 2e^- \longrightarrow 2Ag(s) + 2OH^-(aq)$
Overall: $Zn(s) + Ag_2O(s) + H_2O(l) \longrightarrow 2Ag(s) + Zn(OH)_2(s)$
19.49 $Ni(s)|Ni^{2+}(aq)||Pb^{2+}(aq)|Pb(s)$
19.51 $Ni(s)|Ni^{2+}(1\ M)||H^+(1\ M)|H_2(g)|Pt$
19.53 $2Ag^+(aq) + Fe(s) \longrightarrow Fe^{2+}(aq) + 2Ag(s)$
19.55 Anode: $Cd(s) \longrightarrow Cd^{2+}(aq) + 2e^-$
Cathode: $Ni^{2+}(aq) + 2e^- \longrightarrow Ni(s)$
Overall: $Cd(s) + Ni^{2+}(aq) \longrightarrow Cd^{2+}(aq) + Ni(s)$
19.57 -69 kJ **19.59** -96 kJ **19.61** $NO_3^-(aq), O_2(g),$
$MnO_4^-(aq)$ **19.63** Strongest is $Zn(s)$; weakest is $Cu^+(aq)$.
19.65 (a) not spontaneous (b) spontaneous **19.67** Cl_2 will
oxidize Br^-; $Cl_2(g) + 2Br^-(aq) \longrightarrow Br_2(l) + 2Cl^-(aq)$
19.69 1.54 V **19.71** 1.28 V **19.73** -3.6×10^5 J
19.75 -1.6×10^5 J **19.77** 3.16 V **19.79** 2.07 V
19.81 10^{14} **19.83** 1×10^6 **19.85** 0.57 V **19.87** 0.29 V
19.89 $4 \times 10^{-3}\ M$ **19.91** (a) cathode: $Ca^{2+}(l) + 2e^- \longrightarrow$
$Ca(l)$; anode: $S^{2-}(l) \longrightarrow S(l) + 2e^-$ (b) $Cs^+(l) + e^- \longrightarrow Cs(l)$
$4OH^-(l) \longrightarrow O_2(g) + 2H_2O(g) + 4e^-$ **19.93** (a) anode:
$2H_2O(l) \longrightarrow O_2(g) + 4H^+(aq) + 4e^-$; cathode: $2H_2O(l) + 2e^- \longrightarrow$
$H_2(g) + 2OH^-(aq)$; overall: $2H_2O(l) \longrightarrow 2H_2(g) + O_2(g)$
(b) anode: $2Br^-(aq) \longrightarrow Br_2(l) + 2e^-$; cathode: $2H_2O(l) +$
$2e^- \longrightarrow H_2(g) + 2OH^-(aq)$; overall: $2Br^-(aq) + 2H_2O(l) \longrightarrow$
$Br_2(l) + H_2(g) + 2OH^-(aq)$ **19.95** 3.87×10^7 C **19.97** 0.360 g
19.99 (a) $3Fe + 2HNO_3 + 6H^+ \longrightarrow 3Fe^{2+} + 2NO + 4H_2O$
(b) $3Fe^{2+} + HNO_3 + 3H^+ \longrightarrow 3Fe^{3+} + NO + 2H_2O$
(c) $Fe + HNO_3 + 3H^+ \longrightarrow Fe^{3+} + NO + 2H_2O$

19.101 (a) $16MnO_4^- + 24S^{2-} + 32H_2O \longrightarrow$
$$16MnO_2 + 3S_8 + 64OH^-$$
(b) $IO_3^- + 3HSO_3^- \longrightarrow I^- + 3SO_4^{2-} + 3H^+$
(c) $3Fe(OH)_2 + CrO_4^{2-} + 4H_2O \longrightarrow$
$$3Fe(OH)_3 + Cr(OH)_4^- + OH^-$$
(d) $Cl_2 + 2OH^- \longrightarrow Cl^- + ClO^- + H_2O$
19.103 $4Fe(OH)_2 + O_2 + 2H_2O \longrightarrow 4Fe(OH)_3$
19.105 $Ca(s)|Ca^{2+}(aq)||Cl_2(g)|Cl^-(aq)|Pt(s)$; anode: $Ca(s) \longrightarrow$
$Ca^{2+}(aq) + 2e^-$; cathode: $Cl_2(g) + 2e^- \longrightarrow 2Cl^-(aq)$; 4.12 V
19.107 (a) spontaneous (b) Fe^{3+} will oxidize Sn^{2+} to Sn^{4+}.
19.109 0.36 V **19.111** (a) 2.2 (b) 0.3 M
19.113 (a) 1.0 F, 9.6×10^4 C (b) 2.0 F, 1.9×10^5 C
(c) 0.11 F, 1.1×10^4 C (d) 2.8×10^{-2} F, 2.7×10^3 C
19.115 2.83×10^{-4} g As **19.117** (a) $Cd(s) + 2Ag^+(aq) \rightleftharpoons$
$2Ag(s) + Cd^{2+}(aq)$; 1.20 V (b) It would increase. (c) no effect
19.119 anode: $2H_2O(l) \longrightarrow O_2(g) + 4H^+(aq) + 4e^-$; cathode:
$Cu^{2+}(aq) + 2e^- \longrightarrow Cu(s)$ **19.121** (a) 1.48×10^3 s
(b) 0.398 g **19.123** (a) 0.323 faraday (b) $3+$
19.125 (a) 1.06 V (b) $8.8 \times 10^{-3}\ M$ **19.127** (a) -23.2 kJ
(b) -0.28 V for $Co^{2+} + 2e \longrightarrow Co(s)$ **19.139** 11.7 kJ/K
19.141 -0.05 V; not spontaneous **19.143** -0.04 V; not spontaneous **19.145** $K_{sp} = 1 \times 10^{-7}$

CHAPTER 20

20.23 (a) 0.1% (b) If you had a large quantity of material, 0.1%
still would be a significant quantity; also, if the material were
particularly toxic in addition to being radioactive, it would be
significant. **20.25** Some of the expected mass is in the form of
energy: the mass defect. **20.27** (a) At $t = 0$ min, the container
contains 16 spheres; at $t = 30$ min, the container contains 2 spheres.
(b) Incorrect at $t = 5$ minutes; at $t = 5$ min, there should be fewer
than 750 atoms. **20.29** The large, positively charged He nucleus
that makes up alpha (α) radiation is unable to pass through the
atoms that make up solid materials such as wood without coming
into contact or being deflected by the nuclei. Gamma (γ) radiation,
however, with its small wavelength and high energy, can pass
through large amounts of material without interaction, just as x rays
can pass through skin and other soft tissue. **20.31** Irradiation of
an atom with gamma radiation does not result in the creation of
radioactive elements; therefore, the food cannot become radioactive.
The addition of a radioactive element directly to the meat would
make the meat radioactive. Under the right conditions, nuclear
bombardment could also lead to the production of radioactive
elements. **20.33** $^{87}_{37}Rb \longrightarrow ^{87}_{38}Sr + ^{0}_{-1}e$ **20.35** $^{232}_{90}Th \longrightarrow ^{4}_{2}He$
$+ ^{228}_{88}Ra$ **20.37** $^{18}_{9}F \longrightarrow ^{18}_{8}O + ^{0}_{1}e$ **20.39** $^{210}_{84}Po \longrightarrow ^{4}_{2}He +$
$^{206}_{82}Pb$ **20.41** (a) $^{122}_{51}Sb$ (b) $^{204}_{85}At$ (c) $^{80}_{37}Rb$
20.43 (a) α emission (b) positron emission or electron capture
(c) β emission **20.45** $^{235}_{92}U$ decay series; $^{232}_{90}Th$ decay series.
Alpha emission decreases the mass number by 4. Beta emission has
no effect upon the mass number. **20.47** (a) $^{26}_{12}Mg(d, \alpha)^{24}_{11}Na$
(b) $^{16}_{8}O(n, p)^{16}_{7}N$ **20.49** (a) $^{27}_{13}Al + ^{2}_{1}H \longrightarrow ^{25}_{12}Mg + ^{4}_{2}He$
(b) $^{10}_{5}B + ^{4}_{2}He \longrightarrow ^{1}_{1}H + ^{13}_{6}C$ **20.51** 1.22×10^9 kJ/mol
20.53 (a) $^{4}_{2}He$ (b) α **20.55** plutonium-239 **20.57** $1.79 \times 10^{-9}\ s^{-1}$
20.59 $9.1 \times 10^{-8}\ s^{-1}$ **20.61** 1.3×10^{13} y **20.63** $3.84 \times 10^{-12}/s$
20.65 2.1×10^2 Ci **20.67** 5.7×10^{-4} g **20.69** 0.574, 3.4 μg
20.71 4.16 s **20.73** 44.6 d **20.75** 5.3×10^3 y
20.77 5 disintegrations/(min·g) **20.79** -4.37×10^{-9} g

20.81 -1.688×10^{12} J; -17.50 MeV   **20.83** 0.03436 amu, 32.01 MeV, 5.336 MeV   **20.85** Na-20 is expected to decay by electron capture or positron emission. Na-26 is expected to decay by beta emission.   **20.87** 7 alpha emissions and 4 beta emissions

20.89 $^{209}_{83}\text{Bi} + ^{4}_{2}\text{He} \longrightarrow ^{211}_{85}\text{At} + 2^{1}_{0}n$ **20.91** $^{246}_{98}\text{Cf}$ **20.93** 6.3 y

20.95 2.42 pm   **20.97** -6.02×10^{14} J; -1.64×10^{5} kJ

20.99 (a) $^{47}_{20}\text{Ca} \longrightarrow ^{47}_{21}\text{Sc} + ^{0}_{-1}\beta$ (b) 41 µg

20.101 (a) $^{82}_{35}\text{Br} \longrightarrow ^{82}_{36}\text{Kr} + ^{0}_{-1}\beta$; $2\text{H}^{82}\text{Br}(g) \longrightarrow \text{H}_2 + 2\text{Kr}$

(b) 0.0119 mol; 0.401 atm   **20.117** 1.75×10^{13} nuclei/s

20.119 0.001 L   **20.121** 2.732×10^{9} kJ; 4.91×10^{7} L

CHAPTER 21

21.71 It would react with the oxygen by the following equation: $\text{C}(s) + \text{O}_2(g) \longrightarrow \text{CO}_2(g)$.   **21.73** The metallic character decreases from left to right and increases going down a column.

21.75 This means that aluminum hydroxide reacts with both acids and bases. For example.

$\text{Al(OH)}_3(s) + 3\text{HCl}(aq) \longrightarrow 3\text{H}_2\text{O}(l) + \text{AlCl}_3(aq)$

$\text{Al(OH)}_3(s) + \text{NaOH}(aq) \longrightarrow \text{Na}^+(aq) + \text{Al(OH)}_4^{-}(aq)$

21.77 Oxygen is a very electronegative element, and its bonding involves only the s and p orbitals, in contrast to bonding using the d orbitals in sulfur, etc. Molecular oxygen is a reactive gas but forms mainly compounds in which its oxidation state is -2, compared to compounds of sulfur, etc., which exhibit positive oxidation states as well as the -2 state.

21.79 HBr cannot be prepared by adding sulfuric acid to NaBr because the hot concentrated acid will oxidize the bromide ion to bromine.   **21.81** $\text{Fe}_2\text{O}_3 + 3\text{H}_2 \longrightarrow 2\text{Fe} + 3\text{H}_2\text{O}$

21.83 3.69×10^{4} g   **21.85** -417.9 kJ; exothermic

21.87 The diagram is similar to the one for Na.   **21.89** 2.62×10^{19}

21.91 $\text{CO}_2(g) + \text{NH}_3(g) + \text{NaCl}(aq) + \text{H}_2\text{O}(l) \longrightarrow$
$$\text{NaHCO}_3(s) + \text{NH}_4\text{Cl}(aq)$$

$2\text{NaHCO}_3(s) \xrightarrow{\Delta} \text{Na}_2\text{CO}_3(s) + \text{CO}_2(g) + \text{H}_2\text{O}(g)$

$\text{Ca(OH)}_2(aq) + \text{Na}_2\text{CO}_3(aq) \longrightarrow 2\text{NaOH}(aq) + \text{CaCO}_3(s)$

21.93 (a) $2\text{K}(s) + \text{Br}_2(l) \longrightarrow 2\text{KBr}(s)$

(b) $2\text{K}(s) + 2\text{H}_2\text{O}(l) \longrightarrow 2\text{KOH}(aq) + \text{H}_2(g)$

(c) $2\text{NaOH}(s) + \text{CO}_2(g) \longrightarrow \text{Na}_2\text{CO}_3(s) + \text{H}_2\text{O}(l)$

(d) $\text{Li}_2\text{CO}_3(aq) + 2\text{HNO}_3(aq) \longrightarrow$
$$2\text{LiNO}_3(aq) + \text{H}_2\text{O}(l) + \text{CO}_2(g)$$

(e) $\text{K}_2\text{SO}_4(aq) + \text{Pb(NO}_3)_2(aq) \longrightarrow \text{PbSO}_4(s) + 2\text{KNO}_3(aq)$

21.95 $^{227}_{89}\text{Ac} \longrightarrow ^{4}_{2}\text{He} + ^{223}_{87}\text{Fr}$ **21.97** Add CO_3^{2-} to each solution. Calcium carbonate will precipitate from the calcium hydroxide solution.   **21.99** Add Na_2SO_4 to the solution. $\text{BaSO}_4(s)$ can then be filtered from the solution. The filtrate will contain Mg^{2+} ions.

21.101 $^{230}_{90}\text{Th} \longrightarrow ^{226}_{88}\text{Ra} + ^{4}_{2}\text{He}$

21.103 (a) $\text{BaCO}_3(s) \xrightarrow{\Delta} \text{BaO}(s) + \text{CO}_2(g)$

(b) $\text{Ba}(s) + 2\text{H}_2\text{O}(l) \longrightarrow \text{Ba(OH)}_2(aq) + \text{H}_2(g)$

(c) $\text{Mg(OH)}_2(s) + 2\text{HNO}_3(aq) \longrightarrow \text{Mg(NO}_3)_2(aq) + 2\text{H}_2\text{O}(l)$

(d) $\text{Mg}(s) + \text{NiCl}_2(aq) \longrightarrow \text{MgCl}_2(aq) + \text{Ni}(s)$

(e) $2\text{NaOH}(aq) + \text{MgSO}_4(aq) \longrightarrow \text{Mg(OH)}_2(s) + \text{Na}_2\text{SO}_4(aq)$

21.105 0.22 g Ca(OH)_2

21.107 $\text{Al(H}_2\text{O)}_6^{3+}(aq) + \text{HCO}_3^{-}(aq) \longrightarrow$
$$\text{Al(H}_2\text{O)}_5\text{OH}^{2+}(aq) + \text{H}_2\text{O}(l) + \text{CO}_2(g)$$

21.109 Test portions of solutions of each compound with the others. If one solution is poured into one of the other solutions and no precipitate forms, that means that BaCl_2 was mixed with KOH and the third solution is $\text{Al}_2(\text{SO}_4)_3$. Adding KOH to $\text{Al}_2(\text{SO}_4)_3$ will form a precipitate of Al(OH)_3, which will dissolve when an excess

of KOH is added. BaCl_2 and $\text{Al}_2(\text{SO}_4)_3$ will form a precipitate of BaSO_4.   **21.111** $\text{Sn(H}_2\text{O)}_6^{2+}(aq) + \text{H}_2\text{O}(l) \longrightarrow$
$$\text{Sn(H}_2\text{O)}_5(\text{OH})^+(aq) + \text{H}_3\text{O}^+(aq)$$

21.113 $\text{PbO}_2 + 4\text{HCl} \longrightarrow \text{PbCl}_2 + \text{Cl}_2 + 2\text{H}_2\text{O}$

21.115 (a) $\text{Al}_2\text{O}_3(s) + 3\text{H}_2\text{SO}_4(aq) \longrightarrow$
$$\text{Al}_2(\text{SO}_4)_3(aq) + 3\text{H}_2\text{O}(l)$$

(b) $\text{Al}(s) + 3\text{AgNO}_3(aq) \longrightarrow \text{Al(NO}_3)_3(aq) + 3\text{Ag}(s)$

(c) $\text{Pb(NO}_3)_2(aq) + 2\text{NaI}(aq) \longrightarrow \text{PbI}_2(s) + 2\text{NaNO}_3(aq)$

(d) $8\text{Al}(s) + 3\text{Mn}_3\text{O}_4(s) \longrightarrow 4\text{Al}_2\text{O}_3(s) + 9\text{Mn}(s)$

(e) $2\text{Ga(OH)}_3(s) \xrightarrow{\Delta} \text{Ga}_2\text{O}_3(s) + 3\text{H}_2\text{O}(l)$

21.117 -4.2×10^{9} kJ   **21.119** (a) -1 (b) $+1$ (c) -4

(d) $+6$ **21.121** (a) Each C atom has sp^3 hybridization and forms four σ bonds, one bond to each of three H atoms, and one bond to the other C atom.   (b) Since the Si atom is bonded to six F atoms, Si has six sp^3d^2 hybrid orbitals.   (c) The double bond between two of the C atoms consists of a σ bond and a π bond. The σ bond is formed by the overlap of an sp^2 hybrid orbital from each of the two C atoms. The π bond is formed by the overlap of the unhybridized $2p$ orbital from each of the two C atoms. The single bond between the center C atom and the other C atom is a σ bond formed by the overlap of an sp^2 hybrid orbital from the center C atom with an sp^3 hybrid orbital from the outer C atom.   (d) Since the Si atom is bonded to four H atoms, Si has four sp^3 hybrid orbitals.

21.123 (a) 74.87 kJ   (b) 137.15 kJ   **21.125** (a) $\text{CO}_2(g) + \text{Ba(OH)}_2(aq) \longrightarrow \text{BaCO}_3(s) + \text{H}_2\text{O}(l)$

(b) $\text{MgCO}_3(s) + 2\text{HBr}(aq) \longrightarrow \text{MgBr}_2(aq) + \text{H}_2\text{O}(l) + \text{CO}_2(g)$

21.127 $\text{C} + \text{O}_2$ (from air) $\longrightarrow \text{CO}_2$

$\text{NaOH} + \text{CO}_2 \longrightarrow \text{NaHCO}_3$

$2\text{NaHCO}_3 \xrightarrow{\Delta} \text{Na}_2\text{CO}_3 + \text{H}_2\text{O} + \text{CO}_2$

21.129 Each Si atom has four tetrahedral bonds to other Si atoms, with an sp^3 orbital on one Si atom overlapping an sp^3 orbital on another Si atom.   **21.131** 10.7 kg   **21.133** Spodumene consists of a long chain of SiO_4 tetrahedra linked together, with the negative charge of this chain balanced by lithium and aluminum cations. Figure 21.36 shows the linking of two SiO_4 tetrahedra. Note that in this linkage, one O atom is shared by the two tetrahedra. The repeating unit of the SiO_4 chain of spodumene consists of an Si atom with two unshared O atoms and two shared O atoms (each shared atom counting as $\frac{1}{2}$ O atom to each repeating unit). The repeating unit also has a charge of $2-$ on it. Thus, the formula of the repeating unit is SiO_3^{2-}. Two of these repeating units would have a $4-$ charge, which in spodumene is balanced by an Li^+ ion and an Al^{3+} ion, giving the formula $\text{LiAl(SiO}_3)_2$.

21.135 2.53 g NH_3

21.137 $4\text{NH}_3(g) + 5\text{O}_2(g) \xrightarrow{\text{Pt}} 4\text{NO}(g) + 6\text{H}_2\text{O}(g)$

$2\text{NO}(g) + \text{O}_2(g) \longrightarrow 2\text{NO}_2(g)$

$3\text{NO}_2(g) + \text{H}_2\text{O}(l) \longrightarrow 2\text{HNO}_3(aq) + \text{NO}(g)$

$\text{HNO}_3(g) + \text{NH}_3(aq) \longrightarrow \text{NH}_4\text{NO}_3(aq)$

$\text{NH}_4\text{NO}_3(aq) \longrightarrow \text{NH}_4\text{NO}_3(s)$

$\text{NH}_4\text{NO}_3(s) \xrightarrow{\Delta} \text{N}_2\text{O}(g) + 2\text{H}_2\text{O}(g)$

21.139 $4\text{Zn} + 10\text{H}^+ + \text{NO}_3^- \longrightarrow 4\text{Zn}^{2+} + \text{NH}_4^+ + 3\text{H}_2\text{O}$

21.141 Tetrahedral. Each bond is formed by the overlap of a $4p$ orbital from Br with an sp^3 orbital from P.

21.143 $\text{H}_3\text{PO}_3 + \text{H}_2\text{SO}_4 \longrightarrow \text{H}_3\text{PO}_4 + \text{SO}_2 + \text{H}_2\text{O}$

21.145 14.1 g H_3PO_4 **21.147** (a) $4\text{Li} + \text{O}_2 \longrightarrow 2\text{Li}_2\text{O}$

(b) $4\text{CH}_3\text{NH}_2 + 9\text{O}_2 \longrightarrow 4\text{CO}_2 + 10\text{H}_2\text{O} + 2\text{N}_2$

(c) $2(\text{C}_2\text{H}_5)_2\text{S} + 15\text{O}_2 \longrightarrow 8\text{CO}_2 + 10\text{H}_2\text{O} + 2\text{SO}_2$

21.149 (a) $+6$ (b) $+6$ (c) -2 (d) $+4$
21.151 $8H_2SeO_3 + 16H_2S \longrightarrow Se_8 + 2S_8 + 24H_2O$
21.153 49.1 g
21.155 $Ba(ClO_3)_2(aq) + H_2SO_4(aq) \longrightarrow 2HClO_3(aq) + BaSO_4(s)$
21.157 $8H^+ + 6HCl + K_2Cr_2O_7 \longrightarrow$
$$3Cl_2 + 2Cr^{3+} + 7H_2O + 2K^+$$
21.159 (a) sp^3; bent (b) sp^3; trigonal pyramidal
(c) sp^3d; T-shaped
21.161 (a) $Br_2(l) + 2NaOH(aq) \longrightarrow$
$$BrO^-(aq) + Br^-(aq) + H_2O(l) + 2Na^+(aq)$$
(b) $NaBr(s) + H_3PO_4(aq) \xrightarrow{\Delta}$
$$HBr(g) + Na^+(aq) + H_2PO_4^-(aq)$$
21.163 0.13 V; reaction occurs

21.165 sp^3d^2, square planar

21.167 $2XeF_2 + 4OH^- \longrightarrow 2Xe + 4F^- + O_2 + 2H_2O$
21.169 0.584 metric tons **21.171** 8.184% **21.173** -8.50×10^2 kJ; -425 kJ/mol Fe **21.175** 84.5% **21.177** 6.957 g
21.179 1.36×10^3 K **21.181** $E° = 0.19$ V; -37 kJ; yes
21.183 7.73×10^{-2} g **21.185** 69.6% **21.187** 12.6 hr
21.189 2.58%

CHAPTER 22

22.31 $[Co(NH_3)_4(NO_2)_2]Cl$ **22.33** "Hexacyano" means that there are six CN^- ligands bonded to the iron cation. The Roman numeral II means that the oxidation state of the iron cation is $+2$, so that the overall charge of the complex ion is -4. This requires four potassium ions to counterbalance the -4 charge.
22.35 $[Co(NH_3)_4Br_2]Cl$ $[Co(NH_3)_4BrCl]Br$
22.37 (a) $+2$ (b) $+4$ (c) $+2$ (d) $+6$
22.39 $3Fe^{2+} + NO_3^- + 4H^+ \longrightarrow 3Fe^{3+} + NO + 2H_2O$
22.41 (a) 4 (b) 6 (c) 4 (d) 6
22.43 (a) $+2$ (b) $+3$ (c) $+3$ (d) $+3$
22.45 (a) $+3$ (b) *Name* *Formula* (c) 6 (d) -3
ammine NH_3
chloro Cl^-
oxalato $C_2O_4^{2-}$
22.47 (a) potassium hexafluoroferrate(III)
(b) diamminediaquacopper(II) ion
(c) ammonium aquapentafluoroferrate(III)
(d) dicyanoargentate(I) ion
22.49 (a) pentacarbonyliron(0)
(b) dicyanobis(ethylenediamine)rhodium(III) ion
(c) tetraamminesulfatochromium(III) chloride
(d) tetraoxomanganate(VII) ion
22.51 (a) $K_3[Mn(CN)_6]$ (b) $Na_2[Zn(CN)_4]$
(c) $[Co(NH_3)_4Cl_2]NO_3$ (d) $[Cr(NH_3)_6]_2[CuCl_4]_3$

22.53 (a)

cis   *trans*

(b) no geometric isomerism (c) no geometric isomerism

(d)

cis

trans

22.55 (a) Has optical isomers, similar to those in Figure 22.16 B and C. (b) No **22.57** (a) 2 unpaired electrons (b) 3 unpaired electrons (c) 2 unpaired electrons **22.59** (a) 8 electrons in square planar field (low spin) (b) 7 electrons in square planar field (low spin) (c) 5 electrons in tetrahedral field (high spin) (d) 7 electrons in tetrahedral field (high spin)
22.61 purple **22.63** Yes, H_2O is a weaker-bonding ligand.
22.65 239 kJ/mol **22.67** no d electrons
22.69 3 isomers

Yes, it does rule out a planar hexagonal geometry.
22.73 $[Cu^{2+}] = 6.1 \times 10^{-4}$ M; $[NH_3] = 2.4 \times 10^{-3}$ M; $[Cu(NH_3)_4^{2+}] = 0.10$ M

CHAPTER 23

23.19 (a) The molecules with carbon chains in the C_5–C_{12} range.
(b) The molecules with carbon chains greater than C_{11}.
(c) Low-molecular-mass hydrocarbons have fewer polarizable electrons; therefore, they have weaker London forces than the larger chains and boil at a lower temperature. (d) The more compact 2,3-dimethylbutane would boil at a lower temperature.
23.21 This compound would violate the octet rule.
23.23 (a) trimethylamine, C_3H_9N; acetaldehyde, C_2H_4O;
2-propanol, C_3H_8O; acetic acid, $C_2H_4O_2$
(b) trimethylamine: CH_3 acetaldehyde: O
CH_3NCH_3 CH_3CH

2-propanol: OH   acetic acid: O
CH_3CHCH_3 CH_3COH

(c) trimethylamine: amine (tertiary); acetaldehyde: aldehyde;
2-propanol: alcohol; acetic acid: carboxylic acid
23.25 The molecules increase regularly in molecular mass. Therefore, you expect their intermolecular forces, and thus their melting points, to increase. **23.27** $CH_3CH_2CH_2CH_3$

23.29 (a)

cis-3-Hexene

trans-3-Hexene

(b)

cis-3-Methyl-3-hexene

trans-3-Methyl-3-hexene

23.31 (a) $C_2H_4 + 3O_2 \longrightarrow 2CO_2 + 2H_2O$
(b) $3CH_2{=}CH_2 + 2MnO_4^- + 4H_2O \longrightarrow$

$$3CH_2{-}CH_2 + 2MnO_2 + 2OH^-$$
with OH, OH on the carbons

(c) $CH_2{=}CH_2 + Br_2 \longrightarrow CH_2{-}CH_2$
with Br, Br on the carbons

(d)

(e)

23.33 One possibility: $C_2H_6 + Cl_2 \longrightarrow C_2H_5Cl + HCl$

23.35

23.37 (a) 2,3,4-trimethylpentane (b) 2,2,6,6-tetramethylheptane
(c) 4-ethyloctane (d) 3,4-dimethyloctane

23.39 (a)

(b)

(c)

(d)

23. 41 (a) 2-pentene (b) 2,5-dimethyl-2-hexene

23.43 (a)

(b)

23.45 cis-2-pentene, trans-2-pentene **23.47** (a) 2-butyne
(b) 3-methyl-1-pentyne

23.49 (a)

(b)

23.51 (a)

ketone

(b)

alcohol

(c)

carboxylic acid

(d)

aldehyde

23.53 (a) 1-pentanol (b) 2-pentanol (c) 2-propyl-1-pentanol
(d) 6-methyl-4-octanol **23.55** (a) secondary alcohol
(b) secondary alcohol (c) primary alcohol (d) primary alcohol
23.57 (a) ethyl propyl ether (b) methyl isopropyl ether
23.59 (a) butanone (b) butanal (c) 4,4-dimethylpentanal
(d) 3-methyl-2-pentanone
23.61 (a) secondary amine (b) secondary amine
23.63 (a) 3-methylbutanoic acid (b) trans-5-methyl-2-hexene
(c) 2,5-dimethyl-4-heptanone (d) 4-methyl-2-pentyne

23.65 (a)

(b)

(c)

(d)

23.67 (a) Addition of dichromate ion in acidic solution to propi-
onaldehyde will cause the reagent to change from orange to green
as the aldehyde is oxidized. Under similar conditions, acetone
would not react. (b) Add Br_2 in CCl_4 to each compound. First
compound reacts; the color of Br_2 fades. Benzene does not react.
23.69 (a) ethylene (b) toluene (c) methylamine (d) methanol
23.71 1-butene or 2-butene

CHAPTER 24

24.21 (a) $-A-A-A-A-A-A-$ and
$-B-B-B-B-B-B-$
(b) $-A-B-A-B-A-B-$
(c) $-A-A-C-A-A-C-$

24.23

24.25 The corresponding amino-acid sequence is Arg-Val-Arg-
Asp-Leu-Thr. The triplet UGA is the code to end the sequence.

24.27 $nCF_2 = CF_2 \longrightarrow -CF_2-CF_2-CF_2-CF_2-CF_2-CF_2-$

24.29 $HOCH_2CH_2OH$ and $HOOCCH_2CH_2COOH$

24.31 (a) would give a polymer having alternating single and double bonds, in which resonance might be expected to give a conducting polymer.

24.33

$$CH_3 - \underset{\underset{NH_3^+}{|}}{\overset{\overset{H}{|}}{C}} - COO^-$$

24.35 Two dipeptides are possible:

and

24.37 A:T, 1:1, G:C, 1:1

24.39

24.41 3; 2; guanine-cytosine bonding is stronger. **24.43** 16; no

24.45 hydrogen bonds; less readily

24.47 gly-ser-arg-phe-gly-leu-lys-end

24.49 CUG, ACU, CCC, UGG

24.51 CUU GCU GUU GAA GAU UGU AUG UGG AAA

24.53

$$-\underset{\underset{Cl}{|}}{\overset{\overset{H}{|}}{C}}-\underset{\underset{Cl}{|}}{\overset{\overset{H}{|}}{C}}-\underset{\underset{Cl}{|}}{\overset{\overset{H}{|}}{C}}-\underset{\underset{Cl}{|}}{\overset{\overset{H}{|}}{C}}-$$

24.55 $HOOC-C_6H_4-COOH$, $NH_2-C_6H_4-NH_2$

24.57 $CH_3SCH_2CH_2\underset{\underset{NH_2}{|}}{CH}-COOH$ has a nonpolar side chain

24.59

$$^+H_3N-\underset{\underset{\underset{OH}{|}}{\overset{|}{CH_2}}}{\overset{\overset{COO^-}{|}}{\underset{|}{C}}}-H$$

24.61 $CH_3SCH_2CH_2\underset{\underset{NH_2}{|}}{CH}-\overset{\overset{O}{\|}}{C}-NH-\underset{\underset{CH_2SH}{|}}{CH}-COOH$

$HSCH_2\underset{\underset{NH_2}{|}}{CH}-\overset{\overset{O}{\|}}{C}-NH-\underset{\underset{\underset{CH_2SCH_3}{|}}{CH_2}}{CH}-COOH$

24.63 720   **24.65** adenine, ribose, phosphate ion

Glossary

The number given in blue at the end of a definition indicates the section where the term was introduced. In some cases, more than one section is indicated. In a few cases, the term is defined in an introductory passage just *before* the section indicated.

Absolute entropy see *Standard entropy*.

Absolute temperature scale a temperature scale in which the lowest temperature that can be attained theoretically is zero. (1.6)

Accuracy the closeness of a single measurement to its true value. (1.5)

Acid (Arrhenius definition) a substance that produces hydrogen ions, H^+ (hydronium ion, H_3O^+), when it dissolves in water. (4.4 and 15.1) (Brønsted–Lowry definition) the species (molecule or ion) that donates a proton to another species in a proton-transfer reaction. (4.4 and 15.2)

Acid–base indicator a dye used to distinguish between acidic and basic solutions by means of the color changes it undergoes in these solutions. (4.4)

Acid–base titration curve a plot of the pH of a solution of acid (or base) against the volume of added base (or acid). (16.7)

Acidic oxide an oxide that reacts with bases. (8.7)

Acid-ionization (or acid-dissociation) constant (K_a) the equilibrium constant for the ionization of a weak acid. (16.1)

Acid rain rain having a pH lower than that of natural rain, which has a pH of 5.6. (16.2)

Acid salt a salt that has an acidic hydrogen atom and can undergo neutralization with bases. (4.4)

Actinides elements in the last of the two rows at the bottom of the periodic table; actinium plus the 14 elements following it in the periodic table, in which the 5*f* subshell is filling. (22.1)

Activated complex (transition state) an unstable grouping of atoms that can break up to form products. (13.5)

Activation energy (E_a) the minimum energy of collision required for two molecules to react. (13.5)

Activity of a radioactive source the number of nuclear disintegrations per unit time occurring in a radioactive material. (20.3)

Activity series a listing of the elements in order of their ease of losing electrons during reactions in aqueous solution. (4.5)

Addition polymer a polymer formed by linking together many molecules by addition reactions. (24.1)

Addition reaction a reaction in which parts of a reactant are added to each carbon atom of a carbon–carbon double bond, which then becomes a C—C single bond. (23.3)

Adsorption the binding or attraction of molecules to a surface. (13.9) See *Chemisorption* and *Physical adsorption*.

Aerosol a colloid consisting of liquid droplets or solid particles dispersed throughout a gas. (12.9)

Alcohol a compound obtained by substituting a hydroxyl group (—OH) for an —H atom on a tetrahedral (sp^3 hybridized) carbon atom of a hydrocarbon group. (23.6)

Aldehyde a compound containing a carbonyl group with at least one H atom attached to it. (23.6)

Aliphatic hydrocarbon a saturated or unsaturated hydrocarbon; a hydrocarbon that does not contain benzene rings. (23.1)

Alkali metals the Group IA elements; they are reactive metals. (2.5 and 8.7)

Alkaline dry cell a voltaic cell that is similar to the Leclanché dry cell but uses potassium hydroxide in place of ammonium chloride. (19.8)

Alkaline earth metals the Group IIA elements; they are reactive metals, though less reactive than the alkali metals. (8.7)

Alkane an acyclic saturated hydrocarbon (one without a ring of carbon atoms); a saturated hydrocarbon with the general formula C_nH_{2n+2}. (23.2)

Alkene a hydrocarbon that has the general formula C_nH_{2n} and contains a carbon–carbon double bond. (23.3)

Alkyl group an alkane less one hydrogen atom. (23.5)

Alkyne an unsaturated hydrocarbon containing a carbon–carbon triple bond. The general formula is C_nH_{2n-2}. (23.3)

Allotrope one of two or more distinct forms of an element in the same physical state. (6.8)

Alloy a material with metallic properties that is either a compound or a mixture. (21.2)

Alpha emission emission of a ^4_2He nucleus, or alpha particle, from an unstable nucleus. (20.1)

Amide bond see *Peptide bond*.

Amide a compound derived from the reaction of ammonia, or a primary or secondary amine, with a carboxylic acid. (23.7)

Amine a compound that is structurally derived by replacing one or more hydrogen atoms of ammonia with hydrocarbon groups. (23.7)

Amino acid a compound containing an amino group (—NH_2) and a carboxyl group (—COOH). (24.3)

Amorphous solid a solid that has a disordered structure; it lacks the well-defined arrangement of basic units (atoms, molecules, or ions) found in a crystal. (11.7)

Ampere (A) the base unit of current in the International System (SI). (19.11)

Amphiprotic species a species that can act as either an acid or a base (that is, it can either lose or gain a proton). (15.2)

Amphoteric hydroxide a metal hydroxide that reacts with both bases and acids. (17.5)

Amphoteric oxide an oxide that has both acidic and basic properties. (8.7)

Angstrom (Å) a non-SI unit of length; $1 Å = 10^{-10} m$. (1.6)

Angular geometry see *Bent geometry*.

Angular momentum quantum number (*l*) also known as the azimuthal quantum number. The quantum number that distinguishes orbitals of given *n* having different shapes; it can have any integer value from 0 to $n - 1$. (7.5)

Anion a negatively charged ion. (2.6)

Anode the electrode at which oxidation occurs. (19.2)

Antibonding orbitals molecular orbitals having zero values in the region between two nuclei and therefore concentrated in other regions. (10.5)

Aromatic hydrocarbon a hydrocarbon that contains a benzene ring or similar structural feature. (23.1)

Arrhenius equation the mathematical equation $k = Ae^{-E_a/RT}$, which expresses the dependence of the rate constant on temperature. (13.6)

Association colloid a colloid in which the dispersed phase consists of micelles. (12.9)

Atmosphere (atm) a unit of pressure equal to exactly 760 mmHg; $1 atm = 101.325 kPa$ (exact). (5.1)

Atom an extremely small particle of matter that retains its identity during chemical reactions. (2.1)

Atomic mass as a general term, the mass of an individual atom; but usually we mean the average atomic mass for the naturally occurring element, expressed in atomic mass units. (2.4)

Atomic mass unit (amu) a mass unit equal to exactly one-twelfth the mass of a carbon-12 atom. (2.4)

Atomic number (Z) the number of protons in the nucleus of an atom. (2.3)

Atomic orbital a wave function for an electron in an atom; pictured qualitatively by describing the region of space where there is a high probability of finding the electron. (7.5)

Atomic symbol a one- or two-letter notation used to represent an atom corresponding to a particular element. A temporary name with a three letter notation (denoting the atomic number) is given to newly discovered elements. (2.1)

Atomic theory an explanation of the structure of matter in terms of different combinations of very small particles (atoms). (2.1)

Aufbau principle see *Building-up principle.*

Autoionization see *Self-ionization.*

Avogadro's law equal volumes of any two gases at the same temperature and pressure contain the same number of molecules. (5.2)

Avogadro's number (N_A) the number of atoms in a 12-g sample of carbon-12, equal to 6.02×10^{23} to three significant figures. (3.2)

Axial direction one of two directions pointing from the center of a trigonal bipyramid along its axis. Compare *Equatorial direction.* (10.1)

Azimuthal quantum number see *Angular momentum quantum number.*

Band of stability the region in which stable nuclides lie in a plot of number of protons against number of neutrons. (20.1)

Band theory molecular orbital theory of metals. (21.3)

Bar a unit of pressure equal to 1×10^5 Pa, slightly less than 1 atm. (5.1)

Barometer a device for measuring the pressure of the atmosphere. (5.1)

Base (Arrhenius definition) a substance that produces hydroxide ions, OH^-, when it dissolves in water. (4.4 and 15.1) (Brønsted–Lowry definition) the species (molecule or ion) that accepts a proton in a proton-transfer reaction. (4.4 and 15.2)

Base-ionization (or base-dissociation) constant (K_b) the equilibrium constant for the ionization of a weak base. Thus K_b for NH_3 is 1.8×10^{-5}. (16.3)

Base pairing the hydrogen bonding of complementary bases. (24.4)

Basic oxide an oxide that reacts with acids. (8.7)

Bayer process a chemical procedure in which purified aluminum oxide, Al_2O_3, is separated from the aluminum ore bauxite. (21.2)

Bent geometry (angular geometry) nonlinear molecular geometry, in the case of a molecule of three atoms. (10.1)

Beta emission emission of a high-speed electron from an unstable nucleus. (20.1)

Bidentate ligand a ligand that bonds to a metal atom through two atoms of the ligand. (22.3)

Bimolecular reaction an elementary reaction that involves two reactant molecules. (13.7)

Binary compound a compound composed of only two elements. (2.8)

Binary hydride a compound that contains hydrogen and one other element. (21.7)

Binding energy (of a nucleus) the energy needed to break a nucleus into its individual protons and neutrons. (20.6)

Body-centered cubic unit cell a cubic unit cell in which there is a lattice point at the center of the unit cell as well as at the corners. (11.7)

Boiling point the temperature at which the vapor pressure of a liquid equals the pressure exerted on the liquid (atmospheric pressure, unless the vessel containing the liquid is closed). (11.2)

Boiling-point elevation a colligative property of a solution equal to the boiling point of the solution minus the boiling point of the pure solvent. (12.6)

Bond distance see *Bond length.*

Bond energy the average enthalpy change for the breaking of a bond in a molecule in the gas phase. (9.11)

Bonding orbitals molecular orbitals that are concentrated in the regions between nuclei. (10.5)

Bonding pair an electron pair shared between two atoms. (9.4)

Bond length (bond distance) the distance between the nuclei in a bond. (9.10)

Bond order in a Lewis formula, the number of pairs of electrons in a bond. (9.10)   In molecular orbital theory, one-half the difference between the number of bonding electrons and the number of antibonding electrons. (10.5)

Boyle's law the volume of a sample of gas at a given temperature varies inversely with the applied pressure. (5.2)

Brønsted–Lowry concept a concept of acids and bases in which an acid is the species donating a proton in a proton-transfer reaction, whereas a base is the species accepting a proton in such a reaction. (4.4 and 15.2)

Buckminsterfullerene a molecular form of carbon (C_{60}) informally called "buckyball," referring to its soccer-ball shape; a fullerene. (21.8)

Buffer a solution characterized by the ability to resist changes in pH when limited amounts of acid or base are added to it. (16.6)

Building-up principle (Aufbau principle) a scheme used to reproduce the electron configurations of the ground states of atoms by successively filling subshells with electrons in a specific order (the building-up order). (8.2)

Calorie (cal) a non-SI unit of energy commonly used by chemists, originally defined as the amount of energy needed to raise the temperature of 1 g of water by 1°C; now defined as 1 cal = 4.184 J (exact). (6.1)

Calorimeter a device used to measure the heat absorbed or evolved during a physical or chemical change. (6.6)

Carboxylic acid a compound containing the carboxyl group, —COOH, whose H atom is acidic. (23.6)

Catalysis the increase in rate of a reaction as the result of the addition of a catalyst. (13.9)

Catalyst a substance that increases the rate of reaction without being consumed in the overall reaction. (2.9 and 13.1)

Catenation the covalent bonding of two or more atoms of the same element to one another. (21.7)

Cathode the electrode at which reduction occurs. (19.2)

Cathode rays the rays emitted by the cathode (negative electrode) in a gas discharge tube (tube of low-pressure gas through which an electric current is discharged). (2.2)

Cation a positively charged ion. (2.6)

Cation exchange resin a resin (organic polymer) that removes cations from solution and replaces them with hydrogen ions. (11.10)

Cell potential the maximum potential difference between the electrodes of a voltaic cell. (19.4)

Cell reaction the net reaction that occurs in a voltaic cell. (19.2)

Celsius scale the temperature scale in general scientific use. There are exactly 100 units between the freezing point and the normal boiling point of water. (1.6)

Chain reaction, nuclear a self-sustaining series of nuclear fissions caused by the absorption of neutrons released from previous nuclear fissions. (20.7)

Change of state (phase transition) a change of a substance from one state to another. (11.2)

Charles's law the volume occupied by any sample of gas at a constant pressure is directly proportional to the absolute temperature. (5.2)

Chelate a complex formed by polydentate ligands. (22.3)

Chemical bond a strong attractive force that exists between certain atoms in a substance. (Ch. 9 opener)

Chemical change see *Chemical reaction.*

Chemical equation the symbolic representation of a chemical reaction in terms of chemical formulas. (2.9)

Chemical equilibrium the state reached by a reaction mixture when the rates of forward and reverse reactions have become equal. (14.1)

Chemical formula a notation that uses atomic symbols with numerical subscripts to convey the relative proportions of atoms of the different elements in a substance. (2.6)

Chemical kinetics the study of how reaction rates change under varying conditions and of what molecular events occur during the overall reaction. (13.1)

Chemical nomenclature the systematic naming of chemical compounds. (2.8)

Chemical property a characteristic of a material involving its chemical change. (1.4)

Chemical reaction (chemical change) a change in which one or more kinds of matter are transformed into a new kind of matter or several new kinds of matter. (1.4)   The rearrangement of the atoms present in the reacting substances to give new chemical combinations present in the substances formed by the reaction. (2.1)

Chemisorption the binding of a species to a surface by chemical bonding forces. (13.9)

Chiral possessing the quality of handedness. A chiral object has a mirror image that is not identical to the object. (22.5)

Chlor–alkali membrane cell a cell for the electrolysis of aqueous sodium chloride in which the anode and cathode compartments are separated by a special plastic membrane that allows only cations to pass through it. (19.10)

Chlor–alkali mercury cell a cell for the electrolysis of aqueous sodium chloride in which mercury metal is used as the cathode. (19.10)

Chromatography a name given to a group of similar separation techniques that depend on how fast a substance moves, in a stream of gas or liquid, past a stationary phase to which the substance may be slightly attracted. (1.5)

cis-trans **isomers** see *Geometric isomers*

Clausius–Clapeyron equation an equation that expresses the relation between the vapor pressure P of a liquid and the absolute temperature T: $\ln P = -\Delta H_{vap}/RT + B$, where B is a constant. (11.2)

Claus process a method of obtaining free sulfur by the partial burning of hydrogen sulfide. (21.10)

Coagulation the process by which the dispersed phase of a colloid is made to aggregate and thereby separate from the continuous phase. (12.9)

Codon a sequence of three bases in a messenger RNA molecule that serves as the code for a particular amino acid. (24.4)

Colligative properties properties that depend on the concentration of solute molecules or ions in a solution but not on the chemical identity of the solute. (12.4)

Collision theory the theory that in order for reaction to occur, reactant molecules must collide with an energy greater than some minimum value and with proper orientation. (13.5)

Colloid a dispersion of particles of one substance (the dispersed phase) throughout another substance or solution (the continuous phase). (12.9)

Combination reaction a reaction in which two substances combine to form a third substance. (4.5)

Combustion reaction a reaction of a substance with oxygen, usually with the rapid release of heat to produce a flame. (4.5)

Common-ion effect the shift in an ionic equilibrium caused by the addition of a solute that provides an ion that takes part in the equilibrium. (16.5 and 17.2)

Complementary bases nucleotide bases that form strong hydrogen bonds with one another. (24.4)

Complete ionic equation a chemical equation in which strong electrolytes (such as soluble ionic compounds) are written as separate ions in the solution. (4.2)

Complex (coordination compound) a compound consisting either of complex ions and other ions of opposite charge or of a neutral complex species. (22.3)

Complex ion an ion formed from a metal ion with a Lewis base attached to it by a coordinate covalent bond. (17.5 and 22.3)

Compound a substance composed of two or more elements chemically combined. (1.4)   A type of matter composed of atoms of two or more elements chemically combined in fixed proportions. (2.1)

Concentration a general term referring to the quantity of solute in a standard quantity of solvent or solution. (4.7 and 12.4)

Condensation the change of a gas to either the liquid or the solid state. (11.2)

Condensation polymer a polymer formed by linking many molecules together by condensation reactions. (24.1)

Condensation reaction a reaction in which two molecules or ions are chemically joined by the elimination of a small molecule such as water. (21.8)

Condensed (structural) formula a structural formula in which the bonds around each carbon atom are not explicitly written. (23.2)

Conjugate acid in a conjugate acid–base pair, the species that can donate a proton. (15.2)

Conjugate acid–base pair two species in an acid–base reaction, one acid and one base, that differ by the loss or gain of a proton. (15.2)

Conjugate base in a conjugate acid–base pair, the species that can accept a proton. (15.2)

Constitutional (structural) isomers isomers that differ in how the atoms are joined together (22.5); compounds with the same molecular formula but different structural formulas. (23.2)

Contact process an industrial method for the manufacture of sulfuric acid. It consists of the reaction of sulfur dioxide with oxygen to form sulfur trioxide using a catalyst of vanadium(V) oxide, followed by the reaction of sulfur trioxide with water. (21.10)

Continuous spectrum a spectrum containing light of all wavelengths. (7.3)

Control rods cylinders composed of substances that absorb neutrons, such as boron and cadmium, and can therefore slow a nuclear chain reaction. (20.7)

Conversion factor a factor equal to 1 that converts a quantity expressed in one unit to a quantity expressed in another unit. (1.8)

Coordinate covalent bond a bond formed when both electrons of the bond are donated by one atom. (9.4)

Coordination compound a compound consisting either of complex ions and other ions of opposite charge or of a neutral complex species. (22.3)

Coordination isomers isomers consisting of complex cations and complex anions that differ in the way the ligands are distributed between the metal atoms. (22.5)

Coordination number in a crystal, the number of nearest-neighbor atoms of an atom. (11.8)   In a complex, the total number of bonds the metal atom forms with ligands. (22.3)

Copolymer a polymer consisting of two or more different monomer units. (24.1)

Covalent bond a chemical bond formed by the sharing of a pair of electrons between atoms. (9.4)

Covalent network solid a solid that consists of atoms held together in large networks or chains by covalent bonds. (11.6)

Covalent radii values assigned to atoms in such a way that the sum of covalent radii of atoms A and B predicts an approximate A—B bond length. (9.10)

Critical mass the smallest mass of fissionable material in which a chain reaction can be sustained. (20.7)

Critical pressure the vapor pressure at the critical temperature; it is the minimum pressure that must be applied to a gas at the critical temperature to liquefy it. (11.3)

Critical temperature the temperature above which the liquid state of a substance no longer exists regardless of the pressure. (11.3)

Crystal a kind of solid having a regular three-dimensional arrangement of atoms, molecules, or ions. (2.6)

Crystal field splitting (Δ) the difference in energy between the two sets of *d* orbitals on a central metal ion that arises from the interaction of the orbitals with the electric field of the ligands. (22.7)

Crystal field theory a model of the electronic structure of transition-metal complexes that considers how the energies of the *d* orbitals of a metal ion are affected by the electric field of the ligands. (22.7)

Crystal lattice the geometric arrangement of lattice points of a crystal, in which we choose one lattice point at the same location within each of the basic units of the crystal. (11.7)

Crystalline solid a solid composed of one or more crystals; each crystal has a well-defined ordered structure in three dimensions. (11.7)

Crystal systems the seven basic shapes possible for unit cells; a classification of crystals. (11.7)

Cubic close-packed structure (ccp) a crystal structure composed of close-packed atoms (or other units) with the stacking ABCABCABCA···. It has a face-centered cubic unit cell. (11.8)

Curie (Ci) a unit of activity, equal to 3.700×10^{10} disintegrations per second. (20.3)

Cycloalkane a cyclic saturated hydrocarbon; that is, a saturated hydrocarbon in which the carbon atoms form a ring; the general formula is C_nH_{2n}. (23.2)

Cyclotron a type of particle accelerator consisting of two hollow, semicircular metal electrodes, called dees (because the shape resembles the letter D), in which charged particles are accelerated by stages to higher and higher kinetic energies. Ions introduced at the center of the cyclotron are accelerated in the space between the two dees. (20.2)

Dalton's law of partial pressures the sum of the partial pressures of all the different gases in a mixture is equal to the total pressure of the mixture. (5.5)

***d*-Block transition elements** those transition elements with an unfilled *d* subshell in common oxidation states. (8.2)

de Broglie relation the equation $\lambda = h/mv$. (7.4)

Decomposition reaction a reaction in which a single compound reacts to give two or more substances. (4.5)

Degree of ionization the fraction of molecules that react with water to give ions. (16.1)

Delocalized bonding a type of bonding in which a bonding pair of electrons is spread over a number of atoms rather than localized between two. (9.7)

Denitrifying bacteria bacteria that use nitrate ion, NO_3^-, as a source of energy; they convert the ion to gaseous nitrogen. (21.9)

Density the mass per unit volume of a substance or solution. (1.7)

Deoxyribonucleic acid (DNA) the hereditary constituent of cells; it consists of two polymer strands of deoxyribonucleotide units. (24.4)

Deposition the change of a vapor to a solid. (11.2)

Derived unit see *SI derived unit*.

Desalinate remove ions from brackish (slightly salty) water or seawater, to make drinkable or industrially usable water. (12.7)

Deuterons nucleus of a hydrogen-2 atom. (20.2)

Dextrorotatory refers to a compound whose solution rotates the plane of polarized light to the right (when looking toward the source of light). (22.5)

Diamagnetic substance a substance that is not attracted by a magnetic field or is very slightly repelled by such a field. This property generally means that the substance has only paired electrons. (8.4)

Diffusion the process whereby a gas spreads out through another gas to occupy the space uniformly. (5.7)

Dimensional analysis (factor-label method) the method of calculation in which one carries along the units for quantities. (1.8)

Dipole–dipole force an attractive intermolecular force resulting from the tendency of polar molecules to align themselves such that the positive end of one molecule is near the negative end of another. (11.5)

Dipole moment a quantitative measure of the degree of charge separation in a molecule. (10.2)

Dispersion forces see *London forces*.

Displacement reaction (single-replacement reaction) a reaction in which an element reacts with a compound, displacing another element from it. (4.5)

Dissociation constant of a complex ion (K_d) the reciprocal, or inverse, value of the formation constant. (17.5)

Distillation the process in which a liquid is vaporized then condensed; used to separate substances of different volatilities. (1.4)

Distorted tetrahedral geometry see *Seesaw geometry*.

Disulfide linkage a covalent linkage formed between two cysteine groups within a protein molecule by oxidation of the two groups. (24.3)

Double bond a covalent bond in which two pairs of electrons are shared by two atoms. (9.4)

Downs cell a commercial electrochemical cell used to obtain sodium metal by the electrolysis of molten sodium chloride. (19.9)

Dow process a commercial method for isolating magnesium from seawater. (21.2)

Dry cell see *Alkaline dry cell* and *Zinc–carbon dry cell*.

Effective nuclear charge the positive charge that an electron experiences from the nucleus, equal to the nuclear charge but reduced by any shielding or screening from any intervening electron distribution. (8.6)

Effusion the process in which a gas flows through a small hole in a container. (5.7)

Elastomer elastic or rubbery type of polymer. (24.1)

Electrochemical cell a system consisting of electrodes that dip into an electrolyte and in which a chemical reaction either uses or generates an electric current. (19.2)

Electrolysis the process of producing a chemical change in an electrolytic cell. (19.9)

Electrolyte a substance, such as sodium chloride, that dissolves in water to give an electrically conducting solution. (4.1)

Electrolytic cell an electrochemical cell in which an electric current drives an otherwise nonspontaneous reaction. (19.1)

Electromagnetic spectrum the range of frequencies or wavelengths of electromagnetic radiation. (7.1)

Electromotive force (emf) see *Cell potential*.

Electron a very light, negatively charged particle that exists in the region around the atom's positively charged nucleus. (2.2)

Electron affinity the energy change for the process of adding an electron to a neutral atom in the gaseous state to form a negative ion. (8.6)

Electron capture the decay of an unstable nucleus by capturing, or picking up, an electron from an inner orbital of an atom. (20.1)

Electron configuration the particular distribution of electrons among available subshells. (8.1)

Electronegativity a measure of the ability of an atom in a molecule to draw bonding electrons to itself. (9.5)

Electron spin quantum number (m_s) see *Spin quantum number.*

Electron volt (eV) the quantity of energy that would have to be imparted to an electron (whose charge is 1.602×10^{-19} C) to accelerate it by one volt potential difference. (20.2)

Element a substance that cannot be decomposed by any chemical reaction into simpler substances. (1.4)   A type of matter composed of only one kind of atom, each atom of a given kind having the same properties. (2.1)   A substance whose atoms all have the same atomic number. (2.3)

Elementary reaction a single molecular event, such as a collision of molecules, resulting in a reaction. (13.7)

Empirical formula (simplest formula) the formula of a substance written with the smallest integer (whole-number) subscripts. (3.5)

Emulsion a colloid consisting of liquid droplets dispersed throughout another liquid. (12.9)

Enantiomers (optical isomers) isomers that are nonsuperimposable mirror images of one another. (22.5)

Endothermic process a chemical reaction or physical change in which heat is absorbed. (6.2)

Energy the potential or capacity to move matter. (6.1)

Energy levels specific energy values in an atom. (7.3)

Enthalpy (H) an extensive property of a substance that can be used to obtain the heat absorbed or evolved in a chemical reaction at constant pressure. (6.3)   It equals the quantity $U + PV$. (18.1)

Enthalpy of formation see *Standard enthalpy of formation.*

Enthalpy of reaction (ΔH) the change in enthalpy for a reaction at a given temperature and pressure; it equals the heat of reaction at constant pressure. (6.3)

Entropy (S) a thermodynamic quantity that is a measure of how dispersed the energy of a system is among the different possible ways that a system can contain energy. (18.2)

Enzyme a protein that catalyzes a biochemical reaction. (24.3)

Equatorial direction one of the three directions pointing from the center of a trigonal bipyramid to a vertex other than one on the axis. Compare *Axial direction.* (10.1)

Equilibrium see *Chemical equilibrium.*

Equilibrium constant K_c the value obtained for the equilibrium-constant expression when equilibrium concentrations are substituted. (14.2)

Equilibrium constant K_p an equilibrium constant for a gas reaction, similar to K_c, but in which concentrations of gases are replaced by partial pressures (in atm). (14.2)

Equilibrium-constant expression an expression obtained for a reaction by multiplying the concentrations of products, dividing by the concentrations of reactants, and raising each concentration term to a power equal to the coefficient in the chemical equation. (14.2)

Equivalence point the point in a titration when a stoichiometric amount of reactant has been added. (16.7)

Ester a compound formed from a carboxylic acid, RCOOH, and an alcohol, R'OH. (23.6)

Ether a compound formally obtained by replacing both H atoms of H_2O by hydrocarbon groups R and R'. (23.6)

Exact number a number that arises when you count items or sometimes when you define a unit. (1.5)

Exchange (metathesis) reaction a reaction between compounds that, when written as a molecular equation, appears to involve the exchange of parts between the two reactants. (4.3)

Excited state a quantum-mechanical state of an atom or molecule associated with any energy level except the lowest, which is the ground state. (8.2)

Exclusion principle see *Pauli exclusion principle.*

Exothermic process a chemical reaction or physical change in which heat is evolved. (6.2)

Experiment an observation of natural phenomena carried out in a controlled manner so that the results can be duplicated and rational conclusions obtained. (1.2)

Face-centered cubic unit cell a cubic unit cell in which there are lattice points at the center of each face of the unit cell in addition to those at the corners. (11.7)

Factor-label method see *Dimensional analysis.*

Faraday constant (F) the magnitude of charge on one mole of electrons, equal to 9.6485×10^4 C. (19.4)

f-Block transition elements (inner transition elements) the elements with a partially filled f subshell in common oxidation states. (8.2)

Fibrous proteins proteins that form long coils or align themselves in parallel to form long, water-insoluble fibers. (24.3)

First ionization energy (first ionization potential) the minimum energy needed to remove the highest-energy (that is, the outermost) electron from a neutral atom in the gaseous state. (8.6)

First law of thermodynamics the change in internal energy of a system, ΔU, equals $q + w$. (18.1)

Formal charge (of an atom in a Lewis formula) the hypothetical charge you obtain by assuming that bonding electrons are equally shared between bonded atoms and that the electrons of each lone pair belong completely to one atom. (9.9)

Formation constant (stability constant) of a complex ion (K_f) the equilibrium constant for the formation of a complex ion from the aqueous metal ion and the ligands. (17.5)

Formula see *Chemical formula* and *Molecular formula.*

Formula unit the group of atoms or ions explicitly symbolized in the formula. (2.6)

Formula mass (FM) the sum of the atomic masses of all atoms in a formula unit of a compound. (3.1)

Fractional (isotopic) abundance the fraction of the total number of atoms that is composed of a particular isotope. (2.4)

Fractional precipitation the technique of separating two or more ions from a solution by adding a reactant that precipitates first one ion, then another, and so forth. (17.3)

Frasch process a mining procedure in which underground deposits of solid sulfur are melted in place with superheated water, and the molten sulfur is forced upward as a froth using air under pressure. (21.10)

Free energy (G) a thermodynamic quantity defined by the equation $G = H - TS$. (18.4)

Free energy of formation see *Standard free energy of formation.*

Freezing the change of a liquid to the solid state. (11.2)

Freezing point the temperature at which a pure liquid changes to a crystalline solid, or freezes. (11.2)

Freezing-point depression a colligative property of a solution equal to the freezing point of the pure solvent minus the freezing point of the solution. (12.6)

Frequency (ν) the number of wavelengths of a wave that pass a fixed point in one unit of time (usually one second). (7.1)

Frequency factor the symbol A in the Arrhenius equation, assumed to be a constant. (13.6)

Fuel cell essentially a battery, but it differs by operating with a continuous supply of energetic reactants, or fuel. (19.8)

Fuel rods the cylinders that contain fissionable material for a nuclear reactor. (20.7)

Fullerene a family of molecules consisting of a closed cage of carbon atoms arranged in pentagons as well as hexagons. (21.8)

Functional group a reactive portion of a molecule that undergoes predictable reactions. (2.7 and 23.6)

Fusion see *Melting;* see also *Nuclear fusion.*

Galvanic cell see *Voltaic cell.*

Gamma emission emission from an excited nucleus of a gamma photon, corresponding to radiation with a wavelength of about 10^{-12} m. (20.1)

Gamma photon a particle of electromagnetic radiation of short wavelength (about 1 pm, or 10^{-12} m) and high energy. (20.1)

Gas the form of matter that is an easily compressible fluid; a given quantity of gas will fit into a container of almost any size and shape. (1.4)

Gas chromatography a chromatographic separation method in which a gaseous mixture of vaporized substances is separated into its components by passing the mixture through a column of packing material. Substances in the gaseous mixture are attracted to the packing material to different extents and thus move through the column at different rates. (1.5)

Geiger counter a kind of ionization counter used to count particles emitted by radioactive nuclei. It consists of a metal tube filled with gas, such as argon. (20.3)

Gene a sequence of nucleotides in a DNA molecule that codes for a given protein. (24.4)

Geometric isomers isomers in which the atoms are joined to one another in the same way but differ because some atoms occupy different relative positions in space. (10.4, 22.5, and 23.3)

Glass electrode a compact electrode used to determine pH by cell potential measurements. (19.7)

Globular proteins proteins in which long coils fold into compact, roughly spherical shapes. (24.3)

Goldschmidt process a method of preparing a metal by reduction of its oxide with powdered aluminum. (21.6)

Graham's law of effusion the rate of effusion of gas molecules from a particular hole is inversely proportional to the square root of the molecular weight of the gas at constant temperature and pressure. (5.7)

Gravimetric analysis a type of quantitative analysis in which the amount of a species in a material is determined by converting the species to a product that can be isolated completely and weighed. (4.9)

Ground state a quantum-mechanical state of an atom or molecule associated with the lowest energy level. States associated with higher energy levels are called *excited states.* (8.2)

Group (of the periodic table) the elements in any one column of the periodic table. (2.5)

Haber process an industrial process for the preparation of ammonia from nitrogen and hydrogen with a specially prepared catalyst, high temperature, and high pressure. (3.6 and 21.9)

Half-cell the portion of an electrochemical cell in which a half-reaction takes place. (19.2)

Half-life ($t_{1/2}$) the time it takes for the reactant concentration to decrease to one-half of its initial value. (13.4)   The time it takes for one-half of the nuclei in a sample to decay. (20.4)

Half-reaction one of two parts of an oxidation–reduction reaction, one part of which involves a loss of electrons (or increase of oxidation number) and the other a gain of electrons (or decrease of oxidation number). (4.5 and 19.1)

Hall–Héroult process the commercial method for producing aluminum by the electrolysis of a molten mixture of aluminum oxide in cryolite, Na_3AlF_6. (21.2)

Halogens the Group VIIA elements; they are reactive non-metals. (2.5 and 8.7)

Heat the energy that flows into or out of a system because of a difference in temperature between the thermodynamic system and its surroundings. (6.2)

Heat capacity (C) the quantity of heat needed to raise the temperature of a sample of substance one degree Celsius (or one kelvin). (6.6)

Heat of formation see *Standard enthalpy of formation.*

Heat of fusion (enthalpy of fusion) the heat needed for the melting of a solid. (11.2)

Heat of reaction the heat absorbed (or evolved) during a chemical reaction; it equals the value of q required to return the chemical system to a given temperature at the completion of the reaction. (6.2)

Heat of solution the heat absorbed (or evolved) when an ionic substance dissolves in water. (12.3)

Heat of vaporization (enthalpy of vaporization) the heat needed for the vaporization of a liquid. (11.2)

Henderson–Hasselbalch equation an equation relating the pH of a buffer for different concentrations of conjugate acid and base: pH = pK_a + log [base]/[acid]. (16.6)

Henry's law the solubility of a gas is directly proportional to the partial pressure of the gas above the solution. (12.3)

Hess's law of heat summation for a chemical equation that can be written as the sum of two or more steps, the enthalpy change for the overall equation equals the sum of the enthalpy changes for the individual steps. (6.7)

Heterogeneous catalysis the use of a catalyst that exists in a different phase from the reacting species, usually a solid catalyst in contact with a gaseous or liquid solution of reactants. (13.9)

Heterogeneous equilibrium an equilibrium that involves reactants and products in more than one phase. (14.3)

Heterogeneous mixture a mixture that consists of physically distinct parts, each with different properties. (1.4)

Heteronuclear diatomic molecules molecules composed of two different nuclei. (10.6)

Hexagonal close-packed structure (hcp) a crystal structure composed of close-packed atoms (or other units) with the stacking ABABABA · · ·; the structure has a hexagonal unit cell. (11.8)

High-spin complex ion a complex ion in which there is minimum pairing of electrons in the orbitals of the metal atom. (22.7)

Homogeneous catalysis the use of a catalyst in the same phase as the reacting species. (13.9)

Homogeneous equilibrium an equilibrium that involves reactants and products in a single phase. (14.3)

Homogeneous mixture (solution) a mixture that is uniform in its properties throughout given samples. (1.4)

Homologous series a series of compounds in which one compound differs from a preceding one by a fixed group of atoms, for example, a —CH_2— group. (23.2)

Homonuclear diatomic molecules molecules composed of two like nuclei. (10.6)

Homopolymer a polymer whose monomer units are all alike. (24.1)

Hund's rule the lowest-energy arrangement of electrons in a subshell is obtained by putting electrons into separate orbitals of the subshell with the same spin before pairing electrons. (8.4)

Hybrid orbitals orbitals used to describe bonding that are obtained by taking combinations of atomic orbitals of the isolated atoms. (10.3)

Hydrate a compound that contains water molecules weakly bound in its crystals. (2.8)

Hydration the attraction of ions for water molecules. (12.2)

Hydrocarbons compounds containing only carbon and hydrogen. (2.7 and 23.1)

Hydrogen bonding a weak to moderate attractive force that exists between a hydrogen atom covalently bonded to a very electronegative atom and a lone pair of electrons on another small, electronegative atom. It is represented in formulas by a series of dots. (11.5)

Hydrologic cycle the natural cycle of water from the oceans to fresh water sources and back to the oceans. (11.10)

Hydrolysis the reaction of an ion with water to produce the conjugate acid and hydroxide ion or the conjugate base and hydrogen ion. (16.4)

Hydronium ion the H_3O^+ ion; also called the hydrogen ion and written $H^+(aq)$. (4.4)

Hydrophilic colloid a colloid in which there is a strong attraction between the dispersed phase and the continuous phase (water). (12.9)

Hydrophobic colloid a colloid in which there is a lack of attraction between the dispersed phase and the continuous phase (water). (12.9)

Hypothesis a tentative explanation of some regularity of nature. (1.2)

Ideal gas law the equation $PV = nRT$, which combines all of the gas laws. (5.3)

Ideal solution a solution of two or more substances each of which follows Raoult's law. (12.5)

Immiscible fluids fluids that do not mix but form separate layers. (12.1)

Inert gases see *Noble gases.*

Initiator a compound that produces free radicals in a reaction for the preparation of an addition polymer. (24.1)

Inner transition elements the two rows of elements at the bottom of the periodic table (2.5); the elements with a partially filled *f* subshell in common oxidation states. (8.2 and 22.1)

Inorganic compounds compounds composed of elements other than carbon. A few simple compounds of carbon, including carbon monoxide, carbon dioxide, carbonates, and cyanides, are generally considered to be inorganic. (2.8)

Integrated rate law a mathematical relationship between concentration and time. (13.4)

Intermolecular forces the forces of interaction between molecules. (11.5)

Internal energy (U) the sum of the kinetic and the potential energies of the particles making up a system. (6.1 and 18.1)

International System of Units (SI) a particular choice of metric units that was adopted by the General Conference of Weights and Measures in 1960. (1.6)

Ion an electrically charged particle obtained from an atom or a chemically bonded group of atoms by adding or removing electrons. (2.6)

Ion exchange a process in which a water solution is passed through a column of a material that replaces one kind of ion in solution with another kind. (11.10)

Ionic bond a chemical bond formed by the electrostatic attraction between positive and negative ions. (9.1)

Ionic compound a compound composed of cations and anions. (2.6)

Ionic equation see *Complete ionic equation.*

Ionic radius a measure of the size of the spherical region around the nucleus of an ion within which the electrons are most likely to be found. (9.3)

Ionic solid a solid that consists of cations and anions held together by the electrical attraction of opposite charges (ionic bonds). (11.6)

Ionization energy the energy needed to remove an electron from an atom (or molecule). Often used to mean *first ionization energy.* (8.6)

Ion product (Q_c) the product of ion concentrations in a solution, each concentration raised to a power equal to the number of ions in the formula of the ionic compound. (17.3)

Ion-product constant for water (K_w) the equilibrium value of the ion product $[H_3O^+][OH^-]$. (15.6)

Ion-selective electrode an electrode whose cell potential depends on the concentration of a particular ion in solution. (19.7)

Isoelectronic refers to different species that have the same number and configuration of electrons. (9.3)

Isomers compounds of the same molecular formula but with different arrangements of the atoms. (10.4)

Isotope dilution a technique to determine the quantity of a substance in a mixture or the total volume of solution by adding a known amount of an isotope to it. (20.5)

Isotopes atoms whose nuclei have the same atomic number but different mass numbers; that is, the nuclei have the same number of protons but different numbers of neutrons. (2.3)

Joule (J) the SI unit of energy; $1 J = 1 kg \cdot m^2/s^2$. (6.1)

Kelvin (K) the SI base unit of temperature; a unit on the absolute temperature scale. (1.6)

Ketone a compound containing a carbonyl group with two hydrocarbon groups attached to it. (23.6)

Kilogram (kg) the SI base unit for mass; equal to about 2.2 pounds. (1.6)

Kinetic energy the energy associated with an object by virtue of its motion. (6.1)

Kinetic-molecular theory (kinetic theory) the theory that a gas consists of molecules in constant random motion. (5.5)

Kinetics, chemical see *Chemical kinetics.*

Lanthanides the first of the two rows of elements at the bottom of the periodic table; lanthanum plus the 14 elements following it in the periodic table, in which the 4*f* subshell is filling. (22.1)

Laser a source of intense, highly directed beam of monochromatic light; the word *laser* is an acronym meaning *l*ight *a*mplifi-cation by *s*timulated *e*mission of *r*adiation. (7.3)

Lattice energy the change in energy that occurs when an ionic solid is separated into isolated ions in the gas phase. (9.1 and 12.2)

Law a concise statement or mathematical equation about a fundamental relationship or regularity of nature. (1.2)

Law of combining volumes a relation stating that gases at the same temperature and pressure react with one another in volume ratios of small whole numbers. (5.2)

Law of conservation of energy energy may be converted from one form to another, but the total quantity of energy remains constant. (6.1)

Law of conservation of mass the total mass remains constant during a chemical change (chemical reaction). (1.3)

Law of definite proportions (law of constant composition) a pure compound, whatever its source, always contains definite or constant proportions of the elements by mass. (1.4)

Law of effusion see *Graham's law of effusion.*

Law of heat summation see *Hess's law of heat summation.*

Law of mass action the values of the equilibrium-constant expression K_c are constant for a particular reaction at a given temperature, whatever equilibrium concentrations are substituted. (14.2)

Law of multiple proportions when two elements form more than one compound, the masses of one element in these compounds for a fixed mass of the other element are in ratios of small whole numbers. (2.1)

Law of partial pressures see *Dalton's law of partial pressures.*

Lead storage cell a voltaic cell that consists of electrodes of lead alloy grids; one electrode is packed with a spongy lead to form the anode, and the other is packed with lead dioxide to form the cathode. (19.8)

Le Châtelier's principle when a system in equilibrium is disturbed by a change of temperature, pressure, or concentration variable, the system shifts in equilibrium composition in a way that tends to counteract this change of variable. (12.3 and 14.7)

Leclanché dry cell see *Zinc–carbon dry cell.*

Levorotatory refers to a compound whose solution rotates the plane of polarized light to the left (when looking toward the source of light). (22.5)

Lewis acid a species that can form a covalent bond by accepting an electron pair from another species. (15.3)

Lewis base a species that can form a covalent bond by donating an electron pair to another species. (15.3)

Lewis electron-dot formula a formula in which dots are used to represent valence electrons. (9.4)

Lewis electron-dot symbol a symbol in which the electrons in the valence shell of an atom or ion are represented by dots placed around the letter symbol of the element. (9.1)

Ligand a Lewis base that bonds to a metal ion to form a complex ion. (17.5 and 22.3)

Limiting reactant (limiting reagent) the reactant that is entirely consumed when a reaction goes to completion. (3.8)

Linear geometry a molecular geometry in which all atoms line up along a straight line. (10.1)

Line spectrum a spectrum showing only certain colors or specific wavelengths of light. (7.3)

Linkage isomers isomers of a complex that differ in the atom of a ligand that is bonded to the metal atom. (22.5)

Lipids biological substances like fats and oils that are soluble in organic solvents, such as chloroform and carbon tetrachloride. (12.9)

Liquefaction the process in which a substance that is normally a gas changes to the liquid state. (11.2)

Liquid the form of matter that is a relatively incompressible fluid; a liquid has a fixed volume but no fixed shape. (1.4)

Liter (L) a unit of volume equal to a cubic decimeter (equal to approximately one quart). (1.7)

Lithium–iodine battery a voltaic cell in which the anode is lithium metal and the cathode is an I_2 complex. (19.8)

London forces (dispersion forces) the weak attractive forces between molecules resulting from the small, instantaneous dipoles that occur because of the varying positions of the electrons during their motion about nuclei. (11.5)

Lone pair (nonbonding pair) an electron pair that remains on one atom and is not shared. (9.4)

Low-spin complex ion a complex ion in which there is more pairing of electrons in the orbitals of the metal atom than in a corresponding high-spin complex ion. (22.7)

Magic number the number of nuclear particles in a completed shell of protons or neutrons. (20.1)

Magnetic quantum number (m_l) the quantum number that distinguishes orbitals of given n and l—that is, of given energy and shape—but having a different orientation in space; the allowed values are the integers from $-l$ to $+l$. (7.5)

Main-group element (representative element) an element in an A column of the periodic table, in which an outer s or p subshell is filling. (2.5 and 8.2)

Manometer a device that measures the pressure of a gas or liquid in a sealed vessel. (5.1)

Markownikoff's rule a generalization stating that the major product formed by the addition of an unsymmetrical reagent such as H—Cl, H—Br, or H—OH is the one obtained when the H atom of the reagent adds to the carbon atom of the multiple bond that already has the greater number of hydrogen atoms attached to it. (23.3)

Mass the quantity of matter in a material. (1.3)

Mass defect the total nucleon mass minus the atomic mass of a nucleus. (20.6)

Mass number (A) the total number of protons and neutrons in a nucleus. (2.3)

Mass percentage parts per hundred parts of the total, by mass. (3.3)

Mass percentage of solute the percentage by mass of solute contained in a solution. (12.4)

Mass spectrometer an instrument, such as one based on Thomson's principles, that measures the mass-to-charge ratios of atoms. (2.4)

Material any particular kind of matter. (1.1)

Matter all of the objects around you (1.1); whatever occupies space and can be perceived by our senses. (1.3)

Maxwell's distribution of molecular speeds a theoretical relationship that predicts the relative number of molecules at various speeds for a sample of gas at a particular temperature. (5.7)

Melting (fusion) the change of a solid to the liquid state. (11.2)

Melting point the temperature at which a crystalline solid changes to a liquid, or melts. (11.2)

Messenger RNA a relatively small RNA molecule that can diffuse about the cell and attach itself to a ribosome, where it serves as a pattern for protein synthesis. (24.4)

Metal a substance or mixture that has a characteristic luster, or shine, is generally a good conductor of heat and electricity and is malleable and ductile. (2.5 and 21.2)

Metallic solid a solid that consists of positive cores of atoms held together by a surrounding "sea" of electrons (metallic bonding). (11.6)

Metalloid (semimetal) an element having both metallic and nonmetallic properties. (2.5)

Metallurgy the scientific study of the production of metals from their ores and the making of alloys having various useful properties. (21.2)

Metal refining in metallurgy, the purification of a metal. (21.2)

Metaphosphoric acids acids with the general formula $(HPO_3)_n$. (21.9)

Metastable nucleus a nucleus in an excited state with a life-time of at least one nanosecond (10^{-9} s). (20.1)

Metathesis reaction see *Exchange reaction.*

Meter (m) the SI base unit of length. (1.6)

Micelle a colloidal-sized particle formed in water by the association of molecules or ions each of which has a hydrophobic end and a hydrophilic end. (12.9)

Millimeters of mercury (mmHg) a unit of pressure also known as the *torr.* A unit of pressure equal to that exerted by a column of mercury 1 mm high at 0.00°C. (5.1)

Mineral a naturally occurring inorganic solid substance or solid solution with definite crystalline form. (21.2)

Miscible fluids fluids that mix with or dissolve in each other in all proportions. (12.1)

Mixture a material that can be separated by physical means into two or more substances. (1.4)

Moderator a substance that slows down neutrons in a nuclear fission reactor. (20.7)

Molality the moles of solute per kilogram of solvent. (12.4)

Molar concentration (molarity), M the moles of solute dissolved in one liter (cubic decimeter) of solution. (4.7)

Molar gas constant (R) the constant of proportionality relating the molar volume of a gas to T/P. (5.3)

Molar gas volume (V_m) the volume of one mole of gas. (5.2)

Molarity see *Molar concentration.*

Molar mass the mass of one mole of substance. In grams, it is numerically equal to the formula mass in atomic mass units. (3.2)

Mole (mol) the quantity of a given substance that contains as many molecules or formula units as the number of atoms in exactly 12 g of carbon-12. The amount of substance containing Avogadro's number of molecules or formula units. (3.2)

Molecular equation a chemical equation in which the reactants and products are written as if they were molecular substances, even though they may actually exist in solution as ions. (4.2)

Molecular formula a chemical formula that gives the exact number of different atoms of an element in a molecule. (2.6)

Molecular geometry the general shape of a molecule, as determined by the relative positions of the atomic nuclei. (10.1)

Molecularity the number of molecules on the reactant side of an elementary reaction. (13.7)

Molecular orbital theory a theory of the electronic structure of molecules in terms of molecular orbitals, which may spread over several atoms or the entire molecule. (10.5)

Molecular solid a solid that consists of atoms or molecules held together by intermolecular forces. (11.6)

Molecular substance a substance that is composed of molecules, all of which are alike. (2.6)

Molecular mass (MM) the sum of the atomic masses of all the atoms in a molecule. (3.1)

Molecule a definite group of atoms that are chemically bonded together—that is, tightly connected by attractive forces. (2.6)

Mole fraction the fraction of moles of a component in the total moles of a mixture. (5.5)   The moles of a component substance divided by the total moles of solution. (12.4)

Mole percent percent, in terms of moles, of a component in a solution; obtained by multiplying mole fraction by 100. (12.4)

Monatomic ion an ion formed from a single atom. (2.8)

Monodentate ligand a ligand that bonds to a metal atom through one atom of the ligand. (22.3)

Monomer the small molecules that are linked together to form a polymer (2.6); a compound used to make a polymer (and from which the polymer's repeating unit arises). (24.1)

Monoprotic acid an acid that yields one acidic hydrogen per molecule. (4.4)

Monosaccharides simple sugars, each containing three to nine carbon atoms, generally all but one of which bear a hydroxyl group, the remaining one being part of a carbonyl group. (24.4)

Nernst equation an equation relating the cell potential, E_{cell}, to its standard potential cell, $E°_{cell}$, and the reaction quotient, Q. At 25°C, the equation is $E_{cell} = E°_{cell} - (0.0592/n)\log Q$. (19.7)

Net ionic equation an ionic equation from which spectator ions have been canceled. (4.2)

Neutralization reaction a reaction of an acid and a base that results in an ionic compound and possibly water. (4.4)

Neutron a particle found in the nucleus of an atom; it has a mass almost identical to that of the proton but no electric charge. (2.3)

Neutron activation analysis an analysis of elements in a sample based on the conversion of stable isotopes to radioactive isotopes by bombarding a sample with neutrons. (20.5)

Nickel–cadmium cell a voltaic cell consisting of an anode of cadmium and a cathode of hydrated nickel oxide (approximately NiOOH) on nickel; the electrolyte is potassium hydroxide. (19.8)

Nitrogen cycle the circulation of the element nitrogen in the biosphere, from nitrogen fixation to the release of free nitrogen by denitrifying bacteria. (21.9)

Nitrogen-fixing bacteria bacteria that can produce nitrogen compounds in the soil from atmospheric nitrogen. (21.9)

Noble-gas core an inner-shell configuration corresponding to one of the noble gases. (8.2)

Noble gases (inert gases; rare gases) the Group VIIIA elements; all are gases consisting of uncombined atoms. They are relatively unreactive elements. (8.7)

Nomenclature see *Chemical nomenclature.*

Nonbonding pair see *Lone pair.*

Nonelectrolyte a substance, such as sucrose, or table sugar ($C_{12}H_{22}O_{11}$), that dissolves in water to give a nonconducting or very poorly conducting solution. (4.1)

Nonmetal an element that does not exhibit the characteristics of a metal. (2.5)

Nonstoichiometric compound a compound whose composition varies from its idealized formula. (11.7)

Nuclear bombardment reaction a nuclear reaction in which a nucleus is bombarded, or struck, by another nucleus or by a nuclear particle. (20.1)

Nuclear equation a symbolic representation of a nuclear reaction. (20.1)

Nuclear fission a nuclear reaction in which a heavy nucleus splits into lighter nuclei and energy is released. (20.6)

Nuclear fission reactor a device that permits a controlled chain reaction of nuclear fissions. (20.7)

Nuclear force a strong force of attraction between nucleons that acts only at very short distances (about 10^{-15} m). (20.1)

Nuclear fusion a nuclear reaction in which light nuclei combine to give a stabler, heavier nucleus plus possibly several neutrons, and energy is released. (20.6)

Nucleic acids polynucleotides folded or coiled into specific three-dimensional shapes. (24.4)

Nucleotides the building blocks of nucleic acids. (24.4)

Nucleus the atom's central core; it has most of the atom's mass and one or more units of positive charge. (2.2)

Nuclide a particular atom characterized by a definite atomic number and mass number. (2.3)

Nuclide symbol a symbol for a nuclide, in which the atomic number is given as a left subscript and the mass number is given as a left superscript to the symbol of the element. (2.3)

Number of significant figures the number of digits reported for the value of a measured or calculated quantity, indicating the precision of the value. (1.5)

Octahedral geometry the geometry of a molecule in which six atoms occupy the vertices of a regular octahedron (a figure with eight faces and six vertices) with the central atom at the center of the octahedron. (10.1)

Octet rule the tendency of atoms in molecules to have eight electrons in their valence shells (two for hydrogen atoms). (9.4)

Optical isomers (enantiomers) isomers that are nonsuperimposable mirror images of one another. (22.5)

Optically active having the ability to rotate the plane of light waves, either as a pure substance or in solution. (22.5)

Orbital diagram a diagram to show how the orbitals of a sub-shell are occupied by electrons. (8.1)

Ore a rock or mineral from which a metal or nonmetal can be economically produced. (21.2)

Organic compounds compounds that contain carbon combined with other elements, such as hydrogen, oxygen, and nitrogen. (2.7 and 23.2)

Osmosis the phenomenon of solvent flow through a semipermeable membrane to equalize the solute concentrations on both sides of the membrane. (12.7)

Osmotic pressure a colligative property of a solution equal to the pressure that, when applied to the solution, just stops osmosis. (12.7)

Ostwald process an industrial preparation of nitrogen monoxide starting from the catalytic oxidation of ammonia to nitric oxide. (21.9)

Overall order of a reaction the sum of the orders of the reactant species in the rate law. (13.3)

Oxidation the part of an oxidation–reduction reaction in which there is a loss of electrons by a species (or an increase in the oxidation number of an atom). (4.5)

Oxidation number (oxidation state) either the actual charge on an atom in a substance, if the atom exists as a monatomic ion, or a hypothetical charge assigned by simple rules. (4.5)

Oxidation potential the negative of the standard electrode potential. (19.5)

Oxidation–reduction reaction (redox reaction) a reaction in which electrons are transferred between species or in which atoms change oxidation number. (4.5)

Oxide a binary compound with oxygen in the -2 oxidation state. (21.10)

Oxidizing agent a species that oxidizes another species; it is itself reduced. (4.5)

Oxoacid an acid containing hydrogen, oxygen, and another element. (2.8)   A substance in which O atoms (and possibly other electronegative atoms) are bonded to a central atom, with one or more H atoms usually bonded to the O atoms. (9.6)

Pairing energy (P) the energy required to put two electrons into the same orbital. (22.7)

Paramagnetic substance a substance that is weakly attracted by a magnetic field; this attraction generally results from unpaired electrons. (8.4)

Partial pressure the pressure exerted by a particular gas in a mixture. (5.5)

Particle accelerator a device used to accelerate electrons, protons, and alpha particles and other ions to very high speeds. (20.2)

Pascal (Pa) the SI unit of pressure; $1\ Pa = 1\ kg/(m \cdot s^2)$. (5.1)

Pauli exclusion principle no two electrons in an atom can have the same four quantum numbers. It follows from this that an orbital can hold no more than two electrons and can hold two only if they have different spin quantum numbers. (8.1)

Peptide (amide) bond the C—N bond resulting from a condensation reaction between the carboxyl group of one amino acid and the amino group of a second amino acid. (24.3)

Percentage composition the mass percentages of each element in a compound. (3.3)

Percentage yield the actual yield (experimentally determined) expressed as a percentage of the theoretical yield (calculated). (3.8)

Period (of the periodic table) the elements in any one horizontal row of the periodic table. (2.5)

Periodic law when the elements are arranged by atomic number, their physical and chemical properties vary periodically. (8.6)

Periodic table a tabular arrangement of elements in rows and columns, highlighting the regular repetition of properties of the elements. (2.5)

Peroxide a compound with oxygen in the -1 oxidation state. (21.10)

pH the negative of the logarithm of the molar hydrogen-ion concentration. (15.8)

Phase one of several different homogeneous materials present in the portion of matter under study. (1.4)

Phase diagram a graphical way to summarize the conditions under which the different states of a substance are stable. (11.3)

Phase transition see *Change of state*.

Phospholipid a type of lipid that contains a phosphate group. These molecules have hydrophobic and hydrophilic ends, and they aggregate to give a layer structure. The process is similar to the formation of micelles. (12.9)

Phospholipid bilayer a part of a biological membrane consisting of two layers of phospholipid molecules. (12.9)

Photoelectric effect the ejection of electrons from the surface of a metal or other material when light shines on it. (7.2)

Photon particle of electromagnetic energy with energy E proportional to the observed frequency of light: $E = h\nu$. (7.2)

Physical adsorption adsorption in which the attraction is provided by weak intermolecular forces. (13.9)

Physical change a change in the form of matter but not in its chemical identity. (1.4)

Physical property a characteristic that can be observed for a material without changing its chemical identity. (1.4)

Pi (π) bond a bond that has an electron distribution above and below the bond axis. (10.4)

Planck's constant (h) a physical constant with the value 6.63×10^{-34} J·s. It is the proportionality constant relating the frequency of light to the energy of a photon. (7.2)

Plasma an electrically neutral gas of ions and electrons. (20.7)

Polar covalent bond a covalent bond in which the bonding electrons spend more time near one atom than near the other. (9.5)

Polyamide a polymer formed by reacting a substance containing two amine groups with a substance containing two carboxylic acid groups. (24.1)

Polyatomic ion an ion consisting of two or more atoms chemically bonded together and carrying a net electric charge. (2.8)

Polydentate ligand a ligand that can bond with two or more atoms to a metal atom. (22.3)

Polyester a polymer formed by reacting a substance containing two alcohol groups with a substance containing two carboxylic acid groups. (24.1)

Polymer a very large molecule made up of a number of smaller molecules repeatedly linked together. (2.6); a chemical species of very high molecular mass that is made up from many repeating units of low molecular mass. (24.1)

Polymerase chain reaction (PCR) a technique used to amplify the quantity of DNA in a sample. (24.4)

Polynucleotide a linear polymer of nucleotide units. (24.4)

Polypeptide a polymer formed by the linking of many amino acids by peptide bonds. (24.3)

Polyphosphoric acids acids with the general formula $H_{n+2}P_nO_{3n-1}$ formed from linear chains of P—O bonds. (21.9)

Polyprotic acid an acid that yields two or more acidic hydrogens per molecule. (4.4 and 16.2)

Positron a particle that is similar to an electron and has the same mass but has a positive charge. (20.1)

Positron emission emission of a positron from an unstable nucleus. (20.1)

Potential difference the difference in electrical potential (electrical pressure) between two points. (19.4)

Potential energy the energy an object has by virtue of its position in a field of force. (6.1)

Precipitate an insoluble solid compound formed during a chemical reaction in solution. (4.3)

Precision the closeness of the set of values obtained from identical measurements of a quantity. (1.5)

Pressure the force exerted per unit area of surface. (5.1)

Primary alcohol an alcohol in which the hydroxyl group is attached to a carbon atom that is itself bonded to only one other carbon atom. (23.6)

Primary structure (of a protein) the order, or sequence, of the amino-acid units in the protein. (24.3)

Principal quantum number (n) the quantum number on which the energy of an electron in an atom principally depends; it can have any positive integer value: 1, 2, 3, ... (7.5)

Product a substance that results from a chemical reaction. (2.9)

Protein a biological polymer of small molecules called amino acids; a polypeptide that has a biological function. (24.3)

Proton a particle found in the nucleus of the atom; it has a positive charge equal in magnitude, but opposite in sign, to that of the electron and a mass 1836 times that of the electron. (2.3)

Pseudo-noble-gas core the noble-gas core together with $(n - 1)d^{10}$ electrons. (8.2)

Qualitative analysis the determination of the identity of substances present in a mixture. (17.7)

Quantitative analysis the determination of the amount of a substance or species present in a material. (4.9)

Quantum (wave) mechanics the branch of physics that mathematically describes the wave properties of submicroscopic particles. (7.4)

Racemic mixture a mixture of equal amounts of optical isomers. (22.5)

Rad the dosage of radiation that deposits 1×10^{-2} J of energy per kilogram of tissue. (20.3)

Radioactive decay the process in which a nucleus spontaneously disintegrates, giving off radiation. (20.1)

Radioactive decay constant (k) rate constant for radioactive decay. (20.4)

Radioactive decay series a sequence in which one radioactive nucleus decays to a second, which then decays to a third, and so on. (20.1)

Radioactive tracer a very small amount of radioactive isotope added to a chemical, biological, or physical system to facilitate study of the system. (20.5)

Radioactivity spontaneous radiation from unstable elements. (20.1)

Raoult's law the partial pressure of solvent, P_A, over a solution equals the vapor pressure of the pure solvent, P_A°, times the mole fraction of the solvent, X_A, in solution: $P_A = P_A^\circ X_A$. (12.5)

Rare gases see *Noble gases*.

Rate constant a proportionality constant in the relationship between rate and concentrations. (13.3)

Rate-determining step the slowest step in a reaction mechanism. (13.8)

Rate law an equation that relates the rate of a reaction to the concentrations of reactants (and catalyst) raised to various powers. (13.3)

Reactant a starting substance in a chemical reaction. (2.9)

Reaction intermediate a species produced during a reaction that does not appear in the net equation because it reacts in a subsequent step in the mechanism. (13.7)

Reaction mechanism the set of elementary reactions whose overall effect is given by the net chemical equation. (13.7)

Reaction order the exponent of the concentration of a given reactant species in the rate law, as determined experimentally. (13.3) See also *Overall reaction order*.

Reaction quotient (Q_c) an expression that has the same form as the equilibrium-constant expression but whose concentration values are not necessarily those at equilibrium. (14.5)

Reaction rate the increase in molar concentration of product of a reaction per unit time or the decrease in molar concentration of reactant per unit time. (13.1)

Redox reaction see *Oxidation–reduction reaction*.

Reducing agent a species that reduces another species; it is itself oxidized. (4.5)

Reduction the part of an oxidation–reduction reaction in which there is a gain of electrons by a species (or a decrease of oxidation number of an atom). (4.5)

Reduction potential see *Standard electrode potential*.

Reference form the stablest form (physical state and allotrope) of an element under standard thermodynamic conditions. (6.8)

Rem a unit of radiation dosage used to relate various kinds of radiation in terms of biological destruction. It equals the rad times a factor for the type of radiation, called the relative biological effectiveness (RBE): rems = rads × RBE. (20.3)

Refining see *Metal refining*.

Representative element see *Main-group element*.

Resonance description a representation in which you describe the electron structure of a molecule having delocalized bonding by writing all possible electron-dot formulas. (9.7)

Reverse osmosis a process in which a solvent, such as water, is forced by a pressure greater than the osmotic pressure to flow through a semipermeable membrane from a concentrated solution to a more dilute one. (12.7)

Ribonucleic acid (RNA) a constituent of cells that is used to manufacture proteins from genetic information. It is a polymer of ribonucleotide units. (24.4)

Ribosomal RNA the RNA in a ribosome. (24.4)

Ribosomes tiny cellular particles on which protein synthesis takes place. (24.4)

Roasting the process of heating a mineral in air to obtain the oxide. (21.2)

Root-mean-square (rms) molecular speed a type of average molecular speed, equal to the speed of a molecule having the average molecular kinetic energy. It equals $\sqrt{3RT/M_m}$, where M_m is the molar mass. (5.7)

Rounding the procedure of dropping nonsignificant digits in a calculation result and adjusting the last digit reported. (1.5)

Salt an ionic compound that is a product of a neutralization reaction. (4.4)

Salt bridge a tube of an electrolyte in a gel that is connected to the two half-cells of a voltaic cell; it allows the flow of ions but prevents the mixing of the different solutions that would allow direct reaction of the cell reactants. (19.2)

Saturated hydrocarbon a hydrocarbon that has only single bonds between carbon atoms; all carbon atoms are bonded to the maximum number of hydrogen atoms (that is, the hydrocarbon is *saturated* with hydrogen). A saturated hydrocarbon molecule can be cyclic or acyclic. (23.1)

Saturated solution a solution that is in equilibrium with respect to a given dissolved substance. (12.2)

Scientific method the general process of advancing scientific knowledge through observation, the framing of laws, hypotheses, or theories, and the conducting of more experiments. (1.2)

Scientific notation the representation of a number in the form $A \times 10^n$, where A is a number with a single nonzero digit to the left of the decimal point and n is an integer, or whole number. (1.5)

Scintillation counter a device that detects nuclear radiations from flashes of light generated in a material by the radiation. (20.3)

Second (s) the SI base unit of time. (1.6)

Secondary alcohol an alcohol in which the hydroxyl group is attached to a carbon atom that is itself bonded to two carbon atoms. (23.6)

Secondary structure (of a protein) the relatively simple coiled or parallel arrangement of a protein molecule. (24.3)

Second law of thermodynamics the total entropy of a system and its surroundings always increases for a spontaneous process. Also, for a spontaneous process at a given temperature, the change in entropy of the system is greater than the heat divided by the absolute temperature. (18.2)

Seesaw geometry the geometry of a molecule having four atoms bonded to a central atom, in which two of these outer atoms occupy axial positions of a trigonal bipyramid and the other two occupy equatorial positions. (10.1)

Self-ionization (autoionization) a reaction in which two like molecules react to give ions. (15.6)

Semimetal see *Metalloid*.

Shell model of the nucleus a nuclear model in which protons and neutrons exist in levels, or shells, analogous to the shell structure that exists for electrons in an atom. (20.1)

SI see *International System*.

SI base units the SI units of measurement from which all others can be derived. (1.6)

SI derived unit a unit derived by combining SI base units. (1.7)

SI prefix a prefix used in the International System to indicate a power of 10. (1.6)

Sigma (σ) bond a bond that has a cylindrical shape about the bond axis. (10.4)

Significant figures those digits in a measured number (or in the result of a calculation with measured numbers) that include all certain digits plus a final digit having some uncertainty. (1.5)

Silica a covalent network solid of SiO_2 in which each silicon atom is covalently bonded in tetrahedral directions to four oxygen atoms; each oxygen atom is in turn bonded to another silicon atom. (21.8)

Silicate a compound of silicon and oxygen (with one or more metals) that may be formally regarded as a derivative of silicic acid, H_4SiO_4 or $Si(OH)_4$. (21.8)

Silicone a polymer that contains chains or rings of Si—O with one or more of the bonding positions on each Si atom occupied by an organic group. (21.8)

Simple cubic unit cell a cubic unit cell in which lattice points are situated only at the corners of the unit cell. (11.7)

Simplest formula see *Empirical formula*.

Single bond a covalent bond in which a single pair of electrons is shared by two atoms. (9.4)

Single-replacement reaction see *Displacement reaction*.

Sol a colloid that consists of solid particles dispersed in a liquid. (12.9)

Solid the form of matter characterized by rigidity; a solid is relatively incompressible and has fixed shape and volume. (1.4)

Solubility the amount of a substance that dissolves in a given quantity of solvent (such as water) at a given temperature to give a saturated solution. (12.2)

Solubility product constant (K_{sp}) the equilibrium constant for the solubility equilibrium of a slightly soluble (or nearly insoluble) ionic compound. (17.1)

Solute in the case of a solution of a gas or solid dissolved in a liquid, the gas or solid; in other cases, the component in smaller amount. (12.1)

Solution see *Homogeneous mixture*.

Solvay process an industrial method for obtaining sodium carbonate from sodium chloride and limestone. (21.4)

Solvent in a solution of a gas or solid dissolved in a liquid, the liquid; in other cases, the component in greater amount. (12.1)

Specific heat capacity (specific heat) the quantity of heat required to raise the temperature of one gram of a substance by one degree Celsius (or one kelvin) at constant pressure. (6.6)

Spectator ion an ion in an ionic equation that does not take part in the reaction. (4.2)

Spectrochemical series an arrangement of ligands according to the relative magnitudes of the crystal field splittings they induce in the d orbitals of a metal ion. (22.7)

Spin quantum number (m_s) the quantum number that refers to the two possible orientations of the spin axis of an electron; its possible values are $+\frac{1}{2}$ and $-\frac{1}{2}$. (7.5)

Spontaneous fission the spontaneous decay of an unstable nucleus in which a heavy nucleus of mass number greater than 89 splits into lighter nuclei and energy is released. (20.1)

Spontaneous process a physical or chemical change that occurs by itself. (18.2)

Square planar geometry the geometry of a molecule in which a central atom is surrounded by four other atoms arranged in a square and in a plane containing the central atom. (10.1)

Square pyramidal geometry the geometry of a molecule in which a central atom is at the apex of a pyramid and four other atoms form the square base of the pyramid. (10.1)

Stability constant (of a complex) see *Formation constant*.

Standard electrode potential ($E°$) the electrode potential when the concentrations of solutes are 1 M, the gas pressures are 1 atm, and the temperature has a specified value—usually 25°C. (19.5)

Standard potential ($E°_{cell}$) the potential of a voltaic cell operating under standard-state conditions (solute concentrations are 1 M, gas pressures are 1 atm, and the temperature has a specified value—usually 25°C). (19.5)

Standard enthalpy of formation (standard heat of formation), $\Delta H°_f$ the enthalpy change for the formation of one mole of a substance in its standard state from its elements in their reference forms and in their standard states. (6.8)

Standard (absolute) entropy ($S°$) the entropy value for the standard state of a species. (18.3)

Standard free energy of formation ($\Delta G°_f$) the free-energy change that occurs when one mole of substance is formed from its elements in their stablest states at 1 atm and at a specified temperature (usually 25°C). (18.4)

Standard heat of formation see *Standard enthalpy of formation*.

Standard state the standard thermodynamic conditions (1 atm and usually 25°C) chosen for substances when listing or comparing thermochemical data. (6.8)

Standard temperature and pressure (STP) the reference conditions for gases, chosen by convention to be 0°C and 1 atm. (5.2)

State function a property of a system that depends only on its present state, which is determined by variables such as temperature and pressure and is independent of any previous history of the system. (6.3 and 18.1)

States of matter the three forms that matter can commonly assume—solid, liquid, and gas. (1.4)

Steam-reforming process an industrial preparation in which steam and hydrocarbons from natural gas or petroleum react at high temperature and pressure in the presence of a catalyst to form carbon monoxide and hydrogen. (21.7)

Stereoisomers isomers in which the atoms are bonded to each other in the same order but that differ in the precise arrangement of the atoms in space. (22.5)

Stock system a system of chemical nomenclature in which the charge on a metal atom or oxidation number of an atom is denoted by a Roman numeral in parentheses following the element name. (2.8)

Stoichiometry the calculation of the quantities of reactants and products involved in a chemical reaction. (3.6)

Stratosphere the region of the atmosphere occurring at 10 to 15 km above the ground level wherein the temperature increases with increasing altitude; it lies just above the troposphere, the lower portion of the atmosphere. (10.7)

Strong acid an acid that ionizes completely in water; it is a strong electrolyte. (4.4 and 15.1)

Strong base a base that is present in aqueous solution entirely as ions, one of which is OH^-; it is a strong electrolyte. (4.4 and 15.1)

Strong electrolyte an electrolyte that exists in solution almost entirely as ions. (4.1)

Structural formula a chemical formula that shows how the atoms are bonded to one another in a molecule. (2.6)

Structural isomers see *Constitutional isomers.*
Sublimation the change of a solid directly to the vapor. (11.2)
Substance a kind of matter that cannot be separated into other kinds of matter by any physical process. (1.4)
Substitution reaction a reaction in which a part of the reacting molecule is substituted for an H atom on a hydrocarbon or a hydrocarbon group. (23.2)
Substrate the substance whose reaction an enzyme catalyzes. (13.9)
Superoxide a binary compound with oxygen in the $-\frac{1}{2}$ oxidation state; it contains the superoxide ion, O_2^-. (21.10)
Supersaturated solution a solution that contains more dissolved substance than does a saturated solution; the solution is not in equilibrium with the solid substance. (12.2)
Surface tension the energy required to increase the surface area of a liquid by a unit amount. (11.4)
Surroundings everything in the vicinity of a thermodynamic system. (6.2)
Synthesis gas reaction a chemical reaction in which a mixture of CO and H_2 gases is used in the industrial preparation of a number of organic compounds, including methanol, CH_3OH. (21.7)
System (thermodynamic) the substance or mixture of substances under study in which a change occurs. (6.2)

Termolecular reaction an elementary reaction that involves three reactant molecules. (13.7)
Tertiary alcohol an alcohol in which the hydroxyl group is attached to a carbon atom that is itself bonded to three carbon atoms. (23.6)
Tertiary structure (of a protein) the structure associated with the way the protein coil is folded. (24.3)
Tetrahedral geometry the geometry of a molecule in which four atoms bonded to a central atom occupy the vertices of a tetrahedron with the central atom at the center of this tetrahedron. (10.1)
Theoretical yield the maximum amount of product that can be obtained by a reaction from given amounts of reactants. (3.8)
Theory a tested explanation of basic natural phenomena. (1.2)
Thermal equilibrium a state in which heat does not flow between a system and its surroundings because they are both at the same temperature. (6.2)
Thermochemical equation the chemical equation for a reaction (including phase labels) in which the equation is given a molar interpretation, and the enthalpy of reaction for these molar amounts is written directly after the equation. (6.4)
Thermochemistry the study of the quantity of heat absorbed or evolved by chemical reactions. (6.1)
Thermodynamic equilibrium constant (K) the equilibrium constant in which the concentrations of gases are expressed in partial pressures in atmospheres, whereas the concentrations of solutes in liquid solutions are expressed in molarities. (18.6)
Thermodynamics the study of the relationship between heat and other forms of energy involved in a chemical or physical process. (6.1 and Ch. 18 opener)
Thermodynamic system see *System.*
Third law of thermodynamics a substance that is perfectly crystalline at 0 K has an entropy of zero. (18.3)
Titration a procedure for determining the amount of substance A by adding a carefully measured volume of a solution with known concentration of B until the reaction of A and B is just complete. (4.10)
Torr see *Millimeters of mercury.*
Transfer RNA (tRNA) a small RNA molecule; it binds to a particular amino acid, carries it to a ribosome, and then attaches itself (through base pairing) to a messenger RNA codon. (24.4)

Transition elements the B columns of elements in the periodic table. (2.5); the *d*-block transition elements in which a *d* subshell is being filled. (8.2); those metallic elements that have an incompletely filled *d* subshell or easily give rise to common ions that have incompletely filled *d* subshells. (22.1)
Transition state see *Activated complex.*
Transition-state theory a theory that explains the reaction resulting from the collision of two molecules in terms of an activated complex (transition state). (13.5)
Transmutation the change of one element to another by bombardment of the nucleus of the element with nuclear particles or nuclei. (20.2)
Transuranium elements those elements with atomic numbers greater than that of uranium ($Z = 92$), the naturally occurring element of greatest Z. (20.2)
Trigonal bipyramidal geometry the geometry of a molecule in which five atoms bonded to a central atom occupy the vertices of a trigonal bipyramid (formed by placing two trigonal pyramids base to base) with the central atom at the center of this trigonal bipyramid. (10.1)
Trigonal planar geometry the geometry of a molecule in which a central atom is surrounded by three other atoms arranged in a triangle and in a plane containing the central atom. (10.1)
Trigonal pyramidal geometry the geometry of a molecule in which a central atom is at the apex of a pyramid and three other atoms form the triangular base of the pyramid. (10.1)
Triple bond a covalent bond in which three pairs of electrons are shared by two atoms. (9.4)
Triple point the point on a phase diagram representing the temperature and pressure at which three phases of a substance coexist in equilibrium. (11.3)
T-shaped geometry the geometry of a molecule in which three atoms are bonded to a central atom to form a T. (10.1)
Tyndall effect the scattering of light by colloidal-size particles. (12.9)

Uncertainty principle a relation stating that the product of the uncertainty in position and the uncertainty in momentum (mass times speed) of a particle can be no smaller than Planck's constant divided by 4π. (7.4)
Unimolecular reaction an elementary reaction that involves one reactant molecule. (13.7)
Unit a fixed standard of measurement. (1.5)
Unit cell the smallest boxlike unit (each box having faces that are parallelograms) from which you can imagine constructing a crystal by stacking the units in three dimensions. (11.7)
Unsaturated hydrocarbon a hydrocarbon that has at least one double or triple bond between carbon atoms; not all carbon atoms are bonded to the maximum number of hydrogen atoms (that is, the hydrocarbon is *unsaturated* with hydrogen). (23.1)
Unsaturated solution a solution that is not in equilibrium with respect to a given dissolved substance and in which more of the substance can dissolve. (12.2)

Valence bond theory an approximate theory to explain the electron pair or covalent bond in terms of quantum mechanics. (10.3)
Valence electron an electron in an atom outside the noble-gas or pseudo-noble-gas core. (8.2)
Valence-shell electron-pair repulsion (VSEPR) model predicts the shapes of molecules and ions by assuming that the valence-shell electron pairs are arranged about each atom so that electron pairs are kept as far away from one another as possible, thus minimizing electron-pair repulsions. (10.1)

van der Waals forces a general term for those intermolecular forces that include dipole–dipole and London forces. (11.5)

van der Waals equation an equation that is similar to the ideal gas law but includes two constants, *a* and *b*, to account for deviations from ideal behavior. (5.8)

Vapor the gaseous state of any kind of matter that normally exists as a liquid or solid. (1.4)

Vaporization the change of a solid or a liquid to the vapor. (11.2)

Vapor pressure the partial pressure of the vapor over the liquid, measured at equilibrium at a given temperature. (11.2)

Vapor-pressure lowering a colligative property equal to the vapor pressure of the pure solvent minus the vapor pressure of the solution. (12.5)

Viscosity the resistance to flow that is exhibited by all liquids and gases. (11.4)

Volatile refers to a liquid or solid having a relatively high vapor pressure at normal temperatures. (11.2)

Volt (V) the SI unit of potential difference. (19.4)

Voltaic cell (galvanic cell) an electrochemical cell in which a spontaneous reaction generates an electric current. (19.1)

Volumetric analysis a method of analysis based on titration. (4.10)

Wavelength (λ) the distance between any two adjacent identical points of a wave. (7.1)

Wave mechanics see *Quantum mechanics*.

Weak acid an acid that is only partly ionized in water; it is a weak electrolyte. (4.4 and 15.1)

Weak base a base that is only partly ionized in water; it is a weak electrolyte. (4.4 and 15.1)

Weak electrolyte an electrolyte that dissolves in water to give a relatively small percentage of ions. (4.1)

Work the energy exchange that results when a force *F* moves an object through a distance *d*; it equals $F \times d$. (18.1)

Zinc–carbon (Leclanché) dry cell a voltaic cell that has a zinc can as the anode; a graphite rod in the center, surrounded by a paste of manganese dioxide, ammonium and zinc chlorides, and carbon black, is the cathode. (19.8)

Zwitterion an amino acid in the doubly ionized form, in which the carboxyl group has lost an H^+ to give $-COO^-$ and the amino group has gained an H^+ to give $-NH_3^+$. (24.3)

Illustrations

The following figures are reprinted with permission from *Chemistry: The Practical Science* by Paul Kelter, Michael Mosher, and Andrew Scott. Copyright © 2008 by Houghton Mifflin Company: Figure 1.6, p. 4; Figure 1.12, p. 10; Figure 1.23, p. 21; Figure 2.6, p. 46; Figure 2.8, p. 47; Figure 2.18, p. 56 (bottom row, left and right); Figure 3.1, p. 86; Figure 4.7, p. 137; Figure 5.2, p. 177; Figure 5.13, p. 186; Figure 5.18, p. 194; Figure 5.28, p. 204; Figure 7.9, p. 271; Figure 8.17, p. 313; Figure 8.18 (bottom), p. 315; chapter opener 9, p. 328; Figure 9.10, p. 342; bottom, p. 345; Figure 9.15, p. 346; Figure 10.3 (bottom row), p. 376; Figure 10.16 (left, right), p. 385; Figure 11.2, p. 420; Figure 11.19 (center), p. 435; Figure 11.25 (center), p. 441; Figure 12.7, p. 484; Figure 12.16, p. 492; Figure 12.27, p. 507; Example 13.11, p. 556; Figure 14.1, p. 581; Figure 15.1 (top), p. 634; Figure 16.1 (right), p. 653; Figure 16.4 (bottom), p. 659; Figure 16.5 (bottom), p. 661; Exercise 16.9, p. 671; Problem 16.38, p. 692; Figure 18.9, p. 751; Problem 18.106, p. 767; p. 802; Figure 20.3, p. 825; top, p. 829; Figure 20.12, p. 837; Figure 20.18, p. 853; p. 854 (top, bottom); Figure 20.19, p. 855; Figure 22.9 (right), p. 943; Figure 22.18, p. 951; Figure 22.19, p. 952; Figure 22.29, p. 961; Figure 23.3 (bottom), p. 971; p. 978; Figure 23.14 (bottom row), p. 983; p. 1014; Figure 24.8, p. 1016 (right); Figure 24.9, p. 1016; Figure 24.10, p. 1017; Figure 24.11, p. 1018; p. 1020; Figure 24.13, p. 1022; Table 24.3, p. 1024; Figure 24.17, p. 1024

Photos

Photographs used in the title bars of "A Chemist Looks at" and "Instrumental Methods" feature boxes: Getty Images © 2003. Photographs © Houghton Mifflin Company. All rights reserved: Pages vii (top), viii (two photos), ix (top), xiii (top), xv (top), xvii, 3, 6, 10, 11, 17, 23, 24 (right), 42 (two photos), 72, 86 (left), 90, 94 (two photos), 105, 106, 124 (left), 127 (two photos), 128 (two photos), 130, 134, 137 (top), 143, 145 (top three photos), 149 (two photos), 151, 155 (three photos), 157, 161 (three photos), 175 (two photos), 181 (two photos), 184 (two photos), 200 (two photos), 203 (two photos), 204, 205, 224 (two photos), 228, 229 (two photos), 235 (two photos), 263 (left), 293 (right), 319, 320 (bottom), 321, 337, 341 (two photos), 373 (bottom), 376 (five photos), 385, 386 (two photos), 418 (two photos), 419, 433, 435 (right), 457 (bottom), 480 (two photos), 488 (two photos), 489, 502, 509, 530 (three photos), 545 (two photos), 580 (left), 586, 592 (right), 603 (three photos), 608, 623 (top), 630, 641, 642, 652 (right), 665, 668 (three photos), 699 (two photos), 702, 704, 705, 707, 711 (three photos), 715, 731 (right), 770 (two photos), 774, 778, 782, 798 (two photos), 800 (two photos), 804, 866 (top), 871 (two photos), 880 (top), 887 (top), 888 (bottom), 889 (top), 900, 901, 904 (left), 909, 911 (three photos), 915, 916, 917, 930 (two photos), 932, 936 (top two photos), 943, 948 (two photos), 949 (two photos), 968 (left), 969 (left), 976, 977, 979 (two photos), 982 (two photos), 993, 1004 (two photos), 1005, 1009, 1010.

Photographs by James Scherer. © Houghton Mifflin Company. All rights reserved: Pages x (bottom), xii (two photos), xiii (bottom), 7 (two photos), 12 (two photos), 17 (three photos), 24 (left), 45 (three photos), 58 (bottom), 59, 69, 91, 92, 111, 125, 137 (bottom two photos), 145 (bottom), 146, 150, 152, 159 (two photos), 176, 185, 190 (bottom), 245, 264 (four photos), 320 (top), 338, 361 (three photos), 421 (two photos), 436, 447, 482 (three photos), 512 (two photos), 513, 524 (two photos), 525 (two photos), 610 (three photos), 624, 643, 676, 717 (three photos), 732, 771, 877 (top), 880 (bottom two photos), 881, 882 (two photos), 883, 884 (bottom), 885, 887 (bottom three photos), 891 (two photos), 892, 897, 903, 904 (center, right), 905, 906, 913, 936 (bottom), 959, 981, 1006

Credits for all other photos are listed below, with page numbers in boldface.
ix (bottom) NASA; **x (top)** Courtesy: IBM Research, Almaden Research Center; **x (center)** © Richard Megna/FUNDAMENTAL PHOTOGRAPHS, NYC; **xi (bottom)** © BIOS/Peter Arnold Inc.; **xiv (center)** © Richard Megna/FUNDAMENTAL PHOTOGRAPHS, NYC; **xiv (bottom)** © Paul Silverman/FUNDAMENTAL PHOTOGRAPHS, NYC; **xv (bottom)** Alexander Tsiara/Photo Researchers, Inc.; **xvi (top)** Jacana/Photo Researchers, Inc.; **1 (top)** Mark Schneider/Getty Images; **1 (bottom)** © Lawrence Manning/Corbis; **2** Copyright Doug Elbinger; **4** © Yoav Levy/Phototake; **15** Courtesy PerkinElmer; **20** National Institue of Standards and Technology, © Geoffrey Wheeler; **28** Spencer Grant/PhotoEdit;

41 (left) Courtesy: IBM Research, Almaden Research Center; **41 (right)** Image courtesy of IBM Zurich Research Laboratory; **43** Photo courtesy of Digital Instruments; **45** The Cavendish Laboratory; **49** G. Tompkinson/Photo Researchers, Inc.; **52** Edgar Fahs Smith Collection, University of Pennsylvania; **55** A. Zschau/GSI; **57** Teflon® is a registered trademark of DuPont; **58 (top)** E. R. Degginger/www.color-pic.com; **86 (right)** © Handout/Reuters/Corbis; **124 (right)** Siede Preis/Getty Images; **132** © Royalty-Free/CORBIS; **186** Courtesy Schwarz Pharma; **187** AP Images; **190 (top)** © Royalty-Free/CORBIS; **194** Paul McConville/Getty Images; **223 (left)** © Joseph P. Sinnot/FUNDAMENTAL PHOTOGRAPHS, NYC; **223 (right)** Harry Taylor/Getty Images; **225** © Reuters/Corbis; **227** Tennessee Valley Authority; **251** NASA; **259 (left)** © Royalty-Free/CORBIS; **259 (right)** NASA; **263 (right)** Mark Hamilton/Alamy; **270** Photo courtesy of MDS Nordion; **271** AP Images; **277 (top)** SEM instrument photo courtesy of JEOL USA; **277 (bottom)** Biophoto Associates/Photo Researchers, Inc.; **280** Courtesy: IBM Research, Almaden Research Center; **281** Courtesy: IBM Research, Almaden Research Center; **293 (left)** © Richard Megna/FUNDAMENTAL PHOTOGRAPHS, NYC; **294** © Lebrecht Music & Arts/The Image Works; **296** Paul Shambroom/Photo Researchers, Inc.; **310** Courtesy of A. Geim, University of Nijmegen; **311** University of Chicago Library; **328 (left)** © Clyde H. Smith/Peter Arnold Inc.; **328 (right)** © David Stoecklein/Corbis; **329** E. R. Degginger/www.color-pic.com; **335** Reprinted with permission from *Chem. Eng. News*, March 30, 1998, 76(13), p. 33. Copyright 1998 American Chemical Society; **344** © Craig Hammell/CORBIS; **362** Courtesy of Nicolet; **373 (top)** Michael Rosenfeld/Getty Images; **400** © Yoav Levy/Phototake; **409** NOAA/National Oceanic and Atmospheric Administration; **435 (left)** imagebroker/Alamy; **443** © BIOS/Peter Arnold Inc.; **457 (top)** Courtesy of UCAR Carbon Company, Inc.; **461** From G. D. Preston, "Diffraction of X-Rays by Crystals at Elevated Temperatures," 1939, in *Proceedings of the Royal Society*, A, Volume 172, plate 4, figure 5A; **462** Courtesy of Bruker Analytical X-Ray Systems, Inc., Madison, Wisconsin, USA; **478 (left)** Edu Lyra/Getty Images; **478 (right)** Radius Images/Alamy; **486 (two photos)** Bill Longcore/Photo Researchers, Inc.; **492** © Royalty-Free/CORBIS; **507 (three photos)** David Phillips/Photo Researchers, Inc.; **523 (left)** © Thomas Eisner and Daniel Aneshansley, Cornell University/Visuals Unlimited; **523 (right)** © David Bebber/Reuters/Corbis; **563** Delphi Automotive Systems; **565** California Institute of Technology; **580 (right)** Novastock/Photo Researchers, Inc.; **581** Courtesy © Eastman Kodak Company; **592 (left)** E. R. Degginger/www.color-pic.com; **594** American Gas Association; **623 (bottom)** © Royalty-Free/ CORBIS; **652 (left)** © Richard Megna/FUNDAMENTAL PHOTOGRAPHS, NYC; **663 (left)** © NYC Parks Photo Archive/FUNDAMENTAL PHOTOGRAPHS, NYC; **663 (right)** © Kristen Brochmann/FUNDAMENTAL PHOTOGRAPHS, NYC; **700** © C. Allan Morgan/Peter Arnold Inc.; **710 (top)** © ISM/Phototake; **710 (bottom)** © Barrie Rokeach; **714** E. R. Degginger/www.color-pic.com; **716** © Richard Megna/FUNDAMENTAL PHOTOGRAPHS, NYC; **731 (left)** © Paul Silverman/FUNDAMENTAL PHOTOGRAPHS, NYC; **736** Nelson Morris/Photo Researchers, Inc.; **796** Corning Science Products; **806** Courtesy Kennecott Utah Copper Corporation; **820 (top)** Courtesy of James L. Marshall, JMC Services; **820 (bottom)** CENTRE JEAN PERRIN/Photo Researchers, Inc.; **821** Alexander Tsiara/Photo Researchers, Inc.; **827** AIP Emilio Segre Visual Archives; **834** Fermilab Visual Media Services; **835** Lawrence Berkeley Laboratory; **836** Oak Ridge National Laboratory; **837** Courtesy of Bicron, division of Saint-Gobain Industrial Ceramics, Inc.; **847** Courtesy of DuPont Pharmaceuticals; **848 (left)** Photo of the Philips CardioMD system courtesy of Philips Medical Systems; **848 (right)** Courtesy of Siemens Medical Systems; **849 (left)** Wellcome/Photo Researchers, Inc.; **849 (right)** Alexander Tsiara/Photo Researchers, Inc.; **857** Princeton Plasma Physics Laboratory; **866 (bottom)** GK Hart/Vikki Hart/Getty Images; **870** Jacana/Photo Researchers, Inc.; **872** Hank Morgan/Photo Researchers, Inc.; **876** Argonne National Laboratory; **877 (bottom)** Courtesy of DuPont Magazine; **878** Courtesy: Medtronic, Inc.; **884 (top)** Phil Degginger/www.color-pic.com; **886** Courtesy of Sweetwater Technology; **888 (top)** Courtesy of Smithsonian Institution; **889 (bottom)** Courtesy of Engelhard Corporation; **890** E. R. Degginger/www.color-pic.com; **895** NASA; **898** Richard Luria/Photo Researchers, Inc.; **899** Mark Schneider/Photo Researchers, Inc.; **910** Farrell Grehan/Photo Researchers, Inc.; **919** Argonne National Laboratory; **968 (right)** Thomas Northcut/Getty Images; **969 (left)** © Arthur R. Hill/Visuals Unlimited; **1007** Bryn Campbell/Getty Images; **1009** AP Images; **1022** © Manfred Kage/Peter Arnold Inc.; **1025** By permission of Gang-Yu Liu, Wayne State University

Index